W9-CSF-051

HIGH-PRESSURE SCIENCE AND TECHNOLOGY—1993

HIGH - PRESSURE SCIENCE AND TECHNOLOGY—1993

Proceedings of the joint International Association for Research and Advancement of High Pressure Science and Technology and American Physical Society Topical Group on Shock Compression of Condensed Matter Conference held at Colorado Springs, Colorado, June 28–July 2, 1993

Edited by:

S. C. SCHMIDT
Los Alamos National Laboratory
Los Alamos, New Mexico, USA

J. W. SHANER
Los Alamos National Laboratory
Los Alamos, New Mexico, USA

G. A. SAMARA
Sandia National Laboratories
Albuquerque, New Mexico, USA

M. ROSS
Lawrence Livermore National Laboratory
Los Alamos, New Mexico, USA

American Institute of Physics
AIP Conference Proceedings 309
PART 2

New York

L.C. Catalog Card No. 93-72821
ISBN 1-56396-219-5 (set)
ISBN 1-56396-217-9 (Part 1)
ISBN 1-56396-218-7 (Part 2)
DOE CONF-921145

Printed in the United States of America.

CONTENTS
PART 1

CHAPTER IX: SUPERCONDUCTIVITY

CHAPTER X: CERAMICS

PART 2

CHAPTER XIV: MECHANICAL PROPERTIES: MACROSCOPIC ASPECTS

CHAPTER XX: OPTICAL STUDIES

CHAPTER XIV

MECHANICAL PROPERTIES: Macroscopic Aspects

MOLECULAR DYNAMICS OF VOID COLLAPSE MECHANISMS IN SHOCKED MEDIA

J. W. Mintmire[†], D. H. Robertson[†], M. L. Elert[‡], D. W. Brenner[†], and C. T. White[†]

[†]Chemistry Division
U. S. Naval Research Laboratory
Washington, DC 20375

[‡]Department of Chemistry
U. S. Naval Academy
Annapolis, MD 21402

We have carried out a series of molecular dynamics simulations on a model system to study the dynamics of void defect collapse during pressure-wave propagation in condensed-phase systems. Three-dimensional molecular-dynamics methods were used for a model system of identical particles arranged as diatomic molecules aligned with the center of mass of each molecule at fcc lattice sites, using a {111} layering for the two-dimensional boundary conditions. The diatoms were internally coupled via a harmonic potential; all other interactions were modeled with Morse potentials between all particles other than the immediate diatomic partner. Using this model, we have investigated the effect of a cylindrical void at right angles to the direction of layering (and impact). Depending on the energy density of the incident pressure wave, the void defect can either collapse smoothly and symmetrically (as in a balloon gradually losing air), or asymmetrically and turbulently. In the latter case, we note the transient formation (for periods of several hundreds of femtoseconds) of "*hot spots*" at the void location both in terms of the local effective temperature and the vibrational energies of the diatoms.

INTRODUCTION

The transition from shock to detonation of condensed-phase energetic materials is believed to involve local *hot-spots*[1–5], regions in the heterogenous material which under shock have a higher local temperature than the surrounding regions. A range of defect types have been studied[6–12] as candidates for these initiation sites, including structural defects such as voids and shear bands. How energy is transferred from the pressure front into the internal vibrational modes, ultimately leading to chemical reactions, is one of the critical questions to be answered in studies of the predetonation process. Both molecular dynamics[6–8] and model quantum approaches[9] have been used to study this problem.

In this paper we present results from a series of molecular dynamics simulations of the interaction of a nanoscale cylindrical void with a shock wave propagating in a model three-dimensional condensed-phase system. The void is positioned transverse to the direction of shock wave propagation. The calculations reported herein included 10448 identical particles arranged in diatomic molecules, the center-of-mass of each diatom roughly located at fcc lattice sites using a {111} layering in the direction of wave propagation, and periodic boundary conditions imposed in two dimensions. The system was shocked using the impact of a four-layer flyer plate. We followed the resulting effects of this impact on a range of local properties, and find the formation of local "*hot spots*" when the impact energy is sufficient to result in a turbulent collapse of the void. This paper is an extension of earlier preliminary results reported for smaller systems.[13]

APPROACH

The molecular dynamics simulations were carried out on a model condensed-phase system constructed from an fcc lattice of 42 close-packed layers of atomic dimers stacked in a {111} direction; this direction was assigned the z axis. Periodic boundary conditions were imposed in the x and y directions (*i.e.*, a finite number of layers having infinite extent) with the periodic unit cell containing 16 rows of 8 diatoms in each row, with the row direction aligned in the x direction.

Two types of interatomic interactions were assumed. Within each diatom the particles interacted via a harmonic potential in the diatomic bond distance r, $V_{diatom}(r) \equiv \frac{1}{2}K(r - r_0)^2$, with a spring constant $K = 500$ J/m^2 and equilibrium bond distance $r_0 = 0.16$ nm. Each atom was assumed to have a mass of 14 amu ($\sim 2.3 \times 10^{-26}$ kg). These harmonic parameters and the atomic masses were chosen to approximate the behavior of bonds in organic molecules in a molecular crystal, with the spring constant roughly that of the force constant of a typical carbon-carbon single bond.[14] The harmonic potential prevents dissociation of the diatom over the course of the simulation allowing easy analysis of the vibrational energy distribution.

Interactions between atoms in different dimers were modeled with a Morse potential with a well depth of 3.2×10^{-21} J and an equilibrium separation of 0.5 nm. These values are of the order of those typically found for van der Waals interactions in molecular crystals. A crystal with 3D periodic boundary conditions corresponding to a block of 8×12×6 dimers was equilibrated to a temperature of 100 K, with a longitudinal sound velocity of 3 km/sec estimated from a numerical evaluation of the bulk modulus of the crystal. The relaxed nearest-neighbor equilibrium distance between center-of-masses of the dimer pairs is about 0.55 nm. The shock was simulated by a finite thickness slab constructed from the {111} layers of the crystal. Two-dimensional periodicity was imposed over a region roughly 4.2×7.5 nm, corresponding to an 8×16 pattern of dimers in a layer. The slab was roughly 18 nm thick (42 layers).

We chose a Cartesian coordinate system with the x and y directions along the periodic boundary repeat vectors, and the z direction normal to the {111} layering. A cylindrical void with a diameter of roughly 2.0 nm of 152 pairs per periodic cell (with the central axis of the cylinder lying parallel to the x axis) was removed from the system. The atomic trajectories were calculated using a standard leap-frog algorithm with a 0.5 fs time step. Simulations of shock waves have been simulated by using layers 1–4 as a flyer plate, moving the plate back by 0.2 nm and giving it varying impact velocities. The examples we discuss herein used impact velocities of 1, 3, and 5 km/sec.

RESULTS

We have calculated several local properties using the approach of Hardy,[15] assuming a Gaussian broadening function with a full-width at half-maximum of 0.2 nm. In Figure 1 we depict averages over the x-y plane of the z-component of the atomic velocities as a function of z coordinate for an impact velocity of 3 km/sec at four different points of time. We note that the void is initially centered at a z coordinate of roughly 7.5 nm. We see from inspection of Figure 1 that the wave front velocity is approximately 6 km/sec, substantially faster than the sound velocity of 3 km sec. As expected, the average particle velocities are slower than the shock velocity. The 5 km/sec impact simulation also has a shock front velocity of near 6 km/sec, and only marginally faster than that of the 3 km/sec impact simulation. For the 1 km/sec impact simulation, however, the wave front is sufficiently weak that the shock front velocity drops to about 4 km/sec. These results are similar to those we have obtained using more sophisticated bond-order potentials in two-dimensional simulations.[16–18] The most prominent feature of Figure 1 is the peak in the 1.0 ps curve at a z coordinate of about 6 nm. This arises from the acceleration of particles spalling into the void. This feature is noticed in all three simulations discussed in this article, with correspondingly higher average particle velocities behind the shock front.

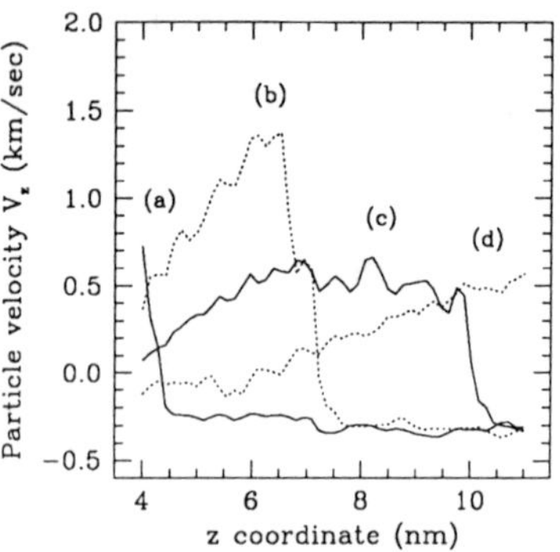

Figure 1. Planar average of local z component of particle velocity as a function of z coordinate for simulation times of (a) 0.5, (b) 1.0, (c) 1.5, and (d) 2.0 ps respectively from left to right.

In addition to planar averages over the x-y plane, we have also looked at the local properties over a 7×7 square section of the y-z plane, averaging just over the x coordinate. In Figure 2 we see a depiction of the two-dimensional field generated by taking the z-component of the average particle velocity for the 3 km/sec simulation at 1.2 ps, just as the shock front is passing the void. The location of the void can be noted in the depiction of the local particle density given in the base plane of the figure. We see that the particles immediately in front of the void are being spalled into the void at velocities substantially faster than the average particle velocities in the rest of the solid. Even so, we note that the wave front remains well ahead of the pulse of particles spalling into the void, as this pulse travels at a velocity related to the average particle velocity which is slower than the shock front velocity. In this simulation as well in the 1 km/sec impact simulation, we find that the void collapses smoothly and relatively symmetrically; the high pressure of the shock front surrounds the void before the spalled material can lead to a turbulent collapse of the void. We also get a transient increase in the local kinetic energy in the vicinity of the void as it collapses smoothly, but this increase dissipates to that resulting if no void is present over a period of about 1 ps.

Figure 2. x coordinate average of the local particle velocity over 7×7 nm square projection of the y-z plane for the 3 km/sec impact simulation at a point of time 1.2 ps into the simulation. Contours in base plane depict local particle density over same area.

Figure 3 depicts a similar snapshot of the local particle velocity for the 5 km/sec impact simulation at 0.95 ps when the shock front is collapsing the void. The shock front velocity is still about 6 km/sec, but the additional energy in the front results in particles at the leading edge of the void being thrust by the pressure of the front into the void at velocities of about 6 km/sec, comparable to the velocity of the shock front. At these velocities the shock front does not have time to surround the void before the particles spalled directly into the void slam into the material at the rear of the void. This process leads to a turbulent collapse of the void, and a significant transfer of energy to the vibrational modes of the dimers. Figure 4 depicts the local effective temperature of the vibrational modes at 4 ps into the simulation for the 5 km/sec impact simulation. By this time the shock wave has reached the end of our slab of material, and the kinetic energy in the vicinity of the void has equilibrated with the immediately surrounding material. But as Figure 4 shows, the effective vibrational temperature in the vicinity of the void is still substantially (by more than a factor of 6) higher than the initial effective temperature of about 100 K, and than the effective vibrational temperature of particles in the surrounding area.

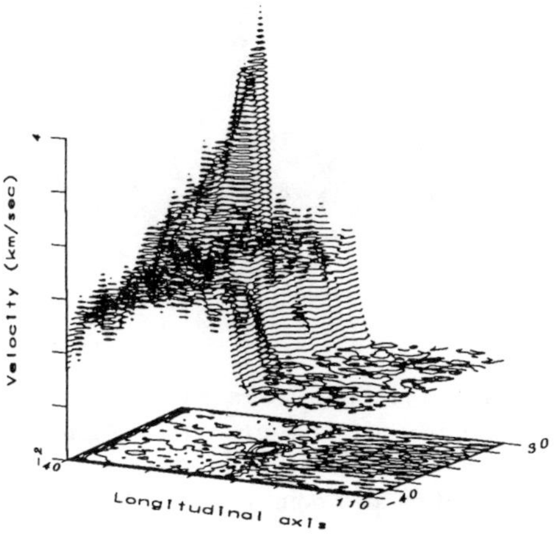

Figure 3. x coordinate average of the local particle velocity over 7×7 nm square projection of the y-z plane for the 5 km/sec impact simulation at a point of time 0.95 ps into the simulation. Contours in base plane depict local particle density over same area.

SUMMARY

We have carried out a series of molecular dynamics simulations on a model system to study the effects of voids on hot-spot formation during pressure-wave propagation in condensed-phase systems. Three-dimensional molecular-dynamics methods were used for a model system of diatomic molecules arranged in a {111} layering of an fcc lattice. Using this model, we have investigated the effects of impact strength on the resulting excitation of the vibrational modes of the model dimer. We find that substantial excitation of the vibrational modes is obtained if the shock strength is sufficient to accelerate particles on the leading edge of the void defect to velocities comparable to the shock front velocity. In our simulations this condition leads to a turbulent collapse of the void rather than a relatively smooth and symmetric collapse of the void; we speculate that this turbulent collapse is instrumental in the vibrational excitation.

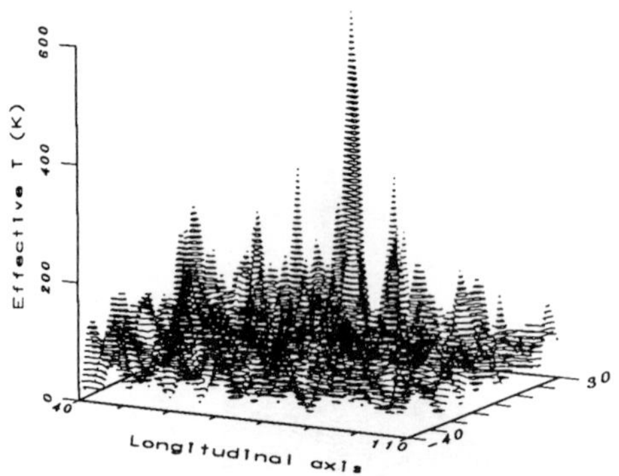

Figure 4. x coordinate average of the local effective vibrational temperature over 7×7 nm square projection of the y-z plane for the 5 km/sec impact simulation at a point of time 4.0 ps into the simulation.

ACKNOWLEDGMENTS

This work was supported by the Office of Naval Research through NRL and the ONR Physics Division. Computational support for this project was supported in part by a grant of computer resources from the Naval Research Laboratory.

REFERENCES

[1] J. N. Johnson, P. K. Tang, and C. A. Forest, *J. Appl. Phys.* **57** (1985) 4323.

[2] J. N. Johnson, *Proc. R. Soc. London, Ser. A* **413** (1987) 329.

[3] S. A. Bordzilovskii, S. M. Karakhanov, and V. F. Lobanov, *Fiz. Goreniya Vzryva* **23** (1987) 132 [*Combustion, Explosion, and Shock Waves* **23** (1987) 624].

[4] P. K. Tang, *J. Appl. Phys.* **63** (1988) 1041.

[5] F. E. Walker and A. M. Karo, in: *Shock Waves in Condensed Matter*, eds. S. C. Schmidt and N. C. Holmes (Elsevier, Amsterdam, 1988), 543–546.

[6] A. M. Karo and J. R. Hardy, *Int. J. Quantum Chem. Symp.* **20** (1986) 763.

[7] A. M. Karo, T. M. Deboni, J. R. Hardy, and G. A. Weiss, *Int. J. Quantum Chem. Symp.* **24** (1990) 277.

[8] D. H. Tsai, in: *Chemistry and Physics of Energetic Materials*, ed. S. N. Bulusu, NATO ASI Series C, Vol. 309 (Kluwer, Dordrecht, 1990) pp. 195–227; D. H. Tsai, *J. Chem. Phys.* **95** (1991) 7497.

[9] D. D. Dlott and M. D. Fayer, *J. Chem. Phys.* **92** (1990) 2798.

[10. C. S. Coffey, *J. de Physique Colloq.* **48** (1987) C4–253.

[11] F. A. Bandak, D. H. Tsai, R. W. Armstrong, and A. S. Douglas, *Phys. Rev. B* **47** (1993) 11681.

[12] F. A. Bandak, R. W. Armstrong, and A. S. Douglas, *Phys. Rev. B* **46** (1992) 3228.

[13] J. W. Mintmire, D. H. Robertson, D. W. Brenner, and C. T. White, "Molecular dynamics simulations of pressure wave effects at voids in a condensed-phase material," in *Shock Compression of Condensed Matter 1991*, Eds., S. C. Schmidt, R. D. Dick, J. W. Forbes, and D. G. Tasker, Elsevier, Amsterdam, 1992, pp. 147–150

[14] D. W. Brenner, *Phys. Rev. B* **42** (1990) 9458.

[15] R. J. Hardy, *J. Chem. Phys.* **76** (1982) 622.

[16] D. W. Brenner, D. H. Robertson, M. L. Elert, and C. T. White, *Phys. Rev. Lett.* **70** (1993) 2174.

[17] C. T. White, D. H. Robertson, M. L. Elert, and D. W. Brenner, "Molecular dynamics simulations of shock-induced chemistry: application to chemically sustained shock waves," in *Microscopic Simulations of Complex Hydrodynamic Phenomena*, Eds., M. Mareschal and B. L. Holian, Plenum, New York, 1992, pp. 111–123.

[18] C. T. White, D. H. Robertson, and D. W. Brenner, *Physica A* **188** (1992) 357.

INVERSE METHOD AND CONSISTENCY EXAMINATION FOR LAGRANGIAN ANALYSIS*

Huayou CAI
Institute of Rock and Soil Mechanics, Academia Sinica, Wuhan, Hubei 470073, PRC.
Z.P.TANG Bo YANG
Department of Modern Mechanics, University of Science and Technology of China, Hefei, Anhui 230026, PRC.

The recurrence formulas of inverse method for calculation of unknown σ(h,t) from pure particle velocity measurements are presented. It seems more flexible but needs consistency check, since it offers various fitting functions for unknown stresses along pathlines. The concept of consistency examination (CE) is reasonable, but it does not work well sometimes in practical use. The reason is analyzed and a new idea for qualitative consistency check is suggested based on c_σ and c_u relation for nonsimple waves.

INTRODUCTION

Lagrangian analysis was first introduced by Fowles at al[1] in early 70's and it has proved to be a useful tool for investigating materials dynamic properties and wave intrinsic features. But the problem is the whole stress field cannot be determined from particle velocity records only due to mathematical incompleteness. To solve this obstacle, there are normally two ways, i.e. Seaman's method[2] or to extrapolate the fitting surface[3]. Here we introduce another way, i.e. inverse method.

However, all these methods have uncertainties, even substantial errors and need to check. The consistency examination (CE) suggested first by Gupta[4] is necessary, but it fails sometimes. We try to discuss the reason and improvement.

INVERSE METHOD

According to path line method, the momentum equation could be written in following differential form[2]

$$-2\rho_o\Delta u_k = \left(\frac{d\sigma_{jk}}{dh} + \frac{d\sigma_{j+1,k}}{dh}\right)\Delta t_k - (\sigma_{j+1,k} - \sigma_{jk})\theta_k, \quad (1)$$

where

$$\Delta u_k = u_{j+1,k} - u_{jk},\ \Delta t_k = t_{j+1,k} - t_{jk},\ \theta_k = \frac{dt_{j+1,k}}{dh} + dt_k,$$

ρ_o is the initial density, the subscripts j and k represent the jth pathline and k^{th} gauge line. The unknown stress $\sigma_{j+1,k}$ can be calculated from Eq. (1) inversely, if its function form along pathline is chosen. This is so-called inverse method which Seaman[2] also mentioned and denied. For a polynomial fitting:

$$\sigma_{j+1,k} = \sum_{n=0}^{N} a_n h_k{}^n, \quad (2)$$

where N and a_n are fitting power and coefficients, respectively, one can derive a recurrence formula of matrix as follows[5]

$$\sum_{i=1}^{K} A_{ki}\sigma_{j+1,i} = \sum_{i=1}^{K} B_{ki}\sigma_{ji} + C_k, \qquad k = 1, 2, ..., K \quad (3)$$

where K is the number of gauges, and

$$\begin{aligned} A_{ki} &= \xi'_{ki}\Delta t_k - \delta_{ki}\theta_k \\ B_{ki} &= -\xi'_{ki}\Delta t_k - \delta_{ki}\theta_k, \\ C_k &= -2\rho_o\Delta u_k \end{aligned} \quad (4)$$

where δ_{ki} is Kronecker matrix, ξ'_{ki} is the derivative of fitting matrix ξ_{ki} with respect to h, and the latter is only related to h and N. Other symbols are same as in Eq.(1). The unknown stress $\sigma_{j+1,i}$ along $(j+1)^{th}$ pathline could be calculated using Eq.(3) if stress along j^{th} pathline is known. For the

* Work performed at National Lab. for Shock Waves and Detonation Phys., Southwest Inst. of Fluids Phys., PRC.

exponential fitting

$$\ln\sigma_{j+1,k} = \sum_{n=0}^{N} b_n h_k^n. \quad (5)$$

Eq.(1) will reduce to nonlinear equations of matrix for unknown $\sigma_{j+1,k}$

$$\sigma_{j+1,k}\sum_{i=1}^{K}\zeta'_{ki}\ln(\sigma_{j+1,i})\Delta t_k - \sigma_{j+1,k}\theta_k + 2\rho_o\Delta u_k$$
$$+\sigma_{jk}\sum_{i=1}^{K}\zeta'_{ki}\ln(\sigma_{ji})\Delta t_k + \sigma_{jk}\theta_k = 0, \quad k = 1,2,\ldots,K, \quad (6)$$

where ζ_{ki} is the fitting matrix, others are same as in Eq.(1). Eq.(6) could be solved for unknown $\sigma_{j+1,k}$ using Newton's iteration method.

Practical calculations indicate that exponential fitting is convergent and more reliable for many materials, and polynomial fitting with N=2 is similar to Seaman's assumption and may diverge in some cases. Taking semi-infinite viscoelastic bar with Maxwell model as an example, the constitutive equation is

$$\sigma + p\dot{\sigma} = q\dot{\varepsilon} \quad (7)$$

where ε is strain and p, q are constants. for a step loading $\sigma(0,t)=\sigma_0 H(t)$, H(t) is Heaviside function, at the end of the bar, we have analytical expressions of σ(h,t) and u(h,t), so we can compare various results of σ(h,t) calculated from analytical u(h,t) with different approaches. The results shown in Fig.1 indicate that the inverse method with exponential fitting (dashlines) are much better than Seaman's (dot-dash lines) for this material. The latter is divergent and has substantial error. When inverse method of polynomial fitting of N=2 is used, the results are similar to Seaman's. It reveals that Seaman's assumption means indeed a strong restriction imposed on constitutive behavior of materials for arbitrary pathlines. To those materials Seaman's assumption is approximately valid, the calculated results will be fine, otherwise, may not. It appears that inverse method may be more flexible, since it offers various fitting choices. However, consistency check is needed, since we do not have analytical solution in experiments.

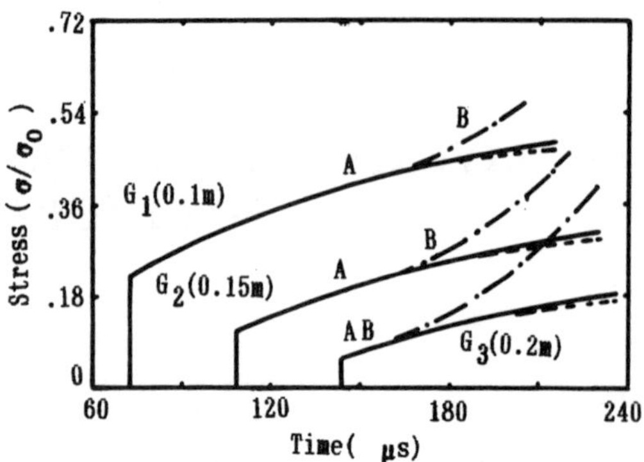

Fig.1 Comparison of σ(h,t) from analytical u(h,t) in a Maxwell bar with different approaches.
——— Analytical
----- Inverse Method with exponential fitting (N=2)
-·-·- Seaman's Method or inverse method with polynomial fitting of N=2.

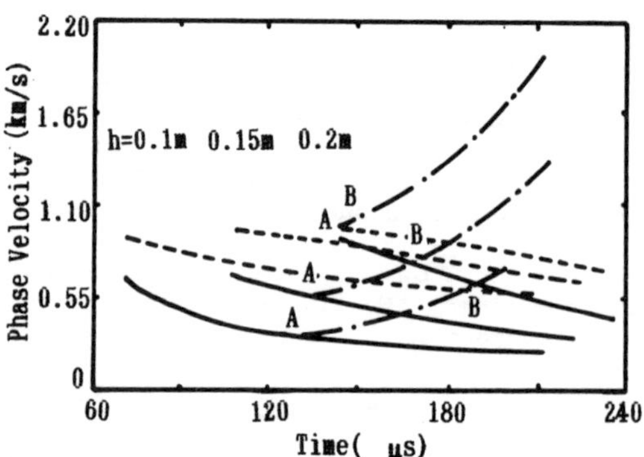

Fig.2 Comparison of C_σ and C_u for consistency examination.
----- C_u curves
——— Analytical C_σ curves
-·-·- C_σ curves of calculated σ'(h,t) with Seaman's assumption.

CONSISTENCY EXAMINATION

The idea of CE is first presented by Gupta[4]. It is quite reasonable, but sometimes it does not work efficiently. Here we analyze briefly.

If calculated stress σ'(h,t) from measured u(h,t) has an error $\sigma_E(h,t)$ compared to the real stress $\sigma(h,t)$, then the rebuilt particle velocity $u'(h,t)$ from $\sigma'(h,t)$ based on momentum equation will be

$$u'(h,t) = u(h,t) + u_E(h,t) \tag{8}$$

where

$$u_E(h,t) = -\frac{1}{\rho_o}\int_{t_o}^{t} \frac{\partial \sigma_E(h,t)}{\partial h} d\tau, \tag{9}$$

where $u_E(h,t)$ is the particle velocity error caused by $\sigma_E(h,t)$. The derivation $u_E(h,t)$ is the basis for reliability judgment. However, if $\partial\sigma_E(h,t)/\partial h \approx 0$, i.e. error $\sigma_E \approx \sigma_E(t)$, it leads to $u_E \approx 0$ and $u'(h,t) \approx u(h,t)$ no matter how large σ_E is. In this case CE method fails.

In order to judge the reliability qualitatively in such situation, an idea of comparing C_σ and C_u is suggested here. For loading part of a nonsimple attenuating wave, we have[3] $C_\sigma < C_u < C_V$, and for a growing wave, $C_V < C_u < C_\sigma$, C_σ, C_u, C_V are phase speeds. The error of σ with t will change C_σ directly, since $C_\sigma = -(\frac{\partial \sigma}{\partial t})_h / (\frac{\partial \sigma}{\partial h})$. Hence, if the inequality mentioned above for C_σ of calculated $\sigma'(h,t)$ is not valid, the results of $\sigma'(h,t)$ must have substantial errors. Unfortunately, this judgment only offers single constraint boundary for C_σ in both cases. However, the trends of C_σ and C_u curves should be roughly similar, with some delay or advance. It may help the judgment. If their trends are different, an unreliability may produce. The C_σ-C_u comparisons of Fig.2 based on Fig.1 show that after point B, calculated C_σ with Seaman's assumption (dot-dash lines) exceeds C_u and non-physical error occurs after that point. Furthermore, the trends of calculated C_σ and C_u begin to differ from A. It hints that substantial error may start from point A. The resulted C_σ curves from exponential fit of inverse method are quite close to analytical curves.

DISCUSSION AND CONCLUSION

Both Seaman's method and inverse method may produce substantial errors and should be used with care. Inverse method can offer various fitting functions for unknown stresses along pathlines, and may be more flexible. The inverse method with exponential fitting normally has better results.

To evaluate the reliability of results of Lagrangian analysis, a validated CE is needed. Here we suggest a qualitative method of comparing C_σ and C_u. Further investigation involved in CE is necessary.

REFERENCES

[1] R.Fowles and R.F.Williams, J. Appl. Phys., 41, p.360 (1970).
[2] L.Seaman, J. Appl. Phys., 45, p.4303 (1974).
[3] J.B.Aidum and Y.M.Gupta, J. Appl. Phys., 69, p.6998-7014 (1991).
[4] Y.M.Gupta, Polym. Eng. Sci., 24, p.851 (1984).
[5] H.Y.Cai and Z.P.Tang, J. of USTC, 20, p.48-56 (1990).
[6] Y.Sano, J. Appl. Phys., 69, p.3525 (1991).

PHASE TRANSITIONS IN SPHERICAL STRESS WAVES

E.A.Kozlov[1], A.V.Zhukov[2]
[1]Research Institute of Technical Physics
P.O. Box 245
Chelyabinsk-70, Russia, 454070
[2]Research Institute of Applied Mathematics & Mechanics
Tomsk, Russia, 634050

Generalization is obtained for solutions [1,9] concerning the focusing of elastic and phase precursors in steel spheres under their loading [2,3] by the detonation of the superimposed explosive charge. Numerical calculations are performed while using the kinetic model of the $\alpha \rightleftarrows \varepsilon$ phase transition in iron [7,8] and with allowance for the plasto-elastic behaviour of the materials [4-9]. The results with respect to structure and stress waves parameters are presented. The influence of the $\alpha \rightleftarrows \varepsilon$ phase transitions on the stress waves evolution, the character of energy cumulation and the value of the explosion products energy transferred to the sphere are analysed.

INTRODUCTION

E.I.Zababakhin has considered [1] polymorphism as one of the possible reasons limiting the energy cumulation at the front of converging shock waves. The strong influence of the $\alpha \rightleftarrows \varepsilon$ phase transition in iron and steels on the value and character of the central vacuum cavity, being formed under loading of the initially full spheres of α- and γ-Fe, by spherically converging shock waves, has been found in [2,3].

The influence of the shear- and spall strength on the size of the cavity formed in the spheres of materials not undergone the polymorphous transitions has been analysed in [4].

In the works [5-8],[9] and [1] the influence of the $\alpha \rightleftarrows \varepsilon$ phase transition on the structure and parameters of the stress waves in iron has been considered under the conditions of plane, cylindrical and spherical geometries, respectively. In particular, in [1] the analytical solutions on the focusing of the elastic precursor or only the phase one in the α-Fe sphere has been published. The aim of this work is

- to obtain the generalization of the solutions [1,4,9];
- to make the computation-theoretical prediction concerning the influence of the $\alpha \rightleftarrows \varepsilon$ phase transition kinetics in iron on the stress waves structure and parameters change in the sphere of α-Fe for the subsequent comparison of computational and experimental results;
- to analyse the influence of the $\alpha \rightleftarrows \varepsilon$ phase transition and the plasto-elastic properties of iron on the value of the explosion product energy transferred to steel spheres for the subsequent comparison with the results of the calorimeter measurements [10] on the conserved samples.

The presented results have not only the scientific interest but also the definite practical one that is connected with using [3,11-13] of the spherical ampoules of conservation for studying into the behaviour and properties as well as for obtaining and synthesizing new materials.

STATEMENT OF THE PROBLEM AND MODELS

Non-stationary flows in the α-Fe full sphere, 64 mm in diameter, are analysed under loading by the detonation of the superimposed TNT-RDX 3/7 charge (ρ = 1.72 g/cm^3, D = 8.05 km/s, Q = 5.47 kJ/g) having 8 mm in thickness and initiated over the external surface at the instant of time t = 0.

The statement of the problem and the equations describing the motion of the plasto-elastic solid without phase transition for the case of the spherical symmetry are published in [4]. These equations correspond with the mass-, impulse- and energy conservation laws. The plasto-elastic model and the fracture criterion used for the calculation of the cavity formation dynamics after the reflection of the converging wave from the sphere center have also been described in [4].

For closing the equations set,as opposed to [5,6,9], thermodynamically full equations of state for the α- and ε-phases of iron and the model for describing the kinetics of the direct $\alpha \rightarrow \varepsilon$ and reverse $\varepsilon \rightarrow \alpha$ transition from [7,8] have been additionally used in our case.

In the considered phase transition model, the kinetics constants were assumed to be equal for the direct and reverse transition, their values were determined by modelling of plane waves structure in iron.

In plasto-elastic calculations, as a first approximation, the shear modules and the yield strength of the α - and ε -phases of iron were also assumed to be equal, G = 820 GPa and Y = 0.5 GPa. Moreover, the problem was solved in the plasto-elastic approximation with constant values of yield strength and shear modules. For describing a plastic flow we used the standard procedure [4-9] to determine the components of the deviator part of the stress tensor according to von Mises' criterion.

SOLUTION PROCEDURE

For numerical solving the set of equations, the two-step difference scheme described in [7] has been used. The sphere of iron, 32 mm in radius, was divided into 128 Lagrange cells with Δr = 0.25 mm which were numbered from the center to the external surface of the sphere. The coordinate (r) and the particle velocity (u) are related to the cells boundaries but radial stress component (σ_r), specific internal energy (E) and temperature (T) - to the cells centers.

CALCULATIONS RESULTS

The main results of the comparative calculations are outlined which demonstrate the influence of the reversible $\alpha \rightleftharpoons \varepsilon$ phase transition in iron on the basic parameters of the flows arising in steel spheres. The stress distributions along the sphere radius for different instants of time are given in Figure 1a and 1b without and with taking into account $\alpha \rightleftharpoons \varepsilon$ phase transition, respectively. In the left part of each figure the stress waves profiles are shown prior to focusing and in the right one- after focusing. Numbers over the curves show the corresponding instants of time in microseconds. The initiation moment of the explosive on its external surface is assumed to be the zero time reference. The pressure distribution in the explosive layer is given for the instant of time t = 0.745 μs.

In Figure 1b the peculiarities of the wave with phase transitions are distinctly seen on the plots at the instants of time t = 3 μs and 5 μs. The elastic precursor is small in amplitude but it is presented and its role can be estimated. The elastic precursor wave is propagating in the considered model without its cumulation when focusing. The velocity of the phase precursor spreading is not constant. It begins to increase appreciably after the elastic precursor focus-

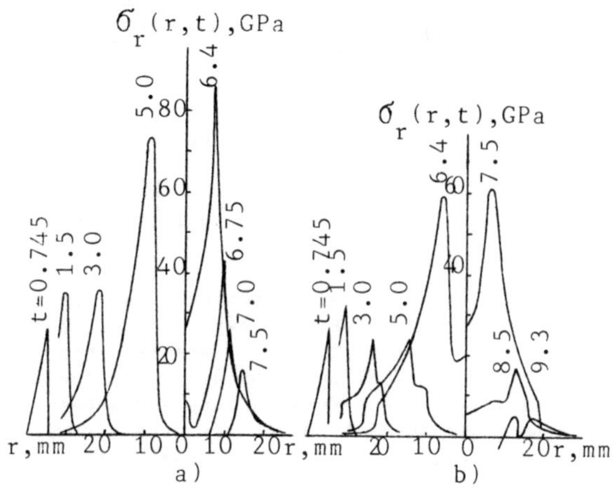

Figure 1. Stress distribution $\sigma_r(r,t)$ along the steel sphere radius for different instants of time without (a) and with (b) $\alpha \rightleftharpoons \varepsilon$ phase transition.

ing at t=5.1 μs. As opposed to the amplitude of the phase precursor (the first plastic wave), the amplitude of the second plastic wave is sharply changed in time. At first it is decreased due to an unloading wave going from the sphere surface, but then, after passing the minimum, it starts to be intensified when it approaches the center. The moment of

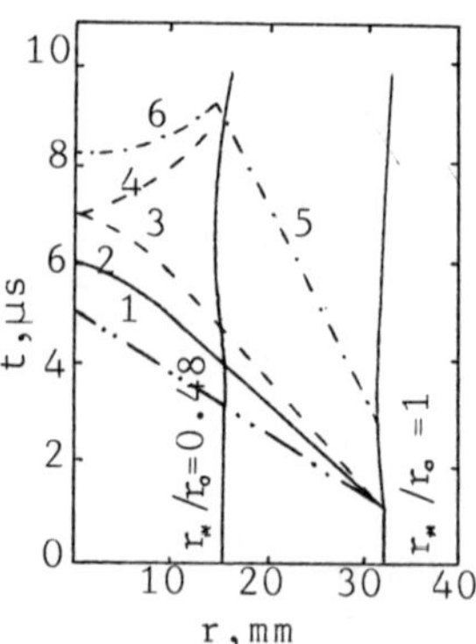

Figure 2. Diagram of wave processing in the α- Fe sphere in Lagrange coordinates (r,t). 1 - elastic precursor, 2 - phase precursor, 3 - second plastic wave ($\sigma_r(r,t)$ maximum in a converging wave), 4 - maximum stress after focusing, 5 - shock rarefaction wave from the sphere surface. 6 - shock rarefaction wave from the sphere center.
Trajectories of Lagrange particles with r_*/r_o = 0.48 and r_*/r_o = 1 are shown.

this wave focusing begins at t = 6.95 μs. The shock rarefaction wave arising as a result of the inverse $\varepsilon \rightarrow \alpha$ phase transition is moving with the velocity equal to 2.5 km/s.

After focusing in the sphere two rarefaction waves are generated which are moving to meet each other (from the surface and from the center of the sphere) as can be seen in Figure 1b (with t = 7.5 μs) and Figure 2.

The meeting of these rarefaction waves leading to the formation of the sharply changing tensile stresses is realized in the point r = 14 mm at t = 9.3 μs. I.e., in the sphere two regions of tensile stresses are formed. One of them is stipulated by the usual inertial scatter of the material, the other one appears as a result of meeting of two shock rarefaction waves arising due to the $\varepsilon \rightarrow \alpha$ transition proceeding.

In Figure 3 stress distributions of $\sigma_r(r_*,t)$ are given in normal and logarithmic coordinates for some of the separated Lagrange particles both for the case of the $\alpha \rightleftarrows \varepsilon$ phase transition absence (a,c) and its availability (b,d). Numbers over the curves denote the relative Lagrange radius of the particle r_*/r_0.

The curves for r_*/r_0 = 1 describe the loading impulse forms on the sphere surface. The peculiarity of this curve in Figure 3b for t = 2.5 μs is connected with proceeding of the $\varepsilon \rightarrow \alpha$ transition in the rarefaction wave. The curves presented in the logarithmic scale

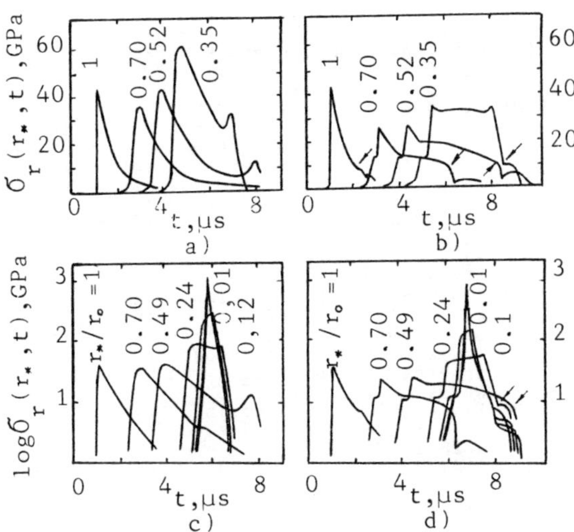

Figure 3. Changes of $\sigma_r(r,t)$ radial stresses in time for some separated Lagrange particles without (a,c) and with (b,d) $\alpha \rightleftarrows \varepsilon$ phase transition. Number over the curves denotes the relative radius of the particle r_*/r_0. The onset of the $\varepsilon \rightarrow \alpha$ transition is noted by arrows.

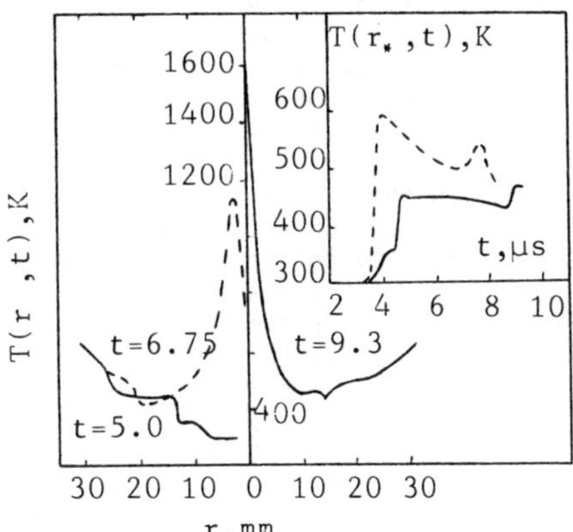

Figure 4. Temperature distribution T(r,t) along the radius of the α-Fe sphere. On the cutting-in the temperature profiles at the point with r_*/r_0=0.48 are shown by a solid line with the $\alpha \rightleftarrows \varepsilon$ phase transition availability and by a dashed line-without this transition.

allows to follow the cumulation character of the main plastic wave as well as to analyse the fast unloading corresponding to the shock rarefaction wave. The lower values of the stresses $\sigma_r^{\varepsilon\rightarrow\alpha}$ corresponding to the onset of the $\varepsilon \rightarrow \alpha$ phase transition for the deeply located Lagrange particles (Figure 3d) are connected with the higher heating of the material by the converging plastic wave and with a negative slope at (T,p) - coordinates of the $\alpha \rightleftarrows \varepsilon$ phase equilibrium boundary. Moreover, it should be noted that in the upper layers (Figure 3b, Lagrange particles with r_*/r_0 = 1; 0.70 and 0.52) the $\varepsilon \rightarrow \alpha$ transition takes place in the rarefaction wave going from the surface of loading and is characterized by a certain minimum on the curve $\sigma_r(r,t)$. For the deeply located Lagrange particles at r_*/r_0 < 0.44 (Figure 3b, r_*/r_0 = 0.35) the $\varepsilon \rightarrow \alpha$ transition takes place in the rarefaction wave from the center and, prior to the sharp drop in stress, the presence of some plateau is typical.

In Figure 4 the distributions of temperature T(r,t) for three fixed instants of time are given. For t = 5.0 μs one can see the temperature increase up to 350 K in the phase precursor front, up to 450 K - in the second plastic wave, and temperature increment roughly up to 40 K - in the shock rarefaction wave front. At the instant of time t = 6.75 μs (the dashed line, for illustration) the growth of temperature is seen in the self-focusing wave. The temperature distribution for t = 9.3 μs can be considered as the residual one [10].

We note that the $\varepsilon \rightleftharpoons \gamma$ phase transition not considered in this paper can be realized for the deep radii at $r_* < 2.5$ mm. The influence of the $\alpha \rightleftharpoons \varepsilon$ phase transition on the temperature profile change for the Lagrange particle located at $r_*/r_0 = 0.48$ is clearly demonstrated on the cutting - in of Figure 4.

In Figure 5 changing in time of the energies transferred to the steels spheres is shown. For steel with the $\alpha \rightleftharpoons \varepsilon$ phase transition the results are denoted by a solid line. In the case of this transition absence the calculated data are presented by a dashed line.

The total energy of the sphere reaches quickly its maximum and is not changed in the following. The kinetic and potential energies have sharp breaks in the point of the main plastic wave focusing. The energy released under the detonation of the explosive material layer, 8 mm in thickness and with calorific power Q = 5.47 kJ/g. amounts to 1.230 MJ. Without the phase transition in steel, 13% of this energy is transferred to the ball, whereas with the $\alpha \rightleftharpoons \varepsilon$ phase transition - 17%.

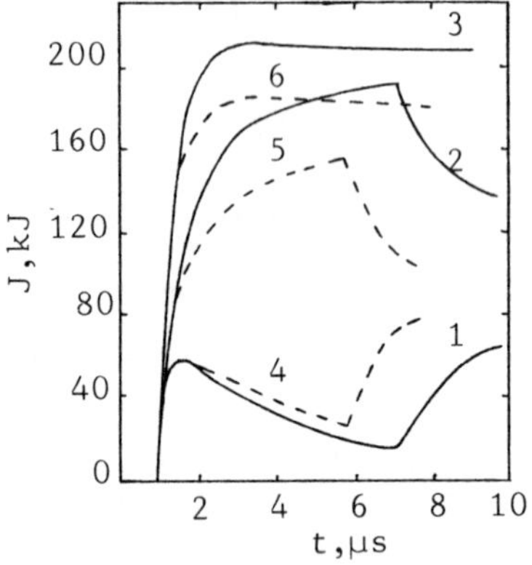

Figure 5. Energy absorbed by the sphere with (1-3) and without (4-6) $\alpha \rightleftharpoons \varepsilon$ phase transition. 1.4 -kinetic energy calculated according to the counting cells velocity; 2.5 -potential energy; 3.6 -total energy of the sphere.

CONCLUSION

The presented comparative calculations results show that the $\alpha \rightleftharpoons \varepsilon$ phase transition in α -Fe exerts a sufficient influence on the structure and stress waves parameters in the steel full sphere loaded by detonation of high explosive charge. Up to a moment of the elastic precursor focusing, the parameters of the converging phase precursor are little affected. The $\alpha \rightleftharpoons \varepsilon$ phase transition availability contributes to the more complete transfer of high explosive products energy to the compressed full sphere.

[1] E.I.Zababakhin, I.E.Zababakhin, *Unrestricted Cumulation Phenomenon*, Moscow: NAUKA, 1988, ch.6, pp.79-95.

[2] E.A.Kozlov, "Experimental check of E.I. Zababakhin hypothesis concerning limitation of energy cumulation in the spherically converging shock-wave front in medium with phase transitions", *in Proceedings of the Conference on SHOCK COMPRESSION OF CONDENSED MATTER 1991, S.C. Schmidt et al., (eds.), 1992 Elsevier Science Publishers B.V.*, pp. 169-176.

[3] E.A. Kozlov, *High Pressure Research* 10, pp. 541-582 (1992).

[4] S.M.Bakhrakh, N.P.Kovalev, B.A.Nadykto et al., *Reports of Ac. Sci. USSR* 215, 5, pp. 1090-1093 (1974).

[5] R.I.Nigmatulin, *Russ.J.Appl.Mech.& Tech. Phys.* 1, pp. 88-95 (1970).

[6] N.Kh. Akhmadeev, R.I. Nigmatulin, *Russ. J.Appl. Mech. & Tech. Phys.* 5, pp. 128-135 (1976).

[7] A.V.Zhukov, A.I. Korneev, V.G. Simonenko. *Russ.Ac.Sci.J. Solid State Mechanics* 4, pp. 138-143 (1984).

[8] A.V.Zhukov, *Russ. J.Appl.Mech.& Tech. Phys.* 3, pp. 112-114 (1986).

[9] M.N.Kravchenko, *Vestnik - Proc. of Moscow State Univ., Ser.1, Math. & Mech.*, 1, pp. 81-85 (1987).

[10] O.N.Averkov, S.P.Gryadobitov, E.A. Kozlov et al., "A solid-state calorimeter for measuring the internal energy increment of metal samples, capable for surviving explosive loading, *in Proceedings of the Conference on SHOCK COMPRESSION OF CONDENSED MATTER 1991, S.C.Schmidt et al., (eds.), 1992 Elsevier Science Publishers B.V.*, pp. 859-862.

[11] E.A.Kozlov, B.V.Litvinov, I.G.Kabin et al., "The acquisition and investigation of submicrocrystal structure materials in experiments on loading of metal spheres by spherically converging shock waves, *ibid*, pp. 535-537.

[12] B.V.Litvinov, E.A.Kozlov, Yu.N.Zhugin et al., *Reports of Ac.Sci. USSR* 319, 6, pp. 1428-1429 (1991).

[13] E.A.Kozlov, M.A.Lebedev, B.V.Litvinov, *Russ.J.Phys.of Comb.& Expl.* 2, pp. 118-122 (1993).

AN IMPROVED COMPUTATIONAL CONSTITUTIVE MODEL FOR BRITTLE MATERIALS

Gordon R. Johnson and Tim J. Holmquist
Alliant Techsystems
600 Second Street N.E.
Hopkins, Minnesota 55343

An improved computational constitutive model for brittle materials is presented. It is applicable for brittle materials subjected to large strains, high strain rates and high pressures, and is well-suited for computations in both Lagrangian and Eulerian codes. The equivalent strength is dependent on the intact strength, fractured strength, strain, strain rate, pressure, and damage. The pressure includes the effect of bulking, which is introduced through the transfer of internal energy from decreased shear and deviator stresses to potential internal energy associated with increased hydrostatic pressure. Examples are presented to illustrate the model.

INTRODUCTION

The original Johnson-Holmquist model [1] for brittle materials includes pressure-dependent strength, damage and fracture, significant strength after fracture, bulking, and strain rate effects. After the model was first reported, it was implemented into several codes and applied to a variety of applications. It soon became apparent that there were several concerns.

The model does not allow for gradual softening, and some materials (such as Boron Carbide) clearly show a gradual softening during flyer plate impact tests [2]. Also, results for some applications are very sensitive to the constants used in the model and there is not a straightforward process available to determine accurate constants. Finally, the jump conditions between fractured material (damage = D = 1.0) and intact material (D < 1.0) caused some problems for Eulerian codes, whereby the material could tend to heal itself after fracture had occurred.

The new model was developed to address these concerns. The original model subsequently will be referred to as the JH-1 model and the new model as the JH-2 model.

DESCRIPTION OF THE JH-2 MODEL

A general overview of the JH-2 model is shown in Figure 1. Although it is very similar to the JH-1 model, there are several differences.

- The material begins to soften when the damage begins to accumulate (D > 0). This allows for gradual softening of the material under increasing plastic strain. (The JH-1 model does not soften until D = 1.0, and then the softening occurs instantaneously.)

- The strength and pressure are normalized by the strength and pressure components of the Hugoniot Elastic Limit (HEL), which allows for many of the constants to be dimensionless. This can be very helpful when comparing different materials, and when estimating constants for materials which have an insufficient data base to determine constants.

- The strength and damage are analytic functions of the pressure and other variables. This allows for parametric variation of the constants in a more systematic manner. (The JH-1 model uses multiple linear segments.)

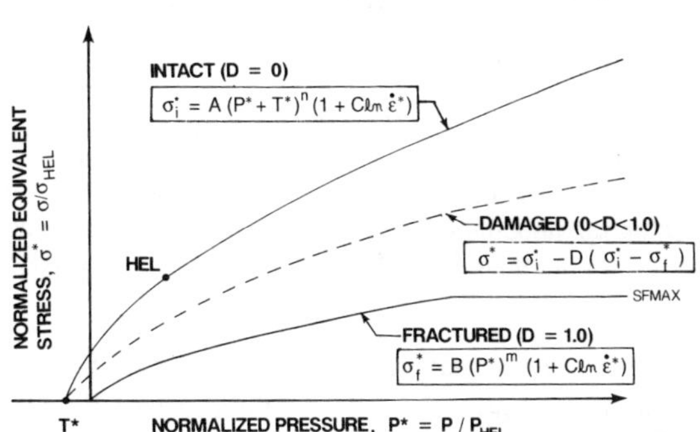

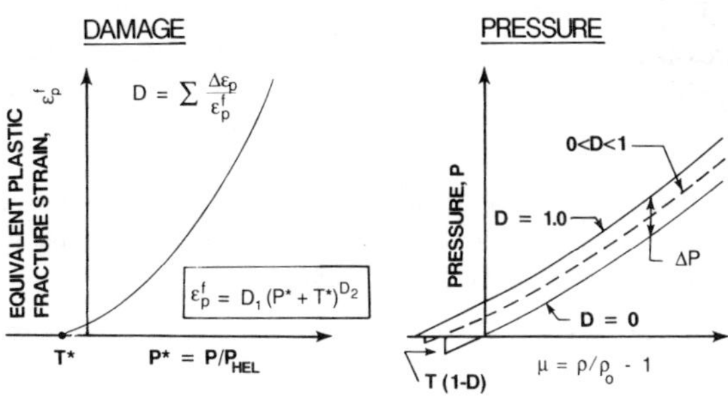

Figure 1. Description of the JH-2 ceramic model

- The strength generally is a smoothly varying function of the intact strength, fracture strength, strain rate, and damage. It is well-suited for implementation into Eulerian codes.

Returning to Figure 1, the normalized equivalent stress is

$$\sigma^* = \sigma_i^* - D(\sigma_i^* - \sigma_f^*)\,, \tag{1}$$

where σ_i^* is the normalized intact equivalent stress, σ_f^* is the normalized fracture stress, and D is the damage ($0 \le D \le 1.0$).

The normalized equivalent stresses (σ^*, σ_i^*, σ_f^*) have the general form

$$\sigma^* = \sigma/\sigma_{HEL}\,, \tag{2}$$

where σ is the actual equivalent stress and σ_{HEL} is the equivalent stress at the HEL.

The normalized intact strength is given by

$$\sigma_i^* = A(P^* + T^*)^N\,(1 + C{\bullet}\ln\dot{\varepsilon}^*)\,, \tag{3}$$

and the normalized fracture strength is given by

$$\sigma_f^* = B(P^*)^M\,(1 + C{\bullet}\ln\dot{\varepsilon}^*)\,. \tag{4}$$

Note that the normalized fracture strength can be limited by $\sigma_f^* \le$ SFMAX. This optional fracture strength parameter is included to provide more flexibility in defining the important fracture strength. It also allows the user to use the same fracture strength as used for the JH-1 model (when M = 1.0).

The material constants are A, B, C, M, N, and SFMAX. The normalized pressure is $P^* = P/P_{HEL}$, where P is the actual pressure and P_{HEL} is the pressure at the HEL. The normalized maximum tensile hydrostatic pressure is $T^* = T/P_{HEL}$, where T is the maximum tensile hydrostatic pressure the material can withstand. The dimensionless strain rate is $\dot{\varepsilon}^* = \dot{\varepsilon}/\dot{\varepsilon}_o$, where $\dot{\varepsilon}$ is the actual strain rate and $\dot{\varepsilon}_o = 1.0\ s^{-1}$ is the reference strain rate.

The damage for fracture is accumulated in a manner similar to that used in the JH-1 model [1] and the Johnson-Cook fracture model [3]. It is expressed as

$$D = \Sigma\,\Delta\varepsilon^P/\varepsilon_f^P\,, \tag{5}$$

where $\Delta\varepsilon^P$ is the plastic strain during a cycle of integration and $\varepsilon_f^P = f(P)$ is the plastic strain to fracture under a constant pressure, P. The specific expression is

$$\varepsilon_f^P = D_1(P^* + T^*)^{D_2}, \tag{6}$$

where D_1 and D_2 are constants and P^* and T^* are as defined previously in Equation (3). Again, the material cannot undergo any plastic strain at $P^* = -T^*$; but ε_f^P increases as P^* increases.

A physical explanation of damage and fracture is shown in Figure 2. If the material is held under a constant pressure and then subjected to a straining deformation at a constant strain rate, the damage begins to accumulate when the material begins to flow plastically (at $\sigma = \sigma_i$). The material then begins to soften (relative to the intact strength). This softening could be related to the material going from a larger particle size to a smaller particle size under increased plastic strain. When the material is completely damaged (D = 1.0), the strength does not decrease with increased plastic strain (at $\sigma = \sigma_f$).

Unfortunately, it is not generally possible to perform these tests at sufficiently high pressures of interest. As a result, the damage functions and fracture strength must be inferred from other data.

The hydrostatic pressure before fracture begins (D = 0) is simply

$$P = K1{\bullet}\mu + K2{\bullet}\mu^2 + K3{\bullet}\mu^3\,, \tag{7}$$

where K1, K2, and K3 are constants (K1 is the bulk modulus); and $\mu = \rho/\rho_o - 1$ for current density ρ and initial density ρ_o. For tensile pressure ($\mu < 0$), Equation (7) is replaced by $P = K1{\bullet}\mu$. Energy effects are assumed to be insignificant [4].

After damage begins to accumulate (D > 0), bulking (pressure increase and/or volumetric strain increase) can occur [5]. Now an additional incremental pressure, ΔP, is added, such that

$$P = K1{\bullet}\mu + K2{\bullet}\mu^2 + K3{\bullet}\mu^3 + \Delta P\,. \tag{8}$$

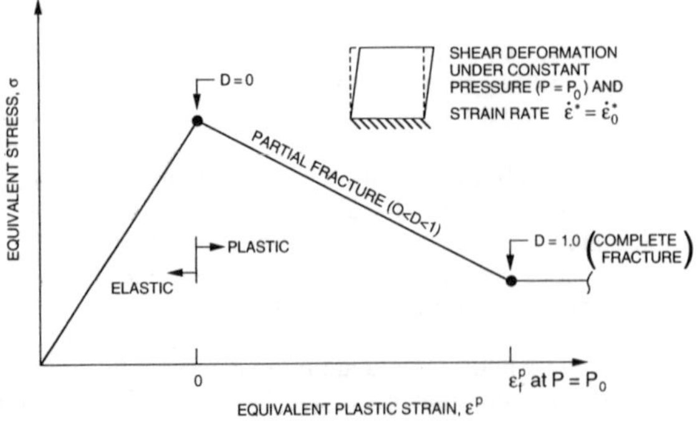

Figure 2. Strength, damage, and fracture under a constant pressure and strain rate

The pressure increment is determined from energy considerations; it varies from $\Delta P = 0$ at $D = 0$ to $\Delta P = \Delta P_{max}$ at $D = 1.0$. Figure 3 shows how ΔP increases as D increases. The incremental internal elastic energy decrease (due to decreased shear and deviator stresses) is converted to potential internal energy by incrementally increasing ΔP. The decrease in the shear and deviator stresses occurs because the strength, σ, decreases as the damage, D, increases, as shown in Figure 1 and Equation (1).

The general expression for the elastic internal energy of the shear and deviator stresses is

$$U = \sigma^2/6G\,, \tag{9}$$

where σ is the equivalent plastic flow stress and G is the shear modulus of elasticity [6].

The incremental energy loss is

$$\Delta U = U_{D(t)} - U_{D(t+\Delta t)}\,, \tag{10}$$

where $U_{D(t)}$ and $U_{D(t+\Delta t)}$ are computed from Equation (9) using $\sigma_{t+\Delta t}$ for both energies.

If the energy loss, ΔU, is converted to potential hydrostatic energy through ΔP, an approximate equation for this energy conservation is

$$(\Delta P_{t+\Delta t} - \Delta P_t)\mu_{t+\Delta t} + (\Delta P^2_{t+\Delta t} - \Delta P^2_t)/2\cdot K1 = \beta\cdot\Delta U. \tag{11}$$

The first term $[(\Delta P_{t+\Delta t} - \Delta P_t)\mu_{t+\Delta t}]$ is the approximate potential energy for $\mu > 0$ and the second term $[(\Delta P^2_{t+\Delta t} - \Delta P^2_t)/2\cdot K1]$ is the corresponding potential energy for $\mu < 0$.

Solving for the updated ΔP gives

$$\Delta P_{t+\Delta t} = -K1\cdot\mu_{t+\Delta t} + \sqrt{(K1\cdot\mu_{t+\Delta t} + \Delta P_t)^2 + 2\cdot\beta\cdot K1\cdot\Delta U} \tag{12}$$

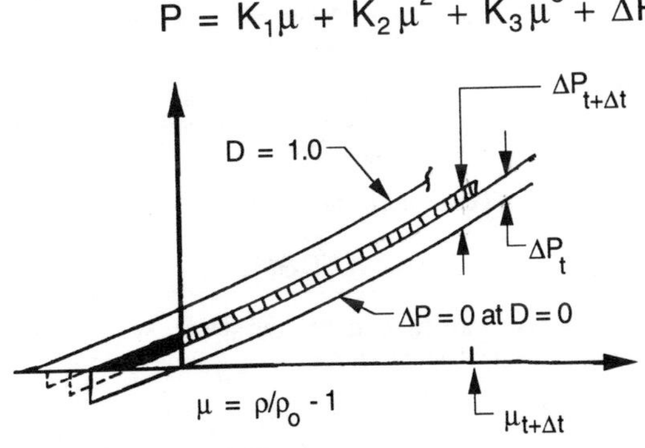

Figure 3. Description of incremental bulking pressure

As was the case for the JH-1 model, the JH-2 model also gives $\Delta P = 0$ when $\beta = 0$, where β is the fraction ($0 \le \beta \le 1$) of the elastic energy loss converted to potential hydrostatic energy.

EXAMPLES USING THE JH-2 MODEL

Various features of the JH-2 model can be illustrated by the three examples shown in Figure 4. The tensile strength of the material is T = 0.2 GPa, the HEL = 2.79 GPa, the intact strength is assumed to be $\sigma_i^* = 0.93(P^* + T^*)^{0.6}$, the modulus of elasticity is E = 220 GPa, and Poisson's ratio is $\upsilon = 0.22$. There is no strain rate effect so that C = 0 in Equations (3) and (4). From the preceding constants, the following additional constants can be obtained:

$$K1 = \frac{E}{3(1-2\nu)} = 130.95\ \text{GPa}\,, \tag{13}$$

$$G = \frac{E}{2(1+\nu)} = 90.16\ \text{GPa}\,, \tag{14}$$

$$P_{HEL} = K1\cdot\mu_{HEL} + K2\cdot\mu^2_{HEL} + K3\cdot\mu^3_{HEL} = 1.46\ \text{GPa}, \tag{15}$$

$$\sigma_{HEL} = \frac{3}{2}(HEL - P_{HEL})\,, \tag{16}$$

where HEL is the net axial stress for the Hugoniot Elastic Limit, P_{HEL} is the pressure component of the HEL, and $\mu_{HEL} = 0.01117$ is the corresponding μ at P_{HEL} (for K2 = K3 = 0). For a known HEL and G, μ_{HEL} can be obtained iteratively from

$$HEL = K1\cdot\mu_{HEL} + K2\cdot\mu^2_{HEL} + K3\cdot\mu^3_{HEL} + \frac{4}{3}G\left(\frac{\mu_{HEL}}{1+\mu_{HEL}}\right). \tag{17}$$

Because the height is H = 1.0m and the area is A = 1.0m^2, the deflection is $\delta = -\varepsilon_z$ and the force is $F = -\sigma_z$. For all three cases, the force, F, is slowly applied until δ = 0.05m, and then it is slowly released until F = 0. The paths are shown for strength versus pressure and for force versus deflection.

For Case A, the material cannot develop any plastic strain ($\varepsilon_f^P = 0$) or any strength after fracture ($\sigma_f = 0$). All of the elastic energy loss (of deviator and shear stresses) is converted to potential hydrostatic energy (β = 1.0). Because there is no plastic work, the external work must also vanish. This is shown in the force versus deflection relationship for Case A. The pressure jump (ΔP = 0.56 GPa) provides for this conservation of energy.

Case B is similar to Case A except the material is allowed to accumulate some plastic strain during fracture. Taking D1 = 0.005 and D2 = 1.0 in Equation (6) gives a pressure dependent fracture strain, ε_f^P. It can be seen in Figure 4 that the material gradually softens between point 2

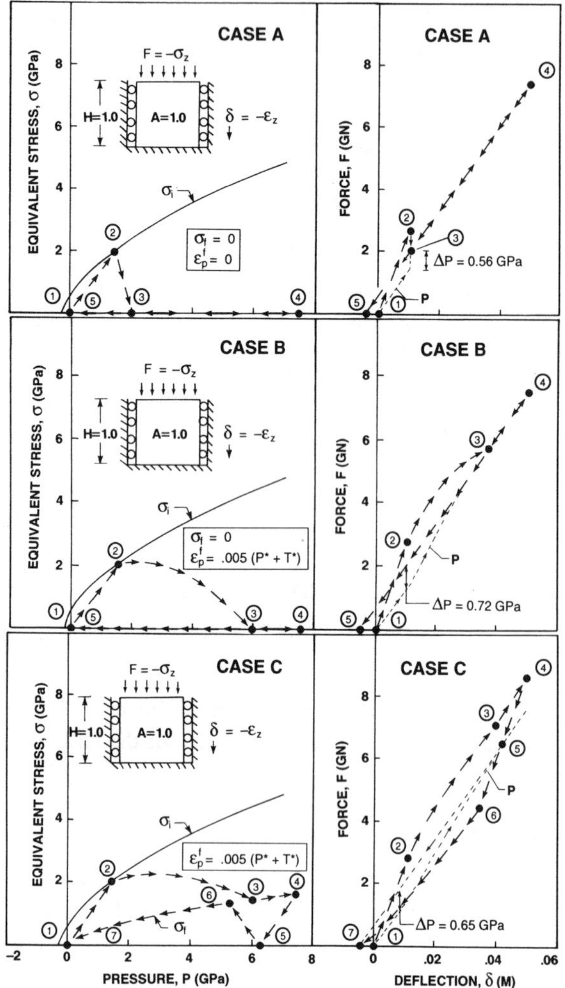

Figure 4. Examples of material responses with the JH-2 model

(where the damage begins to accumulate) and point 3 (where the damage is complete and there is no strength). The bulking pressure, ΔP, is also generated between these two points.

Case C is similar to Case B except that there is strength in the fractured material $[\sigma_f^* = 0.31(P^*)^{0.6}]$. The constants from Equation (4) are assumed to be B = 0.31, m = 0.6, and C = 0. Here the response is very complex, with the primary regions of interest as follows:

From Points 1 to 2 the material loads elastically until the intact strength, σ_i, is encountered at point 2. From Points 2 to 3 the material flows plastically, moving from the intact strength at point 2 to the fracture strength at point 3. The damage goes from D = 0 at point 2 to D = 1.0 at point 3. Similarly, the bulking pressure goes from ΔP = 0 at point 2 to ΔP = 0.65 GPa at point 3. From Points 3 to 4 the material continues to flow plastically along the fracture strength envelope, σ_f. From Points 4 to 5 the loading direction is reversed at point 4 and the material unloads elastically. At point 4, the axial deviator stress is in compression. At point 5, the axial deviator stress is completely unloaded such that the resulting stress is due only to the hydrostatic pressure. From Points 5 to 6 the elastic unloading continues and the axial deviator stress goes into tension. The net axial stress remains in compression, however, because the pressure is greater than the deviator stress. The fracture stress, σ_f, is encountered at point 6. From Points 6 to 7 the material unloads plastically along the fracture strength envelope. At point 7, both the pressure and the axial deviator stress (strength) go to zero.

SUMMARY AND CONCLUSIONS

A new computational constitutive model has been presented for brittle materials. Examples have also been presented to illustrate the complex behavior of various materials under well-defined loading conditions.

REFERENCES

[1] G.R. Johnson and T.J. Holmquist, "A Computational Constitutive Model for Brittle Materials Subjected to Large Strains, High Strain Rates and High Pressures," *Shock-Wave and High-Strain-Rate Phenomena in Materials*, edited by M.A. Meyers, L.E. Murr, and K.P. Staudhammer, Marcel Dekker Inc., New York, pp. 1075-1081, 1992.

[2] M.E. Kipp and D.E. Grady, "Shock Compression and Release in High-Strength Ceramics," Sandia Report, SAND89-1461·UC-704, July 1989.

[3] G.R. Johnson and W. H. Cook, "Fracture Characteristics of Three Metals Subjected to Various Strains, Strain Rates, Temperatures and Pressures," *Journal of Engineering Fracture Mechanics*, Vol. 21, pp. 31–48, 1985.

[4] W.H. Gust and E.B. Royce, "Dynamic Yield Strengths of B_4C, BeO, and Al_2O_3 Ceramics," *Journal of Applied Physics*, Vol. 42, pp. 276–295, 1971.

[5] W.F. Brace, B.W. Paulding, and C. Scholz, "Dilatency in the Fracture of Crystalline Rocks," *Journal of Geophysical Research*, Vol. 71, pp. 3939–3953, 1966.

[6] J.D. Walker, Personal Communication.

ACKNOWLEDGMENT

This work was funded by the Defense Advanced Research Projects Agency (DARPA).

DISCUSSION OF STRESS TENSOR NONUNIQUENESS WITH APPLICATION TO NONUNIFORM, PARTICULATE SYSTEMS

J. B. Aidun
Los Alamos National Laboratory
Los Alamos, New Mexico, USA 87545

The indeterminacy of the mechanical stress tensor has been noted in several developments of expressions for stress in a system of particles. It is generally agreed that physical quantities related to the stress tensor must be insensitive to this nonuniqueness, but there is no definitive prescription for insuring it. Kröner's tensor decomposition theorem is applied to the mechanical stress tensor σ_{ij} to show that its complete determination requires specification of its "incompatibility," $\in_{ijk} \in_{lmn} \partial_j \partial_m \sigma_{kn}$, in addition to its divergence, which is obtained from the momentum conservation relation. For a particulate system, stress tensor incompatibility is shown to vanish to recover the correct expression for macroscopically observable traction. This result removes concern about nonuniqueness without requiring equilibrium or arbitrarily-defined force lines.

INTRODUCTION

Expressions for the configurational (interaction) contribution to the stress density tensor, $\underline{\underline{\sigma}}$, for particulate systems can be derived from the momentum conservation relation.[1-3] This part of the stress density tensor, exclusive of kinetic contributions, will be referred to here as the mechanical stress tensor. This quantity is of interest for molecular dynamics simulations, where the continuum stress can be obtained from it as an appropriate space and time average.[1,4] Because momentum conservation involves only the divergence of the stress density, mechanical stress expressions developed from it are indeterminate up to the addition of a divergence-free tensor, as has been commented on by several authors.[1-3,5] It is generally agreed that physical quantities related to the stress tensor must be insensitive to this nonuniqueness. Nielsen and Martin claim that the divergence-free part of the stress density $\underline{\underline{\sigma}}$ (incorrectly identified as the curl of an arbitrary tensor) does not contribute to volume integrals of $\underline{\underline{\sigma}}$ over all space for finite systems, over a periodic cell for periodic systems, or to surface integrals of $\underline{\underline{\sigma}}$ over infinite planes.[3] At least for classical systems, these claims are unsubstantiated and the divergence-free part of $\underline{\underline{\sigma}}$ must either be constrained, or physical quantities must be invariant to it. Here the physical content of the stress tensor is discussed and it is argued that its divergence-free part must vanish to yield the correct expression for traction, which is a physical observable.

THEORY

Kröner's decomposition theorem[6] provides the framework for evaluating stress tensor nonuniqueness. Like the Helmholtz decomposition theorem for vectors, Kröner's decomposition theorem for second rank tensors establishes that the information required to uniquely determine a tensor (to within a constant) is its divergence and incompatibility. The incompatibility operator, Inc, is defined as

$$\mathrm{Inc}\,\underline{\underline{A}} \equiv \underline{\nabla} \times [\underline{\nabla} \times \underline{\underline{A}}\,]^T \qquad (1a)$$

or

$$[\mathrm{Inc}\,\underline{\underline{A}}]_{ij} \equiv \in_{ikl} \in_{jmn} \partial_k\, \partial_m\, A_{ln} \qquad (1b)$$

Defining the deformation operator, Def, as

$$\mathrm{Def}\,\underline{a} \equiv \frac{1}{2}[\,\underline{\nabla a} + (\underline{\nabla a})^T] \qquad (2a)$$

or $$[\mathrm{Def}\,\underline{a}]_{ij} \equiv \frac{1}{2}(\partial_i a_j + \partial_j a_i), \qquad (2b)$$

the stress tensor can be decomposed as[6]

$$\underline{\underline{\sigma}} = \mathrm{Def}\,\underline{a} + \mathrm{Inc}\,\underline{\underline{C}}^S + \underline{\underline{\sigma}}^A + \underline{\underline{K}} \qquad (3)$$

where $\underline{\underline{K}}$ is a constant tensor. Superscript S (A) denotes the (anti)symmetric part of the tensor and superscript T denotes a transpose. The vector $\underline{\sigma}^A$, which generates the antisymmetric part of the stress tensor according to

$$\sigma^A_{ij} \equiv \epsilon_{ijk}\, \sigma^A_k , \qquad (4)$$

is subject to the Helmholtz decomposition,

$$\underline{\sigma}^A = \underline{\nabla} e + \underline{\nabla} \times \underline{G}\,. \qquad (5)$$

Substituting from Eqs. (4) and (5), the indicial form of the tensor decompostion, Eq. (3), becomes

$$\sigma_{ij} = \frac{1}{2}(\partial_i a_j + \partial_j a_i) + \epsilon_{ikl}\,\epsilon_{jmn}\,\partial_k\,\partial_m\, C^S_{ln} + \epsilon_{ijk}\,\partial_k\, e + \partial_i G_j - \partial_j G_i + K_{ij} \qquad (6)$$

Kröner[6] demonstrated that the decomposition quantities $\underline{a}$ and $\underline{\underline{C}}^S$ are determined by Div $\underline{\underline{\sigma}}^S$ and Inc $\underline{\underline{\sigma}}^S$, respectively, while $\underline{G}$ and $\underline{\nabla} e$ are determined from Div $\underline{\underline{\sigma}}^A$ and Inc $\underline{\underline{\sigma}}^A$, as follows:

$$\underline{G}(\underline{r}_1) = \frac{-1}{4\pi} \int_V \frac{\mathrm{Div}\,\underline{\underline{\sigma}}^A(\underline{r}_2)}{r_{12}}\, d^3 r_2\,, \qquad (7)$$

where, without loss of generality, Div $\underline{G}$ is taken to vanish;

$$(\underline{\nabla} e)_i = -\frac{1}{2} \epsilon_{ijk} (\underline{\nabla} e \times \underline{\underline{I}})_{jk}\,, \qquad (8a)$$

where

$$\underline{\nabla} e(\underline{r}_1) \times \underline{\underline{I}} = \frac{-1}{4\pi} \int_V \frac{\mathrm{Inc}\,\underline{\underline{\sigma}}^A(\underline{r}_2)}{r_{12}}\, d^3 r_2 \qquad (8b)$$

and $\underline{\underline{I}}$ is the identity tensor. Hence, a general second rank tensor is completely determined by its divergence and incompatibility. Like Helmholtz' theorem,[7] Kröner's decomposition theorem applies to a continuous (tensor) field having continuous first derivatives and occupying either a finite or infinite region. It is not restricted only to fields with infinite extent, as Kröner indicated. If the integration volume V is taken to be finite, $\underline{\underline{K}}$ may be nonzero. If V is all of space, then $r^2|\underline{\underline{\sigma}}|$ must be bounded for large r.

DISCUSSION

To evaluate the physical content of $\underline{\underline{\sigma}}$, recall that it is introduced in the development of the continuum momentum conservation relation so that a local differential relation can be obtained. Using the purely mathematical procedure of representing the traction vector as the contraction of a tensor with the system surface normal,[8] the surface integral of the traction is converted into a volume integral of the stress tensor divergence by application of the divergence theorem. This mathematical representation of traction constrains only the stress tensor divergence,

$$\underline{\nabla} \cdot \underline{\underline{\sigma}} = \underline{\nabla} \cdot [\mathrm{Def}\,\underline{a} + \underline{\nabla}\,\underline{G} - (\underline{\nabla}\,\underline{G})^T] \equiv \underline{\nabla} \cdot \underline{\underline{\Gamma}}\,, \qquad (9)$$

which suffices for determining $\underline{a}$ and $\underline{G}$ only. Having no knowledge of Inc $\underline{\underline{\sigma}}$ leaves the stress tensor indeterminate by $\underline{\underline{\Lambda}} \equiv \underline{\underline{\sigma}} - \underline{\underline{\Gamma}}$:

$$\Lambda_{ij} = \epsilon_{ikl}\,\epsilon_{jmn}\,\partial_k\,\partial_m\, C^S_{ln} + \epsilon_{ijk}\,\partial_k\, e\,. \qquad (10)$$

The following relations hold:

$$\underline{\underline{\sigma}} = \underline{\underline{\Gamma}} + \underline{\underline{\Lambda}}\,; \quad \mathrm{Div}\,\underline{\underline{\sigma}} = \mathrm{Div}\,\underline{\underline{\Gamma}}\,; \quad \mathrm{Inc}\,\underline{\underline{\sigma}} = \mathrm{Inc}\,\underline{\underline{\Lambda}}\,;$$

but $$\mathrm{Curl}\,\underline{\underline{\sigma}} = \mathrm{Curl}\,(\underline{\underline{\Gamma}} + \underline{\underline{\Lambda}}). \qquad (11a\text{-}d)$$

This kind of indeterminacy is typical in continuum field equations.[3] It occurs as the additive constant for scalar potentials, the gauge for the vector potential, and the divergence-free tensor for stress-energy tensors.[9,10] If no dynamical principle constrains Inc $\underline{\underline{\sigma}}$, it does not contribute to any observable quantity and is, thus, unphysical and completely arbitrary.[3,10,11] Hence, though the stress tensor $\underline{\underline{\sigma}}$ has some physical content, if it is nonunique it is not itself a physical quantity. Tractions are physical quantities. In discrete systems where the fundamental mechanics assumption of material continuity does not hold, a traction, $\underline{t}$, is the areal average force applied to a finite area S,

$$\underline{t} = \int_S d\underline{S}\cdot\underline{\underline{\sigma}} \Big/ \int_S d\underline{S} \ . \tag{12}$$

$\underline{\nabla}\cdot\underline{\underline{\sigma}}$ is also a physical quantity. It is the force produced indirectly at a location in the interior of the system by application of tractions at its surface.

Though the divergence-free part of the stress-energy tensor may be completely arbitrary for some fields,[9,10] a generalization of Irving and Kirkwood's argument[1] demonstrates that the divergence-free part of the mechanical stress tensor considered here is constrained by its relation to traction: When $\underline{\nabla}\cdot\underline{\underline{\sigma}} = 0$, as for a stress-free state, the traction also vanishes, and Eq. (12) reduces to

$$0 = \underline{\underline{\Gamma}} + \underline{\underline{\Lambda}} \,, \tag{13}$$

because S is arbitrary. Because $\underline{\underline{\Gamma}}$ has no constant part, Eqs. (11b) and (13) provide that $\underline{\underline{\Gamma}}$ and $\underline{\underline{\Lambda}}$ are each zero. Hence, the correct expression for the force or traction on a finite surface is obtained only for the choice of a null Inc $\underline{\underline{\sigma}}$ tensor. This result holds for a general internal potential and does not require specification of paths along which forces act. In contrast, Irving and Kirkwood's argument depends on the choice for the arbitrarily-defined force lines. For a general potential, as well as from the more fundamental quantum mechanical viewpoint, paths of interactions between particles cannot be identified, only the total force on a particle.

The indeterminacy of the divergence-free part of $\underline{\underline{\sigma}}$ occurs as an integration-contour dependence in Schofield and Henderson's expression.[2] Consistent with Irving and Kirkwood's arbitrary definition of interactions as being along the line of centers between particles,[1] they regard the integration contour as the path along which forces act.[2,12] From this they conclude that the nonuniqueness of the stress density expression is equivalent to uncertainty as to exactly where the forces between particles are acting. However, their expression holds for a general internal potential, in which case a contour integral multiplies the total internal force on each particle. Hence, the integral and the cited nonuniqueness are not simply related to interactions between particles.

Baus and Lovett[5,13] recently presented independent arguments that lead them to conclude that, for a symmetric stress tensor, constraining Inc $\underline{\underline{\sigma}}^S$ to vanish makes earlier stress tensor expressions unique.[1,2] Though the present discussion leads to a similar conclusion, their arguments based on equilibrium continuum relations are not applicable to the dynamic systems treated in those earlier developements. In their analysis they define stress as the strain derivative of free energy and invoke strain compatibility.[5] The equivalence of the purported nonuniqueness in strain derivatives of free energy and the nonuniqueness of the mechanical stress tensor defined in the continuum momentum conservation relation remains to be established. Additionally, when stress is defined as the strain derivative of free energy, it lacks the clear applicability to discrete, dynamic systems possessed by the earlier stress density tensors to which it is supposed to be equivalent. Two factors contribute to this deficiency. First, this stress definition is specifically suited to conditions at or near thermodynamic equilibrium. Second, strain cannot be defined as a point quantity in a discrete system, but only as an average quantity in some region, as done, for example, in [14]. In contrast, the present argument for vanishing of Inc $\underline{\underline{\sigma}}$ is independent of strain-related concepts and applies in general to dynamic systems with arbitrary constitutive behavior, which includes those with nonsymmetric stress tensors.

CONCLUSION

The constraint on the divergence-free part of the stress tensor discussed here removes serveral difficulties encountered in attempts to derive expressions for physical observables that are invariant to the choice of $\underline{\underline{\Lambda}}$.[2,5,15] No such invariance is required[2] because $\underline{\underline{\Lambda}}$ is physically limited to being the null tensor.

REFERENCES

[1] J. H. Irving and J. G. Kirkwood, "The statistical mechanical theory of transport pro-cesses. IV. The equations of hydrodynamics," *J. Chem. Phys.* **18**, 817 (1950).

[2] P. Schofield and J. R. Henderson, "Statistical mechanics of inhomogeneous fluids," *Proc. R. Soc. Lond. A* 379, 231. (1982)

[3] O. H. Nielsen and R. M. Martin, "Quantum-mechanical theory of stress and force," *Phys. Rev. B* **32**, 3780 (1985).

[4] A. Klemm, "The evaluation of parial pressures from MD-simulations of liquids," *Z. Naturforsch,* **33a,** 778 (1978).

[5] M. Baus and R. Lovett, "Stress-strain relations in nonuniform equilibrium fluids," *Phys. Rev. A* **44,** 1211 (1991).

[6] E. Kröner, "Kontinuumstheorie der Versetzungen und Eigenspannungen," *Ergeb. angew. Math.* 5 (1958); I. Raasch and C. S. Hartley, Technical Report No. 6 (english translation), 15 December 1971, College of Engineering, University of Florida, Gainesville, FL 32601 prepared under Office of Naval Research contract No. N0004-68-A-0173-0002.

[7] M. S. Schwartz, S. Green, and W. A. Rutledge, *Vector Analysis with Applications to Geometry and Physics,* New York: Harper and Bro.s, 1960.

[8] L. E. Malvern, *Introduction to the Mechanics of a Continuous Medium,* Englewood Cliffs: Prentice-Hall, 1969.

[9] J. D. Jackson, *Classical Electrodynamics,* second ed., New York: Wiley and Sons, 1975.

[10] H. Goldstein, *Classical Mechanics*, second ed., Reading: Addison-Wesley 1980, p. 561.

[11] J. A. McLennan, "Symmetry of the stress tensor," *Physica* **32**, 689 (1966).

[12] S. M. Thompson, K. E. Gubbins, J. P. R. B. Walton, R. A. R. Chantry, and J. S. Rowlinson, "A molecular dynamics study of liquid drops," J. *Chem. Phys.* **81**, 530 (1984).

[13] M. Baus and R. Lovett, "Generalization of the stress tensor to nonuniform fluids and solids and its relation to Saint-Venant's strain compatibility conditions," *Phys. Rev. Lett.* 65, 1781 (1990); M. Baus and R. Lovett, "Baus and Lovett Reply," *Phys. Rev. Lett.* 67, 407 (1991).

[14] M. D. Kluge, D. Wolf, J. F. Lutsko, and S. R. Phillpot, "Formalism for the calculation of local elastic constants at grain boundaries by means of atomistic simulation," *J. Appl. Phys.* **67**, 2370 (1990).

[15] M. J. P. Nijmeijer, C. Bruin, A. B. van Woerkom, A. F. Bakker, and J. M. J. van Leeuwen, "Molecular dynamics of the surface tension of a drop," *J. Chem. Phys.* **96,** 565 (1992).

CONSTITUTIVE RELATIONS FOR THE PLASTIC DEFORMATION OF METALS

Frank J. Zerilli
Research and Technology Department
Naval Surface Warfare Center Dahlgren Division, White Oak Detachment
10901 New Hampshire Avenue
Silver Spring, MD 20903-5640

and

Ronald W. Armstrong
Department of Mechanical Engineering
University of Maryland
College Park, MD 20742

The application of dislocation mechanics leads to simple constitutive relations for metals which describe reasonably well the basic features of metal deformation, including the flow stress and tensile instability strain as functions of temperature, strain rate, and grain size. The equations have been applied to describing the stress/strain behavior of the fcc metals copper and aluminum, the bcc metals iron, tantalum, and tungsten, the hcp metals titanium and zirconium, and alloy steels HY-80, HY-100, and HY-130.

INTRODUCTION

In recent years there has been a great deal of interest in constitutive relations that could describe material behavior sufficiently well enough to produce accurate predictions of deformation and fracture when used in large scale computer simulations. Considerable research has been done in developing a dislocation mechanics basis for describing material behavior and most of the recent work has drawn upon this body of knowledge.

One of the simplest dislocation mechanics formulations was described in 1987 by Zerilli and Armstrong[1] in which heuristic arguments, based on the idea of the thermally activated motion of dislocations, were used to derive relations for face-centered-cubic (fcc) and body-centered-cubic (bcc) metals.

The nature of the dislocation interactions leads to different forms for the fcc and bcc equations. For bcc metals, the motion of dislocations is governed by the interaction produced by the overall lattice potential (Peierls-Nabarro stress) which leads to little increase in flow stress ("strain hardening") with strain. For fcc metals, the motion of dislocations is constrained by their mutual intersections, leading to substantial strain hardening. Hexagonal-close-packed (hcp) metals have a stress-strain behavior falling somewhere between bcc and fcc metals.

THERMAL ACTIVATION MODEL

In the thermal activation picture, the dislocations are assumed to move in a periodic potential and the average dislocation velocity is determined by the thermodynamic probability for achieving sufficient energy at temperature T to move past a peak in the potential.

By simple geometry, the glide plane shear strain rate $\dot{\gamma}$ is related to the average dislocation velocity v by

$$\dot{\gamma} = Nbv \tag{1}$$

where N is the areal density of dislocations and b is the dislocation Burgers vector. The average dislocation velocity can then be written in terms of a Gibbs free energy, a function of T and the thermal component of stress, τ. The form of the Gibbs function is determined by assuming that the area of activation

$$A = -\frac{1}{b}\left(\frac{\partial G}{\partial \tau}\right)_T \tag{2}$$

is inversely proportional to the glide plane shear stress[2].

The inverse proportionality of A to glide plane shear stress was derived by Hartley for the dislocation intersection mechanism[3] (for small stress). For the Peierls-Nabarro stress, Feltham[4] showed that A is proportional to $\tau^{-1/2}$ for small stresses and to $\tau^{-3/2}$ for large stresses with an intermediate range in which A is inversely proportional to τ. The inverse proportionality is also confirmed by experimental evidence[5]. At very

Table 1. Constants for fcc metals.

	B_0 (MPa)	β_0 (10^{-3} K^{-1})	β_1 (10^{-3} K^{-1})	σ_G (MPa)	k (MPa $mm^{1/2}$)
Copper (OFHC)	890	2.8	0.115	46.5	5
Aluminum (99.99%)	150	0.89	0.183	7	1.5

high shear stress, A approaches a non-zero constant, A_0.

The result is that the thermal component of stress may be written as

$$\sigma_{Th} = Be^{-\beta T} \tag{3}$$

where

$$B \propto \frac{1}{A_0}, \tag{4}$$

and

$$\beta = \beta_0 - \beta_1 \ln\dot{\epsilon}. \tag{5}$$

For bcc metals, A_0 may be considered constant in accordance with intrinsic Peierls stress control but for fcc metals, according to the argument given in Ref. 1, A_0, determined by dislocation intersections, is proportional to the inverse square root of strain. Therefore, for fcc metals, B may be written

$$B = B_0 \epsilon^{1/2}. \tag{6}$$

To obtain the total flow stress, a constant term describing the influence of solutes and grain boundaries must be added to the thermal stress so that the complete constitutive relation for fcc metals is

$$\sigma = \sigma_{Th} + \sigma_G + k\ell^{-1/2} \tag{7}$$

where σ_G is the contribution due to solutes and initial dislocation density, k is the microstructural stress intensity and ℓ is the average grain diameter. For bcc metals, an additional empirical term of the form $K\varepsilon^n$ is added to describe the strain dependence. In theory n is 1/2 in this case as well.

In summary, the relation for fcc metals is

$$\sigma = c_0 + B_0 \epsilon^{1/2} e^{-\beta T} \tag{8}$$

and for bcc metals is

$$\sigma = c_0 + Be^{-\beta T} + K\epsilon^n \tag{9}$$

where

$$c_0 = \sigma_G + k\ell^{-1/2}. \tag{10}$$

APPLICATION TO SPECIFIC MATERIALS

The constitutive relations have been applied to the description of several materials and they have been found to describe the major features of the material deformation behavior reasonably well. These features include the flow stress and tensile instability strain as functions of temperature, strain rate, and grain size. The equations do not describe features such as the upper and lower yield points, related strain aging phenomena, and deformation twinning, all common in bcc and hcp metals. Of these, deformation twinning is the most important when an accurate prediction of deformation is required.

Tables 1 through 4 summarize constants for materials that have been examined to date.

FCC Metals

The constants shown for copper in Table 1 have produced good results[1,6] in predicting its deformation behavior under a variety of conditions of temperature, strain rate, and grain size in cylinder impacts and

Table 2. Constants for bcc metals.

	B (MPa)	β_0 (10^{-3} K^{-1})	β_1 (10^{-3} K^{-1})	σ_G (MPa)	k (MPa $mm^{1/2}$)	K (MPa)	n
Iron (ARMCO)	1033	6.98	0.415	0	22	266	0.289
Tantalum	1125	5.35	0.327	0-250	9-19	310	0.44
Tungsten	25000	6.66	0.307	20 (c_0)	25	860	0.443

Table 3. Constants for hcp metals.

	B (MPa)	β_0 (10^{-3} K^{-1})	β_1 (10^{-3} K^{-1})	c_0 (MPa)	k (MPa mm$^{1/2}$)	K (MPa)	n
Titanium	1100	2.4	0.17	54	13	300	0.5
Zirconium	600	2.26	0.132	21	8	76	0.51

expanding ring experiments. The constants for aluminum were obtained only recently from data reported by Christodoulou and Jonas[7] for strain rates from $5\text{x}10^{-4}$ s^{-1} to $5\text{x}10^{-2}$ s^{-1}.

Deformation Twinning

Deformation twinning is important in certain bcc metals and is a stress level dependent phenomenon. The dependence of the twinning stress on grain size is similar to the dependence of the athermal part of the flow stress on grain size[6,8] and may be written

$$\sigma_T = \sigma_{T0} + k_T \ell^{-1/2} \tag{11}$$

where, for iron, σ_{T0} is 330 MPa and k_T is 90 MPa-mm$^{-1/2}$. Twinning occurs at a flow stress level of 600 MPa for iron with a grain size of 100 microns. This stress will be achieved in impacts of 200 ms^{-1} in which strain rates of 10^4 s^{-1} are generated. It has been shown to occur in fcc metals, but generally at very much higher stress levels. For copper, the stress levels are in the range of 1600 to 2800 MPa.[9]

Twinning must be taken into account when modelling the deformation of iron at moderately high strain rates. A method that has been successfully used to include the effect of twinning in numerical simulations is based upon the premise that twinning effectively refines the grain size[10]. If a grain reaches the stress level given by Eq. (11), it is considered twinned and a constant increment is added to the flow stress. Once twinned, the new twinning threshold stress is much higher than the original and so further twinning is unlikely to occur. A more recent twinning model is based on the idea that enough twinning will occur in a grain to accomodate the excess by which the Von Mises equivalent stress exceeds the twinning threshold stress.

BCC Metals

Tantalum, a bcc metal, shows little susceptibility to twinning, and so the constants in Table 2 give a good description of its deformation behavior[11]. A range of values for σ_G are given. The value to be used for a particular material would depend on the solute concentration and could be determined by a yield stress measurement.

The constants for tungsten were obtained from experimental data of Bechtold and Shewmon[12] and Bechtold[13] which covered strain rates from 10^{-2} s^{-1} to 10^{-5} s^{-1} and temperatures from 450 K to 1175 K. The table shows one of three sets of constants that could equally well fit this high temperature, low strain rate data[14]. The constants were applied to predicting the ductile-brittle transition behavior.

Flyer plate impact experiments for iron and tantalum have also been successfully described by the bcc equations[15].

HCP Metals

Included in Table 3 are the hcp metals, titanium and zirconium both of which tend to exhibit a behavior similar to bcc metals. The constants were obtained from data published by Ramachandran, Santhanam, and Reed-Hill[16]. Titanium twins readily so the effect of twinning must be taken into account in numerical simulations[17].

Table 4. Constants for bcc alloy steels.

	B (MPa)	β_0 (10^{-3} K^{-1})	β_1 (10^{-3} K^{-1})	c_0 (MPa)	k (MPa mm$^{1/2}$)	K (MPa)	n
HY-80	870	7.1	0.34	440	22	1120	0.58
HY-100	770	8.6	0.36	800	22	1100	0.73
HY-130	1033	7.0	0.42	710	22	950	0.79

Alloy Steels

The thermal stress constants for the alloy steels HY-80 and HY-100 shown in Table 4 were obtained from data of Harding[18]. For HY-130, the thermal stress constants for Armco iron were used. The Armco iron thermal constants would also give a good result for HY-80 and HY-100. For all three steels, the strain hardening constants were determined from the work of Holmquist[19]. The constants give a reasonably good prediction for the deformation of HY-130 in a Taylor cylinder impact test[20].

Tensile Instability

The condition for stability against necking in a tensile test is that the rate of strain hardening of the test material be sufficient to overcome loss of load bearing capability due to reduction of cross section. In mathematical terms,

$$\frac{d\sigma}{d\epsilon} > \sigma. \tag{12}$$

The equations (8)-(10), (12) have successfully described the necking behavior of copper[2,6] and tantalum[11,21] as functions of temperature and strain rate, showing the contrasting behavior of fcc and bcc metals: the uniform strain before necking increases with strain rate for fcc metals and decreases with strain rate for bcc metals. The fcc instability condition was used[2] to discount dislocation drag being responsible for observations of a significant upturn in flow stress of copper at strain rates greater than 10^3 s^{-1}.

More recently, the fcc and bcc equations have been applied to differentiating the shear banding susceptibilities of copper, iron, and related materials[22]. An increasing value of microstructural stress intensity, k, favors shear banding behavior.

ACKNOWLEDGEMENTS

This work was supported by the NSWC Independent Research Program.

REFERENCES

[1] F. J. Zerilli and R. W. Armstrong, *J. Appl. Phys.* **61**, p. 1816 (1987).

[2] F. J. Zerilli and R. W. Armstrong, *Acta metall. mater.* **40**, pp. 1803-1808 (1992).

[3] C. S. Hartley, in *Second International Conference on the Strength of Metals and Alloys, Vol. II*, Metals Park: American Society for Metals, 1970, p. 429 ff.

[4] P. Feltham, *Brit. J. Appl. Phys.* **2**, p. 377 (1969).

[5] R. W. Armstrong, *(Indian) Journal of Scientific and Industrial Research* **32**, p. 591-598 (1973); R. W. Armstrong and J. D. Campbell, in *The Microstructure and Design of Alloys*, Vol 1, Cambridge: Institute of Metals and the Iron and Steel Institute, 1973, p. 529 ff.

[6] R. W. Armstrong and F. J. Zerilli, *J. Physique, Coll.*, **49**(9), p. 529 (1988).

[7] N. Christodoulou and J. J. Jonas, *Acta metall.* **32**, pp. 1655-1668 (1984).

[8] R. W. Armstrong and P. J. Worthington, in *Metallurgical Effects at High Strain Rates,* New York: Plenum, 1974, p.401.

[9] W. C. Leslie in *Metallurgical Effects at High Strain Rates*, edited by R. W. Rohde, B. M. Butcher, J. R. Holland, and C. H. Karnes, New York: Plenum, 1974, p. 571.

[10] F. J. Zerilli and R. W. Armstrong, in *Shock Waves in Condensed Matter 1987*, Amsterdam: Elsevier, 1988, p. 273 ff.

[11] F. J. Zerilli and R. W. Armstrong, *J. Appl. Phys.* **68**, p. 1580 (1990).

[12] J. H. Bechtold and P. G. Shewmon, *Trans. ASM*, **46**, pp. 397-408 (1954).

[13] J. H. Bechtold, *Trans. AIME* **206**, pp. 142-146 (1956).

[14] V. Ramachandran, R. W. Armstrong, and F. J. Zerilli, in *Tungsten and Tungsten Alloys - Recent Advances*, Warrendale, PA: The Minerals, Metals and Materials Society, 1991, pp. 111-119.

[15] F. J. Zerilli and R. W. Armstrong, in *Shock Compression of Condensed Matter - 1991*, Amsterdam: Elsevier, 1992, p. 257.

[16] V. Ramachandran, A. T. Santhanam, and R. E. Reed-Hill, *Indian J. Tech.*, **11**, pp. 485-492 (1973).

[17] W. H. Holt, W. Mock, F. J. Zerilli, and J. B. Clark, submitted to *Mechanics of Materials*.

[18] J. Harding, *Metals Technology*, pp. 6-16 (January 1977).

[19] T. J. Holmquist, Naval Surface Warfare Center Technical Report TR 88-252 (1987).

[20] W. H. Holt, W. Mock, Jr., and F. J. Zerilli, unpublished result.

[21] F. J. Zerilli and R. W. Armstrong, in *Shock Compression of Condensed Matter 1989*, Amsterdam: Elsevier, 1990, p. 357 ff.

[22] R. W. Armstrong and F. J. Zerilli, submitted to *Mechanics of Materials*.

A RATE-DEPENDENT CONSTITUTIVE MODEL* FOR MOLYBDENUM

Daniel J. Steinberg

Lawrence Livermore National Laboratory
P.O. Box 808, Livermore, CA, 94551, USA

The Steinberg-Guinan-Lund rate-dependent constitutive model has been successfully applied to molybdenum. The model reproduces yield strength vs strain-rate and temperature data and also successfully simulates rate-dependent phenomena, such as shock-smearing, precursor decay, and precursor on reshock, as observed in one-dimensional gas-gun experiments. The spall strength of molybdenum was determined to be 1.5 GPa.

INTRODUCTION

The dynamic yield strength of BCC metals depends strongly on strain rate. In 1989, Steinberg and Lund[1] described a constitutive model, valid for strain rates from 10^{-4} to 10^6 s^{-1}, for use with hydrodynamic computer codes. Using this model, several experimentally observed, rate-dependent, shock-induced phenomena were successfully calculated for tantalum (Ta). These include precursor decay and shock-smearing, i.e., the slow increase in stress between the precursor and the main shock. The model also predicts a precursor on reshock, and this rate-dependent phenomenon was successfully calculated for tungsten (W).[2] The major purpose of this paper is to apply this model to molybdenum (Mo). For Mo, there is a much larger and more complete body of data than for either Ta or W. Therefore, application of the model to Mo is a stringent test of the model's validity.

BASIC EQUATIONS

The yield strength Y is a function of plastic strain ε_p, plastic strain rate $\dot{\varepsilon}_p$, pressure P and temperature T:

$$Y = \left[Y_T(\dot{\varepsilon}_p,T) + Y_A f(\varepsilon_p)\right] G(P,T)/G_0 \,, \tag{1}$$

where $Y_T(\dot{\varepsilon}_p,T)$ is the thermally activated part of the yield strength. The second, or athermal, term is similar in form to the Steinberg-Guinan model, where $f(\varepsilon_p)$ is the work-hardening function and $G(P,T)/G_0$ is the shear modulus divided by the modulus at STP conditions.[3]

$$G(P,T) = G_0\left[1 + AP\eta^{-1/3} - B(T-300)\right] \,, \tag{2}$$

where η is compression, and A and B are the logarithmic derivatives of G with respect to pressure and temperature at T = 300 K and P = 0. The work hardening function is $f(\varepsilon_p) = (1+\beta\varepsilon_p)^n$, where β and n are fit to work-hardening data.

The thermally activated term is written as

$$\dot{\varepsilon}_p = \left\{\frac{1}{C_1}\exp\left[\frac{2U_K}{kT}\left(1-\frac{Y_T}{Y_P}\right)^2\right] + \frac{C_2}{Y_T}\right\}^{-1} . \tag{3}$$

Here Y_P is the Peierls stress, $2U_K$ is the energy to form a pair of kinks in a dislocation segment of length L, and k is the Boltzmann constant. The constant C_2 is the drag coefficient D divided by the dislocation density ρ times the square of the Burgers' vector b. The constant C_1 is $\rho Lab^2\nu/2w^2$, where a is the distance between Peierls valleys, w is the width of a kink loop, and ν is the Debye frequency. The thermally activated contribution Y_T is limited to be $\leq Y_P$. A complete description of the model, as well as how to implement it in a hydrodynamic code, is given in Refs. 1 and 3.

DETERMINING THE MODEL PARAMETERS

Because the terms defining C_1 and C_2 are not well known, it is easier to use non-shock-wave data for Y as a function of $\dot{\varepsilon}_p$ and T to determine them and then use the time-resolved shock-wave data to validate the model. Briggs and Campbell[4] have made measurements for strain rates from 1.7×10^{-4} to 60 s^{-1} and temperatures from 77 to 600 K. These data are shown in Figs. 1 and 2 along with the model fit. (The dashed lines are visual aids only.) The values of C_1, U_K, Y_p, and Y_A used in the fit are 35.2 μs^{-1}, 0.372 eV, 1.67 GPa, and 0.25 GPa respectively. The values for G_0 and B are 125 GPa and 1.52×10^{-4} K^{-1}, both from Ref. 5. Briggs and Campbell estimate that the measured stress values are accurate to within about ±5%. The model fit is within this accuracy except at the highest strain rates (25 and 60 s^{-1}) and temperatures above about 400 K. The worst disagreement is approximately 10% at $\dot{\varepsilon}_p$ = 60 s^{-1} and T = 450 K. Briggs and Campbell also show the stress reaching a maximum at temperatures less than about 150 K.

* Work performed under the auspices of the U.S. Department of Energy by the Lawrence Livermore National Laboratory under contract No. W-7405-ENG-48.

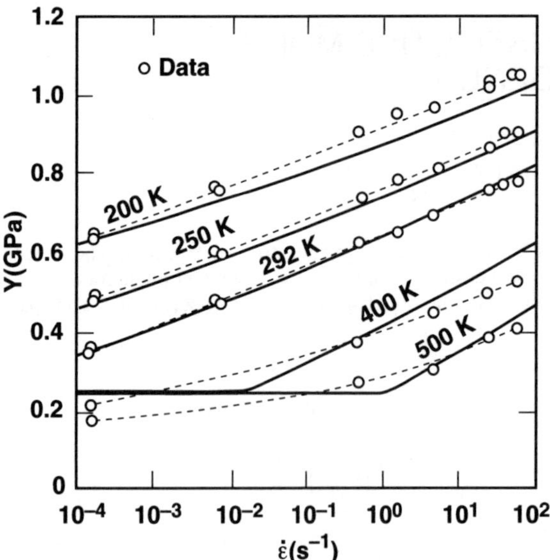

Figure 1. Comparison of the model and experimental data for Y vs $\dot{\varepsilon}_p$ at different temperatures.

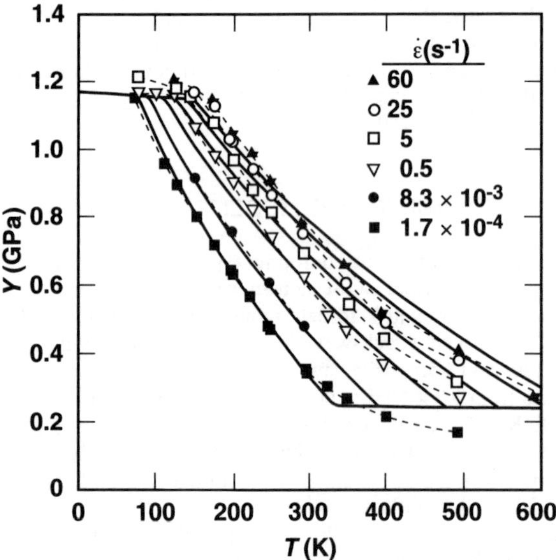

Figure 2. Comparison of the model and experimental data for Y vs T at different strain rates.

The value for Y_A depends on the grain size, the previous mechanical history of the material, impurity level, what kind of impurities, and whether or not these impurities are located at the grain boundaries. Consequently, the value for Y_A used to fit the data of Briggs and Campbell will not necessarily work when calculating the recent time-resolved shock-wave data of Furnish and Chhabildas.[6] The value for Y_A to be used in the hydrodynamic calculations must be found by normalizing at the Hugoniot elastic limit (HEL) to at least one time-resolved shock-wave experiment. This is not an unusual approach. Even for a rate-independent constitutive model, it is necessary to determine the yield strength at the HEL (Y_0) by using at least one time-resolved experiment. The best value for Y_A was found to be 0.9 GPa. Previous experience with Ta and W showed that Y_A was about one-half the value for Y_0. This appears to hold true for Mo as well, as Y_0 is 1.6 GPa.

For the remaining parameters in the model, the value of A is 11.4 TPa^{-1}, determined from the work of Katahara et al.[7] The work-hardening parameters, β and n, were determined from the combined data of Nishihara et al.,[8] Okazaki et al.,[9] Beardmore and Thornton,[10] and Dubensky and Stephens.[11] These values are $\beta = 20$ and $n = 0.15$.

For Ta, static data was taken at strain rates as high as $2 \times 10^4\ \text{s}^{-1}$, which allowed C_2 to be determined from these data. Because the maximum strain rate is only 60 s^{-1} here, it is not possible to determine C_2 in this way. This parameter must also be determined from at least one shock wave profile. I used the highest stress experiment because it is at the highest strain rate and therefore the most sensitive to the choice of C_2. The best agreement was obtained when $C_2 = 1.2$ GPa · µs, and this value was used in all subsequent calculations.

The hydrodynamic equation of state is a Mie-Grüneisen with a linear shock-velocity, particle-velocity relation where the bulk sound speed is 5.143 mm/µs, the slope is 1.255, and the initial density is 10.2 Mg/m^3. The Grüneisen gamma is written as $\gamma_\eta = \gamma_0 + d(\eta - 1)$ where the initial value of gamma γ_0 is 1.59 and the first order volume correction d is 0.3.

COMPARISON OF EXPERIMENTAL AND CALCULATED SHOCK-WAVE PROFILES

The time-resolved, shock-wave profile data of Furnish and Chhabildas are classic, one-dimensional, uniaxial-strain, plate-impact experiments. A gas gun drives a flyer at a target and a velocimeter, such as a VISAR, records the velocity of the interface between the target and a transparent window whose mechanical and optical properties are well known. For these experiments, the first flyer was sometimes backed by a very low-shock impedance material for shock and release experiments, and at other times by a very high-shock impedance material to produce double shocks in the target. In all cases, the transparent window was a single-crystal sapphire. Details for most of the experiments can be found in Ref. 6.

Comparisons of the experimental interface or free-surface velocity vs time and the hydrocode simulations are shown in Figs. 3–5. The results from all the calculations were independent of zone size. Each figure shows two experiments, a shock and release and a double shock and release. The peak stresses are approximately 6.4 and 9.0, 11.2 and 15.6, and 15.1 and 16.3 GPa, respectively. All

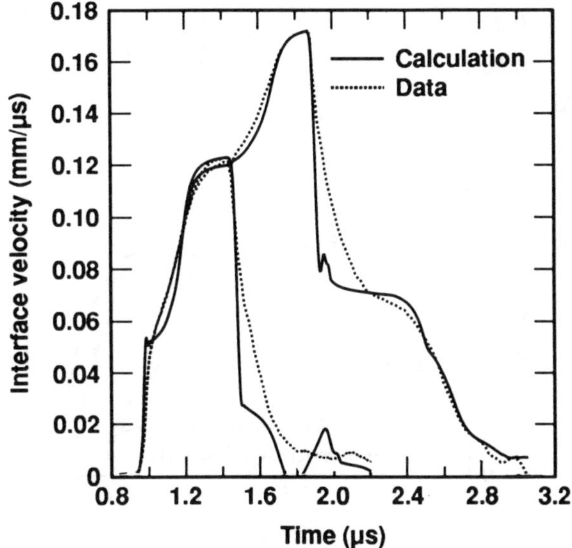

Figure 3. Comparison of measured and calculated interface velocity for a pair of low-stress single and double shock experiments.

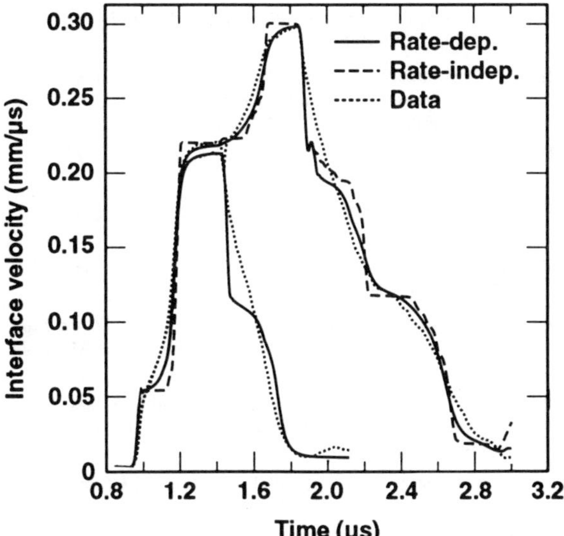

Figure 4. Comparison of measured and calculated interface velocity for a pair of medium-stress single and double shock experiments.

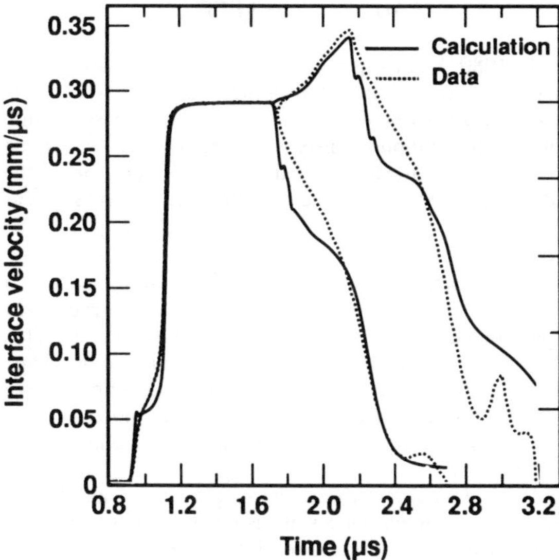

Figure 5. Comparison of measured and calculated interface velocity for a pair of high-stress single and double shock experiments.

experiments are normalized to the calculated first peak velocity. This normalization was within the absolute experimental accuracy of the VISAR and averaged –0.76% with a maximum difference of –1.7%. For the double-shock experiment in Fig. 5, the calculated release profile begins to deviate from the data at about 2.6 μs because the experiment is no longer one dimensional by this time.

The calculated initial rise on all experiments exhibits the characteristic shallow S-shaped curve indicative of shock smearing. The agreement with experiment is good except that initially the data show more smearing than does the calculation. Viscoelasticity may be responsible for this discrepancy. For the double-shock cases, the calculated initial rise of the second shock begins with the arrival of the elastic precursor and also shows a shallow S-shape, both effects in good agreement with the data. In the release portion of the curves, all the calculations initially fall too steeply compared with the data. This appears to be due to the lack of a Bauschinger effect in the calculations. More will be said about this below.

While the remainder of the release profiles exhibit structure, it is still smoothly varying. Indeed, the only sharp break in any profile occurs at the initial arrival of the release wave. This lack of clear structure is also reproduced very well in the calculations and appears to be due to the inclusion of rate-dependence in the model. For comparison, a second calculation is shown in Fig. 4 where our rate-independent model[3] is used with an initial yield strength of 1.6 GPa. It is clear that in this case both the shock-loading and release curves show significantly more structure.

Finally, using unpublished free-surface velocity data from Chhabildas and the model of Cochran and Banner,[12] the spall strength was found to be 1.5 GPa. In addition, the model predicts the precursor decay data for targets varying from 1.5 to 13 mm.

BAUSCHINGER EFFECT

In 1980, Steinberg, Cochran and Guinan[3] described a method to model the Bauschinger effect. They first determined the true deviator stress vs deviator strain in a quasi-static compression-tension experiment. Next, an effective shear modulus for the unloading portion of the curve (G_{eff}) was calculated by differentiating the stress as a function of the strain. It was found that G_{eff} could be represented quite well, as a function of the deviator stress, by simply using two straight lines. This prescription, which described the shape of the unloading curve, was programmed into a hydrodynamic computer code. This approach was extremely successful in simulating the shape of the release curves in time-resolved, shock-wave experiments carried out at strain rates as much as nine orders of magnitude greater than the quasi-static experiments.

While this approach can be very practical and useful under certain circumstances, it has no physical justification. In addition, under certain circumstances, it can be incompatible with the rate-dependent model. I have used it for Mo only to show that certain modeling deficiencies can be corrected by including the Bauschinger effect.

Figure 6 shows our compression-tension data for Mo. (The small bump in the release curve is an artifact of the experiment and was neglected in the differentiation.) The data showed that the slope of the release curve, up to the point where it crosses the hydrostat, is a constant, and from there on, varies linearly with the deviatoric stress down to zero. This is an example of the so-called default version of the model which works well for most of the materials we have studied. In this case no new parameters need to be determined.

Figure 7 shows a pair of experiments, initially shocked to about 6.6 and 11.4 GPa. Two sets of calculations are shown, one with and one without our Bauschinger model. It is clear that including the Bauschinger effect significantly improves the agreement between data and calculation.

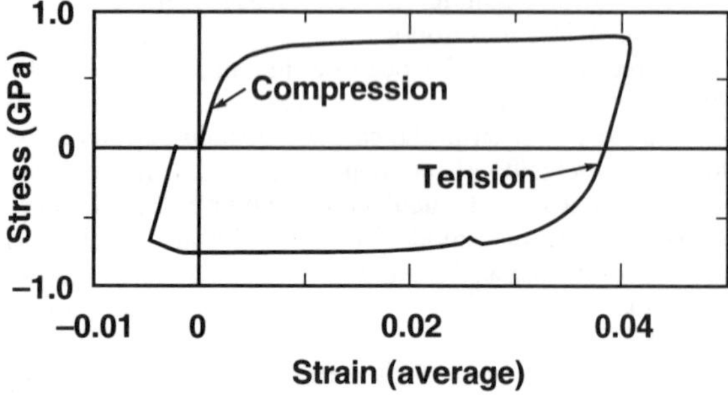

Figure 6. Compression-tension data.

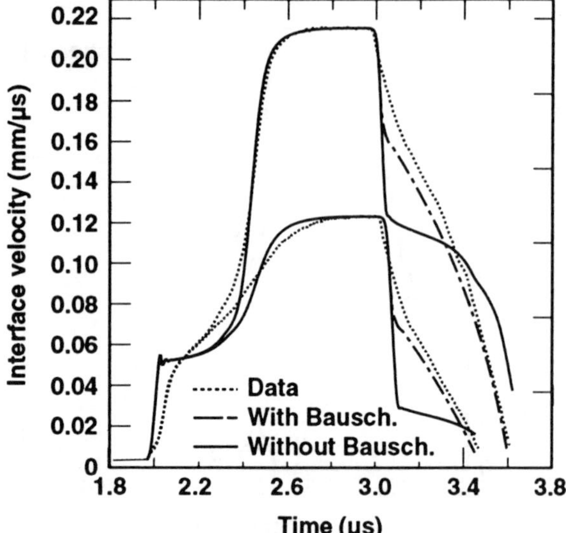

Figure 7. Comparison of measured and calculated interface velocity with and without a Bauschinger model.

REFERENCES

[1] D. J. Steinberg and C. M. Lund, *J. Appl. Phys.* 65, pp. 1528-1533 (1989).

[2] D. J. Steinberg, *3e Symp. Int'l sur le Comportement des Milieux Denses sous Hautes Pressions Dynamiques,* Paris: Assoc. Française de Pyrotechnie, 1989, pp. 233-239.

[3] D. Steinberg, S. Cochran, and M. Guinan, *J. Appl. Phys.* 51, pp. 1498-1504 (1980).

[4] T. L. Briggs and J. D. Campbell, *Acta Met.* 20, pp. 711-723 (1972).

[5] M. W. Guinan and D. J. Steinberg, *J. Phys. Chem.* Solids 35, pp. 1501-1512 (1974).

[6] M. D. Furnish and L. C. Chhabildas, *High Strain Rate Behavior of Refractory Metals and Alloys,* The Minerals, Metals and Materials Soc. 1992, pp. 229-240.

[7] K. Katahara, M. Manghnani, L. Ming, and E. Fisher, *High-Pressure Research, Applications in Geophysics,* NY: Academic, 1977, pp. 351-366.

[8] M. Nishihara, S. Miura, and T. Hirano, *High Temp.–High Press.* 4, pp. 281-291 (1972).

[9] K. Okazaki, Y. Eguchi, and K. Tanoue, *Trans. JIM* 16, pp. 257-269 (1975).

[10] P. Beardmore and P. H. Thornton, *Metall. Trans.* 1, pp. 775-779 (1970).

[11] R. G. Dubensky and R. I. Stephens, *Materials Technology–An Interamerican Approach,* NY: ASME, 1968, pp. 510-515.

[12] S. Cochran and D. Banner, *J. Appl. Phys.* 48, pp. 2729-2737 (1977).

DISLOCATION-DRAG CONTRIBUTION TO HIGH-RATE PLASTIC DEFORMATION IN SHOCK-LOADED TANTALUM

D. L. Tonks, R. S. Hixson, J. N. Johnson, and G. T. Gray III
Los Alamos National Laboratory
Los Alamos, NM 87545 USA

Time-resolved plastic waves in plate-impact experiments give information on the relationship between applied shear stress and plastic strain rate at low plastic strain. This information is essentially different from that obtained at intermediate strain rates using Hopkinson bar techniques, because in the former case the material deformation state is driven briefly into the regime dominated by dislocation drag rather than thermal activation. Two VISAR records of the particle velocity at the tantalum/sapphire (window) interface are obtained for symmetric impact producing peak in situ longitudinal stresses of approximately 75 kbar and 111 kbar. The risetimes of the plastic waves are about 100 ns and 60 ns, respectively, with peak strain rates of about $2x10^5$/s and $1x10^6$/s, respectively, as determined by weak-shock analysis [Wallace, Phys. Rev. B *22*, 1487 (1980), and Tonks, Los Alamos DataShoP Report LA-12068-MS (1991)]. These data show a much stronger dependence of plastic strain rate on applied shear stress than previously predicted by linear viscous drag models in combination with thermal activation through a large Peierls barrier. The data also show complex evolution of the mobile dislocation density during early stages of high-rate plastic flow. This measurement and analysis aid significantly in establishing the fundamental picture of dynamic deformation of BCC metals and the evolution of the internal material state at early times following shock compression.

INTRODUCTION

Earlier work [1-5] has provided a micromechanical picture of weak shock wave plasticity in FCC metals, i.e. dislocation/dislocation interactions, rapid workhardening, and dislocation drag accompanied by rapid dislocation multiplication. No significant Peierls barrier (dislocation - lattice friction) is in evidence in FCC metals.

The micromechanical shock response of BCC metals, on the other hand, has not been much studied by shock time resolved techniques. The purpose of this paper is to present some initial results for Ta, a model BCC metal, and interpret the results in terms of dislocation behavior. This behavior is rather different from that of typical FCC metals in that a strong Peierls barrier is active and little dislocation workhardening is evident at the small strains that occur in the weak shock waves studied here

EXPERIMENTAL

Two Ta shots, Ta2 and Ta6, were performed with in situ shock strengths of about 75 kbar and 111 kbar under conditions of symmetric impact. The projectile velocities for Ta2 and Ta6 were 0.253 mm/μs and 0.371 mm/μs, respectively. The impactor thicknesses were 2.23 mm and 1.76 mm, respectively. The sample thicknesses were 5.20 mm and 5.00 mm, respectively. A VISAR apparatus was used to measure the particle velocities through a sapphire window. Other experimental details are given in Ref. 6.

THEORETICAL

The data was smoothed somewhat and an elastic impedance correction was used to convert the Ta - sapphire interface velocity to an internal Ta particle velocity. This involved dividing the particle velocity data by 1.218. The velocity profiles resulting from both the smoothing and the impedance correction are shown in Fig. 1.

The velocity profiles of Fig. 1 were analyzed using Wallace's weak shock analysis [1] to obtain deviatoric stresses, normal stresses, plastic strains, and compressions. The Wallace analysis relies on a plausible assumption about the precursor evolution and a steady wave analysis of the main or plastic

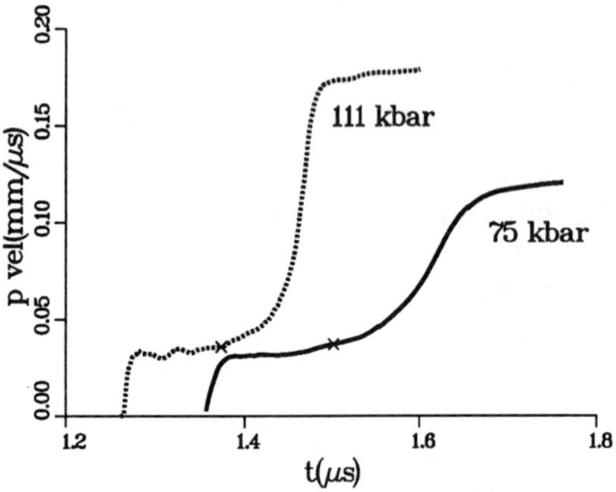

Figure 1. In situ particle velocity versus time.

wave portion. These allow the equations of motion to be integrated to obtain, from the particle velocity profiles, normal stresses and compressions through the shock front. These quantities are then used with a thermoelastic model for material behavior to obtain the deviatoric stresses and plastic strains.

The precursor consists of the first rise and the part immediately following, both of which travel faster than the steady plastic wave portion and, thus, stretch out in front of it. In the Wallace analysis, in time - distance snapshots, the precursor is assumed to stretch in a straight line between the first elastic rise and a point, called point c, where the plastic (steady) wave portion starts. The choices for point c are shown by x's in Fig. 1.

Judging by Fig. 1, the precursor stretching assumption is plausible for shot Ta2, but shot Ta6 has precursor ringing which is not included in the analysis. This ringing is probably an experimental artifact. Hence, the Wallace precursor analysis probably gives real results for plastic wave portion, because the analysis has the effect of ignoring the ringing and placing a straight line through it.

The values for the shock velocity used in the analysis of shots Ta2 and Ta6 were 3.54 mm/μs and 3.614 mm/μs, respectively. They were obtained from the spread in time between the first precursor peak and the halfway point of the plastic wave portion. It was assumed that the first precursor peak traveled through the sample thickness with a calculated longitudinal sound velocity.

The elastic constants and material density were obtained from Chhabildas. [7] The values used for λ and μ are 1.457 Mbar and 0.720 Mbar, respectively. The density value used is 16.66 gm/cm^3. The values 3.79 and 1.02, obtained from Katahara [8], were used for the isothermal pressure derivatives of the bulk and shear moduli, respectively.

The calculated deviatoric stresses versus time are found in Fig. 2. In shot Ta6, once the ringing is over with, the values should be reliable again, as noted above. Note that the final deviatoric stress is not greater than the stress of the first rise. This suggests little work hardening through the shock path. For shot Ta6, this is exaggerated, possibly because, for this stronger shock wave and slightly thinner sample thickness, the precursor has not decayed as much as for shot Ta2. The ringing in shot Ta6 could be caused by a dip after the precursor peak.

The deviatoric stress used here is: $\tau = -(\tau_{xx} - \tau_{yy})/2$, where τ_{xx} and τ_{yy} are the stresses along, and normal to, the shock direction.

Fig. 3 shows the deviatoric stress versus the plastic strain. The curve for shot Ta6 (circles) has a short secondary branch near the top of the first rise due to the ringing. Comparison of the stress value for the first rise with the final stress indicates the lack of workhardening.

In Fig. 4, points with strain rates lower than 1/s, e.g. due to ringing, were placed on the x-axis.

A short error analysis was done. The sensitivity of the results was assessed, to the value of the shock velocity and to the unspecified degree of freedom in the third order elastic constants. (The two pressure derivatives given earlier are not sufficient to determine the three third order elastic constants. [2]) The results indicate that only the deviatoric stress is very sensitive to the uncertainties. The peak and final deviatoric stresses are uncertain by about 10% and 25%, respectively.

DISCUSSION

Insight into the nature of shock wave plasticity in Ta can be obtained by comparing shock wave results with results from Hopkinson bar experiments using a plot of deviatoric stress versus plastic strain rate. Fig. 5 gives such a comparison with model results from Hoge and Mukherjee.[9]

The shock wave results in Fig. 5 are mostly

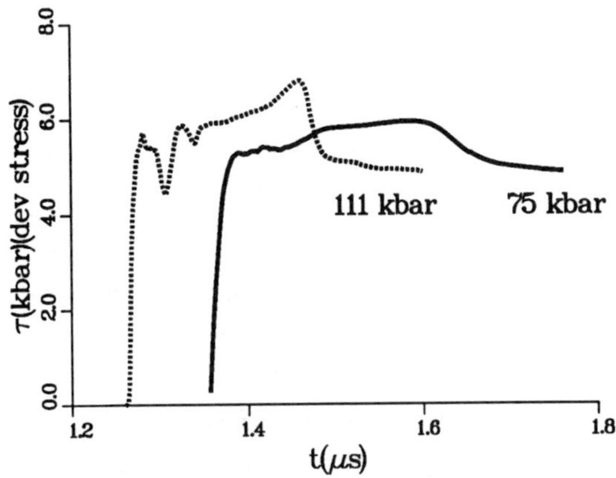

Figure 2. Deviatoric stress versus time.

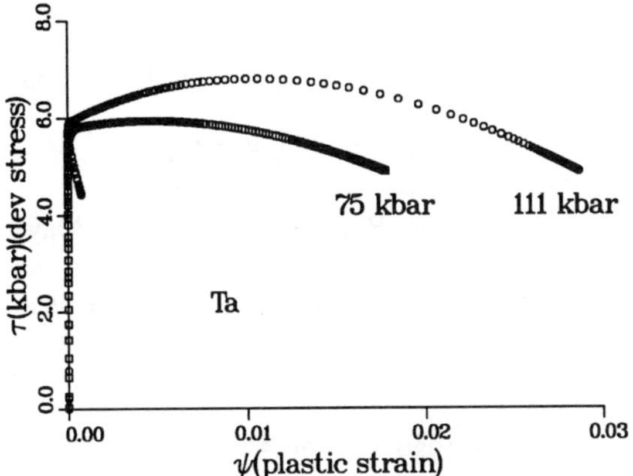

Figure 3. Deviatoric stress versus plastic strain.

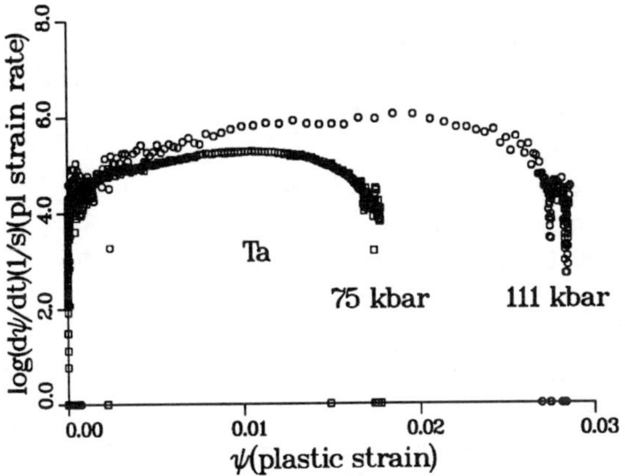

Figure 4. Log plastic strain rate versus pl. strain.

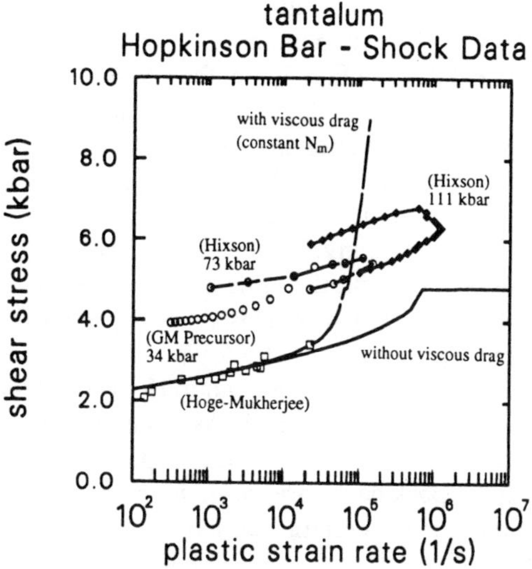

Figure 5. Deviatoric stress versus plastic strain rate: shock and Hopkinson bar data, and model.[9]

from the plastic wave portion, where most of the plastic straining occurs. The most salient feature of the shock stresses is that they mostly lie significantly above the Hopkinson bar data and the model Peierls barrier stresses without drag. It is worth noting that the peak deviatoric stress of the 111 kbar shot, about 7 kbar, is significantly higher than the liquid nitrogen yield stress at Hopkinson bar strain rates, [10] which is about 5 kbar. These comparisons strongly suggest that the peak deviatoric stress in the shock waves is higher than the Peierls barrier; and that the mechanism of dislocation motion in the plastic wave is dislocation drag.

Another feature is the loop formed by the shock data. In Fig. 5, the top portions of the loops for shots Ta2 and Ta6 occur early in the shock path, while the lower portions occur late in the shock path. (Note that the two late path portions overlap. Also, the loop portions that close the loops were not plotted.) This looping indicates that the mobile dislocation density is changing. [11] For example, picking a particular stress occurring in a loop will yield two corresponding points with different strain rates, the one later in time being greater than the one earlier. Since the two points have the *same* stress, the dislocation velocities are probably similar. Therefore, since the point later in the shock path has a higher strain rate, the corresponding mobile dislocation density must be higher.

This is important in understanding the slopes of the shock curves in Fig. 5, i. e. the strain rate sensitivity. It is apparently determined *both* by the dislocation - velocity relation and the mobile dislocation density evolution. Note, also, from Fig. 5, that the strain rate sensitivity of the Hopkinson bar data, which is known to involve thermal activation of dislocations, is about the same as the flatter portions of the shock waves. This similarity makes it difficult to predict, in the shock wave data, where thermal activated dislocation motion leaves off, and where dislocation drag begins. As discussed earlier, from the deviatoric stresses, drag is probably operating at the peak deviatoric stress in the shock wave, but it is not certain where it takes over.

In Fig. 5, the model curve with linear viscous drag and constant mobile dislocation density, obviously fails to predict the shock wave strain rate sensitivity. The shock data is much less strain rate sensitive that the model prediction.[9] This is, in part, due to the neglect in the model of mobile dislocation density evolution, which is important in the shock wave plasticity, as discussed above.

The lack of workhardening is evident in the shock wave data from the low values of final deviatoric stress. This is consistent with results of mechanical tests on recovered shocked Ta, in which little shock hardening is found with post Hopkinson bar testing. [12,13] Electron microscopy indicates that edge dislocations are swept out and the screw dislocations remain straight under the influence of the high shock stresses necessary to overcome the large Peierls barrier. This will significantly affect work hardening by suppressing the storage of new dislocation line length. The absence of shock-enhanced hardening in Ta is consistent with the lack of a depenence of the Stage-II hardening rate in polycrystalline Ta on strain rate.[12,13]

This means that, at the end of the plastic shock wave portion, the *total* dislocation density is not significantly increased from its initial value. Thus, the evolution of *mobile* dislocation density evident in the shock wave results must involve mostly the freeing of dislocations already present and the addition of those (relatively few) geometrically necessary to meet the applied strain rate.

In conclusion, the Ta results here suggest that the general nature of BCC shock wave behavior is dislocation drag above a strong Peierls barrier with evolution of the mobile dislocation density while the total dislocation density remains fairly constant. The strain rate sensitivity of much of the shock path is sufficiently similar to that of thermally activated Hopkinson bar data to obscure the transition point between thermally activated behavior and drag. Nevertheless, additional research to sort out these interesting effects appears worthwhile.

ACKNOWLEDGMENT

This work was supported by the US DOE.

REFERENCES

[1] D. C. Wallace, *Phys Rev. B* 22, pp. 1477-1486 and 1487-1494 (1980).

[2] D. L. Tonks, *J. Appl. Phys.* 66, pp. 1951-1960 (1989).

[3] D. L. Tonks, *The DataShoP, A Database of Weak-Shock Constitutive Data*, Los Alamos National Laboratory Report LA-12068-MS, May 1991.

[4] R. H. Warnes and D. L. Tonks, "Measurement and Analysis of 3-GPa Shock Wave Profiles in Annealed OFE Copper," in *Proceedings of the APS Topical Conference on Shock Compression of Condensed Matter*, 1989, pp. 329-332.

[5] J. N. Johnson and D. L. Tonks, "Dynamic Plasticity in Transition from Thermal Activation to Viscous Drag," in *Proceedings of the APS Topical Conference on Shock Compression of Condensed Matter*, 1991, pp. 371-378.

[6]J. N. Johnson, R. S. Hixson, D. L. Tonks, and G. T. Gray III, this volume.

[7] L. C. Chhabildas, private communication, 1992.

[8] K. W. Katahara, M. H. Manghnani, and E. S. Fisher, *J. Appl. Phys.* 47, pp. 434-439 (1976).

[9] K. G. Hoge and A. K. Mukherjee, *J. of Mat. Sci.* 12, pp. 1666-1672 (1977).

[10]G. T. Gray III, private communication.

[11] D. L. Tonks, *J. Appl. Phys.* 70, pp. 4233-4237 (1991).

[12] D. H. Lassila and G. T. Gray III, *J. Physique IV*, pp. C3-19,C3-26 (1991).

[13]R. T. Gray III, this volume.

DISLOCATION MECHANICS BASED CONSTITUTIVE RELATIONS FOR PLASTIC FLOW AND STRENGTH OF HY STEELS

R.W. Armstrong
University of Maryland
College Park, MD 20742

* F.J. Zerilli, ** W.H. Holt and **W. Mock, Jr.
Naval Surface Warfare Center
* Silver Spring, MD 20903 and ** Dahlgren, VA 22448

The plastic deformation and fracturing properties of high yield (HY) steels are described relative to reference strength properties established for Armco iron and plain carbon steels. The higher yield strengths are produced by a combination of solid solution and precipitation strengthening mechanisms whose embrittling action is offset by the addition of effective grain size strengthening that contributes to suppressing the ductile-brittle transition temperature. The strain rate and temperature dependencies of the flow stress are essentially unchanged. Carbide particles and plates, particularly at grain boundaries, are the eventual sources of cleavage or ductile fracturing.

INTRODUCTION

A combined dislocation mechanics/thermal activation description has been given for the stress/strain behavior of body-centered-cubic (bcc) Armco iron [1], tantalum [2], and tungsten [3] materials in the following set of equations:

$$\sigma = c_o + B_o e^{-\beta T} + K\epsilon^n \quad (1)$$

where

$$\beta = \beta_o - \beta_1 \ln\dot{\epsilon} \quad (2)$$

and

$$c_o = \sigma_G + k\ell^{-1/2} \ . \quad (3)$$

In Eqs. (1) to (3), σ is the von Mises equivalent stress, ϵ is the equivalent strain, $\dot{\epsilon}$ is the strain rate, T is the absolute temperature, and ℓ is the average polycrystal grain diameter. The material parameters: B_o, β_o and β_1 relate to the thermally-activated Peierls stress mechanism for bcc metals; K and n characterize the strain hardening; σ_G is an athermal stress component attributed to dislocation density and alloying effects; and, k is the (Hall-Petch) microstructural stress intensity for transmitting plastic flow across grain boundaries.

Equations (1)-(3), with constants determined from conventional laboratory tensile or compression tests, have been applied to predicting for Armco iron and tantalum, the full shape of (Taylor-type) solid cylinder [1,2] and flyer plate [4] impact test results, and to predicting for tungsten [3] the grain size and strain rate dependencies of the onset of brittleness as characterized by the ductile-brittle transition temperature (DBTT). Here, we are concerned with relating the reference material constants for Armco iron to those for HY naval steels and with applying the same equations plus whatever modifications are necessary for prediction of the HY material behaviors.

ARMCO IRON, HIGH STRENGTH LOW ALLOY, AND HY STEEL CONNECTIONS

Thermal activation parameters: B_o, β_o and β_1 comparable to those of Armco iron, were shown [5] to apply equally well for an experimental study of the temperature and strain rate dependence of the cleavage fracture toughness of ferritic steel, by Curry [6], and for specification of Charpy V-notch transition temperature results obtained for mild steel by Sandström and Bergström [7], as listed in Table 1. Important results have been reported by Marchand and Duffy [8] for HY 100 steel material. In agreement with the trends indicated for Eqs. (1)-(3), the stress/strain curves obtained at lower temperatures were shifted upwards in a nearly parallel manner with a reduced uniform elongation to the maximum load point [9] and essentially parallel shifts were obtained at increasing strain values for the strain rate dependence of the flow stress.

Table 1. Comparison of mild steel [6], C-Mn steel [7] and Armco iron [1] thermal activation constants.

Material	B_o, MPa	β_o, K^{-1}	β_1, K^{-1}
mild steel	1170	0.0066	0.00034
C-Mn steel	1000	0.0075	0.00040
Armco iron	1033	0.0070	0.00042

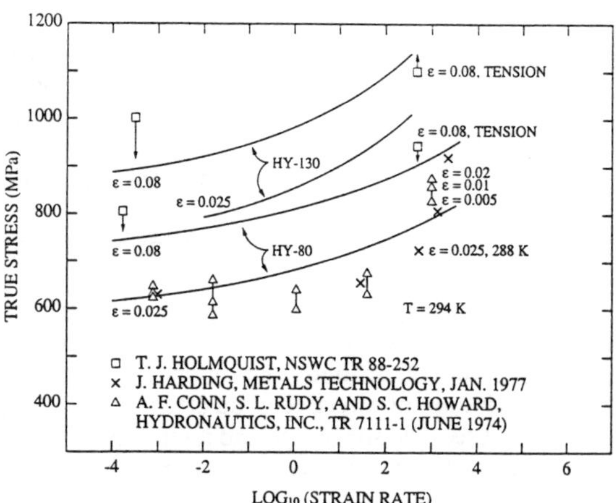

Figure 1. Comparison of experimental and computed strain rate dependencies of the flow stresses for HY-80 and HY-130 materials.

Figure 1 gives an example of the effort to obtain material constants for HY 80 and HY 130 materials, spanning HY 100 measurements not shown, as gleaned from rather limited measurements reported thus far and exhibiting not untypical significant experimental scatter at the higher strain rates of interest [10]-[12]. The parameters listed in Table 2 were obtained from "best fit" curves adapted to such measurements. The computed curves are similar to those better fitted to the tantalum results previously described [2]. The analysis of measurements has led to the list of constants given in Table 2. For HY 130, only values of σ_G, K, and n are taken to be significantly different from the constants for Armco iron.

TAYLOR CYLINDER IMPACT COMPARISON

An HY 130 cylinder impact test result is shown in Figure 2 as obtained at a velocity of 189 m/s with the 40 mm bore gas gun facility [13] at NAVSWC Dahlgren, VA. For improved control of the impacting process, a stationary cylinder specimen 6.35 mm diameter and 25.5 mm in length was impacted with a larger 34 mm diameter 6.20 mm thick hardened steel disk carried in a sabot, as previously described for the impact deformation and fracture of tungsten material [14].

In Figure 2, good agreement has been obtained with the use of Equation (1) in an EPIC code computation for the test result, employing the constants given in Table 2. Deformation twinning, that is important at large grain sizes in Armco iron, is presumed not to be of importance for the deformation of HY 130 because of its small grain size.

THE DUCTILE-BRITTLE TRANSITION

At very large strain rates and/or low temperatures, and in the presence of a tensile stress-state, steel and related bcc metals show a transition in behavior from ductile plastic flow to brittle cleavage fracturing. As mentioned earlier, Eqs. (1)-(3) have been applied to describing the grain size and strain rate dependencies for this DBTT in tungsten material [3]. The condition

Table 2. Thermal activation, grain size, and strain hardening parameters for HY-80, HY-100, and HY-130 steels

	B_o (MPa)	β_0 (10^{-3} K^{-1})	β_1 (10^{-3} K^{-1})	c_0 (MPa)	k (MPa $mm^{1/2}$)	K (MPa)	n
HY-80	870	7.1	0.34	440	22	1120	0.58
HY-100	770	8.6	0.36	800	22	1100	0.73
HY-130	1033	7.0	0.42	710	22	950	0.79

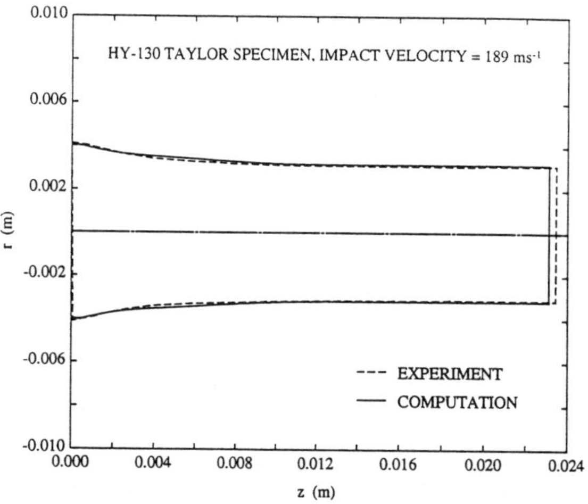

Figure 2. Comparison of experimental and computed cylinder impact test results for HY-130 steel.

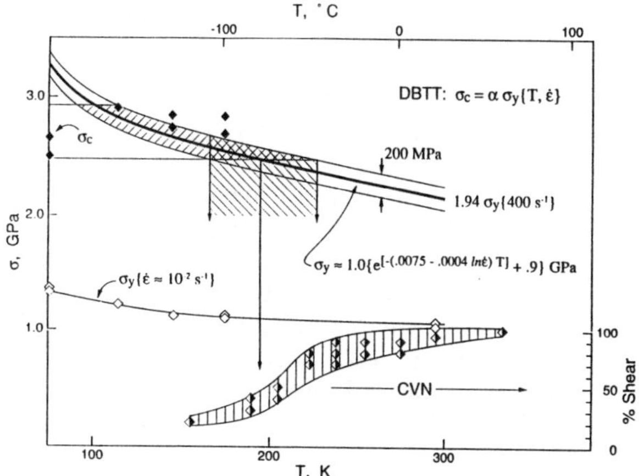

Figure 3. Ductile-brittle transition temperature analysis of yield stress, cleavage stress and Charpy V-notch transition temperature measurements for HY-130 weld metal [17].

is specified for Charpy V-notch impact testing by equating the effective yield stress at the notch root and the cleavage fracture stress of the material in the equation [15]:

$$\alpha\sigma_y = \sigma_c \tag{4}$$

where α is the multiplier for the raised yield stress in the triaxial stress-state at the notch root and σ_c is the cleavage fracture stress that follows a Hall-Petch grain size dependence, as for Eq. (1) but with a significantly larger value of microstructural stress intensity, k_c, in the relation

$$\sigma_c = \sigma_{oc} + k_c \ell^{-1/2} \tag{5}$$

The value of the cleavage friction stress, σ_{oc}, for the microslip required to initiate unstable cleavage fracturing is normally taken to be athermal. The influence of grain boundary carbide on lowering σ_c has been described by Petch [16].

Figure 3 shows an application of this analysis to yield stress, cleavage stress and Charpy V-notch impact measurements made on a candidate HY 130 weld metal material [17]. As indicated, the mildly temperature dependent reference yield stress measurements, made at a strain rate of 0.01 /s, are raised by the measured [7] triaxial stress-state factor α = 1.94 and plastic strain rate of 400 /s in the notch to give a computed moderately strong yield stress dependence on temperature that crosses a horizontal band of measurements established separately at low temperatures for the cleavage fracture stress. Extrapolation of the lowest cleavage stress measurement to its intersection with the limiting edges of the band of computed yield stress values gives a range of temperatures for yielding or cleavage being equally favorable that are in line with the Charpy test results specifying the ductile-brittle transition in terms of the percentage of shear fracturing observed for the broken specimens. The analysis may relate to reported observations at higher strain rates of the spall-induced brittle and/or cleavage fracture behavior of carbon steel materials where a highest spall strength was measured for finer grained material [18].

ACKNOWLEDGEMENTS

This work was supported at NAVSWC by the Independent Research Program and, for R.W. Armstrong, both at the David Taylor Research Center Annapolis Laboratory through an Intergovernment Personnel Appointment and at the University of Maryland through the Office of Naval Research, Contract N00014-89-J-1944.

REFERENCES

1. F.J. Zerilli and R.W. Armstrong, J. Appl. Phys. 61, 1816 (1987).

2. F.J. Zerilli and R.W. Armstrong, J. Appl. Phys. 68, 1580 (1990).

3. V. Ramachandran, R.W. Armstrong and F.J. Zerilli, in Tungsten and Tungsten Alloys - Recent Advances, ed. by A. Crowson and E.S. Chen, (The Minerals, Metals and Materials Society, Warrendale, PA, 1991) p. 111.

4. F.J. Zerilli and R.W. Armstrong, in Shock Compression of Condensed Matter 1991, ed. by S.C. Schmidt, R.D. Dick and D.G. Tasker, (Elsevier Science Publishers B.V., Amsterdam, 1992) p. 257.

5. R.W. Armstrong, L. Roberson Link and G.R. Speich, in Processing, Microstructure and Properties of HSLA Steels, ed. by A.J. DeArdo, (The Metallurgical Society, Warrendale, PA, 1988) p. 305.

6. D.A. Curry, Mater. Sci. Eng. 43, 135 (1980).

7. R. Sandström and Y. Bergström, Metal Sci. 18, 177 (1984).

8. A. Marchand and J. Duffy, J. Mech. Phys. Sol. 36, 251 (1988).

9. F.J. Zerilli and R.W. Armstrong, in Shock Compression of Condensed Matter - 1989, ed. by S.C. Schmidt, J.N. Johnson and L.W. Davison, (Elsevier Publishers B.V., Amsterdam, 1990) p. 357.

10. A.F. Conn, S.L. Rudy and S.C. Howard, Technical Report TR 7111-1, Hydronautics, Inc. (1974).

11. J. Harding, Met. Tech. 4, 6 (1977).

12. T.J. Holmquist, Report NSWC 88-252, Naval Surface Warfare Center (1988).

13. W. Mock, Jr., and W.H. Holt, Report NSWC TR-3473, Naval Surface Warfare Center (1976).

14. W.H. Holt, W. Mock, Jr., V. Ramachandran and R.W. Armstrong, in Tungsten and Tungsten Alloys - Recent Advances, ed. by A. Crowson and E.S. Chen, (The Minerals, Metals and Materials Society, Warrendale, PA, 1991), p. 285.

15. R.W. Armstrong, in Fracture 1969, (Chapman and Hall, London, U.K., 1969) p. 314.

16. N.J. Petch, Acta Metall. 34, 1387 (1986).

17. J.J. DeLoach, G.L. Franke and R.W. Armstrong, David Taylor Research Center Annapolis Laboratory, unpublished results (1989).

18. A.K. Zurek, P.S. Follansbee and J. Hack, Metall. Trans. 21A, 431 (1990).

SHEAR-BANDING IN Ti-6Al-4V

D C Swift
AWE Aldermaston
Reading RG7 4PR, UK

The yield stress of materials exhibiting work-hardening and thermal softening can reach a maximum, at which they are unstable to further strain. Deformation then localises as shear bands. This critical strain has been calculated using parameters for the Steinberg – Guinan strength model. A simple model to predict the onset of shear-banding in the impact of flat-ended rods on plates produces results consistent with known experiments in steel/Ti-6Al-4V, using the calculated critical strain. Conduction effects can modify the critical strain by reducing the rate of thermal softening, introducing a dependence on strain rate. The magnitude of the conduction effects caused by a microstructure of spherical grains in a matrix and by solitary inclusions is estimated. Comparison with experiments indicates that the rate-dependence is consistent with conduction between the phases of the Ti-6Al-4V microstructure.

INTRODUCTION

Materials are stable to small amounts of plastic strain because they harden on working, but they also soften on heating. If the amount of heat lost by conduction from the deforming material is sufficiently small, these competing effects result in a strength which first increases with strain, but tends to a maximum and can result in failure before the bulk material melts or fractures.

In a heterogenous material, some regions reach their maximum strength first, and as they subsequently weaken, the neighbouring material must support an increased stress, so nearby weak sites will tend to fail sooner. If the applied stress remains great enough, the weakening region will grow and spread, forming a shear band.

CONDITIONS FOR FAILURE

The condition for the onset of failure at any position in the deforming material can be derived by considering the variation of the yield strength Y with plastic strain ϵ. A necessary condition for the onset of failure is that Y has reached a maximum:

$$\frac{dY}{d\epsilon} \leq 0 \tag{1}$$

where if Y is a function only of ϵ, strain rate $\dot{\epsilon}$ and temperature T,

$$\frac{dY}{d\epsilon} = \frac{\partial Y}{\partial \epsilon} + \frac{\partial Y}{\partial \dot{\epsilon}}\frac{d\dot{\epsilon}}{d\epsilon} + \frac{\partial Y}{\partial T}\frac{dT}{d\epsilon}. \tag{2}$$

Temperature term and adiabaticity

It is convenient to split the rate of change of temperature with strain into source and sink terms:

$$\frac{dT}{d\epsilon} = \frac{\partial T}{\partial \epsilon} + \frac{\partial T}{\partial t}\frac{dt}{d\epsilon} \tag{3}$$

where the first term on the right hand side represents heat generation through plastic work and the second term handles heat conduction. The heat generated is

$$\frac{\partial T}{\partial \epsilon} = \frac{f_{ph} Y}{\rho c} \tag{4}$$

where ρ is the density, c the specific heat capacity and f_{ph} the fraction of plastic work converted to heat – typically 90 to 95%.

The heat conduction equation is used to express the time derivative of the temperature in terms of the local space derivatives in the material:

$$\frac{\partial T}{\partial t} = \frac{k}{\rho c}\nabla^2 T \tag{5}$$

where k is the heat conductivity. $\nabla^2 T$ is negative inside a positive temperature blip: it acts as a sink term for regions of elevated temperature.

Table 1: Strains to Failure in Ti-6Al-4V.

$\dot{\epsilon}$ (μs^{-1})	ϵ_c
6×10^{-9}	0.8 ± 0.2
7.4×10^{-8}	0.4 ± 0.1
9.55×10^{-7}	0.3 ± 0.1
6.33×10^{-6}	0.2 ± 0.05

The conduction term is linked closely to a material's microstructure and introduces a rate-dependence. To understand it better, we define the *adiabaticity*:

$$A \equiv 1 + \frac{k}{f_{ph} Y \dot{\epsilon}} \nabla^2 T. \tag{6}$$

Heat conduction can be neglected if $A \sim 1$, becomes more important as the adiabaticity falls, and is dominant for $A \sim 0$.

Adiabatic strain to failure

Assuming the adiabaticity has a simple relation to the strain, it is straightforward to calculate the strain ϵ_c at which the failure condition (Eq. 1) is satisfied.

Neglecting the melting term and initial strain from manufacture, the Steinberg – Guinan model has the following form for the yield function:

$$Y = Y_0(1 + \beta\epsilon)^N \left[1 + \alpha p/\eta^{\frac{1}{3}} - h(T - T_0)\right] \tag{7}$$

where $\beta > 0$, $h > 0$, $\alpha > 0$, and $0 < N < 1$. The critical strain for the onset of failure is then

$$\epsilon_c = \frac{1}{\beta}\left[\left(\frac{\rho c N \beta}{h f_{ph} Y_0 A}\right)^{\frac{1}{N+1}} - 1\right]. \tag{8}$$

For Ti-6Al-4V, ϵ_c is calculated from Steinberg - Guinan coefficients[1] to be 0.16, assuming $A = 1$ and $f_{ph} = 1$. The variation of ϵ_c against $\dot{\epsilon}$ was estimated from previous experimental data.[2] The observed values can be seen to tend approximately to 0.16 as $\dot{\epsilon}$ increases.

APPLICATION TO IMPACT EXPERIMENTS

Impact experiments are a useful source of data to test shear-banding models.[3, 4] Attempts have been made to mimic these experiments with hydrocode calculations, with the melt term in the Steinberg – Guinan model adjusted to make the yield strength Y tend rapidly to zero for strains greater than ϵ_c, but these have so far been unsuccessful, with the appearance and propagation of shear bands seeming rather mesh-dependent. However, a simple model can be derived to predict the onset of shear-banding in restricted circumstances.

Simple model for a rod impacting a plate

When a flat-nosed rod, travelling with a speed u_0, impacts normally on a flat plate, the states in both impactor and target can be calculated from the intersection of the Hugoniot curves in $p - u$ space, where p is the pressure in the shocked region. This 1D picture persists until complicated by rarefaction waves propagating from the outside of either material.

The model proceeds by assuming that the 1D states persist over the whole of the front of the impactor and the corresponding region of the target, and that the lateral expansion of the impactor is negligible. (Fig. 1.) As the impactor indents the target, material in line with the edge of the impactor experiences essentially 1D compression, and a shear wave travels along the plate sideways from the impact site.

If the material ahead of the impactor is pushed at a speed u, a region of shear strain $\epsilon_r = u/u_p$ results, growing sideways at the plastic wavespeed u_p. If $\epsilon_r \geq \epsilon_c$, the deformation localises into a shear band. The critical post-impact particle speed u_c is defined as the particle speed required to produce a shear strain greater than ϵ_c:

$$u_c = \epsilon_c u_p, \tag{9}$$

If u_0 exceeds the value needed to produce u_c after impact, the target is liable to exhibit shear-banding. u_p for Ti-6Al-4V is about $500\,\mathrm{m\,s^{-1}}$, implying $u_c \sim 80\,\mathrm{m\,s^{-1}}$.

The 1D state after an impact

The intersection point of the Hugoniots depends on whether they are purely hydrodynamic, elas-

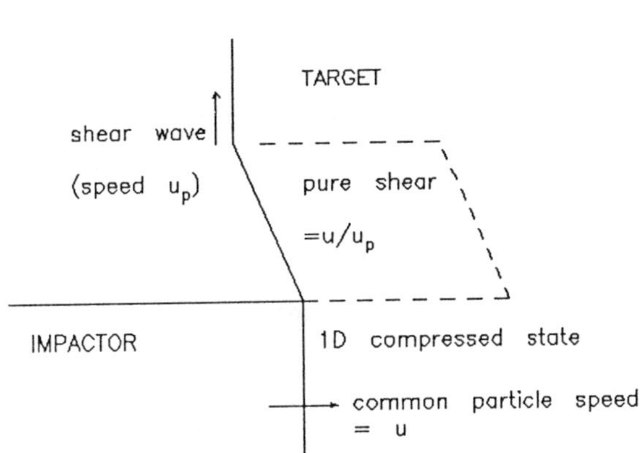

Figure 1: Assumed picture shortly after impact.

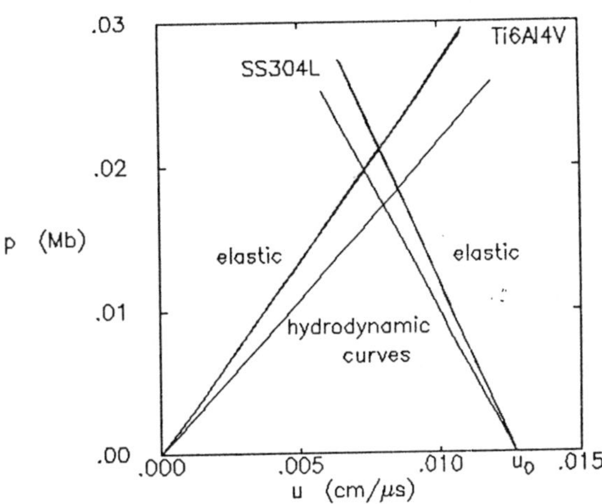

Figure 2: Comparison of hydrodynamic and elastic Hugoniot curves.

tic or elastoplastic, and which strain measure is used. This is illustrated in Fig. 2 using material data for steel (SS304L) and Ti-6Al-4V,[1] where the speed of the impactor was adjusted to give an intersection at $u = u_c$ for hydrodynamic Hugoniots. The elastic Hugoniots are also shown (different strain measures almost indistinguishable), and the elastoplastic curves would lie in between. The impactor speed required to give an intersection at u_p is about $127\,\mathrm{m\,s^{-1}}$ for hydrodynamic Hugoniots, or $129\,\mathrm{m\,s^{-1}}$ for elastic. Different strain measures make a difference of about 1%.

Comparison with experiments

Experimental evidence[3, 4] on steel/Ti-6Al-4V impacts cites the formation of complete shear bands at impactor speeds as low as $247\,\mathrm{m\,s^{-1}}$, and perforation or plugging at higher speeds. This is consistent with the minimum impact speeds calculated, since at the lowest speeds predicted above, edge-rarefactions would quench a shear band before it penetrated the target.

THE EFFECT OF HEAT CONDUCTION

When a material is deformed, initial variations in the strength lead to variations in the temperature. Since temperature variations drive heat conduction and strength is temperature dependent, the inhomogeneity of the strength causes some of the strain rate dependence.

This hinges on the contribution of the $\nabla^2 T$ term to Eq. 1. Simple relations can be found by assuming $\nabla^2 T$ is constant in each region of the microstructure. To avoid solving a full continuum problem, the strength is assumed to be a function of the mean temperature in a region:

$$\bar{T} = \frac{E}{\rho c V} \tag{10}$$

where E is the total internal energy of the region of volume V. Conserving energy flow around the microstructure produces a set of simultaneous equations for the time evolution of $\bar{T}$ in each region.

Spherical grains in a matrix

In a material consisting of spherical grains of one phase embedded in a matrix of another, The local temperature distribution is roughly spherically symmetric about the centre of each grain. If the matrix is stronger than the grains, both phases experience the same strain rate.

To simplify the solution, it is assumed that the difference between the strength of the phases is constant, and that strains are relatively small so that the microstructure does not change during the deformation. The values of $\nabla^2 T$ are then

$$\begin{array}{ll} \frac{\dot{\epsilon} f_{ph}(Y_2 - Y_1)}{k(1 + V_1/V_2)} \left[1 - e^{-\epsilon/\tau\dot{\epsilon}}\right] & \text{(grain)} \\ \frac{\dot{\epsilon} f_{ph}(Y_1 - Y_2)}{k(1 + V_2/V_1)} \left[1 - e^{-\epsilon/\tau\dot{\epsilon}}\right] & \text{(matrix)} \end{array} \tag{11}$$

where

$$\tau \equiv \frac{\rho c S}{k(1 + V_1/V_2)} \tag{12}$$

and S is a factor determined by the microstructure. Because the rate-dependence enters the failure condition (Eq. 1) as $\nabla^2 T/\dot{\epsilon}$, these relations predict that the only rate-dependence from conduction between grains and the matrix occurs on timescales $\sim \tau$. A rigorous treatment of Y_1 and Y_2 would give more detailed rate-dependent behaviour.

For Ti-6Al-4V which has undergone a range of forming processes,[5] a fair approximation to the microstructure is spheres of the α-phase of radius $5\,\mu$m, embedded in a matrix of the β-phase, typically a twentieth as thick as the grain size. $\nabla^2 T$ is larger for the β-phase:

$$(\nabla^2 T)_\beta \sim -2.5 \times 10^9 \dot{\epsilon} \left[1 - e^{-30\epsilon/\dot{\epsilon}}\right] \text{ K cm}^{-2} \tag{13}$$

where $\dot{\epsilon}$ is in μs^{-1}. This equation can be used to estimate the contribution to $\nabla^2 T$ from the inhomogeneity of the microstructure, and compares reasonably with experimental values deduced from Eq. 8 (Table 2).

Solitary inclusions

A similar analysis can be applied to the case of a solitary inclusion stronger than the surrounding homogeneous matrix. The rate-dependence deduced is however negligible for all plausible inclusion sizes in Ti-6Al-4V.

Table 2: Estimated Experimental and Microstructural $\nabla^2 T$.

$\dot{\epsilon}$ (μs^{-1})	Estimated $\nabla^2 T$ (K cm^{-2})	Microstructural $\nabla^2 T$ (K cm^{-2})
6×10^{-9}	$-(2.7 \pm 0.3) \times 10$	-16
7.4×10^{-8}	$-(2.2 \pm 0.6) \times 10^2$	-1.9×10^2
9.55×10^{-7}	$-(1.8 \pm 1.2) \times 10^3$	-2.5×10^3
6.33×10^{-6}	$-(3 \pm 7) \times 10^4$	-1.7×10^4

CONCLUSIONS

The analysis presented for adiabatic strains to failure is supported by the asymptotic value approached in Ti-6Al-4V as the strain rate is increased. This is also consistent with a simplified model of shear-banding in impact experiments.

Heat conduction in the microstructure of this alloy can probably account for the rate dependence at strain rates up to about $10^{-5}\,\mu s^{-1}$, whereas the effect of inclusions is much smaller.

REFERENCES

[1] D J Steinberg, *Equation of State and Strength Properties of Selected Materials*, UCRL-MA-106439, 1991.

[2] A U Sulijoadikusumo and O W Dillon Jr, "Work Softening of Ti-6Al-4V due to Adiabatic Heating", in R W Rohde, B M Butcher, J R Holland and C H Karnes (Eds), *Metallurgical Effects at High Strain Rates*, Plenum, 1973.

[3] R E Winter, *Philosophical Magazine*, 31, 4, p 765 (1975).

[4] B E Ringers *Modeling Adiabatic Shear*, BRL-TR-2662, 1985.

[5] *Metals Handbook*, 8th Ed, Vol 8, Am Soc Metals, 1973.

QUASI-ELASTIC BEHAVIOR OF PURE TITANIUM AND TA6V4 TITANIUM ALLOY AT HIGH PRESSURE

P. Andriot, P. Lalle, and J.P. Dejean

C.E.A. - CENTRE D'ETUDES SCIENTIFIQUES ET TECHNIQUES D'AQUITAINE B.P. n° 2 - 33114 - LE BARP - FRANCE

PEROT-FABRY velocimeter wave profile measurements were made on pure titanium and on TA6V4 alloy to measure the velocity and the amplitude of quasi-elastic waves during release. The two materials behave nearly in the same way : when the Hugoniot stress reaches 64 GPa, the velocity of these waves equals 8 km/s, the deviatoric part of the stress during elastic release is around 1.4 GPa and the Poisson's ratio value is 0.37.

I - INTRODUCTION

The ten per cent amount in weight of foreign metals (e.g. 6 % aluminium and 4 % vanadium) makes the Hugoniot Elastic Limit (HEL) of TA6V4 definitely larger than that of pure titanium. Eight shots were made to measure the amplitude of the quasi-elastic waves in release after shock in order to verify whether this difference between TA6V4 and pure Ti elastic properties at low pressure is true also at high pressure.

II - EXPERIMENTAL PROCEDURE

To measure the velocity and the amplitude of the quasi elastic release waves after shock we used simultaneously the methods described by McQUEEN, FRITZ and MORRIS [1] and ASAY and CHHABILDAS [2]. Let us consider the experiment sketched in figure 1. Here a projectile impacts a stepped target. The first part of the target is made of the same material as that of the projectile. The second part is made of a different material and is termed the "window". The velocity versus time of the target-window boundary is recorded in front of each step In the "optical analyzer" [1] ΔT is the difference between the times when the shock and the beginning of the release wave reach the target/window boundary. According to [1] the Lagrangian velocity C_L of the release wavc obeys :

$$C_L = Us\,\frac{H/e + 1}{H/e - 1} \qquad (1)$$

U_s is the shock velocity and H and e are defined in figure 1 caption. According to [2] the stress-strain and stress -material velocity curves are get from the measured u_w (t) curve by

$$\begin{aligned} du_p &= \tfrac{1}{2}\left(du_W + \frac{d\sigma_W}{\rho_o C_1}\right) \\ d\sigma &= \rho_o C_2\, du_p \qquad (2) \\ d\varepsilon &= \frac{d\sigma}{\rho_o C_2^2} \end{aligned}$$

where ρo is the initial density of the target material, u_p is the material velocity, σ is the stress. C_2 the lagrangian velocity of the wave which produces the increases $d\sigma_w$ and du_w in stress and material velocity in the window, C_1 the lagrangian velocity of this wave when it reaches the window.

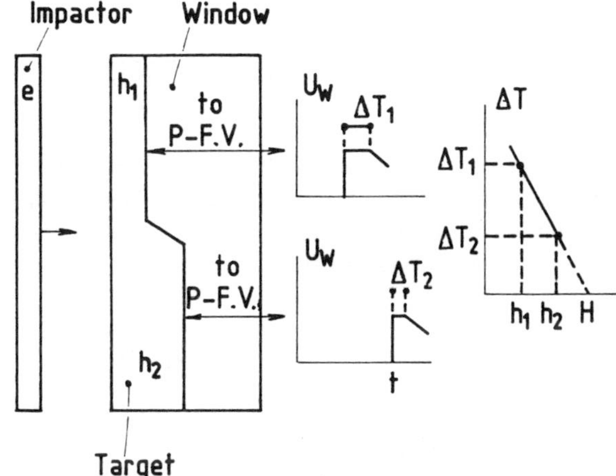

Figure 1. McQUEEN et al. optical analyser. H is the target thickness when the release wave catches the shock, e the impactor thickness.

The C_2 measurement is explained in figure 2 which is a schematic diagram of the waves trajectories in eulerian time-distance coordinates.

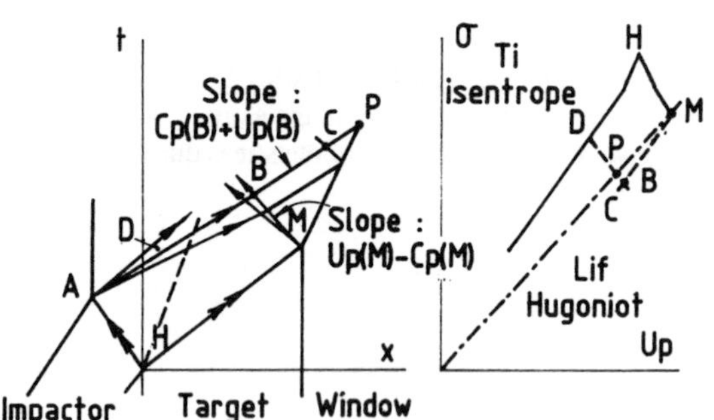

Figure 2 : The areas of the t - x diagram are in the corresponding state of σ- up diagram.

In the fan of release waves originating at the back of the projectile, a line in x - t diagram has a slope $u_p + c(\sigma)$, where C (σ) is the eulerian sound velocity corresponding to stress σ . To find the unknown velocity C (D) we assume that between the points labelled B and C, and C and P, the sound velocity Cp is that of plastic waves. This velocity is calculated by assuming that a release isentropic curve is the mirror image of the Hugoniot in σ-u_p coordinates. Then :

$$Us = C_O + S\, Up$$

(3)

$$Cp(\sigma) = Co \frac{\rho o}{\rho} \sqrt{1 + \frac{4 \sigma S}{\rho_o C_o^2}}$$

The coordinates of the point P are obtained by integrating the experimental u_w (t) curve. From this, we find the coordinates of points C and B, and the quantity of interest, the eulerian sound velocity C(D) :

$$c(D) = (x_B - x_A)/(t_B - t_A) - u_p(D)$$

III - IMPACT STUDIES

III-1 - Experiments

Shock loading is produced by symmetric impact of a projectile thrown by explosive against a target made of the same material, as shown in figure 3.

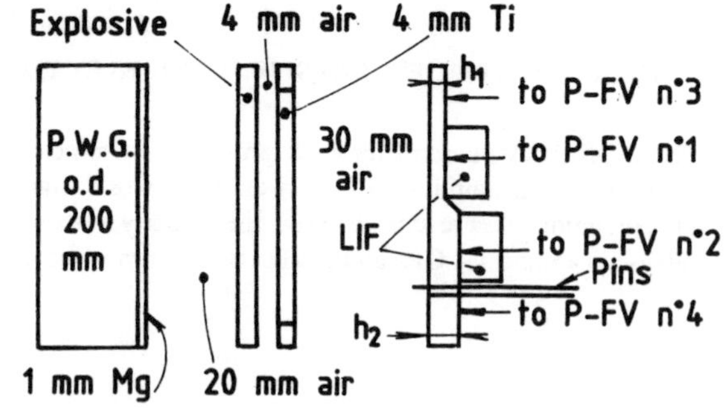

Figure 3 :Experimental arrangement

Sixteen ferroelectric pins (DYNASEN CA 1135) gives the time of impact in front of the velocity measurements. Variation of the impactor velocity is obtained by varying the thickness of the explosive. The air spacing between explosive and projectile ensures a nearly isentropic acceleration and avoids spalling. In each experiment, for the two steps of the target, the target/window interface velocity and the target free surface velocity were recorded with 1 % accuracy by mean of a four beams PEROT-FABRY velocimeter. The window was made of lithium fluoride (LiF). The optical behavior of LiF under shock compression is known.

The initial density of the samples is 4.515 +/- 0.01 g/cm³ for pure titanium (T40 titanium) and 4.419 +/- 0.01 g/cm³ for TA6V4.

III-2 - Hugoniot parameters

The test parameters and the resulting Hugoniot data are listed in table 1

Table 1

Shot n°	Material	Target h1 (mm)	Thickness h2 (mm)	Particle Velocity km/s	Shock Velocity km/s	Hugoniot stress GPa
T1	T40	3.00	12.01	1,72 ± 0,05	6.67 ± 0.15	51.8
T2	T40	2.99	10.00	1.72 ± 0;05	6.63 ± 0.25	51.5
T3	T40	3.02	10.00	1.77 ± 0.05	6.82 ± 0.25	54.5
T4	T40	3.01	7.99	1.99 ± 0.05	7.07 ± 0.25	63.5
TA1	TA6V4	3.02	11.97	1.73 ± 0.05	7.04 ± 0.3	53.8
TA2	TA6V4	3.03	10.00	1.75 ± 0.05	6.74 ± 0.25	52.1
TA3	TA6V4	3.02	10.01	1.80 ± 0.05	6.88 ± 0.25	54.7
TA4	TA6V4	2.98	8.00	2.03 ± 0.05	7.14 ± 0.25	64

The U_s-u_p data relative to pure titanium or to TA6V4 alloy are not straight lines. For pure Ti, STEINBERG [3] gives :

(5) $U_S = 5.02 + [1.536 - 5.138\ U_p + 10.83 U_p^{\ 2}]\ U_p$

This expression, for $1.4 < u_p < 2.0$ km/s, which reproduces also the data in [4] can be approximated by

(6) $Us = 4.83 + 1.11\ U_p$

For TA6V4 alloy one gets, for $U_p > 1.4$ km/s from [3] and [5] respectively.

(7) $U_S = 5.13 + 1.028\ U_p$

(8) $U_S = 5.03 + 1.056\ U_p$

All these expressions agree with the present results.

III-3 - Quasi-elastic waves in release after shock

Examples of the records of the target/window interface velocity versus time are plotted in figure 4.

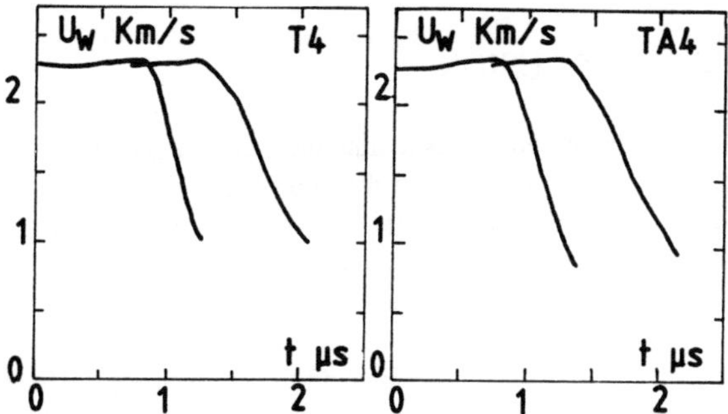

Figure 4 : Interface velocity versus time

The beginning of the release does not show up as an abrupt decrease in interface velocity but rather as a crossover, the velocity of the wave varying slowly from its initial value down to the plastic wave velocity. The ideal stress-strain curve sketched in figure 5 is a simplified version of real experimental curves. The release data thus obtained are listed in table II, where the quantities σ'_d, σ'_H and σ'_r are defined in figure 5.

Comments :

(i) The listed value of C_L is the eulerian velocity of the beginning of release. The Poisson's ratio has been calculated from this value and those of plastic wave velocity (equ. 3) by

$$(9)\qquad \nu = \left\{3 - \left(\frac{C_L}{C_P}\right)^2\right\} \Big/ \left\{3 + \left(\frac{C_L}{C_P}\right)^2\right\}$$

The two materials exhibit an increase in Poisson's ratio with increasing pressure.

Table 2.

Shot n°	Hugoniot * stress GPa	Density * g/cm^3	C_L km/s	ν Poisson's ratio	$\sigma'_d = \sigma'_H + \sigma'_r$ GPa
T1	52.1	6.06	7.68	0.36	1.6
T2	52.5	6.07	7.8	0.35	1.6
T3	54.5	6.11	7.8	0.35	1.4
T4	64.1	6.31	8.0	0.36	1.6
TA1	48.6	5.87	7.8	0.34	1.7
TA2	51.2	5.93	7.85	0.34	1.65
TA3	54.3	6.00	7.9	0.34	1.8
TA4	63.5	6.19	7.9	0.37	1.6

* Hugoniot stress and density have been calculated from the known Hugoniot and the measured values of the initial velocity in LiF and of the waves velocity. The uncertainty in C_L is around 0.3 km/s, and that in σ'_d about 0.2 GPa.

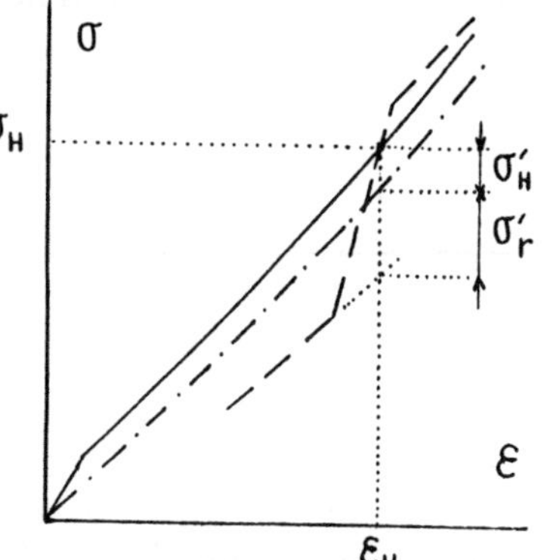

Figure 5. Idealized stress-strain curves. The continuous line is the Hugoniot, the dot-dashed line the pressure, and dashed lines are re-shock and release pathes.The measured amplitude of the deviatoric stress during the release is $\sigma'_d = \sigma'_H + \sigma'_r$.

(ii) Using equations (2) needs to know C_o and S in (3). Our first attempt in TA6V4 data reduction was made with the coefficients of equation (7). This procedure leads to a large discrepancy between measured and calculated values of plastic wave velocity. The examples of σ-ε curves shown in figure 6, and the σ'_d values in table II were obtained with the same coefficients of equation (6) for Ti and TA6V4, leading to a difference between calculated and measured C_p values within the experimental error.

(iii) The HEL value for titanium is 1.5 GPa and the corresponding yield stress Yo 0.85 GPa [3]. For TA6V4 HEL ~ 2.8 GPa, Yo ~1.5 GPa [5]. This large difference in Yo does not appear in our ($\sigma'_H + \sigma'_r$) measured values. We have not performed re-shock experiments, so the actual σ'_H value is unknown, and our experiments give only the quantity ($\sigma'_H + \sigma'_r$) . Deducing Y needs some assumption on σ'_H. If we assume as STEINBERG, COCHRAN and GUINAN (SCG) did in their original model, that the Hugoniot state lies on the "upper" yield curve, then $Y = 3/4\ (\sigma'_H + \sigma'_r)$ and one gets Y = 1.1 GPa when σ_H ~ 64GPa for Ti and TA6V4. The large difference in low pressure elastic properties exhibited by the two materials disappears at high pressure. The S.C.G. model predictions sligthly underestimate the C_L value, and slightly overestimate the Y value. The model correctly reproduces the observed slight decrease in Y when σ_h varies from 50 GPa to 64 GPa.We emphasize that all these comparisons lie on the previous assumption on σ'_H.

III-4 - Spall strength

The spall strength was calculated from the free surface velocity versus time curves according to ROMANCHENKO and STEPANOV formula [6] and the results are listed in table 3.

Table 3

Shot n°	Material	Hugoniot stress (GPa)	ΔV* m/s	Spall strength (GPa)	Spall thickness (mm)
T1	Ti	51.8	220	3.1	2
T2	Ti	51.5	275	3.7	2
T3	Ti	54.5	275	3.7	2
T4	Ti	63.5	275	3.8	2.6
TA2	TA6V4	52.1	270	3.6	2.2
TA3	TA6V4	54.7	315	4.2	2.2
TA4	TA6V4	64	320	4.2	2.6

* ΔV is the difference between the maximum velocity and the pull back velocityFor all the shots, the strain rate was around $1.7 \times 10^5\ s^{-1}$

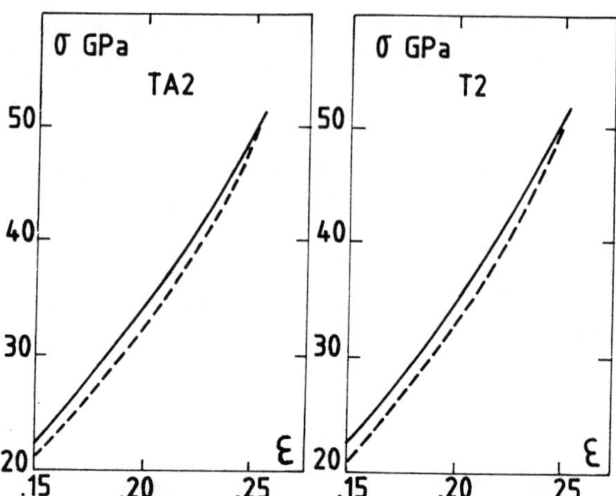

figure 6.Release paths for Titanium and TA6V4. The continuous curve is the Hugoniot.

IV - CONCLUSION

At the Hugoniot elastic limit the yield stress of TA6V4 is greater than that of pure titanium. When the Hugoniot stress is 64 GPa the amplitude of quasi elastic waves in release is the same for the two materials.

REFERENCES

[1] - McQueen, Fritz and Morris"The velocity of sound behind strong shock in 2024A1" in APS shock waves in condensed matter (1983)

[2] - Asay and Chhabildas in "shock waves and high strain rate phenomena in metals" Meyer and Murr, eds, Plenum Publishers (1981).

[3] - Steinberg "Equation of state and strength properties of selected materials" UCRL - MA - 106439 (1991).

[4] -Lasl Shock Hugoniot Data, marsh ed (1979)

[5] - Morris, Winckler and Mitchell "Ti - 6 % A1 - 4 % V alloy wave profile measurements in the shadow region "in shock waves in Condensed matter 1987, Schmidt and Holmes eds, Elsevier Science Publishers (1988).

[6] - Romanchenko and Stepanov "Dependance of the critical stress on the loading time parameters during spall in copper, aluminum and steel", J. Appl. Mech. and Technical Phys. (1981) p. 561.

VISCOPLASTICITY AND POROSITY EFFECTS ON THE SHOCK PROPAGATION IN PMMA AND POROUS ALUMINUM OXIDE

Fangyun LU, Shi HUAN
Department of Applied Physics
Changsha Institute of Technology
Changsha, Hunan, P. R. China, 410073
Jing DING
Department of Engineering Mechanics
Beijing Institute of Technology
Beijing, P. R. China, 100081

Peak pressure of the shock wave will drop gradually when the shock propagates in an inert material. Viscoplasticity and porosity are sources for shock wave attenuation. Plexiglass and porous Al_2O_3 have been investigated in this work. Two shock attenuation mechanisms, which are reflected in constitutive relationships, have been discussed and shock attenuation are simulated successfully.

INTRODUCTION

The peak pressure of a shock wave attenuates while propagating in an inert material. It results from two main factors: viscoplasticity and porosity of materials. The attenuation of shock wave in porous Al_2O_3 and continuous PMMA has been studied by the authors[1]. A 2-D Lagrangian technique was used. Experimental results showed that the shock rising time is different for different materials. The attenuation in porous Al_2O_3 is obviously larger than that in PMMA. For a porous Al_2O_3 sample of 3 mm thick, the relative attenuation is about 42%. However, only 28% is reached for PMMA with the same thickness. Experimental results also show that the viscoplasticity is an important and even a dominant factor besides porosity for shock attenuation.

In this paper, the attenuation of shock propagation in the continuous PMMA and porous Al_2O_3 is simulated with a Lagrangian computational program in which a characteristic line method has been used. The materials are described with viscoplastic constitutive law. All computational results are compared with experimental data and a detailed analysis has been made.

COMPUTATIONAL MODEL

Viscoplastic constitutive law gives a good description on the behavior of materials. For the studied materials, a constitutive relationship by P. Perzyna[2] is employed:

$$\dot{e}_{ij} = \frac{1}{2\mu}\dot{s}_{ij} + \gamma^0 < \Phi(F) > \frac{\partial F}{\partial \sigma_{ij}} \tag{1}$$

where, e_{ij}: deviator strain components; s_{ij}: deviator stress components; σ_{ij}: stress components; γ_{ij}: parameter related to viscosity of the materials; μ: shear modulus of the material. F is a static yield function expressed as

$$F = \frac{\sqrt{J_2'}}{k} - 1 \tag{2}$$

in which k is the shear yield limit of the material, J_2' is the second invariant of deviator strsses, $J_2' = s_{ij}s_{ij}/2$, $<\Phi(F)>$ is a function characterizing the plastic yield of the material defined as:

$$< \Phi(F) > = \begin{cases} \Phi(F) & if\ F > 0 \\ 0 & if\ F \leqslant 0 \end{cases} \tag{3}$$

Conservative equations describing the propagation of one-dimensional shock waves are[3]

$$\rho \frac{\partial u}{\partial t} = \frac{\partial s}{\partial X} - \frac{\partial P}{\partial X} \tag{4}$$

$$\frac{\partial u}{\partial X} = -\frac{1}{K}\frac{\partial P}{\partial t} \tag{5}$$

$$\frac{2}{3}\frac{\partial u}{\partial X} = \frac{1}{2\mu}\frac{\partial s}{\partial t} + \gamma < \Phi(F) > \frac{s}{\sqrt{J_2'}} \tag{6}$$

where, ρ, u, K are density, particle velocity and bulk modulus, respectively, P and s are pressure and deviator stress behind the wave front, X is lagrangian coordinate and t is time.

Eqs. (4) — (6) is a partial differential equation group of hyperbolic type. Using characteristic method, we can find its three characteristic lines and their corresponding compatible equations:

$$Along\ dX/dt = \pm C_L$$

$$du \pm \frac{1}{\rho C_L} \mp \frac{1}{\rho C_L} ds = \pm \frac{2\mu}{\rho C_L}\gamma < \Phi(F) > \frac{s}{\sqrt[2]{J_2'}} dt \tag{7}$$

$$Along\ dX/dt = 0$$

$$\frac{2}{3K}dP \pm \frac{1}{2\mu}ds = -\gamma < \Phi(F) > \frac{s}{\sqrt[2]{J_2'}} dt \tag{8}$$

where, $C_L = \sqrt{(4\mu + 3K)/3\rho_0}$. These equations can be solved by using the differential characteristic line method[4]. Parameters used in calculation are given in Table 1.

Table 1. Computational Parameters

	ρ (g/cm^3)	μ (GPa)	K (GPa)	k (GPa)	γ (1/S)
Al_2O_3	3.83	74.13	185.32	2.0	5×10^5
PMMA	1.18	3.54	8.86	1.5	7.5×10^5

For Al_2O_3,

$$\Phi(F) = \sum_{a=1}^{5} B_a F^a \tag{9}$$

where, $B_1=0.338$; $B_2=-0.147$; $B_3=0.327$; $B_4=-0.334$; $B_5=0.128$.

For PMMA,

$$\Phi(F) = F^{5.5} \tag{10}$$

RESULTS AND DISCUSSION

Attenuation of shock front pressure

Propagation of shock wave with 8.0 GPa incident pressure in PMMA is investigated. The propagation of waves in P—X plane is shown in Fig. 1. It can be seen that the calculation results give a good simulation to the attenuation of wave front pressure. Comparing the computational result with the experimental data[1] shows a good agreement. It demonstrates that the elastic-viscoplastic constitutive relationship can effectively describe the behavior of PMMA. For porous Al_2O_3, the attenuation of a shock wave with an input pressure of 6.69 GPa has been studied. Calculation results are shown in Fig. 2. Compared with experimental data in Ref. 1, the calculation results differed more and more with the propagation of shock waves in the media and the gradual attenuation of pressure on the wave front. This may be resulted from the fact that the effect of porosity was neglected in the constituitve relationship. In the case of high shock pressure, the porous material compacted rapidly , therefore its behavior is close to that of dense media and its elastic-viscoplastic property appears as the principal cause of shock attenuation. In the case of low shock pressure, porosity play an important role (as shown in Fig. 5 of ref. 1). The experimental results with porosity effect included differ greatly with the computational curves where only elastic-viscoplastic effect has been considered.

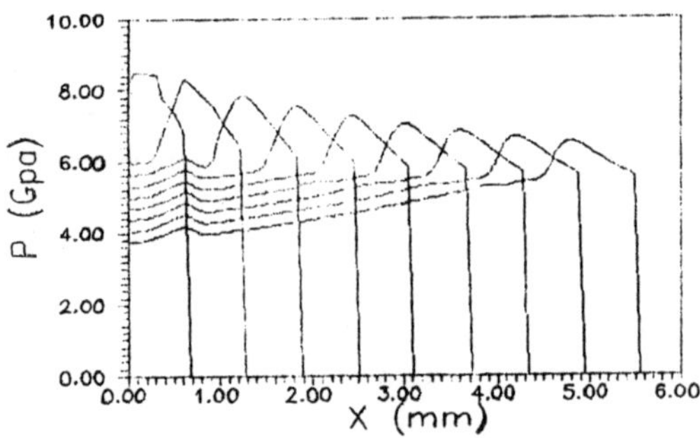

Fig. 1 Propagation of shock waves in PMMA

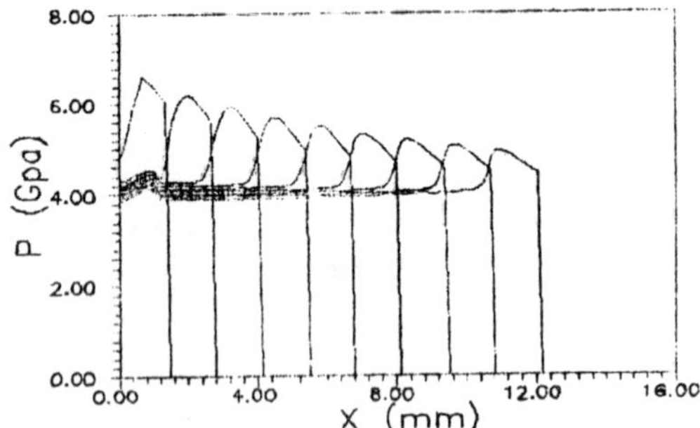

Fig. 2 Propagation of shock waves in porous Al_2O_3

Pressure attenuation behind shock front

The elastic-viscoplastic constitutive law is used to calculate the attenuation process of shock pressure of Lagrangian particles behind the incident waves front. In Fig. 3, the solid line showed the recorded experimental curve of shock pressure of the particle with a distance of 2.84mm from the incident surface of shock waves. It can be seen that the shock pressure decreased rapidly with time and it was accordant with the dot line which was the calculation curves in the correspondent position. This may be concluded that the attenuation of shock pressure actually originated from elastic-viscoplasticity of the material. Fig. 4 is the shock attenuation curves of shock pressure in Al_2O_3 on the Lagrangian position 3.42mm from the incident surface, in which solid curves represented experimental data while dot line calculation results. It can be seen that the attenuation rule of two curves is agreeable qualitively. Shock pressure kept a smooth decaying trend after a period of linear fall, but experimental curves had a small fluctuation. This can be explained as that matters suffering shock compaction can be simulated with elastic-viscoplastic model approximately. However, in the compaction process, some energy have deposited in the porous media. For this, the shock pressure behind the wave front in Al_2O_3 does not drop as fast as in the simulated case, resulting in the difference between experiments and calculation. On the other hand, plexiglass (PMMA) has a low yield strength than Al_2O_3, so it is always in the plastic state under the studied pressure, and viscoplastic effects penetrate the whole process, while the shock pressure in Al_2O_3 is limited, resulting in a smooth attenuation.

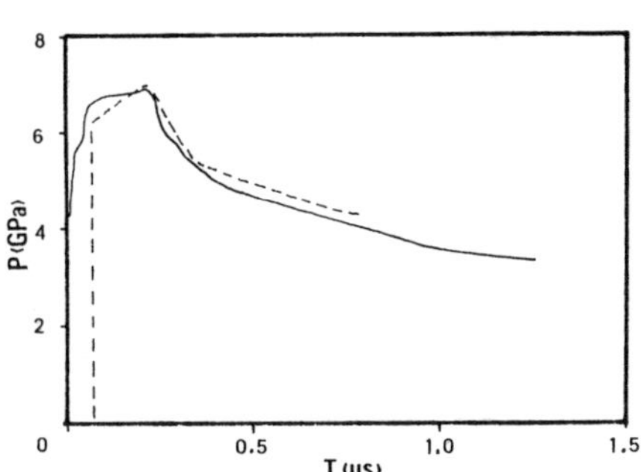

Fig. 3 Attenuation of shock pressure in PMMA, X=2.84mm

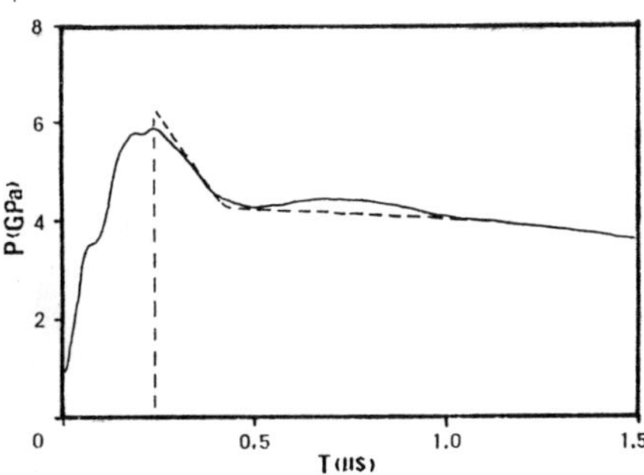

Fig. 4 Attenuation of shock pressure in Al_2O_3, X=3.42mm

CONCLUSIONS

From experiments and calculations, following conclusions can be obtained:

(1) Applying elastic-viscoplastic constitutive model to the shock propagation in dense media is successful.

(2) Both porosity and viscoplasticity are existed in the rising period. The effect of porosity could not be neglected under the condition of low pressure.

(3) The attenuation of shock pressure behind the shock front could be described well with an elastic-viscoplastic constitutive model.

REFERENCES

[1] S. HUAN, F. Y. LU, J. DING, "*Attenuation of Two-dimensional Axisymmetric Shock Waves in Porous Al_2O_3*" in Shock Compression of Condensed Matter 1991, Elsevier Science Publishers B. V., 1992, pp. 261—264.

[2] X. H. Yang, G. T. Yang, B. G. Xu, *Introduction of Viscoplastic Mechanics*, Beijing: Chinese Railway Press, 1985.

[3] L. L. Wang, *Foundation of Stress Waves*, Beijing: National Defence Industrial Press, 1985.

[4] Y. Liu, B. H. Li, T. H. Chou, "*A Quasi-Characteristic Line Method to Solve Problems of Nonlinear Waves*", J. of China University of Science and Technology, Vol. 16, No. 1, p. 123 (1986.)

A MODEL OF PLASTICITY WITH STRAIN-HARDENING FOR SHOCK-WAVE BEHAVIOR OF NON POROUS AND POROUS ALUMINA

J.Y. TRANCHET and J. CAGNOUX
DGA/Centre d'Etudes de Gramat
46500 - GRAMAT FRANCE

Earlier works showed that the Hugoniot Elastic Limit and the beginning of the plastic wave in alumina are due to motion of dislocations in the grains. These physical interpretations justify the development of a model of plasticity with strain-hardening, which is described in this paper. Parameters of the model are identified with shock-wave data obtained for Lucalox, a fully dense alumina. The effect of initial porosity on elastic properties of alumina is empirically taken into account. This model is used for aluminas with porosities ranging from 0 from to 20%, without changing its parameters. Results are in good agreement with experimental data. For high shock levels, the effect of irreversible closure of pores and damage have to be modeled.

INTRODUCTION

The development of ceramic armors is at the origin of the great interest in modeling the behavior of aluminas submitted to shock loading. In the past, microcracking was considered as the phenomenon which controlled the shock wave behavior of ceramics, especially the onset of HEL. Several models were developed, based on this assumption. Munson and Lawrence [1] used a viscoplastic model for a fully dense alumina "in the well-established sense of permanent deformation of the sample because the macroscopic manifestations and terminology are convenient". Steinberg [2] used the general formalism of Grady [3], which was applied to tension behavior of rocks. He justified this by the experimental results of Lankford [4] concerning dynamic loading in uniaxial compressive stress of several ceramics. It leads one to suppose that the micromechanical process is the same in uniaxial strain as in uniaxial stress loading.

This hypothesis was contradicted by Cagnoux and Cosculluela [5]. They showed that the transition from the uniaxial stress state to the uniaxial strain state involved drastic changes in the micromechanical behavior of aluminas. Furthermore, soft recovery experiments performed by Longy and Cagnoux [6] clearly demonstrated that the onset of aluminas'HEL is controlled by a real plastic deformation of grains due to motion of dislocations.

According to these micromechanical considerations, a plasticity with strain-hardening model is proposed in this paper. This model is implemented in a WONDY-V-like one dimensional finite difference lagrangian code.

Comparisons of numerical calculations with experimental results are discussed for aluminas of initial porosities ranging from 0 to 20 per cent (Table 1).

Table 1 : Material characterization

Alumina	Purity (% Al_2O_3)	Grain size (μm)	Density (g/cm^3)
Lucalox (1)	99.9	?	3.969
AL 23 (2)	99.9	20 -70	3.82 - 3.91
A 16-17 (3)	99.9	~ 0.6	3.29 - 3.42

(1) General Electric Co.
(2) Degussa France.
(3) See Reference 6.

MODELING

In previous studies [5,6], it is shown that some aluminas like A16-17, can undergo shock levels above their HEL without entailing any microcracking. TEM studies revealed that motion of dislocations inside the grains of aluminas controled the onset of the HEL. From a macroscopic point of view, the measurements of the shear stress of AL 23 alumina showed an increasing shear strength for shock amplitude above HEL (Figure 1). Rosenberg et al. [7] displayed a similar result for AD 85.

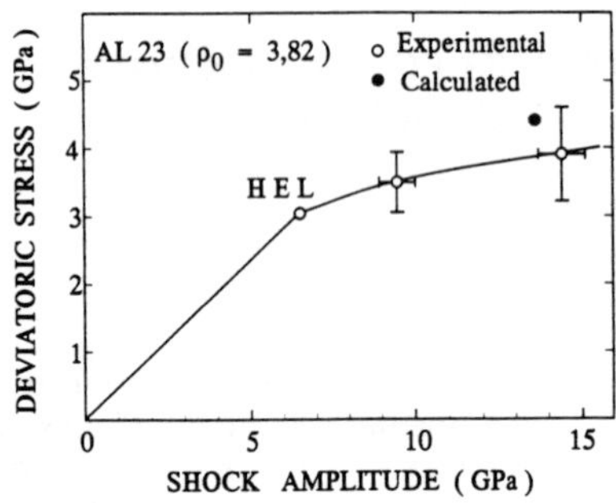

FIGURE 1
Experimental results for shear strength of shock loaded AL23 alumina [5].

According to the difficult motion of dislocations in Al_2O_3 crystal at standard temperature and to the general form of the macroscopic velocity signals (Figures 2 to 7), which was recognized by Davison and Graham [8] as being typical of strain-hardening behavior, we have chosen a plasticity with strain-hardening model written as,

$$Y = (Y_{0d} + C_{2d}\,\varepsilon_p^{n_d}) \, . \, f(\alpha_0)$$

where ,

Y is the yield strength of the tested alumina,

Y_{0d} is the initial yield strength of the dense alumina,

C_{2d}, n_d are the strain-hardening parameters,

ε_p is the plastic deformation,

α_0 is the initial porosity of the tested alumina.

$f(\alpha_0)$ is an empirical function, which gives the initial yield strength of the tested aluminas as a function of their initial porosities. In the paper, influences of other micro-structural parameters, like the grain size which is pointed out as an important parameter for yield strength [6], are not explicitly taken into account but are integrated in the f function.

The C_{2d} and n_d parameters are set in order to fit experimental results of a fully dense alumina. In this way, the effects of plasticity and those of an eventual pore closure are distinguished. The data of Munson and Lawrence [1] concerning Lucalox do not contain impact test velocities . We have assessed them by Hugoniot considerations. Figure 2 shows the comparisons of numerical calculation with experimental result concerning Lucalox.

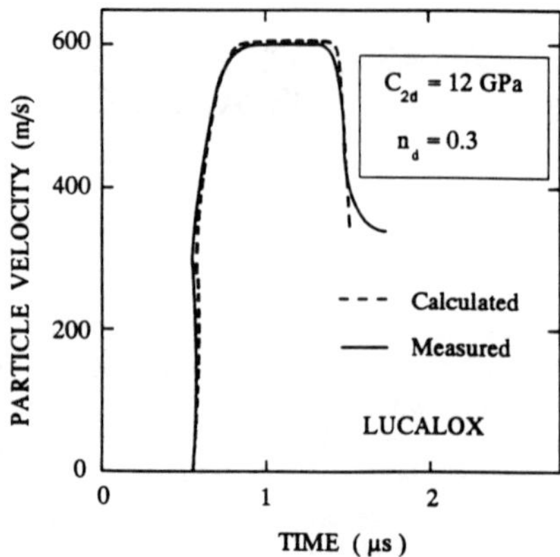

FIGURE 2
Measured [1] and predicted [9] particle velocity in Lucalox.

This model is then applied to AL 23 aluminas for three different initial porosities. The comparisons of numerical and experimental results is displayed in figures 3, 4 and 5. The calculated shear strength is in accordance with the measured one shown in figure 1. We have also applied the model to A16-17 aluminas for two different higher initial porosities. The numerical calculations are compared to experimental results in figures 6 and 7. Experiment configurations are given in Table 2.

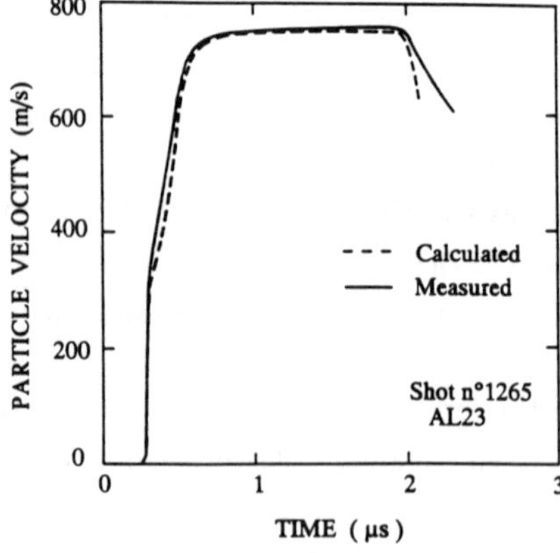

FIGURE 3
Measured [5] and predicted [9] particle velocity in AL23.

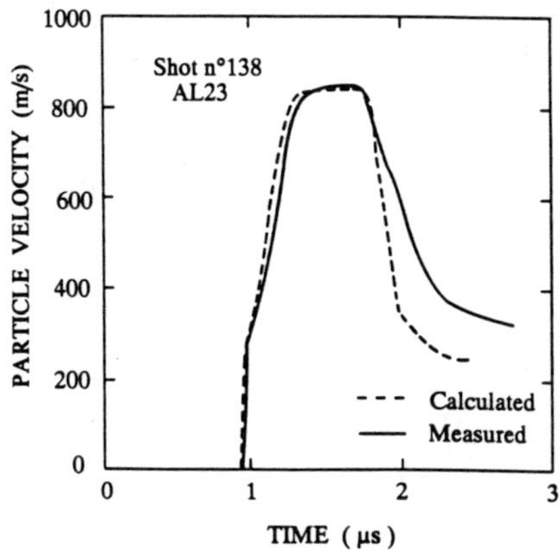

FIGURE 4
Measured [5] and predicted [9] particle velocity in AL23.

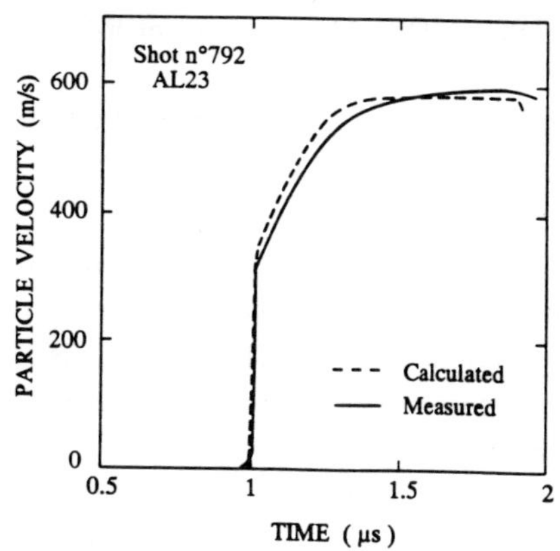

FIGURE 5
Measured [5] and predicted [9] particle velocity in AL23.

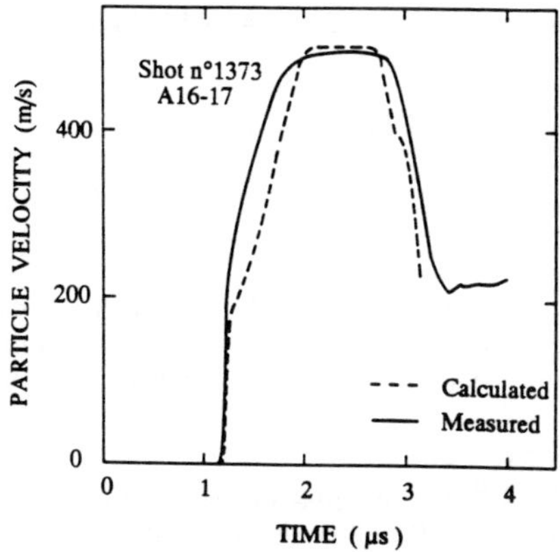

FIGURE 6
Measured [6] and predicted [9] particle velocity in A16-17.

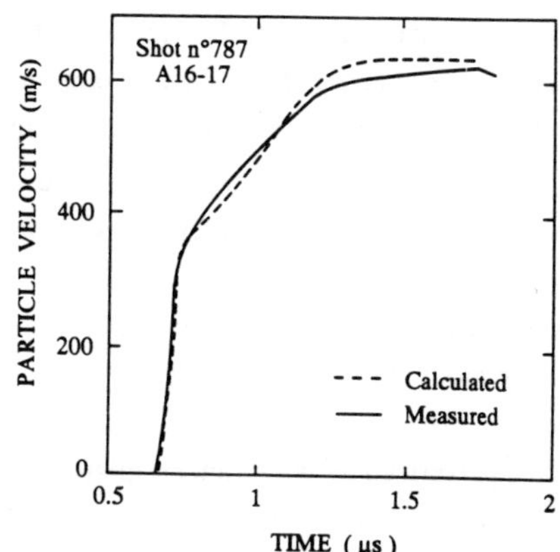

FIGURE 7
Measured [9] and predicted [9] particle velocity in A16-17.

Table 2 : Experiment configurations

Shot N°	Impactor			Specimen			Type of Visar measurement
	nature	thickness (mm)	density (g/cm³)	nature	thickness (mm)	density (g/cm³)	
1265	Cu	4.45	8.92	AL 23	10.02	3.91	PMMA (1)
138	AL 23	5.02	3.86	AL 23	9.97	3.86	LiF (1)
792	AL 23	5.00	3.82	AL 23	10.00	3.82	FS (2)
1373	Cu	4.06	8.92	A16-17	10.05	3.42	Fused silica (1)
787	A16-17	4.85	3.27	A16-17	9.85	3.29	FS

(1) Window (2) Free surface measurement

DISCUSSIONS AND CONCLUSIONS

During the compression phase, numerical calculations are in good agreement with experimental results concerning AL 23 aluminas (Figures 3, 4 and 5). For more porous aluminas like A16-17, comparisons are surprisingly accurate. An effect of pore closure was expected. A lagrangian analysis of the experimental signals shows that the pore closure is relatively low for these shock levels (Figure 8).

This explains the accuracy of our modeling results in this phase. For higher shock levels, the behavior is complicated by two phenomena : pore closure and/or microcracking.

Microcracking is not detectable during the compression phase, but is strongly coupled with the behavior during the release phase. For Lucalox and A16-17, the release phase is reproduced in a satisfying manner. For A16-17, soft-recovery experiments showed no damage up to 2 HEL [6]. For Lucalox, this good agreement leads us to suppose that there is no important microcracking in this experiment.

On the contrary, the release phase of AL 23 aluminas are very badly modeled, especially for the high shock levels. Recent soft-recovery experiments showed that this alumina is pulverized by intergranular microcracks at 15 GPa. This damage explains the experimental results in figures 3 and 4.

As a conclusion, we have shown that such a plasticity model based on the micromechanical reality is able to reproduce the behavior of numerous aluminas in the stress domain of 0-2 HEL. In this domain, the predictibility of the model could be enhanced by a Petch-Hall approach, which would allow to introduce the grain size parameter in the calculation of the yield strength of the aluminas.

For higher shock levels, two phenomena have to be taken into account.

1. The damage, nucleated during the compression phase, coupled with the release behavior.

2. The pore closure in high porous aluminas.

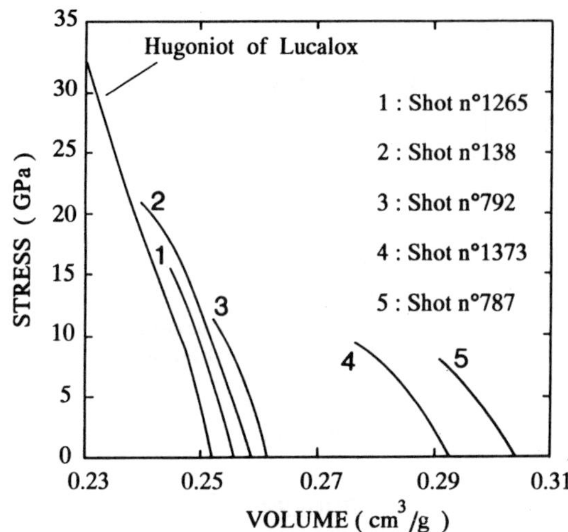

FIGURE 8
Stress-strain paths for AL23 and A16-17 aluminas.

REFERENCES

1. D.E. Munson and R.J. Lawrence, *J. appl. Phys.* 50 (1979), 6272.

2. D.J. Steinberg, "Computer Studies of the Dynamic Strength of Ceramics", Lawrence Livermore National Laboratory Report UCRL - ID - 106004 (Sept. 1990).

3. D. Grady, "The Mechanics of Fracture under High-Rate Stress Loading", in *Mechanics of Geomaterials*, ed. Bazant (London, 1985), p. 129.

4. J. Lankford, *J. Mat. Sci.* 20, (1985), 53.

5. J. Cagnoux and A. Cosculluela, "*Influence of Grain Size on Triaxial Dynamic Behavior of Alumina, in Dynamic Failure of Materials*", eds. H.P. Rossmanith and A.J. Rosakis (Elsevier Applied Science, 1991) pp. 73-84.

6. F. Longy and J. Cagnoux, *J. Am. Ceram.* Soc. 72 (1989), 971.

7. Z. Rosenberg, D. Yaziv, Y. Yeshurun, and S.J. Bless, *J. Appl. Phys.* 62 (1987), 1120.

8. L. Davison and R.A. Graham, in *Shock compression of solids*, Physics Reports 55, N° 4 (North Holland Publishing Company, 1979) pp. 255-379.

9. This paper.

MODELING FLOW BEHAVIOR OF 93W-5Ni-2Fe TUNGSTEN HEAVY ALLOY

Tusit Weerasooriya
Army Research Laboratory-Materials Directorate
Watertown, Massachusetts, USA, 02172-0001

Low (0.0001 and 0.1 s^{-1}) and high (600 s^{-1}) strain rate torsional experiments were performed using the Torsional Kolsky bar set-up for a tungsten heavy alloy (WHA) at room temperature. In addition, low (197°K) and high temperature (408°K) tests were performed at the strain rate of 0.1 s^{-1}. We modeled the deformation behavior of WHA using Johnson-Cook (JC) and Power-Law (PL) models. The model constants were determined from low rate tests at both room and other temperatures. We examine the ability of JC and PL models to reproduce the experimental adiabatic stress-strain curve at 600 s^{-1}. The constants for WHA alloy for these two models are summarized in this paper.

INTRODUCTION

It has been observed by Weerasooriya and Beaulieu[1] and Andrews et. al.[2] that tungsten heavy alloys (WHAs) can fail by shear localization at high rates of shear loading. To simulate this failure, it is necessary to obtain accurate thermo-viscoplastic constitutive models representing the deformation behavior at different strain rates and temperatures. Two such models are obtained using a systematically obtained set of shear stress-strain data that covers a wide spectrum of shear strain rates and temperatures. This paper describes an evaluation of the ability of these models to predict the high rate deformation behavior under shear loading.

EXPERIMENTS

Material

The 93%W alloy that was used for the experiments in this report was obtained from Teledyne. Chemical composition and some of the mechanical properties of this alloy from the manufacturer are:

W	92.85%
Ni	4.9%
Fe	2.25%

Density = 17.69 - 17.76 g/cc

Hardness = HRC 39-40
UTS = 1103 MPa (160,000 psi)
Elongation = 13%

This alloy was processed and swaged to 17% by Teledyne. The procedure that has been used for processing is given elsewhere.[3]

The microstructure of the alloy consists of two phases: nearly pure W spherical grains of bcc crystal structure and W-Ni-Fe matrix of fcc crystal structure.[3] The size of the W grains are approximately 27 µm and are mostly surrounded by a thin layer of matrix material.

Specimen Geometry

Geometry of the test specimen is given elsewhere.[1] The gage section of the test specimen is a thin wall tube (0.38 mm wall thickness) of 0.254 mm gage length and outside and inside diameters of 10.16 and 9.40 mm, respectively. The wall thickness corresponds to an average of 14 W grains.

Procedure

Torsional tests were conducted at high and slow rates at room temperature. A shear strain rate of 600 s^{-1} was used for all high rate tests. Slow rate tests were performed at shear strain rates of either 0.0001 or 0.1 s^{-1}. In addition, to find the effect of temperature on deformation behavior, low

(197°K) and high (408°K) temperature tests were conducted at the shear strain rate of 0.1 s^{-1}.

High Rate Tests

The high rate (600 s^{-1}) tests were conducted using a torsional Split-Hopkinson Bar. This torsional Hopkinson bar and its data acquisition and reduction procedure are described elsewhere in detail.[4] It consists of two bars and a clamp. The hexagonal flanged thin wall specimen is attached between the two bars. A torque is stored between the non-specimen end of the input bar and the clamp. The high strain rate of loading is applied to the specimen by the sudden release of the stored-torque by breaking the clamp. This incident torsional stress pulse travels towards the specimen after its release; at the specimen, part of the pulse transmits through the specimen to the output bar and the remainder reflects back to the input bar. From the measured incident, reflected and transmitted pulses, the stress, strain and strain-rate of the specimen can be inferred as a function of time. When the shear bands initiate, the strain and strain-rate that are determined by this method represent actually average values in the gage section of the specimen.

Slow Rate Tests

Slow shear strain rate (0.0001 and 0.1 s^{-1}) tests at room temperature were conducted using the torsional Hopkinson bar set-up which was modified for this purpose. A servomotor with a reducer (3600:1) was attached to the non-specimen end of the output bar. During slow rate testing, the input bar was held stationary using the clamp of the torsional Split-Hopkinson bar. Average engineering shear strain of the specimen was calculated using the relative angular displacement. Shear stress was calculated using the thin wall tube assumption for the gage section of the specimen. All the low and high temperature tests at the shear strain rate of 0.1 s^{-1} were conducted using the slow rate set-up of the Hopkinson bar.

Results

Shear stress and engineering shear strain information were obtained from above data assuming specimen gage area as a thin wall tube. Details of the procedure used in obtaining shear stress and shear strain are given elsewhere.[1]

Shear stress versus average shear strain data for three different strain rates (0.0001, 0.1 and 600 s^{-1}) at room temperature for this WHA is given in Figure 1. For slow strain rates (0.0001 and 0.1 s^{-1}), flow stress increases with increasing shear strain (work hardening). In contrast, at the high strain rate of 600 s^{-1}, flow stress decreases with increasing shear strain (softening). This indicates that the thermal softening is dominating over strain hardening and strain-rate hardening during deformation at high strain rates. The difference in deformation at high strain rate is due to adiabatic heating of the material.

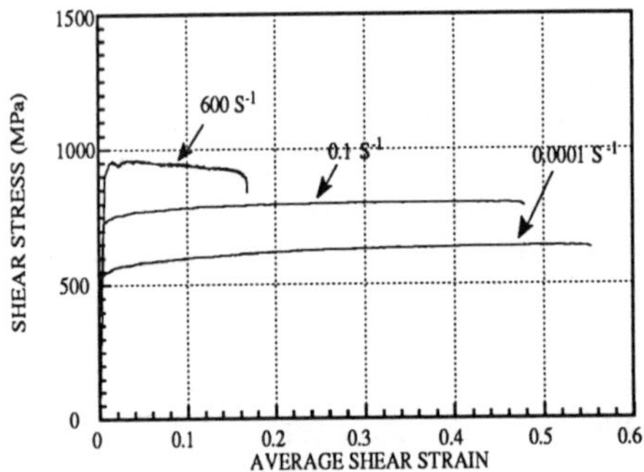

Figure 1. Shear stress - average shear strain at three different strain rates.

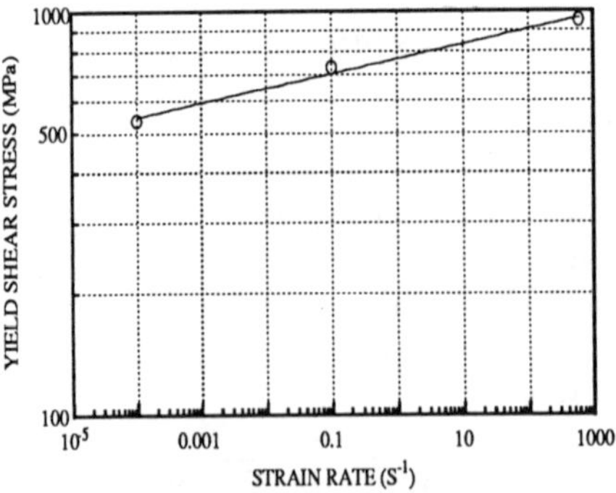

Figure 2. Semi-logarithmic plot of shear yield stress as a function of strain rate.

Yield stress of WHA at room temperature is plotted as a function of strain rate in logarithmic and semi-logarithmic scales in Figures 2 and 3, respectively. From these linear plots, it can be seen that the yield stress can be represented by either a power (compatible with Power-Law) or logarithmic (compatible Johnson-Cook Model) function of strain rate. Therefore, in this paper these two models are considered for their ability to predict the adiabatic stress-strain behavior at high rate. A similar evaluation of other non-state variable and state variable based models will be presented in a future publication.

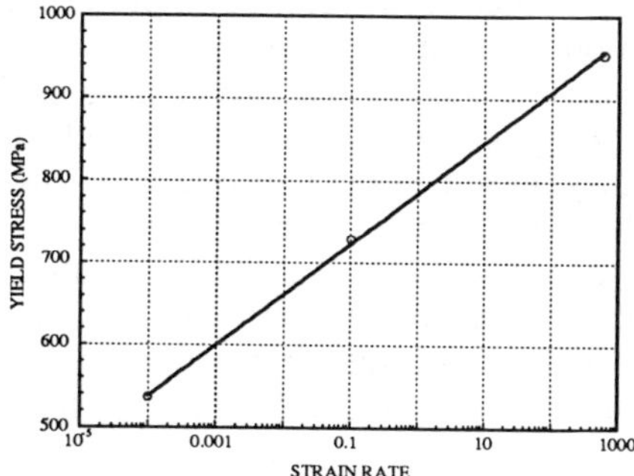

Figure 3. Logarithmic plot of shear yield stress as a function of strain rate.

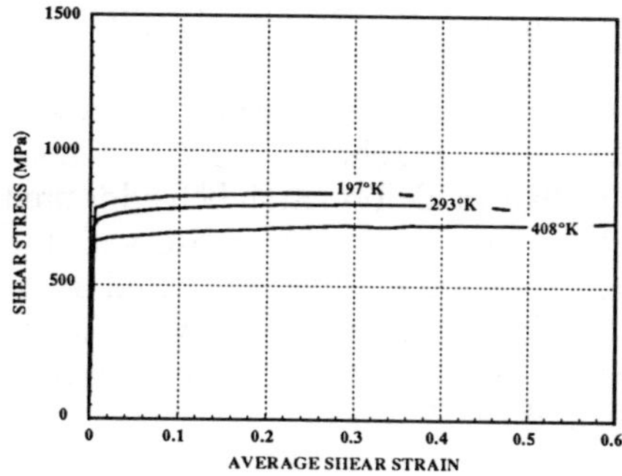

Figure 4. Shear stress - average shear strain at 0.1 s^{-1} for three different temperatures.

Shear stress versus average shear strain plots for three different temperatures (197°K, 293°K and 408°K), at the strain rate of 0.1 s^{-1} are given in Figure 4. For the three temperatures, flow stress increases with increasing strain showing work hardening. Flow stress decreases with increasing temperature at a given strain.

MODELS

Model constants of the two models discussed below were obtained from room temperature stress-strain data at strain rates of 0.0001 and 0.1 s^{-1} and 0.1 s^{-1} strain rate stress-strain data at 408°K. Lower temperature data were not used in obtaining the power constant (α) of the temperature. Value of α obtained from the lower temperature data significantly differ from the value obtained from the higher temperature stress-strain data. Since we are trying to predict the adiabatic stress-strain behavior using these models, low temperature data was not used in obtaining the model constants; when the material is deforming adiabatically, the temperature of the deforming material elements will be at a higher temperature than the room temperature.

Power Law (PL) Model

Many researchers have proposed a power law relationship for the flow stress (τ) as a function of strain (γ), strain rate ($\dot{\gamma}$) and temperature (θ) of the form

$$\tau = \tau_o \left(\frac{\gamma}{\gamma_y}\right)^n \left(\frac{\dot{\gamma}}{\dot{\gamma}_o}\right)^m \left(\frac{\theta}{\theta_o}\right)^\alpha \qquad (1)$$

to describe the dynamic stress-strain behavior.

Here, n, m and α are model constants to be determined from the experimental stress-strain data for this material. τ_o is the yield stress at the reference strain rate ($\dot{\gamma}_o$) and the reference (room) temperature (θ_o). γ_y is the strain at yield.

PL model constants that were obtained from experiments data are:

$\dot{\gamma}_o = 0.1\ s^{-1}$; $\theta_o = 293°K$; $\tau_o = 729.1$ MPa;
$\gamma_y = 0.02228$; $n = 0.0404$; $m = 0.03686$; $\alpha = -0.35$

Johnson-Cook (JC) Model

Johnson and Cook proposed a phenomenological thermo-viscoplastic relationship for flow stress (τ) as a function of plastic shear strain (γ_p), shear strain rate ($\dot{\gamma}$) and temperature (θ°K). This relationship is

$$\tau = \left(\tau_{yo} + B \cdot \gamma_p^n\right)\left(1 + C \cdot \ln\left(\frac{\dot{\gamma}}{\dot{\gamma}_o}\right)\right)(1-T)^{\alpha} \quad (2)$$

$$\text{where } T = \left(\frac{\theta - \theta_o}{\theta_M - \theta_o}\right)$$

Here, τ_{yo} is the yield stress at the reference (room) temperature and the reference strain rate ($\dot{\gamma}_o$). θ_M is the melting temperature and θ_o is room temperature. Since we also conducted lower temperature tests, here, the temperature term is modified from the original JC model. In this model, B, C, n, m and α are model constants to be determined from the experimental data.

JC model constants that were obtained from experimental data are:.

$\dot{\gamma}_o = 0.1 s^{-1}$; $\theta_o = 293°K$; $\theta_M = 3683°K$; $\alpha = 4$; $\tau_{yo} = 729MPa$; $n = 0.413$; $B = 139MPa$; $C = 0.0366$

MODEL PREDICTIONS

The stress-strain behavior was calculated for slow rates using the above models. The calculated stress-strain behavior agreed with the experimental data except for the low temperature case. This is obvious as we did not use the lower temperature data for the model constant determination.

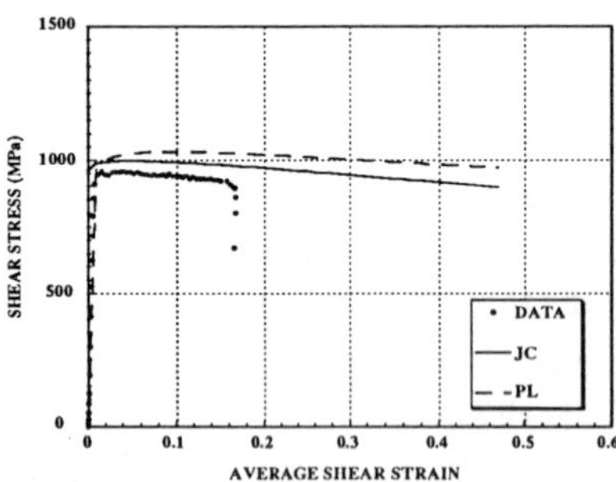

Figure 5. Comparison of predicted and experimental shear stress-strain at room temperature and 600 s^{-1} strain rate.

Using the above models, adiabatic shear stress-shear strain behavior was predicted to compare with the experimental stress-strain behavior. Figure 5 shows the predictions from the two models with the experimental data. Both model predictions show the thermal softening as observed in the experiments. Predicted stresses are always higher than that of experiments. This difference is almost twice for the power-law compared to the JC model.

DISCUSSION

Though the models predicted the thermal softening behavior, they over predicted the high rate experiments. It does show the need to use a more rigorous calculation taking into account the experimentally observed strain localization in predicting the high rate behavior.[1] Similar calculations are being performed.

The two models that are considered in this paper are phenomenologically based. Other physically based state variable and non-state variable models may give a better prediction. Also, experiments show that the temperature in the localized area reaches at least about 873°K.[2] The highest temperature test that was used in model constant determination is 408°K. If the model constants were calibrated with additional temperature data representing the deformation in the range 408-873°K, models would represent the deformation in the localized area more closely. Future work will cover these aspects.

SUMMARY AND CONCLUSIONS

The model constants were obtained for the Power-law and the Johnson-Cook models. The high rate adiabatic deformation behavior predicted by these models show the observed thermal softening. Both models over predicted the stress-strain behavior; difference in the prediction and the experiments for the PL model is approximately double that of the JC model.

REFERENCES

[1] T. Weerasooriya and P. A. Beaulieu, "Effects of Strain Rate on the Deformation and Failure Behavior of 93W-5Ni-2Fe under Shear Loading," to appear in *J. of Mat. Science and Engineering*, 1993.

[2] E. W. Andrews, A. F. Bower and J. Juffy, "Shear Band Formation in a Tungsten Heavy Alloy," to appear in *Mechanics of Materials*, 1993.

[3] T. Weerasooriya and P. A. Beaulieu, "Deformation and Failure Behavior of 93W-5Ni-2Fe at Different Shear Strain Rate Loading," Proc. of the Int. Conf. W and W Alloys - 1992, Edited by A. Bose and R. J. Dowding.

[4] T. Weerasooriya, "The MTL Torsional Split-Hopkinson Bar," U. S. Army Materials Technology Laboratory, MTL TR 90-27, 1990.

DEVIATORIC STRESS MEASUREMENTS AT HIGH PRESSURE AND TEMPERATURE

Donald J. Weidner, Yanbin Wang, Yue Meng, and Michael T. Vaughan
CHiPR, Dept. of Earth and Space Sciences
University at Stony Brook.
Stony Brook, NY 11794, USA

X-ray diffraction of samples at high pressure and temperature provide information not only on the unit cell dimensions, but also on the deviatoric stress in the sample. Macroscopic stress is defined by the relative strains inferred from the different diffraction lines in an elastically anisotropic sample. Cubic materials are particularly useful for determining the macroscopic stress since, under hydrostatic stress, all diffraction lines will display the same strain. Measurements on samples with a superconducting wiggler synchrotron source in a large volume high pressure apparatus (SAM85), capable of generating 15 GPa pressure and 1500°C temperature have been inverted for deviatoric stress as a function of pressure and temperature for NaCl and gold. Deviatoric stress determinations provide information on the yield strength of the sample. In addition, the presence of deviatoric stress will significantly affect the pressure calibration based on a diffraction standard. Measurements in a diamond anvil cell at room temperature with a neon pressure medium demonstrate that a systematic pressure error of up to 2 GPa occurs at about 30 GPa using gold as the pressure standard. This error is significantly reduced by heating to only 100°C. Microscopic deviatoric stress is inferred from peak broadening. Strength measurements have been made on diamond at temperatures up to 1500°C at 10 GPa in SAM85 from this type of data.

INTRODUCTION

Departure from hydrostatic conditions generally occurs in all high pressure experiments where the individual sample grains are not completely surrounded by a fluid. A macroscopic deviatoric stress that is coherent from grain to grain and homogeneous at least over a portion of the sample volume will occur when the geometry of the loading system and cell assembly is lower than cubic. A microscopic deviatoric stress, that varies on the scale of the grain size in both magnitude and orientation, will generally accompany compression of poly-crystalline samples that are elastically anisotropic or heterogeneous.

We present here x-ray methods of estimating the magnitude of both types of deviatoric stress. We generally find that the magnitude of the deviatoric stress for a powdered polycrystalline sample is comparable to the magnitude of the hydrostatic component unless the yield strength of the sample is exceeded.

Special care must be exercised in using the inferred volume of a pressure standard to calibrate pressure if there is a macroscopic deviatoric stress present in the standard. A systematic error in the inferred pressure is related to the magnitude of the deviatoric stress multiplied by the ratio of the bulk to shear modulus. This ratio can be as high as 6 when using gold as the pressure standard.

DEVIATORIC STRESS

Macroscopic Stress

In this study, we report deviatoric stress measurements in a DIA type apparatus (SAM85) [1,2] and a diamond anvil cell [3] using energy dispersive analysis of white radiation generated

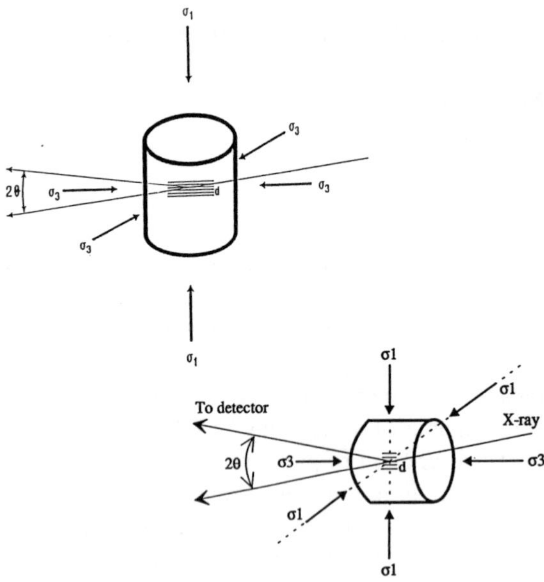

Figure 1. Stress geometry with respect to sample chamber and x-ray diffraction vector in DIA type apparatus (top figure) and diamond anvil cell (bottom figure). Because of very small 2θ angle (5° - 15°) used, only the lattice planes that are perpendicular to σ_1 will give rise to diffraction signals.

by the superconducting wiggler at X-17 at the National Synchrotron Light Source. The geometry of both types of sample cells is cylindrical giving rise to a cylindrical stress field as illustrated in Figure 1. In these experiments, 2θ ranges from 5° to 15°. Thus, the diffraction vector is within 5° of the unique stress axis for the DIA geometry and 8° of the radial stress axis for the diamond cell. Since each diffraction line corresponds only to those grains that are oriented with the particular lattice planes perpendicular to the diffraction vector, the deduced lattice spacings are appropriate for these grains that are appropriately oriented with respect to the macroscopic stress field. Thus, the observed strain, $\delta d_{hkl}/d_{hkl}$, reflects the effect of the macroscopic stress acting on an oriented subset of grains. Ignoring the difference between the diffraction vector and the stress field we obtain for the DIA configuration:

$$\delta d_{hkl}/d_{hkl} = \sigma_1 S_{11} + \sigma_3(S_{12} + S_{13})(1) \quad (1)$$

and for the diamond cell configuration:

$$\delta d_{hkl}/d_{hkl} = \sigma_1(S_{11} + \langle S_{12}\rangle) + \sigma_3\langle S_{13}\rangle \quad (2)$$

where S_{ij}'s are components of the elastic compliance tensor in a coordinate system rotated to align the crystals with the stress field, and $\langle S_{ij}\rangle$ represents an average value of S_{ij} in the plane perpendicular to the x-ray diffraction vector. Even cubic materials that are elastically anisotropic, such as gold or NaCl, will yield different values for $\delta d_{hkl}/d_{hkl}$ corresponding to different diffraction vectors. Knowing the elastic properties of the material, measurements of the lattice spacings corresponding to two or more diffraction lines can thereby define the two unknown stress components.

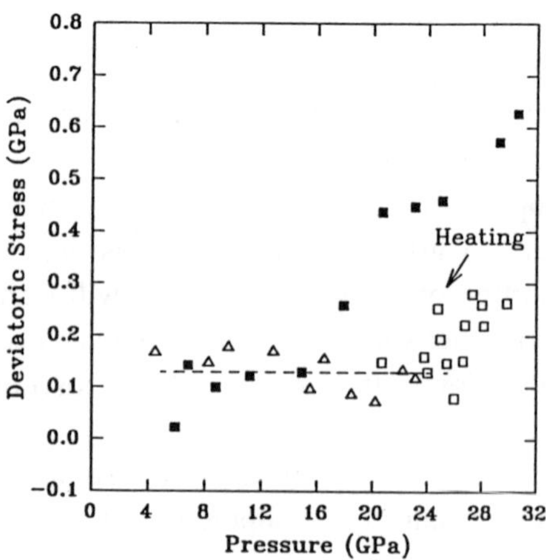

Figure 2. Macroscopic deviatoric stress as a function of pressure at room temperature (solid squares) and at high temperatures (open symbols) for Au pressure marker in Ne pressure medium with a diamond anvil cell. $(\sigma_3 - \sigma_1)$ at 700K are presented by the open triangles. The labeled arrow indicates the direction of increasing temperature.

Figure 2 illustrates the macroscopic deviatoric stress in gold as a function of pressure at room temperature and as temperature is raised to 700K in a diamond anvil cell using Ne as the pressure medium. The deviatoric stress increases significantly at pressure above 16 GPa to a value of 0.6 GPa and then decreases quickly with temperature; dropping by 70% in the first 100K increase in temperature. This probably reflects the strength of the Ne pressure medium.

Microscopic Deviatoric Stress

While the loading system can generate a uniform deviatoric stress field throughout the sample, heterogeneities within the sample along with elastic anisotropy will be responsible for generating stresses which vary from grain to grain. The effect of this microscopic deviatoric stress field will be the broadening of x-ray diffraction lines and the amount of line broadening is determined by the distribution of longitudinal strain parallel to the diffraction vector.

The microscopic stress in the sample can be generated by mechanisms such as anisotropic elastic properties of the sample, heterogeneous elastic properties including porosity, and additional effects of a macroscopic deviatoric stress field [4].

Theories regarding stress induced by thermal expansion in a polyphase aggregate made of anisotropic grains is applicable to the current problem. Studies such as [4,5,6] allow one to estimate properties of the microscopic deviatoric stress for particular material properties. These studies reveal that the microscopic stress varies within the individual grains, but as Evans and Clarke [7] point out, the grain size should not affect the amplitude of the microscopic stress field.

We show here results using a polycrystalline MgO rod as a sample. The peak width is a convolution of the instrument response, sample response function, and the longitudinal elastic strain distribution parallel to the diffraction vector. By assuming that the room P,T spectra included the first two of these, we calculate the full-width at half-maximum strain distribution for Gaussian functions. They are plotted as a function of pressure and temperature in figures 3. The measurements include three diffraction lines and several positions within the sample cell. While there is a fair amount of scatter as pressure is increased, we generally see that the deviatoric strains saturate at a fairly low pressure. If we assume that the strains should increase linearly with applied load, we conclude that at 10 GPa the

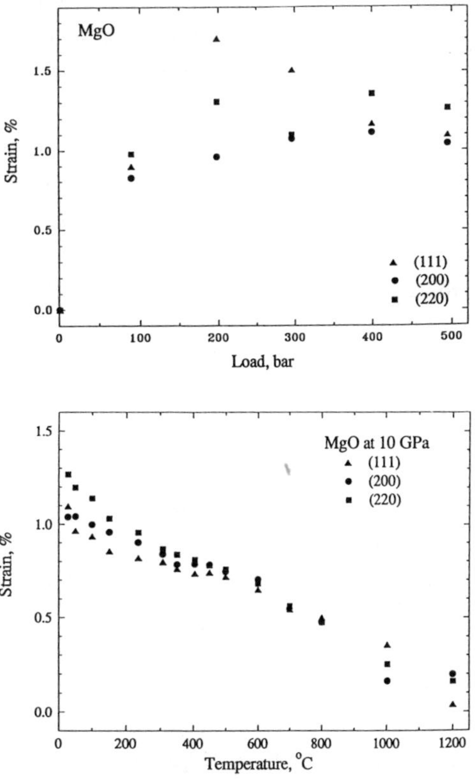

Figure 3: Microscopic strains in MgO, obtained from peak broadening, as a function of pressure (plotted as load force in top figure) and as a function of temperature at 10 GPa (in bottom figure). Saturation is observed at 200 bar load (about 3 GPa).

sample has been deformed by a few per cent. As temperature increases, there is considerably less scatter and the strains monotonically decrease to about zero at 1200°C. At this point the peaks have returned to their room pressure widths. On reducing the temperature to 25°C the peaks retained their narrow width indicating that thermally induced stress which might cancel pressure induced stress was not operative. By multiplying the strain by an appropriate aggregate elastic modulus, strain can be converted to stress.

APPLICATIONS

Yield Strength

We recently [Weidner, Wang, and Vaughan, *in preparation*] demonstrate that these data are useful to define yield strength as a function of pressure and temperature. The saturation of deviatoric stress as pressure is increased is most likely controlled by the strength of the sample or sample media. In the case of Au in figure 2, Ne is probably the strength limiting component. Microscopic stress is most likely limited by the sample yield strength.

Pressure Calibration

The lattice spacings that are deduced from the x-ray pattern for a sample oriented in a stress field as described above does not yield an accurate volume strain unless the deviatoric stress is properly considered. This will give rise to an error in the pressure that is deduced from an x-ray pressure standard. Defining P_R as the average of the three principal stresses and P_M as the pressure measured by ignoring the deviatoric stress, we find for the DIA geometry, assuming an elastically isotropic sample:

$$P_R - P_M = (\sigma_1 - \sigma_3)K/\mu \quad (3)$$

where K is the bulk modulus and μ is the shear modulus. For the diamond anvil cell geometry the effect is reduce by a factor of 1/2. Since K/μ is 6.2 for gold and 1.6 for NaCl, we see that a macroscopic deviatoric stress in gold will give rise to a large systematic error in the deduced sample pressure.

The effects of the deviatoric stress on pressure calibration of the data displayed in Figure 2 are significant. If we ignore the deviatoric stress, then our pressure calculated from the gold standard would be in error by as much as 2 GPa at the highest pressures.

REFERENCES

[1] D. J. Weidner, M. T. Vaughan, J. Ko, Y. Wang, K. Leinenweber, X. Liu, A. Yeganeh-Haeri, R. E. G. Pacalo, and Y. Zhao, Large volume high pressure research using the wiggler port at NSLS, *High Pressure Research*, 8, 617-623, 1992a.

[2] D. J. Weidner, M. T. Vaughan, J. Ko, Y. Wang, X. Liu, A. Yeganeh-Haeri, R. E. G. Pacalo, and Y. Zhao, Characterization of stress, pressure, and temperature in SAM-85, a DIA type high pressure apparatus, *Proceedings of the US Japan High Pressure Conference*, ed. Y. Syono and M. Manghnani, Terra Scientific Publishing Co., Tokyo, 13-17, 1992.

[3] Y. Meng, D. J. Weidner, and Y. Fei, Deviatoric stress in a quasi-hydrostatic diamond anvil cell: effect on the volume based pressure calibration, *Geophys. Res. Lett.* in press, 1993.

[4] V. Tvergaard and J. W. Hutchinson, Microcracking in ceramics induced by thermal expansion or elastic anisotropy, *J. Am. Ceram. Soc.*, 71, 157-166, 1988.

[5] J. B. Walsh, Theoretical bounds for thermal expansion, specific heat, and strain energy due to internal stress, *J. Geophys. Res.*, 78, 7637-7646, 1973.

[6] W. Kreher, Residual stresses and stored elastic energy of composites and polycrystals, *J. Mech. Phys. Solids*, 38, 115-128, 1990.

[7] A. G. Evans and D. R. Clarke, Residual stresses and microcracking induced by thermal contraction inhomogeneity, *Thermal Stresses in Severe Environments*, ed. D. P. H. Hasselman and R. A. Heller, Plenum Press, 629-649, 1980.

NEW METHOD OF PROCESSING COMPOSITIONS BASED ON HIGH MOLECULAR POLYETHYLENE

Beloshenko V. A, Slobodina, V. G., Grinjov V. G., Prut E. V.
Donetsk Physico-Technical Institute
Ukrainian Academy of Sciences
Donetsk, 340114, UKRAINE

The mechanical properties of HMPE and polymerization-filled compositions on its basis obtained by the method of solid-phase extrusion of a powder billet have been studied. It has been shown that the proposed method, as compared with hot compaction increases the elastic and strength characteristics of polymers under compression tests.

INTRODUCTION

Recently, the obtaining of items by using filled polymers has been receiving considerable interest. The method of polymerization filling [1] extends the possibilities of the existing methods of introducing fillers into a polymer die. One of the perspective directions of using this method is creation of compositions based on polyethylene possessing high molecular mass. Such compositions are characterized by improved physical and mechanical properties as compared to those obtained under mechanical mixing of high-molecular polyethylene (HMPE) and corresponding fillers [2].

Because of the high viscosity of the melt the processing of HMPE-based compositions by conventional high-production methods is difficult. In this connection we have developed a new method of processing based on using the high pressure technique. It consists in preliminary compaction of a powder billet, uncombined heating of the billet up to the temperatures close to the melting one, plunger extrusion in a heated high-pressure container. The results obtained for HMPE and its compositions with kaoline and aluminum are given below as an example of the above method realization.

EXPERIMENTAL RESULTS AND DISCUSSION

HMPE with molecular mass of $\sim 10^6$ has been used. The size of kaoline and aluminum particles was 5 μm and 10 μm, respectively. Kaoline and aluminum content amounted to 28 and 54 percent by weight, respectively. Plunger extrusion was performed to different degrees of drawing λ, which was varied at the expense of using dies of different diameters. λ was calculated according to the formula: $\lambda = d_b^2/d_d^2$, where d_b, d_d is the diameter of the billet and of the calibrating die parallel. For comparison the samples obtained by hot compaction (λ=1) have been tested. The value of die swelling ψ related with relaxation of a share of viscous-elastic strain experienced by the polymer under extrusion is found by the formula: $\psi = \frac{d^2{}_e - d^2{}_b}{d^2{}_b - d^2{}_d} \cdot 100\%$, where d_e is the diameter of extrudate. The strain-strength characteristics have been studied under the uniaxial compression with samples of cylindrical form.

The Table shows the diameter of container operating channel d, the degree of drawing λ, the extrusion pressure P, the value of swelling ψ, the elastic modulus E, the breaking stress σ_b, relative deformation under failure ε_f. It is seen that P increases the λ, the P (ln λ) dependence being the nonlinear one. This evidences the strain hardening of the material while the processing [3]. Lower values of P observed for HMPE and its compositions with kaoline are due to the known scaling effect;: in case of HMPE composition with Al, the container and, consequently, the die were of lesser diameter. ψ decreases with λ increase and with introduction of the filler which is explained by a more difficult process of relaxation of viscous-elastic deformations.

The elastic properties of extrudates exceed those of test specimens already at λ =3. Further increase of λ improves the mechanical characteristics, however, at $\lambda \geq 7$ the decrease of E and σ_b is observed. The increase of the strain-strength indices observed under λ increase is due to the formation of orientated structure [3]. The decrease of E, σ_b at $\lambda > 7$ is explained by the attainment of the limiting values of λ under which the destruction processes start prevailing over the processes of orientational hardening. this is confirmed by the fact that it has not already been a success to obtain good-quality composition of extrudates with $\lambda \geq 9$ -there are spiral-type cracks resulting in failure of the samples. In case of HMPE this effect is realized at λ=7. Evidently, the filler particles act as stoppers for the crack distribution.

CONCLUSION

Thus, the method of plunger extrusion of a powder billet makes it possible to improve the elastic and strength properties of HMPE and compositions on its basis considerably as compared with hot compaction. Due to subdivision of powder processing into three separate stages, it is more productive as well. the proposed method has no alternative when producing long-size shapes and can be realized with commercial equipment.

Table. The influence of plunger extrusion on properties of polymers.

Polymer	d, mm	λ	P, MPa	Ψ, %	$E \cdot 10^3$ (MPa)	σ_b (MPa)	ε_f, %
HMPE	20	1	-	-	6.4	(28)	(9.7)
		3	70	6.3	6.9	32	11.7
		4	140	4.8	8.4	30	11.0
		5	160	2.9	11.4	30	10.0
		6	220	1.0	12.3	34	10.6
HMPE+ Kaoline	20	1	-	-	7.1	(31)	10.0
		3	100	2.6	6.8	31	10.0
		4	150	1.3	8.1	41	10.0
		5	175	1.15	9.3	40	9.0
		6	200	0.96	13.0	43	7.0
		7	220	0.2	14.5	47	7.0
HMPE+ Al	12	1	-	-	7.2	(26)	(8.1)
		3	260	2.8	8.2	37	7.4
		5	480	1.9	11.6	41	5.3
		6	600	0.6	10.9	40	5.4
		7	800	0.7	11.0	38	4.8
		9	900	0	9.0	34	6.1

For λ=1 instead of σ_b and σ_f a conventional yield point and its respective relative deformation are taken.

REFERENCES

[1] F. S. Djachkovskii, L. A. Novokshonova. Synthesis and properties of polimeriation-filled polyolefins. Usp. Khimii, 53, pp. 200-222 (1984).

[2] L. . Bunina, V. A. Teleshov, V. I. Sergeev, S. B. Ainbinder, K. I. Tsirule. Tribological and physicomechanical properties of componores. Plastics, 8, pp. 13-15 (1985).

[3] A. Ciferri and J. M. Ward. Ultra-high modulis polymers. London: Appl. Sci. Publishers, 1979, Ch.1.

FLOW STRESS AND MATERIAL MODEL STUDY AT HIGH STRAIN RATE AND LOW TEMPERATURE

R. Kandasamy and N. S. Brar,
University of Dayton Research Institute
300 College Park
Dayton, OH 45469-0182

The flow stress of M200 maraging steel, C1008 steel, and 6061-T6 aluminum at low temperatures to 123 K and at a strain rate of about 10^3 s^{-1} is measured using split Hopkinson bar (SHB). Liquid nitrogen is used to cool the specimen to the desired temperature. The flow stress of M200 increased to 1.93 GPa at 123 K, an increase of 22 percent compared to 1.58 GPa at room temperature. In the case of 6061-T6 aluminum the flow stress remains at about 390 MPa at temperatures in the range 293 to 123 K. For C1008 steel, the flow stress increased to 860 MPa at 123 K from its room temperature value of 610 MPa. The failure strain for C1008 steel at 123 K was 0.02, compared to 0.2 at room temperature, suggesting a ductile to brittle transition. The Johnson-Cook material model constant "m", which accounts for temperature effect, is 0.5 for C1008 at temperatures in the range 123 K to 950 K.

INTRODUCTION

All metals and alloys exhibit dependence of flow stress on temperature and strain rate to varying degrees. The effect of strain rate on the flow stress of materials has been studied very extensively. However, there are a very few investigations on the combined effect of strain rate and temperature, especially lower temperatures, on the flow stress of materials. Harding has reported the flow stress of various steels and α-titanium at strain rates in the range 10^{-3} to $2.5x10^3$ s^{-1} and at temperatures in the range 77 and 288 K[1-2]. Hoge and Mukerjee studied the flow stress of tantalum at strain rates from 10^{-5} to $2x10^4$ s^{-1} and at temperatures in the range 78 and 800 K[3]. In both these studies split Hopkinson bar (SHB) configuration was used to determine flow stress at strain rates $5x10^2$ to $3x10^3$ s^{-1}. Rosenberg et al[4] from our laboratory designed induction heating technique to raise the temperature of SHB specimens to 1000 K and reported flow stress of four alloys as a function of temperature at a strain rate of about 10^3 s^{-1}. Two recent studies from our laboratory reported the high temperature and high strain rate flow behavior of AF1410, HY100, HY130, and ARMCO steels [5-6].

We have fabricated a very simple technique to perform SHB experiments at lower temperatures to 120 K. Three objectives of the present work are: (1) describe the specimen cooling technique, (2) to measure the flow stress of C1008 and M200 steels and 6061-T6 Aluminum at low temperatures, and (3) to evaluate Johnson-Cook material model constant "m", which accounts for the temperature effect for C1008 steel in the temperature range 123 K to 950 K.

SPLIT HOPKINSON BAR

The University of Dayton Research Institute split Hopkinson bar consists of a striker bar and two pressure bars mounted and aligned longitudinally in bearings that support them rigidly in a horizontal plane[7-8]. The bars are 0.5-in (12.7 mm) in diameter Inconel 718. The striker bar (76.2 cm long) is launched with a torsional spring arrangement. The complete description of SHB and specimen configuration are given in References 7 and 8.

Specimen Cooling Technique

A polyurethene box measuring inside about 6x6x6 cm with a wall thickness of 2.5 cm was fabricated using 5 minute epoxy. Holes measuring about 1.4 cm were made through the opposing sides of the box to accommodate the two pressure bars as shown in the Figure 1. The specimen was about 3 cm above the bottom surface of the box. A polyurethene lid with a hole for a thermocouple was placed on top of the box. The level of liquid Nitrogen in the box and the amount of Nitrogen vapors were adjusted to obtain the required temperature. Temperature was monitored by inserting ungrounded Omega thermocouple probe No. SCASS-03236 through an elliptical hole in the collar. The thermocouple tip (diameter 0.9 mm) was placed in contact with the specimen to monitor the temperature continuously. The specimen was maintained at a predetermined temperature for about 2 to 3 minutes before firing the striker bar.

Portion of the two pressure bars in contact with the specimen were also subjected to lower temperatures. Elastic modulus of Inconel increases by only 4% at 120 K compared to that at room temperature[9]. Secondly, the strain gauges mounted on the pressure bars 36-in from the specimen are not affected by the

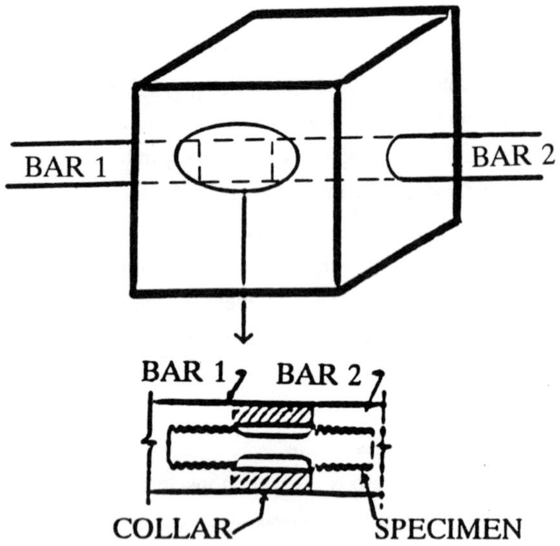

Figure 1. Specimen cooling configuration

lower temperatures near the specimen. Thus the cooling of the ends of the pressure bars near the specimen do not effect the stress and strain evaluated from the strain gauge profiles.

Materials

Three materials with different mechanical behavior were chosen in this study: (i) C1008 steel, a rate dependent material; (ii) 6061-T6 Aluminum, a rate independent material; and (iii) M200 maraging steel, a high strength material.

RESULTS AND DISCUSSION

The tests on the three materials were conducted at a strain rate of about 10^3 s^{-1} and at 293 K (room temperature), 198 K and 123 K. Two tests were performed at each temperature in order to check repeatability. True stress and true strain data for C1008 steel which also include the elevated temperature data[4] are shown in Figure 2. Flow stress results for the three materials are summarized in Table 1.

Flow stress at different temperatures for the three materials are plotted in Figure 3. For C1008 steel the variation in the flow stress at lower temperatures is most dramatic. It increased from 610 MPa at room temperature to 860 MPa at 123 K, an increase of about 41%. This increase in flow stress of C1008 is accompanied by a drastic reduction in ductility as the temperature is lowered from 198 to 123 K. Failure strain at 123 K is about 0.02 compared to about 0.2 at 198 K (Figure 2). This suggests a transition in the behavior of C1008 from ductile to brittle as the temperature is lowered to 123 K. SEM fractographs of the failed surface of the specimens at 198 K and at 123 K are shown in Figure 4(a) and (b). Figure 4(a) exhibits a dimple type of failure resulting from the tensile shear at 198 K, whereas in Figure 4(b) a transgranular fracture characteristic of brittle failure at 123 K is observed. The flow stress at high temperatures decreases to a level value of about 400 MPa above 600 K (Figure 3).

Flow stress for 6061-T6 Al remains about 390 MPa as the temperature is lowered from 298 K (room

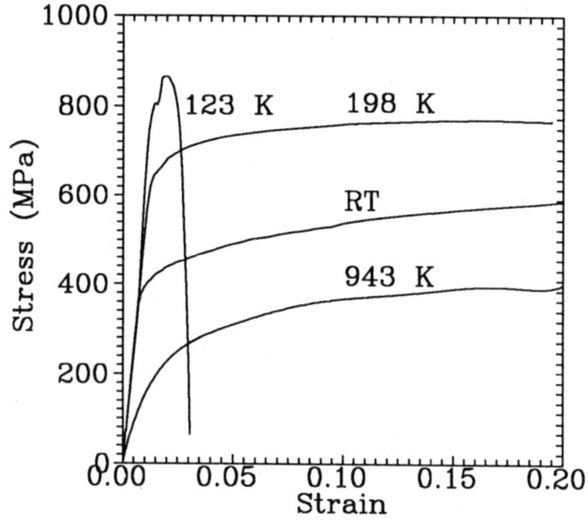

Figure 2. Stress-strain data for C1008 steel

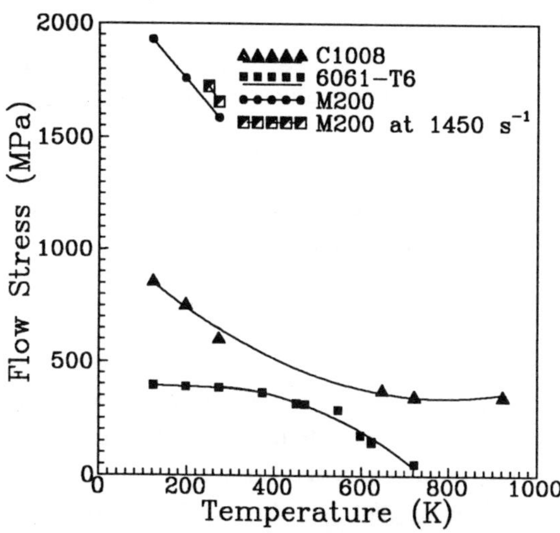

Figure 3. Flow stress-temperature plot for C1008, 6061-T6 and M200

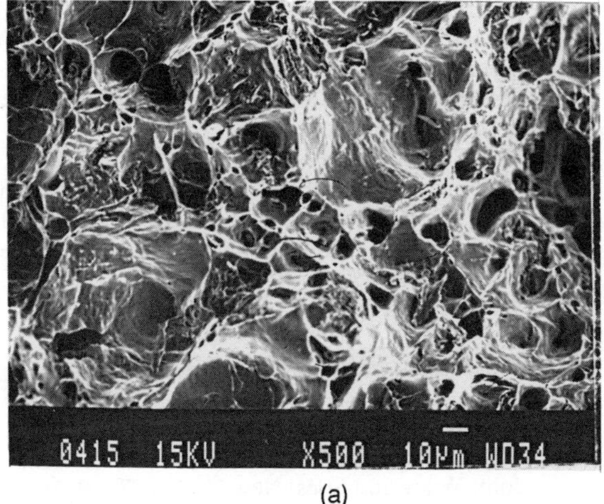

(a)

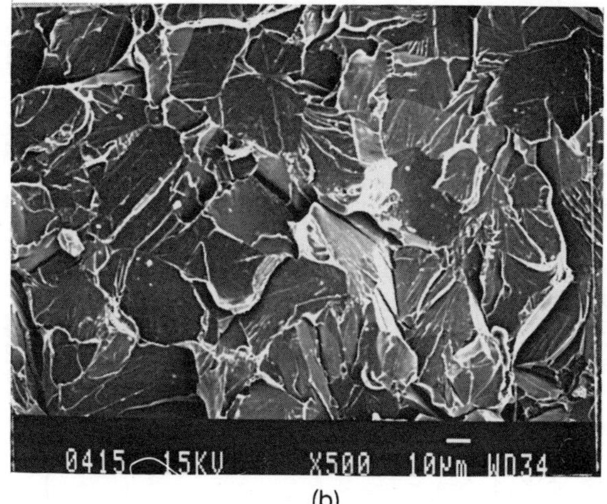

(b)

Figure 4. SEM fractographs of failed specimens at (a) 198 K and (b) 123 K

Table 1. Flow stress at different temperatures

Temperature (K)	σ_{flow} at 5% Strain (MPa)		
	C1008	6061-T6	M200
293	610	385	1585
198	760	390	1760
123	860*	395	1930

* at 2% strain

temperature) to 123 K. However, the flow stress decreases drastically to a value of 62 MPa as the temperature is raised from 298 K to about 700 K (Figure 3). Flow stress of M200 maraging steel at room temperature is 1.58 GPa and it increases to about 1.93 GPa at a temperature of 123 K. This increase of about 22% in flow stress of M200 steel as the temperature is lowered from room temperature to 123 K is approximately half that of 41% in the case of C1008 Steel. We have shown two data points for flow stress at 273 K and 298 K at a strain rate of 1450 s^{-1} to show the combined effect of strain rate and temperature. The trend in these data suggest that M200 steel is strain rate sensitive at temperatures in the range 273-298 K (Figure 3).

MATERIAL MODEL

The Johnson-Cook material model[10] is defined as

$$\sigma = [A+B\epsilon^n]\,[1+C\ln\dot{\epsilon}^*]\,[1-T^{*m}]$$

Where σ is the flow stress, A, B, C, m and n are material constants, $\dot{\epsilon}^* = \dot{\epsilon}/\dot{\epsilon}_0$ is the dimensionless effective plastic strain rate for $\dot{\epsilon}_0 = 1\ s^{-1}$ and T^* is the homologous temperature, defined as $T^* = (T - T_{room})/(T_{melt} - T_{room})$. The constant "m" accounts for temperature effect on the flow stress above room temperature. In this study the homologous temperature T^* is redefined as $T^* = (T - T_{low})/(T_{melt} - T_{low})$. The flow stress ratio $\sigma/\sigma_{low} = 1 - T^{*m}$, where σ_{low} is the flow stress at T_{low}. T_{low} represents the lowest test temperature instead of room temperature as defined in the model. The model curves for m = 0.5 and m = 0.6 are plotted in Figure 5. Experimental data on σ/σ_{low} of C1008 steel at different temperatures shown in Figure 5, exhibits good agreement for m = 0.5.

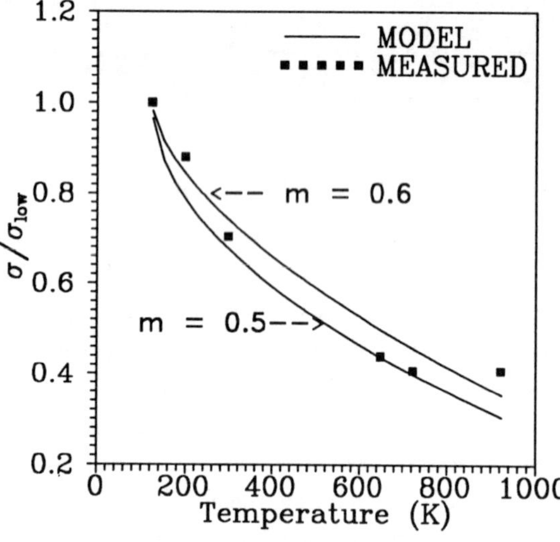

Figure 5. Johnson - Cook model constant "m" for C1008 steel

ACKNOWLEDGMENTS

We thank R. John, B. Azzi, H. Williams and E. Strader of our laboratory for helping us in performing the experiments.

REFERENCES

[1] J. Harding, Metals Technology, **4**, 6 (1977).

[2] J. Harding, Archives of Mechanics, **27**, 715 (1975).

[3] K. G. Hoge, and A. K. Mukherjee, J. of Materials Science, **12**, 1666 (1977).

[4] Z. Rosenberg, D. Dawicke, E. Strader, and S. J. Bless, Exp. Mech., **26**, 275 (1986).

[5] R. Banerjee and R. John, "Static and Dynamic Characterization of AF1410, HY100, and HY130 Alloy Steels at Room and Elevated Temperatures," The University of Dayton Research Institute Report, UDR-TR-92-41, May 1992.

[6] R. Banerjee and A. M. Rajendran, "Static and Dynamic Characterization of ARMCO 33 at Room and Elevated Temperatures," The University of Dayton Research Institute Report, UDR-TR-91-84, June 1991.

[7] T. Nicholas, Exp. Mech., **21**, 117, (1980).

[8] Impact Dynamics, Eds., J.A. Zukas, T. Nicholas, H.L. Swift, L.B. Greszczuk, and D.R. Curran, John Wiley and Sons, New York, 277 (1982).

[9] MIL-Handbook No. 5D, 6-55 (May 1985).

[10] T. Nicholas and A. M. Rajendran, In High Velocity Impact Dynamic, Ed. J. A. Zukas, John Wiley & Sons, Inc., New York, 127-298, (1990).

HIGH STRAIN RATE FAILURE OF ARMCO IRON

W.Arnold
Deutsche Aerospace AG
Postfach 1340
D-86523 Schrobenhausen, FRG

Using the planar impact technique together with a VISAR laser interferometer, failure of Armco iron under dynamic loading was investigated. Spall strength and incipient increase of damage were evaluated from measured wave profiles. These were compared with microscopic damage which showed to be in good agreement with the above mentioned macroscopic damage. Spall strength was independent from loading stress and microscopic features like grain size or twin density but dependent on a macroscopically defined spall strain rate.

INTRODUCTION

In a former study[1] the spallation behavior of Armco iron with 80 μm grain size was investigated using planar impact technique. These incipient explorations were extended to Armco iron with different grain sizes of 20 μm, 40 μm and 400 μm, in order to determine the influence of the grain size on the failure behavior. In addition a strongly prestrained Armco iron (Armco k, ε = 60%) and the alloy steel 42CrMo4 were also tested.

The results demonstrated in the following, represent an excerpt of a comprehensive study[2] about Armco iron concerning the dynamic yield and fracture behavior. Whereas the yielding behavior was already submitted at the last APS-conference[3], the objective of this paper is, to study the incipient increase of damage macroscopically and to compare it with the real produced microscopic damage. Furthermore the influence of microscopic features like grain size and deformation twins and of a macroscopic spall strain rate on the spallation strength, were also investigated.

EXPERIMENTAL

The technique to produce and measure Armco iron wave profiles by planar impact tests and a VISAR velocity interferometer were described earlier[1]. The materials investigated were the same as those in the yielding study[3]. Grain size was chosen to denote the different Armco irons.

INCIPIENT DAMAGE

Macroscopic Investigation

To describe the produced incipient damage in the target a macroscopic damage value was introduced[4] as ratio R of free surface velocities

$$R = \frac{u_C}{u_A} \tag{1}$$

defined in the wave profile of Figure 1. The corresponding pulse duration τ of the tensile stress was determined according to equation (2):

$$\tau = t_B - t_A \tag{2}$$

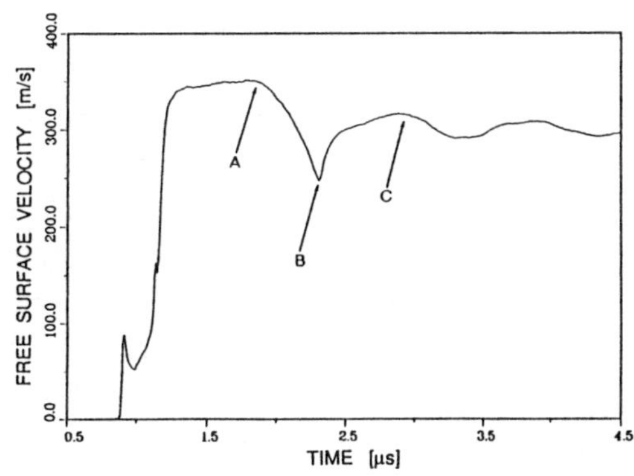

Figure 1. Wave profile for the definition of the damage value R, the pulse duration τ and the spall strength σ_{sp}.

The dependency from the pulse duration was investigated by Armco 80. This was realized by varying the thickness of the target between 1.4 mm and 8 mm with corresponding half thickness of the projectile. A typical damage curve is shown in Figure 2 for the projectile/target combination of 2 mm/4 mm with the damage value R as a function of the loading Hugoniot-stress σ.

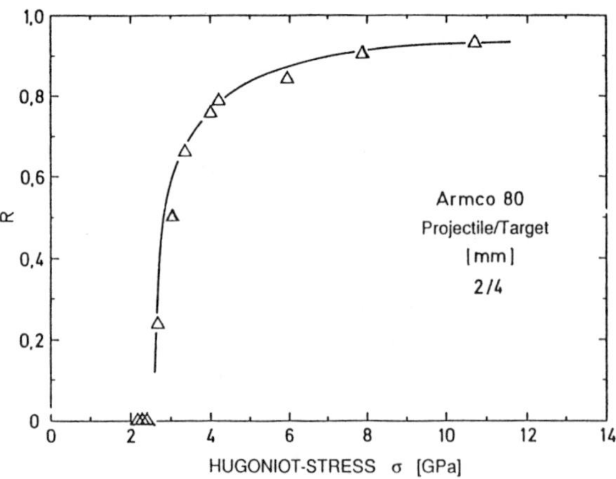

Figure 2. Damage R as a function of Hugoniot-stress for Armco 80.

All measured damage curves showed a similar behavior of starting at a distinct threshold stress, afterwards a rather fast increase in damage and finally a saturation where complete spallation is reached. The influence of the pulse duration can be clearly seen by superposition of the corresponding damage curves produced with different projectile/target thicknesses in one diagram (Fig. 3). Principally the damage increases with increasing pulse duration but fixed loading stress.

By determining the Hugoniot stress σ_R from Figure 3 which is necessary to cause the damage R (e.g. R = 50%), this stress σ_R as a function of the corresponding pulse duration shows a hyperbolic relation in Figure 4. For short pulse durations a considerably larger stress amplitude is necessary to produce the same extent of damage than for long pulse durations.

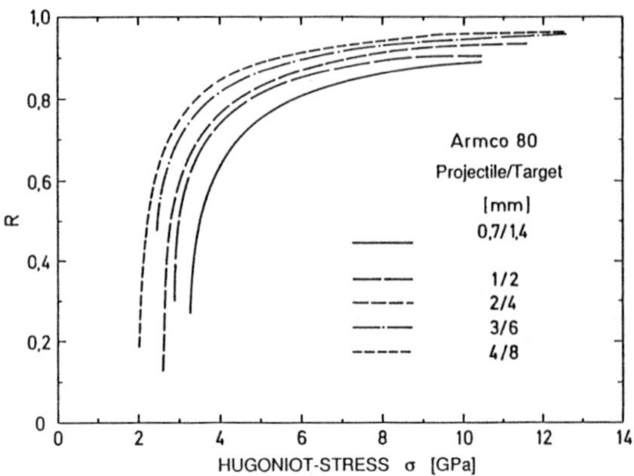

Figure 3. Influence of the pulse duration on the damage of Armco 80. Pulse duration is proportional to the projectile thickness.

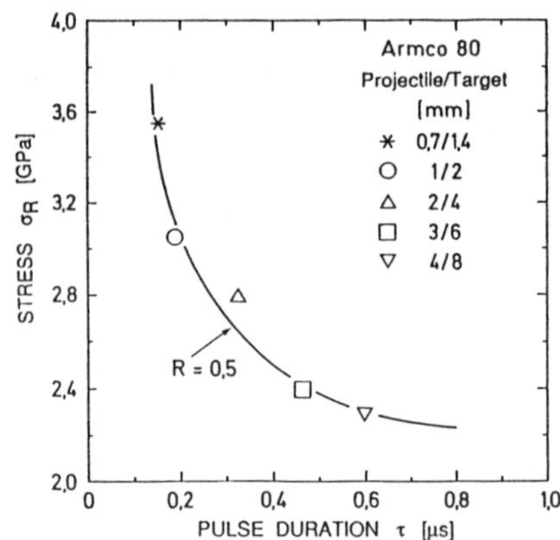

Figure 4. Necessary Hugoniot-stress σ_R to produce the same damage (R=50%) as a function of the pulse duration for Armco 80.

Microscopic Investigation

After the impact the targets were softly recovered to investigate the microstructure. The details of preparation and statistical evaluation can be looked up in former papers [1,2]. Two microscopic damage values were defined [2]. On the one hand the statistical parameter of crack distribution R_1, which is proportional to the average crack radius and on the other hand the dimensionless value $N_0R_1^3$, which is proportional to the whole produced crack volume. N_0 denotes the total number of produced cracks per volume unit.

The comparison of these microscopic damage values with the macroscopic defined damage value R showed good agreement. Not only the threshold stress was correctly prognosticated by R, but also the further development of the damage. In addition the trends corresponding to the relation of pulse duration were correctly reproduced. Therefore the macroscopically introduced value R gives a realistic description of the real produced microscopic damage.

SPALLATION

Corresponding to Figure 1 the spall strength was calculated from the pull back velocity

$$u_{pb} = u_A - u_B \quad (3)$$

using the procedure introduced by Romanchenko and Stepanov[5]. As was already the case with the macroscopic damage R, the spall strength also showed a distinct dependence from the pulse duration, but no influence from the intensity of the Hugoniot-stress was ascertained. Thereby an influence of twin density on the dynamic fracture behavior can be excluded, because of the strong variation of the twin density within the considered region of Hugoniot-stress[3]. The average spall strength of Armco 80 as a function of the pulse duration gives the hyperbolic relationship of Figure 5, analogous to that of σ_R (Fig. 4).

The hyperbolic nature of the spall strength curve suggests the definition of a spall strain rate:

$$\dot{\varepsilon}_{sp} = \frac{1}{2c_o} \cdot \frac{u_{pb}}{\tau} \quad (4)$$

c_o: bulk shock velocity

Figure 6 illustrates the spall strength as a linear function of this spall strain rate. It turns out that the important parameter describing the spallation of Armco 80 is the macroscopic spall strain rate.

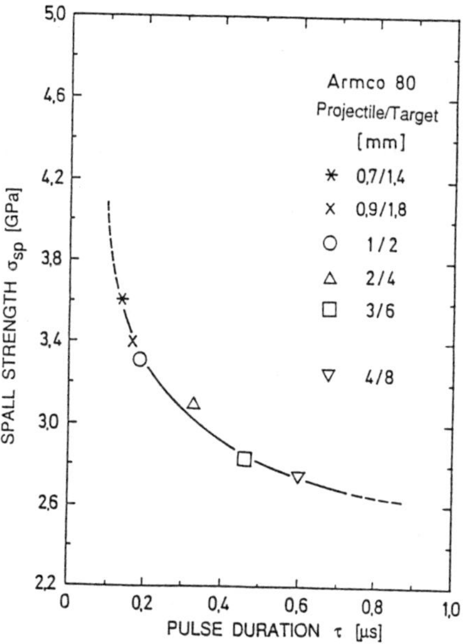

Figure 5. Spall strength as a function of the pulse duration for Armco 80.

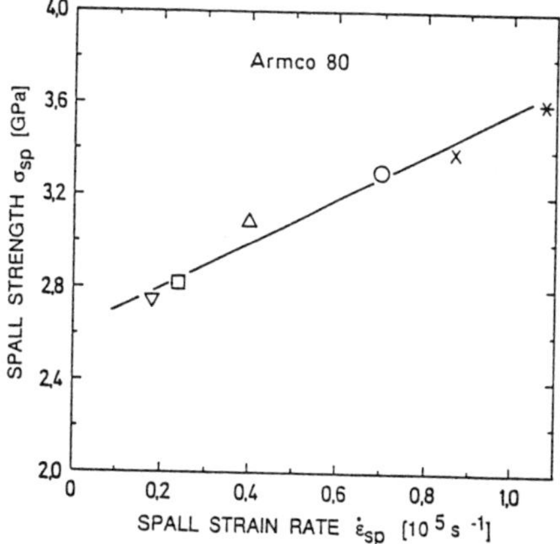

Figure 6: Linear relationship between the spall strength and the spall strain rate of Armco 80.

The results of the spall strength for the other materials under investigation were obtained in an analogous way. Here the material features were varied but the projectile/target thicknesses were fixed at 3 mm/6 mm. Once more there was no relationship between the spall strength and the loading Hugoniot-stress observed with these materials. The formation of deformation twins during the compression phase of the shock wave has obviously no influence on the tensile phase for the ductile Armco materials. Contrary to what was expected, no correlation between the spall strength and the grain size, or other material features like hardness or flow stress were determined.

Another linear relationship was obtained by drawing the spall strength versus the spall strain rate as done in Figure 7. It seems that for all these different materials with different microstructures and grain sizes, the macroscopically defined spall strain rate is the decisive parameter for the spall strength and general for the dynamic fracture behavior.

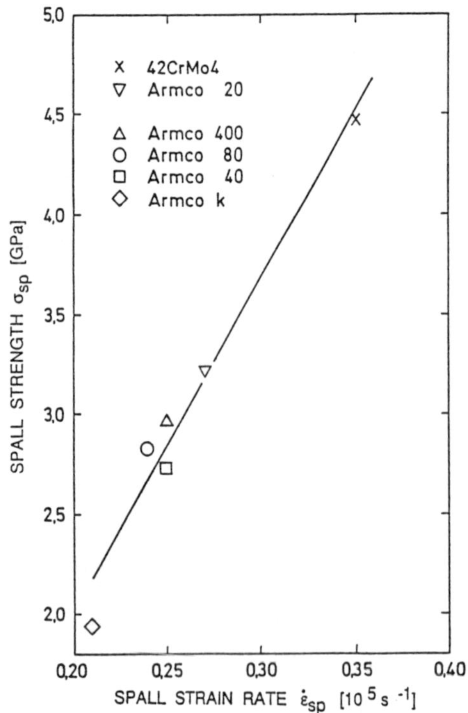

Figure 7. Linear relationship between the spall strength and the spall strain rate for all investigated materials.

CONCLUSION

From the measured wave profiles, statements about the extent of damage and the spall strength can be made. Thereby the macroscopic damage value R correlates well with the actual produced microscopic damage. The spall strength shows to be independent from the amplitude of the tensile stress but especially for short pulses dependent on pulse duration. There is practically no influence on the spall strength by microstructural features like grain size or deformation twins. The important parameter is the spall strain rate.

REFERENCES

[1] W.Arnold, M.Held and A.J.Stilp, Spallation Behavior of Armco Iron, in *Proceedings of the Conference on Shock Compression of Condensed Matter*, Albuquerque, New Mexico, August 14-17, 1989, pp. 421-424.

[2] W.Arnold, Dynamisches Werkstoffverhalten von Armco-Eisen bei Stoßwellenbelastung, Ph.D. Thesis, VDI Fortschrittberichte, VDI-Verlag, Reihe 5, Nr. 247, 1991.

[3] W.Arnold, Influence of Twinning on the Elasto-Plastic Behavior of Armco-Iron, in *Proceedings of the Conference on Shock Compression of Condensed Matter*, Williamsburg, Virginia, June 17-20, 1991, pp. 539-542.

[4] S.Cochran and D. Banner, Spall Studies in Uranium, *J.Appl. Phys.* 66, pp. 4067-4073 (1989).

[5] V.I. Romanchenko and G.V. Stepanov, Dependence of the Critical Stresses on the Loading Time Parameters During Spall in Copper, Aluminum and Steel, *J.Appl. Mech. and Tech. Phys.* 21, pp. 555-561 (1980).

FAILURE WAVES IN UNIAXIAL COMPRESSION OF AN ALUMINOSILICATE GLASS

G. Raiser and R.J. Clifton
Division of Engineering
Brown University
Providence, RI 02912

Recent plate impact experiments on glass specimens have apparently resulted in the generation of failure waves under uniaxial compression. Herein similar experiments are reported and interpreted for an aluminosilicate glass as a means for examining possible explanations of the observed behavior. This investigation bears on the understanding of the behavior of glasses and ceramics under high rate loading.

INTRODUCTION

Recently, Kanel et al.[1] reported a loss of strength in impacted plates of K19 glass (similar to soda lime glass) that they described as the propagation of a "failure wave". More comprehensive studies by Brar et al.[2,3] give a threshold impact stress of about 3.8 GPa for this effect to occur in soda lime glass. In their spall experiments, a wave with speed 2.2±0.2 mm/μsec propagates into the glass from the impact face. Behind this wave the tensile strength drops and the transverse stress increases, indicating a decrease in shear strength. Both investigations exhibit a small "recompression" when the initial compressive wave reflects from the rear surface of the glass, returns as an unloading wave, and interacts with the failure wave. They interpret this recompression as indicating that the material on the impact side of the failure wave has lower impedance because it is fractured.

These results raise fundamental questions. How can extensive cracking occur under the uniaxial strain compression which is generated in plate impact experiments, since any crack would have to open against high compressive stresses? Why does failure at the impact surface begin immediately, but in the interior the same compressive stress state is supported for an extended time prior to failure?

One hypothesis for explaining this behavior is that there is indeed a propagating boundary of broken material, but that the mechanism responsible for the failure wave is the surface roughness of the glass — not its bulk behavior. Even with highly polished samples, as used by Brar et al.[2,3], local stresses around asperities at the impact face could be large enough to initiate cracks. The state of uniaxial compression induced in plate impact experiments could cause these cracks to propagate at approximately 45° to the impact face (planes of maximum shear) in a manner analogous to Mode II fracture. Using the Rayleigh wave speed as the maximum crack speed one would obtain a limiting failure wave speed of approximately 2.1 mm/μsec — which is within the tolerances of the estimates of 2.2±0.2 mm/μsec by Brar et al.[3].

Another hypothesis is that this phenomenon is associated with transformations to crystalline phases or to amorphous phases with higher coordination numbers. The resulting local heterogeneities would generate large residual stresses and/or microcracks, causing low spall strength in regions behind the failure wave. Several investigators have reported the occurrence of phase transformations within shocked glass. Wackerle[4] showed evidence of phase changes in fused silica. Chhabildas and Grady[5] concluded that irreversible densification in the stress range of 8.2 GPa to 14 GPa corresponded to a transformation to quartz. Stress levels up to 35 GPa appear to have produced transformations to both Coesite and Stishovite. Kleeman and Ahrens[6] have recovered samples of Stishovite, identified by x-ray techniques, which was obtained by the shock loading of quartz at pressures above 9.0 GPa.

There is further support for the possibility that the glass undergoes a phase transformation. An amorphous material will, when subjected to large compressive stresses tend to become more ordered[7]. Gibbons and Ahrens[8] observed permanent changes in the refractive index of soda lime glass at shock compression levels above 4.0 GPa. If this is an indication of a phase change, then the reported minimum impact stress of 3.8 GPa for

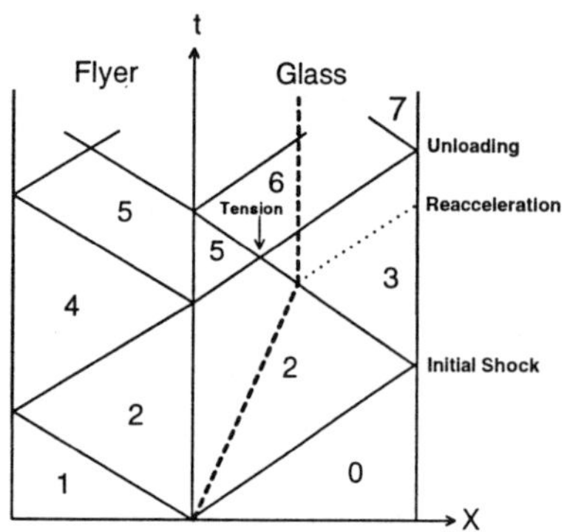

Figure 1. Lagrangian t-X diagram for Shots GLASS1 to GLASS4 showing an aluminum flyer plate impacting a glass target plate with the first occurrence of tension behind a failure wave.

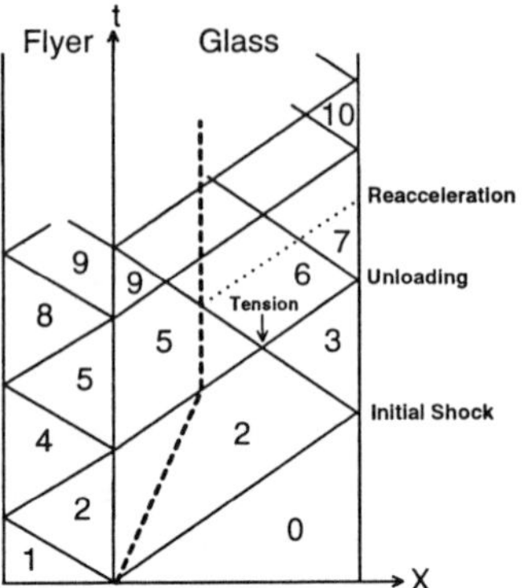

Figure 2. Lagrangian t-X diagram for Shots 92-01 and 93-04 showing a steel flyer plate impacting a glass target plate with the first occurrence of tension ahead of a failure wave.

failure wave formation reported by Brar et al.[2,3] would correspond to the level required to transform soda lime glass.

Several experiments have been conducted to test the two hypotheses. For the results of these experiments to be applicable to the understanding of ceramic behavior, the glass chosen is Corning's C1723, an aluminosilicate with a chemical composition that is similar to that of the intergranular glassy phase found in typical aluminum oxide ceramics[9].

EXPERIMENTS

The experiments called GLASS1 to GLASS4 (See Table 1.) were conducted to examine the surface roughness explanation for the failure wave effect. These experiments were performed at Sandia National Laboratories. The Lagrangian t-X diagram shown in Figure 1 indicates that plate thicknesses were chosen such that the location where tensile stresses are first obtained (i.e. the spall plane) would be behind the expected failure wave. The 6061-T6 aluminum flyer plate is lapped and polished on both sides to a roughness of 0.02 μm rms. The target plate is cut, lapped, and polished to a 60-40 finish with an average roughness of 0.04 μm rms. In shots requiring a "rough" glass impact face, the glass is lapped for one half-hour using 15 μm B_4C powder, giving a surface roughness of 0.52 μm rms.

The experiments 92-01 and 93-04 were conducted to determine whether or not the glass had a substantial tensile strength in front of the expected failure wave. These experiments were conducted at Brown University. A Lagrangian t-X diagram is shown in Figure 2. The Hampden steel flyer plate is lapped and polished to a roughness better than 0.03 μm rms. The glass target plate is lapped and polished as for the "smooth-surface" shots at Sandia.

EXPERIMENTAL RESULTS

Velocity-time profiles for the spall Shots GLASS1 to GLASS4 are shown in Figure 3. Maximum compressive stresses for Shots GLASS1 and GLASS2 were in the range 7.5-7.9 GPa, while those for GLASS3 and GLASS4 were in the range 3.3-3.5 GPa. For the two higher amplitude curves (shots 1 and 2) the lack of unloading at the expected time (~1.9-2.0 μsec) is a clear indication that the glass has lost its spall strength in the region where tension first develops. For the two lower amplitude curves (shots 3 and 4), the almost complete drop in particle velocity at the estimated unloading time shows that the glass has a spall strength of at least 3.5 GPa.

Shots GLASS1 to GLASS4 indicate that the glass, when subjected to a sufficiently large compressive stress, loses its spall strength in the region where the reported failure wave has already passed. If the glass is subjected to a sufficiently small initial compressive stress then the spall strength is retained. These observations are consistent with the published results of the previous failure wave experiments by Brar et al.[2,3].

For GLASS2 there appears to be a small increase in velocity before the estimated unloading wave arrival. This increase could be evidence of a reflection from

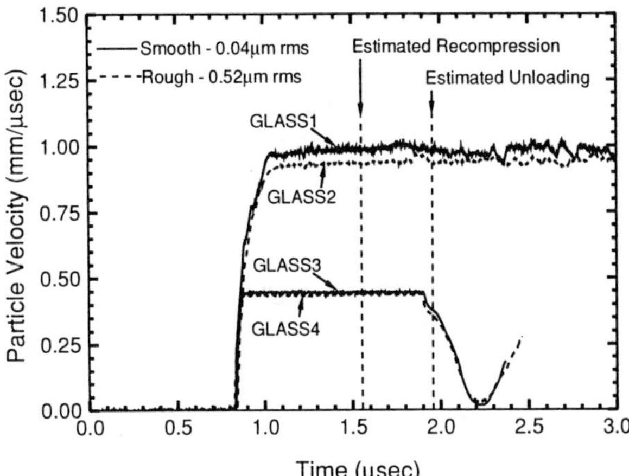

Figure 3. Free-surface velocity-time profiles for Shots GLASS1 to GLASS4.

a slower moving failure wave or phase transformation boundary. In such a case, the velocity of the failure wave or phase boundary estimated from this arrival would be $c_p = 1.35$ mm/μsec. Finally, since no significant differences are observed between shots with specimens of different impact surface roughnesses, no evidence of a surface effect on failure waves has been obtained.

The velocity-time profiles for shots 92-01 and 93-04 are shown in Figure 4. The impact stresses for these two shots were 5.3 GPa and 8.4 GPa, respectively. For Shot 92-01, a velocity level of approximately 0.61 mm/μsec is reached before the expected unloading arrives. The subsequent drop to approximately 0.28 mm/μsec and constant velocity thereafter indicates that the glass did not spall. This is expected as the tensile stress generated was 2.8 GPa and the previous shots indicate that the spall strength of this material is at least 3.5 GPa. The lack of any signal prior to the next unloading wave arrival indicates that the glass has retained its tensile strength and no failure or phase transformation is indicated.

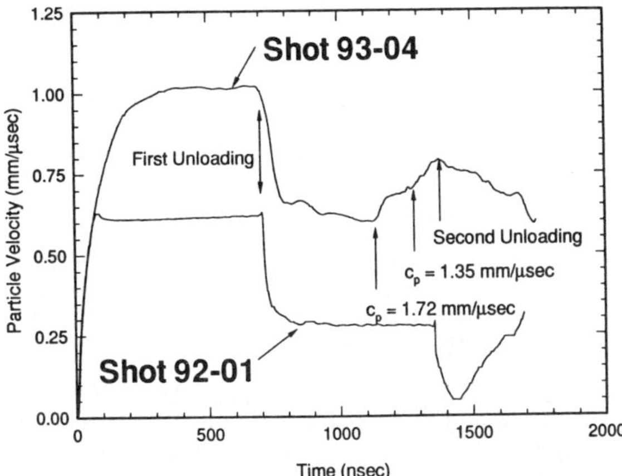

Figure 4. Free-surface velocity-time profiles for Shots 92-01 and 93-04.

For Shot 93-04 the particle velocity levels off at approximately 1.02 mm/μsec during the initial compressive pulse. The velocity then begins to drop near the time expected for the unloading wave arrival. There is a slow decrease after this drop, due mostly to incomplete unloading arising from nonlinear effects in the steel flyer and glass target at this stress level. The main conclusion from this unloading behavior is that this glass did not spall initially even though the impact stress was higher than for any of the previous experiments on this glass. The drop in particle velocity corresponds to a spall strength of at least 4.4 GPa ahead of the failure wave. Another observation from Shot 93-04 is that the velocity increases well before the next expected unloading wave arrival — even before the expected arrival of the reflected wave based on the failure wave velocity of 1.35 mm/μsec calculated for shot GLASS2. The actual arrival corresponds to a failure wave velocity of $c_p = 1.72$ mm/μsec. Finally, since the particle velocity is steadily increasing after this reacceleration arrival, there appears to be either a progressive spallation of the glass, or a finite width of the region over which the phase transformation is completed.

DISCUSSION

From experiments GLASS1 and GLASS2, one can conclude that material behind the failure wave has no spall strength. These experiments, along with Shots 92-01 and 93-04, confirm (for the Corning 1723 aluminosilicate glass) the phenomenon discussed by Kanel et al.[1] and Brar et al.[2,3]. Surface roughness does not appear to play a significant role in the formation of a failure wave.

There are several indications that failure waves may result from phase transformations. The ramp-like wave front suggests a nonlinear elastic response in which the slope of the stress-strain curve decreases monotonically, as expected for a stress path which is approaching the barrier between two energy wells. The increase in the inferred failure wave velocity with increasing stress (i.e. from 1.35 mm/μsec to 1.72 mm/μsec with the increase in stress from 7.5 GPa to 8.4 GPa for Shots GLASS2 and

Table 1. Summary of Spall Experiments on Glass

Shot No.	Impact Stress GPa	Projectile Velocity V_o, mm/μs	Flyer Material	Flyer Thickness mm	Glass Thickness mm	Glass Surface Roughness Å rms
GLASS1	7.88	0.961	Al6061-T6	3.581	5.126	100
GLASS2	7.51	0.965	Al6061-T6	3.581	5.008	5300
GLASS3	3.42	0.450	Al6061-T6	3.577	5.115	700
GLASS4	3.33	0.443	Al6061-T6	3.593	5.040	5100
92-01	5.27	0.438	Hampden Steel	2.080	5.140	300
93-04	8.36	0.695	Hampden Steel	2.045	5.126	300

93-04) is compatible with expectations of a phase transformation. Furthermore, phase changes have been reported by other investigators[4–7,10] who have conducted impact tests on such related materials as soda lime glass, fused silica, quartz, tektite, and a perthitic feldspar. Because of the large strains involved in phase transformations, stress-induced microcracking can be expected to result from heterogeneous nucleation and growth of transformed regions. This microcracking could explain the observed loss of spall strength.

ACKNOWLEDGMENTS

This research was supported by the National Science Foundation through the NSF-MRG at Brown University. Additional support was provided by Sandia National Laboratories where four of the shots were conducted. The assistance of Dr. J. L. Wise, Dr. D. E. Grady and Mr. Dave Cox of Sandia is gratefully acknowledged.

REFERENCES

[1] G. I. Kanel, S. V. Rasorenov, and V. E. Fortov, "The Failure Waves and Spallations in Homogeneous Brittle Materials," *Shock Compression of Condensed Matter 1991*, S.C. Schmidt, R.D. Dick, J.W. Forbes, D.G. Tasker (editors), pp. 451-454.

[2] N. S. Brar, S. J. Bless, and Z. Rosenberg, "Impact-Induced Failure Waves in Glass Bars and Plates," *Appl. Phys. Lett.* 59, pp. 3396-3398, 1991.

[3] N. S. Brar, Z. Rosenberg, and S. J. Bless, "Spall Strength and Failure Waves in Glass," *J. de Physique IV* 1, p. C3-639, 1991.

[4] J. M. Wackerle, "Shock-Wave Compression of Quartz," *J. Appl. Phys.* 33, 922-937, 1962.

[5] L. C. Chhabildas and D. E. Grady, "Shock Loading Behaviour of Fused Quartz," *Shock Waves in Condensed Matter - 1983*, J.R. Asay, R.A. Graham, G.K. Straub (editors), pp. 175-179.

[6] J. D. Kleeman and T. J. Ahrens, "Shock- Induced Transition of Quartz to Stishovite," *J. Geophys. Res.* 78, pp. 5954-5960, 1973.

[7] L. I. Manevich and G. M. Sigalov "Structural Transitions in a One-Dimensional Model of Glasses," *Sov. Phys. Solid State* 34, pp. 210-214, 1992.

[8] R. V. Gibbons and T. J. Ahrens, "Shock Metamorphism of Silicate Glasses," *J. Geophys. Res.* 76, pp. 5489-5498, 1971.

[9] S. M. Weiderhorn, B. J. Hockey, R. F. Krause Jr. and K. Jakus, "Creep and Fracture of a Vitreous-Bonded Aluminum Oxide," *J. Mater. Sci.* 21, pp. 810-824, 1986.

[10] D. E. Grady, W. J. Murri and P. S. DeCarli, "Hugoniot Sound Velocities and Phase Transformations in Two Silicates," *J. Geophys. Res.* 80, pp. 4857-4861, 1975.

SPALLATIONS NEAR THE ULTIMATE STRENGTH OF SOLIDS

G.I. KANEL, S.V. RAZORENOV, A.V.UTKIN

High Energy Density Research Center, Russia Academy of Sciences,
Izhorskaya 13/19, Moscow, Russia, 127412

K.BAUMUNG, H.U. KAROW, V.LICHT

Kernforschungszentrum Karlsruhe,
Institute of Neutron Physics and Reactor Technic,
P.O.Box 3640, D-W7500 Karlsruhe, Germany

Spall strength measurements of aluminum, single crystals of molybdenum, niobium and aluminum oxide were performed over a wide range load durations. A very large dynamic tensile strength (20 GPa) has been registered for sapphire. Dynamic strength of metals at nanoseconds load durations reaches 35% of ultimate theoretical strength. Extrapolation of obtained results shows that ultimate strength can be reached at $\sim 10^{-10}$ s load duration for single crystals and $\sim 10^{-12}$ s for polycrystalline metals.

INTRODUCTION

Previous works have shown that spall strength of copper single crystals 3-4 times exceeds the strength of commercial grade copper [1]; strength of quartz [2] exceeds the strength of quartzite by one order of magnitude. Spall strength increases with decreasing load duration. So, experiments with pure homogeneous single crystals in the shortest load durations range give a chance to reach the ultimate strength of solids.

The objective of this work is an estimation of conditions where ultimate strength of matter can be realized. The spall strength measurements were performed for aluminum, molybdenum and niobium of various incident structure, ruby and sapphire over a wide range of shock load intensities and durations.

MATERIALS

Poly-crystalline aluminum samples were foils 33 or 100 μm thick. Polycrystalline molybdenum specimens of 40 mm in diameter were cut from 0.75-mm-thick rolled sheet or from sintered rod.

Undeformed molybdenum single crystal specimens were cut from a 14 mm-diameter bar. They were 0.3 to 4.5 mm thick and oriented for shock load in the <110>, <111> and <100> directions. Deformed molybdenum and niobium single crystals were prepared by rolling in the <110> direction along the (001) plane. They were 30 to 300 μm thick. The initial dislocation density was about 10^{10} cm^{-2}. It has been shown [3] that deformed molybdenum and niobium retain a single-crystalline structure.

Measurements were performed also with *Z*-cut sapphire and ruby. Specimens were 2 to 3 mm thick and 15 to 20 mm of diameter. Ruby samples were coated by aluminum or silver for work with laser interferometer. In case of sapphire uncoated samples were used.

EXPERIMENTS

Plane shock waves were created by impact of 0.01 to 2 mm thick flyer plates. Explosive facilities [4] were used to launch plane, 0.2 to 2 mm thick aluminum impactors to velocities ranging from 0.6 to 5.3 km/s. Shorter impact pulses were created with high-power proton beams at Karlsruhe Light-Ion Facility ("KALIF"). KALIF is a 1.8 MV, 600 kA, 40 ns pulsed power accelerator delivering up to 40 kJ proton beam energy at a peak power density of 1 TW/cm^2. Shock load pulses in the samples were generated at KALIF in two ways: directly by the ion beam induced ablation pressure, or by impacting of 10 to 50 μm thick aluminum flyer plates accelerated by the ablation pressure to velocities up to 4 to 5 km/s. So, the experiments were performed in the shock pressures range 4 to 100 GPa and load durations between 10^{-8} and 10^{-6} s.

Free surface velocity histories were monitored by VISAR [5] and ORVIS [6] type laser velocimeters. Part of measurements were performed with water "windows". Water windows were used to recovery metal samples and also to maintain the reflectivity of the mirror coating in experiments with ruby.

RESULTS

Figures 1 shows the free surface velocity profiles for undeformed and deformed molybdenum single crystals. Undeformed single crystals demonstrate pronounced elastic precursors with characteristic spikes of 3.7±0.5 GPa peak magnitude. The experiments with deformed single crystals were carried out in the high pressure range, where the two-wave structure can not be observed.

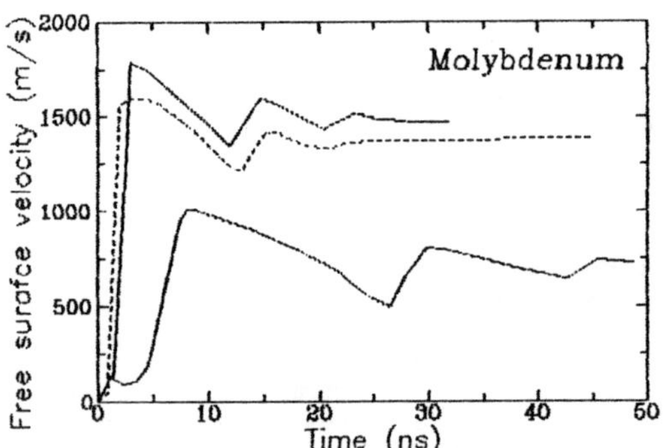

Figure 1. Typical free surface velocity histories for molybdenum single crystals. Load direction is <110>. Solid lines present results for undeformed samples, dashed line is the result of experiment with deformed sample.

Free surface velocity profiles for deformed niobium single crystals are presented in Figure 2. Experimental profiles show more viscous response of niobium in comparison with molybdenum single crystals: deceleration of spall plate is observed during relatively long time after the spall fracture beginning.

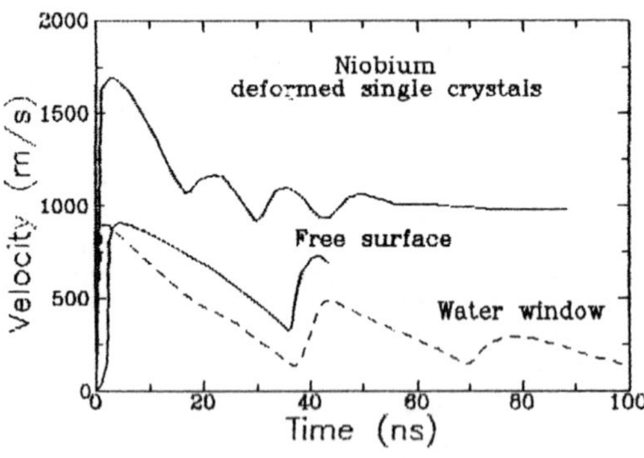

Figure 2. Results of measurements for deformed niobium single crystals. Solid lines are free surface velocity histories, dashed line is particle velocity profile at the boundary with water window.

After reflection of the initial compression pulse from the free surface tensile stresses are generated inside the sample. Spalling is initiated when stress reaches the fracturing magnitude and compression wave appears in the extended material due to stress relaxation. This wave appears in the free surface velocity profile as the so-called "spall pulse". The velocity pullback ΔU_{fs} ahead of the spall pulse is proportional to the tensile stress in a spall plane. This value is called the "spall strength" S:

$$S = \frac{1}{2} \rho_o C_b (\Delta U_{fs} + \delta)$$

where C_b is the bulk sound velocity, δ is a small correction for profile distortion related with elastic-plastic properties of the material [4]. Nonlinearity of matter compressibility was taken into account in the case of high tensile stresses. In fact, this correction does not exceed 10% for the range investigated.

Results of spall strength measurements for metals are summarized in Figure 3 as a function of expansion rate in the incident unloading wave which was calculated as [4]:

$$\dot{V}/V_o = \dot{U}_1/2C_b,$$

where $\dot{U}_1$ is a free surface velocity gradient in the incident unloading wave. Figure 3 contains also results of previous measurements [4,7] for aluminum. For both, poly-crystalline molybdenum and single crystals the spall strength approximately varies as the strain rate to the power of 0.3. For aluminum the index of a power is equal to 0.2.

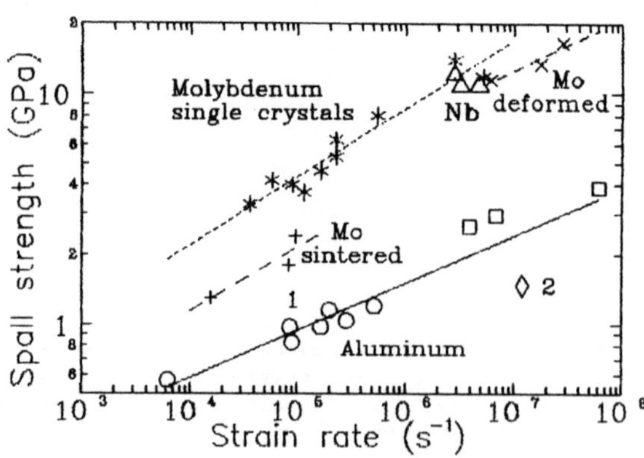

Figure 3. Results of the spall strength measurements for metals. Published data for aluminum are included: 1 - ref. [4], 2 - [7].

Very high tensile stresses in the practically undistorted initial structure were realized in sapphire and ruby. Figure 4 shows experimental profiles. Spall strength for ruby was found equal to 8.6 GPa in case of 15.1 GPa shock wave intensity, and 10 GPa in case of 13.5 GPa peak stress. Spall pulses have drastically steep fronts as a result of very fast fracture of this brittle material. There was not observed any spallation in one of two shots with sapphire where shock intensity was

23 GPa and peak value of tensile stress reached 20 GPa. In other shot with 24 GPa peak stress the spallation was observed at 10.4 GPa tensile stress. Hugoniot elastic limit for sapphire is equal to approximately 14 to 20 GPa [8].

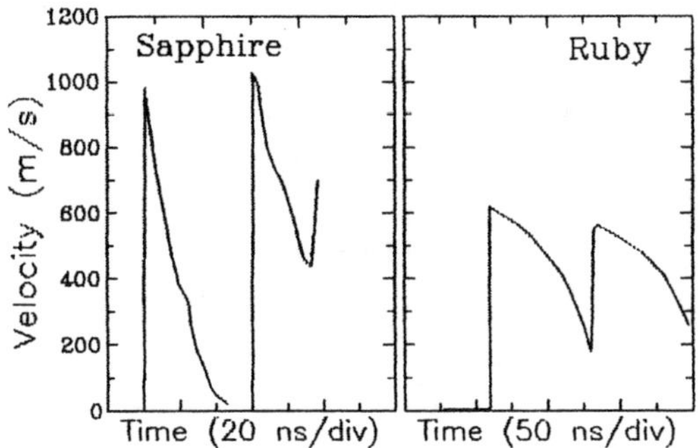

Figure 4. Velocity histories for ruby and sapphire samples. Measurements for ruby were performed with water window.

DISCUSSION

The measured values of spall strength of molybdenum single crystals were not quite reproducible. The scatter of experimental data is too big to reveal the influence of the orientation on resistance to spall fracture. Nearly spherical stress tensor in conditions of one-dimensional shock loading and high isotropy of cubic lattice are reasons of small influence of the orientation on spall strength.

A comparison of the initial load pulse duration and the period of velocity oscillations after spalling shows that there is no discernible delay of fracture. This correlates with weak dependence of the spall strength on the strain rate or, conversely, strong dependence of the initial damage rate on stress.

The spall strength of molybdenum single crystals is approximately twice the strength of poly-crystalline material. As mentioned above, in case of copper [1] this difference amounted to a factor of 3 to 4. The difference between deformed and undeformed single crystals is not so large. However it must be pointed out that the amount of dislocations generated by high-speed plastic deformation at the shock front is comparable with initial dislocation density in the deformed single crystal.

Primary sites of damage nucleation in commercial grade materials are stress concentrators like e.g. grain boundaries and second-phase particles. In pure single crystals a damage nucleation may result only from dislocation interaction during plastic deformation. In this case a concentration of damage nucleation sites has to increase with plastic deformation i.e. with increasing shock load intensity, but results of measurements for molybdenum single crystals do not show any remarkable influence of the peak shock pressure in the range of 4 to 100 GPa on the spall strength. Nevertheless one can conclude that damage nucleation on the dislocation level requires higher tensile stresses and can be realized in single crystals only.

It is interesting to compare measured spall strength values with ultimate theoretical strength. Various estimations of the ultimate tensile strength give significances around approximately $K/10$ to $K/6$, where K is a bulk module. Ultimate tensile strength can be estimated also through the minimum of the $P(V)$ Hugoniot curve as:

$$S_{th} = \frac{\rho_o c_o^2}{4b}$$

where c_o, b are coefficients of the linear relation between shock front velocity and particle velocity. Such estimations give S_{th} = 55 GPa for molybdenum, 36 GPa for niobium, and 14 GPa for aluminum. Ultimate measured values of spall strength are 16.5, 12.4, and 3.9 GPa accordingly. In other words, up to 35% of theoretical strength is reached in single cristals at nanosecond load durations. An extrapolation of obtained spall strength data shows that ultimate strength of molybdenum single crystals has to be reached at strain rate about $5 \cdot 10^8$ s^{-1} which corresponds to 0.5-1 ns of load duration. This value is only by one order of magnitude smaller than shortest shock compression pulse realized in performed experiments, and exceeds a period of atomic oscillations in solids by 3 to 4 orders of magnitude. More than 25% of ultimate theoretical strength is realized for poly-crystalline aluminum at 2 ns load duration. According to extrapolation, ultimate strength in aluminum has to be reached at load duration approximately 2 ps what is near in order to the atomic oscillations period.

Shock pulses in case of sapphire did not exceed the elastic limit. The high homogeneity of matter before the fracture has provided its greatest spall strength in comparison with all known data.

ACNOWLEDGMENT

The experiments with explosive acceleration of impactors and VISAR measurements were carried out in Institute of Chemical Physics (Chernogolovka, Russia). The measurements using the KALIF proton beam and the ORVIS system were performed in the Institute of Neutron Physics and Reactor Engineering (INR) at

Kernforschungszentrum Karlsruhe, Germany. The German Federal Ministry for Research and Technology and the Russian Ministry for Science and Technical Strategy have supported this Project. The authors would like to express their special thanks to Prof. V.Fortov and Prof. G.Kesler for stimulations of this collaborative research

Deformed and undeformed single crystals were prepared at Institute of Solid State Physics, Russia Academy of Sciences. The authors would like to thank Dr. V.G.Glebovsky, Drs. L.N. Pronina and I.M.Aristova and engineer A.V. Mazilkin for providing the samples.

REFERENCES

[1] G.I.Kanel, S.V.Rasorenov, V.E.Fortov. The Dynamic Strength of Copper Single Crystals.- in: Shock-Wave and High Strain-Rate Phenomena in Materials. Ed.: M.A.Meyers, K.Murr, K.Staudhammer, Marcel Dekker, inc., 1992, pp. 775-782.

[2] G.I.Kanel, S.V.Rasorenov, V.E.Fortov. The failure wave and spallations in homogeneous brittle materials. - in: Shock Compression of Condensed matter 1991, ed.: S.C.Schmidt, R.D.Dick, J.W.Forbes, D.G.Tasker, Els. Sc. Publ. B.V., 1992, pp. 451-454.

[3] L.N.Pronina, I.Aristova. Electron microscopy examination of the softening process of the high-purity (001) [110] molybdenum single-crystal sheet.- High Temperatures - High Pressures, v.22, pp.9-11 (1990).

[4] A.V.Bushman, G.I.Kanel, A.L.Ni, V.E.Fortov. Intense Dynamic Loading of Condensed Matter. Taylor & Francis, 1993, 287 pp.

[5] J.R.Asay, L.M.Barker. Interferometric measurement of shock-induced internal particle velocity and spatial variations of particle velocity. - J.Appl.Phys., v.45, No 6, pp. 2540-2546 (1974).

[6] D.D.Bloomquist, S.A.Sheffield. Optically recording interferometer for velocity measurements with subnanosecond resolution. - J.Appl.Phys., v.54, No 4, pp.1717-1722, (1983).

[7] Paisley D.L., Warnes R.H., and Kopp R.A. Laser-driven flat plate impacts to 100 GPa with sub-nanosecond pulse duration and resolution for material property studied. - In: "Shock Compression of Condensed Matter", Ed.: S.C.Schmidt, R.D.Dick, J.W.Forbes and D.G. Tasker, Els. Sci. Publ. B.V., 1992, pp.825-828.

[8] R.A.Graham, W.P.Brooks. Shock-wave compression of sapphire from 15 to 420 kbar. The effects of large anisotropic compression. - J. Phys. Chem. Solids, v.32, pp. 2311-2330 (1971).

EXPERIMENTAL AND NUMERICAL STUDIES OF Ti-6Al-4V SPALLATION BY LASER AND IMPACT LOADINGS

L. TOLLIER[1], F. COTTET[2], M. BOUSTIE[2], J.P. ANSART[3]

1 LALP / ETCA, 16 bis Avenue Prieur de la Cote d'Or - 94114 ARCUEIL - FRANCE
2 LED / ENSMA, rue Guillaume VII - 86000 POITIERS - FRANCE
3 CEA - 91 BRUYERES-LE-CHATEL - FRANCE

Laser induced shock wave technique provides a useful means for studying spall fracture in a complementary range of stress and loading duration (0.1 - 0.2 TPa ; 1 - 20 ns) in relation to conventional shocks by flyer impacts (20 - 40 GPa ; 1 - 10 μs). A set of laser and impact experiments on Ti-6Al-4V material was analysed in term of spall fracture stress Y_S versus time t necessary to produce significant damage in material. A cumulative damage criterion for dynamic fracture, included in a one-dimensional finite difference hydrodynamic code, permitted us to investigate these experiments. It is shown that this simple model for fracture, according to keep constant the product $Y_S{}^2t$, reproduce quite well the fracture behaviour over a wide range of shock loadings.

INTRODUCTION

Shocked-waves induced by high-power pulsed Laser irradiation are distinguished by a strong amplitude (from a few gigapascals to the megabar) and a very short pulse duration (a few nanosecondes). This second characteristic is the main specificity of Laser-driven shock in comparison with conventionnal dynamic techniques like plate-impact experimental studies or experiments performed by direct application of explosives.

The irradiation of a solid target create at the front surface a plasma which generate a compression wave in the material. In the case of a thin foil target and a high amplitude shock front, a fracture occurs in the sample. This fracture, also called spallation, results of a planar separation of the material parallel to the wave front due to a dynamic tensile stress component perpendicular to this plane. This tension area is caused by the crossing of two release waves. The first-one is the rarefaction wave following the shock front generated by the Laser irradiation and the second-one consists in the reflected release wave produced as the shock front reaches the rear surface of the target. Spallation in ductile materials is a cumulative phenomenon which occurs when the magnitude and duration of the tension exceed the ability of the solid to maintain its integrity.

The object of this paper is the responses characterization of the Titanium alloy Ti-6Al-4V subject to the application of high-pressure shock-waves produced by high-power pulsed Lasers. First this paper describes the criterion used for the material responses and spallation numerical simulation, then the validation of this model by an experimental study. Secondly it presents the analysis of the evolution of the critical spallation tensile stress and the comparison with experimental results obtained by plate-impact techniques.

SIMULATIONS AND EXPERIMENTS OF SPALLATION IN Ti-6Al-4V

Simulations

The numerical simulation were realized with the one-dimensional finite-difference hydrodnamic Lagrangian code SHYLAC [1]. we simulate an elastic-plastic behavior of the Ti-6Al-4V with a elastic limit determined by the Von-Mises criterion. The code uses the Mie-Grüneisen state equation. The effects of dynamical failure in ductile materials were described with a cumulative-damage model (Tuler-Butcher criterion [2]).

This criterion supposes that a failure occurs when the tensile stress (σ) exceeds the ultimate strength (σ_R) during certain time. In theory, spallation phenomenon appears when the material meets the following condition :

$$\int_0^t \frac{(\sigma - \sigma_R)^A}{K} dt > 1$$

To determine the three parameters of the criterion for the Ti-6Al-4V (σ_R, A, K) we compare the numerical results with the spall thickness and spall threshold observed in a post-mortem examination of recovered shocked samples. The initial loading conditions of the Laser-driven shock are reproduced by a gaussian pressure pulse described by two parameters : the maximum amplitude and the duration at medium height (τ).

Spall experiments on Ti-6Al-4V

The experiments were performed with the Phosphate Neodymium Glass laser of the LULI Laboratory (Ecole Polytechnique) operating at 1.06 µm wavelength. This laser is able to deliver its energy in different pulse durations : 2.5 ns and 27 ns in these spall experiments. Maximum output energy is 100 J for Gaussian pulses of 2.5 ns FWHM (full width at half maximum), and 170 J for 27 ns FWMH pulses.
We used different focal spots of 0.5 and 1 mm diameters to attain estimated pressures of 120 - 220 GPa (2.5 ns), and 33 - 80 GPa (27 ns). For the experiments realized in this study, we used the following pressure law [3]:

$$P = 12 * \phi_a^{2/3}$$

P : pressure (Mbar)
ϕ_a : absorbed flux (10^{14} W/cm^2)

The aborbed flux is estimated as 80% of the incident flux. This law has been established for the flux interval 10^{13} W/cm^2 - 10^{15} W/cm^2, but it can be extrapolated for lower flux by experimental results [4].
The material used in those experiments is a Titanium alloy composed of 90% Titanium, 6% Aluminium, 4% Vanadium : Ti-6Al-4V. The samples are very thin foil targets with a 2 cm^2 area (larger than the focal spot to suppress the border effects) and a thickness from 250 µm to 900 µm. In order to avoid the ionization of the air at these incident laser intensities, the targets are placed in a vacuum chamber.
By observing a polished section of the sample in the center of the focal spot with an optical microscope, we note the presence of spallation or not and the spall thickness (Figure 1). These observations allow us to verify that the spallation fracture of Ti-6Al-4V is a ductile failure. The spall thickness is the parameter that we used to compare the experiments with the numerical results.

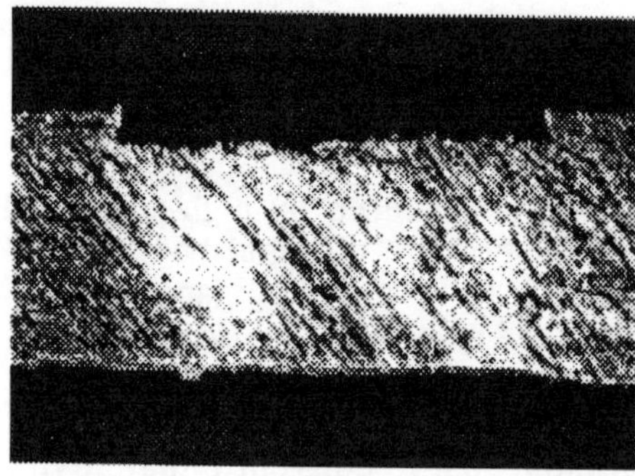

Figure 1. section of a sample which shows a spall at the rear surface (top of the figure) [1 cm = 155 µm]

A comparison of experimental and numerical results is plotted on the diagram of Figure 2, in a spall thickness - target thickness plane.
The shape of the initial loading conditions [P =120GPa - τ = 2.5ns] is the most one-dimensional in the experiments realized in this study. The Tuler-Butcher criterion parameters determined for the simulations are the following ones :

A = 2	σ_R = 4.5 GPa	K = 1 GPa^2.µs

Another shape of laser irradiation [P = 220 GPa - τ = 2.5 ns] is plotted on Figure 3 in the same plane as Figure 2. The focal spot diameter was 0,6 mm and the target thickness was varying from 300 µm to 700 µm. We can see on this diagram that the numerical code is unable to simulate the experimental upper spallation threshold.

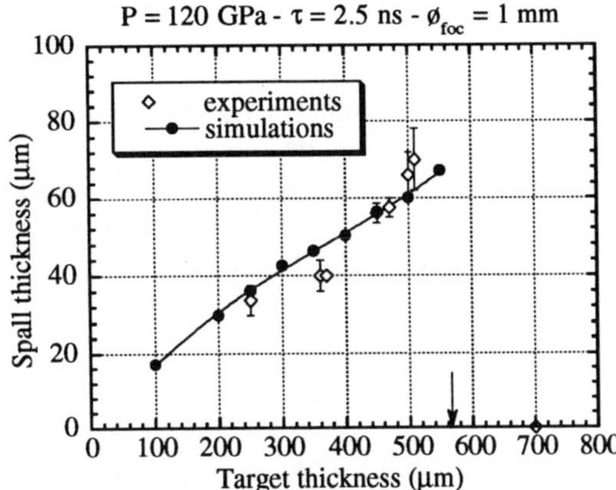

Figure 2. comparison of experimental and numerical spall thickness results (the black arrow shows the numerical upper spallation threshold)

The reason is that the code is one-dimensional and doesn't take the two-dimensional hydrodynamic attenuation of the shock wave. This effect becomes important when the target thickness is greater than the focal spot diameter.

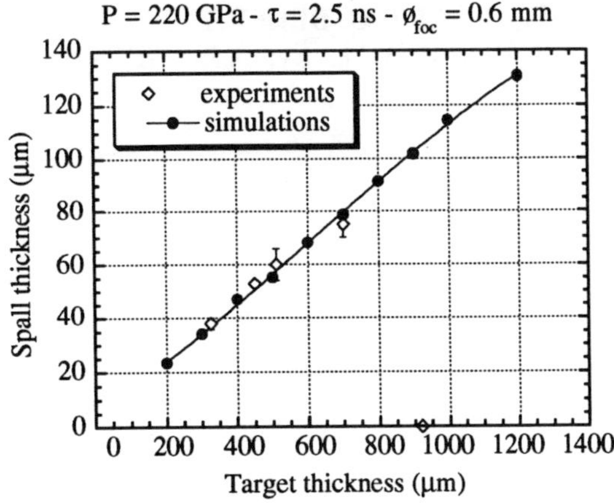

Figure 3. comparison of experimental and numerical spall thickness results for two dimensional loading shape

EVOLUTION OF SPALL FRACTURE STRESS AS A FUNCTION OF THE APPLICATION TIME

The tensile stress at the instant of rupture is one of the important data of spallation process, so we have studied its evolution as a function of the time during which the stress is maintained.The stress profiles generated by plate-impact are very different from the laser-driven stress profiles, especially concerning the maximum induced pressure amplitude and the compressive pulse duration.

So, for the Ti-6Al-4V, the spallation tensile stress is of about a few GPa with plate-impact shocks and of about a few 10 GPa for the laser-driven shocks. These two shock generation systems result in two separate fields in a tensile stress - duration plane.

In order to simulate the stress profil in the rupture plane, we used the parameters of the Tuler-Butcher criterion determined in this study.

The Figure 4 shows a simulation in the fracture plane of a stress profil as a function of the time. The application time during which the stress is maintained is calculated as the duration at medium height as shown on the figure.

Simulations results performed in this study and plate-impact experimental results [5] have been compared on the Figure 5.

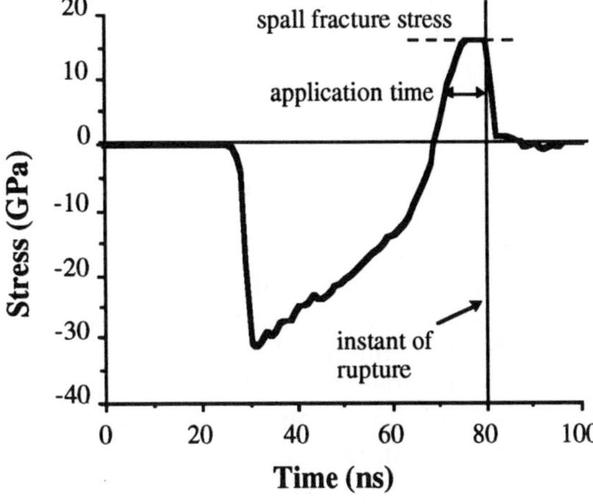

Figure 4. simulation of the loading shape P=33GPa - τ=27ns on a 300μm sample of Ti-6Al-4V

They appear to follow the same evolution : the rupture tensile stress increases when its duration decreases. This evolution is the one reproduced by the Tuler-Butcher damage criterion that we can express with the following equation :

$$[\text{spall fracture stress}]^2 \times \text{duration} = \text{constant}$$

So the result of the numerical study validate this criterion for a larger field of time and stress.

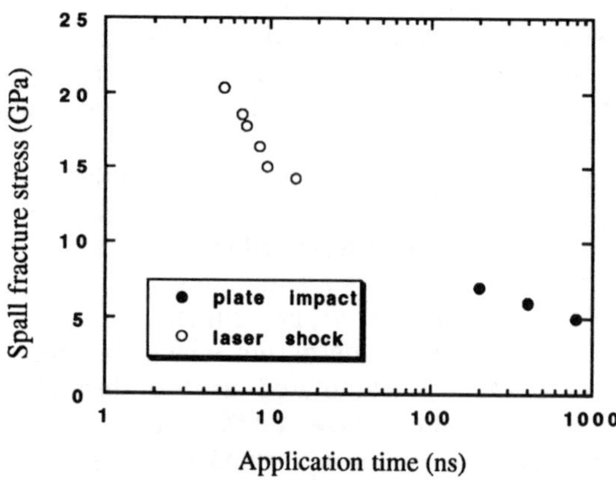

Figure 5. comparison of numerical results obtained in this study and experimental results produced with the plate-impact technique

CONCLUSION

Laser-driven shock waves generation in materials give the possibility to study their behaviour in loading shapes that are different from the conventional techniques (strong pressures and very short durations).
The study of the Titanium alloy Ti-6Al-4V responses under laser-driven shocks allowed us to obtain the following results:

• caracterization of damage in Ti-6Al-4V under laser irradiation.

• determination of the Tuler-Butcher criterion parameters by comparing experiments and one-dimensional simulations :

$A = 2$	$\sigma_R = 4.5$ GPa	$K = 1$ GPa^2.µs

• study of the evolution of the spall fracture stress versus time t necessary to produce significant damage, comparison with impact experiments results [3] and validation of the criterion for a wide range of shock loading.

REFERENCES

[1] : F. COTTET & M. BOUSTIE, J. Appl. Phys. 66 , 4067 (1989)

[2] : F.R. TULER, B.M. BUTCHER, Journal of Fracture Mechanics 4 (4) , (1968)

[3] : R. FABBRO, C.E. MAX & E. FABRE, Phys. Fluids, 28, 1463 (1985)

[4] : F. COTTET & J.P. ROMAIN, Phys. Rev. A., 25, 576 (1982)

[5] : J.P. ANSART, D. BEDERE, R. DORMEVAL Symp. Int. HDP (1989)

METAL FRACTURE AT HYDROSTATIC EXTRUSION

Ya. E. Belgelzimer, B. M. Efros, N. V. Shishkova
Department of Hydrostatic Treatment of Materials
Donetsk Physico-Technical Institute of the Ukrainian Academy of Sciences
72, R. Luxembourg St., Donetsk, Ukraine, 340114

In the paper a mathematical model of multiple material failure at simple loading based on the percolation theory is presented. On the basis of this model the porosity corresponding to formation of macrodiscontinuity is evaluated. A kinetic equation for porosity with an account of the formation and the curing of microdisdiscontinuities is proposed. Conditions for obtaining the state with unlimited deformability at forming of metal sunder external pressure are analyzed. The proposed mathematical model of metal failure is explained by an example of hydroextrusion process. Namely, the relationship for the extrudate damage are obtained and the conditions for the axial cavity opening are discussed.

INTRODUCTION

According to the current ideas [1, 2] the metal failure at plastic strain is a multistage and multiscale process. It is developed at various structural levels. An the lower level failure provokes the higher-level one, i.e. the secondary defects are nucleated from the coalescence of the primary ones, the tertiary defects being formed from the secondary ones, etc. The progress of defects at the same level is self-modeled up to a certain moment, i.e. as the damage degree increased the geometry of the defect cascade is transformed according to the similarity principle (scaling law) [2]. Violation of the self-modeling is due to formation of another level defect [2].

Effective methods for the study of the above processes can be taken from the percolation theory [3]. We present some concepts of this theory which re the basis for the below model of material failure at the plastic strain under pressure.

1. PERCOLATION MODEL OF FAILURE

Assume that a certain amount of a large volume of space v is randomly occupied with a substance. At v<<1 the substance forms small regions separated from one another. As v increases these regions start to coalesce thus originating the bound formation (clusters). The cluster sizes increase and at some critical value v_c a cluster is formed which spread over the entire volume. This cluster is referred to as an infinite cluster. For three-dimensional regions, $v_c \approx 0.17$ [3]. The clusters are of completely random shapes. But on the average, the geometry of randomly arranged substance has quite definite properties. One of them is reflected by the hypothesis of similarity according to which the cluster size distribution function related to a mean value at given v is unchanged and independent of v. The similarity is upset at the moment of the infinite cluster formation.

Let us assume the following model of failure. At each level there is a corresponding simple defect, i.e. the fracture atom. the bound set (cluster) of fracture atoms forms the defects of this level. An infinite cluster of fracture atoms of one level gives a fracture atom of another level. Thus the defects are considered to correspond to the clusters. This results in similarity principle for defects substantiated in [2] which states that at a continuous fracture the cascade of defects is transformed in similar manner, and all the linear sizes of cascade grow proportionally to a statistically average size of defects. Actually the similarity principle, in the given case, is a manifestation of regularity in the cluster development characterized by the similarity hypothesis of the percolation theory.

According to the similarity principle, the cluster geometry of the defect cascade is completely determined by relative volume of defects. In [4], we obtain the kinetic equation for this quantity which is further referred to as porosity.

This equation is :

$$\frac{d\Theta}{d\gamma} = \left[\alpha\sqrt{1+\frac{3}{2}\Theta\left(\frac{\sigma}{\tau}\right)^2} + \frac{3}{2}\Theta\frac{\sigma}{\tau}\right], \quad (1)$$

where Θ- porosity, γ- intensity of shear strain, σ- hydrostatic constituent of stress tensor, τ- intensity of tangential stress, α- internal friction coefficient.

This relation implies that both the formation of micropores and their curing (at $\sigma < 0$) take place at plastic strain. The processes correspond to the first and the second terms in the right-hand side of relation (1) respectively.

From the equation (1) it follows that at (See original) = const < 0, the some equilibrium porosity (Θ_e) steady in the material under deformation. The value of this porosity is a root of an equation:

$$\alpha\sqrt{1+\frac{3}{2}\Theta_e\left(\frac{\sigma}{\tau}\right)^2} + \frac{3}{2}\Theta_e\frac{\sigma}{\tau} = 0. \quad (2)$$

According to [5] the criterion of metal failure at pressure treatment is the appearance of simple defect at macrolevel. On the basis of the proposed model we evaluate the "critical" loosening due to which this effect appears in material.

According to [1] the formation of microdiscontinuity with the linear size of the order of 0.1 μm is an elementary act of failure. the coalescene of these defects gives microdiscontinuities with the size of the order of the linear size of structural heterogeneity)of block, grain), The coalescence of the latter ones results in the appearance of a macrocracks. In terms of the proposed model we have : microdiscontinuity of about 0.1 μm, the first-level fracture atom; microdiscontinuity of size of structural heterogeneity, the second-level fracture atom;

percolation theory the relative portion of this substance should reach its critical value v_c for the formation of an infinite cluster of any substance. therefore, the nucleation of the third-level fracture atom per unit volume requires v of the second-level fracture atoms and $v_c \cdot v_c$ of the first-level ones. thus the critical loosening is evaluated as $\Theta_c = v_c^2$. Substituting $v_c = 0.17$ into the latter expression, we obtain $\Theta_c \approx 3\%$ which corresponds by the order of magnitude to experimental value $\Theta_c \approx 1\%$ [1]. At $\Theta_c < \Theta_e$ the solid fractures before reaches its equilibrium value. And at $\Theta_c > \Theta_e$ the value Θ_e will be reached before the solid starts to fracture. The state with unlimited deformability should correspond to the given condition.

2. PECULIARITY OF THE MATERIAL FAILURE AT HYDROEXTRUSION

Thus the proposed model allows one to determine the conditions which provide the plastic strain of metals without failure external pressure. The above model of metal failure can be explained by an example of steel loosening at hydrostatic extrusion [6, 7]. According to [1, 8] for steels $\alpha \sim 10^{-2}$, $\Theta < 10^{-2}$. It follows [5] that at hydrostatic extrusion $\sigma/\tau \sim 1.3$. In view of this fact and neglecting the terms of the second order smallness in Eq. (1) one gets the simplified kinetic equation for porosity

$$d\Theta = \left(\alpha + \frac{2}{3}\Theta\frac{\sigma}{\tau}\right)d\gamma. \tag{3}$$

It follows from Ref. [9] that at small magnitude of the contact friction which is typical of the hydroextrusion, along the die axis

$$\frac{\sigma}{\tau} = -\sqrt{3}\ln\left(\frac{\rho}{\rho_2}\right)^2 - \frac{2}{\sqrt{3}}, \tag{4}$$

$$d\gamma = -\frac{2\sqrt{3}}{\rho}d\rho, \tag{5}$$

where ρ is the radius of the arbitrary point along the die axis, ρ_1, ρ_2 is the radius of the deformation area boundaries.

Substituting relationships (4), (5) into Eq. (3) one gets the following differential equation for deformation of Θ:

$$\frac{d\Theta}{dx} - 18\Theta x - 6\Theta = -2\sqrt{3}\alpha, \tag{6}$$

where $x = \ln(\rho/\rho_2)$.

Initial condition: $\Theta = \Theta_1$, at $x = x_1$, where Θ_1 is the porosity of the initial billet, $x_1 = \ln(\rho_1/\rho_2)$.

The solution of Eq. (6) at this initial condition has the form

$$\Theta(x) = e^{-F(x)}\left[\Theta_1 - 2\sqrt{3}\alpha\int_{x_1}^{x} e^{F(x)}dx\right], \tag{7}$$

where $F(x) = 3\cdot(x_1 - x)\cdot[2+3(x+x_1)]$. Substituting x=0 into Eq. (7) one gets the expression for the porosity of the extrudate Θ_2:

$$\Theta_2 = \Theta_1 e^{-3x_1(2+3x_1)} + 2\sqrt{3}\alpha\int_0^{x_1} e^{-3x(2+3x)}dx.$$

Replacing the variables in the integral one can reduce the latter to the probability integral for which there are the tables [10]. Having performed simple transforms one gets:

$$\Theta_2 = \Theta_1 \exp\left[-\frac{2}{3}\varepsilon\left(2+\frac{3}{2}\varepsilon\right)+2\alpha e\sqrt{\frac{\pi}{3}}\cdot\right.$$

$$\left.\cdot\left\{\Phi\left[\sqrt{2}\left(1+\frac{3}{2}\varepsilon\right)\right]-\Phi(\sqrt{2})\right\}\right., \tag{8}$$

where $\Phi(z) = \frac{1}{\sqrt{2\pi}}\int_{-\infty}^{z} e^{-\frac{1}{2}\xi^2}d\xi$ is the normal distribution function [10], $\varepsilon = \ln(\rho_1/\rho_2)^2$ is the logarithmic deformation at hydrostatic extrusion. Fig. 1 presents the plots of $\Theta_2 = \Theta_2(\varepsilon)$ at various magnitudes of α and Θ_1.

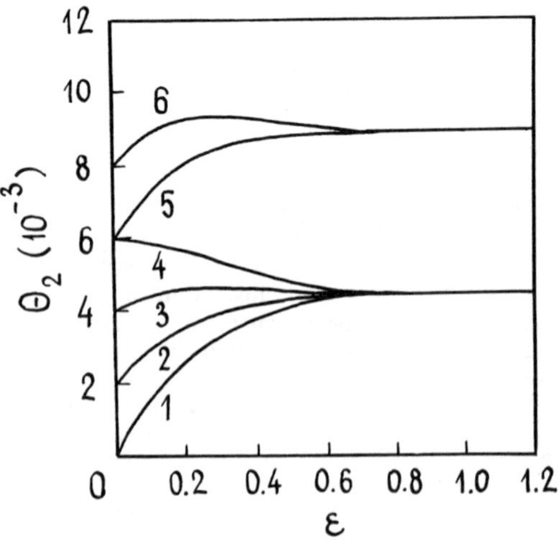

Figure 1. Extrudate porosity as a function of logarithmic deformation at hydrostatic extrusion:

1 - $\Theta_1 = 0$, $\alpha = 10^{-2}$;
2 - $\Theta_1 = 2 \cdot 10^{-3}$, $\alpha = 10^{-2}$;
3 - $\Theta_1 = 4 \cdot 10^{-3}$, $\alpha = 10^{-2}$;
4 - $\Theta_1 = 6 \cdot 10^{-3}$, $\alpha = 10^{-2}$;
5 - $\Theta_1 = 6 \cdot 10^{-3}$, $\alpha = 2 \cdot 10^{-2}$;
6 - $\Theta_1 = 8 \cdot 10^{-3}$, $\alpha = 2 \cdot 10^{-2}$.

It is clear from this figure that at the hydroextrusion there are three versions of dependence of the extrudate porosity on the deformation rate: porosity growth with the increase in the deformation rate; decrease in porosity with the deformation rate growth; dependence with the porosity maximum.

All the above cases are implemented in practice. the first one is typical of the hydroextrusion of metals with small initial damage [11], the second case is observed at the hydroextrusion of billets with a great amount of microdiscontinuities [7]. The third case is realized at the hydroextrusion of tool steels when at small and great deformations the extrudate quality is high whereas at medium deformations plasticity drops up to the axial destruction of the extrudate [11].

Now let us determine the deformation rate at which the extrudate porosity is maximum. For this purpose we find derivative $d\Theta_2/d\varepsilon$. Eq. (8) yields

$$\frac{d\Theta_2}{d\varepsilon} = exp(1-t^2)(\alpha\sqrt{3} - 3\Theta_1 t), \qquad (9)$$

where $t = 1 + \frac{3}{2}\varepsilon$

At $\varepsilon = \varepsilon_m$ where

$$\varepsilon_m = \frac{2}{3}\left(\frac{\alpha}{\sqrt{3}\Theta_1} - 1\right), \qquad (10)$$

the number of defects in the extrudate is maximum.

Fig. 2 presents the plots $\varepsilon_m = \varepsilon_m(\Theta_1)$ at various magnitudes of α.

The proposed mathematical model allows one to write the condition at which the hydroextrusion will result in formation of axial cracks in the extrudate. thus according to it. 1 and Eq. (8) this condition has the form:

$$\Theta_1 exp\left[-\frac{3}{2}\varepsilon\left(2+\frac{3}{2}\varepsilon\right)\right] + 2\alpha e\sqrt{\frac{\pi}{3}} \cdot \left\{\Phi\left[\sqrt{2}\left(1+\frac{3}{2}\varepsilon\right)\right] - \Phi(\sqrt{2})\right\} < \Theta_c . \qquad (11)$$

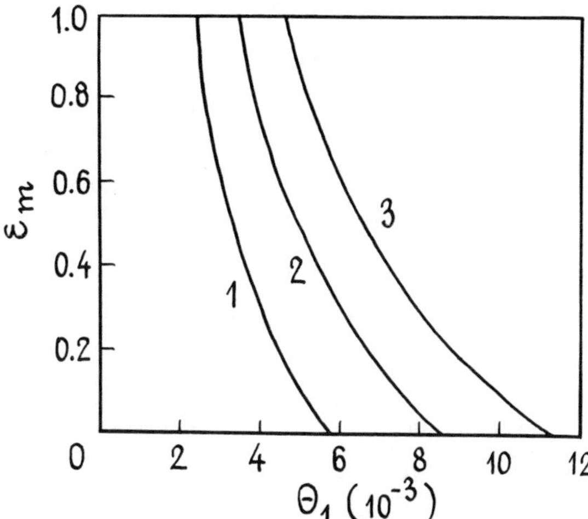

Figure 2. Deformation producing maximum loosening of metal as a function of the billet porosity: 1-$\alpha = 10^{-2}$; 2-$\alpha = 1.5 \cdot 10^{-2}$; 3-$\alpha = 2.0 \cdot 10^{-2}$.

Let us consider the case with $\Theta_1 = 0$. thus Eq. (11) yields the following equation for determination of the critical deformation ε_c.

$$\Phi\left[\sqrt{2}\left(1+\frac{3}{2}\varepsilon_c\right)\right] - \Phi(\sqrt{2}) = \frac{\Theta_c}{2\alpha e}\sqrt{\frac{3}{\pi}} . \qquad (12)$$

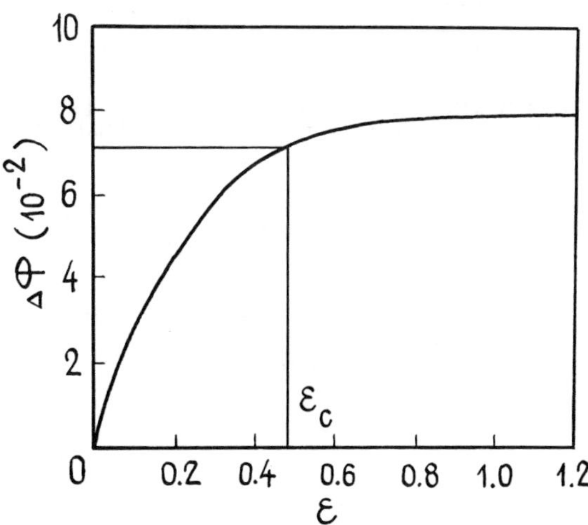

Fig. 3 shows the plot of the dependence of the left-hand side of Eq. (12) on the magnitude ε. Using this plot one can easily find the magnitudes ε_c. Thus at $\alpha = 0.02$ and $\Theta_c = 8 \cdot 10^{-3}$ the right-hand side of Eq. (12) is equal to $7.19 \cdot 10^{-2}$ and the critical deformation $\varepsilon_c = 0.47$.

CONCLUSION

The proposed model of metal failure is illustrated by an example of the hydroextrusion process. In this case the model make it possible to explain the reduction in the extrudate plasticity at medium deformation rates, thus determining the most unfavorable deformation from this point of view. On the basis of his model the condition for hydroextrusion without axial failure of the extrudate is obtained (Eq. (11)).

REFERENCES

[1] V. I. Betekhtin, V. I. Vladimirov, A. G. Kadomtsev, A. I. Petrov, Plastic strain and crystal body failure. Report 1. Deformation and development of microcracks, Problemy prochnosti N7, pp. 38-45 (1979).

[2] G. L. Barenblatt, L. P. Botvina, Scaling principles in mechanics and physics of failure, Fiziko khimicheskaja mekhanika materialov, 22, N 1. pp. 57-62 (1986).

[3] V. I. Shklovskii, A. L. Efros, Electronic properties of doped semiconductors, M.: Nauka, 1979, 416 p.

[4] Ya Beigelimer, L. loladze, B. Efros. On viscous destruction of materials under pressure in Proceedings of the XIII AIRAPT Conference on High Pressure and Technology "Recent trends in High Pressure Research", 1992, pp. 734-736.

[5] V. L. Kolmogorov, Stresses, strains, Failure, M.: Metallurgija, 1970, 229 pp.

[6] B. Avitzur, Metal forming:Processes and Analysis, New York-McGraw-Hill, 1968, 640p.

[7] B. I. Beresnev, K. I. Ezerskii, E. V. Trushin, B. I. Kamenetskii, High pressures in modern technologies of material treatment, M. : Nauka, 1988, 245pp.

[8] V. V. Novozhilov, On plastic loosening, Prikladnaja matematika i mekhanica, 29, N4, pp. 680-689 (1965).

[9] V. V. Sokolovskii, Theory of plasticity, M.: Vysshaja Shkola, 1969, 607 pp.

[10] E. S. Ventzel, Probability theory, M.: Nuka, 1969, 576 pp.

[11] Yu F. Cherny, V. Z. Spuskanjuk, A. A. Ljadskaja, A. I. Opanashuk. Hydropressin of tool steels, Kiev:Tekhnika, 1987.-216pp.

DENSITY SCALING OF VISCOSITY MEASURED VIA DIAMOND CELL VISCOMETRY

H.E. King, Jr.; R.L. Cook; and C.A. Herbst
Corporate Research Science Laboratories
Exxon Research and Engineering Co.
Annandale, NJ 08801

The use of the rolling-ball and centrifugal-force diamond anvil cell viscometers are described. Together they cover a ten decade range in viscosity at pressures up to 10 GPa. Using data from these, we test two theories for density-modulated viscosity: modified Enskog theory and free-volume theory. The latter theory is able to model viscosities ranging from those of super-critical fluids up to those of a glass. The physical significance of the resulting fit parameters is discussed.

INTRODUCTION

At present there is no accepted model for the structural origin of the large ($>10^{15}$) viscosity changes one observes in going from a liquid to a glass. Development of mode-coupling theory may eventually provide such a model,[1] but also important are scaling relations. Density scaling of the viscosity provides an important framework for understanding the structural origins of viscosity, and as we will show, free-volume theory can describe viscosities across the entire density range up to the glassy state.

Experimentally, it is clear that both low temperatures and high pressures cause the viscosity to increase. Analysis of this behavior has suggested that a significant component of this increase can be ascribed to a scaling relationship between density and viscosity.[2] The exact form of this is still uncertain however. Thermal data change the density by only a small amount ($\approx$5%) and there is the complexity of separating the density effects from the intrinsic thermal ones. High pressure directly alters the density but those studies, too, give an incomplete picture. In one type of study, gases and super-critical fluids are compressed a considerable amount ($\Delta\rho>10^2$) but the viscosity variation is small, $\Delta\eta\approx10$. In a second type study, ordinary liquids are compressed by a few percent causing a rise in viscosity of up to three orders of magnitude. The limited viscosity range of these studies makes such data inadequate to fully test scaling theories. Data spanning many orders of magnitude are needed. Pressure studies of this type[3, 4] can provide significant insight into the density scaling of viscosity.

THE DIAMOND-ANVIL CELL VISCOMETER

There have been many devices used in measuring high pressure viscosity (see Cook et al [4] for a review). The diamond cell viscometer excels in two significant ways over previous techniques: 1) an extremely wide pressure range (easily compressing any fluid beyond its 300K liquid stability field) and 2) a wide range of accessible viscosities, from 1 to 10^{10} cP. It can also give quite accurate results (few percent error); thus allowing one to precisely define the pressure-viscosity dependence over a much wider range than previously accessible.

The Rolling Ball Viscometer

The rolling-ball viscometer (more fully described in King et al.[5]) is shown in Fig. 1. Measurements are made by recording the velocity of the rolling ball inside the pressure chamber. The pressure chamber consists of a 200-500 μm diameter hole drilled in a 250 μm thick piece of stainless steel which is compressed between two flat diamond surfaces. An image of the ball, a nickel alloy about 50 μm in diameter, rolling down the surface of one of the diamonds is relayed via a video camera to a video dimension analyzer (VDA). This linear tracking device gives a velocity which is converted into viscosity, η, by a modified Stokes equation, in which the excess drag caused by the small sample chamber is described by a multiplicitative constant. Pressure is measured in the usual manner using the ruby manometer, except that we use a neon reference system to increase the accuracy at low pressures.[6] The fluid density varies with pressure and is calculated from the Tait equation of state. Using a Merrill-Bassett pressure clamp we can access pressures from 0.2 to 10 GPa and viscosities from 10^{-1} to 10^7cP. The resulting viscosity data have a precision of $\approx$4%.

The Centrifugal Force Viscometer

To measure higher viscosities, we must supply a larger driving force than gravity. We use centrifugal force instead of gravity to drive the ball in the diamond-anvil cell viscometer.[3, 4] By applying a maximum acceleration of 1700 g to the ball we are able to measure viscosities up to 4 x 10^9 cP while maintaining an

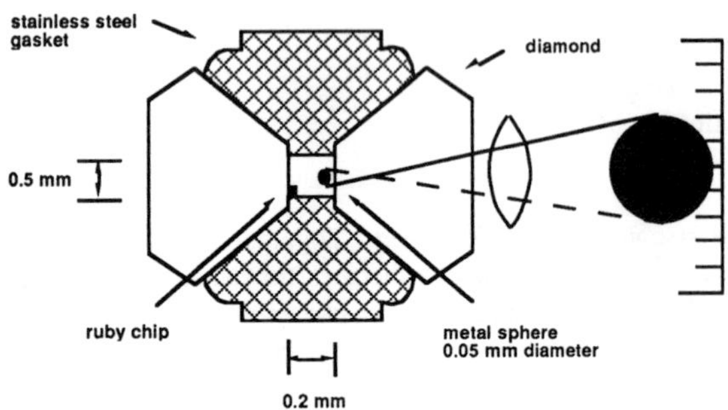

Figure 1. The diamond anvil cell viscometer.

acceptable uncertainty of ≈8%. Data on methanol obtained from both the rolling ball and centrifugal viscometers are shown in Figs. 2 and 3.

DENSITY MEDIATED VISCOSITY

High pressure, isothermal studies provide direct data on density-mediated viscosity, and two main theories have been used in interpreting the results.

Modified Enskog Theory

Dymond pioneered the use of this theory. The usefulness of high-pressure viscosity data in testing density scaling was apparent to him, and in a series of papers over the last 25 years he and his collaborators have utilized data from super critical fluids and other liquids up to their freezing pressures to extensively refine and test the modified-Enskog theory(MET). Dymond's approach[7] in utilizing MET are now summarized and its implications when applied to a wider range of viscosities are considered below.

The starting point is an analytical theory first given by Enskog:

$$\frac{\eta_E}{\eta_B}=\frac{(1-\xi)^3}{1-\frac{\xi}{2}}+3.2\xi+12.176\frac{\xi^2-\frac{\xi^3}{2}}{(1-\xi)^3} \qquad (1)$$

The ratio of Enskog to Boltzman viscosity, is completely determined by ξ, the packing fraction. This is defined as V_∞/V, where V_∞, an excluded volume, is determined by the molecular diameter, $V_\infty = \pi\sigma^3/6$. (Note that in defining ξ, V_∞ is also sometimes equated with the close packed volume.) The Boltzman viscosity is that of the fully expanded, gaseous state and is defined through,

$$\eta_B=\frac{5\pi^{1/6}(RT)^{1/2}}{16\bullet 6^{2/3}N_A^{1/3}M^{1/6}V_\infty^{2/3}} \qquad (2)$$

This form of the equation presumes that V_∞ is given in terms of volume per mass (cm^3/gm). Eqn. 1, has been shown through molecular dynamics simulations[8] to be accurate only up to packing fractions of 0.25. Above these densities, it systematically underestimates the viscosity with the correction (η/η_E) reaching 2.2 for ξ=0.49. (For $\xi\approx0.5$ the hard sphere liquid transforms to a close packed crystal). To include this correction in the model, an empirical functional form relating the correction term to the packing fraction is constructed. We find that the following form is an accurate representation:

$$\frac{\eta}{\eta_E}=1+e^{[29.742(\xi-0.4888)]} \qquad (3)$$

In some instances, Dymond includes a further modification for non-spherical molecules[9] which would appear as a multiplicative correction to η_B. This term is not considered here. It does not alter the density dependence, nor is it appropriate for the spherical molecules we examine.

The resulting Modified Enskog Theory, the product of Eqns. 1, 2 and 3, relates the viscosity to the volume, with V_∞ being the only adjustable parameter. Utilizing a simple molecular parameter, such as diameter, in predicting viscosity is quite appealing. For example, the viscosity of the normal alkane series has been predicted by assigning a volume increment to each CH_2 segment[9]. Also deviations from hard sphere behavior at low temperatures in argon have been quantified by the deviation of viscosity from that predicted by MET.[10]

We now fit MET to the viscosity data for methane[11] at 298K and methanol[4] at 293K. The former is, of course, a super-critical fluid and undergoes compression of several orders of magnitude up to its crystallization point of approximately 1.6 GPa. Methanol is a liquid, and like many, can be super-pressed well above its 3.5 GPa equilibrium crystallization point. We have measured its viscosity up to the point of crystallization, P=8.3 GPa, giving a compression range of 44%. We plot the resulting

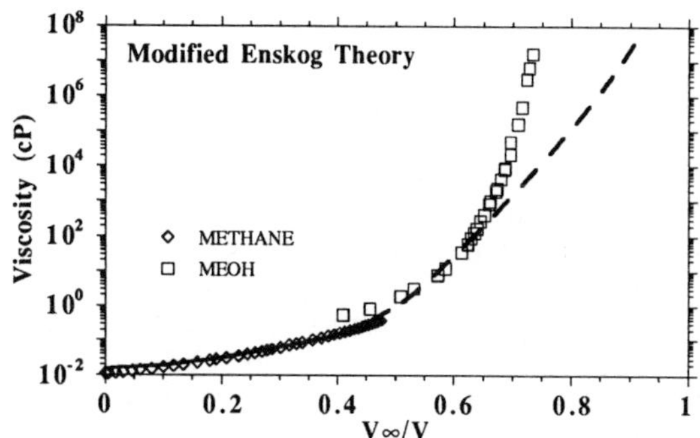

Figure 2. Fits of modified Enskog theory to methane (solid line) and methanol (dashed line) data.

fits along with the data in Fig. 2. In this figure, the observed volume is ratioed to the best-fit values for V_∞, methane = 22.24±0.04 Å^3 and methanol= 27.6±0.1 Å^3. As previously found[9], the methane data are adequately described by MET, but it's clear that the methanol data are not. The theory fails because it does not describe the strong divergence of viscosity as the packing fraction approaches unity. The origin of this is clear; the correction from molecular dynamics is limited to ξ values within the hard-sphere fluid range; this packing fraction range barely overlaps densities for ordinary liquids. Therefore, unless the liquid crystallizes at a low pressure, MET would not be expected to reproduce the high pressure behavior. Its use is limited to those fluids which crystallize near the close-packed ξ, thus limiting their viscosity rise to 1-2 orders of magnitude.

Free Volume Theory

Originally an empirical observation,[2] this theory was later[12] given a microscopic, statistical physics basis. In this form, motion of the molecules is constrained by the number of near-neighbor holes which exceed some critical size. One can derive a distribution of such holes and relate the viscosity to this "free volume". The resulting form of the equation is quite simple

$$\ln\left(\frac{\eta}{\eta_0}\right) = BV_\infty\left[\frac{1}{V-V_\infty} - \frac{1}{V_0-V_\infty}\right] \qquad (4)$$

The subscript 0 refers to some reference state, typically ambient pressure. The two variable parameters are V_∞, an excluded volume term, and B, a term which in the original theory was of order unity and proportional to V_∞. As will be seen, the actual meaning of B is more subtle. We have found this functional form to be quite powerful in fitting high-pressure viscosity data[3, 4]. This is now demonstrated by again considering the methane and methanol data. These were fit with Eqn. 8, and the following values were obtained: methane V_∞= 21.6±0.1 Å^3, B= 4.18±0.05 and methanol V_∞= 33.8±0.1 Å^3, B= 2.22±0.05. The resulting fits are plotted along with the data in Fig. 3.

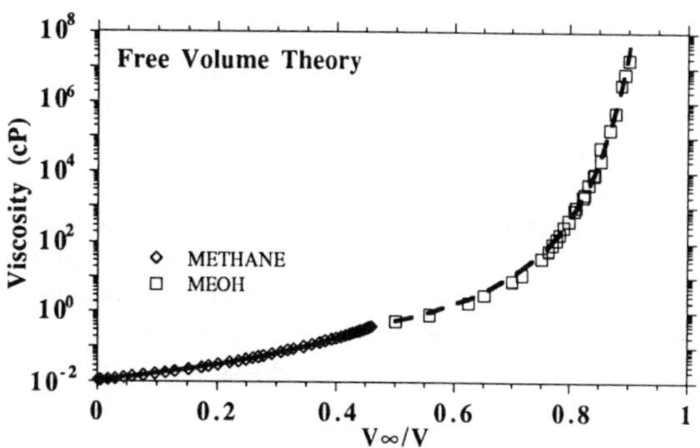

Figure 3. Fits of free-volume theory to methane (solid line) and methanol (dashed line) data.

FVT is able to fit both data sets extraordinarily well. This function has also been used to fit over 25 liquids, and similar good fits are obtained. In addition, we find that extrapolation of the function to $\eta=10^{15}$cP, the approximate η at the glass transition for many liquids, allows one to calculate glass transition pressures which are in good agreement with other determinations. Dymond[13] has suggested that FVT and MET are equivalent, but comparison of Figs. 2 and 3 shows that functionally they are quite different and can only be numerically equal for the small packing fraction region.

The functional form of FVT thus seems to describe the data. We now attempt to attach physical significance to the resulting parameters.

The FVT parameter V_∞ is that volume at which the viscosity diverges. Molecular dynamics simulations[14] suggest that $V_\infty = 1.57 \bullet V_{HS}$, a value slightly expanded from the close packed volume, $1.35 \bullet V_{HS}$. Our best-fit values for V_∞ are typically more nearly equal to the actual hard-sphere volumes. For example, the effective hard sphere volumes from the Carnaghan-Starling equation of state[15] are methane= 24.1 Å^3 and methanol= 29.2 Å^3. This level of agreement, about 15%, is typical for a wide variety of compounds. Thus V_∞ can be roughly correlated with molecular volume, but to make quantitative use of the volume in estimating viscosity better accuracy is desired. We are currently investigating this question.

The parameter B determines the amount of curvature in a plot of viscosity versus density. Small B values cause the curve to assume a strongly hyperbolic shape with a sharp upturn in viscosity as $V \rightarrow V_\infty$. In the original theory, B was independent of molecule type except that it was though to vary slightly with molecular size and shape. We find that B for a variety of chemically dissimilar liquids varies between ≈0.7 and 10. In the MD simulation mentioned above, B= 0.68. Functionally it can be shown that B plays the role for pressure data that fragility[16] plays for temperature data. The subject of fragility has been extensively discussed and cannot be reviewed here. But a significant outcome of identifying B with fragility is that it should then be related to the entropy difference between the liquid and glass. This is not a part of the original free-volume theory, and suggests that one could perhaps improve the underlying physics by altering its assumptions.

SUMMARY

We have developed a diamond cell viscometer which is capable of measuring viscosity data over extreme ranges of pressure and viscosity. Using this device we have explored the scaling relationship between viscosity and density. Owing to the large accessible viscosity range (10^{-1} to 10^{10} cP) and high precision, we are able to test density-modulated viscosity theories. We find that free-volume theory provides an excellent fit to the data, and can be extrapolated to give an accurate estimate of the glass transition pressure. The resulting fit parameters can be identified with molecular properties of the fluid, but an accurate prediction of the coefficients will require further refinement of the model.

REFERENCES

[1] Cummins, H.Z., *et al.*, *Physical Review* E47, pp. 4223-39 (1993).

[2] Doolittle, A.K., *Journal of Applied Physics* 22, pp. 1471-1475 (1951).

[3] Herbst, C.A., R.L. Cook, and H.E. King Jr., *Nature* 361, pp. 518-520 (1993).

[4] Cook, R.L., C.A. Herbst, and H.E. King Jr., *Journal of Physical Chemistry* 97, pp. 2355-61 (1993).

[5] King, H.E., Jr., E. Herbolzheimer, and R.L. Cook, *Journal of Applied Physics* 71, pp. 2071-2081 (1992).

[6]King, H.E., Jr. and C.T. Prewitt, *Review of Scientific Instruments* 51, pp. 1037 (1980).

[7] Dymond, J.H., *Physica* 144B, pp. 267-276 (1987).

[8] Alder, B.J., D.M. Gass, and T.E. Wainwright, *Journal of Chemical Physics* 53, pp. 3813-3826 (1970).

[9] Assael, M.J., *et al.*, *International Journal of Thermophysics* 13, pp. 269-281 (1992).

[10] Van Der Gulik, P.S. and N.J. Trappeniers, *Physica* 135A, pp. 1-20 (1986).

[11] Van Der Gulik, P.S., R. Mostert, and H.R. Van Den Berg, *Physica* A151, pp. 153-166 (1988).

[12] Cohen, M.H. and D. Turnbull, *Journal of Chemical Physics* 31, pp. 1164-1169 (1959).

[13]Dymond, J.H. and T.A. Brawn. . in *Proc. 7th Symp. Thermophys. Prop.* Am. Soc. Mech. Eng., pp. 660-7 (1977).

[14] Woodcock, L.V. and C.A. Angell, *Physical Review Letters* 47, pp. 1129-1132 (1981).

[15] Ben-Amotz, D. and D.R. Herschbach, *Journal of Physical Chemistry* 94, pp. 1038-1047 (1990).

[16] Böhmer, R., *et al.*, *Journal of Chemical Physics* in press, pp. (1993).

EVALUATION OF TEMPERATURE DEPENDENCE ON RUBY FLUORESCENCE AT HIGH PRESSURE BY VISCOSITY MEASUREMENT OF LUBRICANTS

I. Fujishiro, Y. Nakamura and H. Yamanokuchi
Faculty of Engineering,
Mie University,
1515 Kamihama-cho, Tsu, Mie 514, Japan.

Heating a diamond-anvil cell (DAC) filled with a liquid medium induces a pressure increment in a pressure chamber due to the restriction of thermal expansion of the liquid medium. The pressure increment was measured with high sensitivity up to an elevated temperature (200℃) by means of the viscosity measurements for the reference lubricant that have established viscosity-pressure-temperature data. The reference lubricant was Dioctylsebacate, whose viscosity under high pressure and temperature was described in an ASME report. Considering the effect of such a pressure increment in DAC, the temperature coefficient of ruby R_1 was found to be 0.00641 nm/℃ up to 120℃ at 850 MPa. By using this coefficient, the pressure increment for a synthetic lubricant, PAO68, was evaluated, and the viscosity was then obtained at elevated temperature under high pressure.

INTRODUCTION

A diamond-anvil cell (DAC) has been used in various fields of high pressure research. The authors earlier employed DAC for the measurement of lubricant's viscosity [1][2] by means of a falling sphere in a gasket hole suggested by Piermarini et al. [3], and developed this viscometry up to an elevated temperature of 100℃ [4]. In this experiment, the pressure increment in the pressure chamber was observed without compression of a gasket hole by means of ruby fluorescent shift using a temperature coefficient of 0.0068 nm/℃. This might be due to the restriction of thermal expansion of the liquid medium in the pressure chamber because of the larger thermal expansion coefficient of liquid than DAC body (stainless steel). However, the temperature coefficient of the ruby fluorescent shift is not confirmed under both high temperature and high pressure condition. The evaluation of pressure increment in DAC is necessary for accurate viscosity measurement at elevated temperatures.

In the present study, the pressure increment was measured with high sensitivity up to elevated temperature (200℃) by means of the viscosity measurements for the reference lubricant that have established viscosity-pressure-temperature data. The lubricant was Dioctylsebacate (DOS) whose viscosity under high pressure and elevated temperature was described in an ASME report [5]. Furthermore, the obtained pressure increment was compared with that estimated from the pressure-volume-temperature (*PVT*) relation of ASME. Considering the effect of such a pressure increment in DAC, the temperature coefficient of ruby R_1 was found to be 0.00641 nm/℃ up to 120℃ at 850 MPa. By using this coefficient, the pressure increment for a synthetic lubricant, PAO68, was evaluated and the viscosity was then obtained at elevated temperature under high pressure.

TEMPERATURE DEPENDENCE ON RUBY FLUORESCENCE AT ATMOSPHERIC PRESSURE

Wavelength shift ($\Delta\lambda$, nm) of ruby R_1

fluorescence by temperature rise was expressed by Piermarini et al. [6] as follows,

$$\Delta\lambda = 0.0068\Delta T \qquad (1)$$

where ΔT is the temperature increment (°C). Yamaoka et al. [7] made experiments and found the linearity between the ruby shift and the temperature from 80°C to 500°C and gave the following least square fit equation.

$$\Delta\lambda = 0.00680T - 0.242 \qquad (2)$$

where T is the temperature (°C). In their experimental results, Eq. (2) could not be applied for the ruby R_1 shift from room temperature (20°C) to about 100°C, and we tried to express their result for around those temperatures as follows

$$\Delta\lambda = 0.00572T - 0.127 \qquad (3)$$

RESULTS AND DISCUSSION

Evaluation of Pressure Increment by Viscosity Measurement in DAC

To evaluate the pressure increment in the DAC pressure chamber due to the restriction of thermal expansion of the liquid medium, the viscosity of the liquid lubricant having the established viscosity–pressure–temperature data was measured. The reference liquid was DOS whose viscosity up to about 220℃ and up to about 1 GPa was described in the ASME report. The viscosity was measured by heating DAC a few times with a flexible heater in order to confirm reproducibility of the measurement at several pressures, (e.g., 310 MPa, 590MPa, 640MPa, 800 MPa). Figure 1 shows some results of those experiments. At 310 MPa, the reproducibility between the two heatings can be observed. At 800 MPa, after first heating a viscosity decrease (pressure drops to 730 MPa) is observed at 20℃. This may be caused by pressure leakage between the gasket and diamond anvils due to the heating. However, there was no viscosity decrease after the second heating, i.e., gasket sealing against the pressure leakage seems to be completed after the first heating in some experiments. The isobaric viscosity from ASME is also indicated in the figure. The obtained viscosity is larger than the isobaric one with increasing tempera–ture, which implies a pressure increment in the pressure chamber by heating DAC without loading (compressing the gasket hole). Such a pressure increment was evaluated by calibrating the obtained viscosity to the above ASME data. The result of the experiment at 730 MPa is depicted in Fig. 2. Using the *PVT* data of ASME for the sample liquid (DOS) and thermal expansion of DAC body (stainless steel), the pressure increment was also evaluated and depicted in the figure. This evaluation is based

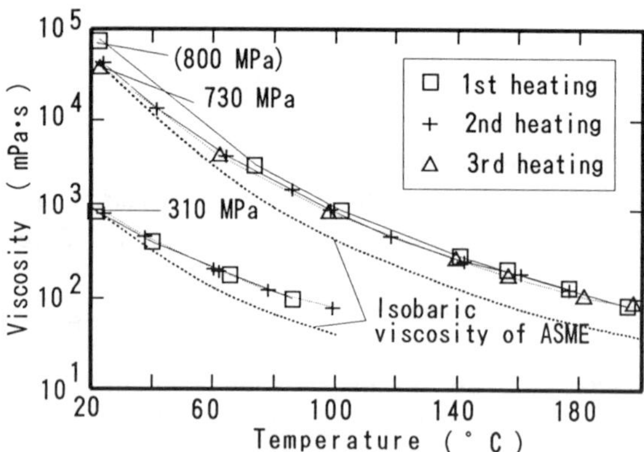

Figure 1. Viscosity change with temperature under high pressure.

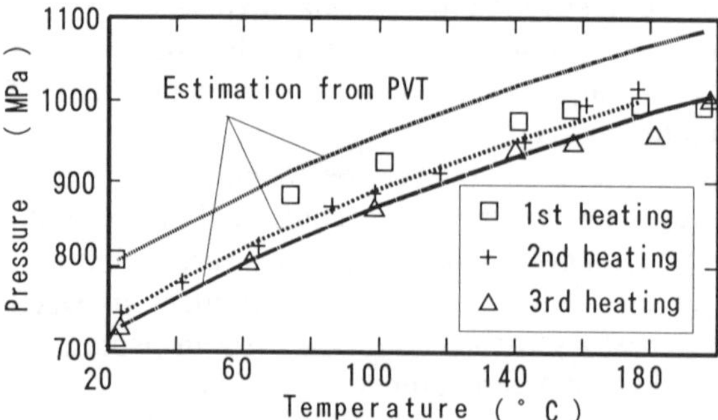

Figure 2. Pressure increment obtained by viscosity measurement of DOS.

on the assumption that thermal expansion of DOS due to elevated temperature is restricted to that of the DAC body. The *PVT*-based evaluation almost agrees with that from the viscosity measurement for the second and third heating in Fig. 2. Figure 3 shows a pressure increment diagram for various pressure obtained from the *PVT* data for DOS, assuming no leakage of pressure medium from the gasket of DAC.

Temperature Dependence on Ruby Fluorescence at High Pressure

The ruby R_1 fluorescent shift $\Delta\lambda$ $(\Delta P, T)$ (nm) was measured at elevated temperature up to 120℃ under pressure of about 700 MPa for DOS in DAC, where ΔP (MPa) is the pressure increment described above. Then the shift $\Delta\lambda$ (T) only due to the temperature elevation was obtained by subtracting the shift $\Delta\lambda$ (ΔP) $(= \Delta P \times 0.365 \times 10^{-3})$ due to the pressure increment from $\Delta\lambda$ $(\Delta P, T)$, which follows

$$\Delta\lambda(T) = \Delta\lambda(\Delta P, T) - \Delta P \times 0.365 \times 10^{-3} \quad (4)$$

Figure 4 shows the result. The linearity between $\Delta\lambda$ and T and the reproducibility between two experiments can be observed. Those data was expressed as the following linear equation.

$$\Delta\lambda\ (T) = 0.00641T - 0.119 \quad (5)$$

From comparing the obtained temperature coefficient, 0.00641 nm/℃, with that of the atmospheric pressure described in the previous part, the obtained value is somewhat smaller than the 0.00680 by Piermarini et al. and Yamaoka et al. from 80℃ to 500℃, and it is larger than 0.00572 by the regression line of the authors (Eq. (3)) up to 100℃. It is noticed that the present evaluation is based on the assumption that the pressure factor 0.365×10^{-3} of ruby fluorescent shift is constant under both elevated temperature and high pressure condition. However, even if this pressure factor may be varied, no trouble may result provided that this coefficient is employed only for the evaluation of the pressure increment for other lubricant in DAC.

Viscosity Measurement of Lubricant Using Eq. (5)

Using Eq. (5), the viscosity was measured for the lubricant, PAO68 (Polyalphaolefine), as

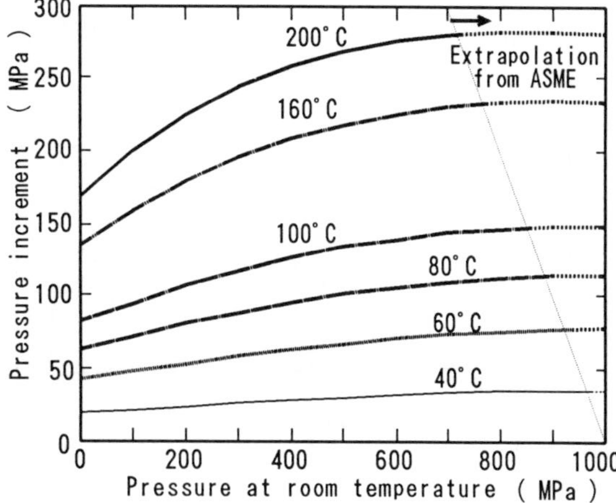

Figure 3. Pressure increment due to heating DAC estimated from PVT relation.

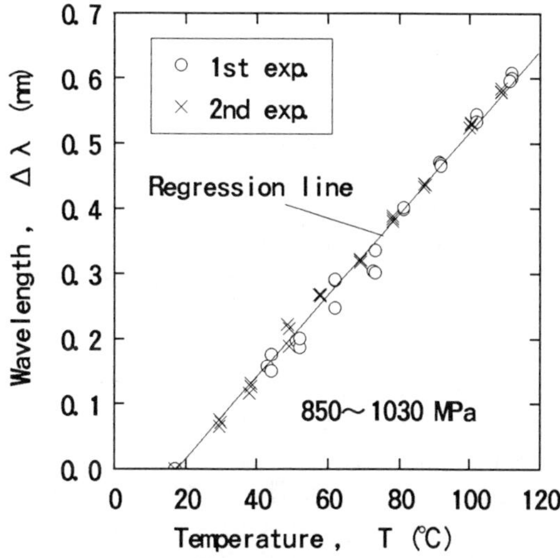

Figure 4. Ruby fluorescent shift at elevated temperatue under high pressure.

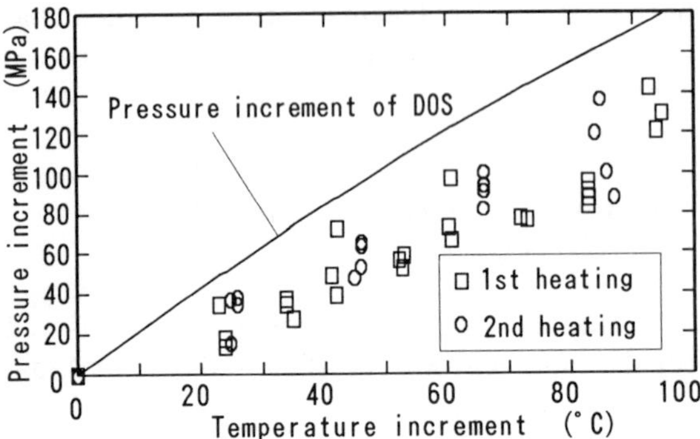

Figure 5. Pressure increment of PAO68 by ruby fluorescence.

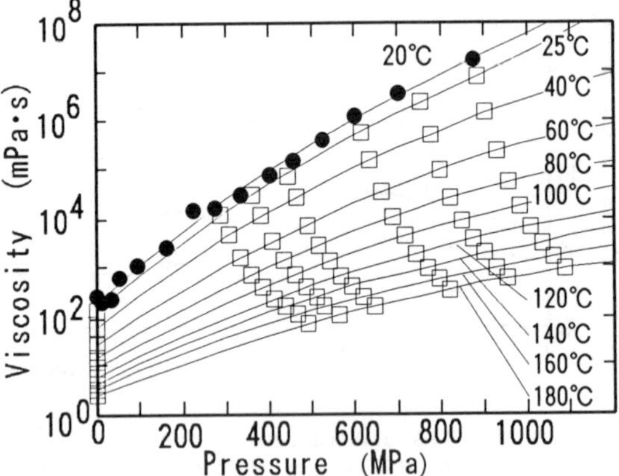

Figure 6. Viscosity-pressure-temperature relation of PAO68.

a synthetic paraffinic oil at an elevated temperature under high pressure. The evaluation of the pressure increment in DAC for PAO68 is shown in Fig. 5 together with that of DOS. The amount of pressure increment for PAO68 is about two-thirds smaller than that for DOS. Over 100℃, the pressure increment was extrapolated by the least square fit curve of those results up to 100℃. The obtained viscosity is depicted in Fig. 6 considering the pressure increment in the pressure chamber of DAC in this manner. The logarithm of viscosity is convex toward the viscosity axis for every temperature. The slope becomes small with increasing temperature.

ACKNOWLEDGMENTS

This study was supported by Grants-in-Aid for Science Research (03555031 and 03402027) from the Ministry of Education, Science and Culture of Japan. The technical assistance of Mr. K. Murai (Mie University) is acknowledged.

REFERENCES

[1] I. Fujishiro, Y. Nakamura and S. Matsuhiro, "Viscosity Measurement of Lubricants Under High Pressure," Bull. JSME, 29-250 pp.1280-1287 (1986).

[2] I. Fujishiro, Y. Nakamura and S. Inoue, "Viscosity Measurements of Blended Lubricant Oils at High Pressure by Diamond-Anvil Cell," Proc. of Japan Int. Tribology Conference Nagoya, I, pp.385-390 (1990).

[3] G. J. Piermarini, R. A. Forman and S. Block, "Viscosity Measurement in the Diamond Anvil Pressure Cell," Rev. Sci. Instrum., 49-8, pp.1061-1066 (1978).

[4] I. Fujishiro, Y. Nakamura, C. Guihe and Y. Fujii, "Pressure and Temperature Effects on Viscosity of Synthetic Lubricants," JSME Int. J. Ser.Ⅲ, 33-2, pp.213-218 (1990).

[5] ASME, *Pressure-Viscosity Report*, Vol. Ⅱ, New York, ASME Research Pub., Appendix VII, pp.198-200 (1953).

[6] J. D. Barnett, S. Block, S. and G. J. Piermarini, "An Optical Fluorescence System for Quantitative Pressure Measurement in the Diamond-Anvil Cell," Rev. Sci. Instrum., 44-1, pp.1-9 (1973).

[7] S. Yamaoka, O. Shimomura and O. Fukunaga, "Simultaneous Measurement of Temperature and Pressure by the Ruby Fluorescence Line," Proc. Japan Acad., 56-3, Ser.B, pp.103-107 (1980).

COMPUTER SIMULATION OF MOLECULAR RESPONSE AT A SHOCK FRONT

J. Belak
Lawrence Livermore National Laboratory
Livermore, California 94551

Molecular dynamics simulations of the response of small molecules at a shock front are presented. The simulations are performed in the reference frame of the shock and the results provide a unique insight into the sequence of states through which the material transforms during shock loading. The calculated up-pumping time (time for the translational and vibrational kinetic energy to equilibrate) for small molecules is quite fast, a few picoseconds for butane and about 10 ps for nitromethane. This is somewhat faster than the 100 ps suggested by recent experiment.

INTRODUCTION

The purpose of this paper is to address one of the outstanding questions in shock physics; that is, what is the sequence of states through which the material transforms in going from the initial state in front of the shock to the final high-temperature and high-pressure state behind the shock? For example, during shock loading of high explosive molecules, such as HMX, the shock wave dumps a huge initiation energy into the translational motion of the molecules. This energy is slowly transferred into internal vibrational motion of the molecules, weakening the chemical bonds. This process, known as multiphonon up-pumping, continues to be a hot research topic.[1]

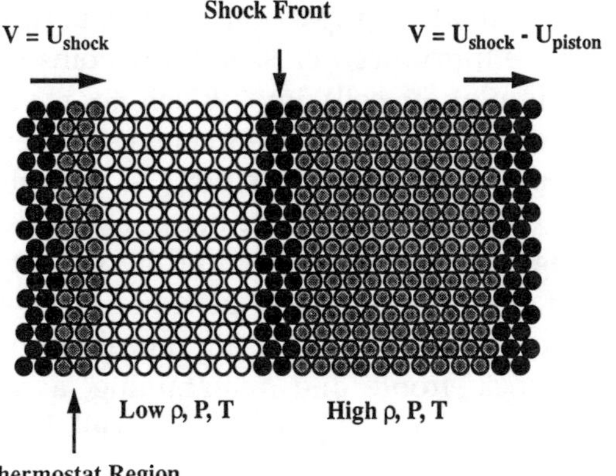

Fig 1. A schematic illustration of the constant velocity boundary condition used to simulate shock propagation within the reference frame of the shock.

In this work we present molecular dynamics simulations of the response of small molecules at a shock front. The simulations are performed in the reference frame of the shock and the results suggest that the up-pumping time (time for the translational and vibrational kinetic energy to equilibrate) for small molecules is quite fast, a few picoseconds for butane and about 10 ps for nitromethane. This is somewhat faster than the 100 ps suggested by recent experiment.[1]

MODEL

The molecular dynamics (MD) computer simulation method[2] is an ideal approach to study this and related problems such as the reactive dynamics of chemically-sustained shocks.[3] The MD method has been applied to the study of shock problems with significant success.[4-10] In these previous studies the shock was generated by either driving a fixed wall into the material (material reference frame) or driving the material into a stationary wall (piston reference frame). In this work we take an alternate approach and perform the simulation within the reference frame of the shock. This coordinate frame is especially useful. For in this frame only, the flux of mass, momentum and energy have constant values everywhere when the profile is steady.[11]

We perform the simulation as follows:[12] all atoms within a boundary region (see Figure 1) are constrained to propagate at a constant velocity. Atoms are continually inserted from the left, while atoms that leave the box are discarded—the system is open. The system is initially equilibrated at the desired temperature and density using the standard periodic boundary conditions. The final configuration from this periodic simulation is used to generate the configuration of incoming material. In addition to sampling the incoming velocities from a Maxwell-Boltzmann distribution, we pass this incoming material through a small thermostat region to assure that the initial temperature is as desired. The remaining interior atoms are purely Newtonian and we retain the periodic boundary condition within the plane of the shock. The shock wave simulation is performed by imposing a constant velocity (U_{shock}) to the incoming material and a slower constant velocity (U_{shock}-U_{piston}) to the departing material. As we increase the piston velocity, material piles up at the departing boundary until, above a critical velocity, a sharp density discontinuity propagates into the simulation cell (to the left in Figure 1). We associate this density discontinuity with a shock front. By decreasing the piston velocity, we make the shock front stationary with respect to the simulation cell and, in doing so, we are able to study shock propagation for arbitrarily long periods of time.

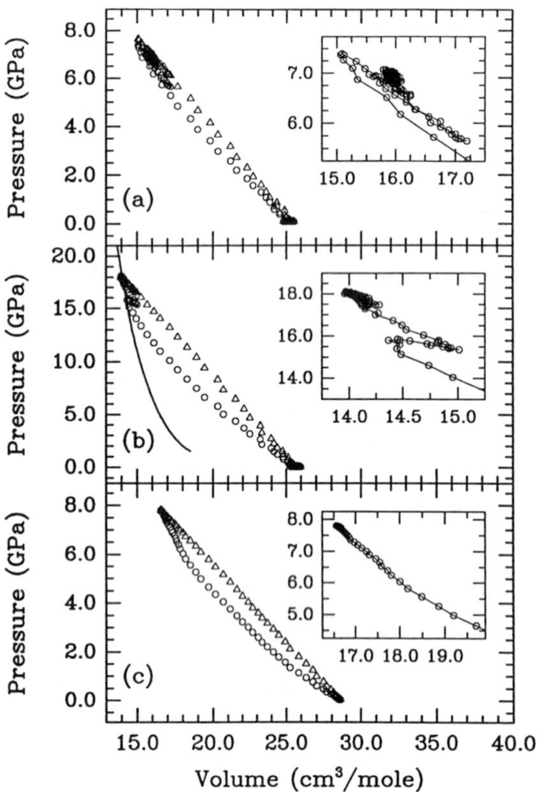

Fig 2. The sequence of states in P-V space that simulated argon follows as it goes through a shock front. In each case, the inset shows the approach to the final state.

RESULTS AND DISCUSSION

To facilitate comparison with experiment, we have introduced cross-sectional bins (1000 per simulation cell) into which to measure physical observables. The averages presented here are relative (in position) to the shock front. One observable of primary interest is the average flow velocity. We find the velocity to maintain a well-defined plateau (U_{shock}) in front of the shock, decreasing rapidly through the shock front, and maintaining a well-defined plateau (U_{shock}-U_{piston}) well behind the shock.

In Figure 2, we show the path in P-V space for three simulations of solid and liquid argon using the potential model due to Ross *et al*,[13] which gives excellent agreement with the experimental Hugoniot up to shock velocities of 9 km/s. The open triangles represent the longitudinal component of the pressure tensor (P_{xx}) which varies linearly with volume through the shock front. This is a direct consequence of conservation of momentum. The straight line is known as the Raleigh line and the area beneath this line is equal to the change in internal energy between the initial and final states.[11] The pressure, however, includes both the longitudinal and transverse components of the pressure tensor ($P = (P_{xx}+P_{yy}+P_{zz})/3$) and the sequence of pressure states (open circles) does not vary linearly with volume.

The sequence of pressure states for a 7 GPa shock in solid argon is shown in Figure 2a. At the shock front, the pressure over-shoots the final state, then oscillates with diminishing amplitude, finally rising slightly at nearly constant volume as the system melts. In Figure 2b, we show the sequence of states for a stronger shock (18 GPa) in the solid. The pressure, while increasing in the solid, does not overshoot the final state and the melting does not occur at constant volume. We also show in this figure, for comparison, our calculated Hugoniot curve (locus of final PV states) for shocks along the [100] axis in solid argon. Finally, we show in Figure 2c, the sequence of states for a

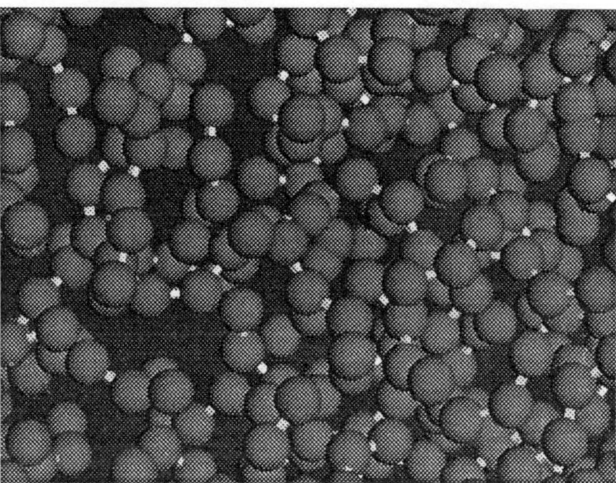

Fig 3. A 10 GPa shock wave in liquid butane.

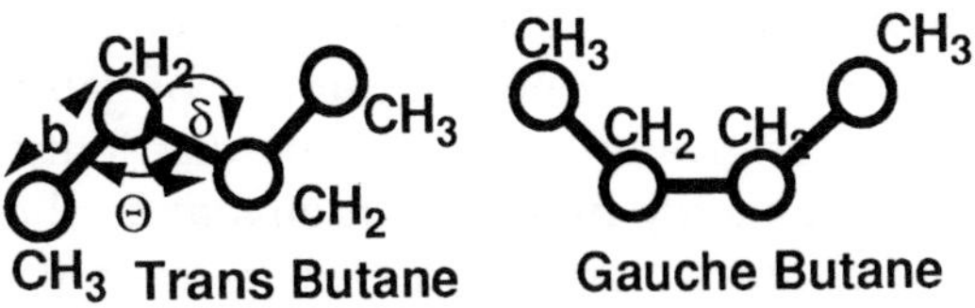

Fig 4. The trans and gauche configurations of butane.

liquid-state shock of similar strength to the solid-state shock shown in Figure 2a. The pressure rises smoothly with decreasing volume, though we note a slight kink in the curve near the final state, possibly due to the fluid responding in a solid-like manner during the short time scale involved in loading and later relaxing out of the non-equilibrium state.

In Figure 3, we show a 0.6 nm thick cross-sectional snapshot of a 10 GPa shock wave in liquid butane. Butane is the simplest molecule exhibiting all of the degrees of freedom (bond length, angles and torsions) required to simulate larger high-explosive molecules. The thermodynamics and potential models are well-known.[14] Here, we use a united-atom approximation. In the room temperature liquid in front of the shock, butane forms a trans config-

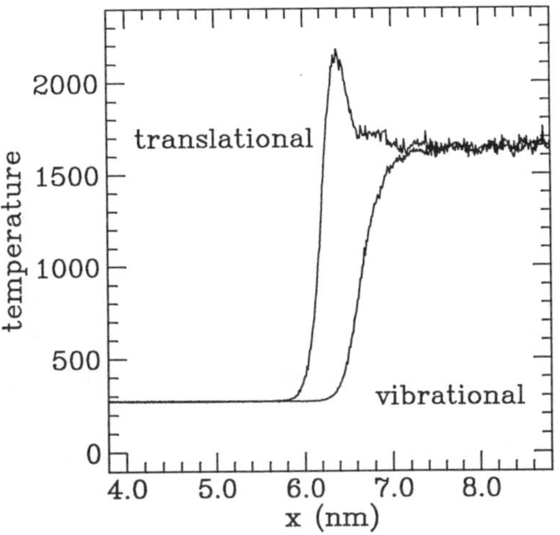

Fig 5. The translational and vibrational kinetic energy of liquid butane as a function of position through a 10 GPa shock.

uration as shown in Figure 4, while behind the shock we find a significant number of gauche defects. Of greater interest is the distribution of kinetic energy into translational and vibrational degrees of freedom. This is shown in Figure 5. For each bin we calculate the expectation value of the center of mass (CM) kinetic energy, rotational kinetic energy about the CM, and the total kinetic energy. In Figure 5 the curve marked *translational* is the sum of the CM and rotational kinetic energy and the curve marked *vibrational* is the difference between the *translational* energy and the total kinetic energy. The *translational* energy leads the *vibrational* energy by a few nanometers (a few picoseconds). Preliminary simulations using available intermolecular[15] and intramolecular[16] potential models for nitromethane suggest a lead time of nearly 10 ps.

In summary we note that our simulations give unique insight into the sequence of states through which the material transforms during shock loading. The calculated up-pumping time for small molecules is quite fast, a few picoseconds for butane and nearly 10 ps for nitromethane. This is somewhat faster than suggested by recent experiment. In future work we plan to project the molecular motion onto the normal coordinates for vibrational motion. This should lead to further insight into the doorways for energy transport into the molecule.

ACKNOWLEDGEMENTS

The author is indebted to Dave Boercker, Marvin Ross and Clark Souers for many useful suggestions and enlightening discussions. This work was performed at Lawrence Livermore National Laboratory under the auspices of the U.S. DOE through Contract No. W-7405-ENG-48.

REFERENCES

[1] A. Tokmakoff, M.D. Fayer, and D.D. Dlott, J. Phys. Chem. **97**, 1901 (1993); and references therein.

[2] M.P. Allen and D.J. Tildesley, *Computer Simulation of Liquids*, (Clarendon Press, Oxford, 1987).

[3] D.H. Robertson, D.W. Brenner, and C.T. White, Phys. Rev. Lett. **67**, 3132 (1991).

[4] D.H. Tsai and C.W. Beckett, J. Geophys. Res. **71**, 2601 (1966).

[5] D.H. Tsai and R.A. MacDonald, F. Phys. C **11**, L365 (1978).

[6] A. Paskin and G.J. Dienes, J. Appl. Phys. **43**, 1605 (1972).

[7] A. Paskin, A. Gohar, and G.J. Dienes, J. Phys. C **11**, L857 (1978).

[8] B.L. Holian and G.K. Straub, Phys. Rev. Lett. **43**, 1598 (1979).

[9] B.L. Holian, W.G. Hoover, B. Moran, and G.K. Straub, Phys. Rev. A **22**, 2798 (1980).

[10] B.L. Holian, Phys. Rev. A **37**, 2562 (1988).

[11] Ya. B. Zel'dovich and Yu. P. Razier, *Physics of Shock Waves and High-Temperature Hydrodynamic Phenomena* (Academic Press, New York, 1966).

[12] J. Belak, *Conservation of Momentum through a Shock Front*, Lawrence Livermore National Laboratory Report UCRL-JC-109989, (1992).

[13] M. Ross, H.K. Mao, P.M. Bell, and J.A. Xu, J. Chem. Phys. **85**, 1028 (1986).

[14] J.-P. Ryckaert and A. Bellemans, Chem. Phys. Lett. **30**, 123 (1975).

[15] J. Caillet and P. Claverie, Acta Cryst. **A31**, 448 (1975).

[16] B.M. Rice and D.L. Thompson, J. Chem. Phys. **93**, 7986 (1990).

MOLECULAR DYNAMICS INVESTIGATION OF SHOCK WAVE IN ONE–DIMENSION

Jihai Wang,Wenshan Duan,Yuansheng Pan
Beijing Institute of Applied Physics and Computational Mathematics
No 6 Huayuan Road, P.O.Box 8009
Beijing,P.R.China, 100088

The propagation and the refraction of shock wave in one–dimensional lattice are investigated by molecular dynamics(MD). Far from the piston, the distribution of velocity near every pick agrees with related solitary wave solutions, which are obtained exactly for Toda lattice and approximatly for other potentials. Dependence of wave velocity on particle velocity also agrees with corresponding relations for solitons. By using averaging parameters to describe interaction between molecules of different matters, the refraction of shock wave is calculated that shows not only qualitative but also quantitative agreement of MD calculation with results of macroscopic continuum mechanics.

INTRODUCTION

In dependence on the development of computer technique,the MD gets a wide application in many fields of science[1]. The first work was accomplished just after the appearance of computer[2]. However, in present condition, we are limited by solving many–body problems of classical mechanics. It is necessary to research the foundation of numerical simulation. We are interested mainly in the dynamic problems[3,4]. Therfore, the propagation and the refraction of shock wave in one–dimensional lattice are treated as simple examples. The exact soliton solutions for Toda one–dimensional chains were obtained[5]. Several authors show that the leading edge of shock front in one–dimensional MD calculation can be represented by solitons[6,7]. In the first part of our work, we compare the soliton solution with results of shock wave given by MD numerical simulation. There is a good quantitative agreement between them. By using averaging parameters, we consider the shock wave refraction in one–dimensional lattice, which consists of molcules of different matters. This treatment gives not only right property of reflected wave, but also quantitative agreement of MD calculation for pressure and velocity at interface with results of macroscopic continuum mechanics.

SOLITON SOLUTIONS

The equation of motion of every inner molecule can be written by

$$m\frac{d^2 r_n}{dt^2} = F(r_n - r_{n-1}) - F(r_{n+1} - r_n) \tag{1}$$

where

$$F = -\frac{\partial\Phi}{\partial r}$$

and Φ is the interaction potential.

By using the Toda potential[5], the equation (1) can be rewritten to the dimensionless form

$$Q'' = e^{Q_{n-1} - Q_n} - e^{Q_n - Q_{n+1}} \tag{2}$$

Toda had got a solution for displacement[5]. Here we give the solution by other way. Taking

$$Q_n = S_{n-1} - S_n$$

$$S_n = \ln f_n$$

we get

$$f_{n+1} f_{n-1} - f_n^2 = f_n'' f_n - f_n'^2$$

By noting

$$\omega^2 = 4\sinh^2\frac{\alpha}{2} \tag{3}$$

the solitary wave solution can be obtained

$$Q_n = \ln[\frac{1 + e^{an - \omega t + \delta - \alpha}}{1 + e^{an - \omega t + \delta}}] \tag{4}$$

and the dimensionless velocity is

$$Q_n' = \frac{\omega}{2}\sinh\frac{\alpha}{2}\,\mathrm{sech}\frac{1}{2}(an - \omega t + \delta - \alpha)\mathrm{sech}\frac{1}{2}(an - \omega t + \delta) \tag{5}$$

It's shown that

$$\lim_{n\to\infty} Q_n = -\alpha$$

Thus the parameter α is the displacement at infinite. From formula (5) we obtain

$$Q'_{max} = \sinh^2\frac{\alpha}{2}\,\mathrm{sech}^2\frac{\alpha}{2} \tag{6}$$

$$D = \sinh\frac{\alpha}{2} / \frac{\alpha}{2}$$

where the D is wave velocity.

For other potentials, it is differcult to obtain exact soliton solution. However, for weak wave, we can use the continuum approximation[7,8]. For small displacement the equation (1) can be transformed to the Bousnesq equation

$$\frac{\partial^2 w}{\partial t^2} = \gamma\frac{\partial^2 w}{\partial n^2} + \frac{\gamma}{12}\frac{\partial^4 w}{\partial n^4} + \beta\frac{\partial^2 (w^2)}{\partial n^2} \tag{7}$$

where

$$w = \frac{\partial r_n}{\partial n}$$

$$\gamma = -\frac{\partial F}{\partial r} / m$$

$$\beta = -\frac{\partial^2 F}{\partial r^2} / 2m$$

The solution of equation (7) can be given[8] by

$$w = \frac{a^2\gamma}{8\beta}\,\mathrm{sech}^2\frac{1}{2}(an - \omega t + \delta)$$

where

$$\omega^2 = \gamma(a^2 + \frac{a^4}{12}) \tag{8}$$

Using

$$Q' = -\frac{\omega}{a} w$$

we can obtain

$$Q' = -\frac{\gamma a \omega}{8\beta}\,\mathrm{sech}^2\frac{1}{2}(an - \omega t + \delta) \tag{9}$$

From these formulas we can get relation between wave velocity D and amplitude of soliton Q'_{max} in following dimensional form

$$D = c_0(1 - \frac{2}{3}\frac{\beta x_0}{\gamma}\frac{Q'_{max}}{D})^{\frac{1}{2}} \tag{10}$$

where the x_0 is the equilibrium distance and c_0 is sound speed

In order to include the higher derivative of potential, we take the next term of expansion[7] and get

$$\frac{\partial^2 r_n}{\partial t^2} = -\frac{F'(0)}{m}[\frac{\partial^2 r_n}{\partial n^2} + \frac{1}{12}\frac{\partial^4 r_n}{\partial n^4}]$$

$$-\frac{F''(0)}{2m}\frac{\partial^2}{\partial n^2}[(\frac{\partial r_n}{\partial n})^2] - \frac{1}{6}\frac{F'''(0)}{m}\frac{\partial}{\partial n}[(\frac{\partial r_n}{\partial n})^3]$$

Taking the traveling wave solution

$$r = r(\zeta)$$

$$\zeta = t - \frac{n}{D}$$

$$\frac{\partial r}{\partial n} = -\frac{1}{D} r'$$

and

$$r' = P$$

we have

$$P' = -\frac{F'(0)}{m}\frac{P'}{D^2} - \frac{F'(0)}{12m}\frac{1}{D^4}P''' + \frac{F''(0)}{m}\frac{PP'}{D^3}$$

$$-\frac{1}{2}\frac{F'''(0)}{m}\frac{P^2P'}{D^4}$$

Following reference [7] for Toda lattice , we integrate this P equation and get a equation of motion of pseudoparticle in the variable ζ,

$$P''(\zeta) = -\frac{\partial\Psi(P)}{\partial P}$$

where the pseudopotential takes the form

$$\Psi(P) = 6D^2[1 + \frac{D^2 m}{F'(0)}]P + 6D\frac{F''(0)}{F'(0)}P^2$$

$$-2D\frac{F''(0)}{F'(0)}P^3 + \frac{1}{2}\frac{F'''(0)}{F'(0)}P^4$$

The pseudoparticle gets a maximum Q'_{max} where $\Psi(P)=0$. Thus we get a formula for wave velocity:

$$D = c_0[1 - \frac{1}{3}\frac{F''(0)}{F'(0)}\frac{Q'_{max}}{D} + \frac{1}{12}\frac{F'''(0)}{F'(0)}\frac{Q'^2_{max}}{D^2}]^{\frac{1}{2}} \tag{11}$$

COMPARISON OF SOLITON WITH SHOCK FRONT

As shown by many authors[6,7], in the certain condition, the oscillations in leading edge of shock front are not decay and

$$u_p = \frac{1}{2} u_{max} \tag{12}$$

where u_P is piston velocity, which induces the propagation of shock wave. Using this relation we can compare the above solitary wave solutions with our MD calculation in one–dimension. In the figures 1–3, the comparison of numerical results of velocity profile of shock wave with solitons are ploted. It is shown that the distribution of velocity near every pick agrees with related solitons very well, which are calculated by formula (5) for Toda potential or by (9) for Morse and L–J potentials. Moreover, the relation between wave velocity and soliton amplitude also agrees with the numerical relation between shock wave velocity and piston velocity in the condition (12), as shown in figures 4, 5, 6 for Toda, Morse and L–J potentials respectively. Because the soliton relation (11) contains the information of potential constants, this agreement provides a possibility to determine the interaction constants from shock wave experiments for metals. As well known, the shock velocity for metals can be expressed by

$$D = c_0 + \lambda u_P + \kappa u_P^2$$

where the λ and κ can be determined by experiment, and for most metals the κ equals zero. Comparing this formula with (11), we obtain the following dimensional formulas:

$$F'(0) = -c_0^2 m / x_0$$

$$F''(0) = 3\lambda c_0^2 m / x_0^3$$

$$F'''(0) = -3c_0^2 m[3\lambda^2 + 2\kappa c_0] / x_0 \qquad (13)$$

which provides a possibility to determine the potential constants from shock experiment.

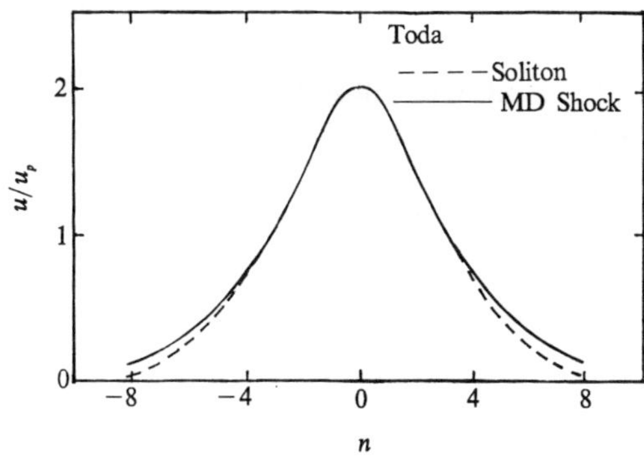

Figure 1. Velocity distribution for Toda lattice.

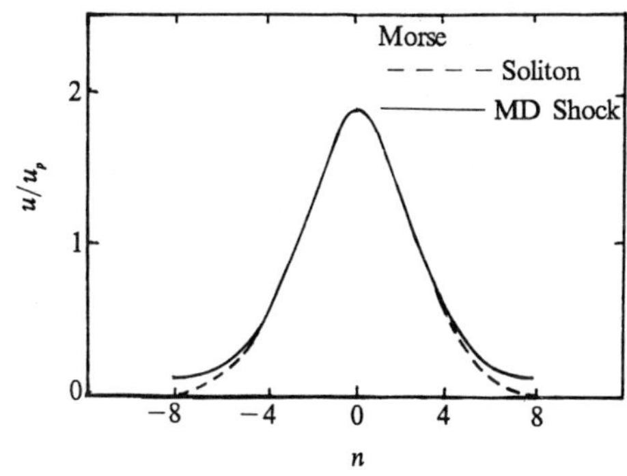

Figure 2. Velocity distribution for Morse lattice.

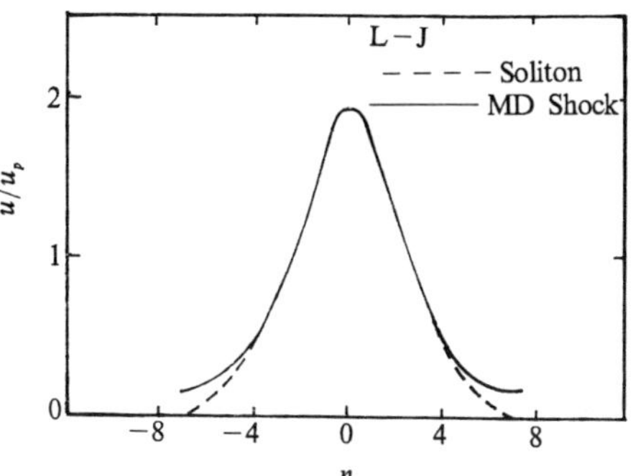

Figure 3. Velocity distribution for L–J lattice.

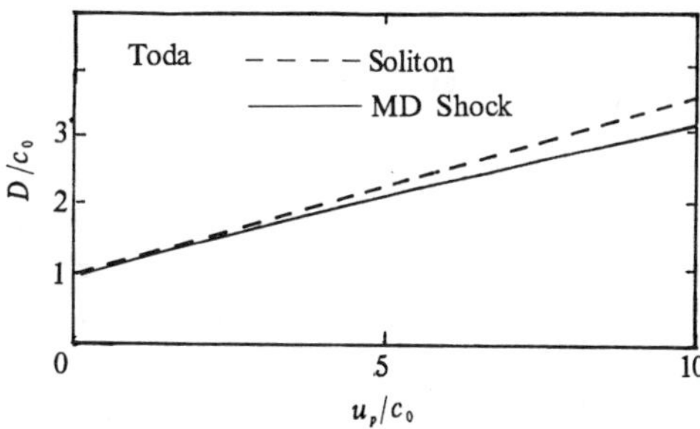

Figure 4. Dependence of wave velocity D on the piston velocity u_P for Toda lattice.

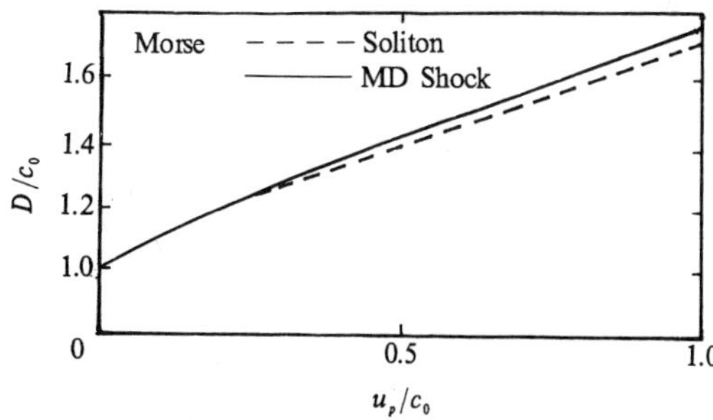

Figure 5. Dependence of wave velocity D on the piston velocity u_P for Morse lattice.

SHOCK REFRACTION

In order to extend the MD calculation to the heterogeneous media, we use the average constants which describe the intermolecular interaction of different matters. The primary constants of Morse potential are taken from reference [9]. The shock wave is formed in

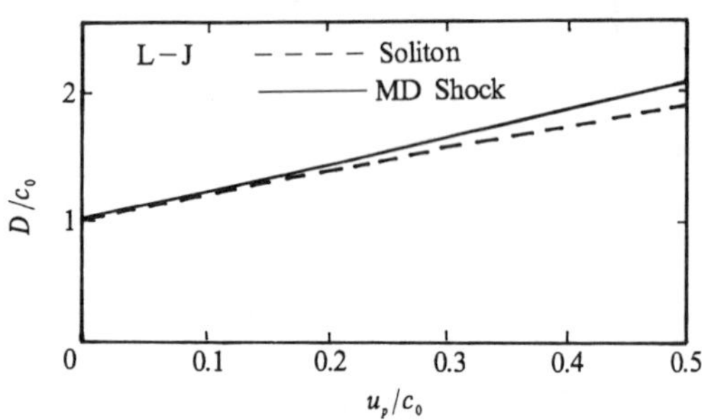

Figure 6. Dependence of wave velocity D on the piston velocity u_P for L–J lattice.

first matter by using the motion of first molecule with constant velocity. When this shock disturbance arrives at the interface of the different molecules, there is a shock refraction. The average velocity may be increased or decreased in dependence on the property of reflected wave at interface. The averaged velocity and pressure go to constant values respectively and the relaxation time is varing from $10^{-10}$to 10^{-12}sec. The equilibrium values calculated by MD method are compared with results of macroscopic continuum mechanics. The related values of velocity and pressure are given in Table 1. It is shown that there is a good agreement between MD calculations and results of macroscopic continuum mechanics.

REFERENCES

[1] W. G. Hoover, *Ann. Rev. Phys. Chem.* 13, pp 103–127 (1983)

[2] E. Fermi, J. R. Pasta and S. M. Ulam. *Studies of Nonlinear Problems,* Los Alamos Report LA 1940 (1955)

[3] Jihai Wang and Jinglin Zhang, in*Shock Compressionof Condensed Matter 1991* S. C. Schmidt, R. D. Dick, J. W. Forbes,D. G. Tasker (editors). ElsevierScience Publisshers B. V,1992, pp151–154

[4] Jihai Wang and Jinglin Zhang, in*Proceedings of the International Symposium on Intense Dynamic Loading and Its Effects,* Chengdu, China, June 9–12, 1992 pp 248–251.

[5] M. Toda,*Phys. Rep. C* 18, 1–123(1975).

[6] T. G. Hill and L. Knopoff, *J. Geophys. Res.* 85, pp 7025–7030(1980)

[7] B. L. Holian, H. Flaschka and D. W. Mclaughlin,*Phys. Rev.A* A24, pp 2595–2623 (1981)

[8] R. K. Dodd, J. C. Eilbeck, J. D. Gibbon and H. C. Morris, *Solitons and Nonlinear Wave Equations,* London NewYork, Academic Press,1982, pp6–9

[9] L. A. Girfalco and V. G. Weizer, *Phys. Rev.* 114, pp 687–690 (1959)

Table 1. Velocity and pressure of shock refraction.

Material 1	Material 2	Piston velocity (10^4cm / sec)	Velocity(10^4cm / sec)		Pressure(10^{-1}GPa)	
			MD calcul.	Macroscopic	MD calcul.	Macroscopic
Al	Cu	2.5	1.65	1.49	5.80	5.53
		5.0	3.30	3.03	11.5	11.9
		7.5	4.80	4.60	16.7	19.0
Cu	Al	2.5	3.30	3.49	5.40	5.46
		5.0	6.80	7.01	11.8	11.8
		7.5	9.80	10.3	17.1	18.6
Al	Pb	5.0	2.80	3.60	10.4	10.6
Pb	Al	5.0	7.10	6.46	11.2	10.8

A 1D MODEL FOR GLASS DYNAMIC BEHAVIOUR UNDER EXPLOSIVE LOADING

T. DE RESSEGUIER, F. COTTET and A. MIGAULT,
L.E.D., E.N.S.M.A., 20, rue Guillaume VII, 86034 POITIERS Cédex FRANCE

The object of this paper is the investigation of the dynamic behaviour of soda-lime glass. An experimental study of its response to a plane detonation wave has been carried out. The observed double wave structure has been related to the process of permanent densification induced in glass under strong compression. A 1D numerical modelling of this phenomenon has been worked out, on the basis of our experimental results completed by data reported in the literature. Satisfying agreement between measured velocity records and calculations gives us confidence that the model is able to predict the response of soda-lime glass to a variety of dynamic solicitations.

I. INTRODUCTION

Glass materials' constitutive properties under shock loading have been a topic of interest for many years. A large amount of experimental work has revealed a complex behaviour, that has been discussed in terms of shear strength, crushing under compression, failure waves, phase transformations [1], and permanent densification [2]. Some authors involve several of these phenomena in their analysis, and many uncertainties remain. In this paper, we present an experimental study of the response of soda-lime glass to explosive loading, then we propose a model able to account for this response.

II. EXPERIMENTAL SET-UP

We have used the wellknown technique of electromagnetic velocity gauges. The propagation of a plane stress wave in a target gives rise to a 1D motion of its material points along the direction of propagation. A conducting gauge embedded in the sample moves with the surrounding material. When this motion takes place in a uniform magnetic field, it generates an electromotive force. If the gauge, the magnetic field lines and the direction of propagation are mutually perpendicular, the particle velocity u is proportional to the gauge output voltage V.

The specimens consist of plates of soda-lime, window glass. The main compounds of this glass are SiO_2 (71.2%), Na_2O (13.7%), and CaO (9.5%). Its initial density is ρ_o = 2512 kg.m^{-3}, and the longitudinal sound speed has been measured as 5760 m.s^{-1} by an ultrasonic method.

A 1D compression wave is produced with a cylindrical charge of explosive (nitromethane) separated from the glass specimen by a polymethyl methacrylate (PMMA) shield. Peak loading stress in the glass is controlled by the thickness of the PMMA shield. The stress range is 3 to 15 GPa. Stress unloading is provided by a Taylor wave, so that the input pulse provided to the glass target produces a slowly decaying, approximately triangular particle velocity profile in the glass.

The gauges are U-shaped strips made from 25 μm thick copper foils. The crossbar of the U is the only active element, oriented perpendicularly to the magnetic field direction (see Fig. 1a). The leads of the U are brought out of the side of the target, along magnetic field lines. The active length of the gauges was calculated as a function of their dimensions, on the basis of a simple integral model. Their overall response time was estimated to be less than 30 ns in our conditions.

Two types of experiments are reported. In both cases, a multiple gauge configuration permits measurement of particle velocity histories at a variety of depths in the target. Three gauges are connected in series. The loop is connected to a digital oscilloscope with a 2 ns sampling period. The recorded signals present three steps corres-ponding to the responses of the three gauges, reached successively by the compressive front.

III. WAVE PROPAGATION IN GLASS

The first target, designed to study wave propagation in glass, consists of a stack of glass plates bonded together, with the gauges mounted between the plates (see Fig. 1a). A typical test oscillogram is shown in Figure 1b. It indicates that the initial shock separates into two waves :

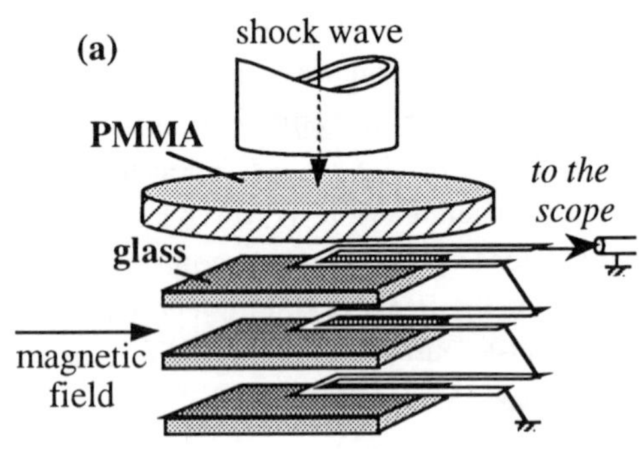

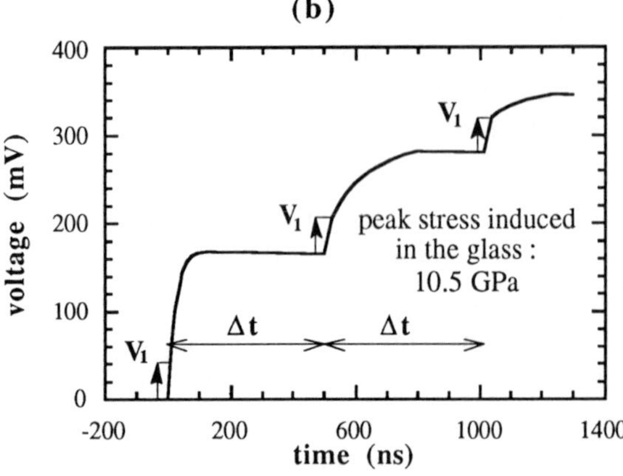

Figure 1. Wave propagation in glass : exploded view of the target (a) and typical oscillogram (b).

The first one produces a rapid jump in particle velocity. The amplitude of this jump, deduced from the voltage V_1, has a constant value $u_1 = 210$ m.s^{-1} within an experimental error of ± 7%, regardless of the depth in the glass sample or the peak stress. This first compressive wave can be regarded as a steady shock front. The time interval Δt is the transit time of this shock through the glass plate separating two gauges. It indicates a shock velocity of 5710 m.s^{-1}, constant over the range of stresses with an accuracy of 5%, in good agreement with the longitudinal sound speed in the glass.

The second wave gradually rises the particle velocity from u_1 to its final value. It is an unsteady wave, whose risetime increases with propagation distance in the glass target. However, in other experiments, above a 12 GPa-peak stress induced in the glass, this second wave front is observed to steepen, giving rise to a second shock transition to the final velocity.

IV. GLASS HUGONIOT

The second target (see Fig. 2a) is designed to permit a simultaneous measurement of the characteristics of the incident shock in PMMA, and the response induced in the glass by this shock. Figure 2b shows a typical oscillogram.

The duration of the first step gives the transit time of the incident shock in the PMMA plate separating the first two gauges. Thus, we have a mean value of the shock velocity. Neglecting the attenuation in this thin plate, we assimilate this value to the shock velocity at the interface. The Hugoniot data for PMMA [3] then provide the characteristics of the state (a) attained in PMMA at the interface. The particle velocity u_a thus obtained is in good agreement with the amplitude of the first jump in the signal.

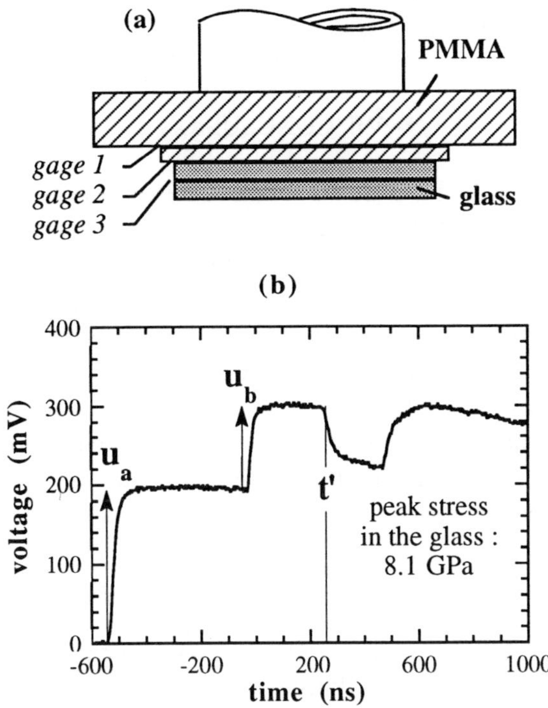

Figure 2. Determination of the glass Hugoniot : target set-up (a) and typical test oscillogram (b).

When the incident shock front reaches the interface, a transmitted shock enters the glass sample, and a reflected shock propagates back into the PMMA plate. The common state (b) achieved in both materials is located on the reflected shock curve of PMMA. The amplitude of the second step gives the particle velocity u_b induced in the glass. The break after this second step at time t' is due to the slowing down of the first gauge under the action of the reflected shock.

Finally, we infer from the measurements of u_b and state (a) the shock state (b) in the (σ,u) plane. This impedance mismatch technique gives one point on the glass Hugoniot at each shot. The resulting data are shown in Figure 3. They are in satisfying agreement with other measurements in an almost similar glass [1,4].

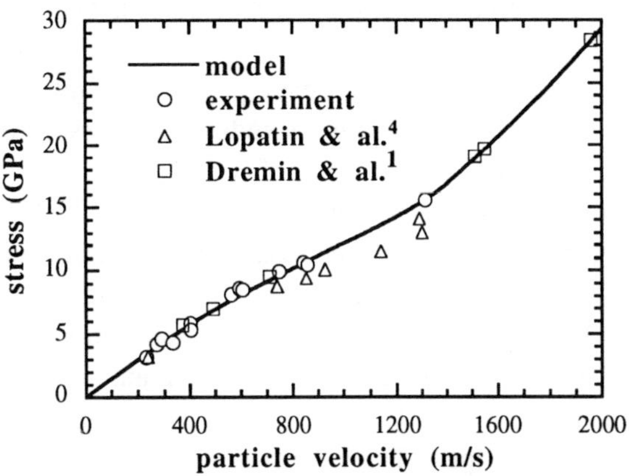

Figure 3. Hugoniot for soda-lime glass. Our results (open dots) are compared to data from the literature [1,4]. The solid curve results from the model presented in section VI.

V. PERMANENT DENSIFICATION OF SODA-LIME GLASS UNDER COMPRESSION

The experimental observations reported above have been interpreted in terms of permanent densification. This phenomenon has been observed in a variety of silica materials, and has been described as an internal rearrangement of the SiO_4 tetrahedra, occurring under both static or dynamic compression [2].

The steady shock precursor corresponds to a reversible compression of glass, up to a threshold stress $\sigma_1 = \rho_o C_L u_1 = 3$ GPa, where C_L is the longitudinal sound speed. Above this limit, permanent densification is assumed to occur, increasingly with the applied peak stress. A sharp reduction in compressibility of glass was reported for a threshold stress σ_2 of about 17 GPa [1]. We associate this limit to the completion of the densification process. This result provides an estimate of the maximum densification $\rho_{do}/\rho_o \approx 1.235$, where ρ_{do} is the maximum density of the glass after release to the ambient pressure. Other workers found the same order of magnitude in glass materials under plate impact.

VI. NUMERICAL MODELLING OF SODA-LIME GLASS DYNAMIC BEHAVIOUR

A model has been developed to account for the singular behaviour of soda-lime glass. We have used our 1D code SHYLAC [5]. Shear strength effects are considered secondary to the densification, so that the stress tensor is assumed to be spherical. Permanent densification is included in the glass equation of state through a "P-α" model [6] relating the thermodynamic state of the real glass to the one of a densified glass ("d" subscripts). The reference Hugoniot of this densified glass has been fitted by a third order polynomial, on the basis of the high pressure data and the maximum densification ρ_{do}/ρ_o. The degree of compaction $\alpha = V/V_d$ is defined as the volume ratio between the real glass and the densified glass, under fixed conditions of pressure and temperature. We assume $E = E_d$ and $P = P_d/\alpha$, where P is the pressure and E is the internal energy, as it is generally done for the description of porous materials. The stress volume plane is separated into three regions :

- a reversible compression region, for $\sigma \leq \sigma_1$, where $\alpha = \alpha_o = V_o/V_{do}$
- a densification region for $\sigma_1 \leq \sigma \leq \sigma_2$, where $\alpha = \alpha(\sigma)$ decreases with the applied stress
- a high stress region for $\sigma_2 \leq \sigma$, where $\alpha = 1$, when the glass is completely densified.

The variations of α with σ in the densification region are given by a polynomial relationship, so that $\alpha(\sigma)$ has a first order derivative at σ_2 and a second order derivative at σ_1.

The calculated Hugoniot in the (σ,u) coordinates is plotted in Figure 3. It is shown to fit successfully the set of experimental data. We have applied triangular stress-time profiles reproducing the explosive loading into glass targets, and we have calculated the responses of the gauges in the experimental conditions. A comparison of experimental and simulated oscillograms is shown in Figure 4, for the target described in Figure 2a. The agreement is good over the investigated range, as for the velocities of the waves and the deformation of the fronts.

VII. CONCLUSION

The proposed model, limited to a 1D configuration, is simple to implement, and it involves a minimum number of parameters, namely α_o, σ_1 and σ_2, which have precise physical meaning. The widespread consistancy of calculated and measured particle velocity profiles on the whole investigated field gives us confidence that this model is able to predict the response of soda-lime glass on a wide range of loading conditions.

REFERENCES

1 A.N. Dremin and G.A.Adadurov, *Soviet Physics-Solid State* **6**(6), (1964).

2 J. Cagnoux, AIP Conference Proceedings, ed. H.C. Wolfe, New York (1982).

3 LASL Shock Hugoniot Data, ed. S.P. Marsh, Univ. of California Press (1980).

4 C.M. Lopatin, S.J. Bless, and N.S. Brar, *J. Appl. Phys.* **66**(2), 593 (1989).

5 F. Cottet and M. Boustie, *J. Appl. Phys.* **66**, 4067 (1989).

6 W. Herrmann, *J. Appl. Phys.* **40**(6), 2490 (1969).

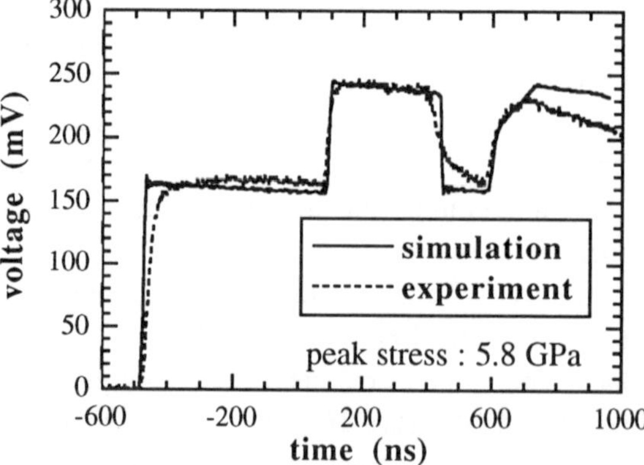

Figure 4. Comparison of measured and calculated responses for a 5.8 GPa - stress in the glass.

MEASUREMENT AND ANALYSIS OF THREE 1.5-GPA SHOCK-WAVE PROFILES IN COPPER

Richard H. Warnes and Davis L. Tonks
Los Alamos National Laboratory
Los Alamos, NM 87545 USA

Three wave-profile experiments were performed on OFE fully annealed (600 °C for one hour) copper using a 101.6-mm-diam gas gun at impact velocities of 86 m/s. A symmetric impact produced a 1.5-GPa shock wave in the target. A sapphire window was bonded to the front (non-impact) face of the target, and a four-detector push-pull velocity interferometer (VISAR) measured the velocity of the copper/sapphire interface. The impactor thickness (4 mm) was the same in all experiments; the target thicknesses were 10, 20, and 30 mm. The stresses and strains, including the deviatoric stresses and strains, have been extracted from these data using a quasi-Lagrangian analysis. (The waves are not steady.) The use of three separate shots in Lagrangian analysis yields only approximate results for the deviatoric stresses; but the results for the normal stresses, and for the strains, are fairly accurate. Even though the strain rates fall in the Hopkinson bar regime, the mechanism of dislocation motion appears to be dislocation drag, as is the case for stronger shock waves in Cu.

INTRODUCTION

The three experiments presented here are part of a series of experiments to measure and model the elastic-plastic response of OFE fully annealed copper subjected to shock and reshock and shock and release loading at initial pressures of 1.5 and 3 GPa. Some of the 3-GPa experiments and analyses have already been reported [1]. This paper presents the very lowest pressure experiments and analyses.

EXPERIMENTS

A 101.6-mm-diam gas gun was used to produce a symmetric impact in OFE copper at an impact velocity of about 86 m/s. The copper in both the impactor and the target was fully annealed (600°C for one hour). A single-crystal sapphire window [2] was bonded to the front (non-impact) face of the copper target.

The impactor velocity was measured with an array of electrical contact pins recording on digitizers with a resolution of 5 ns. The velocity of the target/sapphire interface was measured with a four-detector push-pull VISAR [3] recording on digitizing oscilloscopes sampling at either 1 or 2 gigasamples/s.

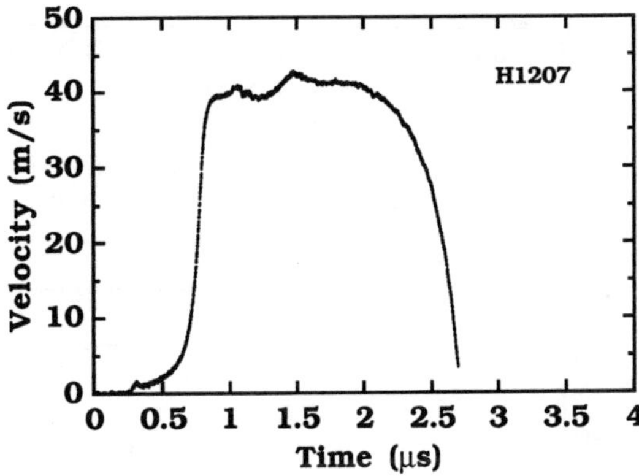

Figure 1. Experiment H1207; 10-mm target. The velocity is at the Cu/sapphire interface.

In these three low stress, low strain rate experiments the impactor thickness was 4 mm, and the target thicknesses were 10 mm, 20 mm, and 30 mm. Details of the experiments are given in Tables 1 and 2. The wave profiles at the target/sapphire window interfaces are plotted in Figs. 1-3.

Table 1. Dimensions of components in the experiments.

	Impactor		Target		Sapphire Window	
Experiment No.	Thickness (mm)	Diam (mm)	Thickness (mm)	Diam (mm)	Thickness (mm)	Diam (mm)
H1207	3.988	59.957	9.970	54.953	25.0	50.0
H1208	3.988	59.944	19.952	54.953	25.0	50.0
H1230	3.988	59.944	29.972	54.940	25.0	50.0

Table 2. Impact velocities and VISAR setup.

Experiment No.	Impactor Velocity (m/s)	Impactor Tilt (mrad)	Fringe Constant (m/s)
H1207	85.7 ±0.1	0.85	39.07
H1208	85.2 ±0.3	0.66	39.07
H1230	86.2 ±0.1	1.21	39.07

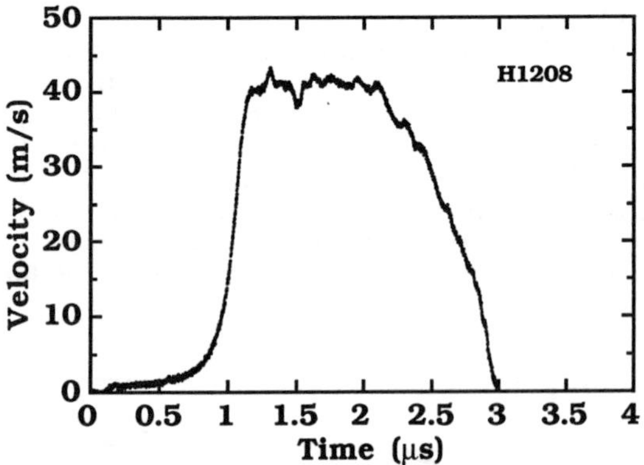

Figure 2. Experiment H1208; 20-mm target. The velocity is at the Cu/sapphire interface.

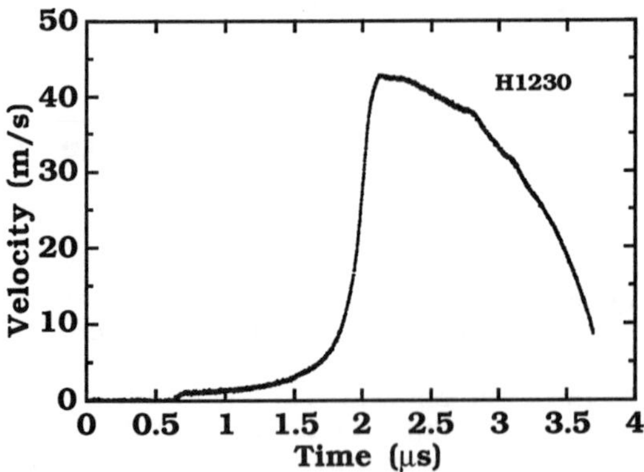

Figure 3. Experiment H1230; 30-mm target. The velocity is at the Cu/sapphire interface.

THEORETICAL ANALYSIS

The particle velocity data were smoothed by local least-squares fitting to eliminate local ringing that changed the sign of the acceleration. This resulted in no drastic changes to the data.

Theoretically, Lagrangian analysis requires progressive snapshots of the same wave. The data available here, however, are from three different experiments with three different sample thicknesses. (See Table 1.) Shot-to-shot variations cloud the straightforward application of the technique to these data. For example, as seen in Figs. 1-3, experiment H1230 has a somewhat larger peak velocity than the others. In order to apply the Lagrangian method, these variations must be eliminated in some fashion. Therefore, the profiles for experiments H1207 and H1208 were scaled in velocity to make their peak velocities identical to that of shot H1230. (The adjustments were minor, less than eight percent.) The method of analysis used here consists of a Lagrangian analysis together with this and other methods of eliminating shot-to-shot variations (to be described shortly). It will be called a pseudo-Lagrangian analysis.

To estimate the extent of the error, each wave was analyzed using the steady wave analysis of Wallace [4] and the results were compared to that of the pseudo-Lagrangian method used here. The steady wave results are surely not correct, but provide some sort of bound on the correct result. As seen in Figs. 4-7, the results from both analyses compared fairly closely for all quantities except the deviatoric stress, which is the quantity most sensitive to error. Nevertheless, the two versions of the deviatoric stress, Fig. 5, are similar, differing at most by about 30%.

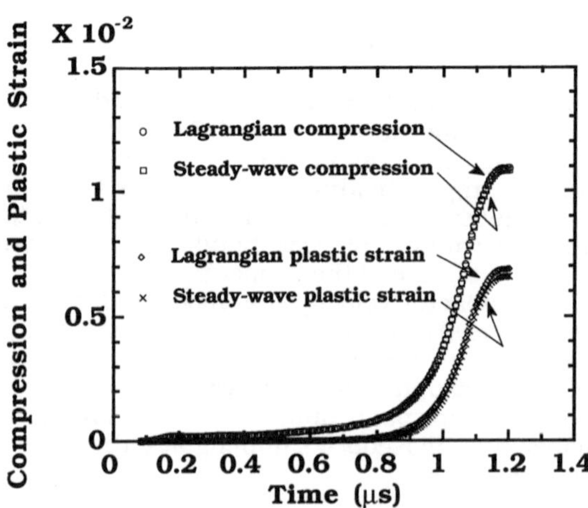

Figure 4. Calculated compression and plastic strains versus time for the H1208 gauge position.

A 3% elastic impedance correction was applied to the measured interface velocity to estimate the in situ Cu particle velocity without the presence of the sapphire. For a correction this small, the elastic theory is adequate, [5].

The Lagrangian method of paths was used, [7]. Each profile was divided into three monotonic parts separated by the peak of the first rise, the following dip, and the top of the plastic wave. Points with the same relative velocity in corresponding parts in the three profiles were connected to form paths.

The equations used for the pseudo-Lagrangian analysis are

$$\sigma(t) = -\rho_0 \int \left(\frac{\partial u}{\partial t} \right)_h dh \Big|_t \tag{1}$$

and

$$\varepsilon = -\int \left(\frac{\partial u}{\partial h} \right)_t dt \Big|_h , \tag{2}$$

where u is the particle velocity, σ is the normal stress defined positive in compression, ε is the compression or volumetric strain, h is the Lagrangian position, ρ_0 is the initial density, and t is the time. The normal stress and compression were found at the sample thickness (20 mm) corresponding to shot H1208 using these formulas. Eq. (1) was integrated along a line of constant time in the h-t plane inward from an undisturbed position in front of the shock wave. Eq. (2) was integrated along a line of constant h corresponding to the H1208 sample thickness. The H1208 position is in the center of the data and, thus, extrapolations there are minimized.

Once σ and ε were obtained, the thermoelastic equations of Wallace [4] were used to obtain the deviatoric stress and plastic strains. The material parameters used are given in [5,6].

The steady wave procedure used to obtain the steady wave results are also described in these references. In the calculations here, the rise to the first peak was assumed elastic and the velocity of point "c" used in the analysis [4] was taken to be 10 m/s.

The absolute timing measurements of the transit time for the three profiles proved to be too inaccurate to obtain physically reasonable results; negative deviatoric stresses were obtained. Using the points of first motion to aid in aligning the three records in time also led to negative deviatoric stresses. To set the relative timing of the three profiles, the peaks of the first rise were taken to have traversed the sample thicknesses at the longitudinal sound velocity. This assumption, together with the velocity versus time record for each profile, established the timing for all profile points.

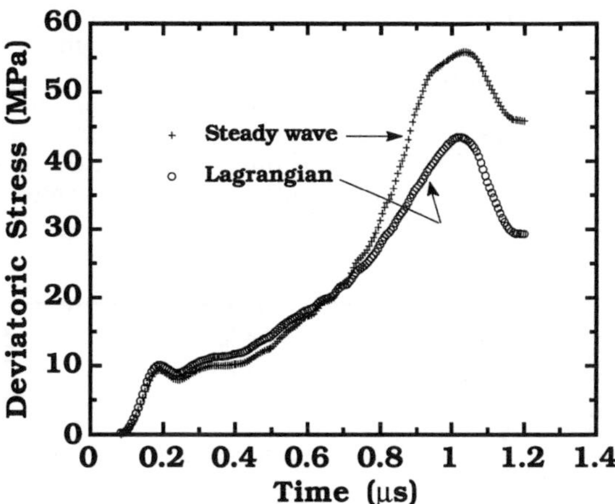

Figure 5. Calculated deviatoric stress versus time for the H1208 gauge position.

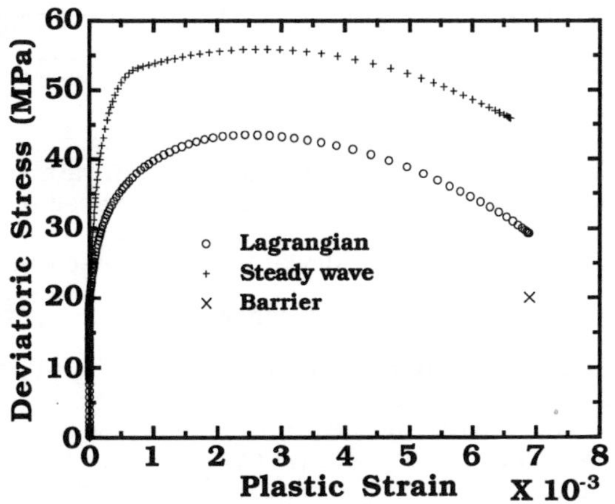

Figure 6. Calculated deviatoric stress versus plastic strain for the H1208 gauge position. The X is a calculated value for the internal barrier strength at the top of the shock wave.

Both linear and quadratic fitting of the data were tried. Both gave about the same results for the stresses and strains at the H1208 target thickness. The calculated peak deviatoric stress, however, was about 10% lower for the quadratic fit than for the linear fit. For the thicknesses corresponding to the other two experiments the quadratic fit gave regions of negative deviatoric stress. These results are not shown here. Since the linear fit did not produce this problem, only the linear results are given here. One would think that the quadratic fit would give better results because it was based on all of the data. The reason it did not may be due to the shot-to-shot variations.

An additional restriction is that only data from shots H1208 and H1230 were used in the linear fit. Using data from shots H1207 and H1208 in the linear fit also produced negative deviatoric stresses.

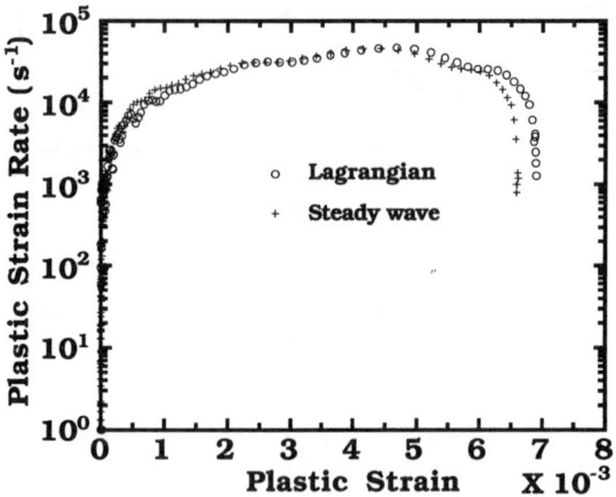

Figure 7. Calculated plastic strain rate versus plastic strain for the H1208 gauge position.

We note that the deviatoric stress used here is: $\tau = \left(-\frac{1}{2}\right)\left(\tau_{xx} - \tau_{yy}\right)$, where τ_{xx} and τ_{yy} are the stresses along, and normal to, the shock direction, respectively.

The curves of the deviatoric stress versus plastic strain, Fig. 6, and of the strain rate versus plastic strain, Fig. 7, closely resemble those for stronger Cu shock-wave profiles that are dominated by dislocation drag [1]. The very fast rise in plastic strain rate with plastic strain and the peaking of the deviatoric stress about midway in plastic strain are typical of shock-wave dislocation drag processes in which the initial stress loading is higher than any initial barriers and faster than any buildup of internal work hardening. Hence, the mechanism of plastic flow here is probably influenced by dislocation drag also.

Evidence for this was obtained by calculating, for the end of the shock path of Fig. 6, the mechanical threshold stress using the model of [8]. Because of the small strains involved, the results of this model should be considered fairly rough, accurate to, say, 40%. The resulting value of 20 MPa for the mechanical threshold stress should be compared with the final deviatoric stress of Fig. 6. Due to the uncertainties involved, these two values are roughly the same. As can be seen, after the first rise the deviatoric stresses of the shock path lie above this value, which is an upper bound for the evolving threshold stress, indicating that the dislocations are being driven by stresses greater than the opposition of internal barriers. Hence, even though the strain rates here fall in the range of Hopkinson bar data, which is dominated by thermally activated dislocation motion, the stress loading here is higher than internal barriers and so abrupt that dislocation drag is the mechanism of dislocation motion.

ACKNOWLEDGMENTS

This work is supported by the United States Department of Energy under Contract W-7405-ENG-36.

REFERENCES

[1] R. H. Warnes and D. L. Tonks, "Measurement and Analysis of 3-GPa Shock Wave Profiles in Annealed OFE Copper," in *Proceedings of the APS Topical Conference on Shock Compression of Condensed Matter*, 1989, pp. 329-332.

[2] L. M. Barker and R. E. Hollenbach, *J. Appl. Phys* 41, pp. 4208-4226 (1970).

[3] W. F. Hemsing, *Rev. Sci. Instrum.* 50(1), pp. 73-78 (1979).

[4] D. C. Wallace, *Phys Rev. B* 22, pp. 1477-1486 and 1487-1494 (1980).

[5] D. L. Tonks, *J. Appl. Phys.* 66, pp.1951-1960 (1989).

[6] D. L. Tonks, "The DataShoP, A Database of Weak-Shock Constitutive Data," Los Alamos National Laboratory Report LA-12068-MS, (1991).

[7] L. Seaman, *J. Appl. Phys.* 45, p. 4303 (1974).

[8] J. N. Johnson and D. L. Tonks, "Dynamic Plasticity in Transition from Thermal Activation to Viscous Drag," in *Proceedings of the APS Topical Conference on Shock Compression of Condensed Matter*, 1991, pp. 371-378.

FREE SURFACE VELOCITY PROFILES IN MOLYBDENUM SHOCK COMPRESSED AT 1400°C

Thomas S. Duffy and Thomas J. Ahrens
Seismological Laboratory
California Institute of Technology
Pasadena, CA 91125

The equation of state, constitutive properties and unloading wave velocities of molybdenum have been determined from free surface velocity profiles on samples shock compressed from a 1400°C initial state. The equation of state of 1400°C molybdenum agrees with previous streak camera measurements and the combined equation of state between 12 and 96 GPa is: $U_S = 4.78\ (0.02) + 1.42\ (0.02)\ u_p$. Unloading wave velocities measured between 12 and 81 GPa range from 6.30 to 7.91 km/s and are 4-8% below extrapolated 25°C compressional velocities. The yield strength, Y, was found to be 0.79-0.94 GPa, compared with values of 1.3-1.6 GPa from ambient-temperature experiments.

INTRODUCTION

Shock-compression methods are uniquely capable of producing high pressure (P) and high temperature (T) states of matter. One limitation of shock techniques is that pressure and temperature cannot be varied independently (for non-porous samples). By shock compressing a sample preheated to a known high temperature, it is possible to delineate the separate effects of P and T on material properties.

In this study, we report new wave profile measurements on molybdenum shock-compressed between 12 and 81 GPa from a 1400°C initial state. The results provide insight into the effects of temperature on the elastic, constitutive, and equation of state (EOS) properties under shock compression. For the first time, we have extended the range of optical velocity interferometric techniques to materials at significantly high initial temperatures (>250°C).

EXPERIMENTAL TECHNIQUE

Molybdenum (Mo) was chosen for study because of its role as a high-pressure standard. In addition, its 1400°C equation of state (EOS) has been studied previously [1], and shock compression data above 150 GPa [2] reveal complex behavior. Shock compression of Mo (99.95% purity) was carried out using foam-backed aluminum and tantalum flyer plates to impact 5.5-mm thick Mo samples with velocities between 0.95 and 2.28 km/s. Prior to impact, the samples were heated to near 1400°C using a radio-frequency heating system [1], and the temperature was measured to ±1°C by a thermocouple. The motion of the rear free surface of the Mo sample was recorded using a VISAR. The time resolution of our VISAR is ~2–3 ns, the precision is ±1%, and velocity changes of a few m/s are resolvable.

RESULTS

Four experiments were conducted on Mo samples, three of which yielded free surface velocity profiles. In the fourth experiment, data recording failures prevented a wave profile from being obtained but the arrival times of the shock front and the initial unloading wave could be read from the partial fringe records. The velocity profiles are shown in Fig. 1.

Compressive States

To establish timing for the experiments, the toe of the elastic precursor was assumed to propagate at the ambient-pressure compressional wave velocity which was calculated to be 6.10 km/s from the linear modulus-temperature trend in high T ultrasonic data to 700°C [3]. The time difference between the precursor and the midpoint of the shock established the shock velocity and, together with the particle

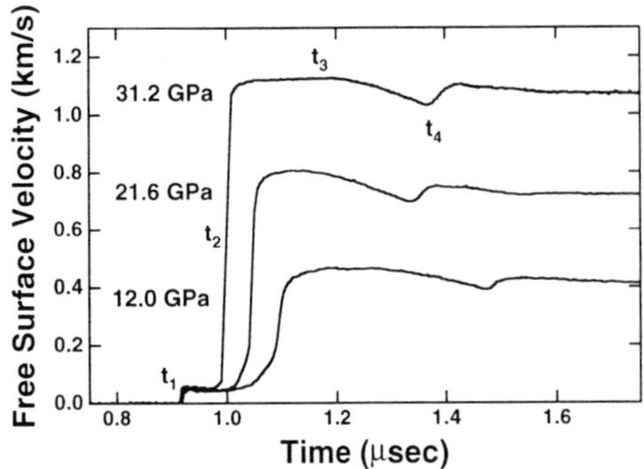

Fig. 1. Free surface velocity histories recorded at the rear surface of 1400°C molybdenum.

velocity, the Hugoniot state was obtained. The particle velocity was calculated from the measured free surface velocity by accounting for elastic-plastic interactions at the free surface [4]. The Hugoniot states are consistent with previous data [1] and the combined equation of state is: U_S = 4.78(0.02) + 1.42(0.02) u_p, where U_S and u_p are the shock and particle velocities, respectively (Fig. 2).

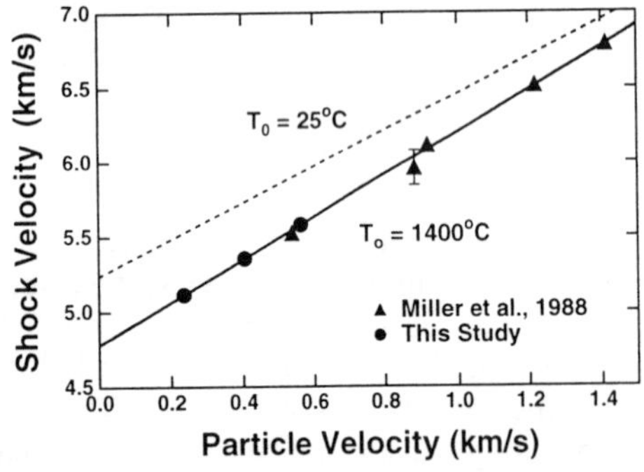

Fig. 2. Hugoniot equation of state of 1400°C molybdenum. Solid line is a least squares fit to the data. Dashed line shows the 25°C Hugoniot.

The elastic precursor manifests itself as a sharp jump in velocity which then relaxes by as much as 25%. No such relaxation was observed in Mo samples compressed from ambient temperature [5]. The amplitude of the Hugoniot elastic limit (HEL) is 1.46-1.73 GPa. HEL values for Mo compressed to 7-15 GPa from ambient temperature are 2.3-2.8 GPa for slightly thicker samples (6.1 mm) [5]. Thus, at 1400°C, the HEL amplitude of Mo is reduced by ~35%.

Assuming a von Mises yield condition, the compressive yield strength, *Y*, is related to the HEL amplitude through:

$$Y = \frac{(1-2\upsilon)}{(1-\upsilon)}\sigma_{\mathrm{HEL}}, \qquad (1)$$

where υ is Poisson's ratio which is calculated to be 0.313 at 1400°C [3]. The yield strength at the HEL is 0.79-0.94GPa for the three experiments while the ambient T data of [5] yields Y = 1.3-1.6 GPa.

Material strength has been observed to decrease at high shock stress in aluminum, presumably because of thermal effects [6]. However, there is little quantitative information on thermal softening under dynamic compression. Yield strength is plotted as a function of initial temperature in Fig. 3. In the constitutive model of [7], thermal effects are approximated by assuming that the ratio Y/G is constant, where G is the shear modulus. According to Fig. 3, the yield strength of Mo decreases at a faster rate than the shear modulus. An alternative representation is that the yield strength is the following linear function of homologous temperature:

$$Y = 1.59(1-T/T_m), \qquad (2)$$

where T_m is the melting temperature. This relationship was obtained from the 25°C yield strength at 12.6 GPa and by requiring that Y = 0 GPa at the melting point. This relationship predicts a yield strength at 1400°C of 0.65 GPa, 22-45% below the measured values.

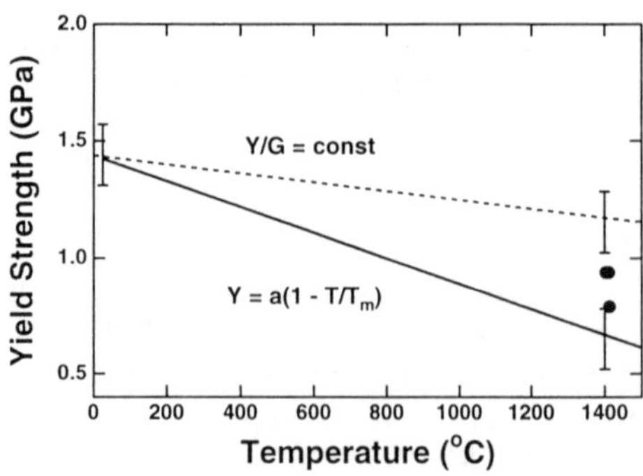

Fig. 3. Yield strength of Mo at the HEL as a function of initial temperature. Error bars show range of values from [5].

Unloading States

Decompression of the sample results from a rarefaction wave propagating from the rear of the impactor (Fig. 4 (inset)). Unloading wave velocities, V_P, calculated from the rarefaction arrival time and the known shock and release properties of the impactors are shown in Fig. 4. The 1400°C Hugoniot velocities are offset to significantly lower values than ambient temperature ultrasonic data to 0.5 GPa [5] extrapolated via finite strain theory. The decrease results from the effect of temperature on the elastic wave velocity.

Reflection of the shock from the Mo rear surface perturbs a region near the free surface through which the rarefaction wave must pass (Fig. 4, inset). The uncertainty thus introduced was minimized by including a correction term and by restricting the perturbed region to less than 10% of the sample thickness.

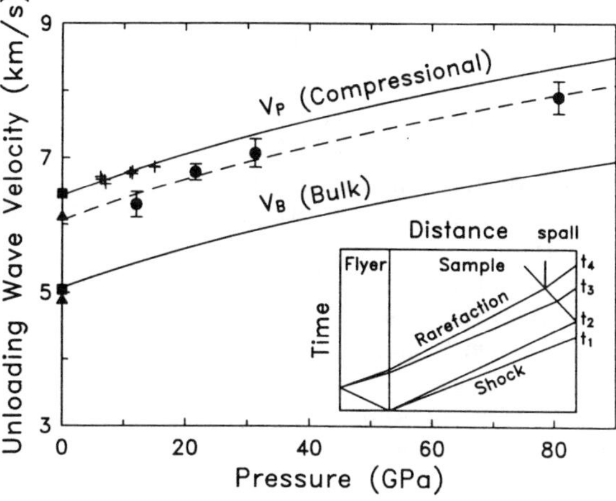

Fig. 4. Unloading wave velocity in molybdenum shock-compressed at 25°C (pluses) and at 1400°C (filled circles). The solid lines show extrapolated compressional and bulk velocities at 25°C. The dashed line is fit to the 1400°C Hugoniot velocities using Birch's Law. Inset is a distance-time diagram (in Lagrangian coordinates) of wave propagation through the flyer and sample.

The temperature coefficient of V_P was calculated from the Hugoniot and room temperature data at a given pressure:

$$\left(\partial V_P/\partial T\right)_P = \frac{V_P(H) - V_P(25^\circ\mathrm{C})}{T(H) - 25^\circ\mathrm{C}}, \tag{3}$$

where H refers to Hugoniot conditions. *T(H)* includes both the initial temperature and the shock-induced temperature increase which ranges from 129 ± 22°C at 12 GPa to 1037 ±186°C at 81 GPa.

At high pressure, Mo values are consistent with the ambient-pressure value of $\left(\partial V_P/\partial T\right)_P$ from ultrasonics [3] and suggest a decrease in $\left|\left(\partial V_P/\partial T\right)_P\right|$ with pressure. The highest pressure Mo data yield a 31-38% decrease in $\left|\left(\partial V_P/\partial T\right)_P\right|$ from -0.26 m/s/°C at ambient pressure to -0.16 m/s/°C (31 GPa) and -0.18 m/s/°C (81 GPa).

To examine the reliability of the extrapolated ultrasonic data, Hugoniot sound velocities were computed from wave profiles measured on Mo samples shocked from 25°C to 7-15 GPa [5], a region where shock heating effects are small. As shown in Fig. 4, the Hugoniot measurements are consistent with the ultrasonic data. Similar agreement between extrapolated ultrasonic data and Hugoniot measurements to 35 GPa has been observed for Al, Cu, and W [9] as well as for MgO [10]. It has been argued from micromechanical theory [11] that, due to plastic flow, the measured Hugoniot rarefaction velocity can be less than the elastic wave velocity. The results of Fig. 4 suggest this effect is not significant for Mo.

Acoustic velocities in Mo shock-compressed from a 25°C initial state to pressures between 150 and 441 GPa have also been reported [2]. These data indicate that a solid-solid phase transition occurs at around 210 GPa and Mo melts near 390 GPa. Fig. 5 compares available compressional and bulk sound velocity data for Mo, including ultrasonic [8], shock compression [this study, 2, 5], and isobaric expansion data [12]. The trend of the data between 150 and 190 GPa (ρ = 13.7-14.5 g/cm^3) differs significantly from the trend of the present data.

The interaction of unloading waves depicted in the inset to Fig. 4 leads to the development of tensile stresses within the specimen which leads to dynamic fracture. The characteristic signature of spall is the "pull-back" in free surface velocity seen in Fig. 1. From the amplitude of the pull-back signal, an estimate of the spall strength can be obtained [13]. Near 12 GPa, the spall strength of high-temperature Mo is found to be 2.4 GPa, only slightly different from the value of 2.31 GPa reported for room-temperature Mo

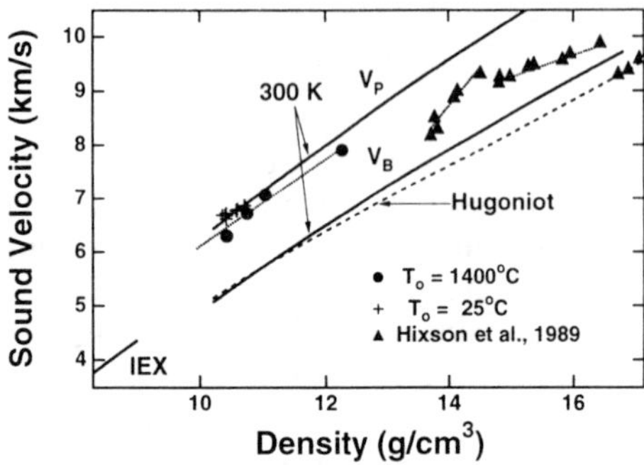

Fig. 5. Compressional and bulk sound velocity data for Mo. Solid lines are extrapolated ultrasonic data [8]. Dashed line is bulk velocity calculated from Hugoniot slope [2]. The solid circles are data from this study, while pluses and triangles are Hugoniot data from [5] and [2]. Dotted lines show linear fits to the data. IEX - isobaric expansion measurements on liquid Mo [12].

[14]. Thus, in contrast to the compressive yield strength, the spall strength appears to be temperature-insensitive for this material.

SUMMARY

Free surface velocities have been measured on molybdenum preheated to 1400°C in order to investigate its high-temperature properties under shock compression. Equation of state measurements on 1400°C Mo are in excellent agreement with the results of earlier streak camera experiments. The Hugoniot elastic limit stress ranges from 1.5-1.7 GPa between 12 and 31 GPa at ~1400°C, which is significantly below ~25°C values of 2.3-2.6 GPa. Spall-strength measurements near 12 GPa indicate this quantity is only weakly temperature sensitive in Mo.

Unloading wave velocities between 12-81 GPa lie 4-8% below extrapolated room temperature values. Velocity trends to 81 GPa are inconsistent with measured velocities between 150 and 190 GPa from a 25°C initial state [2]. This may be a consequence of high-pressure structural changes in Mo caused by electronic changes, but no evidence of anomalous effects are observed to 81 GPa in the high-temperature data.

ACKNOWLEDGMENTS

We thank L. Rowan, E. Gelle, M. Long for experimental assistance and M. Furnish for providing us with copies of his data. We also thank L. S. Durango for editorial assistance. This work was supported by the NSF. Division of Geological and Planetary Sciences, California Institute of Technology contribution 5290.

REFERENCES

[1] G. H. Miller, T. J. Ahrens, and E. M. Stolper, *J. Appl. Phys.* 63, 4469-4475 (1988).

[2] R. S. Hixson, D. A. Boness, J. W. Shaner, and J. A. Moriarty, *Phys. Rev. Lett*, 62, 637-640 (1989).

[3] J. M. Dickinson and P. E. Armstrong, *J. Appl. Phys.,* 38, 602-606 (1967).

[4] D. E. Grady, in *Metallurgical Applications of Shock-Wave and High Strain Rate Phenomena*, 1986, pp. 763-780.

[5] M. D. Furnish and L. C. Chhabildas, in *High Strain Rate Behavior of Refractory Metals and Alloys*, 1992, pp. 229-240.

[6] J. R. Asay and G. I. Kerley, *Int. J. Impact Eng.*, 5, 69-99 (1987).

[7] D. J. Steinberg, S. G. Cochran, and M. W. Guinan, *J. Appl. Phys.* 51, 1498-1504 (1980).

[8] K. W. Katahara, M. H. Manghnani and E. S. Fischer, *J. Phys. F: Metal Phys.*, 9, 773-790 (1979).

[9] T. S. Duffy and T. J. Ahrens, *J. Geophys. Res.*, 97, 4503-4520 (1992).

[10] T. S. Duffy and T. J. Ahrens, this volume.

[11] J. N. Johnson, R. S. Hixson, G. T. Gray and C. E. Morris *J. Appl. Phys.* 72, 429-441 (1992).

[12] R. S. Hixson, *Int. J. Thermo.*, 13, 477-487 (1992).

[13] V. I. Romanchenko and G. V. Stepanov *J. Appl. Mech. Tech. Phys.*, 21, 555-561 (1980).

[14] L. C. Chhabildas, L. M. Barker, J. R. Asay and T. G. Trucano *Int. J. Impact Eng.*, 10, 107-124 (1990).

EXPERIMENTAL MEASUREMENTS OF 2169 STAINLESS STEEL UNDER DYNAMIC LOADING

Shihui HUANG Xiaogang JIN Zeren LI Xiang WANG Kai GUAN*
Lab for Shock Wave and Detonation Physics Research
Southwest Institute of Fluid Physics
P. O. Box 523, Chengdu, Sichuan, 610003, China

Symmetric planar impact experiments were performed for 21%Cr-8%Ni-9% Mn stainless steel on a 57mm single-stage gas-gun. The time resolved motion of target back free surface was monitored with a laser velocity interferometer (VISAR) and the VISAR data were recorded by HP 54111D digital oscilloscope. The measured velocity histories exhibit a typical two-wave loading structure. The peak stresses range from 8GPa-17GPa. The Hugoniot Elastic Limit (HEL), Hugoniot, shock strain rate and shock viscosity were obtained for the steel from the experimental results. Combining with the experimental results of the same kind of steel、obtained from the explosively loading techniques under pressures of 50-250GPa and the underground explosion under pressure of 2. 32TPa, some discussions were presented.

INTRODUCTION

21Cr-6Ni-9Mn stainless steel is one of the Austenitic stainless steel with nitrogen. Because of its high yield strength and excellent anticorrosion at ambient and low temperatures, it has been used in areas of controllable nuclear fusion study、petro-chemical industry、aerospace engineering、low temperature superconducting engineering and so on. Several studies on the dynamic behavior of this material have been reported in the last decade. [1][2] The present paper reports our recent impact experimental results of 2169 stainless steel on a gas gun in the stress range of 8～17GPa. The data were also utilized to numerically simulate the shock wave profile with that material model in another publication.

EXPERIMENTAL TECHNIQUE AND RESULTS

We performed our experiments with a 57mm gas gun in Lab for Shock Wave and Detonation Physics Research, Southwest Institute of Fluid Physics. The impact velocity of this gun ranges from 40m/s up to about 1400m/s. The projectile velocity before impact was measured by recording the time intervals between impact on electrical shorting pins in the muzzle of the gun and the time intervals were recorded by a multichronometer with 2ns time resolution. The velocity measuring accuracy is about 1%.

All experimental data were obtained from symmetric plate impact tests. The samples were cut from ϕ65 bar of 2169 steel. Its chemical composition and physical parameters are listed in Tables 1 and 2. Both flyers and targets in the experiments were flat plates with diameter of 55mm and thick-

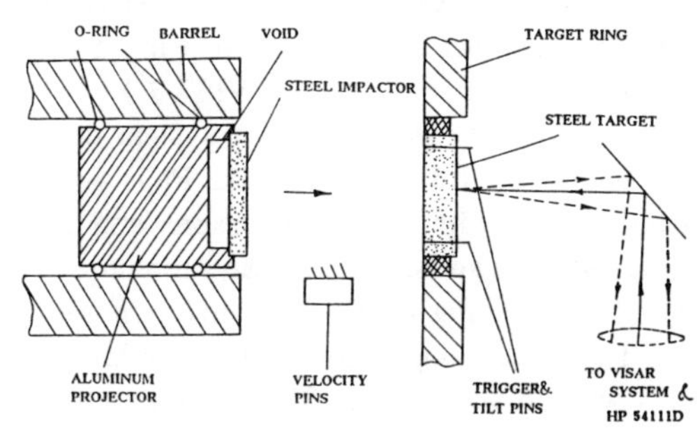

Fig. 1 Experimental impact configuration to determine elastic-plastic loading in 2169 stainless steel

* Southwest Institute of Mechanical Manufacture

This work performed under the auspices of National Natural Science Foundation of China and China Academy of Engineering Physics.

Table 1. Chemical composition of 2169 stainless steel for different experiments(values in weight percent)

	C	Mn	Cr	Ni	N_2	Si	P	S	Fe
Sample in our test	0.037	8.95	20.53	7.64	0.29	0.41	0.012	0.007	62.10
Sample in M. S. Yang's[3]	0.04	8.61	20.38	7.86	0.265	0.51	0.016	0.005	62.31
Sample in J. L. Wise's[1]	0.02	9.38	19.81	7.23	0.30	0.09	0.011	0.010	63.15

Table 2. Physical constants of 2169 stainless steel

Density ρ_0 (g/cm³)	Melting Point (℃)	Logitudinal Wave Velocity c_l (km/s)	Shear Wave Velocity c_s (km/s)	Elastic Modulus (kg/mm²)	Specific Heat (cal/g℃)	Poisson's Ratio
7.806	1,410	5.732[1]	3.170[1]	20300	0.115	0.280

ness of 4mm、8mm and 10mm, respectively. The plates were annealed at 1050℃ in a vacuum furnace for 1 hour, then cooled down in water. Its average grain size is about 44μm and hardness in RC is HRC 10.8. In order to obtain a good flatness and parallelism of samples, all those plates were lapped by using diamond paste to get a final surface finish better than 1μm. The dynamic tilt was monitored by four pins installed flush in the target plate in the experiment. The tilt in our experiment is less than 1×10^{-3} rad.

The experimental configuration is indicated in Fig. 1. The time-resolved motion of the free surface of 2169 stainless steel was monitored using a laser velocity interferometer system (VISAR). This JSG-Ⅱ laser velocity interferometer system developed by Southwest Institute of Fluid Physics is a measuring system with double precisions and four detectors, which can simultaneously monitor the velocity of the moving object with different sensitivities. The measuring range is from 40m/s to 3000m/s with an accuracy of 3% and a time resolution of 2ns. MS 120 He-Ne laser with 25mW power in single frequency was used in the VISAR system. The output of VISAR was recorded by a HP 54111D digital oscilloscope with a frequency response of 500MHz. The composite risetime of the system was estimated to be ~5ns.

The impact conditions for the series of experiments are summarized in Table 3.

The four free surface velocity profiles measured by VISAR system are shown in Fig. 2, where the profiles are time correlated by alignment of the elastic precursor waves. Although the measured velocity histories show a little differences from test to test, the main features are approximately reproducible. The profiles exhibit a typical two-wave loading structure: The precursor possesses a rapidly rising ramp and a following shallower ramp, then it develops gradually to an abrupt rising plastic wave from the foot of the plastic wave.

The average stress amplitude of Hugoniot Elastic Limit (HEL) was estimated to be 1.32GPa at a particle velocity of 0.059km/s.

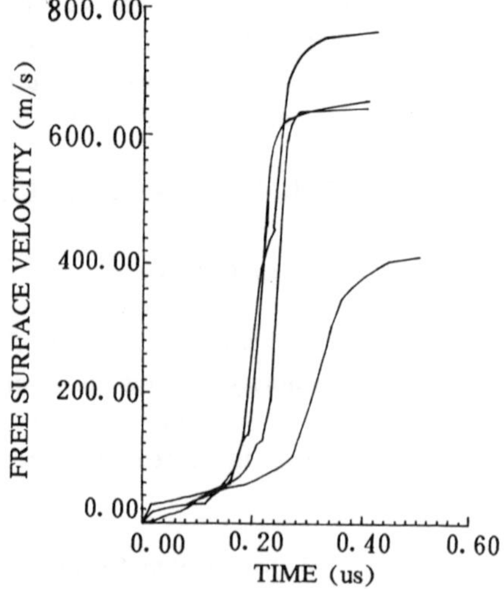

Fig. 2 Free surface velocity histories in experiment

Table 3. Experimental results for 2169 stainless steel impact tests

Shot No.	Sample Thickness (mm)	Impact Velocity (m/s)	Hugoniot Elastic Limit (GPa)	Shock Velocity (m/s)	Shock Stress (GPa)	Shock Strain	Maximum Strain Rate (s^{-1})	Viscosity (Pa—s)
No. 1	9.920	441.3	1.30	4,821	8.18	0.043	3.5×10^5	702
No. 4	7.884	667.5	1.37	4,974	12.9	0.065	1.4×10^6	427
No. 7	9.931	676.1	1.32	5,022	12.7	0.063	1.9×10^6	285
No. 8	9.955	859.0	1.30	5,107	16.8	0.081	3.2×10^6	304

The shock velocity, or the velocity of the plastic wave, U_s, was determined using the midpoint velocity of the wave between the peak free surface velocity U_f and HEL free surface velocity U_{fHEL}, where the elastic precursor wave velocity of $C_l=5.732$km/s was taken from the experimental measurements by J. L. Wise et al. [1] The shock wave speeds determined from our experiment are given in Table 3. Particle velocity was evaluated from the peak free surface velocity by using the free surface approximation. The shock velocity-particle velocity data are plotted in Figure 3. A linear、least-squares fit to the data provides:

$$U_s = 4.524 + 1.383U_p, \quad 221 \leqslant U_p \leqslant 430\text{m/s} \tag{1}$$

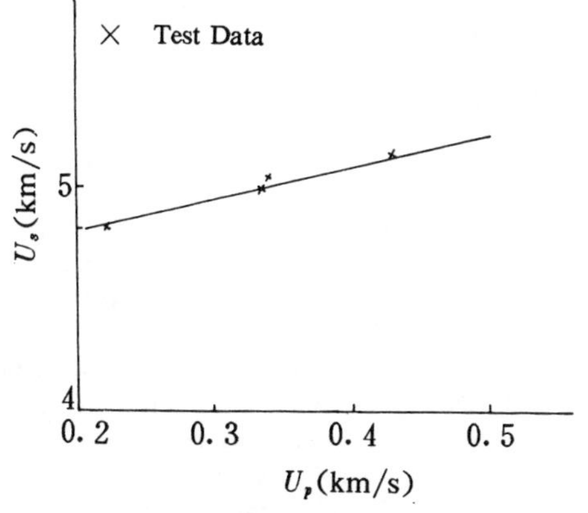

Fig. 3 Experimental U_s-U_p data for 2169 stainless steel

The Hugoniot stress σ_f and strain ε_f were calculated and reported in Table 3 according the following expressions[5]:

$$\sigma_f = \sigma_{HEL} + \frac{\rho_0 U_s}{2}(U_f - U_{fHEL} + \frac{c_l - c_0}{c_l c_0}\frac{\sigma_{HEL}}{\rho_0})$$

$$\varepsilon_f = \frac{\sigma_{HEL}}{\rho_0 c_l^2} + \frac{\sigma_f - \sigma_{HEL}}{\rho_0 U_s^2} \tag{2}$$

where ρ_0, the initial density of the material; c_0 and c_l, the bulk velocity and longitudinal wave speed, respectively.

The maximum strain rate can be calculated using the relation:

$$\dot{\varepsilon} = \frac{1}{2U_s}\frac{dU_f}{dt} \tag{3}$$

where the time derivative is taken at the steepest part of the velocity profile.

The effective viscosity η, which is defined by

$$\Delta\sigma = \eta\dot{\varepsilon} \tag{4}$$

were also estimated by the relation

$$\Delta\sigma = \frac{1}{2}s\sigma_f\varepsilon_f \tag{5}$$

where σ_f and ε_f are the final Hugoniot stress and strain achieved in shock compression, s is the slope of U_s-U_p relation.

DISCUSSION

several experimental studies on the dynamic compression behavior of 2169 stainless steel have been carried out in our institute for the past years. M. S. Yang et al[3] measured the shock Hugoniot in the pressure range of 50~250GPa using the explosively loading techniques. In their experiment, the impedance-match method was adopted and OFHC copper was taken as a standard material. The composition of the samples is listed in Table 1. The least-square fit to their data results in

$$U_s = 4.693^{\pm 0.055} + 1.339^{\pm 0.023} U_p \qquad 1.238 \leqslant U_p \leqslant 3.425\text{km/s} \qquad (6)$$

which is plotted in Fig. 4.

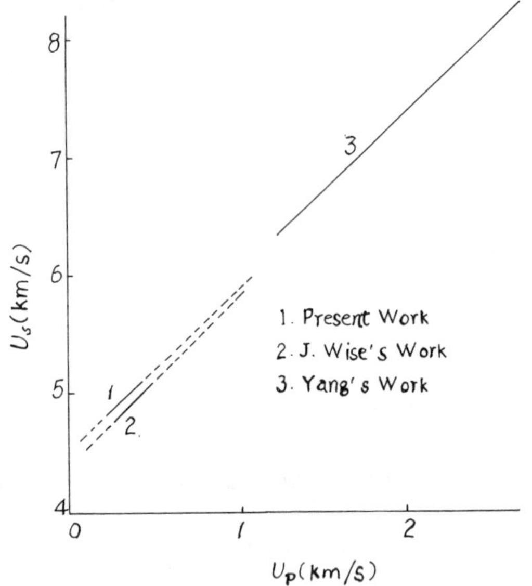

Fig. 4 Comparison of present U_s-U_p measurements with some previously reported results

X. G. Jin et al obtained ultrahigh pressure of about 2TPa in 2169 stainless steel using an underground explosion. With iron as the standard material, they provided the following experimental results of 2169 steel:

shock velocity $U_s = 22.12$km/s,
particle velocity $U_p = 13.39$km/s,
shock pressure $P = 2.31$TPa,
compression ratio $\sigma = 2.53$.

The above results are in good agreements with extrapolations from both Yang′ s and present data. The corresponding relative errors are 2.3% and 4.2%, respectively.

J. L. Wise and D. E. Mikkola in Sandia National Labs reported their research results on Hugoniot and wave-profile measurements on 2169 stainless steel on the gun impact experiment.

The relation between shock velocity and particle velocity from their data is

$$U_s = 4.403 + 1.441 U_p \qquad 0.25 \leqslant U_p \leqslant 0.49\text{km/s} \qquad (7)$$

Considering the fact that 2169 stainless steel consists of so many different elements and the difference of compositions between Wise′ s and present work, the agreement between above two experimental results is pretty good. From Fig. 4, it could also be observed that because the sample composition in present experiment is much closer with Yang′ s than Wise′ s, the agreement between Yang′ s data and the extrapolation from present data is better than that between Yang′ s and the extrapolation from Wise′ s.

Also, the difference between the longitudinal wave velocities among different samples should be considered.

ACKNOWLEDGEMENTS

The authors would like to thank Prof. Musong Yang for his helpful discussion and providing his experimental data for this paper. The following colleagues who took an active part in the preparation and conducting the experiments are also thanked: Zhiyi Wang, Xiaosong Wang, Qiuwei Fu, Zizheng Gong and Qiang Wu.

REFERENCES

[1] J. L. Wise and D. E. Mikkola, "Hugoniot and wave-profile measurements on shock-loaded stainless steel (21Cr-6Ni-9Mn)" in *Proceedings of the Conference on Shock Waves in Condensed Matter*, 1988, pp. 261-264

[2] X. G. Jin et al., *Chinese Journal of High Pressure*, 2 (1), 1988 pp17-23.

[3] M. S. Yang et al, Private communication, 1984.

[4] F. Q. JING "Shock wave physics research in China" in *Proceedings of the conference on Shock Compression of Condensed Matter*, 1990, pp33-44.

[5] D. E. Grady "Steady-wave risetime and spall measurements on uranium (3-15GPa)" in *Proceedings of the conference on Shock-Wave and High-Strain-Rate Phenomena in Materials*, 1986, pp763-780

THE INFLUENCE OF SHOCK INDUCED POLYMORPHIC TRANSITION IN STEEL ON 2D WAVES PROPAGATION.

A.FANGET, P.L HEREIL and J.M SIBEAUD.

Centre d'Etudes de Gramat, 46500 France.

Steel presents a well known polymorphic transition at the pressure of 13. GPa. This implies a new field of repartition for the waves crossing the sample and consequently a different loading field. At first, the modelisation of the polymorphic transition of a particular steel is shown validated by the comparaison between experimental(1) and numerical (1D lagrangian discretisation) results of the free surface velocity in plates impact configuration. The second part involves the influence of the polymorphic transition of the steel for two dimensional experiments and numerical simulations (2D lagrangian configuration). The repartition, in the sample of the thermodymanical variables, is shown for a 2D impact configurations.

INTRODUCTION

A modelisation of the direct and reverse polymorphic phase transitions for the low–alloy martensitic steel (27NCD10) has been built by P.L Hereil and F.Doubax [1]. In this work, they have used original plate impact configuration to observe the reverse phase transition and they have implemented the model in a one–dimensionnal wave propagation code. This paper is the extension of the utilisation of this model in 2D impact configurations where experimental and numerical results are compared.

MODEL REVIEW

The constitutive relations consist in a two–phase equation of state and a thermodynamic model for the non–equilibrium phase change. The equilibrium surface of the first and second phase are elabored respectively by the Murnaghan and Keane equations of state. Their interdependence in the phase transition domain is realized by the equality of the Gibbs free energies of the two phases on the phase boundary in the (pressure, temperature) coordinates. In the mixed region, the physical assumptioms are :

No surface energy between the two phases.

Existence of an internal parameter λ which is the mass fraction of the second phase.

The equilibrium functions λ_{eq} for direct and reverse are respectively given by the expressions :

$$\lambda_{eq} = 1 - exp\left[\beta\ (G_1 - G_2)\right]$$

$$\lambda_{eq} = exp\left[\beta\ (G_1 - G_2)\right]$$

where β is a constant, G_1 and G_2 represent the Gibbs free energies of the two phases. The kinetic transformation is expressed by :

$$d\lambda/dt = (\lambda_{eq} - \lambda)/\tau$$

with $\tau = \phi_0 / (|G_1 - G_2|)$

The parameters of the model are recalled in table I.

EXPERIMENTAL CONFIGURATIONS.

1. Material properties.

The investigated material is a low–alloy martensitic steel elaborated by rolling. Alloying agents and impurities are (in wt%) : C (0.270), Mn (0.670), Ni (2.24), Cr (2.16), Cu (0.17), Mo (0.48) and others (0.01). Its Rockwell C hardeness is approximatively 25 and its volumic mass is 7835 kg/m^3 · Ultrasonic measurement yield mean values of longitudinal C_l and shear C_s wave velocities : C_l = 5895 m/s and C_s = 3225 m/s. Corresponding value for Poisson's ratio is ν = 0.286.

Table I
Parameters of the model

	alpha phase	epsilon phase
K_0(Gpa)	15.5	21.5
n_0	5.5	6.5
n_i	–	4.5
Cv(J/kg/K)	444.7	446.6
Γ	1.735	2.0
β(kg/J)	9.10^{-5}	9.10^{-5}

2. Studied configurations .

Three experimentations have been done. The first is the recall of plate impact test to validate the implementation of the model in this configuration. The two others concern the impact of kinetic projectile on plate. Two thicknesses of plate for experimentations have been done. The relevant experimental parameters are summarized in Table I. An Interferometric Doppler Laser (IDL) system has been used to mesure the free surface velocity of the rear of the plate.

The first 2D configuration concerns the impact of a projectile with a flat noze against a 5 mm thick plate. Though this configuration in the first microsecond involves an unidimensionnal behaviour, it is caracterized by the fact that the values of the radius of the projectile and the width of the plate are proportionnal of a factor 2. So the release wave from the free boundary of the projectile and the plate can converge in the same locus.

The purpose of the second 2D configuration where now the thickness of the plate is 25 mm is to separate the two phase waves. So the release wave from the free surface of the projectile can "catch" the second phase wave. By this way, one can know if the celerity of the waves in the different phases are well simulated, because the free surface velocity is very lower than them. A comparison will be done between two calculations, one with the phase polymorphic change, the other without.

The initial conditions for the relevant numerical configurations are summarized in table II.

RESULTS AND DISCUSSION.

The modelisation of the polymorphic phase change has been implemented in the hydrodynamic lagrangian code EPIC2. It discretizes the equations of the continuum mechanics by the finite elements approach.

1. Unidimensionnal test.

For this test, the mesh size used in the numerical simulation is dx=.02 mm. Figure 1 presentes the comparison between experimental and numerical results about the evolution of free surface velocity. The numerical signal is spreaded than experimental one, in particular for the elastic precursor where the spreading comes from the pseudo viscosity essentially. The free surface velocity levels of the polymorphic changement and maximal value are in of good accuracy with experimental results. They average values are respectively 659 m/s and 1032 m/s. In the numerical simulation, the "plateau" showing the phase change is flatter than in the record. It means that the slope noted experimentally comes specifically from the plastic behaviour of the material. In these calculations, we used a simple rigid plastic behaviour and a more sophisticated model is needed.

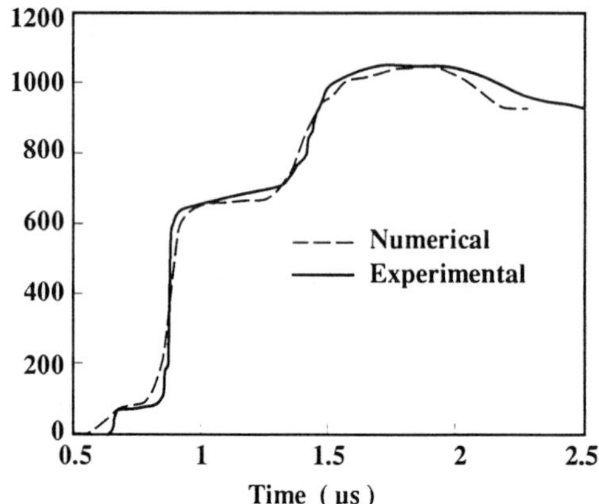

Figure 1 : Free surface velocity. case 1D

2. 2D configuration (plate thickness = 5 mm).

In the plate the average size of the cell is dx = .1 mm, the mesh is triangular with four triangles per cell. This 2D configuration allows to have an unidimensionnal loading and a 2D unloading. The figure 2 shows the isobars of phase change at the time 2 µs. The projectile for a large part is in the ε and α phase while the target is totally relaxed and presents two tension areas. The experimental–numerical comparison, done on the free surface velocity, shows a good fitting (figure 3). The same remark about the spread of the signal at the phase change level can be done than in 1D configuration. The consequence is that the simulated second shock anticipates the real shock.

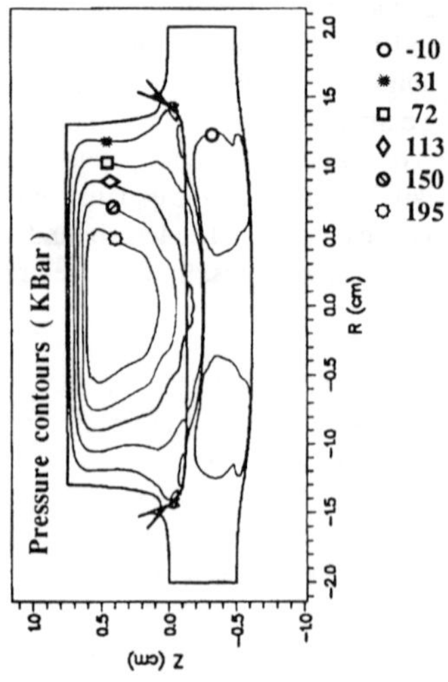

Figure 2 : Isopressures case 2D, ep=5 mm, T = 2 µs

Table II
Configurations parameters.

Cases	Impactor Material	Impactor projectile (mm)	Target thickness (mm)	Impact velocity (m/s)
1D	Steel	plate 4.03	7.985	1105.
2D	Steel	cylinder ϕ = 13	5.	1270.
2D	Steel	cylinder ϕ = 13	25.	1300.

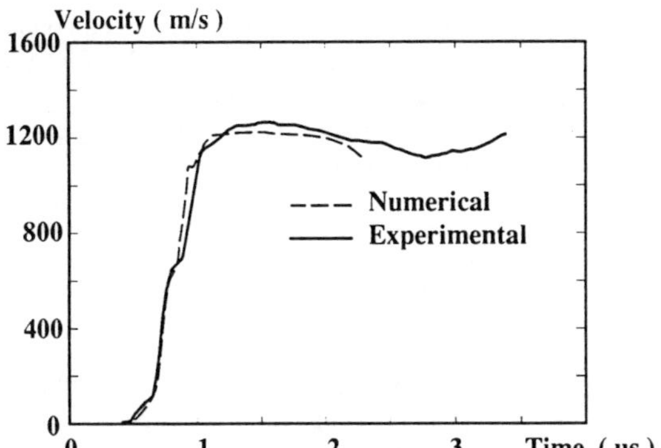

Figure 3 : Free surface velocity case 2D, ep = 5 mm

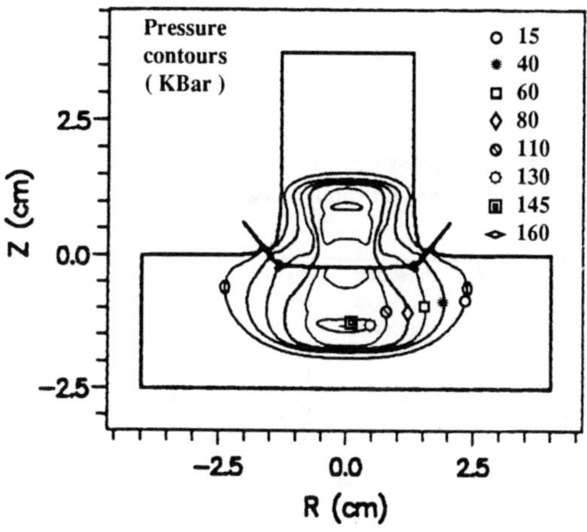

Figure 4 : Isopressures case 2D, ep= 25 mm, T = 3.5 ms, with polymorphic phase change.

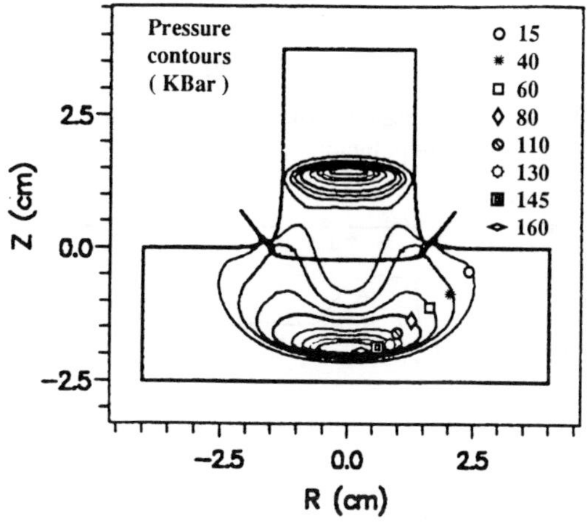

Figure 5 : Isopressures case 2D, ep= 25 mm, T = 3.5 ms, without polymorphic phase change.

3. 2D configuration (plate thickness = 25 mm)

In the plate the average size of the cell is dx = .26 mm, the mesh is triangular with four triangles by cell. As we mentionned previously, the released waves coming from the free interface projectile–target catch the second wave in the simulation made with the polymorphic phase change. Figure 4 shows this phenomenon at 3.5 µs. The maximal value in pressure in the plate is less than 130 10^8 Pa, so any polymorphic phase transformation can take place far away this area. Without the phase change model, as we can see figure 5, the maximal value of pressure is more than 160 10^8 Pa. On the contrary, at the interface projectile–target, the level of pressure is less, in the case where no phase change is taken in account, because the velocity of the release waves goes faster. At 5.5 µs, the isopressure contours are (specially about the location of tension zones) for the two cases, very different (see figures 6 and 7). If damaging model had been used, the effect of the recompression due to the relaxation stress on the free surface velocity would have been deleted for the simulation with phase change. In this kind of penetration the area which is submitted to the phase change is very confined at the interface projectile–target. Figure 8 shows the comparison experimental–numerical results about the free surface velocity .There is a gap between the results coming from the discretisation but not only.

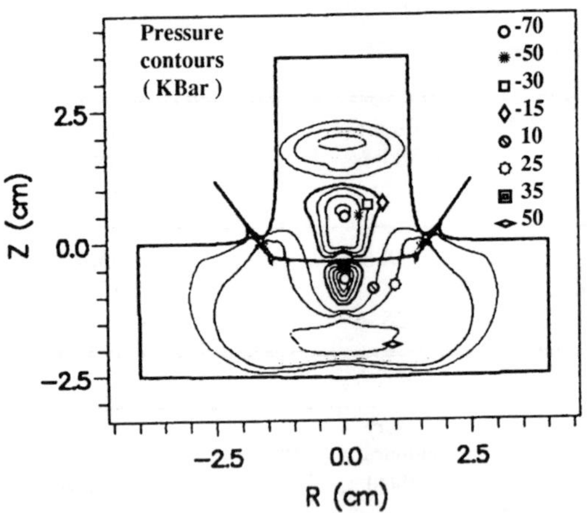

Figure 6 : Isopressures case 2D, ep= 25 mm, T = 5.5 ms, with polymorphic phase change.

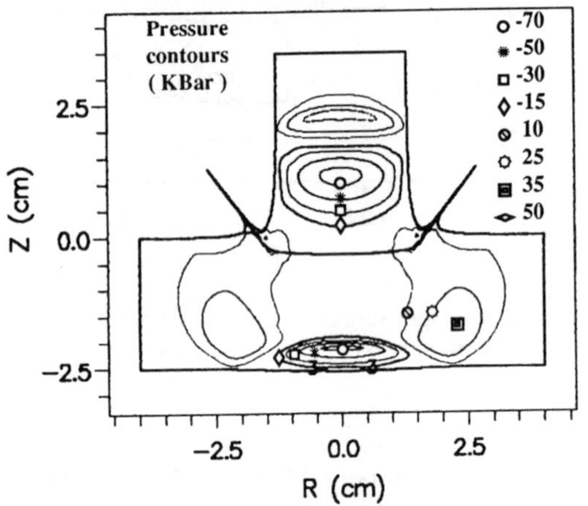

Figure 7 : Isopressures case 2D, ep= 25 mm, T = 5.5 ms, without polymorphic phase change.

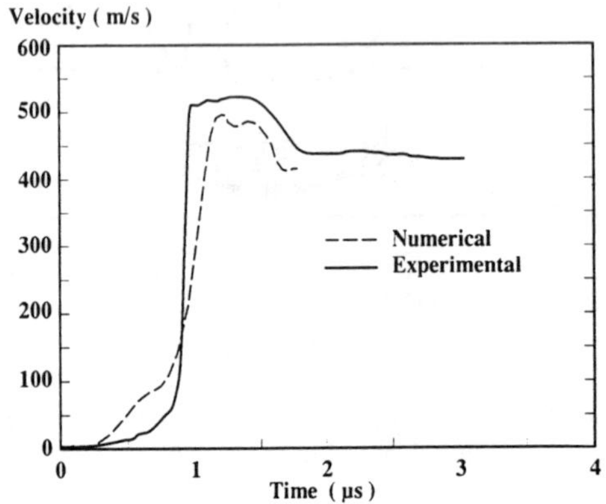

Figure 8 : Free surface velocity case 2D, ep = 25 mm

CONCLUSION.

The polymorphic phase change is well implemented in the EPIC2 code. Nevertheless, the 1D calculation shows that the model of behaviour of the material must be changed for the model of behaviour of the material must be changed for a more sophisticated one. Two D configuration shows , for the studied impact velocities, that the polymorphic phase change takes place in a restrictive area which is localized around the interface projectile–target. This point is important and it need to have a very good numerical treatment of the interface to avoid numerical dispertion due to the boundary conditions. The change of the propagation of the wave yields to a repartition very different of tension areas. With the damage model developed in [2], we hope getting good fitting with experimental results.

ACKNOWLEDGEMENT

We want to acknowledge P.LEYDE for this help in the use of EPIC2 code and A.Halgand for the experimental data.

REFERENCES

1. P.L. Hereil, F.Doubax : Shock Compression of Condensed Matter June 17–20 1991

2. F.Doubax : Ph.D Universite de P. Sabatier de Toulouse 19 juin 1992

STRESSES IN PAINTED STEEL COUPONS FROM STONE IMPACT

A. C. Ramamurthy[1], S. J. Bless[2], N. S. Brar[3]
[1]Canton, MI*
[2]Institute for Advanced Technology, Austin, TX
[3]University of Dayton Research Institute, Dayton, OH

* Present address: Ford Motor Company, Redford, MI

Abstract—Impacts of stones on painted steel coupons was studied using an air gun to launch standard rocks. Shock stress was measured with manganin gauges behind the coupons, and it was concluded that the paint layers cause significant shock attenuation, especially when thicker viscoelastic materials are used.

Impact chipping of automotive paint from stones and other lofted road debris is a problem of increasing concern to the automobile industry. Damage to upper pigment layers presents a cosmetic problem. However, damage to the relatively brittle and thin phosphate layer on the surface of the steel substrate will usually lead to impact induced corrosion.

Qualitative studies of impact damage to paint have been carried out for some time [1, 2]. Recently time resolved temperature measurements have shown that significant heating can occur during stone impact onto painted substrates [3]. Numerical techniques have also recently been applied to stone impacts with some success [4], new techniques have been developing for quantifying impact damage [5], and new experimental apparatus for precision impact studies has also recently appeared [6]. A comprehensive review of stone impact phenomena associated with paint chipping will be appearing in [7].

In the present study, stone projectiles were fired at a variety of different types of targets. The projectiles were cone cylinders made of Cedar City tonalite; these projectiles were originally developed to study the vulnerability of missiles to lofted stones. The projectile diameters were 19mm. The volume was essentially the same as a 19mm diameter sphere.

In the first study, a nominal impact velocity of 40 m/s was employed. A plastic barrel was used with compressed air and styrofoam sabots. Velocity was measured with two laser PIN diode time-of-arrival stations. Impact stress was measured with 50-Ω Dynasen ytterbium gauges. The sensitive area was 3.2mm square.

Targets consisted of painted 0.8mm thick cold rolled steel plates. The gauges were placed between the rear surface (unpainted side) of the steel plates and a relatively thick substrate. Steel was used for initial experiments to develop techniques; then Lexan blocks were employed. In order to avoid damaging the relatively expensive gauges, a 0.08mm sheet of PMMA was placed between the gauge and the paint coupon. Initial experiments with sharp pointed projectiles resulted in considerable scatter, so it later tests the nose of the projectile was ground flat to a 6.3mm diameter area.

Two types of targets were used: standard paint specimens (approximately 50 μm clearcoat, 25 μm basecoat, 25 μm primer, and 25 μm electrocoat). The other specimen design had an additional layer: 0.35mm layer of polyurethane film manufactured by 3M Corporation. It was known that the polyurethane film reduces impact induced corrosion, and we wanted to find out how it modified the impact induced stress waves.

All targets were dented by the impacts. Projectiles striking base panels always broke, whereas projectiles striking coated panels did not break. A typical stress-time record from a standard specimen in shown in Figure 1. The initial peak is due to the impact shock, and the negative phase is due to stretching of the gauge by subsequent in-plane strain. Brar has found that the apparent stress rise in ytterbium due to in-plane strain does indeed go through a negative followed by a positive phase [8]. The relaxation of the gauge is due to projectile rebound. Values of peak shock stress are listed in Table 1. For the standard material, it was about 0.2 kbar.

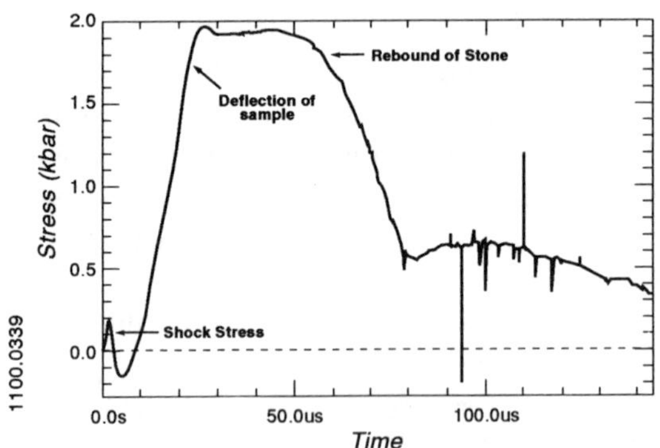

Fig. 1. **Gauge record from first test in Table 1.**

Table 1
Stresses Measured in Panels Backed by Lexan Blocks

Stone mass (g)	Impact velocity (m/s)	Target	Shock (kbar)	Duration (μs)
9.8	41	base	0.19	55
9.4	42	base	0.22	58
9.4	44	coated	0	
9.4	42	coated	0.05	65

An impedance match solution for these impacts (granite striking steel over plastic) gives a peak stress in the steel of 5 kbar. After a few reverberations in the steel (lasting about 0.7 μs), the stress should relax to 1 kbar (granite striking plastic). Although the time scale for the first pulse is about right, the peak stress levels are much lower than these values. We tentatively conclude that the stress reduction is due to the neglect of shock attenuation in the paint layer. This is born out by the observation that peak stress levels were significantly less in the specimens with the extra 3-M coating, although total load durations were similar—about 60 μs.

The stress records also give the duration of the contact. This is about 60 μs. The duration of loading may be estimated from several different assumptions. Timoshenko's equation for contact duration is [7],

$$t_1 = \frac{2.943\left(1.25\,\pi\rho_1\left(K_1+K_2\right)\right)^{2/5}R}{V^{1/5}} \quad , \qquad (1)$$

where R is projectile radius, V is impact velocity, and $K = (1-\nu^2)/\pi E$, where ν and E have their usual meanings as elastic constants, and subscripts 1 and 2 refer to the projectile and target. This equation is based on the assumption that the projectile is spherical and that the projectile and target remain elastic.

If the projectile collapses, then the duration would be given by:

$$t_2 = 2\frac{R}{V} \quad , \qquad (2)$$

where V is the impact velocity. These contrast with the normal shock equation for plate projectiles, where the impact duration is:

$$t_3 = 2\frac{R}{C_L} \quad , \qquad (3)$$

(for projectile impedance < target impedance) where C_L is the sound velocity.

We estimate these times by taking R = 9.5 mm, E_2 = 210 GPa, ν_2 = 0.33, ν_1 = 0.2, E_1 = 72 GPa, ρ = 2.65 g/cm^3, and V = 40 m/s, C_L = 6mm/μs, giving t_1 = 27μs, t_2 = 475μs, and t_3 = 3 μs. The shock phase duration agree with t_3, as might be expected. But the measured contact duration is about 2 t_1. The difference cannot be due to shatter, since the projectiles hitting coated targets did not shatter. The assumptions regarding target properties should be conservative, so the discrepancy is probably because the target is effectively much softer than predicted by a thick steel solution.

The efficacy of the 3-M coating in reducing impact induced corrosion is presumably due to the additional stress attenuation, indicated by the lower shock stress measured by the gauge and the fact that the stones did not shatter when hitting coated specimens. However, whether the attenuation is due the energy absorbing properties of the polymer or simply the additional thickness remains to be determined.

In additional studies we measured the rebound velocity of stones striking unsupported paint coupons. The same shape stones were used; mass was about 2.18 g. These stones did not break. Post impact deflection and rebound velocity were measured in these tests. Two types of panels were tested. Some had the paint scheme as before (type 1), while in type 3 panels a 110μm layer of Stoneguard© was added below the color coats. Stoneguard© is also known to be very effective at reducing impact damage.

Figure 2 shows the variation of deflection with impact velocity. It is clear that there is a critical velocity for the onset of deflection of about 18 m/s. The deflection is not linear in velocity. Instead, it is approximately quadratic, with a threshold of about 18 m/s. The deflection also did not correlate well with the change in momentum where rebound was measured. Thus, deflection seems to correlate principally with impact energy.

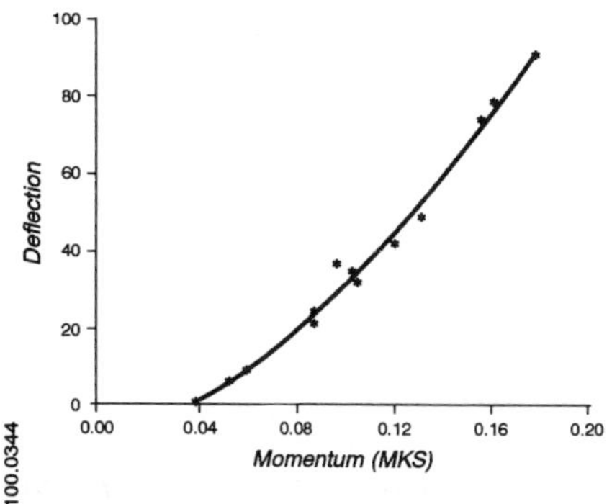

Fig. 2. **Deflection vs impact momentum for type 1 panels.**

Data for rebound velocities are shown in Table 2. For both types of panels, the rebound velocity was about 20% of the impact velocity.

In summary, we have shown that the peak stresses caused when stones strike paint specimens are commensurate with shock wave loading. Coatings which are known to reduce impact damage also significantly reduce shock loads. Deflection is associated with impact energy, and paint systems which reduce impact damage do not reduce deflection. Therefore, the hypothesis that damage is due to shock loading is worth further investigation. Moreover, principles of shock physics might be useful in reducing impact damage to painted substrates.

Table 2
Velocity Measurements from Stones Hitting Unbacked Panels

Impact velocity (m/s)	**Target type**	**Rebound velocity (m/s)**
47	1	10.4
27	1	6.4
40	1	5.6
55	1	5.4
30	3	9
67	3	5
32	3	6.6

REFERENCES:

1. U. Zorll, *Metalloberflache*, 29, 577, 1975.

2. E. Ladstadter, *Farbe und Lack*, 83, 9, 1977.

3. A. T .Zehnder, A. C. Ramamurthy, S. J. Bless, N. S. Brar, *Int. J. Impact Engng,* 13, 133, 1993.

4. A. C. Ramamurthy, W. I. Lorenzen, A. M. Rajendran, D. Grove, *Proc. ACS, PMSE Div.,* 67, 43, 1992.

5. A. C. Ramamurthy, T. Ahmed, L. D. Fauro, R. L. Thomas, D. B. K. Hohnke, R. Cooper, Paper # 930051, 1993 Ann. Congress SAE, Detroit, MI, March 1, 1993.

6. A. C. Ramamurthy, W. M. Isbell, V. A. Venditto, T. Jennings, paper at 1993 SAE Auto. Corrosion and Prevention, Oct 4, 1993.

7. A. C. Ramamurthy, W. I. Lorenzen, S. J. Bless, Prog. Org. Coat,. Dec. 1993.

8. N. S. Brar, unpublished data.

SHOCK COMPRESSION AND QUASIELASTIC RELEASE IN TANTALUM

J. N. Johnson, R. S. Hixson, D. L. Tonks, and G. T. Gray III
Los Alamos National Laboratory
Los Alamos, New Mexico, USA 87545

Previous studies of quasielastic release in shock-loaded FCC metals have shown a strong influence of the defect state on the leading edge, or first observable arrival, of the release wave. This is due to the large density of pinned dislocation segments behind the shock front, their relatively large pinning separation, and a very short response time as determined by the drag coefficient in the shock-compressed state. This effect is entirely equivalent to problems associated with elastic moduli determination using ultrasonic methods. This is particularly true for FCC metals, which have an especially low Peierls stress, or inherent lattice resistance, that has little influence in pinning dislocation segments and inhibiting anelastic deformation. BCC metals, on the other hand, have a large Peierls stress that essentially holds dislocation segments in place at low net applied shear stresses and thus allows fully elastic deformation to occur in the complete absence of anelastic behavior. Shock-compression and release experiments have been performed on tantalum (BCC), with the observation that the leading release disturbance is indeed elastic. This conclusion is established by examination of experimental VISAR records taken at the tantalum/sapphire (window) interface in a symmetric-impact experiment which subjects the sample to a peak longitudinal stress of approximately 7.3 GPa, in comparison with characteristic code calculations.

INTRODUCTION

One of the unique aspects of shock-compression science is the ability to make very accurate time-resolved (~1 ns) optical measurements of particle velocity at a position on the surface of an impacted solid sample. If the sample material is transparent, these measurements can be made *in situ.* More often, as in the case of metals, measurements are made at the planar interface between the sample and a transparent window material chosen to provide a reasonably good acoustic impedance match with the sample.

These data contain much information concerning variation of elastic moduli with compression, the onset and continuation of high-rate plastic flow, and quasielastic release from the shocked state.

The term "quasielastic" comes from the common observation that release waves in shocked metals (and perhaps most nonmetals) do not exhibit ideal elastic-plastic behavior.

The initial treatment of elastic-plastic deformation in shock-loaded solids was based on rate-independent, ideally plastic deformation. However, it was soon recognized that this description was unable to account for time-dependent effects, particularly the complex release-wave properties observed in almost all, if not all, metals. Measured release waves exhibit a great deal of anelastic, or quasielastic, structure prior to fully plastic, reverse yielding when the stress state encounters the yield surface on the opposite side of the shock hydrostat.

Analysis of quasielastic release in shock-compressed solids involves quantifying microstructural effects such as pinned dislocation segments and dislocation pile-ups. This includes the evolution of internal stresses that control the motion of these defects as the applied stress is released in the unloading wave propagating into the shocked state [1-4]. In previous work [4] several conclusions are reached in regard to the type of defects related to quasielastic release-wave behavior in FCC metals. The first is that pinned segments are responsible for the reverse inelastic deformation observed in the quasielastic regime, and secondly the distance L between pinning points is ~ 500 b, where b is the lattice spacing (or magnitude of the Burgers vector). The line density of pinned dislocation segments is on the order of 10^{-5} b^{-2} (approximately 10^{10} cm^{-2}). These observations seem reasonable enough, but the inferred value of the viscous drag coefficient B in the shock-compressed state is unusual. For 6061-T6 aluminum, oxygen-free-electronic (OFE) copper, and a silicon-bronze alloy (all shock loaded to 10 - 20 GPa) it is found that the viscous drag coefficient must be approximately 1 dyne s cm^{-2} in order for calculated quasielastic release waves to be in even approximate agreement with measurement. This is three orders of magnitude greater than experimentally observed under ambient conditions [5]. These results pertain explicitly to the assumption that the leading observable release disturbance is fully elastic.

Preliminary molecular dynamics studies [6] suggest that the viscous drag coefficient in copper is essentially unchanged by compression to 10 - 20 GPa. This information served as a strong impetus to investigate quasielastic behavior related to lower values (0.001 - 0.1 dyne s cm^{-2}) of the viscous drag coefficient in FCC metals [6]. The results given in reference [7] show that for $B \le 0.1$ dyne s cm^{-2} the leading <u>observable</u> release-wave disturbance in FCC metals does not propagate with the elastic wave speed c_e given by

$$\rho c_e^2 = K + \frac{4}{3}G \ , \tag{1}$$

but with the "relaxed" velocity c_r defined by

$$\rho c_r^2 = K + \frac{4G/3}{1+(nL^2/4)} \ , \tag{2}$$

where ρ is the material density, K and G are the adiabatic bulk and shear moduli, respectively, and nL^2 is the product of density (length per unit volume) of pinned segments and the average pinning separation squared. All of the quantities in Equations (1) and (2) are evaluated in the shock-compressed state ahead of the release wave.

For normal values of B, the shear modulus determined from release-wave measurements corresponds to the elastic shear modulus $G(\varepsilon)$ only when $nL^2 \ll 1$: this is also one of the conditions required of ultrasonic measurement in the accurate determination of elastic moduli [8,9]. Unfortunately, experimentalists have little or no control over nL^2 behind the shock front in shock-release experiments.

The specific results obtained so far apply only to FCC metals, for which the Peierls stress provided by the lattice is usually quite small. Other solids may possibly possess sufficient natural resistance to reverse motion of dislocation segments to insure that the initial release from the shocked state is fully elastic.

This brings us to the question of whether or not the leading observable release wave in tantalum, a typical BCC metal, propagates with the fully elastic speed, in contrast with results obtained for FCC metals. The answer to that question is yes, the leading portion of the release wave in tantalum does propagate with the fully elastic wave speed. This is a consequence of the effective pinning of bowed out dislocation segments provided by the finite Peierls stress of the lattice.

MICROMECHANICAL SOURCE OF ANELASTICITY IN THE RELEASE WAVE

The quasielastic nature of release waves in aluminum, copper, and Si-bronze comes from internal stresses acting on dislocations due to their curvature between pinning points provided by lattice impurities, point defects, or other dislocations. This is shown schematically in Figure 1. The relationship between radius of curvature R and applied shear stress τ in the shock-compressed state is $R = Gb/\tau$ under equilibrium conditions. In the transient situation the back stress β given by

$$\beta = Gb/R \tag{3}$$

is not in equilibrium with τ, but obeys the evolutionary law given by [4]

$$\dot{\beta} = \frac{(1/GB)\beta^2(\tau - \beta)}{[1 - (\beta L/2Gb)^2]^{-1/2} - 1} . \tag{4}$$

PINNED DISLOCATION SEGMENTS

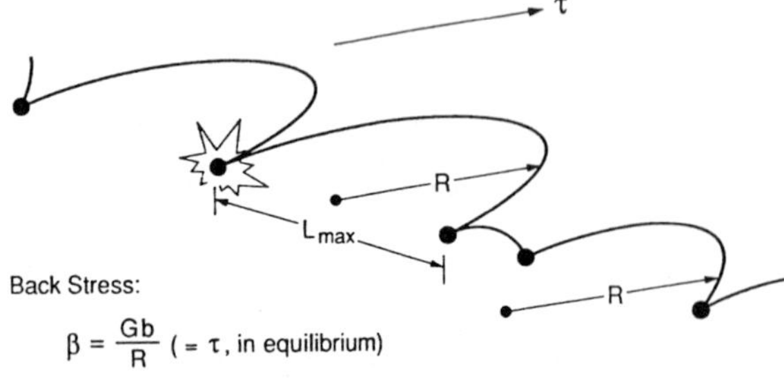

Figure 1. Pinned dislocation segments under the influence of an applied shear stress τ.

The release of applied stress allows reverse dislocation motion to occur immediately upon arrival of the unloading wave. There are two characteristic times associated with the accumulation of reverse plastic strain [4]: $(B/G)(L/b)^2$ and $B/(nb^2)$.

The first time constant controls the readjustment of the internal stress β due to dislocation curvature and the second controls the rate of accumulation of plastic strain. Because of the small values of B and L/b (~500), the first time constant is very small (~1 ns) and the readjustment of the dislocation segments takes place almost instantaneously, even in comparison to the best VISAR time resolution currently available. This means that the leading observable release disturbance in FCC metals is not fully elastic. Measured release-wave speeds are related to an effective elastic shear modulus given by

$$G_{eff} \sim \frac{G}{1 + nL^2/4}. \tag{5}$$

For pure materials, $nL^2 \sim 1$ and the shear modulus, as determined by release-wave speeds, is a few tens of percent lower than the true elastic shear modulus G.

As an aside, the above expression for the effective shear modulus suggests a means by which n can be determined in the shock-compressed state, once L, G, and G_{eff} are known.

Figures 2 and 3 show two calculations for 6061-T6 aluminum [10], each with B = 0.1 dyne s cm^{-2}; Figure 2 has a value of $nb^2 = 2.5 \times 10^{-5}$, and Figure 3 is for $nb^2 = 0$. The latter case shows the effect of "freezing out" the anelastic contribution from the pinned dislocation segments. The elastic shear modulus in the shock-compressed state is taken to be 92 GPa. The vertical arrows indicate the first observable arrival of the quasielastic release wave in each case. It is clear from these results that the presence of mobile dislocation segments has a strong influence on the first arrival of the release wave. The effective shear modulus as obtained from first-arrival information alone is G = 65 GPa.

RESULTS FOR TANTALUM

The quasielastic release wave in shock-loaded tantalum was studied using a 50-mm-diameter gas gun. Projectile velocity and tilt were measured immediately before impact by means of a stepped circular array of shorting pins surrounding the target disk. For this experiment the tilt was

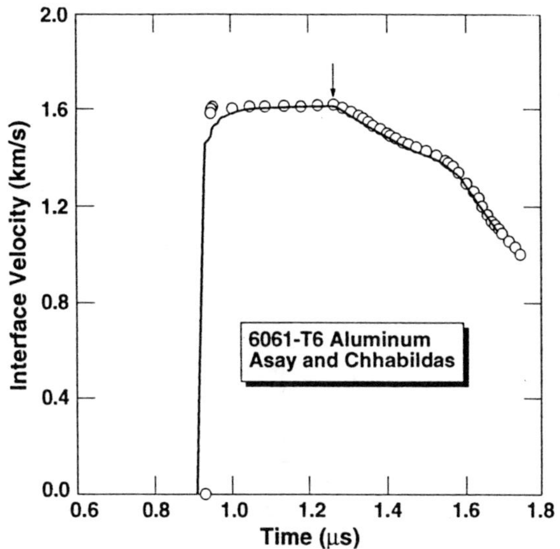

Figure 2. Measured (circles) and calculated (line) wave profiles in 6061-T6 aluminum: $nb^2 = 2.5 \times 10^{-5}$.

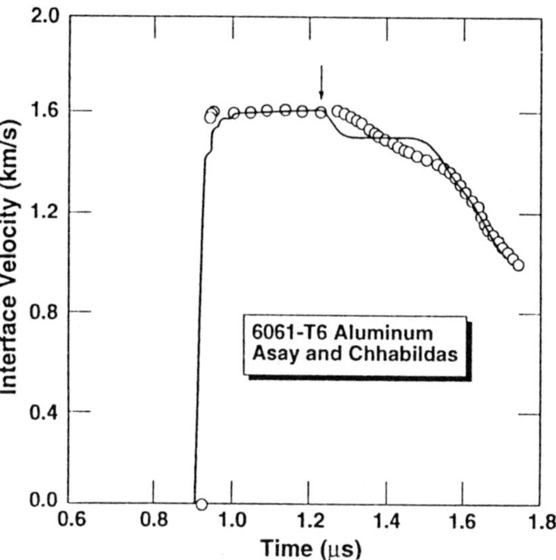

Figure 3. Measured (circles) and calculated (line) wave profiles in 6061-T6 aluminum: $nb^2 = 0$.

approximately 1.0-1.5 mrad, and the impact velocity was very close to 0.256 km/s. Symmetric impact was used to generate an initial 7.3-GPa shock followed by release.

The shock-release profile was measured using a push/pull VISAR [11]. The wave profile was measured at the target-window interface with a Z-cut sapphire window. This target geometry minimized, to the extent possible, hydrodynamic perturbations at the target-window interface.

These data are shown in Figures 4 and 5 in comparison with numerical simulations of this experiment using characteristic methods [4]. Figure 4 shows the effect of quasielastic release with ($nb^2 = 5 \times 10^{-5}$). Figure 5 shows material behavior in the absence of anelasticity in the release wave ($nb^2 = 0$). The viscous drag coefficient is taken to be B = 0.1 dyne s cm^{-2} in both cases. The influence of the Peierls stress is taken into account by assuming the dislocation velocity goes very rapidly to zero when the absolute magnitude of the shear stress falls below 0.45 GPa [12]. This is the effect that is responsible for pinning the dislocation segments as unloading begins in the release wave.

The results presented here show the quasielastic nature of the release wave in tantalum and the improved fit to the data when this is taken into account in way described previously [4]. However, it is seen that the first arrival time of the release wave is unaffected by the presence of pinned dislocation segments in the shock-compressed state. This is consistent with the existence of a strong lattice resistance (Peierls force) to dislocation motion in BCC materials.

The micromechanical model of pinned dislocation segments for FCC metals has been used in this calculation for tantalum. It is recognized that the shape of expanding dislocation loops in FCC and BCC metals is likely different, and that dislocation storage effects differ greatly between these two crystal structures [13]. However, the essential picture of bowed dislocation segments remains approximately the same. While the fundamental mechanism for generating back stress is unchanged, the effect of varied dislocation morphology will alter global slip activity from areal to lineal glide [14]. This rationale is consistent with substructure observations that show residual long, straight screw dislocations after deformation in tantalum at low temperatures or high strain rates [15].

The elastic properties of tantalum have been described in two ways. The first is the small anisotropy approximation [16], in which the isotropic bulk and shear moduli are assumed to be functions of density. In this approximation the bulk sound speed $c_0 = 3.43$ cm/μs, the slope of the shock-velocity/particle-velocity relationship is s = 1.19, and Poisson's ratio is assumed constant at ν = 0.331 [17]. Because of the relatively large Hugoniot elastic limit in comparison to the peak longitudinal stress of 7.3 GPa (Figures 4 and 5), the small anisotropy approximation may not be as valid as it is for aluminum at 21.7 GPa (Figures 2 and 3).

For this reason we also investigated the effect of using weak-shock analysis [16,18] involving second- and third-order elastic moduli. This will provide a check on the reasonableness of the small anisotropy approximation, and will be further confirmation of fully elastic behavior in the initial portion of the release wave. The independent isotropic elastic moduli used in these calculations are given by

$$C_{11} = 289.7 \text{ GPa}, \qquad C_{12} = 145.7 \text{ GPa},$$

$$C_{111} = -1622 \text{ GPa}, \quad C_{112} = -1100 \text{ GPa}, \quad C_{123} = 838.9 \text{ GPa},$$

based on calculations using the zero-pressure bulk sound speed [19] in conjunction with pressure and temperature

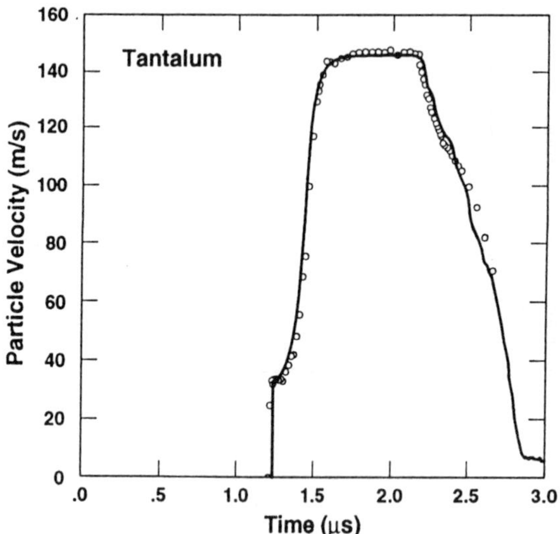

Figure 4. Measured (circles) and calculated (line) wave profiles in tantalum: $nb^2 = 5 \times 10^{-5}$.

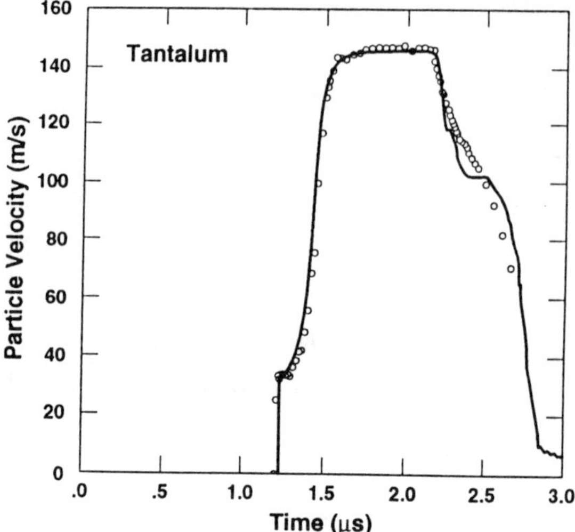

Figure 5. Measured (circles) and calculated (line) wave profiles in tantalum: $nb^2 = 0$.

derivatives of the the bulk and shear moduli [20,21]. Differences between wave profiles (Figures 4 and 5) using either the small anisotropy approximation or the weak-shock analysis are negligible.

SUMMARY AND CONCLUSIONS

Previous work showed that release waves in FCC metals were quasielastic in nature, and that the leading observable release disturbance propagated with a speed controlled by an effective shear modulus defined by $G_{eff} \sim G/[1 + nL^2/4]$, where G is the fully elastic shear modulus, n is the density of mobile dislocation segments behind the shock front, and L is their pinning separation. Experimentalists have little or no control over n and L in a shock/release cycle, and for this reason release-wave arrival times may be of questionable use in obtaining elastic moduli in the shocked state for FCC metals.

For BCC metals, in particular tantalum, the finite Peierls stress serves as an effective additional pinning mechanism that prohibits reverse dislocation motion immediately upon release from the shocked state. The leading observable release-wave disturbance in tantalum correctly samples fully elastic material response.

REFERENCES

[1] J. N. Johnson, P. S. Lomdahl, and J. M. Wills, *Acta Metall.* **39**, pp. 3015-3026 (1991).
[2] J. N. Johnson and P. S. Lomdahl, *J. de Physique IV*, Colloque C3, **1**, pp. 223-228 (1991).
[3] J. N. Johnson, G. T. Gray III, R. S. Hixson, and C. E. Morris, *J. Appl. Phys.* **72**, pp. 429-441 (1992).
[4] D. L. Tonks, in *Shock Waves in Condensed Matter 1991* (edited by S. C. Schmidt, R. D. Dick, J. W. Forbes, and D. G. Tasker) Amsterdam: Elsevier, 1992, pp. 269-272.
[5] J. J. Gilman, *Micromechanics of Flow in Solids*, New York: McGraw-Hill Book Co., 1969, ch. 5.
[6] J. B. Aidun, Personal Communication (1992).
[7] J. N. Johnson, *J. Phys. Chem. Sol.* (in press, 1993).
[8] J. S. Koehler, in *Imperfections in Nearly Perfect Solids* (edited by W. Shockley, *et al.*), New York: John Wiley and Sons, 1952, ch. 7.
[9] A. Granato and K. Lücke, *J. Appl. Phys.* **27**, pp. 583-593 (1956).
[10] J. R. Asay and L. C. Chhabildas, in *Shock Waves and High-Strain-rate Phenomena in Metals* (edited by M. A. Meyers and L. E. Murr), New York: Plenum, 1982, Ch. 26.
[11] W. F. Hemsing, *Rev. Sci. Instrum.*, pp. 73-78 (1979).
[12] K. G. Hoge and A. K. Mukherjee, *J. Mat. Sci.* **12**, pp. 1666-1672 (1977).
[13] G. T. Gray III, this volume.
[14] U. F. Kocks, in *The Mechanics of Dislocations* (edited by E. C. Aifanatis and J. P. Hirth) American Society for Metals, 1985, pp. 81-83.
[15] G. Welsch, R. Gibala, and T. E. Mitchell, *Phys. Stat. Sol. (a)* **30**, pp. 117-132.
[16] D. C. Wallace, Los Alamos Rep. LA-10119 (1985).
[17] S. P. Marsh, LASL Shock Hugoniot Data, Berkeley: University of California Press, 1980, p.136.
[18] D. C. Wallace, *Phys. Rev. B* **22**, pp. 1487-1494 (1980).
[19] A. C. Mitchell and W. J. Nellis , *J. Appl. Phys.* **52**, pp. 3363-3374 (1981).
[20] R. G. Leisure, D. K. Hsu, and B. A. Seiber, *J. Appl. Phys.* **44**, pp. 3394-3397 (1973).
[21] K. W. Katahara, M. H. Manghnani, and E. S. Fisher, *J. Appl. Phys.* **47**, pp. 434-439 (1976).

DYNAMICAL BEHAVIOR OF TANTALUM*

Michael D. Furnish[1], Lalit C. Chhabildas[1] and Daniel J. Steinberg[2]

[1]Experimental Impact Physics Dept. 1433, Sandia National Laboratories, Albuquerque NM 87185
[2]MS L-35, Lawrence Livermore National Laboratory, Livermore, CA 94551

We have performed four dynamic impact tests on tantalum to determine its high-pressure yield and viscoelastic properties. Our experiments used compressed gas gun techniques to produce a combination of shocks, reshocks and releases over the pressure range 0-12 GPa in samples 5.0 and 7.3 mm thick. Profiles were recorded using VISAR (velocity interferometry) techniques. Elastic precursors suggest a yield strength of 0.95 GPa, which is somewhat above literature values. As with other metals, release waves do not show a perfect elastic-plastic behavior, indicating a slight Baushinger effect. Lagrangian sound velocities for singly shocked states are consistent with earlier results (about 4.5 km/sec).

INTRODUCTION

As part of an effort to characterize the viscoplastic behavior of a variety of refractory metals we have undertaken a study of the dynamical properties of molybdenum, tantalum, vanadium and tungsten (all body-centered cubic materials), using time resolved velocity interferometry techniques. The detailed results obtained to date for tungsten, vanadium, molybdenum and tantalum (higher stress regimes) are summarized elsewhere[1,2,3,4] In this paper, the most recent results on tantalum are summarized. The experiments were conducted over a pressure range of 3.5 to 12 GPa. Most of the physical phenomena of interest contribute significantly to the observed wave behavior for loading and unloading in this pressure range. The viscoelastic behavior of tantalum can be deduced from the rise time (and release time) measurements of stress or particle velocity profiles. Specific viscoelastic properties of interest include the Hugoniot Elastic Limit (HEL), its dependence on run distance and final stress amplitude, the strain rate in the plastic loading wave, properties of release, reshock and release/reshock cycles, and yield strength in the shocked state; metallurgical properties of virgin and recovered material are also of interest. These are the first reshock experiments of this nature for fully dense tantalum.

The objective of the present paper is to present the data obtained from the impact experiments conducted with tantalum and interpretations of the loading/unloading properties from the observed wave profiles.

IMPACT EXPERIMENTS

Method and Matrix

A suite of four impact tests was designed to allow the observation of strength effects, the Hugoniot, and release properties. The configurations used are shown schematically in Fig. 1, with relevant dimensions given in Table 1.

Sapphire impactors and windows were chosen because sapphire is an extremely high-impedance, elastic material with well-studied optical and mechanical properties in the stress regime of interest (stresses up to about 9 GPa are achieved in the windows in the present study).

Results and Discussion

The first two experiments conducted (Ta 1 and Ta 2) utilized samples of similar thickness and impact velocity, but differed in that Ta 2 provided a reshock of the sample followed by a release, while

*Sponsored by the U.S. Department of Energy and conducted under the auspices of the U. S. Department of Energy under Contract DE-AC04-76DP00789.

Table 1. Shot parameters for tantalum tests. Note that WC (Tungsten Carbide) reshock plates in tests Ta 2 and Ta 4 are backed by PMMA.

	Ta 1	Ta 2	Ta 3	Ta 4
Sapphire Backer	PMMA	WC	PMMA	WC
Backer Thickness	6.1575 mm	1.796 mm	6.097 mm	1.600 mm
Sapphire FP Thick	3.1896 mm	3.180 mm	3.1735 mm	3.171 mm
Sample Thickness	7.273 mm	7.277	5.0205 mm	5.0225 mm
Sample Diameter	50.8635 mm	50.8635 mm	50.828 mm	50.825 mm
Sample Density	16.65 gm/cm^3	16.65 gm/cm^3	16.65 gm/cm^3	16.65 gm/cm^3
Window Thickness	25.2805 mm	25.320 mm	25.382 mm	25.402 mm
Impact Velocity	305 m/sec	305 m/sec	442 m/sec	133 m/sec
Velocity per Fringe	40.60 m/sec	40.60 m/sec	40.60 m/sec	40.33 m/sec

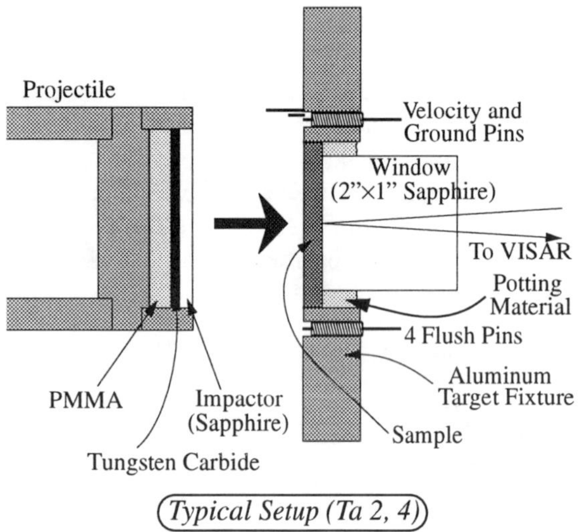

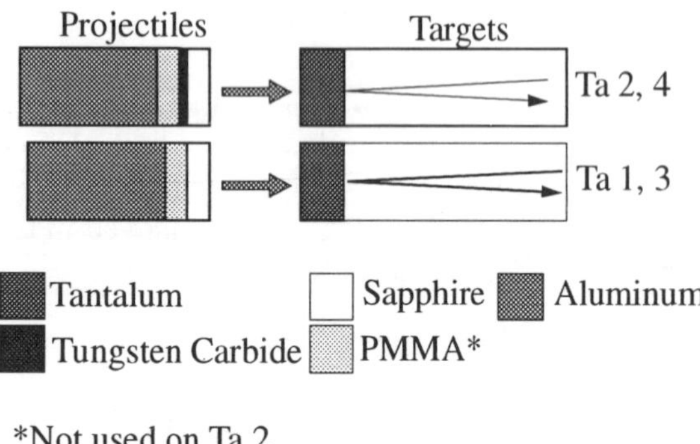

Figure 1. Impact configurations used

Ta 1 provided a simple release.

The resulting wave profiles are shown in Figures 2 and 3, together with 1-dimensional simulations performed with the wavecode WONDY V utilizing a Mie-Grüneisen model for tantalum (C_0 = 3.414 km/sec, S = 1.201, ρ_0 = 16.65 gm/cm^3), and an elastic-perfectly-plastic behavior with a yield strength of 0.7 GPa.

The precursors provided an accurate fiducial, and were used to establish timing of the profiles relative to impact. We made use of the relation,

$$C_l = (4.146{+}0.291P(\text{GPa}))\ \text{km/sec}$$

for the pressure dependence of the tantalum longitudinal wave velocity[5]. The half-maximum point of the precursor (corresponding to about 1 GPa sample stress) was taken to represent the precursor arrival time; the waveform was translated in time to

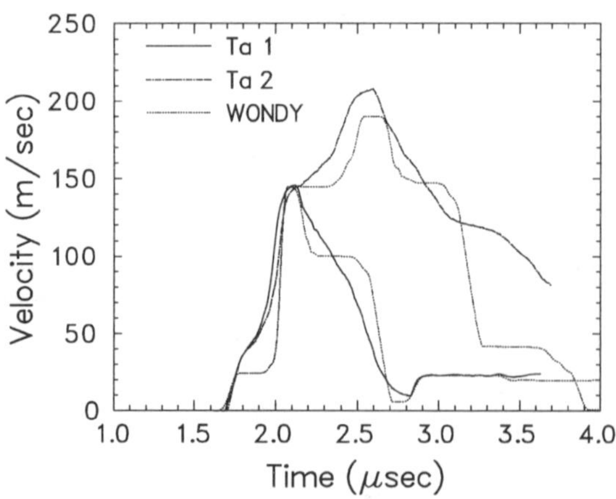

Figure 2. Wave profiles for Ta 1 and Ta 2.

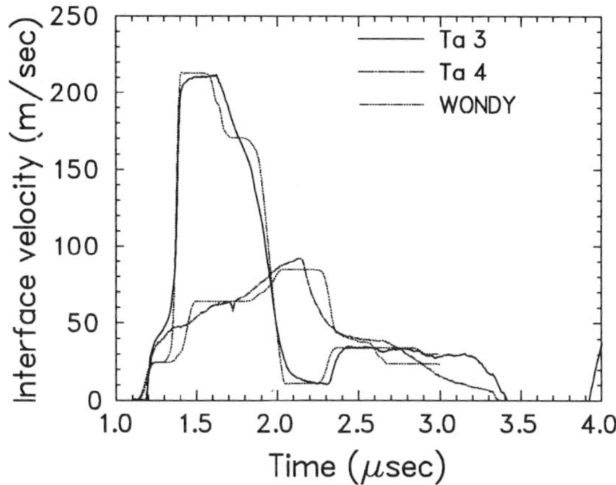

Figure 3. Wave profiles for Ta 3 and Ta 4.

Table 2. Hugoniot states for tantalum. (Note that arrival of Ta 4 second wave is poorly defined)

Test #	Particle Vel. km/s	Stress GPa	Density gm/cm^3	Shock Vel. km/s
Hugoniot states (Lagrangian analysis)				
Ta 1	0.125	7.94	17.22	3.64
Ta 2	0.130	7.86	17.22	3.61
Ta 3	0.183	11.41	17.51	3.63
Ta 4	0.054	3.46	16.89	3.30
Hugoniot states (Impedance match analysis)				
Ta 1	0.129	8.02	17.25	3.65
Ta 2	0.130	7.99	17.26	3.60
Ta 3	0.189	11.61	17.56	3.63
Ta 4	0.056	3.46	16.91	3.22
Elastic precursor states				
Ta 1	0.026	1.83	16.756	4.175
Ta 2	0.027	1.89	16.759	4.175
Ta 3	0.025	1.72	16.749	4.177
Ta 4	0.030	2.06	16.769	4.175

be consistent with a precursor velocity of 4.175 km/sec at this amplitude.

Precursor states were computed by impedance match methods; *i.e.* from shock velocity and plateau level in the wave profiles and from the known elastic properties of the Z-cut sapphire windows; these are summarized in Table 2.

Hugoniot conditions were calculated by two methods: impedance match (referenced to the post-precursor state) and finite-velocity-increment Lagrangian analysis. Results for the two methods differ slightly, and are presented in Table 2 and plotted in Figure 4. Some difference is expected because the waveforms are not sharp steps in this material (Figure 5). Advancing the arrival times to the sample positions shown in Figure 5 brings the calculations into agreement. Shock velocities are presented in Lagrangian form, *i.e.* as original specimen thickness divided by transit time.

The Lagrangian analysis yielded tabular relations between wave speed, stress, strain, strain rate,

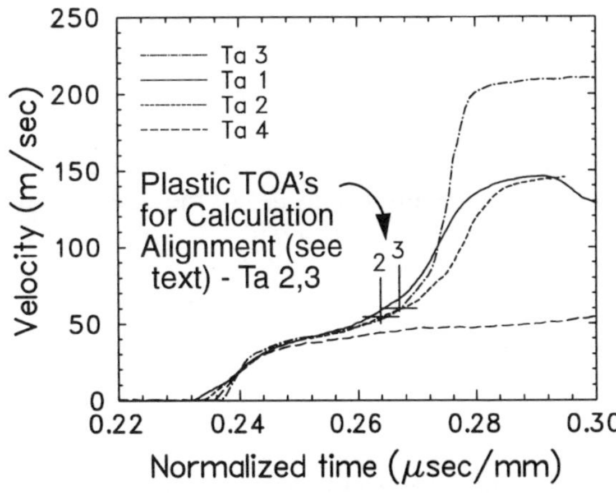

Figure 5. Details of loading profiles to Hugoniot.

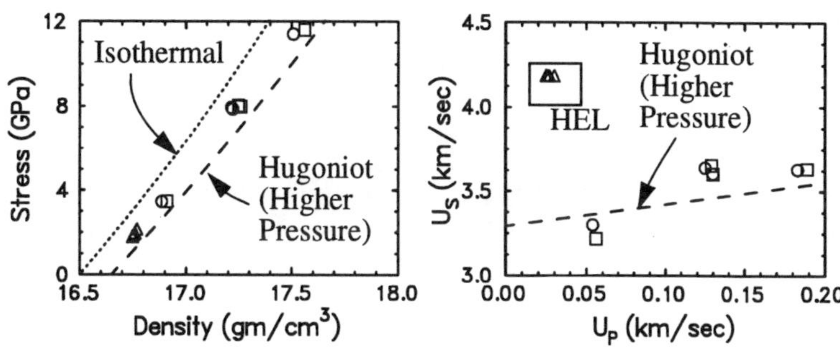

Figure 4. Present measurements (σ vs. ρ; shock velocity vs. particle velocity) of tantalum. Isothermal curve is from Birch-Murnighan fit to static data with K_0 = 194 GPa and K' = 3.98[6]. Dashed Hugoniot shown is ρ_0=16.65 gm/cm^3, C_0 = 3.293 km/s, S = 1.307

□ ○ Present Data (Impedance match, Lagrangian analysis, respectively.)

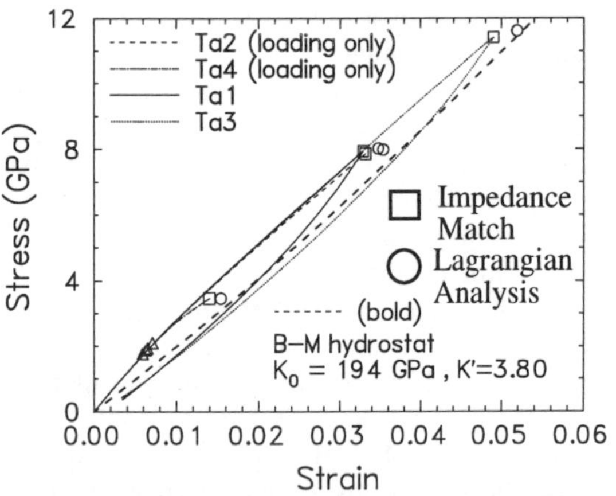

Figure 6. Stress/strain paths for tantalum tests

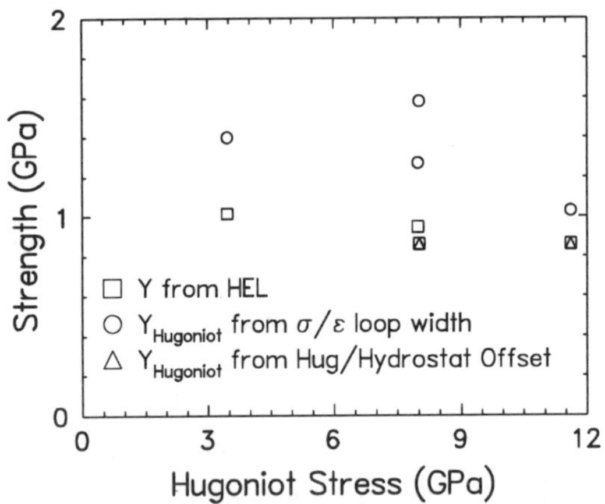

Figure 7. Strength vs. Hugoniot Stress

particle velocity and window velocity. For those experiments with a reshock following the initial shock (Ta 2 and Ta 4), this analysis was cut off after the initial shock arrival at the window. Space does not permit a detailed analysis of these results, but it is instructive to consider some particular results.

The stress/strain paths traversed in these tests are shown in Figure 6. These do not assure steady wave behavior; the discrepancy between these results and the impedance-match results suggests nonsteady wave propagation.

The yield strength of material at the Hugoniot state may be determined as 3/4 of the width of the stress/strain loop. Alternatively, for stress regimes where shock heating is minimal (such as the present), it may be calculated as 3/2 of the offset between the Hugoniot and the hydrostat (i.e. delta stress at constant strain). For fully dense tantalum, the hydrostat has been determined to 10 GPa by Ming and Manghnani [6] and may be written in terms of the Birch-Murnighan equation with K_0 = 194 GPa and K' = 3.98.

The initial strength of tantalum may be calculated from the precursor amplitude according to:

$$Y = \sigma_{HEL} \cdot (1-2\nu)/(1-\nu) \quad (\nu \equiv \text{Poisson's ratio})$$

Using the precursor amplitudes from Table 2, the loading and Hugoniot strengths may be plotted against Hugoniot stress; the results are presented as Figure 7. These results show reasonable agreement with the shock loading and quasi-isentropic loading results from Chhabildas and Asay[3].

Hugoniot Lagrangian sound velocities calculated in the Lagrangian analysis were 4.5 to 4.6 km/sec for the two tests affording release from the Hugoniot state.

REFERENCES

[1] L. C. Chhabildas and L. M. Barker, Dynamic quasi-isentropic compression of tungsten, pp. 111-114 in Shock Waves in Condensed Matter - 1987, S. C. Schmidt and N. C. Holmes, eds., Elsevier Science Publishers B.V, 1988.

[2] L. C. Chhabildas, L. M. Barker, J. R. Asay and T. G. Trucano, Relationship of fragment size to normalized spall strength for materials, Int. J. Impact Engng, 10, 107-124, 1990.

[3] L. C. Chhabildas and J. R. Asay, Dynamic yield strength and spall strength measurements under quasi-isentropic loading, to be published in the proceedings of the 1990 Explomet Conference, "Shock Waves and High Strain Rate Phenomena in Metals", edited by L. E. Murr, K. P. Staudhammer and M. A Meyers, 1991.

[4] M. D. Furnish and L. C. Chhabildas, Dynamic material properties of refractory materials: Molybdenum, in High Strain Rate Behavior of Refractory Metals and Alloys, (R. Asfahani, E. Chen and A. Crowson, eds), The Minerals, Metals and Materials Society, 1992

[5] M. W. Guinan and D. J. Steinberg, Pressure and temperature derivation of the isotropic polycrystalline shear modulus for 65 elements, J. Phys. Chem. Sol. 35, 1501, 1974.

[6] L. Ming and M. H. Manghnani, Isothermal compression of bcc transition metals to 100 kbar, J. Appl. Phys., 49, 208-212, 1978.

INFLUENCE OF PEAK PRESSURE AND TEMPERATURE ON THE SHOCK-LOADING RESPONSE OF TANTALUM

G. T. Gray III
Los Alamos National Laboratory
Los Alamos, New Mexico, USA 87545

While the deformation response of tantalum subjected to high-rate loading has attracted considerable study, few studies have systematically investigated the influence of peak shock pressure and starting temperature on the shock response of tantalum. In this study the deformation behavior of annealed tantalum has been compared to tantalum shock pre-strained to 7 and 15 GPa at 25°C as well as to 7 GPa after first preheating to 200° and 400°C. The reload yield behavior of shock prestrained Ta was found to exhibit no enhanced shock hardening compared to Ta deformed quasi-statically or dynamically to an equivalent strain level. In addition the reload yield behavior of Ta shock prestrained to 7 GPa at 200 or 400°C was found to exhibit increased hardening compared to the shock prestraining at 25°C. The shock-hardening response of Ta is discussed in terms of defect storage and compared to that seen in fcc metals.

INTRODUCTION

The passage of shock waves through materials has been shown to alter to varying degrees the structure/property response of a broad range of metals and alloys. Specific examples of post-shock material response have been discussed previously[1-3]. These effects have been particularly well documented in a diverse number of face-centered-cubic(fcc) metals such as copper and nickel, and fcc alloys including brass and austenitic stainless steels. Shock response studies on body-centered-cubic (bcc) metals have preferentially focused on iron and ferritic steels due to extensive interest in the α–ε pressure-induced transition. Fewer studies have been undertaken on other bcc metals such as niobium, molybdenum, tantalum, or tungsten. Shock-loaded fcc metals and alloys have been repeatedly shown to exhibit increased hardening behavior in reload tests after shock recovery compared to the same metal deformed at low strain rate to an equivalent strain level[1-3]. Figure 1 illustrates an example of this substantially increased reload yield strength response for polycrystalline copper and high-purity nickel[4,5].

While fcc, bcc, and hcp metals exhibit a large number of similarities in general physical and

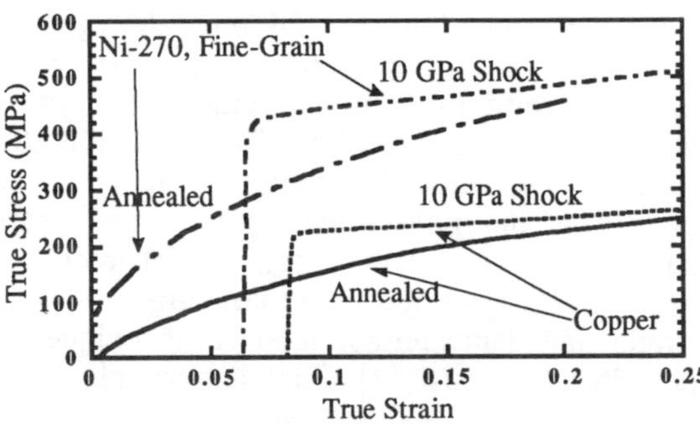

Figure 1. Reload stress-strain response of shock-loaded Cu and Ni compared to that observed during quasi-static deformation.

mechanical properties, significant differences also exist. For example, annealed bcc and hcp metals and alloys exhibit pronounced strain-rate and temperature-dependent properties. This dependence is due to their strong inherent lattice resistance to dislocation motion compared to fcc metals in which the lattice resistance is small Recently, the high-strain rate and shock response of bcc metals, in particular the refractory metals tantalum, niobium, and tungsten, has received increased interest for ballistic applications. While the detailed response of refractory metals to a wide range of deformation paths has been widely examined, systematic studies of the shock response of these metals has received limited attention. Early work by Dieter[1] in 1961 noted that bcc metals other than iron exhibited no or minimal improvement in overall mechanical properties after shock loading. Only iron which displays an allotropic transition and extensive twinning during shock deformation showed a pronounced effect of shock loading on defect storage. Niobium revealed minimal twinning and displayed virtually no increased hardening compared to quasi-static rolling to equivalent strain levels. The purpose of the present study was to investigate the influence of peak pressure and temperature on the shock-loading response of tantalum.

EXPERIMENTAL

Commercial purity tantalum plate 5 mm thick with a measured composition (in wt. %) of Carbon-6 ppm, Nitrogen-24 ppm, Oxygen-56 ppm, Hydrogen-<1 ppm, Iron-19 ppm, Nickel-25 ppm, Chromium-9 ppm, Tungsten-41 ppm, Niobium-26 ppm and balance Ta was used in this study. The plate was studied in an annealed condition and possessing an equiaxed grain structure ~68μm in diameter. Shock recovery experiments were performed utilizing an 80-mm single-stage launcher and recovery techniques as described previously[3]. Tantalum samples were shock loaded in Ta shock-recovery assemblies to 7 and 20 GPa for 1 μs pulse durations under symmetric impact conditions. Elevated temperature shock-loading experiments at 7 GPa were conducted at nominally 220° and 400°C using a resistive heating-element furnace placed circumferentially around the outer momentum trapping ring of the assembly. Compression samples were EDM machined from the as-received Ta and shocked samples, and reloaded at strain rates ranging from 0.001 to 3000 s^{-1}.

RESULTS AND DISCUSSION

The reload mechanical response of shock prestrained tantalum was found to depend on both the peak shock pressure and the temperature at which shock prestraining was performed. Figure 2 presents a plot of the quasi-static reload stress-strain behavior of the annealed starting Ta, as well as the samples shocked at room temperature to 7 and 20 GPa. Figure 3 shows a plot of the same shocked Ta shock prestrained samples reloaded dynamically using a Split-Hopkinson Pressure Bar at a strain rate of 3000 s^{-1}. The reload shock curves in Figures 2 and 3 have been offset with respect to the annealed Ta response at low and high strain rate by the transient strain generated by the shock defined as 4/3 ln (V/V_0), where V and V_0 are the final and initial volumes of Ta during the shock cycle. Contrary to the results reviewed for Cu and Ni in Figure 1, Ta shocked to 7 and 20 GPa does not exhibit an increased shock hardening response compared to Ta quasi-statically deformed to an equivalent strain level. The reload mechanical response following shock prestraining to 7 GPa exhibits a reduced flow stress level compared to the quasi-static loading path. The 20 GPa reload stress-strain curve follows nearly the identical yield and hardening path as the low-rate annealed response at the equivalent strain level. The dynamic reload stress-strain response in Figure 3 shows the same response as that seen in the quasi-static reloads although the overall flow stress levels are higher, consistent with the high rate-sensitivity of Ta.

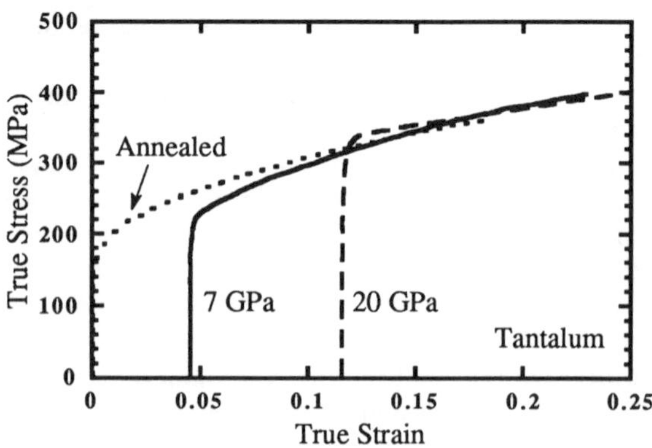

Figure 2. Quasi-static stress-strain response of shock recovered Ta after 7 and 20 GPa shocks. Reload curves are offset by the transient strains due to the shocks as compared to quasi-static deformation of annealed Ta.

The reload flow stress response of shocked Ta does not display the often documented increased defect storage response of shock loading in fcc

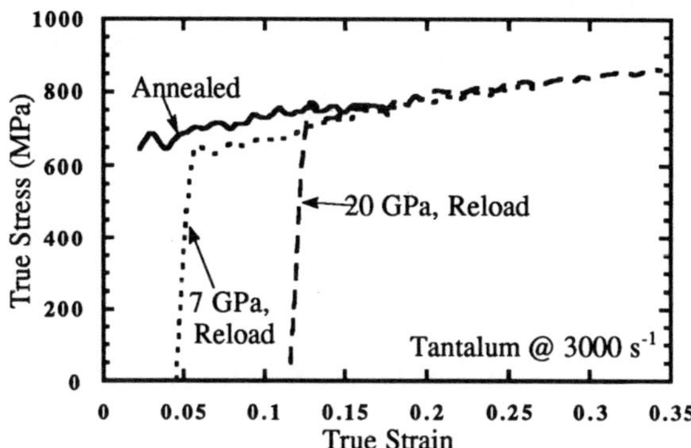

Figure 3. High-strain-rate reload stress-strain response of shock prestrained tantalum.

metals compared to conventional strain-rate loading paths[3]. This observation is identical to that seen previously by Lassila and Gray[6]. Increased hardening during shock loading in the fcc case has been qualitatively linked to the subsonic restriction on dislocation velocity, requiring the generation and storage of a larger number of dislocations for a given strain. Observations of a strong dependence of the initial Stage II work-hardening rate[5,7] on strain rate in fcc metals supports this fact and the data for Cu and Ni in Figure 1. This increased hardening response clearly shows that the inherent dislocation-dislocation micro-mechanisms responsible for defect storage are altered in the shock. The exact phenomena responsible for this increased hardening efficiency in the shock has yet to be adequately explained or modeled[5,7]. However, its manifestation in high SFE fcc metals suggests that it is linked to both: (a) increased dislocation interactions resulting from enhanced dislocation nucleation at the higher stress levels achieved at high strain rates, and (b) suppression of dynamic recovery processes, which depend on cross-slip. Cross-slip is made more difficult when deformation occurs at higher strain rates due to reduced thermal activation[8] and more planar slip results. The absence of shock-enhanced hardening in low-SFE Si-Bronze[9] and low-SFE Ni-based 230-alloy[10] is consistent with differences in cross-slip reducing the amount of total defect storage in the shock cycle. More "homogeneous" dislocation nucleation or widespread multiplication from existing sources with increasing stress levels at high/shock strain rates will lead to reduced dislocation slip distances prior to tangling with other defects.

The results in this study on Ta, similar to those described by Dieter for Nb[1], reveal that increased hardening due to shock loading in Ta is not observed. In both Nb and the current Ta, this behavior is consistent with defect storage being dislocation controlled; no significant twinning occurred in the Ta at 7 or 20 GPa. Accordingly, defect storage phenomena may be viewed using the framework of dislocation kinetics as is the case for low-rate plasticity[5,9]. The observation of no enhanced shock hardening is believed to reflect the influence of the large lattice friction (Peierls Stress) component of the flow stress in both Ta and Nb. At low temperatures and high-rates, the Peierls stress(~0.48 GPa shear stress for Ta) is a significant portion of the flow stress.

As such, under high-rate loading dislocation motion in Ta will be significantly restricted and cross-slip inhibited or totally suppressed. These effects will be particularly pronounced on screw dislocations which have a higher Peierls barrier than edge segments in bcc metals[11]. The predominance of long straight screw segments in Ta following low temperature or shock deformation is consistent with this mechanism[6,9]. This disparity in cross-slip ability in a bcc metal where defect generation is dominated by dislocation processes will significantly alter defect storage in bcc metals at high-rate or low temperatures leading to similar hardening behavior from quasi-static to shock-loading rates. The suppression of cross-slip in Ta at shock-loading strain rates will change dislocation motion from 'areal' to 'lineal' glide[12]. This will significantly affect work hardening by suppressing the storage of new dislocation line length. The absence of shock-enhanced hardening in Ta is consistent with the lack of a dependence of the Stage-II hardening rate in polycrystalline Ta on strain rate.

Further, the lack of an enhanced shock-hardening response in Ta supports the importance of

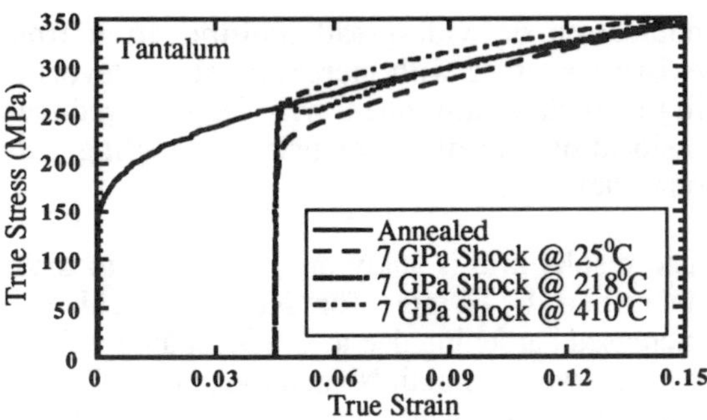

Figure 4. Reload stress-strain response of Ta shock prestrained to 7 GPa at three different starting temperatures.

dislocation kinetics in describing the thermally-activated generation and storage of dislocations in bcc metals. In accordance with this idea the influence of temperature on defect storage in the shock process was investigated. Tantalum shock assemblies were preheated to elevated temperatures and shock loaded to a peak pressure of 7 GPa. The reload stress-strain response of the shock-recovered Ta as a function of shock preheat temperature is shown in Figure 4. Increasing the temperature at which shock prestraining was conducted increased the reload yield strength of the shocked Ta. This result suggests that the temperature increase either increases the reload response by: 1) directly increasing defect storage during the shock by increasing thermally activated cross-slip, or 2) post-shock pinning of the dislocations generated in the shock by mobile interstitials; this pinning is aided by thermally-activated diffusion of the interstitials, i.e. assisting static strain-aging. The yield drop evident in the 218°C shock prestrained curve is consistent with at least some strain-aging contribution, supporting the assertion that interstitial effects are important.

SUMMARY AND CONCLUSIONS

Based upon a study of the variation of peak shock pressure and temperature at which shock prestraining was conducted on the mechanical response of tantalum, the following conclusions can be drawn: 1) the reload yield behavior of shock prestrained Ta exhibits no enhanced shock hardening compared to Ta deformed quasi-statically or dynamically to an equivalent strain level; the absence of shock-enhanced hardening in Ta is consistent with the lack of a dependence of the Stage-II hardening rate in polycrystalline Ta on strain rate, and 2) the reload yield behavior of Ta shock prestrained to 7 GPa at 200 or 400°C exhibits increased hardening compared to shock prestraining at 25°C.

ACKNOWLEDGMENTS

The author wishes to acknowledge C. Trujillo, W. Wright, and M.F. Lopez for their assistance with the experimental aspects of this study. This work was performed under the auspices of the U.S. Department of Energy.

REFERENCES

[1] G.E. Dieter, in *Resp. of Metals to High Vel.Def.,* Interscience Publ., NY, pp. 409 (1961).
[2] L.E. Murr, in *Shock Waves and High Strain Rate Phen. in Metals,* (ed. by M.A. Meyers and L.E. Murr) Plenum Press, NY, pp. 607 (1981).
[3] G.T. Gray III, in *High Pres. Shock Comp.of Solids,* (ed. by J.R. Asay and M. Shahinpoor) New York: Springer-Verlag,ch. 6, (1993).
[4] G.T. Gray III and P.S. Follansbee, in *Impact Loading and Dynamic Behavior of Materials,* (ed. by C.Y. Chiem, H.-D. Kunze, and L.W. Meyer) DFG, Germany, pp. 541 (1988).
[5] P.S. Follansbee and G.T. Gray III, *Int. J. Plasticity* **7**, pp. 651-660 (1991).
[6] D. Lassila and G.T. Gray III, in *DYMAT 91,* J.de Physique IV, vol. 1, pp. C3-19 (1991)
[7] P.S. Follansbee and U.F. Kocks, *Acta Metall.* **36**, pp. 81-93 (1988).
[8] G.T. Gray III, in *Modeling the Def. of Crystal.* (ed. by T.C. Lowe, A.D. Rollett, P.S. Follansbee, and G.S. Daehn)TMS, pp. 145 (1991).
[9] G.T. Gray III, *Shock Waves ,* (1993) in press.
[10] K.S. Vecchio and G.T. Gray III, this volume.
[11] V. Vitek, in *Disl. and Prop. of Real Matls.,* Inst. of Metals, London, pp. 30-50 (1985).
[12] U. F. Kocks, in *The Mech. of Disl.*(ed. by E. C. Aifanatis and J. P. Hirth) Amer. Soc. for Metals, 1985, pp. 81-83.

SHOCK COMPRESSION AND RELEASE OF POLYCRYSTALLINE MAGNESIUM OXIDE

Thomas S. Duffy and Thomas J. Ahrens
Lindhurst Laboratory of Experimental Geophysics
Seismological Laboratory
California Institute of Technology
Pasadena, CA 91125

Release wave profile and Hugoniot equation of state data for low-porosity polycrystalline MgO are reported to 36 and 133 GPa, respectively. At low pressure, the Hugoniot lies above single-crystal data, reflecting material strength of 3.1±0.8 GPa. Unloading wave velocities to 27 GPa are consistent with extrapolated compressional sound velocities. The unloading profiles can be fit using a viscoplastic model, but there are significant differences between waveforms for different experimental geometries.

INTRODUCTION

Magnesium oxide is of geophysical interest because it is potentially a major constituent of the Earth's lower mantle. Its exceptional stability from ambient conditions to pressures above 200 GPa under both dynamic and static loading also makes it a significant material for study. Previously, wave profile data on single-crystal MgO shocked between 4.8 and 11.2 GPa were reported [1]. Study of polycrystalline MgO is of interest because of the wide range of response of ceramic materials to shock deformation [2]. In this work, we have measured the equation of state (EOS), unloading wave velocities, and wave profiles on nearly fully dense polycrystalline MgO under shock compression.

EXPERIMENTAL METHOD

Samples

Low-porosity polycrystalline magnesium oxide (MgO) samples were obtained commercially (Cercom Inc.) as 1.25" diameter hot-pressed disks. Microprobe analysis revealed the presence of less than 0.5% impurities. The average crystal density was found via the Archimedean method to be 3.571 ±0.004 g/cm^3, and the average bulk density obtained by weighing and measuring the samples was 3.562 ±0.006 g/cm^3, both of which are within better than 1% of the x-ray density (3.584 g/cm^3). Sample flatness variations were less than 0.01 mm. The longitudinal sound velocity was measured ultrasonically to be 9.81 km/s.

Equation of State Experiments

Equation of state experiments were conducted on MgO specimens using both a propellant and a light gas gun. The velocity of Ta and Mg flyer plates was measured to ~0.1-1% by recording x-ray shadowgraphs immediately prior to impact. Wave velocities were determined from the destruction of flat and inclined mirrors in contact with the sample and the driver plate. The measured shock and flyer plate velocities were combined with impedance-matching techniques and the Rankine-Hugoniot equations to constrain the shock velocity, particle velocity, stress, and density of the shock-compressed state.

Wave Profile Measurements

Wave profile measurements were conducted for both forward and reverse ballistics geometries using a VISAR. In the reverse impacts, a 3-4 mm thick MgO sample was used to impact a 2-mm thick Al 6061 buffer with an LiF window (8-mm thick) attached to it. The sample was backed by low-density foam. In the forward geometry, an MgO flyer was used to impact an MgO target to which a 2-mm thick Al 6061 buffer and an LiF window (8-mm thick) were attached. The combined thickness of the MgO flyer and sample was nominally 7 mm in these experiments. In both geometries, the VISAR was used to monitor the velocity of the buffer-window interface. A total of five reverse ballistic and four forward ballistic experiments were performed.

RESULTS

The Hugoniot states determined from the EOS experiments are shown in Fig. 1 and Table 1. Also shown in Fig. 1 are single-crystal Hugoniot data [3] for MgO. The elastic precursor was resolved in only one experiment from which a velocity of 9.77 ±0.12 km/s was obtained, in agreement with the ultrasonically measured value.

Wave profiles representing a subset of the reverse and forward ballistic experiments are shown in Figs. 2 and 3. Some chaotic variations in particle velocity are evident in the velocity plateau region. This may reflect differential motion of grains, material reorganization, or heterogeneous faulting and has been observed previously in ceramics [2]. The measured interface particle velocities are consistent with values calculated using the equation of state discussed below.

Unloading wave velocities were determined from the reverse-impact experiments (Fig. 4) using the arrival time difference between the shock and unloading waves. Shock states in the buffer and sample were determined from the particle velocity at the buffer-sample interface and impedance matching. Unloading wave velocities in the buffer were determined from the time difference between the shock and the arrival of the reverberation through the buffer.

DISCUSSION

Equation of State

While single-crystal and porous polycrystalline MgO have been studied extensively using shock techniques, the present study represents the first EOS determination for low-porosity (<1%) polycrystalline MgO. The shock velocity-particle velocity data of Table 1 can be described by the relation:

$$U_S = 6.87\ (0.10) + 1.24\ (0.04)\ u_p \qquad (1)$$

where U_S is the shock velocity and u_p is the particle velocity. For MgO, the bulk velocity from ultrasonic data [4] is 6.73 km/s, which is 2.1% below the U_S-u_p intercept. Also shown in Fig. 1 is the static isotherm

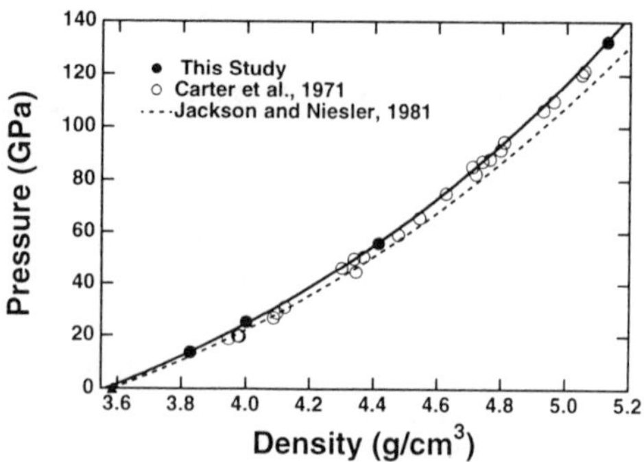

Figure 1. Stress-density states achieved in shock compression of MgO. Open symbols are for single-crystal MgO. Solid symbols are data of this study. The solid curve is a fit to the present Hugoniot data and the dashed curve is the static isotherm [4].

for MgO constructed from 0-3 GPa ultrasonic elasticity data [4] and the Birch-Murnaghan equation. The polycrystalline MgO data lie above the single-crystal data at low stresses and above the static isotherm at all stresses. The coincidence of the single-crystal data and the static isotherm at low stresses has been used to infer that MgO undergoes a significant loss of strength above the Hugoniot elastic limit [1]. In contrast, magnesia does not undergo such a collapse. Below 56 GPa, the stress difference between the static isotherm and the polycrystalline Hugoniot data is 1.5-2.5 GPa, when thermal effects have been subtracted by employing the Mie-Gruneisen equation. For an elastic-plastic material, the yield strength is three-halves the stress difference between the Hugoniot and the static isotherm, implying that the yield strength of polycrystalline MgO is 3.1 ±0.8 GPa at these stresses.

Table 1. EOS experiments on polycrystalline MgO.

Experiment	u_p (km/s)	U_S (km/s)	σ (GPa)	ρ (g/cm^3)
233	3.37(1)	11.04(7)	132.6(8)	5.13(3)
840	0.89(1)	7.96(11)	25.3(3)	4.00(2)
841	1.74(2)	9.01(13)	55.9(9)	4.42(3)
843	0.51(1)	7.53(12)	13.8(2)	3.83(2)

Unloading Wave Velocities

Compressional and bulk sound velocities were calculated to 30 GPa from ultrasonic data [4] extrapolated using finite strain theory [5]. The results are shown in Fig. 4 along with measured Hugoniot unloading velocities plotted as a function of mean pressure. The Hugoniot unloading velocities agree with the ultrasonic extrapolations within their experimental precision (2-3%). This implies that the unloading wave is traveling with the compressional elastic wave velocity and that extrapolation of ultrasonic data is suitable over this pressure range.

Using the finite strain equations, Hugoniot measurements can be inverted to obtain elastic moduli and their pressure derivatives along the Hugoniot. By combining the present Hugoniot data with the ambient-pressure compressional velocity, the following values for the longitudinal elastic modulus, C_{L0}, and its pressure derivative C'_{L0} are obtained: $C_{L0} = 335 \pm 1$ GPa and $C'_{L0} = 7.0 \pm 0.4$. The ultrasonically determined parameters are: $C_{L0} = 336.9 \pm 0.3$ GPa and

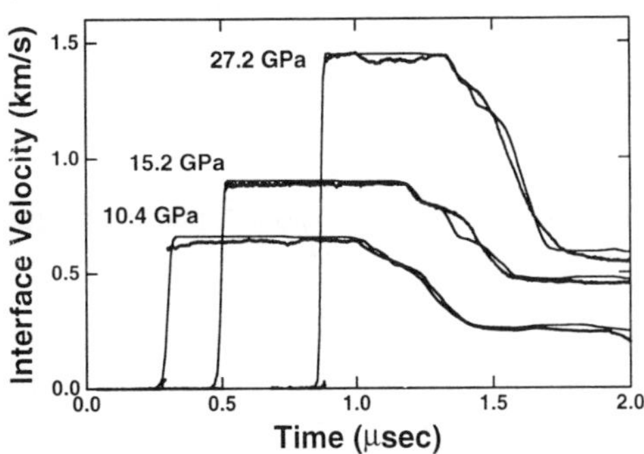

Figure 2. Interface particle velocity histories for reverse-impacts. Peak stresses are listed next to each profile. The times are arbitrary and have been shifted for display purposes. Points are experimental data, curves are wavecode simulations.

$C'_{L0} = 7.4 \pm 0.2$ [4]. Thermal effects on the compressional sound velocity are calculated to be less than 1% at these pressures.

Grady [1] reported three wave profiles on single-crystal MgO shocked along [100] between 4.8 and 11.2 GPa (mean pressures of 3.5 - 9.9 GPa). The initial unloading velocities are 4-6% below the extrapolated sound velocity in this direction at high pressure (Fig. 4). Single-crystal MgO collapses to the hydrostat upon shock compression above the HEL. The unloading wave velocities indicate that material strength has recovered substantially in the ~500 ns time interval between shock and release arrivals. The different behaviors of polycrystalline and single-crystal MgO are a reflection of different yielding processes in single and polycrystals.

Constitutive Modeling

Numerical simulations of the particle velocity histories were carried out using WONDY [6]. Models tested included an elastic perfectly plastic (EPP) model as well as those including a Bauschinger effect and strain-rate dependent stress relaxation. The Al

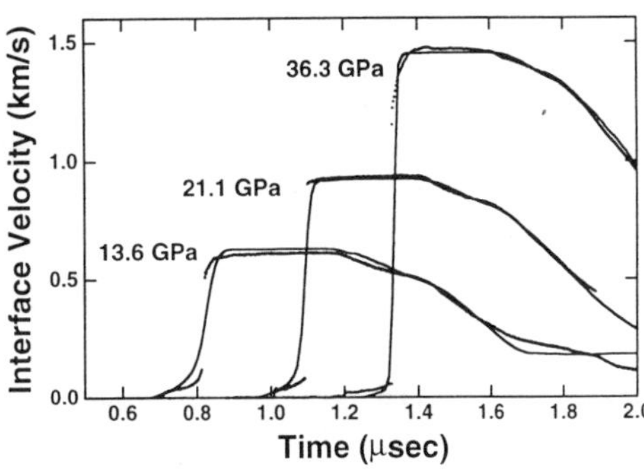

Figure 3. Interface particle velocity histories for forward impacts.

6061 buffers were described using the viscoplastic model of [7]. The LiF windows were treated as elastic perfectly plastic.

The EPP model could not fit the wave profiles in detail but revealed that the measured profiles were not significantly dispersive. The amplitude and shape of the precursor transmitted through the buffer in the forward impacts could only be matched by MgO yield strengths between 1-1.5 GPa, while the initial unloading of the reverse impacts was best fit by a yield strength of 2.5 GPa. The precursor velocities in the forward experiments were variable and could not be reproduced consistently.

Separate viscoplastic models which included a Bauschinger effect and stress relaxation were arrived at for the forward and reverse experiments (Figs. 2 and 3). While the main features of the profiles can be fit with a simple model, there are some complicating features. The reverse impacts exhibit significantly sharper initial releases than the forward impacts. This may be an indication of non-steady wave propagation. A large fraction of the sample in the forward impacts is subjected to partial unloading due to wave reflection at the sample-buffer interface. This may produce a damaged region that could affect subsequent unloading waves. The lowest-amplitude reverse experiment has a weak and diffuse elastic release, similar to the forward impacts. This illustrates that the shape of the profile in MgO is dependent both on peak stress and propagation distance.

SUMMARY

Equation of state and wave profile measurements have been performed on low-porosity (<1%) polycrystalline MgO. The equation of state differs from single-crystal MgO, reflecting different levels of strength in single and polycrystals.

Wavecode simulations of the particle velocity histories were performed to assess whether a viscoplastic material model could accurately describe the dynamic behavior of MgO. While reasonable fits were obtained, separate models were required for the forward- and reverse-impacts because of the different nature of the waveforms observed under these two conditions.

There are several lines of evidence which suggest that polycrystalline MgO, in contrast to single crystals, retains its strength when shock-compressed in the 10-37 GPa range. First, the temperature-corrected stress-volume states measured in the EOS experiments lie 1.5-2.5 GPa above the hydrostat. Second, the initial unloading wave velocity corresponds to extrapolations of ultrasonically measured compressional wave speeds. Third, the initial portion of the unloading wave, particularly for the reverse experiments, is sharp and non-dispersive.

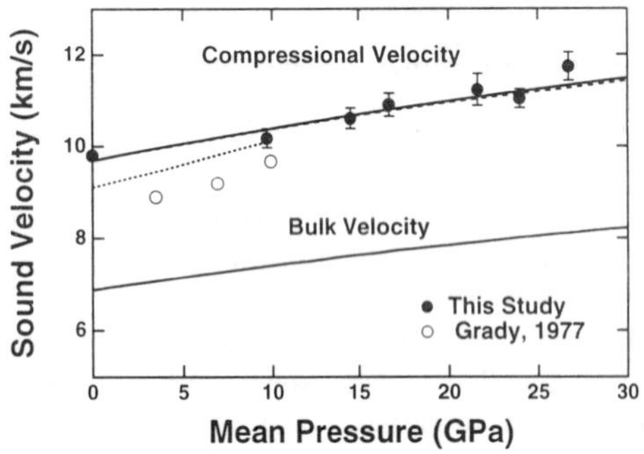

Figure 4. Unloading wave velocities in MgO. The solid symbols are for polycrystalline MgO, and the open symbols are for single-crystals shocked along [100][1]. The solid curves are extrapolated ultrasonic data, and the dashed curve shows the expected effect of Hugoniot temperature on V_p. The dotted curve shows the extrapolated compressional velocity along [100].

ACKNOWLEDGMENTS

We thank M. Long, A. Devora, and E. Gelle for experimental assistance and L. S. Durango for editorial assistance. We are grateful to Dr. S. Rigden (ANU) for the ultrasonic sound velocity measurements. This research was supported by the NSF. Division of Geological and Planetary Sciences, California Institute of Technology contribution 5291.

REFERENCES

[1] D. E. Grady, "Processes occurring in shock wave compression of rocks and minerals", in *High-Pressure Research: Applications to Geophysics*, 1977, pp. 389-438.

[2] M. E. Kipp and D. E. Grady, "Shock compression and release in high-strength ceramics", *Sandia Natl. Lab., Rep. SAND89-1461*, 1989.

[3] W. J. Carter, S. P. Marsh, J. N. Fritz, and R. G. McQueen, "The equation of state of selected materials for high-pressure reference", in *Accurate Characterization of the High Pressure Environment*, 1971, pp. 147-158.

[4] I. Jackson and H. Niesler, "The elasticity of periclase to 3 GPa and some geophysical implications", in *High Pressure Research in Geophysics*, 1982, pp. 93-133.

[5] C. Sammis, D. Anderson, and T. Jordan, *J. Geophys. Res.*, 75, 4478-4480 (1970).

[6] M. E. Kipp and R. J. Lawrence, "WONDY V - A one-dimensional finite-difference wave propagation code", *Sandia Natl. Lab., Rep. SAND81-0930*, 1982.

[7] R. J. Lawrence and J. R. Asay, "High-pressure multiple-shock response of aluminum", in *High Pressure Science and Technology*, 1979, pp. 88-98.

TIME-RESOLVED SHOCK COMPRESSION OF POROUS RUTILE: WAVE DISPERSION IN POROUS SOLIDS

M. U. Anderson, R. A. Graham, and G. T. Holman
Sandia National Laboratories, Albuquerque, New Mexico 87185-5800

Rutile (TiO_2) samples at 60% of solid density have been shock-loaded from 0.21 to 6.1 GPa with sample thickness of 4 mm and studied with the PVDF piezoelectric polymer stress-rate gauge. The technique uses a copper capsule to contain the sample which has PVDF gauge packages in direct contact with the front and rear surfaces. A precise measure is made of the compressive stress wave velocity through the sample, as well as the input and propagated shock stress. The initial density is known from the sample preparation process, and the amount of shock-compression is calculated from the measurement of shock velocity and input stress. Shock states and re-shock states are measured. The observed data are consistent with previously published high pressure data. It is observed that rutile has a "crush strength" near 6 GPa. Propagated stress-pulse rise times vary from 234 to 916 nsec. Propagated stress-pulse rise times of shock-compressed HMX, 2Al + Fe_2O_3, 3Ni + Al, and 5Ti + 3Si are presented.

INTRODUCTION

Shock compression of highly porous rutile (TiO_2) has been investigated with a time-resolved shock compression technique. The rutile material was chosen to: (1) develop an understanding of a highly porous single component system under shock compression, and fully qualify the time-resolved shock compression technique, (2) provide data for the extensive numerical simulation data base on rutile[1], (3) compare with the information learned through previous sample preservation (recovery) work on rutile[1], and (4) compare with the existing high pressure shock compression work on rutile as reported by Bugaeva et al.[2] The present work is part of an overall study of shock-induced solid state chemistry.[3-5]

EXPERIMENTAL TECHNIQUE

The time-resolved shock compression technique used in the present study subjects the powder sample to controlled shock-loading from either a compressed-gas gun, or high explosive loading.[6] The sample was encased in a copper capsule with PVDF[7] gauge packages at both input and propagated locations as in Figure 1. High explosive loading is described in Holman's[8] paper in the present proceedings.

The material used in the present study was "Puratronic" grade, high purity powder from Johnson-Matthey. Particle sizes range from 1 - 800μm. Powder samples were pressed to 60% of 4.26 gm/cm^3. Difficulty was encountered when pressing the samples due to the high crush strength of rutile, consistent with shock-compression observations.

Sample Preparation

The powder samples were pressed directly into the instrumented copper capsule to achieve intimate contact at the PVDF gauge package/sample interface. The piezoelectric polymer PVDF measures stress-rate directly and is sensitive to sample imperfections such as density gradients, or μm size voids at the PVDF interface.

The powder samples were pressed in three uniform layers using a tool steel die at sample pressures of 500 MPa for each layer. The copper containment ring began to expand radially at sample pressures above 350 MPa unless externally supported. Sample densities achieved averaged 59.5%, $\pm$ 0.9%.

At shock-pressures below 2 GPa, the PVDF/sample impedance mismatch required use of a buffer material to isolate the front and rear surfaces of the sample from the copper. The polymer TPX was chosen to impedance match the rutile at low pressure. During the sample compaction process, the TPX was observed to compress by 10% at 500 MPa sample pressure, changing the TPX buffered sample to 56.8% dense, with a sample thickness uncertainty of $\pm$ 75μm.

The experimental arrangement as shown in Figure 1, consists of a powder sample encased in a copper capsule with PVDF gauge packages at both input and propagated locations. A precise measure is made of the compressive stress-wave velocity through the sample, as well as the input and propagated stresses. The initial density is known from the sample preparation process, and the amount of shock-compression is calculated from measurement of wave velocity and input stress.

The conservation of momentum assumption used in the calculation is known to be violated by observation of the propagated wave dispersion. The pressure-versus-relative volume states identified using this technique provide a reasonable measure of material response under shock compression even though the exact volume is not identified.

Time-Resolved Measurements

The shock-loading wave enters the capsule from the left as shown in Figure 1, and propagates through the powder sample with PVDF gauge packages monitoring the input and propagated wave stress profiles, and identifying the transit time between gauge locations. Each PVDF gauge package is described in the footnotes to Table I.

The input PVDF gauge generates a piezoelectric current as the shock-loading pulse transits the gauge, with a risetime less than the shock transit time through the 25μm film thickness (typical risetimes are 4 - 10 nanoseconds). The input shock propagates through the 125μm Kel-F insulation film to the Kel-F/rutile material boundary where a reflection is caused by the impedance mis-match of the powder. This reflected release wave arrives at the input PVDF gauge ~ 90 nanoseconds after the initial input shock as shown in the records of Figure 1.

The piezoelectric current is recorded with two complementary amplifier sensitivities connected to a

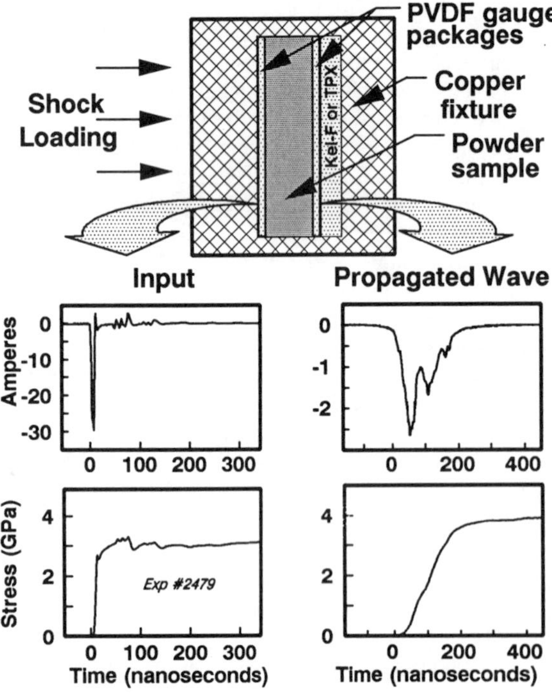

Figure 1. Highly porous powder sample encased in copper capsule is subjected to shock-loading from the left. PVDF gauge packages in direct contact with the sample generate current pulses (upper row) that measure wave velocity, and input and propagated stresses. The current pulses are numerically integrated to yield the stress profile.

current viewing resistor at the PVDF gauge. Combination of both amplifier recordings provides a high resolution current-versus-time profile which is then numerically integrated and converted to stress-versus-time using the PVDFSTRESS computer code[9].

The shock-loading wave propagates through the 4 mm thick rutile sample and arrives at the propagated PVDF gauge location as a dispersed loading wave which generates a piezoelectric current with magnitude and duration altered by an order of magnitude from the input gauge, as shown in the lower right corner of Figure 1, with the resulting stress-versus-time profile.

PVDF provides an unusually sensitive stress profile measurement since the piezoelectric current is stress-rate dependent. The ability to distinguish small changes in the local slope of a loading wave provide information on the dynamic compaction process characteristic of each material. The structure of each propagated wave provides a characteristic signature for each unique material system.

RESULTS

Shock-loading and re-shock states are observed during gas gun experiments. The shock-loading pulse travels through the sample to the back gauge package, which is a close impedance match at the higher pressures of this study, continues through the 0.7 mm thick Kel-F buffer, re-shocks at the copper interface with the re-shock returning to the rear surface of the sample after 500 nanoseconds. The copper re-shock propagates back to the copper front surface where the sample is re-shocked a second time. When the appropriate gauge package is used to mechanically buffer the shear stresses that the electrodes encounter, recording times of 6 microseconds have been observed during gas gun experiments.

Under high explosive loading conditions, the initial shock through the sample with the 500 nanosecond delayed re-shock from the copper backer is observed. The high explosive Taylor wave is observed behind the shock front at both input and backer gauge locations for ~ 1 microsecond, but subsequent re-shocks through the sample are not observed.

The structure of the shock-loading pulse propagated through 4 mm of 60% dense rutile show a characteristic trend of dispersion that results in risetimes ranging from 234 - 916 nanoseconds as measured by PVDF in current-mode. A consistent trend of propagated risetime increasing inversely with stress as shown in Figure 2.

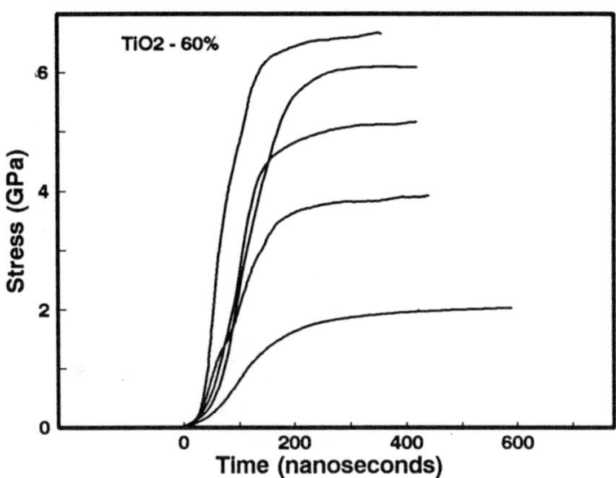

Figure 2. The dispersed structure of an input shock propagated through 4mm of 60% dense rutile shows risetime increasing inversely with stress.

The shock-compression behavior of 60% dense rutile shows a high crush strength with a well-defined path toward solid density that shows good agreement with existing high pressure data.

The pressure-versus-relative volume data are shown in Figure 3 for rutile at 60% dense with the P-V points calculated from known initial density, measured input stress, and measured wave velocity using conservation of momentum and mass relationships.

The risetime of the propagated wave is sufficiently long to require different methods of analysis, the wave velocity from toe-to-toe, and half max-to-half max.

For the toe-to-toe measurement, the transit times are chosen from the current-versus-time data as the leading edge of the pulse referred to as time = 0 in Figure 1. For half max-to-half max measurement, the time at which the current returns to the baseline is taken to be the time and level of propagated stress, from which the time at half max stress is chosen. The solid and open symbols indicate toe-to-toe and half max-to-half max calculations respectively. The high pressure work of Bugaeva covers the stress range from 20.2 to 192 GPa for 60% dense rutile with the 20.2 GPa data point shown in the upper left corner.

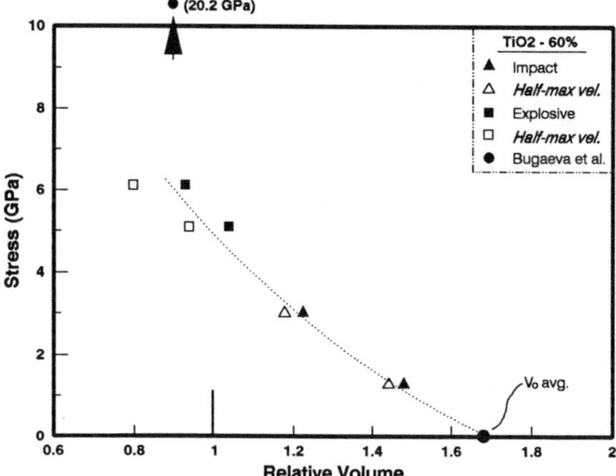

Figure 3. Measured stress-versus-relative volume states for 60% dense TiO_2 using toe-to-toe and half max-to-half max wave speeds in calculations represented with solid and open symbols respectively

Table I. Summary of time-resolved shock compression experiments

Experiment number[A]	Input Condition[B]	Configuration[C]	Input Stress[D] (GPa)	Wave Velocity[E] (km/s)	Prop. Risetime[F] (nsec)	Output Stress[G] (GPa)	Relative Volume[H]	V_o
-----	-----	-----					-----	-----
2496 (a)	0.231	2	0.21	1.344 (1.182)	916 (400)	0.32 TPX	1.674 (1.649)	1.760
2474 (a)	0.420	1	1.29	1.964 (1.822)	490 (194)	1.98 Kel-F	1.477 (1.440)	1.706
2479 (a)	0.704	1	3.02	2.099 (1.998)	382 (132)	3.68 Kel-F	1.223 (1.176)	1.676
BE055 (b)	TNT	3	5.10	2.293 (2.132)	348 (116)	5.11 Kel-F	1.035 (0.935)	1.671
2471 (a)	1.045	1	-----	2.514 (2.407)	234 (94)	6.52 Kel-F	-----	1.662
BE061 (b)	Comp-B	3	6.10	2.313 (2.138)	300 (132)	6.08 Kel-F	0.925 (0.796)	1.684

A: (a) impact loading; (b) explosive loading; **B:** symmetric impact velocity (km/s) Cu > Cu or explosive type; **C:** configuration, (nominal thickness): 1: Cu(6.35mm)/Kel-F(125μm)/PVDF(25μm)/Kel-F(125μm)/TiO_2(4mm)/Kel-F(125μm)/PVDF(25μm)/Kel-F(0.74mm)/Cu(9.52mm); 2: Cu(6.35mm)/TPX(9.4mm)/PVDF(25μm)/FEP(25μm)/TiO_2(4mm)/FEP(25μm)/PVDF(25μm)/TPX(9.40mm)/Cu(6.35mm); 3: P-040/explosive(25.4mm)/Cu(12.7mm)/Cu(6.35mm)/Kel-F(125μm)/PVDF(25μm)/Kel-F(125μm)/TiO_2(4mm)/Kel-F(125μm)/PVDF(25μm)/Kel-F(0.74mm)/Cu(9.52mm) **D:** PVDF measurement **E:** wave speed toe-to-toe(half max-to-half max) **F:** Propagated wave toe-to-peak(10-90%) **G:** PVDF measurements (in polymer backing material) **H:** calculated from PVDF input stress and toe-to-toe wave speed(half max-to-half max wave speed)

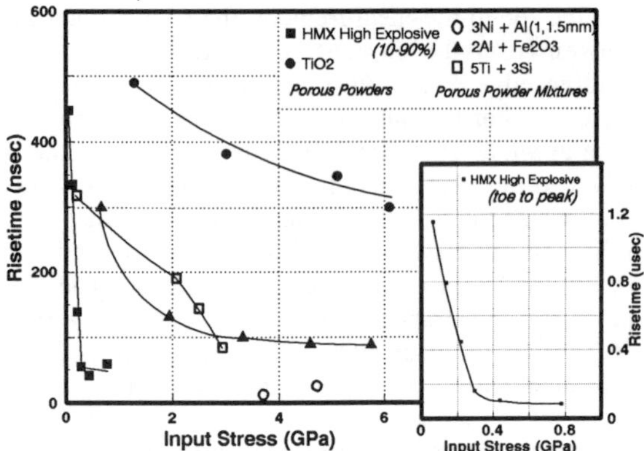

Figure 4. The 4 mm propagated wave risetime-versus-input stress is shown for five different material systems. Strongly material-dependent response is observed.

The risetime-versus-input stress relationship of the propagated wave through 4 mm thick samples is shown for four different highly porous powder systems in Figure 4. The single component systems rutile and HMX high explosive[10], the unreactive two component systems, 2Al + Fe_2O_3[8] and 3Ni + Al, and the reactive two component system 5Ti + 3Si[11].

The HMX has long risetimes at low stress followed by a rapid decrease in risetime due to the low crush-strength, and the onset of reaction. Rutile demonstrates a more constant trend of risetime decrease with increasing stress and a very high crush-strength without the effects of reaction. The 2Al + Fe_2O_3 mixture exhibits a rapid decrease in risetime due to the aluminum crush-up followed by very little risetime decrease due to the Fe_2O_3 crush-up. The 5Ti + 3Si mixture crush-strength is initially similar to 2Al + Fe_2O_3 followed by decrease in risetime due to reaction. The 3Ni + Al mixture show 13 and 26 nanosecond risetimes for 1.5 and 1mm sample thicknesses respectively.

DISCUSSION & CONCLUSION

The shock-compression of rutile shows a pressure-versus-volume relationship that crushes toward solid density in the pressure range of the present study, and shows good agreement with existing high pressure work. The propagated wave risetimes show a consistent trend of increasing inversely with input stress.

The rutile, HMX, 2Al + Fe_2O_3, 3Ni + Al, and 5Ti + 3Si data illustrate the strongly material-dependent risetime characteristics which appear to be both morphologically and material dependent.

Properly packaged PVDF provide recording times of 6 microseconds, and unusual sensitivity to details while measuring stress-rate profiles.

The data provide a significant data base on materials behavior adequate for the advanced modeling in progress by Baer[12], that is required to realistically describe shock compression loading of porous solids.

ACKNOWLEDGEMENTS

The authors would like to acknowledge the excellent support of Heidi Anderson, Dave Wackerbarth and the explosive firing site staff at New Mexico Tech. Supported by the U.S. Department of Energy under contract number DE-AC04-76DP00789.

REFERENCES

1. R. A. Graham, *Solids under High Pressure Shock Compression: Mechanics, Physics and Chemistry,* Springer-Verlag (1993).
2. V. A. Bugaeva, M. A. Podurets, G. V. Simakov, G. S. Telegin and R. F. Trunin, "The dynamic compressibility and equations of state of rutile-structure minerals", in *Izvestiya, Academy of Sciences, USSR, Physics of the Solid Earth,* Vol. 15, No. 1, 1979, pp.19-25.
3. R. A. Graham and N. N. Thadhani, "Solid State Reactivity of Shock-Processed Solids", in *Shock Waves in Materials Science,* edited by A. B. Sawaoka, Springer-Verlag (1993).
4. N. N. Thadhani, "Shock-Induced Chemical Reactions and Synthesis of Materials", *Progress in Materials Science,* 37, 117-226, 1993.
5. R. A. Graham, B. Morosin, Y. Horie, E. L. Venturini, M. Boslough, M. J. Carr, and D. L. Williamson, "Chemical Synthesis Under High Pressure Shock Loading", in *Shock Waves in Condensed Matter,* edited by Y. M. Gupta, Plenum (1986) pp 693-711.
6. R. A. Graham, M. U. Anderson, Y. Horie, S-K. You, and G. T. Holman, "Pressure Measurements in Chemically Reacting Powder Mixtures with the Bauer Piezoelectric Polymer Gauge", *Shock Waves,* in press.
7. R. A. Graham, M. U. Anderson, F. Bauer, and R. E. Setchell, "Piezoelectric Polarization of the Ferroelectric Polymer PVDF from 10 MPa to 10 GPa: Studies of Loading-Path Dependence", *Shock Compression of Condensed Matter - 1991,* eds. S. C. Schmidt, et al, North-Holland, (1992), pp 883-886.
8. G. T. Holman Jr., R. A. Graham, M. U. Anderson, present proceedings, in press.
9. D. E. Wackerbarth, M. U. Anderson, R. A. Graham, SAND92-0046, February, 1992, Sandia National Laboratories.
10. S. A. Sheffield, R. L. Gustavsen, R. R. Alcon, R. A. Graham, M. U. Anderson, present proceedings, in press.
11. E. W. Dunbar, R. A. Graham, M. U. Anderson, G. T. Holman Jr., N. N. Thadhani, present proceedings, in press.
12. M. R. Baer, present proceedings, in press.

SHOCK COMPRESSION AND ISENTROPIC RELEASE OF RHYOLITE

W. Yang, G. Chen, W. W. Anderson and Thomas. J. Ahrens
Lindhurst Laboratory of Experimental Geophysics, Seismological Laboratory
California Institute of Technology, Pasadena, CA 91125

A series of shock compression experiments have been conducted on rhyolite at pressure ranging from 6 to 33 GPa. A velocity interferometer (VISAR) was employed to monitor the particle velocity of an aluminum reflector with a diffused surface bonded to the rhyolite sample. In the forward ballistic experiments, a slow rise shock wave front is observed at 6 GPa. While in the forward experiments their release waves are smeared, in a reverse ballistic experiment, the particle velocity variation at the shock wave plateau and the isentropic release wave arrival have been clearly observed. Using Swegle's mixed phase model, we simulated the experimental results with WONDY code. Like quartz and granite, the rhyolite data could be fit to a frozen release model which has some hysteric behavior. The Eulerian sound velocity at shock pressure 8.7 GPa has been determined to be 5.6 km/s.

INTRODUCTION

The shock loading and unloading of silicate geological materials are of interest for the description of impact and explosively driven shock waves in crustal rock. Shock propagation in quartz have been studied extensively at pressures up to 650 GPa by Trunin et al [1], Al'tshuler et al [2], Wackerle [3] and Fowles [4]. Release isentropes have been measured by Grady et al [5] in quartz-bearing rock, Grady and Murri [6] in feldspar, and by Poderets et al [7] and Chhabildas [8,9] in single crystal quartz. It has been found that the phase transition from quartz to stishovite occurs in mixed phase region from 14 to 40 GPa. Upon isentropic release, the high density phase does not immediately undergo the reverse transformation to the low density quartz phase. Recently, Swegle [10] constructed a thermodynamically consistent mixed phase model which can be used to analyze loading and unloading shock wave data in quartz-bearing rocks and reported several data for granite and rhyolite. The release behavior of rhyolite was previously less well studied. We conducted a series of release isentrope measurements on rhyolite, using a VISAR [11] to monitor the compression and release particle velocities of an Al buffer bonded to a rhyolite sample. Numerical simulations with WONDY code [12] were conducted and used to fit the data. The Eulerian sound velocity of rhyolite at high pressure in one reverse ballistic experiment was also determined.

EXPERIMENTS

The VISAR used in the present experiments incorporated the push-pull modification [13] for improved signal quality. The time resolution of the data are ~3 ns and the velocity precision ~1%. Two type of experiments have been conducted----forward and reverse ballistic. The forward ballistic target assembly (Figure 1a) consists of an aluminum driver plate (2 mm thick), a rhyolite target (6 mm thick), a diffuse reflecting Al2024 or Al6061 buffer (0.8 mm thick) and a LiF window (12 mm thick). The flyer plate used are Al2024 (5 mm thick) and W (4 mm thick). For the reverse ballistic experiment, the flyer plate was rhyolite and it impacted the Al6061 buffer directly (Figure 1b). Table 1 lists the experimental parameters.

RESULTS AND SIMULATIONS

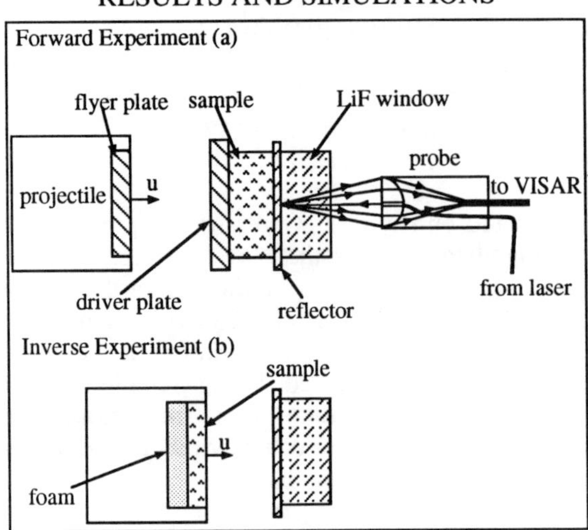

Figure 1. Experimental assembly.

Table 1. Experimental Parameters

I. Forward Ballistic Experiments		
Shot No.	Flyer plate velocity (km/s)	Rhyolite sample density (g/cm^3)
886	1.45 (Al2024)	2.298
887	1.06 (Al2024)	2.29
888	1.97 (Al2024)	2.29
896	2.55 (W)	2.35
II. Reverse Ballistic Experiment		
Shot No.	Rhyolite flyer velocity (km/s)	Rhyolite sample density (g/cm^3)
895	1.48	2.28

The forward ballistic experimental results are shown in Figure 2. At low pressure 6 GPa, the shock wave front rises very slowly (~280 ns), make it very difficult to determine the elastic precursor's amplitude. The observed low amplitude precursor is due to the strength of the Al buffer. As pressure increases, the shock front rise-time becomes shorter. For shock pressures >9 GPa, the wave front becomes nearly a step function. The long rise time at low pressures arises from heterogeneity of the rhyolite sample. The grain size is up to a few millimeters. The particle velocities at the shock wave plateau and

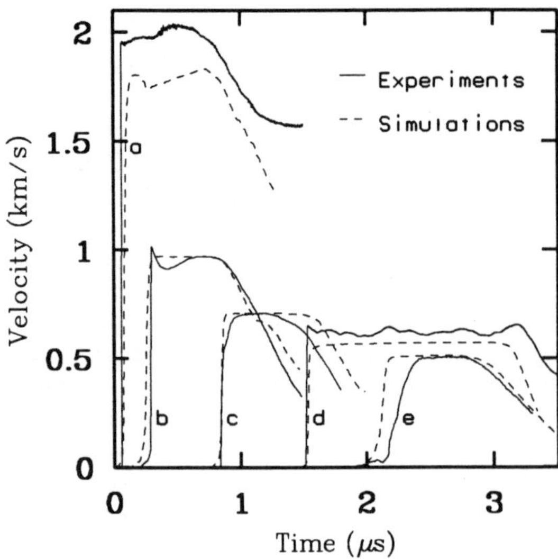

Figure 2. Particle velocity profiles. a. shot 896, 33 GPa; b. shot 888, 12 GPa; c. shot 886, 8.7 GPa; d. shot 895, 8.7 GPa; e. shot 887, 6 GPa.

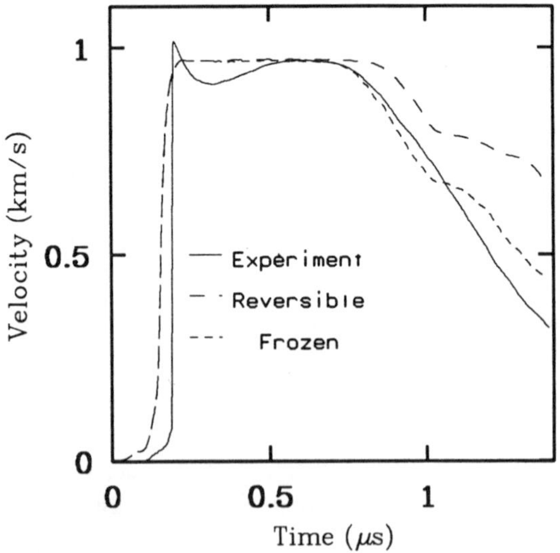

Figure 3. Comparison of simulation models. The frozen model clearly fits better than the reversible one.

release region, however, are smoothed out by the complex wave reflections between different layers of materials. The gradual velocity increase of Figure 2a is due to the compression wave reflected from the W flyer plate. The dashed lines are numerical simulation results using the

Table 2. Rhyolite Equation of State Parameters

	LPP		HPP
ρ_o(g/cm^3)	2.50		4.21
K_o(GPa)	37.0		350
K_o'	6.27		3.3
γ_o	0.7		1.2
ν		0.2	
Y_o(GPa)		2.1	

LPP-low pressure phase; HPP-high pressure phase; γ_o-Gruneisen's parameter; ν-Poisson's ratio.

WONDY code and Swegle's mixed-phase model. The strength of rhyolite is obtained from a streak camera experiment which provided the Hugoniot elastic limit of 2.8 GPa. Rhyolite is assumed frozen during release region (that is, when pressure decreases, high density phase will not transform back to low density phase). The mixed phase region is chosen as 5-41 GPa. A reversible model is also used, but the frozen model best fits the experimental particle velocity profile (Figure 3). In our simulation model, the sample porosity is closed when pressure reaches 1 GPa. Rhyolite parameters used in the simulation are given in Table 2. Dynamic strength Y_o, bulk modulus K_o and its derivative K_o' are obtained from our impedance match [14] experiments. The experimental particle profile and simulation for the reverse ballistic experiment is shown in Figure 2d. The oscillation of the particle velocity at the shock wave plateau reflects the heterogeneity of the sample. The clear onset of the release wave makes it possible to calculate the sound velocity of rhyolite at high pressure. The high pressure sound velocity of Al6061 is provided by Duffy [15]. The Eulerian sound velocity for this shot was determined to be 5.6 km/s at 8.7 GPa. Due to the heterogeneity of the sample, it is unclear whether this is a longitudinal or bulk release wave. Figure 4 shows the simulation of the isentropic release trajectories of rhyolite from Hugoniot states similar to our experiments on the pressure volume plane. The hysteric frozen release behavior can cause strong attenuation of shock wave propagation.

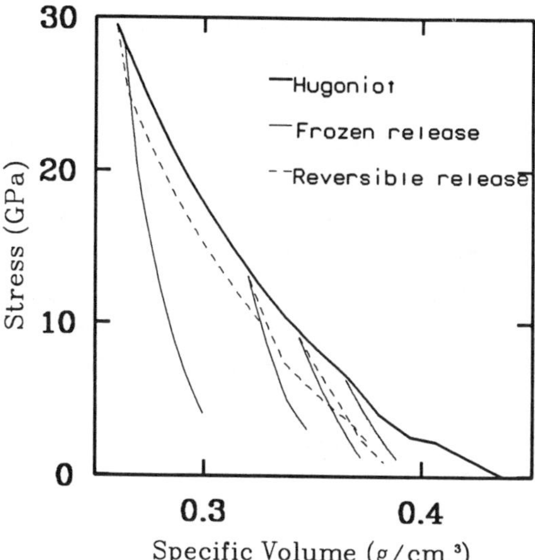

Figure 4. Isentropic release curves of rhyolite.

CONCLUSIONS

Like quartz and granite, rhyolite appears to have release isentrope trajectory which is frozen up to 33 GPa. Sample heterogeneity causes slow wave front rise at low shock pressures. Particle velocity oscillation has been observed at the shock wave plateau. Eulerian sound velocity of rhyolite at shock pressure 8.7 GPa is determined with a reverse ballistic experiment.

ACKNOWLEDGMENTS

This research is supported under Contract F49670-92-J-0402 and Mission Research Corp. Subcontract #SC-0064-90-0002. Division of Geological and Planetary Sciences Contribution #5325.

REFERENCES

[1] R. F. Trunin and G. V. Simakov et al,

Dynamic compressibility of quartz and quartzite at high pressure, *Izv. Acad. Sci. USSR Phys. Solid Earth*, no. 1, p. 13-20,1971.

[2] L. V., Al'tshuler et al, Shock-wave Compression of periclase and quartz and the composition of the earth's lower mantle, *Izv. Acad. Sci. USSR Phys. Solid Earth*, no 10, pp. 657-660,1965.

[3] J. Wackerle, Shock-wave compression of quartz, *J. Apply. Phys.*, 33, p. 922-937, 1962.

[4] G. R. Fowles, Dynamic compression of quartz, *J. Geophys. Res.*, 72, p. 5729-5742, 1967.

[5] D. E. Grady, Shock deformation of brittle solids, *J. Geophys. Res.*, 85, B2, p. 913-924, 1980.

[6] D. E. Grady et al, Quartz to stishovite: Wave propagation in the mixed phase region, *J. Geophys. Res.*, 79, p. 332-338, 1974.

[7] M. A Podurets et al., *Izv. Acad. Sci. USSR Phys. Solid Earth*, no. 12, p. 419-424, 1976.

[8] L. C. Chhabildas and D. E. Grady, Dynamic material response of quartz at high strain rates, in *Mat. Res. Soc. Symp. Proc. Vol. 22*, edited by C. Homan et al, North Holland, Elsever Science Publishing, 1984, p.147.

[9] L. C. Chhabildas, Shock loading and release behavior of X-cut quartz, in *Shock Waves in Condensed Matter*, edited by Y. M. Gupta, Plenum Publishing Corp., 1986.

[10] J. W. Swegle, Irreversible phase transitions and wave propagation in silicate geologic materials, SAND89-1443,1989.

[11] L. M. Barker and R. E. Hollenbach, Laser interferometer for measuring high velocities of any reflecting surface, *J. Appl. Phys.*, 43, p. 4669-4675, 1972.

[12] M. E. Kipp and R. J. Lawrence, WONDY V - A one-dimensional finite-difference wave propagation code, SAND81-0930, 1982.

[13] W. F. Hemsing, Velocity sensing interferometer (VISAR) modification, *Rev. Sci. Instrum.*, 50, p. 73-78, 1979.

[14] T. J. Ahrens, in *Methods of Experimental Physics*, New York: Academic Press, 1987, Vol. 24, Part A, p. 185-234.

[15] T. S. Duffy, Elastic properties of metals and minerals under shock compression, Ph. D thesis, California Institute of Technology, 1992, pp. 296.

SHOCK RESPONSE OF POROUS 2Al + Fe_2O_3 POWDER MIXTURES

G.T. Holman, Jr., R.A. Graham, and M.U. Anderson, Sandia National Laboratories,
Albuquerque, NM. 87185

Time-resolved pressure measurements have been conducted on 2Al + Fe_2O_3 powder mixtures using the (PVDF) stress-rate gauge. These measurements were made on samples which were 53% of solid density. Measurements were made at pressures from 0.67 to more than 10 GPa utilizing both impact loading with a compressed gas gun and direct contact high explosive loading. The sample is pressed to the desired density in a copper capsule. PVDF gauges were positioned in front of and behind the powder sample in direct contact with the sample. These gauges measure the input and propagated stress-rate and are used for a precise measurement of velocity through the 4 mm thick sample. In the case of high explosive loading, gauges are also installed on the explosive side and on the capsule side of a metal driver plate to measure the shock velocity through the driver so that the driver pressure can be determined. The response of 2Al + Fe_2O_3 under shock compression appears to demonstrate a more complex behavior than other materials. At approximately 4.6 GPa, the material compresses to beyond solid density. There was no evidence of chemical reaction.

INTRODUCTION

For more than ten years, shock-compression studies have been performed on highly porous powders and powder mixtures. Early experiments used the sample preservation technique. The experiments subjected the sample to a controlled shock using a plane wave generated by a high explosive. The sample was then recovered and analyzed using X-ray diffraction (XRD), scanning electron microscopy (SEM), differential thermal analysis (DTA), as well as other techniques.[1-5] Later, the need for time-resolved measurements on porous powders became essential to understand the dynamic response of porous materials under shock compression. This need led to a measurement technique being developed which utilizes the piezoelectric polymer, PVDF, as a gauge[6] to measure the time-resolved response of these porous materials under shock compression.[7]

The present study is one of three papers describing parallel work performed on three different materials. One material is a single component sample, TiO_2.[8] The second material is a powder mixture which has a relatively low pressure for initiation of reaction, 5Ti + 3Si.[9] The third is the classical thermite 2Al + Fe_2O_3 which reacts at a pressure greater than 15 GPa based on earlier sample preservation work.[1]

EXPERIMENTAL CONFIGURATION

The aluminum and hematite (Fe_2O_3) powder in the mixture were acquired from the Aluminum Company Of America, ALCOA, and Fisher Scientific, respectively. The aluminum powder was manufactured and shipped as ALCOA lot #1401/S2-80202. ALCOA quoted 90% of the powder (by weight) between 3μm and 12.8μm. A sample of the 1401 aluminum powder has been measured, and has a narrow size distribution ranging from 2μm to 17μm with 15μm making up the largest volume, (25%).

The hematite in the mixture was Fisher Scientific stock #I116-3. Fisher quotes 100% of this material to be 15μm or smaller. The measured sample shows a distribution from 1μm to 27μm and 45% of the sample per volume at a size of 22μm.

The porous powder sample is pressed into a capsule in three layers using a hardened steel plug. The top of each of the first two layers is loosened before the next layer is added to lessen the chances of a layered effect of the sample. After all three layers are pressed, the back capsule plug is pressed against the sample. A 50 mm diameter, 9.5 mm thick disc of Kel-F is mounted to the back plug between the gauge and the copper plug. This polymer provides a closer impedance match to the sample than the copper. Delaying the time of re-shock from the copper plug provides for a longer viewing time of the propagated wave. There is approximately $\pm$ 1.5% thickness uncertainty with this design rather than the usual $\pm$ 0.5%. The polymer deflects at a lower pressure than the pressure needed to compress the powder to 53% of solid density. Since the length of the hardened steel packing plug is known to $\pm$ 5 μm, and the powder level with respect to the top of the capsule can be measured to $\pm$ 10 μm, the sample thickness can be determined to the accuracy stated above.

As shown in Figure 1, a PVDF gauge package is placed on either side of the sample. The gauge packages are comprised of different thicknesses of either Kel-F or Teflon along with the 25 μm PVDF gauge itself. Approximately 0.2 μm of aluminum is vapor deposited on the powder side of the package to provide an opaque barrier.

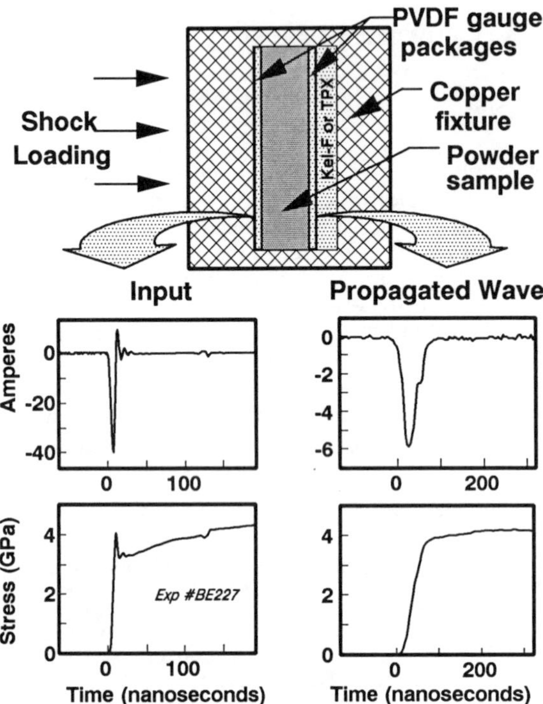

Figure 1. The copper capsule containing the porous powder sample. Gauge packages are shown on both sides of the sample. Typical input and propagated stress-rate current waveforms are shown at the top and stress profiles are shown at the bottom.

Two loading experimental configurations were utilized to measure the time-resolved response. The first technique utilized a gas gun facility which provides well controlled symmetric impact loading.[10] This method of impact loading also has the advantage of enabling small incremental pressure changes to be achieved. The second method is explosive loading where a P-40 plane wave generator, and a 102 mm diameter, 25 mm thick high explosive are used to provide the input stress wave into the target. Explosive loading offers the advantage of higher input stress, but has at least two distinct disadvantages: 1) limited selection of input stress levels, and 2) electrical noise radiated by the explosive to the data acquisition system at the lower signal levels. Measured current-time pulses and resulting stress-time records are shown in Figure 1.

Impact loading

In this configuration, an aluminum projectile with a copper impact face is accelerated into a copper capsule which contains a 50 mm diameter, 4 mm thick porous powder sample. Charged pins are used to measure the projectile velocity to an accuracy of $\pm$ 0.1%. Each gauge output goes to a current viewing resistor (CVR). There are two signal lines from each CVR. These signals are monitored using digitizing signal analyzers operated at one nanosecond per point. The output of each CVR is monitored by the same analyzer at the same horizontal sweep. One analyzer monitors the two gauge outputs at a sensitivity based on the expected output. The other signal analyzer monitors the outputs at 10 or more times the sensitivity of the first. These current-versus-time signals are a measure of the input and propagated stress-rates. The time between the two signals determines the wave velocity. The signals from the primary and sensitive channels are combined to increase resolution. The stress-rate signals are integrated and processed with a numerical fit using the software program PVDF Stress.[11] The propagated stress measurement is characteristic of the state in the polymer.

Several shock reverberations were observed during impact loading. The front gauge typically remained active for more than eight microseconds.

Explosive loading

As shown in Figure 2, a P-40 plane wave generator and a 102 mm diameter, 25 mm thick high explosive are used to produce the input stress to the sample. A 114 mm diameter, 12.7 mm thick metal driver plate (aluminum or copper) is placed between the explosive and the copper capsule containing the sample. The explosive, the driver plate, and the capsule are in direct contact. PVDF gauge packages are mounted on the explosive side and on the capsule of the driver plate. The time difference between the two gauges measures the shock velocity in the driver plate so that input pressure in the driver can be determined. The gauge package on the explosive side of the driver plate is coated with approximately 0.2 μm of aluminum to provide an opaque shield between the explosive and the gauge.

The capsule containing the sample and the method used to monitor the current output from the gauges are essentially the same as that used in impact experiments. Late time signal reverberations have not been observed during explosive loading experiments. There is evidence of the Taylor wave from the explosive as seen by a slow decay on the back side of the stress signal. At pressures of approximately 17.5 GPa into the gauge package, the gauge output begins to become erroneous. This pressure range is coincident with the explosive driving configuration of Composition B with an aluminum driver plate. More work will be needed on the gauge packaging before higher input stresses can be successfully measured.

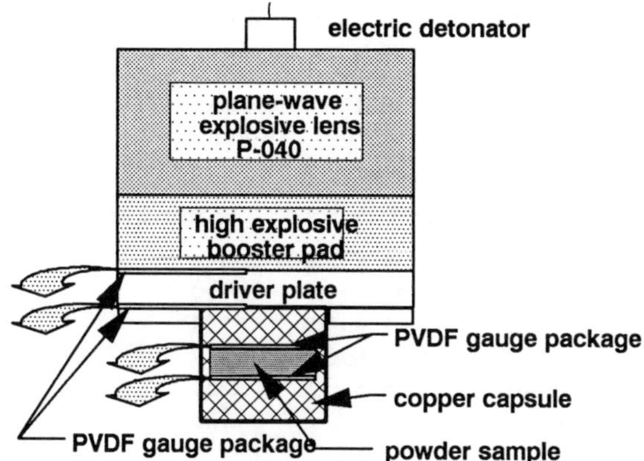

Figure 2. An established method of planar loading as seen above. A plane wave generator is used to change a point detonation into a plane wave over the surface of the HE. Explosive loading results in higher pressures than can be achieved with impact loading. Two gauges are used to measure the shock velocity through the metal driver plate.

RESULTS

The propagated waveforms in the porous samples are observed to be dispersive when compared to a solid. A comparison of the propagated stress waves through 2Al + Fe_2O_3 at different input stresses is shown in Figure 3. The risetimes, though long, are virtually constant at input pressures above 3.3 GPa.[8]

The measured input stress and sample wave speed are used to calculate a point on the pressure-vs-relative volume curve. Conservation of momentum equations are used in these calculations even though the pressure pulse in the porous powder is not a true shock wave. For this reason, the p-v points as plotted on the curve are somewhat uncertain.

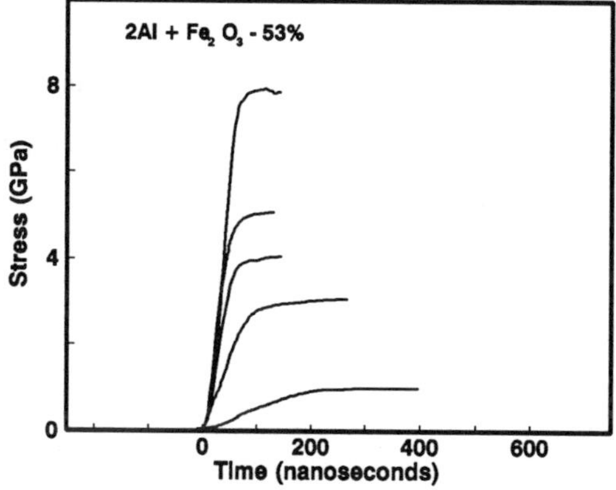

Figure 3. The propagated stress waveforms show small changes in risetime with increased loading pressure above 3 GPa.

Since the compression of porous solids is so large, the uncertainty of compression is not large. As shown in Figure 4, the p-v plot for 2Al + Fe_2O_3 exhibits two different crush up slopes. At lower pressures (up to 0.67 GPa), there is a large compression toward solid density. At pressures between 0.67 GPa and 3.2 GPa the slope becomes more steep, and there is a smaller compression toward solid density. There have been two possibilities suggested to explain this phenomenon. One possibility suggests that the initial slope is the effect of the crush strength of the aluminum and the second slope due to the crush strength of Fe_2O_3. Another possibility is that this could be the effect of voids being filled as a result of particle size differences of the two materials resulting in the initial jump toward solid density. At an input pressure of 4.6 GPa, the sample has been compressed beyond solid density. Prior sample preservation studies on 2Al + Fe_2O_3 indicate a pressure of reaction threshold above 15 GPa.[1]

CONCLUSIONS

The propagated wave in 2Al + Fe_2O_3 is quite dispersive as is the case with most porous materials. The response of this material under shock compression appears to be more complex than TiO_2[8] or 5Ti + Si[9] as indicated by the wave dispersion and the data plotted in the pressure-vs-volume plane.

Modeling of this material response is being done by Baer.[12]

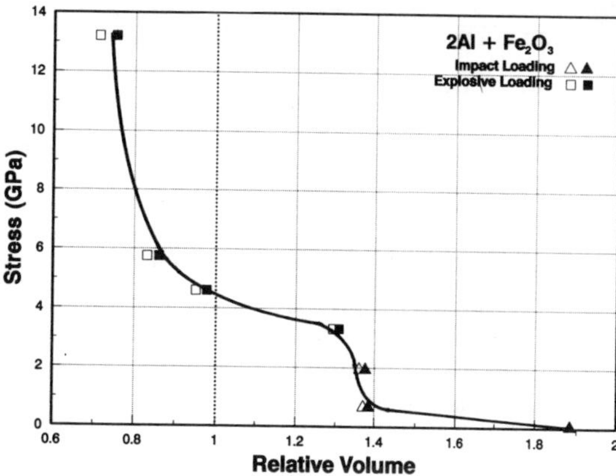

Figure 4. A plot of pressure-vs-relative volume. The solid symbols represent calculations based on the wave speed being measured from the breakaway of the input signal to the breakaway of the propagated signal. The open symbols represent calculations based on the wave speed being measured from half-max to half-max.

Table 1. Experimental parameters and results from shock compression experiments on $2Al + Fe_2O_3$ powder mixtures with unshocked density of 2.245 ± .026 grams/cm³ (53%) of solid.

Experiment Number[A] ----	Input Condition[B] ----	Config-uration[C] ----	Input Stress[D] (GPa)	Wave Velocity[E] (km/s)	Risetime[F] (nsec)	Output Stress[G] (GPa)	Relative Volume[H] ----
2485 (a)	0.314	1	0.67	1.050	300 (162)	0.95 Kel-F	1.385
2484 (a)	0.635	1	1.94	1.795	132 (78)	3.02 Kel-F	1.377
BE-227 (b)	Baratol/Cu	4	3.32	2.198	100 (44)	4.01 Kel-F	1.293
BE-057 (b)	TNT/Cu	3	4.59	2.059	90 (39)	4.11 Kel-F	0.977
BE-059 (b)	Comp B/Cu	3	5.75	2.168	89 (40)	5.05 Kel-F	0.861
BE-233 (b)	PBX9404/Al	5	13.2[I]	3.128	96 (48)	7.89 Kel-F	0.755

A: (a) Impact Loading; (b) Explosive Loading; B: Symetric impact velocity (km/s) copper on copper or explosive loading; C: Configuration, nominal thicknesses in parentheses: 1: Cu (6.5mm)/FEP (12.7μm)/PVDF (25μm)/FEP (12.7μm)/2Al + Fe_2O_3 (4mm)/FEP (12.7μm)/PVDF (25μm)/FEP (12.7μm)/Kel-F (8.9mm)/Cu (6.35mm); 2: P-40/Explosive (25.4mm)/Cu (12.7mm)/Cu (6.3mm)/Kel-F (125μm)/PVDF (25μm)/FEP (25μm)/2Al + Fe_2O_3 (4mm)/FEP (25μm)/PVDF (25μm)/FEP (25μm)/Kel-F (9.52mm)/Cu (6.35mm); 3: P-40/Explosive (25.4mm)/Cu (12.7mm)/Cu or Al (6.5mm)/FEP (12.7μm)/PVDF (25μm)/FEP (12.7μm)/2Al + Fe_2O_3 (4mm)/FEP (12.7μm)/PVDF (25μm)/FEP (12.7μm)/Kel-F (9.52mm)/Cu (6.30mm); D: PVDF Measurement; E: Wave speed: Toe-Toe/10-90%; F: Propagated wave; G: PVDF measurement in polymer backing material; H: Calculated from PVDF input stress and wave speed; I: Value calculated using Hugoniot program rather than the actual measurement.

ACKNOWLEDGEMENTS

The authors would like to thank Heidi Anderson and Dave Wackerbarth, Ktech Corporation for their excellent technical assistance. The authors would also like to acknowledge New Mexico Tech for their firing site support. Work supported by USDOE Contract #DE-AC04-76DPOO789.

REFERENCES

1. R. A. Graham, *Solids Under High Pressure Shock Compression: Mechanics, Physics and Chemistry,* Springer-Verlag (1993).
2. R. A. Graham and N. N. Thadhani, "Solid State Reactivity of Shock-Processed Solids", in *Shock Waves in Materials Science,* edited by A. B. Sawaoka, Springer-Verlag (1993).
3. N. N. Thadhani, "Shock-Induced Chemical Reactions and Synthesis of Materials", *Progress in Materials Science* , 37, 117-226, 1993.
4. R. A. Graham, "Issues in Shock-Induced Solid State Chemistry", in Third International Symposium on High Dynamic Pressures, edited by R. Cheret, CEA, Paris (1989) pp 175-180.
5. R. A. Graham, B. Morosin, Y. Horie, E. L. Venturini, M. Boslough, M. J. Carr, and D. L. Williamson, "Chemical Synthesis Under High Pressure Shock Loading", in *Shock Waves in Consensed Condensed Matter,* edited by Y. M. Gupta, Plenum (1986) pp 693-711.
6. R.A. Graham, M.U. Anderson, F. Bauer, and R.E. Setchell, "Piezoelectric Polarization of the Ferroelectric Polymer PVDF from 10 MPa to 10 GPa: Studies of Loading-Path Dependence", *Shock Compression of Condensed Matter-1991*, eds. S.C. Schmidt, et al, North-Holland, (1992), pp 883-886.
7. R.A. Graham, M.U. Anderson, Y. Horie, S-K. You, and G.T. Holman, "Pressure Measurements in Chemically Reacting Powder Mixtures With The Bauer Piezoelectric Polymer Gauge", *Shock Waves,* in press.
8. M.U. Anderson, R.A. Graham, and G.T. Holman, present proceedings, in press.
9. E.W. Dunbar, R.A. Graham, M.U. Anderson, G.T. Holman, N.N. Thadhani, present proceedings, in press.
10. R.E. Setchell, "Sandia 25-Meter Compressed Helium/Air Gun", *Shock Waves in Condensed Matter-1981*, eds. W.J. Nellis, L. Seaman, and R.A. Graham, (AIP, 1982) pp. 657-660.
11. D. E. Wackerbarth, M. U. Anderson, R. A. Graham, SAND92-0046, February, 1992, Sandia National Laboratories.
12. M.R. Baer, present proceedings, in press.

RESPONSE OF THE HIGH-FILLED ELASTOMERS TO SHOCK-WAVE LOADING.

G.I. KANEL',

High Energy Density Research Center, Russia Academy of Sciences, Izhorskaya 13/19, Moscow, 127412

A.V. UTKIN, and Z.G.TOLSTIKOVA

Institute of Chemical Physsics of Russia Academy of Sciences, Chernogolovka, Moscow region, 142432, Russia

The behavior of a rubber and two model elastomers at shock and rarefaction waves was studied. The evolution of shock pulses with 0.2 to 6 GPa peak intensity was registered with manganin gauges and laser velocimeter VISAR. A comparison of measured rarefaction front velocities and estimated sound velocities indicate to the solidification of shock compressed rubber. An abrupt decreasing of the resistance to tension of elastomers was observed under tensile stresses of 15 to 30 MPa in the spall conditions.

INTRODUCTION

Elastomers are specified by an ability to undergo large reversible deformations and a pronounced frequency dependence of elastic modules. These elastomers properties are extended on the response of rubber to the dynamic tension at shock wave reflection from the free surface [1,2]. In case of composite propellants and its simulators [3,4] spall fracture is initiated in filler grains under the incident pulse intensity of about 50 MPa. Then cracks stretch into the binder where they are stopped. The rupture of samples were observed only after 145 MPa impact stress [4].

In this paper results of the experimental studying of the rubber and two high-filled elastomers mechanical properties are presented.

BEHAVIOUR OF RUBBER UNDER SHOCK COMPRESSION

Samples were cut out from the rubber sheet 10 mm thick. Measured density and sound velocity at normal conditions are equal to 1.34 g/cm^3 and 1.5 km/s, correspondingly. One-dimensional shock pulses were generated by aluminum impactors 4-7 mm thick or explosive plane-wave generators. Manganin gauges were used to measure the pressure profiles P(t) inside the sample at different distances [1].

The shock wave pressure profile evolution in rubber does not content any specific peculiarities. Figure 1 shows results of measuring of the shock wave velocities (dark points - the experiment, curve 1 - resulted Hugoniot) and Lagrangian sound velocity (light points) for rubber as a function of pressure. Curve 2 presents an estimation of the bulk sound velocity for shock-compressed rubber in a quasiacoustic approach, curve 3 is the upper estimation of sound velocity. The quasiacoustic approach is based on the assumption of coincidence of Hugoniot and unloading isentrope in pressure - particle velocities coordinates. This approach gives a good agreement with experimental sound velocity values for metals at pressures up to 100 GPa [5]. The upper estimate of sound velocity was fulfilled by differentiation of rubber Hugoniot in pressure - density coordinates.

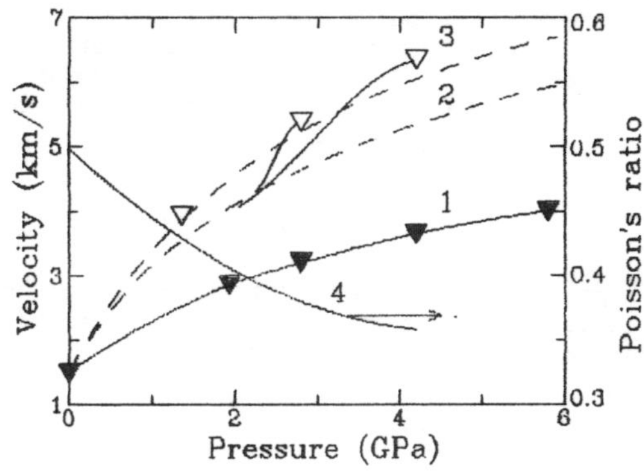

FIGURE 1. Dependence of shock wave velocity (1), Lagrangian sound velocity (2,3) and Poisson's ratio (4) upon the pressure.

The rarefaction wave front velocity exceeds the upper estimation of equilibrium bulk sound velocity. As the unloading proceeds (solid line originated from the light points in Fig.1) the measured wave velocities come near to curve 2. It is naturally to connect such a character of rarefaction wave velocity behavior with the elastic-plastic properties of the shock-compressed rubber. In this case the rarefaction front is an elastic wave and Poisson's ratio can be calculated from relation between the rarefaction front velocity and a sound velocity on curve 2 at the same pressure. Calculated Poisson's ratio values are presented in Fig.1 by curve 4. Poisson's ratio decreases from typical for elastomers value (about 0.5) down to 0.36 at pressure of 4.2 GPa, typical for solids. It means that solidification of rubber occurs under shock-wave compression.

Earlier, glass transition of rubber was observed under static compression [6] at the normal temperature. Within the framework of obtained experimental data it is impossible to exactly identify the mechanism of glassing, nevertheless the ability for elastomers to glass in shock waves is demonstrated distinctly.

RESISTANCE TO SPALL FRACTURE OF ELASTOMERS

Spallation of rubber and two high-filled elastomers was investigated through the free surface velocity profiles measurements. Shock waves were generated in samples by PMMA impactors. Free surface velocity was registered with VISAR [7]. To reflect the laser beam the aluminum foil 8 μm thick was glued with epoxy upon the samples surface. Part of experiments with rubber were performed with liquid windows.

A typical free surface velocity profile of solids at spallation contains usually the initial part of the incident shock wave and so-called "spall pulse" which is a result of fracture under tension in the reflected rarefaction wave. The velocity drop ahead of the spall pulse Δu_{fs} is proportional to the material spall strength σ:

$$\sigma = 0.5 \cdot \rho_0 \cdot c_0 \cdot \Delta u_{fs}. \qquad (1)$$

Experimental results for rubber are presented in Figure 2, where curve 1 has been obtained in a shot with ethanol window, and

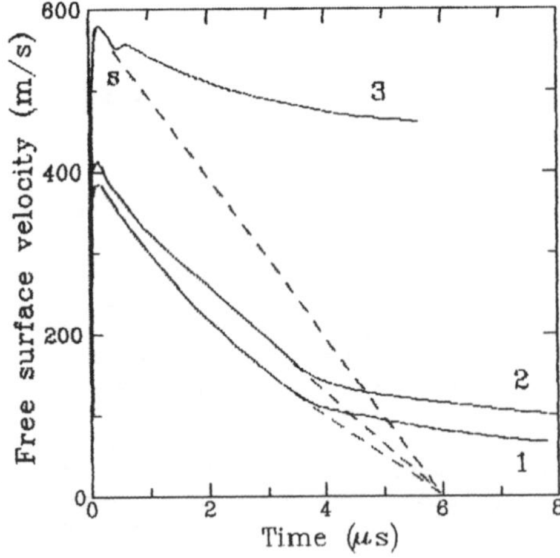

FIGURE 2. Experimental particle velocity profiles for rubber.

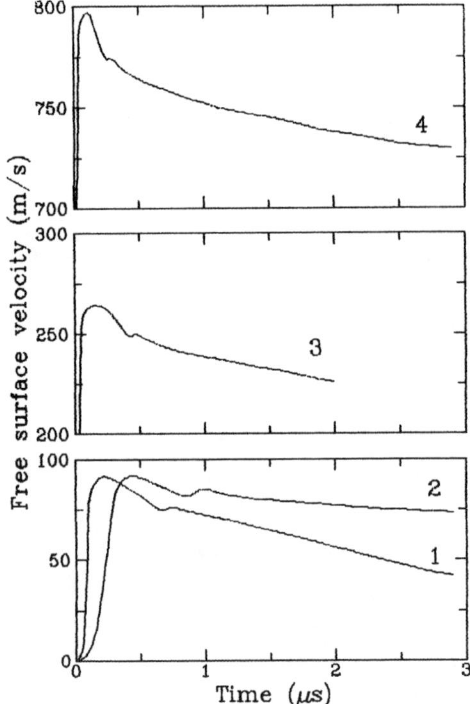

FIGURE 3. Experimental free surface velocity profiles for high-filled elastomers.
1,3,4 - fine-dispersed filler; 2 - coarse-dispersed filler.

curve 2 in a shot with hexane window. The shock compressibility of window materials is known [8,9]. The dashed line shows the free surface velocity profile calculated from results of window tests in the assumption of absent of any rubber destruction at tension. If the material has not got any remarkable tensile strength, the free surface velocity after the shock front arrival must be constant.

The measured free surface velocity profile (curve 3) occupies some intermediate position between these two extreme cases. Initial part of the profile corresponds to the incident shock and unloading waves. A small spall pulse is fixed in the point S. Then the slow surface velocity decreasing is observed during relatively large time. Visual examination of the recovered sample does not reveal any remarkable destructions. The value of rubber spall strength calculated from (2) for point S is equal to 27±3 MPa.

Figure 3 presents the free surface velocity histories for some butadienenitrile caoutchouc based filled elastomer. The filler contention was equal to 75 mass %, including 61.6% of KCl. Two compositions were differed by the filler particle size: a coarse-dispersed samples with 160-200 μm of KCl particle size, and a fine-dispersed composition with that of 20-50 μm. The initial density of the material ρ_0 was equal to 1.6 g/cm^3, sound velocity at normal conditions was 1.85 km/s. Samples were disks 4.5-5.0 mm thick with diameter of 70 mm.

The measured free surface velocity profiles for tested high-filled elastomers are similar to rubber. Measured values of spall strength are 24 to 30 MPa for fine-dispersed samples and $\simeq$15 MPa for coarse-dispersed. In shots 1,2 samples were recovered. As well as rubber, these model elastomer samples were not scabbed after shock loading. The peak shock pressure in shots 1,2 was equal to ~150 MPa what exceeds significantly the measured spall strength value.

It is known the voids formation precedes rupture of elastomers. These voids are nucleating under stresses essentially lower then the rupture stresses. Nucleation of microdiscontinuitis is not yet of destruction itself. Thus in tests with three-axial tension of natural caoutchouc vulcanizers [10] the voids appeared at stresses of 1 to 3 MPa and insignificant deformation. After that samples underwent further large deformation reaching several hundred percents. So one can suppose the obtained spall strength values of 15 to 30 MPa characterize the nucleation of microdiscontinuities in elastomers, but not complete rupture.

The velocity deceleration behind the spall pulse is determined by the resistance to the material tension. For tested materials the resistance to tension is highest for rubber (curve 3 in Fig.2); it is lower for the elastomer with a fine-dispersed filler (curves 1,3,4 in Fig.3) and lowest for the coarse-dispersed elastomer (curve 2 in Fig.3). The observed deceleration of free surface inversely proportional to the size of filler's particles. For the fine-dispersed filler the velocity deceleration is 3.5 times as high as that of coarse-dispersed sample. One can see also the influence of filler particle size on the shock front rise time. The rise time for coarse-dispersed composition is twice as much as for the fine-dispersed sample.

REFERENCES

[1] Yu.B.Kolmikov, G.I.Kanel, I.P.Parhomenko et al.,Zh. Prikl. Mekh. Tekh. Fiz., N1, 126 (1990).

[2] G.R.Danker, C.D.Newlander, N.J.Colella, "Analytical modeling of Dynamic Tensile Behavior in Loaded Vamac Elastomers", in Shock Compression of Condensed Matter, Elsevier Science Publishers B.V., 1990, p.213.

[3] L.J.Weirick, "Characterization of Booster-Rocket Propellants and their Simulators", in The 9-th Symposium (Int) on Detonation, V.1, Portland, USA, 1989, pp.462-470.

[4] F.Huang, C.Bai, J.Ding, "Mechanical Response of a Composite Propellant to Dynamic Loading", in Shock Compression of Condensed Matter, 1991.

[5] A.V.Bushman, G.I.Kanel, A.L.Ni, V.E.Fortov. Intense Dynamic Loading of Condensed Matter. Taylor & Francis, 1993, 287 pp.

[6] C.W.Weaver, M.S.Paterson, J. Polym. Sci., 7, pt.A-2, N3, 587 (1969).

[7] J.R.Asay, L.M.Barker, J. Appl. Phys., 45, 2540 (1974)

[8] J.M.Walsh, M.H.Rice, J. Chem. Phys. 37, 815 (1957)

[9] I.J.Ahrens, M.N.Ruderman, J. Appl. Phys. 37, 4758 (1966)

[10] A.N.Gent, P.B.Lindley, Proc. Roy. Soc. (London) 249 **A**, 195 (1959).

EFFECT OF EPOXY BOND RESPONSE ON COMBINED COMPRESSION-SHEAR WAVE PROPAGATION IN SOLIDS

R. Feng & Y. M. Gupta
Shock Dynamics Center
Washington State University
Pullman, WA 99164-2814

Thin epoxy bonds are commonly used for assembling samples in plate impact experiments. A good understanding of the bond response is essential to understanding large amplitude shear wave propagation in plate impact experiments involving combined compression and shear wave propagation in inelastic materials. Toward this end, we have carried out numerical calculations and modeled the epoxy as a thermal softening, elastic/viscoplastic material. Results are presented for different model parameters to understand the inter-relationship between the bond response and shear wave amplitudes. Numerical solution are compared with experimental measurements obtained using EMV gauges embedded in fused silica layers. Over the stress range examined, the fused silica behaves as a nonlinear elastic solid and the measurements can be related to the bond response.

INTRODUCTION

The use of epoxy as a bonding material is a common practice in plate impact experiments. With suitable care, an epoxy bond can be made very thin (~0.5-5 μm). Such a thin bond has negligible influence on the propagation of compression waves if the rise time of the wave is larger than the reverberation times in the bond. However, the response of an epoxy bond in combined compression-shear wave experiments can significantly influence the amplitude of the transmitted shear wave. To relate the material or sample response to measured shear wave amplitudes, it is important to understand the role of epoxy bond strength and failure under dynamic loading.

Evidence of the influence of bond response has been observed in combined compression-shear wave experiments on *elastic solids* using electromagnetic particle velocity (EMV) gauges.[1,2] Figure 1 shows a typical experiment involving elastic impactor and specimen discs (14° inclined). Two EMV gauges are vapor-deposited (and subsequently electroplated) on the second and third pieces of the specimen. All three pieces are then bonded using EPON 815 epoxy. A magnetic field, $\boldsymbol{B}$ is applied during the experiment. Upon

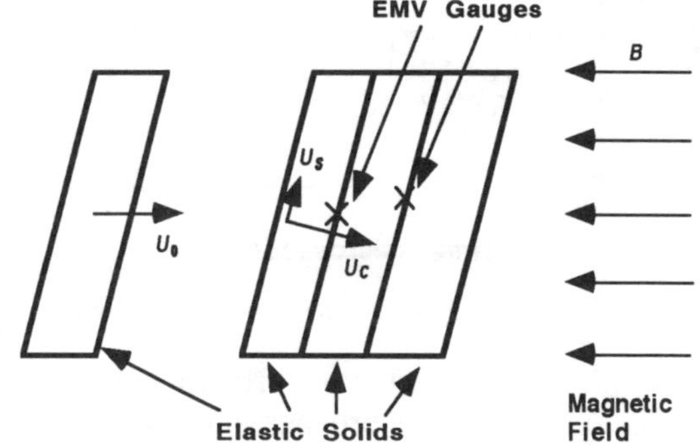

Figure 1. Compression-shear experiment using EMV gauges

impact, the momentum imparted splits into a normal component (compression wave) and a transverse component (shear wave). The induced EMF in a gauge produces a voltage which can be written as the following[1,2]

$$\varepsilon = \boldsymbol{l} \cdot (\boldsymbol{U} \times \boldsymbol{B}) \tag{1}$$

where $\boldsymbol{l}$ denotes the gauge length vector and $\boldsymbol{U}$ is the particle velocity. For the configuration shown in Figure 1, the fast traveling compressive wave produces a negative signal and the slower traveling shear wave produces a positive signal. After the arrival of both waves at a gauge location, the voltage should add to zero provided the full shear wave amplitude has been transmitted. Representative data from Conner's work[1] on fused silica are shown in Figure 2. In the two experiments at lower compressive stresses, the voltage did return to zero after the arrival of the shear wave. However, in the experiment at a compressive stress of 54 *kbar*, the voltage change associated with shear decreased after about one third of its expected value and showed a time-dependent decay. Since fused silica is known to be elastic at this stress level, the thin epoxy bond is responsible for perturbing the transmitted shear wave.

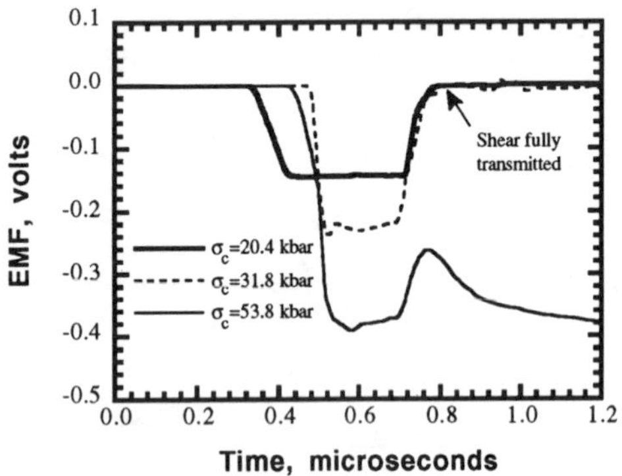

Figure 2. Compression-shear measurements in SiO_2

Despite the growing efforts in combined compression-shear wave propagation studies, little has been done to characterize the influence of bond response on the propagation of large amplitude shear waves. Prakash & Clifton[3] recently investigated the behavior of frictional bonds at the impact surface in inclined plate impact experiments. They observed a time-dependent decay in frictional bond strength and simulated it using a phenomenological model of interfacial plasticity. We present here a numerical study of the epoxy bond response under combined compression-shear loading. We will use the experimental results on fused silica (Figure 2) to guide the development of our phenomenological models for epoxy bond.

EPOXY BOND RESPONSE

The Hugoniot of a commonly used epoxy (EPON 815) has been characterized[4] and is used as a reference to construct an equation-of-state of the Mie-Grüneisen type. The specific heat of the epoxy at ambient pressure is available in the handbook by Lee & Neville[5]. The other properties needed to describe epoxy behavior under combined compression-shear loading are approximated by those reported for polymethyl methacrylate (PMMA).[6-9] The computational configuration consists of an impactor (SiO_2 or sapphire) and a sandwich target (SiO_2-epoxy-SiO_2). The epoxy bond has a thickness of 2.5 μm (typical of the experiment[1]) and is usually divided into 5 cells. Because of the time scales involved in the computation, heat conduction is neglected. An explicit wave propagation code[10] is used to carry out numerical calculations.

The softening shear response (Figure 2) was first modeled as stress relaxation in the bond using the following overstress relaxation model (in incremental form):

$$s_{ij}^{i+1} = \left(s_{ij}^{i} + 2G\Delta e_{ij}\right)\left[1 - \left(1 - \frac{\tau_Y}{\sqrt{J_2'}}\right)\frac{\Delta t}{T_R}\right] \tag{1}$$

where $\boldsymbol{s}$ and $\Delta \boldsymbol{e}$ are the deviatoric stress and strain increment tensors, respectively; J_2' is the second invariant of $\boldsymbol{s}$; Δt is the time step; and T_R is the relaxation time. Both shear modulus, G and yield stress, τ_Y are assumed to be linearly dependent on the mean stress.

A better simulation of the observed softening pattern was achieved by introducing a temperature dependence into the yield stress, τ_Y:

$$\tau_Y(p,\theta) = \left(\tau_0 + \alpha p\right)\exp\left[-\beta\left(\theta - \theta_0\right)\right] \tag{2}$$

where θ and θ_0 are the current and initial temperatures, respectively; p is the mean compressive stress ($p=-\sigma_{mm}/3$); τ_0 is the initial yield stress (0.5-1 $kbar^6$); and α (0.1-0.3) and β are the coefficients that govern pressure and temperature dependence. The temperature dependence shown in equation (2) is commonly used for polymer melts.[7] In computing the temperature increase, we assume that 90% of the inelastic work done contributes to the change of entropy. This issue is discussed in detail by Wallace.[11]

Finally, an elastic/viscoplastic thermal-softening model was also used to examine the influence of other material parameters. In this model, the inelastic response of epoxy is assumed to be non-strain-hardening and governed by a J_2' yield condition:

$$\sqrt{J_2'} - (\tau_0 + \alpha p) f(\theta) g(\dot{\gamma}) = 0 \qquad (3)$$

where f and g are the temperature and strain rate functions, respectively; and $\dot{\gamma}$ is the effective inelastic strain rate. A typical plot of f and g is presented in Figure 3.

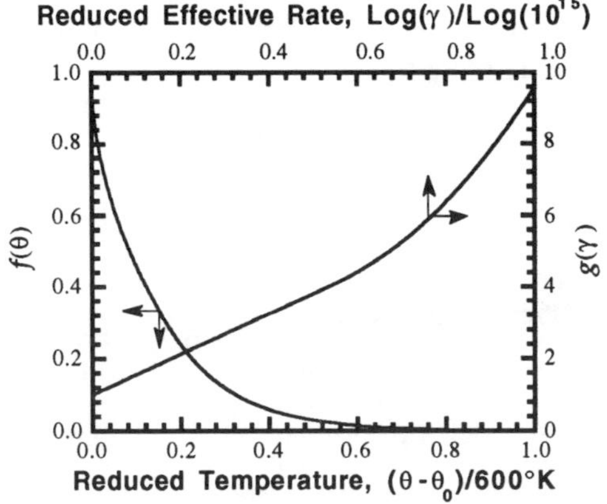

Figure 3. Temperature and rate dependencies of yield stress

For most of the computations, non-slipping interfacial conditions were imposed. In an attempt to identify whether the bond undergoes a cohesive failure or an adhesive one, we also used a stress-controlled interfacial sliding condition.

RESULTS AND DISCUSSION

Results of the overstress relaxation model are summarized in Figure 4. The time step in this series of computations was 65 *ps*. For a relaxation time much larger than the computation time step (say 1 *μs*), the shear wave is transmitted without loss in amplitude. As T_R decreases, the amount of shear amplitude transmitted also decreases. However, a single relaxation time scale does not provide the type of time-dependent evolution observed in experiments (Figure 2). This lead us to add a thermal softening mechanism into the constitutive model.

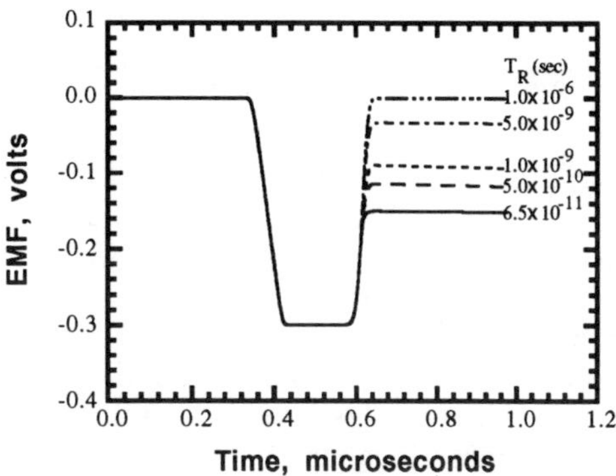

Figure 4. Results of overstress relaxation model

The results of the overstress model with thermal softening are presented in Figure 5. Increasing the temperature dependence (using larger β's) not only reduces the maximum shear transmitted but also develops the type of softening evolution observed in the experiments. Note, that the EMF change associated with shear motion does not vanish even with a larger β. Further examination of velocity profiles inside the epoxy bond indicates that shear localization happened in every simulation involving softening response. This is not surprising since the system of governing equations resembles that of a classic shear band problem. The difference is that in this case, the material has no strain-hardening at all. The shear deformation is localized well after the whole system has become predominantly elliptic. Hence, the information that the shear stress diminishes in the shear band is not transmitted to the material being bonded. Explicit strain-rate dependence was therefore used in the modeling to provide some control on localization.

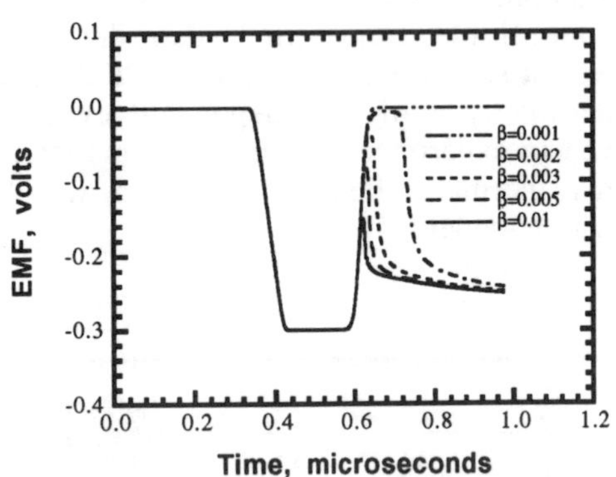

Figure 5. Results of thermal softening and relaxation

In practice, we modeled the epoxy as a thermal softening, elastic/viscoplastic material. The model only provides a limited transport mechanism once the shear localization is developed. Nevertheless, with certain sets of parameters, shear localization is prevented. One such result is shown in Figure 6 as the solid line. The result is not qualitatively different from that presented in Figure 5, except that in this case the softening is not trapped within the bond. Overall, the thermal softening mechanism provides a reasonable explanation to the experimentally observed phenomenon (Figure 2).

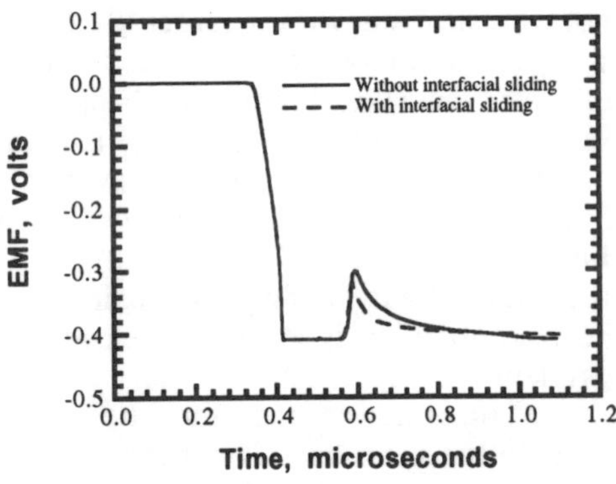

Figure 6. Results of elastic-viscoplastic model

An interesting result was obtained when stress-controlled interfacial sliding was used as an interfacial condition. By doing so, localization was either avoided or initiated at interfaces. However, as shown in Figure 6 (the broken line), the output is not much different from that obtained with continuous interfacial conditions. The results suggest that the bond failure might occur within a very narrow band which can be inside the bond or at bond-sample interface.

CONCLUSIONS

A phenomenological model for thin epoxy bond behavior has been developed that provides a method to examine the influence of the bond response on compression-shear wave propagation. Good agreement was observed with the experimental results reported in Ref. 1. Although the model presented is by no means unique or rigorous, it provides insight into the bond response for combined compression-shear wave propagation. Finally, we emphasize that a good understanding of the bond response is necessary for a rigorous analysis of shear wave amplitudes in inelastic materials.

REFERENCES

[1] M. P. Conner, MS Thesis, Washington State University, 1988.

[2] Y. M. Gupta, *J. Geophys. Res.*, **88**, pp. 4304-4312 (1983).

[3] V. Prakash and R. J. Clifton, in *"Experimental Techniques in the Dynamics of Deformable Solids"*, edited by K. T. Ramesh, New York: ASME, 1993, AMD-Vol. **165**, pp. 33-48.

[4] M. V. Thiel, *Compendium of Shock Wave Data*, Lawrence Livermore Laboratory, 1977.

[5] H. Lee and K. Neville, *Handbook of Epoxy Resins*, New York: McGraw-Hill, 1967.

[6] R. A. Duckett, S. Rabinowitz, and I. M. Ward, *J. Mater. Sci.*, **5**, pp. 909-915 (1970).

[7] J. A. Brydson, *Plow Properties of Polymer Melts* , New York: Van Nostrand Reinhold, 1970.

[8] L. M. Barker and R. E. Hollenbach, *J. Appl. Phys.*, **41**, pp. 4208-4226 (1970).

[9] Y. M. Gupta, *J. Appl. Phys.*, **51**, pp. 5352-5361, (1980).

[10] Y. M. Gupta, *COPS Wave Propagation Program* (unpublished)

[11] D. C. Wallace, *Phys. Rev.* B, **22**, pp. 1477-1486 (1980).

THE EFFECT OF AN ELECTRIC FIELD ON THE HIGH STRAIN - RATE PROPERTIES OF POLYMETHYL METHACRYLATE

Jeffery J. Davis
Department of Physics,
The American University
4400 Massachusetts Ave. N.W.
Washington DC 20016
and
Naval Surface Warfare Center
10901 New Hampshire Ave.
Silver Spring MD 20903

Experimental data is presented on the effect of an electric field on the high strain - rate mechanical strength properties of polymethyl methacrylate (PMMA). While more experiments are need to be performed in order to understand the cause of this effect, the data presented correlates well with the results that have been observed in the past on the effect of an electric field on the low strain - rate properties of PMMA.[1]

INTRODUCTION

The effect of an electric field on polymers has been examined extensively by others[2-7] and the high strain - rate properties of polymers have been examined extensively by others[8-10]. However, the effect of an electric field on the high strain - rate mechanical strength properties of bulk polymers have not yet been investigated. In the present work, polymethyl methacrylate (PMMA) has been subjected simultaneously to an electric field and a compressive strain pulse.

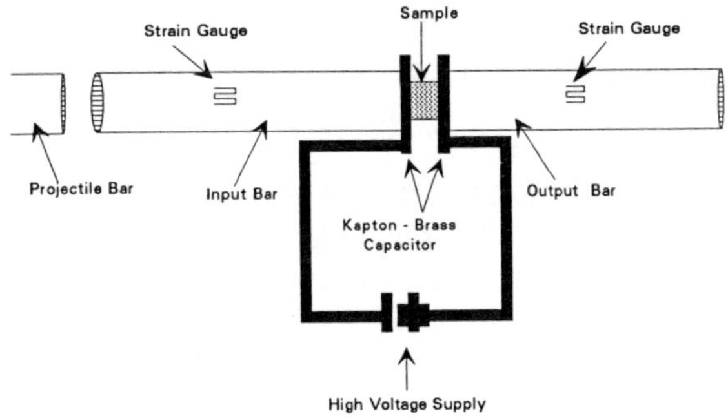

Figure 1. Experimental setup - Hopkinson split pressure bar and capacitor.

EXPERIMENTAL TECHNIQUE

A standard Hopkinson Split Pressure Bar (HSPB) was used to generate stress in PMMA up to 1 kBar at strain rates of 10^3 s^{-1}. A schematic of the HSPB is shown in Figure 1. The input and output bars measured 0.0254 m diameter by 1.2192 m long. The projectile bar was 0.0254 m diameter by 0.3048 m long. All three were made from 4130 steel with a Brinell hardness of 223. The bars will remain elastic up to 10 kBars which is well below the stress levels to which they were subjected. The incident strain pulse had a rise time of 6.6 μs. Each bar had two strain gauges which were epoxied to the center of the bars 180° apart. The gauges were Micro Measurements Division of Measurements Group model # EA-13-062AQ-350. A constant current circuit was attached to the gauges and the change in voltages were measured by a Nicolet digital oscilloscope. The data was then transferred to a computer for analysis. The dispersion of frequencies was corrected for during the computer analysis.

In order to obtain a high electric field parallel to the 1-D stress wave, each test sample was sandwiched between two electrodes; this package was placed between the bars. Each electrodes consisted of a $2.54 \cdot 10^{-5}$ m thick strip of brass and a $2.54 \cdot 10^{-5}$ m thick sheet of Kapton. This arrangement is shown in Figure 2. The brass - Kapton electrodes have little effect on the stress pulse as evidenced in numerous experiments comparing pulses when the electrodes were removed to those obtained with the electrodes in place.

The electric field was generated by an Associated Research Inc. DC Hypot power supply model # 5220 that was capable of providing 15 kV DC. Actual voltage was limited to approximately 4 kV to 5 kV in order to prevent arcing through the air surrounding the sample. The electrodes were designed to have twice the diameter of the sample in order to eliminate edge effects, so that the field lines were parallel through the sample area. The edges of the electrodes were masked in order to eliminate arcing due to sharp points at the edges.

The PMMA samples were cylindrical disks 0.0203 m diameter by 0.0032 m thick. These were machined from 0.0254 m thick rods. The rods were cast and annealed at the factory. The samples were polished so that the ends were flat and parallel.

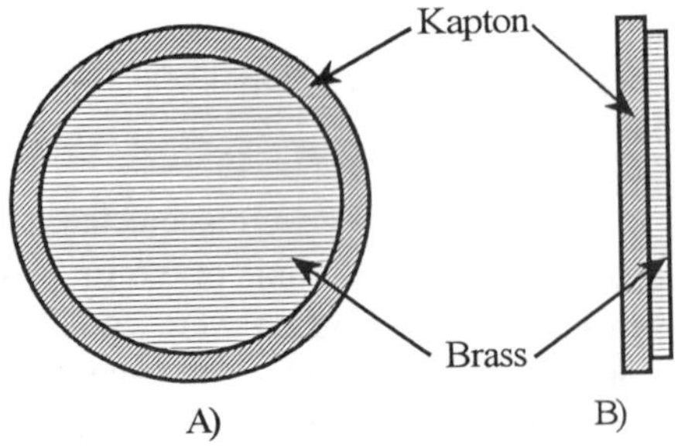

Figure 2. One side of the Kapton - brass capacitor: A) front view and B) side view.

RESULTS

Figure 3 shows the dynamic stress vs. strain curve obtained for two samples of PMMA. Curve number 1 shows the result of a test without an electric field. Curve 2 shows the results of a test conducted with an electric field of $E = 1.26 \cdot 10^6$ V/m. The electric field was applied for thirty minutes prior to testing and maintained during the test. The test duration was less than one second. The strain rate for each test was $10^3 s^{-1}$. The stress - strain curve for the PMMA with no field was linearly fitted. From Hooke's law, the slope of that fit is Young's modules (E). This was determined to be 5.21 GPa for PMMA with no applied electric field. This corresponds to a sound speed, c_s, of 2.09 km/s. This is lower than the standard value for c_s which is 2.70 km/s. However, the experimentally determined value of c_s was typical of our results. The curve for the test sample with the electric field applied had a fit of E = 3.28 GPa, corresponding to a value for c_s of 1.66 km/s.

The cause of this change in the material stiffness is not yet fully understood. From work done on thin films, ion conduction was shown to occur in PMMA.[2] However, this conduction is quite small and would result in a Joule heating of less than one Kelvin. The peak stress in this experiment is well below the region where polarization has been observed to occur in PMMA in the absence of an electric field.[9] In their work on the effect of an electric field on the low strain - rate properties of PMMA[1], Kulichenko and Smirnov concluded that the dipole moment of the polymer did not play a role in the low strain - rate effects. They discussed two possible explanations for the change in plastic flow stress. First, the electric field may influence the process of ionization of the macromolecules and then interact with the macro-ions, altering the bulk plastic properties as a result. Second, the electric field may alter the electrical state of the surface of the sample by charging the surface and thus reduce the surface energy of the material, consequently changing its plastic properties. The current work cannot rule out the hypothesis that the electric field is pre-straining the polymer molecules by

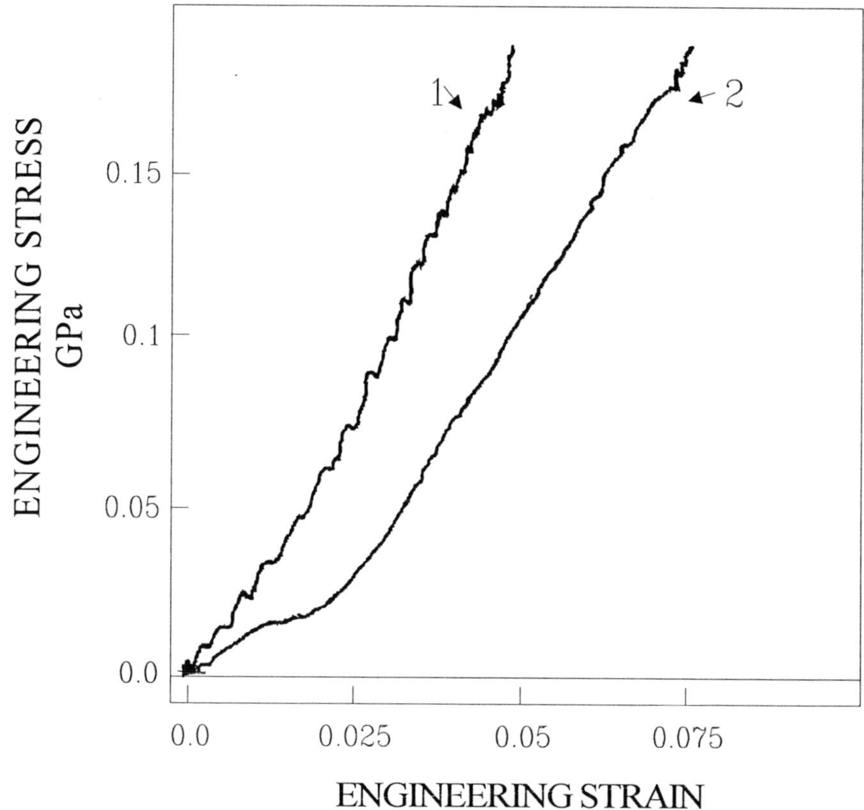

Figure 3. Curve 1 is the stress - strain plot for PMMA with no electric field present. Curve 2 is the stress - strain plot for PMMA with the application of an electric field.

interacting with the positive or negative charges that are associated with the different portions of the polymer chain either from ionization or from dipole moments. However, work on thin films of PMMA suggest that PMMA undergoes electrostriction.[11] This decreases the volume and thus causes the material to stiffen. In a bulk material such as was used in these tests, the result from thin films may not be analogous or applicable; our experimental results show that the electric field causes PMMA to weaken. This would then indicate that the charging of the surface is the more likely choice for the cause of the effect.

CONCLUSIONS

There is a definite shift in the dynamic stress - strain curves of PMMA when a strong electric field is present. The electric field lowers the plastic flow stress. This shift is reproducible. There is not yet an adequate explanation for the effect that an electric field has on the high strain rate mechanical strength properties of bulk polymethyl methacrylate. However, we are in the process of conducting further tests on PMMA and on other polymers and crystals to better clarify a theory.

ACKNOWLEDGMENTS

This research was sponsored by the Advanced Technology Thrust Program at NSWC under Dr. Richard Bardo. The computer aided data analysis technique and program for the Hopkinson Split Pressure Bar was developed by Doug Tasker. The author would like to thank Dr. Bill Wilson and Dr. Diana Woody for their technical assistance through out this work.

REFERENCES

[1] A. N. Kulichenko and B. I. Smirnov, *Sov. Phys. Solid State* 26(3), pp. 570 - 571 (1984).

[2] T. Miyamoto, *Polymer Journal*, Vol. 6 No. 5, pp. 385 - 390 (1974).

[3] G. K. Narula, Rashmi, and P. K. C. Pillai, *Acta Polymerica* 40, pp. 462 - 465 (1989).

[4] V. Adamec, *Kolloid - Z. u. Z. Polymere* 249, pp. 1085 - 1095 (1971).

[5] J. M. Schultz, *Treatise on Material Science and Technology* Vol. 10 Part B, pp. 677 - 740 (1977).

[6] S. M. Lebedev, V. F. Vazhov, and V. Y. Ushakov, *Sov. Phys. Tech. Phys.* 28(4), pp. 475 - 476 (1983).

[7] J. B. Bernstein and C. M. Cooke, *IEEE Transactions on Electrical Insulation* Vol. 26 No. 6, pp. 1080 - 1086 (1991).

[8] J. J. Dick, "Stress-Strain Histories in Shocked Polymethyl Methacrylate," in *Proceedings of the Conference on Shock Waves in Condensed Matter*, 1988, pp. 301 - 304.

[9] S. A. Sheffield and D. D. Bloomquist, "Low Pressure Hugoniot Cusp in Polymeric Materials", in the *Proceedings of the Conference on Shock Waves in Condensed Matter*, 1981, pp. 57 - 61.

[10] R. D. Goolsby and C. Lin, *Instrumented Impact Testing of Plastic and Composite Materials* STP 936, pp. 351 - 367 (1987).

[11] K. Ohara, M. Hennecke, and J. Fuhrmann, Colloid and Polymer Science 260, pp. 164 - 168 (1982).

AN EXPERIMENTAL TECHNIQUE FOR STUDYING SHOCK PROPAGATION IN LARGE-SCALE SAMPLES OF SNOW AND OTHER HIGHLY-POROUS MATERIALS

David C. Erlich and Donald R. Curran
Poulter Laboratory
SRI International
333 Ravenswood Avenue
Menlo Park, CA 94025-3493

Electromagnetic particle-velocity gages were emplaced along a diagonal within large (roughly 40 by 60 by 10 cm) specimens of artificially-made snow ($\rho_o \approx 0.35$ g/cm^3) and a snow-matching grout ($\rho_o \approx 0.25$ g/cm^3), to record transmitted pulse histories at various depths in the specimen. The snow was produced by a leased cryogenic snow-making system at a newly-established permanent cold-temperatures facility at SRI's remote explosives test site. Nearly uniaxial strain loading was achieved by a line detonation wave running through dilute explosives tile (DET) squares in contact with a slanted top face of the specimen block. Peak particle velocities ranged from ≈0.6 mm/μs at the HE interface to ≈0.25 mm/μs at depths of ≈6 cm. Corresponding peak stresses were calculated to be from ≈1.0 to ≈0.25 kbar.

INTRODUCTION

There has been interest recently in the characterization of shock propagation in relatively large-scale samples (depths of ≥ 6 cm) of materials of high porosity (≥ 60%). Previously, gas gun impacts and HE in-contact plane-wave loading techniques have been used to record particle velocity and stress histories under uniaxial strain at several depths within relatively small-scale specimens of materials with moderate-to-high porosity (20-57%) material specimens.[1,2] Embedded gage tests have been reported recently on smaller-scale samples of snow[3-5] and silica aerogels.[6] However, we could not use any of the standard gas gun or HE techniques to test larger-scale specimens of the highly-porous materials.

This paper describes a novel technique developed to study shock transmission and attenuation in snow (porosity of 62%) and in a high-porosity grout, SMG-2 (porosity of 83%), subject to transient pulse loading of ≈1 kbar (100 MPa) peak stress. In addition we briefly describe the cold-temperature and cryogenic snow-making facility that was established at SRI's remote HE test site to enable us to perform the embedded gage tests of snow.

APPROACH

To obtain the relatively low peak stresses in the test materials, we used the dilute explosive tile (DET) low-pressure HE system recently developed at SRI,[7] which has proven to be a reliable method of attaining uniform detonation stresses well below the range available from standard HE formulations. The baseline DET consists of 0.15 g/cm^3 of PETN in an inert matrix of expanded polystyrene beads (bulk DET density is 0.404 g/cm^3, detonation velocity is 1.95 mm/μs), and are generally made in 1-ft. (30.48 cm) or 2-ft. (60.96 cm) squares, at thicknesses of from 0.25 in. (0.635 cm), to 1.0 in. (2.54 cm). Higher PETN-concentration formulations can also be produced for higher pressure detonations, and different tile sizes and shapes are readily formed.

Our approach involves a running line-wave detonation front propagating across a thin layer of Detasheet (sheet explosive), into a thicker slab of DET, and then into a rectangular block of the specimen material, as shown in Figure 1(a). A triangular line-wave generator (a long, narrow triangle of Detasheet with diamond-shaped cutouts) sends a line-wave detonation front into the Detasheet rectangle, where it propagates horizontally at a high velocity, U_{ds}. As it travels, it initiates the DET slab beneath it, which in turn sends a shock wave into the test specimen. If the shock velocity in the specimen is U_s, then the shock front will travel at an angle equal to arcsin (U_s/U_{ds}). If the lateral dimensions of the specimen block is large enough so that no rarefaction waves can arrive from the four lateral sides, then each point in the central region of the specimen will experience a stress pulse that is dependent only upon its vertical position (its distance from the DET interface).

For an idealized linearly elastic material (i.e. wave velocity independent of peak stress), the magnitude of U_s, and hence the orientation of the shock front, does not change as a function of vertical position. Therefore the shock front is a straight line (actually a flat plane in three dimensions), and the flow is precisely uniaxial strain.

For most real materials, however (particularly for highly-porous materials), U_s varies with peak stress, and the peak stress decays as the wave propagates into the specimen. So the shock front changes orientation as it propagates into the specimen. This is shown in Figure 1(b), where the specimen block cross section is trapezoidal, with a sloping upper surface. The shock front in the specimen is an arc; U_{s+} is the wave velocity close to the DET interface, near the depth of the shallowest gage plane; U_{s-} is the wave velocity far from the interface, at

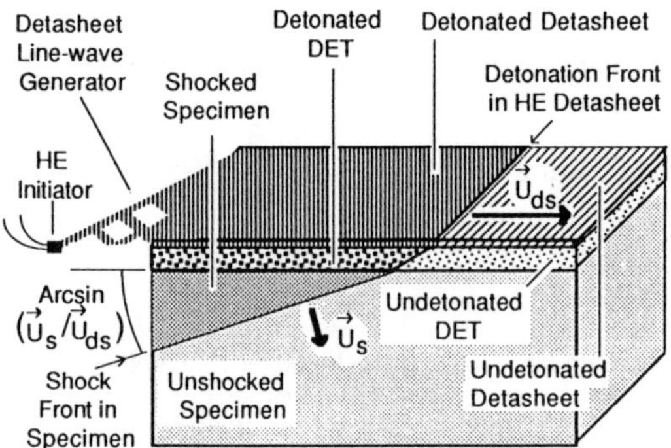

(a) Geometry for Linear Elastic Material (sliced through center)

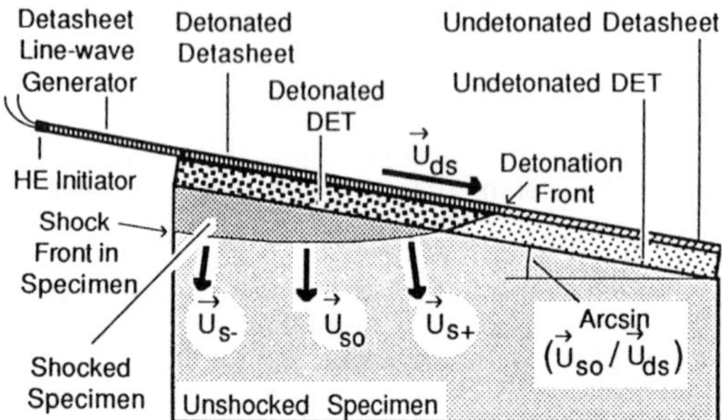

(b) Slanted Geometry for Highly-Porous Material (cross section)

Figure 1. DET in-contact running wave techniques for nearly uniaxial strain loading of large-scale specimens.

about the location of the deepest gage plane; and U_{so} is the wave velocity midway between the two extremes. If we select the slant angle to be arcsin (U_{so}/U_{ds}), then the wave propagates vertically downward midway through the gaged region.

For a highly-porous material like snow or SMG-2, the wave velocity is so much smaller (about one order of magnitude) than the detonation velocity of the Detasheet that the orientation of the shock front only changes by a very small amount as the wave propagates through the material with a rapidly decaying peak stress. For a range of wave velocities from 0.79 to 0.52 mm/µs, the angle between the upper surface of the specimen block and the shock front varies only from 6.6° to 4.3°. So the arc representing the shock front in Figure 1(b) would be much flatter than shown, and the material would experience very nearly uniaxial strain flow (with only negligible amounts of transverse motion), at least during compression. A particle velocity gage oriented to record vertical motion during compression would be in error by ≤0.02%, or one minus cosine of the variation angle (≈±1°) in the shock front, far less than any other experimental uncertainties.

In a highly-porous material the wave velocity during unloading can be much higher than during loading. For an unloading velocity of 1.8 mm/µs, the angle between the unloading wave front and the upper specimen surface can be 15°, which is ≈9.5° more than the slant angle selected from an average shock front velocity (U_{so}) in the gage vicinity. The particle velocity gage recording the unloading would then be in error by ≈1.5%, or one minus the cosine of 9.5°, larger than for the compressive wave, but still well within the range of magnitude of other experimental uncertainties, such as snow density uniformity.

EXPERIMENTAL CONFIGURATION

Figure 2 is a schematic diagram of the experimental configuration. The SMG-2 test samples were trapezoidal solids whose top surface was at a 6° slant. For the snow tests, Lexan containers of a similar trapezoidal shape (with a 4° slant) were filled with snow to form the test samples. To reduce the depth of the snowfall needed, three separate snow containers were used—the gages were all emplaced in the middle container—and then fastened together.

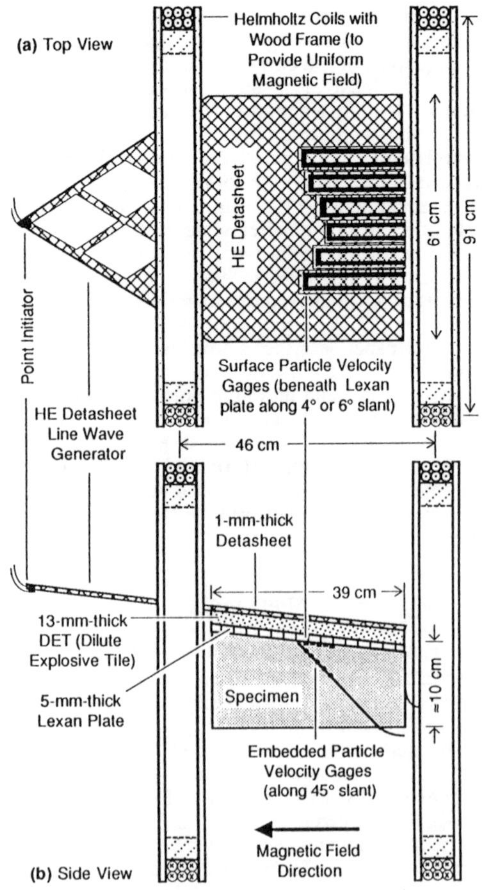

Figure 2. Experimental arrangement for embedded gage tests in highly-porous materials (drawing not to scale).

Thin foil particle electromagnetic particle velocity gages were placed along a ≈45° slope at various depths (from ≈1-6 cm) to record the embedded particle velocity histories. The gages operate on the simple premise that a conductor moving in a magnetic field generates a voltage equal to the product of its length, the field strength, and the velocity of motion, provided each are in a mutually perpendicular orientation. Another set of particle velocity gages were placed at the top surface of the sample, one directly above each of the embedded gages, to record the arrival time (TOA) of the input pulse. By subtracting the TOA of the surface gage from the signal recorded by the corresponding embedded gage, we obtain the wave transit times from the surface to the various gage depths.

The uniform magnetic field was provided by a pair of circular wire coils wrapped on wooden frames and positioned parallel to one another at a separation distance equal to the coil radius (this configuration, known as the Helmholtz coil, provides the maximum uniformity of magnetic field in the region mid-way between the coils near the coil axis). The magnetic field was calibrated for each gage location (never more than a few percent from that at the center of the coil pair), and is monitored during the test by a current probe.

COLD-TEMPERATURE AND SNOW-MAKING FACILITIES

To allow for the testing of snow specimens, a cold-temperature facility was established at SRI International's explosive test site. Permanent equipment set up at this facility include two low-temperature horizontal chest freezers with cryogenic backup for storage at temperatures down to -60°F (-51°C), and a large walk-in freezer for working with cold-temperature specimens at temperatures down to ≈ -10°F (-23°C).

A leased cryogenic snow-making system was used to produce a fine-grained snow (grain size varied from 25 to 400 μm), with a density range of from 0.25 to 0.42 g/cm^3. The system mixed liquid nitrogen (LN), compressed air, and water by a proprietary method and ejected the resultant snow through nozzles into an LN-precooled tent. To minimize the manipulation to which the snow would be subjected (and hence reduce the likelihood of affecting the uniformity of the snow), the snow fell directly into the sample containers into which the gages had already been emplaced. Sampling containers and a densitometer were also filled with snow, in order to determine the density variation as a function of depth and location within the snow tent. The density variation within a particular snowfall was typically ±0.03 g/cm^3 (±10%).

To minimize snow metamorphosis, the snow containers were maintained at temperatures no higher than -5°F (-20°C) during the ≈1-hour duration between filling and HE firing, which took place inside a large sacrificial Styrofoam igloo cooled by electric fans blowing air across piles of dry ice.

TYPICAL EXPERIMENTAL RESULTS AND ANALYSIS

The embedded gage records for an SMG-2 test is shown in Figure 3, where the particle velocity histories for each embedded gage have been plotted against time from the TOA of the corresponding surface gage. Stress histories calculated by Lagrangian analysis[8] from these data are shown in Figure 4. The Lagrangian analysis calculation for the loading and unloading paths yielded excessively large values for the change in specific volume for both SMG-2 and snow. Whether this inaccuracy is due to the density variations within the sample or represent a limit on the applicability of the analysis to highly-porous materials has not yet been determined.

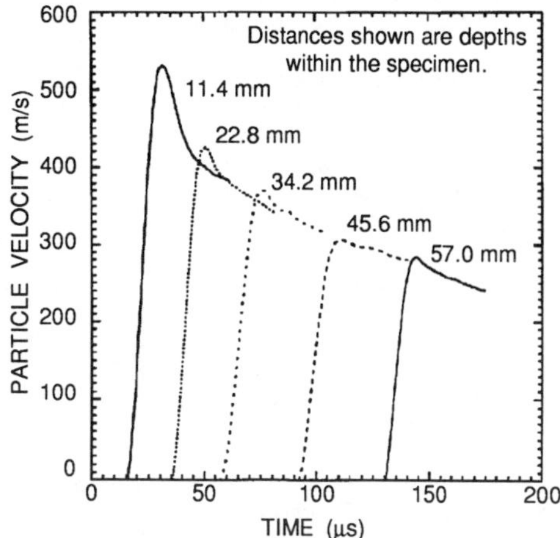

Figure 3. Smoothed embedded particle velocity gage histories from SMG-2 test.

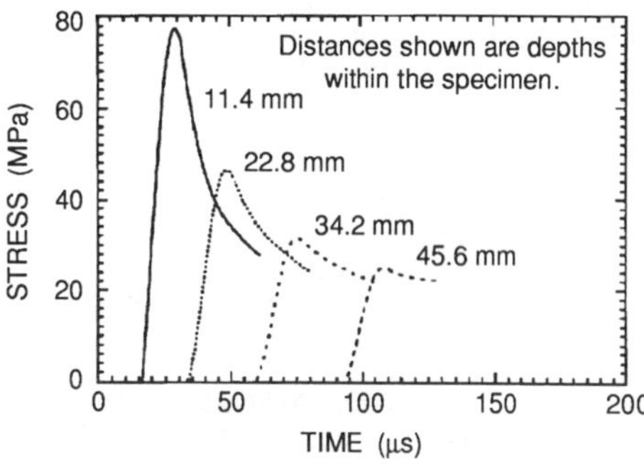

Figure 4. Stress histories calculated by Lagrangian analysis for SMG-2 test.

CONCLUSIONS

We have established a permanent cold-temperature facility for HE testing materials such as snow, ice, frozen rock, etc., and have developed a viable technique for testing large-scale samples of highly-porous (or less porous) materials.

ACKNOWLEDGMENTS

This work was supported by a contract from the Defense Nuclear Agency.

REFERENCES

1 D. C. Erlich and D. R. Curran, "Characterization of the Dynamic Behavior of Porous Solids, Part 6: Dynamic Response of Porous Ceramics - Experiments" SRI Int'l. Final Report for Defense Nuclear Agency, March 1976.

2. J. K. Gran, D. C. Erlich, and L. Seaman, "Experiments and Analyses of Shock-Resistant Advanced Materials (SRAM)," SRI Int'l. Final Report for Naval Research Laboratory, March 1989.

3. J. A. Brown, E. S. Gaffney, G. L. Blaisdell, and J. B. Johnson, "Techniques for Gas Gun Studies of Shock Wave Attenuation in Snow," in *Shock Waves in Condensed Matter 1987*, Amsterdam, the Netherlands: Elsevier Science Publishers, 1988, pp. 657-660.

4. J. B. Johnson, J. A. Brown, and E. S. Gaffney, "Interpretation of the Stress Histories from Shock Impact Tests on Snow Using Embedded Gages," in *Shock Compression of Condensed Matter 1991*, Amsterdam, the Netherlands: Elsevier Science Publishers, 1992, pp. 107-110.

5. J. B. Johnson, et al., "Shock Wave Studies of Snow," in *Shock Compression of Condensed Matter 1989*, Amsterdam, the Netherlands: Elsevier Science Publishers, 1990, pp. 117-120.

6. R. Rabie and J. J. Dick, "Equation of State and Crushing Dynamics of Low-Density Silica Aerogels," in *Shock Compression of Condensed Matter 1991*, Amsterdam, the Netherlands: Elsevier Science Publishers, 1992, pp. 97-100.

7. C. Romander and M. Sanai, "Fabrication, Fielding, and Evaluation of a Dilute Explosive Tile (DET) Charge in DET Demonstration Test and MINERAL FIND 6 Experiment," Technical Report for Defense Nuclear Agency, May, 1962.

8. L. Seaman, "Lagrangian Analysis for Multiple Stress or Particle Velocity Gages in Attenuating Waves," *J. Appl. Phys.*, Vol. 45, 1975, pp. 4303.

THE RESPONSE OF NATURAL SNOW TO EXPLOSIVE SHOCK WAVES

D. J. SOLIE, J. B. JOHNSON and S. A. BARRETT
U.S. Army Corps of Engineers, Cold Regions Research and Engineering Laboratory, Fort Wainwright Alaska, 99703 U.S.A.

Field measurements of shock waves in snow with initial densities from 100 kg/m^3 to 555 kg/m^3 were made in situ in a natural snow cover. A high amplitude, short duration, uniaxial shock impulse (~0.6 GPa for 10 μs) was imparted to the snow using sheet explosive, and the shock arrival time and stress histories were measured at depth in the snow. For dry snow ($\rho_o = 250 \pm 30$ kg/m^3), the shock velocity can be described by a power law and decays rapidly with depth, from over 1000 m/s near the snow/explosive interface to 120 ± 20 m/s at 0.20 m. The shock stress attenuation factor at a propagation depth of 0.20 m is about 4 x 10^{-3}. Tests in which explosive gases were excluded from the snow had higher shock velocities and pressures than tests where the gases penetrated the snow.

INTRODUCTION

Understanding shock wave propagation in natural snow is important in several geophysical applications, including avalanche control and neutralization of snow-covered land mines. Snow strongly attenuates shock waves, but to quantitatively calculate this pressure decrease, the pressure as a function of density (P-ρ) loading and unloading path must be known. In 1991 and 1992 we conducted a series of experiments to measure explosive shock waves in the natural snow pack. This was done to compare with the results of our previous gas gun experiments[1], and to extend those results to higher pressures. We also did this to measure the pressure attenuation at greater depths in the snow. This paper presents the results of one class of these tests for snow with an initial density (ρ_o) of 250 ± 30 kg/m^3.

EXPERIMENTAL METHOD

In our tests, sheet explosive (DuPont Deta Sheet C) was detonated at nine points simultaneously, to generate a plane shock wave in the snow. The initial impulse was ~0.6 GPa for 10 μs. The sheet was oriented parallel with the surface of a natural snow cover which was approximately one meter deep. The sheet was placed either directly on the snow, or elevated above it. Shock arrival times and stress histories were measured by stress gauges imbedded directly in the snow at measured depths below the surface. Two types of gauge packages were used; stress gauges sandwiched between two thin sheets of stainless steel, and gauges epoxied to the top surface of aluminum plates 3.17 mm thick. Gauges used were: C300-50-EKRTE Carbon stress gauges manufactured by Dynasen Inc., and PVDF stress gauges manufactured by Metrivib Inc. (B_25_25) and Dynasen Inc. (pvf2 11-.25-ek).

To install the gauges, a block of snow was removed from the test site exposing a vertical face. The gauges were then carefully inserted into the face horizontally, within the cone of uniaxial stress, and the snow block replaced. The explosive sheet was then positioned directly over the active area of the gauges and the explosive detonated. Signals were recorded on a twelve channel data logger (Tektronix 2520).

ANALYSIS

Measurement Uncertainties

Detonation at the nine points on the sheet occurred within 5 μs, and the total variation in detonation time across the sheet was 15 μs. The uncertainty in gauge position was ± 0.005 m, and the uncertainty in determination of shock arrival time was < 20%. PVDF gauge signals were recorded in charge mode, temperature corrected[2,3], and converted to stresses using a published calibration curve[4]. Carbon gauge signals were reduced using a polynomial fit to the manufacturer-supplied calibration curve. The uncertainty in peak stress was about 40%. Stress enhancement in the snow occurs under the detonation points, however from two dimensional simulations, at depths greater than two cm in the snow, this effect was small[5]. Due to the large impedance mismatch between the snow and gauge package, and the rapid change in the snow's impedance that occurs as the shock front passes, the measured gauge stresses are much greater than those in the snow. Without numerical simulation these signals are complex to interpret.

Modeling

We used the dynamic finite element program PRONTO 2D[6] to model tests and interpret the gauge stress records. Simulations were also used to empirically determine the P-ρ loading and unloading behavior of explosively shocked natural snow following the procedure used in our laboratory tests[1].

RESULTS

The shock arrival time data for 250 kg/m^3 snow shown in Figure 1 can be fit with a power law, where (t_a) is arrival time in seconds and (x) is snow depth in meters.

$$t_a = Ax^{\alpha} \tag{1}$$

A = 0.0166, and α = 1.82 are the coefficients from a least squares fit of the data (r^2= 0.99). Shock velocity (V_s) as a function of snow depth can be determined by rearranging equation (1) and taking the derivative with respect to time.

$$V_s = 33.0\ (x)^{-0.82} \tag{2}$$

This relation is applicable for snow depths of about 0.02 to 0.4 m with an uncertainty of < 20% over the range. Shock velocities decay rapidly in snow, from over 800 m/s at 0.02 m to 120 m/s at 0.2 m.

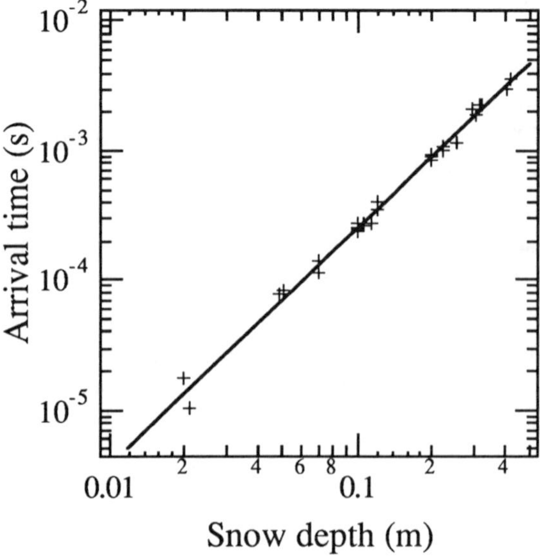

Figure 1. Shock Arrival Vs Snow Depth for ρ_o = 250 ± 30 kg/m^3.

Shock propagation into the snow is clearly not steady with depth. However, if we assume it is constant over a small Δx, and know final density (ρ_f) and V_s at that point, the following Rankine-Hugoniot (R-H) relation can be used incrementally to calculate the peak snow pressure (P).

$$P = \rho_o (1 - \rho_o/\rho_f) V_s^2 \qquad (3)$$

This relation is relatively insensitive to ρ_f, and if the shock velocity is well known, even approximate final density measurements will give reasonably good pressure values. We made post-shot final density measurements at various depths, and used Bakanova's high pressure results[7] to estimate the maximum ρ_f at the explosive/snow interface. The pressure values shown in Figure 2 were calculated iteratively with depth, using equation (3) with approximate final densities and V_s from equation (2). The uncertainty in these values is roughly 50%. When equation (2) is inserted in (3), the exponent of (x) is (-1.64), which is close to the theoretical value of (-1.5) derived from a simple snow plow model[8].

The measured pressure values shown represent the pressure in the snow, unaffected by gauge emplacement. These pressures are reduced from the raw measured gauge values by snow/gauge impedance enhancement factors which were determined from simulations of gauge packages.

Also shown in Figure 2 are the results of two simulations. Seaman at SRI used PUFF[9] with compaction and release data from previous gas gun tests[1]. The CRREL simulation used PRONTO 2D with a P-ρ loading curve that was empirically determined by matching the results with measured shock arrival times. Both simulations agree with the measured results.

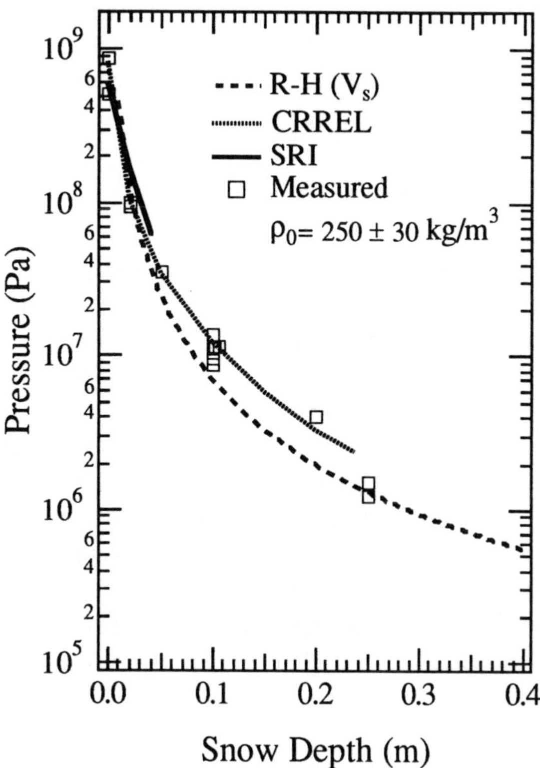

Figure 2. Measured and calculated values of shock pressure attenuation in snow .

Snow is a porous media, and explosive gases from a nearby detonation penetrate into it as the shock front advances. To qualitatively investigate this effect on the shock wave propagation, we placed a thin aluminum membrane between the explosive and the snow to shield the gases. This resulted in a measured decrease in shock arrival time, and an increase in pressure. The mean arrival time from several tests and multiple gauge measurements at 0.10 m was 224 ± 30 μs with an aluminum membrane, and 248 ± 30 μs without. The error conservatively takes into account all timing and positioning uncertainties for the measurements. In a pair of tests, identical except one had a membrane shield, the measured gauge pressure at

0.10 m in the shielded test was nearly twice that measured in the unshielded test. This suggests that the penetrating gases cool rapidly decreasing the energy of the shock wave.

CONCLUSION

Shock waves attenuate rapidly in snow. The decrease with depth in the shock velocity and pressure can both be fit well with a power law. Calculated pressures from simulations of field tests with 250 kg/m^3 density snow using empirically determined P-ρ loading and unloading curves agree with measured pressures, and with a simple Rankine-Hugoniot calculation using measured shock velocities and final densities. Tests in which explosive gases were excluded from the snow had higher shock velocities and pressures than tests where the gases penetrated the snow.

ACKNOWLEDGEMENTS

We especially thank SFC David Dillingham for his help with the explosives and logistics. We thank Jacques Charest and Don Johnson for their guidance in making stress gauge measurements and accommodating our experimental needs. We thank Lynn Seaman for his help and insight during numerous discussions on modeling the snow. This work was funded by DA project 4A762784AT42.

REFERENCES

[1] J. B. Johnson, D. J. Solie, J. A. Brown, and E. S. Gaffney, *J. App. Phys.* 73(10), pp. 4852-4861 (1993).

[2] D. J. Solie, J. B. Johnson, P. K. Dutta, and J. Kalafut, "Effects of temperature on an ISL-PVDF shock sensor between +20°C and -40°C," in *Proceedings of the American Physical Society Topical Conference*, 1991, pp. 891-892.

[3] C. S. Lynch and J.A. Charest, "Practical considerations on the piezofilm gauge technique," in *Proceedings of the American Physical Society Topical Conference*, 1991, pp. 901-904.

[4] R. A. Graham and M. U. Anderson, "Piezoelectric polymer (PVDF) materials characterization," in *PVDF Shock Sensor Workshop Proceedings*, 1990, pp. 57-76.

[5] Lynn Seaman, written communication, 1992.

[6] L. M. Taylor and D. P. Flanagan, *PRONTO 2D: a two-dimensional transient solid dynamics program*, Sandia Rep. Sand86-0594, 1987.

[7] A. A. Bakanova, V. N. Zubarev, Yu. N. Sutulov and R. G. Trunin, *Sov. Phys.-JETP* 41, pp. 544-548 (1975).

[8] J. B. Johnson, *J. of Glaciology* 37(127), pp. 303-312.

[9] L. Seaman, *SRI PUFF 8 computer program for one-dimensional stress wave propagation*, Menlo Park:SRI International, 1978, pp. 1-334.

CHAPTER XV

MECHANICAL PROPERTIES: Microscopic Aspects

MICROMECHANICAL STRENGTH EFFECTS IN SHOCK COMPRESSION OF SOLIDS

J. N. Johnson
Los Alamos National Laboratory
Los Alamos, New Mexico, USA 87545

Time-resolved shock-wave measurements and post-shock recovery techniques have long been used as means of inferring the underlying micromechanics controlling high-rate deformation of solids. This approach requires a considerable amount of subjective interpretation. In spite of this feature, progress has been made in experimentation and theoretical interpretation of the shock-compression/release cycle and some of the results are reviewed here for weak shocks. Weak shocks are defined to be those with peak amplitudes (typically 10 - 20 GPa for most solids) that do not overdrive the elastic precursor. The essential elements of a typical shock-compression/release cycle involve, in order, (a) the elastic precursor, (b) plastic loading wave, (c) pulse duration, (d) release wave, and (e) post-mortem examination. These topics are examined in turn, with some emphasis given to elements (b) and (d). If the plastic loading wave is traveling without change of shape, it is possible to convert the particle-velocity/time records to a shear-stress/plastic-strain-rate path. Shock data in this form can be compared directly with low-to-intermediate strain-rate tests. Results for copper and tantalum show how shock data can be used to determine the transition from the deformation mechanism of thermal activation to that of dislocation drag. An important result of release-wave studies is that the leading observable release disturbance in FCC metals may not be propagating with the ideal, longitudinal elastic-wave speed, but at a lower velocity dependent on the elastic bulk and shear moduli and the product of the dislocation density times the pinning separation squared for dislocation segments in the region behind the shock and ahead of the release wave.

INTRODUCTION

How can an experimentalist look inside a shock-loaded solid on a submicrosecond time scale and examine the micromechanical aspects of material strength and deformation properties? The answer seems to be that general direct observation is very difficult except for a few special materials, and then only for a few special phenomena that can be probed by clever optical means [1-3]. This means that most of our "information" concerning the micromechanical basis for material deformation under shock conditions must come from indirect methods. Measurement of particle velocity, longitudinal stress, impulse, and so on, contains information about the microstructure, if the data can be interpreted properly.

The interpretation of macroscale measurement to provide microscale information is a difficult and nonunique process. This was recognized by Orowan, one of the co-discoverers of the dislocation [4]; and he expressed his reservations about being able to discern the micromechanical basis of material deformation from integral tensile tests as follows:

> *"...The extension of a piece of metal (is) in a sense more complicated than the working of a pocket watch and to hope to derive information about its mechanism from ... the tensile test (is) perhaps as optimistic as would be an attempt to learn about the working of a pocket watch by determining its compressive strength."*

In spite of this very discouraging viewpoint, I want to describe some positive things that have been done to shed light on the micromechanical basis for material deformation and plastic flow in shock-loaded solids. There has been some progress, but it has taken a long time and a great deal of resources, and current interpretations remain open to further investigation.

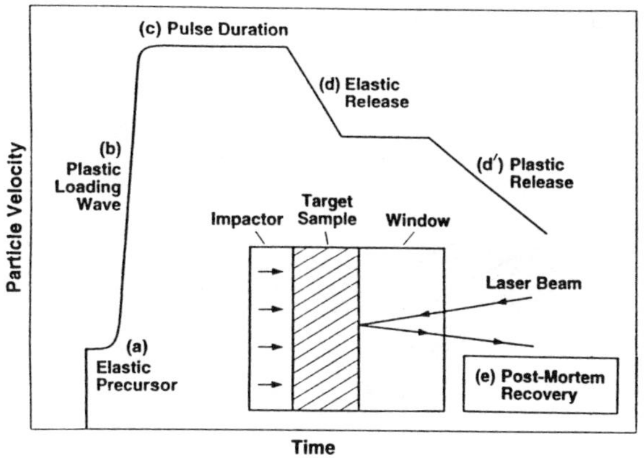

Figure 1. Plate-impact experiment

Figure 1 shows an idealized flat-plate-impact profile of particle velocity as a function of time at some hypothetical gage location interior to the sample. If the sample material is transparent, these measurements can be made *in situ*. More often, as in the case of metals, measurements are made at the planar interface between the sample and a transparent window material chosen to provide a reasonably good acoustic impedance match with the sample. When an approximate impedance match is obtained, spallation is prohibited; the idealized record shown in Figure 1 contains no information about tensile fracture properties of solids; that is a topic for separate discussion.

The main features of the wave profile shown in Figure 1 are (a) the elastic precursor, (b) the plastic compression wave, (c) the nominally flat plateau between compression and release, (d) the elastic-plastic release wave, and (e) post-mortem recovery (following the shock/release cycle). I will deal with each of these topics in turn, with emphasis on (b) and (d).

The micromechanical basis for high-rate plastic deformation is extremely complex. In order to make sense of indirect experimental observations, we need a simplified picture of the deformation process. Figure 2 shows some of the major aspects of plastic deformation on the mesoscale. Pictured here are several dislocation line segments traversing a principal glide plane. The intersections of the straight lines in the glide plane represent atomic positions in a simple cubic lattice. Of course when we consider glide on (111) planes in <110> directions of the FCC lattice, atomic positions are more complicated than this. Also shown in the glide plane are pinning obstacles provided by impurities, interstitials, and other dislocations.

Three major factors contribute resistance to dislocation motion; **(a) the pinning obstacles, (b) the static resistance of the lattice itself (Peierls stress)**, and **(c) the drag resistance** provided by the lattice when the applied stress exceeds the Peierls stress and the dislocation is running in the clear region between pinning obstacles. In this picture (a) and (b) are thermally activated processes, and (c) is a simple mechanical dissipative process.

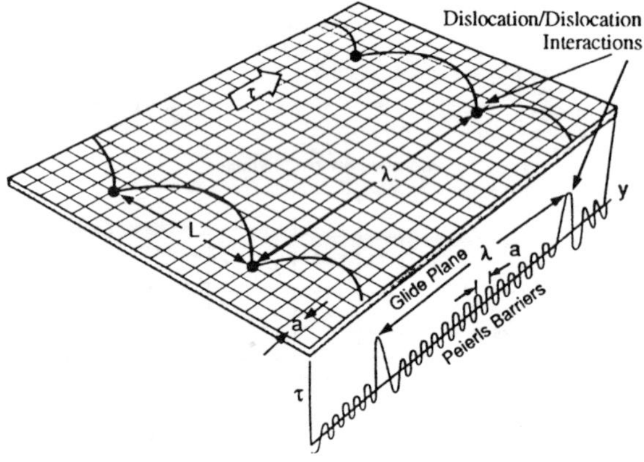

Figure 2. Schematic representation of plastic deformation mechanisms.

Omitted from this diagram are important effects such as dislocation climb, in which a pinned dislocation can climb out of the principal glide plane by cross-slip on an intersecting plane, for example. Nevertheless, the simplified picture shown in Figure 2 provides a means of interpreting shock-wave response as shown in Figure 1. What I intend to present is a broad interpretation of how and when **deformation mechanisms (a), (b), and (c)** contribute to mechanical strength effects in shock-wave compression of FCC and BCC metals, and how the bowed out dislocation segments between pinning obstacles contribute to quasielastic behavior in the "elastic" portion of the elastic-plastic release wave.

COMPRESSION/RELEASE PROFILE

Elastic Precursor

This aspect of shock compression has received a great deal of study, particularly experimental measurement of LiF single crystals [5-7]. Deformation at the elastic precursor front is controlled by **mechanism (c)**, with a great deal of mobile dislocation multiplication. The elastic precursor undergoes extreme excursions in applied shear stress near the impact surface, and for this reason is very hard to characterize fully. Important aspects of the decaying elastic precursor have been reviewed in reference [8].

Plastic Compression Wave

The plastic compression wave is even more complicated in its deformation processes than the elastic precursor, but has seen greater success in micromechanical interpretation.

The important aspect of the plastic compression wave that allows analysis is the fact that it very quickly establishes a steady propagating profile; that is, the particle velocity in the plastic-wave region can be expressed as a function of x - Ut, where U is the shock velocity corresponding to that particular wave amplitude. The rule of thumb [9] is that the transit time to steady propagation is ~ 15 risetimes of the plastic wave front. For example, if the risetime of a 7.3 GPa shock in tantalum is 30 ns, the steady nature of the plastic wave is established in less than 500 ns (propagation distance of ~2 mm). Of course it is always better to establish steady-wave behavior experimentally if the resources are available, but this is not always possible.

When the plastic wave is steady, the longitudinal stress, specific volume, and particle velocity satisfy the mass- and momentum-conservation relationships:

$$\varepsilon = 1 - V/V_0 = u/U \quad , \tag{1}$$

$$\sigma = \rho_0 U u \quad . \tag{2}$$

If u and U are known, ε and σ can be obtained. If additional equation-of-state information is known, it is also possible to obtain the shear stress τ and the longitudinal plastic strain ψ [10-12]. This is the computationally intensive part of the problem. But the important result is that we can then plot the shock data in terms of shear stress, plastic strain, and plastic strain rate. This is the common currency of materials scientists. We do not have to run a hydrocode and show agreement between theory and experiment in order to convince someone that we know the mechanism responsible for shock deformation. The data are simply plotted in the (τ, ψ), $(\psi, \dot{\psi})$, or $(\tau, \dot{\psi})$ planes and the interpretation is almost immediate.

For example, shock compression of copper shows the distinct transition to viscous dislocation drag, **mechanism (c)**, before returning to the thermal activation **mechanism (a)** in the region behind the shock front: Figure 3. The upper solid curves represent the actual τ, ψ paths [13] followed in the shock fronts, while the lower dash and

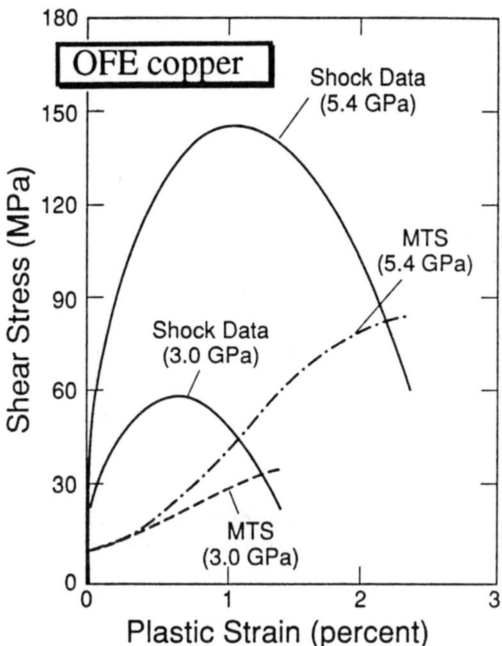

Figure 3. Shear stress paths in shock compression experiments (OFE copper). MTS values are calculated from measured plastic strain rates.

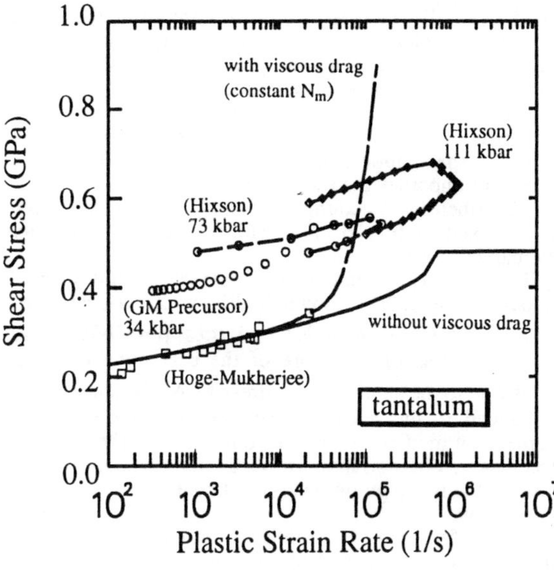

Figure 4. Shear stress paths in shock compression and Hopkinson bar experiments (tantalum).

dash-dot paths give the mechanical threshold stress (MTS) as a function of ψ through two different shock paths. The MTS is the 0 K shear strength, and the actual thermally activated flow stress is somewhat less than this due to finite temperature [14]. At the end of the shock path the shear stress falls below the MTS and the deformation mechanism reverts to thermal activation.

An important question is: what region of $\psi, \dot{\psi}$ space is dominated by thermal activation as compared to viscous drag in OFE copper? The answer is that at high strain rates and low plastic strains viscous dislocation drag, **mechanism (c),** controls material deformation. As deformation proceeds, the MTS increases due to rate-dependent work hardening, **mechanism (a)**, and eventually overtakes the viscous-drag contribution. Hence, for this material, viscous drag plays a dominant role only in the shock front.

Tantalum has also been studied as a typical BCC metal, and it is of interest to determine the dominant deformation mechanisms under various loading conditions. Figure 4 shows shock-compression data [15] in comparison with Hopkinson bar measurements over several decades in plastic strain rate. The flat plateau region on the right is the Peierls stress (~0.48 GPa). Without other deformation mechanisms there would be no resistance to applied shear stress above the Peierls stress. The dashed line rising very steeply at a plastic strain rate on the order of 10^5 s^{-1} is based on the theory of linear dislocation drag with constant mobile dislocation density N_m. The experimental shock data clearly show the importance of rapid mobile dislocation density evolution, and a very strong dependence of plastic strain rate on shear stress in the viscous drag regime. We currently have no constitutive models that adequately represent this material behavior.

It is also clear from the data shown in Figure 4 that thermal activation through the Peierls barriers and viscous dislocation drag, **mechanisms (b) and (c)**, have about the same strain-rate sensitivity, and that there is no clear distinction between the two deformation mechanisms as there is for OFE copper. At larger plastic strains dislocation/dislocation interactions also play a role in determining material strength of tantalum.

Pulse-Duration Effects

The region between compression and release is usually thought of as being nearly constant, without much in the way of microstructural evolution. This appears to be incorrect, based on the numerous observations of pulse duration having an influence on post-shock material strength. Reference [8] contains some added discussion on the possible origins for this effect.

Quasielastic Release

Just as analysis of the elastic precursor can yield information on micromechanical behavior in the vicinity of the initial state, unloading (or reloading) waves contain micromechanical information about the shocked state. In fact, some things simplify the analysis of release waves and other things make it more complicated. Since the sound speed generally increases with compression, the shear stress in the release wave does not undergo the extreme excursion that it does in the precursor. However, the release wave is moving into pre-shocked material for which we have very little direct information about existing microstructure (dislocation density, pinning separation, etc.), and speculation and conjecture therefore become a little more important than we would like.

Nevertheless, something can be said about release from the shocked state [16,17]. These effects are simply summarized here.

The source of quasielastic release is the pinned dislocation segments shown in Figure 2. Because of dislocation curvature there is a back stress $\beta = Gb/R$, where R is the radius of curvature of the segment, acting in opposition to the applied shear stress τ. As the shear stress is reduced in the release wave, the pinned dislocation segment immediately sweeps out area in the reverse direction (as it collapses toward straight equilibrium between the two pinning points) and contributes to reverse plastic flow.

This effect can be quantified, and the quasielastic release-wave profile calculated as shown for OFE copper in Figure 5 [16] using a linearized version of the evolutionary equations. The nondimensional micromechanical constants for this calculation are $B/(nb^2) = 0.002$ GPa ns and $B(L/b)^2 = 0.005$ GPa ns, where B is the viscous drag coefficient, n is the density of pinned segments, L is their pinning separation and b is the magnitude of the Burgers vector. The results shown in Figure 5 are not the whole story, but it does give an indication of the kinds of things that can be learned about micromechanics from release waves.

An important aspect of release-wave behavior in FCC metals is that the leading observable release may not correspond to fully elastic behavior [17]. Instead of sampling the longitudinal modulus $K + 4G/3$ in the shock-compressed state, the leading observable release wave is determined by $K + (4G/3)[1 + nL^2/4]^{-1}$. Since we have little control over the product nL^2 in a shock experiment, care should be exercised in using release wave data to determine elastic moduli in FCC metals.

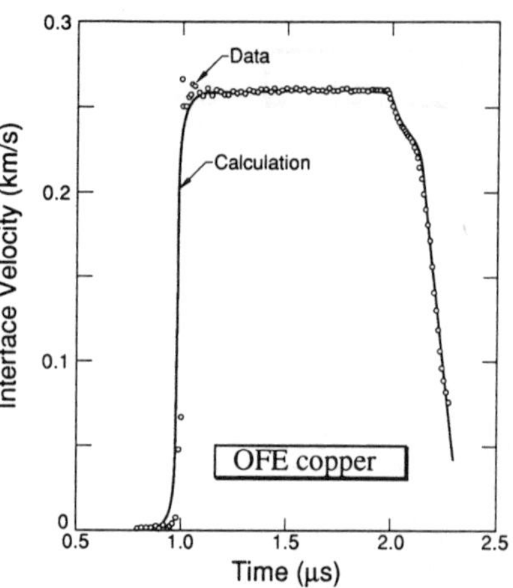

Figure 5. Comparison of experimental data and calculation of quasielastic release in OFE copper shocked to 10 GPa.

Post-Mortem Recovery

Important information on material microstructure can also be obtained from careful recovery experiments. The drawbacks of these experiments are that some additional deformation occurs in the release wave and perhaps in the catching process itself. However, an actual view of the microstructure, even post-mortem, is often very helpful in eliminating false mechanisms from real-time data interpretation. The review article by Gray [18] describes the recovery process and the kinds of information that can be obtained.

SUMMARY

In spite of complex material behavior and incomplete experimental data, shock-compression scientists have been able to piece together a consistent micromechanical picture of high-rate deformation. Direct observation of these processes would aid greatly in establishing uniqueness of interpretation.

REFERENCES

[1] J. S. Wark, R. R. Whitlock, A. A. Hauer, J. E. Swain, and P. J. Solone, *Phys. Rev. B* **40**, pp. 5705-5714 (1989).
[2] P. D. Horn and Y. M. Gupta, *Phys. Rev. B* **39**, pp. 973-979 (1989).
[3] D. S. Moore and S. C. Schmidt, in *Shock Waves in Condensed Matter 1987* (edited by S. C. Schmidt and N. C. Holmes), Amsterdam: Elsevier, 1988, pp. 35-42.
[4] E. Orowan, *Proc. Instn. Mech. Engrs.* **151**, pp. 133-141 (1944).
[5] J. R. Asay, G. R. Fowles, G. E. Duvall, M. H. Miles, and R. F. Tinder, *J. Appl. Phys.* **43**, pp. 2132-2145 (1972).
[6] Y. M. Gupta, G. E. Duvall, and G. R. Fowles, *J. Appl. Phys.* **46**, pp. 532-546 (1975).
[7] G. Meir and R. J. Clifton, *J. Appl. Phys.* **59**, pp. 124-148 (1986).
[8] J. N. Johnson, in *High Pressure Shock Compression of Solids* (edited by J. R. Asay and M. Shahinpoor), New York: Springer-Verlag, 1993, ch. 7.
[9] D. L. Tonks, personal communication (1992).
[10] D. C. Wallace, *Phys. Rev. B* **22**, pp. 1487-1494 (1980).
[11] D. C. Wallace, Los Alamos Rep. LA-10119 (1985).
[12] D. Tonks, Los Alamos Rep. LA-12068-MS (1991).
[13] J. N. Johnson and D. L. Tonks, in *Shock Waves in Condensed Matter 1991* (edited by S. C. Schmidt, R. D. Dick, J. W. Forbes, and D. G. Tasker) Amsterdam: Elsevier, 1992, pp. 371-378.
[14] P. S. Follansbee and U. F. Kocks, *Acta Metall.* **36**, pp. 81-93 (1988).
[15] D. L. Tonks, R. S. Hixson, J. N. Johnson, and G. T. Gray III, this volume.
[16] J. N. Johnson, R. S. Hixson, G. T. Gray III, and C. E. Morris, *J. Appl. Phys.* **72**, pp. 429-441 (1992).
[17] J. N. Johnson, J. Phys. Chem. Solids (in press, 1993).
[18] G. T. Gray III, in *High Pressure Shock Compression of Solids* (edited by J. R. Asay and M. Shahinpoor), New York: Springer-Verlag, 1993, ch. 6.

COMPUTER MODELS OF DYNAMIC FRACTURE AND FRAGMENTATION

D. R. Curran
Poulter Laboratory
SRI International
333 Ravenswood Avenue
Menlo Park, CA, USA, 94025

In the defense community, fracture and fragmentation theory and associated computational models are used to produce descriptions of material damage as well as fragment sizes, velocities, and trajectories for fragmenting warheads and back-of-the-armor debris. Whereas previously such models depended almost exclusively on empirical correlations, emerging physics models of the fracture and fragmentation process that are based on laboratory-measured properties of materials are now available. The models fall into two levels of sophistication, (1) end-state fragmentation models based on extensions of Griffith's energy-balance approach to fracture, and (2) damage evolution models based on characterization of the material's microstructural failure modes. The energy-balance models have the great advantage of simplicity, whereas the microstructural failure models have the advantage of describing the gradual evolution of damage from activation of inherent flaws to microcrack coalescence resulting in fragmentation. Both types of models have been used successfully in conjunction with finite element computer codes to predict fragment sizes, velocities, and trajectories. This paper presents a short review of the above models and concludes with a description of a class of models of intermediate complexity that retain relative simplicity while including dependence on key microstructural features of the material.

COMPUTER MODELS OF THE FRAGMENTATION PROCESS

The geometry of the fragmenting object has a strong effect on the fragmentation. If the microscopic damage occurs near free surfaces, as in the case of exploding thin-walled rings or cylinders, then the microscopic cracks, bands, or voids may tend to coalesce with the free surfaces before they coalesce with each other. In that case, the classical analysis of Mott[1] applies. Mott's model assumes a random distribution of microscopic flaws in the ring wall with an associated distribution of strains-to-failure. The activated flaws are assumed to coalesce with the ring wall surface instantaneously, producing rather slowly diffusing unloading waves that protect adjacent material from further damage. Thus, the fragment size distribution depends on the initial flaw size distribution and the competition between the loading rate and the unloading wave speed.

In more complicated geometries, where most of the fragmentation results from microscopic cracks or shear bands coalescing with each other rather than with free surfaces, it is still true that the fragment size distribution depends on the initial flaw size distribution and the competition between the loading rate and the rate of unloading around the cracks or bands. However, in this case, the unloading rate is governed by the growth (extension) rates of the cracks or bands because the equilibrium size of the unloaded region is proportional to the crack or band size.

In the following paragraphs, we describe current computer models of this complex process, where the models will handle complex geometries and will contain the Mott model as a special case.

NAG/FRAG Models

During the past 20 years, workers at SRI International and elsewhere have developed a family of material fracture and fragmentation models with the name NAG/FRAG (Nucleation And Growth of damage to FRAGmentation). A recent review of these models is given in [2]. The NAG/FRAG models describe in detail the evolution of the damage, and they require as input laboratory-generated data for the nucleation rate of inherent microscopic flaws in the material as well as data for the postnucleation growth (extension) rate of the flaws. Both the nucleation and growth rates are functions of stress and strain. Furthermore, the evolving damage is allowed to soften the material and relax the stresses. In the remainder of this paper, we confine our discussion to one member of the NAG/FRAG family, BFRACT, which describes the behavior of brittle cracks in tension.

As the cracks intersect each other or specimen boundaries, they form fragments, and the BFRACT model describes this process in an average way to predict fragment size distributions. An advantage of the BFRACT approach is that the input parameters to the models can be related to the material's microstructure, thereby giving the materials scientist insight for improving material performance. A disadvantage, however, is the need to perform a significant number of laboratory material property tests to obtain BFRACT model parameters. For scoping calculations, or for applications where end-state fragmentation is the main interest and a description of softening and localization is not needed, simplifications of the BFRACT approach are very useful. In the remainder of this paper, we discuss two such simplifications.

Simplified Tensile Fracture and Fragmentation Models

Energy Balance Approach

Grady and colleagues (for a review, see [3]) have developed a series of spall and fragmentation models based on a global energy balance approach. These models predict the spall strength, the time-to-failure, and the average fragment size for constant strain rate loading conditions, and they have proved very valuable in a variety of applications. The energy balance approach has been used for both brittle and ductile fracture and fragmentation [3]. Here, we will briefly summarize the approach for the brittle case, since it is somewhat more straight- forward and serves to illustrate the approach.

The approach is based on three main assumptions:

1. The sum of the elastic strain energy and the nontranslational kinetic energy must equal or exceed the surface energy dissipated in brittle fracture and fragmentation. In most cases, the nontranslational kinetic energy is negligible, so this assumption becomes

$$(\sigma^2/2) \geq (3\ K_c{}^2/s) \tag{1}$$

where K_c is the fracture toughness and s is the average fragment size (the fragments are assumed to be equisized spheres or cubes of dimension s).

2. There is a "horizon condition" that specifies

$$s \leq 2\ c\ t_s \tag{2}$$

where c is the speed of sound and t_s is the time-to-failure, i.e., the spall time.

3. The material is "favorably disposed," i.e., sufficient flaws are present, so that an equal sign can be used in Eq. (1).

Then, assuming that the material remains linearly elastic up to the peak stress,

$$\sigma_s = \rho c^2 \dot{\varepsilon} t_s \tag{3}$$

and one can then solve Eqs. (1) through (3) for σ_s, t_s, and s:

$$\sigma_s = (3\rho c K_c{}^2 \dot{\varepsilon})^{1/3} \tag{4}$$

$$t_s = (1/c)(\sqrt{3}\ K_c/\rho c \dot{\varepsilon})^{2/3} \tag{5}$$

$$s = 2(\sqrt{3}\ K_c/\rho c \dot{\varepsilon})^{2/3} \tag{6}$$

Thus, Eq. (6) says that the average fragment size is proportional to the strain rate to the inverse 2/3 power, a result that is consistent with much experimental data for brittle materials.

The significant advantage of this simplified approach over the more complex BFRACT model is that no information is required about the flaw size distribution or crack growth rates; only handbook values of elastic modulus and the fracture toughness are required.

A disadvantage is that only the average fragment size is given, whereas in many cases the fragment size distribution is needed. Furthermore, in many cases of interest the applied strain rate is not constant, which in finite element code applications leads to ambiguities as to what strain rate or average strain rate to use in Eq. (6). Also, the model, in contrast to the BFRACT model, does not give the history of microdamage evolution and the associated material softening history, information that is sometimes needed to determine deformation localization in structures.

In the next few paragraphs, we present an attempt to overcome some of these disadvantages while maintaining the advantages of a simplified approach.

Simplified BFRACT Model

In this approach we retain the BFRACT dependence on knowledge of the initial flaw size distribution, but we simplify the picture by assuming that the flaws are all pre-existing penny-shaped cracks. Then, for a given flaw size distribution and remotely applied stress, we know which flaws are activated ("nucleated"); they are those with sizes greater than $(K_c/\sigma)^2$, where K_c is the fracture toughness as before. That is,

$$R_c \geq (K_c/\sigma)^2 \tag{7}$$

where R_c is the critical flaw size.

Any initial flaw size distribution is allowed, but for purposes of illustration let us assume the commonly observed distribution:

$$N_g(R_c) = N_{tc} \exp(-R_c/R_{c1}) \tag{8}$$

where $N_g(R_c)$ is the number of cracks per unit volume with sizes greater than R_c. The c subscripts refer to the flaws (cracks) that have the potential of growing to coalescence to form fragments.

N_{tc} is the total number of flaws per unit volume. A minimum fragment size can thus be defined; it is

$$s_{min} = N_{tc}{}^{-1/3}, \quad s_{min} > R_{c1} \tag{9}$$

That is, if all the flaws grew and coalesced, the average fragment size would be the average distance between the flaw centers (and of, course, the distance between flaw centers is assumed to be greater than the initial flaw sizes).

If we now assume that all active cracks will grow to coalescence, the average fragment size will be the spacing between the active crack centers. Thus,

$$s = [N_g(R_c)]^{-1/3} = s_{min}\exp(R_c/3R_{c1}) = s_{min}\exp(K_c^2/3\sigma^2 R_{c1}) \quad (10)$$

Let σ in Eq. (10) be the peak stress, σ_s, and let σ_s be given approximately by

$$\sigma_s = \rho c^2 \dot{\varepsilon}\, t_s \quad (11)$$

where t_s is the time at peak stress, as before.

If we assume that t_s is given approximately by the time for a crack to propagate the distance s/2 at a velocity of c/3, then

$$t_s = 3s/2c \quad (12)$$

Thus, Eqs. (10) through (12) can be used to solve for σ_s, t_s, and s, similar to the way that Eqs. (1) through (3) were used in the energy balance approach. Furthermore, we approximate the fragment size distribution with the often-observed distribution

$$N_g(R) = (1/8\pi s^3)\exp(-R/s) \quad (13)$$

where $N_g(R)$ is the number of fragments with sizes greater than R.

That is, Eqs. (10) through (12) can be combined to give

$$[\dot{\varepsilon}/A][(s/s_{min})\sqrt{\ln(s/s_{min})}] = 1 \quad (14)$$

where $A = 0.4\, K_c/[\rho c s_{min}\sqrt{(R_{c1})}]$. Equation (14), as plotted in Figure 1, gives a dependence of s on strain rate that is similar to the inverse 2/3 power dependence produced by the energy balance approach. However, in the present case, the results depend not only on the modulus and K_c but also on parameters of the initial flaw size distribution, namely, s_{min} and R_{c1}. The results are dependent on whether there are large numbers of small flaws (small s_{min} and R_{c1}) or small numbers of large flaws (large s_{min} and R_{c1}).

It is interesting to note that when Eq. (14) is applied to material properties and flaw sizes typical for brittle ceramics, it predicts that for strain rates greater than about $10^4\ s^{-1}$ the average fragment size will tend to be almost equal to the initial flaw spacing and relatively independent of strain rate. That is, at such high rates the initial flaws will all rapidly coalesce to form the minimum fragment size. At lower strain rates, on the other hand, the fragment size will have roughly the inverse dependence on the strain rate to the 2/3 power, corresponding to cases where not all the flaws are activated and only the larger ones eventually coalesce to form fragments.

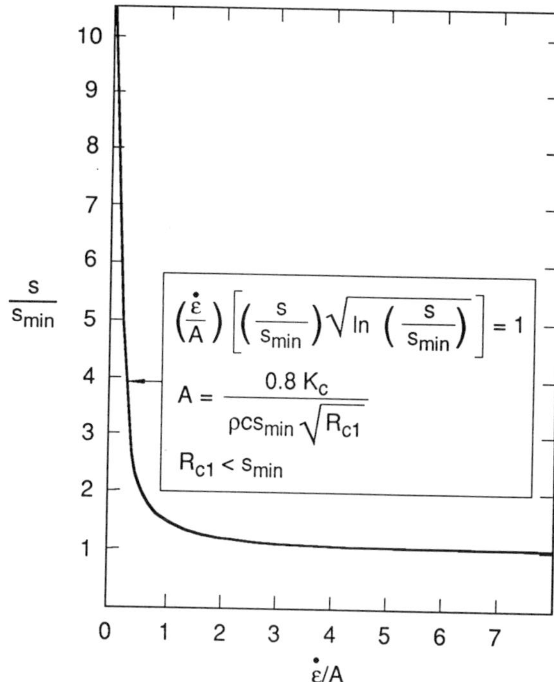

Figure 1. Average fragment size as a function of strain rate.

CONCLUSIONS

Physics models of fragmentation have evolved to the point where they can be used in finite element codes to make fair-to-good predictions of final fragment size and velocity distributions. Simplified versions of these models hold promise in some cases for significantly improving the applicability of such models by decreasing the number of variables needed to be carried along in code calculations of fragmentation in complex structures. However, the simplified models discussed above must be used with caution because they ignore details of damage-induced softening and localization and depend on the "strain rate," which is often a rapidly varying quantity.

REFERENCES

1. N. F. Mott, *Proc. R. Soc. London A* **189**, 300-308 (1947).
2. D. R. Curran, L. Seaman, and D. A. Shockey, *Physics Reports* **147**(5&6) (March 1987).
3. D. E. Grady, *J. Mech. Phys. Solids* **36**(3), 353-384 (1988).

A UNIFIED THEORY OF COLLECTIVE DISLOCATION MOTION INCLUDING BOTH THERMAL ACTIVATION AND VISCOUS DRAG EFFECTS

Jing-Yi Cheng, Guang-Quan Zhou, Z.P.Tang and X.Z.Li
Department of Modern Mechanics
University of Science and Technology of China
Hefei, Anhui 230026, P.R.China

A unified theory of collective dislocation motion including both thermal activation and viscous drag effects is proposed. The theory is able to describe both fast and slow moving dislocation with a simple equation. The experimental dislocation velocity-stress relation data of KCl crystals are fitted with the theory. Good consistency is obtained. The comparison of the theory with the classical theory of single dislocation is also given.

INTRODUCTION

The high and intermediate velocity dislocation motion is usually occurred during the shock compression of crystalline materials according to the strength of shock loadings. The theory and experiment of both thermal activated and viscous drag motion of single dislocation seems quite well established now[1]. But the macroscopic plastic responses of crystals are the results of collective motion of many dislocations, therefore, only having the knowledge of single dislocation, one cannot get a complete picture of the plastic behaviour of crystalline materials. So the effort of using the theoretical results about single dislocation to establish the constitutive laws of macroscopic plastic deformation has not got success in all aspects.

A unified theory of collective dislocation motion including both thermal activation and viscous drag effects is proposed. The theory is able to describe the stress and temperature dependent velocity behaviour of both fast and slow moving dislocations with a simple equation. Since the reported data of the velocity-stress relations of single dislocation are in fact the average results of tens to hundreds dislocations, then, to a certain degree, they are already reflecting the average behaviour of many dislocations. Therefore, the typical experimental data of KCl crystals[3] are fitted with the theory. Good consistency is obtained. Because the theory is established to describe the average behaviour of many dislocations, so it can be used as the start point in establishing the constitutive laws of the plastic deformation of crystalline materials.

DYNAMICS OF SINGLE DISLOCATION

Consider a dislocation line lying in the X direction and gliding in the Y direction under a applied resolved shear stress τ. In the string approximation, the equation of motion is of the form[1]

$$M\frac{\partial^2 y}{\partial t^2}+B\frac{\partial y}{\partial t}-\Gamma\frac{\partial^2 y}{\partial x^2}+\rho(x,y)K(y)=b\tau+f(t) \qquad (1)$$

here M is the mass of the dislocation, B the drag coefficient, Γ the line tension, $\rho(x,y)$ the density of pinning points exerting a force K(y) in the y direction, b the Burgers vector, f(t) the randomly fluctuating (Langevin) thermal force and t the time.

For discrete distributed obstacles with average spacing $\bar{l}$, the distribution function $\rho(x,y)$ is of the form

$$\rho(x,y)=\begin{cases}\rho(x), & y=n\bar{l},\ n=0,\pm1,\pm2,\cdots \\ 0, & y\neq n\bar{l},\ n=0,\pm1,\pm2,\cdots\end{cases} \qquad (2)$$

The movement of a single dislocation through a crystal lattice is then consisted of two fundamental processes: one is interaction of dislocation with obstacles, the other is the viscous drag motion of dislocation in the clear lattice. To deal with the dislocation obstacle interaction process, we consider the potential along the reaction path from one stable equilibrium position to another as sketched in Fig 1. Kramers[3] and Chandrasekhar[4] show that for the case of a system initially in equilibrium in the potential well at point A, the rate of escape across the potential barrier is

$$\nu=\nu_0\exp(-\Delta G/kT) \qquad (3)$$

where ν_0 is the attempt frequency, ΔG the activation energy, k the Boltzmann constant and T the absolute temperature.

The viscous drag-controlled velocity of dislocation in obstacle free region is

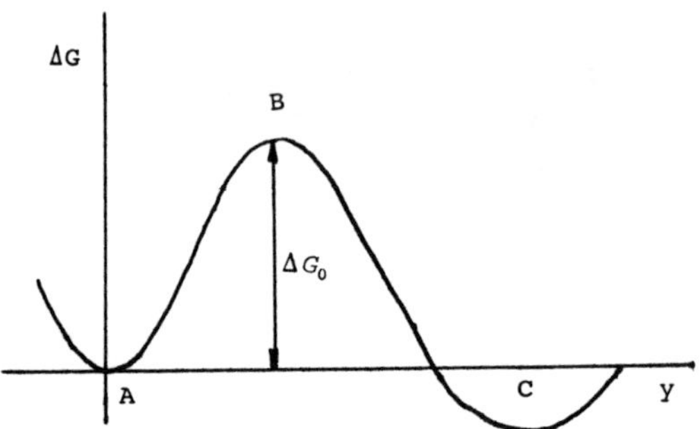

Figure 1. Sketch of reaction path potential

$$V_D=\langle \partial y/\partial t\rangle=\tau b/B \tag{4}$$

where < > expresses the time average. The average velocity V is governed by a mean free path $\bar{l}$ of the dislocation between activated obstacles and the total time for the path (t_T+t_D),

$$\bar{V}=\bar{l}/(t_T+t_D) \tag{5}$$

where $t_T=v^{-1}$ is the average time of thermal activation and $t_D=\bar{l}/V_D$ viscous drag motion time. At sufficiently low velocities such as those probably encountered in conventional tensile tests, one finds, $t_T>>t_D$, so the velocity is governed by the thermal activation mechanism. At sufficiently high velocities such as those encountered in explosive deformation, the behaviour is governed by the viscous drag. In between there is a wide range in which the two effects superimpose.

DYNAMICS OF COLLECTIVE DISLOCATION MOTION

Now consider the collective motion of N dislocation, where N should be a number large enough statistically. If the stress is replaced by a total stress including the stress exerted by all the other dislocations on the given dislocation, the equation of motion of any dislocation in the group should be the same of a single dislocation,

$$\begin{aligned} &M\frac{\partial^2 y_i}{\partial t^2}+B\frac{\partial y_i}{\partial t}-\Gamma\frac{\partial^2 y_i}{\partial x^2}+\rho(x,y_i)K(y_i) \\ &=b\tau+f(t)+\sum_{\substack{j=1\\ j\neq i}}^{N}K_{ij} \qquad (i=1,2,\cdots,N) \end{aligned} \tag{6}$$

where y_i is the coordinate of the i-th dislocation, K_{ij} the interaction force between dislocations. Adding the above equations together, one finds the equation of motion which can be used to describe the average behaviour of many dislocations:

$$\begin{aligned} &M\left(\frac{\partial^2 y}{\partial t^2}\right)_{av}+B\left(\frac{\partial y}{\partial t}\right)_{av}-\Gamma\left(\frac{\partial^2 y}{\partial x^2}\right)_{av} \\ &+\rho_{av}(x)K(y)=b\tau+f(t) \end{aligned} \tag{7}$$

here

$$\left(\frac{\partial^2 y}{\partial t^2}\right)_{av}=\frac{1}{N}\sum_{i=1}^{N}\frac{\partial^2 y_i}{\partial t^2},$$

$$\left(\frac{\partial y}{\partial t}\right)_{av}=\frac{1}{N}\sum_{i=1}^{N}\frac{\partial y_i}{\partial t},$$

$$\left(\frac{\partial^2 y}{\partial x^2}\right)_{av}=\frac{1}{N}\sum_{i=1}^{N}\frac{\partial^2 y_i}{\partial x^2},$$

$$\rho_{av}(x)=\frac{1}{N}\sum_{i=1}^{N}\rho(x,y_i),$$

$$K_{av}(y)=\frac{\sum_{i=1}^{N}\rho(x,y_i)K(y_i)}{\sum_{i=1}^{N}\rho(x,y_i)},$$

and

$$f_{av}(t)=\frac{1}{N}\sum_{i=1}^{N}f_i(t)$$

are average acceleration, average velocity, average curvature, average obstacle distribution function, average obstacle strength and average thermal fluctuation force, respectively. Since the macroscopic mechanical responses of materials exhibit homogeneity in space, then the average obstacles distribution function should be continuous in the direction of dislocation motion, i.e., independent of y coordinate. Therefore, when viewing the dislocation group as a whole, the average obstacle number which interacts with dislocations is the same nevertheless the distance the dislocations move. Although the behaviour of the individual dislocations is like a single dislocation which appears in the state of viscous drag or thermally activated motion alternatively, the average behaviours of the collective dislocation motion is quite different which is always in the state of dislocation-obstacle interaction. If the potential of the average dislocation motion is the same as sketched in Figure 1, then the average rate of escape across the potential barrier is also of the form

$$\bar{\nu}=\bar{\nu}_0\exp(-\overline{\Delta G}/kT) \tag{8}$$

here ν_0 is the average attempt frequency and ΔG the average activation energy. So the average velocity is

$$\bar{V}=d\bar{\nu}_0\exp(-\overline{\Delta G}/kT) \tag{9}$$

where d is the width of the potential barrier.

From the average velocity equation of many dislocations [Equation(9)], it appears that even at very high velocities, the governing mechanism of dislocation motion is the still thermal activation. In fact, the classical theory of thermal activation is established for quasistatic processes, therefore, the classical theory cannot be used for high velocity dislocations which are in the state of equilibrium.

We know that the driving stress or effective stress acting on a moving dislocation is

$$\tau^*=\tau-\tau^I-(B/b)\bar{V} \tag{10}$$

where τ^I is the internal stress and (B/b)V is the viscous drag stress. During the establishment of classical theory of thermal activation, the viscous drag stress is omitted. In fact, this omission is appropriation only at low velocities. At high velocities, we must consider the viscous drag stress. When the stress dependent activation energy ΔG is specified, equation(9) relates stress, temperature and velocity. Without loss of generality, ΔG may be written in the form

$$\overline{\Delta G}=\int_{\tau^*}^{\hat{\tau}^R} b\Delta a^* d\tau^* \tag{11}$$

where $\tau^R=K_{max}/b$ is the maximum obstacle resistance stress, which is the stress needed for dislocation motion at absolute zero temperature, and ΔA^* is the activation area. The function ΔA^* is assumed to be inversely proportional to some negative power of τ^*

$$\Delta A^* \propto (1/\tau^*)^m, \quad (m\geq 0) \tag{12}$$

with different m values, the following expression for ΔG is obtained.

$$\overline{\Delta G}=\begin{cases}\Delta G_0\ln(\hat{\tau}^R/\tau^*) & (m=1)\\ \Delta G_0[1-(\tau^*/\hat{\tau}^R)^{1-m}]^q & (0\leq m<1)\\ \Delta G_0[(\hat{\tau}^R/\tau^*)^{m-1}-1] & (m>1)\end{cases} \tag{13}$$

here ΔG_0 is a constant and q is a modification factor. Equations (9), (10) and (13) give us the complete description of the average behaviour of many dislocations.

DISCUSSION

From equation (9), (10) and (13), we can write the stress-velocity relation as follows

$$\tau=s(\bar{V},T)\hat{\tau}^R+(B/b)\bar{V}+\tau^I \tag{14}$$

where

$$s(\bar{V},T)=\begin{cases}(\bar{V}/V_0)^{kT/\Delta G_0} & (m=1)\\ \{1-[\frac{kT}{\Delta G_0}\ln\frac{V_0}{\bar{V}}]^{1/q}\}^{\frac{1}{1-m}} & (0\leq m<1)\\ \{1-[\frac{kT}{\Delta G_0}\ln\frac{\bar{V}}{V_0}]\}^{\frac{1}{m-1}} & (m>1)\end{cases}$$

and $V_0=d\nu_0$. It is easy to see that to move the dislocations, the applied stress must balance two velocity dependent stress and a velocity dependent stress. Due to smallness of the B value, the viscous drag stress can be omitted for low velocity dislocations. Therefore, the governing mechanism for low velocity dislocations will be thermal activation. Comparing with the classical theory of the single dislocation, we find that, at low velocities, the velocity equation for single and many dislocations are in the same form. It is the reason for why the use of the theoretical result of single dislocation to the establishment of the constitutive laws has obtained great success at low strain rate. At high velocities, the viscous drag force becomes important. Because the term $s(V,T)\tau^R$ increases with increasing velocity at the rate of a few percent per decade of velocity, so the viscous drag dominates the behaviour of high velocity dislocations. Obviously, the average behaviour of collective dislocation motion is qualitatively in accordance with that of a single dislocation. But they have noticeable difference quantitatively. By comparing equations (9) and (5) one knows it clearly.

When combining the equation (5) of single dislocation with the Orowan equation

$$\dot{\gamma}^P=bN_m\bar{V} \tag{15}$$

to get the constitutive equation for high strain rate, we have

$$\tau=\frac{B}{b^2N_m}\dot{\gamma}^P=c\dot{\gamma}^P \tag{16}$$

where N_m is the mobile dislocation density and $c=B/(b^2N_m)$. But experiments show that the correct constitutive equation should be [5]

$$\tau=\tau_0+c\dot{\gamma}^P \tag{17}$$

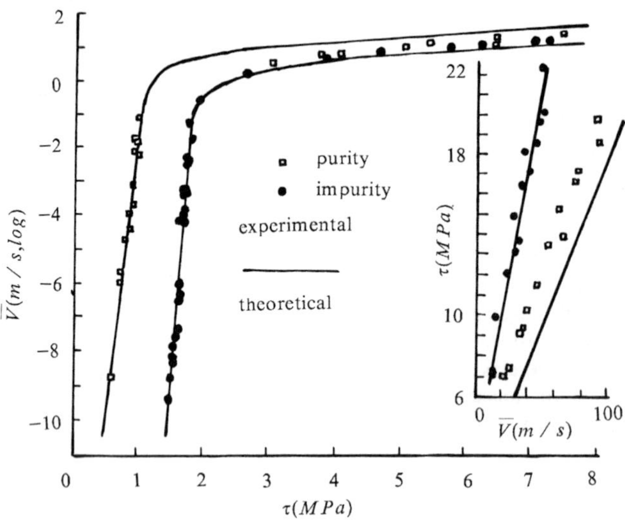

Fig 2. The theoretical and experimental curves of the velocity-stress relation of KCl crystals

where γ_0 is a constant which makes up a large part of the total flow stress. Therefore we can conclude that it is impertinent to use the result of single dislocation to establish constitutive laws for high strain rate deformation. When using the unified theory of collective dislocation motion proposed here, we get exactly the equation(17). The equation of m=0, q=1 is used to fit the typical experimental data of KCl crystals. As showed in Figure 2, at low velocities, the theoretical and experimental curves are in good agreement. At high velocities, good agreement is also obtained for impurity KCl crystal, but for purity crystal some deviation is exhibited. It is because the experiments are the average results of 40-50 dislocations, the obstacles of purity crystals are too few to give the macroscopic average of dislocation-obstacles distribution, so the dislocations behave like single dislocation. But for impurity crystals, the obstacle numbers are large, though the dislocation numbers are too large, yet they already exhibit the macroscopic average behaviour.

CONCLUSION

1. A unified theory of collective dislocation motion including both thermal activation and viscous drag effects is proposed. The theory can be used as the start point in establishing the constitutive laws of macroscopic plastic deformation of crystalline materials.

2. The successes and limits of the classical theory of thermal activation are pointed out.

REFERENCES

[1] E. Nadgornyi, *Progr. Mater. Sci.*, **31** (1988)

[2] S.U. Lubenets and V.I. Startsev, *Sov. Phys. Solid state*, **10** (1968), 15.

[3] H. A. Kramers, *Physica*, **7** (1940), 284.

[4] S. Chandrasekhar, *Rev. Mod. Phys.*, **15** (1943), 1.

[5] P. S. Follansbee, G. Regazzoni and U. F. Kocks, in *Mechanical Properties of Materials at High Rate of Strain* (ed, J.Harding), Inst. Phys. Conf. Ser. **70** (1984), 71.

DAMAGE MODELS WITH INTERMEDIATE CONFIGURATION LARGE STRAIN FORMULATION AND RESULTS

J. F. Guéry
Laboratoire de Détonique et de Dynamique Rapide
SNPE - Centre de Recherche du Bouchet
BP 2 - 91710 Vert-le-Petit - FRANCE

A lot of damage models have been formulated using different definitions of the *damage variable.* In computations, some of them give cell-size dependent results and localization. One can make a link between constitutive relations with intermediate configuration at large strain and damage models using the notion of *distributed body.* Damage is introduced by a natural deformation gradient tensor. It is shown that the Nucleation and Growth models formulated at SRI can be the linear approximation of such models. Numerical results on cell-size independency and non-localization are given.

INTRODUCTION

Damage models with different levels of complexity have been formulated. Curran et al. [1] have shown that damage could be considered as the result of nucleation, growth and coalescence of voids or microcracks. This implies that anisotropic directions might be introduced in an isotropic material by the presence of damage.
For instance, after spalling, a material is fully damaged in one direction and intact in the others. One can also assume that damage results in the opening or closure of these voids or cracks, reducing the apparent moduli of the material in tension and having less sensitive effects in compression. One can see that a single parameter model is not sufficient and that a tensor measure of damage is preferable [2].
In the community of mechanics, large strain or finite strain formulations have been developed during these last three decades. One can use results obtained in elastoplasticity to formulate new generations of damage models.

LARGE STRAIN FORMULATION

As usual, we denote by x and X the positions in the deformed configuration at time t (Eulerian) and in a reference configuration (Lagrangian), and by $\mathbf{F}$ the deformation gradient tensor.

$$x = x(X,t)$$
$$\mathbf{F} = \frac{\partial x}{\partial X}$$

We introduce a third variable X^a. Relations between X^a, X and x define an *intermediate configuration* [3].

$$\mathbf{F} = \frac{\partial x}{\partial X} = \frac{\partial x}{\partial X^a}\frac{\partial X^a}{\partial X} = \mathbf{F^2F^1} \quad (1)$$
$$\mathbf{F^2} = \frac{\partial x}{\partial X^a} \; , \; \mathbf{F^1} = \frac{\partial X^a}{\partial X} \quad (2)$$

X^a can be introduced by the notion of *distributed body.* For instance, for elasto-plastic material, X^a represents the fraction of plastic body and $\mathbf{F^1}$, $\mathbf{F^2}$ the plastic and elastic deformation gradient tensor.

We can assume that "a damaged material is a *distribution* of voids or cracks in an intact material". Thus, X^a represents a measure of the intact material in all the solid. $\mathbf{F^2}$ is the deformation gradient tensor of the intact solid, $\mathbf{F^1}$ is a *damage tensor.*

We note $X^a = X^s$, $\mathbf{F^1} = \mathbf{F^d}$ and $\mathbf{F^2} = \mathbf{F^s}$.

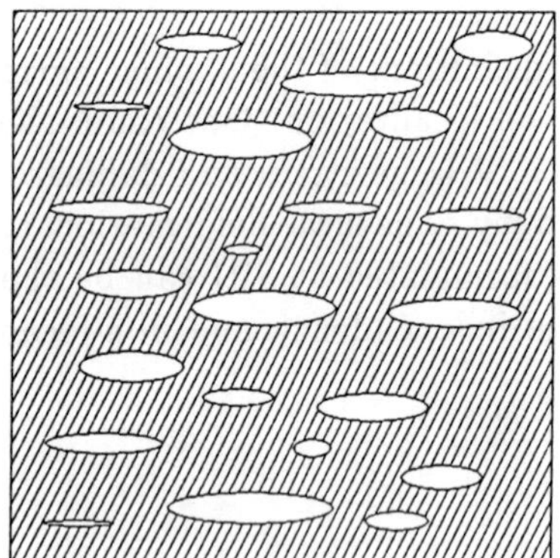

Figure 1: distribution of cracks in a material

For the undamaged material, $X^s = X$ hence $\mathbf{F^s} = \mathbf{F}$.

This description allows an anisotropic description of the damage. The formulation of the damage model will be an evolution law for $\mathbf{F^d}$. With the classical notations, $\mathbf{R}$ is the rotation tensor, $\mathbf{V}$ the left stretch tensor, $\mathbf{B}$ the left Cauchy-Green tensor, $\mathbf{D}$ the rate of deformation tensor and $\mathbf{T}$ the Cauchy stress tensor. We define in the same way:

$$\begin{aligned} \mathbf{B^s} &= \mathbf{F^s}\mathbf{F^{s}}^T \\ \bar{\mathbf{D}}^\mathbf{d} &= \mathbf{R^s}\mathbf{D^d}\mathbf{R^s} \end{aligned}$$

All these quantities must satisfy the Clausius Duhem inequality. We can try to see what it means in a simple case.

If we neglect thermal effects and take the specific free energy ψ as a function of $\mathbf{B^s}$, the dissipation becomes:

$$\begin{aligned} \Phi &= [\mathbf{T} - 2\rho\frac{\partial\psi}{\partial\mathbf{B^s}}\mathbf{B^s}] : \mathbf{D} \\ &+ 2\rho\mathbf{V^s}\frac{\partial\psi}{\partial\mathbf{B^s}}\mathbf{V^s} : \bar{\mathbf{D}}^\mathbf{d} \geq 0 \end{aligned}$$

If the intact material is supposed hyperelastic,

$$\mathbf{T} = 2\rho\frac{\partial\psi}{\partial\mathbf{B^s}}\mathbf{B^s}$$

and $\mathbf{T^d}$ is introduced as:

$$\mathbf{T^d} = \mathbf{V^s}\frac{\partial\psi}{\partial\mathbf{B^s}}\mathbf{V^s}$$

A constitutive function will be a relation between $\bar{\mathbf{D}}^\mathbf{d}$ and $\mathbf{T^d}$. Following Onsager's relations, one can for instance choose a positive linear form ϕ and write:

$$\bar{\mathbf{D}}^\mathbf{d} = \phi[\mathbf{T^d}]$$

The intermediate configuration introduces a stress relaxation in the damaged material since the Cauchy stress tensor $\mathbf{T}$ is a function of the undamaged strain $\mathbf{B^s}$ instead of the total strain $\mathbf{B}$.

For the fully damaged material, the only stresses are in compression or in shearing. In dilatation, $\mathbf{X^s} = x$ thus $\mathbf{B^s} = \mathbf{1}$, $\mathbf{B^d} = \mathbf{B}$ and $\mathbf{T} = \mathbf{0}$. All the deformation is in the opening of cracks or voids. The formulation is more complex in this case.

One can also introduce other internal variables, α_i, related to the microstructure, and rewrite the Clausius Duhem inequality with α_i.

In small strain assumption, we linearize the strain tensors. The multiplicative composition becomes additive.

$$\begin{aligned} \mathbf{F^s} &= \mathbf{1} + \mathbf{H^s} \\ \mathbf{F^d} &= \mathbf{1} + \mathbf{H^d} \\ \mathbf{F} &= \mathbf{1} + \mathbf{H^s} + \mathbf{H^d} \end{aligned}$$

$$\mathbf{E} = \mathbf{E}^s + \mathbf{E}^d \qquad (3)$$

where $\mathbf{E}$ is the Eulerian strain tensor, $\mathbf{E} = \frac{1}{2}(\mathbf{1} - \mathbf{B}^{-1})$.

THE SRI MODEL

In the NAG models formulated at SRI [1], damage is described by the active flaw concentration $\rho_f(X, t, R, \vec{n})$, where X is the lagrangian position, t the time, R and $\vec{n}$ the size and orientation of the crack. The total number of microcracks or voids $N_g(R)$ with sizes greater than or equal to R is:

$$N_g(X, t, R) = \int_R^\infty \int_{all\ \vec{n}} \rho_f \ d\vec{n}\ dR$$

Damage is described by the evolution of the number of cracks and the crack size, using a nucleation law and a growth function:

$$\frac{dN}{dt} = \dot{N}_o \left(exp(\frac{\sigma_n - \sigma_{n0}}{\sigma_1}) - 1 \right)$$

$$\text{for} \quad \sigma \geq \sigma_{n0}$$

$$\frac{dR}{dt} = \frac{1}{4\eta} \left(\sigma_n - \sqrt{\frac{\pi}{4R}} K_{1C} \right)$$

$$\text{for} \quad \sigma_n \geq \sqrt{\frac{\pi}{4R}} K_{1C}$$

where σ_n is the stress normal to the crack plane and $\dot{N}_o$, σ_{n0}, σ_1, η, K_{1C} are some parameters of the model.
Experimental observations show that cracks are nucleated following:

$$N = N_t \ exp(-\frac{R}{R_n})$$

up to a maximal size R_{max}. In its original formulation [1], the model uses one direction of anisotropy, given by one crack orientation $\vec{n}$, and the total strain in this direction is written in an additive decomposition into solid material strain and crack opening:

$$\epsilon = \epsilon^s + \epsilon^c \qquad (4)$$

where:

$$\epsilon^c = \frac{16(1 - \nu^2)}{3E} N R^3 \sigma_n$$

Equations (3) and (4) are equivalent.
A global damage variable τ is introduced, related to the volume fraction of fragmented material. This variable is connected to the processes of coalescence of the cracks.

$$\tau = A \int_{R_{min}}^{R_{max}} R^3 dN$$

Discussions on frame indifference (objectivity), well-posedness and stability of the model have been made elsewhere by Curran [4].

DYNAMIC RESULTS

We have fitted the BFRACT parameters for some solid propellants. The solid material behavior is taken elastic, perfectly plastic:

$$\rho_0 = 1.80 g/cm^3$$
$$K = 9.144 GPa$$
$$\mu = 75 MPa$$
$$\sigma_y = 25 MPa$$

We performed simulations of plate impact experiments. The flyer plate is in PMMA, 3 mm width. The propellant is 6 mm width. The impact velocity is 79 m/s. The results (figures 2 and 3) show cell size independency, which is not obvious for a damage model.

It is not necessary to let the computational cell size be no smaller than a *microstructurally-based* control volume as discussed by Curran [4]. On the contrary we must choose the cell size small enough for insuring numerical convergence. We can apply averaging operators for global results on material volumes larger than microstructural heterogeneities of the material.

Table 1: BFRACT parameters for the propellant.

Parameter	value	unit
$1/4\eta$	15,000	$/MPa/s$
K_{1C}	1.	$MPa\sqrt{cm}$
R_n	0.0021	cm
R_{max}	0.0088	cm
$\dot{N}_0$	1. 10^{17}	$/cm^3/s$
σ_{n0}	109	MPa
σ_1	100	MPa
A	4	-

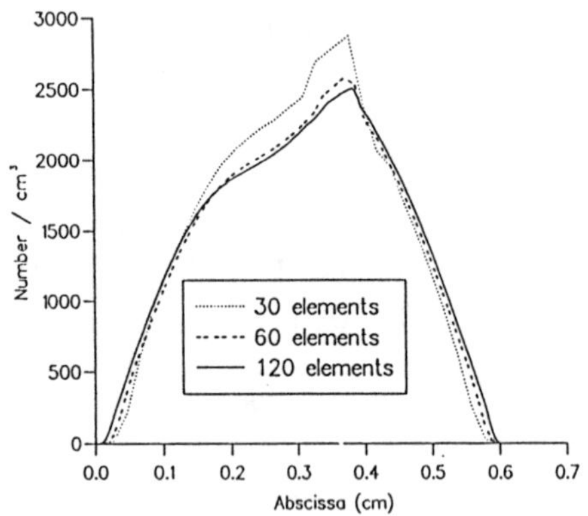

Figure 2: Maximum number of cracks.

CONCLUSION

We have formulated a tensor damage model based on the idea of a *distributed body*. Finite strain formulation is possible using an intermediate configuration. NAG models developed at SRI are the linearized assumption of such damage models and are very interesting for non-locality. Examples of computation are given elsewhere [5].

AKNOWLEDGMENTS

This work was performed under the auspices of the Service Technique des Poudres et

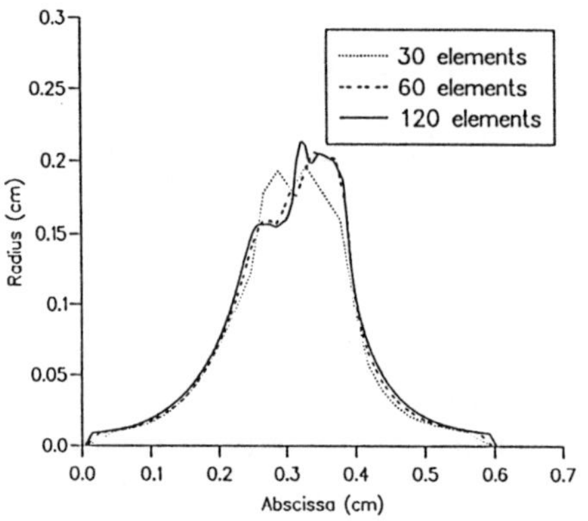

Figure 3: Maximum size of cracks.

Explosifs.
The author wants to thank Lynn Seaman for helpful discussions.

REFERENCE

[1] D. R. Curran, L. Seaman and D. A. Shockey, *Physics Reports* 147, pp. 253-388 (1987).

[2] M. Kachanov, *J. Eng. Mech. Division, ASCE* 106, 1039 (1980)

[3] F. Sidoroff, *Arch. of Mech.* 25, pp. 299-309, 1973.

[4] D. R. Curran, " Appropriate Material Softening and Failure Models for Numerical Calculations", in *Proceedings of the APS Conference on Shock Compression of Condensed Matter*, 1991, pp 395-398.

[5] B. Salvetat and J. F. Guéry, "Visualization and Modelling of Delayed Detonation in the Card Gap test", presented at the Tenth International Symposium on Detonation, Boston, Massachusetts, July 12-16, 1993.

SHOCK-LOADING RESPONSE OF ADVANCED MATERIALS

G. T. Gray III
Los Alamos National Laboratory
Los Alamos, New Mexico, USA 87545

Advanced materials are receiving increasing attention for applications requiring high-leverage materials possessing potentially high pay-offs. While the low-rate deformation response of a broad range of advanced materials is receiving intense scientific study, increased utilization of these material classes under dynamic loading conditions requires an understanding of their high-rate / shock-wave behavior. In this paper the issues relevant to defect generation, storage, and the underlying physical basis needed in predictive models for several advanced materials will be reviewed. Examples of the diversity in the shock response of advanced materials will be illustrated with results from Cu-Nb and 6061-T6-Al_2O_3 composites and the intermetallic compound, Ni_3Al.

INTRODUCTION

Advanced materials, such as composites (metal, ceramic, or polymer-matrix), laminated materials, intermetallics, nanostructured materials, and foams (metallic or polymeric-based) are receiving increasing attention due to their tailor-able properties. These include higher specific strengths, stiffnesses, and high temperature properties. Composites and laminated materials also allow other physical properties besides mechanical properties to be custom designed to specific applications. The high-rate/impact response of advanced materials is relevant to a broad range of service environments such as the crash-worthiness of civilian/military vehicles, foreign-object-damage in aerospace applications, and light-weight armor. Increased utilization of these material classes under dynamic loading conditions requires an understanding of the relationship between high-rate/shock-wave response as a function of microstructure if we are to develop constitutive models to predict material behavior.

In contrast to single-phase materials, advanced materials are: 1) heterogeneous mixtures of often dramatically different phases in terms of structural, physical, and mechanical properties, morphology, volume fractions, etc., 2) elastically and plastically anisotropic, and 3) achieve some of their properties due to interfacial effects that influence the plastic flow and fracture behavior. These three attributes can cause a broad range of effects on the structure/property relationships of composites and intermetallics subjected to shock loading. Increasing utilization of 'advanced materials' in future engineering designs will necessitate a fundamental understanding of how the deformation response these ordered or complex multi-phase structures accommodate high-rate plastic deformation. In this paper the issues relevant to defect generation, storage, and the underlying physical basis needed in predictive models for several advanced materials will be discussed.

EXPERIMENTAL

Shock recovery experiments were performed on two composites and one intermetallic compound with an 80-mm single-stage launcher utilizing recovery techniques as described previously[1]. Cu-15 vol.% Nb, 6061-T6-10 vol.% Al_2O_3, and polycrystalline Ni_3Al samples were shock loaded in symmetric shock-recovery assemblies for 1 μs pulse durations to various shock peak pressures. The Cu-Nb represents a ductile metal-matrix composite exhibiting good interfacial strength and based on negligible solid-solubility of each metal in the other. Aluminum-alumina composites are available with a wide range of reinforcement volume fractions, second-phase morphologies, and second-phase sizes. Figure 1 shows a 6061-T6-Al_2O_3 composite with a second-phase volume fraction of 10 vol.% spherical-alumina particles. Ni_3Al represents an ordered-fcc($L1_2$) intermetallic compound. Compression samples were EDM machined from the as-received and shock-recovered Cu-Nb, 6061-T6-Al_2O_3, and Ni_3Al samples, and reloaded at a strain rate of 0.001 s^{-1} at 298K.

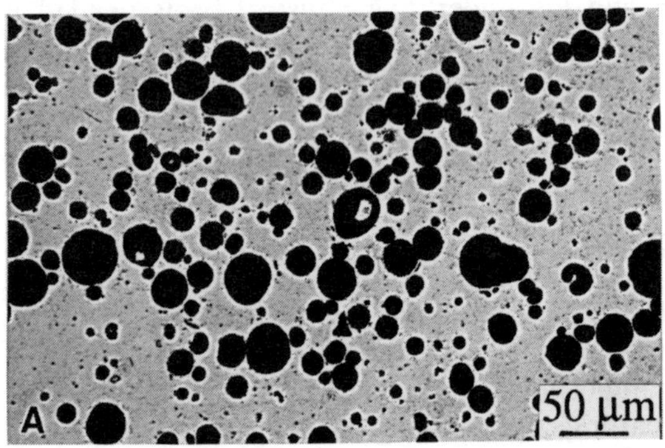

Figure 1. Optical micrograph of a 6061-T6 Al-10 vol. % Al_2O_3 composite with spherical particles.

RESULTS AND DISCUSSION

The Cu-Nb and 6061-T6-Al_2O_3 composites were selected to examine the influence of particulate metal and ceramic-phase additions on material shock response. The Cu-Nb composite represents a ductile second-phase reinforcement where: a) both phases have similar sound speeds of ~ 4 km/s, and b) both phases are expected to deform at low shock pressures (<10 GPa). The 6061-T6-Al_2O_3 case contrarily represents a composite where: a) the reinforcement sound speed is ~2x faster than that of the matrix, and b) at low shock pressures the Al_2O_3 will remain elastic while the matrix will readily deform plastically. Differences in shock velocity are known to influence the dispersive effects of the composite and thereby significantly change the loading and release wave profiles[1]. Systematic studies are crucial to enable modeling of how different composite reinforcement types (particulates, disks, rods), volume fractions, morphologies, etc. affect wave dispersion.

The quasi-static and shock response of the Cu-Nb composite and single-phase pure copper is shown in Figure 2. The Cu-Nb is observed to possess a higher quasi-static yield strength but after ~10% strain to exhibit a similar work-hardening rate. The reload Cu-Nb is also seen to exhibit a fall off in the reload response after yielding rather than sustained hardening. The reload shock curves in Figure 2 have been offset with respect to the annealed responses at low-strain rate by the transient strain generated by the shock defined as $4/3 \ln (V/V_0)$, where V and V_0 are the final and initial volumes of Cu during the shock cycle. Pure Cu is seen to exhibit enhanced shock hardening compared to Cu deformed quasi-statically to an equivalent strain level.

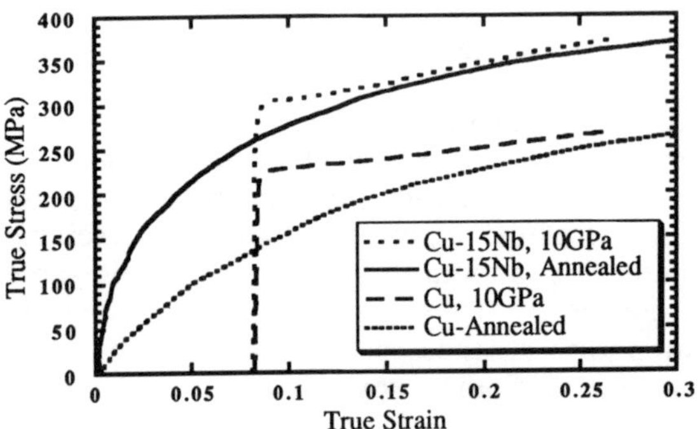

Figure 2. Reload stress-strain response of shock-loaded Cu-Nb composite and Cu compared to that observed during quasi-static deformation for each material.

While the Cu-Nb composite has an increased reload yield strength compared to its quasi-static response it does not exhibit as pronounced a shock-hardening as pure Cu. At a true strain of 0.15, the annealed and shock reload responses of the Cu-Nb are coincident while the shocked Cu curve displays increased flow stress levels over the annealed Cu until a strain of 0.25. Defect generation and storage in the Cu-Nb composite represents a combination of bcc and fcc materials with each possessing drastically different strain-rate and temperature sensitivities. Nb, due to its high inherent lattice resistance (Peierls Stress) under high-rate or shock loading will possess a much higher flow stress than copper thereby acting more "elastic" until higher stress levels are reached. This process might be expected to store a disproportionate amount of the defects in the Cu matrix. Upon quasi-statically reloading the shock-recovered composite sample the Nb now finds itself with a lower inherent flow stress surrounded by a highly work-hardened Cu matrix. This process will tend to reduce the total defect storage in the Cu-Nb and result in an unstable state in the Nb which is consistent with the slight yield fall off in the reloaded shock Cu-Nb sample.

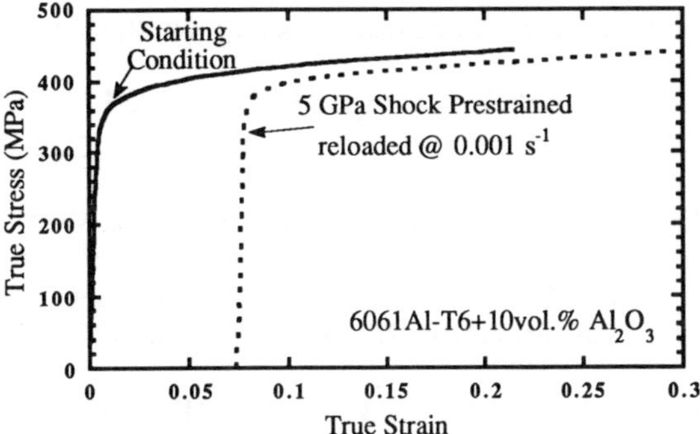

Figure 3. Reload stress-strain response of 6061-T6-Al_2O_3 composite shock prestrained to 5 GPa offset to the quasi-static starting material.

The shock-response of the 6061-T6 Al - 10 vol.% Al_2O_3 composite is substantially different than the Cu-Nb discussed so far (Figure 3). Similar to previous observations on a shock-loaded Al-Zn-Mg-Cu alloy-SiC composite[3,4], the reload stress-strain response of the shocked 6061-Al_2O_3 is lower than the quasi-static stress-strain curve. At first glance this behavior seems inconsistent with the fact that: a) at low strains during quasi-static loading many particulate-ceramic composites exhibit anomalously high apparent work hardening rates due to load transfer to the reinforcement, b) with the imposition of a hydrostatic stress or testing in compression, the process of damage accumulation is suppressed and these composites exhibit continued hardening and enhanced ductility[5]. These facts might suggest that we would expect substantial shock hardening of ceramic-reinforced composites.

However, in the shock process, contrary to a uniaxial test, deformation encompasses a stress and strain path reversal during the compressive loading and release[3]. The lower reload yield stress in shock-loaded hard-second-phase composites is therefore consistent with a Bauschinger effect[3] in two-phase materials. The Bauschinger effect in the reloaded shock samples is manifested in lower yield behavior after the strain-path reversal inherent in the shock and caused by the back stresses built up during the shock release. Constitutive modeling of the high-rate/shock response of advanced composites must also consider additional influences. Residual stresses are formed in many composites during processing due to the thermal expansion mismatches between phases. During cooling dislocations are generated in the matrix in response to these stresses thereby increasing the yield strength of the composite. The role of these unrelieved stresses and dislocation networks on subsequent wave propagation and defect generation/storage mechanisms during shock loading remains to be investigated.

Ordered compounds represent an exciting challenge to our understanding and modeling of defect generation and storage during shock loading. To prevent local disordering of the structure, dislocations in many ordered compounds move in linked pairs which disorder and reorder the lattice as the "superdislocation" moves. Dislocation motion in most ordered intermetallics is accompanied by a large Peierls stress which results in a high temperature and strain-rate sensitivity. Coincident with the restriction of dislocation motion in pairs is the difficulty of dislocation cross-slip to other slip planes.

An important engineering intermetallic that is an exception to many of these properties is Ni_3Al[6]. Ni_3Al displays a low, temperature and rate-sensitivity similar to annealed fcc metals due to a low Peierls barrier to {111}<110> dislocations. The shock response of Ni_3Al contrasted to pure Ni is shown in Figure 4. Ni_3Al is seen to display an enhanced hardening response compared to its quasi-static hardening behavior to an equivalent strain level.

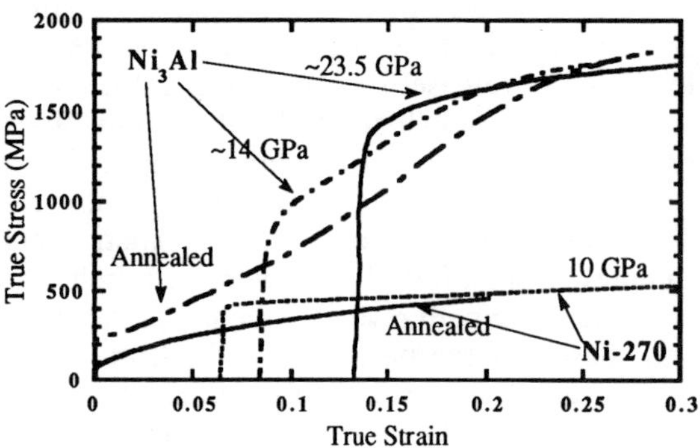

Figure 4. Reload stress-strain response of shock-loaded Ni3Al and Ni compared to that observed during quasi-static deformation.

While it is difficult to compare the behavior of shocked Ni3Al with shocked Ni, several insightful observations are evident from Figure 4. In a simplistic sense this can be considered in terms of a very high value of the saturation stress, σ_{sat}. In Ni3Al sustained hardening at quasi-static rates under ambient conditions is observed to stresses approaching 2 GPa[7]. In contrast Ni exhibits a saturation stress, i e, asymptotic saturation of the flow stress, at a stress level of approximately 450 MPa. Given the nearly identical elastic and shear modulii of Ni and Ni3Al, the approximately 4-fold increase in the "saturation stress" between the two materials clearly demonstrates that drastically different dynamic recovery mechanisms are controlling the transition from Stage II to III in Ni3Al[7].

SUMMARY AND CONCLUSIONS

Preliminary indications of the shock generation and storage mechanisms operative in composites and intermetallics have been elucidated using shock-recovery studies of select advanced materials. The influences of various reinforcement phases and matrix structures in a range of advanced composites and ordered intermetallics will present a considerable challenge to the development of models of defect generation and storage mechanisms during shock loading.

ACKNOWLEDGMENTS

The author wishes to acknowledge C. Trujillo, W. Wright, and M.F. Lopez for their assistance with the experimental aspects of this study. This work was performed under the auspices of the U.S. Department of Energy.

REFERENCES

[1] G.T. Gray III, in *High Pressure Shock Compression of Solids,* (ed. by J.R. Asay and M. Shahinpoor) NY: Springer-Verlag, ch. 6, (1993).

[2] L.M. Baker, *J. Comp. Matls.*, **5**, pp. 140-162, (1971).

[3] G.T. Gray III, R.S. Hixson, and C.E. Morris, in *Shock Comp. of Condensed Matter-1991,* (ed. by S.C. Schmidt, R.D. Dick, J.W. Forbes, and D.G. Tasker) North-Holland (1992) pp. 427-430.

[4] S.I. Hong, G.T. Gray III, and J.J. Lewandowski, *Scripta Metall.*, **27**, pp. 431-436, (1992).

[5] J.D. Embury and G.T. Gray III, in *Mod.of Plastic Def.and its Eng.Appl.* (ed. by S.I. Andersen, J.B. Bilde-Sorensen, N. Hansen, D. Juul Jensen, T. Leffers, H. Lilholt, T. Lorentzen, O.B. Pedersen, and B. Ralph, Riso National Laboratory, Roskilde, Denmark (1992)pp. 39-56..

[6] H.W. Sizek and G.T. Gray III, *Acta Metall. Mater.*, **41**, pp. 1855-1860, (1993).

[7] G. T. Gray III and J. D. Embury, in *High-Temp.Ord.Inter. Alloys-V*, (ed. by I. Baker, R. Darolia, J.D. Whittenberger, and M.H. Yoo), MRS, Pgh., PA , (1993) vol. 288, pp. 585-590.

Using Maxwell–Boltzman's Statistics for Microcracks Distribution Function in a Failure Model.

E. Bar-on
Rafael Ballistics Center, Box 2250(24), Haifa, ISRAEL

D. Z. Yankelevsky
National Building Research Inst., Technion City 32000, Haifa, ISRAEL

The way microcracks are distributed in a solid is formulated in analogy to Boltzmann's molecular velocities distribution. Each crack is associated with a vector, whose magnitude is crack's characteristic half-length and its direction is defined as the normal to crack faces. Crack's orientation distribution is assumed homogeneous and we do not consider interaction between cracks until failure occurs. The derived DF is tested in simulating a measured flaws distribution.

INTRODUCTION

Most materials's behaviour models use some Distribution Function (DF) in order to derive mathematical expressions for flaws distribution in the material. These Distribution Functions are based on experimental observations. Thus, mathematically these functions should decrease as flaw size is increased and integration of the function should result in the number of flaws in the material. No theoretical or physical meaning is given to the DF chosen. Common DF's are based on Weibull DF[1,2], or a survival equation used in Flaw Growth Models[3] of the form of-

$$N = N_0 e^{-\left(\frac{R}{R_0}\right)} \quad (1)$$

Where N is the number of flaws whose size is greater than R_0, N_0 is the total number of flaws in the solid and R is the flaw size.

In this paper we derive a DF in analogy to Boltzman's molecular velocities distribution[4] which can be applied to Micro-Mechanics Models.

MAXWELL-BOLTZMAN'S CRACKS DF

Each crack is represented through a crack vector $\vec{a} = a\hat{n}$, where a is crack's magnitude and $\hat{n}$ is the crack's direction (defined as normal to crack faces)

Let us imagine that at a certain instant all the crack vectors are transferred to the origin of a rectangular coordinate system, where the three axes represent the X, Y, and Z components of the crack vector. We shall call these components a_x, a_y and a_z respectively.

Each crack vector is completely defined by the coordinates of its end point (the arrowhead of the vector). We can therefore speak of these **points,** instead of the vectors themselves, and describe our problem as that of determining the way in which these representative points are distributed in the **crack space.**

Limitations are imposed on the permissible smallness of a volume element in crack space. The element must be large enough to contain a large number of representative points, but small in comparison with the total range of crack lengths. We wish to describe the crack distribution by a **continuous function** of crack length, whereas the actual distribution, since there are only finite number of cracks, is necessarily **discontinuous.** The DF that we will obtain, then, cannot be expected to give correct results if applied to a volume element that contains only a small number of representative points.

dN_{a_X} represents the number of cracks with X lengths component between some arbitrary value a_x and a slightly larger value a_x+da_x. This number depends on the length of the cracks considerd, that is, it will be some function of a_x. The function of a_x is unknown at this point (the derivation of the form of the function is precisely our problem), so all we can do for the present is to write it as $f(a_x)$. Thus, we let -

$$dN_{a_X}=Nf(a_x)da_x \tag{2}$$

Taking this line and going further, we derive the expression for the number of cracks simultaneously having X-components of length between a_x and a_x+da_x, Y-components of length between a_y and a_y+da_y, and Z-components of length between a_z and a_z+da_z -

$$d^3N_{a_Xa_ya_z}=Nf(a_x)f(a_y)f(a_z)da_xda_yda_z \tag{3}$$

This is the number of representative points in a volume element $da_xda_yda_z$. The number of points **per** unit volume, or the "density" of points in crack space, which we shall denote as ρ, is -

$$\rho=\frac{d^3N_{a_Xa_ya_z}}{da_xda_yda_z}=Nf(a_x)f(a_y)f(a_z) \tag{4}$$

The change in density when a_x, a_y and a_z are changed by da_x, da_y, and da_z respectively, is -

$$d\rho=\frac{\partial\rho}{\partial a_x}da_x+\frac{\partial\rho}{\partial a_y}da_y+\frac{\partial\rho}{\partial a_z}da_z \tag{5}$$

Since the crack distribution is isotropic, the density is uniform in any spherical shell centered at the origin. If the changes da_x, da_y, and da_z are such that the second volume element lies in the same spherical shell as the first, then $d\rho=0$. Using the partial derivatives of eq. (4) and substituting it in eq. (5), we obtain -

$$\frac{f'(a_x)}{f(a_x)}da_x+\frac{f'(a_y)}{f(a_y)}da_y+\frac{f'(a_z)}{f(a_z)}da_z=0 \tag{6}$$

But if the second element does lie in the same spherical shell as the first one then -

$$a^2=a_x^2+a_y^2+a_z^2$$

and -

$$a_xda_x+a_yda_y+a_zda_z=0 \tag{7}$$

Using the method of **undetermined multipliers,** known as **Lagrange multipliers,** we multiply equation (7) by a constant λ whose value we shall determine later (λ is then our undetermined multiplier) and add the resulting equation to eq. (6). This gives-

$$\left(\frac{f'(a_x)}{f(a_x)}+\lambda a_x\right)da_x+\left(\frac{f'(a_y)}{f(a_y)}+\lambda a_y\right)da_y+$$

$$\left(\frac{f'(a_z)}{f(a_z)}+\lambda a_z\right)da_z=0 \quad (8)$$

Since da_x, da_y, and da_z are independent, the coefficient of each must vanish. Solving for f we get –

$$f(a)=\alpha e^{-\frac{\lambda a^2}{2}} \quad (9)$$

After some algebraic manipulation, we find that the number of points per unit volume in crack space is –

$$\rho(a)=\frac{d^3Na_xa_ya_z}{da_xda_yda_z}=N\alpha^3e^{-\beta^2a^2} \quad (10)$$

Where – $\beta^2\equiv\frac{\lambda}{2}$

The quantity $\rho(a)$ is the **Maxwell–Boltzman crack distribution function** and is described (qualitatively) in fig. 1.

The constants α and β are evaluated using two integral expressions for the total number of cracks and for the average representative crack.

$$N=4N\int_{a=0}^{a=\infty}\int_{\phi=0}^{\phi=\frac{\pi}{2}}\int_{\theta=0}^{\theta=\frac{\pi}{2}}N\alpha^3e^{-\beta^2a^2}a^2\sin\theta\, da\, d\phi\, d\theta \quad (11)$$

$$\bar{a}=\frac{4N\int_{a=0}^{a=\infty}\int_{\phi=0}^{\phi=\frac{\pi}{2}}\int_{\theta=0}^{\theta=\frac{\pi}{2}}N\alpha^3e^{-\beta^2a^2}a^3\sin\theta\, da\, d\phi\, d\theta}{N} \quad (12)$$

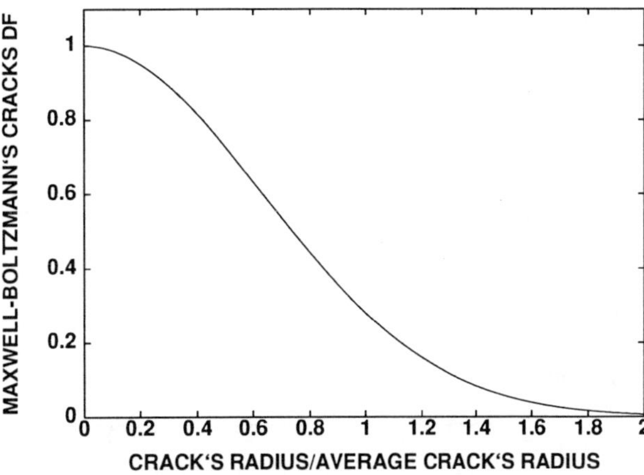

Fig. 1:Maxwell–Boltzmann's cracks DF

Thus we get the expressions for α and β –

$$\alpha^3=\frac{16}{(\pi\bar{a})^3} \text{ and – } \beta^2=\frac{4}{\pi\bar{a}^2}$$

The density, or Boltzman crack distribution function is –

$$\rho(a)=N\frac{16}{(\pi\bar{a})^3}e^{-\frac{4}{\pi}\left(\frac{a}{\bar{a}}\right)^2} \quad (13)$$

In Fig. 2 the size distribution of flaws in Arkansas novaculite is shown. The curve is the calculated distribution function and the dots are experimental measurements[5].

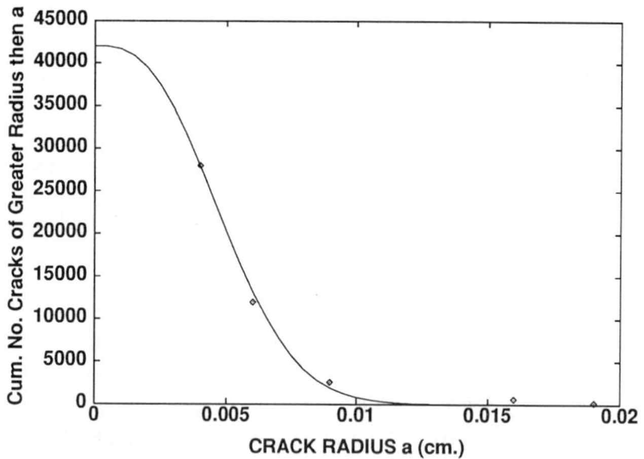

Fig. 2: Size distribution of flaws in Arkansas novaculite

An example for using the DF in Micro-Mechanical Models is the case of Damage Evolution. A volume element in the model is considered failed only if its volume fraction reaches some critical value -

$$\gamma = \int_{\Omega}\int_0^a \rho(a)a^3 da d\Omega \geq 0.6 \tag{14}$$

The integration includes all open cracks, to sum their contribution to the overall crack's volume.

SUMMARY

In this work we have derived, using first principle assumptions, an expression for crack distribution in a solid. This DF can be used in any calculation, where there is a need for the form of flaws distribution, i.e. while calculating Elastic moduli degradation or crack's volume fraction for failure criteria.

REFERENCES

[1] Weibull W., "A Statistical Distribution of Wide Applicability".J. of Appl. Mech., 18, PP. 293-296. 1951.

[2] Grady D. E. and Kipp M. E., "Continuum Modeling of Explosive Fracture in Oil Shale". Int. J. Rock. Mech., Min. Sci. Geomech. Abstr., 17, PP. 147-157. 1980.

[3] Shockey D. A., Curran D. R., Seaman L., Rosenberg J. T. and Peterson C. F., "Fragmentation of Rock under Dynamic Loads". Int. J. Rock Mech. Sci. & Geomech. Abstr., Vol. 11, PP. 303-317. 1974.

[4] Sears W. F., "An Introduction to Thermodynamics, the Kinetic Theory of Gases, and Statistical Mechanics". Addison-Wesley Publishing Co., Cambridge 42, Mass. 1955.

[5] Seaman L., Curran D. R. and Shockey D. A., "Computational Model for Ductile and Brittle Fracture". J. Appl. Phys., 47, PP. 4814-4826. 1976.

A COMPUTER MODEL FOR THE EVOLUTION OF IMPACT DAMAGE IN BRITTLE MATERIALS

S. Shimamura
Department of Applied Science, Faculty of Engineering
Yamaguchi University
Ube 755, Japan

Model simulations have been carried out to explore the evolution of impact damage in brittle materials. Crack growth is modeled as processes of strain energy dissipation using a cubic lattice system. By supplying a large energy to the center of the system surface, the evolution of cracks initiated by this impact shock is pursued. The results of the simulations reveal a characteristic difference in the pattern of impact cracks. The system with a spatially fluctuating distribution of strain energy is resistant to an impact shock. The system with a relatively uniform distribution shows a deep penetration of impact cracks. The evolution of impact damage is discussed in connection with the resistibility of brittle materials to an impact shock.

INTRODUCTION

The resistance of a material to an impact shock is one of the most important characteristics of the material. Since the response of a solid to an impact shock involves complicated processes, a number of investigations on this subject have been described in the literature [1,2]. However the global evaluation of impact damage has hardly been explored to date. Information of this type is required for the foreknowledge of impact fracture of various materials. The main purpose of this paper is to show that a computer model is useful for the global evaluation of the resistibility of a material to an impact shock.

Studies of fracture based on simple models have received considerable interest in recent years from a fundamental point of view [3–5]. There have been several studies of the spatial pattern of cracks reported in the literature [6–9]. The present author has developed a lattice model in order to explore the crack pattern [10,11]. There has also been some information on the crack pattern from experiments, especially from thermal shock experiments [12,13].

In this paper I will show the results of model simulations of crack growth in impact fracture of brittle materials. The model simulations are based on a series of dissipation processes of strain energy. The results of the simulations will reveal that the spatial features of impact cracks and the energy release caused by an impact have a close relation to the characteristics of strain energy distribution.

MODEL SIMULATION

Crack growth can be regarded as dissipation processes of stored strain energy; cracking involves release and spatial transfer of strain energy. From this point of view, we developed a lattice model for crack growth and carried out computer simulations [10,11]. The outline of the model for crack growth is as in the following. We consider a cubic lattice system; a cube is called the grain which is a spatial unit for a series of processes of strain energy in the system. If the strain energies of adjacent two grains, say the ith and jth grains, satisfy the condition, $E_i \times E_j \geq E_t^2$, we generate a crack on the boundary of the two grains, as shown in Fig. 1. Here E_t is a threshold energy for cracking. After the cracking, the strain energies of the two grains both reduce to zero, and an energy, E_r, is released from the system. The rest of strain energies, $E_i + E_j - E_r$, is transferred equally to four grains at the crack tips, as shown in Fig. 1. The crack extends if grains at the crack tips satisfy the cracking condition a a result of this transfer process. Once a crack is generated in the surface layer, the energy transfer is carried out for grains beneath the surface layer, as shown in Fig. 1. Thus a crack can penetrate in the direction perpendicular to the surface.

Computer simulations of impact fracture in the cubic lattice system are carried out through two steps: the random storage of strain energy and the supply of impact energy. First we prepare several systems having different distributions of strain energy by storing strain energy prior to an impact shock. We select a grain in the surface lattice layer at random and give a *strain energy*, ΔE. By repeating this process, we store strain energies

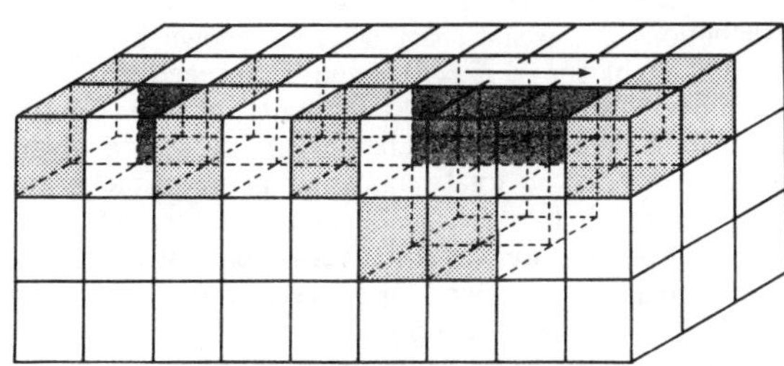

Figure 1. Crack growth and transfer of strain energy in the cubic lattice system.

in grains in the system. If the cracking condition is satisfied during this process, a crack initiates and grows. As we proceed the storage process, the system settles into a stationary state in which the magnitude distribution of strain energies of grains in the system is almost invarient [10]. We have prepared several systems with different characteristics of strain energy distribution by using different values for ΔE.

We next give an impact shock to the system in the stationary state. An *impact shock* is here regarded as a supply of a much larger energy, E_0, than E_t to a central grain of the system surface. We have pursued crack growth caused by this impact energy by carrying out the processes of energy release and transfer described above [14]. The supplied impact energy dissipates through energy release due to crackings and energy transfer, and impact cracks stop.

Simulations have been carried out for systems of 120 × 120 grains on the surface. The effect of the number of grains on the results of simulations was investigated; the characteristic features of crack pattern were not modified by adopting a larger-sized system of 256 × 256 grains. Periodic boundary conditions have been imposed on the sides of the system. We adopted E_t = 20 for the threshold energy, E_r = 1 for the release energy, and E_0 = 1,000 for the impact energy. As for the storage energy, different values have been used as ΔE = 0.5, 1, 2, 3, 4, 5. Since the stationary state is reached at $N_c \sim$ 6,000, where N_c is the number of crackings during the storage process [10], we have supplied the impact energy at this stage. Twenty runs of simulation have been carried out for each ΔE.

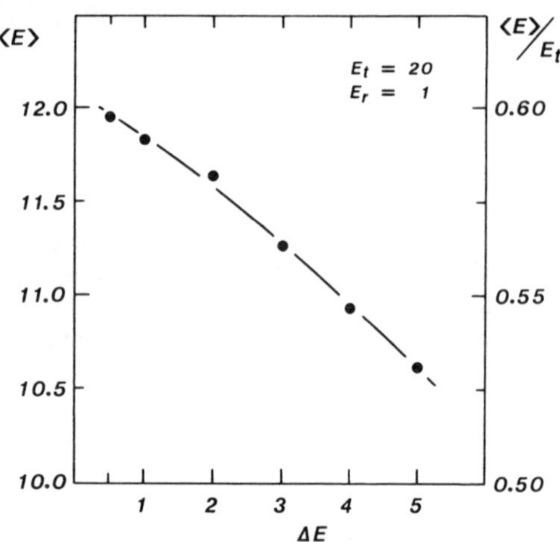

Figure 2. Dependence of the average strain energy per grain in the stationary state, $\langle E \rangle$, on the storage energy, ΔE, for E_t = 20 and E_r = 1. The points are the values averaged over twenty runs of simulation and the line is a guide to the eye.

RESULTS AND DISCUSSION

We first see the features of the system in the stationary state. Figure 2 shows the dependence of the average strain energy per grain, $\langle E \rangle$, in the system on the storage energy, ΔE. The average energy decreases with increasing ΔE. As a result of the storage process and the release and transfer processes due to crackings, the system with a large unit of storage energy is stabilized into a stationary state with a small average strain energy per grain.

Typical patterns of cracks and the strain energy distributions in the stationary state are shown in Figs. 3 (a) and 3 (b) for ΔE = 0.5 and 5, respectively. The magnitude distribution in lower parts of the figures denotes the rate of the number of grains with a given strain energy to the total number of grains. Cracks are relatively rough for ΔE = 0.5 and fine for ΔE = 5. These results are qualitatively consistent with experimental observations [12] of thermal shock–induced cracking, as discussed in a previous paper [11].

The features of crack pattern are associated with the characteristics of strain energy distribution. The system for ΔE = 0.5 has a distribution concentrated around the average strain energy per grain, while the distribution of the system for ΔE = 5 is considerably fluctuating. These characteristics influence the pattern of cracks caused by an impact shock, as seen below. For comparison we have prepared a special system as shown in Fig. 3 (c), in which all grains have the same strain energy as the average strain energy in the system in Fig. 3 (a); in this case there is no cracks prior to an impact shock.

Cracks caused by an impact shock on the systems in Figs. 3 (a), 3 (b) and 3 (c) are shown in Figs. 4 (a), 4 (b) and 4 (c), respectively. The upper parts in the figures show impact cracks on the surface, and the lower parts, the cross–sectional views perpendicular to the surface; only cracks caused by the impact shock are shown on the surface. Impact cracks for ΔE = 0.5 extend considerably on the surface and penetrate deeply into the interior. Impact cracks for ΔE = 5 are limited around an impact point on the surface and its penetration is shallow relatively. In the case of spatially uniform distribution of strain energy in Fig. 4 (c), the pattern of impact cracks is only a straight line; an impact shock results in the extension of an initial crack and a deep penetration. Thus the features of impact cracks reflect the characteristics of strain energy distribution.

The dependence of the penetration depth of impact cracks on ΔE is shown in Fig. 5. As ΔE increases, the penetration depth becomes shallow. This is a consequence of the fact that a larger ΔE leads to a stationary state with a smaller average strain energy, as shown in Fig. 2, and that the distribution of strain energies of grains is more fluctuating. The fluctuation of strain energies among grains is favorable for obstructing crack extension.

The energy released by impact cracks depends on ΔE through the characteristics of strain energy distribution. We here define the energy release rate as $(E_{after} - E_{before})/E_0$, where E_{before} and E_{after} is the total strain energy of the system before and after an

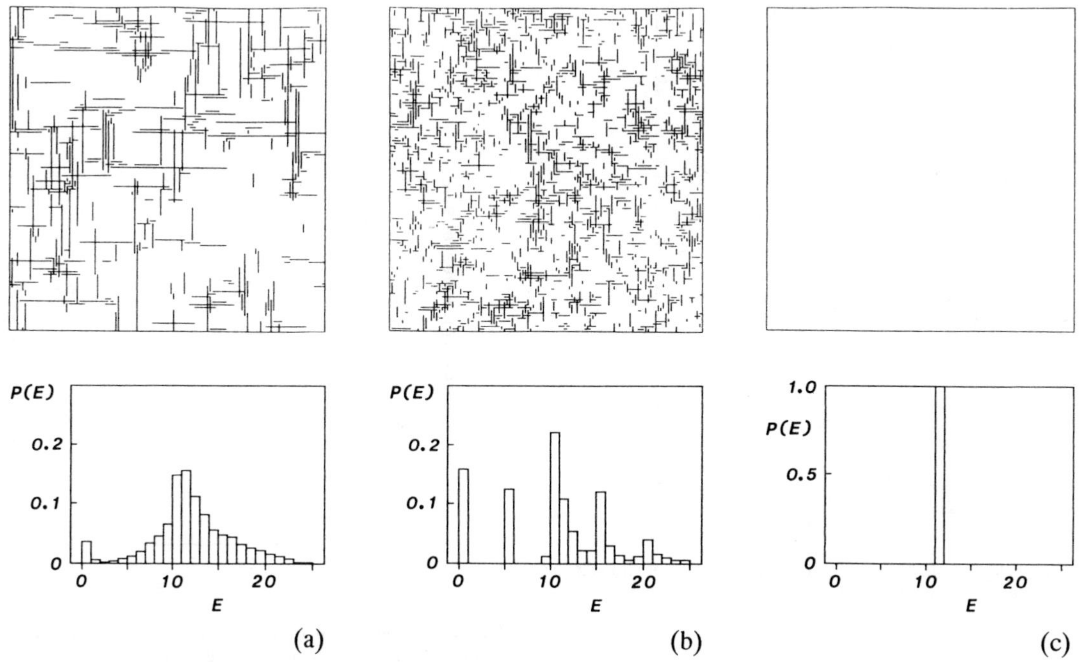

Figure 3. Surface cracks and magnitude distribution of strain energies of grains in the stationary state for $E_r = 1$: (a) $\Delta E = 0.5$; (b) $\Delta E = 5$; (c) a case in which all grains have the same strain energy.

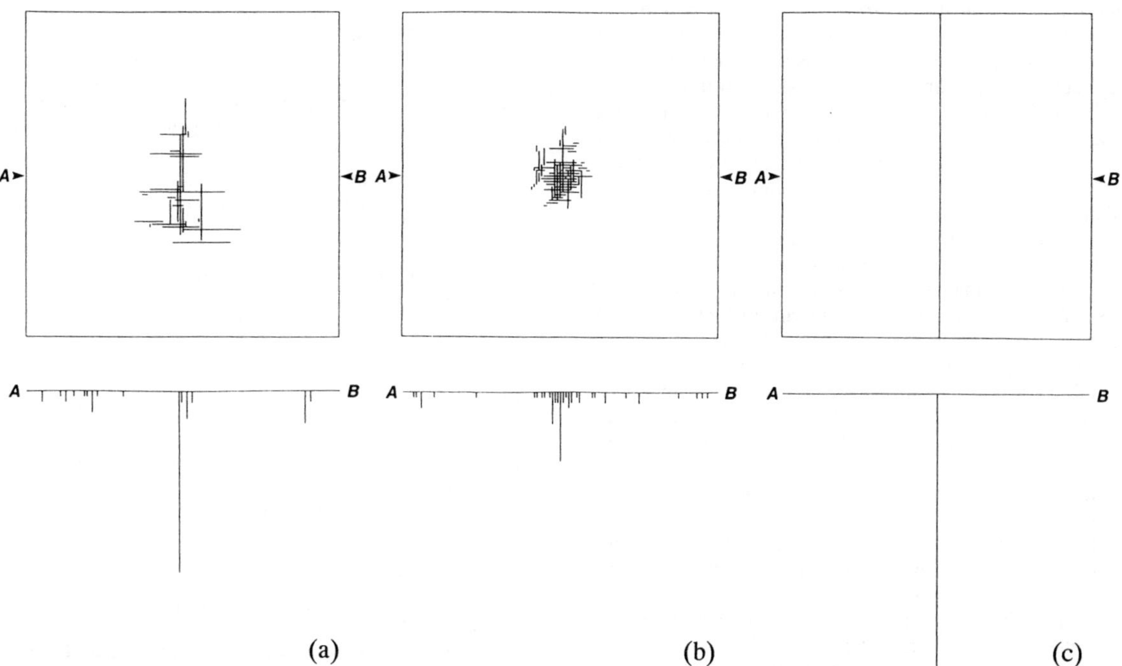

Figure 4. Impact cracks on the surface and crack penetration under $E_0 = 1{,}000$ for the systems in Fig. 3: (a) $\Delta E = 0.5$; (b) $\Delta E = 5$; (c) a case in which all grains have the same strain energy.

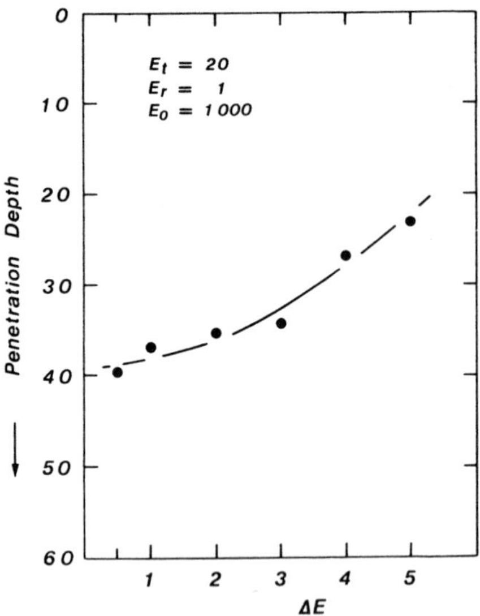

Figure 5. Dependence of the penetration depth of impact cracks on the storage energy, ΔE.

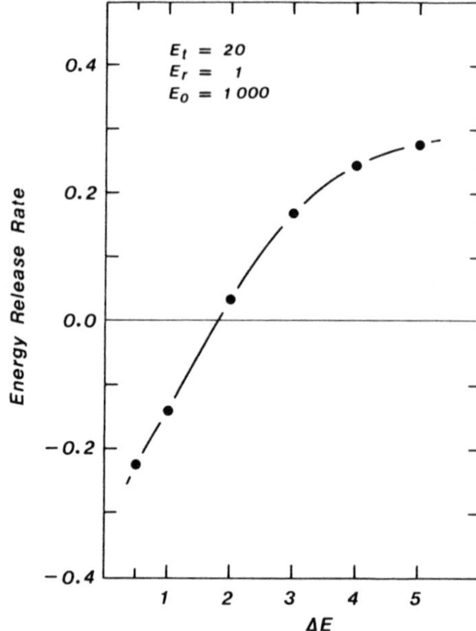

Figure 6. Dependence of the energy release rate due to an impact shock on the storage energy, ΔE.

impact shock, respectively. Then if the energy release rate has a minus sign, the system releases more energy than the impact energy. Figure 6 shows the dependence of the energy release rate on ΔE. As ΔE decreases, the energy release rate changes its sign from plus to minus. Therefore a system for a small ΔE releases part of the strain energy stored prior to an impact shock by the impact shock as a trigger. This is also revealed by a deep penetration of impact cracks, as shown in Fig. 4 (a).

From the present results of simulations, we can make some suggestions on the evolution of impact damage in brittle materials. Various materials are often exposed to a random environment such as irradiation of particles which generates strain energies at random on the surface of the materials [9]. This situation corresponds to the storage process in the present model simulations. Therefore the simulations give us information on the resistibility of those materials to an impact shock. A material which was exposed to intense irradiation corresponding to a large ΔE is expected to show limited damage due to an impact shock. An impact shock on a material which was exposed to weak irradiation for a long time will do severe damage with a danger of fragmentation. Thus the present simulations have some implications in foreknowing the evolution of impact damage.

In conclusion we have carried out model simulations of impact fracture using a lattice model based on energy dissipation of crack growth. The features of impact crack pattern and the energy released by an impact shock are dominated by the characteristics of strain energy distribution prior to the impact shock. The simulations have given us some useful information on the evolution of impact damage in brittle materials.

REFERENCES

[1] S. C. Schmidt, R. D. Dick, J. W. Forbes, and D. G. Tasker (eds.), *Shock Compression of Condensed Matter – 1991*, Amsterdam: North- Holland, 1992.

[2] R. A. Graham, *Solids Under High-Pressure Shock Compression*, New York: Springer-Verlag, 1992.

[3] R. Thomson, in H. Ehrenreich and D. Turnbull (eds.), *Solid State Physics, Vol. 39*, Orlando: Academic Press, 1986, pp. 1–129.

[4] H. J. Herrmann and S. Roux (eds.), *Statistical Models for the Fracture of Disordered Media*, Amsterdam: North-Holland, 1990.

[5] J. C. Charmet, S. Roux, and E. Guyon (eds.), *Disorder and Fracture*, New York: Plenum Press, 1990.

[6] P. Meakin, G. Li, L. M. Sander, E. Louis, and F. Guinea, *J. Phys. A* 22, pp. 1393–1403 (1989).

[7] Y. Mori, K. Kaneko, and M. Wadati, *J. Phys. Soc. Jpn.* 60, pp. 1591–1599 (1991).

[8] S. Aratani and H. Ojima, in K. Takayama (ed.), *Shock Waves, Vol. II*, Berlin: Springer-Verlag, 1992, pp. 1277–1282.

[9] J. Kameda and X. Mao, *J. Mater. Sci.* 27, pp. 983–989 (1992).

[10] S. Shimamura and K. Kuriyama, *J. Mater. Sci.* 26, pp. 6027–6034 (1991).

[11] S. Shimamura and Y. Sotoike, *J. Mater. Res.* 7, pp. 1286–1291 (1992).

[12] V. N. Gurarie and J. S. Williams, *J. Mater. Res.* 5, pp. 1257–1265 (1990).

[13] E. H. Lutz, M. V. Swain, and N. Claussen, *J. Am. Ceram. Soc.* 74, pp. 19–24 (1991).

[14] S. Shimamura and Kazuto Yamamoto, submitted for publication in *J. Mater. Res.*.

INSTABILITY OF PLASTIC FLOW AT DYNAMIC PORE COLLAPSE

V.F. Nesterenko, M.P. Bondar', I.V. Ershov
Lavrentyev Institute of Hydrodynamics
Lavrentyev Avenue, 15
Novosibirsk, Russia, 630090

It has been found experimentally that the high-rate plastic deformation is localized close to the internal area of the collapsing cylindrical pore developing in crack formation under radial strain ε_r from 30% to 100% and its rate $\dot{\varepsilon}_r = 10^4 \div 10^5 sec^{-1}$ in metals and polymers. At critical values of initial grain sizes the shear localization process may lose the features unique for a crystalline structure and becomes analogous to the process in "liquid-like" polymers.

INTRODUCTION

Shear localization due to plastic deformation instability is of significant scientific interest beacuse it determines the material behavior under intense loading. But the detailed mechanism of its formation has not been revealed yet, as well as its dependence on the nature and structural parameters of a medium, which does not allow to control and manage it.

In this paper the investigation results on the instability of a high-velocity pore collapse in a number of qualitatively different materials (copper M1 with different grain sizes, stainless steel X18H9T, Aluminum, Niobium and Teflon) at strain rates 10^{4}-10^{5} sec^{-1} are presented.

EXPERIMENT

The "thick-walled cylinder" method [1, 2] is used in this research, where cylindrical pore collapse results from the action of detonation products on the outer surface of a thick-walled hollow cylinder. The direction of detonation is parallel to cylinder axis. Its wall thickness (10 mm for Cu), inner diameter (10÷11 mm), explosive parameters (density 1 g/cm^3, detonation velocity 4000 m/sec) and sizes (outer diameter (60÷62 mm) were thoroughly selected to approach the complete pore collapse in the vicinity of jet formation in order to preserve the material near the inner surface. The length of cylinders was 70 mm. To provide stationary detonation regime the steel plugs of the same length and diameters were jointed to their both ends. All the assembly was placed in a thin-walled copper tube.

The following materials were chosen for the experiments: copper M1 with different grain sizes d~1000, 100, 30 μm, Aluminum (d~1000 μm), stainless steel X18H10T (d~10 μm), Niobium (d~1000 μm) and Teflon (no grains). The copper cylinder with d~100μm, outer diameter 30÷37 mm was used as a basic cylinder and the cylinders of other materials of less outer diameters were inserted in it.

For the analysis of final structure the cylinders were cutted in the middle in perpendicular to the axis. Cylindrical geometry allows to calculate material strain at a continual level on the basis of initial and final radii provided that a medium is incompressible and to determine strain rates range by measuring the internal surface velocity $V(t)$ up to the beginning of plastic flow instability [1,2].

Internal surface velocity $V(t)$ and the time of collapse were measured by noncontact electromagnetic method (Fig. 1, a). For this purpose the modified assembly was placed in magnetic field (B_0=414 Gs) with the miniature gauge (radius 1 mm) inside the pore.

The typical example of experimental dependence of electric signal from the gauge upon the time is represented in Fig. 1, b.

In the experiments with copper the initial jump of velocity V_0=200 m/sec, the time of pore collapse was 8 μsec.

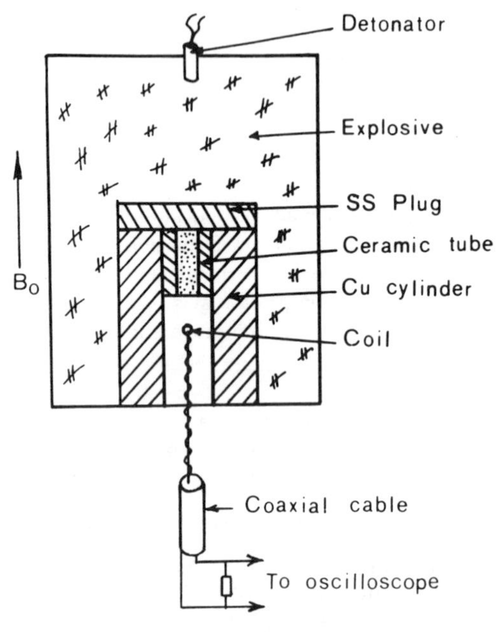

a

b

Fig. 1. The diagram of the experiments on velocity measurement (a) and typical oscillogram (b), the oscillogram scales: 0.05 V/div, 5 μs/div.

It results in initial strain rate on the pore surface $\dot{\varepsilon}_r \sim 0.4 \cdot 10^5 \text{sec}^{-1}$ and mean strain rate $1.3 \cdot 10^5$ sec^{-1} for collapse process for the point with ε_r=100%. The latter is close to the strain rate on pore surface at the moment when ε_r=100% on it. Because in all experiments the relation of explosive mass to the mass of composite cylinder was constant and equal to corresponding value for basic experiment with copper, we consider that strain rates for all materials were in the range $10^4 \div 10^5$ sec^{-1}. Among other studies on shear localization in copper with $\dot{\varepsilon}$ close to our data the works [3, 4] may be cited.

EXPERIMENTAL RESULTS

Presented in Figs. 2, 3, 4 is the final structure of the materials in the vicinity of the cylinder center.

a

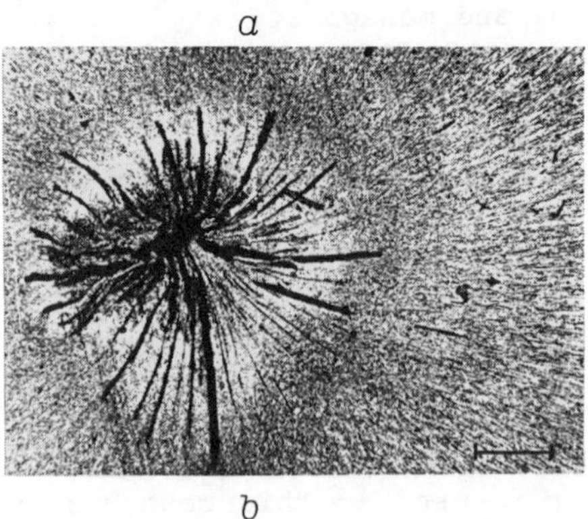

b

Fig. 2. Copper: a - initial grain size ~100 μm, scale 400 μm; b - initial grain size ~30 μm, scale 200 μm.

Fig. 3. Niobium: initial grain size ~1000 μm; scale 600 μm.

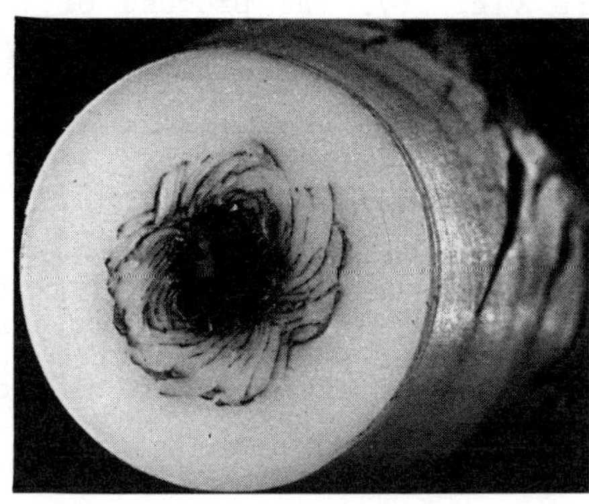

Fig. 4. Teflon, outer sample diameter 25 mm.

The material behavior is characterized by the following peculiarities:

1. The process of cylindrical pore collapse is accompanied by localization of plastic deformation which develops in some cases into spiral system of cracks near the center for all tested materials. The qualitative similarity of the behavior of copper (Fig. 2) and Teflon (Fig. 4) is surprising.

2. There are qualitatively different shear bands: in one of the them the zone of localized plastic flow develops into crack (Fig. 2, a; Fig. 3), in the other - the chain of local pore-cracks turns into continuous crack (Fig. 2, b; Fig. 4).

3. The values of continual deformation near the localized bands heads preceding (on deformation value) to crack formation for Cu are ε_r=30% (d~1000 μm) and 100% (d~100 μm). Calculation of ε_r for Teflon, corresponding to the beginning of crack formation (assuming Teflon to be incompressible and pore closure in collapse process to be complete) gives $\varepsilon_r \approx 40\%$.

4. The differing picture of relative arrangement for shear bands is obtained: for Teflon oncoming bands are observed (Fig. 4), while for metals they were not noticed (Fig. 2, 3).

5. The number of shear bands (or cracks) in the same collapse geometry was: for Cu (d~1000μm) - 30,(d~100μm) - 30, (d~30 μm) - 50, Al (d~1000 μm) - 20, Teflon - 50. For row-grained Nb and Cu shear bands failed to develop into symmetrical picture of cracks (Fig. 3), [2].

Thus, condensed materials with different structure and properties undergo peculiar compulsory structurization on macroscale in the collapse process. It indicates that it is this process and not a phase transitions [5] that will result in a loss of symmetrical character of collapse of any condensed medium.

It is interesting that the decrease of grain size in copper is accompanied with spiral-wise crack formation [1], Fig. 2, b, which qualitatively corresponds to the similar picture for "liquid-like" Teflon (Fig. 4). This fact gives a new turn to a hypothesis on a "liquid-like" state of metals in cumulation process [6]. The hypothesis postulates the uniform flow of medium as in a liquid under normal conditions. But it is well known that it is the liquid structure that provides its instability to high-rate shear localization. In a sense Fig. 2, b clearly demonstrates a "liquid-like" behavior of this type of copper at $\dot{\varepsilon}_r = 10^4 \cdot 10^5$ sec^{-1}, but this results in very non-uniform flow. This rises a new problem in medium description with newly arised elements with the scales far from interatomic ones, or even from grain sizes, after its structurization of shear bands, or even cracks. The grain size decreasing in Cu transforms its behavior to the "liquid-like" one, but, however, does not avoid the shear localization, only retarding their start to larger values of ε_r, paying for that by rapid crack formation afterwards.

The observed similarity of shear localization (Fig. 2, b; Fig. 4) in such qualitatively different materials as fine-grained copper and Teflon indicates the existence of general criterion for selecting this newly arising medium structure among other possible variants. As the criterion the achievement of minimum collapse time as compared with other ways of closure may be proposed. A loss of shear strength in localization bands will accelerate the collapse process as a movement of non-deformable segments, but a great number of them will enhance the vortex character of this process and retard the closure. On this basis it is possible to derive the optimal number of shear zones.

The change of localization process and subsequent crack formation with the increase of grain size in copper [2], and analogous picture in Nb (Fig. 3) testify the essential role of crystalline structure in these conditions of collapse at large grain sizes. The similarity of row-grained Cu and Nb despite of their difference in the heat conductivities, type of lattice and sliding systems is worthy of notice. The transformation of shear zones in Cu with the increase of grain size from ~30 to ~1000 μm testifies the fact that in investigated region of $\dot{\varepsilon}$ the relation of deformation processes on micro and meso levels is of major importance. The origin of shear localization in row-grained copper (d_0~1000 μm) at $\varepsilon_r \simeq 30\%$ evindences the translation instability development. Its structural characteristics are the channels of plastic flow which result from collective dislocation movement. This type of shear localization develops at absence of structural elements of rotational deformation modes [7] or, at high rate deformation, where they can be "frozen". The grain size decrease facilitates the origin of such elements. Therefore the translation-rotational processes of deformation inside the grains on mesolevel promotes the uniform plastic deformation, which retards shear localization to larger ε_r. The final structure to great extent depends on switching on the processes on mesolevel. For example, the mean grain size in Cu (d_0~30 μm) at ρ=7 mm failed to exceed 22 μm, but at $\rho \simeq 0.7$ mm the ultrafine structure may be observed.

Collective nature of shear bands in copper (Fig. 2) as opposed to Teflon (Fig. 4) should be mentioned. This difference (absence and existence of oncoming shear band cracks) may testify the different kinetics of shear development - "relay-race" type in the first case and more or less independent of each other in the second case owing to relatively larger energy of elastic deformation in teflon.

CONCLUSIONS

Thus, the instability of high-rate cylindrical pore collapse in relation to shear localization which develops in some cases into spiral bands (cracks) has been demonstrated for qualitatively different materials. Variation of initial material structure allows, to a certain extent, to manage this process. The observed shear localization at pore collapse arises the problem of correctness a lot of attempts to design, on the basis of uniform viscoelastic flow in pore vicinity, the process of nonequilibrium heating and reaction start at impulse loading of heterogeneous media.

ACKNOWLEDGEMENTS

The authors are grateful to the International Science Foundation for the partial support of their research and to J. Shaner and ISF for the support that made feasible our participation in the AIRAPT/APS conference.

REFERENCES

[1]. V.F. Nesterenko, A.N. Lazaridi, S.A. Pershin. "Localization of deformation in copper by explosion compression of hollow cylinders," *Fizika Goreniya i Vzryva*, V. 25, No. 4 (1989), pp. 154-155.

[2]. M.P. Bondar', V.F. Nesterenko. "Strain correlation at different structural levels for dynamically loaded hollow copper cylinders", *Journal de Physique IV*, V., 1 (1991), pp. C2-163-C3-170.

[3]. S.N. Chang, S. Nemat-Nasser. "Compression-induced high-strain- rate void collapse," In *Shock-wave and high-strain-rate phenomena in materials*, Ed. M.A. Mayers, L.E. Murr, K.P. Staudhammer, Marcel Dekker Inc., 1992, pp. 783-791.

[4]. M.A. Meyers, L.W. Meyer, J. Beatty, V. Andrade, K.S. Vecchio, A.N. Chokshi. "High Strain, High-strain-rate deformation of Copper," in *Shock-wave and high-strain-rate phenomena in materials*, Ed. M.A. Meyers, L.E. Murr, K.P. Staudhammer, Marcel Dekker, Inc., 1992, pp. 529-542.

[5]. E.I. Zababakhin, I.E. Zababakhin, *Phenomena of unrestricted cumulation*, Moscow, Nauka Press, 1988.

[6]. M.A. Lavrentyev, "Cumulative charge and principles of its work", *Uspekhi matematicheskikh nauk*, V. 12, No. 4 (1957),pp. 41-52.

[7]. V.V. Rybin, *Large plastic strains and metal fracture*, Moscow Metallurgija Press, 1986.

DISLOCATION DYNAMICS BEHIND SHOCK FRONT

E.ZARETSKY

Pearlston Center for Aeronautical Engineering Studies, Department of Mechanical Engineering, Ben-Gurion University of the Negev, P.O.Box 653, Beer-Sheva, 84105, Israel.

A new model of stress relaxation based on multiplication and motion of partial dislocations bounding the stacking fault is suggested. High shear stress values leads to stretching of lateral branches of bowed out dislocation segment (half - loop) followed by collapse of those branches. The result of the collapse is the forming of the "fresh" partial dislocation loop bounding the stacking fault area and "initial" dislocation half - loop, both being capable of the next multiplication act. After every collapse time interval ΔT the process leads to the doubling of both the dislocation concentration and stacking faults total area. The time dependence of strain rate has the form $d\varepsilon/dt \sim 2^{t/\Delta T}$. An explanation of twinning, shear bands formation in shocked material and voids nucleation in rarefaction wave is proposed.

INTRODUCTION

Microscopic description of high strain rate plastic deformation needs a high productive dislocation source. However, existing models of such sources need either high initial mobile dislocation density, [1] - [4], or dislocation density surplus in post-shocked material, [5] - [7].

In recent experimental study of pulse X-ray diffraction patterns of shock compressed materials, [8], it was shown that almost all shear deformation in shocked crystal solids is concentrated in stacking faults (SF) . A single SF is a two - dimensional defect of crystal lattice which is a plane region of two atomic layers of alienated structure in maternal lattice, e.g. hexagonal packed (h.p.) bi-layer in face centered cubic (f.c.c.) lattice. The SF region is bounded by partial dislocations with Burgers vectors less than that of perfect dislocation. In particular, in f.c.c. lattice with period a a dislocation of plane (111) with Burgers vector $\frac{a}{2}[\bar{1}10]$ being unstable, dissociates in two partial dislocations with SF between them according to the reaction, [9],

$$\frac{a}{2}[\bar{1}10] = \frac{a}{6}[\bar{2}11] + \text{SF of width } r_0 + \frac{a}{6}[\bar{1}2\bar{1}]. \quad (1)$$

The separation of the partial dislocations r_0 (characterized by energy per square unit γ) can vary under shear stress acting in the SF plane and thus absorb an external stress energy. The formation of three SF in three adjacent lattice planes corresponds to the formation of a thin (three-atomic) twin layer, [9]. The metallography sections of post-shocked samples contain deformation twins, even for the materials, in which no twinning was found after usual deformation, [11].

The purpose of this paper is to present a model of rapid source of dislocations based on stacking faults (and, thus, the partials) evolution under applied shear stress which is both discribe the rate of dislocation generation and explain results of recovery studies of shock-compressed solids.

A PARTIAL DISLOCATION SEGMENT UNDER SHEAR STRESS

The equation of equilibrium of an arc length element ds of partial dislocation which bounds a stacking fault is (see Fig.1a) :

$$\tau b - \gamma - w(2\theta)\frac{d\theta}{ds} = 0, \quad (2)$$

where τb is the component of applied shear stress (in a dislocation glide plane) which always normal to the arc element ds direction [9], b - is the Burgers vector of the partial, γ - is SF specific energy , $w(2\theta)$ - is the self-tension of the dislocation line, [9], θ - is the angle between dislocation Burgers vector and perfect dislocation line tangent, $\frac{d\theta}{ds}$ - is the bowed dislocation segment curvature. De Witt and Koehler, [12], showed that for complete dislocation (in Eqs.(2) $\gamma = 0$) the dislocation line self-tension w is anisotropic and may be presented as

$$w(2\theta) = E + \frac{d^2E}{d\theta^2}, \quad (3)$$

where E is the elastic energy per unit of dislocation length. Their analysis of elastic constants of different materials showed that the self-tension is essentially positive for any θ and thus the bowed-out dislocation line has always a curvature of unchangeable sign. The presence of SF coupled with dislocation changes the character of equilibrium in Eq.(2). The SF energy, from the viewpoint of interaction between the stacking fault and the partial dislocation is anisotropic and may be expressed as

$$\gamma = \gamma(2\theta) = \gamma_o \left(1 - \frac{2\nu}{2-\nu} \cos 2\theta \right), \tag{3a}$$

where ν is Poisson's ratio. From Eq.(2) (with SF energy $\gamma(2\theta)$ from Eq.(3)) it is possible to get some insight into the equilibrium shape of bowed-out partial dislocation for different values of shear stress τ.

For moderate shear stress ($\tau b < \gamma_i = \gamma_o \left(1 - \frac{2\nu}{2-\nu} \right)$) the increase of the stress τ magnitude leads to the stretching of bowed out segment without any change in the sign of curvature. If the value of τb approaches from below to γ_i the segment stretches strongly in the direction of its Burgers vector; the curvature of the dislocation lateral branches approaches to zero and the radius of curvature approaches to infinity (see Fig.1b). When τb value belongs to the interval

$$\gamma_o \left(1 - \frac{2\nu}{2-\nu}\right) < \tau b < \gamma_o \left(1 + \frac{2\nu}{2-\nu} \right), \tag{4}$$

regions of alternate sign of curvature are to appeare on the lateral branches of bowed-out dislocation (see Fig.1c). Finally in the case of high shear stress τ ($\tau b > \gamma_f = \gamma_o \left(1 + \frac{2\nu}{2-\nu} \right)$), the dislocation segment expands up to its equilibrium configuration, which does not contain regions of different curvature sign (see Fig.1d).

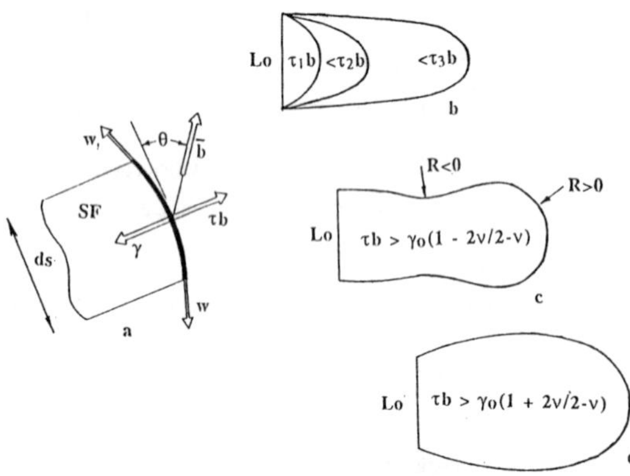

Figure 1. Equilibrium of an arc element of partial dislocation (a) and equilibrium shape of bowed-out partial dislocation segment for different values of acting shear stress (b - d).

MOTION AND MULTIPLICATION OF SF REGION

Eq.(2) describes only local equilibrium of the bowed-out dislocation element, and it is hardly possible, in general, to find explicit expression for the dislocation shape. The dislocation motion under applied shear stress which is accompanied with different type drag forces, makes the problem extremely complicated. To overcome the difficulties, we assume that a dislocation, which is bowing-out to its equilibrium state under high ($\tau b > \gamma_f$) shear stress, has to pass through the stages which are shown in Fig.1b. We will approximate the stretched dislocation segment as a long quasi-rectangular half-loop (see Fig.2a) of width Lo and length X. For a strongly stretched (Lo << X) segment the shape of the top of the half-loop is not essential, [9]. The self energy of the half-loop may be expressed as

$$W = w \left\{2X \left[1 + 2 \left(\frac{l}{X}\right)^2\right] + L_o \right\} + \\ + \gamma_o L_o X \left[1 - \frac{l}{L_o}\right], \tag{5}$$

where the first term in Eq.(5) is the energy of dislocation line self-tension and the second one is the energy of SF bounded by the dislocation line. Equating the self-energy variation to the variation of external stress work

$$\delta W_s = (\tau b - \gamma_i) L_o \delta X - (\gamma_f - \tau b)\, X\, \delta l, \tag{6}$$

gives (neglecting the terms of the first order in ($\delta l / \delta X$) and the terms with dislocation line self-energy w - the later is to be correct for the segments of initial size $L_o >> w/\gamma_o \sim 10 - 100$ å)

$$\frac{\delta l}{\delta X} = - \frac{\tau b - (\gamma_i + \gamma_o)}{\tau b - (\gamma_f - \gamma_o)} \frac{L_o}{X}. \tag{7}$$

Eq.(7) shows that for moderate values of shear stress τ ($\gamma_f - \gamma_o < \tau b < < \gamma_i + \gamma_o$) there is a tendency the stretched lateral branches of the dislocation half-loop with increasing loop length to approach one another ($\delta l/\delta X > 0$). This closing leads to the increase (proportional to $(L_o - l)^{-1}$) of attraction between the lateral branches (both of screw orientation but of alternate direction) and to further collapse of the branches with the formation of a "fresh" half-loop capable of reproduction. This new partial dislocation loop (bordering the SF area) also can be stretched by the applied shear stress, giving the origin to a new multiplication act (see Fig.2b)

To estimate the dislocation output rate of such a source, consider the motion of the top of rectangular half-loop ahead (stretching of the loop) and the lateral branches motion towards one another. Under the assumption of linear viscous drag and neglecting the dislocation mass,

$$B\frac{dX}{dt} = \tau b - \gamma_i \quad (8a)$$

$$B\frac{dl}{dt} = \gamma_f - \tau b\ , \quad (8b)$$

where B is the viscous drag coefficient (of about 10^{-4} Pa sec for a wide group of materials, [13]). For lateral dislocation branches collapse ($l = L_o/2$) Eqs. (8a) and (8b) give for "collapse time", "collapse distance" and "collapse area" (with a factor of 1/2 accuracy)

$$\Delta T = \frac{B\,L_o}{\gamma_f - \tau b}, \quad (9)$$

$$\Delta X = \frac{\tau b - \gamma_i}{\gamma_f - \tau b} L_o, \quad (10)$$

$$\Delta S = \frac{\tau b - \gamma_i}{\gamma_f - \tau b} L_o^2. \quad (10a)$$

Each time interval ΔT one can expect redoubling of each SF area ΔS, characterized by an energy $\gamma_o \Delta S$. Thus the energy dissipation rate per unit of moving dislocation length may be expressed

$$\frac{1}{L_o}\frac{dW}{dt} = \gamma_o \frac{\tau b - \gamma_i}{B}\, 2^{\,t(\gamma_f - \tau b)/ BL_o}\ , \quad (11)$$

The rate of creation of the dislocations in this process is (ρ is the dislocation density):

$$\frac{d\rho}{dt} = c_o \frac{\gamma_f - \gamma_i}{B\,(\gamma_i - \tau b)^2}\, 2^{\,1+t(\gamma_f - \tau b)/ BL_o}\ , \quad (12)$$

where c_o is the initial concentration of "active" dislocation segments. For intermediate ($\gamma_i < \tau b < \gamma_f$, $\tau b \sim \gamma_o$) shear stress τ values, for γ_o = 0.1 J/m^2 (e.g., 0.07 for Cu, 0.2 for Al) and for pinned dislocation segments of length Lo ≈ 1000å Eqs.(9) - (12) give: $\Delta T = 10^{-10}$ - 10^{-9} sec, $\Delta X = L_o$, $\Delta S = L_o^2$. The energy dissipation rate $\frac{1}{L_o}\frac{dW}{dt}$ higher than 1 W/m of dislocation line already at early stage of the multiplication process. For initial source concentration $c_o = 10^{15}$ m^{-3} (this value corresponds the initial "mobile" dislocations density $\rho_o = c_o L_o = 10^8$ m^{-2}), the dislocation generation rate $\frac{d\rho}{dt}$ reaches a value of about 10^{21} dislocations per m sec after 0.5 - 10 nsec from the beginning of multiplication (about ten multiplication acts).

Thus, the dislocation source acts much faster than well-known Frank - Read, [3], or multiple cross glide [4] sources. The SF source productivity is comparable with that of Coffey's grain boundary source, [14], however, the SF source has several advantages from the point of view of experimental results explanation.

SF'S MULTIPLICATION: TWINNING, SHEAR BANDS

Both the head part of half-loop and the tail part of the new loop (Fig.2b) are of edge type and have opposite direction. The repulsion force between them has a component normal to the glide plane, because Burgers vector of partial dislocations always has a slight climb component , [15]. The impossibility to continue the motion in the plane leads to the head part of the half-loop crossing to the next plane with the formation of a double-SF region (middle region in Fig.2c, Roman numerals mark the generation of the loop). The transmission electron microscope studies show a prevalence of overlapped stacking faults in post-shocked samples, [16], [17]. Continuing the multiplication process leads to creation of a faulted structure which is shown in Fig.2d (for six generations).

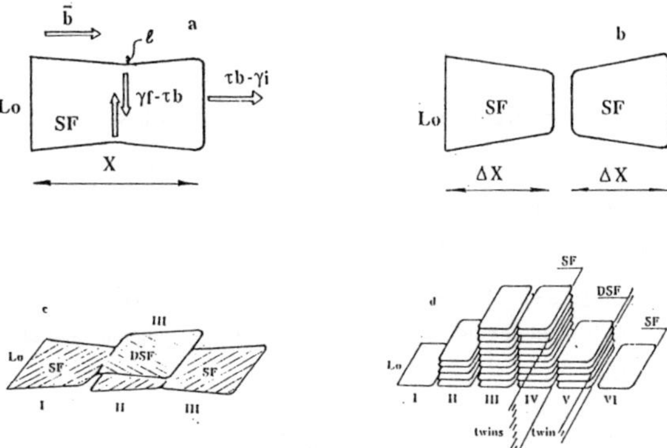

Figure 2. Stretching (a), collapse (b) and crossing with formation of double-stacking fault (c) of rectangular half-loop of partial dislocation. Twin lens formed by six generations of redoubled dislocation loops (d).

In the crystalline material undergoes a shock loading, it is always possible to find glide planes for which the shear stress value τ satisfies the inequalities (4) and where the pinned dislocation segments of length L_o < 1000 å are present. Triggering of the described source leads to the formation of twin lens or shear band.

If the source operates with dislocation creating rate of Eq.(12), the dislocation concentration will achieve the values of $\rho \approx 10^{15}$ - 10^{16}m^{-2} immediately behind the shock front (10 - 20 nsec). It is of one - two orders of magnitude higher than experimentally found (e.g., $\rho \approx 10^{14}$ - 10^{15}m^{-2} , [18]). In order to overcome such a discrepancy Meyers proposed a simultaneous generation of dislocations of opposite sign in his model of homogeneous dislocation generation, [5]. The present model needs not such an assumption. The created partial dislocation loops have lateral branches of screw type and of opposite direction (Fig.2a,b). If the shear stress acting in the loop glide plane releases or is inadequate for further multiplication and if the loop lateral branches are free (not arrested by interactions with dislocations of other slip planes), the SF bordered by the loop will tighten the loop and the lateral branches (attracted because of their screw character) will annihilate.

This dislocation generation in the form of SF packages may be a cause of material fracture in rarefaction wave. It is known that discs of vacancies under compression (or in the absence of external pressure) tend to collapse with creation of Frank partial dislocation loop (immobile because of Burgers vector normal to the loop plane), [9]. The Frank partial dislocation combines with the Shockley partial dislocation (dislocations of above discussed type) to form a perfect dislocation according to the reaction

$$\frac{a}{3}[\overline{1}\overline{1}\overline{1}] \text{ (Frank)} + \frac{a}{6}[\overline{1}2\overline{1}] \text{ (Shockley)} = \\ = \frac{a}{2}[\overline{1}0\overline{1}] \text{ (perfect)}. \qquad (13)$$

In a rarefaction wave in the presence of tension stress the reverse reaction is possible with Frank loop formation and further creation of vacancies disc in the (111) plane. Interaction of SF package (several Shockley partial dislocations of neighbor planes) would create a pillar of vacancies which may be considered as a nucleus of a void. A close mechanism of void formation was pointed by Chang and Nemat-Naser, [19].

CONCLUSION

A mechanism of dislocation generation (dislocation source) during shock deformation of metals is proposed. According to the model the bowed - out segment of partial dislocation (bounding a stacking fault area) begins to multiply when a shear stress τ in the glide plane falls within the bounds $\gamma_i < \tau b < \gamma_f$. In contrast with the other models the present one does not need any assumption of dislocations motion with near - sound velocity, [6], [7], simultaneous creation of opposite sign dislocations, [5], or existence of any string of impurities, [14]. In the same time, the model gives a realistic explanation of the formation of shear bands and twins (both in materials with comparatively high stacking fault energy, as materials with b.c.c. lattice, in which twining is not observed after usual loading but only after a shock deformation). It agrees with results of molecular dynamics modeling of Mogilevsky [20], which showed that stacking faults form spontaneously at early stages of high strain rate deformation. The lower limit of shear stress, ($\tau b = \gamma_f - \gamma_o$), required by source for its successive action, is close to material elastic limit, [21], (τ about 10^{-3} G, G is the material shear modulus) and significantly lower than a shear stress value which is required, according to the model [5], for homogeneous dislocation nucleation . Existence of the upper limit of shear stress required for successfull source operations, $\tau b = \gamma_o + \gamma_i$, possibly corroborates with significant increase of shear stress over the shock amplitude range of 10 - 20 GPa in aluminum 6061-T6, [22]. In this case the dislocation multiplication rate is not enough for providing proper deviatoric stress relaxation.

REFERENCES

1] J.N.Johnson, L.M.Barker, Journ. of Appl. Phys, 40, pp.4321-4334 (1969)

2] J.W.Taylor, Journ. of Appl. Phys,36, pp.3146-3150 (1965)

3] F.C.Frank, W.T.Read, Phys. Rev., 79, pp.722-723 (1950)

4] H.Wiedersich, Journ. of Appl. Phys, 33, pp.854-858 (1962)

5] M.A.Meyers, Scripta Metallurgica,12, pp.21-26 (1978)

6] C.S.Smith, Trans. AIME, 212, pp.574-576 (1958)

7] E.Hornbogen, Acta Metallurgica, 10, pp.978-980 (1962)

8] E.B.Zaretsky, G.I.Kanel', P.A.Mogilevsky, V.E.Fortov, High Temperature Physics , 29, 1002-1008 (1991)

9] J.P.Hirth and J.Lothe, Theory of Dislocations, McGraw-Hill, 1968, New-York

10] S.M.Copley, B.H.Kear, Acta Metallurgica, 16, pp.227 - 231 (1968)

11] J.N.Johnson, R.W.Rohde, Journ.Appl.Phys., 42, pp.4171-4182 (1971)

12] G.deWitt, J.S.Koehler, Phys.Rev.,116, pp.1113-1120 (1959)

13] J.Weerman, J.R.Weertman, in "Dislocations in Solids", v.3 "Moving Dislocations", ed. F.R.N.Nabarro, North-Holland Publishing Company, 1980.

14] C.S.Coffey, Journ.Appl.Phys., 66, pp.1654-1656 (1989)

15] S.Amelinckx, in "Dislocations in Solids", v.2 "Dislocations in Crystals", ed. F.R.N.Nabarro, North-Holland Publishing Company, 1980.

16] H.Fujita, S.Ueda, Acta Metallurgica, 20, pp.759-767 (1972)

17] S.Mahajan, in "Dislocation Modelling of Physical Systems", Eds. M.F.Ashby et al., Pergamon Press, 1981, 217-223.

18] L.E.Murr, D.Kulmann-Wilsdorf, Acta Metallurgica, 26, pp.847 - 857 (1978)

19] S.N.Chang, S.Nemat-Nasser, in:"Shock-Wave and High-Strain-Rate Phenomena in Materials, eds. M.A.Meyers, L.E.Murr, K.P.Staudhammer, Marcel Dekker Inc., 1992, 783-791

20] M.A.Mogilevsky, in "Shock waves and high strain rate phenomena in metals, 1981, Plenum Press, 531-542.

21] P.Jongenburger, Acta Metallurgica, 11, pp.992 - 994 (1963)

22] J.R.Asay, L.C.Chhabildas, in "Shock Waves and High-Strain-Rate Phenomena in Metals", eds. M.A.Meyers and L.E.Murr, Plenum Publishers, 1981, 417-431.

MICROSCOPIC PROCESSES OF PLASTIC DEFORMATION DURING SHOCK OR IMPACT

C.S. Coffey

Naval Surface Warfare Center
White Oak Laboratory
Silver Spring, MD 20903-5640

The movement of dislocations is analyzed as a quantum mechanical process in which the dislocations tunnel through the lattice potential barriers and transit into adjacent potential wells. For simple potential barriers, the predicted dislocation velocity and macroscopic plastic strain rate contain all of the essential features observed in shock and impact experiments.

INTRODUCTION

The creation and motion of dislocations are the major mechanisms by which crystalline solids undergo plastic deformation. However, it appears that the actual processes by which these lattice defects move through an otherwise defect free crystal during an applied shear stress have never been described in detail on a fundamental, quantum mechanical, level. Partly as a result of this, much of the description of the response of crystalline solids to shock or impact is dependent on empirical constitutive relations which often have very limited range of validity.

Here the movement of dislocations in an otherwise defect free crystalline solid is examined by observing that motion occurs when a dislocation core slips past the potential barrier that confines it to an initial lattice potential well and transits into an adjacent potential well. This is analyzed in terms of quantum mechanical tunneling and predictions are obtained for the dislocation velocity and the macroscopic plastic strain rate as functions of both the applied shear stress and temperature.

MOVEMENT OF DISLOCATIONS

An ideal edge dislocation consists of an extra half plane of atoms or molecules inserted in the regular crystal lattice array. The only distortion of the lattice occurs in the vicinity of the core of the dislocation where the extra half plane terminates. The core resides in a potential well formed by its interaction with the surrounding lattice and plastic deformation occurs when the core translates one atomic or molecular spacing in response to an applied shear force. This happens not by somehow forcing the extra half plane of the dislocation past its neighboring atoms or molecules, but by the easier process of moving and realigning the atoms/molecules adjacent to but on the opposite side of the slip plane from the extra half plane of the dislocation. The remaining portion of the plane of atoms/molecules that was immediately ahead of the initial dislocation now becomes the extra half plane of the edge dislocation.

Classically it is impossible to move the core of a dislocation out of its initial potential well and into an adjacent well when the energy of the core is less than the depth of the potential well. It is possible that thermal fluctuations could enable the dislocation to occasionally overcome the potential barrier and move into an adjacent well. However, while thermal processes are important, from an energy basis it is more likely that motion will occur by tunneling through the potential barrier allowing the dislocation to pass directly into the adjacent well.

To describe the tunneling process analytically consider the length of the dislocation to be composed of segments each one atom or molecule in length. Thus, an edge dislocation N atoms or molecules long will be made of N segments, each of which is bound to its adjacent segments by the lattice potential which serves to hold the dislocation together. Dislocation motion occurs when the core section of each segment tunnels through its adjacent potential barrier and transits into the adjacent potential well. The dislocation advances when all of its core segments have advanced into their adjoining potential wells. The lattice potential that maintains the dislocation also prevents the segments or kinks from advancing more than one atomic or molecular spacing ahead of their neighboring segments. This assumption is implicit in the conventional view of dislocation motion due to thermal processes. Otherwise the dislocation would rapidly break up into a collection of point defects and lose its identity.

The lattice distortion due to the termination of the extra half plane of the edge dislocation reduces the barriers of the potential well that the adjacent of atoms/molecules form with the core of the edge dislocation. Consider the simple case in which the core of the dislocation is confined in a shallow potential well established by two constant width potential barriers of depth U and Width W formed by the reduced potential of the distorted lattice. Later, this square barrier approximation will be replaced by a more realistic barrier. The remainder of the lattice has its normal inter atomic or inter molecular potentials.

Beginning with the Schrodinger equation for the quasi-particle dislocation core segment of mass m located in the well U, the probability, T, that the core segment will tunnel through the barrier along the slip plane is[1]

$$T = \frac{1}{1 + \frac{U^2 m}{2E\hbar^2} S(U - E)} \tag{1}$$

where

$$S(U-E) = \frac{\hbar^2}{2m(U-E)} \sinh^2\left(\frac{2m}{\hbar^2}(U-E)\right)^{1/2} W, \tag{2}$$

when E < U, and

$$S(U-E) = \frac{\hbar^2}{2m(E-U)} \sin^2\left[\frac{2m}{\hbar^2}(E-U)\right]^{1/2} W, \tag{3}$$

when E > U.

PLASTIC STRAIN RATE

The plastic strain rate, $d\gamma_p/dt$, is

$$\frac{d\gamma_p}{dt} = Nvb, \tag{4}$$

where N is the number of moving dislocations per unit area of surface, v is the average dislocation velocity and b is the Burgers length.

The dislocation velocity is determined by observing that a dislocation residing in a potential well has both thermal and applied stress induced motions. These cause the dislocation core segments to vibrate back and forth between the walls of their potential wells. Occasionally the segments may tunnel through the barrier and transit into the adjacent well where they continue to oscillate between the walls of the new potential well until tunneling again occurs and the dislocation segment moves into the next potential well. If n is the number of times that a dislocation segment approaches a potential barrier, and T is the probability of tunneling through the barrier, then nT is the average number of potential barriers that the segment tunnels through. With each successful tunneling event, the dislocation segment moves a lattice distance b. To simplify, assume that a sufficiently strong thermal or shear stress gradient exists so that for the most part the dislocation segments do not tunnel back into previously occupied wells. For this case, the average velocity of a segment is approximately

$$v \approx \frac{nTb}{t} \tag{5}$$

where t is the time interval. The time for each successful tunneling event is just the time for the lattice to rearrange itself to accommodate the new position of the core segment. This occurs at the local sound speed, v_0, so that the time required to accomplish tunneling one lattice spacing is $\Delta t = b/v_0$. The appropriate time interval over which to average the dislocation velocity is just $t = n\Delta t$ so that the average segment velocity becomes

$$v = Tv_0 \tag{6}$$

Since a dislocation is made up of a string of these core segments all of which experience the same shear stresses, this is the average velocity with which the dislocation moves.

This form gives the correct limits for the average dislocation velocity both at very low shear stress levels, $\tau \sim 0$, where $T \to 0$ and at high shear stress levels, $\tau >> 0$, where $T \to 1$. Since $T \leq 1$, the velocity of the plastic wave can never exceed the velocity of the elastic wave.

The number of moving dislocations can be estimated by assuming that the dislocations are created by N_s sources whose dislocations intercept a unit surface area of the crystal. To each of these sources is assigned a probability, $p_c(\tau)$, of creating a new dislocation pair at a shear stress τ and a characteristic source size, l_0, beyond which the newly created dislocation pair must propagate before the back stress due their presence is sufficiently reduced to allow the source to create another dislocation pair. The rate at which a single source can create dislocations is[2]

$$\frac{dn}{dt} = 2p_c(\tau)\frac{v}{l_0} \tag{7}$$

The factor of 2 accounts for the creation of a pair of dislocations. If τ resembles a step function, $\tau(t) \approx \tau u(t)$, then integrating (7) gives

$$n(\tau, t) \approx 2T(\tau)p_c(\tau)\frac{v_0}{l_0}t \tag{8}$$

where the time t is the time from first application of the shock or impact. Combining equations (4), (6) and (8), the plastic strain rate from N_s dislocation sources that intercept a unit area is approximately

$$\frac{d\gamma_p}{dt} \approx 2\,T(\tau)^2 \frac{v_0^2 b}{l_0} p_c(\tau)\, N_s\, t \qquad (9)$$

The plastic deformation rate given in equation (9) admits two time regimes of interest. These are delineated by the time required for a newly created dislocation to move away from its source, at a velocity v, and encounter an obstacle which forces it to stop. Let L_0 be the average distance between the dislocation source and an obstacle such as a grain boundary, then at early times after the application of a shock or impact when $t < L_0/v$ the number of moving dislocations increases with time and the plastic strain rate is given by equation (9). However, at later times when $t \geq L_0/v$, the moving dislocations will begin to encounter obstacles and their motion halted. A near steady state is reached where the number of newly created dislocations is offset by the number of recently stopped dislocations. The number of moving dislocations approaches a constant determined by substituting the time $t = L_0/v$ into equation (9) and the plastic strain rate becomes

$$\frac{d\gamma_p}{dt} \approx \frac{2\,T(\tau)\, v_0 b p_c(\tau)\, N_s L_0}{l_0} \qquad (10)$$

THE DISLOCATION ENERGY

Assume local equilibrium, so that the energy density of a dislocation must be the same as the local energy density of the host lattice. During shock or impact the energy will have two components, one due to the shear stress imposed by the shock or impact and the other from the shear stresses arising from the thermal background. The average energy with which a segment of the dislocation core approaches the potential barrier is approximately

$$E \approx \frac{\tau^2 V}{2G} + \frac{k\theta}{2} \qquad (11)$$

where G is the shear modulus. Equation (11) can be substituted directly into equations (9) or (10) and used to predict the average plastic deformation rate of a crystalline solid that has been subjected to a shock or impact.

COMPARISON WITH EXPERIMENT

It is of useful to compare the predicted plastic strain rate given by equation (10) with the experimental results of Campbell and Ferguson obtained with a mild steel over a large temperature range.[3] The material constants were taken as $b = 3\text{x}10^{-10}$m, $W = .5\text{x}10^{-10}$m, $l_0 = 3\text{x}10^{-8}$m, $v_0 = 5.5\text{x}10^3$ m/s, $G = 7.5\text{x}10^{11}$dy/cm^2, $\rho = 8.6\text{x}10^3$kg/m^3, $U = .5\text{x}10^{-13}$ergs. The number of dislocation sources per unit area was determined in conjunction with the mean free path distance, L_0, that a dislocation travels between its source and a blocking obstacle. It was assumed that there was only one source per mean free path, so that $N_s L_0^2 \approx 1$. Taking $L_0 = 10^{-4}$m, the approximate crystal size, then $N_s \approx 10^8\text{m}^{-2}$. The mass of a dislocation core segment was taken as $m \approx \rho b^3$, and the volume, V, of the lattice that is perturbed by the presence of the moving dislocation core was taken as a cylinderical disk centered at the dislocation core and of height b and radius 7b so that $V \approx 150b^3$. For simplicity, it was assumed that the amplitude of the applied shear stress was large enough so that the sources could readily create dislocations allowing $p_c(\tau) \rightarrow 1$.

Figure (1) shows the predicted behavior of the plastic deformation rate as a function of the applied shear stress for approximately the same temperatures as in the experiments of Campbell and Ferguson. These calculations used a somewhat more realistic half sine wave potential barrier $W = W_0(\sin(\pi E_0/2E_\tau))^3$, where E_0 is the dislocation segment energy when $\tau = 0$ and $W_0 = .5\text{x}10^{-10}$m. The boundary conditions were only approximated. The thin lines are the experimental results and the thick lines are the predicted behaviors.

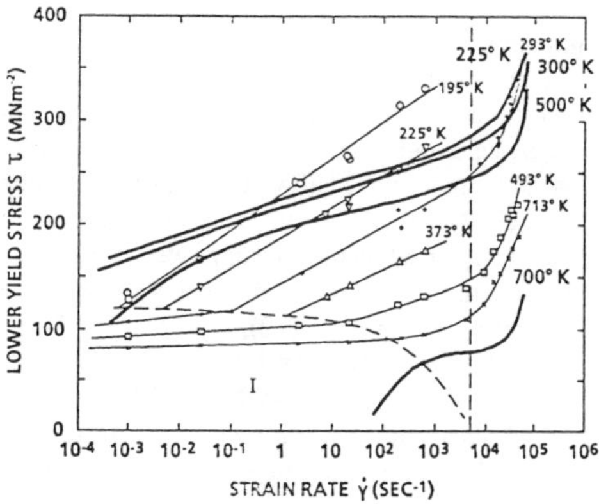

Figure (1). Comparison of predicted and measured strain rate as a function of shear stress.

The predicted rapid increase in strain rate with applied shear stress that occurs at $\gamma_p \approx 4 \times 10^4\ s^{-1}$ at all temperatures is due to the tunneling probability approaching unity as $E \rightarrow U$ and consequently $v \rightarrow v_0$. This behavior is evident in the experiments of Campbell and Ferguson and has been observed in other experiments on steel, copper and ß brass.[4,5,6] The conventional macroscopic constitutive approach makes no attempt to explain this very rapid increase in plastic strain rate at high shear stress levels.

These results can be extended to other materials. The prediction of the dislocation velocity in lithium flouride crystals determined by equation (6) compares reasonably well with the experimental measurements of Johnson and Gilman on LiF at several temperatures.[7]

Finally, these results apply to screw dislocations as well as edge dislocations since the only difference in this analysis between these is the potential barrier that each type of dislocation must tunnel through. This will only alter the tunneling probability, T, and only for mid range shear stresses. The asymptotic behavior at very high and very low amplitude shear stresses will be the same in both cases which is in keeping with the experimental observations of dislocation velocities.[7]

High amplitude shock loading offers a unique analytical view of plastic deformation because the energy with which the dislocations approach the potential barrier approaches the barrier height, $E \rightarrow U$. For this case the plastic strain rate at early times becomes

$$\frac{d\gamma_p}{dt} = 2\frac{\left(\frac{\tau^2 V}{2G} + \frac{k\theta}{2}\right)^2}{U^4}\left(\frac{2\hbar^2 v_0}{mW^2}\right)^2 \frac{b}{l_0} p_c N_s t \quad (12)$$

For a high amplitude shock, the thermal term can be ignored so that at early times, the average plastic strain rate is proportional to the fourth power of the applied shear stress. Swegle and Grady have observed that within a few tens of nanoseconds after the onset of a high amplitude shock the plastic strain rate in a number of different materials varied as the fourth power of the stress level.[8] Choosing representative numerical values for the constants appearing in equation (12), $U = .5 \times 10^{-13}$ ergs, $v_0 = 3 \times 10^3$ m/s, $W = .5\times10^{-10}$ m, $b/l_0 = 10^{-2}$, $G = 7\times10^{11}$ (dynes/cm^2), $\rho = 3\times10^3$ kg/m^3 and $N_s = 10^8$ sources/m^2 and the applied shear stress $\tau = 2$ GPa gives $d\gamma/dt \approx 10^5$ s^{-1} at $t = 10^{-8}$s, which is in the range of the experimental data.

CONCLUSIONS

An analysis of dislocation motion is developed which suggests that dislocations propagate in crystalline solids by quantum mechanical tunneling because it is energetically more favorable to tunnel through the lattice potential barriers than to surmount the barriers by thermal fluctuations. A model of a dislocation localized in a lattice by a simplified lattice potential is developed which gives physical insights and yields approximate predictions of the plastic strain rate and dislocation velocity as functions of temperature and applied shear stress which agree with the central features of experimental observations.

ACKNOWLEDGEMENTS

This work was supported by the Office of Naval Research and by the Naval Surface Warfare Center Independent Research Funds. The author wishes to thank Dr. D. H. Liebenberg of the ONR and Mr. R. H. Riedl of NSWC for their support and encouragement.

REFERENCES

[1] A. Messiah, Quantum Mechanics, Vol. 1. (Wiley, New York, 1961). p. 77.

[2] C. S. Coffey, J. Appl. Phys. 66, 1654 (1989).

[3] J. D. Campbell and W. G. Ferguson, Phil. Mag. 21, 63 (1970).

[4] A. R. Rosenfield and G. T. Hahn, Trans. Am. Soc. Metals 59, 962 (1966).

[5] P. S. Follansbee and U. F. Kocks, Acta Met. 36, 81 (1988).

[6] O. Vohringer, "Deformation Behavior of Metallic Materials", Int. Summer School on Dynamic Behavior of Materials, ENSM, Nantes, (1989).

[7] W. G. Johnston and J. J. Gilman, J. Appl. Phys. 33, 129 (1959).

[8] For LiF the following constants were used, $G = 5.3\times10^{11}$dy/cm^2, $U = .22\times10^{-13}$ergs, $W = 1.5\times10^{-10}$m, $v_0 = 3.6\times10^3$m/s, $b = 3\times10^{-10}$m, $l_0 = 3\times10^{-9}$m, $\rho = 2.5\times10^3$kg/m^3, $m = 6\rho b^3$ and $V = 40b^3$.

[9] J. W. Swegle and D. E. Grady, J. Appl. Phys. 58 (2). 692 (1985).

THE ROLE OF MATERIAL INHOMOGENEITIES IN THE LOCALIZATION OF STRAINS

M. Zhou, R. J. Clifton and A. Needleman

Division of Engineering, Brown University, Providence, RI 02912

Pressure-shear plate impact experiments are conducted to study dynamic shear banding in a two-phase microstructure at strain rates between 10^5 and 10^6 s^{-1}, under pressures of the order of 10 GPa. The material is a tungsten heavy alloy (WHA) which has a microstructure consisting of hard tungsten grains embedded in a soft matrix. Experiments and numerical simulations show that the two-phase alloy is more susceptible to shear banding than either of its constituent phases when tested separately.

1. Introduction

The need to understand dynamic plastic flow is of critical importance in a wide range of applications including high speed machining, high rate forming, explosive welding and armor penetration. At high rates of straining, the thermal softening that occurs because of the heating due to plastic dissipation, together with the lack of time for heat conduction, provides the main driving force for localization. Shear band formation in a tungsten-nickel-iron (W-Ni-Fe) alloy was studied experimentally by Zhou, Clifton and Needleman (1992)[1], using pressure-shear plate impact. The alloy consists of hard, more or less spherical, tungsten grains embedded in a soft nickel-iron-tungsten matrix. Shear banding is especially important in this alloy because its performance as a long rod projectile for penetrating heavy armor appears to depend on the stability of its plastic flow at high strain rates.

There is an extensive literature on the one-dimensional problem of thermal softening induced localization in simple shear, *e.g.* Recht (1964)[2], Clifton (1980)[3], Wright and Walter (1987)[4], Bai (1982)[5], Merzer (1982)[6], Molinari and Clifton (1987)[7], Batra and Kim (1992)[8] and Shawki and Clifton (1989)[9]. Such formulations do not, however, consider the microstructural interactions that can dominate the evolution of localized deformation in composite microstructures, such as that of the WHA alloy considered here.

In the present paper, finite element calculations are carried out to model the experiments of Zhou, Clifton and Needleman (1992)[1]. The tungsten heavy alloy is modelled as a composite consisting of two phases, *i.e.* the hard tungsten grains and the soft matrix. The numerical calculation is carried out using a digitized microstructure of the actual alloy. In addition, calculations are carried out to simulate pressure-shear impact experiments on pure tungsten and a nickel-iron-tungsten alloy which is representative of the matrix material.

2. Material Behavior

The tungsten heavy alloy contains 93% W, 4.9% Ni and 2.1% Fe by weight. Figure 1 shows the microstructure of this material, which is typical of such alloys, consisting of nearly spherical grains of tungsten embedded in a soft matrix. This material is tested in the pressure-shear plate impact experiment described by Clifton and Klopp (1985)[10]. In this experiment, sustained strain rates in excess of 10^5 s^{-1} are achieved by sandwiching a thin foil specimen between two hard elastic plates (Fig. 2). Before unloading waves arrive from lateral boundaries, the stress and deformation states are characterized by plane wave conditions; large strains can be reached because the high pressure inhibits failure. The deformed microstructure of a thin foil of WHA after a pressure-shear plate impact experiment is shown in Fig. 3. The initial thickness of the specimen is $87\mu m$. The micrograph shows deep etching of the grains so that the structure of the deformed matrix and grains are clearly revealed. A band of intense shear deformation, which involves both the tungsten grains and the matrix, is formed in the middle of the thin foil. The width of the band is $5-10\mu m$. Note the tear-drop shape of the grains near the middle of the band. The specimen is slightly

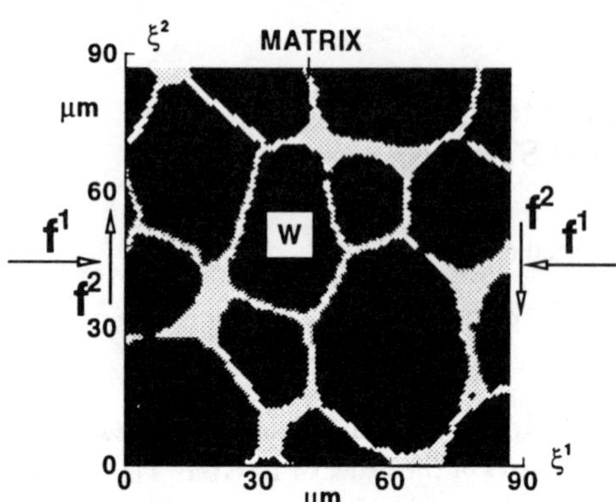

Figure 1 Digitized Microstructure of WHA

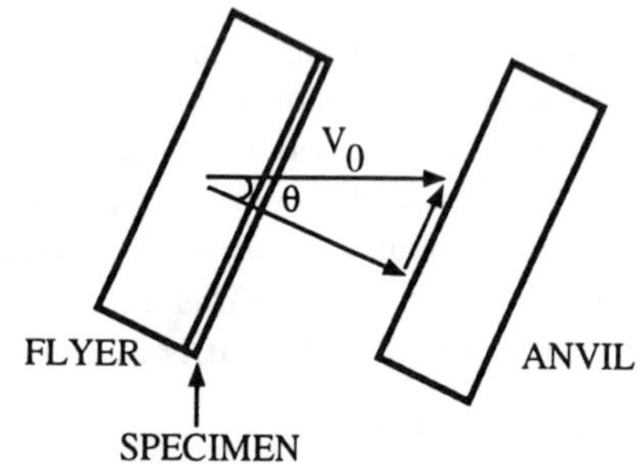

Figure 2 Pressure-shear Plate Impact Experiment

Figure 3 Shear Band in Specimen after Pressure-shear Impact

bent in the micrograph. This occurred after the experiment when the specimen was arrested inside a catcher filled with soft lead plates.

The response of the tungsten grains and the matrix phase over a wide range of strain rate, from 10^{-4} to 7×10^5 s^{-1}, has been characterized based on data from pressure-shear plate impact, torsional Kolsky bar and quasi-static torsion experiments by Zhou, Clifton and Needleman (1992)[1]. Figure 4(a) shows the rate sensitivities of the matrix and the tungsten grains. Figure 4(b) shows the thermal softening behavior of these constituent phases. Results reported by Andrews, Bower and Duffy (1992)[11] on the flow stress at strain rates of the order of 10^3 s^{-1}, Bose and German (1988)[12] and O'Donnell and Woodward (1990)[13] on the temperature dependence of the flow stress for similar tungsten heavy alloys are also shown in Fig. 4. To characterize the thermal softening behavior, it is assumed that the stress-carrying capacity of each material vanishes when the temperature reaches the corresponding melting point. Partly because of their different melting temperatures, pure tungsten and the matrix have very different thermal softening rates.

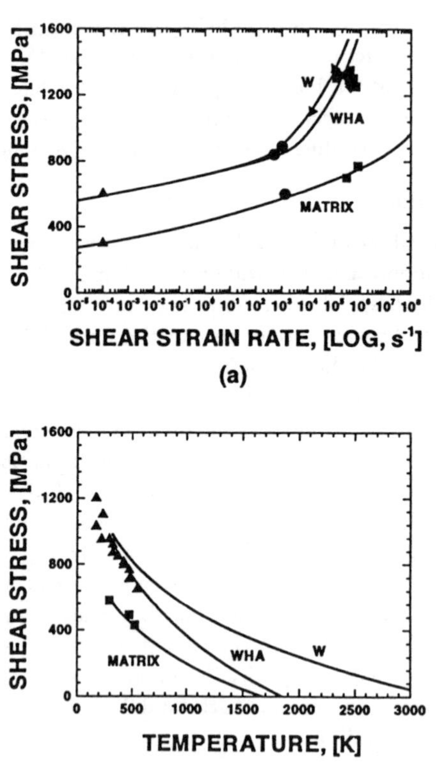

Figure 4 Material Response Characterization

3. Numerical Results

The simulations consider the effects of finite deformation, inertia, thermal softening, rate sensitivity, elasticity, strain hardening and heat conduction. Specific details of the formulation and numerical implementation can be found in Zhou, Needleman and Clifton (1993)[14]. In the numerical analysis, the impact angle, impact velocity and specimen thickness are the same as in the experiment that led to the shear band in Fig. 3, (*i.e.* $\theta = 26.6°$, $V_0 = 202$ m/s and $h = 87\mu m$).

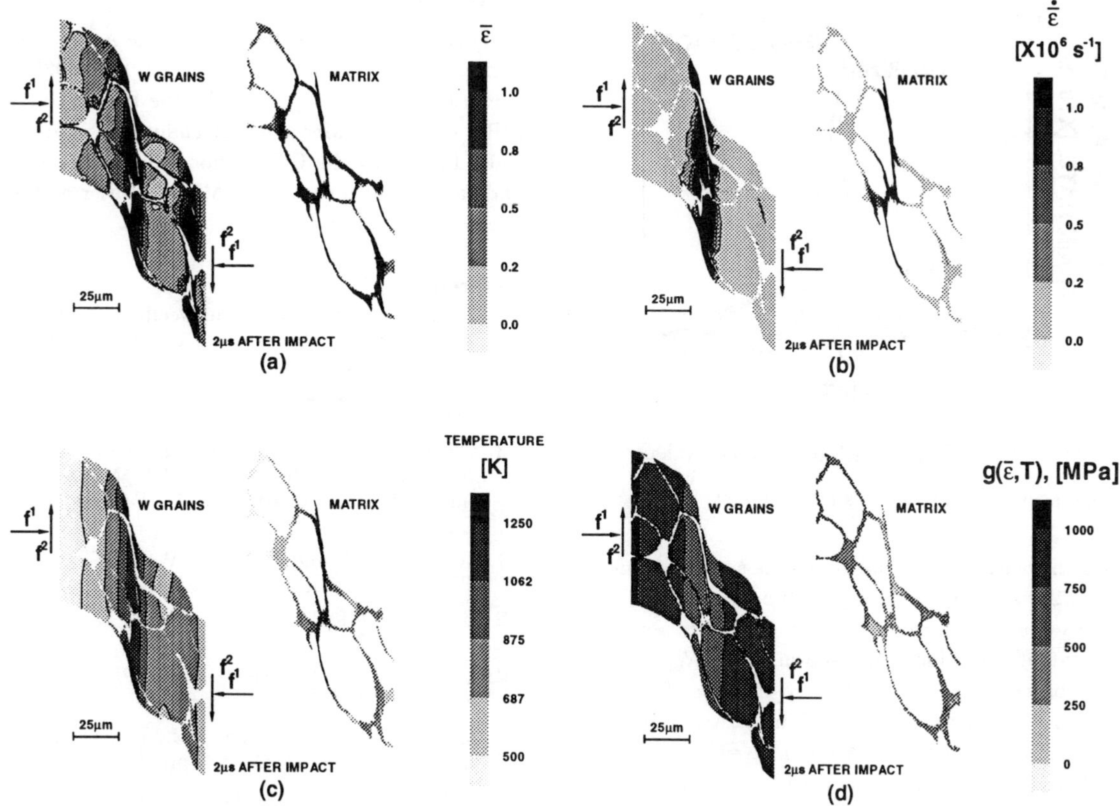

Figure 5 Calculated Distributions of (a) equivalent plastic strain; (b) equivalent plastic strain rate; (c) temperature; and (d) hardness function.

The digitized microstructure shown in Fig. 1 is used for the analysis. The results at $2.0\mu s$ after impact are shown in Fig. 5. The distributions of equivalent plastic strain (Fig. 5a), equivalent plastic strain rate (Fig. 5b) and temperature (Fig. 5c) indicate that a shear band has formed at the center of the specimen. The width of the band is approximately $10\mu m$, which is consistent with the width of the band in the micrograph in Fig. 3. Further calculations with microstructures with different grain shapes, grain arrangement, grain size, grain volume fraction and with adiabatic conditions assumed have shown that the length scale associated with heat conduction determines the shear band width in the circumstances considered, Zhou, Needleman and Clifton (1993)[14]. The largest equivalent plastic strain (Fig. 5a) in the shear band is 8 to 9 and the peak temperature (Fig. 5c) inside the band is approximately 1300 K, which is approximately 75% of the melting temperature of the matrix ($\approx$ 1750 K). In Fig. 5d, $g(\bar{\epsilon},T)$ is a hardness function representing the flow stress of the material as a result of the effects of strain hardening and thermal softening. Clearly, the two phases have different hardness levels. Since more heat is generated inside the band, thermal softening inside the shear bands overcomes the strain hardening and the hardness decreases strongly as the temperature continues to increase. Consequently, $g(\bar{\epsilon},T)$ is significantly lower inside the shear band than outside the band. Both the matrix and the grains are involved in the shear band. The tails of the tear-drop shapes are similar to those in the micrograph of Fig. 3. In addition, the overall shapes of the deformed grains resemble closely those observed in the micrograph of Fig. 3.

To study the effect of material inhomogeneities, simulations were also carried out for impact experiments of pure tungsten and the nickel-iron-tungsten alloy with a composition similar to that of the matrix phase in the WHA composite. Figure 6 shows the distribution of the

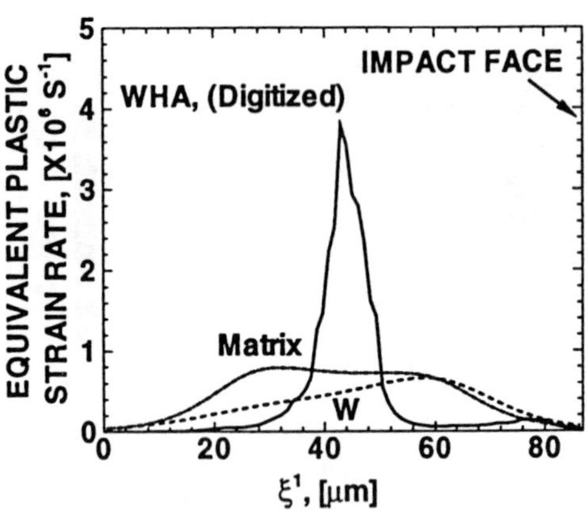

Figure 6 Calculated Distributions of equivalent plastic strain rate at 2.0μs after impact.

equivalent plastic strain rate across the specimen thickness, at 2μs after impact, for pure tungsten and for the matrix. For comparison purposes, the corresponding strain rate distribution is also shown for the WHA simulation based on the digitized microstructure of Fig. 1. The curves for the digitized WHA microstructure represent averages over the ξ^2 direction. Neither the pure tungsten nor the matrix shows the formation of a shear band, but the WHA composite does. This behavior can be explained as follows. Pure tungsten has a much higher flow stress than the matrix. The high flow stress in tungsten causes high rates of heat generation, but, because of the high melting temperature of tungsten, thermal softening is not sufficiently strong to cause localization. Thus, in the composite, the inhomogeneities arising from the presence of the tungsten grains provide perturbations for initiating localization in the matrix at much earlier times. However, in order for a shear band to form the harder tungsten grains must undergo large deformations. The progressive thermo-mechanical coupling between the phases causes both of them to be involved in the formation of the shear band. For all the grain morphologies and volume fractions simulated the band occurred earlier than when localization was calculated for the matrix alone, under the same impact conditions.

Acknowledgement

This research was supported by the Army Research Office through grant No. DAAL03-91-G-0025. The computations were supported by the Brown University MRG on "Micro-Mechanics of Failure-Resistant Materials" funded by the U.S. National Science Foundation and carried out on a Cray YMP computer at the San Diego Supercomputer Center.

References

1. Zhou, M., Clifton, R.J. and Needleman, A., (1992), *Proc. Int. Conf. on Tungsten and Tungsten Alloys*, Nov., Arlington, VA., pp. 343-356.
2. Recht, R.F., (1964), *J. Appl. Mech.*, **86**, pp. 189-193.
3. Clifton, R.J., (1980), *Material Response to Ultra-High Loading Rates*, NMAB-356, National Materials Advisory Board (NRC), Washington, D.C., Chap. 8.
4. Wright, T.W. and Walter, J.W., (1987), *J. Mech. Phys. Solids*, **35**, No. 6, pp. 701-720.
5. Bai, Y.L., (1982), *J. Mech. Phys. Solids*, **30**, No. 4, pp. 195-207.
6. Merzer, A. M., (1982), *J. Mech. Phys. Solids*, **30**, No. 5, pp. 323-338.
7. Molinari, A. and Clifton, R.J., (1987), *Trans. of ASME, J. Appl. Mech.*, **54**, pp. 806-812.
8. Batra, R.C. and Kim, C.H., (1992), *Int. J. Plasticity*, **8**, pp. 425-452.
9. Shawki, T.G. and Clifton, R.J., (1989), *Mech. Mat.*, **8**, pp. 13-43.
10. Clifton, R.J. and Klopp, R.W., (1985), *Metals Handbook*, **8**, Amer. Soc. Metals, Metals Park, 9th ed., pp. 230-239.
11. Andrews, E.W., Bower, A.F. and Duffy, J., (1992), *The 29th Annual Technical Meeting of the Soc. for Engng Sci.*, Sep. 14-16, La Jolla, CA.
12. Bose, A., and German, R.M., (1990), *Metall. Trans. A*, **21A**, pp. 1325-1327.
13. O'Donnell, R.G. and Woodward, R.L., (1990), *Metall. Trans. A*, **21A**, pp. 744-748.
14. Zhou, M., Needleman, A. and Clifton, R. J., (1993), Submitted to *J. Mech. Phys. Solids*.

MICROSTRUCTURE OF DYNAMICALLY COMPACTED AMORPHOUS MATERIALS

P. R. Ruuskanen, A. A. Kiiski and O. Heczko
Technical Research Centre of Finland, Metals Laboratory
P.O. BOX 776
FIN-33101 Tampere, Finland

Bulk amorphous materials were produced by the shock wave technique. Shock waves were generated by high explosives. The experiments were performed inside a vacuum chamber. As starting material amorphous ribbon with a thickness of 25μm produced by rapid solidification was used. Also powder obtained by crushing the amorphous ribbon was compacted. Rings with an outer diameter of 30 mm were obtained. The microstructure of the compacted samples was investigated by an x-ray diffractometer and optical microscope. No crystallization was observed in the samples compacted from the amorphous ribbon or the powder. A complete adhesion between the different ribbon layers was observed. The microstructure of the samples compacted from the amorphous powder consists of homogeneously distributed grains with an average diameter of 5-10 μm. Magnetic hysteresis curves of the samples were measured using a frequency of 1 Hz.

INTRODUCTION

Soft magnetic materials produced by the rapid solidification technique have been widely investigated. These materials have good magnetic properties. However, the practical use of these materials is not as widerspread as could be expected. One reason for this is that amorphous materials are available mostly in the form of thin ribbon. Crushed amorphous materials have been compacted earlier by the shock wave technique and by hot pressing [1,2]. However magnetic properties of these compacts are lower than the magnetic properties of the original ribbon. In this paper we present a technique to compact amorphous ribbon to the form of core rings. Also we show that the magnetic properties are comparable to the magnetic properties of the original ribbon.

EXPERIMENTAL

Fig 1. shows the experimental arrangements to compact the amorphous ribbon and the powder. It consists of a steel tube closed at both ends with thick steel plates. The amorphous ribbon is wound on the copper tube and on both sides of the wound ribbon there are copper rings. The purpose of the copper tube and rings is to damp the reflected waves following the primary shock wave. Explosion experiments were performed inside a vacuum chamber.

As a starting material we used amorphous ribbon prepared by the rapid solidification technique. Also powder prepared by crushing the amorphous ribbon was used. The average particle size after the crushing was 50μm. The shape of the particles was flaky. The composition of the amorphous material was $Fe_{73.5}Cu_1Nb_3Si_{13.5}B_9$. The crystallization temperature is typically 550 °C for this material. By annealing the sample close to the crystallization temperature it is possible to obtain a nanocrystalline structure ith superior soft magnetic properties [3]. Owing to the high crystallization temperature, this material is suitable for the dynamic compaction.

Immediately after explosion the samples were annealed at 450 °C for one hour to release the residual stresses in the compacts. The microstructure of the compacted samples were investigated by optical microscopy and x-ray diffraction using molybdenium kα-radiation. Samples were also annealed at 550 °C to obtain the nanocrystalline microstructure. Magnetic properties were measured with a fluxmeter method using a frequency of 1 Hz.

RESULTS AND DISCUSSION

Microstructure

With the shock wave technique well-consolidated high-density coils were obtained from the amorphous ribbon. The outer diameter of the coils was 30 mm, internal diameter 15 mm and a thickness of 10 mm. Fig. 2 shows the core rings obtained by the shock wave compaction. Fig. 3a shows the outer surface of the compacted ribbon. In the polished surface only some few individual ribbon layers were visible close to the outer and the internal surfaces of the specimen. 98 % of the surface was smooth and no individual ribbon layers were visible. This reveals the perfect welding of the ribbon layers during the compaction. The formation of cracking during compaction was prevented by the copper tube (10) and the copper rings (7) which absorb the reflected shock waves. Fig 3b shows the microstructure of the sample compacted from crushed amorphous ribbon. This sample exhibits porosity and individual particles are visible. In this sample thee were some macrocracks. The most probable reason for the porosity and the cracking of the powder samples is that the pressure generated by the explosive used was too low to form complete joining between the different particles. After the compaction the density of the samples made from crushed ribbon was low, 87 % of the theoretical density.

In Fig. 4 there is a comparison of x-ray curves of different ribbons and compacts. As-quenched ribbon shows a pattern typical of the amorphous microstructure. As shown in the figure, the patterns measured from as-compacted ribbon and as-compated powder annealed at 450 °C are also typical of the amorphous structure. Based on these results we can say that the microstructure of the material remains amorphous during the dynamic compaction. The upper curve in Fig. 4 presents the x-ray curve of nanocrystalline microstructure obtained after annealing the samples at 550 °C for one hour.

Magnetic properties

The magnetic properties of the original wound ribbon and the rings compacted dynamically from amorphous ribbon and crushed ribbon were measured in the nanocrystalline state. Fig. 5 shows the corresponding hysteresis curves measured at a frequency of 1 Hz. Curve (A) in Fig. 5 presents the hysteresis curve of the original non-compacted nanocrystalline ribbon. The maximum flux density of this sample is approximately one Tesla with the magnetizing field strength of 15 A/m. The coercive force of the original ribbon is 2 A/m. The magnetic properties of the sample compacted dynamically from the ribbon are comparable to those measured from the original ribbon, as curve (B) in Fig. 5 shows. The largest change in the hysteresis curve is the coercive force increasing up to 10 A/m because of internal stresses formed by compaction. The curve (C) in Fig. 5 presents the magnetic hysteresis of a sample compacted dynamically from crushed ribbon. As shown, the maximum flux density and permeability are much lower than those of compacted ribbon samples but the coercive force is approximately the same. The internal stresses cause strong magnetic anisotropy in the material due to magnetoelastic coupling. Magnetic anisotropy increases the coercive force and reduce the permeability. By annealing the effect of the anisotropy can be reduced. However the annealing temperature of 550°C is not high enough to remove the anisotropy completely. The role of the compaction-induced magnetic anisotropies will be discussed in more detail elsewhere [4].

CONCLUSION

A method to compact amorphous ribbon and powder is presented. The results show that the shock wave technique offers a convenient way to prepare bulk amorphous and nanocrystalline materials with good soft magnetic properties. The microstructure of the amorphous material do not change during explosion. Magnetic properties of samples compacted from amorphous ribbon are comparable to those ofthe original non-compacted ribbon.

REFERENCES

[1] M. Takagi, Y. Kawamura, M. Araki, Y. Kuroyma, T.Imura, *Materials Science and Engineering* 98, pp.457-460 (1988).

[2] T. Sato, M. Kobayashi, T. Nakagava, H. Ohsumi, *Journal of Materials Science* 1, pp. 39-45 (1990).

[3] Y. Yoshisawa, S. Oguma and K. Yamauchi, J. Appl. Phys. 64(10), p.6044 (1988).

[4] O. Heczko and P. Ruuskanen, to be published in IEEE Trans. Mag. Sept. 1993.

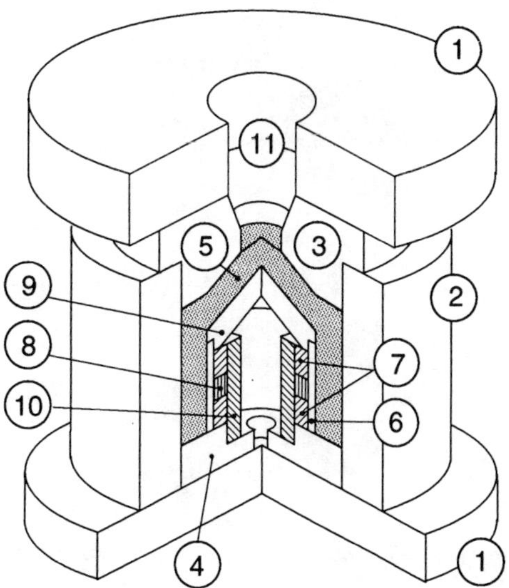

Fig. 1 Experimental set-up for compaction of amorphous ribbon and powder.
1) steel plates, 2) steel tube, 3)aluminium plate, 4) steel ring, 5) explosive material 6) copper tube, 7)copper damping rings,8) material to be consolidated, 9) damping cone, 10) copper damping tube,11) detonator

Fig. 2. Different core rings prepared by the shock wave technique from the amorphous ribbon and the powder. Left: rings from the ribbon, right: rings from the powder.

a)

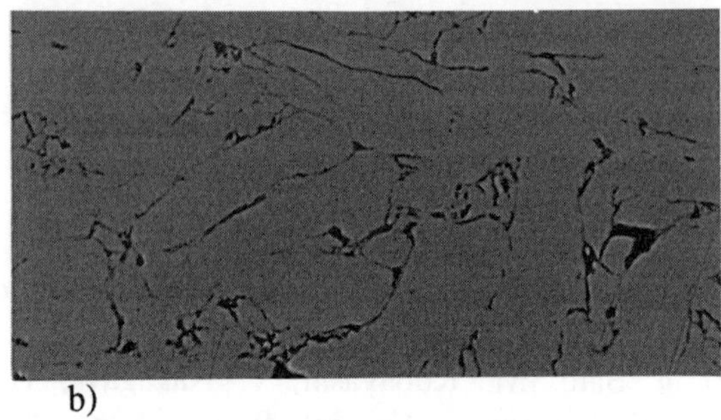

b)

Fig. 3. Microstructure of the dynamically compacted amorphous materials.
a) outer surface of ribbon sample
b) sample compacted from powder
Magnification 300X.

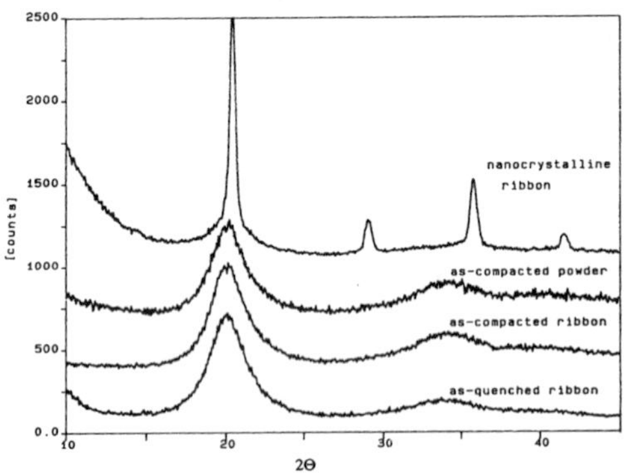

Fig. 4. X-ray diffraction curves of the amorphous and nanocrystalline ribbon and as-compacted ribbon and as-compacted powder.

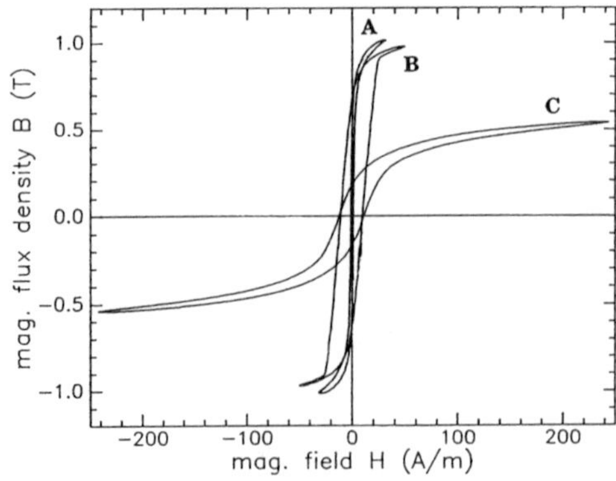

Fig. 5. Magnetic hysteresis curves of the nanocrystalline core rings.
A) original ribbon
B) ring compacted from ribbon
C) ring compacted from powder

GAS-GUN REVERSE-BALLISTIC IMPACT DEFORMATION AND FRACTURE OF ARMCO IRON TAYLOR SPECIMENS OF DIFFERING GRAIN SIZES

W. H. Holt, W. Mock, Jr., J. B. Clark, and F. J. Zerilli, Naval Surface Warfare Center, Dahlgren, VA 22448 and Silver Spring, MD 20903

R. W. Armstrong
University of Maryland, College Park, MD 20742

Taylor cylinder specimens of Armco iron have been prepared with average grain sizes of 20 and 91 microns. For each grain size, impacts were performed at 193 and 295 ms^{-1}. The extent of fracturing that occurred at the specimen perpheries was only minor at the lower velocity but was pronounced at the greater velocity. Radial striations of softened or melted material were observed on the specimen and anvil disk impact surfaces. EPIC-2 predictions using the Zerilli-Armstrong constitutive equation are compared to the measured specimen outlines and to the extent of deformation twinning observed in metallographic examination of specimen longitudinal sections.

INTRODUCTION

Impact-deformed Taylor cylinder[1] specimens have been used as reference shapes in the development of constitutive models for material deformation behavior at high strain rates, and in particular, to account for the effects of deformation twinning[2,3]. The present paper concerns impact deformation experiments with cylinders of Armco iron of differing grain sizes and the influence of associated microstructural changes on constitutive modelling.

IMPACT EXPERIMENTS

A 40 mm bore gas gun was used for the impact experiments[4]. The reverse-ballistic impact configuration with a stationary specimen and a moving anvil (impactor) disk permits precise control of the impact geometry. Impact occurs in vacuum and electrical contact pins are used to measure the sabot velocity. The specimen and impactor disk are soft recovered in a box of cloth rags.

The impactor disks were 34.0 mm in diameter, 19.0 mm thick, and were fabricated from maraging 350 steel (Rockwell C 55-57 hardness). A 4.0 inch diameter as-received bar of Armco iron was cut into two sections. Taylor cylinder specimens machined from the as-received material had equiaxed grains with an average size of 91 microns. Specimens were also machined from the other section after the material was rolled and heat treated to produce equiaxed grains with an average size of 20 microns. The specimens were 6.35 mm in diameter, 25.4 mm long. Prior to impact, the ends of the cylinders and the impact surfaces of the disks were lapped with 0.3 micron aluminum oxide film.

Experiments were performed at 193 and 295 ms^{-1}. After impact deformation and soft recovery, the specimen shapes were digitized via a toolmaker's microscope connected to a computer.

The impact surfaces of all the deformed specimens showed radial striations extending nearly to the specimen edges. Scanning electron microscopy (SEM) examination of the impact surfaces of the specimens and of the impact region of the steel impactor disk showed corresponding striations, and energy-dispersive-analysis-of-x-rays (EDAX) studies determined that the striated material was iron. These patterns on the impact surfaces suggest that during impact deformation and the associated radial flow across the impactor disk surface, the temperature at some regions of the impact surface exceeded the 1535 °C melting temperature[5] of iron. When the impacting disk and specimen separated after impact, ductile fracture surfaces formed on the striations. Similar observations have been made for Taylor impact experiments with titanium[3].

Fractures at the periphery of the deformed end of each specimen were minor for both grain size materials at 193 ms^{-1} (this velocity appears to be near the threshold for fracture). At 295 ms^{-1}, the fracturing was significant, with the fracture planes oriented approximately 45 degrees to the impact surface. The larger grain material showed slightly larger cracks, probably corresponding to the outlines of the larger grains.

Figure 1 shows longitudinal sections of the specimens impacted at 193 ms^{-1} and corresponding microstructural features.

NUMERICAL SIMULATIONS

Numerical simulations of the 193 ms^{-1} impacts were performed with the EPIC-2 material dynamics computer program[6] using the Zerilli-Armstrong constitutive equation for bcc metals[2]:

$$\sigma = c_0 + Be^{-\beta T} + K\varepsilon^n \quad (1)$$

where

$$c_0 = \sigma_G + kl^{-1/2}, \quad (2)$$

$$\beta = \beta_0 - \beta_1 \ln \dot{\varepsilon}, \quad (3)$$

σ is the von Mises equivalent stress, ε is the equivalent strain, T is the absolute temperature, and l is the average grain diameter. The material parameters, B= 1033 Mpa, β_0 = 6.98 x 10-3 K^{-1}, β_1 = 4.15 x 10^{-4} K^{-1}, K = 266 MPa, n = 0.289, σ_G = 0 MPa, and k = 22 MPa-mm $^{1/2}$, were previously published[2] for Armco iron.

Deformation twinning is important in iron and was accounted for in the numerical simulations. The dependence of the twinning stress on grain size is similar to the dependence of the athermal part of the flow stress on grain size and may be written[7]

$$c_T = \sigma_{T0} + k_T l^{-1/2} \quad (4)$$

where, for iron, σ_{T0} is 330 MPa and k_T is 90 MPa-mm$^{1/2}$. The method that was previously used to include the effect of twinning in numerical simulations is based on the premise that twinning effectively refines the grain size[8]. If the stress in a grain reaches the level given by Eq. (2), the grain is considered to be twinned and a constant increment is added to the flow stress. Once twinned, the new twinning threshold stress is much higher than the original, so that further twinning is unlikely to occur.

The twinning model used in this work is based on the idea that enough twinning will occur in a grain to accomodate the excess by which the von Mises equivalent stress exceeds the twinning threshold stress[9]. The previous twinning model required knowledge of the number of twins per grain produced. In this model, the only parameters needed, σ_{T0} and k_T , are known *a priori*.

Figure 2 shows comparisons of the simulations with the experimental specimen outlines for impacts at 193 ms^{-1}, indicating generally good agreement. From Table 1, the simulations predict no twinning for the 20 micron grain size material and significant twinning for the 91 micron material. Some twinning was observed for the 20 micron material and more twinning than predicted was observed in the 91 micron material, suggesting that a value of σ_{T0} somewhat lower than 330 MPa may further improve the agreement with the specimen outlines.

CONCLUSIONS

The outlines of Armco iron Taylor specimens deformed at 193 ms^{-1} can be predicted with generally good agreement when the effect of deformation twinning is included. The observed extent of twinning in the specimens correlates with the predicted influences of grain size on the threshold stress for twinning.

ACKNOWLEDGEMENT

This work was supported by the Independent Research Office, Dahlgren Division, Naval Surface Warfare Center.

REFERENCES

1 G. I. Taylor, Proc. Roy. Soc. A194 (1948) 289.

2 F. J. Zerilli and R. W. Armstrong, J. Appl. Phys. 61 (1987) 1816.

3 W. H. Holt, W. Mock, Jr., F. J. Zerilli, and J. B. Clark, "Experimental and Computational Study of the Impact Deformation of Titanium Taylor Cylinder Specimens," Mechanics of Materials, in press.

4 W. Mock, Jr. and W. H. Holt, Naval Surface Weapons Center Report NSWC TR-3473, 1976.

5 *Handbook of Chemistry and Physics, 57th Edition*, Cleveland: CRC Press, 1976, p. B-171.

6 G. R. Johnson and W. H. Cook, in *Proceedings of the Seventh International Symposium on Ballistics*, 1983, p.523.

7 R. W. Armstrong and F. J. Zerilli, J. Physique, Coll., 49(9), (1988) p. 529.

8 F. J. Zerilli and R. W. Armstrong, in *Shock Waves in Condensed Matter 1987,* Amsterdam: Elsevier, 1988, p.273.

9 F. J. Zerilli and R. W. Armstrong, unpublished work.

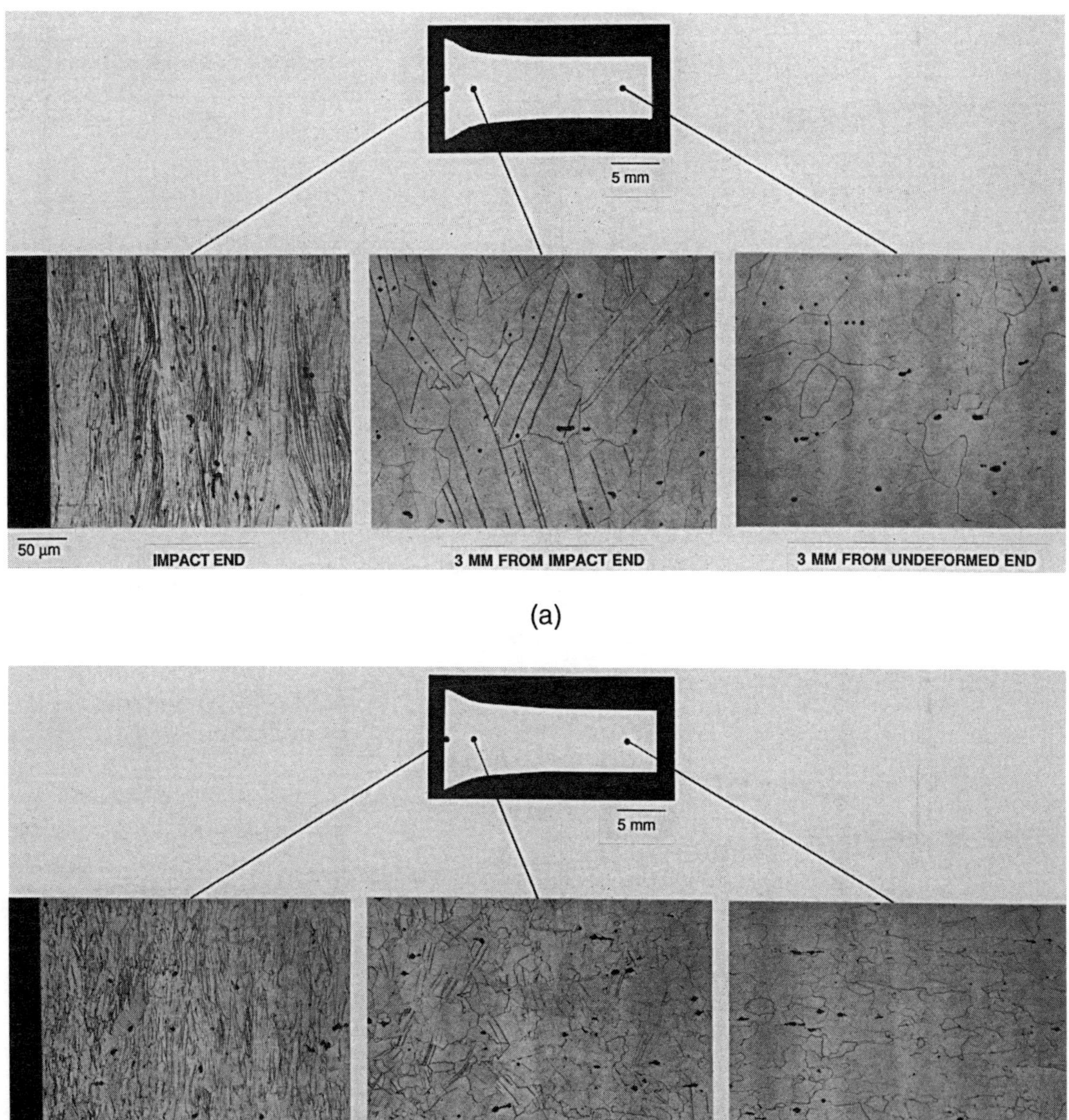

Figure 1. Longitudinal sections of Taylor specimens and corresponding microstructural features for two average grain sizes. Impact velocities 193 ms^{-1}. (a) 91 microns. (b) 20 microns.

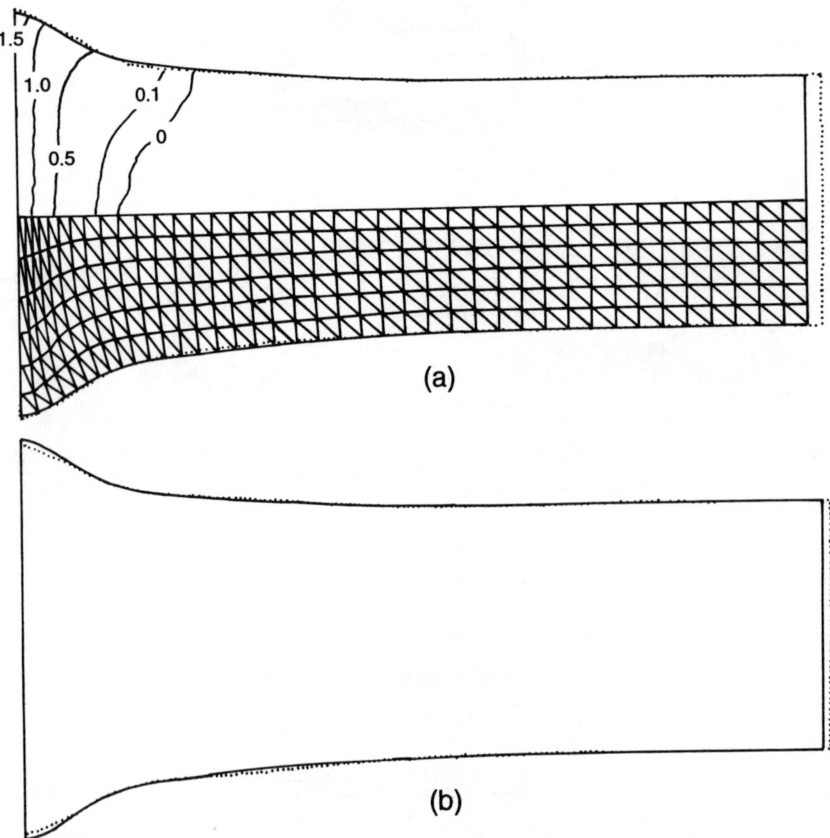

Figure 2. Comparison of computational simulations at 50 microseconds after impact (solid lines) and specimen outlines (dotted lines) for two average grain sizes. Impact velocities 193 ms^{-1}. The contours show predicted numbers of twins per grain. (a) 91 microns. (b) 20 microns. The finite element grid for the initial specimen shape was the same for (a) and (b).

Table 1. Summary of quantities used in simulations. The number of twins per grain, the peak von Mises stress, and the strain rate are predicted by the simulation.

v (ms^{-1})	l_0 (μm)	twins per grain	σ_T (MPa)	σ_{VMmax} (MPa)	$\dot{\varepsilon}$ (10^5 s^{-1})
193	91	2	628	835	3
295	91	2.5	628	880	5
193	20	0	966	864	3
295	20	0	966	898	5

THE EFFECT OF HYDROSTATIC PRESSURIZATION ON THE MICROSTRUCTURE AND MECHANICAL PROPERTIES OF THE $L1_2$ Cu-MODIFIED TITANIUM TRIALUMINIDE

Z. Witczak
High Pressure Research Center, Polish Academy of Sciences
Sokołowska 29/37
01-142 Warszawa, Poland

A porous Cu-modified Al_3Ti-based intermetallic has been subjected to various hydrostatic pressures (up to 2.5 GPa). Density changes and microstructure of the material are related to its microhardness characteristics. Quantitiative metallography has been applied to describe microcracking characteristics of the compound. Plasticity and strength of the compound after pressurization have been determined from uniaxial compression tests. The acoustic emission method was applied to monitor the process of deformation of the material during mechanical testing.

INTRODUCTION

Prospective design materials, Al_3Ti-based intermetallics modified to the $L1_2$ structure as cast are porous. This is a result of the Kirkendall effect that takes place during crystalization and, presumably, homogenisation of the crystalized material. Pores are the sources of microcracks in the material. They can participate in brittle behaviour of the material during deformation even under high hydrostatic pressure [1]. The aim of this work was investigation of the irreversible changes in such materials after pressurization (cold densification), when porosity was significantly reduced.

EXPERIMENTAL

The investigations were carried out on Cu-modified Al_3Ti-based intermetallic compound (Al_5CuTi_2) of a following composition: Al-59.3, Ti-27.8, Cu-12.9 at % [2]. After homogenisation (1050°C/72 h) the material contained the 4.5 % porosity and 1 % other phases (Al_3Ti + AlCu). Cylindrical specimens were encapsulated in thin-wall capsules (copper foil) and subjected to high hydrostatic pressure of the values: 0.5, 1.0, 1.5, 2.0, 2.5 GPa for 15 min.

The density of the material was measured with the helium pycnometer (Accu Pyc 1330V1.02).

A TV analyzer Videoplan 2 was used for measuring cracking parameters of the material. Observations were performed under Nomarski contrast.

Compression tests were performed with the apparatus described elsewhere [3].

RESULTS AND DISCUSSION

A microstructure of the material is presented in Figure 1. Brighter grains of Al_3Ti and AlCu phases are visible. This is characteristic that majority of cracks is situated inside these grains. The parameters of cracking are presented in Table 1. There is no correlation between them and the value of applied pressure.

At the same time there is significant correlation between the density of the material (Fig. 2) and its microhardness (Fig. 3). It can be expressed as

$$\Delta H_v = C\Delta\eta \quad (1)$$

where: H_v - Vickers hardness, η - relative density, C - constant (1625 kG/mm^2).

This relationship is obvious as the change in density of a material is a measure of its permanent deformation, hence its dislocation density.

It is seen from compression tests (Fig. 4, Table 2) that the pressure-induced increase in dislocations density of the material gives rise to its flow stresses and reduces its plasticity, while the rate of work hardening remains constant. The increase in compression strength of the material is not so dramatic but is still significant. These results are opposite to that of Margevicius and Lewandowski [4,5,6] obtained for a NiAl intermetallic compound after pressurization at lower pressures.

Acoustic emission from specimens during compression tests (Fig. 5) shows the process of cracking in the material being compressed. The cumulative number of AE events registered till fracture seems to be constant, independent of the dislocation structure (Fig. 3) and the initial density of cracks in the material (Table 1).

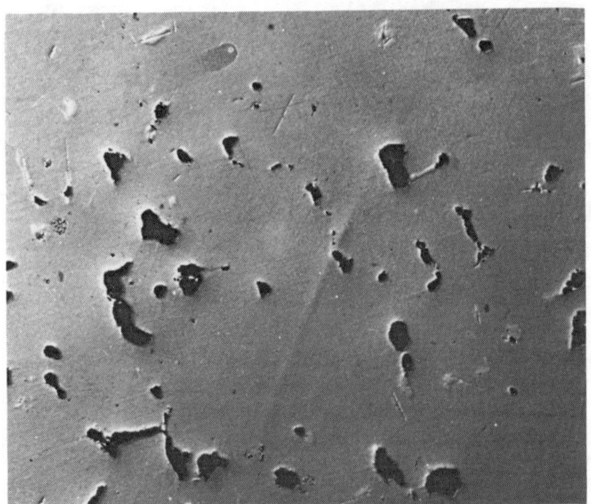

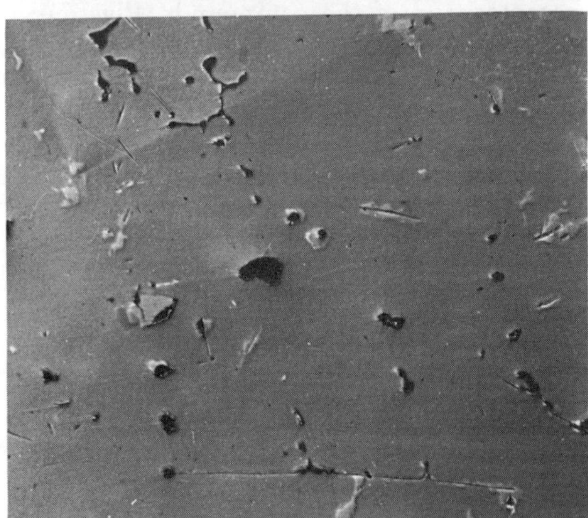

Figure 1. Optical micrographs (under Nomarski contrast) of the material before pressurization (upper) and after 2.5 GPa applied pressure (lower).

Table 1. Parameters of cracking of the material.

p (MPa)	n (mm^{-2})	l_c (μm)	a_c ($\mu m/mm^2$)
0.1	2.98	166	0.471
500	3.80	151	0.572
1000	4.96	117	0.580
1500	8.33	94	0.784
2000	5.17	89	0.461
2500	3.49	117	0.408

p - pressure, n - specific number of cracks, l_c - average length of the crack, a_c - density of cracks.

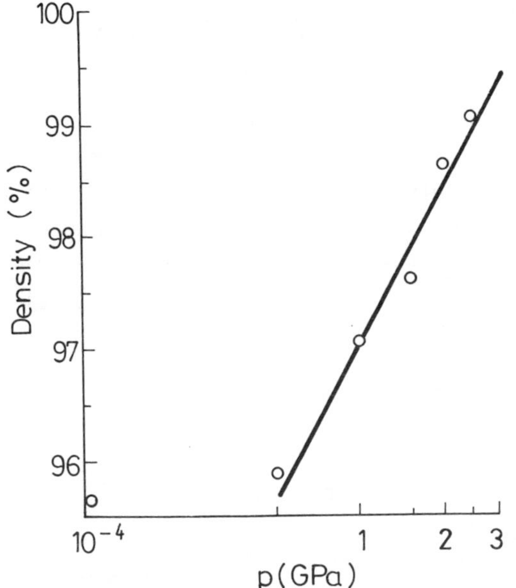

Figure 2. Densification of the material with hydrostatic pressure.

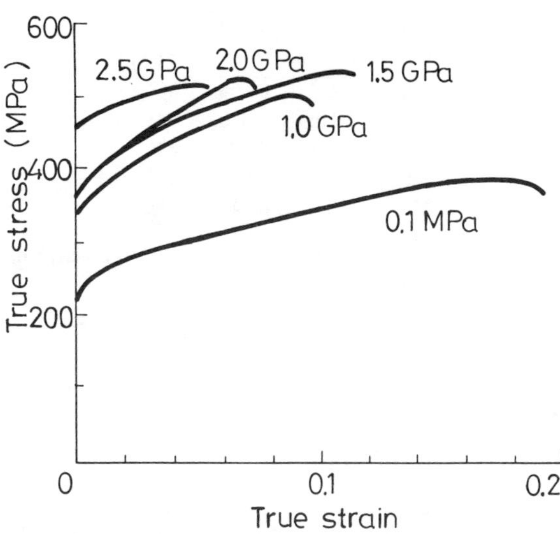

Figure 4. Compressive true stress vs. true strain diagrams after pressurization at various hydrostatic pressures.

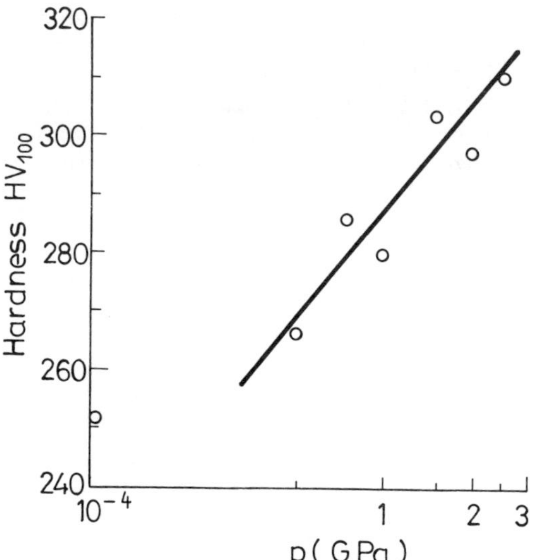

Figure 3. Vickers microhardness (100 G load) vs. previously applied hydrostatic pressure.

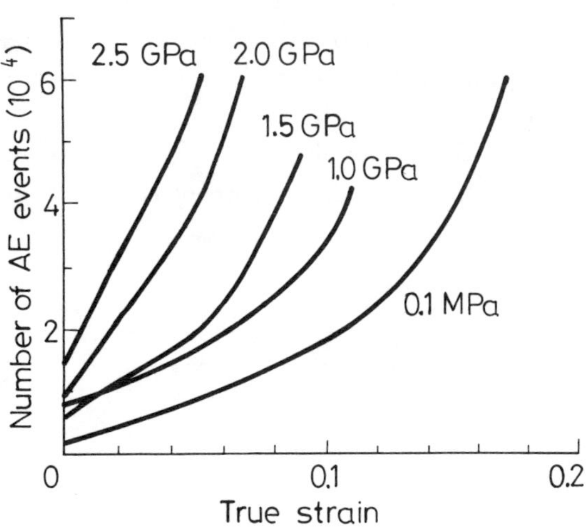

Figure 5. Acoustic emission activity (cumulative number of AE events) during uniaxial compression of the material after pressurization at various pressures.

Table 2. Mechanical properties of the material after pressurization.

p (MPa)	$\sigma_{0.2}$ (MPa)	ϵ_{max}	σ_{max} (MPa)
0.1	230	0.168	385
1000	345	0.090	501
1500	371	0.109	536
2000	368	0.068	524
2500	464	0.049	514

p - pressure, $\sigma_{0.2}$ - yield strength, ϵ_{max} - max. true strain, σ_{max} - compression strength.

CONCLUSIONS

1. Hydrostatic densification of a porous $L1_2$ Cu-modified Al_3Ti intermetallic compound obeys a power law.
2. Microhardness of the material linearly depends on the change of its density.
3. Hydrostatic pressurization does not change the density of craks in the material.
4. Pressure-induced increase in dislocation density of this material reduces its plasticity and significantly increases its flow stresses and compression strength.
5. Cumulative number of acoustic emission events registered till fracture of the material is a constant.

ACKNOWLEDGEMENTS

The author gratefully acknowledges Dr. M.B. Winnicka for the material used in these investigations and Dr. A. Gładki for metallographic measurements. The work was sponsored by the State Committee for Scientific Research in Poland (grant 3-P407-071-04).

REFERENCES

[1] M.B. Winnicka, Z. Witczak and R.A. Varin, *Metall. Trans. A*, submitted (1993).

[2] M.B. Winnicka and R.A. Varin, *Metall. Trans. A*, 23A, pp. 2963-2972 (1992).

[3] Z. Witczak, R. Jemielniak and J. Szczepek, The Apparatus for Mechanical Testing of Materials under High Hydrostatic Pressure with In-situ Acoustic Emission Analyzer, this Conference.

[4] R.W. Margevicius and J.J. Lewandowski, *Scripta Metall. Mater.* 25, pp. 2017–2022 (1991).

[5] R.W. Margevicius, J.J. Lewandowski and I. Locci, *Scripta Metall. Mater.* 26, pp. 1733–1736 (1992).

[6] R.W. Margevicius and J.J. Lewandowski, *Acta Metall. Mater.* 41, 2, pp. 485–496 (1993).

RELATIONSHIP BETWEEN THE SHOCK RESPONSE AND MICROSTRUCTURAL FEATURES OF TITANIUM DIBORIDE (TiB_2)

L. Ewart and D.P. Dandekar
Army Research Laboratory - Materials Directorate
Watertown, MA 02172-0001

Detailed microstructural studies of recovered TiB2 specimens from spall and reshock spall experiments reveal that cracks are the principle from of damage generated with peak compressive stresses of up to 6.7 GPa. Quantifiction of crack lengths and densities suggests that the lower cusp represents a threshold for increased damage production.

INTRODUCTION

During the shock compression of titanium diboride (TiB2) two cusps are observed in the shock wave loading profile; one between 4.2-5.8 GPa and referred to as the first Hugonoit elastic limit (HEL1), and the other between 9-17 GPa and referred to as the second Hugonoit elastic limit (HEL2). Recent investigations [1,2] of HEL1 suggest that the lower cusp corresponds to a threshold above which irreversible damage in the form of cracks and pores is generated. Results from conventional spall experiments [1] (Figure 1) reveal that below the first cusp the spall strength remains constant at 0.3 GPa. Above the first cusp the spall strength falls to 0.06 GPa at a peak compressive stress of 12.84 GPa.

"Reshock" experiments [1] in which the TiB2 is subject to a shock-release-reshock-rerelease cycle prior to tensile loading corroborate the correlation of HEL1 to a threshold above which irreversible damage is produced. In reshock experiments which have a peak stress below HEL1 the average reshock spall strength and the conventionally measured spall strength are the same (Figure 1). However, reshock spall strengths measured above HEL1 are significantly smaller than the single shock spall strengths at comparable peak stresses.

Details regarding the type of damage produced in TiB2 during impact can be inferred from the results of both direct impact and transmission experiments. There is no reduction in the shock wave velocity, no stress relaxation at the impact surface, no attenuation of the stress amplitude as the shock wave propagates through the TIB2, nor a decrease in the release wave velocity (no change in compressibility). The implication, especially with the constancy in the compressibility, is that cracks rather than pores are the primary form of damage.

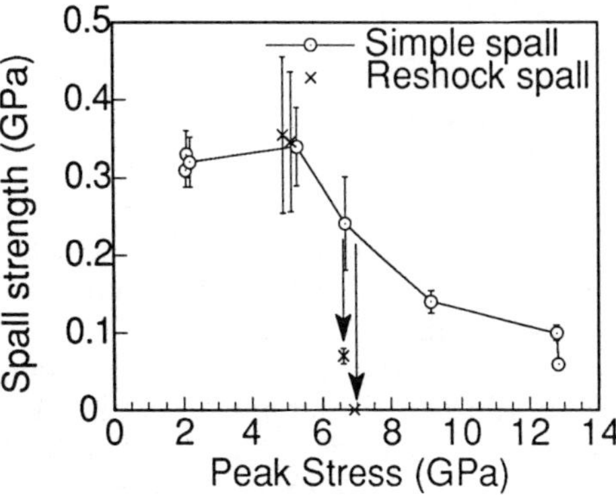

Figure 1. Spall strength as a function of compressive stress.

Theoretical models [3] reveal that pores are significantly more effective than cracks in increasing the compressibility of a brittle material. Since no measurable change in the compressibility of TiB2 occurs, material damage through an increase in the number density and/or length of cracks rather than through an increase in the percent porosity is expected. The generation of cracks as the primary mechanism of damage in TiB2 is also consistent with the loss of tensile strength as seen in the decline of the spall threshold above the lower cusp. A crack is more detrimental to tensile properties than a pore since it has a larger associated stress concentration when subject to an applied tensile stress.

The present research was initiated to ascertain the nature of the lower cusp through detailed microstructural observations. TiB2 was recovered from conventional spall and reshock experiments above and below HEL1. Scanning electron microscopy studies enabled quantification of the crack number densities and lengths and of the pore densities in as-received and shock recovered specimens. The effect of peak stress, reshock and location within the target material on the measured crack and pore features is examined. Estimates of the expected compressibility change due to the damage observed are made based on published models.

EXPERIMENTAL PROCEDURE

The as-received material is hot pressed TiB2 in 6" x 6" x 1" tiles from Ceradyne. The elemental composition in weight percent is: titanium diboride 98.89, tungsten 0.83, carbon 0.3, cobalt 0.2, nitrogen 0.37 and oxygen 0.32. The average grain size is 10 μm. The targets for the shock experiments were machined from 2 of the TiB2 tiles. Details of the shock experiments are given in reference 1. The results of these experiments have been discussed in the introduction and are shown in Figure 1.

Microstructural studies were conducted on as-received TiB2 and on TiB2 specimens recovered from the shock experiments described above. Specimens were recovered from conventional spall experiments having peak compressive stresses of 2, 5 and 6.7 GPa and from a reshock experiment at 5 GPa. All specimens were polished down to 1 μm and etched. Specimens were examined uncoated in an AMRAY 1820 scanning electron microscope. Shock recovered specimens came from material which was within 10 mm of the center of the TiB2 target. The plane of examination for the shock recovered specimens was perpendicular to the spall plane. Sixteen noncontiguous fields of view comprising a 4 column x 4 row grid pattern were analyzed for each specimen. For shock recovered specimens the rows were positioned at the spall plane and at 300, 500 and 700 μm down from the spall plane. In the shock recovered specimens data taken at 300, 500 and 700 μm from the spall plane are outside of the spall zone. Calculations indicate that the 6.7 GPa test has the widest spall zone with penetration 132 μm into the material from the spall plane. The average area of a field of view was 35.6 x 10^3 μm^2. The overall area spanned by a grid pattern averaged 2 mm^2.

RESULTS AND DISCUSSION

Microstructural examinations of the TiB2 before impact testing reveal preexisting cracks and pores. Cracks are present both at grain boundaries and within grains, although intra-granular cracking is more prevalent. Porosity, on the other hand, is mainly intergranular. These observations also apply to all the shock recovered specimens. A representative micrograph is shown in Figure 2. One distinguishing feature of the cracking in the impacted specimens is that it occurs nominally parallel to the spall plane.

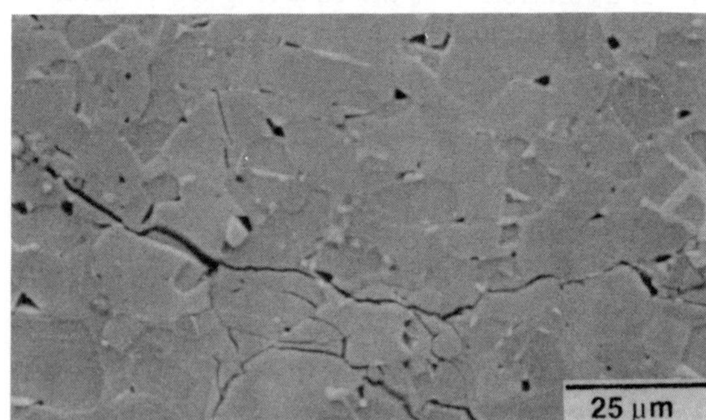

Figure 2. Recovered TiB2 from 6.7 GPa at 300μm below spall plane.

Crack Damage

Effect of Depth

For shock recovered specimens the crack densities and the crack lengths are constant with depth from the spall plane to 700 μm. Increased damage is not seen at the spall plane because the observation area is large compared to the size of the spall zone. Thus, damage in the form of cracking appears homogeneous throughout the body. This has two implications. First, models of material behavior which assume a homogeneous body are applicable. And, second, the material can be sampled at any depth indiscriminately for knowledge of the crack damage sustained.

Effect of Peak Compressive Stress

A comparison in Figure 3 of the as-received TiB2 and the recovered TiB2 from conventional spall experiments indicates that the average number density of cracks increases with increasing peak compressive stress. The largest generation of new cracks occurs when the peak stress exceeds HEL1. The application of up to 5 GPa produces 236 more cracks/mm^2 compared to the starting density of 63 cracks/mm^2. However, when the peak stress is raised above the lower cusp to 6.7 GPa the crack density increases 731 cracks/mm^2 over the starting density.

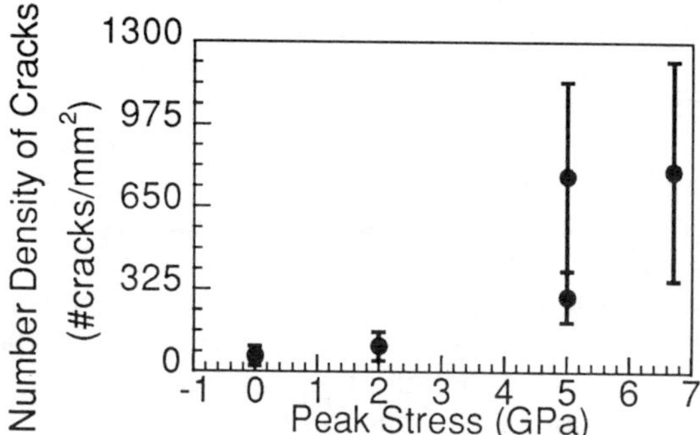

Figure 3. Variations in crack length with stress

The effect of peak compressive stress on the average crack length is the same as discussed above for crack densities. Below HEL1 the average length of a crack increases with peak stress from 5.8 μm at 0 GPa to 11.6 μm at 5 GPa. At 6.7 GPa the crack length jumps to 27.8 μm. Despite the scatter in the data the observed trend in the averages, increasing crack lengths and densities with increasing stress, is believed to exist. The dramatic rise in crack lengths and densities at HEL1 indicates that the lower cusp is a threshold above which there is increased generation of irreversible damage. The result, as seen in Figure 1, is a falling spall threshold.

Effect of Reshock

The conventional spall experiments indicate that peak stresses below the lower cusp produce crack damage in TiB2. Reshock experiments corroborate this observation. Comparing the reshock 5 GPa to the simple 5 GPa experiment in Figure 3 demonstrates that the second shock wave both generates and propagates cracks. Crack densities jump 473 cracks/mm^2 with corresponding increases in the average crack length of 7.8 μm compared to the 5 GPa single shock.

The rise in damage seen in the reshock experiment was not anticipated by comparing the average spall strength of the 5 GPa to the reshock 5 GPa. However, there is increased scatter in the value of the spall threshold measured in the reshock experiments. Consequently, average reshock spall data overlap with the spall data from the 6.7 GPa experiment, as seen in Figure 1. Analytical models [4] indicate that a decline in tensile properties is proportional to increases in the number density of cracks and to the cube of increases in the average crack length. The 5 GPa reshock has crack densities comparable to the 6.7 GPa. However, since the 6.7 GPa has significantly longer cracks than the 5 GPa reshock its spall strength should be and is lower.

Porosity

As with the crack damage, there is no change in the percent porosity with depth in recovered TiB2 specimens. The effect of peak stress, however, is less certain. The two starting tiles had different volume fractions of porosity (1.5 ± .26 and 3.8 ± .55), and it is not known from which tile a given TiB2 specimen came from. No trends are discernable in the data, and the porosity in each shock recovered specimen falls within the range of porosities in the as-received TiB2.

Modeling

With the porosity and the crack damage of the TiB2 microstructure quantified it is instructive to calculate the expected change in compressibility for comparison to the change, or rather the lack there of, in the measured compressibility. Walsh [3] has developed separate equations for the effect of the presence of cracks and pores on the compressibility of brittle materials when subject to hydrostatic pressures. For pores,

$$\beta_{eff}/\beta = 1+3(1-\nu)\eta/2(1-2\nu)(1-\eta) \qquad (1)$$

where β_{eff}/β is the compressibility ratio of the pore filled material to the solid material, ν is the

Poisson's ratio taken to be 0.1144 for TiB2 and η is the volume fraction porosity.

The largest change in the average percent porosity is 2.3% occurring between the as-received tiles. Calculations from equation 1 show that a 2.3% increase in porosity is expected to decrease the compressibility by 4%. However, changes in compressibility of 3% or less can not be detected experimentally due to measurement error.

For an elliptical crack in plane strain,

$$\beta_{eff}/\beta = 1+4\pi(1-\nu^2)c^3/3(1-2\nu)\upsilon \qquad (2)$$

where c is the average crack length and υ is the average region volume. In the calculations presented here it is assumed that the crack number densities per unit volume equal the crack number densities per unit area so that the average region volume is taken to be 6.830 x 10^6 μm^3. It is also assumed that the crack thickness is approximately 1 μm so that c^3 = (the average crack length)^2 x 1 μm (see Figure 2). These calculations, which also include the number density of cracks, are shown in Figure 4. The threshold at the lower cusp is quite obvious. Yet, despite the large increase in damage at HEL1 the change in compressibility is less than 3% and thus, not experimentally detectable.

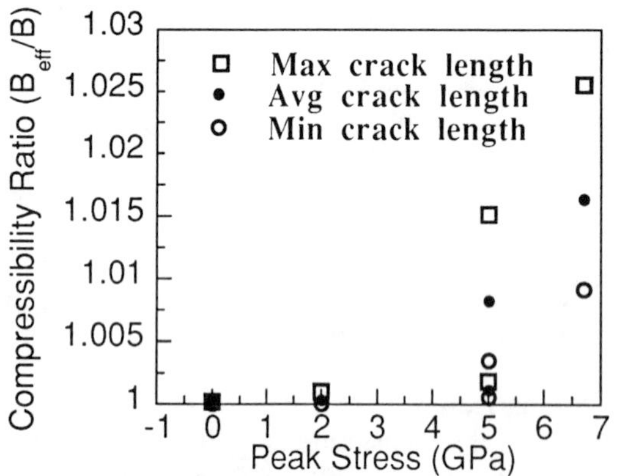

Figure 4. Compressibility ratio as a function of crack length vs. stress.

In plane shock wave experiments materials are deformed under uniaxial strain conditions. However, it is expected that the trends observed using a hydrostatic comparison are representative of the uniaxial strain condition. The actual values calculated in hydrostatic compression will be somewhat smaller than numbers calculated with a uniaxial model.

CONCLUSIONS

A detailed microstructural analysis of as-received and shock recovered TiB2 examining the volume fraction porosity and the crack features has been performed. Shock induced damage, which occurs principally in the form of cracking, has been quantified in terms of average crack lengths and crack number densities. The extent of crack damage is found to be homogeneous throughout each impacted specimen. Crack densities and lengths increase slowly with the peak compressive stress up to HEL1. Dramatic increases in the measured crack features at peak stresses above HEL1 support the existence of a threshold for the generation of increased irreversible crack damage. Predictions of the expected material compressibility based upon the quantitative analysis of crack damage substantiate the lack of observed change in compressibility during shock impact.

REFERENCES

[1] D. P. Dandekar and D. C. Benfanti, Strength of titanium diboride under shock wave loading, *J. Appl. Phys.*, 73, pp. 673-679, 1993, and references therein.

[2] W-D Winkler and A. J. Stilp, Pressure induced macro- and micromechanical phenomena in planar impacted TiB2, in *Shock Compression of Condensed Matter*, 1991, pp. 555-558.

[3] J. B. Walsh, The effect of cracks on the compressibility of rock, *J. of Geophysical Research*, 70, pp.381-389, 1965.

[4] L. G. Margolin, Elastic moduli of a cracked body, *Int. Journ. of Fracture*, 22, pp.65-79, 1983.

PRESSURE EFFECT ON GRAIN BOUNDARY DEWETTING AND PREMELTING TRANSITION IN A Fe-6 at.%Si BICRYSTAL

W.Łojkowski , S. Porowski
High Pressure Research Centre, Polish Academy of Sciences,
Sokołowska 29,
01-142 Warsaw, Poland.

E.I.Rabkin, B.B.Straumal
Institute of Solid State Physics
Russian Academy of Sciences,
142432 Chernogolovka, Russia.

W.Gust
Max-Planck-Institut für Metallforschung
Seestr. 75
W- Stuttgart, FRG

The pressure effect on diffusion of Zn along a 45°<100> grain boundary (GB) in an Fe-6at.%Si bicrystal was studied in the pressure range up to 1 GPa. A Zn layer was deposited on the surface of the bicrystals. It was found that at low pressures the Zn rich liquid wetted the grain boundary perfectly.Next to the GB groove there was a region where Zn diffusion along the grain boundary was enhanced by two orders of magnitude. It is postulated that in the enhanced diffusion region a GB premelting transition has taken place. Increasing pressure caused a dewetting transition at the grain boundary. At the same time the premelted GB region disappeared. The transition pressure was a function of the temperature. There was a minimum transition pressure of 175 MPa at about 790°C. The above results were interpreted based on the heterophase fluctuation theory.

INTRODUCTION

Wetting of grain boundaries (GBs) by liquids is a phenomenon that attracts considerable attention [cf.1,2]. One can distinguish two wetting states:

a) Complete wetting, when the dihedral angle at the intersection of the GB and liquid is zero.

b) Incomplete wetting, when the dihedral angle has a non zero value.

Upon a change of intensive thermodynamic variables a transition between the above two states can take place.

We will further call the a$\Rightarrow$b transition a "de-wetting transition" while the b$\Rightarrow$a transition will be called "wetting transition". In a recent study of wetting of a 45°[100] tilt boundary transition in a Fe-6at.%Si bicrystal by liquid zinc, it was [3,4] discovered that the pressure causes a de-wetting transition. Furthermore, the dihedral angle value increased with increasing pressure. At the annealing temperature of 1178K, the transition pressure was about 0.5GPa.

The wetting angle measurements were carried out parallel to studies of diffusion of zinc along the grain boundary. It was found that complete GB wetting occurred then and only then,

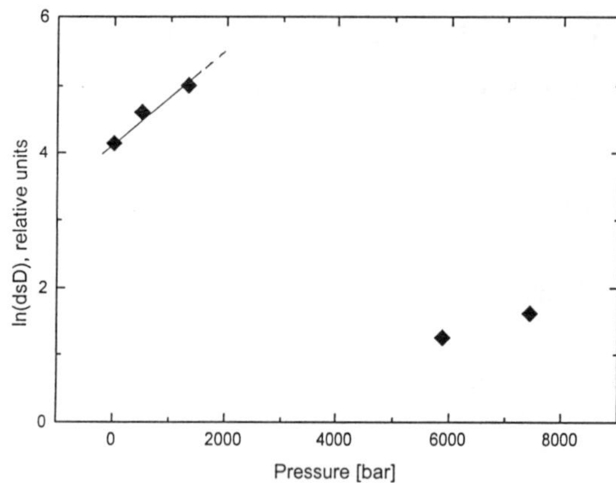

Fig.1 Pressure effect on the triple product for Zn diffusion in the 45°[100] tilt grain boundary in the Fe-6at.%Si bicrystal. D- Zn GB diffusion coefficient, d- GB thickness, s - Zn segregation factor.

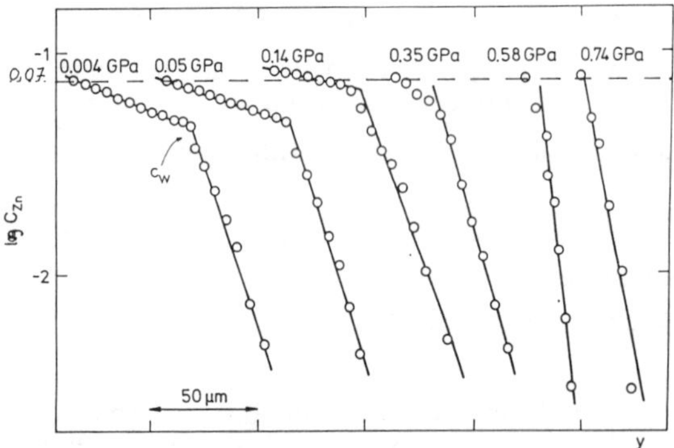

Fig.2. Pressure effect on the concentration profiles of Zn along the grain boundary. y - depth along the GB. Dashed line: the 7% Zn concentration level. according to Rabkin et al [5].

when the GB in the regions adjacent to the liquid zinc layer had undergone a phase transformation, which was identified as GB premelting. The characteristic feature of this transformation was a discontinuity of the GB diffusion coefficient. Figure 1 shows the pressure effect on the Zn GB diffusion coefficient, at constant Zn concentration $C_{Zn}= 0.07$. A similar transition takes place when the Zn concentration decreases. Figure 2 shows the pressure effect on the Zn concentration profiles. Under the conditions that pressure is less than 0.5Gpa, at the high-Zn-concentration side, the GB displays a more than two orders of magnitude higher diffusion coefficient than on the low-zinc-concentration side. The unusually high diffusion coefficient led Rabkin et al. [3-5] to the conclusion that the GB is in a "premelted" state. In other words, under the above conditions a thin liquid-like structure is thermodynamically stable in the GB. Thermodynamic calculations lead to the layer thickness of about 10 nm [5].

The purpose of this paper is to present the results of our study of the pressure effect on the wetting-dewetting transition temperature and to propose an interpretation of the premelting and dewetting transition in terms of the effect of bulk phase transitions on the GB structure.

EXPERIMENTAL

The bicrystals were prepared from vacuum melted Fe-6at.%Si alloy by the floating zone method. The orientation of the bicrystal axis and misorientation of the crystals were measured by X-ray Laue diffraction with the accuracy of ±1°.

The as grown bicrystal was cut by electro-spark cutter into specimens of 12 mm length (parallel to the [100] direction) and 1.5x1.5 mm^2 crosssection. The GB was situated in the middle of the samples, parallel to the [100] axis. A zinc layer was deposited on each sample by immersion into liquid zinc. After the immersion, zinc was removed from all sides of the samples except for the ones perpendicular to the [100] axis. Excess zinc was removed so that only a 100-150µm layer remained. For the high pressure annealing, the specimens were placed in a stainless steel container of I.D. 7.9 mm. In the bottom part of the capsule about 50 mm^3 of zinc were placed to ensure equilibrium zinc vapour concentration in the capsule during high pressure annealing. The capsule was not tight, so that argon under high pressure could penetrate it. The high pressure experiments were carried out in a high pressure cell. The temperature in the capsule was measured with an accuracy of 1±K. Pressure was measured with accuracy better than 1% using a manganin coil.

After the high pressure annealing, the samples were polished and examined by light microscopy and the dihedral angle at the GB grove was measured.

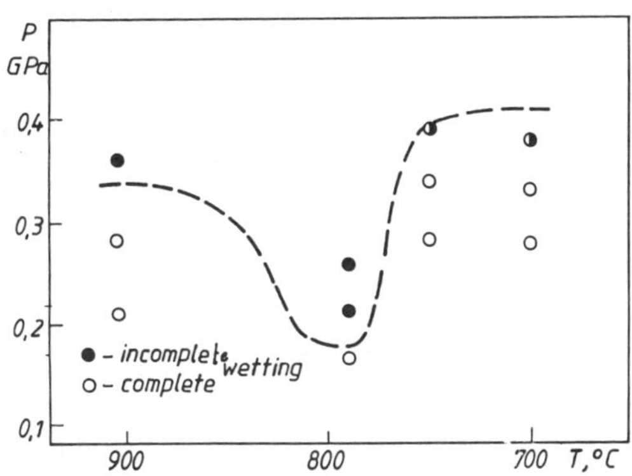

Fig.3. Temperature effect on the wetting-dewetting transition pressure.

RESULTS

The results of anealing are presented in Fig. 3; open circles correspond to complete wetting, whereas the solid circles indicate incomplete-wetting. This figure shows how the pressure at which wetting transition occurs depends on temperature. It can be seen that around T=790°C, the minimum transition pressure was observed. Fig. 4 shows the optical micrographs of the GB groove at the contact place of the liquid zinc and grain boundary after annealing at high pressure. The photographs in the first row indicate the first occurence of incomplete wetting after transition wetting-dewetting.

The second row phtographs correspond to the last occurence of complete wetting prior to the transition. The transition temperature has a minimum close to 1063K (790°C).

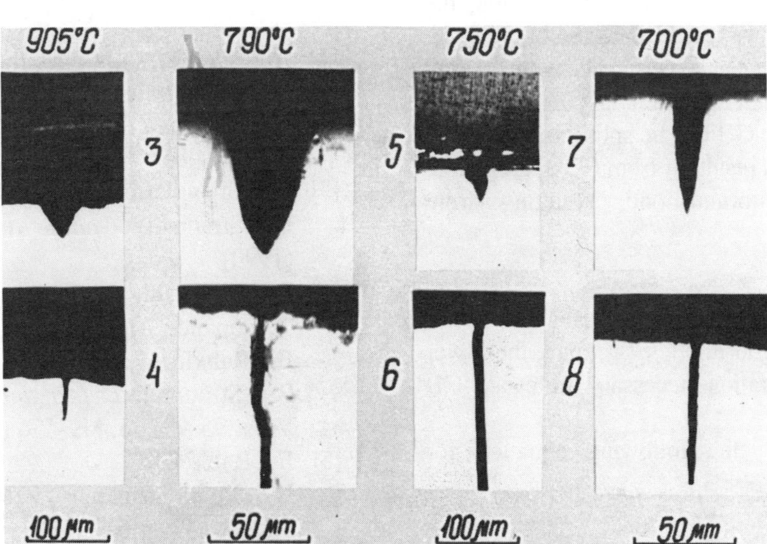

Fig.4. Optical micrographs of the GB groove at the contact place of the liquid Zn and grain boundary.

DISCUSSION

The pressure effect on the wetting transition can be explained under the assumptions that the energy of the pre-melted GB increases with pressure more rapidly than of the GB with regular structure.

The following equations describe the equilibrium of surface tensions for the complete-wetting state:

$$\gamma_{GB} = 2\gamma_{SL} + g \qquad (1)$$

where γ_{GB} is the surface tension of a regular grain boundary, γ_{LS} is the liquid-solid interface surface tension and g is the energy of the pre-melted layer per unit surface [5]. It follows that complete wetting takes place if $2\gamma_{SL}+g<\gamma_{GB}$. Hence, the wetting and premelting behaviour depends on the energy of the thin layer of the grain boundary that is in the pre-melted state.

In order to explain the occurence of the minimum at temperature 790°C Fig. 3, which corresponds to peritectic temperature of Fe 6% Si-Zn, we assume that the energy of the GB depends on the zinc concentration in the grain boundary. The higher the zinc concentration, the more the GB structure reassembles the liquid state. This is so, since all the experiments were carried out above the melting point of Zn. The Zn concentration in the GB can be split into two parts: the equilibrium one resulting from GB segregation, and the nonequilibrium one, resulting from diffusion.

$$C_{Zn} = C_{Segr} + C_{Diff}. \qquad (2)$$

Hence, the higher the C_{Segr} value, the lower the C_{Diff} concentration necessary to cause GB premelting.

We propose the following equation for C_{Segr}:

$$C_{Segr} = C_o \exp\left(\frac{Q + a(T - T_P)}{T}\right) \qquad (3)$$

Where Tp is the peritectic temperature and $a(T-Tp)$ is the energy difference between Zn - liquid phase and the Γ phase, which forms below the peritectic temperature. a=0 for $T>Tp$. In other words, below the peritectic temperature, Zn in the grain boundary forms with iron atoms solid clusters of the Γ phase, and is not any more available for the liquidlike grain boundary phase. As a consequence, at Tp the highest concentration of Zn in liquid clusters in the boundary is present. Therefore, the density of the interface is lowest and the pressure effect on its energy is highest.

This interpretation of the existence of the minimum of transitum pressure at Tp is consistent with the heterophase fluctuation theory, where it is assumed that thermal fluctuations at lattice defects take the structure of the closest neighbourhood phase in the phase diagram [6].

ACKNOWLEDGEMENTS.

W.L. is grateful to the Polish Committee for Science for financial support.

REFERENCES

[1] A.Passerone, N.Eustathopulaos, P.Desrè, *J.Less Common Metall*, 52, p.37 (1977)

[2] A.Passerone, R.Sangiorgi, *Acta Metall.*, 33, p.771 (1985)

[3] L.S.Shvindlerman, W.Łojkowski, E.I.Rabkin, B.B.Straumal, *Coll.de Phys*51, p.TC 629 (1990)

[4] W.Łojkowski, J.Swiderski, Y.Minamino, T.Yamane, J.Kwieciñski, D.A.Molodov, E.I.Rabkin, L.S.Shvindlerman, B.B.Straumal, *Defect and Diffusion Forum*, Vols. 95-98, pp.449-456 (1993)

[5] E.I.Rabkin, V.N.Semenov, L.S.Shvindlerman, B.B.Straumal, *Acta Metall.*, 39, p.627 (1991)

[6] B.S.Bokstein, V.V.Kopetskii, L.S.Shvindlerman, *"Thermodynamics and Kinetics of Grain Boundaries in Metals"*, ed.Metallurgia, Moscow (1986)

LOCAL RAPID QUENCHING IN A POWDER MIXTURE AND ITS UTILIZATION TO SYNTHESIZE NOVEL COMPOUNDS IN THE B-C-N SYSTEM

A.B.SAWAOKA[1], K.DAN[1], H.TAMURA[1], Y.HORIE[2] AND K.YAMADA[3]

[1]Center for Ceramics Research, Tokyo Institute of Technology, Midori, Yokohama 227, Japan
[2]Department of Civil Engineering, North Carolina State University, Raleigh, NC27695-7908, USA
[3]Department of Chemistry, National Defense Academy, Hashirimizu, Yokosuka239, Japan

ABSTRACT

A selective surface heating of particle and local mixing are known as a typical microscopic effect on shock compression of powder. In the case, the thermal conductivity of powder particle is sufficiently high, like diamond, shock compression technique can be used as a means of local heating and rapid quenching of particle surface. Shock compression of powder in a metal capsule causes steep distribution of pressure and temperature by shock waves interaction. A rod-in-cylinder type recovery assembly composed of steel rod having sample cavity and aluminum alloy cylinder is used in this study. After shock-treatment, particle surfaces in the powder mixture of diamond and boron nitride were observed with a high resolution transmission electron microscope. It is demonstrated that this method has a high potential as a tool of new material exploration.

INTRODUCTION

When shock wave is introduced into powder, the shock energy distributes at surface of particles other than interior of them. As a result, the surface is much more heated than the interior. The temperature difference in a powder particle is thus relieved. In the case, the thermal conductivity of powder particle is sufficiently high, like diamond, shock compression technique can be used as a means of local heating and rapid quenching of particle surface. Kondo and Sawai estimated a cooling rate near surface of diamond particle as 10^{13} K/s when the surface was heated at 5,300 K and the core 340 K by shock compression [1]. An unique attempt to explore new materials has been conducted by utilizing such local surface heating and following rapid cooling phenomenon at surface of powder particles [2,3].

Metal capsule is indispensable in the shock recovery experiment. Shock compression process of powder in a metal capsule is complicated because of large difference of shock wave velocity in the powder and metal capsule. A rod-in-cylinder type shock recovery assembly has been used for the higher shock pressure production. This technique was applied to study metallurgical effect on iron and copper [4,5].

An ejection of metal jet from capsule wall into relatively low shock impedance sample is unavoidable during strong shock wave passage. This jetting material is caused as contamination. For avoiding such contamination, a new type of recovery fixture with sample cavity with cylinder shape in long rod was designed. When converging shock waves interact in the powder, a remarkable local temperature increase is expected due to violent particle sliding at the shock wave interaction area. This technique has been applied to explore new compounds in the B-C-N system.

A NEW SHOCK RECOVERY SYSTEM

A cylindrical sample cavity is settled in the rod-in-cylinder type recovery assembly which consists of stainless steel rod and aluminum alloy cylinder. It is expected that Mach disk is formed in the sample cavity containing powder specimen and that the contamination due to metal jetting from wall of sample cavity is negligible small near the central axis except top boundary. Cross section of the recovery assembly is shown in Fig. 1. The dimensions of SUS 304 stainless steel rod are 12 mm in diameter and 60 mm in length, and those of 2024 aluminum alloy cylinder are 12 mm in inner and 24 mm in outer diameter, 60 mm in length. The assembly is placed in the momentum trap type recovery fixture which was described elsewhere [6,7]. The impact velocity of the 3.2 mm thick iron flyer plate onto the end of the assembly were 1.6 or 2.3 km/s. The dimensions of sample cavity are 6 mm in diameter and 15 mm in length which located 25 mm from the impact interface.

A numerical simulation of pressure distribution and history in the recovery assembly was conducted in the case of 2.3 km/s flyer impact velocity. The maximum shock pressure is close to about 100 GPa in the diamond and h-BN mixture [3]. Another simulation indicated, 50% higher pressure can be produced by the use of the rod-in-cylinder recovery system, in comparison with conventional technique in case of same impact velocity [8].

AN ATTEMPT TO EXPLORE NEW COMPOUNDS IN THE B-C-N SYSTEM

Synthetic diamond powder with 10~20 mm

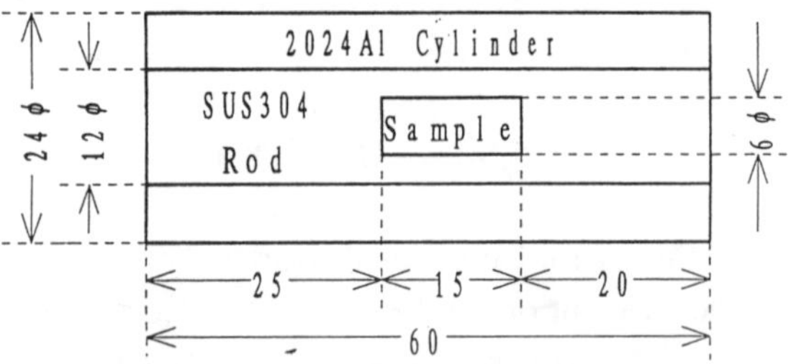

Fig. 1 Schematic Layout of rod-in-cylinder type recovery assembly, a flyer plate impacts onto left end surface.

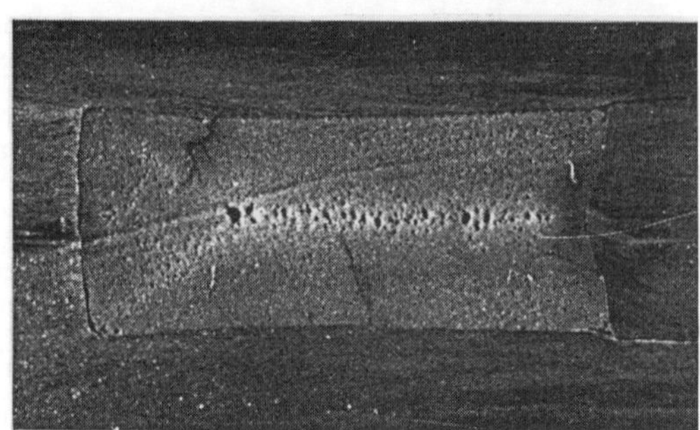

Fig. 2 Cross sectional view of shock-treated powder mixture of diamond and boron nitride; 92:8 in volume %. Flyer plate impact velocity was 1.6 km/s. Impact face was left side.

particle size (300 series, General Electric Co.) and h-BN powder with 1.3 mm (GP grade, Showa Denko Co.) were mixed in the volume ratio of 92:8. This mixture was pressed to 60% of theoretical density in the sample cavity as shown in Fig. 1. Recovery fixtures are shock-treated at impact velocities of flyer plate at 1.6 and 2.3 km/s. Recovered stainless steel capsule was cut into one half on the plane including the central axis and washed in an acetone bath with ultrasonic vibration. Cross section of the sample obtained at 1.6 km/s is shown in Fig. 2. Y-shape white region can be seen on the section. Many holes with diameter of 0.2-0.5 mm formed by grain removal are seen on the Y-shape region. This means that the bonding of diamond particles are not enough in the Y-shape region.

The cross section of the sample was observed by a scanning electron microscope. Five pictures

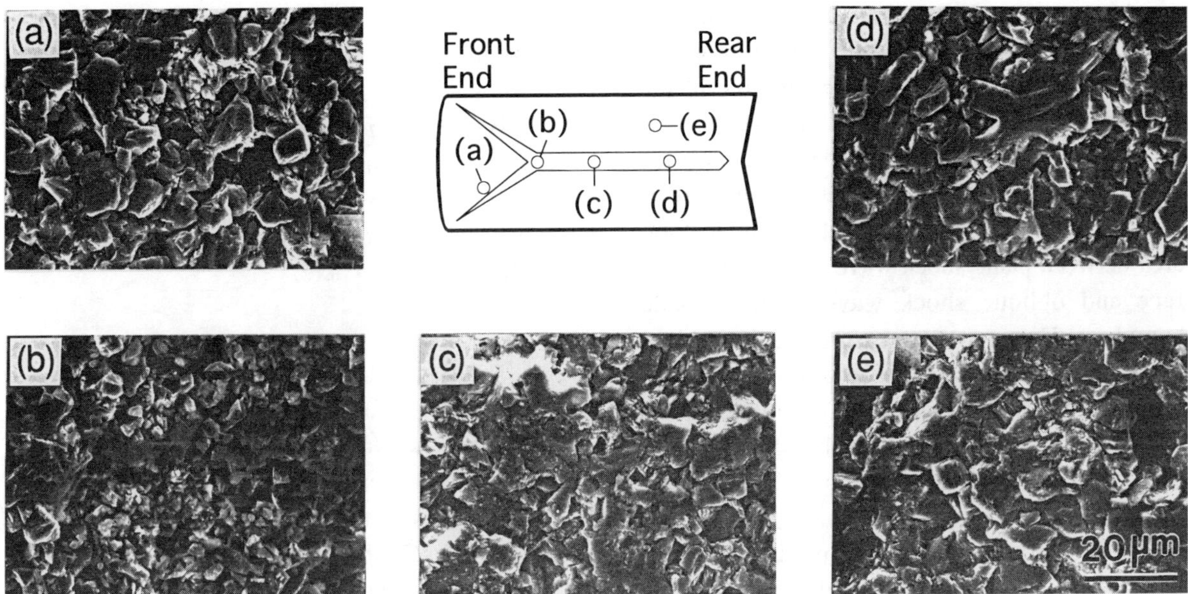

Fig. 3 Scanning electron micrograph of shock-treated powder mixture of diamond and boron nitride; 92:8 in volume % . Starting diamond is 10~20 μm and h-BN is 1.3 μm powder. Flyer plate impact velocity was 1.6 km/s. Impact face was left side.

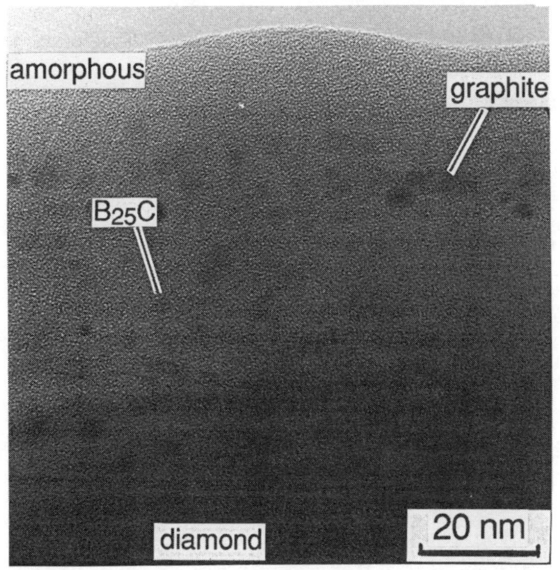

Fig. 4 Transmission electron micrograph of surface of diamond particle, obtained from region (b) in Fig. 3. Two kinds of crystalline fine sphere precipitated in an amorphous layer on diamond particle were observed; one is graphite and the other is $B_{25}C$.

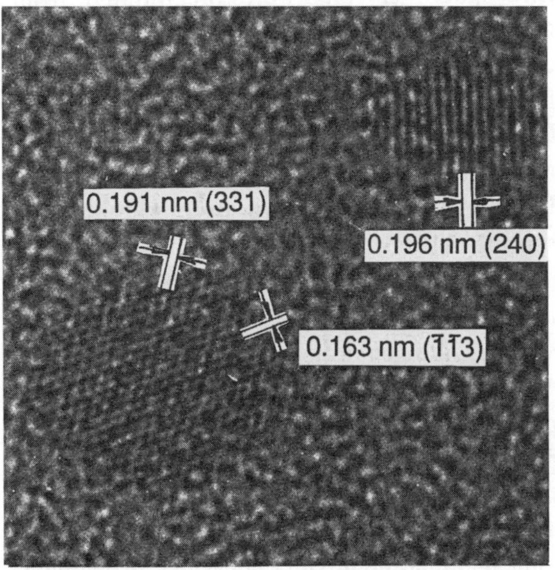

Fig. 5 Lattice images of very small sphere in amorphous layer of diamond particle, obtained from region (b) in Fig. 3. The crystallographic data obtained from this picture suggested, these particles are $B_{25}C$.

are shown in Fig. 3. It is seen, diamond particles were broken into small pieces in the whole region. Crushing tendency is remarkable in the Y-shape region, especially at region (b) in Fig. 3. Why is color of the Y-shape region white? The V-shape region of Y as seen in the left of Fig. 2 corresponds qualitatively to the interaction area between plane shock wave entered from top face and oblique shock wave from the side boundary. Thus a steep pressure gradient might be existed in the V-shape region and caused crashing of diamond particles. Crashing tendency in the white straight region on the central axis is also remarkable, which corresponds to the Mach disk formation.

Microstructures in diamond particles corresponding to the region (b) in Fig. 3 were observed by a high resolution transmission electron microscope. Surface of the diamond particle is surrounded by an amorphous layer with 30~60 nm thickness as seen in Fig. 4. Very fine sphere crystals were precipitated from amorphous layer. There are two kinds of sphere crystals of 3~5 nm in diameter in the amorphous layer. Lattice images of both spheres suggested that one is graphite phase and other is $B_{25}C$ having tetragonal symmetry. Lattice images of $B_{25}C$ particle are shown in Fig. 5. Lattice spacing obtained from the lattice image are 0.196 nm for (240), 0.191 nm for (331) and 0.163 nm for ($\bar{1}\bar{1}3$). It is not clear, this amorphous layer includes nitrogen or not.

Paisley et al. [3] investigated this composite prepared at 2.3 km/s impact velocity by the present authors. A few mg sample was collected from the central white region in this composite. An x-ray diffraction pattern of the sample indicated that the mixture consisted of diamond, graphite, h-BN and unknown phases whose planar spacings are 0.225, 0.1743 and 0.1293 nm. They found two kinds of fine crystals by an electron diffraction of the particle in the mixture. One fine crystal was identified as $B_{25}N$. The other was unidentified phase which has different planar spacing to the unknown phase mentioned above.

$(BN)_{0.26}C_{0.74}$ is known in the B-C-N system which was synthesized by Badzian (9). The present authors also found this compound between diamond and BN particles. Details will be described elsewhere.

ACKNOWLEDGMENTS

The authors would like to thank M.J.Paisley of North Carolina State University for useful discussions on characterization of extreme small amount materials.

This work is supported by Grant-in-Aid Scientific Research for Priority Area "Shock Waves", given by Ministry of Education, Science and Cultures, Japan.

REFERENCES

[1] K.Kondo and S.Sawai, *J. Am. Ceramic Society*, 75, 253, 1992.

[2] K.Dan, H.Kunishige, H.Tamura, A.B.Sawaoka, T.Akaski and H.Kudo, *Yogyo-Kyokai-Shi*, in print (in Japanese).

[3] M.J.Paisley, Y.Horie, R.F.Davis, K.Dan, H.Tamura and A.B.Sawaoka, *J. Mat. Sci. Letters*, in print.

[4] K.Dan, H.Tamura, H,Kunishige, A.B.Sawaoka and T.Mori, in *Shock Waves*-Proceedings, Sendai 1991, p.181, Springer-Verlag, 1992.

[5] K.Dan, H.Tamura, A.B.Sawaoka, T.Mori, M.D.Hwang and Y.Horie, in *this proceedings*.

[6] A.B.Sawaoka, in *Shock waves in Materials Science*, edited by A.B.Sawaoka, Springer Verlag, Tokyo, p.1, 1993.

[7] A.B.Sawaoka and Y.Horie, in *Shock Compression Chemistry of Materials*, KTK Publishers, Tokyo, 1993.

[8] H.Kunishige, Y.Horie and A.B.Sawaoka, in *Proceedings of 1988 National Symp. Shock Wave Phenomena*, pp. 181, 1988.

[9] A.Badzian, Mater. Res. Bull., 16, 1385.

EFFECTS OF SHOCK LOADING ON A SOLID-SOLUTION STRENGTHENED SUPERALLOY

KENNETH S. VECCHIO* and GEORGE T. GRAY III†,
*Dept. of AMES, UC San Diego, 9500 Gilman Dr., La Jolla, CA 92093-0411
†Los Alamos National Lab., Los Alamos, NM, 87544

Ni-based HAYNES® 230™ ALLOY has been studied to determine the effect of shock loading on the post-shock quasistatic and dynamic mechanical response, and microstructural evolution. The compression properties of this material was studied in both the as-received and shock-loaded conditions at strain rates from 10^{-3}/s to 3000/s, and 77 and 293K. Damage evolution was documented via TEM, and correlated with the observed mechanical response. Changes in the deformation mechanisms and second phase distributions resulting from the shock pre-straining and subsequent testing are correlated with changes in the strain hardening behavior of the materials. Comparison of these results with shock loading results on pure Ni revealed distinct differences in strengthening and defect storage mechanisms.

INTRODUCTION

To date most research on shock-loading effects in FCC materials has been directed at either pure metals or metal alloys strengthened by single element solid solutions or precipitates. Shock-loaded fcc metals and alloys have been repeatedly shown to exhibit increased defect storage, and concurrent higher hardening, behavior in reload tests after shock recovery compared to the same metal deformed at low strain rate to an equivalent strain level[1-3]. By comparison relatively little work has probed the response of more complex, engineering alloys which derive their mechanical properties through a combination of strengthening mechanisms.

In the 1970's and early 1980's a new generation of solid-solution strengthened superalloys was introduced with the goal of approaching the strength of the best cobalt-based alloys, with cobalt additions either reduced or eliminated. An example of this effort, and the subject of the present study is HAYNES® 230™ Alloy (hereafter 230 alloy). which is based on the Ni-Cr-W system. 230 alloy is solid-solution strengthened primarily by tungsten, but like alloy X and cobalt-based HAYNES® 188™ Alloy, also relies to a large extent on carbide precipitation strengthening.

The primary solid-solution element in 230 alloy is tungsten. Tungsten was selected in favor of refractory elements such as molybdenum because of its larger atomic diameter (13% greater than nickel) and lower diffusivity in nickel. Tungsten also lowers the stacking fault energy (SFE) of nickel thus restricting cross slip of dislocations. Carbides are important contributors to the overall strengthening observed in these alloys, perhaps to a greater degree than solid-solution strengthening.

The purpose of this study was to investigate the effect of shock-loading on the mechanical properties of 230 alloy, and to correlate these properties to the microstructural changes and substructure evolution as a function of strain rate and test temperature.

EXPERIMENTAL PROCEDURE

230 alloy in the form of hot-rolled bar was produced at Haynes International, Kokomo, IN (Heat Number 8305-9-7178). The chemical composition of this alloy is given in Ref. 4, along with the hot-rolling conditions. Shock recovery experiments were performed at New Mexico Tech., Socorro, NM using shock recovery techniques described elsewhere [5]. Samples were explosively shock-loaded to a shock pressure of 55 GPa for a 1.4μs pulse duration. Compression samples were EDM machined from the as-received bar stock and shock recovered samples. Compression tests were conducted at strain rates ranging from 0.001 to 3000 s^{-1}, at both room temperature (293K) and liquid nitrogen temperature (77K). Samples for transmission

electron microscopy (TEM) were also sectioned from the recovered samples and observed using a CM-30 operating at 300kV.

RESULTS AND DISCUSSION

Figure 1 shows a TEM micrograph of the starting microstructure of 230 alloy processed at 1121°C. The microstructure consists of grains ~20μm in diameter, which contain some annealing twins, large M_6C carbides and smaller $M_{23}C_6$ carbides. The presence of the annealing twins is indicative of an FCC matrix having a low stacking fault energy, resulting from the W solid-solution addition.

Figure 1. TEM micrograph showing the initial microstructure, particularly the dislocation substructure.

Figure 2 presents plots of the true stress-true strain response of 230 alloy at strain rates of 0.001/s and 3000/s, each at temperatures of 293K and 77K. The most striking aspects of these curves is the strong dependence of the yield strength on strain rate and temperature, as well as the apparent dependence of strain hardening rate on strain rate.

Figure 3 is a TEM micrograph of the as-received 230 alloy following deformation at 77K and 3000/s strain rate. The propensity for coarse planar slip was found to increase with increasing strain rate and decreasing temperature, with the most pronounced example shown here. Following low strain rate-room temperature testing, the dislocation substructure was clearly more homogeneous, although still planar in nature consistent with the low SFE of 230 alloy.

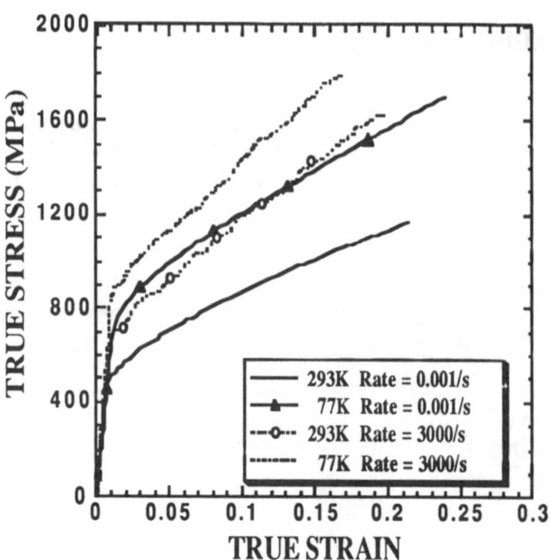

Figure 2. True stress-true strain responses of as-received 230 alloy.

Figure 3. TEM micrograph of as-received 230 alloy deformed at 77K and 3000/s showing planar dislocation arrays.

Figure 4 is a TEM micrograph showing the dislocation substructure and microbands introduced as a results of the shock-loading. The number of microbands varied from grain to grain, and Figure 4 represents a typical density observed; isolated deformation twins were also observed.

Figure 5 presents the reload true stress-true strain response for the shock-recovered 230 alloy material. The material shows a significant increase in yield strength for each test condition compared to the unshocked, as received 230

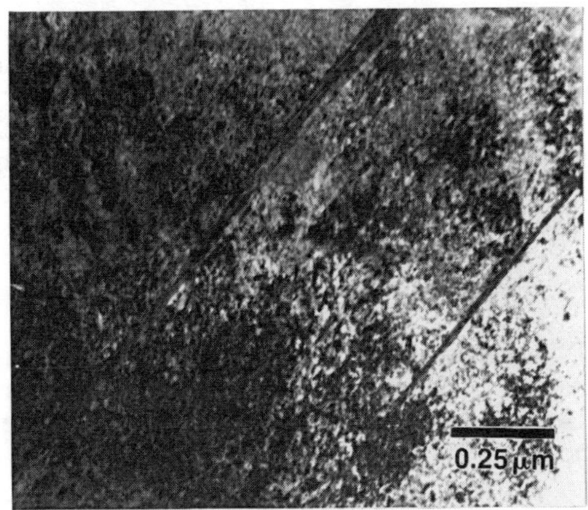

Figure 4. TEM micrograph of shock-loaded 230 alloy showing dislocation debris and microbands.

alloy. Additional tests were conducted, although not shown, in which compression samples were remachined to remove any slight barreling, reloaded to an additional ~20% strain and the process repeated. In those tests performed at 77K and 3000/s, conducted in the manner described above, 230 alloy exhibited sustained work-hardening to a strength level approaching 2.6 GPa at a true strain of ~1, followed by catastrophic shear failure. At that point, the ratio of flow stress to elastic modulus approaches 1/80.

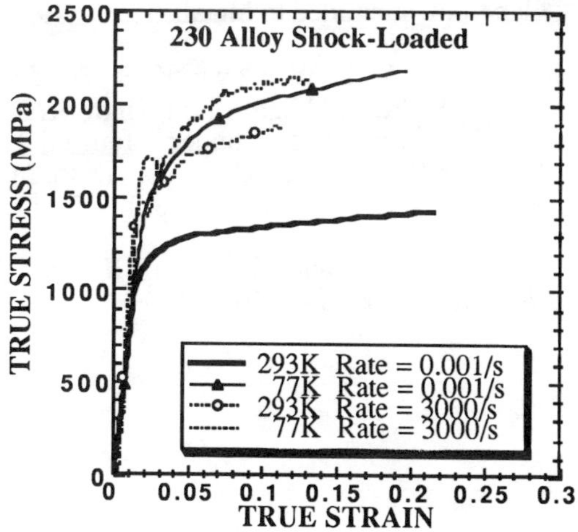

Figure 5. Reload true stress-true strain responses of shock-loaded 230 alloy.

In general, the microstructures of the reloaded shocked specimens were very similar to each other, with the reemergence of planar dislocation arrays. The most distinct change in the microstructure from the as-shocked condition was the presence of very fine scale twins. The greatest density of these microtwins was found in the 0.001/s-293K reload sample (see Figure 6). The microtwins were present in almost every grain of this sample, and may explain the reduced hardening rate observed for this sample during the reload tests, see Figure 5.

Figure 7 shows a plot of the quasi-statically loaded stress-strain response of the as-received 230 alloy and the reload stress-strain curve for the shocked 230 alloy. The reload shock curve in Figure 6 has been offset with respect to the as-received 230 alloy response by the transient strain in the shock defined as 4/3 $\ln(V/V_0)$, where V and V_0 are the final and initial volumes of 230 alloy during the shock cycle. Also shown in this figure are results from a similar study on pure nickel shocked to 10 GPa [6] showing a significant increase in the reload yield strength compared to the annealed material deformed to an equivalent strain. Contrary to the previous results for pure Ni, Ni-based 230 alloy shocked to 55 GPa does not exhibit an increased shock hardening response compared to the 230 alloy quasi-statically deformed.

Figure 7 also shows the significant increase in strength level on 230 alloy compared to pure Ni, as well as the significantly higher strain hardening rate for 230 alloy in both the as-received alloy and the shock recovered material. The influence of multiple strengthening mechanisms is clearly evident from the absolute strength levels achieved by these two different nickel-based materials.

Comparison of the influence of shock loading on the mechanical response of pure Ni and Ni-based 230 alloy reveals that the ability to increase the defect storage capacity of each material must be linked to stacking fault energy (SFE) differences. The higher SFE pure Ni is capable of storing a comparatively higher density of defects as a result of the shock loading, than it achieved through normal quasi-static deformation to equivalent strains. In 230 alloy, although the total defect storage capacity is significantly higher than for pure Ni, the amount of hardening achieved by shock loading was no greater than that which would be attained by normal quasi-static deformation. These results suggest that systematic studies of the influence of SFE on defect storage under shock-loading deformation would be a potentially very insightful avenue for future research.

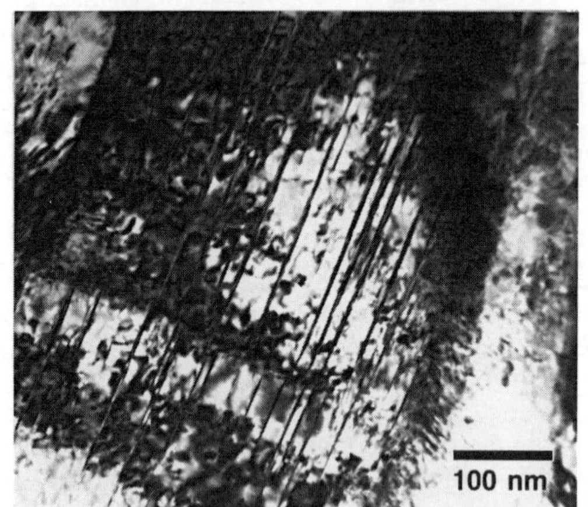

Figure 6. TEM micrograph of the shock-loaded 230 alloy reloaded at a strain rate of 0.001/s and 293K.

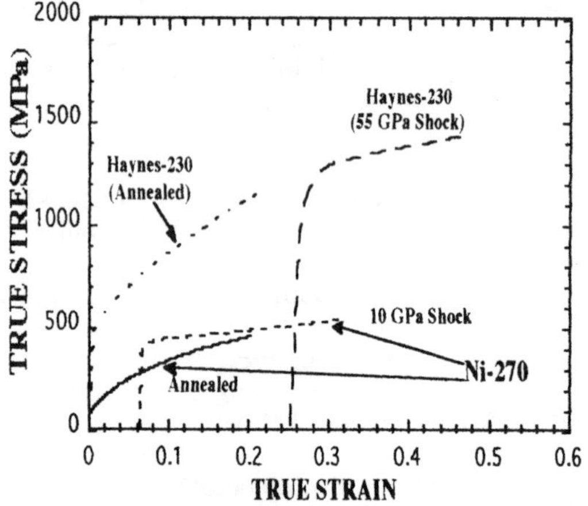

Figure 7. Comparison of as-received and shock-loaded 230 alloy with reload curve of shocked sample offset by transient shock strain. The results from a similar study of pure Ni are also plotted.

CONCLUSIONS

Based on a study of the shock-loading and substructure evolution response of a Ni-based superalloy [HAYNES 230 alloy], the following conclusions can be drawn: 1) substructure evolution in 230 alloy exhibits planar dislocation arrays which is exacerbated by increasing strain rate and decreasing temperature; and 2) contrary to pure Ni, 230 alloys displays no shock enhanced defect storage due to the low cross-slip propensity resulting from the lower SFE due to W alloy additions.

ACKNOWLEDGMENTS

KSV acknowledges support by the U.S. Army Research Office through a URI at UCSD contract #DAAL03-92-G-0108 and GTG acknowledges support by the U.S. Dept. of Energy.

REFERENCES

[1] G.E. Dieter, in *Response of Metals to High Velocity Deformation,* Interscience Publishers, New York, pp. 409-445 (1961).

[2] L.E. Murr, in *Shock Waves and High Strain Rate Phenomena in Metals,* (ed. by M.A. Meyers and L.E. Murr) Plenum Press, N.Y., p. 607 (1981).

[3] G.T. Gray III, in *High Pressure Shock Compression of Solids,* (ed. by J.R. Asay and M. Shahinpoor) N.Y.: Springer-Verlag, ch. 6, (1993).

[4] K. S. Vecchio, M. F. Fitzpatrick, and D. Klarstrom, submitted to Metall. Trans., 1993.

[5] Meyers, M. A., L. W. Meyer, K. S. Vecchio, and U. Andrade, "High Strain, High Strain-Rate Deformation of Copper," Journal De Physique IV, Colloque C3, suppl. au Journal de Physique III, Oct. 1991, **1**, pp. 11-17.

[6] P.S. Follansbee and G.T. Gray III, *Int. J. Plasticity* , **7**, pp. 651-660 (1991).

EFFECT OF HIGH PRESSURE ON GRAIN BOUNDARY MIGRATION IN ALUMINIUM BICRYSTALS.

S.Porowski, W.Łojkowski,
High Pressure Research Centre, Polish Academy of Sciences,
Sokołowska 29,
01-142 Warsaw, Poland.

D.A.Molodov, L.S.Shvindlerman,
Institute of Solid State Physics
RussianAcademy of Sciences,
142432 Chernogolovka, Russia.

G.Gottstein
Institut für Metallkunde und Metallphysik,
RWTH Aachen,
Kopernikusstr.14
W-5100 Aachen, FRG

The effect of high pressures on the migration rate of grain boundaries (GBs) in aluminium bicrystals was studied. The boundaries were of tilt type, with <111>, <100> and <110> tilt axis. For each tilt axis at least two boundaries were studied, one with periodic and another with non-periodic structure. It was found that for the <111> and <100> boundaries the activation volumes (V^*) for migration were independent both on the activation energy and on misorientation. The obtained values were close to 1.2 atomic volume (Ω), which corresponds to V^* for self-diffusion. For the four <110> boundaries investigated V^* was proportional to the activation energy and was in the range 1.1-3.6 Ω. These results indicate that in <111> and <100> boundaries GB migration takes place by single atom transfer, with cooperation of one vacancy. In the case of <110> boundaries it takes place by transfer of groups of atoms by a multi-vacancy-mechanism.

INTRODUCTION

The mechanism of grain boundary (GB) migration attracts considerable interest [1]. One reason is the technological importance of grain growth in polycrystals. Another reason is that understanding the grain boundary migration (GBM) mechanism may help us to understand the GB structure. The GBM rate depends on the GB mobility M and driving force F [cf.1]:

$$v = F \cdot M \qquad (1)$$

where v is the GB migration rate. Pressure affects the GBM rate, since both F and M are a function of pressure [cf.2]:

$$F = F_o + pV^f$$
$$M = M_o \exp\left(\frac{-pV^*}{RT}\right) \qquad (2)$$

V^f is the GB free volume, i.e., the difference of atomic volume for GB atoms and bulk atoms. V^* is the activation volume for GBM. F is a linear function of pressure, so the pressure effect on the driving force for GBM can be neglected. As a consequence, the equation obtains:

$$V^* = -\frac{1}{RT}\frac{\partial \ln v}{\partial P} \qquad (3)$$

V^* reflects the volume expansion of the crystals when atoms jump across the boundary. Hence, investigations of the pressure effect on GBM may permit to evaluate the mechanism of grain boundary migration.

Hahn and Gleiter [3] studied the pressure effect on grain growth in Cd. They obtained the V^* value 0,3Ω, where Ω is the atomic volume. This is considerably lower than 0,8Ω, the activation volume for GB diffusion in Ag and Al [4,5]. The activation volumes for GB diffusion and GB migration can be compared with each other because GB migration can be treated as diffusion perpendicular to the boundary. Hahn and Gleiter concluded that GBM takes place by jumps of atoms without the participation of vacancies. According to Hahn and Gleiter, there are places in GBs where mismatch of the lattices of the crystals causes "loose packing" of the atoms. In such places vacancy-less atomic jumps are possible.

On the other hand, Łojkowski et al [2,6,7] obtained the values V^*=0,8Ω and 0,65 Ω for the activation volume for grain growth in aluminium. The V^* value depended on the thermomechanical story of the polycrystals. The above difference in values indicates, that the activation volume may depend on the structure of boundaries in the polycrystals.

The grain growth rate provides averaged data for boundaries in the polycrystal and gives limited information about the correlation between GB structure and activation volume. For that reason, we studied the pressure effect on the migration rate of well-defined boundaries in aluminium bicrystals.

EXPERIMENTAL

Aluminium bicrystals were prepared by crystallisation from the melt in high purity argon atmosphere. Bi-crystalline seeds were prepared using a 5N material. The Fe content in the bicrystals was less than 20 ppm. The sum of the other impurities didn't exceed 40 ppm in total. 8 boundaries were studied, all of symmetrical tilt type with tilt axis parallel to low index directions: <100>, <110> and <111>. The accuracy of tilt angle determination was ±1°. For <100> and <111> boundaries, one short-period-low Σ coincidence boundary and one general boundary were prepared. Σ is a parameter characterising the periodicity of the GB structure. 1/Σ is the fraction of atoms that belongs to a common to the two crystals Coincidence Site Lattice. The low Σ boundaries will be further called "special boundaries" [cf.8], owing to their special properties: low energy, low activation energy for GB migration. For <110> tilt axis, besides one special boundary, 3 general boundaries were prepared.

Grain boundary migration was measured at constant GB curvature, which ensured constant driving force. Figure 1 shows the idea of the experiment and some experimental results. The bicrystals were annealed under high pressure argon pressure, at pressures up to 1 GPa. After each annealing, the distance the GB migrated was measured. This was possible because the old GB position could be recognised from the groove on the oxide film.

The size of the bicrystals annealed under high pressure was 3x4x15mm^3. The temperature was measured with Pt-PtRh10% thermocouples. The thermocouple indications were corrected for the pressure effect on the thermoelectric power [9]. The accuracy of temperature measurements was ± 2K. The temperature gradient along the bicrystals was less than 2K.

Table 1. Activation Energy and Volume for Grain Boundary Migration in Aluminium Bicrystals

Bicrystals' misorientation			Activation		pre-exp. factor
Axis	Angle	Σ	Energy [kJ/mol]	Volume [V/Ω]	$log(A_0)$
<100>	36.9±0.4	5	113.7±7.9	1.20±0.06	4.4
<100>	31.8±0.4		196.0±11.3	1.19±0.06	10
<111>	37.1±0.4	≈7	161.4±9.2	1.10±0.06	8.3
<111>	32.0±1.0		194.4±45.1	1.19±0.06	10.8
<110>	38.5±0.5	9	181.4±32.2	1.65±0.08	7.7
<110>	36.0±1.0		222.4±13.4	2.22±0.10	10.3
<110>	32.0±1.0		274.6±56.2	3.24±1,7	13.5
<110>	30.0±1.0		291.4±58.9	3.63±0.18	14.1

RESULTS

Fig.1 shows the pressure dependence of the relative GB mobility *A* for three boundaries. A[cm^2/s] is the GB velocity normalised to the driving force, which is proportional to the GB radius of curvature ρ.

$$A = \frac{v}{\rho} \qquad (5)$$

It is clearly seen that the activation volume for the <110> boundary is higher than for the <100> and <111> boundaries. Table 1 lists the activation volumes and activation energies measured. Inspection of Table 1 leads to the following conclusions:

1. for <100> and <111> boundaries, the activation energies for GB migration depend on the GB periodicity, being low for special boundaries, but not on the activation volume.
2. for <110> boundaries, the activation energy is also at minimum for the special boundary. However, it increases with an increase of activation volume. The activation volumes reach high values, up to 3 atomic volumes.

DISCUSSION

The above results are consistent with the following model of GB migration mechanism Fig.2.

For <110> boundaries the surfaces of the crystals that are immediately adjacent to the grain boundary plane are built of close packed rows of atoms parallel to the tilt axis and the GB plane [10]. Atoms are closely bounded with their neighbours in the crystal. The surfaces of the crystals are compactly packed and there are no "loose packed regions" necessary for transfer of atoms. It is only when a number of vacancies condense in one region, that GB migration becomes possible .

For the <100> and <111> boundaries, the V^* value is consistent with a single-vacancy migration mechanism. The difference in behaviour of <100> and <111> boundaries comparing to <110> results from the fact that the <100> and <111> atomic rows are not closey packed [10]. Also the <100> and <111> tilt boundaries have a high free volumxe compared to the <110> tilt boundary [11]. We assume that in such boundaries a single vacancy can produce enough free volume for atoms to jump across the boundary.

The reason for high activation volumes for GBM in bicrystals compared to grain growth remains to be investigated.

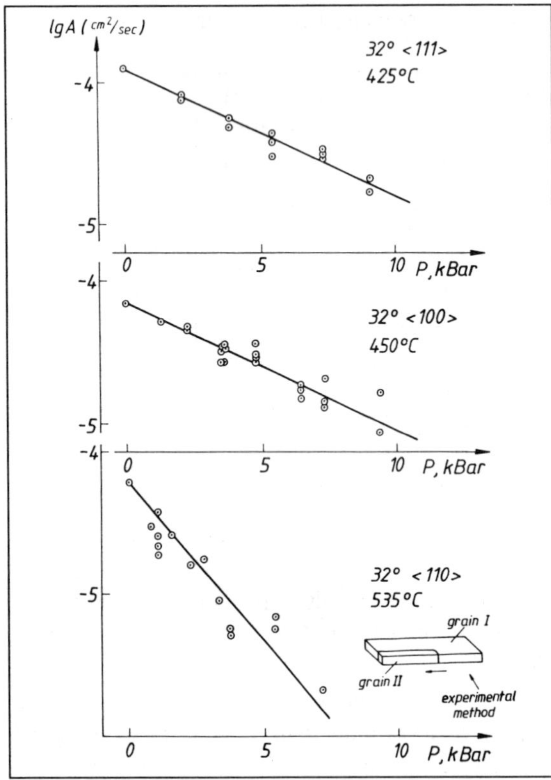

Fig.1. Pressure effect on the normalised GB mobility in Aluminium bicrystals.

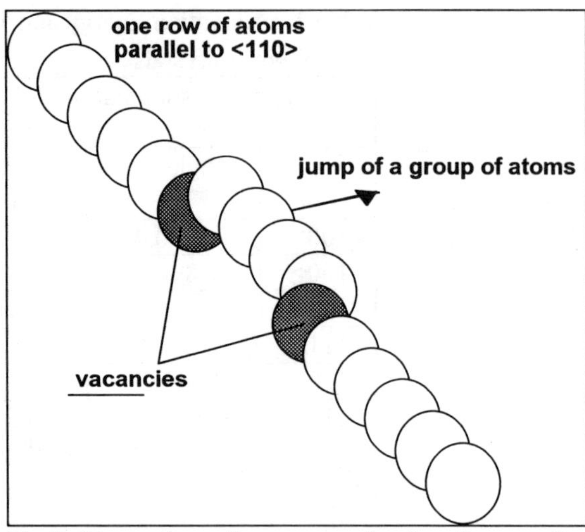

Fig.2. Illustration of group mechanism for transfer of atoms across a <110> tilt grain boundary. To enable transfer of a group of atoms across the boundary, the cooperation of at least two vacancies is necessary.

ACKNOWLEDGEMENTS.

W.L. is grateful to the Polish Committee for Science for financial support.

REFERENCES

[1] C.L.Bauer, *Defect and Diffusion Forum*, Vols.66-69, pp.749-764 (1989)

[2] W.Łojkowski, J.Swiderski, Y.Minamino, T.Yamane, J.Kwieciñski, D.A.Molodov, E.I.Rabkin, L.S.Shvindlerman, B.B.Straumal, *Defect and Diffusion Forum*, Vols. 95-98, pp.449-456 (1993)

[3] H.Hahn and H.Gleiter, *Scripta Met.* 13, p.3 (1979)

[4] G.Martin, D.A.Blackburn, Y.Adda,: *phys.st.sol.*, **23**, p.223 (1967)

[5] G.Erdèlyi, W.Łojkowski, D.LBeke, L.Godèny, F.J. Kedves, *Phil.Mag.A*, 56, p.673 (1987)

[6] W.Łojkowski, *J.de Physique*, *Coll.* C5, suppl. n°10, 49, p.C5-545

[7] W.Łojkowski, J.Swiderski, D.Molodow, E.I.Rabkin, L.S.Shvindlerman, Y.Minamino, J.Kwieciñski, IIB'92, 6-th International Conference on Intergranular and Interphase Boundaries in Materials, Thesaloniki, Greece, June 21-26, 1992

[8] P.H.Pumphrey, in "Grain Boundary Structure and Properties", eds.G.A.Chadwick, D.A.Smith, Academic Press, New York 1986, p.139.

[9] V.M.Cheng, P.C.Allen, D.Lazarus, *Applied Physics Letters*, 26, p.6 (1975)

[10] W.Łojkowski, H.Gleiter, R.Maurer, *Acta Metall*, 36, p.69 (1988)

[11] M.Koiwa, H.Seyzaki, T.Ogura, *Acta Metall.*32, p.171 (1984)

ELECTRON MICROSCOPY OF SHOCK-SYNTHESIZED SILICIDES AND ALUMINIDES

KENNETH S. VECCHIO
Department of Applied Mechanics and Engineering Sciences
University of CA-San Diego, 9500 Gilman Dr., La Jolla, CA 92093-0411

The effects of shock-wave passage through porous (powder) materials are complex, since intense and non-uniform plastic deformation is coupled with the shock-wave effects. Attempts to synthesize niobium and molybdenum silicides and nickel aluminides by the passage of shock waves through elemental powder mixtures resulted in an array of different microstructures. Extensive electron microscopy was employed to characterize both unreacted and reacted regions, and revealed only equilibrium phases. Convergent beam electron diffraction combined with x-ray microanalysis was used to determine the crystal structure and compositions of the reacted products. The extent of reaction was found to vary to different degrees with shock pressure, initial temperature, morphology of the powder particles, elemental system and mixture ratios, among other features. Electron microscopy of partially-reacted regions has led to the development of a new reaction mechanism based on the formation of a liquid-disilicide reaction product at the metal-silicon interface. For the nickel-aluminides the extent of reaction was considerably less for comparable shock pressures, and the nickel particle morphology influenced the reaction kinetics leading to the formation of Ni-aluminide compounds. Comparison of the microstructures produced in each of these systems has led to a better understanding of the role of elemental mixtures on the nature and extent of the reaction.

INTRODUCTION

Shock-induced reactions (or shock synthesis) have been studied since the 1960's but are still poorly understood, partly due to the fact that the reaction kinetics are fast making experimental analysis of the reaction difficult. The effects of shock-wave passage through porous (powder) materials are complex, because intense and non-uniform plastic deformation is coupled with the shock-wave effects. Thus, the particle interiors experience primarily the effects of shock waves, while the surfaces undergo intense plastic deformation which can often result in interfacial melting. Shock synthesis of compounds from powders is triggered by the extraordinarily high energy deposition rate at the surfaces of the powders, thereby changing their configuration, forcing them in close contact, activating them by introducing large densities of defects, and heating them close to or even above their melting temperatures. Since these reactions occur extremely fast, assumptions regarding microstructure evolution and reaction mechanisms based on equilibrium considerations may not apply.

Some fundamental questions regarding these reactions remain unanswered. Prominent among them are the following: (1) How can the extraordinarily high reaction rates encountered in shock compression be explained? (2) Are the phases formed in shock-synthesis unique (morphologically or structurally) and/or non-equilibrium?

This paper presents experimental results coupled with characterization and analysis of Nb- and Mo-silicides and Ni-aluminides formed by shock synthesis directed at providing an answer to these questions. By means of careful electron microscopy, it is shown that the mechanism of shock-induced reactions is quite different than conventional solid-state reactions; however the phases formed are equilibrium phases.

EXPERIMENTAL PROCEDURE

Two elemental powder mixtures were used in this investigation for the synthesis of silicides: Nb-Si and Mo-Si. The powders had irregular shapes, and sizes smaller than 44μm. The purity levels were 99.9% for Nb, Mo and Si. The powders were mixed in the proportions to provide, upon reaction, the intermetallic compounds $NbSi_2$ and $MoSi_2$, for each system respectively. These powders were encapsulated under controlled argon atmosphere in stainless steel capsules. These capsules were subjected to shock compression in a Sawaoka fixture; this fixture is described in detail elsewhere [e.g. 1]

For the Ni-aluminides, flaky morphology Ni (~44μm) and spherical Al (~10-20μm) powders 99.9% purity were used. These powders were mixed in proportions to yield Ni_3Al and then were encapsulated under controlled argon atmosphere in stainless steel capsules. These capsules were subjected to shock compression in the Sandia Momma Bear A fixture with a Baratol explosive; this fixture and shock technique is described in detail elsewhere [e.g. 2]

After shock processing, the specimen capsules were sectioned and analyzed by scanning and transmission electron microscopy. Composition measurements of individual phases were conducted using the ZAF correction procedure with unreacted powder regions and known intermetallics used for standards.

RESULTS AND DISCUSSION

Metal-Si Specimens

SEM backscattered electron micrograph of a polished section of the metal-Si samples shocked at room temperature and low velocity (1.2 km/s) are shown in Figures 1 and 2. Figure 1 shows the unreacted regions of the Nb-Si and Mo-Si samples. Figure 2(a) shows the partially-reacted regions which made up the majority of the sample and consisted of Nb particles surrounded by a reaction layer of $NbSi_2$ nodules and embedded within a two-phase matrix of $NbSi_2$ nodules and silicon. Figure 2(b) shows a similar microstructure for the Mo-Si sample, with the reacted product being $MoSi_2$ nodules.

Figure 3a shows a TEM micrograph of the partially-reacted region of the Nb-Si sample revealing the structure of the nodules and of the surrounding silicon matrix. The $NbSi_2$ nodules are monocrystalline, approximately 1-2μm in diameter, and have facets. They do not show any marked internal structure, such as dislocations, stacking faults, or twins. The silicon surrounding these reacted regions generally shows an annealed structure with a profusion of annealing twins. A few silicon regions exhibit a microcrystalline structure. These regions were either subjected to intense plastic deformation and recrystallized (statically or dynamically) or was molten and rapidly re-solidified. This microstructure is in stark contrast with the previous silicon regions which suggested melting followed by slow re-solidification.

Figure 3b shows a TEM micrograph of the partially-reacted region of the Mo-Si sample revealing the structure of the $MoSi_2$ nodules and the surrounding silicon matrix. The $MoSi_2$ nodules are monocrystalline, approximately 1-2μm in diameter, and have facets. They show significant internal structure, including dislocations and twins. The silicon surrounding these reacted regions generally shows an annealed structure with a profusion of annealing twins suggesting Si melting followed by slow re-solidification.

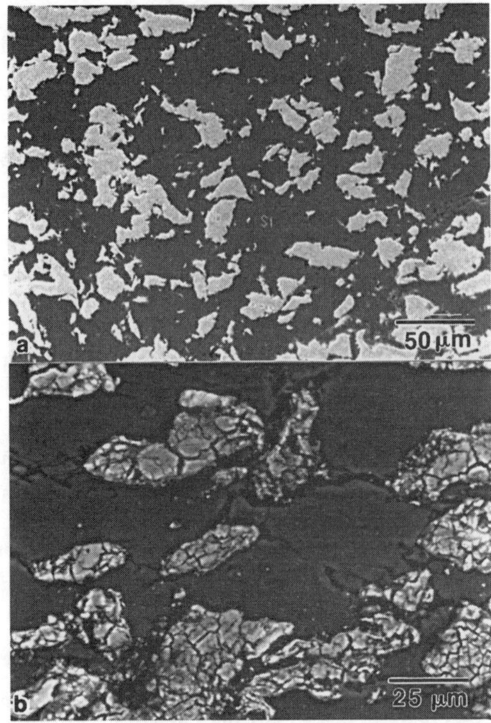

Figure 1. SEM backscattered electron micrograph of the unreacted region of (a) the Nb-Si specimen, and (b) the Mo-Si specimen.

CBED and X-ray Microanalysis

The crystal structure and composition of the $NbSi_2$ nodules was determined by convergent beam electron diffraction (CBED) analysis and x-ray microanalysis, respectively. The symmetry in the CBED patterns allowed the point group to be determined as 622. The established crystal structure for the $NbSi_2$ phase is the C40 hexagonal structure (space group $P6_222$ and point group 622). The microanalysis results were consistent with the disilicide composition.

Similar CBED and microanalysis results of the $MoSi_2$ nodules showed the symmetries were

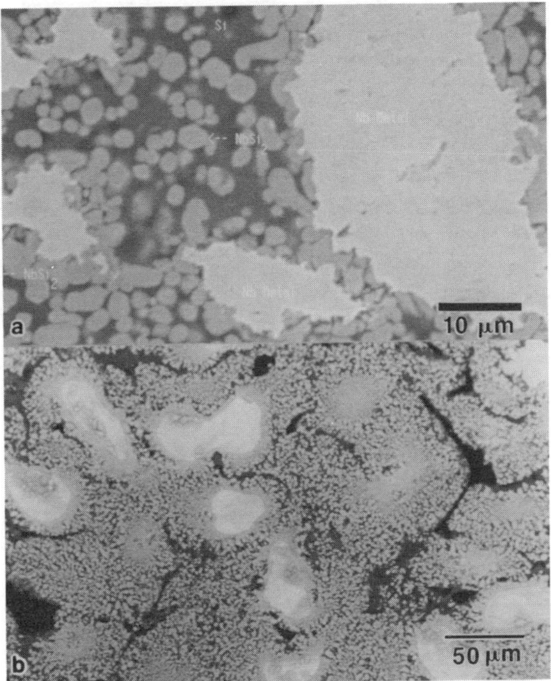

Figure 2. SEM backscattered electron micrograph of the partially-reacted region of (a) the Nb-Si specimen, and (b) the Mo-Si specimen.

consistent with a point group of 4/mmm, space group I4/mmm, and the composition was consistent with the Mo-disilicide phase.

$MoSi_2$ has been reported to exist as two different crystal structures, C40 hexagonal (β-$MoSi_2$) above 1900°C and as $C11_b$ (body-centered tetragonal α-$MoSi_2$) below 1900°C [3]. More recently, Boettinger et al. [4] has reported that pure $MoSi_2$ exists only as the $C11_b$ structure, and that the C40 is only stable at high temperatures as a result of impurities stablizing this phase. The $MoSi_2$ phase observed here is consistent with the tetragonal phase ($C11_b$) suggesting that either this phase is very pure and therefore exists in its true equilibrium structure or was formed from the liquid state first as the high-temperature C40 structure (in an impure form) which subsequently transformed during cooling to the low-temperature $C11_b$ phase.

It is interesting to note at this point that the reacted product in both the Nb-Si and Mo-Si samples was the disilicide phase (either $NbSi_2$ or $MoSi_2$) consistent with the overall bulk powder mixture. However, the formation of these phases does not depend on the bulk powder mixture, but rather on local chemistry and thermodynamics.

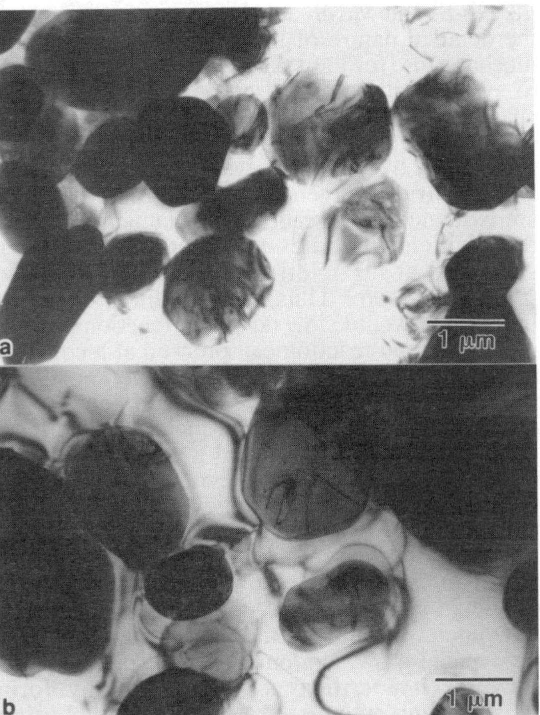

Figure 3. TEM micrographs of the partially-reacted region of (a) the Nb-Si sample and (b) the Mo-Si sample revealing the structure of the nodules and the surrounding silicon matrix.

Ni-Al Specimen

Figure 4 shows the unreacted and partially-reacted regions of the 3Ni-1Al specimen. Again the reaction initiated from the particle interfaces, with the reacted product growing into the lower melting point material (Al). In this case the reacted product is Al_3Ni, and not Ni_3Al as intended by the bulk powder mixture. The Al_3Ni phase forms because Ni dissolves into the Al regions along the interface, enriching the Al with Ni. When sufficient Ni has enriched the Al, the first phase to form must be Al_3Ni according to the phase diagram. Several regions were found in which the Al_3Ni phase existed as a dendritic structure indicating that the Al particles were molten. By comparison with the metal-Si samples, the reacted product is different from the overall bulk powder mixture. This further demonstrates how the reaction depends, at least initially, on the local chemistry and thermodynamics, rather than the bulk powder mixture.

Proposed Reaction Mechanism

The analysis of the partially-reacted regions in

the Nb-Si and Mo-Si shock experiments revealed the detailed nature of the reaction sequence and mechanisms [for the sake of brevity only the Nb-Si system will be discussed below, however this analysis applies equally well to the Mo-Si system]. The preponderance of small $NbSi_2$ particles surrounded by silicon, as well as the existence of $NbSi_2$ particles attached to the niobium particles are evidence for a reaction mechanism in which the disilicide particles are continuously being generated at the interface and ejected into the (molten) silicon. Thus, no permanent diffusion barrier that would slow down the reaction process is formed, and reaction can proceed at a constant rate until the entire metal (Nb, Mo, etc.) or silicon is consumed. The shock-induced reaction is initiated along the solid metal-molten Si interface. After reaction has proceeded to a certain extent, surface (interfacial) forces become dominant, and the liquid reaction product agglomerates, forming a spherule. At this point, reaction kinetics are drastically decreased, due to the reduction in the Nb-Si interfacial area, and solidification of the disilicide sphere starts. As the sphere solidifies, new nuclei form along the Nb-Si interface. The new nuclei grow, agglomerate into spheres when they reach a critical size, and thereby form neighboring spheres. As these neighboring spheres solidify, they exert forces on the first sphere, expelling it into the molten silicon, and thus exposing fresh surfaces. This reaction process can continue unimpeded, until the reactants are consumed. In addition, turbulent flow of the liquid silicon under shock can also contribute to the detachment of the spherules from the interface.

CONCLUSIONS

Electron microscopy observations reveal that the main reaction product in the partially-reacted regions is the disilicide formed from the molten state as spherules with radii of approximately 1-2 μm. These spherules are formed at the metal-Si interface and are expelled into the silicon. The product formed from these reaction depends on local chemistry and thermodynamics, rather than bulk powder mixture.

A reaction mechanism under shock compression for the metal-Si interface is proposed involving the dissolution of (Nb or Mo) into molten Si, producing the molten disilicide, with its subsequent spheroidization, solidification, and expulsion into the surrounding liquid silicon melt. In this reaction mechanism a fresh solid (Nb or Mo)-liquid (Si) interface is continuously maintained, enabling a high reaction rate. A similar reaction may occur in the Ni-Al system.

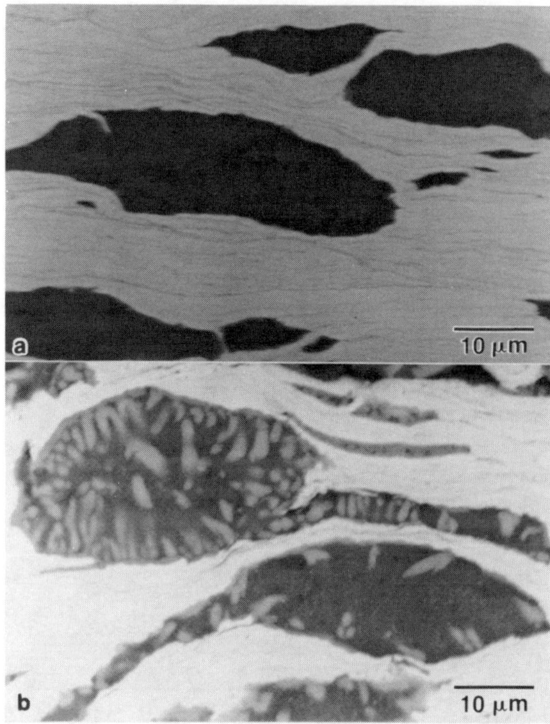

Figure 4. SEM backscattered electron micrograph of (a) the unreacted region and (b) the partially-reacted region of the Ni-Al specimen. In (b) the phase formed from the interface between the Ni (bright regions) and Al (dark regions) particles is Al_3Ni.

REFERENCES

1. A. B. Sawaoka and T. Akashi, U. S. Patent 4655830 (1987).
2. N. N. Thadhani, S. Work, R. A. Graham, and W. F. Hammetter, J. Mater. Res., **7**, pp 1063-1075 (1992).
3. P. Villars, "Pearson's Handbook of Crystallographic Data for Intermetallic Phases," eds. P. Villars and L. D. Calvert, Metals Park, OH, Amer. Soc. for Metals, (1985).
4. W. J. Boettinger, J.H. Perepezko, and P. S. Frankwicz, Mat. Sci. Eng., A155, p. 33 (1992).

MICROSTRUCTURES OF SINGLE–CRYSTAL COPPER RODS SHOCK–TREATED BY A ROD–IN–CYLINDER TECHNIQUE

K.DAN[1], H.TAMURA[1], A.B.SAWAOKA[1], T.MORI[2], M.D.HWANG[3] AND Y.HORIE[3]

[1]Center for Ceramics Research, Tokyo Institute of Technology,
[2]Department of Materials Science and Engineering, Tokyo Institute of Technology, Nagatsuta 4259, Midori, Yokohama 227, Japan
[3]Department of Civil Engineering and Materials Science, North Carolina State University, Raleigh, NC 27695–7908, USA

Two single–crystal copper rods were shock–treated with a rod–in–cylinder technique. One rod was treated in a polycrystal copper cylinder. Strong contrast areas due to shock waves interactions were not observed with an optical microscope. Another rod was shock–treated in a 2024–aluminum cylinder. An area compressed by plane shock waves and an ellipsoidal area compressed by a Mach–wave were distinguishable with an optical microscope. Complex microstructures were found in the ellipsoidal area. We believe that such microstructures were caused by the heterogeneity of particle velocity, shearing stress, pressure and temperature in the shock–treated specimen.

INTRODUCTION

It is well known that extremely high pressure in condensed matter can be obtained by interactions of shock waves. Syono et al. [1] devised a concentric cylindrical assembly composed of an outer cylinder with higher shock velocity and an inner rod with lower shock velocity. This is called rod–in–cylinder–technique. In their experiments, a formation of Mach–disk through interactions of conically converging shock waves is shown with a streak photograph technique. Kunishige et al. [2] calculated pressure distributions in this rod–in–cylinder assembly composed of an inner copper rod and an outer 2024–aluminum–alloy cylinder using the two dimensional hydrocode PISCES.

Deformations of metals are usually accompanied by point defects, dislocations, stacking faults, twins, shear bands, dynamic recrystallizations and phase transition. Shock compressions of metals induce especially mechanical twins and adiabatic shear due to rapid moving of atoms under high strain rate [3]. The propagation and growth of adiabatic shear bands depend on the strain rate and the stress, and they are not interrupted by grain boundaries and other forms of barriers such as inclusions in the structure. Dan et al. [4] observed microstructures of iron rods shock–treated in an outer 2024–aluminum cylinder, with an optical microscope. However the relation of microstructure and shock wave propagation was not clear, since the sample was a polycrystal rod and iron has a phase transition at high pressure condition. It is known that production of the mechanical twins is strongly related to a specific crystallographic direction. For example, they occur in [211] direction of {111} plane in copper.

In the present study, rods of single–crystal copper, of which the axial direction is [100], were shock–treated in rod–in–cylinder assembly. Thus the crystallographical relation is axially symmetric. The object of this research is to investigate metallurgical effects of shock–wave interaction on a shock–treated rod specimen.

EXPERIMENTAL METHODS

Shock experiments were conducted by using a momentum–trap–type recovery system, in which a flyer–plate was accelerated with explosives and impacted normally on one end of a large cylindrical iron block containing sample assemblies. Type I assembly was composed of a 5 mm diameter single–crystal copper rod and a 24 mm diameter polycrystal copper cylinder. Type II assembly had an outer 2024–aluminum cylinder, which replaced the copper one. Single–crystal copper rods were prepared to have the crystallographical direction of 〈001〉 by the Bridgeman method. These assemblies were 60 mm long. One end of the assembly was flush with the surface of the retaining iron block. The impact velocity of a 3.2 mm thick iron flyer–plate was 1.6 km/s, measured with a pin contact method.

Each recovered assembly was cut into two halves along the central axis by machining. Cross sections were polished with silicon carbide emery paper by hand and with 1 μm–diameter alumina slurry. The surfaces were etched with 50 % HNO_3 solution for metallurgical observations. Macrostructures and microstructures were observed with an optical microscope and a transmission electron microscope, respectively.

RESULTS AND DISCUSSIONS

Macrostructure of recovered type I assembly is shown in Figure 1. Light contrast areas are observed on this rod. Strong contrast areas along the center line are not observed. Deformation twins could not be observed at the front part of the rod with the optical microscope. It is reported that the single–crystal copper rod shocked in [001] direction shows no deformation twins with optical microscopy [5]. The present study is consistent with this fact.

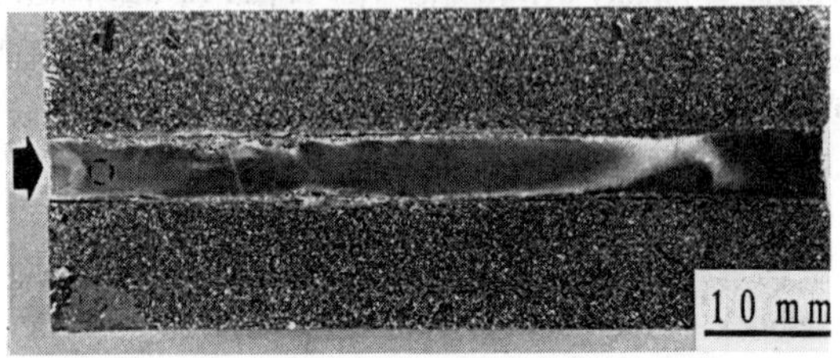

Figure 1. Microphotograph of the shock-treated single-crystal copper rod.

A microstructure of broken circle area shown in Figure 1 is observed with a transmission electron microscope. The result is shown in Figure 2. Many thin lens–shaped mechanical twins are observed. It is reported that such twins have large interface energy, accompanying interface dislocations. The crossing angle of twins are about 87°. Diffraction patterns of this area showed almost (100) and (221) plane.

Figure 2. TEM photograph of the circled area shown in Figure 1

The propagation of shock waves in type II assembly is estimated as shown in Figure 3. The pressure and shock wave velocity of the copper rod at the impact surface are estimated to be 34 GPa and 5.07 km/s by impedance matching method using the polycrystalline Hugoniot data. Those of 2024–aluminum cylinder are estimated to be 20 GPa and 6.75 km/s. In the area between the impact surface and the position ②, the shock front consists of plane shock waves propagating from the impact surface and oblique waves propagating from the interface of the rod and the outer cylinder. The diameter of the plane waves decreases with propagating distance and the oblique waves conically converge. It is reported that the interaction of such oblique waves causes the pressure enhancement in the interaction area and causes furthermore Mach–disk formation [2]. In the area between the position ② and ③, the pressure gradually increases through the interaction of oblique waves. The formation of Mach–disk starts at the position ③. Its diameter increases in the area between the position ③ and ⑤, and decreases in the area between the position ⑤ and ⑦.

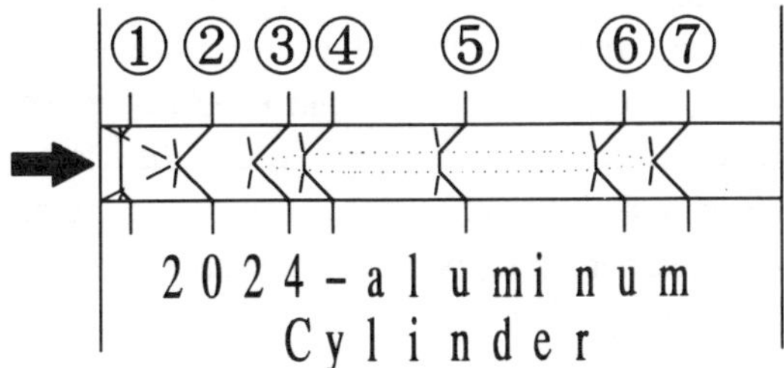

Figure 3. Schematic diagram of shock wave propagations in type II assembly (rod: single–crystal copper, cylinder: 2024–Al)

The pressure profiles on the rod axis (A) and the rod–cylinder interface (B) are calculated by using the DINA2D CODE. They are shown in Figure 4. The pressure difference between (A) and (B) gradually decreases. Then it increases owing to the interactions of oblique waves. This process is similar to that in a rod, that is shock–treated by using annular explosives [6,7] .

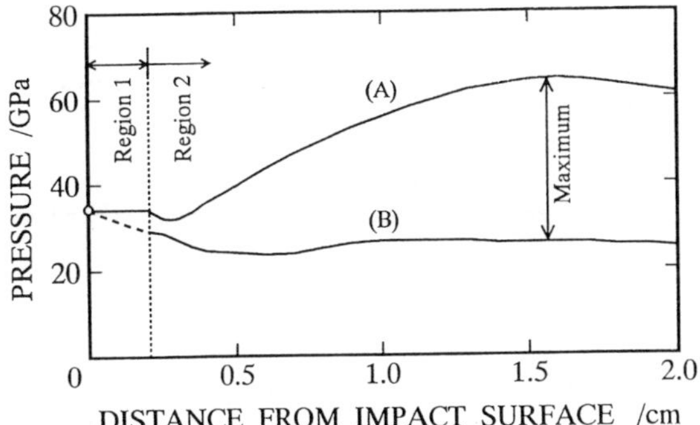

Figure 4.
Maximum pressure profiles in copper rod on the central axis (A) and the outer area (B) calculated by one dimensional impedance matching method (Region I) and DINA2D Code (Region II)

Figure 5 shows macrostructure of the recovered type II assembly. Strongly etched areas, which are symmetric to the central axis, are observed. They correspond to the shock wave propagations shown in Figure 3. They are believed to be a sign of the interactions of conically converging radial shock waves, plane shock waves, and a variety of unloading waves.

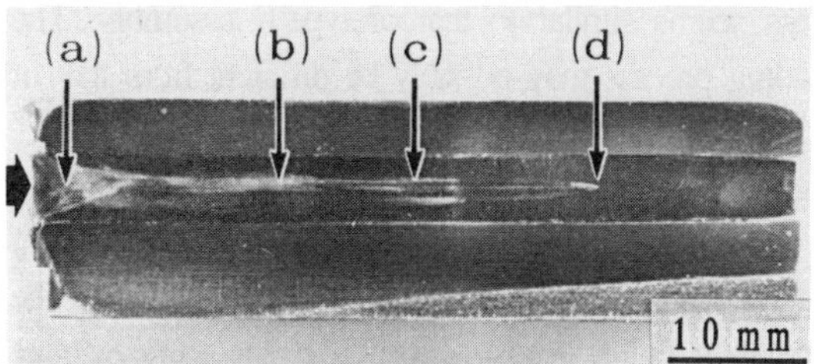

Figure 5.
Macrostructure of recovered type II assembly (rod: single–crystal copper, cylinder: 2024–Al)

Observing the overall microstructures with optical microscopy revealed that long deformation twins were oriented in two different directions within 32 mm from the impact surface. It is reported that such long twins are formed during unloading from 20 GPa, and that they show different features according to the direction of sample cutting, because there are four twin–boundary–planes [5] . In the present study, they were observed in two directions since the sample was cut along ⟨001⟩ direction. The crossing angle was 80 °

Some microstructures are shown in Figure 6 (a)~(d). They correspond to those in Figure 5. Figure 6 (a) shows the microstructure in the area compressed by the plane waves. Many long deformation twins are uniformly arranged in parallel. It seems that the physical condition shown by the broken circle is homogeneous during compression and expansion. The compression

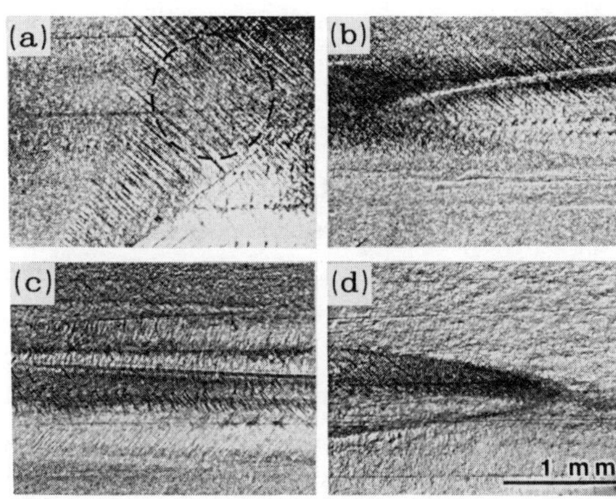

Figure 6. Microstructures of areas (a)~(d) shown in Figure 5

process seems similar to that of type I assembly. The unloading process may possibly be different from that of the type I assembly.

Figure 6 (b) shows microstructures at the area where the Mach–disk was formed. The starting of an ellipsoidal area is distinguished by observation. The deformation twins, whose direction is the same as that of deformation twins shown in Figure 6 (a), cross the ellipsoidal area without bending. Hence it is concluded that these deformation twins were formed after the formation of the ellipsoidal area. The periphery of an ellipsoidal area may be formed through the interaction of Mach–disk and oblique waves. On this periphery, the particle velocity and its direction are discontinuous. Especially the velocity difference would be very large since the pressure difference between the central axis and the outer area is very large as shown in Figure 4. Hence adiabatic shear bands could be formed. It is reported that micro–crystals and very dense dislocation appear through temperature rise after deformation of the bands [8].

Figure 6 (c) shows microstructures around the central part of the ellipsoidal area. Microstructures seem complex. There are many short deformation twins(?), whose direction is the same as that of the long deformation twins, and other microstructures. They must be formed through some effects other than shock waves propagations of Figure 3. Such effects can be induced from the interactions of various kinds of pressure waves coming from the interface of the outer cylinder and the rod. It is reported that a temperature rise is extremely high in such an ellipsoidal area [2]. However in the present study, the driving force of these microstructures has not been made clear yet.

Figure 6 (d) shows microstructures around the end of the ellipsoidal area. Long deformation twins, whose direction is the same as that of Figure 6 (a), are observed in the ellipsoidal area. While there are no deformation twins outside the area, since the pressure of this area is lower than that of the ellipsoidal area. It is supposed that unloading waves finally overtook the shock fronts and that the Mach–disk disappeared.

The ellipsoidal area of high pressure and high temperature, could be obtained by using the rod–in–cylinder technique. In this area, microstructures are very complex. Such microstructures could be formed heterogeneously through rapid changes of particle velocity, shearing stress, pressure and temperature. These rapid and complex changes of physical parameters in a specimen can be utilized for a variety of materials research.

ACKNOWLEDGMENTS

The authors would like to thank Dr. T.Akashi of Sumitomo Coal Mining Co. and Mr. H.Kudo of Izumi Dia. Co. for conducting shock treatments.

This work is supported by a Grant–in–Aid Scientific Research for Priority Area "Shock Waves", given by Ministry of Education, Science and Cultures, Japan.

REFERENCES

[1] Y. Syono, T. Gogo and T. Sato, *Journal of Applied Physics,* 53, pp. 7131–7135(1982).

[2] H. Kunishige, Y. Horie and A.B. Sawaoka, "Computer simulation of conically converging shock wave in the rod–in–cylinder structure" in *Proceedings of the 1988 National Symposium on Shock Wave Phenomena,* 1988, pp. 181–188.

[3] C.Feng, *Shock–Wave and High–Strain–Rate Phenomena in Materials, Marcel Dekker* Inc., 1992, pp. 573–586.

[4] K.Dan, H.Tamura, A.B.Sawaoka, Y.Horie, *Report of the Research Laboratory of Engineering Materials, Tokyo Institute of Technology,* 18, pp.281–294(1993).

[5] C.S Smith and C.M. Fowler, *Response of Metals to High Velocity Deformation,* 1960, pp. 309–341.

[6] K.A.Johnson, K.P.Staudhammer, *Metallurgical Applications of Shock–Wave and High–Strain–Rate Phenomena,* Marcel Dekker Inc., 1986, pp. 525–542.

[7] K.P.Staudhammer, *Shock–Wave and High–Strain–Rate Phenomena in Materials,* Marcel Dekker Inc., 1992, pp. 971–980

[8] Y.Meunier, R.Roux, J.Moureaud, *Shock–Wave and High–strain–Rate Phenomena in Materials,* Marcel Dekka Inc., 1992, pp.637–644.

MICRO-ANALYSIS OF ADIABATIC SHEAR FRACTURE IN EXPLOSIVE-FILLED CYLINDERS

Hu Bayi, Dong Qingdong, Han Changsheng, Wang Desheng, Hu Haibo
Southwest Institute of Fluid Physics
P. O. Box 523-51, Chengdu, Sichuan, 610003, CHINA

In this paper the micro shear fracture characteristics of explosive-filled cylinders made of AISI 1045 steel, Ti-6Al-4V and tungsten alloy are described. The different micro fracture mechanisms of these metal cylinders under internal high explosive loading are also discussed. The study shows that lower the thermal conductivity of the metal and finer the grain, then the metal is more sensitive to adiabatic shearing and it is more easy to form transformed bands.

INTRODUCTION

Dynamic fracture of a metal cylinder under internal impulsive loading is a general problem in fracture mechanics. The study of the damage and fracture mechanism of metal cylinder loaded by explosive impulse is therefore of practical use.

Last year we made a macro-analysis of adiabatic shear fracture of the cylinders made of AISI 1045 steel, Ti-6Al-4V and tungsten alloy under internal high explosive loading[1]. On the basis of that work, we made micro-analysis on the soft-recovered fragments by the scanning electron microscopy. So that we could get a better understanding about the fracture process and mechanism related to the physical characters and microstructures of the metal.

In this paper we briefly introduce the fracture characteristics and mechanism in these metal cylinders loaded by PBX-9404 and discuss the relationship between adiabatic shearing and the characteristics of these shell materials at explosive strain rates (10^3-$10^5 s^{-1}$).

EXPERIMENT AND RESULTS

Fractography

High speed frame photography study[2] shows that the crack first emerges along the axial direction of the cylinder. After the axial cracks have undergone full development, the fragments are formed with the action of annular tensile stress. That is to say the transverse fracture surface of the fragment is produced by the tensile stress. So there must be

(a)

(b)

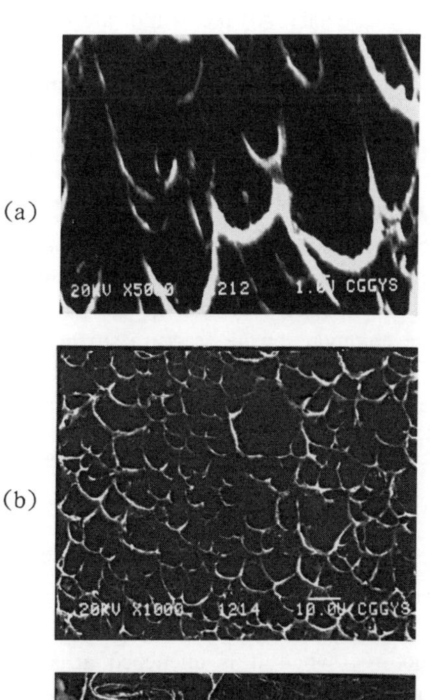

(c)

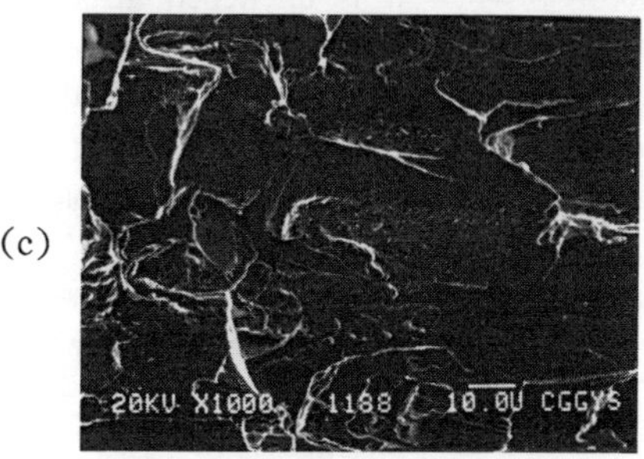

Figure 1. The micro-characteristics of the macro-shear fracture surface (a)AISI 1045 steel; (b)Ti-6Al-4V; (c)tungsten alloy

some mechanical information about the initial damage and rupture of the wall on the axial shear fracture surface of the fragment. Thus we only observe this fracture surface.

Under this loading condition, the micro-morphology of the macro shear fracture surface of the AISI 1045 steel (in normal and heat treatment conditions) and Ti-6Al-4V are all shear dimples. These dimples show evident shear directionality as shown in Figure 1(a) and Figure 1(b). The dimples near the inner surface of the cylinder are deavily oxidized and their shape is somewhat like flattened ellipse, but those near the outside surface of the cylinder are lightly oxidized and their shape is relatively circular. All theses indicate that the material close to the inner surface of the cylinder experience more intensive shear deformation. The high temperature oxidation is also more serious owing to the local plastic shear strain. The adiabatic shear damage is starting from the inner surface of the cylinder and evolving outward.

For the tungsten alloy, the macro shear fracture surfaces are far less smooth and shiny than those of AISI 1045 steel and Ti-6Al-4V alloy, even looks like the common tensile fracture surface, the detailed examination of SEM shows that its microcharacteristics is a new kind of metallographic morphology shown in Figure 1(c).

Metallograph

We first examined the original microstructure of the three kinds of metals. The AISI 1045 steel in normal condition shows a coarse pearlite/ferrite microstructure, when it is quenched at 840℃ and tempered at 400℃, the microstructure becomes finer sorbite. Ti-6Al-4V alloy in annealed condition shows much finer equiaxial $\alpha+\beta$ grains. The grains of the tungsten alloy are much bigger than those of the above two kinds of metals.

From the soft recovered fragments we chose a few typical ones which were sectioned for examination. For the fragments of AISI 1045 steel cylinder (normal condition), the tips of the shear cracks are adiabatic deformed bands in which the initial pearlite/ferrite structure of the steel is kept, but the grain are highly distorted as shown in Figure 2(a). The width of shear bands is in the range of 100

(a)

(b)

Figure 2. The adiabatic shear band in AISI 1045 steel
(a) Deformed band (in normal condition)
(b) Transformed band (after heat treatment)

-400μm. The Pearlite and cementite on the bands are all highly deformed and oriented parallel to the orientation of the shear band. From the deformation of the cementite within the band, we can promptly infer that the mechanism of heat deformation due to high temperature is the physical base for the formation of the adiabatic shear band.

For the heat treated fragments, a narrow plastic flow band was formed. The grains inside the band have the same orientation, but the grains in the matrix near the band experienced little shear strain. This band is usually called as adiabatic transformed band. Figure 2(b) shows its appearance.

The examination for the fragments of Ti-6Al-4V alloy indicates the shear crack is always transformed band, its length is of macro-scale and width about 1-5μm. There are some elliptic holes within some tranformed bands in which the grains' morphology are thoroughly different from that adjacent to it. There are no evident grain bounderies within the band, as shown in Figure 3(a), from which we found this kind of shear band like a rapid river. This phenomenon reveals the material within the band had undergone melting process at high temperature and the hot fluid had been forced to flow rapidly by the shear force. Among some fragments of this alloy we found at the end of the transformed bands are usually deformed bands shown in Figure 3(b). This type of deformed bands is very similar to that of ones found in the same alloy fragments by very low explosion-pressure explosive[1]. This result indicates adiabatic shearing starts from deformed band and its last developing stage is the transformed band.

In fragments of tungsten alloy we never found any indication of adiabatic shearing.

(a)

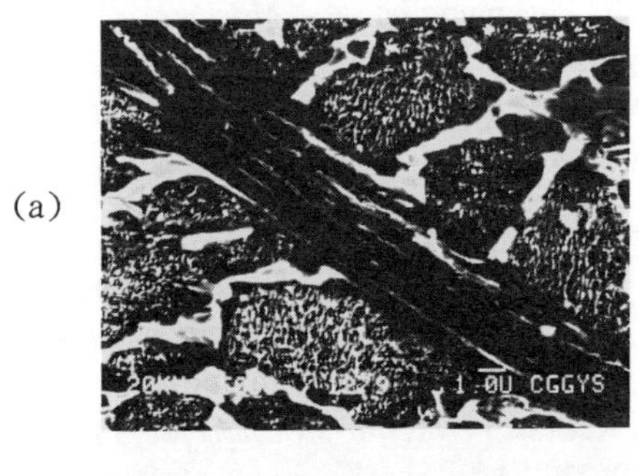

(b)

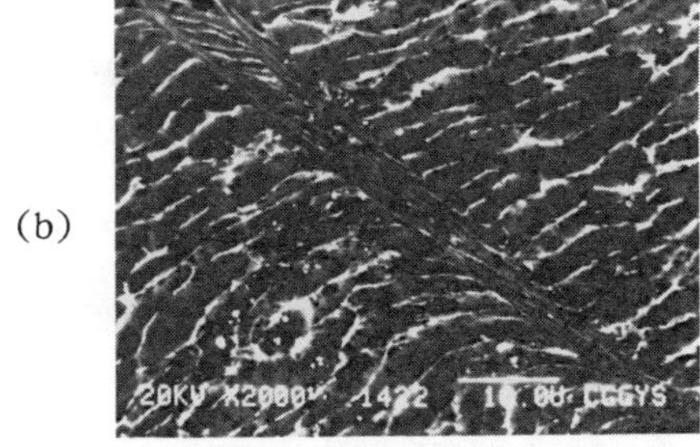

Figure 3. The adiabatic shear bands in Ti-6Al-4V (a) Transformed band; (b) Deformed band

DISCUSSION

How to understand above experimental results? Here we try to make an further approach to the relation between some material properties and the formation of adiabatic shear band.

According to reference 3 the thermal conductivity k(w/m°c) of Ti-6Al-4V, AISI 1045 steel and tungsten alloy and pure Al are 6.8, 48.2, 75.4 and 218.0 respectively, related to the above experimental results, it can be concluded that the lower the thermal conductivity of the metal, the more easy to form adiabatic shear band. For pure Al, because of its high k value, the heat produced by the local plastic deformation is conducted away swiftly and can't form local high temperature. In addition their strong capacity of strain hardening, it is very difficult to form adiabatic shear band in pure Al. On the other hand, for AISI 1045 steel and Ti-6Al-4V alloy, the heat produced by the local plastic deformation can make the temperature of the grain approach its melting point because of their low k value and low melting point. Hence the intense local plastic deformation continues and eventually results in the formation of the adiabatic shear band.

Our experimental observations have shown that when the grain of the metal is fine, it is more easy for a metal to produce adiabatic shear band, especially more advantageous to transformed band. For example, when AISI 1045 steel has been heat treated to fine sorbite, not only the proportion of shear fracture surface increase[1], but it also forms transformed band. The grains of Ti-6Al-4V are much finer than those of AISI 1045 steel and tungsten alloy. The result is that it is acutely sensitive to adiabatic shearing and easily forms transformed band. In Ref. [4-6] the martensite grains are also much finer than the pearlite/ferrite grains of AISI 1045 steel in normal condition, then under explosive loading transformed band emerged. In reference 7 when coarse laminate pearlite was heat treated to fine granular pearlite, transformed band was formed in high carbon steel. Experiments carried out on brass samples[8] reported that the amount of volume containing shear bands decreases with increasing grain size. Wang[9] found in his study of TB-2Ti alloy, that compared to fine grains, the coarse grains and pre-plastic deformation all had the effects to retard the onset and development of adiabatic shear band.

When the grains of a metal are finer, its hardness value is higher and more frequent the activity of the shear band, as reported by shockey[11] and staker[10]. Rogers[12] also found the coarser structure of the grain is responsible for the increased thermal stability. Lee[13] found in rolled 2024 Al alloy that shear bands appeared in the aged-hardened alloy (133VHN), but not in the one that had been annealed (59VHN). All these results coincide with the above understanding.

Why the finer of the grain is, the more intense of the adiabatic shearing? we believe it is due to the results of strengthening on grains boundaries. The more detailed analysis could be seen in reference 15. As Dubois[14] pointed out that the staking fault energy as well as the grain size might be considered as out-standing features ruling the onset and the growth of shear bands.

CONCLUSIONS

The micro-morphology of the macro shear facture surface of the AISI 1045 steel (in normal and heat treatment conditions) and Ti-6Al-4V are all shear dimples. The fragmentation mechanisms of AISI 1045 steel cylinder in normal and Ti-6Al-4V cylinder are the adiabatic shear deformed band and adiabatic shear transformed band respectively. The adiabatic shearing of AISI 1045 steel is more intensive in heat treatment condition than in normal condition. The tungsten alloy is very insensitive to adiabatic shearing, the micro-character of its fragment surface is transgranular cleavage.

Fining and evening the grains of the metal material under certain condition is advantageous to the onset of adiabatic shearing, and impel the deformed band to become into transformed band.

ACKNOWLEDGEMENTS

I would like to thank all my colleagues who helped me in the explosive cylinder experiment. The help of Dr. ZhangGanren in the preparation of this paper is greatly appreciated. I' m grateful to Ms. Gao for performing the type-work.

REFERENCES

1. B. Y. Hu, et al. , *Chinese Journal of Explosion and Shock Waves* 12, pp. 319-325(1992).
2. B. Y. Hu, et al. , *Chinese Journal of Explosion and Shock Waves* 13, pp. 49-54(1993).
3. *The Practical Manual of Engineering Materials*, Beijing, The Publisher of Chinese Normalization, (1989).
4. A. J. Bedford. NASA 73-26915(1973)
5. J. L. Affouard, et al. *Mechanical Properties at High Rates of Strain*. J. Harding, eds, Bristol and London, The Institute of Physics, 1984, pp. 533-540
6. M. E. Backman, et al. *Metallurgical Effects at High Strain-Rates*, R. W. Rhode, et al , eds, New York, Plenum Press, 1973, pp. 531-543
7. H. C. Rogers. *Ann. Rev. Mater. Sci.* 9, pp. 283-311(1979).
8. B. Fargette and D. Whitwham, *Memoires et Etudes Sc. Revue de Met.* , Mars, pp. 197-208(1976)
9. L. L. Wang, et al, *Chinese Journal of Explosion and Shock Waves* 9, pp. 101-119(1989)
10. M. R. Staker, *Scripta Metallurgical*. 14, pp. 677-680(1980)
11. D. A. Shockey, et al, *Shock-wave and High Strain Rate Phenomena in Metals*. L. E. Murr, et al. eds. NY, plenum press, 1981, ch. 15, pp. 249-261
12. H. C. Rogers, et al . *Shock-wave and High Strain Rate Phenomena in Metals*. L. E. Murr, et al. eds. NY, plenum press, 1981, ch. 18, pp. 285-302
13. W. B. Lee and K. C. Chan. *International Journal of Fracture* 52, pp. 207-221(1991).
14. PH. Dubois, et al. *Arch. Mech*, 40, pp. 35-42 (1988).
15. B. Y. Hu, et al, *Chinese Journal of Explosion and Shock Waves* 13, pp. 287-295(1993).

CHAPTER XVI

MATERIAL SYNTHESIS AND SHOCK-INDUCED MODIFICATION

COMPUTATIONAL MODELING OF SHOCK-INDUCED CHEMICAL REACTIONS IN POWDER MIXTURES

Y. Horie
North Carolina State University, Raleigh, NC 27695-7908

A mathematical model called VIR is used to simulate pressure and temperature profiles for Al-Ni and Al-Fe_3O_4 powder mixtures where chemical reactions have been observed to occur during shock duration. A second model based on a continuum mixture theory is applied to describe shock-induced heterogeneous flow in those mixtures that may explain the initiation of the observed fast chemical reactions.

INTRODUCTION

Computational modeling of shock-induced chemical reactions at NCSU was first concerned with the analysis of recovery experiments with diamond-Si(Ti)-C mixtures. Since then the model, now known as VIR, has been tested with a variety of material systems. The acronym VIR signifies the three major "ingredients" of the model: Voids, Inactive and Reactive elements. The basic thermodynamic postulates of this model were similar to those used by Nutt [1]. Major differences are found in the evaluation of mixture internal energies, chemical kinetics, and initiation criteria.

This paper reports an extension of the early model and hydrocode calculations of the real-time measurements [2,3] with the improved model. We shall also show calculations of shock-induced heterogeneous flow in a powder mixture that may describe the initiation of chemical reactions.

VIR MODEL

Key features of the VIR model are (i) multicomponent mixture calculations of constituents properties, (ii) a common particle velocity for all the components, (iii) separate temperatures for active and inactive constituents, (iv) p - α model for pore collapse, (v) a single chemical reaction among R constituents. Shear stress is not considered. The derivation of the basic model is found in [4]. Some elements of the model such as the equations of state and the number of chemical reactions are subject to change depending on the nature of the problems under consideration.

The most important improvement made in the current model is the calculation of pressure and temperatures that eliminated the explicit need for the rate of changes of species specific volumes. This is made possible by imposing a weak assumption on the form of the equations of state that includes most commonly used equations such as Mie-Grüneisen equation and the ideal gas law. Pressure and tempreatures are now calculated by the matrix equation,

$$\begin{bmatrix} \frac{P_m-(P+\eta)}{C_{vi}} - T_i\frac{\Gamma_i}{v_i} & 0 & \frac{\beta_{si}}{v_i} - \frac{\Gamma_i}{v_i}[P_m-(P+\eta)] \\ \frac{P_m}{C_{vm}} - T_m\frac{\Gamma_m}{v_m} + \frac{\lambda_i}{\lambda_m}\frac{P+\eta}{C_{vm}}\frac{\beta_{tm}}{\beta_{ti}}\frac{v_i}{v_m} & \frac{\beta_{sm}}{v_m} - P_m\frac{\Gamma_m}{v_m} & -\frac{\lambda_i}{\lambda_m}\frac{P+\eta}{C_{vm}}\frac{\beta_{tm}}{\beta_{ti}}\frac{v_i}{v_m}C_{vi}(\frac{\Gamma_i}{v_i}) \\ \frac{\lambda_i}{\lambda_m}\frac{v_i}{\beta_{ti}} + \sum_j \frac{\zeta_j v_j}{\beta_{tj}} & -\sum_j \frac{\zeta_j v_j}{\beta_{tj}} C_{vj}(\frac{\Gamma_j}{v_j}) & -\frac{\lambda_i}{\lambda_m}\frac{v_i}{\beta_{ti}}C_{vi}(\frac{\Gamma_i}{v_i}) \end{bmatrix} \begin{Bmatrix} \dot{P}_m \\ \dot{T}_m \\ \dot{T}_i \end{Bmatrix} = \begin{Bmatrix} \frac{\beta_{ti}}{C_{vi}v_i}\dot{q}_i \\ \frac{\beta_{tm}}{C_{vm}v_m}(-\frac{P+\eta}{\lambda_m}\dot{v} + \dot{q}_m + H_0\dot{\xi}) \\ \sum_j \dot{\zeta}_j v_j - \frac{1}{\alpha\lambda_m}(\dot{v} - \dot{\alpha} v_s) \end{Bmatrix} \quad (1)$$

where i and m stand for inactive and reactive subsystems respectively, λ = mass fraction of subsystems, α = distention ratio, η = artificial viscosity, ζ_j = mass fractions of reacting components within subsystem m, $H_0\dot{\xi}$ = rate of internal energy change due to reactions. The inhomogeneous column contains the quantities that are related to the rate equations for internal mechanisms such as heat conduction and chemical kinetics. The term $\dot{v}$ is given by the equation of mass conservation.

MODEL SIMULATION

Ni-Al mixture

A schematic of the test configuration is shown in Figure 1 where a 304 Steel plate impacts on a sample mixture held between two similar steel plates. Chemical initiation is investigated by varying the impact velocity and monitoring pressure at the back plate. The reaction is also checked by a post-shock study of the recovered materials.

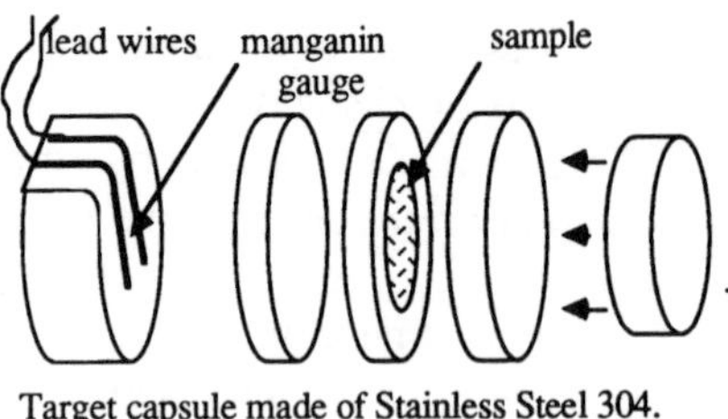

Figure 1. Schematic of test configuration for Ni-Al.

The measured profile for the flyer velocity of 1.4 km/s is compared with calculations in Figure 2. Material properties used were those at ambient conditions or derived from Hugoniot data. The product is assumed to be melted Ni_3Al. The Hugoniot of the product is based on atomic fraction. Unknown data associated with pore collapse and chemical kinetics are treated as adjustable parameters. Crush-up pressure of 4 GPa was selected based on unreacted profiles. Kinetic constants were adjusted to match the peak pressure. The most critical parameter turned out to be the initiation threshold. The value that yields the measured pressure is 1,200 K. Other kinetic constants were chosen to yield the characteristic reaction constant of about 2 μsec. Unfortunately, the gauge failed shortly after the pressure reached the peak value.

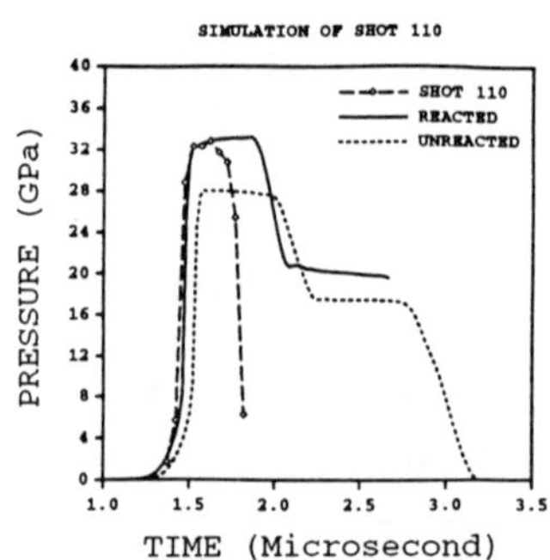

Figure 2. Calculated and experimental profiles for Ni-Al.

There is not much more one can infer from this comparison. But, it needs to be emphasized that the observed excess pressure is not caused by the heat of reaction, but by the interaction of chemistry with shock wave reflection. Such an interaction cannot be predicted by analyses based on the Hugoniot equation. When unreacted the shock strength is 28 GPa. Also, it is important to note that the reaction is taking place in a consolidate mixture.

Al-Fe_3O_4 Mixture

In this experiment a sample disk mounted on a projectile impacts on a transparent lithium floride disk that serves as an optical window for the measurement of temperature of the impact interface [3]. Figure 3 shows measured temperatures for shot 2274 and 2279. Respective impact velocities were 1.3 and 1.2 km/s. Calculated inert shock temperatures were said to be about 1,000 K. Second increases after 2.5 to 3 μsec were attributed to the reflected shock from the rear surface of the sample pellet. Several inferences have been drawn from the measurements. They are (i) a fast, but limited reaction in the first shock, (ii) heterogeneous temperature fields, and (iii) second reaction induced by the reflected shock in shot 2274.

A simulation of the experiments is shown in Figure 4. Material constants are those of [3]. The reaction threshold and time constatnt used were 1,200 K and 2 μsec respectively. Crush-up

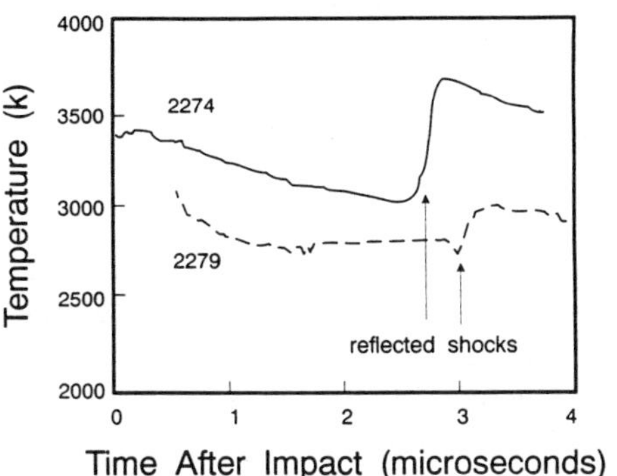

Figure 3. Experimental temperature profiles for Al-Fe_3O_4.

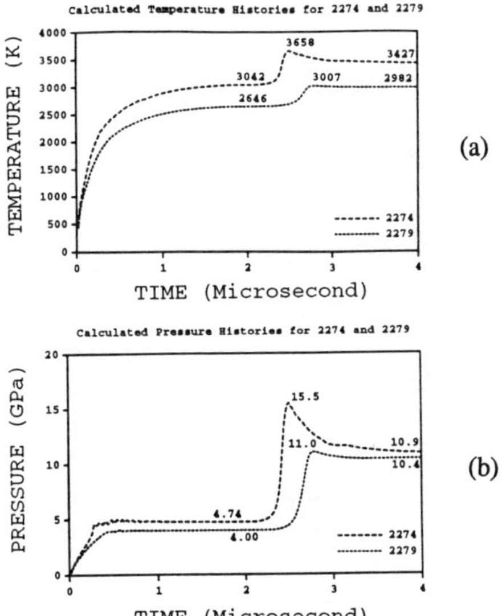

Figure 4. Calculated pressure and temperature profiles.

pressure was 5 GPa.

Disagreements in early time profiles are thought to be caused by hot spots that are not considered in this calculation. But, the calculations describe late stage characteristics fairly well. The difference in magnitudes is no doubt caused by the use of ambient properties that may not be appropriate for this highly exothermic system and the uncertainty in the equation of state properties. The calculations were performed to gain a qualitative insight into the first order phenomena. In this spirit, we may infer from Figure 4(b) that for shot 2274 the presure somehow affects the second reaction strongly or that the temperature rise is a pure pressure effect. Also, the relaxation behind the second shock for shot 2274 is found to require a particular range of initiation temperature: 1,200 ± 100 K. The reason is again attributable to the interaction of reflecting shock with chemistry at the rear interface. The variation of the initiation temperature alters the timing of chemical initiation in relation to shock compression.

SHOCK-INDUCED HETEROGENOUS FLOW

Orthodox mechanisms of mass transport are all too slow to explain the observed reactions. Also, there is evidence that the initiation is of nonthermal origin. Therefore, we have sought some mechanistic understanding of the chemical initiation through the non-equilbrium aspects of hydrodynamic flow in a powder mixture under shock loading. In essence we developed an Eulerian VIR model that has eliminated the conditions of mechanical equilibrium among constituents using a continuum mixture theory [6]. For a simple two component system, the resulting equations resembles those of two-phase flow. However, one of the unique features of this mixture theory is the way in which the volume fractions of constituent species are introduced as independent variables. For details the readers are reffered to [6]. We show only the momentum equation for one of the constituents in a binary system.

$$\rho_a\left(\frac{\partial v_a}{\partial t} + v_a\frac{\partial v_a}{\partial x}\right) = -\alpha_a\frac{\partial P_a}{\partial x} - \delta(v_a - v_b) + (P_b - P_a)\frac{\partial \alpha_a}{\partial x} \qquad (2)$$

$$\frac{\partial \alpha_a}{\partial t} + v_a\frac{\partial \alpha_a}{\partial x}) = \frac{1}{\mu}(P_a - P_b) \qquad (3)$$

where equation (3) is the constitutive equation for α_a. The equation for the second component can be easily found by interchanging the subscript. Equation (2) differs from that for a single component system only in the terms that are associated with the slip velocity (v_a - v_b) and the volume fraction α_a, which are no longer in equilibrium.

To demonstrate shock-induced heterogeneous flow, Equation (2) is used for calculating plane shock wave propagation in a saturated mixture of 50/50 wt % Ni-Al. Results are shown in Figure 5 where shocks were generated by impacting the mixture on another at 1 km/s. The viscosity coefficient is estimated from that of Ni in [7]. The relaxation constant for α_a is based on sound speeds of the elements. The figure shows a slip velocity of 2~300 m/s, which is primarily controlled by the viscocity.

With real powder mixtures there is no gurantee that the calculated heterogeneous flow will indeed occur. Onset of the flow must depend on such factors as particle packing, porosity, particle shape and size distributions, deformation behavior of individual particles, to name a few. However, if it occurs, then surface instabilities of some sort can reduce a characteristic mixing length to a scale at which even orthodox mechanisms can sustain observed fast reactions. A simple estimate of this length is given by $6\sigma/\varepsilon\rho u^2$ where σ is interfacial surface tension, $\rho u^2/2$ kinetic energy of slip, and ε the efficiency of the energy transformation [8].

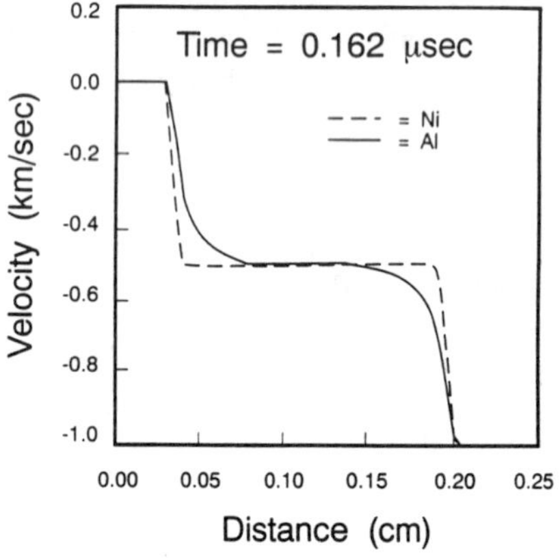

Figure 5. Shock-induced heterogeneous flow in Ni-Al.

For the surface tension of 1 joule/m^2, the length is indeed of the order of 0.1 μm.

SUMMARY

Two types of mathematical models were used to investigate chemical reactions in Ni-Al and Al-Fe_3O_4 powder mixtures. The first model called VIR shows a large pressure effect due to the interaction of chemistry with hydrodynamic flow and the importance of high pressures in chemical initiation. The former cannot be not predicted by Hugoniot analysis. The second continuum mixture model suggests that shock-induced heterogeneous flow may explain the initiation of the chemical reactions.

ACKNOWLEDGEMENTS

Computations were mostly carried out by the author's former students, Drs. M.D. Hwang, S.K. You and L.S. Bennett. This work was partially supported by the North Carolina Supercomputing Center.

REFERENCES

[1]. G.L. Nutt, Lawrence Livermore National Laboratory Report No. UCID 20277, 1984.

[2]. L.S. Bennett, F.Y. Sorrell, I.K. Simonsen, Y. Horie, and K.R. Iyer, *Appl. Phys. Let.* 61, 520 (1992).

[3]. M.B. Boslough, *J. Chem. Phys.* 92, 1839 (1990).

[4]. Y. Horie and A.B. Sawaoka, *Shock Compression Chemistry of Materials*, Tokyo: Tera Scientific Publishing Co., 1993.

[5]. N.N. Thadhani, *Progress in Materials Science* 37, 1993, pp.117-226.

[6]. S.K. You, Ph.D Thesis (unpublished), North Carolina State University, 1992.

[7]. A.V. Bushman, G.I. Kanel , A.L. Ni, and V.E. Fortov, *Intense Dynamic Loading of Condensed Matter*, London: Taylor & Francis, 1993.

[8]. S.J. Board and R.W. Hall, "Thermal Explosions at Molten Tin/Water Intefaces," *Moving Boundary Problems in Heat Flow and Diffusion*, Oxford: Clarendon Press, 1975, pp.259-269.

ENERGY EXPENDITURE AND LIMITATIONS IN SHOCK CONSOLIDATION

M. A. Meyers, D. J. Benson, and S. S. Shang
University of California, San Diego
La Jolla, California, 92093-0411

The energy dissipated by a shock wave as it traverses a powder is assessed. The various energy dissipation processes are analyzed: plastic deformation, interparticle friction, microkinetic energy, defect generation. An expression is developed for the energy requirement to shock consolidate a powder as a function of strength, size, porosity, and temperature, based on a prescribed interparticle melting layer. The corresponding pressures are calculated and it is shown that the activation of flaws occurs at tensile reflected pulses that are a decreasing fraction of the compressive pulse as the powder strength increases. These analytical results are compared to numerical solutions obtained by modeling the compaction of a discrete set of particles with an Eulerian finite element program.

INTRODUCTION

It is very important to estimate the total energy needed to consolidate a material and to determine the shock parameters required to effect such a consolidation by shock waves. This predictive capability has been obtained, for soft materials, through the energy flux models of Gourdin [1] and Schwarz *et al.* [2]. For harder materials, the energy expended in plastic deformation becomes an important component of the overall equation and energy predictions incorporating plastic work have been made by Nesterenko [3] and Ferreira and Meyers [4].

A model for the total energy requirement is developed and applied to some typical "hard" materials: SiC, c-BN, diamond, and Ti_3Al. This estimate of the overall energy enables us to establish the minimum shock energy required for consolidating powders as well as the energy partitioning, when other sources of energy other than shock energy are used. Additionally, the results of the large-scale Eulerian computations using a two-dimensional geometry (cylindrical particles) is presented. The calculational procedure developed by Benson [5] is an extension of the work of Williamson [6] and uses an Eulerian Finite Element Code well suited for the large plastic deformations ocurring in shock consolidation.

Figure 1 shows schematically the various phenomena occurring during shock compaction.These are: (a) The material is plastically deformed; the collapse of the voids requires plastic flow. A plastic deformation energy has to be computed. (b) The plastic flow of the material is a dynamic process, leading to interparticle impact, friction, and plastic flow beyond the flow geometrically necessary to collapse the voids. We will call this component "microkinetic energy". The entire plastic deformation path is changed by virtue of the dynamics of the process. The kinetic energy acquired by the material elements being plastically deformed eventually dissipates into thermal energy. (c) Melting at interparticle regions: It is known that energy is preferentially deposited at the particle surface, leading eventually to their melting. This is the main

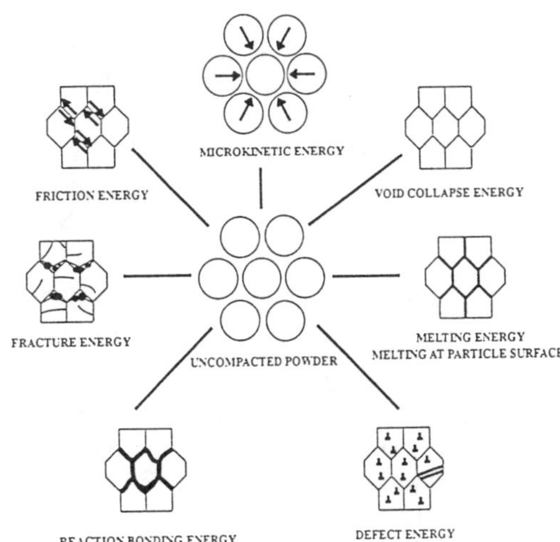

Figure 1. Schematic representation of energy dissipation processes in shock consolidation.

component of Schwarz *et al.* [2]. (d) Defect energy: Point, line, and interfacial defects are produced by the passage of the shock wave. (e) Friction energy: The rearrangement of the powders at the shock front requires relative motions, under the applied stress. Thus, friction may play a role in energy deposition at the shock front. (f) Fracture energy: Brittle materials may consolidate by fracturing. The comminuted particles can more efficiently fill the voids. (g) Gas compression: Compaction is most often conducted with the powder being initially at atmospheric pressure. Thus, the gaps between the powders are filled with gas. Shock compaction of the powders compresses and heats these gases. This effect was considered first by Lotrich, Akashi, and Sawaoka [7]. (h) Shock initiated chemical reactions: Reactive elements or compounds can be added to the powders that are being consolidated. These exothermic reactions can be used to deposit additional energy at the powder surfaces, thereby assisting bonding. This approach was introduced by Akashi and Sawaoka [8].

SIMPLE ANALYTICAL COMPUTATION OF SHOCK COMPACTION ENERGY REQUIREMENTS

The computation of the various components is presented in detail by Shang [9] and only the final expressions are given here.

Void Collapse Energy at Microscopic Level: One of the models that predict the pressure in porous materials as a function of density is the one by Helle *et al* [10]. The pressure is given by:

$$\mathbf{P_y} = 2.97\,\rho^2 \frac{(\rho - \rho_0)}{(1 - \rho_0)}\,\mathbf{Y_y}$$

Y_y is the flow stress of the material. The total energy required to densify the material is given by

$$\mathbf{E_{vc}} = \frac{2.97\ \mathbf{Y_y}}{1 - \rho_0}\left[\frac{(-\rho_f^2 - \rho_0^2)}{2} + \rho_f\,\rho_0\right]$$

Microkinetic Energy: Nesterenko [3] developed a model which describes the relative movement of particles under dynamic compression, as shown in Figure 2. Nesterenko's [3] modification of the Carroll-Holt model enables the introduction of a size scale and the separation of the plastic deformation process into two components, one of which has a substantial microkinetic energy. The external shell, is directly responsible for the microkinetic energy, since it impacts the internal core, which is considered to be stationary. The impact velocity is given by $V=(a_0-c)/t$, and the microkinetic energy is given as

$$\mathbf{E_k} = \frac{1}{2}\,\mathbf{m}\,\mathbf{V}^2 = \frac{1}{2}\,\mathbf{m}\left(\frac{\mathbf{a_0 - c}}{\mathbf{t}}\right)^2$$

where m is the mass of the external shell.

Frictional Energy: The calculation of frictional energy is based on a pyramidal coordination and one-dimensional strain. This leads to:

$$\mathbf{E_f} = \frac{0.1\ \mathbf{P}\,\xi\ \mathbf{Z}\,\mu}{\rho}$$

where μ is friction coefficient, P the applied stress, ρ the density, ξ fraction of contact surface, and Z the coordination number of the powders.

Computation of the total Energy: The following problem is posed: what pressure is required to shock consolidate a specific material, if interparticle melting with a prescribed thickness is needed for good bonding between particles? The shock pressure can be estimated by equating the total shock energy with the sum of the void collapse, defect, microkinetic, and frictional energy, leading to:

$$\mathbf{P} = \frac{2\rho_0\rho}{(\rho - \rho_0)}\left[\frac{1}{2}\mathbf{m}\left(\frac{\mathbf{a_0 - c}}{\mathbf{t}}\right)^2 + \frac{0.1\ \mathbf{P}\,\xi\ \mathbf{Z}\,\mu}{\rho} + \frac{2.97\mathbf{Y_y}}{1 - \rho_0}\left(\frac{-\rho_f^2 - \rho_0^2}{2} + \rho_f\rho_0\right)\right]$$

The defect energy (which is found to be negligible) is a component of the plastic deformation energy. The melting energy is a direct result of the plastic deformation, microkinetic, and friction energies. By considering a prescribed interparticle melting layer, it is possible to calculate the pressure required to consolidate a material as a function

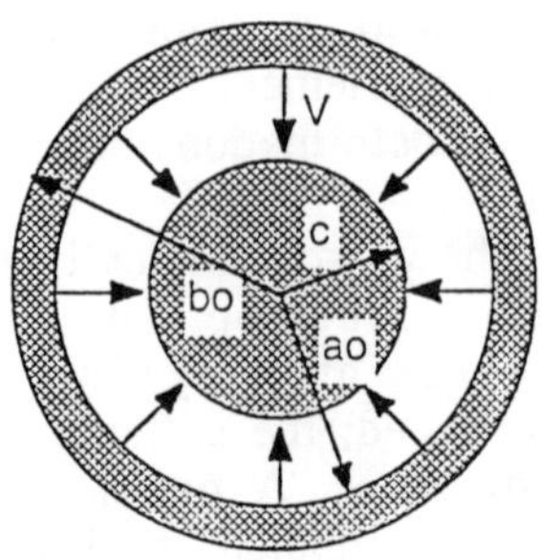

Figure 2. Nesterenko's [3] void collapse model.

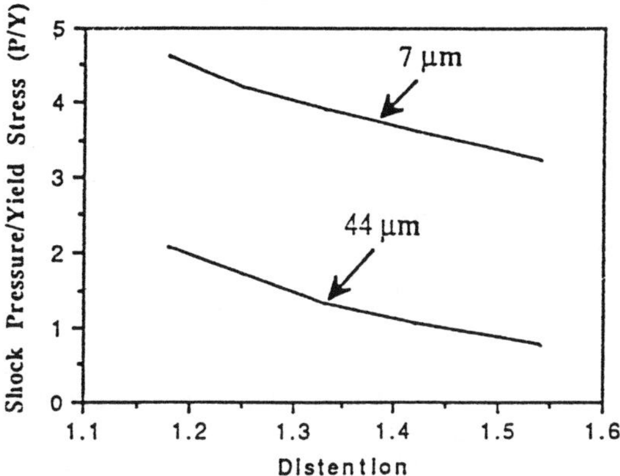

Figure 3. Computed pressure required for shock consolidation of SiC.

of initial density (distention) and particle size. This is shown in Figure 3 for SiC. A normalized plot of P/Y versus distention was produced for different particle sizes. As the distention increases, the P/Y ratio required for shock consolidation of a fixed particle size decreases. Conversely, as the particle size is decreased, the P/Y ratio required increases.

DIRECT NUMERICAL SIMULATION OF SHOCK COMPACTION

The complex deformation pattern occurring in shock consolidation is best captured by computational modeling. The simplifying assumptions in the simple analytical model presented in the previous section are very drastic and the physical processes are only brought out by numerical methods. Benson [11] presents an overview of explicit Lagrangian and Eulerian codes. A model boundary value problem was used to simulate the propagation of the shock wave through the powder. The tridimensional problem is reduced to two dimensions, and spherical particles (of varying diameters) are simulated as cylinders. The green density was taken as 80% of the theoretical density, and calculations were performed for copper and silicon carbide. The Steinberg-Guinan plasticity model [12] was used in combination with the Mie-Gruneisen equation of state. A particle size distribution was assumed based on experimental measurements. As the impact velocity is increased, the "microkinetic" energy of the powders increases, and plastic deformation at the interfaces exceeds significantly the value needed for void collapse. Thus, one can separate this

Figure 4. Configuration for consolidated (a) copper and (b) SiC powders after 1 km/s impact velocity (from Benson and Nellis [5]).

plastic deformation into a "geometrically necessary" component and a "redundant" component; the latter is due to the microkinetic energy and is responsible for the localized temperature spikes that lead to melting and bonding. Figure 4 shows the results of the computation for (a) copper and (b) silicon carbide for a 1 km/s impact velocity, developed by Benson and Nellis [5]. The copper powder is severely deformed with a great amount of "redundant" plastic deformation due to the microkinetic energy. At 1 km/s, the shock energy is only sufficient to collapse the voids in SiC. This explains why the shock pressure required for consolidation of SiC is much higher than for copper.

LIMITATIONS OF SHOCK CONSOLIDATION PROCESS

There exist two major problems in shock consolidation. One is cracking of the compacts at both the microscopic and macroscopic levels. The other is a lack of uniformity in microstructure and mechanical properties within the resulting compacts. Figure 5(a) shows plots of critical flaw size, a, as a function of tensile stress, σ, for materials having different fracture toughnesses, K_{IC}. These plots were made using

a
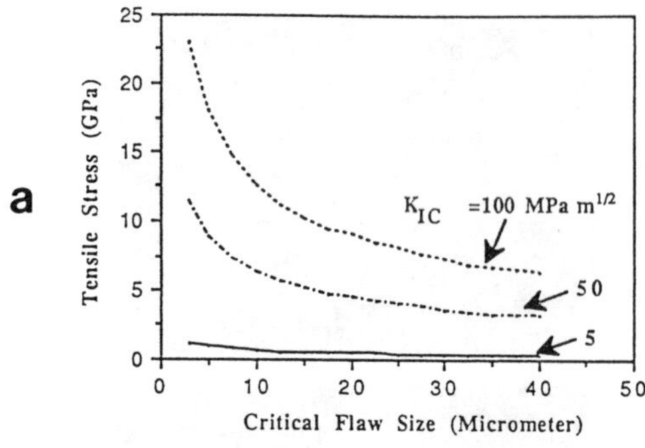

b
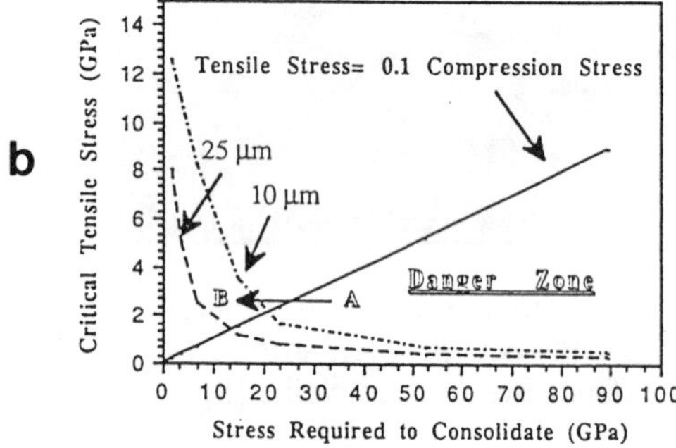

Figure 5. (a) Critical flaw size as a function of tensile stress; (b) variation of critical tensile stress for 10 and 25 µm flaw activation.

the well known fracture mechanics equation: $\sigma = K_{IC}/\sqrt{\pi a}$. It is difficult to conceive a shock consolidation process in which no flaws are left, and the particle size is a good indicator of the inherent flaw size in a shock consolidated material. The three fracture toughnesses given, 5, 50, and 100 MPa $\sqrt{m}$, are characteristic of brittle (ceramics), tough (steel, titanium alloys) and very ductile materials (copper, nickel), respectively. Figure 5(b) shows the critical tensile stresses for 25 µm and 10 µm particle sizes as a function of the compressive stresses needed to consolidate the respective powders. The compressive stresses were taken from Ferreira and Meyers' calculation [4], at a distention corresponding to an initial density of 65% of the theoretical density (this is a typical value for powders). Tensile stresses due to reflections are always present in shock consolidation systems. In well designed systems a significant portion of the tensile stresses is trapped. When the tensile stresses exceed the critical tensile stresses for the specific material, failure occurs; this is shown in Figure 5(b) in a schematic fashion. A realistic line shows $\sigma_t = 0.1\sigma_c$, i.e., the tensile reflections have, at most, an amplitude of 10% of the compressive pulse. Thus, a "Danger Zone" is marked in the figure. By reducing the shock amplitude point [A] (corresponding to a hypothetical material) is changed to [B]. Thus, there are three approaches to be implemented for improved shock consolidation. Reduction of tensile stresses requires systems where the design geometry is optimized. Shock energy can be reduced by thermal or chemical energy in an effort to improve compact quality. The reduction in powder size (e.g., nanocrystalline), reducing a, the flaw size, is the third approach.

This work was supported by the National Science Foundation Grants DMR 8713258 and DMR 91-5835R1 and by the LawrenceLivermore National Laboratory (IGPP).

REFERENCES

1. W.H. Gourdin, *J. Appl. Phys*, 55, p.55 (1984).
2. R.B. Schwarz, P. Kasiraj, T. Vreeland Jr., and T.J. Ahrens, *Acta Metall.*, 32, p. 1243 (1984).
3. V.F. Nesterenko, Proc. Novosibirsk-Conference on Dynamic Compaction, (1988) p. 100.
4. A. Ferreira and M.A. Meyers, in "*Shock Wave and High Strain Rate Phenomena in Materials,*" M. Dekker, 1992, p. 361.
5. D. J. Benson and W. J. Nellis, "Numerical Simulation of the Shock Compaction of Copper Powder," these proceedings.
6. R.L. Williamson, *J. Appl. Phys.*, 68, p. 1287 (1990).
7. V.F. Lotrich, T. Akashi, and A.B. Sawaoka, in *Metallurgical Applications of Shock Wave and High-Strain-Rate Phenomena*, M. Dekker, 1986, p. 277.
8. T. Akashi and A.B. Sawaoka, U.S. Patent 4.655.830 (1987).
9. S.S. Shang, Ph.D. Dissertation, UCSD, 1992.
10. A.S. Helle, K.E. Easterling and M.F. Ashby, *Acta Metall.*, 33, p. 2163 (1985).
11. D.J. Benson, *Comp. Meth. in Appl. Mech. and Eng.*, 99, p. 235 (1992).
12. D.J. Steinberg and M.W. Guinan, Technical Report UCRL-80465, Lawrence Livermore National Laboratory, 1978.

NUMERICAL SIMULATION OF THE SHOCK COMPACTION OF COPPER POWDER

David J. Benson
Dept. of AMES 0411
University of California, San Diego
La Jolla, CA 92093

William J. Nellis
Lawrence Livermore National Laboratory
P. O. Box 808 L-299
Livermore, CA 94550

The shock compaction of an aggregate of randomly distributed copper particles with a nonuniform size distribution is simulated using an Eulerian hydrocode. A shock Hugoniot for a copper powder is calculated from a series of shock compaction simulations and compared to experimental results. The powder particles are modeled as rods in two dimensions. The particle size distribution is generated from a representative powder size distribution via a simple Monte-Carlo method and is initially numerically packed to a dense powder compact using the pseudo-gravity method.

INTRODUCTION

An understanding of the shock physics of powders on the micromechanical level is important in both engineering and science. Experiments measure the average response of many particles to shock compression since the size and time scales involved currently preclude the detailed measurement of the response of individual particles in a powder. Phenomenological models [1] and numerical simulations of closest-packed arrangements of mono-sized steel particles [2] have been used to gain insight on the micromechanical response of powders to shocks.

Real powders generally have a nonuniform shape and size distribution, and the initial density of the powder is well below the theoretical density. The objective of this research is the development of a computational method for analyzing the micromechanical response of real powders to shock compression and the research presented here represents our first step in that direction. We hope to eventually develop the methodology to the point where it can be used to design experiments using a wide variety of materials. Copper was chosen for this study because of the large amount of experimental real time data available in the literature [3]. To verify the accuracy of the calculations, the shock velocity, U_s, versus particle velocity, U_p, relation was calculated and compared to a least squares fit to the experimental data.

THE MODEL PROBLEM

The model problem approximates a single-shock powder compaction experiment with a few simplifications. The most notable simplification is the reduction of the problem from three dimensions to two, with the result that the particles in the calculations are cylinders instead of spheres.

Geometry

The model two-dimensional, plane strain boundary value problem is defined in Figure 1. The initial domain is 30 μm on a side and each side is divided into 100 zones for a total of 10000 zones. The particle size distribution is generated from a representative powder size distribution via a simple Monte-Carlo method and it is initially numerically packed to a dense powder compact using the pseudo-gravity method. A compression wave, generated by a velocity boundary condition, propagates from the upper boundary, through the domain, and is transmitted out through the lower boundary. A square test region in the center of the domain contains the random distribution of cylindrical particles. The left and right edges have the "roller" boundary conditions:

$$\boldsymbol{u} \cdot \boldsymbol{n} = 0 \tag{1}$$
$$\boldsymbol{t} \cdot \boldsymbol{\sigma} \cdot \boldsymbol{n} = 0 \tag{2}$$

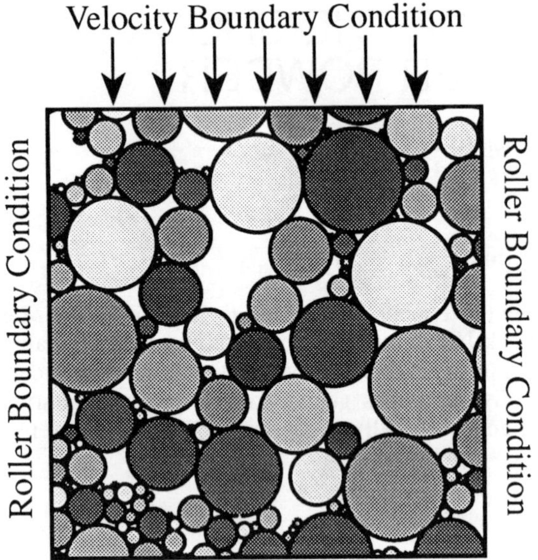

Figure 1. The model boundary value problem with an initial porosity of nineteen percent. Different colors are used to differentiate different copper particles.

The velocity on the upper boundary is ramped up over a period of 0.001 μs with the quadratic function

$$v = \begin{cases} U_p(t/t_{ramp})^2 & \text{if } t < t_{ramp} \\ U_p & \text{otherwise.} \end{cases} \tag{3}$$

The fast rise time generates a shock-wave in the powder. The quadratic temporal rise avoids producing excessive oscillations behind the shock front. U_p is the steady state velocity of the upper boundary, and t_{ramp} is the period over which the velocity ramped up from zero.

Constitutive Model and Equation of State

The Steinberg-Guinan plasticity model [4] and the Gruneisen equation of state are used to model the copper. The differential equations for Steinberg-Guinan plasticity model follow the well-established framework of J_2 flow theory with isotropic hardening defined by

$$\dot{\boldsymbol{\sigma}}' = 2G(\dot{\boldsymbol{\epsilon}}' - \dot{\boldsymbol{\epsilon}}^p) \tag{4}$$

$$\bar{\epsilon}^p = \int_0^t \sqrt{\frac{2}{3}\dot{\boldsymbol{\epsilon}}^p : \dot{\boldsymbol{\epsilon}}^p}\, d\tau \tag{5}$$

$$\sigma_y = \sqrt{\frac{3}{2}\boldsymbol{\sigma}' : \boldsymbol{\sigma}'} \tag{6}$$

where $\boldsymbol{\sigma}'$ is the deviatoric part of the Cauchy stress tensor, $\dot{\boldsymbol{\epsilon}}'$ is the deviatoric strain rate tensor, $\dot{\boldsymbol{\epsilon}}^p$ is the plastic strain rate, and $\bar{\epsilon}^p$ is the equivalent plastic strain.

The shear modulus, G, and the yield strength, σ_y, are temperature and pressure-dependent, and have the same general functional form. The temperature dependence is expressed in the constitutive model in terms of the internal energy per initial volume, E. When the internal energy is below the melt energy, E_m, the yield stress and the shear modulus are

$$G = G_o\left[1 + bPV^{1/3} - h\Delta T\right]\exp\left(-\frac{fE}{E_m - E}\right) \tag{7}$$

$$\sigma_y = \sigma_o'\left[1 + b'PV^{1/3} - h'\Delta T\right]\exp\left(-\frac{fE}{E_m - E}\right) \tag{8}$$

$$\sigma_o' = \min\left\{\sigma_m, \sigma_o\left[1 + \beta(\bar{\epsilon}_o^p + \bar{\epsilon}^p)\right]^n\right\} \tag{9}$$

$$\Delta T = \frac{E - E_c}{3R'} - 300 \tag{10}$$

and after the material melts, they are set to

$$G = G_o/2 \tag{11}$$

$$\sigma_y = \sigma_o/2 \tag{12}$$

where V is the specific volume, P is the pressure, E_c is the cold compression energy, and G_o, σ_o, σ_m, b, b', h, f, β, $\bar{\epsilon}_o^p$, and n are material parameters. The coefficient R' is defined as

$$R' = R\rho/A \tag{13}$$

where R is the gas constant, ρ is the density, and R is the gas constant, and A is the atomic weight.

A Gruneisen equation of state for the pressure is used in compression

$$P = \frac{\rho_o C^2 \mu\left[1 + (1 - \gamma_0/2)\mu - a\mu^2/2\right]}{\left[1 - (S - 1)\mu\right]^2} + (\gamma_0 + a\mu)E \tag{14}$$

$$\mu = \rho/\rho_o - 1 \tag{15}$$

In expansion, the pressure is given by

$$P = \rho_o C^2 \mu + (\gamma_0 + a\mu)E \tag{16}$$

where C and ρ_o are the acoustic wave speed and density at the reference temperature and density, and S is the slope of the $U_s - U_p$ curve.

NUMERICAL SOLUTION PROCEDURE

The boundary value problem was solved using an explicit Eulerian hydrocode called "Raven," which was developed by DB. The spatial discretization uses quadrilateral elements with constant stress and viscous hourglass control. The solution is advanced in time using the central difference method. Spatial operator splitting is used in combination with the MUSCL advection scheme for calculating the transport between elements, and the interfaces are resolved using the method developed by Youngs. A detailed discussion of these methods is presented in a review paper [5].

CALCULATION OF THE SHOCK VELOCITY

The shock velocity is calculated by differencing the location of the shock front with respect to time. Since the shock front is not a straight line at the micromechanical level in a powder, a numerical averaging scheme must be used to calculate a mean location. In a one-dimensional version of the boundary value problem, the location of the centroid of the material behind the shock, y_c, is

$$y_c = (y_p + y_s)/2 \tag{17}$$

where y_p is the location of the boundary that is compressing the material with the specified particle velocity U_p and y_s is the location of the shock front. After taking the derivative of the equation with time, the shock velocity, U_s, is

$$U_s = 2U_c - U_p \tag{18}$$

where U_c is the velocity of the centroid. At each output step, the location y_c is calculated based on the yield stress:

$$y_c = \frac{\int \mathcal{F}_\sigma(\boldsymbol{\sigma}) \cdot y d\Omega}{\int \mathcal{F}_\sigma(\boldsymbol{\sigma}) d\Omega} \tag{19}$$

$$\mathcal{F}_\sigma(\boldsymbol{\sigma}) = \begin{cases} 1 & \text{if } |\sigma(t)| \geq \sigma_y/2 \\ 0 & \text{otherwise} \end{cases} \tag{20}$$

COMPARISON TO EXPERIMENTS

Shock Velocity

The initial densities of the cylindrical and rectangular powders (81 and 84 percent of the solid copper density respectively) used in the calculations are not the same as those used in the experiments performed at Los Alamos [3]. To provide a comparison with the calculated shock velocity -

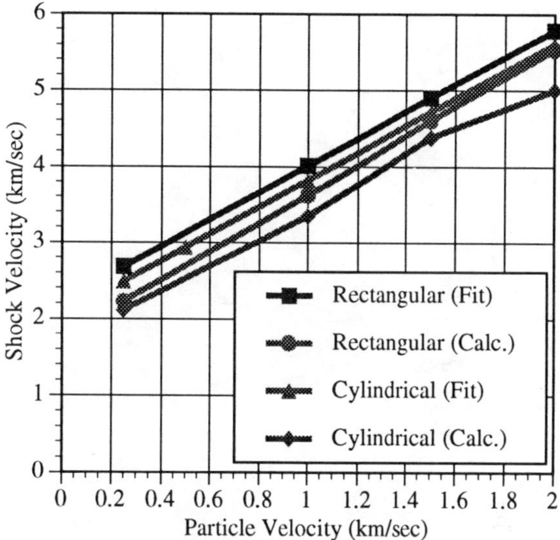

Figure 2. The calculated and interpolated shock velocity - particle velocity relations for copper powders.

particle velocity relations for the two powders, a least squares fit to the experimental $U_s - U_p$ data for the appropriate initial densities was used in Figure 2. The calculations are in surprisingly good agreement with the experimental data given the two-dimensional approximation of the geometry and the modest number of particles in the calculations.

Material Microstructure

As the particle velocity increases, the flow of the copper particles becomes increasingly turbulent, see Figure 3. The general features of the microstructure calculated for a particle velocity of 1.0 km/sec are similar to those in the experiments by Thomas *et al* [6], although the experimental conditions aren't specified for the microphotograph.

ACKNOWLEDGMENTS

This work was supported by the University of California Institute of Geophysics and Planetary Physics branch at LLNL. Calculations were performed at the LLNL Open Computer Facility.

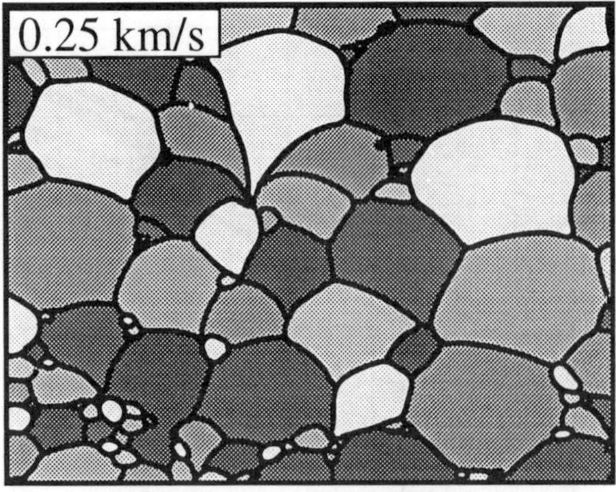

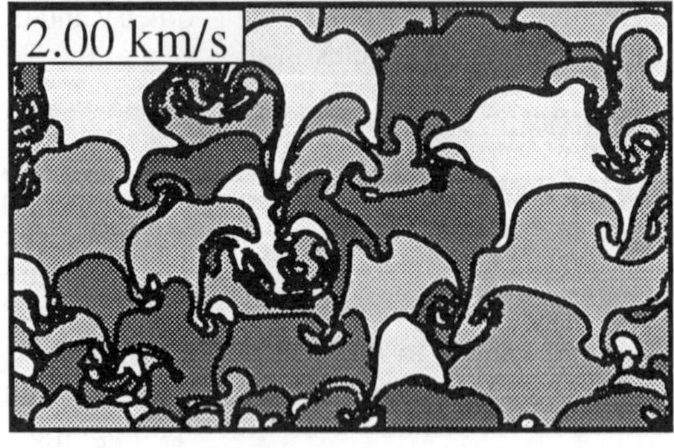

Figure 3. The microstructures of the copper powder after shock compaction with particle velocities of 0.25, 1.00, and 2.00 km/s.

REFERENCES

[1] W. H. Gourdin. Energy deposition and microstructural modification in dynamically consolidated metal powders. *J. Appl. Phys.*, 55(1):172–181, 1984.

[2] R. L. Williamson. Parametric studies of dynamic powder consolidation using a particle-level numerical model. *J. Appl. Phys.*, 68(3):1287–1296, 1990.

[3] S. P. Marsh, editor. *LASL Shock Hugoniot Data*. University of California Press, 1980.

[4] D. J. Steinberg and M. W. Guinan. A high strain rate constitutive model for metals. Technical Report UCRL-80465, Lawrence Livermore National Laboratory, 1978.

[5] D. J. Benson. Computational methods in Lagrangian and Eulerian hydrocodes. *Computer Methods in Applied Mechanics and Engineering*, 99:235–394, 1992.

[6] T. Thomas, P. Bensussan, P. Chartagnac, and Y. Bienvenu. Dynamic compaction of copper powder: Experimental results and 2D numerical calculations. In M. A. Meyers, L. E. Murr, and K. P. Staudhammer, editors, *Shock-Wave and High-Strain-Rate Phenomena in Materials*, pages 433–442. Marcel Dekker, Inc., 1992.

A MIXTURE MODEL FOR SHOCK COMPRESSION OF POROUS MULTI-COMPONENT REACTIVE MATERIALS

M. R. Baer*
Energetic Materials and Fluid Mechanics Dept. 1512
Sandia National Laboratories, Albuquerque,NM, 87185

A multiphase mixture model is presented to describe shock compression of highly porous, multi-component powders. Volume fractions are represented as independent kinematic variables and thermodynamically-admissable phase interaction constitutive models are formulated in the context of a three phase system. Numerical solutions of the multiphase flow equations simulated impact on a porous layer of mixed powders of Al and Fe_2O_3. The multiphase model predicts dispersive compaction waves which have features similar to observed time-resolved pressure measurements.

INTRODUCTION

In contrast to single-phase materials, porous materials contain internal boundaries which greatly influence their thermal and mechanical response to shock loading. At the microscale, heterogeneous materials often have disparate properties and the interactions between constituents greatly influence macroscale response. Much remains to be understood regarding the complex nature of shock compression of distended materials and prior studies have identified anomalous shock behavior in porous materials. For example, experimental studies have shown that Hugoniot descriptions, based on thermodynamic equilibrium, are inaccurate[1-3] and shock loading induces dispersed compaction wave profiles[4-6] and material segregation behavior.[7] Because of the failure of existing models to realistically describe shock behavior, it is important to extend theoretical models of porous materials.

Continuum mechanics has provided a foundation for theoretical study and mixture theory has successfully described various multiphase waves;[8-10] however, much of this analysis has centered on two phase models. This work extends mixture theory to a multi-component system. As a preliminary study, impact-induced compaction wave behavior in a porous layer of mixed powders is treated.

THEORETICAL DESCRIPTION

The foundations of continuum mixture theory are largely based on the works of Truesdell and Toupin[11] and Truesdell and Noll[12]; an overview of theoretical modeling of reactive mixtures can be found in reference 13. In this study, an extension of the multiphase reactive flow model of Baer and Nunziato[8] is presented; only the final forms of this model are given here. The balance equations are given for a multi-component system with each phase denoted with a subscript "a". Associated with each phase are the material partial densities, $\rho_a = \phi_a \gamma_a$, true material density, γ_a, volume fractions, ϕ_a, particle velocities, $\vec{v}_a$, pressures, p_a, temperatures, T_a, and internal energies, e_a. The Eulerian form of the balance laws are given as:

Mass: $$\grave{\rho}_a = -\rho_a \nabla \cdot \vec{v}_a + c_a^{\dagger} \qquad (1)$$

Momentum: $$\rho_a \grave{\vec{v}}_a = \nabla \cdot \underset{\sim}{\sigma}_a + \vec{m}_a^{\dagger} - c_a^{\dagger} \vec{v}_a \qquad (2)$$

Energy: $$\rho_a \grave{e}_a = \underset{\sim}{\sigma}_a : \vec{\nabla} \vec{v}_a + e_a^{\dagger} - (\vec{m}_a^{\dagger} - c_a^{\dagger} \vec{v}_a) \cdot \vec{v}_a - c_a^{\dagger} E_a \qquad (3)$$

where the material derivative for each phase is defined as $\grave{f}_a = \partial f_a / \partial t + \vec{v}_a \cdot \vec{\nabla} f_a$ and the total energy for each phase is given as $E_a = e_a + (\vec{v}_a \cdot \vec{v}_a)/2$. The "†" superscript denotes a phase exchange quantity for mass, $c_a^{\dagger}$, momentum, $\vec{m}_a^{\dagger}$, and energy, $e_a^{\dagger}$ and the stresses are represented as $\underset{\sim}{\sigma}_a = -\phi_a p_a \underset{\sim}{I} + \underset{\sim}{\tau}_a$.

Consistent with derivations used in mixture theory, summation of each balance equation over all phases yields the response of the total mixture corresponding to the well known equations of motion for a single phase material. Thus, summation constraints are imposed on the phase interactions: $\sum c_a^{\dagger} = 0, \sum \vec{m}_a^{\dagger} = 0$ and $\sum e_a^{\dagger} = 0$. The restrictions of the Second Law of Thermodynamics also suggest admissable forms of phase interaction. For the sake of brevity, the algebraic manipulation will not be repeated here and the final forms of these interactions are given as the following:

This work performed at Sandia National Laboratories supported by the U.S. Department of Energy under contract DE-ACO4-76DP00789

$$\vec{m}_a^{\dagger} - c_a^{\dagger} (\vec{v}_a + \vec{v}_i)/2 + p_i \nabla \phi_a = \sum_j \delta_{j,a} (\vec{v}_j - \vec{v}_a) \quad (1)$$

$$e_a^{\dagger} - \vec{m}_a \cdot \vec{v}_a - (e_a - \vec{v}_a \cdot \vec{v}_a/2) c_a^{\dagger} - (\beta_a - p_a) \{\dot{\phi}_a - c_a^{\dagger}/\gamma_a\} = \sum_j \mathcal{H}_{j,a} (T_j - T_a) \quad (2)$$

$$\dot{\phi}_a - c_a^{\dagger}/\gamma_a = \sum_j \tau_{j,a} (p_a - \beta_a - p_j + \beta_j) \quad (3)$$

where $\delta_{j,a}$, $\mathcal{H}_{j,a}$, $\tau_{j,a}$ are exchange coefficients of positive-definite symmetric tensors reflecting interactions between phases. Interface quantities are denoted with a subscript "i". The configurational stress, β_a, is the stress associated with contact forces between phases and is a different stress state than the bulk stress associated with the material compressibility. Model closure is obtained by specifying an independent equation of state for each phase. Hence, the mixture description centers on the determination of appropriate constitutive relations and phase exchange coefficients using micromechanical modeling and/or experimental guidance.

A MODEL APPLICATION

Time-resolved measurements of shock wave structure in porous multicomponent powders are recent advances in the shock physics field;[4-6] hence limited data exists for guidance in theoretical studies. Figure 1 displays a set of wave profiles measured using PDVF gauges between a porous layer of $2Al/Fe_2O_3$ (2.33 g/cc) mixed powders and a layer of Kel F. Varied impact conditions are shown of the output pressure shifted in time to a common datum. The striking feature of these records is the dispersive nature of the shock front. Rise times of 50 to 300 ns were measured which are well in excess of the rise time in crystalline solids.

As an application of the mixture theory, a 6.7 kbar impact on a 4 mm layer of mixed $2Al/Fe_2O_3$ has been modeled. The mixture description is formulated to describe three components - two solid constituents and void. As an approximation, we consider equal phase velocities ($\delta_{j,a} \to \infty$) and an impact condition that is insufficient to produce reaction between the phases, ($c_a^{\dagger} \to 0$). Thus, the model description simplifies to a set of mass conservation equations, a set of energy equations including heat transfer effects between the solid phases, a set of volume fraction rate equations describing variations

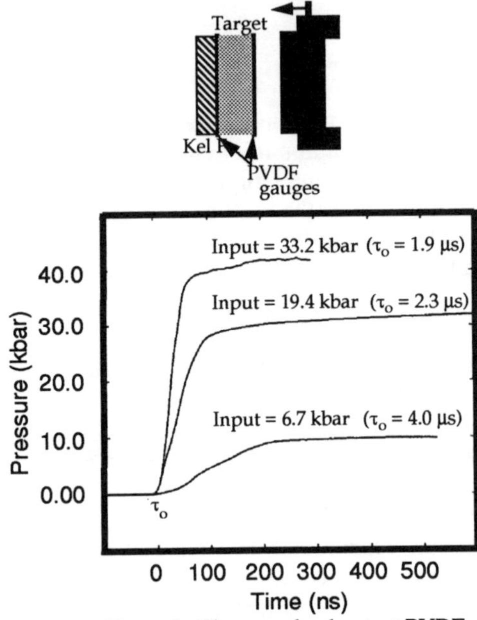

Figure 1. Time-resolved output PVDF pressure measurements from impact on a porous layer of $2Al - Fe_2O_3$.

due to difference in the stress fields, and a single momentum equation describing the mass-averaged velocity of the mixture. Separate thermoelastic equations of state for Al and Fe_2O_3 are formulated using shock Hugoniot data for the crystalline materials[14]. To model the configurational stress, β_a, empirical Konopicky relationships[15] are formulated using yield stresses for each phase[16,17]. Finally, the exchange coefficients for the volume fraction rate equations, $\tau_{j,a}$, are inversely related to material viscosities which are scaled to material sound speed and particle size.

One-dimensional numerical solution of the mixture model is sought using an adaptive finite element method[18] resolving appropriate length scales associated with the shock compression of the porous material. Figure 2 displays an overlay of the pressure, volume fraction and temperature profiles for each solid phase material projected in distance-time space. Input impact conditions occur at the origin of the spatial coordinate. As shown in these plots, compaction of interacting solids proceeds as a dispersive compaction wave traversed the porous layer. Upon interacting with the boundary between the porous material and the Kel F (at the 4 mm spatial coordinate) an impedance mismatch produces a reflected wave back into the compacted material.

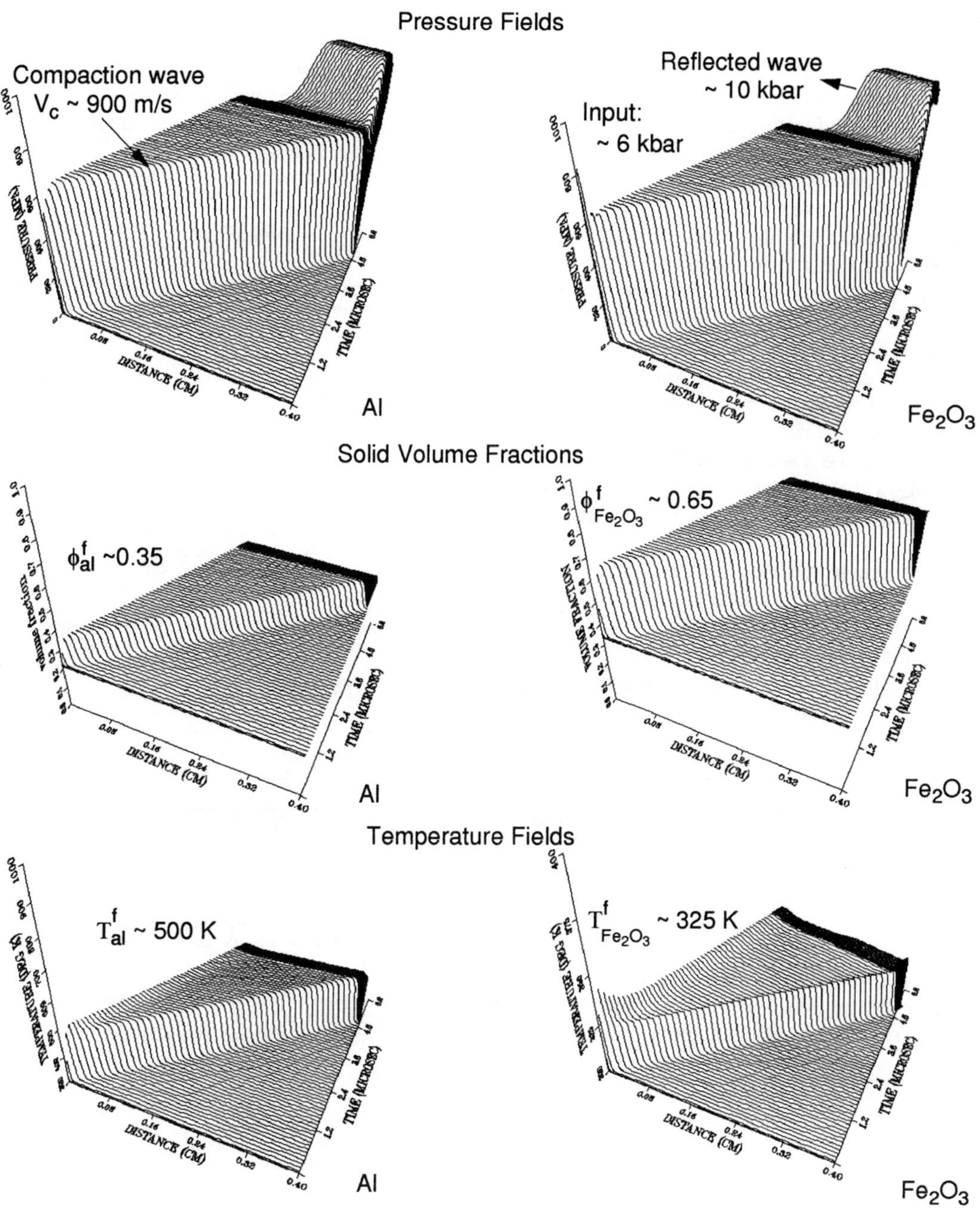

Figure 2. Calculated compaction wave fields in a porous layer of 2 Al/Fe_2O_3 following a 6.7 Kbar impact. Figures in the left column correspond to Al pressure, volume fraction, and temperature (top to bottom) and the right column figures are Fe_2O_3 fields.

At a 6.7 kbar input condition, the compaction shock wave has a speed of ~900 m/s yielding a delay of ~4.5 μs between the input and output gauge locations similar to experimental observation. Upon interaction with the Kel F boundary, the pressure rises to ~10 kbar in a duration of ~200 ns. This corresponds to a wave thickness of ~0.1 mm. Pressure differences between the phases occur primarily at the compaction wave front.

The transient solid volume fraction profiles clearly shows that rapid distortion of the powders occur in a thin shock-like compaction wave which traverse the porous layer. Initially, the volume fractions for Al and Fe_2O_3 are ~0.2 and 0.35, respectively and material flow during compaction increases the volume fractions to 0.35 and 0.65. This suggests that the majority of the material distortion is associated with Fe_2O_3 and all of the open porosity is filled following compaction. Recovery tests on shock compressed powders have suggested similar behavior.

The temperature fields show that thermodynamic equilibrium does not occur during shock compression (at these impact conditions). A larger temperature rise occurs in the consolidated Al than in the Fe_2O_3, however, both temperatures fields are below melting conditions. For this powder configuration (mean particle sizes 15 and 22 μm for Al and Fe_2O_3 powder, respectively), heat transfer is insufficient to rapidly equilibrate these temperatures and thermodynamic equilibrium occurs at much longer time scales.

SUMMARY

In this study, a multi-component mixture model for shock compression of porous materials is presented. This model has been applied to the simulation of impact on a layer of mixed metal powders and predicted wave behavior favorably reproduce experimental observations. Extended study of this approach will now focus on experimental studies of mixed powders with greatly disparate thermophysical properties and conditions which will initiate reactive wave behavior. Prediction of combustion response to shock loading represents the forefront of energetic material research and determining the nature of dispersive shock wave structure in porous materials is a critical step toward a better understanding of the complex reactive behavior of composite materials.

ACKNOWLEDGMENTS

I would like to thank R. A. Graham for insightful discussions and suggestions in the course of this study. I also thank G. T. Holman, R. A. Graham and M. U. Anderson for sharing their PVDF measurements used in this work.

REFERENCES

1 Trofimov, V. S., G. A. Adadurov, S. V. Pershin, and A. N. Dremin, "Anomalous Shock Compressibility of Porous Materials", *Combustion, Explosion and Shock Waves*, Vol 4, No. 2, pp. 244-253, 1968.

2 Linde, R. K. and D. N. Schmidt, "Shock Propagation in Nonreactive Porous Solids", *Journal of Applied Physics*, Vol 37, No. 8., pp 3259-3271, 1966.

3 Dolgoborodov, A. Y., I. M.Voskoboinikov, I. K. Tolstov and A. V. Sudarikov, "Anomalies of the Propagation of Shock Waves in Mixtures", *Combustion, Explosion and Shock Waves*, Vol. 28, No. 3, pp. 106-111, 1992.

4 Holman, G. T., R. A. Graham, M. U. Anderson, "Shock Response of Porous 2Al + Fe_2O_3 Mixtures", 1993 Topical Conference on Shock Compression of Condensed Matter, Colorado Springs, CO, 1993.

5 Anderson, M. U., R. A. Graham, and G. T. Holman, "Time-Resolved Shock Compression of Porous Rutile", 1993 Topical Conference on Shock Compression of Condensed Matter, Colorado Springs, CO, 1993.

6 Dunbar, E., R. A. Graham, N. N. Thadhani, "Time-Resolved Pressure Measurements in Chemically Reacting Powder Mixtures",1993 Topical Conference on Shock Compression of Condensed Matter, Colorado Springs, CO, 1993.

7 Kostyukov, N. A., "Mechanism of Lamination of Particulate Composites in Shock Loading", *J. Applied Mechanics and Technical Physics*, No 1, pp. 84-91, 1990.

8 Baer, M. R. and Nunziato, J. W., "A Two-Phase Mixture Theory for the Deflagration-to-Detonation Transition (DDT) in Reactive Granular Materials," *International Journal of Multiphase Flow*, Vol 12, no. 6, 1986, pp. 861-889.

9 Baer, M. R., "A Numerical Study of Shock Wave Reflection on Low-Density Foam," *Shock Waves*, Vol. 2, pp 121-124., 1993.

10 Baer, M. R., "Numerical Studies of Dynamic Compaction of Inert and Energetic Granular Materials," *Journal of Applied Mechanics*, Vol. 55, 1988, pp. 36-43.

11 Truesdell, C. and R. Toupin, "The Classical Field Theories", **Handbuck der Physik** (Ed. S. Flugge), Vol II/1, Berlin: Springer, 1960.

12 Truesdell, C. and N. Noll, "The Nonlinear Field Theories of Mechanics", **Handbuck der Physik** (Ed. S. Flugge), Vol III/3r, Berlin: Springer, 1965.

13 Truesdell, C., **Rational Thermodynamics**, 2nd Edition, Springer-Verlag, 1984.

14 Marsh, S. P., **LASL Shock Hugoniot Data**, University of California Press, 1980.

15 Konopicky, K., *Radex Rdsch.*, Vol 3, p 141, 1948.

16 Wang, P. T. and M. A. Zaidi, "Thermomechanical Deformation of Powder-Based Porous Aluminum - part I", *Powder Technology*, Vol 66, pp 9-19, 1991.

17 Prasad, Y. A. and Y. B. G. Varma, "Physical and Mechanical Properties of α-Iron Oxide, Iron Oxide-Alumina and Nickel-Alumina Catalysts", *Indian Journal of Technology*, Vol 18, pp. 122-126, 1980.

18 Baer, M. R., Benner, R. E., Gross, R. J., and Nunziato, J. W., "Modeling and Computation of Deflagration-to-Detonation Transition (DDT) in Reactive Granular Materials," **Lectures in Applied Mathematics**, American Mathematical Society, Vol. 24, 1986, pp. 479-498.

EFFECT OF PACKING DENSITY ON SHOCK CONSOLIDATION OF DIAMOND POWDERS

V.S. JOSHI and H.A. GREBE
Energetic Materials Research and Testing Center
New Mexico Institute of Mining and Technology
Socorro, NM 87801, USA

N.N. THADHANI
School of Materials Science and Engineering
Georgia Institute of Technology
Atlanta, GA 30332, USA

Z. IQBAL
Research and Technology
Allied-Signal
Morristown, NJ 07960, USA

Diamond powders of different types and particle size distribution were shock consolidated using a plate impact shock recovery system at 1.6 to 2.2 km/s. Single-piece diamond compacts (approximately 12 mm diameter and 2 - 4 mm thickness) with relative densities in the range of 88 - 94% of Theoretical Maximum Density (TMD) and less than 5% non-diamond phase, were produced. While the effects of several different variables, e.g., powder pre-treatment, particle size and distribution, and impact conditions, were explored, it was established that the initial green-powder-compact density was the most important variable controlling the densification of diamond powders. In this paper, we will present results of some of the consolidation experiments and the role of initial green density in controlling the final compact density and microstructure.

INTRODUCTION

The sintering of diamond powder is generally achieved by static high-pressure techniques using inorganic catalysts or carbide-forming materials as additives.[1] Shock-consolidation of powder offers an alternative route to produce high-density diamond compacts. For diamond powders to attain good interparticle bonding, partitioning of shock energy and its localization at interparticle regions is essential.[2] However, the high hardness and thermal conductivity of diamond limits energy localization, thereby making shock-consolidation of powders more difficult. Some of the attempts to overcome this problem have included powder preheating,[3] use of reactive powder mixtures to generate intrinsic heat,[4] admixing of graphite to provide a low-thermal conductivity phase,[5] and even use of very fine powders such that the temperature rise and subsequent thermal equilibrium for a particular size of particle is well within the shock transit time.[2] These attempts have yielded compacts that in some cases have hardness values ≈ 75% of single crystal diamond;[3,4] however, in all cases the compacts contain extensive cracking, final densities in the range of 80 - 90% of theoretical maximum density, and detectable levels of graphitic or amorphous carbon phases. The objective of our work was to shock consolidate diamond powders (without use of additives), by manipulating the localization of energy via control of particle size distribution and powder packing density.

EXPERIMENTAL PROCEDURE

High purity synthetic diamond powder (Diamond Abrasives Corporation (DAC) - De Beers, Warren - GE 300S) and natural diamond powder (DAC - De Beers) of different particle size distribution and initial packing density (Table 1) were used in the present work. The diamond powders mixed in the appropriate size distribution were pressed into stainless steel capsules embedded in a stainless steel recovery fixture and impacted by an explosively accelerated flyer plate between 1.6 and 2.2 km/s. The recovery fixture is described in detail elsewhere.[6]

A range of powder packing densities from 59% - 75% TMD were achieved by adjusting the particle size distribution. Tap densities as high as 60 - 65% were attained; upon statically pressing the powders, maximum densities in the 70-75% TMD range were attained.

RESULTS AND DISCUSSION

The diamond compacts were recovered in the form of 12 mm diameter x 2 - 4 mm thickness single piece discs. The compacts were free from macro-cracks and had strong mechanical integrity. The recovered compacts were

Table 1. Summary of experimental parameters.

Shot No.(capsule)	Flyer Velocity (km/s)	Powder Size (μm)	Packing Density (%)
NMG 9114 (12)	1.89	4-8	61-64
NMG 9115 (12)	1.68	4-8	55-73
NMG 9124 (12)	1.90	4-12	59-71
NMG 9125 (4)	1.90	1-8	57-62
NMG 9131 (12)	2.15	1-8	63-74
NMG 9132 (4)	1.90	1-12	56-63
NMG 9201 (12)	1.90	1-12	63-74
NMG 9213 (12)	1.84	1-16	64-75
NMG 9240 (12)	1.90	0.5-16	68-84

polished and cleaned prior to measuring their densities. Results of density measurements which were done by the Archimedes water displacement method on the single piece diamond discs are plotted in Figure 1. It is seen that for initial packing densities below 65% consistently result in final densities less than 75%, while for packing densities greater than 65%, the final compact densities range between 85% - 94% theoretical maximum density.

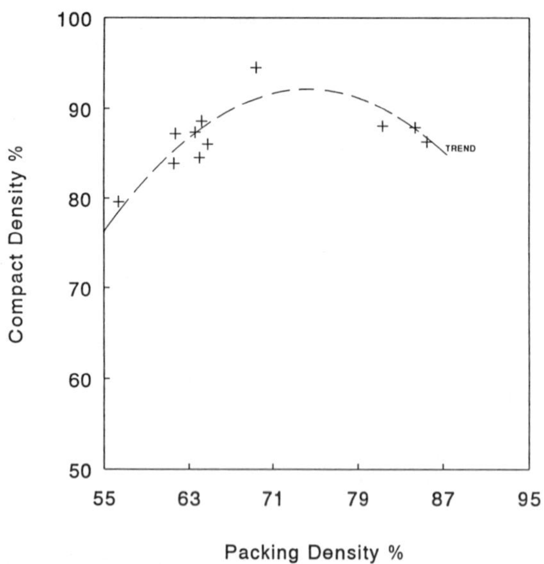

Figure 1. Packing density vs. final compact density for DAC synthetic diamond powder.

Increasing the impact velocity from 1.6 to 1.9 km/s, and therefore the shock consolidation conditions (temperature and pressure), resulted in improved densification with final densities increasing from 70 - 75% to 88 - 94% TMD. Further increase in impact velocity to 2.15 km/s, resulted in marginal increase in density but compact recovery was affected adversely with the compacts being extensively cracked.

Scanning electron microscopy revealed the presence of tiny, smooth areas with possible melted and resolidified microstructure, as shown in Figure 2, for DAC synthetic powder (sample # 9124-10), consolidated at 1.9 km/s. The samples also contained micro-cracks emanating from these melt areas. At higher impact velocity (2.15 km/s), large, glassy regions appear (Figure 3, sample # 9131-10, Warren - GE synthetic powder), containing melted and resolidified material and forming a continuous matrix at the particle interfaces.

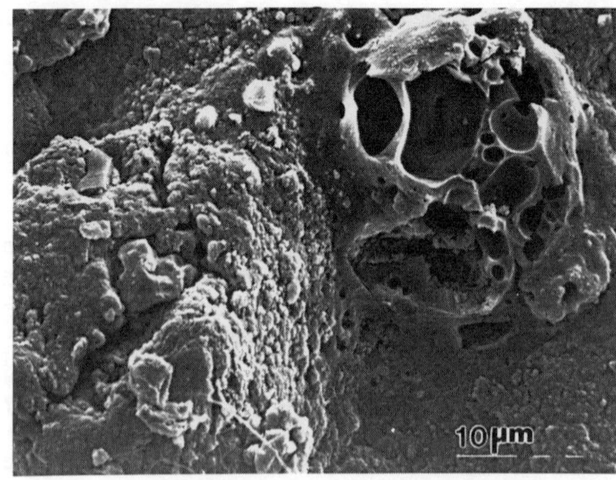

Figure 2. SEM micrograph of DAC synthetic powder compact (sample # 9124-10) showing resolidified structure.

Raman spectroscopy was conducted to detect non-diamond phase. All compacts contained an estimated 3-5% graphitic and/or amorphous carbon phase, which increased with increasing impact velocity and lower packing density. Typical Raman spectra obtained for compacts at two different initial packing densities is shown in Figure 4. Although diamond peaks appear at 1332 cm^{-1} for both compacts, the intensity of the graphite/amorphous carbon peak is larger in the compact with lower initial packing density.

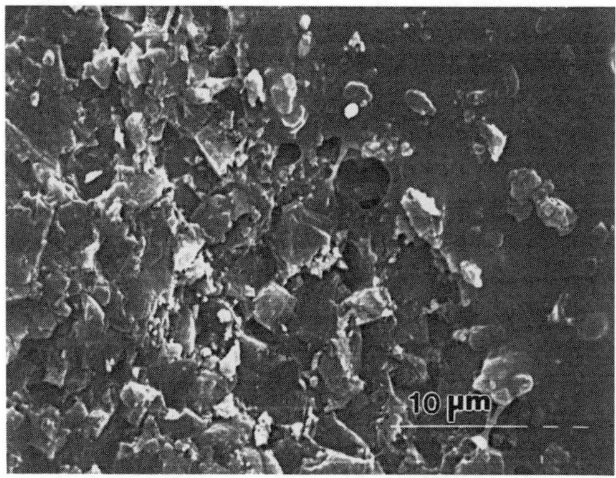

Figure 3. SEM micrograph of Warren - GE synthetic powder compact (sample # 9131-10), showing large melt areas.

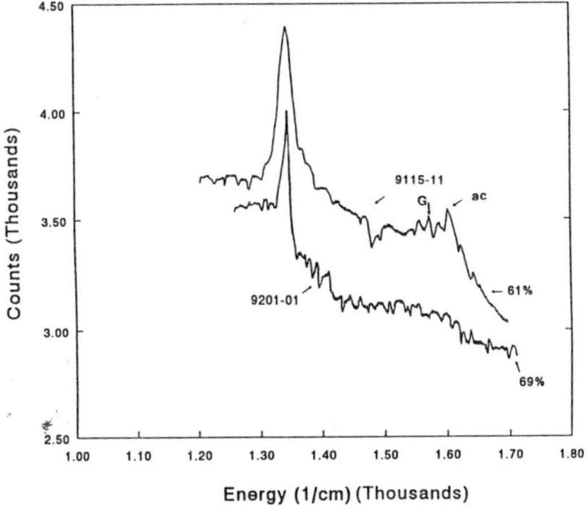

Figure 4. Raman spectra for compact #9201-01 (69% density) and #9115-11 (61% density), showing increased graphite peak.

The melt-like amorphous regions seen in the SEM and identified by Raman, were further characterized by EDX analysis. Presence of Ta as well as other alkaline metals was observed, both in the synthetic and natural diamond powders. These impurities may have been trapped in the diamond particles during the powder comminution step. The presence of the impurities however, significantly lower the thermal conductivity of the diamond powders, thereby allowing heat localization and subsequent melting of particle surfaces. We believe that, although the melting of diamond particle surface is essential for obtaining optimum consolidation, the formation of ≈ 5% melted and resolidified amorphous or graphitic carbon phase weakens the compacts and lowers the final density.

CONCLUSIONS

It has been shown that diamond compacts 12 mm diameter and 2 - 4 mm thickness, made from various types of high purity natural as well as synthetic diamond powders can be consolidated to better than 90% relative density without the use of additives. With initial packing density change from 60 - 65% to 70 - 75%, the final compact densities increased from 70 - 75% range to 88 -94% range. The optimum consolidation conditions are achieved by appropriate selection of powder particle size and distribution.

ACKNOWLEDGEMENTS

This work was supported by NRL Contract No. N00014-91-C-2173. We thank Keith Reckling of Diamond Abrasives Corporation for supplying the De Beers natural and synthetic diamond powder for the initial tests.

REFERENCES

[1]S. Sawai and K. Kondo, "Essential Factors for Shock Compaction of Diamond Composites," *J. Am. Ceram. Soc.*, 73(8), pp. 2428-34, 1990.

[2]K. Kondo and S. Sawai, "Fabricating Nano-crystalline Diamond Ceramics by a Shock Compaction Method," *J. Am. Ceram. Soc.*, 73 (7), pp. 1983-1991, 1990.

[3]K. Hokamoto, S.S. Shang, L.H. Yu, and M.A. Meyers, in *Shock Wave and High-Strain-Rate Phenomena in Materials*, eds. MA. Meyers, L.E. Murr, and K.P. Staudhammer, Mercel Dekker, Inc. NY, 1992, pp. 453-462.

[4]H. Kunishige, Y. Oya, Y. Fukuyama, S. Watanabe, H. Tamura, A.B. Sawaoka, T. Taniguchi and Y. Horie, "Shock Compaction of Diamond in Reactive Mixtures," Report of the Research Laboratory of Engineering Materials, Tokyo Institute of Technology, No. 15, 1990.

[5]D.K. Potter and T.J. Ahrens, "Shock Consolidation of Diamond and Graphite Mixtures to Fused Polycrystalline Diamond," *J. Appl. Phys.*, 63(3), pp. 910-914, 1988.

[6]EMRTC final report #FR-9312, "Dynamic High-Pressure Shock Compaction of Diamond Powders," New Mexico Tech, Socorro NM, pp. 1-84, 1993.

COMBUSTION SYNTHESIS OF AlN AT HIGH PRESSURE OF NITROGEN AND ARGON MIXTURES

M. Boćkowski, I. Grzegory, M. Wróblewski, A. Witek, J.Jun, S. Krukowski, S. Porowski
High Pressure Research Center
Sokołowska 29/37, 01-142 Warsaw, Poland
R. M. Ayral-Marin, J.C. Tedenac
Université Montpellier II, URA 407 C.C 003,
34095 Montpellier, France

The combustion synthesis of AlN was studied for mixtures of argon and nitrogen. The samples of AlN with very low contents of oxygen have been obtained. The influence of partial nitrogen pressure on the degree of conversion, microstructure and content oxygen for obtained AlN samples will be presented.

INTRODUCTION

Aluminum nitride is a high temperature refractory material. Due to its high thermal conductivity, high electrical resistivity and low thermal expansion coefficient, AlN is applied in electronics as heat sink. substrates.[2]

AlN powder has been industrially prepared by the direct nitridation of metallic aluminum or by the carbothermic reaction of alumina, carbon and nitrogen. Dense-sintered aluminum nitride is manufactured either by hot-pressing or pressureless sintering with or without sintering additives. The major drawback of these methods, is relatively high content of oxygen in the samples, which leads to decreasing of thermal conductivity of AlN[3,4].

The first studies of the combustion of bulk aluminum under high nitrogen pressure[1,5], showed that the reaction occurs at temperature higher than 1000°C and at pressures of 0.1-6.5 kbar. However, the combusted samples were inhomogeneous and contained high porosity regions of sintered AlN and regions of AlN/Al cermet.

In this paper, we report the results of the investigation of the combustion synthesis of aluminum nitride, from bulk Al as a starting material, under high pressure of nitrogen and argon mixtures. The addition of argon to nitrogen allows to obtain the oxygen free AlN powder.

EXPERIMENTAL PROCEDURE

Combustion experiments were carried out in the high pressure-high temperature equipment described in the review of Porowski et al[6]. High purity aluminum rod (99.999) 3 mm-diameter, 20 mm-long, was used as a starting material. It was placed into BN crucible in the graphite furnace. The Al rod was heated with a constant rate of 20°C/min at pressures 1.5 and 2.5 kbar of nitrogen and argon mixtures. In order to register the temperature during combustion, three PtRh6%-PtRh30% thermocouples were used. First thermocouple (serving as the furnace controller) was placed 1 cm from the end of the crucible. The two others were inserted into the wall of BN crucible in such a way, that it was possible to measure the temperature of both ends of the sample. This configuration of thermocouples allowed us to determine the combustion wave velocity.

The pressure, during the experiments, was measured by manganine gauge positioned in the low temperature zone of the high pressure chamber.

The Keithley multimeter 199DMM and IBM PC were used to monitor the voltage output of the thermocouples and manganine gauge. The sampling rate was up to 18 times per second.

The microstructure of the obtained samples was observed by scanning electron microscopy (SEM) and an energy dispersive X-ray analyser (EDX) attached to SEM. The degree of conversion of Al to AlN was determined by DTA analysis of the melting of residual Al metal. This analysis was performed in Seteram apparatus.

RESULTS

Fig. 1 shows typical time-temperature profiles measured during heating of the Al sample under high pressure of nitrogen and argon mixtures.

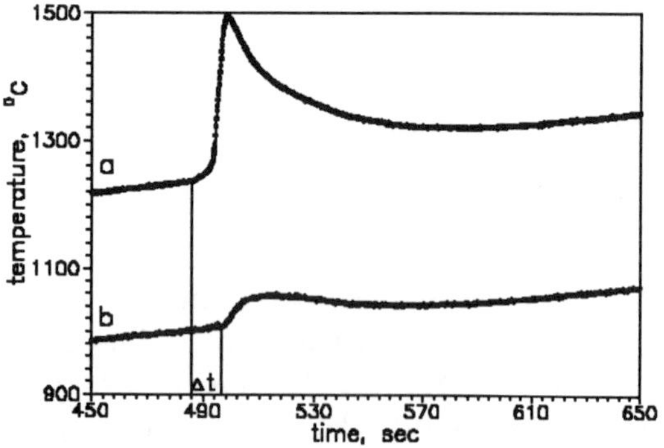

Figure 1. Typical temperature profiles of combustion synthesis of AlN a) in the hotter end of Al rod b) in the cooler end of Al rod

The reaction begins in the hotter end of the Al rod (Fig. 1a) and propagates to the cooler part probably by combustion front moving through the liquid aluminum. The evolution of temperature presented in Fig. 1b is associated with the combustion reaction in the cooler point of Al. At this end, the rate of reaction is lower. The rise of temperature is usually few times slower than for the hotter end. The time difference Δt between the beginnings of the two peaks (see Fig. 1) can be interpreted as a time necessary for the combustion front to travel from one end of the sample to the other. From these data, the avarage combustion front velocity was estimated. Fig 2 shows the velocity as a function of nitrogen partial pressure at fixed total pressures of 1.5 and 2.5 kbar. For the both cases, the velocity increases with partial N_2 pressure. On the other hand, higher total pressure, decreases the velocity of the combustion front.

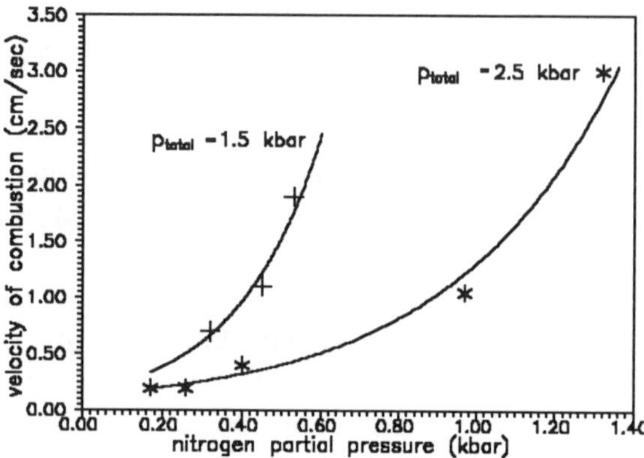

Figure 2. The combustion front velocity as a function of nitrogen partial pressure a) +-at 1.5 kbar of total pressure b) *-at 2.5 kbar of total pressure

In Fig. 3, we have compared the initial portions of time temperature profiles, during the combustion in the mixtures with various N_2 content. The rate of temperature increase in the mixture with lower N_2 content, is evidently smaller.

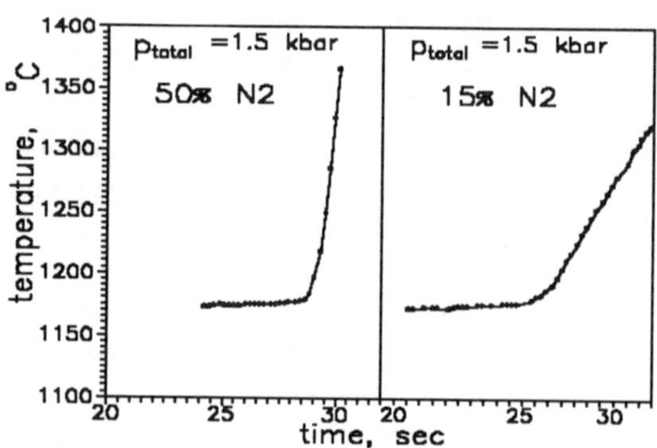

Figure 3. Initials portions of temperature profiles during combustion at 1.5 kbar of nitrogen and argon mixtures with 50% and 15% of nitrogen content

The structure of the combustion products depends on argon partial pressure. Burning of Al in a pure N_2 leads to inhomogeneous sintered AlN samples (Fig. 4). The addition of Ar to the nitrogen improves the homogeneity and for the mixture with argon content above 75% we obtain homogeneous AlN powder. Fig. 5 shows typical microstructure of obtained AlN powders. Particle-size analysis demonstrates, that the powders consist of irregular grains of 1 to 20 μm in size.

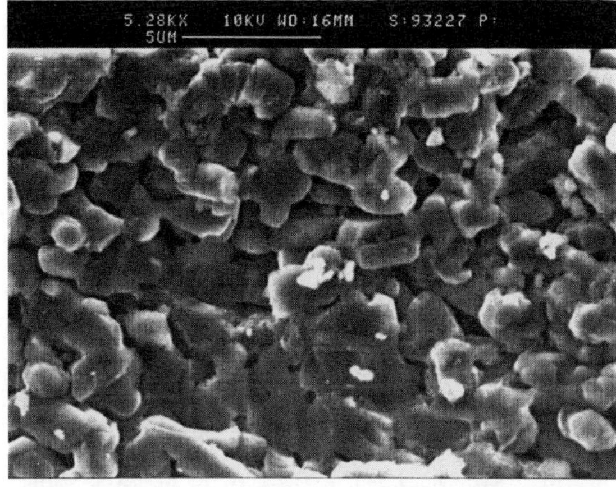

Figure 4. SEM micrograph of the AlN sample combusted in pure nitrogen at pressure 1 kbar (fracture)

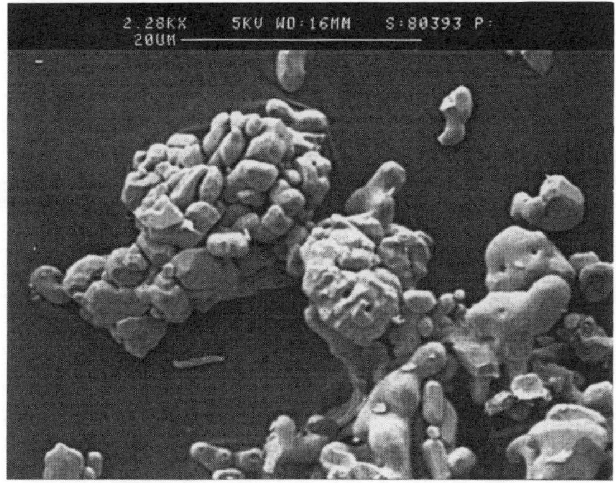

Figure 5. SEM micrograph of the AlN powder (no grided) combusted at 2.6 kbar of nitrogen and argon mixture (15% of N_2)

Fig. 6 presents the EDX spectrum of the AlN synthesized at 2 kbar (in the mixture of 15% N_2 and 85% Ar). It is worth to mention, that there is no traces of oxygen in this powder. The samples obtained after combustion are slightly gray, however the annealing at 1 kbar of N_2 and at 1600°C leads to the change of the colour from gray to white, which indicates 100% conversion.

The measured (by DTA) fractions of Al converted to AlN as a function of the combustion pressure and nitrogen partial pressure are summarized in Table 1.

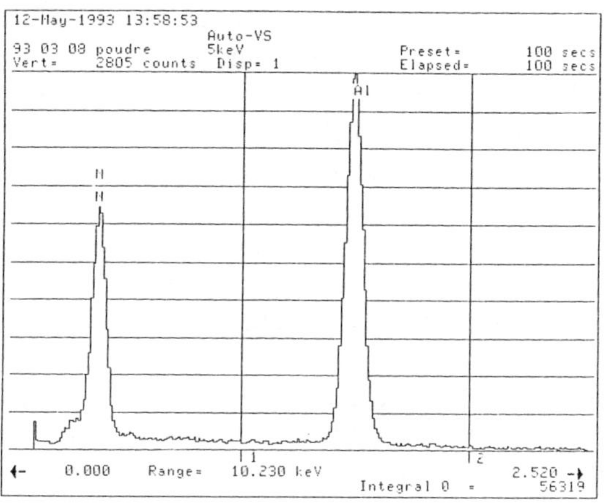

Figure 6. EDX spectrum of the AlN powder after combustion at 2.6 kbar of nitrogen and argon mixture (15% of N_2)

For all combustion reactions, at mixture pressures between 1 and 3 kbar, we obtained almost complete conversion.

Table 1 Fractions of Al converted to AlN as a function of the combustion pressure and nitrogen partial pressure.

No	p of N_2 (kbar)	p of reaction (kbar)	conversion (%)	form of obtained AlN
1	1.32	2.64	99.01	compact
2	0.90	2.75	99.60	compact
3	0.70	2.78	99.78	powder
4	0.42	2.6	99.71	powder
5	0.17	2.65	99.29	powder
6	0.50	1.52	99.75	compact
7	0.42	1.63	98.84	powder
8	0.22	1.48	96.43	powder

DISCUSSION

The mechanism of the combustion of metal powders under high N_2 pressure has been studied, and it was shown that the reaction rate depends on availability of N_2 through the sample[7]. For the bulk aluminum, with no porosity, the mechanism of combustion must be different and it is not yet well understood. In order to interprete our data, we propose the following rough model. After melting of aluminum under high pressure of nitrogen and argon mixtures, AlN layer is formed on the surface of the liquid Al. At higher temperatures the layer cracks, due to the difference in thermal expansion coefficients between melted Al and solid AlN. This leads to the contact of the liquid aluminum with hot nitrogen and synthesis of AlN grains. Due to large enthalpy of AlN formation[3], the combustion front is formed and starts to propagate through the liquid Al. We assume that the combustion front velocity is constant. When the combustion occures under high pressure of N_2, the reaction is so fast, that. the temperature of combustion is enough to sinter the AlN grains. Increasing Ar content reduces availability of the nitrogen to the reaction zone. This leads to decrease of reaction rate and combustion temperature, which gives the possibility to eliminate the process of sintering. Therefore, we obtain the AlN powder. For this model the reduction of availability of N_2 by the argon presence in the mixture is essential.

Our experimental results confirme the proposed model. As it has been shown in Fig. 2, for the same partial pressure of N_2 the velocity of the combustion front is lower, when the argon partial pressure in the mixture is higher. At the same total pressure the rate of reaction strongly depends on the nitrogen partial pressure. Fig. 3 shows that the rate of temperature increase during combustion is significantly lower for the reaction in decreased N_2 content atmosphere.

CONCLUSION

The combustion of bulk Al at high pressure of nitrogen and argon mixtures results in either sintered AlN or AlN powder, as a product. It depends on partial pressure of argon in the mixtures of gases. The model of the combustion, proposed in the discussion, seems to be confirmed by our experimental results. Due to a low surface area of starting material (Al rod), no trace of oxygen has been observed for the combusted samples. This indicates that by the combustion synthesis under high pressure of nitrogen and argon mixtures it is possible to fabricate high purity AlN.

REFERENCES

[1] I. Grzegory, M. Bockowski, J. Jun, *High Pres. Res.*10 pp 288-291 (1992)

[2] L. M. Shepard, *Ceram Bull.* 69 pp 1801-1812 (1990)

[3] D. D. Marchant, T. E. Nemecek, *"Aluminum nitride: preparation, processing and properties"* in *Advances in Ceramics* 26, ed by M. F. Yan, K. Niwa, W. S. Young, pp 18-55 (1991)

[4] N. Kuramoto, H. Tonigushi, J. Aso, *"Synthesis and properties of high purity AlN ceramics"* in Advances in Ceramics 26, ed by M. F. Yan, K. Niwa, W.S. Young, pp 98-118 (1991)

[5] S. Porowski, I. Grzegory, J.Jun, *"Synthesis of metal nitrides under high nitrogen pressure"*, in *High Pressure Chemical Synthesis* ed by J. Jurczak and B. Baranowski (Amsterdam: Elsevier) pp 21-54 (1989)

[6] M. Bockowski, J..Jun, I. Grzegory, R. M. Ayral-Marin, J. C.Tedenac submitted to *Acta. Ceram.*

[7] Z. A. Munir, J. B. Holt, *J. Mater. Sci.* 22, pp 710-714 (1987)

SHOCK SYNTHESIS OF NICKEL - ALUMINIDES

A. J. Strutt, K. S. Vecchio, L. -H. Yu, M. A. Meyers and R. A. Graham †

Dept. of AMES, UC San Diego, La Jolla, CA 92093
† Sandia National Laboratory, Albuquerque, NM 87185

Chemical reactions between nickel and aluminum powder mixtures have been initiated by explosively generated high-pressure shock waves in an attempt to form Ni-Al compounds at temperatures lower than those necessary for conventional alloying. Nickel in the form of powders of "coarse" ~50 μm, "fine" ~5 μm and "flaky" ~40 μm were each reacted with ~15 μm aluminum powder at shock pressures of 7.5 and 16 GPa, in the ratio of 3Ni + 1Al. Evidence of reactions leading to the formation of Ni-Al alloy phases was observed in a specimen after processing at the higher shock energy, but only in the case of "flaky" nickel. Scanning electron microscopy (SEM) of this specimen revealed regions consisting of unreacted Ni and Al particles together with isolated regions of a Ni-Al dendritic structure in the prior-Al areas. Quantitative energy-dispersive X-ray spectroscopy (EDX) of the reaction phase showed this to be Al_3Ni, while the dendritic morphology of the structure indicated that the reaction had proceeded in the liquid state.

INTRODUCTION

The high creep resistance of many intermetallic compounds has led to many earlier studies of their high temperature mechanical properties [1-3].

In the Al-Ni system, two phases - Ni_3Al and NiAl are particularly suitable for elevated temperature applications due to relatively high melting temperatures of 1395°C and 1638°C respectively (Fig.1).

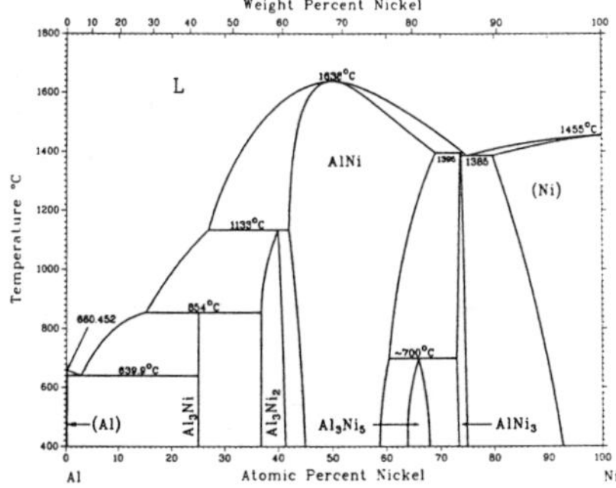

Fig.1 Al-Ni phase diagram [4].

The production of intermetallic compounds by shock induced reaction synthesis (SRS) may be achieved at lower temperatures than those involved in self-propagating high-temperature synthesis (SHS) [5] and as a result, a greater degree of control may be exercised over grain size of the product material. Unlike SHS, SRS need not necessarily involve complete melting of reactants. Reactions may proceed as a result of the high velocity shock wave causing plastic flow and cleansing of particle surfaces [6], with additional heat provided by friction and the exothermic nature of the reaction.

Recent investigations by other workers have shown that in the shock synthesis of Ni-Al powders, the extent of the chemical reaction, and hence the products formed, depended not only on shock energy, but also on powder particle size and morphology [6,7]. However, there is still some uncertainty concerning the mechanism of the initial stages of the reaction. In the current investigation the extent of reaction was deliberately controlled so that the products of early stages of the reaction could be characterized.

EXPERIMENTAL

Aluminum powder with spherical, 10-20 μm sized grains was reacted with Ni powders of sizes and morphologies as shown in Table 1. (all reactants obtained from Aesar-Johnson Matthey).

All powder mixtures were in the ratio of 3Ni:1Al and were shock loaded using the Sandia 'Momma Bear' type fixture shown in Fig.2 with Baratol high explosive and under the pressure and temperature conditions outlined in Table 2.

Shock energy	Ni powder morphology and particle size	Specimen Identification
7.5 GPa	Flaky, 44 μm	2H896
	Spherical, 45-70 μm	4H896
16 GPa	Flaky, 44 μm	1H896
	Spherical, 3-7 μm	3H896

Table 1. Details of powder particle sizes, morphologies and shock pressures.

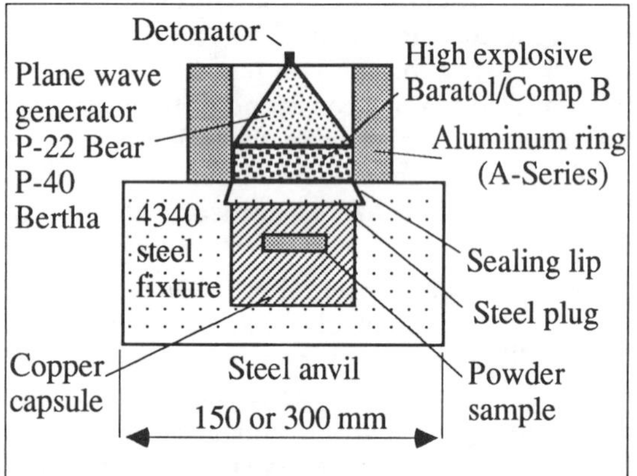

Fig. 2 Schematic representation of the Sandia Momma Bear-A fixture. [8]

The distributions of temperature and shock pressure for this type of fixture have been computed and that for temperature is shown in Fig.3 [6]. (Although the profiles were calculated for Composition-B explosive, the distribution of temperature and pressure profiles is believed to be similar to those for Baratol).

Shocked specimens were examined using SEM in a Cambridge Stereoscan 360 with a backscattered electron detector and at a beam energy of 20 keV. Chemical analysis of micro-constituents in reacted specimens was performed

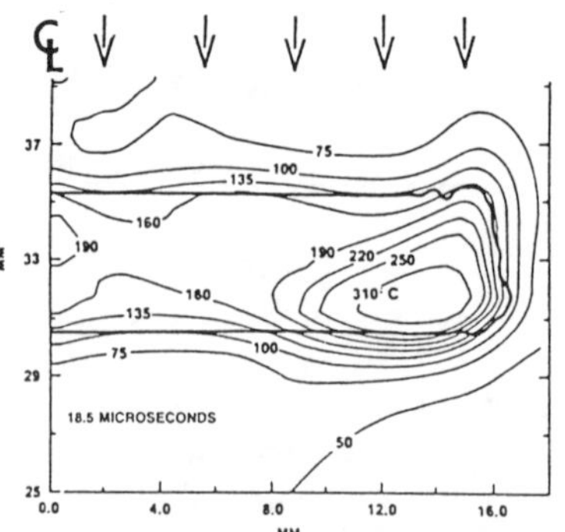

Fig. 3 Typical mean-bulk temperature distribution in powder compacts in Sandia Momma Bear A / Comp B fixture [6].

in the above microscope with the aid of a Link Systems energy-dispersive X-ray detector. Data acquired in this manner were quantified by the ratio technique [9], using a k-factor which had been derived experimentally from an Al_3Ni standard. However, corrections for the effects of selective X-ray absorption were not applied to these data.

RESULTS

SEM micrographs of the shocked specimens are shown in Fig.4. Nickel regions appear lighter than aluminum, due to higher atomic number. In all cases, the plane of the shock wave was parallel to the long edge of the micrographs. No evidence of any reaction could be found in specimens other than in certain areas of specimen 1H896(3Ni:1Al, flaky Ni). The most widely occurring form of reaction product in 1H896 is illustrated in Fig. 5(c) and takes the form of particles of intermediate contrast (and hence of mean atomic number greater than Al, but less than Ni) which nucleate at the interface between Ni and Al and grow into the prior-Al grains.

Fixture (Baratol explosive)	Peak Pressure (GPa)		Mean Bulk Temperature, (°C) *	
	Bulk	Focus	Bulk	Edge
Momma Bear	7.5 ± 2.5	27	225	310
Momma Bear A	16 ± 4.0	32	225	310

Table 2. Characteristics of the Sandia explosive shock-loading fixtures (*calculated temperatures are based on 50 % dense samples).

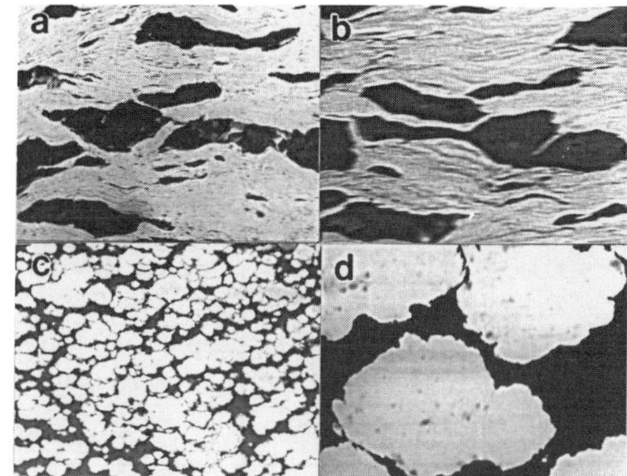

Fig. 4 Backscattered SEM images showing microstructures after shock compaction. (a) 1H896, (b) 2H896, (c) 3H896 and (d) 4H896. (x 150)

Fig. 5(b) shows Al grains typical of unreacted areas in the same specimen, which are identical to the Al-grains in a cold-compacted, un-shocked sample of flake Ni and spherical Al-powders (Fig. 5a).

In an isolated region of 1H896, an apparently more complete stage of reaction occurred, which is illustrated in Fig. 6(a). In this backscattered SEM image, the light area in the bottom right is unreacted Ni, while most of the remaining section of the micrograph shows a prior-Al region after reaction has occurred. The X-ray spectra in Fig. 6(b), (c) and (d) show qualitatively the change in Al:Ni ratio indicated in the backscattered image by the zones of different contrast. The electron interaction volume (and hence the approximate size of the region of X-ray generation) for analyses at 20 kV would be about 1μm^3 and therefore within the boundaries of the various phase regions in Fig. 6(a).

The area represented by Fig.6(a) was located at the bottom edge of the shock-compacted sample, and therefore in the region of highest temperature, as shown in Fig. 3. Quantification of the X-ray spectra yielded the results listed in Table 3. The first line of data corresponds to the Al_3Ni standard while the second is from the

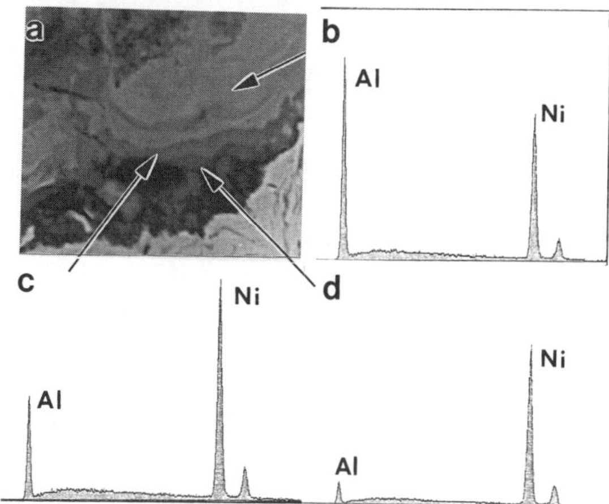

Fig. 6 (a) Backscattered SEM image of the fully-reacted region of specimen 1H896, (x 475) showing the range of reaction products of varying Al:Ni composition ratio, distinguished by varying atomic number-contrast and by the EDX spectra, (b), (c) and (d).

reaction product shown in Fig. 5(c) and is obviously Al_3Ni. The 3 EDX spectra shown in Fig.6 (b), (c) and (d), which correspond to the zones illustrated in Fig.6(a) and to the data on lines 4, 5 and 6 of Table 3 represent Al:Ni ratios consistent with the compositions of Ni_3Al, NiAl and Al_3Ni respectively.

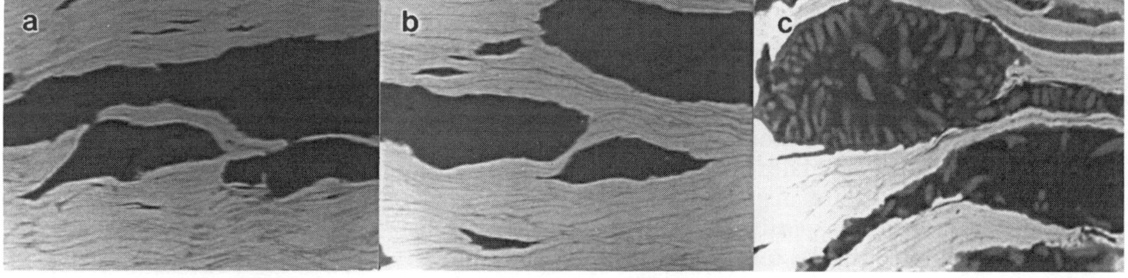

Fig. 5 Backscattered SEM micrographs showing Al-grains in specimen 1H896 before shock compaction (a) and after shock compaction: unreacted (b) and reacted (c). (x 650)

Spectrum I.D.	Description	IAl / INi	C_{Al} / C_{Ni} (weight fraction	Al-content (wt.%)	(at.%)	Theoretical Al-content (at.%)
AL3NI	Al_3Ni standard	0.9	1.38	58.0	75	75
1H8961	Main reaction product in 1H	0.82	1.25	55.6	73	75
1H8962	Ni-particle	0.001	0.002	0.2	1	approx. 0 - 10
1H8963	Ni_3Al reacted region	0.1	0.15	13.0	25	25 -27
1H8964	NiAl	0.32	0.49	32.9	52	approx. 41 - 55
1H8965	Al_3Ni	1.04	1.59	61.4	77	75
1H8966	Al-particle	80.05	122.48	99.2	99.5	100

Table 3. Details of quantitative EDX analyses of Al-Ni phases in specimen 1H 896.

DISCUSSION

In Figs. 5 (c) and 6 (a), the shock-induced reaction probably occurred in the following manner. The reaction commenced at the Al / Ni interface leading to the formation of Al_3Ni which grew into the prior-Al grain (in the Al_3Ni+liquid 2-phase field of the phase diagram). In most regions of the specimen, temperatures were not high enough for the reaction to proceed beyond this stage. However, in the region shown in Fig. 6(a), higher temperatures were attained (and probably sustained for longer), leading to more diffusion of Ni into the Al. At this stage, the Ni-content at the original interface was higher than that required for Al_3Ni, favoring the formation of Al_3Ni_2, and then (due to its higher exothermic energy of formation) AlNi. The final stage of the reaction at the NiAl/Ni interface was the formation of a thin layer of Ni_3Al, although in the center of the prior-Al grain, insufficient Ni-diffusion occurred for the reaction to proceed beyond Al_3Ni.

During the reaction, temperatures were probably above 700°C, thus preventing the formation of Al_3Ni_5, which was not found.

The reactions described above initiate at the Al/Ni grain boundaries due to short diffusion paths and because the temperatures attained during shock compression are increased as a result of frictional heating of particle surfaces. Although partial melting of the Al may occur (to permit the formation of Al_3Ni at the Al/Ni interface) it is unlikely that sufficient temperatures could be reached to permit reaction in the liquid state.

REFERENCES

[1] A. Lawley, J. A. Coll and R. W. Cahn, *Trans. AIME* **218**, pp. 166-176 (1960).

[2] P. R. Strutt, R. S. Polvani and J. C. Ingram, *Met. Trans. A* **7A**, pp. 23-31 (1976)

[3] J. D. Whittenberger, *J. Mater. Sci.* **22**, pp. 394-402.

[4] M. F. Singleton, J. L. Murray and P. Nash in *Binary Alloy Phase Diagrams*, edited by T. B. Massalski, ASM, Metals Park, OH (1987) pp. 181-184.

[5] A. N. Dremin and O. N. Bruesov, *Russ. Chem. Rev.*, **37** pp. 392-402 (1968).

[6] N. N. Thadhani, S. Work, R. A. Graham and W. F. Hammetter, *J. Mater. Res.*, **7** pp. 1063-1075 (1992).

[7] I. Song and N. N. Thadhani, *Met. Trans. A*, **23A** pp. 41-48 (1992).

[8] R. A. Graham and D. M. Webb in *Shock Waves in Condensed Matter 1985*, edited by Y. M. Gupta, Plenum, New York, (1986) pp. 831-836.

[9] G. Cliff and G. W. Lorimer in *Proceedings of the 5th. European Congress on Electron Microscopy*, University of Manchester, UK, Institute of Physics, London and Bristol, (1972) pp. 140-141.

SHOCK COMPACTION OF ALUMINA/ZIRCONIA CERAMICS

John Freim, J. McKittrick and W.J. Nellis*
Materials Science Program, University of California, San Diego, La Jolla, CA 92093-0411
*IGPP, Lawrence Livermore National Laboratory, Livermore, CA 94550

ABSTRACT

Shock compaction has been used as an aid in the densification of alumina/zirconia ceramic composites. Shock compacted specimens have been recovered as singular, macroscopically crack free, dense specimens in repeated trials for shock pressures ranging from approximately 4-12 GPa for both conventional and rapidly solidified material. Recovery of the shocked samples from the steel shock capsules was facilitated by the use of ashless sub-micron-pore paper shims, which also provided support during the subsequent handling and processing steps. The recovered specimens exhibited high as-shocked densities, believed to be a result of plastic flow and deformation of particles, which enhanced the achievement of a high final density after a relatively short high temperature sintering process.

INTRODUCTION

The alumina/zirconia eutectic composition was used in the experiments. Rapidly solidified (RS) material was prepared by heating the powder in an induction furnace from which the melt was quenched between rapidly rotating steel rollers [1]. The high cooling rates resulted in the formation of amorphous, nanocrystalline and lamellar microstructures which have been shown to lead to products with desirable structural properties [2]. Our goal was to examine and compare the physical properties of RS with conventional powders. RS specimens were aggressively attrition milled and microsieved through either 5μm or 20μm. The conventional powders were mixed and loaded into the shock capsules without the milling, sieving and heat treat procedures.

EXPERIMENTAL TECHNIQUE

The materials were shock compacted with the 6.5 meter two stage gas gun facility located at Lawrence Livermore National Laboratory [3] . The starting powders were loaded into stainless steel shock capsules and were subjected to pressures ranging from 4-41 GPa by impacting the capsules with a projectile traveling at a velocity ranging from 0.98 to 1.82 km/s. Specimens were thin compared to their diameter. Compaction was quasi-one-dimensional and was achieved by a reverberating shock wave with a tuneable peak pressure. Upon recovery, the specimens were inspected for pressures ranging from approximately 4-12 GPa. One piece macroscopically crack free samples were produced [2,4]. Some of the samples were post shock annealed at 1600^{0}C for 2 hours to investigate the effect of shock compaction on post sintered properties.

RESULTS AND DISCUSSION

A summary of the results is presented in Table 1. The one-piece nature of the recovered specimens is of significance due to the observance of macrocracks in other materials believed to have originated due to tensile stresses associated with decompression [5,6,7]. Micrographs of the as-shocked material reveal the onset of intraparticle tensile fracture as a function of particle size. Micrographs of samples shocked at 4,6,12 and 30 GPa are presented in Figure 1 along with literature values for the tensile yield strength of alumina whiskers as a function of whisker diameter [8]. For the alumina/zirconia RS eutectic, the onset of particle

Table 1. Summary of Experimental Conditions and Observations

Sample Powder Composition	Projectile Type	Projectile Velocity (km/sec)	Shock Pressure (GPa)	Tapped Density (%)	Relative Density (%)	Observation
conventional	Lexan	1.37	6.1	49%	87%	one piece
conventional	Lexan	1.40	6.3	51%	88%	one piece
conventional	Lexan	1.82	9.1	48%	not measured	one piece
conventional	aluminum	1.05	12.6	53%	97%	three pieces
conventional	aluminum	1.51	19.3	60%	98%	several pieces
conventional	copper	1.36	30.0	50%	-----	powder
conventional	copper	1.76	41.0	53%	-----	powder
RS (sub 20μ)	Lexan	1.01	4.1	50%	89%	one piece
RS (sub 5μ)	Lexan	1.27	5.6	53%	96%	one piece
RS (sub 20μ)	Lexan	1.38	6.2	54%	88%	one piece
RS (sub 20μ)	Lexan	1.42	6.4	53%	89%	one piece
RS (sub 20μ)	aluminum	0.98	11.7	52%	90%	one piece
RS (sub 20μ)	copper	1.48	33.2	49%	-----	powder

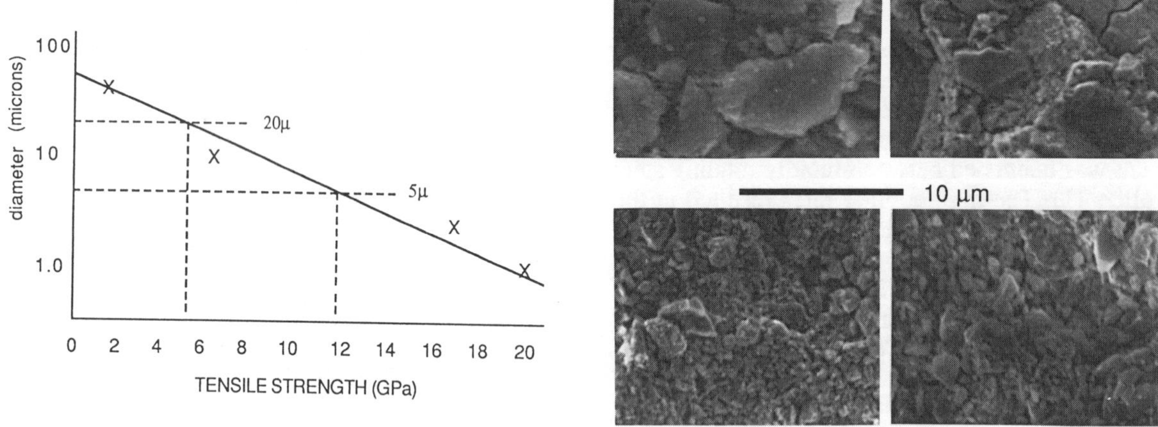

Figure 1. Alumina whisker tensile strength vs. particle size along with micrographs (clockwise from upper left) revealing the increasing extent of fracture in particles shocked at 4, 6, 12, and 30 GPa.

fracture occurred at approximately 6 GPa in 20 μm particles and at approximately 12 GPa in 5 μm particles. Extensive crushing and pulverization of the particles was observed in samples shocked at 30 GPa. These observations correlate closely with the aforementioned alumina tensile yield strengths. With this knowledge it is possible to tailor the particle size of the RS starting material and the shock pressure in order to minimize intraparticle fracture and alleviate associated bulk mechanical strength deficiencies in the compact.

The as-shocked material was recovered by machining the capsules which exposed the specimens in the form of discs 1 cm in diameter and approximately 1 mm thick. The as-shocked

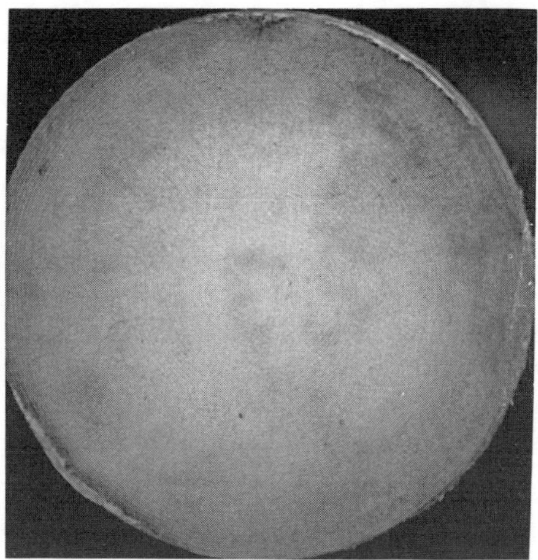

Figure 2. Photograph of a recovered specimen with the paper shims intact. Compact diameter is 1 cm.

Figure 3. Photograph of a recovered specimen sintered at 1600°C for two hours. Compact diameter is 1 cm.

specimens, although relatively dense, were fragile and possessed relatively poor bulk mechanical strengths. In order to facilitate the handling of the recovered specimens, shims consisting of ashless sub-micron-pore filter paper were placed on both sides of the powder as the capsules were loaded. Originally, silver shims were used but the shims tended to stick to the compacts which made their removal difficult without inflicting damage to the samples. The advantage of paper shims is that the recovered sample can be handled with the paper intact, and unlike silver, the paper is easily removed by heating the shimmed compact. A photograph of a recovered specimen with the shims intact is shown in Figure 2. The shims were removed by heating the compact in He at 600°C to minimize any exothermic reactions associated with the combustion of the paper. A specimen which has been sintered at 1600°C for two hours is shown in Figure 3. As shown, the specimen is intact and free of macroscopic cracks. The presence of chipping on the perimeter of the disc is attributed to handling and fixturing during the paper removal and sintering processes which can be overcome with minor modifications.

As-shocked density measurements along with process variables for several specimens are presented in Table 1. The as-shocked densities of the compacts made with rapidly solidified material have ranged from approximately 88% to 96% of single crystal theoretical density. As-shocked densities of compacts made with conventional powder measured from 88% to 97% of ρ_{th}. The densities of the conventional specimens are consistent with the finding of previous research which investigated conventional Al_2O_3 and other starting materials [6,7,9,10]. A micrograph of a compact consisting of conventional powder is shown in Figure 4, and a micrograph of a specimen consisting of RS starting material is shown in Figure 5. The particles appear to be in intimate contact but are not strongly bonded to each other.

CONCLUSIONS/ FUTURE WORK

The shock compaction process appeared to enhance the bulk density through particle plastic deformation and flow, but did not result in interparticle bonding through frictional melting and subsequent fusion of adjacent particles. A high temperature sintering step is necessary to fully densify and induce interparticle bonding in the material. Research is being performed which investigates sintering profiles which are intended to fully densify the material with minimal grain growth.

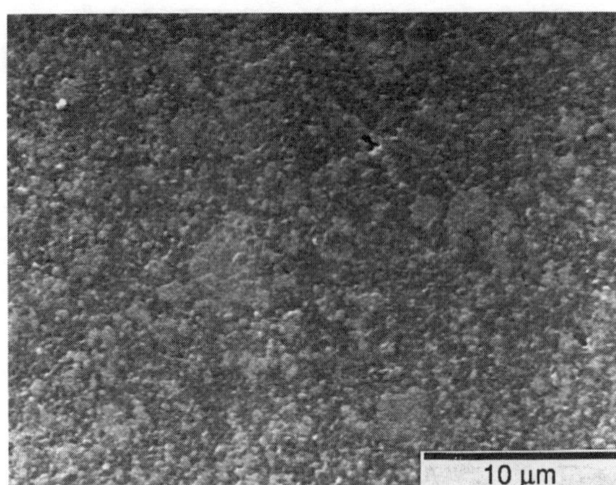

Figure 4. Microstructure of a conventional specimen shocked at 12.6 GPa.

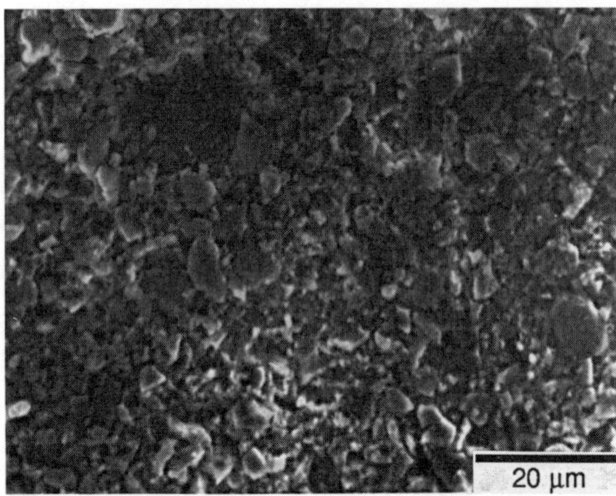

Figure 5. Microstructure of a rapidly solidified specimen shocked at 4.1 GPa.

Acknowledgements
This work was supported by the Institute for Geophysics and Planetary Physics at the Lawrence Livermore National Laboratory.

REFERENCES

[1] J. McKittrick, G. Kalonyi, T. Ando, *J. Non-Cryst. Sol.*, **64**, p. 163, (1987).
[2] B. Tunayoblu, J. McKittrick, W. Nellis, submitted to the *J. Am. Cer. Soc.*, 1992.
[3] A. J. Gratz, W. J. Nellis, J. M. Christie, W. Brocious, J. Swegle, P. Cordier, *Phys. Chem. Minerals*, **19**, pp. 268-288, (1992).
[4] J. M. McKittrick, B. Tunayoblu, J. D. Katz, W. Nellis, "Al_2O_3-ZrO_2 Ceramics With Submicron Microstructures Obtained Through Microwave Sintering, Plasma Sintering and Shock Compaction", in *Mat. Res. Soc. Symp. Proc., Vol. 274*, 1992, pp. 149-154.
[5] C. L. Hoenig, C. S. Yust, *Am. Cer. Soc. Bulletin*, **60** [11], pp.1175-1224, (1981).
[6] E. K. Beauchamp, M. J. Carr, R. A. Graham, *J. Am. Ceram. Soc.*, **68** [12], pp.696-699, (1985).
[7] J. H. Adair, R. R. Willis, V. D. Linse, "Dynamic Compaction of Ceramic Powders", in *Emergent Process Methods for High Technology Ceramics, Materials Research Society Vol. 17*, 1984.
[8] *Engineering Property Data on Selected Ceramics Volume III*, MCIC Report MB-07, Battelle Columbus Laboratories, Columbus, Ohio, pp. 5.4.1-21.
[9] T. Z. Blazynski, "Explosive Compaction of Ceramic and Polymeric Powdered Materials", in *Metallurgical Applications of Shock Waves and High Strain Rate Phenomenon*, 1986, pp. 1013-1022.
[10] R. A. Prummer, G. Ziegler, *Powder Metall. Int.*, **9**, pp. 11-14, (1977).

STRUCTURE AND MAGNETIC PROPERTIES OF CdS NANOCRYSTALLINE MATERIALS SYNTHESIZED UNDER HIGH STATIC PRESSURE

DA-PENG XU[1], XIAO TONG[1], WEN-HUI SU[1,2,3]
LIANG-ZHI XIAO[1], SHOU-TIAN LI[1],

1. Phys. Dept., Jilin University, Changchun 130023, China
2. CCAST (World Lab.) P.O. Box 8730, Beijing 100080, China
3. ICMP, Academia Sinica, Shenyang 110015, China

Using the ultrafine powder as starting materials, CdS nanocrystalline materials were prepared by high static pressure of 0.0-5.0 GPa. The results of XRD show that their diffraction peaks are the same as CdS ultrafine powder, but their XPS and magnetic properties change with synthesizing pressure. In our XPS measurements of CdS nanocrystalline materials and CdS ultrafine powder, two peaks were observed in S region (161.5 and 162.8eV) and their area ratio varies with synthesizing pressure. The magnetic measurements (magnetic balance) show that CdS nanocrystalline materials exhibit a complicated magnetic behavior from diamagnetism to positive magnetism with increasing pressure. The reason of variation is discussed.

INTRODUCTION

At present, many nanocrystalline materials can be obtained by assembling pre-generated small clusters by means of consolidation. But the effect of consolidating conditions such as pressure on the structure and properties of nanocrystalline materials have been rarely studied. As many properties of nanocrystalline materials depend primarily on the grain boundaries or interphases, for application, it is necessary to investigate the influence of synthesizing pressure on the grain boundaries and interphases. In this report, the structure and magnetic properties of CdS nanocrystalline materials consolidated under various pressures have been investigated for the first time by XRD, XPS and magnetic measurement.

EXPERIMENTAL

The ultrafine particles were prepared by chemical method. They have the cubic structure and their distribution of particle sizes is 3 ~10nm, which were examined by TEM. The high static pressure equipment utilized for the synthesis of nanocrystalline materials was a belt type press (0.00~5.00GPa). The consolidation processes are as follow.

The ultrafine particles were placed in a high pressure chamber ($\Phi 5 \times 5$mm) of the press. Firstly the pressure increased to a certain value between 0.00 and 5.00GPa, maintaining for 10 min, then the pressure decreased slowly to atmosphere and the CdS nanocrystalline materials were obtained.

The structure of these samples were checked by D/max-rA X-ray diffractometer and XP spectrometer of ESCALAB MKII model with an angle resolvable aperture using MgKα radiation.

Their magnetic susceptibilities were also measured by the magnetic balance at room temperature and in a field of 12000Gs.

RESULTS AND DISCUSSIONS

Fig. 1 (a ~ d) are the X-ray diffraction spectra of ultrafine particles and nanocrystalline materials synthesized under 1.00, 3.20 and 4.80 GPa at room temperature, respectively. By comparison, Fig. 1 (b), (c) and (d) are essentially similar to Fig. 1 (a). They are all cubic CdS. It shows that the structural changes do not occur under different synthesizing pressure. But the fact that there are only a few wider peaks in Fig. 1 confirms that the size of individual crystallites is very small.

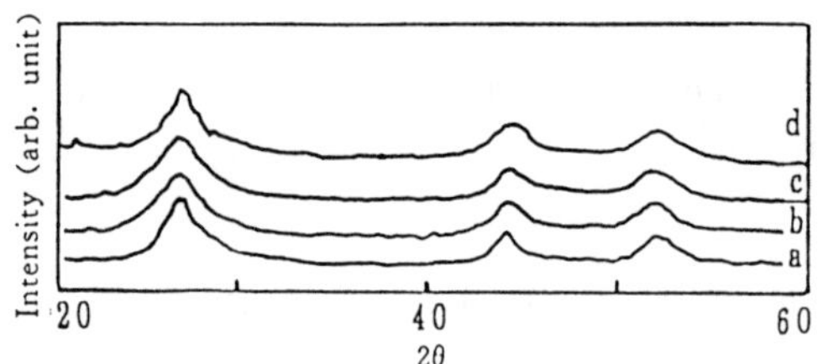

Fig. 1. X-ray diffraction patterns of CdS ultrafine powder (a) and CdS nanocrystalline materials synthesized under 1.0GPa (b), 3.2GPa(c) and 4.8GPa(d).

CdS nanocrystalline materials synthesized under different pressures were treated again by sintering (annealing) at 280, 340, 540 and 600℃ for 4h. The results of XRD (Fig. 2) exhibit that on increasing temperature the peak width narrows and the number of the peaks increases eventually under the same pressure. By annealing at 340℃ for 4h, the peaks of hexagonal CdS appear in the samples [Fig. 2 (b)], and at 600℃ the peaks of cubic CdS disappear, all the samples transform to hexagonal structure. The phase transformation in three samples begins at about 340℃, ends at 600℃.

Comparing Fig. 2 with Fig. 1, the changes of the peak width for nanocrystalline materials are slower than that of ultrafine powder at low temperature, and their changes are the same at

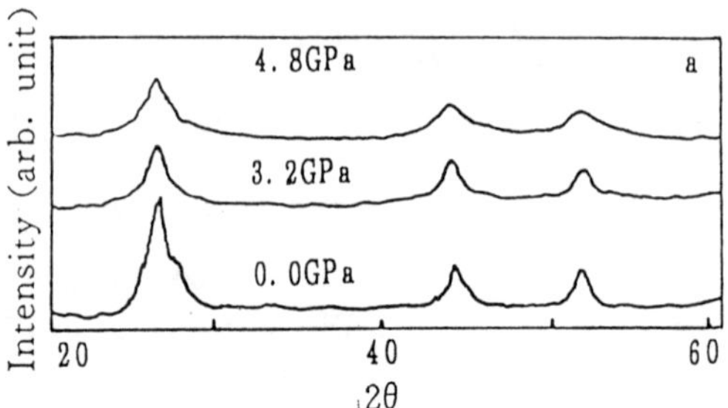

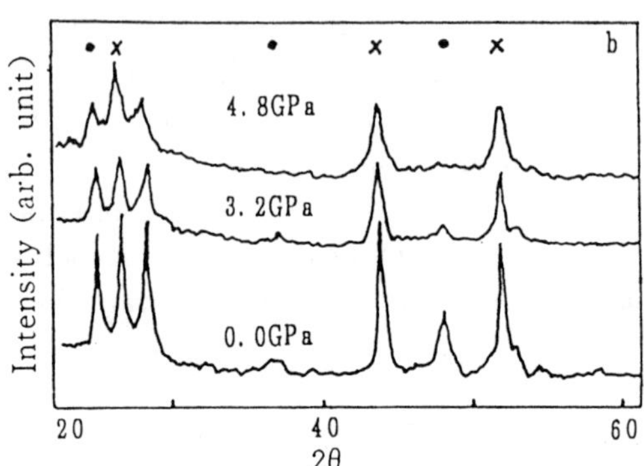

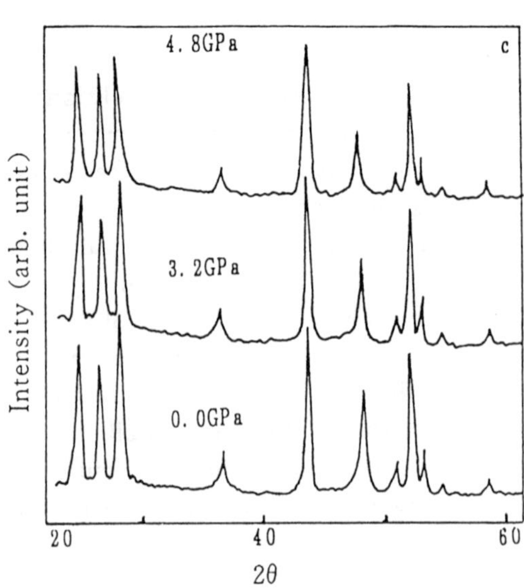

Fig. 2 X-ray diffraction patterns of CdS ultrafine powder and nanocrystalline materials synthesized under high pressure, (a) annealing at 280℃ for 4h
(b) annealing at 340℃ for 4h
(c) annealing at 540℃ for 4h

high temperature (540℃).

The above results show that though the effect of synthesizing pressure on the crystal structure of nanocrystalline materials is not evident, the effect on sintering behavior of nanocrystalline materials is very obvious.

In addition, compared to bulk CdS whose phase transition from cubic to hexagonal structure occurred by annealing at above 700℃ for 36h, the transition temperature of nanocrystalline materials and ultrafine particles decreased about 350℃.

The above samples were examined by XPS in order to get information on grain boundaries and interphases in nanocrystalline materials. In our XPS measurements, the peaks of O(1s) and Cd(3d) have been observed and their peak positions and intensities did not vary with pressure in all the samples. In S region two peaks for all the samples have been detected at about 161.5 and 162.8 eV, respectively. In particular, their area ratio varies with synthesizing pressure (see Table. 1). In XPS measurements of CdS bulk and thin films, only one peak have been detected in S region (about 162eV) which belongs to not only $S2p_{\frac{1}{2}}$ but also $S2p_{\frac{3}{2}}$ since their energy difference is very small [1]. We propose that the two peaks may result from 2p-orbit split of S atoms on nanometer particle surfaces, and that the reason of orbit-split probably is a new-rangement of electrons of S atom on surface which arises from the size quantization in nanometer particles [2]. The evidence support our proposition as follows:

Table 1. The data of the area ratio of two peaks in the S spectral region vs synthesizing pressure for CdS nanocrystalline materials.

P(GPa)	Binding energy (eV)	ratio(%)
0.00	161.52 162.82	75.87 24.13
3.50	161.64 162.84	66.15 33.85
4.00	161.50 162.75	65.17 33.04
4.80	161.75 163.00	70.83 27.97

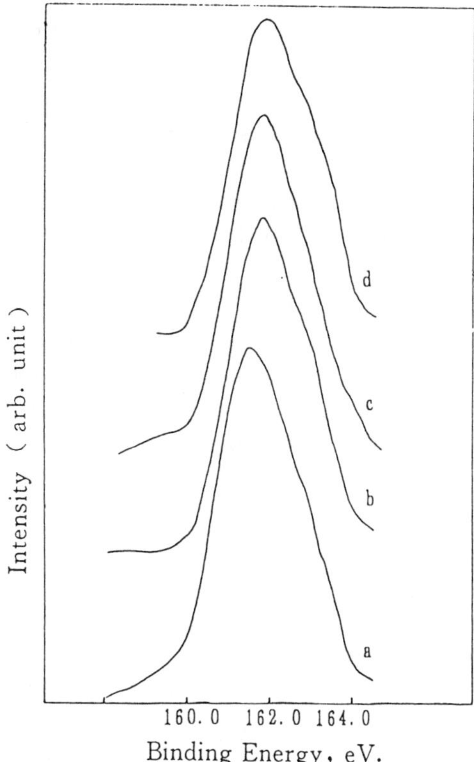

Fig. 3 X-ray photoelectron spectra in the S spectral region.
(a) CdS ultrafine powder,
(b) CdS nanocrystalline materials synthesized under 3.5GPa,
(c) CdS nanocrystalline materials synthesized under 4.0GPa,
(d) CdS nanocrystalline materials synthesized under 4.8GPa.

1. The size quantization in CdS nanometer particles have been observed and studied.

2. Earlier experiment data showed that in

the measurement of XPS of CdS thin films by heating in vacuum from room temperature, the ratio of Cd:S decreased with increasing temperature over the range of 300～600℃ and the S was rich. In our measurements, the Cd:S ratios do not change in all samples (about 3/7), i.e. the S is also rich. As the atoms ratio between lattice and surface of nanometer particles was approximately the same, the S atoms were also rich on the surface.

3. Fig. 1 exhibits the crystal structure of nanocrystalline materials does not vary but the area ratio between the peak at 161.5eV and the one at 162.8eV changes with synthesizing pressure (Fig. 3, Table. 1). Therefore the changes of the area ratio of the two peaks with pressure result from the changes of interphases with pressure, the pressure mainly results in the changes of surface atoms and produces some interphases.

Whether the above reason is right or not, it is clear that XPS data vary with synthesizing pressure. This shows that though the structure of nanocrystalline materials indeed is influenced by synthesizing pressure, the tendency is still ambiguous.

The magnetic susceptibilities of above samples have also been measured at room temperature by magnetic balance in field of 12000 Gs (see Table. 2). The results show that the ultrafine particles is diamagnetic and have a susceptibility $X = 1.38 \times 10^{-6}$ emu/g, which is similar to polycrystals. But the X of nanocrystalline materials vary anomalously with increasing synthesizing pressure. Particularly, there is an interesting phenomenon that the sample synthesized under 4.00GPa exhibits a paramagnetic (positive) susceptibility $X = 8.82 \times 10^{-8}$ emu/g. In earlier measurements, this phenomenon have also been observed in the pressure quenched polycrystals under 4.0GPa, but not interpreted [3]. Comparing nanocrystalline materials with the polycrystals, it is considered that the diamagnetic transition arises from the formation of a special interphase in interfaces of grains under 4.0GPa.

Table 2. Magnetic susceptibility VS synthesizing pressure for CdS nanocrystalline materials, H=12000 Gs.

P(GPa)	0.0	1.0	1.5	2.0	3.0	4.0	4.5	4.8
X(emu/g)	-1.38×10^{-6}	-3.10×10^{-6}	-2.20×10^{-6}	-5.73×10^{-7}	-4.81×10^{-7}	8.82×10^{-8}	-4.0×10^{-7}	-1.27×10^{-6}

ACKNOWLEDGMENT

Thank the NSFC for their support.

REFERENCES

[1] M. Marychurch and G. C. Morris, *Surface Science*, 154, L251-L254 (1985).

[2] A. J. Nozik, Ferd Williams, M. T. Nenadovic, T. Rajh and O. I. Micic, *J. Phys. Chem.*, 89, pp. 397-399 (1985).

[3] R. K. MacCrone and C. G. Homan, *Solid State Communications*, 35, pp. 615-618(1980).

STUDY ON SURFACE PHOTOVOLTAGE SPECTRA OF CdS NANOCRYSTALLINE MATERIALS SYNTHESIZED UNDER HIGH STATIC PRESSURE.

XIAO TONG[1], DA-PENG XU[1], WEN-HUI SU[1,2,3], LIANG-ZHI XIAO[1], SHOU-TIAN LI[1], LI HAN[1],

1. Phys. Dept., Jilin University, Changchun, China.
2. CCAST (World Lab.) P.O. Box 8730, Beijing 100080, China.
3. ICMP, Academia Sinica, Shenyang 110015, China.

Using the ultrafine powder (3～10nm) as starting materials, CdS nanocrystalline materials were synthesized under different pressures (0.0～5.0 GPa). Their surface photovoltage spectra (SPS), UV absorption spectra and laser transient SPS have been observed at room temperature in air. The UV spectra exhibit blueshift of the absorption edge of CdS nanocrystalline materials. The SPS of CdS nanocrystalline materials are different from that of CdS crystals and are similar to that of CdS thin films and the intensities of photovoltage response varying with synthesizing pressure. Their laser transient SPS's show that at $\lambda=532$nm and $\lambda=355$nm, photo-stimulated electron transition processes vary with synthesizing pressure. A kind of mechanism is proposed.

INTRODUCTION

Nanocrystalline materials have recently been developed into a new type of solid materials which differ from glasses and crystals in the sense that they exhibit little short-range or long-range order. Their defect structure such as grain and interphase boundaries, and special properties have attracted much attention of materials scientists. However, at present, the synthesis of nanocrystalline materials is mainly carried out by assembling pre-generated small clusters by means of in situ consolidation (called physical method). In fact, there are many chemical methods by which small clusters can be easily prepared in large quantities. Using the small clusters prepared by chemical methods, the nanocrystalline materials can be synthesized under high pressure (not in situ) and it can expand the theoretical research and applications of nanocrystalline materials. On the other hand, because the special properties of nanocrystalline materials are dependent on their defect structure, it is obvious that they are also effected by different synthesizing pressure to a certain extent. The effects of pressure on the properties of nanocrystalline materials have been seldom studied untill now. In this paper, we have investigated the effect of pressure on the structure of CdS nanocrystalline materials for the first time.

The structure of CdS crystals and thin films have been extensively studied in the past. Here using the ultrafine powder prepared by chemical method as starting materials, CdS nanocrystalline materials were synthesized under different pressures. Photovoltage spectroscopy technique was employed to study the influence of pressure on the structure of CdS nanocrystalline materials.

EXPERIMENTAL

The ultrafine powder was prepared by chemical method and the distribution of particle sizes is 3 ~ 10 nm. The high-static pressure equipment used for synthesizing nanocrystalline materials was a belt type press. The ultrafine powder was placed in high pressure chamber of this press. The pressure was first increased to a value between 0.0GPa and 5.0GPa, maintained for 10min at the value, and then decreased to zero. The pressed compacts were examined by the surface photovoltage spectra, UV absorption spectra and laser transient surface photovoltage spectra.

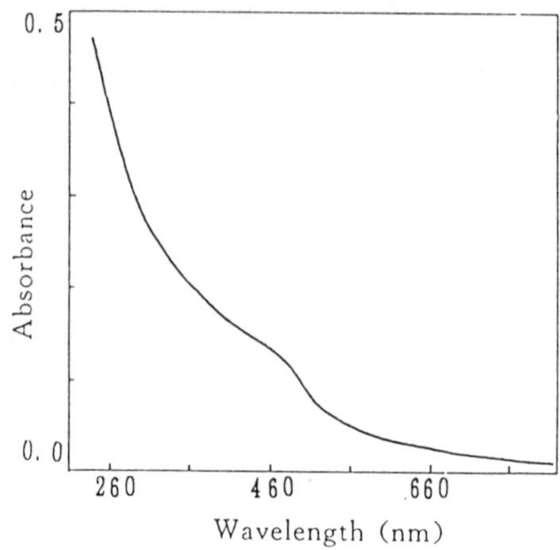

Fig. 1 UV absorption spectrum of CdS ultrafine powder in $C_3H_8O_3$ at 300K.

RESULTS AND DISCUSSIONS

Numerous studies have been carried out on the size-effect of CdS nanometer particles. It has been reported that the particles larger than about 6 nm, i.e. larger than the size of an exciton (7.0 nm), start to absorb close to 515nm (or 2.4ev photon energy), corresponding to the band gap of bulk CdS. With decreasing the size, the absorption threshold shifts to shorter wavelengths [1]. Fig. 1 is the UV absorption spectrum of CdS ultrafine powder used here in $C_3H_8O_3$. The spectrum does not show significant excitonic effects but rather shows a small shift of about 0.2ev in the fundamental absorption edge, reflecting an increase in the band gap (bulk band gap = 2.4ev). Fig. 1 shows that though the ultrafine powder does not have a very uniform size, there are size quantization effects it the spectrum. In addition, the absorption edge in Fig. 1 shows a long tail. It may also arise from the distribution of particle sizes[2].

In general, the properties of nanocrystalline materials are not completely similar to the nanometer particles because there are a lot of interphase boundaries in nanocrystalline materials and the boundaries change with synthesizing pressure. In order to investigate the effect of pressure on the interphases and grain boundaries, the surface photovoltage spectroscopies in CdS nanocrystalline materials synthesized under different pressures (0.00GPa ~ 5.00GPa) have been observed in air (Fig. 2).

In Fig. 2, in the long wavelength range ($\lambda > 500$nm, corresponding to transitions of electrons from the surface states to the band), there are some step-like jumps in the curves and the intensities in photovoltage response of each curve are not the same at the same photon energy. It shows that the surface states which mainly arise from the atoms in grain boundaries and defect structure are different in each sample and vary with synthesizing pressure[3].

In the short wavelength range ($\lambda < 500$nm, photon energy larger than bulk band gap), a characteristic feature of each curve is that there are two peaks (a wider peak in short wavelength range and a sharper peak in long wavelength range) rather than a slow dip as

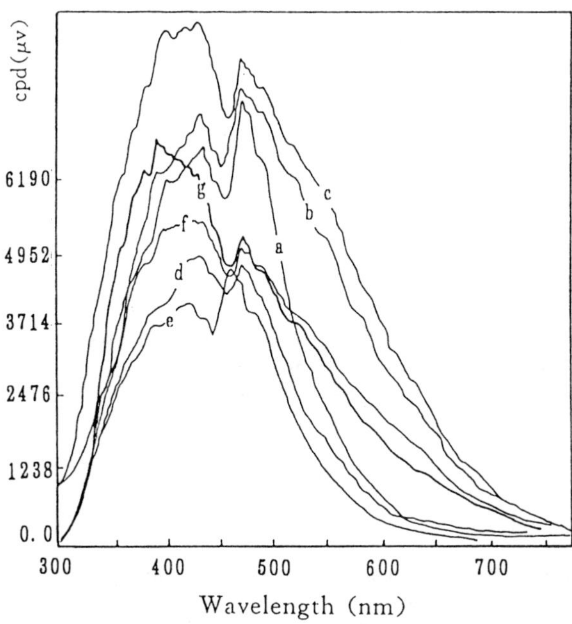

Fig. 2 Surface photovoltage spectra of CdS ultrafine powder and CdS nanocrystalline materials synthesized under various pressures. (a) powder, (b) 1. 0GPa, (c) 1. 5GPa, (d) 3. 2GPa, (e) 4. 0GPa, (f) 4. 5GPa, (g) 4. 8GPa, in room atmosphere.

bulk CdS [4], and their intensities and positions vary also with different synthesizing pressures. Their varying direction with increasing pressure is that firstly the intensities of two peaks increase from 0. 0 GPa to 1. 5 GPa; then that of two peaks begin to decrease untill 4. 0 GPa; finally, that of two peaks increase again up to 4. 8 GPa. In addition, the position of the sharper peak corresponding to that of distinct dip of Fig. 1 shifts to the short wavelength for 10 nm under 4. 0 GPa.

Fig. 3 is laser surface photovoltage transients for the above samples at $\lambda = 532$nm and $\lambda = 355$nm, respectively. The analysis shows that at each wavelength there are two kinds of photo-stimulated electron transition processes in the samples[5]: either a single or a complex process, and photo-stimulated electron transition processes varying with synthesizing pressure. However it is very interesting that the regulation of photo-stimulated electron transition processes varying with pressure is similar to that of Fig. 2.

The above phenomena can be explained those in Fig. 2, where the short wavelength range some peaks arise from the size-effects of small particles[1]. With increasing pressure, the ultrafine particles come into contact closely with each other. This causes the change of atom states in grain boundaries and the formation of some interphases. But under different pressures, the atom states in grain boundaries and interphases formed are different, and the atoms in grain surface will

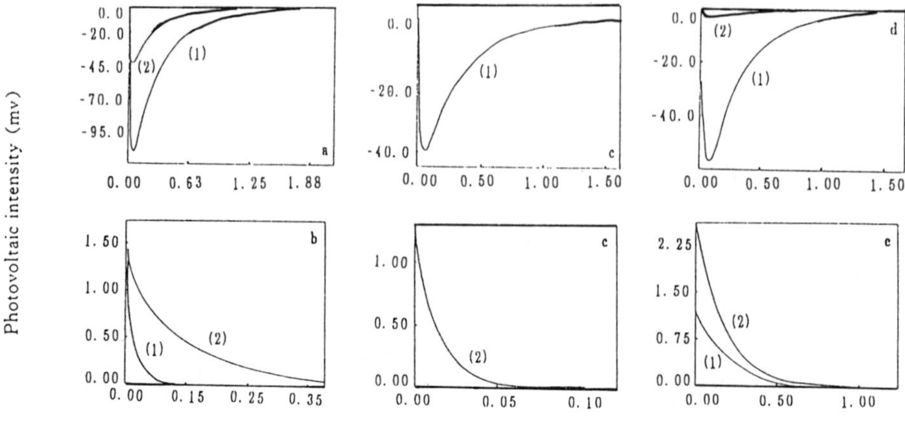

Fig. 3 Surface photovoltage transient spectra of CdS ultra-fine powder and CdS nanocrystalline materials synthesized under various pressures: (a) powder, (b) 2.0GPa, (c) 3.2GPa, (d) 4.0GPa, (e) 4.8GPa, in room atmosphere.
Curve (1) --- wavelength 532 nm, Curve (2) --- wavelength 355 nm.

decrease with increasing pressure while interphases will increase. In addition, because there is a certain distribution of particle sizes, the large particles can be smashed to small ones under high pressure. This will cause again the change of surface states of grain boundaries and interplases. It is proposed that the regulation of photovoltage spectra with synthesizing pressure arises from the above reasons.

CONCLUSION

The present experimental results show that: (1) The properties of nanocrystalline materials are dependent on not only the defect structure but also the size effects under high pressure. (2) The synthesizing pressure can influence the properties of nanocrystalline materials with a regularity. The study of the effect of synthesizing pressure on the structure and properties in nanocrystalline materials very important for theoretical research applications.

ACKNOWLEDGMENT

Thank the NSFC for their support.

REFERENCES

[1] A. J. Nozik, Ferd Williams, M. T. Nenadovic, T. Rajh and O. I. Micic, *J. Phys. Chem.* 89,397-399 (1985).

[2] R. Rossetti, J. L. Eilison, J. M. Gibwon and L. E. Brus, *J. Chem. Phys.* ,80(9),4464-4468 (1984).

[3] J. Lagowski, C. L. Balestra and H. C. Gatos, *Surface Science*, 29, 213-219 (1972).

[4] Harry C. Gatos and Jacek Lagowski, *J. Vac. Sci. Technol.*, 10(1), 130-135 (1973).

[5] Jacek Lagowski, Chester L. Balestra and Harry C. Gatos, *Surface Science*,29,203-212 (1972).

HIGH PRESSURE SYNTHESIS OF CUBIC BORON NITRIDE

S.NAKANO, H.FUJIOKA AND O.FUKUNAGA
Tokyo Institute of Technology
Ookayama,Meguro, Tokyo 152, Japan

High pressure synthesis of cubic boron nitride by solvent catalyst method is reviewed. Alkali and alkaline earths boron nitrogen compounds are used to determine pressure temperature region of cBN formation and we confirmed that the P-T region is separated by the lines corresponding the minimum temperature of liquid formation, the equilibrium between hBN and cBN and the characteristic threshold pressure. This paper discusses the parameters determined for the threshold pressure in various catalytic solvent systems.

INTRODUCTION

Since the first discovery of the solvent catalyst for conversion of hBN to cBN by Wentorf [1], many results supporting the solvent catalyst scheme have been presented [2-4]. However, the mechanism of conversion from hBN to cBN in the solvent still remains unclear. Recently, we presented the results of P-T region of cBN formation and discussed the origin of the threshold pressure, the pressure barrier of cBN formation [5]. This paper presents further experimental results focusing on the catalytic solvent systems.

EXPERIMENTS

Syntheses of catalytic solvents of Li, Mg, Ca and Sr boron nitrogen compounds were carried out by the reaction between metal nitrides and BN under nitrogen atmosphere and identification of phases and impurities was by powder X-ray diffraction (XRD). The Li and Mg compounds were relatively pure but the Ca, and Sr compounds contained oxides, and an unidentified amorphous phase as shown in the Fig. 1. We carried out high pressure high temperature experiments using 10 mm edge cubic anvil apparatus to determine the P-T region of cBN formation. The recovered samples were observed by SEM to determine the sizes and the morphology of the cBN grains.

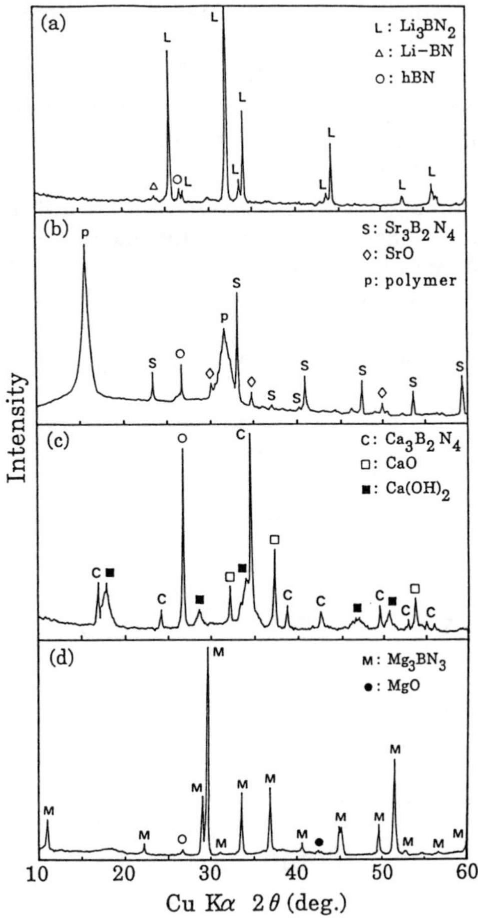

Figure 1. X-ray diffraction peaks of the synthesized solvent catalysts compounds . Note that the Sr-compound was protected by polymer film during the measurements.

EXPERIMENTAL RESULTS

(1) BN-Li_3BN_2 System

Laminating sample configuration of compacted powderd BN(Denka GP) and Li_3BN_2 was used. The runs were carried out at designed P-T conditions for 15 to 30 min. The recovered samples were examined by XRD and SEM. If cBN was identified in the sample, the P-T condition was determined as the point of cBN formation. As shown in the Fig. 2, the formation region of cBN has three boundaries namely the low temperature limit at about 1050 °C, the equilibrium boundary curve which can be expressed as P=T/200 - 3.5(GPa,°C), and the threshold pressure at about 4.8 GPa. The lower temperature limit obtained in the present experiments was lower than that reported previously [6]. We cannot explain this difference. However, Li or Li_3N were used as the mixing agent of hBN in the previous experiments, expecting the formation of Li_3BN_2 at high pressure and high temperature condition. It must be noted that these agents are reactive to the moisture of air to form carbonate and oxide of Li and they deteriorate the effect of catalytic actions. The threshold pressure of the formation of cBN is clearly shown in the Fig.2.

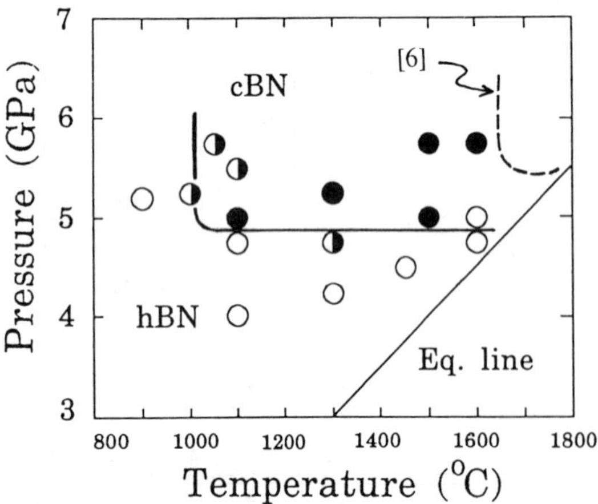

Figure 2. P-T region of cBN formation using Li_3BN_2 as a solvent catalyst.

(2) BN-Mg_3BN_3 System

The Mg boron nitrogen compounds reported previously contained many mistakes in the composition and stability but now it is clear that the Mg boron nitrogen compounds in the system Mg_3N_2-BN are high and low pressure phases of Mg_3BN_3 and an unidentified metastable phase having a composition between Mg_3N_2 and BN [7].

Based on this result, we used low pressure phase of Mg_3BN_3 as a starting agent for high pressure experiments. The P-T region of cBN formation in this system shown in Fig.3, is separated by the lower temperature limit at about 1250 °C, and threshold pressure at about 4.9 GPa. The P-T region of cBN formation is somewhat different from previous data [4] and this was discussed in our recent paper [7]. It is considered that the present results are more reliable as the P-T region of cBN formation in the system BN-Mg_3BN_3.

(3) BN-$Ca_3B_2N_4$ and BN-$Sr_3B_2N_4$ Systems

The P-T region of cBN formation in the BN-$Ca_3B_2N_4$ system has been reported by Sato et al. [4] and Demazeau et al previosly. [9]. The lower temperature boundary of the present data shown in Fig.3 is about 250 °C lower than the data of

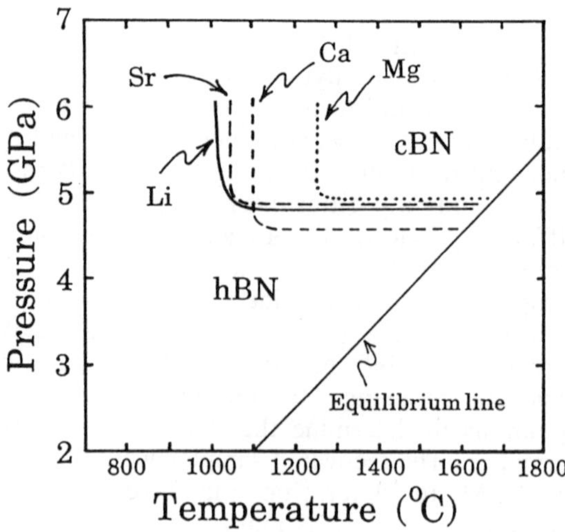

Figure 3. P-T region of cBN formation using Li, Ca, Mg and Sr boron nitrogen compounds as solvent catalysts.

Sato and about 200 °C higher than that of Demazeau at 6 GPa. However, threshold pressures of cBN formation are found within 0.1 GPa at 4.9 GPa. The formation region of cBN in the system BN-$Sr_3B_2N_4$ has not been reported previously. This work shows it to have a lower temperature boundary at 1050 °C and threshold pressure at 4.9 GPa.

(4) Observation of cBN grains

As shown in Fig. 4, the size and morphology of the cBN grains are different by the forming P-T condition. However, the size of cBN is increased with approaching to the equilibrium boundary between hBN and cBN, because this condition corresponded to the lower nucleation density of cBN and relatively higher rate of crystal growth.

The morphology and size of the cBN grains are also affected by the chemical components of the solvent catalyst. Li and Sr boron nitrogen catalysts formed (111) dominated tetraheral crystals. The Ca and Mg boron nitrogen catalysts formed more irregular granules having larger size at maximum 100 µm. These different features of the formed cBN grains may be attributed to the difference of the nucleation density of cBN in the solvent catalyst.

(5) Decomposition of Metal Boron Nitrogen Compounds with Water

We have reported decomposition of Mg_3BN_3 and water system to form cBN and MgO by the high pressure runs [10]. Similar reaction was found in the $Ca_3B_2N_4$ and water system but no cBN formation was observed from Li_3BN_2 or $Sr_3B_2N_4$ system. The structure refinements of Mg_3BN_3 has been carried out [11] and it is confirmed that Mg_3BN_3 contains N=B=N linear chains in the unit cell. This structure will prefer to decompose to MgO and BN because the Mg ion is located at an active site to react with oxygen. The decomposition was observed even at room temperature and at about 5 GPa to form $Mg(OH)_2$.

No structural information of the high pressure form of Li_3BN_2 is available, but if we consider it as a similar structure of the low temperature form of Li_3BN_2 determined by Yamane et al. [12], it also contains the N=B=N chains in the unit cell. However, Li_2O formation is unlikely as a decomposition product with water.

An important difference of the threshold pressure of the cBN formation was found in the system Mg_3BN_3 and water. The threshold pressure was decreased from 4.9 GPa for solvent catalyst reaction to about 3.8 GPa for the decomposition reaction. This data suggested that the threshold pressure of cBN formation is sensitive to the bonding state of boron and nitrogen in the solvent at high pressure.

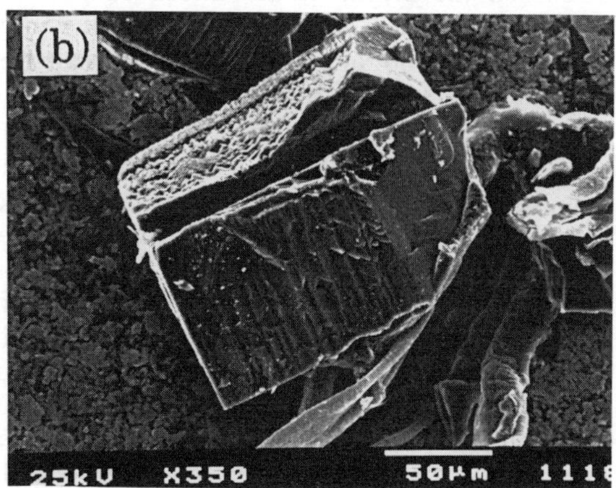

Figure 4. Examples of cBN grains obtained (a) at 4.8 GPa, 1100°C for 15 min in the $Ca_3B_2N_4$ solvent catalyst and (b) at 4.8 GPa, 1600°C for 15 min.

DISCUSSION

(1) Solvent Catalyst of cBN Formation

In the present study, we used metal boron nitrogen compounds which are considerd to be the solvent catalyst of BN. However, the solvent of BN is not so simple in chemical composition and structure of the melts. Interaction among alkali or alkaline earth elements, boron, and nitrogen may be complicated in the high pressure melts. But phenomenologically, transformation reaction are taking place selectively at the boundary between hBN and the solvent catalyst and the cBN formation proceeds from the interface to the hBN zone by the increase of reaction time. This observation is similar to the case of carbon and solvent catalyst system. Thus, the formation mechanism of cBN may not be different from that of diamond.

(2) The Threshold Pressure of cBN Formation

It must be noted that the threshold pressure was not changed by the reaction period. No cBN growth on the seed crystal was observed below threshold pressure while the samples were exposed at sufficiently higher temperature than the lower temperature limit of cBN formation. These data suggested that the pressure barrier of cBN formation is independent of reaction kinetics and nucleation barrier of cBN.

Pressure barrier of the cBN formation has been reported for the P-T region using ammonium salts as catalysts by Kobayashi [13], and he discussed the origin of the threshold pressure relating with the the oxygen contamination. Although, it is not applicable to the present case because BN-solvent catalyst system in these experiments are free from oxygen contamination.

It was confirmed in the present experiments that the threshold pressure, the pressure barrier of cBN formation, was widely observed throughout the P-T region of cBN formation in the solvent catalysts system. The origin of the threshold pressure is still unclear but it can be assumed that the value of threshold pressure can be controlled by the control of the bonding state of boron and nitrogen in the solvents. More clear information of the threshold pressure will be obtained from solubility measurements of BN in the catlytic solvent.

REFERENCES

[1] R.H.Wentorf Jr., J. Chem. Phys., 34, pp.809-12(1961).

[2] R.C.DeVries and J.F.Fleischer, J, Cryst Growth, 13/14,.pp.88-92(1972).

[3] T.Endo, O.Fukunaga and M.Iwata, J.Mat.Sci., 16,.pp.2227-32(1981).

[4] T.Sato, T.Endo, S.Kashima, O.Fukunaga and M.Iwata, J. Mater. Sci., 18 pp.3054-62(1983).

[5] S.Nakano, and O.Fukunaga,"New Concept of the Synthesis of Cubic Boron Nitride" in Recent Trends in High Pressure Research, edited by A.K.Signh 1992, pp.687-90

[6] K.Kudaka et al. Japanese J Chemical Industries, 69, pp.365-69(1966).

[7] S.Nakano, H.Ikawa and O.Fukunaga, Diamond and Related Mater., 2, pp.1168-74(1993).

[8] S.Nakano, H.Ikawa and O.Fukunaga, Diamond and Related Mater.,

[9] J.Demazeau, L.Vel and G.Biardeau, "Flouronitrides; New Flux-Precursors for Preparation Cubic-BN" in New Diamond Science and Technology, 1991, pp.1045-49.

[10] S.Nakano, H.Ikawa and O.Fukunaga, J. Am. Ceram. Soc., 75, pp.240-43(1992)

[11] H.Hiraguchi et al., J. Appl. Cryst., 24, pp.286-92(1991).

[12] H.Yamane, S.Kikkawa and M.Koizumi, J.Solid State Chem., 71, pp.1-11(1987)

[13] Kobayashi, J. Chem. Phys., 70, pp.5898-905(1979).

HIGH PRESSURE SYNTHESIS OF SERIAL HIGHER BORON SUBOXIDES WITH CAGE STRUCTURES

Xiao-Yang Liu[a], Xu-Dong Zhao[a], Wen-Hui Su[a,b],

a. Solid State Phys. Grp., Jilin Univ., Changchun 130023

b. ICMP, Academia Sinica, Shenyang, 110015 and CCAST (World Lab.), Beijing, 100080 China.

Under the extreme conditions of high pressure (5.0GPa~8.0GPa) and high temperature (1500℃~1700℃), the serial boron suboxides, such as B_nO (n=2,4,6,7,8,10,12,16,18,20,22,26) have been synthesized by high pressure quenching and characterized by XRD, SIMS, IR, XPS, TG-DTA and chemical analysis. The result of XRD shows that the boron suboxide B_2O has a tetragonal symmetry with lattice constants(nm), a=b=0.9447, c=1.6166, and the B_7O crystallizes in the hexagonal system with lattice constants (nm) a=0.5435, c=1.2415 which correspond to average values derived from a least squares fitting of XRD data. The results of XRD, IR and XPS show that when n>4 the boron suboxides possess cage structures composed of closely packed, slightly distorted B12 icosahedra in which each icosahedron may bonded to oxygen atoms located in interstices among them. After being heated to high temperature in N_2, those boron suboxides become superhard materials and their microhardness is close to that of c-BN. The result of TG-DTA shows that as the temperature increases up to 1200℃ in air, there occurs no thermal transitions in the samples.

INTRODUCTION

The chemistry of boron is an active subject because of their abundance of chemical structures and physical properties. Especially, higher borides differ from conventional compounds in their bondings and structures, so they exhibit a number of distinctive physical properties, and the boron suboxides perhaps is the earliest boron-rich compounds studied by chemists. In 1909, B_7O was first thought to exist by Weintraub[1] and later proven. From then on, the B_2O[2,3], B_6O[4,5], B_7O[6] were synthesized by chemists. Since Andizej R. Badzian[7]pointed out that the boron suboxide can be a kind of superhard material, scientists began to pay more attention to these borides. In the former work, two methods were often used to synthesize boron suboxide: one is to reduce B_2O_3 with B, Mg or Si under high temperature, another is to oxidize B with ZnO under very high temperature for long time. In this paper. Under the extreme conditions of high pressure(5.0GPa~8.0GPa) and high temperature, using high pressure quenching, the serial boron suboxides such as B_nO(n =2,4,6,7,8,10,12,14,16,18,20,22,26) have been synthesized by reducting B_2O_3 with boron. Furthermore, B_7O have been prepared by oxidizing B with ZnO. The prepared serial boron suboxides have been characterized by XRD, SIMS, IR, XPS, TG-DTA and chemical analysis.

EXPERIMENT AND RESULTS

The synthesis of boron suboxides is conducted on 500 ton Bridgman and 2000 ton belt-type apparatus. The reaction equation is

$$(3n-2)B+B_2O_3=3B_nO \qquad (1)$$

Further more, another method is applied to the synthesis of B_7O. The equation is

$$7B+ZnO=B_7O+Zn \quad (2)$$

Boron was mixed with B_2O_3 or ZnO powder and ground uniformly, then they were placed in the high pressure chamber (h-BN) and the pressure was increased up to expected value, the temperature was then increased up to expected value, too. After 20 min, the samples were quenched to room temperature under high pressure, and the pressure was finally released. As to reaction (2), the products were put into 6N chlorhydric acid to remove the metal zinc, at last the B_7O can be obtained. After many experiments, the best reaction condition is found to be 5.0GPa ~ 8.0GPa, 1500℃~ 1700℃ for reaction (1); 3.5 ~ 4.0GPa, 1200℃ for reaction(2), respectively.

The XRD spectra of the prepared B_2O and B_7O are shown in Figure 1 and 2 respectively.

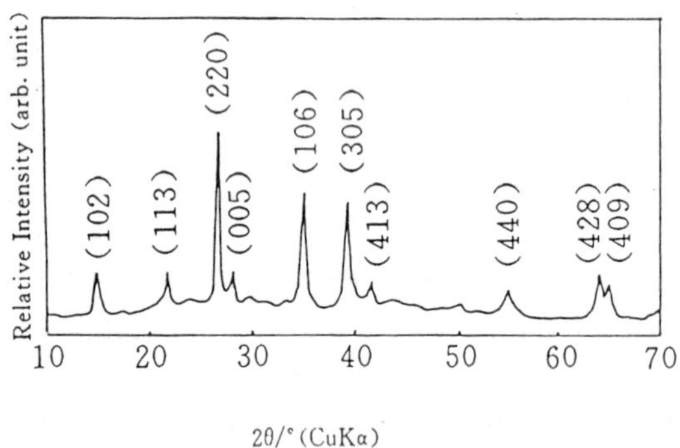

Fig. 1 X-ray Diffraction Pattern of Boron Suboxide B_2O

The results show that the B_2O has a tetragonal symmetry with lattice constants (nm) a=b= 0.9447 c=1.6166. The B_7O crystallizes in the hexagonal system with lattice constants(nm) a =0.5435, c=1.2415, which are average values derived from a least squares fitting of XRD data. The XRD results of B_nO show that the

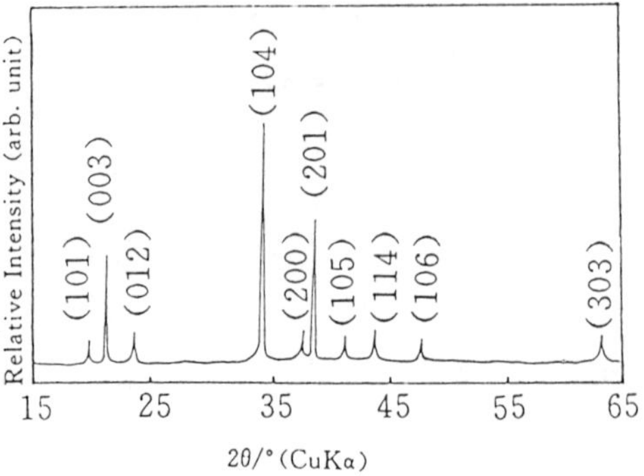

Fig. 2 X-ray Diffraction Pattern of Boron Suboxide B_7O

B_nO have a tetragonal symmetry when $n<4$, a hexagonal symmetry when $n>4$.

The results of SIMS indicate that the products are composed of boron and oxygen, and the impurities of C, and N are on the degree of ppm. The contamination was caused by the graphite heater and h-BN capsule. Chemical analysis shows that the ratio of boron and oxygen is in accordance with the chemical formula B_nO.

In order to investigate the bonding characters of B_nO, IR studies are carried and IR data of B_2O and B_7O are listed in Table 1. Comparison with that of boron and B_2O_3, we have found that the structure of B_2O is similar to that of B_2O_3, and the struture of B_7O is close to that of B. Following, we tried to define the absorb peaks according to the former work. In B_2O spectra, the peaks at 1632 cm^{-1} and 1062cm^{-1} are due to B-B bond vibration, the peaks at 1452cm^{-1} and 1196cm^{-1} to B-O bond vibration, the peaks at 883cm^{-1}, 783cm^{-1}, 644cm^{-1} and 544cm^{-1} to O-B-Obond vibration. In B_7O, the peak at 785cm^{-1} is deduced by the expansion vibration of cage skeleton, the peaks at 1072cm^{-1}, 883cm^{-1} and 669cm^{-1} are due to oxygen-boron cluster (OB_3 and OB_5) vibration, the peaks at 547cm^{-1} to O-B-O flexural vibration, the peak at 1244cm^{-1} to B-O expan-

Table 1 Position of IR Absorption Bands (cm^{-1})

B_2O	B_7O	B	B_2O_3
1632		1630	
1452		1448	1468
	1244	1225	
1196		1194	1198
		1128	1107
1062	1072	1083	
		1037	1026
883	883	884	883
783	785	793	803
644	669		676
	653	648	650
	618		
	594		
547	547	547	547

sion vibration, and the other peaks at lower wavenumber to B-B vibration[9—11].

The peak at about 790cm^{-1} is an evidence for the existence of boron cage. Above peak exists in the samples of B_nO when $n>4$, and doesn't when $n<4$. So we guess that the structure of B_2O is a three-dimension netted texture in which the boron could bond to boron or oxygen. The structure of B_7O is composed of slightly distorted boron cage of B12 icosahedra in which each boron atom bonds to other one or oxygen atoms. In order to prove these guesses, the B_nO was examined by XPS.

XPS could be used for investigating the chemical environment of boron in boride. The XPS of B_2O and B_7O are shown in Figure 3 compared with that of boron and B_2O_3. The data of their XPS are listed in Table 2. The result show that the B1s binding energy of B_2O and B_7O are different because of chemical environment among them. The two binding energy of B_2O mean two boron bonding states in the structure: B-B and B-O. The three binding energies of B_7O mean three boron bonding states in B_7O: B-O, B-B in boron cage and B-B between boron cage. The results are in correspondence to those of IR. As to the XPS results of serial boron suboxides B_nO we found that there are two bonding states when $n<4$ and three states when $n>4$.

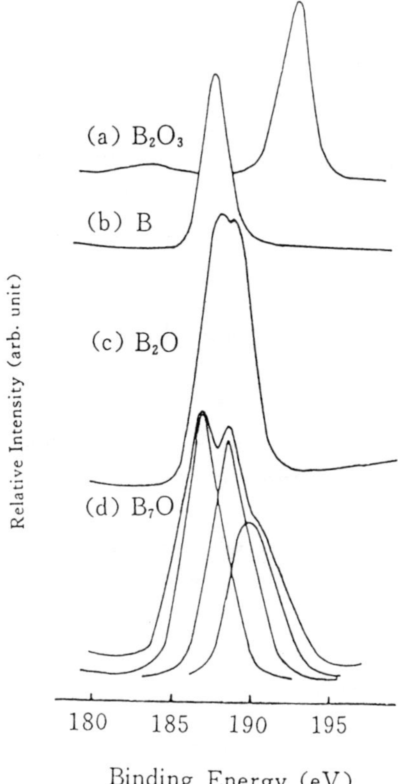

Fig. 3 B1S XPS of (a) B, (b) B_2O_3, (c) B_2O and (d) B_7O

Table 2 Binding Energy of B1s

B. E. (eV)	B	B_2O_3	B_2O	B_7O
	187.2	193.9	187.23	186.94
Bls(eV)			188.62	188.56
				189.62

These boron suboxides B_nO, after being heated to high temperature in N_2, did become superhard materials whose microhardness is close to that of c-BN. The TG-DTA result of those retreated boron suboxide shows that there are no thermal transitions when the temperature is increased up to 1200℃ in air, indicating that the boron suboxide can be a kind of refractory superhard materials.

CONCLUSION

Under high pressure and high temperature, the serial boron suboxides have been synthesized. In the structure of boron suboxide B_nO, the boron cage of B12 icosahedron exists when $n > 4$ and it doesn't when $n < 4$. After being heated to high temperature those boron suboxides become superhard material whose microhardness is close to that of c-BN.

ACKNOWLEDGMENT

This work was supported by the National Natural Science Foundation of China.

REFERENCE

[1] E. Weintraub, Trans Amer. *Electrochem. Soc.* 16, pp. 165-184 (1909).

[2] H. Tracy Hall and Lane A Compton. *Inorg. Chem.* 4(8), pp. 1213-1216 (1965).

[3] Tadashi Endo Tsugio Sato and Masahiko Shimada, *J. Mat. Sci. Lett.* 6, pp. 683-685 (1987).

[4] H. F. Rizzo, W. C. Simmons and H. O. Bielstein, *J. Eletrochem Soc.* 109 (11), pp. 1079-1082 (1962).

[5] Rheniamin F. Goosey. Anderson S. C. *USP* 3,816,586, 1974.

[6] C. E. Holocombe Jr. and O. J. Horne Jr, *J. Amer. Cera. Soc.* 55(2) pp. 106-109(1972).

[7] Andizej Badzid. *Appl. Phys. Lett.* 53 (25). pp. 2495-2497 (1988).

[8] Hongjian Liu, Yifeng Wang and Wenhui Su; *Chin. J. High Pressure Phys*, 4(4), pp. 284-290 (1990).

[9] W. E. Keller et al., *J. Chem. Phys.*, 20, pp. 1749-1752 (1952).

[10] G. F. Lanthier et al., *J. Inorg. Nucl. Chem.* 32, pp. 1807-1812 (1970).

[11] Kogno Nakanoto, "*Infrared and Raman Spectra of Inorgnic and Coordination Compounds*" *3rd Ed.*, John Willevy & Sons, (1975).

INVESTIGATIONS INTO THE DETONATIVE SYNTHESIS OF βBN

R.Trębiński, E.Włodarczyk, S.Cudziło, J.Paszula, W.Trzciński
Faculty of Chemistry and Technical Physics
Military University of Technology
Kaliskiego str.2
Warsaw, Poland, 01-489

The work contains the description of investigations into the detonative synthesis of the sphaleritic modification of boron nitride and the analysis of the influence of synthesis conditions on the yield of βBN. The influence of the detonation parameters and the conditions of the products scatter into the explosion chamber on the yield has been determined.

INTRODUCTION

The possibility of αBN→βBN transformation under the dynamic load was for a long time a merit of controversy. The authors of [1] identified in the shocked aBN only the wurtzite modification γBN, whereas it was stated in [2] that the transformation product is the sphaleritic modification. By the authors of [3] the product is a mixture of both modifications. In accordance with the results of [4] and [5] the only product of the transformation under shock loading is the wurtzite modification. However further investigations ([6]-[9]) proved that in the case when the shock compression is accompanied by a high increase of the temperature αBN→βBN transformation is possible. The high thermal activation is necessary in respect of the diffusive mechanism of the transformation - [10]. Whereas diamond can arise from graphite on the way of a purely martensitic transition ([11], [12]), the martensitic transformation αBN→βBN is prohibited.

In accordance with the estimations made in [7]-[9] the diffusive transformation in shocked αBN in the time about 1 μs needs the value of the temperature being about 3300 K. Such a high temperature on the shock wave front results in the final temperature being high enough to cause the inverse transformation. This can be partially omitted in a variation of the dynamical synthesis - so called detonative synthesis. It consists in direct action of high pressure and temperature of the detonation products on particles of αBN mixed with an explosive. Under this high energy action αBN transforms into the dense modifications - βBN and γBN. As a result of expansion of the explosion gases the transformation product is cooled, owing to which the inverse transformation after the drop in pressure is prevented. In accordance with information given in patents [13] and [14] the detonative synthesis provides the product with the content of βBN up to 85%.

The use of the turbostratic αBN (BNt) is a factor increasing the content of βBN in the product of the detonative synthesis. BNt is a material with the high density of the turbostratic stacking faults, consisting in a mutual torsion of the crystalline planes of the graphitic boron nitride. Due to this imperfection of the crystalline structure BNt does not transform into the wurtzite modification. When it is subjected to the action of high pressure and temperature, it transforms only into the sphaleritic modification ([8],[9]).

In the present work the results of investigations, aimed on the determination of the influence of detonation parameters and conditions of the scatter of detonation products in an explosion chamber on the yield of the detonative synthesis of βBN from BNt, are presented.

DESCRIPTION OF EXPERIMENTS

Two kinds of reactive mixtures were used with various content of boron nitride: plastic mixtures -

X10, X15, X20 and pressed mixtures - P15, P20, P25. Compositions of the mixtures are given in Table 1. Graphitic boron nitride synthesized in the temperature 1200 - 1300 °C, supplied by WISTOM Ent., was used for preparing mixtures. Its granulation was 40-63 μm.

Table 1. Composition and density of mixtures.

Mixture	Composition		Density [kg/m^3]
X10	RDX/BNt/binder*	65/10/25	1440
X15	RDX/BNt/binder	60/15/25	1510
X20	RDX/BNt/binder	55/20/25	1560
P15	RDX/BNt/nitrocel.	83/15/2	1690
P20	RDX/BNt/nitrocel.	78/20/2	1700
P25	RDX/BNt/nitrocel.	74/24/2	1730

* water/ammonium nitrite/glycol/polyacryloamid 60/20/15/5

Cylindrical charges of plastic mixtures of a diameter of 40 mm and mass of about 0.5 kg were moulded. Charges of pressed mixtures were formed by joining cylindrical blocks of a diameter 42.3 mm, a height of 44 mm and mass of about 100 g. In tests 16,19-26 charges were composed of five blocks and in tests 17 and 18 - of four blocks. In tests 17,18,21,22,25 and 26 charges were put into polyethylene sleeves of a diameter 100 mm and of a length of 300 mm filled with water. Charges were detonated in an explosion chamber of a capacity of about 4 m3. Following operations were performed: detonation of a charge, depressurizing of the chamber 15 min after the shot, recovering solid products by washing them out by the use of water with a detergent, filtering off and drying the solid products, chemical treatment in order to isolate dense modifications of boron nitride.

Results of tests are presented in Table 2. In the table the information concerning the application of water envelopes ("+") and the yield of the synthesis are given. The yield was calculated as a ratio of the mass of the product after the chemical treatment to the mass of αBN in the charge.

Table 2. Results of experimental shots (TN - test number, M - mixture, WE - water envelope, Y - yield [%]).

TN	M	WE	Y	TN	M	WE	Y
1	X10	-	3.7	14	X20	-	4.7
2	X10	-	4.1	15	X20	-	4.8
3	X10	-	4.2	16	P15	-	3.0
4	X10	-	4.1	17	P15	+	4.8
5	X10	-	4.0	18	P15	+	5.3
6	X15	-	3.9	19	P20	-	2.4
7	X15	-	4.4	20	P20	-	2.1
8	X15	-	4.6	21	P20	+	4.6
9	X15	-	3.9	22	P20	+	4.5
10	X15	-	3.9	23	P25	-	2.1
11	X20	-	3.9	24	P25	-	1.9
12	X20	-	5.9	25	P25	+	4.0
13	X20	-	6.0	26	P25	+	3.9

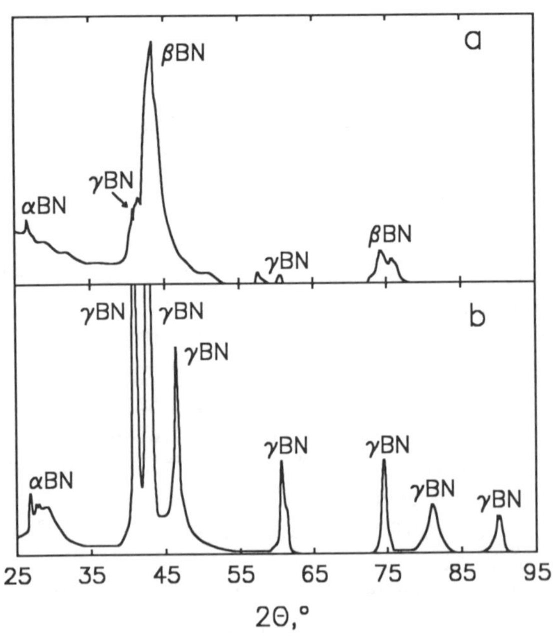

Figure 1. X-ray diffraction patterns of (a) product of detonative synthesis (X10 mixture) - dominating βBN, (b) product of dynamical synthesis in a closed container - dominating γBN.

The identification of the product was accomplished by the X-ray diffractometry. A diffraction pattern of a sample obtained after the chemical treatment of the solid products of the X10 mixture detonation is presented in Fig.1a. Two basic lines 43.7° and 74.1° correspond to βBN. Two weak lines 40.8° and 60.6° can be attributed to γBN. Other lines characteristic for γBN are not observed. A diffraction pattern of a γBN sample, produced by the dynamical synthesis in a closed container from a high grade αBN, is presented in Fig.1b for comparison. Confrontation of both diffraction patterns leads to the conclusion that the content of γBN in the product of the detonative synthesis is very low. On the base of crude assessments it does not exceed 5%. The content of αBN (line 26.6°) is similar. Therefore the results of X-ray analysis prove that βBN is the dominating phase in the product of the detonative synthesis.

MEASUREMENTS AND CALCULATION OF DETONATION PARAMETERS

The methodology of detonation parameters measurements is presented in [15]. Only the detonation velocity D and mass velocity u were measured for the pressed mixtures. The results of measurements for both types of mixtures are given in Table 3 in the column denoted by E.

Theoretical calculations of the detonation parameters were performed by the use of the thermodynamic code TIGER with the set of coefficients in the BKW equation of state recommended in [16]. Results of calculations are given in Table 3 in column denoted by "BKW".

Some records of variations of the velocity of the boundary: explosive - plexiglas plate are shown in Fig.2. Sharp throws of the velocity inside the reaction zone can be observed. They can be attributed to a transformation accompanied by a volume decrease in shocked αBN. It was shown in [17] that this can cause the realization of the "weak detonation" regime. We estimated parameters of the weak detonation by the method described in [15]. Results of calculations are presented in Table 3 in columns denoted by "AD-1"(parameters before the mass velocity throw) and "AD-2" (the end of the throw). The values of the temperature in the column "AD-1" were assessed with the assumption that there is no heat exchange between detonation products and αBN.

Table 3. Results of measurements and calculations of detonation parameters (M -mixture, P - parameter, E - results of measurements).

M	P	BKW	AD-1	AD-2	E
X10	D,m/s	6830	6960	6960	6920
	u,m/s	1630	1690	1400	1260
	p,GPa	15.5	16.9	14.0	14.3
	T,K	2100	2430	-	-
X15	D,m/s	6750	7070	7070	7030
	u,m/s	1550	1680	1320	1270
	p,GPa	15.3	17.9	14.1	15.0
	T,K	1860	2360	-	-
X20	D,m/s	6580	7040	7040	6660
	u,m/s	1450	1610	1200	1100
	p,GPa	14.4	17.7	13.2	11.6
	T,K	1620	2280	-	-
P15	D,m/s	7620	7610	7610	7340
	u,m/s	1900	1800	1420	1050
	p,GPa	23.6	23.2	18.2	-
	T,K	2690	3440	-	-
P20	D,m/s	7360	7460	7460	7370
	u,m/s	1790	1730	1290	1040
	p,GPa	21.6	21.9	16.3	-
	T,K	2480	3350	-	-
P25	D,m/s	7150	7400	7400	7190
	u,m/s	1690	1680	1190	1130
	p,GPa	20.2	21.9	15.2	-
	T,K	2250	3290	-	-

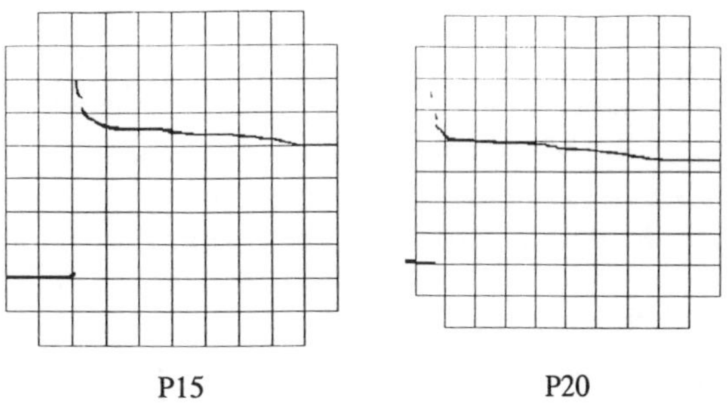

Figure 2. Records of the time variations of the velocity of the boundary explosive-plexiglas plate obtained by the use of electromagnetic gages (1div=0.1 μs).

CONCLUSIONS

1. The product of the detonative synthesis of dense modifications of boron nitride from BNt consists in at least 90% of βBN.

2. Calculated values of temperature are lower than 3000 K. It suggests that the transformation runs only in this stage of the process, in which due to the lack of the thermal equilibrium "hot points" with the temperature higher than 3000 K are present. Approximate calculations prove that the temperature relaxation time for BN grains of the size of 40-60 μm is one order of magnitude longer that the chemical reaction time. Therefore we can make use of the results of the temperature value calculations made under assumption of no heat exchange to assess the temperature value in "hot points" - column AD-1 in Table 3. Confrontation of the temperature values in "hot points" and after attaining the equilibrium suggests that only a small part of the raw material can transform into βBN. Therefore a deficit of the energy supplied to BN grains in the detonation process seems to be a basic reason of the low yield.

3. Measured values of the mass velocity are close to the values calculated for the weak detonation regime. It is an argument for the hypothesis of the weak detonation regime in mixtures containing αBN. Another evidence of the weak detonation regime is a characteristic "plateau" on the records of the mass velocity (see Fig.2). In accordance with the conclusions of the analysis performed in [17] the weak detonation regime is caused by the polymorphic transformation of αBN inside the reaction zone. In our opinion the throw of the mass velocity can be attributed to the first stage of the transformation, consisting in a deformation of the plains of graphitic boron nitride, that loose their initial flatness. In the case of boron nitride with the perfect lattice the deformation results in forming covalent bonds between atoms belonging to neighboring deformed plains. As a result the wurtzitic modification of boron nitride forms. The deformation of plains of the turbostratic boron nitride cannot cause formation of the bonds, because of a mutual turn of the plains. Therefore a certain intermediate structure is formed with some features of an amorphous structure. If it is subjected to the action of the high temperature, the diffusive processes of recrystallization will cause formation of βBN.

4. Processes taking part during scatter of detonation products (reflection of shock waves against the wall of the chamber, formation of "hot nucleus" in the center of the chamber, effects of two-phase flow - [18],[19]) cause diminishing of the yield by causing the inverse transformation. The use of water envelope prevents the inverse transformation and increases the yield (twice in conditions of our experiments).

REFERENCES

[1] G.A.Adadurov et al, *Dokl.Akad.Nauk SSSR* 172, pp.1066-1068, (1967)

[2] N.L.Coleburn, J.W.Forbes, *J.Chem.Phys.* 48, pp. 555-559, (1968).

[3] I.N.Dulin et al, *Sov.Phys.of Sol.* 11, pp.1252-1257, (1969).

[4] T.Soma et al, *Mat.Res.Bull.* 9, pp. 755-762, (1974).

[5] A.V.Kurdyumov, I.N.Frantzevich, *Dokl.Akad.Nauk SSSR* 221, pp. 588-589, (1975).

[6] T.V.Bavina et al, *Phys.Comb.Expl.* 11, pp. 773-776, (1975).

[7] A.V.Kurdyumov et al, Dokl.Akad.Nauk.SSSR 246, pp. 1113-1115, (1979).

[8] N.I.Borimchuk et al, Proc. of the Fifth Allunion Conf. on Detonation, Krasnoyarsk 1991, Russia, pp. 43-47.

[9] N.I.Borimchuk et al, *Sov.Chem.Phys.* 9, pp.1686-1688, (1990).

[10] A.V.Kurdyumov, A.N.Pilyankyevitch, *Phase transformations in carbon and boron nitride* [in Russian], Kiev: Naukova Dumka, 1979.

[11] E.J.Wheeler, D.Lewis, *Mat.Res.Bull.* 10, pp.687-694, (1975).

[12] A.V.Kurdyumov et al, *Sov.Powder Metall.* 1, pp.34-40, (1988).

[13] G.A.Adadurov et al, *Method of obtaining diamond and/or diamond-like modification of boron nitride*, GB Patent 2090239A, 7.07.1982.

[14] G.A.Adadurov et al, *Method of obtaining superhard material on the base of cubic boron nitride* , USSR Patent 90364(AC),15.12.1982.

[15] S.Cudzilo et al, *J.Tech.Phys.* 33, pp.79-92, (1992).

[16] P.Crawford, *Getting started with TIGER,* Lawrence Livermore National Laboratory 1986.

[17] R.Trebinski et al, *J.Tech.Phys.* 31, pp. 129-154, (1990).

[18] R.Trebinski et al, *J.Tech.Phys.* 32, pp. 199-218, (1991).

[19] R.Trebinski et al, *J.Tech.Phys.* 32, pp. 417-433, (1991).

STUDY ON THE SYNTHESIS PROCESS OF $CeTbO_3$ COMPOUND UNDER HIGH PRESSURE AND HIGH TEMPERATURE

Liu Hongjian[1] Su Wenhui[1,2,3] Li Liping[1] and Wang Yifeng[1]

1. Group of Rare Earth Solid State Physics, Jilin University, Changchun 130023, People's Republic of China

2. International Center for Material Physics, Chines Academy of Sciences, Shenyang 110015, People's Republic of China

3. China Center of Advanced Science and Technology (World Laboratory), PO Box 8730, Beijing 100080, People's Republic of China

The electric resistances of $CeTbO_3$, CeO_2, Tb_4O_7 and mixture $CeO_2+Tb_4O_7$ (Tb:Ce=1:1) have been measured in situ from room temperature to 800℃ under 0.5GPa. The results show that these samples are all of semiconducting properties, but up-and-down changes in mixture and Tb_4O_7 system have been found under 0.5GPa above 600℃. X-ray diffraction and X-ray photoelectron spectra show that corresponding to this irregular resistance change, there is a change in structure which close relates to the valence fluctuation from Tb^{4+} to Tb^{3+}. The results suggest that during $Tb^{4+} \rightarrow Tb^{3+}$, the reaction forming $CeTbO_3$ compound begin at about 600℃ and finish at about 1000℃.

INTRODUCTION

In the early of 1960's, Schneider et al. have reported some ABO_3 type rare earth oxides prepared by the method of high temperature solid state reactions [1,2], recent years the high pressures were employed to synthesize compounds, obtaining some ABO_3 double-rare earth oxides [3]. Around the synthesizing products the solid state reactions between rare earth oxides were investigated [4,5], but it is few to study the reaction process directly by using dynamic measurement methods. In this paper the dynamic measurement method was employed to investigate the chemical reaction, expecting to understand the synthesis process of $CeTbO_3$ compound through the dynamic information coming from reaction process.

EXPERIMENTAL

The CeO_2, Tb_4O_7, mixture of ($4CeO_2+Tb_4O_7$) and $CeTbO_3$ compound prepared before were used as starting materials for high pressure experiments. The in situ resistance was measured on the 1.97MN (200 ton) Bridgman press [6]. At first the pressure rose to 0.5GPa, then the temperature increased gradually and the resistances at some constant temperatures were measured. After high pressure experiment, the above samples were tested by X-ray diffraction and X-ray photoelectron spectrum methods as a additional evidence.

RESULTS AND DISCUSSIONS

The resistance-temperature variation showed that under the pressure of 0.5GPa, for the cases of $CeTbO_3$ and CeO_2, they have a semiconducting characteristic and exhibit a higher structural stability, however, for the Tb_4O_7 and the mixture, they are different, there appear the up-and-down changes in resistance above 600℃, predicting the change of inner electronic state. The resistance-temperature curves for the mixture of $(CeO_2+Tb_4O_7)$ with 4:1 mole ratio are shown in Fig. 1.

The experimental results suggest that the irregular resistance change in the system of mixture above 600℃ may be considered coming from Tb_4O_7. The Tb_4O_7 has a defect fluorite structure in which Tb^{3+}, Tb^{4+} ions are about 50% respectively, forming some oxygen deficiencies. Therefore the carrier should consist of intrinsic carriers and anion deficiencies, but the latter one may be the predominant conductivity mechanism at high temperature. When one Tb^{4+} transits to Tb^{3+}, there occur 0.5 oxygen deficiencies due to the condition of electrical neutrality. If the small amount oxygen deficiencies produced by the pressing are ignored, the contribution to conductivity of the sample comes from the intrinsic carriers and the innate oxygen deficiencies at the initial stage of increasing temperature. As increasing temperature, a certain amount of new producing oxygen deficiencies will take part in conducting, but they are not large. It is only close to the transition temperature, a large number of deficiencies would be produced and they influence seriously on the conductivity. The present experimental results, the resistance in the mixture and Tb_4O_7 showing up-and-down change above 600℃, may be supposed as the beginning of $Tb^{4+}\rightarrow Tb^{3+}$, the transition temperature is about 600℃. At this temperature a great deal of Tb^{4+} transit to Tb^{3+}, resulting in abrupt increase in oxygen deficiency. If maintaining the temperature oxygen deficiencies would increase as time passing until the saturate value. The new producing deficiencies are in disorder state because the constant temperature and pressure, and no contribution to the conductivity but increasing the scattering effect on the intrinsic carriers (point defect scattering). At the same time the producing of deficiencies also decreases the concentration of intrinsic carrier. Therefore the conductivity will be lowered than before, i.e., the resistance increases as time passing at a certain temperature. When further increasing temperature the deficiencies produced before become more active and partly take part in conducting, which make the resistance decrease again as increasing temperature. In concluding, it may explain the up-and-down change of resistance-temperature curves for the increasing temperature process in Fig. 1, and similarly for the decreasing temperature process.

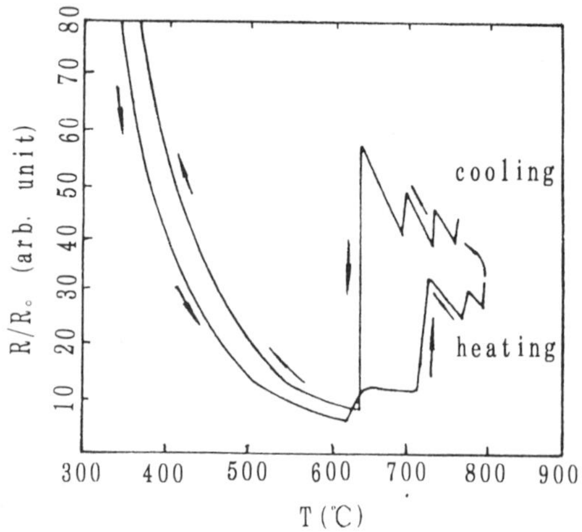

Figure 1. Resistance-temperature curve of $(4CeO_2 + Tb_4O_7)$ mixture under 0.5GPa (the interval of up-and-down change is related to the maintaining temperature time)

Referring the resistance-temperature variation in the products of mixture under 0.5GPa the samples prepared under 0.5GPa, and 400℃, 650℃, and 800℃ are selected to be checked by X-ray diffraction and X-ray photoelectron spectrum methods as an additional experiment. The X-ray diffraction spectra are shown in Fig. 2, exhibiting change in the

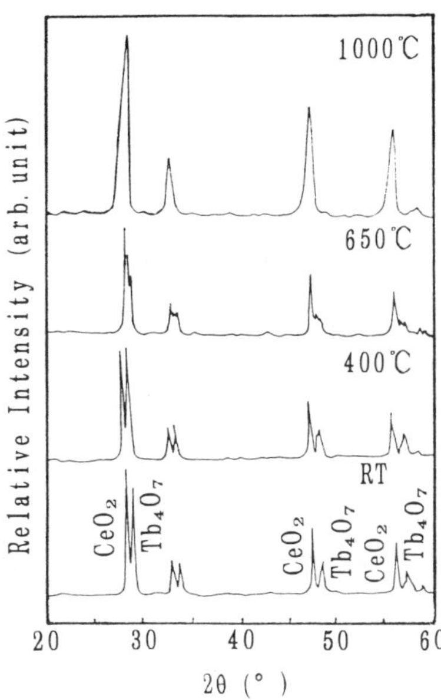

Figure 2. X-ray diffraction spectra of ($4CeO_2+Tb_4O_7$) mixture treated at different temperatures (p=0.5GPa)

diffraction patterns as increasing temperature. At room temperature it is a simple superposition of CeO_2 and Tb_4O_7 diffraction peaks, and at 400℃ there is no obvious change here. But at 650℃ the peaks corresponding to Tb_4O_7 take place splitting, forming fluorite phase (F), cubic phase (C) and only a little monoclinic phase (B) [4]. Here C phase is $TbO_{1.5+X}$, B phase Tb_2O_3, they are all resulted from the transition of $Tb^{4+} \rightarrow Tb^{3+}$. At 1000℃, a single phase of fluorite structure $CeTbO_3$ occurs. The Tb_{4d} photoelectron spectra in the samples prepared under 0.5GPa and 400℃, 650℃, 738℃, 800℃, 1185℃ are shown in Fig. 3. As increasing temperature the intensity in Tb_{4d} photoelectron spectra peaking at 155ev gradually decreases until disappearing. The characteristic

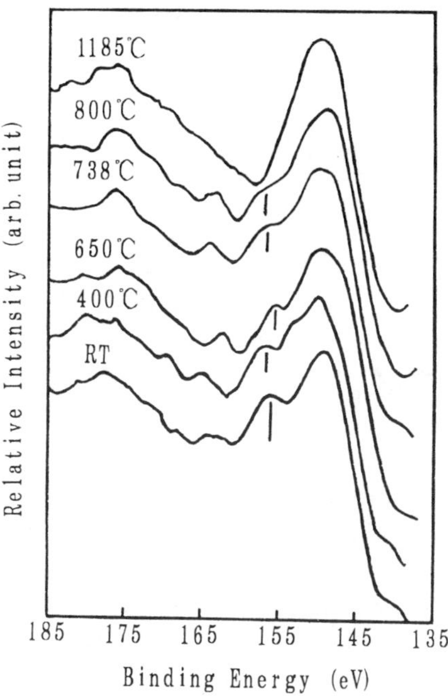

Figure 3. Tb4d X-ray photoelectron spectra of ($4CeO_2+Tb_4O_7$) mixture treated at different temperatures (p=0.5GPa)

levels of Tb^{3+} and Tb^{4+} in compounds have been determined to be 149.45 and 156.20ev respectively, the approximate relationship between the intensity ratio, I, of the higher binding energy peak to the lower one and the content of Tb^{4+}/Tb, Z, is $I=-0.98Z^2+2.15Z$ ($0 \leqslant Z \leqslant 1$) [7]. According to Fig. 3, the intensity I for these samples are obtained, then the Z values of Tb^{4+}/Tb can be calculated by the above relationship, they are listed in Table 1. It can be seen that the Tb^{3+} content increases as increasiing temperature, meaning the occurrence of $Tb^{4+} \rightarrow Tb^{3+}$ under high pressure. As increasing temperature to 650℃, the Tb^{3+} content increases obviously, closing to 1185℃ the Tb ions in compounds are basically in Tb^{3+}.

The X-ray diffraction and X-ray photoelectron spectra are well agreement with the in

Table 1. The XPS data for the samples prepared under 0.5GPa and different temperatures

sample	I	Z(Tb^{4+}/Tb)	Tb^{3+}
RT	0.82	0.49	0.51
400℃	0.82	0.49	0.51
650 ℃	0.78	0.46	0.54
738 ℃	0.78	0.46	0.54
800℃	0.73	0.42	0.58
1185℃	0	0	1.0

RT: room temperature

situ resistance measuring results. So it may be suggested that the compound $CeTbO_3$ forms due to the transition of Tb^{4+} to Tb^{3+} in the mixture, which makes the fluorite Tb_4O_7 be gradually disintegrated and the Tb^{3+} ions enter the perfect fluorite structure of CeO_2, finally the $CeTbO_3$ compound with fluorite structure be synthesized. The present results showed that the in situ resistance measurement may be an available method to study the reaction process concerning valence fluctuation and charge transference.

ACKNOWLEDGMENTS

This work has been supported by the National Natural Science Foundation of China and the Science Foundation of National Education Committee of China.

REFERENCES

[1] S. J. Schneider and R. S. Roth, *J. Res. NBS.*, 64A, pp. 317-332 (1960).
[2] S. J. Schneider, R. S. Roth and J. L. Waring, *J. Res. NBS.*, 65A(4), pp. 345-374 (1961)
[3] Su Wenhui, Wu Daiming, Li Xiaoyuan and Ma Xianfeng, *Physica*, 139&140B, pp. 658-660 (1986).
[4] Zhou Jianshi and Su Wenhui, *Chinese J. Rare Earth Soc.*, 6 (2), pp. 57-60 (1988).
[5] Su Wenhui, Wu Daiming, Ma Xianfeng and Qian Zhengnan, *Physica*, 139&140B, pp. 661-663 (1986).
[6] Liu Hongjian, Su Wenhui, Qian Zhengnan, Wang Yifeng, Wu Daiming and Cui Shuojing, *Chinese J. High Pressure Physics*, 2(2), pp. 146-152(1988).
[7] Li Liping, Wei Quan, Wang Yifeng, Liu Hongjian and Su Wenhui, *Chemical J. Chinese Universities*, 13 (2), pp. 217-220 (1992).

SHOCK SYNTHESIS OF NIOBIUM SILICIDES

L. H. Yu, W. J. Nellis+, M. A. Meyers, and K. S. Vecchio
University of California, San Diego
La Jolla, California, 92093-0411
+Lawrence Livermore National Laboratory
Livermore, California, 94550

Elemental powder mixtures with two sizes (<5 µm and 15-45 µm) were shock compressed at 20, 46, and 70 GPa using a 20 mm-bore two-stage gun. Specimens were 10 mm in diameter and 0.5 mm thick. The powders were contained in a Cu capsule and impacted by a Cu projectile. The results for small <5 µm powder particles indicate that the experiments produced unreacted, partially reacted, and fully reacted $NbSi_2$, respectively, as predicted. Results for the larger 15-45 µm particles at 46 GPa indicate that reactions to form $NbSi_2$ did not occur during shock compression. This observation is consistent with the expectation that larger powder particles require more time to react. All the micrographs indicate that the powders are relatively mobile in the capsule and that some reactions are caused by plastic deformation after release of the shock.

INTRODUCTION

Following the first report by Batsanov, Deribas, and co-workers [1], a considerable amount of activity has taken place in the field of shock-induced chemical reactions. Recently, Vecchio *et al.* [2] and Meyers *et al.* [3] have attempted to develop a quantitative predictive understanding of shock-induced reactions in silicide systems. The results reported here represent the extension of this work. The particle size was varied in order to assess its effect on reaction kinetics.

EXPERIMENTAL TECHNIQUES

The niobium and silicon powders were obtained from CERAC and had sizes smaller than 44 µm (-325 mesh). The powders were separated in a vibrating microsieve, yielding two size ranges: <5 µm and 15-44 µm. The powders were mixed in the stoichiometric proportion $NbSi_2$ (twice the atomic composition for Si vs. for Nb). The powders were encapsulated in the LLNL capsule configuration shown in Figure 1(a) using a laser ruler, a microbalance, and a mechanical powder-tapping device. In this way, the initial specimen powder density (60% of theoretical) was obtained reproducibly in the specimens. The capsule diameter is 10 mm and thickness is 0.5 mm; this ensures a shock geometry that is close to one-dimensional (planar front propagating through powder) in contrast to the earlier experiments [2-4], in which the capsule geometry was such that two-dimensional effects dominated. Each Cu capsule was embedded in a steel recovery fixture and mounted in the target chamber of the 20 mm-bore two-stage gas gun at LLNL. The capsule recovery fixture assembly was impacted by copper flyer plate mounted in a plastic sabot [5, 6]. Three impact velocities of 0.96, 1.92, and 2.66 km/s yield shock pressures, in copper, of 20, 46, and 70 GPa, respectively. The pressure in the specimen powder "rings up" to the impact pressure. The first pulse traveling through the porous medium generates a lower pressure in the first wave, by virtue of the shock-impedance. The three pressures were chosen specifically to achieve unreacted, partially reacted, and fully reacted $NbSi_2$ from Nb + 2Si powder mixtures, based on previous shock melting calculations for Fe powders [7], a similar transition metal, which showed that about 50 GPa are required to achieve melting. Melting and temperatures close to it in the solid state are expected to produce rapid chemical reactions. To enhance the reaction rate in this fast experiment (~0.5 µsec), small particles (<5 µm) were used. Lower reaction rates were expected for larger particles, one experiment was done with 15-45 µm particles at intermediate pressure. To obtain relatively high quench rates to "catch" the high-pressure state, a thin (0.5 mm) specimen layer was used in a Cu capsule with a high cooling rate.

RESULTS AND DISCUSSION

Three impact experiments were conducted for the < 5 µm powder, at velocities of 0.96, 1.92, and 2.66 km/s. The objective of these experiments was to determine the threshold energy for shock synthesis, a concept proposed by Krueger *et al.* [8]. The unreacted, partially reacted, and fully reacted regions are shown in Figure 1(b). As shown in Figure 1, the elemental powder mixtures were essentially unreacted, partially reacted, and fully reacted at 20, 46,and 70 GPa, respectively. These observations are made by optical inspection of material near mid-radii where undesirable late-time edge effects on axis and on the outer boundary are ignored. The larger particles at 46 GPa are essentially unreacted on shock compression.

Figure 1 shows that the capsules underwent considerable deformation with increasing pressure, with material being pushed into the periphery, and by the formation of a central jet along the axis of the disk. On the periphery, the material was pushed into the threaded area of the capsule by the high hydrostatic stresses and, most probably, pressure gradients due to shock wave convergence along the axis of the disk. Figure 1(b) shows that there is a strong preference for reaction in the regions where the material underwent intense late-time plastic deformation (periphery and central axis) on release. Whereas the material was virtually unreacted at the 0.96 km/s impact, it was fully reacted after 2.66 km/s impact. Figure 1(b) does not show any marked effect of particle size at the 1.9 km/s impact velocity. The only difference is that the central jet is partially reacted for the large particles. Scanning electron microscopy observations show the observed differences.

Figure 2 shows unreacted (a) and trace amounts of partially reacted (b) regions from the

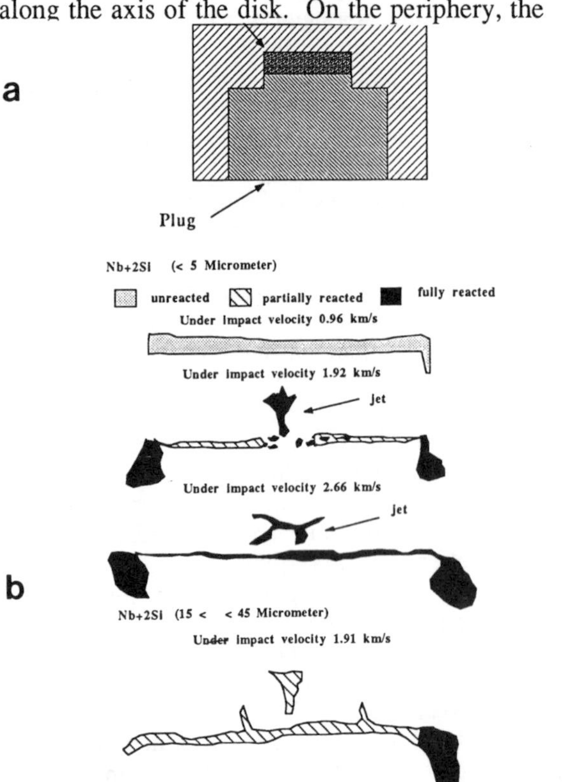

Figure 1(a). Capsule used for shock recovery experiments in the LLNL 6.5-meter-long 2-stage gas gun. (b). Unreacted, partially reacted, and fully reacted regions for capsules; notice late time formations of central jet and lateral extrusions, probably caused on release.

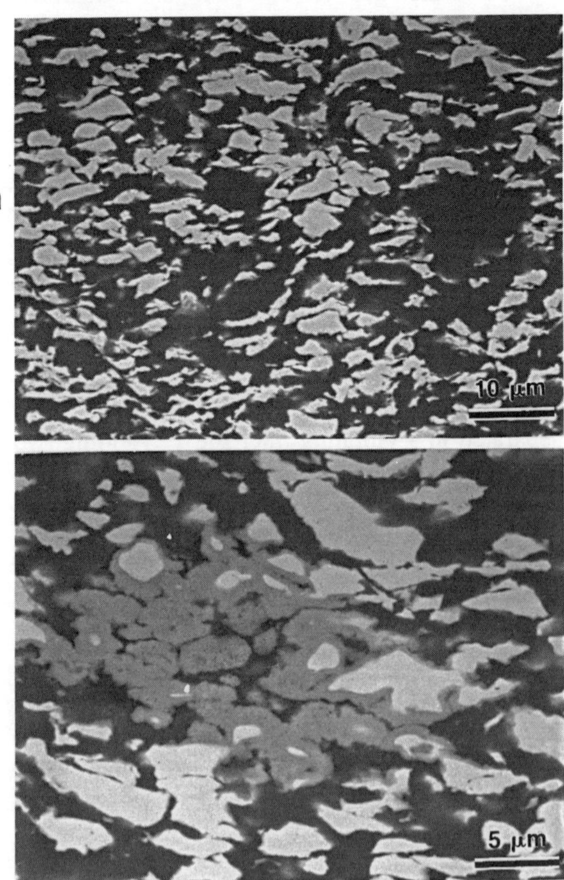

Figure 2. Fine (<5 μm) powder impacted at 0.96 km/s; (a) unreacted area; (b) partially reacted area (possibly, after shock-wave passage).

fine powder impacted at 0.96 km/s. The partially reacted region shown in Figure 2(b) represents only trace amounts. It is probable that the partial reaction occurred after shock-wave passage, through diffusive processes. As the impact velocity is increased to 1.92 km/s, the material (fine powder) was either partially or fully reacted. The periphery and core were fully reacted, and the imtermediate region was partially reacted, as can be seen from Figure 1(b). The fully reacted region probably caused by release at late time showed profuse evidence of full-scale melting and some capsule melting (Figure 3(a) and (c)). Dendritic growth is evident in Figure 3(c) showing the edge of the capsule, while the center shows particulate $NbSi_2$ in (probably) a Si matrix. The partially-reacted region (Figure 3(b)) shows $NbSi_2$ spherules (gray) in the silicon matrix and along the Nb-Si interfaces. This mechanism of reaction is shown in Figure 4 [2, 3]. Reaction is initiated at the Nb (solid)-Si (liquid) interface (a). After it has proceeded to a certain extent (c), surface (interfacial) forces become dominant, and the liquid reaction product agglomerates, forming spherules (d). These spherules then solidify and are extracted from the interface by the motion of the liquid silicon or by forces exerted by the next generation of spherules that is being formed.

At 2.66 km/s impact velocity, the fine powder is fully reacted, with the morphology of the product consisting of a mixture of particulate silicides (center) and dendritic growth (corners).

The 15-45 μm powder exhibited, at the impact velocity of 1.91 km/s, features similar to the <5 μm powder (see Figure 5). The principal difference is the larger Nb particles; see Figures 5(a) and 3(b). The total Nb-Si interface available for reaction is greater for the <5 μm powder, aiding the reaction. The kinetics are accelerated for the small powder size. In the fully reacted region (periphery), massive Nb particles can still be seen for the 15-45 μm powders (Figure 5(b)), whereas they are totally consumed for the <5 μm powder (Figure 3(c)).

An additional surprising effect was established. Dremin and Breusov [9] and Al'tshuler [10] suggested that local heating of material in zones of intense slip could influence the kinetics of reaction, and Yu [11] and Shang

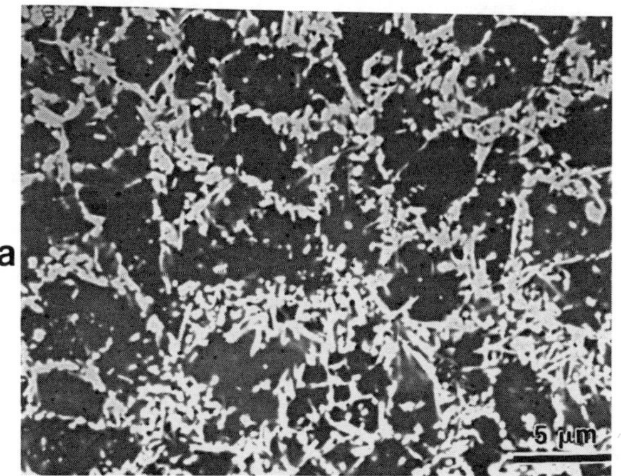

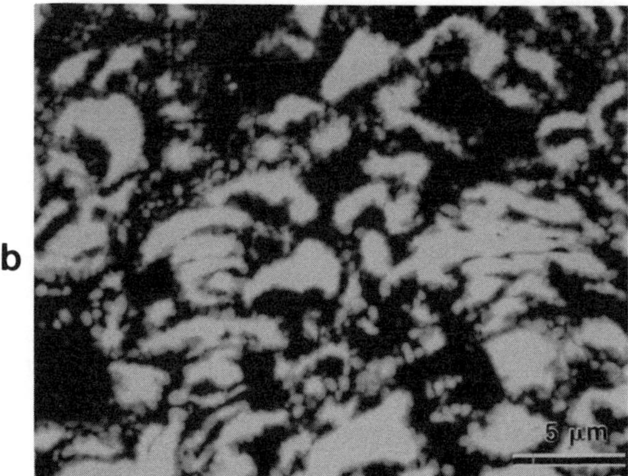

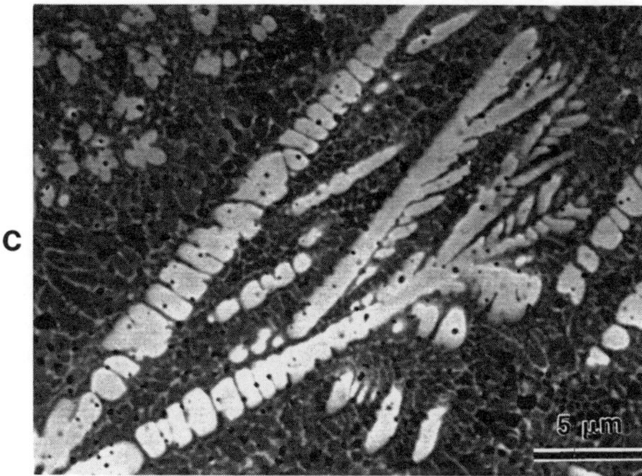

Figure 3. Fine (<5 μm) powder impacted at 1.91 km/s; (a) fully reacted area in center region; (b) partially reacted area; (c) fully reacted area from extruded peripheral region.

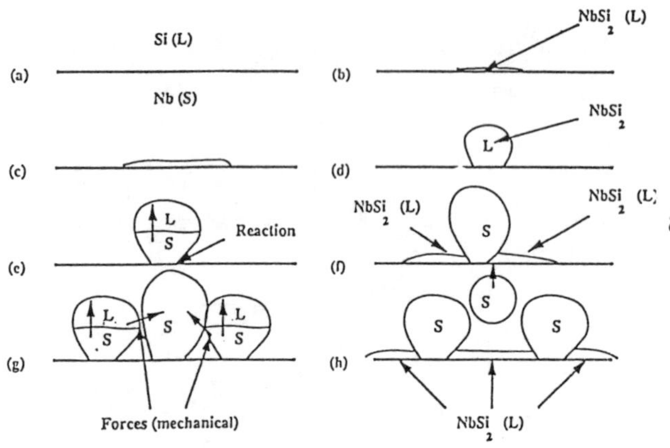

Figure 4. Idealized representation of propagation of reaction at Si-Nb interface (Nb-solid; Si-liquid).

[12] observed a reaction enhancement in regions of localized shear. The results reported herein strongly suggest that shear strains play an important role in shock-induced chemical reactions, confirming suggestions [9, 10] and observations [11, 12]. The peripheral and central regions experienced more extreme reaction because the additional plastic strains on release at late time. The energy deposited into the powders by the shock can be expressed as $E_1=1/2\ P(V_{00}-V)$, whereas the plastic deformation energy can be taken as $E_2=\tau\gamma$, where τ and γ are shear stress and strain. The total energy contributing to initiation of reaction is $E_1 + E_2$. Thus, E_2 can contribute significantly to process.

Work at LLNL was performed under the auspices of USDOE under contract W-7405-Eng-48 with support from the LLNL branch of the UC Institute of Geophysics and Planetary Physics; work at UCSD was supported by NSF grant DMR-91-5835R1.

REFERENCES

1. S. S. Batsanov, A. A. Deribas, E. V. Dulepov, M. G. Ermakov, V. M. Kudinov, *Comb. Expl. Shock Waves USSR* **1**, p. 47 (1965).
2. K. S. Vecchio, L.-H. Yu, and M. A. Meyers, *Acta Met. et Mat.*, in press (1993).
3. M. A. Meyers, L.-H. Yu, and K. S. Vecchio, *Acta Met. et Mat.*, in press (1993).
4. L. H. Yu and M. A. Meyers, *J. Matl. Sci.*, **26**, p. 601 (1991).
5. C. L. Seaman, E. A. Early, M. B. Maple, W. J. Nellis, J. B. Holt, M. Kamegai, and G. S. Smith, in *Shock Compression in Condensed Matter - 1989*, Elsevier, 1990.

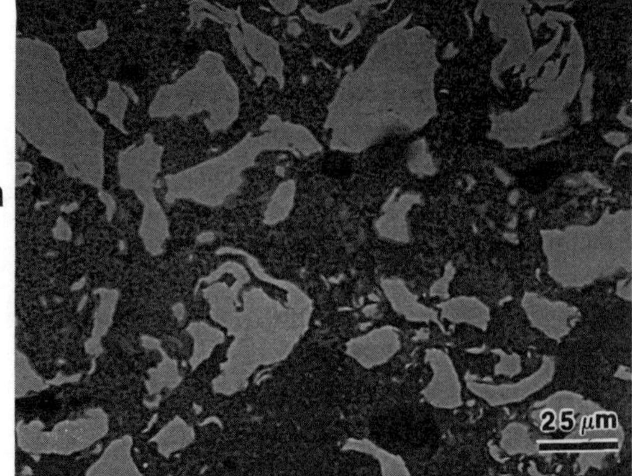

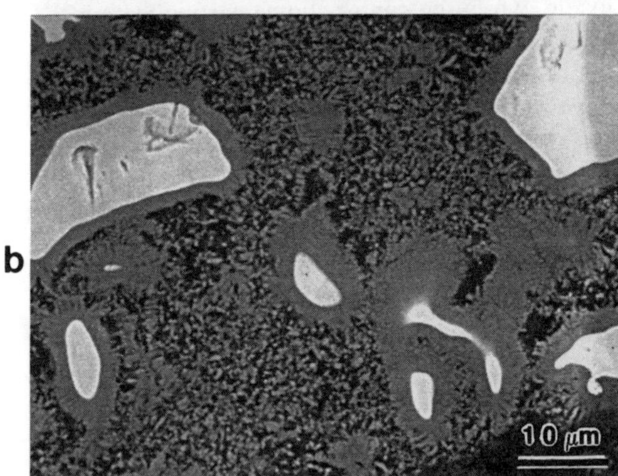

Figure 5. Coarse (5-44 µm) powder impacted at 1.91 km/s; (a) partially reacted area; (b) fully reacted area showing remnants of Nb particles.

6. A. J. Gratz, W. J. Nellis, J. M. Christie, W. Brocious, J. Swegle, and P. Cordier, *Phys. and Chem. of Min.*, **19**, p. 267 (1992).
7. W. J. Nellis, W. H. Gourdin, and M. B. Maple, in *Shock Waves in Condensed Matter*, Elsevier, 1987.
8. B.R. Krueger, A. H. Mutz, and T. Vreeland, Jr., *J. Appl. Phys.* **70**, p. 5362 (1991).
9. A. N. Dremin and O. N. Breusov, *Russian Chem. Rev.* **37**, p. 392 (1968).
10. L. V. Al'tshuler, *J. Appl. Mech. Tech. Phys.* **19**, p. 496 (1978).
11. L. H. Yu, Ph.D. Thesis, NMIMT (1992).
12. S. S. Shang, Ph.D. Thesis, UCSD (1992).

CONSOLIDATION OF TANTALUM NITRIDE SYSTEM POWDERS BY SHOCK COMPRESSION

Suguru TASHIRO, Tsutomu MASHIMO and Minoru NISHIDA
High Energy Rate Laboratory
Kumamoto University
Kumamoto 860, Japan

Shock compression recovery experiments were performed on the CoSn-type tantalum nitride (TaN) system powders to prepare the B1-type TaN system bulk bodies through the shock-induced CoSn-B1 phase transition. The starting materials were pure TaN powder and TaN-Al, TaN-TiN, TaN-TaC system mixture powders. As a result, almost single phase B1-type tantalum nitride bulk bodies with good stoichometric composition were prepared by shock compression. The pure tantalum nitride bulk bodies showed the higher hardnesses than the sintered CoSn-type one by a static pressure. The TaN-Al, TaN-TiN and TaN-TaC system bulk bodies with good dispersion were also prepared by shock compression.

INTRODUCTION

B1-type tantalum nitride is expected to have high hardness and superconductive property, while the stable phase of tantalum nitride is a hexagonal structure (CoSn-type) at the standard condition. [1] The B1-type phase tantalum nitride materials have been, so far, synthesized by means of high pressure, [2] high temperature nitrogen atmosphere, [3] self-propagating high temperature synthesis (combustion synthesis), [4] plasma jet synthesis. [5] However, the materials prepared by these methods were mixtures with other compounds such as Ta N or nonstoichometric B1-type phase. [2-5] In addition, by the second to forth methods, bulk materials of the B1-type phase can not be prepared. Recently, we succeeded in the synthesis of the almost single phase B1-type tantalum nitride with stoichometric composition by shock compression. [6]

In order to examine the mechanical and electrical properties, or to realized the industrial uses, the bulk body of B1-type phase is indispensable. In this study, the shock-compression recovery experiments of the pure CoSn-type tantalum nitride powder and TaN-Al, TaN-TiN, TaN-TaC system mixture powders were performed to prepare the B1-type tantalum nitride system bulk bodies. The recovered samples were examined by means of the X-ray powder diffraction (XRD), the instrumental chemical analysis and Vickers microhardness measurements.

EXPERIMENTAL PROCEDURE

Powder sample of CoSn-type phase tantalum nitride was provided by Japan New Metals Co., Ltd. The sample particle has a shape of pole-like or plate-like of about 1 μm in length and 0.2 μm in width. The starting material was confirmed to consist of the CoSn-type phase, whose lattice parameters were determined to be a_0=0.51923+(1) nm and c_0=0.29083+(1) nm by the XRD method. [6] The contents of nitrogen (N), oxygen (O) and carbon (C) of the samples were measured to be 6.63, 0.58 and 0.35 wt%, respectively, by the instrumental chemical analyses. Small amount of impurities were Si, Nb, Fe, Ti, Ni, etc. In addition, the weak X-ray diffraction lines (for the (111), (200) and (220) planes) of the cubic tantalum carbide (TaC) were detected, while the other carbide (TaC) were detected, while the other carbides or oxides could not be detected. It was assumed that oxygen was contained not as bulk tantalum oxides, but as admolecules or surface reaction layers. Considering the existense of tantalum carbide (TaC), the chemical formula of the starting material was estimated to be $TaN_{0.97-1.00}$.

For the mixture powder sample, the CoSn-type tantalum nitride powder were mixed with Al powder (99.99% purity, Rare Metallic Co., Ltd.), TiN powder (99.9% purity, CEREX Co., Ltd.) or TaC powders (Mitsui Metal Mining Co., Ltd.), respectively using a planetary ball mill (P-7) of Fritsh Co., Ltd. or an agate mortar, in an air atmosphere. The mole ratio of TaN:Al, TaN:TiN and TaN:TaC were 10:1, 1:1 and 1:1, respectively. In the treatment by using the ball mill, 5 gm of the powder specimen was contained into the mill pot with 4 ml ethanol. The pure tantalum nitride powder was not treated by the ball mill.

Shock compression recovery experiments were conducted using a powder gun. [7-9] The pure TaN powder or the TaN-Al, TaN-TiN, TaN-TaC system powder was enclosed in an iron capsule (SS-41) or stainless steel capsule (SUS-405) of about 12 mm inside diameter and 5 mm inside height. The porosities of these samples were about 70 %. Shock loading was carried out by impacting the sample capsule with a tungsten flat impact plate of 2 mm in thickness, which was accelerated to 1.2-1.5 km/s. For the pure tantalum nitride powder, one sample was shock-loaded twice (double shock compression).

The recovered capsules were carefully peeled out on the lathe. The XRD measurements were carried out by using Cu-Kα radiation with a Rigaku Goniometer (RAD-1B). Instrumental chemical analysis of N, O and C contents were carried out by the innert-gas fusion thermal conductivity method and the combustion in oxygen nondispersive infrared absorption method each with TC-436, WR-112 of LECO Corp. The measurement error for N, O and C contents were estimated to be less than 0.07, 0.02 and 0.01 wt%, respectively, by the experiments using the Si_3N_4 and TiN standard samples. The hardness measurments were carried out with a Vickers type diamond pyramid indenter for 30 sec at a load of 100 g using the microhardness tester, type-M of Shimadzu Co., Ltd. The measurements of 2-3 times were performed for each sample.

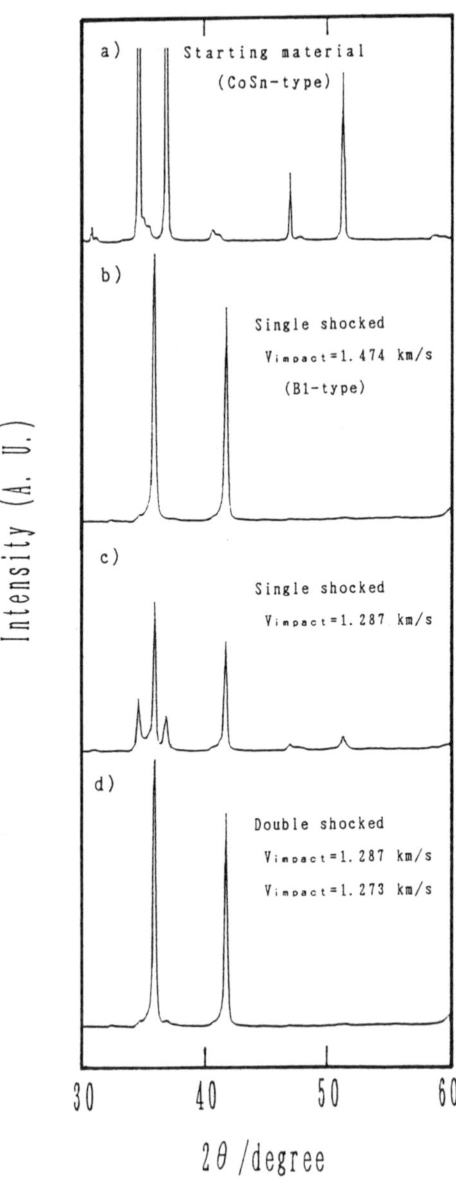

Figure 1. Powder XRD patterns of the starting material and the shock-loaded samples.

RESULTS AND DISCUSSION

Figure 1 showed the XRD patterns of the starting material (a), the recovered samples from the shock compression with the impact velocity of 1.474 km/s (b) and 1.287 km/s (c), and one (d) from the double shock compressions with the impact velocity of c sample. The XRD pattern of the single shock-loaded sample with the impact velocity of 1.273 km/s (c) showed the existence of two phases, which were identified as B1-type phase (about 70 wt%) and CoSn-type phase (about 30 wt%). But, the XRD patteren of the double shock-loaded sample (d) showed the existence of only B1-type phase. The XRD patterns of the single shock-loaded sample with the impact velocity of 1.474 km/s (b) and the double shock-loaded sample (d) consisted of almost single phase of B1-type tantalum nitride.

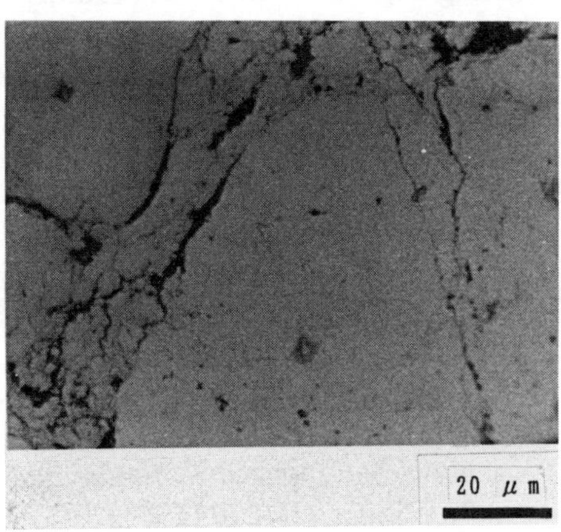

Figure 2. Optical photograph of the polished surface of the double shock-loaded sample (d).

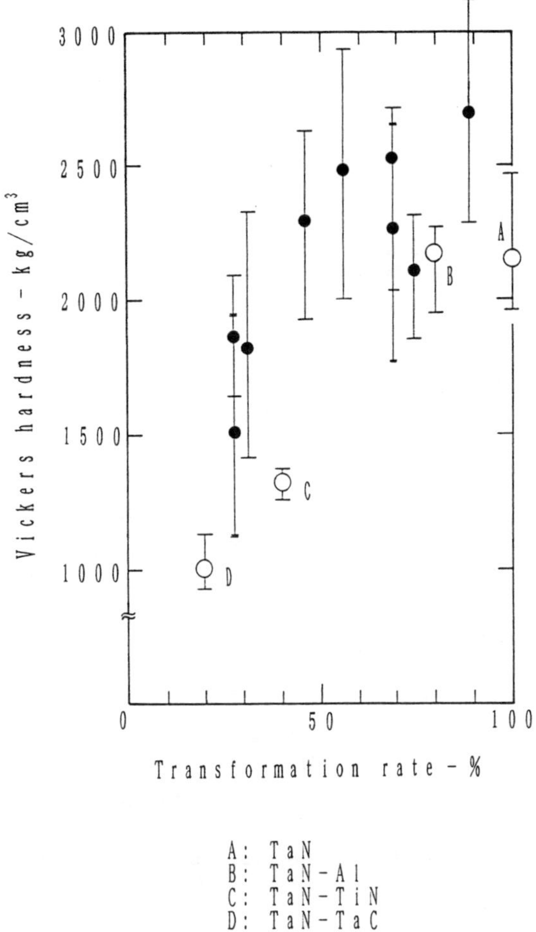

Figure 3. Vickers microhardness results versus the transformastion rate of the B1-type tantalum nitride.

By the chemical analysis results, the contents of N, O and C of the pure tantalum nitride sample recovered from the single shock compression with the impact velocity of 1.474 km/s (b) or one from the double shock compressions (d) were 6.60, 0.68 and 0.34 wt%, or 6.57, 1.88 and 0.39 wt%, respectively. The nitrogen contents of the starting material and the recovered ones were almost the same. The carbon content also did not change, whose amounts were consistent with those of cubic TaC estimated by the XRD method. However, the oxygen content slightly increased, but the tantalum oxides could not be detected by the XRD method. This may be due to adsorbed oxygen as admolecules or surface reaction layers during or after shock compression. Considering the existence of TaC, the chemical formula of the shock synthesized B1-type one ((b) and (d)) was estimated to be $TaN_{0.98}$ [6] and $TaN_{1.00}$, respectively. As a result, it was assumed that the shock consolidated B1-type phase samples maintained good stoichometry.

The bulk body samples of the pure tantalum nitride with small cracks were recovered from shock compression. Figure 2 shows an optical photograph of the polished surface of the pure tantalum nitride bulk body recovered from the double shock compressions (d). In the figure, the traces of square by the Vickers hardness measurements can be seen. Figure 3 shows the hardness measurement versus the transformation rate of the B1-type phases. The transformation rates were estimated by the intensities of the XRD peaks of the CoSn-type and B1-type phases. The hardness increased with the transformation rate by about two times. This suggested that the B1-type phase had much higher hardness value than the CoSn-type one. It is expected that if the well sintered B1-type phase bulk body is prepared, very high hard material be realized.

On the other hand, the TaN-Al, TaN-TiN and TaN-TaC system bulk bodies were also prepared by shock compression. Particularly, the TaN-Al system bulk body prepared by shock compression showed a good consolidated feature, and had the high hardness. The transformation rate of the sample was about 80%, when the porosity was 70% and the impact velocity was 1.287 km/s. However, the shock consolidated TaN-TiN and TaN-TaC system bulk bodies showed many cracks, and had the lower hardnesses. The transformation rates of B1-type phase of these samples were both very low, although the dispersion state of TiN or TaC seems to be homogeneous. The further experiments are now under study on these mixture systems.

ACKNOWLEDGMERNTS

The authors would like to thank Prof. T. Sata of Kumamoto Institute of Technology for his support in the XRD analyses, and also Mr. T. Egashira for his experimental efforts. They would like to acknowlegdge Toshiba Tungaloy Co. Ltd. and Japan New Metals Co. Ltd. for their experimental supports. They would also like to acknowlegdge the Matsuda Foundation's Research Grant. for the financial support.

REFERENCE

[1] N. Terao, Jpn. J. Appl. Phys. 10, pp. 248-259 (1971).

[2] L.G. Boiko and S.V. Popova, JETP Lett. 12, pp. 70-71 (1970).

[3] R. Kieffer, P. Ettmayer, M. Freudhofmeier and J. Gatterer, Monatsche. Chem. 102, pp. 483-489 (1971).

[4] V.F. Petrunin, N.I. Sorokin, I.P. Borovinskaya and A.N. Pityulin; Trans. Poroshkovaya Metallurgina, No. 3, pp. 62-64 (1980).

[5] O. Matsumoto, E. Hayashi and Y. Kanzaki, J. Less. Common Met. 60, pp. 147-149 (1978).

[6] T. Mashimo, S. Tashiro, T. Toya, M. Nishida, H. Yamazaki, S. Yamaya, K. Oh-ishi and Y. Syono, J. Mater. Sci. 28, pp. 3439-3443 (1993).

[7] A. Nakamura, T. Mashimo, M. Nishida and. S. Matsuzaki, "Shock-compression recovery experiments using the keyed-powder gun," in Proc. 1989 National Symp. on Shock Wave, 1990, pp. 145-153.

[8] T. Mashimo, S. Ozaki and K. Nagayama, Rev. Sci. Instr. 55, pp. 226-230 (1984).

[9] T. Mashimo, "Measurement facililities combined with keyed-powder gun for impact-shock study of solids, " in Proc. 1988 National Symp. on Shock Wave, 1989, pp. 105-118.

MECHANISTIC STUDY OF SHOCK-INDUCED SOLID-STATE CHEMISTRY IN TI- AND TA-BASED CARBIDE AND BORIDE SYSTEMS

V. S. Joshi*, N. N. Thadhani, R. A. Graham*****

* Energetic Materials Research and Testing Center, New Mexico Tech, Socorro, NM 87801, USA
** School of Materials Science and Engineering, Georgia Institute of Technology, Atlanta, GA 30332, USA
*** Advanced Materials Physics Department, Sandia National Laboratories, Albuquerque, NM 87125, USA

Shock chemistry experiments were performed on mixtures of Ti-C, Ti-B, Ta-C and Ta-B powders, to study the effect of density differential amongst the powder mixture constituents, in all systems with otherwise very high heats of reaction. The experiments were performed at a wide range of shock conditions, using the Sandia Bear fixtures and the CETR/Sawaoka 12-capsule plate-impact system, to establish the reaction threshold for respective systems. It was observed that the density differential between the constituents, and the heat of reaction do not significantly affect the reaction threshold. Instead, the propensity for reaction increases with increasing degree of mixing of constituents either by simultaneous deformation or fracture. In this paper we present the microscopic and macroscopic characteristics of the shock compressed compacts to delineate the mechanistic processes influencing shock-induced chemical reactions in Ti- and Ta-based carbide and boride forming powder mixtures.

INTRODUCTION

The conceptual model of shock-induced chemical reactions proposed by Graham,[1] identified the important role of *configuration change* and *mixing* between reactants prior to reaction initiation. Shock-compression of powders changes the configuration of reactants and produces a highly activated state with mechanically altered inter-material contacts and intimate mixing. The configuration of reactant powders at the inception of reaction, therefore, depends on their morphological characteristics, initial porosity, volumetric ratio, shock-compression conditions, as well as the ability of the powders to plastically deform, flow and mix with each other. For example, prior work[2] on intermetallic forming Ni-Al powder mixtures has shown that flaky morphology Ni powders deform and flow more readily than spherical Ni particles. A finer recrystallized structure of the Ni flakes, and their deformation via additional modes (bending and torsion), causes them to deform more extensively than spherical Ni powders. Thus, the configuration produced with flaky morphology powders exhibit a greater propensity for chemical reaction, than that produced with spherical powders.

Configuration change and mixing during shock-compression are also affected by differences in the density of reactants. Density differences can result in a mixture having (on a volumetric scale) an abundance of heavier reactant if the mixture is prepared on an atomic stoichiometry basis. In addition, the impedance mismatch between reactants, can also result in a dissimilar deformation behavior. The purpose of the present study, was to investigate the influence of density differential between reactants in Ti- and Ta-based carbide and boride forming powder mixtures. These refractory metal systems include reactants with high melting temperature and reactions that are highly exothermic. The density difference between Ta and C, and Ta and B, is greater than that between Ti and C, and Ti and B; however, the heat of reaction of Ti systems is greater than that of Ta systems, and likewise the heat of reaction for formation of borides is greater than that of carbides (see Table 1).

EXPERIMENTAL PROCEDURE

Mixtures of equiaxed (-325 mesh) powders of Ti and Ta with graphitic C and crystalline B were prepared with equiatomic as well as equivolumetric reactant distributions.

Table 1. Properties of reactants and products.[3]

	Ti	Ta	B	C	TiC	TaC	TiB_2	TaB_2
Density (gm/cm^3)	4.54	16.65	2.34	2.26	4.93	14.47	4.52	12.6
Melt Temp (°C)	1670	2996	2079	3652*	3067	3985	3225	3037
ΔH_R** (KJ/gm)					-3.06	-0.74	-4.65	-1.03
T_R** (°C)					2937	2423	2917	2997

* Sublimation
** For compounds with highest value

In a few cases, amorphous carbon and fine amorphous boron were also used. Mixing of the powder was performed using a mechanical V-shaped blender in a 6-8 hour mixing cycle. The respective powder mixtures were packed in capsules with packing densities in the range of 45% -55% theoretical density.

The recovery experiments were conducted over a range of shock-compression conditions, using the Sandia Momma Bear A fixture with Comp B explosive (22 GPa peak pressure)[4] and the 12-capsule CETR/Sawaoka system at impact velocity of 0.9 km/s (peak pressure 60-100 GPa).[5] The shock-compressed samples were recovered by peeling the capsules. Optical and scanning electron microscopy were used to characterize the polished cross-sectional surfaces of the compacts.

The respective *focus* (axial extreme pressure), *edge* (peripheral low-pressure high-temperature), and *bulk* (moderate-pressure low temperature) regions were carefully distinguished and analyzed separately. For each of these areas *regions of reaction* and *no-reaction* were identified based on the microstructural contrast; presence of voids or porosity in regions of otherwise uniform contrast indicate occurrence of reaction. Due to the high heat of reaction associated with carbide/boride systems, the temperature rise due to reaction exceeds the melting point of products, resulting in a microstructure characteristic of melted and resolidified material (Figure 1). Analysis of *unreacted* regions was performed with great detail to observe features of deformation, flow, and mixing, produced in the shock-compressed configuration at the conditions below the threshold of reaction initiation. The shock-compressed unreacted configuration of respective *focus, edge* and *bulk* regions of individual samples were compared amongst themselves as well as with samples of the other carbide/boride systems, to establish the effect of shock conditions and to obtain reaction thresholds for each of the respective systems. The results of this comparative analysis is presented and discussed in the following sections.

RESULTS

Table 2 provides details of experimental conditions, including powder characteristics, mixture ratios, powder packing densities and generalized summary of microstructural observations evaluating regions of *reaction* and *no-reaction* in respective samples. Based on this generalized analysis,[6] the following reaction threshold conditions were inferred:

(a) Ti and C (graphite) system has the highest reaction threshold, with reaction occurring only in focus region (>60 GPa peak pressure) of CETR/Sawaoka capsules;
(b) Ta and C (graphite) system show partial reaction in focus and bulk regions (≈ 50 GPa peak pressure) of CETR/Sawaoka compacts;
(c) Ti and B and Ta and B systems show complete reaction in CETR/Sawaoka fixture and partial reaction in Momma Bear fixture (≈ 22 GPa);
(d) Ti and amorphous C and Ta and amorphous B show the lowest threshold conditions and undergo complete reaction even with Momma Bear fixture (<22 GPa).

Microstructure of Shock-Compressed Configuration

Typical SEM micrographs of shock-compressed, unreacted areas of Ti+C (graphite), Ta+C (graphite), Ti+B, and Ta+B compacts are shown in Figs. 2,3,4 and 5 respectively.

SEM micrograph of sample # 9207 (Ti+C) in Figure 2 shows no deformation of Ti particles, whereas graphite has deformed to fill space between the Ta particles. Similar feature is observed in compact # 10H917II (MBA-CB), where Ta particles have retained their original configuration, as shown in Figure 3. Contrast to this, both

Figure 1. Typical SEM micrographs of fully reacted region of Ta+B sample #9022-04.

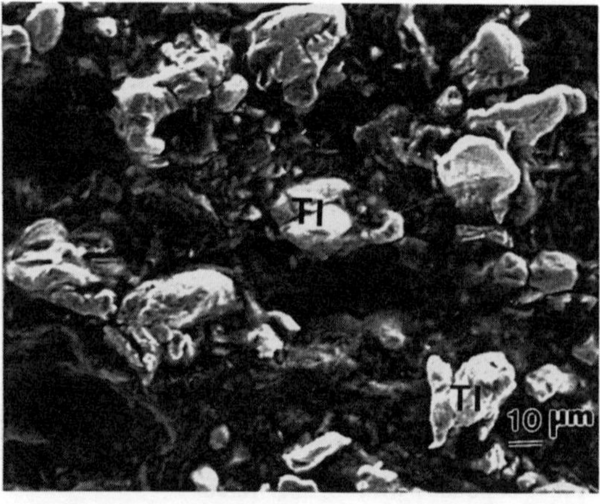

Figure 2. SEM micrograph of unreacted region of Ti+C compact #9207 (CETR-S).

Table 2. Summary of Experiments on Carbides and Borides.

Sample Number	Shock Assembly	Mixture	Atomic Ratio	Powder Morphology A	Powder Morphology B**	Packing Density	Optical Microscopy	XRD Results
901112	CETR-S	Ti-C	1:1	coarse	coarse	43	reacted (focus)	TiC, Ti, C
44H896	MBA-CB	Ti-C	1:1	coarse	coarse	45	mostly unreacted	Ti, C
9207	MBA-CB	Ti-C	1:2	coarse	coarse	45	reacted (focus)	Ti, C, TiC
9228	MBA-CB	Ti-C*	1:2	coarse	coarse	44	reacted	TiC
04H896	MBA-CB	Ti-B	1:2	coarse	submic	40	reacted (bulk)	TiB_2, Ti, B
40H906	MBA-CB	Ti-B	1:2	coarse	coarse	43	reacted (edge)	TiB_2, TiB, Ti, B
902205	CETR-S	Ta-C	1:1	coarse	coarse	55	partial reaction	TaC, Ta_2C
10H917	MBA-CB	Ta-C	1:1	coarse	coarse	50	reaction (local)	TaC, Ta, C
9208	MBA-CB	Ta-C	1:2	coarse	coarse	45	unreacted	Ta, C
9229	MBA-CB	Ta-C*	1:2	coarse	coarse	45	reacted	TaC
902204	CETR-S	Ta-B	1:2	coarse	coarse	55	reacted	TaB, TaB_2, Ta_3B_4
02H917	MBA-CB	Ta-B	1:2	coarse	coarse	44	reaction (local)	TaB, TaB_2, Ta, B

* uses amorphous carbon.
** B here refers to the second constituent.

Ti and Ta particles in boride systems have deformed and filled the fractured gaps in the boron particles of sample #40H906 (MBA-CB) and #2H917II (MBA-CB), shown in Figures 4 and 5 respectively.

DISCUSSION

In the present study, while the Ta-C and Ta-B systems have large density differentials, the Ti-C and Ti-B systems have lesser density differentials. Ta is harder than Ti, and likewise B and C have dissimilar deformation characteristics. Thus, working with such contrasts in systems of very high heats of reaction, together with the fact that the temperatures rise due to shock alone, in the Momma Bear fixtures cannot melt either boron or carbon, provided important clues about the reaction mechanism.

In the comparisons made so far, if density differential

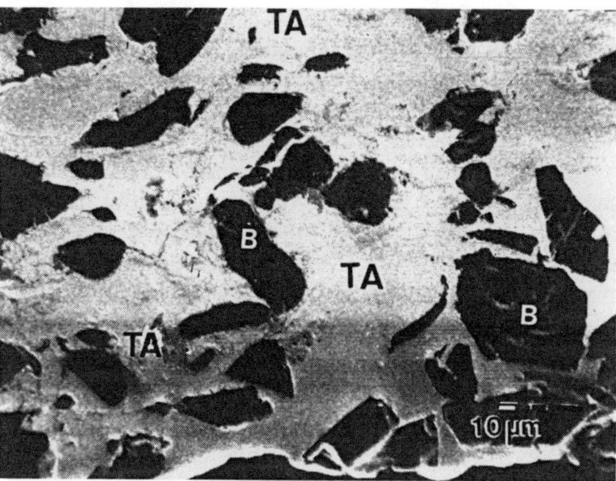

Figure 4. SEM micrograph of unreacted region of Ta+B compact #40H906 (MBA-CB).

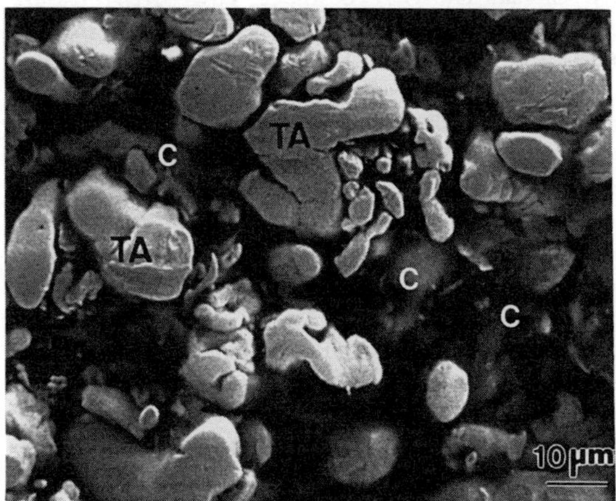

Figure 3. SEM micrograph of unreacted region of Ta+C compact #10H917II (MBA-CB).

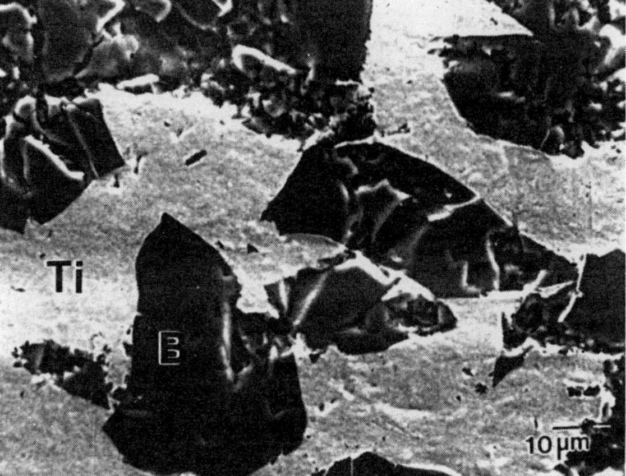

Figure 5. SEM micrograph of unreacted region of Ti+B compact #2H917.

of constituent was a contributing factor, carbon would behave similar to boron, as the ratios of densities (Ta/C) and (Ta/B) are similar (7.36 and 7.11). Similarly, the ratios of densities (Ti/C) and (Ti/B) are 2.0 and 1.92. Thus, it can be inferred that density differential is not a significant factor.

Experiments conducted by changing volumetric ratio of the constituent in the powder mixture did not alter the reaction behavior. This is in agreement with some of the earlier works,[7] wherein the emphasis has been placed on deformation of both the constituents, for the initiation of reaction.

The systems selected in the present study are all associated with very high heats of reaction. However, from the results it can be seen that Ti-B system had maximum reaction, in line with its highest heat of reaction among all the systems under study. The Ti-C and the Ta-B systems did not react to the same extent. The Ta-C system had even less reaction, seen only in localized regions. These results indicate that the systems under study with highest heat of reaction make it possible for the reaction to be self sustained resulting in more reaction occurring in the bulk. Thus, heat of reaction influences only the extent of reaction, after reaction initiation.

Comparison of two compacts in the Ti-2B subsystem, partially reacted compact #40H906 and fully reacted compact #04H896 points to the increased reactivity observed due to presence of submicron boron powder. The increased reactivity of this mixture is perhaps due to the shock-compressed configuration with increased contact surface area, and enhanced mixing of the constituents. However, it is clearly seen from the study that the coarse boron powder also reacts with Ti and Ta only if boron particles are fractured and disintegrated followed by penetration of metallic constituent during shock compression. Thus, mixing of boron (either by deformation or by fracture) with Ti or Ta is essential for reaction initiation.

The role of the form of elemental carbon, as graphite or amorphous material, is clearly differentiable. The mixture containing amorphous carbon reacted fully in both Ti and Ta mixtures, whereas the corresponding compacts containing graphite did not react fully. This condition, thus proves that amorphous carbon is more reactive than graphite under shock-waves, suggesting the importance of the high-strain-rate compressibility of constituents, which is one of the main differences between graphite and amorphous carbon.

Careful comparison of reacted and unreacted areas of the various systems shows that the graphite simply deformed and flowed around the Ti or Ta particles. The relatively easy flow of the graphite results in its minimum mixing with the Ti or Ta particles. On the other hand, the boron systems show fracture and sometimes plastic deformation of the boron particles, along with extensive deformation in both Ti and Ta and so become intimately mixed with them. Thus, deformation and mixing of both constituents is a prerequisite to the occurrence of reaction. Another feature observed in some regions was the melting of Ti, but no reaction was seen in those areas. This type of structure indicates that reaction can occur without melting. In fact, it has been seen that melting of any constituent actually inhibits further reaction. The feature indicates the solid-state nature of these reactions.

CONCLUSION

It is shown that configuration change and intimate mixing of constituents during shock compression of powder mixtures are the most significant mechanistic aspects of shock-induced chemical reaction. The study also indicates that the reaction initiates at temperatures below the melting point of either component, and hence shock-induced chemical reaction is essentially a solid-state reaction.

ACKNOWLEDGMENTS

This work was supported by Sandia National Laboratories under grant No. 42-5737. The authors also thank G.T. Holman Jr. (SNL) for providing old samples and useful suggestions.

REFERENCES

[1] R.A. Graham, *Solids Under High Pressure Shock Compression: Mechanics, Physics and Chemistry*, New York: Springer-Verlag, 1993, pp. 1-221.

[2] E. Dunbar, *Effect of Volumetric Distribution of Starting Powders on Shock-Induced Chemical Reactions*, M.S. Thesis, New Mexico Tech., 1991, pp. 1-110.

[3] O. Kubaschewski and C.B. Alcock, *Metallurgical Thermochemistry*, New York, Pergamon Press, 1988, 3rd edition, pp. 312-316.

[4] R.A. Graham and A.B. Sawaoka, eds., *High Pressure Explosive Processing of Ceramics*, Switzerland, Trans Tech Publications, 1987, pp. 29-64.

[5] N.N. Thadhani, G.T. Holman, B. Romero and R.A. Graham, *The CETR/Sawaoka 12-Capsule Plate Impact Shock Recovery Fixture: Design and Experimentation*, CETR Report A-01-91, New Mexico Tech., 1991, pp. 1-15.

[6] V.S. Joshi, *Shock-Induced Chemical Reactions in Ti-and Ta-based Carbide and Boride Systems*, M.S. Thesis, New Mexico Tech., 1992, pp. 1-117.

[7] N.N. Thadhani, A. Advani, E. Dunbar, I. Song, and H.A. Grebe, "Shock-Induced Reactions Synthesis (SRS) of Tungsten-Rhenium Intermetallic Compounds," in *Proceedings of TMS Symposium on High Strain Rate Behavior of Refractory Materials*, Cincinnati, Ohio, Oct. 21-24, 1991, pp. 211-228.

TIME-RESOLVED PRESSURE MEASUREMENTS IN CHEMICALLY REACTING POWDER MIXTURES

E. Dunbar*, R.A. Graham**, G.T. Holman**, M.U. Anderson**, N.N. Thadhani***,
*New Mexico Tech, EMRTC, Socorro, NM 87801; **Sandia National Laboratories, Albuquerque, NM 87185;
***Georgia Institute of Technology, School of Materials Science and Engineering, Atlanta, GA 30332

PVDF piezoelectric polymer stress-rate gauges have been used to detect and record stress pulses input to and propagated through powder mixtures of 5Ti+3Si at densities of 53%. Data are obtained for the porous solid "crush-up" and in the chemically reacting state. Wave speed is determined to an accuracy of 0.1% and serves as a sensitive and overt indication of chemical reactions. Compressed-gas gun and high explosive loading experiments show a crush strength of about 1 GPa. Strong exothermic chemical transformation is indicated by large increases in wave speed to expanded volume states. The degree of reaction is approximately 50%. The pressure measurements are supplemented by studies of shock treated powder mixtures preserved for post-shock analysis which determine the effect of particle size and morphology on reaction threshold and degree of reaction. The materials response is consistent with Graham's CONMAH conceptual model of shock-induced solid state chemistry reaction.

Work supported by U.S.DOE Contract #DE-AC04-76DP00789.

INTRODUCTION

The ability to form intermetallic compounds by intense stress waves passing through elemental constituent metal powders has been well demonstrated [1]. The present work is concerned with study of the processes occurring during shock loading of metal powders and the subsequent reaction of the powders, with both time-resolved pressure measurements as well as shock recovery experiments. The piezoelectric polymer PVDF stress rate gauges are used for the time-resolved measurements [2,3]. The correlation of data between the two techniques permit a better understanding of processes occurring during shock loading of reactive powder mixtures. These experiments are designed to quantify the concepts suggested by Graham's CONMAH conceptual model of shock-induced solid state chemical processes [4].

EXPERIMENTAL

A total of seventeen experiments were carried out, with seven of those being instrumented with the PVDF gauge and the other ten being the recovery experiments using the Bear fixtures designed by Sandia National Laboratories [5]. Three powder morphologies were used in the experiments: coarse, medium, and fine. All of the instrumented shock compression experiments were carried out using the medium morphology powder, which is -325 mesh for both the Ti and Si. The recovery experiments were carried out using all three morphologies. The coarse powder has particle sizes of 105-149 μm for the Ti and 45-149 μm for the Si, whereas the fine morphology has particle sizes of 1-3 μm for the Ti and less than 10 μm for the Si. All of the powder morphologies were mixed in the atomic ratio of 5Ti+3Si, which corresponds to a weight distribution of 74% Ti and 26% Si and a volume distribution of 60% Ti and 40% Si.

The shock compression experiments were carried out on the 25 meter gas gun located at Sandia National Laboratories, which is precisely controlled in velocity, planarity, and tilt. The symmetric impact of impactor and target materials provide a controlled shock compression of the target, which is shown schematically in Figure 1, as are the representative traces of gauge output in current vs. time and the integrated trace of stress vs. time. The sample consisted of several configurations, which are listed in Table 1 and were changed in order to match more closely the impedance of the powder mixture and delay the reshock of the powder mixture in order to more clearly see the features during shock compression [2]. The higher pressure shock compression experiments were carried out using high explosive loading utilizing P-040 plane wave lenses and 25.4 mm thick explosive in contact with an Al driver plate, which acted as the driver on the copper capsule target with the same design as those for the gun experiments.

The typical PVDF gauge package configuration consists of insulating films of FEP Teflon on both sides of the 25 μm PVDF elements, with Al sputtering of 2000 Å on the powder sides of the gauge package to prevent pyroelectric effects from affecting gauge response during possible reaction of the powder mixture.

The PVDF gauge used has been studied and standardized so that the behavior during loading is well understood. The gauges have all been of high quality, biaxially stretched PVDF film, poled using the Bauer

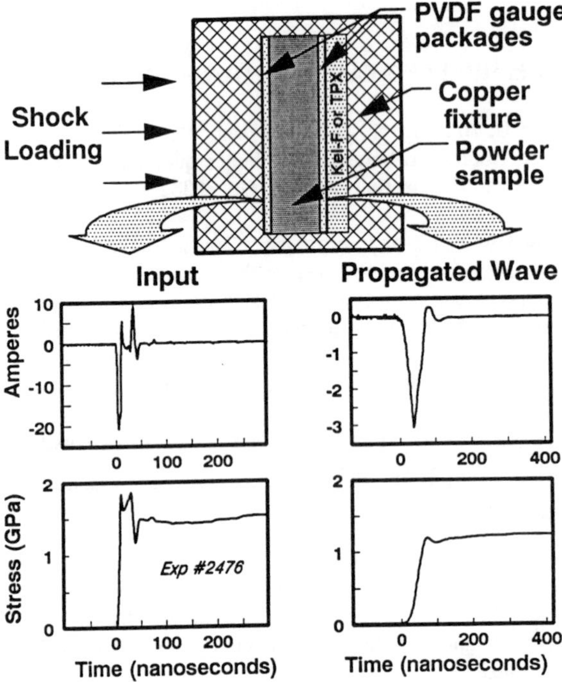

Figure 1. Experimental configuration for shock compression experiments, with characteristic current vs time and stress vs time plots from PVDF gauges for input and propagated waves. Polymer backing and locations of gauges relative to powder mixture are shown for single configuration, other configuration has TPX on both sides of powder and gauges to impedance match the mixture.

poling process to a remanent polarization of 9.2 μC/cm^2, and have identical gold over platinum electrodes/leads [2]. Each PVDF gauge is tested to verify electric characteristics, essential for accurate measurements of current vs. time which are integrated to stress vs. time. The piezoelectric data obtained from the gauge is in the form of a current vs. time trace, which is then analyzed using the PVDFSTRESS program [6].

The recovery shots were done using two configurations listed in Table 2, which include the Momma Bear Baratol and Poppa Bear Baratol configurations [5]. The peak bulk pressures as predicted by a two-dimensional computer model are 7.5$\pm$2.5 GPa and 5$\pm$1 GPa, respectively [5]. The samples were sectioned and polished to view the cross-section of the hockey-puck shaped sample in order to see if reaction had occurred. A typical reacted sample has no contrast when viewed, whereas an unreacted sample will show contrast between the constituent powders. Both optical and scanning electron microscopy (SEM) were performed on all recovery samples.

RESULTS AND DISCUSSION

The results of the shock compression and recovery experiments are summarized in Tables 1 and 2, respectively. The data obtained in the shock compression experiments is highly accurate due to the design and set-up of the gas gun with measuring capabilities to accurately record the velocity of the impact. The input stress is the stress in the powder at the front gauge and varies from 0.21 GPa to over 2.5 GPa. The wave speed measures the transit time through the powder and gives an explicit measure of wave speed as a reaction occurs. The risetime of the propagated wave has been reported with two different values, namely toe-to-peak and 10% to 90% values [7]. The toe-to-peak value was measured using the current vs. time data with the toe being where the pulse leaves the baseline and the peak being where it returns to the baseline. From the peak value, the half-maximum values are then calculated. The half-maximum values are used for volume calculations. The dispersion of the stress pulse with respect to backing material and pressure can be seen in Figure 2. The output stress is actually the stress in the polymer-backing material in the capsule. The backing material influences both the pressure and the risetime of the propagated wave, due to the behavior of a polymer. The relative volume of the sample can then be calculated from these measured values and a stress (pressure)-volume curve can be plotted to show the Hugoniot of the powder mixture, which is shown in Figure 3. Although the stress pulses are not shock waves, the analysis using the conservation equations is used as the basis for a common comparison between the lower pressure and higher pressure experiments. Such an analysis of a dispersed wave causes some error for the relative volume calculations; however the principal features of such an approximation are not altered.

The observed shift of the Hugoniot to the right indicates an increase in volume during compression of the powder mixture. This increase in volume arises due to the reaction of the powder mixture and the high temperature associated with that reaction. The high temperature causes the reaction products to expand, thereby allowing for an expansion of the products instead of a compression. In an inert powder, the Hugoniot would continue to curve to the left indicating a decreasing volume due to the high stress (pressure). Crush-up to solid density is occurring at 1 GPa, and at stresses above that the reaction begins to occur, which shifts the Hugoniot to the right. Further indication of reaction is the increase in stress observed at the propagated wave gauge. Although the stress measured at this position is actually the stress in the material backing the powder, the increase is observable. The increase in stress is caused by the energy added to the wave due to the reaction, as well as the expansion of reaction products due

Table 1. Experimental parameters and results from shock compression experiments on 5Ti+3Si powder mixture, with constant density of 1.930±0.012 g/cm³.

Experiment Number[A]	Impact Velocity[B] (km/s)	Configuration[C]	Input Stress[D] (GPa)	Wave Velocity[E] (km/s)	Risetime[F] (ns)	Output Stress[G] (GPa)	Relative Volume[H]
2462 (a)	0.280	2	0.21	0.766 (0.750)	319 (127)	0.42 (Kel-F)	1.539 (1.527)
2475 (a)	0.434	3	0.77	0.878 (0.825)	1176 (500)	0.69 (TPX)	0.909 (0.774)
2476 (a)	0.650	3	1.49	1.314 (1.295)	83 (37)	1.17 (TPX)	1.042 (1.024)
2463 (a)	0.871	2	2.08	1.646 (1.597)	191 (156)	3.95 (Kel-F)	1.141 (1.089)
2407 (a)	0.972	1	2.5	1.842 (1.827)	145 (68)	11.0 (Cu)	1.169 (1.157)
BE-231 (b)	TNT	4	2.94	2.090 (2.064)	85 (17)	5.4 (Kel-F)	1.227 (1.211)
BE-232 (b)	PBX-9404	4	11.5[I]	2.786[I] (N/A)	N/A	N/A	0.442[I] (N/A)

A: (a) impact loading; (b) explosive loading; **B:** symmetric impact, Cu on Cu or explosive loading; **C:** Configuration, nominal thickness in parentheses: 1: Cu (6.5mm)→FEP (50μm)→PVDF (25μm)→FEP (62.5μm)→5Ti+3Si (4mm)→FEP (62.5μm)→PVDF (25μm)→FEP (50μm)→Cu (9.5mm); 2: Cu (6.5mm)→Kel-F (125μm)→PVDF (25μm)→Kel-F (125μm)→5Ti+3Si (4mm)→Kel-F (125μm)→PVDF (25μm)→Kel-F (125μm)→Kel-F (0.7mm)→Cu (8.8mm); 3: Cu (6.5mm)→TPX (9.5mm)→PVDF (25μm)→FEP (12.7μm)→5Ti+3Si (4mm)→FEP (12.7μm)→PVDF (25μm)→ TPX (9.5mm)→Cu (6.5mm); 4: P-040→Explosive (25.4mm)→Al (12.7mm)→Cu (6.5mm)→FEP (12.7μm)→PVDF (25μm)→FEP (12.7μm)→5Ti+3Si (4mm)→FEP (12.7μm)→PVDF (25μm)→ Kel-F (9.5mm)→Cu (6.5mm); **D:** PVDF measurement; **E:** wave speed from toe to peak (half maximum value); **F:** propagated wave, toe to peak (10-90%); **G:** PVDF measurement (polymer backing material); **H:** Calculated from PVDF input stress and toe to peak wave speed (half maximum value); **I:** Values computed based on predictions, not on measurements.

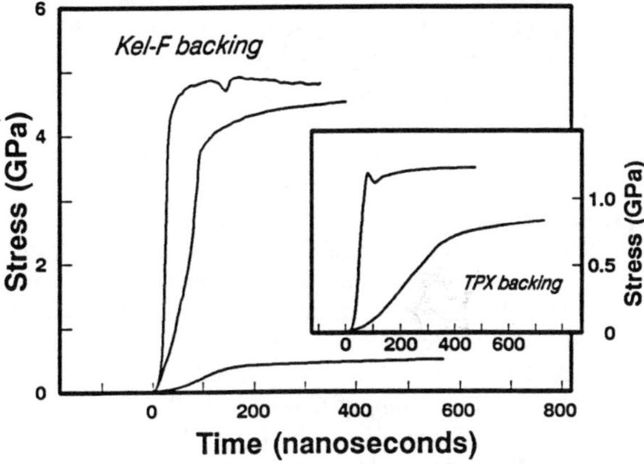

Figure 2. Overlays of propagated waves showing large difference in shape of wave and risetimes for different stresses with a Kel-F polymer backing material. Overlays in box are same for TPX polymer backing material. Note the difference in risetimes and pressure between the different backing materials.

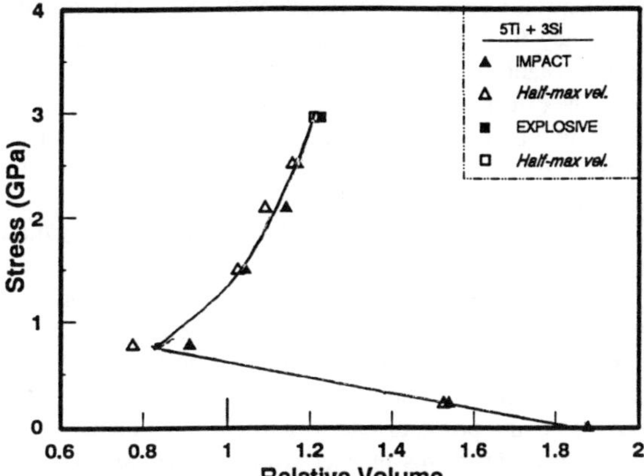

Figure 3. Relative volume vs. stress showing Hugoniot of powder mixture. Crush-up to solid density is observed at about 1 GPa, then reaction begins as evidenced by shift of curve to the right due to expansion of products from heat of reaction.

to the large heat of reaction. The amount of reaction occurring is approximately 50% at a stress level of 2.5 GPa, based on calculations done by Graham et al. [8].

In the recovery experiments, two-dimensional loading effects inherent to the capsule design cause the pressure experienced by the powder to increase in two stages. The first stage is a planar wave which is of low pressure, while the second stage is due to radial waves that load the powder to a much higher pressure. The radial waves act to focus the pressure which causes the high pressure. However, even at the higher pressure, the powder mixture may not react due to the change in initial configuration caused by the initial loading. As can be immediately seen, the pressures in the recovery fixtures are much higher than in the shock compression experiments, which should

Table 2. Experimental parameters and results for recovery experiments on 5Ti+3Si powder mixture.

Experiment Number	Packing Density (g/cm³)	Configuration[A]	Powder Morphology[B]	Reaction
NMG-9122	1.92 (52.8%)	PB-B	medium	none
NMG-9121	1.93 (53.1%)	MB-B	medium	complete
NMG-9120	1.95 (53.6%)	MB-B	medium	complete
NMG-9212	1.625 (44.7%)	PB-B	medium	complete
NMG-9123	2.147 (59.0%)	PB-B	medium	none
NMG-9211	2.33 (64.1%)	MB-B	medium	none
NMG-9252	1.633 (44.9%)	PB-B	coarse	none
NMG-9251	1.916 (52.7%)	MB-B	coarse	none
NMG-9254	1.626 (44.7%)	PB-B	fine	none
NMG-9253	1.989 (54.7%)	MB-B	fine	localized

A: MB-B = Momma Bear Baratol, Peak P = 7.5 GPa; PB-B = Poppa Bear Baratol, Peak P = 5 GPa [5]; **B:** fine: Ti 1-3 μm; Si < 10 μm; medium: Ti and Si -325 mesh (<45 μm), coarse: Ti 105-149 μm; Si 45-149 μm

indicate that all of the samples should react. In the table, it is seen that as initial packing density is increased, the tendency for reaction decreases with constant pressure. Tendency for reaction also decreases with lower pressure at a constant initial packing density.

The effect of powder morphology plays a large role in determining the reaction threshold based on starting packing density. As the size of the powder increases, the reaction threshold density decreases, whereas the opposite is true to a certain extent. As the density of the medium morphology powder increased, the reaction decreased. These results were fairly consistent with the exception of the fine morphology, where the 45% dense experiment was expected to react. However, the void morphology within the initial configuration may not have allowed enough mixing of the powders due to particle agglomeration. It was consistent in this manner with the CONMAH model with regards to configuration and mixing not being enough of a factor to cause reaction. For the coarse morphology powder, the particles are too big to be sufficiently attain mixing on a fine scale which would lead to reaction, even though the configuration changed a fair amount. Further work describing the configuration changes and mixing in shocked but unreacted powder mixtures has been done by Thadhani et al. [9].

CONCLUSION

Reaction in the 5Ti+3Si system has been observed in shock compression experiments as evidenced by the shift to the right of the Hugoniot in the P-V plane. Crush-up of the powder mixture occurs at 1 GPa, and above that pressure the reaction begins. The recovery experiments have shown the effect of powder morphology for inhibiting reaction in the coarse and fine morphology due to a change in configuration and lack of mixing due to void morphology. The effect of initial packing density on reaction was also shown, which establishes a threshold density for the medium morphology powder and shows that powder morphology changes the threshold density due to CONMAH effects. Further shock compression experiments on the coarse and fine morphology are planned and should reveal the effect on reaction more clearly. These results provide explicit data on the processes of the present CONMAH model.

REFERENCES

[1] R.A. Graham, B. Morosin, B. Dodson. "The Chemistry of Shock Compression: A Bibliography". Sandia Report SAND83-1887, October 1983, Sandia National Laboratories.

[2] M.U. Anderson, R.A. Graham, and D.E. Wackerbarth, "Prediction and Data Analysis of Current Pulses from Impact-Loaded Piezoelectric Polymers (PVDF)," in *Shock Compression of Condensed Matter-1989*, S.C. Schmidt, J.N. Johnson, L.W. Davison, eds. Elsevier Science Publishers B.V., 1990, pp. 805-808.

[3] R.A. Graham, M.U. Anderson, F. Bauer, and R.E. Setchell, "Piezoelectric Polarization of the Ferroelectric Polymer PVDF From 10 MPa to 10 GPa: Studies of Loading-Path Dependence," in *Shock Compression of Condensed Matter-1991*, edited by S.C. Schmidt, et al., North Holland, 1992, pp. 883-886.

[4] R.A. Graham, "Issues in Shock-Induced Chemical Synthesis of Intermetallic Compounds," in *Proc. of 3rd Inter. Symposium on High Dynamic Pressures.* LaGrande Motte, France, June 5-9, Associacion Française de Pyrotechnie, 1989, p. 175-198.

[5] R.A. Graham and A.B. Sawaoka, eds. *High Pressure Explosive Processing of Ceramics,* Netherlands, Trans Tech Publications, 1987, ch. 4, pp 29-64.

[6] D.E. Wackerbarth, M.U. Anderson, R.A. Graham, "PVDFSTRESS: A PC-Based Computer Program to Reduce Bauer PVDF Stress-Rate Gauge Data", Sandia Report SAND92-0046, February 1992, Sandia National Laboratories.

[7] M.U. Anderson, R.A. Graham, G.T. Holman, "Time-Resolved Shock Compression of Porous Rutile", to be published, this proceedings.

[8] R.A. Graham, M.U. Anderson, Y. Horie, S-K. You, G.T. Holman, to be published, *Shock Waves.*

[9] N.N. Thadhani, E. Dunbar, R.A. Graham, "Characteristics of Shock Compressed Configuration of Ti and Si Powder Mixtures", to be published, this proceedings.

CHARACTERISTICS OF SHOCK-COMPRESSED CONFIGURATION OF Ti AND Si POWDER MIXTURES

N.N. Thadhani,[*] E. Dunbar,[**] and R.A. Graham[***]

[*] Georgia Tech, School of Materials Science and Engineering, , Atlanta, GA 30062,
[**]New Mexico Tech, EMRTC, , Socorro, NM 87801, and
[***]Sandia National Laboratories, Albuquerque, NM 87185.

Shock-compression recovery experiments were performed on mixtures of Ti and Si powders of **fine**, **medium**, and **coarse** morphology, and packed at different initial densities, using the Sandia Momma and Poppa Bear fixtures with Baratol explosive. The shock-compressed configuration revealed characteristics typical of either chemically reacted material with **fine** equiaxed grains, or unreacted material with densely packed Ti and Si particles. The unreacted configuration showed that Ti particles were extensively deformed, irrespective of powder morphology and shock conditions generated by either fixture. In contrast Si particles showed different characteristics depending on the powder morphology, packing density, and shock conditions. The microstructural characteristics of unreacted configuration of Ti and Si powder mixtures were investigated. Mechanistic processes occurring prior to the inception of *shock-induced chemical reactions* in this system are described.

Work supported by Sandia National Laboratories Document No. 42-5737 at New Mexico Tech, and also in part by the U.S. Army Research Office Contract # DAAH04-93-G-0062 at Georgia Institute of Technology.

INTRODUCTION

Titanium-silicon represents an higly exothermic intermetallic forming system, with associated heat of reaction of -138kcal/mole, volume change of -27.8%, and calculated reaction temperature of 2500K for the formation of Ti_5Si_3.[1] Shock-compression experiments[2] on Ti-Si powder mixtures have shown that chemical reactions in this system occur at shock pressures of only a few GPa, and corresponding bulk temperatures significantly below the melt temperature of Si. The equilibrium shock temperature (and shock energy) does not influence the reaction behavior. Rather, by altering the shock pressure and initial packing density, but maintaining the same bulk temperature, it is found that the propensity for reaction initiation largely depends on particle size, with **fine** powder morphologies reacting at lower pressures and lower initial porosities[2].

The objective of our present work is to study this system in detail via controlled instrumented and recovery experiments on the same types of powder mixtures and under similar loading conditions. The results of real-time measurements are discussed by Dunbar et al[3] in this proceedings. Results of recovery experiments focussing on characteristics of shock-compressed unreacted configuration of Ti-Si powder mixtures at conditions below the reaction threshold, will be described here.

EXPERIMENTAL PROCEDURE

Shock recovery experiments were performed on Ti-Si powder mixtures of three types of powder morphologies, **coarse** (105-149 μm Ti and 45-149 μm Si, **medium** (10-45 μm Ti and Si), and **fine** (1-3 μm Ti and < 5 μm Si). The powders were mixed in a mortar and pestle (without organic mixing agents) in a volumetric distribution corresponding to the Ti_5Si_3 atomic stoichiometry compound. SEM images of the respective powder mixtures are shown in Fig. 1.

The various powder mixtures were shock loaded using the Sandia[4] Poppa Bear fixture with Baratol explosive (PB-B) and Momma Bear fixture with Baratol explosive (MB-B). In these fixtures the loading history is dominated by an initial low-pressure planar wave, followed by a radial wave focussing effect, resulting in peak pressures of 5 ± 1 GPa for PB-B system and 7.5 ± 2.5 GPa for MB-B system.[4]

Six experiments were performed on powder mixtures of **medium** morphology packed at initial density ranging between 53% to 64% (or porosity of 47% to 36%) with MB-B fixture, and 45% to 53% (or porosity of 55% to 47%) with PB-B fixture. Two experiments were performed on **fine** and **coarse** morphology powders, each with packing density of 64% (36% porosity) with MB-B, and 53% (47% porosity) with PB-B fixture.

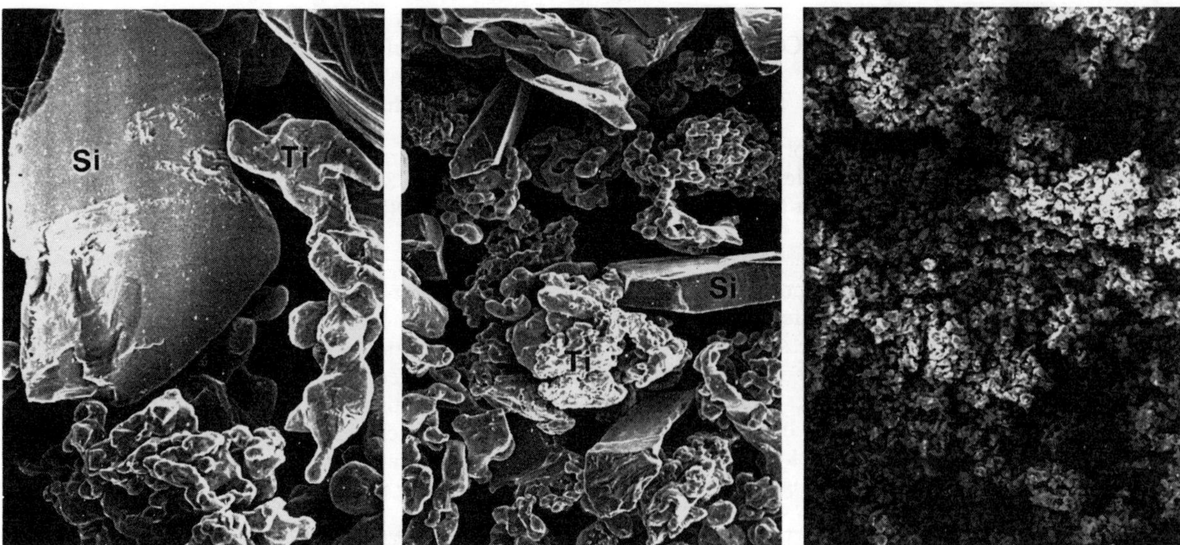

Fig. 1. SEM images showing morphologies of Ti-Si powder mixtures: (a) **coarse** (b) **medium**, and (c) **fine** powders. Si particles are generally blocky single crystals and have a shiny contrast, while Ti particles are rounded polycrystalline aggregates with grainy contrast.

RESULTS

Overall results of shock recovery experiments, characterized by optical/SEM analysis are illustrated in the reaction map in Figure 2. For **medium** morphology powders, MB-B experiments showed complete reaction in samples with 47% porosity, and no reaction with 36% porosity. The **PB-B** experiments showed no reaction with 41% and 47% porosity, but complete reaction with 55% porosity. No reactions were observed with **coarse** powders for MB-B experiments with 47% porosity, and PB-B experiments with 55% porosity; likewise no reactions were observed with **fine** powders for PB-B experiment with 55% porosity, while only localized reactions in peripheral edge regions of the compacts were observed for MB-B experiment with 47% porosity.

Time-resolved experiments (discussed elsewhere in this proceedings[3]) were performed primarily on **medium** morphology Ti-Si powders at shock pressures up to 3 GPa. The results of time-resolved experiments concur with the recovery experiments, and provide clear evidence of the occurrence of *shock-induced chemical reactions* in Ti-Si powder mixtures. Differences in stress recorded by the PVDF gages in cases of complete reaction and no-reaction, and concomitant shift in the measured P-V Hugoniot are conclusive evidence of "shock-induced reactions" occurring during the shock state and not due to post-shock activation effects similar to "shock-assisted" reactions.[6]

In general, the microstructure of the fully reacted samples showed an equiaxed grain structure, along with presence of spherical voids, typical of a fully reacted, melted, and resolidified material. The size of the equiaxed Ti_5Si_3 grains was measured to be ≈10 μm. A typical fully reacted microstructure is shown in Figure 3.

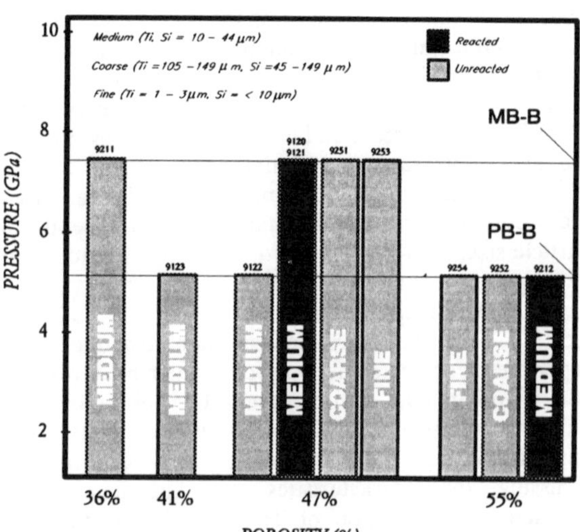

Fig. 2. Reaction map showing effect of initial density, powder morphology, and shock conditions.

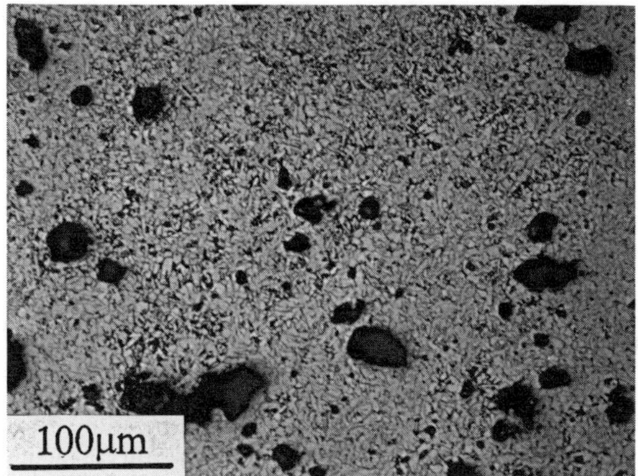

Fig. 3. Optical micrograph showing fully reacted microstructure.

Unreacted samples from experiments performed at shock conditions below the threshold are of principal interest in the present work. Such samples provide the configuration of powder mixtures in the shock-compressed state at various stages prior to inception of reaction. In order to compare the microstructure resulting from the effects of different variables, analysis was performed along identical regions of every microstructural compact, namely the central bulk area.

The most revealing effects are observed in samples of the three different morphologies, packed at similar density in the PB-B shock recovery fixture; the three corresponding optical micrographs are shown in Figure 4 (a-c). The grainy-contrast **fine**, **medium**, and **coarse** morphology Ti particles in all cases show extensive deformation. The **fine** morphology Ti particles are also seen to form large agglomerates ≈ 200 μm diameter. The shiny-contrast **fine** morphology Si particles show extensive deformation and flow around Ti particles (Fig. 4(a)). On the other hand the shiny-contrast **coarse** Si particles show extensive fracture and fragmentation (Fig. 4(b)). The **medium** morphology Si powders show some cracking, as well as deformation and flow, the latter case observed particularly when Si is isolated and surrounded by Ti particles (Fig. 4 (c)).

The effect of shock pressure was best revealed on **medium** morphology Ti-Si powders. Optical micrographs of powders shock-compressed with the low pressure PB-B fixture and the higher pressure MB-B fixture are shown in Figure 5 (a,b). While extensive deformation of the grainy-contrast Ti particles is commonly observed in both micrographs, the mixtures shock-compressed with the higher pressure MB-B fixture (Fig. 6(b)) show more cracking than the those with the PB-B fixture. There is also evidence of possible melting of Si, in certain localized regions of the MB-B samples.

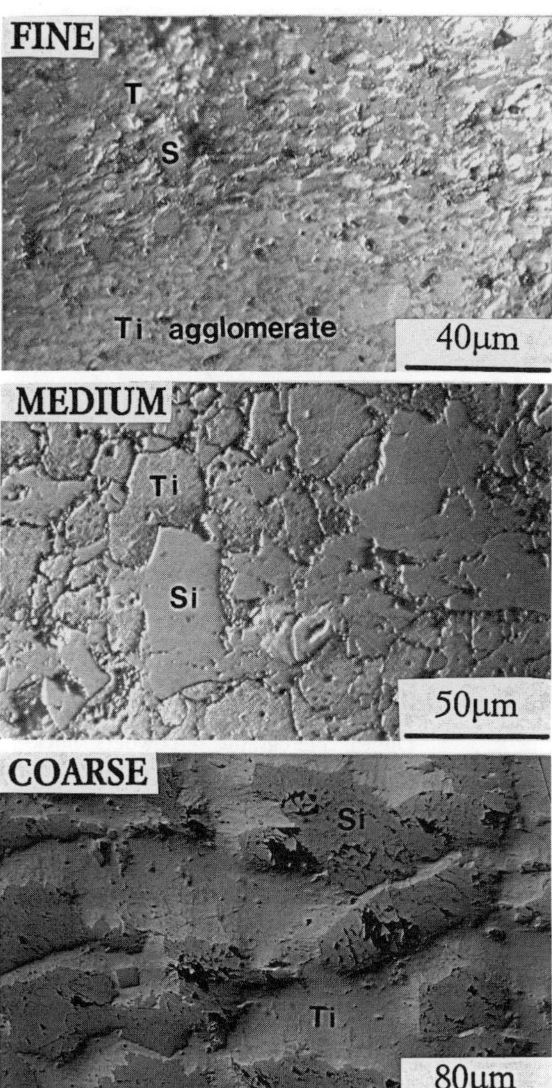

Fig. 4. Optical micrographs of **fine**, **medium**, and **coarse** morphology powders shock compressed with PB-B fixture at same packing density.

DISCUSSION

The overall scenario revealed by recovery experiments illustrates that *shock-induced chemical reactions* in Ti-Si powder mixtures occur predominately with **medium** morphology powders. The reaction thresholds for **medium** morphology powders are shock conditions generated with PB-B system with initial porosity of 55%, or with MB-B system and 47% initial

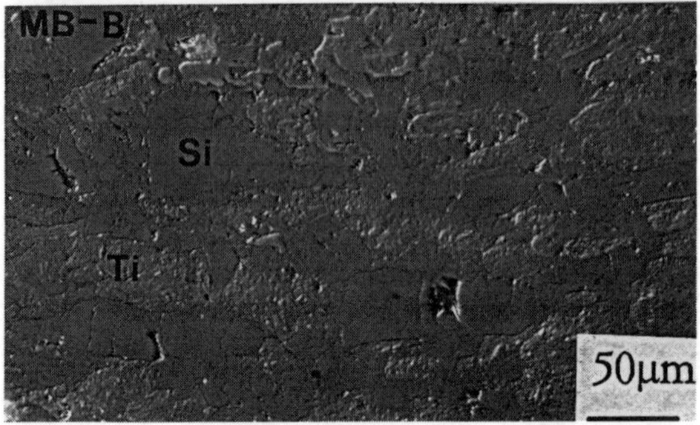

Fig. 5. Optical micrographs of powders shock-compressed with the low pressure PB-B fixture and the higher pressure MB-B fixture.

porosity. The picture emerging from the shock-compressed unreacted configuration of Ti-Si powder mixtures provides clues of mechanistic processes that cause reactions in **medium** morphology powders and not in **fine** or **coarse** morphology powders. As shown in the micrographs in Figures 4 and 5, both Ti and Si **medium** morphology powders simultaneously undergo extensive deformation and flow leading to more intimate mixing between them. In contrast **coarse** morphology Si powders fracture and fragment at low stresses, prior to deformation of Ti particles, therefore, there is only limited mixing between the deformed Ti and Si fragments. **Fine** morphology Ti and Si powders are expected to undergo extensive deformation, and therefore the greatest propensity for reaction initiation. However, while **fine** Si particles do show extensive deformation and flow, the **fine** Ti particles tend to agglomerate, thereby limiting interparticle mixing.

Mechanistic Considerations

Simultaneous deformation of constituents is therefore, the important property needed to provide an ideal configuration for initiation of *shock-induced chemical reactions*. Morphological variations and porosity affect reaction initiation characteristics, by altering simultaneous deformability of the constituents. The deformation response of Si is also different when it is shock-compressed with other metals in a binary mixture, e.g., with Ni, Nb, Mo, instead of Ti. Prior work[5,6] shows that Ni-Si and Ti-Si systems have the highest propensity for reaction initiation, while Nb-Si and Mo-Si systems have the lowest propensity. The Ni-Si and Ti-Si systems are favored because of the small difference in the yield strength of constituents which allows simultaneous deformation, plastic flow, and mixing to occur. In contrast, large yield strength differences amongst constituents in Mo-Si and Nb-Si, inhibit complete mixing since the metal constituent has deform at higher stresses, and then mix with fragments of the brittle Si. Thus, simultaneous deformation and mixing is the first step towards providing the configuration for initiation of *shock-induced chemical reactions* consistent with Graham's CONMAH model[7].

SUMMARY

Shock-induced chemical reactions in Ti-Si powder mixtures occur at lower thresholds with **medium** morphology powders. In contrast, mixing is inhibited with **coarse** and **fine** powders due to fragmentation or agglomeration problems which limit the propensity for reaction initiation. Effects of powder morphology, initial porosity, and shock conditions, on resulting microstructure of shock-compressed unreacted Ti-Si powders, reveal the importance of the deformation response of Si, and its subsequent mixing with Ti, in providing the configuration needed for reaction initiation.

REFERENCES

1. O. Kubaschewski and C.B. Alcock, *Metallurgical Thermochemistry*, 5th ed, Pergamon Press, 1979.
2. B.R. Krueger, A.H. Mutz, and T. Vreeland, Jr., *Met. Trans.*, **23A**, 55 (1991).
3. E. Dunbar, R.A. Graham, G.T. Holman, M.U. Anderson, and N.N. Thadhani, "Time-resolved Pressure Measurements in Chemically Reacting Powder Mixtures," to be published, this volume.
4. R.A. Graham, "Explosive Processing Methods," in *High Pressure Explosive Processing of Ceramics*, eds. R.A. Graham and A.B. Sawaoka, Trans Tech Publications, 1987, pp. 17-64.
5. L.H. Yu, Ph.D. dissertation, New Mexico Tech, Socorro, New Mexico, 1992.
6. N.N. Thadhani, *Progress in Matls. Sci.*, **37**(2), 117 (1993).
7. R.A. Graham, "Solids Under High Pressure Shock Compression: Mechanics Physics, and Chemistry," *Springer Verlag*, 1992.

HIGH-PRESSURE SYNTHESIS AND MAGNETIC PROPERTIES OF $T_{1-x}T'_xGe_4$ (T, T' : 3d TRANSITION METAL)

H. TAKIZAWA, K. YAMAZAKI, T. ENDO, and M. SHIMADA

Department of Molecular Chemistry and Engineering,
Faculty of Engineering,Tohoku University,
Aoba-ku, Sendai, Miyagi 980, Japan

Synthesis of the pseudo-binary compounds, $T_{1-x}T'_xGe_4$ (T: Ti, V, Cr, T': Fe, Co) with the various average number of 3d electrons have been studied under high-pressure/temperature condition. Single phase $T_{1-x}T'_xGe_4$ compounds are synthesized at 6 GPa and 650-750°C in the definite composition: $Cr_{0.5}Fe_{0.5}Ge_4$, $Cr_{0.5}Co_{0.5}Ge_4$, $Ti_{0.25}Fe_{0.75}Ge_4$, and $V_{0.25}Fe_{0.75}Ge_4$. All these compounds have the superstructure related to the β-$NiHg_4$-type. These pseudo-binary compounds are new family of electron compounds in which both the average valence electron number and the average size of the transition metal atoms are important factors on determining the crystal structure.

INTRODUCTION

In the binary transition metal - germanium system, a large number of intermetallic compounds have been synthesized. Among these germanides, the compounds containing more than 67 at.% Ge were rarely investigated because of little synthesis of compounds. Recent investigations on the synthesis of transition metal germanides demonstrate that the high-pressure synthesis is a suitable method for the preparation of new germanides with high germanium contents [1, 2].

In our previous study [2], two new germanides, $MnGe_4$ and $CoGe_4$, were synthesized under high-pressure/temperature condition of 5.5-6 GPa and 600-700°C. The crystal structures of $MnGe_4$ and $CoGe_4$ are closely related to the β-$NiHg_4$-type structure; the size of the unit cells of $MnGe_4$ and $CoGe_4$ correspond to four and eight times the size of β-$NiHg_4$-type cells. No other TGe_4 (T : 3d transition metal) compounds have not yet been synthesized.

The solid solution systems, $Mn_{1-x}Co_xGe_4$ and $Mn_{1-x}Fe_xGe_4$, were also synthesized at 6 GPa and 650-750°C and their structural and magnetic properties were examined [3]. In both solid solution systems, it is found that structural change is closely related to the variation of the average valence electron number of the transition metal atoms. This fact indicates that the electron concentration in the 3d-band is an important factor on determining the crystal structure and the magnetic properties.

In the present study, pseudo-binary compounds, $T_{1-x}T'_xGe_4$ (T: Ti, V, Cr, T': Fe, Co) have been synthesized to evaluate the contributions of the electron concentration and the size factors on the formation of new family of electron compounds, TGe_4.

EXPERIMENTAL

Powders of transition metal elements (>99.9% purity) and germanium powder (>99.99% purity) were used as starting materials. These powders were mixed in the atomic ratio $Ge/(T_{1-x}T'_x)=4.5$ (T: Ti, V, Cr, T': Fe, Co) and uniaxially pressed at 100 MPa to form a pellet; the excess of germanium was added to prevent the formation of germanide phases with lower germanium contents. The pellet was put into a cylindrical BN capsule, which was placed in a carbon heater. The assemblage was put into a cell constructed with NaCl and subjected to high-pressure/temperature condition using the belt-type high-pressure equipment. Figure 1 shows the detailed cell assemblage of the belt-type equipment. The high-pressure/tem

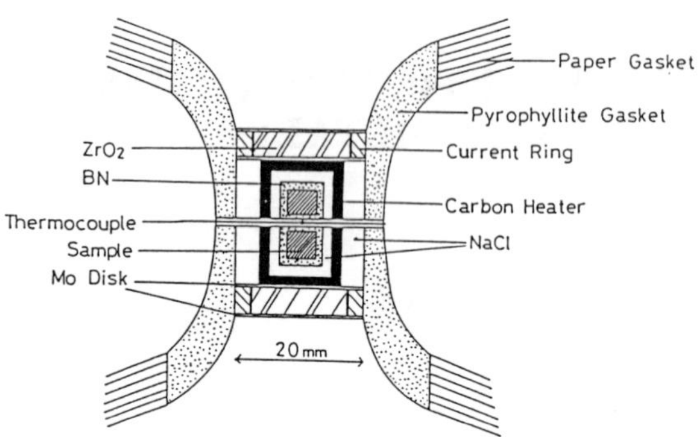

Figure 1. Cell assemblage for the Belt-type equipment.

perature treatment was carried out at 6 GPa and 650-750°C for 1 hr, and then the sample was quenched to room temperature prior to releasing the applied pressure. The high-pressure reaction was repeated several times to obtain a well homogenized sample. The pellet thus obtained was pulverized and the residual germanium was removed by leaching with 5N NaOH + 3% H_2O_2 solutions at room temperature.

The resulting phase was identified by X-ray powder diffraction analysis using Ni-filtered Cu-Kα or Fe-filtered CoKα radiation. Lattice parameters were determined by a least-squares method using silicon (a=0.543088 nm) as an internal standard. Magnetic measurements were carried out in the temperature range 77-450K.

RESULTS AND DISCUSSION

Formation of the Pseudo-Binary Compound

Synthesis of $T_{1-x}T'_xGe_4$ compounds with the following combinations of transition metal atoms were attempted in the various composition of x at 6 GPa and 650-750°C; (T, T') = (Ti, Fe), (Ti, Co), (V, Fe), (V, Co), (Cr, Fe), and (Cr, Co). It is notable that $T_{1-x}T'_xGe_4$ compounds are obtained in the pseudo-binary $Ti_{1-x}Fe_xGe_4$, $V_{1-x}Fe_xGe_4$, $Cr_{1-x}Fe_xGe_4$, and $Cr_{1-x}Co_xGe_4$ systems in which each end members do not form TGe_4 compounds except $CoGe_4$ [2]. Among these pseudo-binary systems, $Cr_{1-x}Fe_xGe_4$, and $Cr_{1-x}Co_xGe_4$ have the narrow single phase region; $0.5 \leq x \leq 0.6$ for $Cr_{1-x}Fe_xGe_4$, and $0.47 \leq x \leq 0.53$ for $Cr_{1-x}Co_xGe_4$. Other pseudo-binary compounds have the definite composition of $Ti_{0.25}Fe_{0.75}Ge_4$ and $V_{0.25}Fe_{0.75}Ge_4$.

Figure 2 shows the X-ray powder diffraction pattern of $Cr_{0.5}Fe_{0.5}Ge_4$ synthesized at 6 GPa and 700°C. All diffraction peaks can be completely indexed as the pseudo-tetragonal structure ($2c \approx a > b$) with lattice constants of a=1.1116(5)nm, b=1.0941(5)nm, and c=0.5556(3)nm. This pseudo-tetragonal structure is isostructural with the β-$NiHg_4$-related structure appeared in $Mn_{1-x}T_xGe_4$ (T:Fe,Co) system [3]. $Ti_{0.25}Fe_{0.75}Ge_4$, $V_{0.25}Fe_{0.75}Ge_4$, and $Cr_{0.5}Co_{0.5}Ge_4$ also have the same pseudo-tetragonal structure. The unit cell parameters of $T_{1-x}T'_xGe_4$ compounds are listed in Table 1.

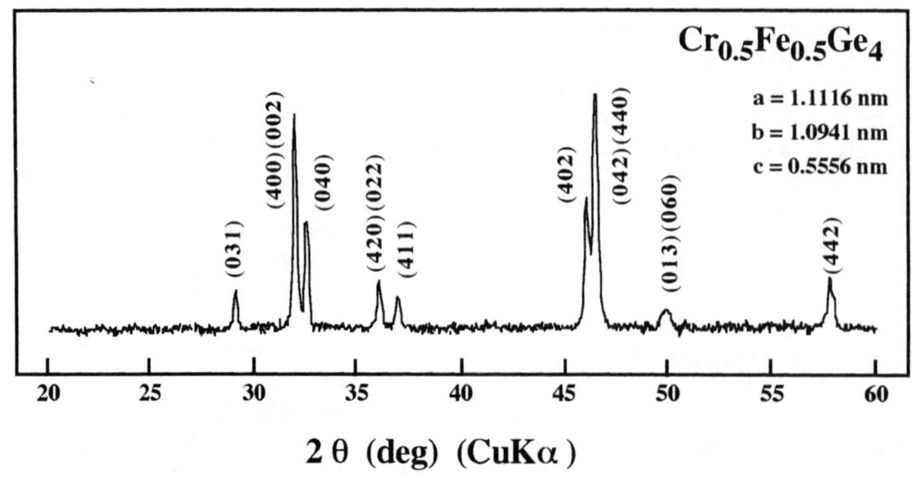

Figure 2. The X-ray powder diffraction pattern of $Cr_{0.5}Fe_{0.5}Ge_4$ synthesized at 6 GPa and 700°C.

Table 1. The unit cell parameters of $T_{1-x}T'_xGe_4$ (T: Ti, V, Cr, T': Fe, Co)

compound	unit cell parameters			
	a (nm)	b (nm)	c (nm)	v (nm^3)
$Cr_{0.5}Fe_{0.5}Ge_4$	1.1116(5)	1.0941(5)	0.5556(3)	0.6757(8)
$Cr_{0.4}Fe_{0.6}Ge_4$	1.1055(5)	1.0865(5)	0.5529(3)	0.6641(8)
$V_{0.25}Fe_{0.75}Ge_4$	1.1032(5)	1.0825(5)	0.5513(3)	0.6584(8)
$Ti_{0.25}Fe_{0.75}Ge_4$	1.1049(5)	1.0855(5)	0.5525(3)	0.6626(8)
$Cr_{0.5}Co_{0.5}Ge_4$	1.1117(5)	1.0932(5)	0.5559(3)	0.6756(5)

Structure Determination Factors

The structure map of $T_{1-x}T'_xGe_4$ compounds are plotted in Figure 3 in relation to the unit cell volume and the average valence electron number of the transition metal atoms. The previous results on the $Mn_{1-x}T_xGe_4$ (T: Fe, Co) system [3] and the additional results on $Mn_{0.8}Cr_{0.2}Ge_4$ (tetragonal) and $Mn_{1-x}Ni_xGe_4$ (orthorhombic, x=0.067, 0.133) are also plotted in Figure 3.

As seen in this figure, the formation of $T_{1-x}T'_xGe_4$ compound is limited in the enclosed area, unit cell volumes of 0.658-0.684 nm^3 and 6.8-7.8 valence electrons. The tetragonal modification occurs in the upper left side and the orthorhombic modification occurs in the upper middle region. The occurrence of these two modifications depends on both average valence electron number and the size factor. In contrast, it is clear that the occurrence of the pseudo-tetragonal modification is mainly controlled by the size factor rather than the average valence electron number.

The various kinds of electron compounds occur in alloys and intermetallic compounds. A typical example of such compounds is the Hume-Rothery phases. The crystal structure of the Hume-Rothery phases is controlled by the valence electron number/atom ratio [4]. Another example of electron compounds is the Laves phases with the $MgZn_2$, $MgCu_2$, and $MgNi_2$-type structures [5-7]. The Laves phases frequently occur at the composition of AB_2 in alloy systems in which the atomic radius ratio of the constituent atoms is approximately 1.2. The stabilization of various stacking

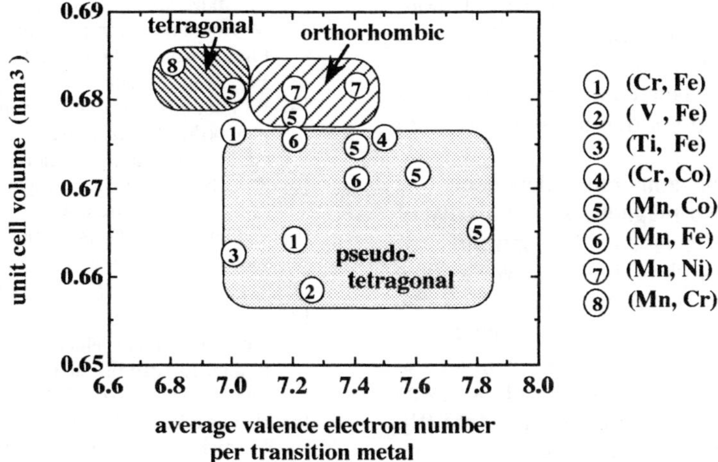

Figure 3. The structure map for the $T_{1-x}T'_xGe_4$ compounds (T, T': 3d transition metal)

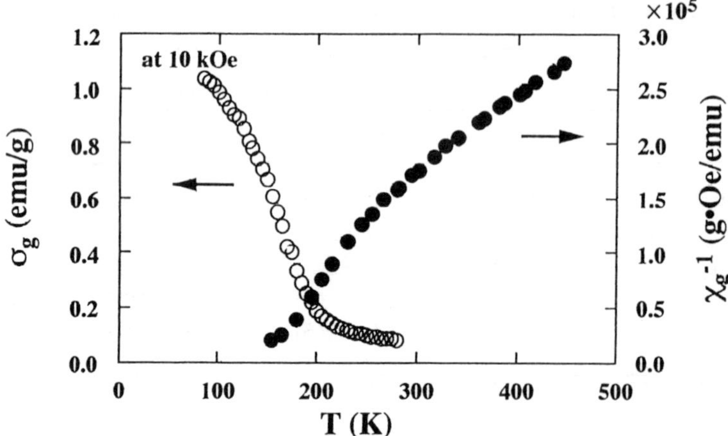

Figure 4. Temperature dependence of the magnetization and magnetic susceptibility of $Cr_{0.5}Fe_{0.5}Ge_4$.

variants in the Laves phases strongly depends on the valence electron concentration of the constituent elements [7]. The TGe_4 compounds are new family of electron compounds in which both electron concentration and size factor are important factors on the structure determination.

Magnetic Properties

The magnetization and magnetic susceptibility of $T_{1-x}T'_xGe_4$ compounds were measured in the temperature range 77-450K. Both $Cr_{0.5}Fe_{0.5}Ge_4$ and $Cr_{0.5}Co_{0.5}Ge_4$ are weakly ferromagnets with the Curie temperature of 190K and 240K, respectively. The saturation magnetic moments (μ_s) per transition metal atom, extrapolated to 0K, are considerably small for both compounds; 0.07 μ_B for $Cr_{0.5}Fe_{0.5}Ge_4$ and 0.03 μ_B for $Cr_{0.5}Co_{0.5}Ge_4$. These weakly ferromagnetic behaviours are probably intrinsic behaviours and not due to the presence of magnetic impurities.

Figure 4 shows the temperature dependence of the magnetization and magnetic susceptibility of $Cr_{0.5}Fe_{0.5}Ge_4$. The magnetic susceptibility of $Cr_{0.5}Fe_{0.5}Ge_4$ does not obey the Curie-Weiss-type relation of $M\chi_g=M\chi_c+C/(T-\theta_p)$, where M is the formula weight and χ_c is the temperature-independent magnetic susceptibility. Similar deviation from the Curie-Weiss-type relation was also observed in weakly ferromagnetic MnSi [8]. Such behaviour of the magnetic susceptibility can be explained by the effect of spin fluctuations in the itinerant electron weakly ferromagnets.

ACKNOWLEDGMENTS

This work has been supported in part by a Grant-in-Aid for Scientific Research of the Ministry of Education, Science and Culture.

REFERENCES

[1] V.I. Larchev and S.V. Popova, The new phase $IrSn_4$ and $RhGe_4$ formed by high pressure treatment, *J. Less-Common Metals*, **98**, L1 (1984).

[2] H. Takizawa, T. Sato, T. Endo and M. Shimada, High pressure synthesis and electrical and magnetic properties of $MnGe_4$ and $CoGe_4$, *J. Solid State Chem.*, **88**, 384 (1990).

[3] H. Takizawa, K. Yamazaki, T. Endo and M. Shimada, High-pressure synthesis, crystal structure, and magnetic properties of $Mn_{1-x}T_xGe_4$ (T: Co, Fe), *J. Solid State Chem.*, in press. (1993).

[4] W. Hume-Rothery, R. E. Schmalman and C. W. Haworth, *The Structure of Metals and Alloys*, 5th ed. [Inst. of Metals, London, 1958], p. 235.

[5] R. L. Berry and G. V. Raynor, The crystal chemistry of the Laves phases, *Acta Crystallogr.*, **6**, 178 (1953).

[6] Y. Ohta and D. G. Pettifor, Size versus electronic factors in transition metal Laves phase stability, *J. Phys.: Condens. Matter*, **2**, 8189 (1990).

[7] Y. Komura and Y. Kitano, Long-period stacking variants and their electron-concentration dependence in the Mg-base Friauf-Laves phase, *Acta Crystallogr., B*, **33**, 2496 (1977).

[8] H. Yasuoka, V. Jaccarino, R. C. Sherwood and J. H. Wernick, NMR and susceptibility study of MnSi above T_c, *J. Phys. Soc. Japan*, **44**, 842 (1978).

CHAPTER XVII

HIGH-PRESSURE CHEMISTRY AND EXPLOSIVES

IN-SITU STUDY OF THE SOLUBILITY OF HYDROGEN IN RHENIUM AT HIGH PRESSURE

J.V. Badding, D.C. Nesting, and R.B. Baron
Department of Chemistry
Pennsylvania State University
University Park, PA, 16802

The solubility of hydrogen in rhenium at high pressure has been investigated using diamond anvil cell techniques and synchrotron X-ray diffraction. Rhenium incorporates hydrogen with a stoichiometry of $ReH_{0.25}$, in good agreement with earlier quenching experiments.

INTRODUCTION

Many transition metal hydrides that are not stable under ambient conditions can be synthesized under high pressures of hydrogen. Hydrogen was shown to begin to incorporate into rhenium at approximately 2 GPa at 250 °C [1,2] by electrical resistivity measurements. By measurement of the amount of hydrogen evolved from samples quenched to low temperatures, it was shown that the solubility of hydrogen in rhenium increases monotonically with pressure. The hydrogen stoichiometry increased from $ReH_{0.06}$ at 7 GPa and 250 °C to $ReH_{0.13}$ by 9 GPa. At a lower temperature (170 °C) and 9 GPa the amount of hydrogen incorporated was even more, 0.22 moles of H per Re [1, 2]. X-ray diffraction [1] and neutron diffraction [3] measurements on the quenched samples showed that upon incorporation of hydrogen the crystal structure remains the same (hcp), but with a larger unit cell volume that scales with the amount of hydrogen incorporated. Because rhenium is often used as a gasket material in diamond cell experiments with hydrogen, it is important to characterize the formation, stoichiometry, and properties of phases in the rhenium-hydrogen system at high pressure. Using diamond cell techniques and synchrotron radiation, we have characterized in-situ the solubility of hydrogen in rhenium at high pressure.

EXPERIMENTAL

Hydrogen at a pressure of 0.2 GPa and powdered rhenium (Aesar) were loaded together into a Mao-Bell diamond anvil cell with a T301 steel gasket. The molar ratio of hydrogen to rhenium was estimated to be larger than a factor of 10. Pressures were measured with ruby fluorescence. Energy dispersive synchrotron diffraction measurements were performed at line X17C at the National Synchrotron Light Source. All diffraction patterns were collected at 25 °C.

RESULTS AND DISCUSSION

At 2.3 GPa the diffraction pattern (Figure 1) is characteristic of rhenium metal. By 5.3 GPa, small shoulders on the hcp rhenium diffraction peaks appear due to the incorporation of hydrogen in an hcp lattice with a larger unit cell volume. At 8.3 GPa the coexistence of the two phases can clearly be seen. Similar two phase behavior has been observed in other metal-hydrogen systems [4]. It is likely that incorporation of hydrogen begins at pressures lower than 5.3 GPa, but could not be observed because the differences in the diffraction patterns for the two phases were too

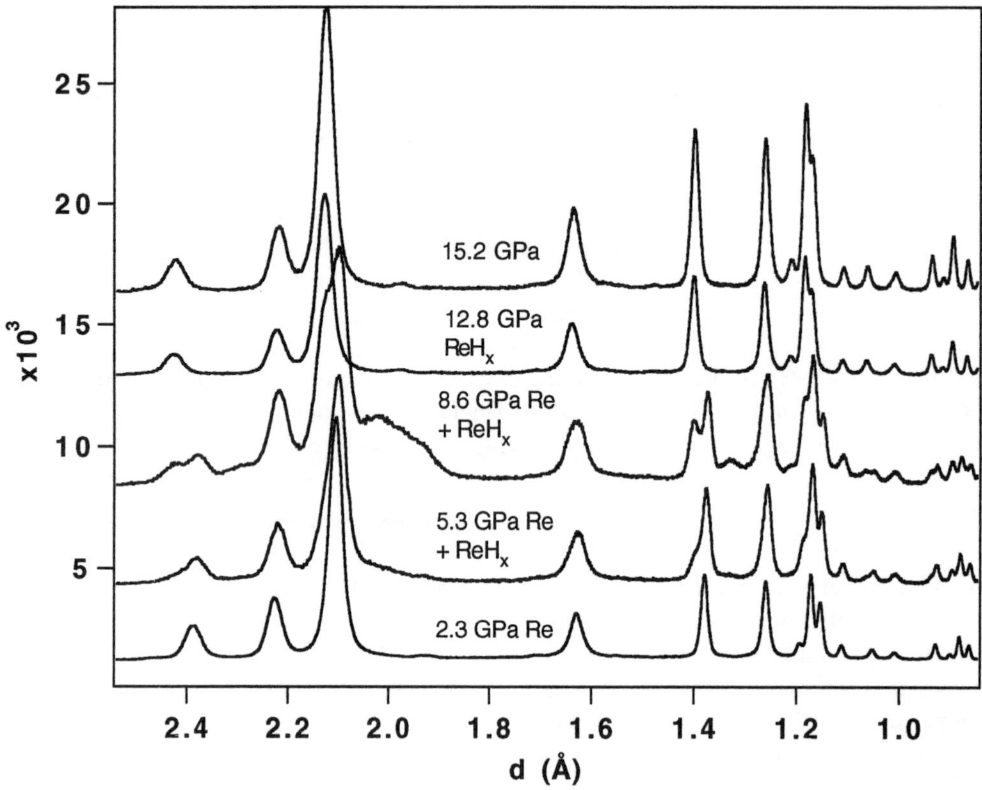

Figure 1. Energy dispersive diffraction patterns at different pressures.

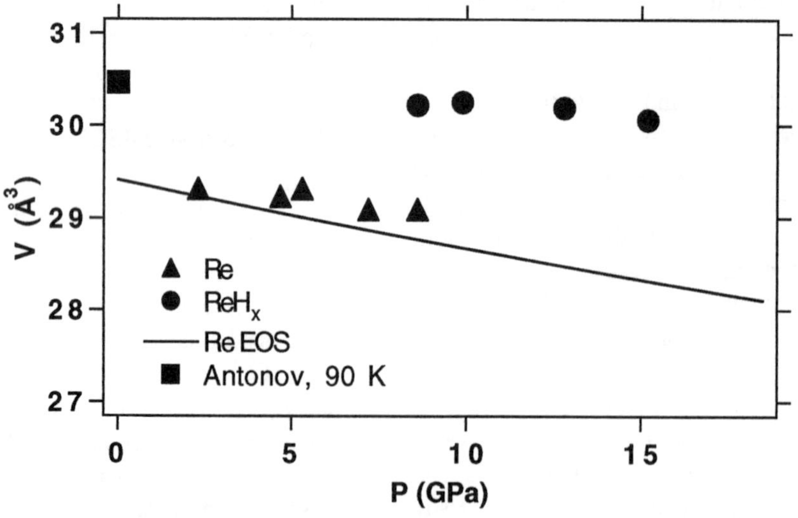

Figure 2. Volume vs. pressure for rhenium and rhenium hydride. The line is the equation of state of Re [5]. The solid square corresponds to the volume measured on a sample compressed to 9 GPa at 170 °C and quenched to 90 K [1].

small. By 12.8 GPa, all of the metal has been converted to the new phase.

Based on the magnitude of the increase in the unit cell volume upon incorporation of hydrogen into rhenium (Figure 2), the stoichiometry of can be estimated. The difference in the unit cell volumes at 8.6 GPa between rhenium (28.77 Å^3) [5] and the hydrogen-containing phase (30.22Å^3) is 1.45 Å^3. Assuming a cell volume increase of approximately 2.9 Å^3 per hydrogen [6], a stoichiometry of $ReH_{0.25}$ results, which compares favorably with the earlier determination of the stoichiometry at 9 GPa and 170 °C ($ReH_{0.22}$) [1].

Steel gaskets used in high pressure hydrogen experiments in the diamond cell are disrupted

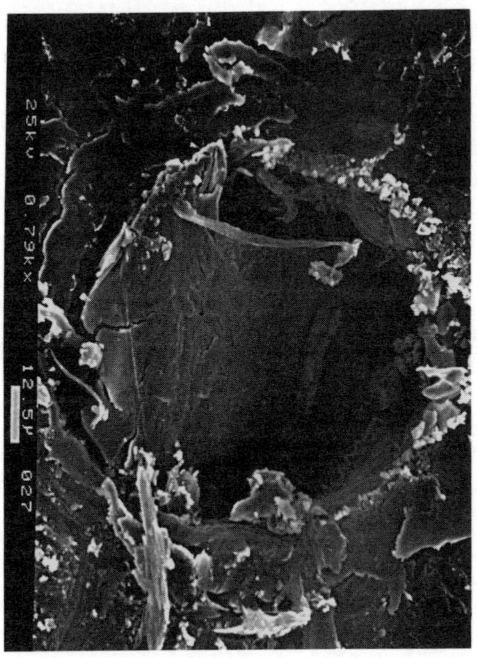

Figure 3. SEM photograph of iron sample in a T301 steel gasket after exposure to hydrogen at 5 GPa. Both the steel and iron are severely cracked and disrupted after the formation of the hydride.

and embrittled by the formation of a hydride at 3.5 GPa with a stoichiometry close to FeH (Figure 3) [4, 7]. The use of rhenium gaskets in high pressure hydrogen experiments generally results in less hole deformation and higher sample stability [4, 8]. At 16 GPa much less hydrogen is incorporated into rhenium than iron, which suggests that the superior properties of rhenium gaskets are due to smaller changes in the materials properties of the metal.

REFERENCES

1. V. E. Antonov, I. T. Belash, V. Y. Malyshyev, E. G. Ponyatovskii, N. A. Tulina, Dokl. Akad. Nauk SSSR 269, pp. 617-619 (1983).
2. E. G. Ponyatovskii, V. E. Antonov, "High Hydrogen Pressures. Synthesis and Properties of New Hydrides," in Problems in Solid State Physics, A. M. Prokhorov, A. S. Prokhorov, Eds. (MIR, Moscow, 1984), pp. 109-172.
3. V. A. Somenkov, V. P. Glazkov, A. V. Irodova, S. S. Shilstein, J. Less Comm. Met. 129, pp. 171-180 (1987).
4. J. V. Badding, R. J. Hemley, H. K. Mao, Science 253, pp. 421-424 (1991).
5. Y. K. Vohra, S. J. Duclos, A. L. Ruoff, Phys. Rev. B 36, pp. 9790-9792 (1987).
6. B. Baranowski, "Pressure Dependence of Hydrogen Volume in Some Metallic Hydrides," in Molecular Systems Under High Pressure, R. Pucci, G. Piccitto, Eds. (Elsevier, North-Holland, 1991), pp. 139-156.
7. M. Yamakata, T. Yagi, W. Utsumi, Y. Fukai, Proc. Japan Acad. 68B, pp. 172-176 (1992).
8. R. J. Hemley, H. K. Mao, Science 249, pp. 391-394 (1990).

SELF DIFFUSION IN LIQUID HYDROGEN FLUORIDE AT PRESSURES UP TO 600 MPa

N. Karger, H.-D. Lüdemann
Institut für Biophysik und Physikalische Biochemie
Universität Regensburg
93040 Regensburg, Germany

Self diffusion coefficients D of waterfree HF and DF have been determined between the melting pressure curve and 373 K at pressures up to 600 MPa. The technique employed is the nuclear magnetic resonance method with pulsed magnetic field gradients.
The isobaric temperature dependence of D shows a slight deviation from Arrhenius behaviour. Activation energies for HF rise from 9.5 kJ/mole at 360 K to 11.3 kJ/mole at 200 K and are pressure independent. Increase of pressure hinders self diffusion. All isotherms of D show a pronounced decrease of slope with rising pressure. The isotope effect D_{HF}/D_{DF} rises from 1.05 at 373 K to 1.2 at 200 K, which can be explained by the strong influence of hydrogen bonds upon molecular mobility.

INTRODUCTION

The energy of the hydrogen bonds formed in liquid HF is comparable to this interaction in water [1]. However, fluid HF does not show any anomalies in its thermodynamic properties, except for a very large compressibility. This is doubtless due to the different H-bond-geometries in HF and H_2O. Water forms a 3-dimensional, distorted tetrahedral network of H-bonds, whereas liquid hydrogen fluoride consists of H-bonded chains, that are branched and intertwined.
While water has been studied extensively with just about every experimental technique available, there is only a limited number of experimental publications about waterfree liquid hydrogen fluoride. This work adds another piece to our knowledge of H-bonded liquids and thus aids in the development of a comprehensive picture for the description of the dynamical and structural properties of such liquids.

EXPERIMENTAL

HF (DF) has been synthesized from benzoyl fluoride (C_6H_5COF) and water. At 80-90°C these compounds react to benzoic acid and hydrogen fluoride. When an excess of benzoyl fluoride is used, practically waterfree HF (DF) can be

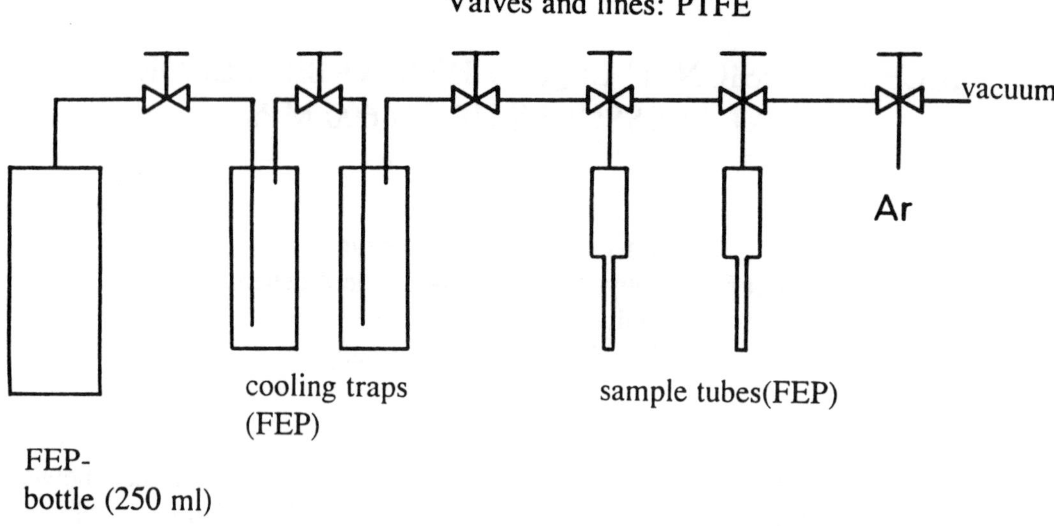

Fig. 1: Teflon distilling apparatus

obtained. The resulting HF (DF) was further purified by double distillations and condensed into the FEP sample tubes, which were then sealed by welding the upper end with hot (≈360°C) pliers.
The whole distillation was performed in an Ar-atmosphere.
The distilling apparatus is depicted in Fig. 1 and is made entirely of teflon (PTFE). For the sample tubes, FEP (fluor ethylene propylene) has been used.
Details of the autoclave used for the measurements and the high pressure equipment have been published elsewhere [2]. The pressure medium used was a 4:1 mixture of methanol and ethanol.
All diffusion coefficients were determined by the NMR-spin echo technique with pulsed magnetic field gradients. The nucleus studied is the ^{19}F-nucleus at a resonance frequency of 94.2 MHz. The overall accuracy of the results is ± 5 %.

RESULTS

The isobars of the self diffusion coefficient D of HF and DF show a slight deviation from Arrhenius behaviour (Fig. 2) only.
In HF, the activation energy rises from 9.5 kJ/mole at 360 K to 11.3 kJ/mole at 200 K. It is pressure independent within experimental error. The activation energies in DF are approximately 0.4 kJ/mole higher than in HF.
Also shown in Fig. 2 are isobars of D for methane and water. Methane, which does not form hydrogen-bonds, exhibits a much smaller activation energy of about 2.8 kJ/mole. On the other hand, water, which forms upon cooling a 3-dimensional network of H-bonds, shows a higher

activation energy which increases drastically at low temperatures.

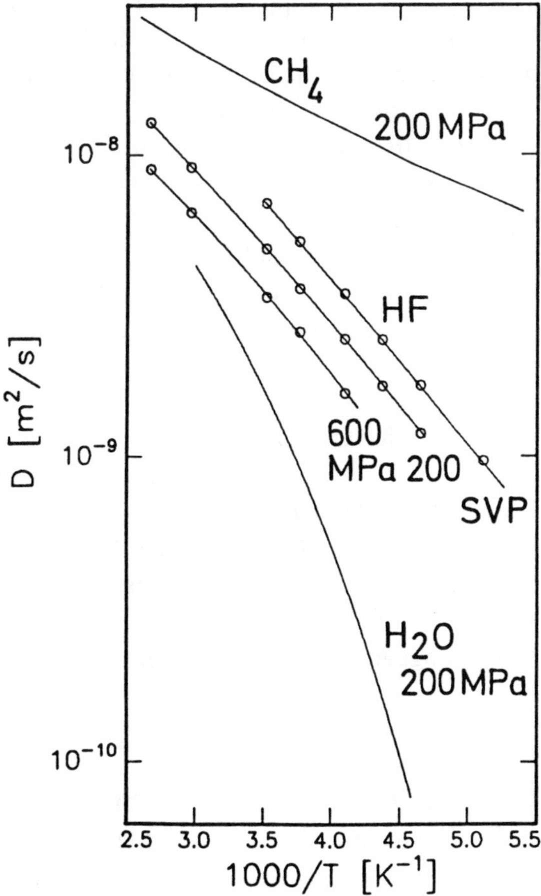

Fig. 2: Isobaric behaviour of D in HF, CH_4 and water

In Fig. 3, some isotherms of D for HF are presented and compared to the behaviour of methane and water. While cold water shows the well-known anomalous behaviour, namely a maximum of the mobility around 150 MPa, hydrogen fluoride exhibits a monotonic decrease of D with pressure. This pressure dependence, however, is small compared to the 140 K-isotherms of D in methane, which shows a much steeper pressure dependence.

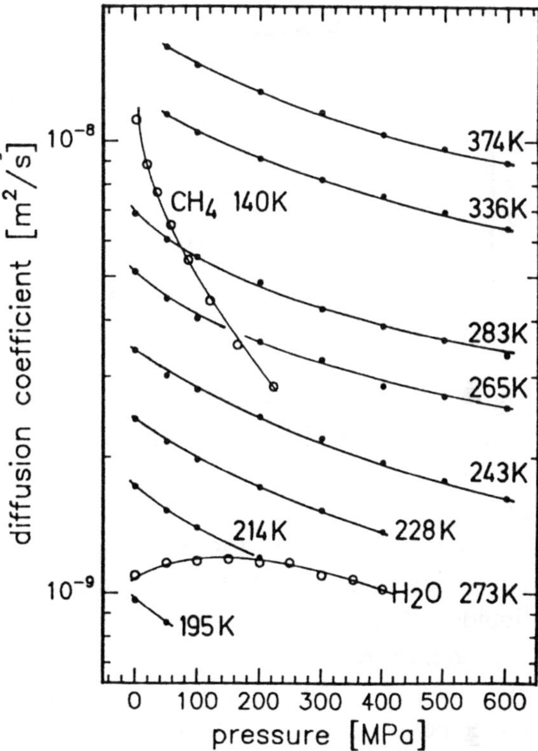

Fig. 3: Isotherms of D for HF, CH_4 and water

The dynamic isotope effect, D_r = D(HF)/D(DF), is plotted in Fig. 4 for the extreme pressures. It shows a similar temperature dependence as in water, namely a pronounced increase at low temperatures.

DISCUSSION

As expected, translational mobility in hydrogen fluoride is strongly influenced by the hydrogen-bond-structure of the liquid. This can be seen from the following

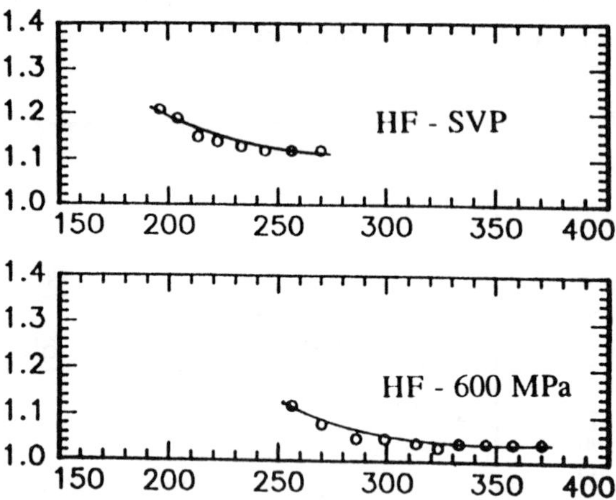

Fig. 4: Dynamic isotope effect in hydrogen fluoride as a function of temperature [K]

results:
The activation energy for diffusion in HF is higher than in non-hydrogen-bonded liquids. The much higher temperature-dependence of E_A in water can be explained by the ability of the H_2O-molecules to form a 3-dimensional stable network of H-bonds upon cooling; whereas hydrogen fluoride forms a chain structure, which does not hinder diffusion as much as the tetrahedral network in water.
Initial compression of cold water enhances the rotational and translational mobility of the H_2O-molecules [3]. This is due to the fact that hydrostatic pressure forces the O-O-O-angles out of their optimum configuration and thereby weakens the H-bonds.
In recent Monte Carlo-simulations [1], this effect was also found for HF. However, due to its high compressibility, a net decrease of D with rising pressure is observed. In contrast, in methane, where there is no enhancement of mobility due to the breaking of H-bonds, a much steeper decrease of D with pressure is observed.

The dynamic isotope effect in hydrogen fluoride is also dominated by the hydrogen-bond- structure. The drastic increase of D_r with falling temperature cannot be explained by kinetic theories, which would predict a temperature-independent value of $D_r = \sqrt{m(DF)/m(HF)}$.
As in water and monohydric alcohols [4], this behaviour is ascribed to the higher hydrogen-bond energy in the deuterated species.

ACKNOWLEDGEMENTS

The expert technical help of Mr. G. Niesner and Mr. R. Knott made this work feasible. This work was supported by a grant from the Deutsche Forschungsgemeinschaft (DFG).

REFERENCES

[1]Honda, K. , Kitaura, K., Nishimoto, K. Bull. Chem. Soc. Jpn. 65, 3122 (1992)

[2]Vardag, T., Karger, N., Lüdemann, H.-D., Ber. Bunsenges. Phys. Chem. 95, 859 (1991)

[3]Angell, C.A.
Ann. Rev. Phys. Chem. 34, 630 (1983)

[4]Karger, N., Vardag, T., Lüdemann, H.-D., J. Chem. Phys. 93, 3437 (1990)

EXPERIMENTAL EVIDENCE FOR A TWO-STEP MECHANISM OF DIFFUSION-CONTROLLED UNIMOLECULAR REACTIONS

T. Asano, K. Cosstick, and H. Furuta
Department of Chemistry, Faculty of Engineering
Oita University
Oita 870-11, Japan

Reaction rates of thermal Z/E isomerization of benzaldehyde anils (**1** and **3**) and azoarenes (**4** and **5**) have been measured under pressure (≤600MPa) in glycerol triacetate (GTA). Pressure effects expected from the transition state theory (TST) were observed at the beginning of pressurization. At higher pressures, an increase in pressure retarded the reaction suggesting that the diffusion-control was realized by an increase in solvent viscosity. The results were analyzed on the basis of eq 2 which can be derived by assuming a two-step mechanism (eq 3). The observed and the TST-expected rate constants at high pressures were inserted to eq 2 in order to estimate the diffusion-limited rate constants. The k_{dif} values thus obtained gave linear Arrhenius plots and showed inverse fractional dependence on the solvent viscosity. Compared at the same viscosity, the diffusion-limited rate constant was almost independent of temperature in **1**, **2**, **4**, and **5**.

INTRODUCTION

As shown in eq 1, photochemically produced Z-isomers of N-[4-(dimethylamino)benzylidene]-4-nitroaniline **1** and 4-(Dimethylamino)-4'-nitro-azobenzene **2** thermally isomerize to their E-isomers with an activation energy of *ca.* 50kJ mol^{-1}. At the previous AIRAPT Conference [1], we reported that these Z/E isomerizations could be retarded by an increase in pressure when viscous solvents such as glycerol triacetate (GTA) were used as a reaction medium. Since such pressure-induced retardation was not observed in usual solvents, it was concluded that the diffusion-control was realized by an pressure-induced increase in the solvent viscosity. The results were analyzed on the basis of eq 2 which was originally derived for diffusion-controlled bimolecular processes by Noyes [2].

$$k_{obs} = (1/k_{TST} + 1/k_{dif})^{-1} \qquad (2)$$

By inserting the observed rate constants k_{obs} and the ones expected from the transition state theory (TST) k_{TST} to this equation, rate constants for the diffusion-limited rate process k_{dif} were calculated and they were shown to give linear Arrhenius plots. In this paper, the results of kinetic measurements in GTA for **1**-**5** will be presented and the relation between the k_{dif} values and the molecular structure will be discussed.

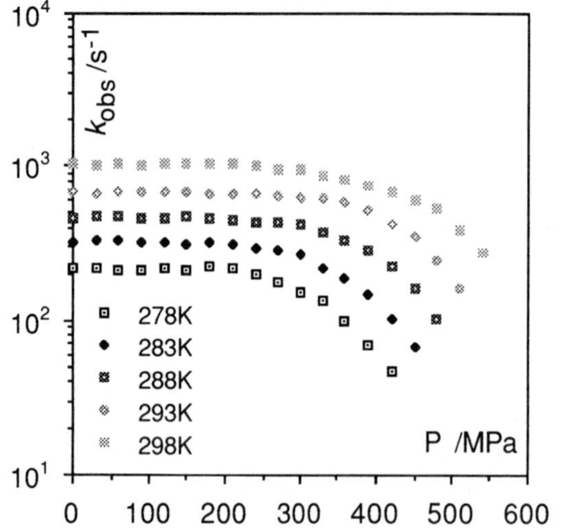

Figure 1. Pressure effects on the isomerization of **1**.

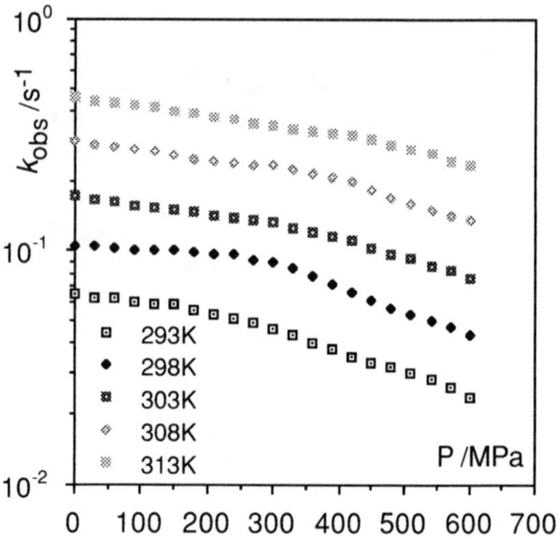

Figure 2. Pressure effects on the isomerization of **3**

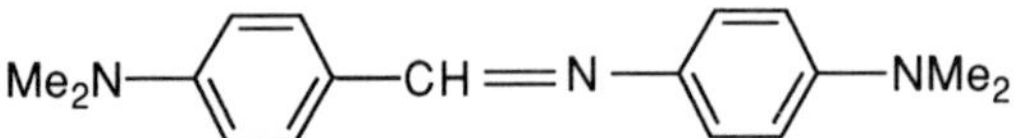

RESULTS

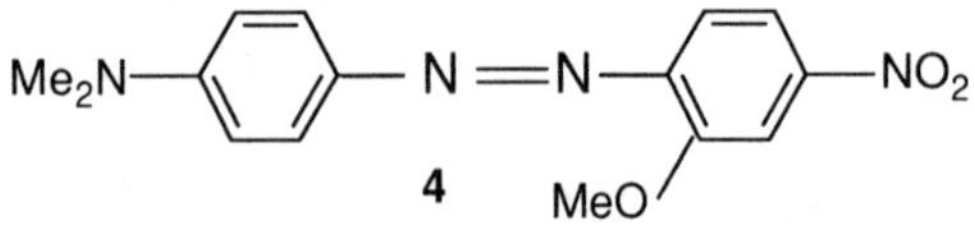

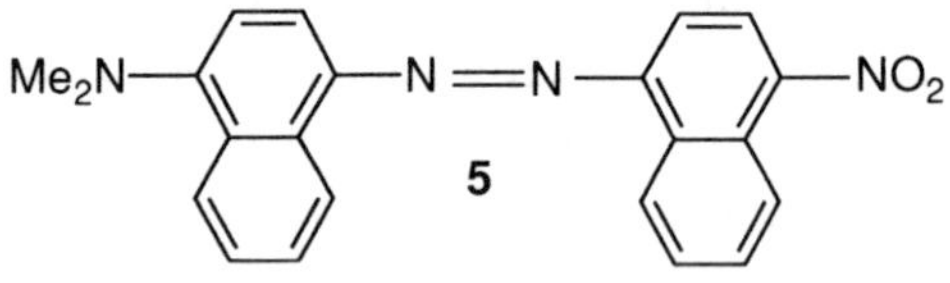

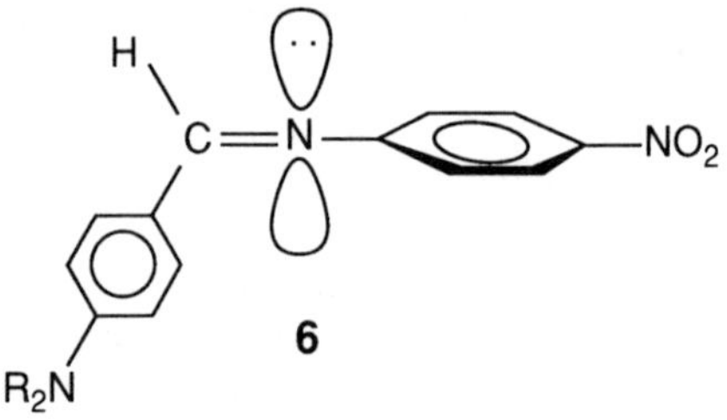

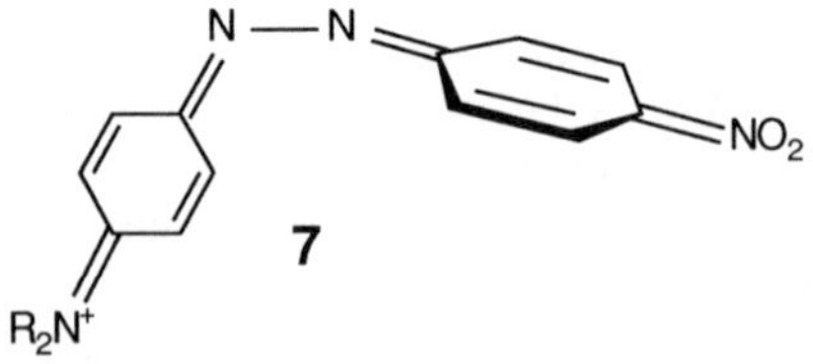

Isomerization about the CH=N bond

In the previous communication [3], we reported preliminary results of pressure-effect study on the isomerization of **1** in GTA. The measurements were completed and the results are shown in Figure 1 The results of similar measurements on **3** are shown in Figure 2. It can be seen clearly from Figure 1 that there are two stages in the pressure effect. At the first stage the rate constant was almost unaffected by pressure as expected from the isomerization mechanism. The reaction is effected by nitrogen inversion [4] and the transition state may be depicted as **6.** Since neither charge separation nor bond scission takes place during the activation step, activation volume will be close to zero. In other words, the pressure effect observed at the first stage shows the validity of TST in GTA at lower pressures. At the second stage, the pressure increase resulted in strong retardation. Because of a slight suppression of the reaction at the first stage ($\Delta V^{\neq} \approx 2 cm^3 mol^{-1}$), the $\ln k_{obs}$ - P plots for **3** (Figure 2) look somewhat different from that for **1**. However, pressure-induced retardation became pronounced at higher pressures.

Table 1. Activation Energies (Ea /kJ mol^{-1}) and Frequency Factors (A /s^{-1}) for the Activation-Limited Rate Process at 0.1MPa and for the Diffusion-Limited Rate Process at Various Pressures in the Z/E Isomerization of Some Benzaldehyde Anils and Azoarenes

	1		**2**		**3**		**4**		**5**	
P /MPa	Ea	A	Ea	A	Ea	A	Ea	A	Ea	A
0.1	53.5	2.4×10^{12}	49.8	6.9×10^{8}	75.4	1.7×10^{12}	50.8	3.2×10^{8}	27.2	2.3×10^{8}
270									111	2.0×10^{24}
300									115	6.3×10^{24}
330	150	3.8×10^{30}							130	2.4×10^{27}
360	142	8.9×10^{28}							148	3.5×10^{30}
390	141	2.7×10^{28}							165	2.7×10^{33}
420	127	4.4×10^{25}								
450	135	8.6×10^{23}	120	7.3×10^{22}						
480							134	4.2×10^{24}		
500			118	1.1×10^{22}						
510					159	1.1×10^{27}	133	2.5×10^{24}		
540					152	7.8×10^{23}	135	3.7×10^{24}		
550			128	5.1×10^{23}						
570					140	4.6×10^{23}	140	5.5×10^{24}		
600			142	8.0×10^{25}	139	2.1×10^{23}	146	1.5×10^{26}		

Isomerization about the N=N Bond

In polar solvents such as GTA, azoarenes with a strongly electron-donating and an electron-attracting substituent in its 4- and 4'-positions, respectively, isomerize *via* rotation mechanism, i.e., the nitrogen-nitrogen π bond is heterolytically cleaved and rotation about the remaining σ bond leads to the E-isomer. The transition state **7** is highly polar and strong electrostriction results in pressure-induced acceleration ($\Delta V^{\neq} << 0$). The pressure effects for **4** and **5** are shown in Figure 3. In accordance with this mechanism, the reaction was accelerated by an increase in pressure at the first stage and then strong retardation was observed as in **1**.

DISCUSSION

The results presented here suggest that the thermal Z/E isomerization in anils and azoarenes becomes diffusion-controlled at high pressures in GTA. If they proceed *via* two-step mechanism (eq 3) as proposed by Sumi [6], the observed rate constant is given by eq 2 where $k_{dif} = k_1$ and $k_{TST} = k_1k_2/k_{-1}$.

$$\mathrm{Z} \underset{k_{-1}}{\overset{k_1}{\rightleftharpoons}} \mathrm{M} \xrightarrow{k_2} \mathrm{E} \qquad (3)$$

$$k_{-1} + k_2 >> k_1$$

The diffusion-limited rate constants were calculated [7]. The Arrhenius plots for the k_{dif} values were linear indicating that the rate constant is related to a process which needs some activation. The activation energies Ea and the frequency factors A are listed in Table 1 along with the values for the activation-limited rate process at 0.1MPa. Sterically bulkier azonaphthalene **5** is expected to give smaller k_{dif} values. However, the rate constants were actually larger in **5** than in **2**. For example, at 278K and 300MPa, the values were 1050 and 36.1s^{-1} , respectively. The larger frequency factor for **5** gives this unexpected result. If the k_{dif} values are the rate constants for the diffusion-limited rate process, it must be corre-

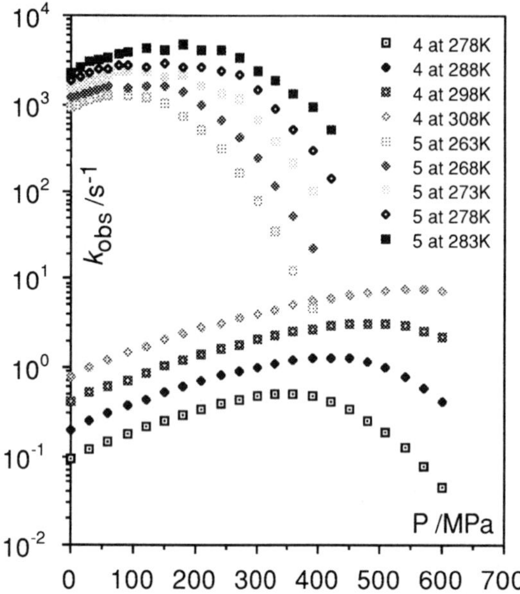

Figure 3. Pressure effects on the isomerization of **4** and **5**.

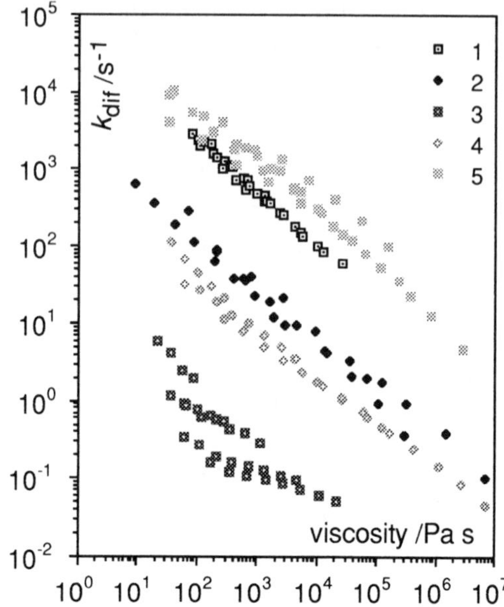

Figure 4. Plots of k_{dif} against solvent viscosity

lated with the solvent viscosity. Such correlations are illustrated in Figure 4. In **1**, **2**, **4**, and **5**, all of the points flock around one straight line. The parameter α in eq 4 were 0.70 (**1**), 0.64 (**2**), 0.60 (**4**), 0.62 (**5**).

$$k_{dif} = B\eta^{-\alpha} \qquad (4)$$

This temperature independence of k_{dif} at the same viscosity suggests that the intermediate M is energetically close to the Z-isomer.

CONCLUSION

Dynamic solvent effects on the rate of thermal *Z*/*E* isomerizations about a carbon-nitrogen and a nitrogen-nitrogen double bond can be analyzed on the basis of eq 2. suggesting the operation of a two-step mechanism as depicted by eq 3.

ACKNOWLEDGMENT

The authors are grateful to Professor Sumi, University of Tsukuba, for his valuable suggestions in the preparation of this manuscript.

REFERENCES

[1] K. Cosstick, T. Asano, and N. Ohno,"Pressure-Induced Retardation of Steric Isomerizations in Highly Viscous Media," in *Proceedings of XIII AIRAPT Conference on High Pressure Science and Technology*, 1991, pp.556-558.

[2] R. M. Noyes, *Prog. React. Kinet.*, **1**, 129 (1961).

[3] K. Cosstick, T. Asano, and N. Ohno, *High Press. Res.*, **11**, 37 (1992).

[4] T. Asano, T. Okada, and W. G. Herkstroeter, *J. Org. Chem.*, **54**, 379 (1989).

[5] T. Asano and T. Okada, *J. Org. Chem.*, **51**, 4454 (1986).

[6] H. Sumi, *J. Phys. Chem.*, **95**, 3334 (1991)..

[7] TST-expected rate constants at high pressures were estimated by extrapolating the results at the first stage of pressurization either by eq a or b [8], where k_P and $k_{0.1}$ are the observed rate constants at P and 0.1MPa, respectively.

$$\ln(k_P/k_{0.1}) = a + bP \qquad (a)$$

$$\ln(k_P/k_{0.1}) = aP + bP/(1+cP) \qquad (b)$$

[8] T. Asano and T. Okada, *J. Phys. Chem.*, **88**, 238 (1984).

PRESSURE EFFECTS ON MENSCHUTKIN REACTIONS IN BUTAN-1-OL AND PENTAN-1-OL

Pinheiro, L. M. V., Calado, A. R. T., and Viana, C. A. N.
FFUL/FCUL/CECUL/IBRC
Cç.Bento Rocha Cabral, 14, 1200 Lisboa, Portugal

In this work results concerning pressure and solvent effects on the Menschutkin reactions rates were determined. The reaction of triethylamine with ethyl iodide was followed conductimetrically at seven different pressures in the range 1 - 2000 bar at 40 °C in the pure solvents butan-1-ol and pentan-1-ol. Special attention was paid to pressure effects from which volumic properties of the solvent were determined.

INTRODUCTION

High pressure kinetics has been proved to be an effective tool to study the transition states of chemical reactions in solution, in terms of activation volumes. Kinetics of polar and ionic reactions in solution, namely solvolytic and Menschutkin reactions are strongly accelerated by high pressure and so negative volumes of activation are produced on account of increasing ionic and dipolar solvation due to the activated complex formation [1-4]. Volumes of activation are thus very discriminative in terms of solvent effects on the reactions [1-8]. The dependence of rate constants of reaction of triethylamine with ethyl iodide in butan-1-ol (1-BuOH) and pentan-1--ol (1-PeOH) on pressure are discussed in terms of volume of activation and extrasolvation numbers. The results are compared with enthalpy and entropy of activation previously studied in this systems and other ones [9].

EXPERIMENTAL

The rate constants of the reaction of triethylamine with ethyl iodide in butan-1-ol and pentan-1-ol were determined using the conductimetric technique and obtained with high accuracy (about 0.1% to the titulimetric 1%).

The purification of the reactants and solvents has been described elsewhere[9,10].

Standard curves relating mole fraction to experimental conductances were determined and used as a calibration method for the kinetic measurements. Duplicate measurements of both calibration and kinetic experiments were made at 1, 100, 250, 500, 1000, 1500 and 2000 bar at 40° C for each solvent.

An autobalanced WAYNE KERR B905 bridge (accuracy 0.05%) and conductivity cells with platinum electrodes with a rod and ring electrode configuration were used for the study of pressure effects. Cell constants ranged from 0.2 to 0.3 cm^{-1}. At least eight different standard solutions of tetraethylammonium iodide of different mole fraction were used to obtain standard mole fraction - conductivity calibration curves corresponding to concentration ranges of, approximately 6.7×10^{-5} - 2.0×10^{-3} mol dm^{-3} for primary alcohol solutions. Calibration curves relating mole fraction (x) to conductivity (κ) of the form $x = a + b\kappa + c\kappa^2$ have been obtained and so reported previously [10].

Both reactants were at the same initial mole fraction, accurate to 0.02 %, and corresponding to concentrations of approximately 3×10^{-2} mol dm^{-3} for primary alcohol solutions.

RESULTS AND DISCUSSION

A collection of accurate rate constants for Menschutkin reactions in two different solvents at several pressures was obtained with standard deviations below 0.5 %.

A second-order rate law was assumed and the equation $x_P/[x^0_R(x^0_R - x_P)] = kt$ (where x_P is the mole fraction of the product and x_R is the mole fraction of either reactant) was used to obtain the rate constants. In Table 1 the rate constants at 40°C as a function of pressure and solvent are presented.

The accuracy and the large number of data in determining the rate constants, justified the calculation of the thermodynamic functions of activation.

Experimental data (lnk,p) were fitted to the Golinkin & Hyne equation [11] ($\ln k = a + bp + cp^2$).

Activation volumes ($\Delta V^{\neq}$) are related to the pressure dependence of reaction rates (k) by $[\Delta V^{\neq} = -RT(\partial \ln k/\partial p)_T]$ and were obtained, using the Golinkin & Hyne equation [11], as a function of pressure and solvent (Table 2).

The ($\Delta V^{\neq}$) parameter was dissected in two components as follows:

$$\Delta V^{\neq} = \Delta V^{\neq}_1 + \Delta V^{\neq}_2 \qquad (1)$$

where ($\Delta V^{\neq}_1$) is concerned with intramolecular structural modifications in the substrate and ($\Delta V^{\neq}_2$) is an intermolecular term concerning substrate-solvent interactions.

The solvent loses all or part of its free volume in the process of activation and so the intermolecular volume of activation ($\Delta V^{\neq}_2$) is related to the solvent free volume (V_m - V_s) assuming that the process of electrostriction compresses the neighbouring solvent. Equating the volume of activation in terms of the solvent free volume it is possible to obtain [1,2]

$$\Delta V^{\neq} = \Delta V^{\neq}_1 - n(V_m - V_s) \qquad (2)$$

where (V_m) and (V_s) are the solvent molar volume and the solid volume in the bulk, respectively, ie, the liquid volume and the non-operable volume, and (n) is the extrasolvation number (it is a measure of difference between the number of molecules that solvate the activated complex and the reactants).

Considering that ($\Delta V^{\neq}_1$) varies much less with (V_m) than ($\Delta V^{\neq}_2$) it can be assumed that $(\partial \Delta V^{\neq}/\partial V_m) = n$. Such a derivative is determined through ($\Delta V^{\neq}$,V_m) variations which are always very approximately linear (correlation factor, r = = 0.99). An example is shown in Figure 1.

The extrasolvation numbers (n) were determined for each solvent [2,9] (Table 3). As can be seen the (n) values decrease as the carbon chain lenght of the solvent increases. Such value suggest a more intricate activated complex, which is in accord with previous results shown [9] (Table 3).

The values of these thermodynamic functions permitted to obtain information concerned to mechanism, revealing accordance with other thermodynamic functions in systems previously studied [9,12-14].

The variations in enthalpy of activation ($\Delta H^{\neq}$) are generally high which is in accord with

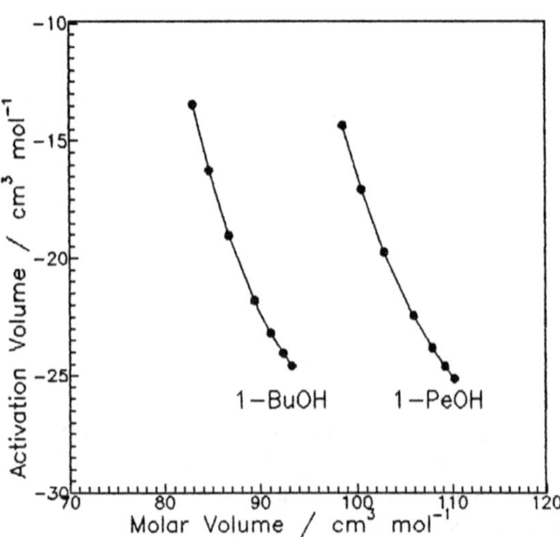

Figure 1. Activation Volumes of the reaction of Et_3N with EtI as a function of Molar Volume (T = 313.15 K)

the high covalent bond energy for both N-C and C-I. In this step a large solvent assistance would be required which agrees with the negative values of the entropy of activation ($\Delta S^{\neq} < 0$).

The high values of the enthalpies of activation [9], ($\Delta H^{\neq}$) (and their constancy or otherwise,) are well related to the extrasolvation numbers and to the high negative values of the volumes of activation (Table 3).

This is all in accordance with the higher polarity of the activated complex giving it a more solvated state compared with that of the reactants.

Table 1. Rate constants as a function of pressure and solvent (T = 313.15 K)

Solvent	$(k\pm\sigma k)\times10^5$/(mole fraction)$^{-1}$s^{-1}						
p/bar	1	100	250	500	1000	1500	2000
1-BuOH	10.910±	11.979±	13.822±	17.163±	25.773±	36.812±	49.577±
	±0.007	±0.008	±0.001	±0.001	±0.021	±0.033	±0.073
1-PeOH	6.958±	8.002±	9.133±	11.238±	16.545±	22.749±	31.150±
	±0.008	±0.020	±0.002	±0.015	±0.024	±0.017	±0.064

Table 2 Volumes of activation as a function of pressure and solvent (T = 313.15 K)

Solvent	$-\Delta V^{\neq}\pm\sigma(\Delta V^{\neq})$/cm^3 mol^{-1}						
p/bar	1	100	250	500	1000	1500	2000
1-BuOH	25.13±	24.60±	23.79±	22.44±	19.74±	17.04±	14.33±
	±0.13	±0.12	±0.10	±0.02	±0.03	±0.08	±0.14
1-PeOH	24.58±	24.02±	23.19±	21.80±	19.01±	16.23±	13.44±
	±1.17	±1.06	±0.89	±0.62	±0.31	±0.70	±1.25

Table 3. Thermodynamic functions of activation (T = 313.15 K; p = 1 bar)

Solvent	$\Delta G^{\neq}\pm\sigma(\Delta G^{\neq})$ /kJmol^{-1}	$\Delta H^{\neq}\pm\sigma(\Delta H^{\neq})$ /kJmol^{-1}	$-\Delta S^{\neq}\pm\sigma(\Delta S^{\neq})$ /JK^{-1}mol^{-1}	$-\Delta V^{\neq}\pm\sigma(\Delta V^{\neq})$ /cm^3 mol^{-1}	n
1-BuOH	101.21±0.01	76.4±1.2	79.1±4.2	25.1±0.1	1.0
1-PeOH	101.71±0.01	76.9±1.4	79.3±4.5	24.6±1.2	0.9

REFERENCES

[1] C. A. N. Viana, Rev. Fac. Cienc Univ. Lisboa, Ser. B, 11, 5, (1967-1968).

[2] C. A. N. Viana and G. J. Hills, Hydrogen-Bonded Solvent Systems, ed. A. K. Covington and P. Jones, Taylor and Francis: London, (1968), pp. 261-273.

[3] C. A. N. Viana and R. M. C. Goncalves, J. Chem., Faraday I, 76, 753-757, (1980).

[4] C. Cameron, P. P. S. Saluja, N. A. Floriano and E. Whalley, J. Phys. Chem., 92, 3417-3421, (1988)

[5] Y. Kondo, M. Ohnishi and N. Tokura, Bull. Chem. Soc. Jpn., 45, 3579-3583,(1972).

[6] T. Asano and W. J. le Noble, Rev. Phys. Chem. Jpn., 43, 82, (1973).

[7] T. Asano, T. Yano and T. Okada, J. Am. Chem. Soc., 104, 4900, (1982).

[8] C. A. Eckert, Ann. Rev. Phys. Chem., 23, 239

(1972).
[9] C. A. N. Viana, A. R. T. Calado and L. M. V. Pinheiro, J. Chem. Res. (S), 6-7,(1992); (M), 0173-0181, (1992).
[10] C. A. N. Viana and A. R. T. Calado, Port. Electrochim. Acta, 6, 149-166, (1988).
[11] H. S. Golinkin, W. G. Laidlaw and J. B. Hyne, Can. J. Chem., 44, 2193-2203, (1966).
[12] E. M. Arnett and R. Reich, J. Am. Chem. Soc., 102, 5892-5902, (1980).
[13] M. H. Abraham, Pure Appl. Chem., 57, 1055-1064, (1985).
[14] J. L. M. Abboud, A. Douhal, M. J. Arin, M. T. H. Diez, H. Homan and G. Guihneuf, J. Phys. Chem., 93, 214-220, (1989).

AUTOXIDATION OF LINOLENIC ACID UNDER HIGH PRESSURE

Kowalski, E.; Tauscher B.
Federal Research Centre for Nutrition
Engesserstr. 20
76131 Karlsruhe
Germany

Ludwig H.
University of Heidelberg
Institute for Physical Chemistry
INF 346
69120 Heidelberg
Germany

We studied the reactions of linolenic acid under conditions of high pressure sterilisation, with special emphasis on hydroperoxides forming in the second reaction step of autoxidation. Reaction products were seperated by HPLC and detected by UV at 234 nm.

A comparative study on forming the first reaction products under atmospheric pressure and at 350 Mpa, at 313 K was carried out by measuring the absorption at 234 nm.

INTRODUCTION

During the last years the use of hydrostatic pressure up to 700 MPa to sterilize food has gained in importance [1]. One of the main advantages as compared to conventional sterilization methods is that pressure does not affect covalent bonds and therefore less chemical reactions are expected in pressure processed food. Whether a chemical reaction is promoted by pressure depends on the activation volume of the system concerned.

$$\Delta V^{\ddagger} = -RT\frac{\partial \ln k}{\partial p}$$

Reactions may be promoted if the activation volume is negative; the transition state has less volume than the educt. In principle forming of a covalent bond during the reaction is favoured by pressure, while breaking (forming of radicals) of covalent bonds is inhibited.

If there is no effect on the reaction in the range of 100 to 500 MPa, further increase in pressure will have no significant effect [2].

O
C
OH

Linolenic acid

Linolenic acid is a nutrient which, however, oxidizes readily to physiologically less valuable and even toxic products. Linolenic acid present e.g. in soybean oil, is essential for the retinal development in children, fluidity of membranes, and as part of human brain tissue [3]. Therefore it is important to make sure that the linolenic acid is not affected during processing of the food. The mechanism for the autoxidation is according to the following scheme:

initiation

$$initiator \longrightarrow free\ radicals$$

propagation

$$R\cdot + O_2 \longrightarrow ROO\cdot +$$
$$ROO\cdot + 2RH \longrightarrow ROOH + R\cdot$$

termination

$$\left.\begin{array}{llll} R\cdot & + & R\cdot & \longrightarrow \\ R\cdot & + & ROO\cdot & \longrightarrow \\ ROO\cdot & + & ROO\cdot & \longrightarrow \end{array}\right\} \textit{non radical products}$$

The first oxidation products of linolenic acid are hydroperoxides formed during the propagation step.

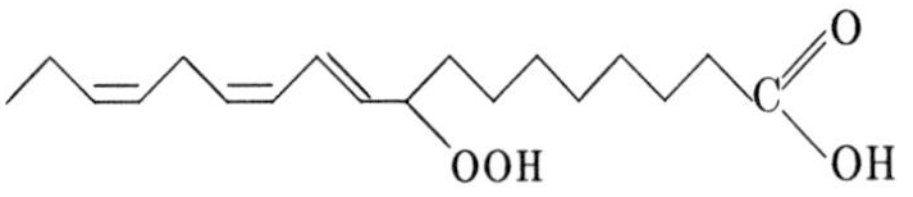

9-hydroperoxy-octadecatrienoic acid

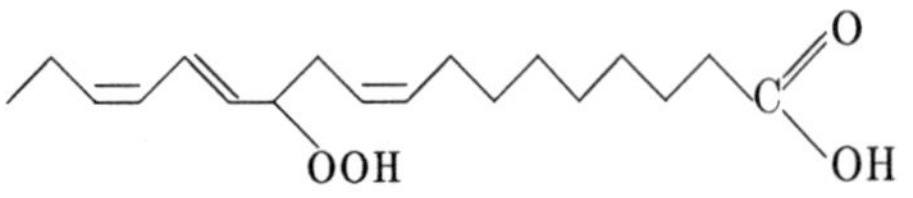

12-hydroperoxy-octadecatrienoic acid

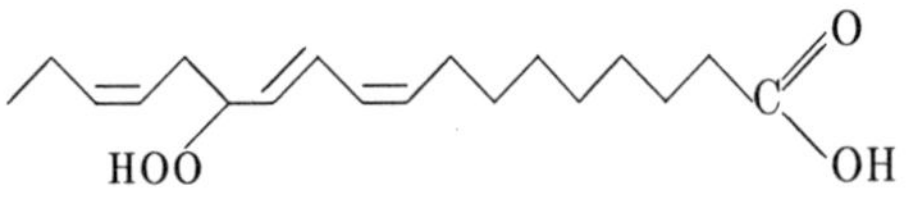

13-hydroperoxy-octadecatrienoic acid

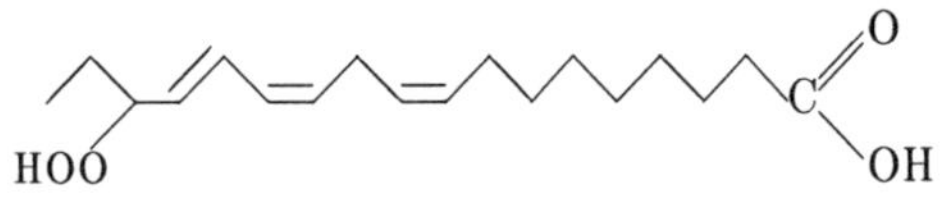

16-hydroperoxy-octadecatrienoic acid

For each of the four hydroperoxides, geometric isomers exist, each having a conjugated diene system in either cis–trans (as shown above) or trans–trans configuration, and an isolated double bond that is always cis [4].

MATERIAL AND METHODS

GENERAL

Linolenic acid was purchased from ROTH (Karlsruhe), and used without further purification. Derivatizating reagent Diazald was obtained from ALDRICH, all solvents from MERCK (Darmstadt), HPLC–Eurosphere column from KNAUR (Berlin).

SAMPLE PREPARATION

100 μl aliquots of linolenic acid were pipetted into small bags of LD–polyethylene–aluminium laminate and heat sealed. 10 ml oxygen were added to each bag using a syringe; then the bag was sealed again.

PRESSURE TREATMENT

The apparatus used consisted of three separate autoclaves (12 ml volume each), thermostated by water. Pressure up to 350 MPa was generated by an air-driven hydraulic pump.

ANALYTICAL

UV–Absorption

5 μl linolenic acid were added to 5 ml 80 % ethanol. The absorption at 234 nm (conjugated diene absorption) was measured using a BECKMANN DU–6 Spectrophotometer.

HPLC

Before separating the oxidation products by HPLC, free acids were converted into the corresponding methylesters using diazomethane.

Analytical HPLC was carried out on a 12 × 0.4 cm Eurosphere 80C–8 column. The products were eluted using a gradient of acetonitrile/water = 50/50 to 80/20 in 20 minutes at a flow rate of 1 ml · min^{-1} [5].

Column effluents were continously monitored by an ultraviolet detector, set at 234 nm and 215 nm, via a 10 μl flow cell.

RESULTS AND DISCUSSION

UV absorption at 234 nm after different times of pressure treatment and at atmospheric pressure shows differences in the amount of primary oxidation products of the conjugated diene structure; this may be correlated to the amount of hydroperoxides.

Figure 1 shows that forming of primary oxidation products is favoured by pressure, though to a limited extent; the curve shows a maximum. This is in agreement with theoretical considerations, according to which the propagation step should be promoted under pressure. The limitation may be due to the small amount of radicals present in the linolenic acid and to the fact that pressure does not favour generation of new radicals.

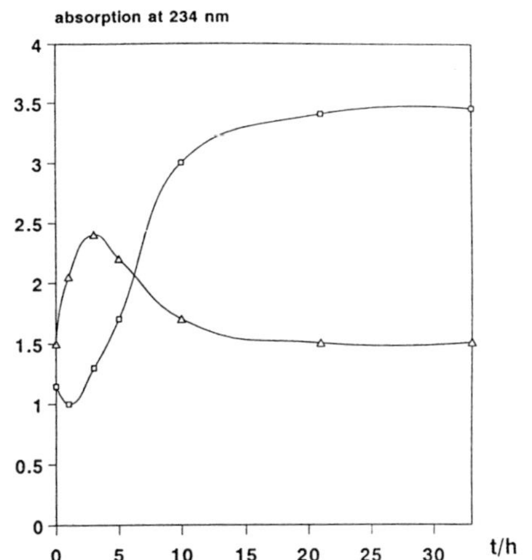

Fig. 1 : Absorption of linolenic acid (in 80% ethanol) at 234 nm after different times of pressure treatment and at atmospheric pressure. (T = 313 K)
△ : 350 MPa □ : 0.1 MPa

Separation of the oxidation products was carried out using HPLC; the conjugated dienes were detected at 234 nm, at 215 nm methyl linolenate has its absorption maximum.

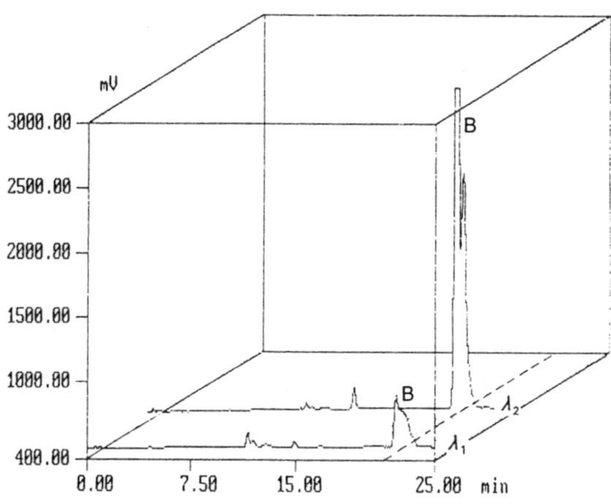

Fig. 2 : HPLC chromatogram of purchased methyl linolenate (*B*) detected at λ_1 = 234nm and λ_2 = 215nm

Figure 2 shows the derivatized linolenic acid as used for the experiments, detected at two different wavelengths; the peak (*B*) appearing after about 23 minutes corresponds to methyl linolenate.

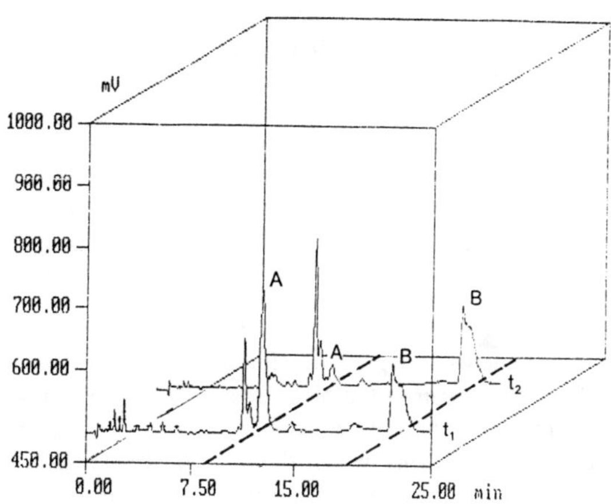

Fig. 3 : HPLC chromatogram of oxidized methyl linolenate after t_1 = 1h and t_2 = 21h at 350 MPa and 313 K; UV detection at 234 nm

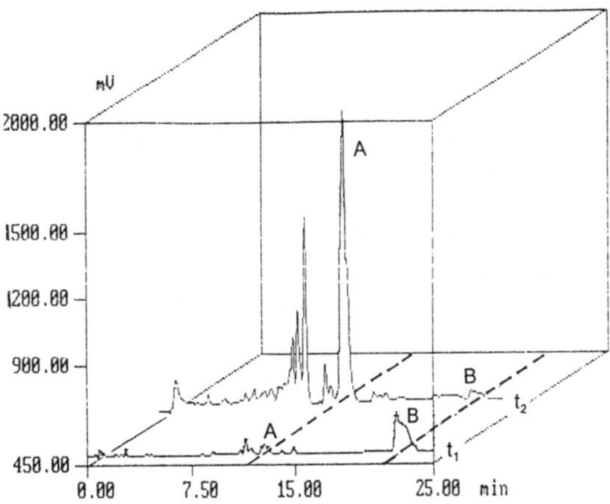

Fig. 4 : HPLC chromatogram of oxidized methyl linolenate after t_1 = 1h and t_2 = 21h at atmospheric pressure (0.1 MPa) and 313 K; UV detection at 234 nm

Figures 3 and 4 show the oxidation products detected at 234 nm after different times of treatment. Figure 3 shows pressure treated methyl linolenate (*B*) and its oxidation products; the main difference between the treatment of 1 hour and 21 hours is the amount of the substance (*A*) appearing at about 8 minutes. It decreases with increasing duration of the pressure treatment. Figure 4 shows for the same peak as above (*A*) the following oxidation behaviour at atmospheric pressure : *A* is increasing with increasing oxidation time. There are also extra peaks appearing after about 10 minutes.
It is obvious also, that the amount of methyl linolenate (*B*) left after 21 hours of pressure treatment (350 MPa) is nearly unchanged, while it decreases at atmospheric pressure.

Generally it can be said that autoxidation of linolenic acid is influenced by pressure. In the first stage of oxidation under pressure (350 MPa) more primary oxidation products form than at atmospheric pressure. A second stage follows, during which diene absorption increases in the sample oxidized at atmospheric pressure, but decreases for the sample exposed to high pressure. Finally a saturation point is reached for both samples, however, at different concentrations of conjugated dienes.

This simplified model has to be extended by further experiments to identify the different products.

References

[1] J.C. Cheftel, *IAA,* pp. 141–153,(1991)

[2] Le Noble, *Organic High Pressure Chemistry,* ELSEVIER,1988, ch.9, pp. 254–282

[3] F.D. Gunstone, *Prog. Lipid Res.* Vol. 31, No. 2, pp. 145–161 (1992)

[4] O.R. Fennema, *Food Chemistry* DEKKER INC,1985, ch. 4, pp. 139–245

[5] E. Kaplan, *Journal of Chromatogr.* 350, pp. 435–443 (1985)

SOLID STATE CHEMICAL REACTIONS AT THE SHOCK FRONT

K.R. Iyer
U.S. Army Research Office, Research Triangle Park, NC 27709
and
L.S. Bennett, F.Y. Sorrell, and Y. Horie
North Carolina State University, Raleigh, NC 27695

Instrumented high velocity impact recovery experiments were performed to study solid state reactions in mixtures of nickel and aluminum powders during the passage of shock waves. "Excess pressure" due to the release of energy from the exothermic reaction was measured for a range of impact velocities. An impact velocity threshold for the initiation of reaction at the reflected shock front was established and this threshold value was found to be dependent on the particle size of the powder. Microscopic examination of the recovered specimens show features which corroborate hypothesized extent of reaction based on pressure measurements.

INTRODUCTION

Until as recently as 1987, the possibility of chemical reaction at the shock front was speculative. Thadhani [1] has written an exhaustive review of the subject of shock-induced chemical reactions which also covers the subject of chemical reactions at the shock front. This investigation is based on the premise that the examination of the post-shock recovery specimen alone will not establish when the reaction took place. It is clear that understanding the kinetics of such reactions, which are obviously beyond the realm of diffusion mechanisms, will require measurements of changes at the shock front. The energy released by exothermic reactions is expected to manifest itself as pressure and temperature. We chose to attempt to make time-resolved pressure measurements when a green compact of a suitable mixture of powders of nickel and aluminum is subjected to planar high velocity impact.

EXPERIMENTS

The details of the recovery fixture, powder gun assembly, velocity and pressure measurement techniques, and the preparation of specimens have been described in previous publications [2-4]. Gauges located in front of the specimen to measure the incident wave on the specimen did not survive to produce reliable measurements. Manganin gauge epoxied to the back of the rear cover disc survived for about a microsecond and produced reproducible records during the half a microsecond between the reflection of the compression wave from the rear cover disc and the arrival of release wave. The recording digitizing oscilloscope gave a data point every 50 nanoseconds.

Green compacts of 55% of the theoretical density of solid mixture of Ni and Al powders were impacted by a 304 stainless steel flyer plate at the front surface of a lexan projectile driven to a series of velocities in a 19mm powder gun. The size of the Al powder was 20 μm in all the experiments; two series of experiments, one with Ni powder of 3-7 μm and another with $<3\mu$m size were performed. Experiments with pure Al powder compact and Ni powder compacts were also performed to compare the calculated peak reflected pressure values with the measured values and validate the reliability of the measurement technique. A 2.6:1 Ni to Al atomic weight percent ratio was maintained to keep the impedance of the fully densified mixture lower than that of the 304 SS in order for the wave reflected from the rear cover disc to be compressive. After the experiment, portions of the specimen, strongly adhered to the rear cover disc, were recovered and subjected to metallographic examination, usually in the polished and unetched condition. Nondispersive Energy X-ray spectroscopy in the Scanning Electron Microscope helped identify the reaction products qualitatively.

RESULTS

Figure 1 shows a typical pressure-time record. The impact velocity was 1075 m/s. The predicted value is the reflected peak pressure at the interface of a fully dense inert mixture of Ni and Al in the ratio of 2.6:1 by atomic weight and 304 SS rear cover plate. The shock properties were calculated from published data for Ni and Al and on the bases of simple mixture theory and the assumption of complete densification by the passage of the incident shock wave through the specimen. Temperature effects due to the heating of the specimen were not considered. In a series of experiments with increasing impact velocity, a threshold velocity, below which the measured peak pressure was slightly lower than the predicted peak pressure and above which the measured value was much higher than the predicted value, was

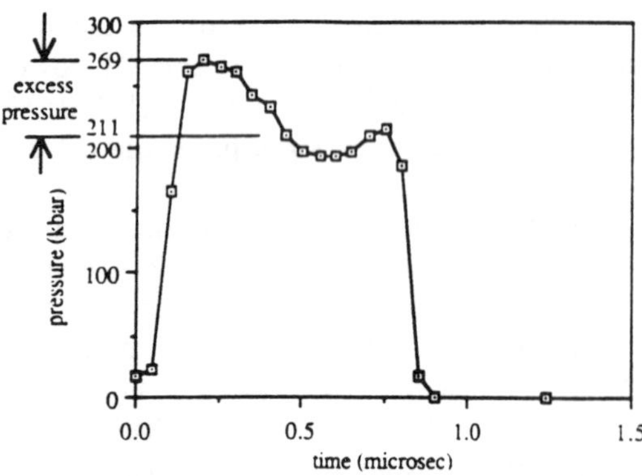

Figure 1. Typical Pressure-Time data for an impact experiment. (1075 m/s. 3-7μm Ni powder)

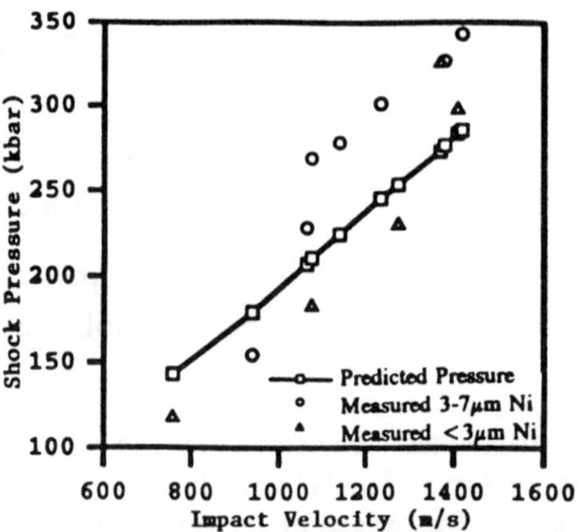

Figure 2. Measured reflected shock pressure vs impact velocity for two series of experiments.

observed. Above the threshold the "excess pressure" was about the same irrespective of the impact velocity. In another series of similar experiments with a smaller size Ni powder in the mixture, the threshold at which the excess pressure was observed was shifted to a higher impact velocity. Results of both series of experiments are summarized in Figure 2.

At low velocities of impact, the recovered specimens did not show any sign of compound formation. At high enough but lower than the threshold impact velocity, specimens revealed regions of reaction products. Figure 3 is a photo micrograph of a recovered specimen with regions of unreacted Al surrounded by rings of light and

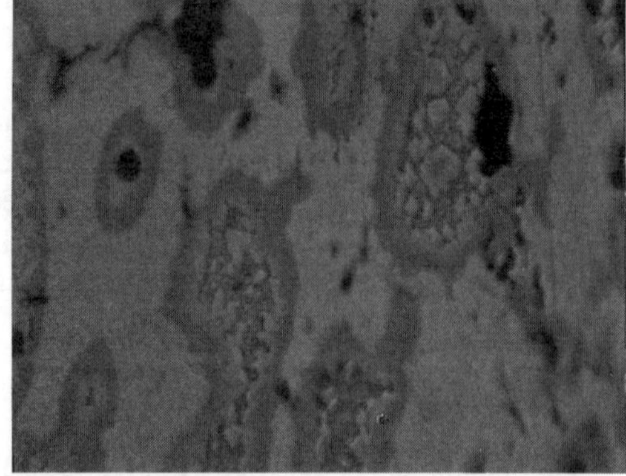

Figure 3. Photomicrograph of a sub-threshold recovery specimen. No "excess pressure" was evident in this experiment. (1075 m/s. < 3μm Ni) 300X

gray regions of Al +Ni compound and unreacted Ni. Above the threshold but at the lower velocity region all the aluminum had combined with nickel but Ni-rich and Al-free regions are still present. At higher velocities reaction products were found all over with a range of Al-Ni ratios. Figure 4 shows regions of compound melting.

DISCUSSION

At impact velocities near but lower than threshold velocity, consistent with our previously reported results [2] on the Sn-S system, reaction products were found but the measured peak pressure was lower than the predicted value. Heating by the shock is sufficient to melt the aluminum in the mixture thus making any reaction diffusion-controlled and the post-shock reaction proceeds but is arrested by the massive quenching by the fixture. Above the threshold, the "excess pressure" recorded is reproducible and much larger than the possible experimental errors in measurement (3%). Exothermic reaction at the reflected shock front is a definite possibility. Obviously, the extent of reaction in the recovered specimen is more than what could have occurred during the passage of the reflected shock wave because the reaction could continue by diffusion in the post-shock specimen until, as explained before, the fixture would arrest the reaction. It is reasonable to expect the same amount of reaction in the reflected shock front irrespective of the impact velocity especially if one considers the small range of impact velocities in this investigation. But at higher impact velocities, the specimen is heated to a greater extent and the diffusion controlled reaction proceeds further. Small regions of what is considered to be molten and solidified reaction products could be found only in specimens impacted at the high velocities. The pressure-time traces at these velocities also showed greater drops after the peak value of pressure.

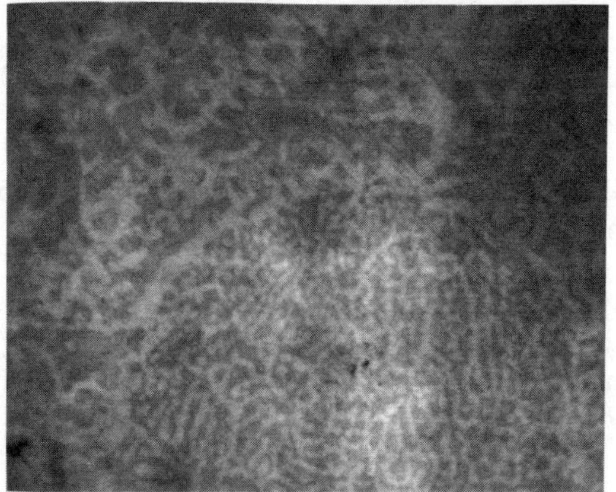

Figure 4. Scanning electron micrograph of a post-threshold specimen. Melting of the product is indicated. (1380 m/s. 3-7μm Ni) 750X

In an experiment in which the back cover plate of 304 stainless steel was replaced by lexan whose impedance is less than that of the dense mixture of Ni + Al. The recovered specimen did not show any sign of reaction even though the impact velocity was about 1300 m/s. Complete pore collapse and a certain similarity with recovered specimens impacted at velocities lower than the threshold value were observed; this would lead one to believe that heating by pore collapse alone may not be sufficient to trigger and sustain the reaction by shock wave. Unfortunately, a pressure-time trace was not obtained in this experiment. Nevertheless, the possibility of the incident shock densifying and conditioning the mixture such that the reaction took place only in the reflected shock is indicated. It would have been preferable to conduct an experiment at high enough impact velocity which corresponded to the energy levels of the reflected shock in the specimen. Currently we do not have facilities in our laboratory for that.

The effect of the smaller Ni particle size in the second series of experiments was to shift the threshold velocity to a higher value. The impact velocity for the ultrafast reaction thresholds of the two Ni-Al mixtures appears to be inversely related to the particle size. This may be a clue to a physical description of the ultrafast reaction mechanisms. The mixture constituents have different impedances and it is not realistic to assume that the particle velocities are immediately in equilibrium during and just behind the shock front. So a relative particle velocity may exist between the constituents [5]. In fact this relative particle velocity may be greatly increased during the reflected shock front where it is possible for the constituents to be moving in opposite directions for a short period [6]. This relative particle velocity will be equilibrated by inter-particle shear which is also inversely related to the particle size. A recent Eulerian model of this process shows that this equilibration takes place in about 100 nanoseconds [6], i.e., in and just behind the reflected shock front. This inter-particle shear will rapidly expose fresh reaction surfaces and cause extreme mass mixing. Dremin and Breusov [7] have indicated that reaction nucleation and propagation may occur under these conditions within these time constraints. If a critical value in inter-particle shear must be overcome for these ultrafast reactions to occur, they will occur at different impact velocities for different particle size mixtures.

CONCLUSIONS

Time-resolved measurements of the reflected shock pressure profile through exothermic mixtures have yielded measured peak pressures in excess of those predicted for the inert systems. This excess pressure is attributed to the heat released by ultrafast exothermic reactions at the shock front. Ultrafast reaction thresholds have been observed and the reactions have been observed to occur in the reflected shock front. The reaction takes place in about 100 nanosecond. The occurrence of ultrafast reaction thresholds has been corroborated through material analysis of the recovered specimens. Assuming that the ultrafast reaction product is $NiAl_3$, Hugoniot calculations which account for the heat of reaction show that the excess pressure represents a nearly complete reaction. A change in the size of the nickel particles used in the Ni-Al mixture resulted in a substantial shift in the ultrafast reaction threshold. This hints at a physical description of the reaction mechanism. The ultrafast reaction mechanism may be related to interparticle shear which is necessary to equilibrate relative particle velocities within and just behind the shock front and may rapidly expose fresh reaction surfaces for ultrafast reactions.

ACKNOWLEDGEMENT

This work was funded by the U.S. Army Research Office under Grant # DAAL03-89-C-0037 to North Carolina State University

REFERENCES

[1] N. N. Thadhani, Progress in Material Science, 37, pp. 117-226 (1993).

[2] L. S. Bennett et.al, "Shock Compression of Condensed Matter 1991," Ed. S.C. Schmidt and others, Elsevier Science Publishers B.V. pp. 605-608 (1992).

[3] L. S. Bennett et.al., Appl. Phys. Lett. 61(5), pp. 520-521) (1992).

[4] L. S. Bennett, "Experimental Investigation of Exothermic Reactions During Shock Loading," Ph.D. Thesis, North Carolina State University, 1992.

[5] S. S. Batsonov et. al., Combustion,Explosion, and Shock waves, 22(6), pp. 765-768 (1987).

[6] S.K. Yu, "Computational Modeling of Non-Equilibrium Flow in Condensed Media," Ph.D. Thesis, North Carolina State University, 1992.

[7] A. N. Dremin and O. N. Breusov, Russian Chemical Reviews, 37(5), 392-402 (1968).

MOLECULAR DYNAMICS STUDIES OF SHOCK INITIATION IN A MODEL ENERGETIC MATERIAL

P J Haskins and M D Cook
DRA, Fort Halstead, Sevenoaks, Kent TN14 7BP, UK

In this paper we report the results of molecular dynamics simulations of shock initiation in an energetic material. An Abell-Tersoff potential has been used to represent a lattice of diatomic molecules capable of undergoing an exothermic reaction. This model system has been employed to investigate the critical conditions for initiation of a chemically sustained shock wave. The effect of shock pulses of differing amplitude and duration have been studied, and some variations in the potential parameters have been considered to examine the influence of potential barriers on the initiation thresholds. Finally the results of these simulations are compared with the classical picture of initiation in homogeneous explosives.

INTRODUCTION

In a number of recent papers [1,2,3] Brenner and co-workers have described the use of a modified Abell-Tersoff potential in molecular dynamics simulations of chemically sustained shock waves. Building on this work we have written a fast molecular dynamics code incorporating this potential and carried out studies of initiation thresholds.

For a full description of the Abell-Tersoff potential the reader is referred to [1], but it is worth noting that the versatility of this potential makes it particularly attractive, enabling the potential barriers or exothermicity of the reaction to be easily adjusted. The main purpose of this study was to look at how various factors influence the critical conditions for obtaining a sustained reaction, and to compare the results of these model simulations with the known behaviour of real systems and the classical thermal explosion theory description.

GENERAL PROPERTIES OF THE MODEL

The simulations described here all involved an initial lattice of AB diatomic molecules capable of undergoing exothermic reaction to A_2 and B_2 molecules. Both 2D and 3D simulations have been carried out, although the majority of the results to date are for 2D systems. For both 2D and 3D simulations the initial lattice was at near zero pressure and temperature. In the 2D simulations the molecules in the initial lattice were inclined at 45 degrees to the direction of the shock (x axis), whilst in the 3D simulations an alpha face centred cubic lattice was used. Periodic boundary conditions were imposed on the y axis (2D), or the y and z axes (3D). An initial shock was input to the lattice by impacting it with a flyer composed of the same AB molecules. By varying the thickness and velocity of this flyer it was possible to alter the duration and amplitude of the shock.

In the calculations reported here two sets of potential parameters have been employed. The first set were identical to those in [1], and had well depths of 2eV and 5eV for the heteronuclear and homonuclear diatomics respectively. A second series of simulations was carried out with these well depths reduced to 1ev and 4ev. This had the effect of halving the unimolecular A-B bond dissociation energy whilst leaving the exothermicity of the reaction unaltered.

We find, as did Brenner et.al. [1,3], that provided the initial stimulus is sufficiently strong a chemically sustained shock wave is formed which travels at a velocity which is independent of the initiating stimulus. In the 2D simulations this wave, which we will henceforth refer to as a detonation, travels at ca. 6 km/s, for both sets of potential parameters. Although no systematic 3D studies have as yet been completed the simulations to date show very similar results to those from the 2D calculations, albeit with a slightly reduced velocity of detonation. By way of illustration Figure 1 shows a snapshot of part of a 3D simulation taken at 3.2ps after impact of the flyer. For simplicity the view is normal to the x and y axes, making the undisturbed alpha fcc lattice appear 2D. The dense reaction zone behind the leading shock, and the A_2 and B_2 product molecules emerging from the rear of this zone are clearly visible.

INITIATION STUDIES

Pulse Amplitude and Duration Effects

Using the original well depths of 2ev and 5ev for the heteronuclear and homonuclear molecules we ran a number of 2D simulations with different flyer velocities and thicknesses. The flyer thicknesses ranged from $5A^o$ to $37.5A^o$, and the effect of this variation in flyer thickness on the critical velocities to achieve detonation is shown in table 1.

Table 1. Threshold velocities for initiation as a function of flyer thickness. AB well depth = 2eV.

Flyer Thickness (A^o)	Flyer Velocity (km/s)
5.0	8.5-8.25
10.0	5.8-5.6
12.5	5.3-5.1
17.5	4.3-4.2
37.5	4.15-4.1

The velocities quoted in Table 1 are those of the slowest simulation which produced a stable detonation and the fastest which did not. It should be noted that at velocities just below the threshold, chemical reaction does occur but fails to build to a stable detonation. The shock durations for these impacts has been calculated (by determining the shock-particle velocity relationship (Hugoniot) for the initial lattice) and the results are shown in Figure 2 as a plot of shock energy versus pulse duration. The most notable features of this plot are the strong dependence of shock energy on duration for very short pulses, and the weak dependence on duration for longer pulses. This is discussed later in the section on thermal explosion theory.

Activation Barrier Effects

By carrying out further simulations of the type described above, but with the well depths decreased by 1ev, it was possible to see the effect of reducing the activation barrier whilst retaining the same exothermicity. Table 2 shows the critical velocities for this system.

Table 2. Threshold velocities for initiation as a function of flyer thickness. AB well depth = 1eV.

Flyer Thickness (A^o)	Flyer Velocity (km/s)
5.0	3.6-3.4
10.0	3.1-3.0
12.5	2.95-2.75
17.5	2.6-2.4
37.5	2.5-2.4

In Figure 3 we again show the results in the form of threshold shock energies versus pulse duration. (It should be noted that the Hugoniot for this system is significantly different from that with the original potential parameters.) It can clearly be seen that a very similar shape of response curve is obtained with the reduced activation barrier, but that the critical energies / velocities are, as expected, much lower.

Interpretation by Thermal Explosion Theory

Since the initial lattice we are impacting contains no defects we are in essence studying initiation in a homogeneous explosive. Initiation in such systems has traditionally been interpreted in terms of thermal explosion theory [4,5]. The essential concept in such interpretations is that after the initial shock heating there is an induction time before significant chemical reaction (and therefore release of energy) takes place. Provided no

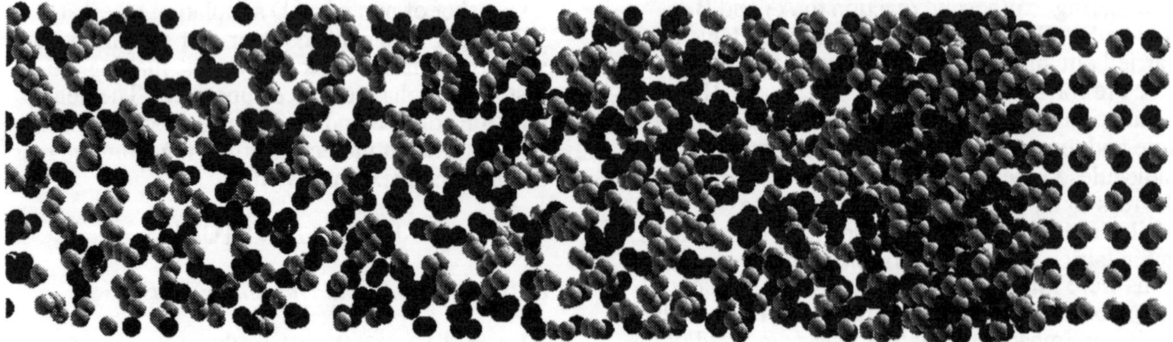

Figure 1. A snapshot of part of a 3D simulation. The shock wave is moving from left to right, and the A and B atoms are displayed as light and dark.

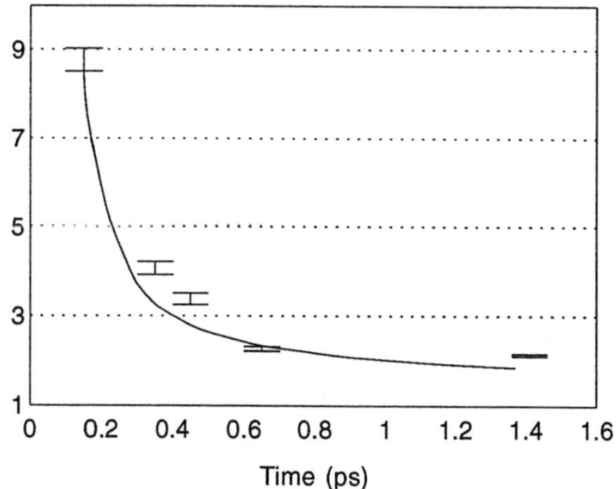

Figure 2. Shock Energy - Pulse Duration threshold curve. A-B well depth = 2eV.

I Molecular dynamics results.

— Thermal explosion theory prediction with W = 13.0, and v = $1.3\text{x}10^{13}$.

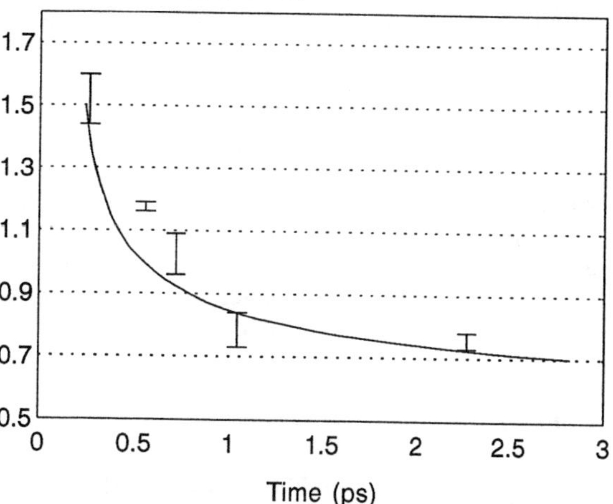

Figure 3. Shock Energy - Pulse Duration threshold curve. A-B well depth = 1eV.

I Molecular dynamics results.

— Thermal explosion theory prediction with W = 6.5, and v = $1.3\text{x}10^{13}$.

rarefaction cools the shocked material before the induction period is complete then detonation is assumed to occur.

It should be noted that the concept of an induction time, before which any significant reaction occurs, will break down for very strong shocks where the shock heating can become comparable to that from the exothermic decomposition. Under these extreme conditions (which some of the molecular dynamics runs simulate) it is not strictly correct to separate the hydrodynamics and the chemistry. However, even in these circumstances it is instructive to calculate the time required for any given percentage of the material to have reacted, and base an approximate initiation criterion on this. Here we have attempted to fit the molecular dynamics results to a simple model of this kind, based on a single reaction step.

For a single step, first order process, controlled by Arhenius kinetics Hubbard and Johnson [4] have shown that the time for a fraction (f) of the original material to have reacted is given by:

$$t = v^{-1}\int_0^f (1-f)^{-1} \exp(W/(E_o+Qf))\, df \qquad (1)$$

where v is the frequency factor, E_o is the shock energy, Q the exothermicity of the reaction and W is given by:

$$W = C_v E_a / R \qquad (2)$$

in which E_a is the activation energy, C_v the specific heat (assumed constant), and R the molar gas constant. We have used the above expressions to calculate threshold response curves for the shock energies used in the molecular dynamics simulations. By choosing suitable values for W and v it was possible to obtain good fits to the molecular dynamics results (See figures 2 and 3). In the calculations shown here the induction time was taken to be that for f=0.9 (ie the time for 90% of the material to react), but similar quality fits could be obtained with a wide range of values for f, albeit with slightly different values for W and v. Q was fixed at 3eV/ molecule (=10.29MJ/kg) in all the calculations.

There are a number of points to note concerning the thermal explosion response curves. Firstly, they provide a reasonably good fit to the molecular dynamics results for both sets of potential parameters. The strong dependence of shock energy on pulse duration for short pulses and the weak dependence for longer pulses is well represented. Secondly, the results for the potential with the halved unimolecular bond strength are well-fitted by using a value for W which is half that used to fit the results from the original potential, whilst the frequency factor v remains unchanged. Finally, it is interesting to note that the values of W and v required to achieve the fits are chemically sensible. Whilst C_V is not known exactly, if we assume the classical estimate for a diatomic of 5R/2 then the values of W needed to obtain a fit imply activation energies of ca. 1.5 and 0.75 eV for the two potential sets. These values, which amount to 75% of the unimolecular bond strengths, seem eminently reasonable.

Comparison with Real Systems

Experimental data on homogeneous explosives generally shows a fairly weak dependence of critical shock energy on pulse duration. This is entirely consistent with both the molecular dynamics results and the thermal explosion theory predictions for 'relatively long' duration shocks. Extrapolation of the thermal explosion fit shown in figure 2 would predict a critical flyer velocity of 2.1 km/s for a 2mm thick flyer. This is a very plausible value, suggesting that the original potential parameters provide a realistic simulation of typical homogeneous explosives. It is also interesting to note that a threshold pulse amplitude - duration curve similar to figures 2 and 3 has been observed experimentally for TATB [6] impacted by thin flyers. Whilst TATB is normally regarded as a heterogeneous explosive, it may be that in this, and possibly other insensitive explosives, the homogeneous initiation mechanism plays an important and possibly dominant role.

CONCLUSIONS

The results reported here have shown that a molecular dynamics model based on the Abell-Tersoff potential is capable of representing initiation in a way which is consistent with both the known behaviour of real homogeneous explosives and a simple thermal explosion model. The fit to a thermal explosion model was surprisingly good when one considers the approximate nature of the model. No doubt improved fits could be obtained by allowing for multiple reaction steps and variation in Cv. However, at very high shock energies only a reactive flow model could accurately represent the true behaviour of the system.

We feel that molecular dynamics has much to offer in studies of initiation and growth of reaction, and will continue to grow in importance as our ability to handle more complex potentials increases. In the near future we hope to investigate the influence of other factors, such as exothermicity and the presence of defects, on initiation thresholds.

REFERENCES

[1] D W Brenner, M L Elert and C T White, "Incorporation of Reactive Dynamics in Simulations of Chemically-Sustained Shock Waves" *in Proceedings of the APS Topical Conference on Shock Compression of Condensed Matter*, North Holland, 1989, pp 263-266.

[2] D W Brenner, "Molecular Potentials for Simulating Shock-Induced Chemistry" *in Proceedings of the APS Topical Conference on Shock Compression of Condensed Matter*, North Holland, 1991, pp 115-121.

[3] D H Robertson, D W Brenner, M L Elert and C T White, "Simulations of Chemically-Sustained Shock Fronts in a Model Energetic Material" *in Proceedings of the APS Topical Conference on Shock Compression of Condensed Matter*, North Holland, 1991, pp 123-126.

[4] H W Hubbard and M H Johnson, "Initiation of Detonations", *J. Appl. Phys.* 30, pp 765-769 (1958).

[5] A W Campbell, W C Davis and J R Travis, "Shock Initiation of Detonation in Liquid Explosives", *Phys. Fluids* 4, pp 498-510 (1961).

[6] C A Honodel, J R Humphrey, R C Weingart, R S Lee and P Kramer, "Shock Initiation of TATB Formulations", *in Proceedings of the Seventh Symposium (International) on Detonation*, 1981, pp 425-434.

MOLECULAR DYNAMICS SIMULATIONS OF SHOCK PROCESSES

D. H. Robertson*
Chemistry Division†
Naval Research Laboratory
Washington, DC 20375-5340

Shock waves in condensed-phase material occur on a time and length scale that makes them ideal for study using molecular dynamics (MD) techniques. However, the potential energy surface used in these MD simulations limits the shock-related phenomena that can be simulated. We have developed many-body potentials to study the coupling of shock waves with varying physical and chemical processes such as polymorphic phase transitions and chemical reactivity. We have shown that MD simulations using these many-body potentials can model such complex phenomena as shock wave splitting resulting from the presence of a polymorphic phase transition and chemically sustained shock waves. These chemically sustained shock waves can show differing qualitative behavior depending on whether or not a polymorphic phase transition is present.

INTRODUCTION

Shock waves and their aftermath are evident in common occurrences such as a thunder clap or the craters visible on the moon. Various physical and chemical processes can accompany these shock waves. For example, polymorphic phase transitions can result in the presence of split shock waves[1,2] and chemical reactivity can couple to shock waves resulting in detonations.[3] A more detailed atomic-level understanding of the physical and chemical response of material under these extreme shock-loading conditions could result in the production of new stronger, more stress-resistant materials and safer, more reliable explosives. However, atomic-level information of shock processes is currently unobtainable through experiment and unavailable from continuum calculations. Therefore, alternate methods for probing these atomic-scale details are necessary.

The time (sub-picosecond) and length (sub-nanometer) scales associated with shock waves in condensed-phase materials makes them ideal for investigation using molecular dynamics (MD) simulations. Indeed, early MD shock wave simulations in Lennard-Jones systems have shown that atomic-scale simulations can be of sufficient size to reproduce continuum results.[4,5] However, to model interesting shock wave behavior, such as split shock waves or detonations, potentials capable of supporting chemical reactions or distinct phases are necessary. The processes modeled by these potentials must also occur on a time scale accessible to the MD simulations. Additionally, these potentials must permit the efficient computation of simulations containing thousands of atoms so that the simulation will be of sufficient size and duration to allow comparison with continuum theory and predictions.

At the Naval Research Laboratory, we have been developing a series of reactive many-body potentials that allow atomic resolution MD studies of such processes as the initial steps of diamond chemical vapor deposition,[6] detonations,[7-14] adhesion and friction,[15-17] hypervelocity impacts,[18,19] the early stages of fullerene formation,[20] and phase changes.[21] In this paper, we present results that use these many-body potentials to probe the atomic-level details of such interesting shock-related phenomena as split shock waves and chemically sustained shock waves (CSSW). These simulations can possibly uncover atomic-scale information that is currently inaccessible by experiment or unavailable from continuum calculations .

MODEL AND METHOD

The model potentials used in these MD shock simulations are based on the empirical bond-order formalism first introduced by Abell[22] and subsequently used by Tersoff.[23] This potential form has a many-body term that allows the interatomic interactions to vary depending on the local bonding environment. Our adaptation of the Abell-Tersoff formalism is parameterized[8-11,21] to generate diatomic molecules as the most stable, low-pressure species. An additional nonbonding term is added to allow these molecules to condense into a stable molecule solid with a speed of sound of 2 km/s. The diatomic molecules in this model can be composed of either like atoms, A_2 and B_2 (binding energy of 5 eV), or dissimilar atoms, AB (binding energy of 2 eV). For simulations starting with AB

---

* Work done in collaboration with D.W. Brenner, J.W. Mintmire, M. L. Elert, and C. T. White.

† Permanent address: Department of Chemistry, Indiana University - Purdue University at Indianapolis, 402 N. Blackford St., Indianapolis, IN 46202.

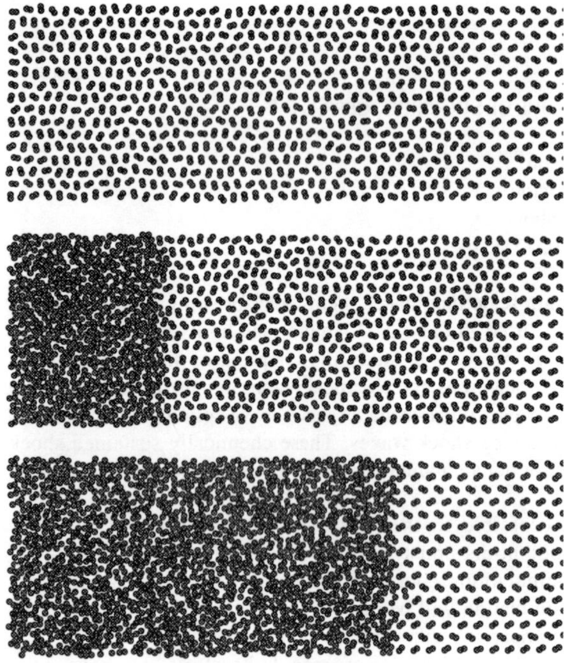

Figure 1. Snapshots at 2 ps for simulations with piston velocities of 2, 5, and 8 km/s, from top to bottom respectively. The shock waves are traveling from left to right. The positions are offset to align the pistons.

molecules, this parameterization allows for the possibility of an exothermic release of 3 eV per AB reactant if the AB molecules undergo reaction to form the more stable products, A_2 and B_2. In contrast, for simulations starting with only A_2 or B_2 molecules, reactions can occur but they have no net exothermicity. This model then allows the shock-induced behavior of both nonenergetic and energetic material to be probed at the atomic level.

Currently, these model simulations are performed in two dimensions. The crystal is set up with a free boundary to the left, infinite material to the right (simulated by adding material as needed in front of the shock wave) and periodic boundary conditions enforced in the remaining directions (perpendicular to shock direction). This allows the crystal edge to be either driven by a piston or impacted by a flyer plate. After establishing the initial and boundary conditions, the atomic positions on this potential energy surface are updated by integrating Hamilton's equations of motion using a Nordsiek predictor-corrector method.[24]

RESULTS AND DISCUSSION

First we discuss results from simulations of shock waves generated in the nonenergetic A_2 material by driving the

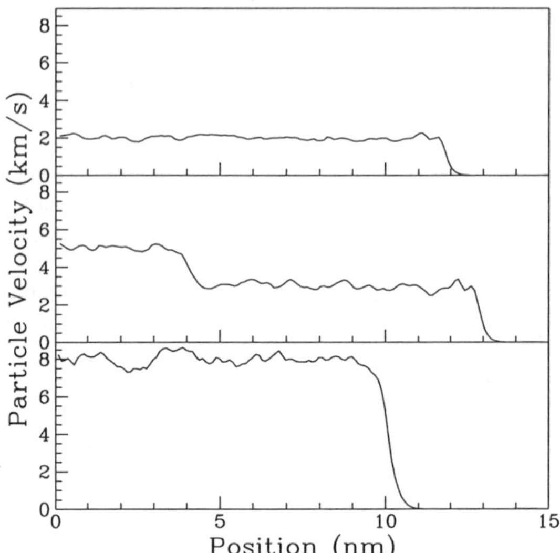

Figure 2. The sectional averages of the particle velocities corresponding to the snapshots in Fig. 1

crystal edge with a constant velocity piston.[21] Figure 1 presents snapshots of the atomic positions at 2 ps for simulations with piston velocities of 2.0, 5.0 and 8.0 km/s, from top to bottom, respectively. The shock front positions are clearly visible as sharp changes in density between adjacent regions. Figure 2 plots the particle velocity as a function of distance from the piston for the snapshots in Fig. 1. The split shock wave structure is clearly visible in the center plot of Fig. 2. Also note that the particle velocity (the second shock for the split shock wave) rapidly reaches the velocity of the rear boundary condition (piston velocity) for each of the various piston velocities. The other properties of these shock waves such as pressure and density show similar profiles.

An extensive analysis of this system and its associated Hugoniot has been presented earlier.[21] In the 2.0 km/s piston simulation a single compaction shock wave forms in which the individual molecules are heated, compressed and disoriented but retain their molecular identity and no phase change is evident. In the 5.0 km/s simulation the final shocked state is sufficient to induce the polymorphic phase change and a split shock wave structure is formed. The leading compaction shock heats and compresses the molecules up to the point of transition which then lose their molecular identity as they pass through the slower, second shock wave and enter a high-pressure dissociative region. Finally, in the 8.0 km/s piston simulation, the dissociative shock velocity has exceeded the compaction shock velocity and the material passes directly from the molecular solid into the dissociative region without the intervening

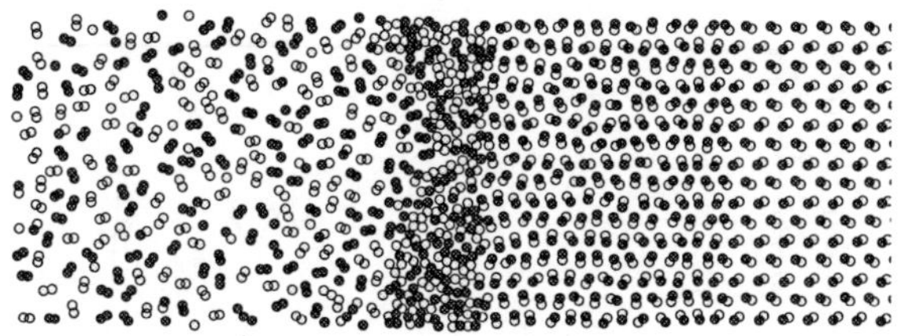

Figure 3. Snapshot of the chemically sustained shock wave resulting from impact of a 6 km/s flyer plate at 3 ps after impact. The two types of atoms are denoted as light and dark. The shock wave is propagating from left to right.

presence of an initial compaction shock wave. These simulations give excellent quantitative agreement with the continuum theory and its predictions for shock-induced polymorphic phase transitions.[21] We have also used this model to show that hypervelocity impacts can induce dissociative phase transitions in target materials.[19]

If, in place of A_2, the energetic AB molecules are used in the 2-D crystal then the possibility exists for exothermic chemical reactions. The shock waves in these AB simulations are initiated by a flyer plate impact instead of applying a constant velocity piston. Figure 3 shows a atomic positions for a simulation resulting from the impact of energetic material by a 6 km/s flyer plate. The split shock wave structure (similar to the nonenergetic simulations discussed above) is clearly visible. The particle velocity profile shown in Figure 4 for this snapshot exhibits a profile similar to the center plot of Fig. 2, except that instead of leveling off at the piston the particle velocity drops abruptly as products are formed in the rear of the shock wave. Therefore the chemical energy released as the reactants form products acts as a piston driving the shock wave allowing for the formation of a constant velocity self-sustaining shock wave. After initiation, the shock wave velocities rapidly relax to constant values of 6.4 and 7.2 km/s. Additionally, due to the presence of this dissociative phase, a rarefaction shock (seen as the rapid density drop in the rear of the dissociative phase in Fig. 3) follows this split shock waves at a velocity of 5.9 km/s. The majority of products are formed as the atoms move through this rarefaction shock. Further detail has been presented elsewhere.[10,11]

In the above CSSW simulation it is fortuitous that the model parameterization and initial conditions generates a final shocked state of the material (before expansion in the rear) that allows the formation of a stable split shock wave. These CSSW simulations do not necessarily have to show a split shock wave structure. The presence of a split shock wave is dependent on the final state of the high-pressure region before expansion which is in turn dependent on such properties as the amount of energy release, initial state, and phase transition characteristics of the model and crystal

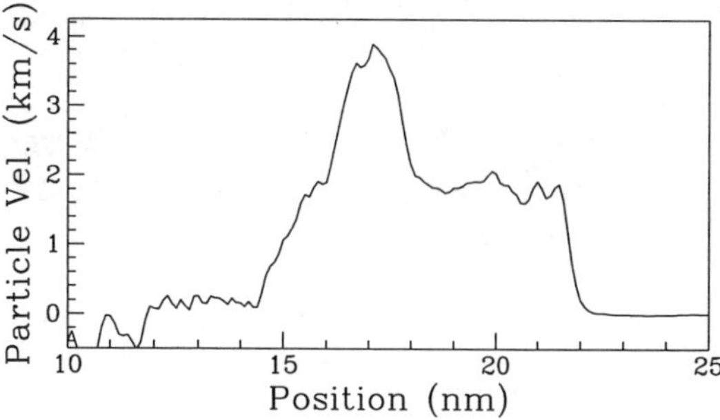

Figure 4. Plot of the particle velocities of the snapshot in Fig. 3.

structure. If an adjustment is made to AB equilibrium bond distance in the potential parameterization so that the volume collapse associated with the dissociative phase transition is reduced then the split shock wave disappears from the CSSW and the qualitative behavior of the CSSW changes.[12,13] A snapshot of this simulation using the modified parameterization is shown in Figure 5. In this snapshot only a single shock wave is evident and the CSSW does not exhibit the rear rarefaction shock. Likewise the particle velocity profile in Figure 6 shows a gradual decrease after the shock peak in contrast to the profile in Fig. 4. The behavior of this CSSW is similar to that predicted by the Zel'dovich-von Neumann-Doering (ZND) model for detonations.[12,13]

An additional way to change the characteristics of the CSSW that exhibits a split shock wave is to increase the exothermicity of the $AB \rightarrow {}^1/_2A_2 + {}^1/_2B_2$ reaction. This should increase the CSSW peak pressure and the shock velocity. Preliminary results indicate that this system shows behavior similar to the first model of CSSW except without the presence of a split shock wave. The particle velocity profile should be square topped with a rapid rise as the initial shock wave passes followed by an abrupt decrease associated with the rarefaction shock. The effect of changing the exothermicity and other model characteristics is under further study.

Conclusions

Chemically reactive potentials with the possibility for a polymorphic phase transition have been used in MD simulations to study coupling of shock waves to chemical and physical properties. Piston-driven shock wave simulations of a nonenergetic material show the presence of a split shock wave depending on the piston velocity. These results are in agreement with the behavior expected from experiments and continuum theory. Simulations using an energetic material are shown to develop stable, constant velocity, chemically sustained shock waves. The qualitative

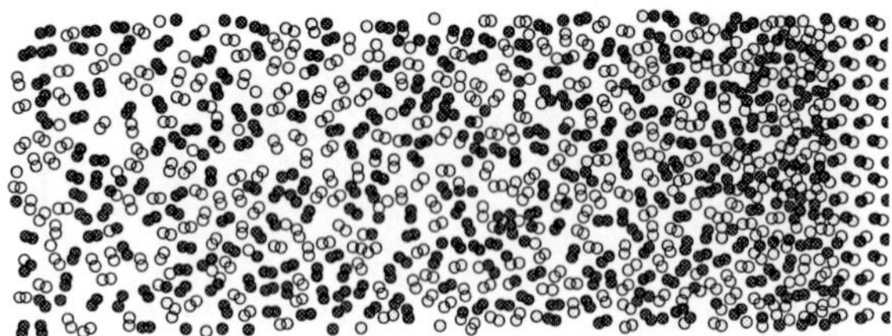

Figure 5. Snapshot of the chemically sustained shock wave resulting from impact of a 6 km/s flyer plate at 3 ps after impact for the modified potential.

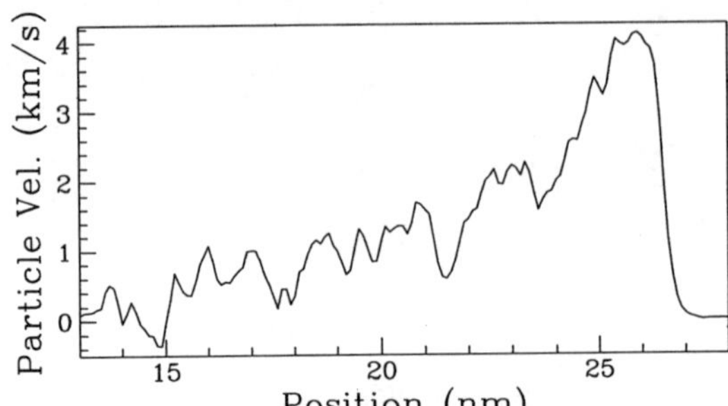

Figure 6. Particle velocity profile of the snapshot in Fig. 5.

behavior of these CSSWs can vary. A split shock wave is evident in one parameterization of the model. With a change in parameterization to remove this split shock wave, the behavior changes to that expected from ZND theory. A third behavior is also predicted that includes the dissociative phase transition but does not include the split shock wave structure.

MD simulations with reactive many-body potentials have been shown to be able to probe the atomic level details of shock-related phenomena. These simulations have been able to reproduce such complex behavior as shock wave splitting induced by a polymorphic phase transition as well as suggest the possibility for chemically sustained shock waves to include polymorphic phase transitions and thereby show interesting unanticipated behavior. Further studies, more complex models, and faster computers should increase the ability to probe these atomic level details by MD techniques.

ACKNOWLEDGMENTS

This work was supported in part by the ONR through NRL and the ONR Physics Division.

REFERENCES

[1] D. Bancroft, E.L. Peterson, and S. Minshall, *J. Appl. Phys.* **27**, 291 (1956).
[2] G.E. Duvall and R.A. Graham, *Rev. Mod. Phys.* **49**, 523 (1977).
[3] W.C. Davis, *Sci. Am.* **256**, 106 (1987).
[4] B.L. Holian, W.G. Hoover, W. Moran, and G.K. Straub, *Phys. Rev.* **22**, 2798 (1980).
[5] A.N. Dremin and V.Yu Klimenko, *Prog. Astronaut. Aeronaut.* **75**, 253 (1981).
[6] D.W. Brenner, *Phys. Rev. B* **42**, 9458 (1990).
[7] M.L. Elert, D.M. Deaven, D.W. Brenner, and C.T. White, *Phys. Rev. B* **39**, 1453 (1989).
[8] D.W. Brenner, M.L. Elert, and C.T. White, *Shock Compression of Condensed Matter - 1989*, S.C. Schmidt, J.N. Johnson, and L.W. Davison, eds., B.V.: Elsevier Science Publishers, 1990, p. 263.
[9] D.W. Brenner, *Shock Compression of Condensed Matter - 1991*, S.C. Schmidt, R.D. Dick, J.W. Forbes, and D.G. Tasker, eds., Amsterdam: North-Holland, 1992, p. 115.
[10] D.H. Robertson, D.W. Brenner, M.L. Elert, and C.T. White, *ibid.*, p. 123.
[11] C.T. White, D.H. Robertson, M.L. Elert, and D.W. Brenner, *Macroscopic Simulations of Complex Hydrodynamic Phenomena*, M. Mareschal and B.L. Holian, eds., New York: Plenum Press, 1992, p. 111.
[12] D.W. Brenner, D.H. Robertson, M.L. Elert, and C.T. White, *Phys. Rev. Lett.* **70**, 2174 (1993).
[13] C.T. White, D.H. Robertson, M.L. Elert, J.W. Mintmire, and D.W. Brenner, *MRS Proc.* **296**, 123 (1993).
[14] D.H. Robertson, D.W. Brenner, and C.T. White, *MRS Proc.* **296**, 183 (1993).
[15] J.A. Harrison, C.T. White, R.J. Colton, and D.W. Brenner, *Phys. Rev. B* **46**, 9700 (1992).
[16] J.A. Harrison, C.T. White, R.J. Colton, and D.W. Brenner, *Surf. Sci.* **271**, 57 (1992).
[17] D.W. Brenner and J.A. Harrison, *Ceramics Bulletin* **71**, 1821 (1992).
[18] R.C. Mowrey, D.W. Brenner, B.I. Dunlap, J.W. Mintmire, and C.T. White, *J. Chem. Phys.* **95**, 7138 (1991).
[19] C.T. White, D.H. Robertson, and D.W. Brenner, *Physica A* **188**, 357 (1992).
[20] D.H. Robertson, D.W. Brenner, and C.T. White, *J. Phys. Chem.* **96**, 6133 (1992).
[21] D.H. Robertson, D.W. Brenner, and C.T. White, *Phys. Rev. Let.* **67**, 3132 (1991).
[22] G.C. Abell, *Phys. Rev. B* **31**, 6184 (1985).
[23] J. Tersoff, *Phys. Rev. B* **37**, 6991 (1988).
[24] C.W. Gear, *Numerical Initial Value Problems in Ordinary Differential Equations*, Englewood Cliffs: Prentice-Hall, 1971.

STRAIN-INDUCED CHEMICAL REACTIONS

John J. Gilman
Lawrence Berkeley Laboratory
Berkeley, California 94720

The uniaxial displacements at leading edges of detonation fronts in solids create large shear-strains. These bend the covalent bonds, and cause piezoelectric effects, thereby closing the HOMO-LUMO energy gaps, and leading to ultra-fast athermal chemical reactions. specific examples are discussed: ammonium, azide, and nitrate ions; and PETN. It is shown that their properties are consistent with the proposed mechanism.

At the leading edge of a plane detonation front moving along the x-axis, the longitudinal and transverse strains are ϵ_{xx}, and $\epsilon_{yy}=\epsilon_{zz}=0$, respectively. Thus the state of strain consists of an isotropic compression$=3\epsilon_{xx}$, plus shears$=\epsilon_{xy}=\epsilon_{yz}=(\epsilon_{xx}-\epsilon_{yy})/2=\epsilon_{xx}/2$. The strain energy density associated with these shear strains is 4G/3 (G= shear modulus), while that associated with the isotropic compression is B=bulk modulus. Thus, for a stiff solid with G=(3/4)B, the shear and dilatational strain energy densities are equal.

Even if the shears relax in part of the volume, large ones remain at the shock interface. From the viewpoint of chemistry, shear strains are more important than dilatations because they change shapes; just as chemical reactions do. Also, they facilitate chemical reactions through their effects on electronic structures. Their general effect is to bend chemical bonds. This has three major effects: 1. reduction of HOMO-LUMO energy gaps [1]; 2. polarization of non-centrosymmetric structures; and 3. creation or movement of defects (particularly dislocations)[2]. Nonlinear effects can also be expected when strong gradients are present as they are at detonation fronts.

Strains play an especially important role at detonation fronts. When they reach critical values which cause the bonding electrons in the material to become delocalized, stored chemical energy begins to be released into the dense plasma behind the front, tending to make it expand. This creates a pressure spike whose gradients drive the front forward, and the reaction products backward. A computational model of this phenomenology that is con- consistent with observations was developed by Wilkins [3]. A critical parameter of the model is the magnitude of the strain at which the bonding electrons become delocalized. In other words, the critical strain at which decomposition begins. When this strain level is reached in the model, the heat of reaction of the medium is immediately released. This is similar to the physical situation because the bonding electrons can become delocalized in very short time periods, of the order of femtoseconds.

Although it is impractical to attempt to calculate the critical strains from quantum chemistry, estimates can be made by means of "molecular mechanics". These estimates are justified by the theorems of molecular orbital theory regarding the effect of bond-bending on wave functions [16].

Let us start with the azides. Explosion of them consists principally of decomposition of the azide ion, yielding nitrogen gas. The ion consists of three nitrogen atoms (usually in a linear array) bound together by a σ-orbital and two π-orbitals. If the ion is bent, the π-orbitals must be substantially disturbed, thereby raising the bonding level (HOMO) and lowering the antibonding level (LUMO).

Initially the energy gap in $Pb(N_3)_2$ is 1.64 eV. (the first exciton level is 1.26 eV.) Bending a linear triad shortens its length. If the bend angle is δ, the longitudinal strain is $(1 - \cos \delta)/2$. Bending changes the energy by $(k_\delta \delta^2)/2$ where k_δ is the bending force constant = 4.63 eV/rad. Thus the bending energy equals the initial gap when δ =

0.84 rad., or the critical longitudinal strain = 0.17.

Since the compressive strains at detonation fronts in lead azide are observed to be as much as 0.5, this is a very reasonable estimate.

Next, consider the ammonium ion. Strain of this has two effects because the ion is not centrosymmetric. One effect is the reduction of the HOMO-LUMO gap through bond-bending; and the other is polarization of the ion through internal charge displacement.

Figure 1

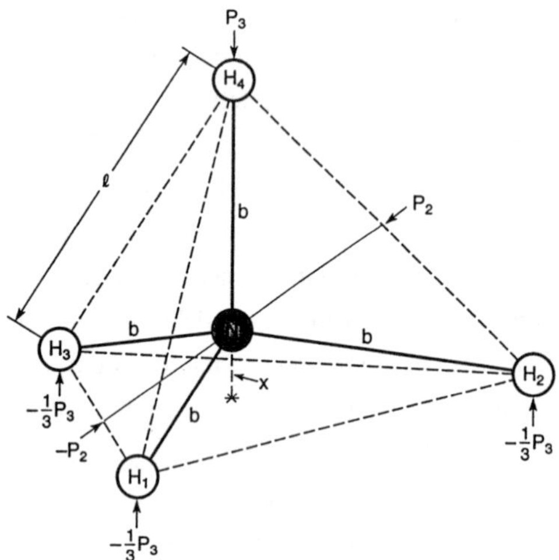

Figure 1 shows a schematic unstrained ammonium ion which has the form of a tetrahedron with hydrogen nuclei at the corners, each a bond length, b away from the central nitrogen nucleus. The molecule has two principal symmetry axes: one two-fold, the other three-fold. There are two principal deformation modes: one can be caused by the forces $\pm P_2$ acting along the two-fold axis; and the other by $\pm P_3$ acting along the three-fold axis.

The first one increases the bond angles H_1N_3, and H_2NH_4, while the second increases H_iNH_j (i,j = 1,2,3). In each case the complementary angles are decreased.

Evidence has been presented elsewhere that bending of covalent bonds raises the HOMO energy level while lowering the LUMO level [1]. In several covalently bonded crystals (Si, Ge, Sn, InSb, GaSb, AlSb, InAs, and GaP) when compression increases the tetrahedral bond angle from 109.5° to 149.5°, the HOMO-LUMO gap vanishes and the crystal structure changes from the diamond-type to the beta-tin-type. Also, the bonding electrons become delocalized (at finite temperatures the gap need not completely vanish). The critical angle is consistent with the quantum theory of the angular dependence of the energies of sp^3 bonds.

Similar effects are expected during the compression of ammonium type ions; and for other tetrahedral ions and molecules such as SO_4^{2-}, $C(CH_2OH)_4$((pentaerythritol and its derivatives), ClO_4^-, and IO_4^-.

Compression along the two-fold axis brings planes o like atoms closer together symmetrically so there is no net charge displacement and therefore no induced polarization.

On the other hand, compression along the three-fold axis not only bends bonds, but at constant bond length, brings the N-atom closer to the $H_1H_2H_3$ plane, thereby causing a net charge dispacement. That is, it leads to piezoelectrically induced internal electric fields. If ϵ_{33} is the compressive strain along the three-fold axis, and the bond length is b, then the distance, x = b/3 changes, producing an internal displacement Δx which is a measure of the local separation of the centers of positive and negative charge (creation of a local dipole). $\Delta=(3b/4)\epsilon_{33}$, so the electrostatic energy change is about $(q^2/b)(\Delta x/b)$, or $(3q^2/4b)\epsilon_{33}$.

Letting: q be one electronic charge, b = 1.1 Å for ammonium, and the strain be 0.2; the change in energy is about 2 eV. Note that the local electric field is very high; about 2.4 x 10^{10} V/m.

Perhaps the most common chemical group in energetic materials is the nitrate ion. It usually has the form of a planar equilateral triangle (Figure 2), and is piezoelectric for strains parallel to its plane. A vertical strain, ϵ_{33} causes the distance x to change by: $\Delta x = (3b/2)\epsilon_{33}$, in this case. This separates the centers of charge creating a dipole of approximate energy: $(3q^2/2b)\epsilon_{33}$. It takes ~4.6 eV to photoexcite KNO_3 [4]. The bond length, b is about 1.25 Å. Thus the strain needed to equal the excitation gap would be about 0.56 without taking into account

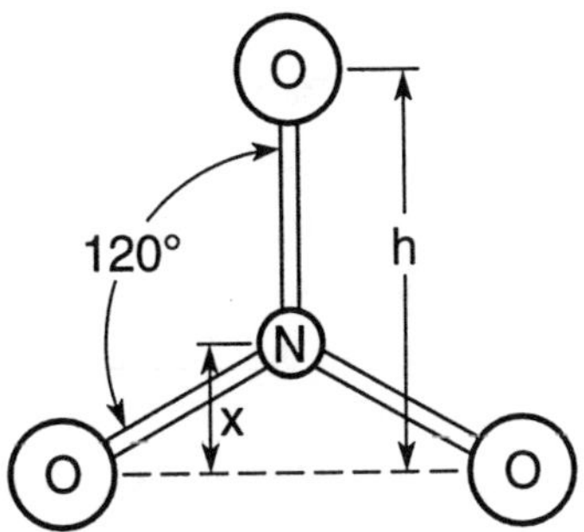

Figure 2

the effect of bond-bending. As before, δ = change of angle = $3\epsilon/\sin(\theta/2)$, so the bond-bending work, $k_{\delta 2}/2$ = $9k_\delta \epsilon^2/2\sin(\theta/2)$. To get the total energy change, the bending work and the dipole energy are added together and set equal to the excitation energy, U_e; yielding a quadratic equation in ϵ:

$$4.9 = 8.6\epsilon + 69.7\epsilon^2$$

The solution is $\epsilon = 0.21$, and by substituting this back into the equation it may be seen that the bond-bending term makes the largest contribution to reducing the effective gap; thereby starting the reaction.

In general computational models the two effects (bending and dipole formation) cannot be separated; especially since the electron distribution will change with the deformation, but the separation is instructive in this simple model.

The final example that will be considered is that of PETN. It is of special interest because Dick and coworkers [5] have shown that, not only is it affected by deformation, but its response depends on the orientation of the principal deformation axes relative to the crystal axes. In other words its observed behavior is anisotropic.

PETN illustrates another factor. Namely, that more than one part of a molecule may be strongly affected by deformation; especially shear. The structure of the molecule is shown schematically in Figure 3. At the very center is a carbon atom surrounded by four other carbons at the corners of a compressed tetrahedron. Attached to each of these are two hydrogens and one nitrate group. Thus bending might occur either at the quasi-tetrahedral

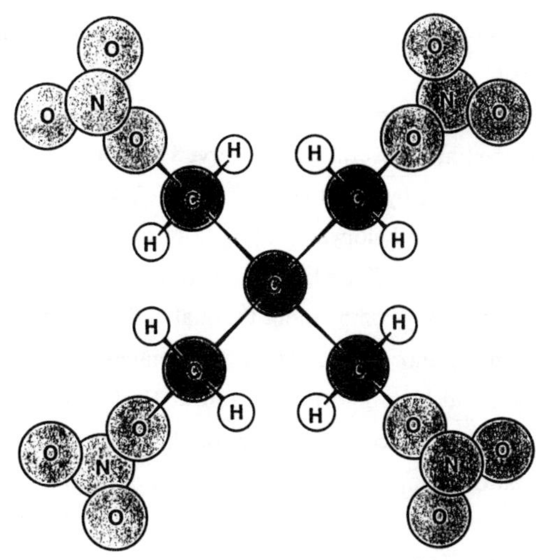

Figure 3

C-C-C angles, at the O-N-O angles of the nitrate groups, or at the C-C-O angles. Based on force constant data [6], the dependence of the energies on bend angles are: 8.2, 4.4, and 19.4 eV/rad., respectively. Thus, for a given imposed strain, the nitrate group has the largest effect.

Since the bond-bending force constants are smaller than the bond-stretching constants, bending is the easiest way for the atomic structure to respond to compression. It has been shown [1] that the mechanical work needed to bend the bonds enough to cause metallization is just equal to the energy gap between the HOMO and LUMO levels.

With the bonding electrons delocalized, the ion-cores can rearrange readily into product configurations, as in a dense plasma, thereby releasing the heat of reaction [7].

A homologous series of secondary explosives is is the amino-nitro-benzenes. They have been studied by Rogers [8], and by Sharma [9]) among others. The latter author has studied their "shake-up" spectra which measure their HOMO-LUMO gaps. The gap correlates with their sensitivities. The correlation starts with trinitro-benzene, and ends with triamino-trinitro-benzene (TATB).

It has been shown by Zhou and Parr [10] that the resonance energy per π-electron correlates quite well with the HOMO-LUMO energy gap for a large number of aromatic molecules. Thus the chemical hardnesses of energetic molecules partially determine their sensitivities to shock.

Athermal reactions induced by shear have been known for a long time. Several were observed by Bridgman [11], and interpreted by Teller [12]. They have been extensively studied by Enikolopyan [13] in more recent years, but they seem to have been largely ignored in the explosives literature. They complement thermal activation mechanisms, being more important at low temperatures, high stresses, and high deformation rates. Explicit phenomenological evidence and theory for their importance in detonation fronts has been presented by Trofimov and Trofimova [14].

The new idea presented here is that bond-bending is the important factor in starting fast chemical reactions in secondary explosives. This idea removes most of the conceptual inconsistencies of the past, thereby resolving most of the questions recently posed by Dremin [15]. Also, it may provide a new tool for controlling reactions so that energetic materials can be designed with high energy densities combined with low sensitivities.

REFERENCES

1. J. J. Gilman, Phil. Mag. B, 67, 207 (1993).
2. R. W. Armstrong, C. S. Coffey, and W. L. Elban, Adv. Chem. Reaction Dynamics, Eds. Rentzepsis and Capellos, D. Reidel Pub. Co.,p.469 (1986).
3. M. L. Wilkins, 1964, Fundamental Methods in Hydrodynamics, Vol.3 - Methods in Comp. Phys., Ed. by Alder, Fernbach, and Rotenberg, Academic Press, New York, p.260 (1964).
4. V. A. Ananev, M. B. Miklin, and V. A. Nevostruev, High Energy Chem., 24, 122 (1990).
5. J. J. Dick, E. Garcia, and D. C. Shaw, Shock Compression of Condensed Matter - 1991, Proc. APS Topical Conf. at Williamsburg, Virginia, North-Holland Publishers, 349 (1992).
6. G. Herzberg, Molecular Spectra and Molecular Structure - II. Infrared and Raman Spectra of Polyatomic Molecules, D. Van Nostrand, New York (1945).
7. M. A. Cook, The Science of High Explosives, p.157, Reinhold Publishing, New York (1958).
8. J. W. Rogers, reported in C & E News (August 10 issue), p.25 (1987).
9. J. Sharma, Shock Compression of Condensed Matter - 1991, Proc. APS Topical Conf. at Williamsburg, Virginia, North-Holland Publishers, 639 (1992).
10. Z. Zhou, and R. G. Parr, J. Amer. Chem. Soc., 111, 7371 (1989).
11. P. W. Bridgman, Phys. Rev., 48, 825 (1935).
12. E. Teller, J. Chem. Phys., 36, 901 (1962).
13. N. S. Enikolopyan, Dokl. Akad. Nauk SSSR, 302, 630 (1988).
14. V. S. Trofimov and G. P. Trofimova, Combustion, Explosions, and Shock Waves (English - translated from Fizika Goreniya i Vzryva), 26, 136 (1990).
15. A. N. Dremin, Phil. Trans. Roy. Soc. Lond., 339, 355 (1992).
16. R. McWeeny, Coulson's Valence, 3rd Edition, p.196, Oxford University Press (1979).

ACKNOWLEDGMENT

This work was supported by the Director, Office of Energy Research, Office of Basic Energy Sciences, Materials Materials Sciences Division, of the U.S. Department of Energy under Contract #DEAC0376F00098.

A STUDY OF THE CURVATURE OF A TWO-DIMENSIONAL DETONATION WAVE AT AN EXPLOSIVE-CONFINEMENT INTERFACE

Pierre Vidal[1], Michael Cowperthwaite[2], Henri-Noël Presles[1] and Eric Bouton[1].

[1]Laboratoire d'Energétique et de Détonique, URA 193 CNRS, ENSMA, 86034 Poitiers, France.

[2]SRI International, Poulter Laboratory, 333 Ravenswood avenue, Menlo Park CA 94025, USA.

We present a theoretical study of the interaction of a constant-velocity two-dimensional detonation wave with its surrounding medium. For the case of pure refraction, we obtain exact expressions for the interface curvatures of the shock fronts in both the explosive (X) and its confinement (C) in terms of the detonation velocity D, the material properties of X and C and, if the flow is cylindrically symmetric, the radius of the explosive charge. These relations are obtained from the constraints imposed on the flow derivatives of the pressure P and the flow turning angle θ by the conservation laws, the boundary conditions at the curved shock fronts and the contact conditions matching P and θ along the interface. This model is used in our numerical analysis of a polytropic explosive with a pressure-dependent decomposition rate and a polytropic confinement. We find that, for a given D, the explosive's interface curvature C_x decreases as the confinement's density increases and that, depending on the pressure exponent in the decomposition rate, the slope of the D versus C_x plot can be positive, infinite or negative. Such results can be applied to the experimental determination of decomposition rates in condensed explosives.

INTRODUCTION

A detonation wave (DW) in a chemical explosive is a very fast propagation of combustion reactions induced by a shock compression. Such a wave is called self-sustaining (SS) when the shock is supported solely by the release of chemical energy. According to the earliest models, the SS-DW shock front is flat and its velocity D* is determined by the equation of state of the combustion products and the amount of chemical energy released. The detonation of a condensed explosive (X) however generates very high pressure levels (>0.1 Mbar) which deform any material that can be used to confine X. For example, the propagation of a DW along the longitudinal symmetry axis of a slab or cylinder of explosive produces a lateral compression of the confinement (C), thus a lateral expansion of the flow in X which reduces the amount of chemical energy supporting the propagation of the shock. Consequences of this loss are a curved shock front in X, shown schematically as OI in Figure 1, a SS-DW velocity D lower than D*, and the existence of a slab or cylinder critical transverse size below which a SS-DW cannot be obtained. These features are commonly referred to as the diameter effect because experiments are usually carried out in cylindrical explosive charges. In most experiments, X and C are initially at rest and their shock properties are such that a shock, sustained by the lateral expansion of the flow in X and shown as O'I in Figure 1, is refracted into C. A consideration of the characteristic lines for flows in X and C then suggests that the matching of OI and O'I can be made by two types of refraction [1] :

1 - a singular refraction or matching of OI and O'I by reflexion of an expansion fan into X, centered at the interaction point I. In a shock-fixed frame (SFF), the flow is exactly sonic at point I at the shock in X and supersonic in C.

2 - a pure refraction or matching of OI and O'I without any wave reflected into X or C. In a SFF, the flow in the vicinity of I is subsonic in X and supersonic in C.

In such situations only can the acoustic perturbations be carried from C to OI through the subsonic reaction zone in X, thereby accounting for the above described diameter effect.

In this paper, we derive exact expressions for the curvatures of OI and O'I at point I for the case of pure refraction [2]. We then present the results of calculations performed with these expressions subjected to the assumptions that X and C are governed by polytropic equations of state and that the chemical energy release rate in X obeys a pressure-dependent law [3].

ANALYSIS OF THE REFRACTION

Our study is based upon the two-dimensional (2D) Zeldovich-Von Neuman-Doring (ZND) model [4],[5] : a 2D axisymmetric (2DA) or 2D plane (2DP) adiabatic inviscid reactive flow sustains a symmetrically curved shock propagating at constant velocity D in a quiescent explosive. In a SFF, the flows in X and C are steady-state in the vicinity of OI and O'I. We shall use the subscript H to denote a shocked state in X or C and use x and c as subscripts or superscripts to denote states in X and C respectively. We shall omit x and c when referring to X or C indistinctively. Our other nomenclature is given in Table 1. To describe such 2DP (α= 0) or 2DA (α=1) flows in a SFF, we first write the balance equations for mass, momentum and energy in a system of curvilinear orthogonal coordinates (l,n) defined by the streamlines and their normals as :

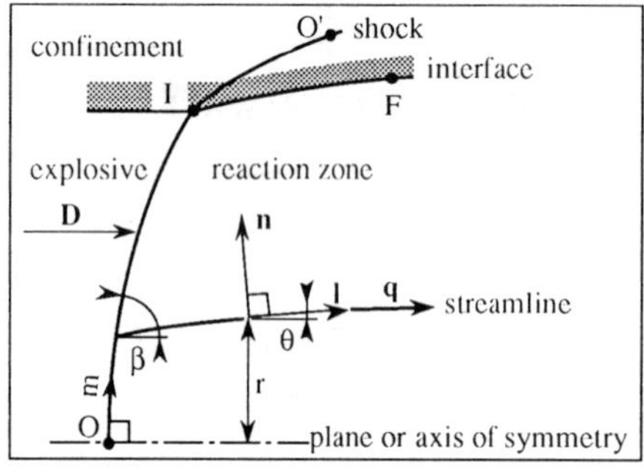

Figure 1. Two-dimensional detonation

β	: shock inclination angle
θ	: streamline angle
P	: pressure
ρ	: specific mass
λ	: extent of chemical reaction
q	: particle speed
c	: sound speed
e	: specific internal energy
s	: specific entropy
t	: time
d( )/dt	: material derivative ($= q\partial(\ )/\partial l$ for a steady-state flow)

Table. Nomenclature

$$\frac{\partial Ln(\rho)}{\partial l} + \frac{\partial Ln(q)}{\partial l} + \frac{\partial \theta}{\partial n} = \frac{-\alpha \sin(\theta)}{r} \quad (1)$$

$$\frac{\partial Ln(q)}{\partial l} + \frac{1}{\rho q^2}\frac{\partial P}{\partial l} = 0 \quad (2)$$

$$\frac{\partial \theta}{\partial l} + \frac{1}{\rho q^2}\frac{\partial P}{\partial n} = 0 \quad (3)$$

$$\frac{-\partial Ln(\rho)}{\partial l} + \frac{1}{\rho c^2}\frac{\partial P}{\partial l} = \sigma.\mathbf{w}/q \quad (4)$$

The (frozen) sound speed c and the thermicity vector σ can be expressed as functions of P, ρ and λ by using a specified e(P, ρ, λ) equation of state. The decomposition rate vector **w** is also to be considered as depending on P, ρ and λ. In nonreactive media, λ, σ and **w** are equal to zero.

$$c^2 = \left.\frac{\partial P}{\partial \rho}\right)_{\lambda,S} = \frac{\frac{P}{\rho^2} - \left.\frac{\partial e}{\partial \rho}\right)_{\lambda,P}}{\left.\frac{\partial e}{\partial P}\right)_{\lambda,\rho}}$$

$$\rho c^2 \sigma = \left.\frac{\partial P}{\partial \lambda}\right)_{e,\rho} \quad ; \quad \frac{d^0\lambda}{dt} = w(P,\rho,\lambda)$$

We next recall [6] that the shock values of any dependent variable g = (ρ , q , P, θ) can be expressed as a function of β and D by using the jump relations for an oblique shock and the equation of state of the medium under consideration. λ_H is equal to zero (ZND model). The shock values of the partial derivatives of the latter variables thus satisfy the following geometrical identity (Figure 1) :

$$\cos(\beta-\theta_H)\left(\frac{\partial g}{\partial l}\right)_H + \sin(\beta-\theta_H)\left(\frac{\partial g}{\partial n}\right)_H = \frac{dg_H}{d\beta}C \quad (5)$$

where $C = \frac{d\beta}{dm} = \sin(\beta)\frac{d\beta}{dr_H}$ denotes the curvature of a meridian shock line. Applying the identity (5) to the variables P and θ yields two relations which, together with the relations (1) to (4), defines a linear nonhomogeneous system of six equations in the shock values of the six partial derivatives involved in it. Upon resolution, we obtain in particular

$$\left(\frac{\partial P}{\partial l}\right)_H = A_P C - B_P \quad (6)$$

$$\left(\frac{\partial \theta}{\partial l}\right)_H = A_\theta C - B_\theta \quad (7)$$

$$(\rho_H q_H^2)^{-1}\Delta A_p = \cos(\beta-\theta_H)\frac{1}{\rho_H q_H^2}\frac{dP_H}{d\beta} + \sin(\beta-\theta_H)\frac{d\theta_H}{d\beta}$$

$$(\rho_H q_H^2)^{-1}\Delta B_p = \sin^2(\beta-\theta_H)\left\{\frac{\sigma_H w_H}{q_H} - \frac{\alpha\sin(\theta_H)}{r_H}\right\}$$

$$\Delta A_\theta = -(1-M_H^2)\sin(\beta-\theta_H)\frac{1}{\rho_H q_H^2}\frac{dP_H}{d\beta} + \cos(\beta-\theta_H)\frac{d\theta_H}{d\beta}$$

$$\Delta B_\theta = \cos(\beta-\theta_H)\sin(\beta-\theta_H)\left\{\frac{\sigma_H w_H}{q_H} - \frac{\alpha\sin(\theta_H)}{r_H}\right\}$$

$$\Delta = 1 - M_H^2\sin^2(\beta-\theta_H) \quad ; \quad M = q/c$$

The coefficients A_P, A_θ, B_P, B_θ and Δ are function of β and D. The coefficients B_P and B_θ also depend on r_H for a 2DA explosive charge.

We finally write the contact conditions for X and C by matching the pressures and the flow directions along the interface IF as :

$$P_x = P_c \quad (8)$$

$$\theta_x = \theta_c \quad (9)$$

$$\left(\frac{\partial P}{\partial l}\right)_x = \left(\frac{\partial P}{\partial l}\right)_c \quad (10)$$

$$\left(\frac{\partial \theta}{\partial l}\right)_x = \left(\frac{\partial \theta}{\partial l}\right)_c \quad (11)$$

These matching conditions apply along the interface IF. It is important to acknowledge that they also apply at the

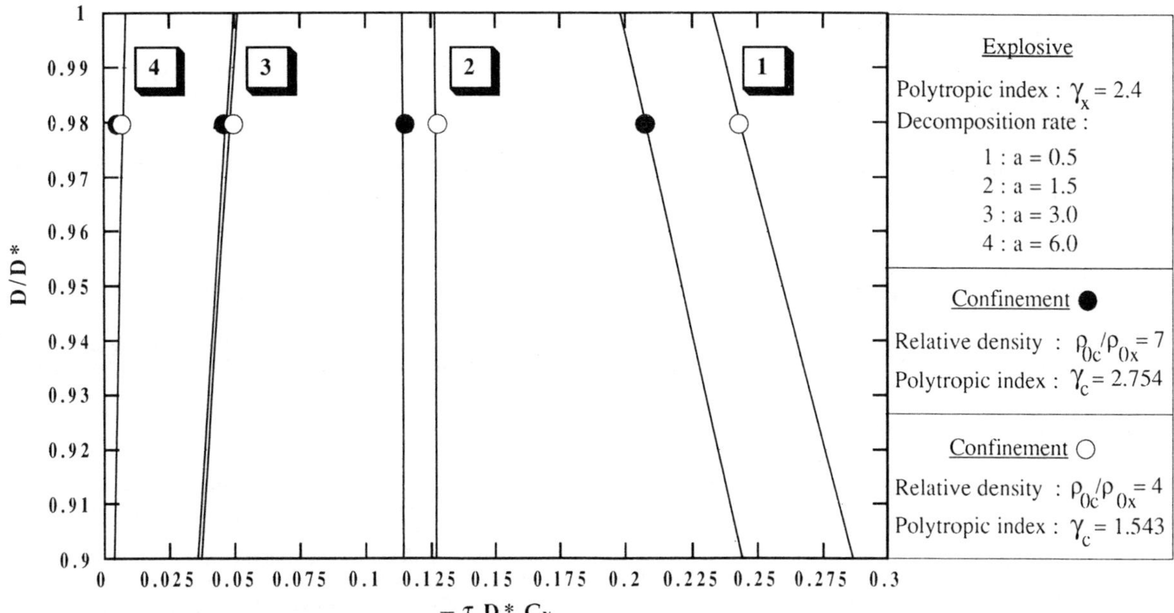

Figure 2. Plots of the nondimensionalized detonation velocity D/D* versus the nondimensionalized explosive's interface curvature $\tau D^* C_x$ for a polytropic explosive, two polytropic confinement and the decomposition rate law $w_x = \tau^{-1} (P_x/P_{ref})^a (1 - \lambda_x)^b$. (Two-dimensional explosive charge).

intersection point I of shocks OI and O'I when there is no reflected wave in X or C as for a pure refraction. The shock relations (6) and (7) can thus be used to evaluate the derivatives in relations (10) and (11) at point I. This operation yields a linear nonhomogeneous system of two equations in the two interface values, C_x and C_c, of the curvatures of shocks OI and O'I. We obtain

$$C_x = \frac{(B^x_\theta - B^c_\theta) A^c_p - (B^x_p - B^c_p) A^c_\theta}{\bar{\Delta}} \tag{12}$$

$$C_c = \frac{(B^x_\theta - B^c_\theta) A^x_p - (B^x_p - B^c_p) A^x_\theta}{\bar{\Delta}} \tag{13}$$

$$\bar{\Delta} = A^x_\theta A^c_p - A^x_p A^c_\theta$$

The conditions (8) and (9) define the values of the shock angles β_x and β_c at I as functions of the velocity D and the material shock properties of X and C. The interface values of the curvatures of OI and O'I consequently depend on D, the material shock properties of X and C, the chemical decomposition rates and, for a 2DA explosive charge, on the radius of the explosive charge.

RESULTS OF A MODEL CALCULATION

We have specialized the above results to the case of a 2DP explosive charge ($\alpha = 0$) bounded with a nonreactive confinement ($\lambda_c = 0$, $\sigma_c = 0$, $w_c = 0$) and have introduced in our analysis the following simplifying assumptions (the subscript 0 will denote the initial conditions):

1 - The inital pressure P_0 can be neglected with respect to the shock pressure P_H. In condensed explosives, typical P_0/P_H ratios are 10^{-5}.

2 - A global irreversible reaction can model the exothermic process in the reaction zone of X:

Explosive → Products

Such a reaction is accordingly described by a single scalar variable λ_x that represents the mass fraction of burnt explosive and specifies the fraction of heat released per unit mass of X.

3 - The material properties of X and C are governed by polytropic equations of state:

$$e(P, \rho, \lambda) = e_0 - \lambda Q + \frac{P}{\rho(\gamma - 1)} \tag{14}$$

where γ and Q denote the polytropic index and the total amount of heat avalaible per unit mass respectively. Here, Q_c is equal to zero since we have chosen a nonreactive confinement.

4 - The global chemical decomposition rate of X obeys a pressure-dependent law in the form:

$$w_x = \tau^{-1}\left(\frac{P_x}{P_{ref}}\right)^a (1-\lambda_x)^b \qquad (15)$$

where τ is a characteristic chemical time, P_{ref} is a characteristic pressure and a and b are nondimensional constants.

Assumptions 1, 2 and 3 lead to the following one-dimensional SS-DW velocity [4], [5]:

$$D^* = \sqrt{2(\gamma_x^2 -1)Q_x} \qquad (16)$$

The velocity D*, the initial specific mass ρ_{0x} and the characteristic time τ were used to nondimensionalize the other variables and, without loss in generality, the characteristic pressure P_{ref} was set equal to $\rho_{0x}D^{*2}$.

We next used formula (12) to determine how the relationship between the explosive's interface curvature C_x and the DW velocity D depends on the properties of C and of the parameter a of the decomposition rate (15). The control parameters of our calculations are the nondimensional velocity D/D*, the polytropic indices γ_x and γ_c, the relative density ρ_{0c}/ρ_{0x}, and the parameter a of the decomposition rate. The values of D*, ρ_{0x}, ρ_{0c}, γ_x and γ_c were chosen to model the liquid explosive nitromethane ($D^*= 0.63$cm/μs, $\rho_{0x}= 1.128$ gr/cm^3, $\gamma_x = 2.4$) confined in steel ($\rho_{0c}/\rho_{0x} = 7$, $\gamma_c = 2.75$)) or titanium ($\rho_{0c}/\rho_{0x}= 4$, $\gamma_c = 1.54$) tubes [7],[8]. These materials meet the pure refraction conditions in the range of the selected values for D/D* (0.9-1.0). The values of the angles β_x and β_c at point I were found to be practically independent of D :

$$\beta_x = 81.15 \text{ degrees and } \beta_c = 23.21 \text{ degrees for } \frac{\rho_{0c}}{\rho_{0x}} = 7$$

$$\beta_x = 73.87 \text{ degrees and } \beta_c = 24.43 \text{ degrees for } \frac{\rho_{0c}}{\rho_{0x}} = 4$$

Our results are summarized in Figure 2 which plots the nondimensionalized wave velocity D/D* versus the nondimensionalized interface curvature τD^*C_x.The curves exhibits the following trends:

1 - The explosive's interface curvature, as defined here, is found to be negative. The concave face of the DW shock front is thus oriented towards the reaction zone.

2 - For a given velocity D, the absolute value of the explosive's interface-shock-curvature, $-C_x$, decreases as the confinement's density increases. Also, the distance between curves associated with two confinements and the same value of the parameter a decreases as the value of a increases.

3- Depending on the pressure exponent in the decomposition rate, the slope of the curves can be positive infinite or negative.

4- The same considerations apply to the dependence of the normal velocity $D\sin(\beta_x)$ and the explosive's interface curvature.

CONCLUSIONS

Current models for curved self-sustaining detonation waves are based upon a compatibility relation between the normal velocity and the curvature of the detonation shock front that only depends on the properties of the explosive [9]. Our results, on the contrary, indicate that such a compatibility relation is not unique but is determined by the properties of the material that bounds the explosive. Our formulas (12) and (13) for the explosive and confinement interface shock curvatures have been obtained without approximating the flows behind the curved shock fronts and without restricting the forms of the equations of state and the chemical decomposition rates. These formulas can thus be used to calibrate shock equations of state and decomposition rates in condensed explosives from velocity measurements and shock-front shape records of confined two-dimensional self-sustaining detonation waves.

REFERENCES

[1] D.S. Stewart, J.B. Bdzil, Examples of detonation shock dynamics for detonation wave spread applications, in *Proceedings of the Ninth Symposium (International) on Detonation*, OCNR 113291-7,1, 1989, pp. 773-783. (See the discussion by Bdzil at the end of the paper)

[2] P. Vidal, M. Cowperthwaite, H.-N. Presles, D. Fontaine, Sur la courbure d'une onde de détonation bidimensionnelle à l'interface d'un explosif et de son confinement, *C.R. Acad. Sci. Paris*, t.315, Série II, pp. 791-794, 1992.

[3] P. Vidal, M. Cowperthwaite, H.-N. Presles, D. Fontaine, Non-unicité de la relation entre la célérité et la courbure du front de choc de l'onde de détonation, *C.R. Acad. Sci. Paris*, t.316, Série II, pp. 177-180, 1993.

[4] Ya.B. Zeldovich, S.A. Kompaneets,*Theory of detonation*, New York, Academic Press, 1960.

[5] W. Fickett, W.C. Davis, *Detonation*, University of California Press, 1979.

[6] R. Courant, K. Friedrichs, *Supersonic flow and shock waves*, Intersciences, 1948.

[7] S.P. Marsh, *LASL Shock Hugoniot Data*, Berkeley, University of California Press, 1980.

[8] H.-N. Presles, *Contribution à l'étude de la détonation de mélanges liquides binaires à base de nitrométhane*, Thèse de doctorat ès sciences physiques, Université de Poitiers, 1979.

[9] D.S. Stewart, J.B. Bdzil, The shock dynamics of stable multidimensional detonation, *Combustion and flames*, 72,pp. 311-323, 1988.

A NEW APPROACH TO THE WOOD AND KIRKWOOD AXIAL DETONATION PROBLEM

Michael Cowperthwaite
Poulter Laboratory
SRI International
333 Ravenswood Avenue
Menlo Park, California 94025-3493

A new approach to Wood and Kirkwood's classical, two-dimensional, axial detonation problem, based on different methods for constructing first integrals of the flow equations, provides an exact solution for such axial flow in a polytropic explosive with an arbitrary rate of decomposition. This solution includes the constraints imposed on the axial flow derivatives by the curved shock, the axial and radial momentum equations, and the rate law. A new axial condition for detonation failure is postulated and used to show that detonation failure can occur before the slope of the curve relating the axial radius of curvature of the shock (Sa) and the detonation velocity deficit (D/D_∞) becomes infinite.

INTRODUCTION

This paper presents significant features of my new approach to the problem of steady-state (SS), axial flow in a cylindrically symmetric (CS), ZND detonation. This new approach to this axial flow problem (AFP) is here called the Cowperthwaite approach (CA) and differs from the traditional approaches adopted respectively by Wood and Kirkwood (WKA),[1] Fickett and Davis (FDA),[2] and Bdzil (BA)[3] by formulating a different procedure for constructing first integrals of the flow equations. This procedure in the CA uses methods of differential geometry, Bernoulli's equation (B = 0), and the solution for ID detonation and provides an exact solution to the AFP for polytropic explosive with an arbitrary rate of decomposition. In contrast to the WKA and BA, the CA allows the equation for the axial radial particle velocity gradient (w_r^a) to be obtained from the continuity equation without making approximations. In contrast to the FDA, the CA first allows the relationship between the detonation velocity (D) and the heat of decomposition (Q) to be determined without solving an eigen-value problem, and then allows the constraints imposed on axial flow by the curved shock, the axial and radial momentum equations, and the rate law to be incorporated into the solution.

GOVERNING EQUATIONS

In a cylindrical (z, r) coordinate system that is attached to the shock and travels along the axis of the charge from right to left with a velocity -D, we write our equations expressing the balance of mass, axial momentum, and energy for axial flow as

$$B = \frac{u^2}{2} + \frac{c^2}{k-1} - \lambda Q - \frac{D^2}{2} = 0 \qquad (1)$$

$$\frac{p}{p_H}\left(\frac{c_H}{c}\right)^{2k/k-1} = \exp\left(-k\int_0^\lambda \frac{Qd\lambda}{c^2}\right) = \frac{\rho}{\rho_H}\left(\frac{c_H}{c}\right)^{2/k-1} \qquad (2)$$

$$-\frac{d\ln\rho u}{dt} = 2w_r^a = (k-1)\frac{Q}{c^2}\frac{d\lambda}{dt} - \left(1-\frac{u^2}{c^2}\right)\frac{1}{u}\frac{du}{dt} \qquad (3)$$

In these equations, t denotes time, u = dz/dt, w = dr/dt, the subscript H denotes the shock where the extent of decomposition $\lambda = 0$, and the superscript a denotes the axis. Bernoulli's equation, B = 0, and the equation for the pressure (p) are both obtained by integrating equations expressing the conservation of axial momentum and energy for polytropic explosive with an index k; the equation for the density (ρ) is obtained from the equation $c^2 = kp/\rho$ defining the sound speed c. In Equation (3), the first equation for w_r^a is the continuity equation, and the second equation is a combination of the continuity, axial momentum and energy equations. Following WK, we write the equation expressing the conservation of radial momentum on the axis, with a now used as a subscript, as

$$\left[\rho\left(\frac{dw_r}{dt} + (w_r)^2\right)\right]_a = -\left(\frac{\partial 2p}{\partial r^2}\right)_a \qquad (4)$$

We call the shock locus OS, use the subcript o to denote the initial state, and use s_H and β respectively to denote the length along OS and the angle a tangent to OS makes with the axis of the change. Then $dr_H/dz = \tan\beta$ for β in the range $\beta_s \le \beta \le \pi/2$, and the axial radius of curvature of OS (S_a) is given by the equations

$$\frac{1}{S_a} = -\left(\frac{d\beta}{dr_H}\right)^a = \left(\frac{d^2z}{dr_H^2}\right)^a \qquad (5)$$

We resolve the axial velocity of the explosive entering OS into a perpendicular component $D_\perp = D\sin\beta$, and a parallel component $D_{11} = D\cos\beta$, and use the Rankine-Hugoniot (RH) jump conditions and the polytropic ($D_\perp - u_\perp$) Hugoniot, $2D_\perp = (k+1)\,u_\perp$, to write the equations for shocked states as,

$$(k+1)u_H = D(k+\cos 2\beta) \qquad (6)$$

$$(k+1)w_H = D \sin 2\beta \tag{7}$$

$$\frac{\rho_H}{\rho_o} = \frac{D_\perp}{D_\perp - u_\perp} = \frac{k+1}{k-1} \tag{8}$$

$$p_H = p_H^a \sin^2\beta \tag{9}$$

with $p_H^a = 2\rho_o D^2/(k+1)$. Applying the directional derivative along the shock, $d()_H/dr = (\partial/\partial r)_H + (\partial/\partial z)_H \cot\beta$, to Equations (7) and (9), setting $\beta = \pi/2$, and using Equations (4) and (5) with the equation $(d^2p_H/dr^2)^a = -2p_H^a/(S_a)^2$ to evaluate the indefinite form obtained from Equation (9) gives the constraints imposed on the axial flow derivatives by the RH jump conditions and the axial and radial momentum equations as

$$w_{rH}^a = \frac{2D}{(k+1)S_a} \tag{10}$$

$$\left(\frac{du}{dt}\right)_H^a - \frac{4D^2(k-2)}{(k+1)^2 S_a} = -S_a\left(\frac{dw_r^a}{dt}\right)_H \tag{11}$$

THE WRA AND FDA TO THE AFP

Some comments about the WKA and FDA to axial flow are now presented to show why, in my opinion, a new approach was required to address the AFP. The BA is not mentioned here because it is an extension of the WKA. Following the classical treatment of SS shocks, WK construct first integrals of the continuity and axial momentum equations as RH jump conditions containing w_r^a terms, and then approximate OS as a spherical isobar and use Equation (4) to determine w_r^a. Following phase-plane methods for differential equations (DEs), FD use the second equation for w_r^a in Equation (3), B = 0, and prescribed forms for w_r^a and $d\lambda/dt$ to obtain a DE in the (λ–u^2) plane containing D as a parameter. They then integrate this DE with different values of D to determine the integral curve passing through the shock and the sonic point (a saddle), that is defined by the first integral of the mass, axial momentum and energy equations for axial flow. Because the constraint imposed on axial flow by OS and the radial momentum equation is ignored in this approach, however, the integral curve obtained by solving this eigen-value problem will not provide a solution to the AFP unless its associated values of D, S_a, and $(du/dt)_H^a$ satisfy Equation (11). The CA to bypass these problems with w_r^a is based on the concept that Equation (3) can be used to obtain w_r^a as a part of the solution to the AFP when the flow equations are written as shown in Equations (1) through (3) and expressions for u and c can be found that satisfy B = 0 and reduce to the equations for u and c for ID detonation. This concept is valid because such an expression for c can be used to evaluate the integral in Equation (2) and thereby obtain the equations for p and ρ without using the continuity equation. Methods of differential geometry were used to construct such equations for u and c and also provide a means of incorporating Equation (11) into the solution.

THE CA APPROACH TO THE AFP

The CA approach to the AFP is based on the tangent vector $\tilde{A}_1 = \tilde{\Lambda}_1\, \partial/\partial\lambda + \tilde{U}_1\, \partial/\partial u + \tilde{C}_1\, \partial/\partial c$ that satisfies the invariant condition $\tilde{A}_1 B = B = 0$ and has first integrals, $u_H = u_H(u, \lambda, k)$ and $c_H = c_H(c, \lambda, k)$ that are also the equations for u and c for ID detonation. To construct such a tangent vector $\tilde{A}$ for axial flow, that reduces to $\tilde{A}_1$ when $w_r^a = 0$ and satisfies the invariant condition $\tilde{A}B = aB = 0$, I introduce the parameters a, b, ε_1, and ε_2 and extend $\tilde{A}_1$ by setting,

$$\tilde{\Lambda} = a(1-\lambda) \tag{12}$$

$$\tilde{U} = \frac{au}{2} - \frac{bkD}{2(k+1)}(1+\varepsilon_1) \tag{13}$$

$$\tilde{C} = \frac{ac}{2} + \frac{bk(k-1)Du(1+\varepsilon_1)}{4(k+1)c} - \frac{a\varepsilon_2 k^2 D^2}{4(k+1)c} \tag{14}$$

I then integrate the differential system defined by these equations to obtain equations for the first integrals u_H and c_H that give our required equations for u and c when b/a = 1 as

$$(k+1)u = D[k(1+\varepsilon_1) - (1+k\varepsilon_1)(1-\lambda)^{1/2}] \tag{15}$$

and

$$(k+1)^2c^2 = kD^2[C_1 - C_2(1-\lambda)^{1/2} + C_3(1-\lambda)] \tag{16}$$

with $2C_1 = k[(k+1)(1+\varepsilon_3) - (k-1)(1+\varepsilon_1)^2]$, $C_2 = -(k-1)(1+\varepsilon_1)(1+k\varepsilon_1)$, $2C_3 = (k-1)[4 + (1+\varepsilon_1)\{k(1-\varepsilon_1) - 2\}] - k(k+1)(1+\varepsilon_3)$ and $\varepsilon_3 = \varepsilon_2 - 1$.

Setting $a = b = \varepsilon_2 = 1$ and $\varepsilon_1 = 0$ in Equations (12) through (14) gives the equations defining $\tilde{A}_1$, and setting $\varepsilon_3 = \varepsilon_1 = 0$ in Equations (15) and (16) gives the corresponding equations for ID detonation. The condition for $\tilde{A}B = aB = 0$,

$$D^2[k^2(\varepsilon_2 - 1) + 1] = 2(k^2-1)Q = D_\infty^2 \tag{17}$$

bypasses the eigen-value problem and allows us to introduce the parameter ε_3 in terms of the detonation velocity deficit D/D_∞ as $k^2\varepsilon_3 = (D_\infty/D)^2 - 1$. Using Equation (16) to perform the integration in Equation (2) leads to the following equations for p and ρ.

$$\frac{p}{p_H} = \left(\frac{c}{c_H}\right)^{K_1}\left(\frac{R_+ - (1-\lambda)^{1/2}}{R_+ - 1}\right)^{NC_2/C_3} \tag{18}$$

$$\frac{\rho}{\rho_H} = \left(\frac{c}{c_H}\right)^{K_1-2}\left(\frac{R_+ - (1-\lambda)^{1/2}}{R_+ - 1}\right)^{NC_2/C_3} \tag{19}$$

with the nonideal paramters $K_1 = 2(k + (k-1)NR_-)/k-1$, $2C_3R_+ = C_2 - (R)^{1/2}$, $2C_3R_- = C_2 + (R)^{1/2}$, $R = C_2^2 - 4C_1C_4$, and $(k-1)R^{1/2}N = (k+1)(D_\infty/D)^2$. Evaluating these nonideal parameters as ε_1 and $\varepsilon_3 \to 0$ and $C_1 \to k$, $-C_2 \to (k-1)$ and $C_3 \to -1$ shows that $R_+ \to k$, $R_- \to -1$, $R^{1/2} \to (k+1)$ and $N \to (k-1)^{-1}$, and also shows that Equations (18) and (19) reduce to the equations for p and ρ for ID detonation. Substituting, Equations (15) and (19) or Equations (15), (16), and (17), respectively into the first or the second equations in Equation (3) gives the equation for w_r^a which we write here with $U_1 = k(1+\varepsilon_1)$ and $U_2 = -(1+k\varepsilon_1)$ as

$$2\,w_r^a = \frac{D^2}{2c^2(k+1)}\left[k^2\,\varepsilon_3+1+\frac{U_2(U_2+U_1(1-\lambda)^{1/2})}{(k+1)}\left(\frac{c^2}{u^2}-1\right)\right] \times \frac{d\lambda}{dt} \qquad (20)$$

to show that the second Chapman-Jouguet (CJ) condition is automatically satisfied at the sonic point where $\hat{u} = \hat{c}$.

I eliminate $\hat{u}$ from the equations obtained, by setting $\hat{c} = \hat{u}$ and $\lambda = \hat{\lambda}$ in B = 0 and $u = \hat{u}$ and $\lambda = \hat{\lambda}$ in Equation (15) to derive the equation for $\hat{\lambda}$ as,

$$k^2[(1+\varepsilon_1)^2-(1+\varepsilon_3)] - 2k(1+\varepsilon_1)(1+k\,\varepsilon_1)(1-\hat{\lambda})^{1/2} + [(1+k^2\varepsilon_3) + (1+k\varepsilon_1)^2]\,(1-\hat{\lambda}) = 0 \qquad (21)$$

I evaluate Equation (20) at the shock front to obtain my equation for $(w_r^a)_H$ as

$$(w_r^a)_H = \frac{(k+1)}{8(k-1)}\,[k\,\varepsilon_3-\varepsilon_1]\left(\frac{d\lambda}{dt}\right)_H \qquad (22)$$

and combine this equation with Equation (10) to derive my equation defining the D/D_∞ versus Sa^{-1} relationship as

$$\frac{D_\infty}{Sa} = \frac{(k+1)^2}{16(k-1)}\,[k\,\varepsilon_3-\varepsilon_1]\,[k^2\varepsilon_3+1]^{1/2}\left(\frac{d\lambda}{dt}\right)_H \qquad (23)$$

I finally use Equation (11) to derive a relationship between ε_1 and ε_2 that closes my solution to the AFP and ensures that it accounts for the constraints imposed on axial flow by OS, the axial and radial momentum equations and the rate law. In this derivation, I evaluate the left-hand side of Equation (11) with Equations (10) and (22) and the equation for $(du/dt)_H^a$ obtained from Equation (15), and I evaluate the right-hand side of Equation (11) with the equation for $d(w_r^a)/dt$ obtained by differentiating the continuity equation with du/dt and dρ/dt derived from Equations (15) and (19).

Because the ε_1–ε_3 relationship derived in this way contains $(d\lambda/dt)_H^2$ and $(d^2\lambda/dt^2)_H$ terms, a particular solution for axial flow can only be constructed by determining the particular form this relationship takes for a prescribed rate of decomposition. For the rate law considered here,

$$\frac{d\lambda}{dt} = \frac{2}{\alpha}\left(\frac{p}{2\hat{p}_\infty}\right)^n (1-\lambda)^m \qquad \text{(RI)}$$

with $\hat{p}_\infty$, the ID CJ pressure, α a characteristic chemical time, and n and m variable parameters, the ε_1–ε_3 relationship takes the form,

$$\begin{aligned}&k\varepsilon_3[(k-7)-2n(k-1)]\,\varepsilon_1^2\\ &-2[4k+(k-1)\{n+4(m-1)\}\\ &+k^2\{(3k-5)-(k-1)n\}\varepsilon_3]\,\varepsilon_1\varepsilon_3\\ &+[2k\{2(k+1)+(k-1)[n+4(m-1)]\}\\ &+k^3(k+1)\varepsilon_3]\,\varepsilon_3^2\end{aligned} = 0 \qquad (24)$$

The parameters n and m enter Equation (24) because they govern the dependence of dλ/dt on the thermodynamic state. The ε_1–ε_3 relationship for the following rate law obtained by setting $p = p_H$ in RI

$$\frac{d\lambda}{dt} = \frac{2}{\alpha}\left(\frac{D}{D_\infty}\right)^{2n} (1-\lambda)^m \qquad \text{(RI)'}$$

is obtained from Equation (24) by setting n = 0, and no longer contains n because n now determines the dependence of dλ/dt on the shocked state.

Thus in the CA to the AFP in polytropic explosive, the invariant condition $\tilde{A}B = aB = 0$ defines the $\varepsilon_3 - D/D_\infty$ relationship, and the rate law defines the particular form taken by the $\varepsilon_1 - \varepsilon_3$ relationship. The solution for a prescribed rate law and value of k, is obtained by first constructing their ε_1–ε_3 relationship and then by using this relationship and the ε_3–D/D_∞ relationship to calculate values of ε_1 and ε_3 associated with different values of D/D_∞. Equations (15), (16), and (18) through (20) can then be used to determine how the variations of u/D, c/D, p/p_H, ρ/ρ_H, and w_r^a with λ depend on D/D_∞, and Equations (21) through (23) can be used to determine the dependence of $\hat{\lambda}$, $(w_r^a)_H$, and $D_\infty\alpha/Sa$ on D/D_∞. Such calculations have been performed with (RI), (RI)', and k = 3 but because of space limitations only some results pertaining to $D_\infty\alpha/Sa$ and $(w_r^a)_H$ for RI will be presented here.

THE DEPENDENCE OF $D_\infty\alpha/Sa$ AND $(w_r^a)_H$ ON D/D_∞ AND A NEW AXIAL CONDITION FOR DETONATION FAILURE

We first note from Equations (23) and (22) that both $D_\infty\alpha/Sa$ and $(w_r^a)_H$ depend explicitly on the reaction rate at the shock front but implicitly on the charge diameter through ε_1 and ε_3. We next note that $\alpha(d\lambda/dt)_H = 2(D/D_\infty)^{2n}$ for RI and use Equations (17) and (23) to show that the $D_\infty\alpha/Sa$ versus D/D_∞ relationship for RI and k = 3 is governed by the equations

$$\frac{D}{D_\infty} = \frac{1}{(9\varepsilon_3+1)} \quad (25)$$

$$\frac{D_\infty \alpha}{Sa} = \frac{(3\varepsilon_3-\varepsilon_1)}{(9\varepsilon_3-1)^{(2n-1)/2}} \quad (26)$$

with the $\varepsilon_1 - \varepsilon_3$ relationship given by Equation (24) with k = 3. Plots of values of D/D_∞ and $D_\infty\alpha/Sa$ calculated from these equations with n = 1, 2, 3, and 4 and m = 1/2 and 1 are shown in Figure 1. These plots exhibit similar features to the corresponding curves presented by Bdzil,[3] in that the plots with n = 1 are single-valued but those with n = 2, 3, and 4 are double-valued, and at the points labelled with a solid circle have an infinite slope where $d(D_\infty\alpha/Sa)/d\varepsilon_3 = 0$. We denote the value of D/D_∞ at such points by $(D/D_\infty)_f^B$, call the condition $d(D_\infty\alpha/Sa)/d\varepsilon_3 = 0$, Bdzil's axial condition for detonation failure $(BAC)_f$, and see that it will be satisfied when the denominator in Equation (26) increases faster with ε_3 than the numerator. An analysis with the equations obtained by differentiating Equations (25) and (26) with respect to ε_3 shows (1) that the D/D_∞ versus $D_\infty\alpha/Sa$ curves for RI and k = 3 will be double-valued and satisfy $(BAC)_f$ when n > 1.5 and (2) that their initial slopes are given by the equation,

$$\left(\frac{d(D/D_\infty)}{d(D_\infty\alpha/Sa)}\right)_\infty = -\frac{3}{4}(2+n+4m) \quad (27)$$

A more detailed comparison of my curves and Bdzil's can be obtained by recognizing that the variable parameter, say $\bar{n}$, in Bdzil's rate law (BRL) governs the shocked state and that $(d\lambda/dt)_H \propto (D/D_\infty)^{4+\bar{n}}$ for BRL while $(d\lambda/dt)_H \propto (D/D_\infty)^{2n}$ for RI. We according set $2n = 4 + \bar{n}$ and see that my n > 1.5 condition for the curves to be double-valued is equivalent to Bdzil's $\bar{n} > -1$ condition, and that the curves in Figure 1 with m = 1/2 and n = 1 and 4 correspond respectively to Bdzil's curves with $\bar{n} = -2$ and $\bar{n} = 4$. The three pairs of corresponding curves (n = 2.5, $\bar{n}$ = 1), (n = 4, $\bar{n}$ = 4) and (n = 6, $\bar{n}$ = 8) have essentially the same values of $(D/D_\infty)_f^B$ where their slopes become infinite, but show contrasting behavior with respect to their initial slopes. While the initial slopes of my curves are given by Equation (27) with m = 1/2, the initial slopes of Bdzil's curves are the same. This difference is explained by the fact that while my n and m parameters govern the dependence of RI on the thermodynamic state and appear in its $\varepsilon_1 - \varepsilon_3$ relationship, Bdzil's $\bar{n}$ parameter governs the dependence of BRL on the shocked state and will thus not appear in the $\varepsilon_1 - \varepsilon_3$ relationship determined by this rate law.

Finally, to formulate a new axial condition for detonation failure, we write Equation (22) for RI and k = 3 as

$$\alpha\,(w_r^a)_H = \frac{(3\,\varepsilon_3 - \varepsilon_1)}{2\,(9\varepsilon_3 + 1)^n} \quad (28)$$

Using Equation (28) to perform an analysis similar to that used for the D/D_∞ versus $D_\infty\alpha/Sa$ curves, shows that the D/D_∞ versus $(w_r^a)_H$ curves will be double-valued for n > 1, and for a given value of n > 1.5 will exhibit an infinite slope at a higher value of D/D_∞ than the D/D_∞ versus $D_\infty\alpha/Sa$ curve with the same value of n. Here for physical reasons, we choose the condition $d(w_r^a)_H\,\alpha/d\varepsilon_3 = 0$ rather than $d(D_\infty\alpha/Sa)/d\varepsilon_3 = 0$ to be the axial failure condition. Points satisfying this axial failure condition $d(w_r^a)_H\,\alpha/d\varepsilon_3 = 0$ are denoted by the subscript f and shown as solid squares on the D/D_∞ versus $D_\infty\alpha/Sa$ curves in Figure 1. With this axial failure condition D/D_∞ versus $D_\infty\alpha/Sa$ curves with n > 1 will have $(D/D_\infty)_f$ points, and those with n > 1.5, as shown in Figure 1, will exhibit $(D/D_\infty)_f$ points before their slopes become infinite.

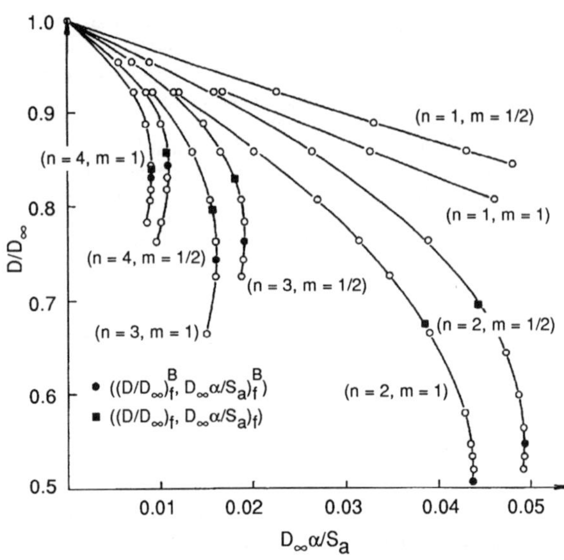

Figure 1. Plots of the detonation velocity deficit (D/D_∞) versus a nondimensionalized axial radius of curvature $(D_\infty\alpha/S_a)$ for a polytropic explosion with k = 3 and the decomposition rated $\lambda/dt = 2\,(p/2\hat{p}_\infty)^n(1 - \lambda)^m/\alpha$.

ACKNOWLEDGMENTS

I gratefully acknowledge the CNRS for supporting this work while I spent a year at Laboratoire d'Energétique et de Détonique, U.R.A. n°193 au C.N.R.S. as an Associate Research Director, and also acknowledge discussions with Dr. H. N. Presles and Dr. P. Vidal.

REFERENCES

1. W. W. Wood and J. G. Kirkwood, J. Chem.Phys. 22, pp. 1920-1924 (1954).

2. W. Fickell and W. C. Davis, Detonation (University of California Press, Berkeley and Los Angeles, CA, 1979) Chapter 5, pp. 212-219.

3. J. B. Bdzil, J. Fluid Mech. 108, pp. 195-226 (1981).

A DEVELOPED UNIFIED CRITICAL CRITERION FOR THE INITIATION OF BARE EXPLOSIVES

Zhao Feng Sun Chengwei Wei Yuzhang
Laboratory for Shock Wave and Detonation Physics Research
Southwest Institute of Fluid Physics
P. O. Box 523, Chengdu 610003, Sichuan, P. R. China

An unified critical criterion is developed to predict the bare heterogeneous explosives based on the critical energy criterion. This unified model can be applied to flat-end plate or projectile with various thickness and shapes of profile. And it has been applied to PBX-9404, JO-9159, HNS-I_4 (HNS-I/$F_{23\text{-}14}$ = 97.5/2.5) and Tetryle explosives. The predicted results are compared with some published experimental values, which shows a good agreement is achieved. The characteristic of the criterion is that only one empirical parameter (critical energy for one-dimensional shock initiation) is there in it.

INTRODUCTION

In 1969 a critical energy criterion was proposed by walker and wasley[1] as follows

$$pu\tau = Const = E_c \qquad (1)$$

where p is the shock pressure at the impacted surface, u is the particle velocity in the target, τ is taken to be the shock duration of the impact. Equation (1) means that at the surface if the hydrodynamic energy from the shock per area reaches a special value E_c, the explosive will explode.

However, when impact takes place on a small surface, the one-dimensional critical energy criterion becomes invalid because of lateral rarefication. Many scholares have investigated this problem. James[2] suggested a criterion for long-rod, and Moulard[3] gave a criterion which includes five empirical parameters. But we still need a criterion which can deal with one-dimensional to two-dimensional problem with clear physical concept.

CRITERION FOR CYLINDER FLAT-END PROJECTILE

It should be noted that the initiation of HE not only depends on imported energy but also on the distribution of the energy. One-dimensional criterion tells us that the initiation of HE needs critical energy $E_c = pu\tau$, and the high pressure volume with p generated by flying-plate in HE is $(D-u) \cdot \tau$ before the rear rarefication reaches the HE. Based on the concept metioned above, considering the energy transimitted from projectile and the variation of high pressure region in HE within the time τ, the unified critical criterion is derived[4] as follws

$$\begin{cases} pu\tau \cdot q_1 q_2 = E_c \\ q_1 = [1 - \dfrac{c\tau}{R_0} + \dfrac{1}{3}(\dfrac{c\tau}{R_0})^2] \\ q_2 = 1 - \dfrac{2}{3}\dfrac{c\tau}{R_0} + \dfrac{1}{6}(\dfrac{c\tau}{R_0})^2] \end{cases} \qquad (2)$$

Equation (2) represents the critical criterion for long rod. Obviously, as $R_o \to \infty$, it becomes one-dimensional critical energy criterion equation (1). In equation (2) p and u are calculated according to Hugoniot relation.

As rarefication from the lateral and the rear of projectile disturbs the high region in it we can simply chose the total time interval τ as

$$\tau = min\left\{\frac{2l}{w}, \frac{R_0}{c}\right\} \qquad (3)$$

where w and c are shock velocity and rarefication velocity in the projectile respectively, we will discuss this problem further in section 4.

CRITERION FOR FLAT-END PROJECTILE WITH DIFFERENT SHAPES OF PROFILE

For rectangle projectile with sidelines a and b

($b \leqslant a$), we get the criterion as

$$\begin{cases} pu\tau q_1 q_2 = E_c \\ q_1 = 1 - (a+b)\dfrac{c\tau}{ab} + \dfrac{4}{3}\dfrac{c^2\tau^2}{ab} \\ q_2 = 1 - \dfrac{2}{3}\dfrac{(a+b)}{ab}c\tau + \dfrac{2}{3}\dfrac{c^2\tau^2}{ab} \\ \tau = min\{b/w, 2l/c\} \end{cases} \quad (4)$$

For a equilateral triangle, we have

$$\begin{cases} pu\tau q_1 q_2 = E_c \\ q_1 = 1 - 2\sqrt{3}\dfrac{c\tau}{a_0} + 4(\dfrac{c\tau}{a_0})^2 \\ q_2 = 1 - \dfrac{4}{3}\sqrt{3}\dfrac{c\tau}{a_0} + 2(\dfrac{c\tau}{a_0})^2 \\ \tau = min\{\dfrac{\sqrt{3}a_0}{6w}, \dfrac{2l}{c}\} \end{cases} \quad (5)$$

where a_0 is the sideline. And for a annulation, we have

$$\begin{cases} pu\tau q_1 q_2 = E_c \\ q_1 = 1 - \dfrac{c\tau}{R_2 - R_1} \\ q_2 = 1 - \dfrac{2}{3}\dfrac{c\tau}{R_2 - R_1} \\ \tau = min\{\dfrac{R_2 - R_1}{2w}, \dfrac{2l}{c}\} \end{cases} \quad (6)$$

where R_1 and R_2 are inside and ontside radiuses respectively. And R_1 should be larger than a critical value.

To sum up, the criterion for flat-end projectile with various shapes of profile is as follows

$$pu\frac{\int_0^\tau S(t)dt}{S(0)} \cdot \frac{\int_0^\tau V(t)dt}{(D-u)\cdot S(0)\dfrac{1}{2}\tau^2} = E_c \quad (7)$$

where $s(t)=\pi(R_o-ct)^2$, $V(t)$ is high pressure region in HE generated by projectile, and $S(0)=S(t)|_{t=0}$.

COMPARATION OF THE MODEL WITH EXPERIMENTS

Suppose the shock wave velocity D and particle velocity u satisfy the linear relation, $D=a+bu$. Constants a, b of six material (include HE) are listed in Table 1. The D~u relation and shock jump-tion relation are used to calculate the pressure and particle velocity at impact surface. The velocity of rarefication wave is assumed to be equal to shock wave velocity.

Figure 1 and 2 represent the relationship between critical pressure p and action time τ of JO-9159 and HNS-I_4 with MYLAR flying-plate respectively, where solid lines are calculated with equation (2) and symbles are experimental results of 50% initiation possibility from [5] and [6] respectively.

Table 1 Hugoniot data for several materials

	DENSITY/(g/cm³)	a/(km/s)	b
PBX—9404(HE)[2]	1.84	2.43	2.57
STEEL[2]	7.84	3.596	1.6863
JO-9159(HE)	1.84	2.43	2.57
MYLAR[7]	1.4	2.54	1.49
HNS-I_4(HE)[8]	1.57	1.00	3.21
TETRYL(HE)[2]	1.54	2.17	2.76

It can be seen that the predicted results of our criterion are consistent with the experiments.

From calculation it is discovered that as the thickness of projectile L, as well as its diameter d satisfy $L/d \geqslant 1/8$ approximately, the critical pressure would not decrease as L increases. That is to say the pressure is in P_{min} at $L/d \approx 1/8$. At this situation, $L \geqslant d/8$, the increase of thickness may has no influence on the critical pressure because of lateral rarefication.

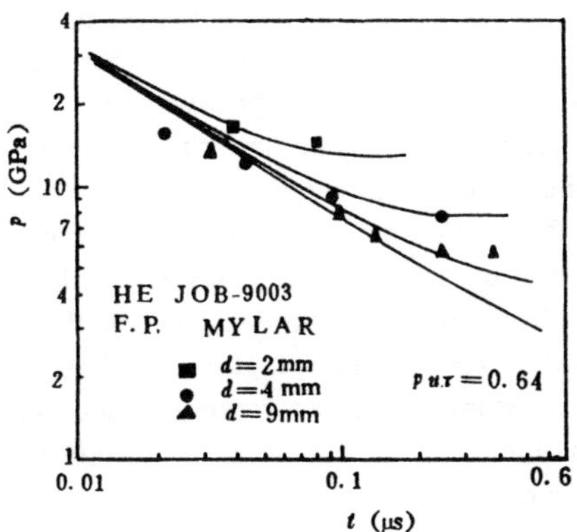

Fig. 1 Relationship between critical pressure and action time (flyer thickness) with different diameter
Solid lines are calculated, others are measured

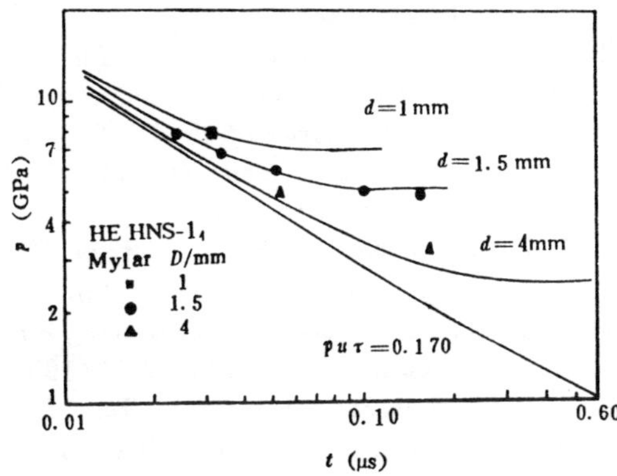

Fig. 2 Relationship between critical pressure and action time (flyer thickness) with different diameters
Solid lines are calculated, other are measured

Figure 3 and 4 indicate critical velocities of HE with flat-end steel rod, where lines are calculated from Eq, (2), and experimental results are from reference [2]. Because $L/d \approx 1$ in experiments, the U_{min} (corresponding to P_{min}) is chosen as the critical velocity. It can be seen that the predicted u are agreement with the experimental value.

DISCUSSION AND CONCLUSION

When L/d is approximate equal to 1/8, the

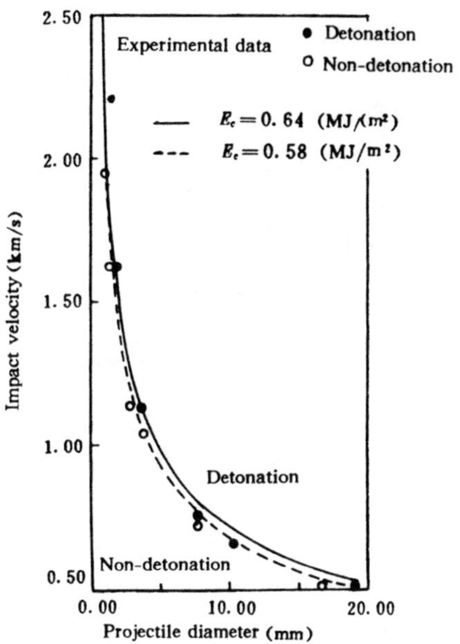

Fig. 3 Steel rods impacting PBX-9404 HE

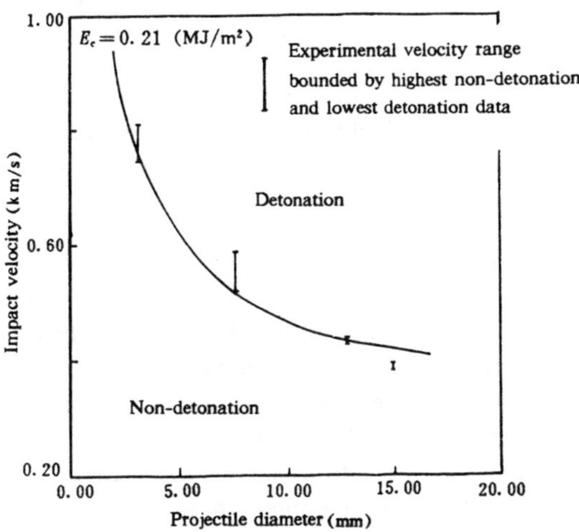

Fig. 4 Steel (brass) rods impacting Tetryl HE

pressure in Eq. (2) becomes minimum, that is, the increase of L could not enable the critical pressure or velocity to decrease. It indicates the projectile has become to act as a lony rod, which changes current accepted value[2] of $L/d=1/4$ or $L/d=1/12$.

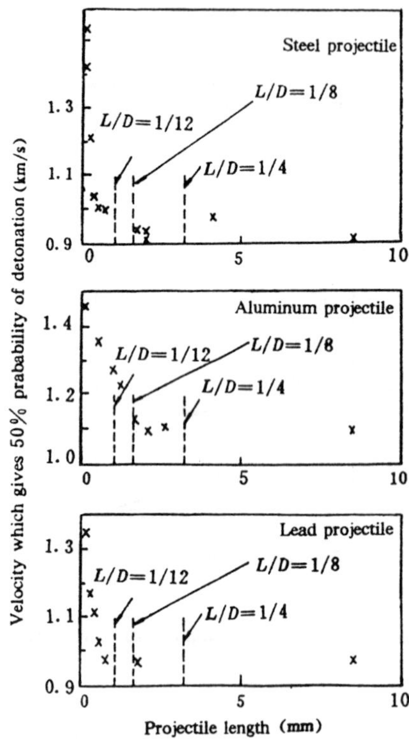

Fig. 5 Projectiles of constant diameter and decreasing length impacting RDX/Wax 83/17

Figure 5 indicates experimental results. The projectile with decreasing thickness but same diameter, impact an RDX/wax explosive[2]. We plot $L/d = 1/4, 1/8$ and $1/12$ on the figure. It can be seen that constant velocity is approximately accquired for $L \geqslant d/8$. Hence $L/d \approx 1/8$ may be reasonable as a change-overpoint from projectile to long rod behaviour. The accurate value of L/d can be accquired by resolving the minimum pressure for various projectile and the total acting duraction τ will be changed for different projectile.

In order to give a reasonable fit to experimental data, we use a E_c which is smaller than the experimental critical energy. The reason may be the diameter of projectile or plate in experiments are limited, and the effect of edge always exist. And in our criterion, E_c should be the critical energy under ideal one-dimensional condition.

The criterion developed in this paper can basically be used to flat-end projectile with various shapes of profile and thickness. The calculations for PBX-9404, HNS-I_4 Tetryl and JO-9159 indicate that one parameter E_c can represents the character of initiation of these HE. And it is convinent for application.

REFERENCES

[1] F. E. Walker and R. J. Wasley, *Explosivestof* 17(1), pp. 9-16 (1969)

[2] H. R. James, *Propellants, Explosives, Protechnics* 13, pp. 35-41 (1988)

[3] H. Moulard, "Critical conditions for shock initiation of detonation by small projectile impact", in *Proceedings of the 7th Symposium (Int) on Detonation*, White Oak Maryland: NSWC 1977, pp. 316-324

[4] F. Zhao et al, *Explosion and Shock Waves* (Chinese Journal) 13(1), pp. 41-48 (1993)

[5] Z. Zhou and Y. Wei, *Explosion and Shock Waves* (Chinese Journal) 12(1), pp. 77-82(1992)

[6] Z. Wang et al, *Explosion and Shock Waves* (Chinese Journal) 7(2), pp. 154-159 (1987)

[7] K. C. Weingart, et al, "Shock initiation of PBX-9404 by electrically driven flyer plates", in *Proceeding of the 6th Symposium (Int) on Detonation* White Oak Maryland: NSWC, 1977, pp. 201-209

[8] J. Roth, "Shock sensitivity and shock hugoniots of High-Density Granular Explosives", in *Proceeding of the 5th Symposium (Int) on Detonation*, White Oak Maryland: NSWC, 1971, pp. 139-140

THE SHAPE OF DETONATION FRONT AND THE DETONATION VELOCITY*

Yuanhang He and Jing Ding
Department of Engineering Mechanics
Beijing Institute of Technology,
Beijing, P. R. China, 100081

The governing equation for the steady-state detonation front is given in this paper. The boundary condition which is decoupled from the flow variables in the reaction zone can be obtained from the stability analysis. The shape of detonation front is calculated.

INTRODUCTION

The flow structure of a two-dimentional (2-D) Steady-state detonation has been studied extensively by many authors in past decade. The detonation wave is usually considered as a nonreactive shock front followed by a reaction zone. Speaking generally, as soon as the detonation velocity reaches its steady value, the configuration of the flow as well as its free boundary would be fixed. It is determined only by the detonation velocity and the initial parameters. However, this problem is complicated by the boundary conditions which are coupled with the flow variables, although simple reaction rate law and equation of state are used in the 2-D steady-state Euler equation. Bdzil[1,2] presented an analytical theory for the 2-D steady-state detonation with a small curvation shock front. Based on a transverse analysis of the flow variables in the infinitesimal neighborhood of the shock front, Chaisse et al.[3] measured the curvature of the shock front on the symmetrical axis and determined the shape of the shock front theoretically.

In this paper, we derive the governing equation for the shock front from the conservations of mass and momentum accross the shock front. With the aid of stability analysis, we determined the boundary value. It is shown that the shape of the shock front is dependent only on the detonation velocity and the deflection angle of streamline on the lateral boundary.

THEORY

Governing Equation

In the coodinate system attaching the shock front which travels with the steady detonation velocity D as shown in Figure 1, the oblique shock relationships give:

$$\rho_0 D\cos\theta = \rho_+ u\cos(\theta + \chi) \qquad (1)$$

$$P_+ = P_0 + \rho_0 D\cos\theta[D\cos\theta - u_+ \cos(\theta + \chi)] \qquad (2)$$

$$D\sin\theta = u_+ \sin(\theta + \chi) \qquad (3)$$

where P, ρ, u are the pressure, density and particle velocity respectively. The subscripts "0" and "+" imply the variables of explosive ahead andbehind immediately to the shock front. We take the polytropic equation of state:

$$P_+ = A_0[(\rho_+ / \rho_0)^\gamma - 1] \qquad (4)$$

for describing the unreacted explosive. Combining the four equations, we get the governing equation for the shape of shock front.

$$[y + \mathrm{tg}\chi]^{\gamma+1} - y^\gamma[1 - y\mathrm{tg}\chi]^\gamma[y + (A_1 + 1)\mathrm{tg}\chi] = 0 \qquad (5)$$

where

$$y = \mathrm{tg}\theta = \frac{dz_s(r)}{dt} \qquad (6)$$

$$A_1 = \frac{D^2}{A_0\rho_0^{\gamma-1}} \qquad (7)$$

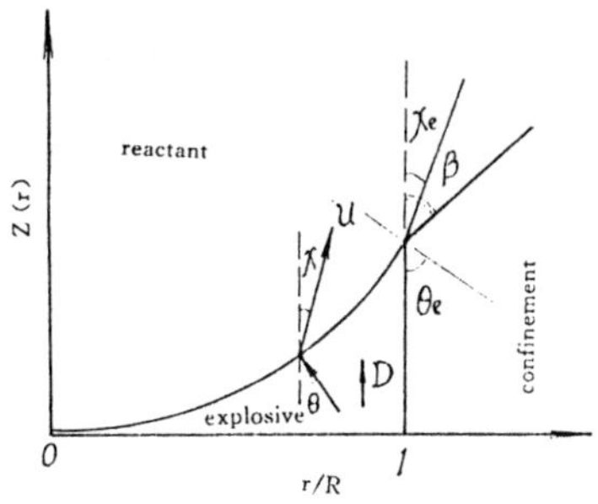

Figure 1. The configuration of 2-D steady-state detonation R is the radius of charge.

* This work is supported by the NSFC.

If an another relationship between θ and χ is found or the function $\chi(r)$ is given, equation (5) can be solved.

Deflection of Streamline

For a steady-state detonation, the configuration of its free boundary is fixed. The curved front and the deflecting streamline illustrate the edge effect. Following to Whitham's theory, the speed of the edge disturbance along the detonation front is $D\int_0^r K(r)dr$ for the cylindrical charge. It is obvious that the strength of the disturbance increases as the distence from the axis increases. Thus the deflection angle χ can be written as:

$$\chi(r) = \sum_i a_i \left(\frac{r}{R}\right)^i \chi_e \qquad (8)$$

where the cofficient $a_i \geqslant 0$ and $\sum_i a_i = 1$. R is the radius of charge. For the solid explosive, equation (8) can be taken as

$$\chi(r) = \left(\frac{r}{R}\right)^2 \chi_e \qquad (9)$$

The boundary condition χ_e will be determined below.

Boundary Condition.

On the boundary $r=R$, we have the relationship for the edge values θ_e, χ_e

$$(\mathrm{tg}\theta_e + \mathrm{tg}\chi_e)^{\gamma+1} - (\mathrm{tg}\theta_e)^{\gamma}(1-\mathrm{tg}\theta_e\mathrm{tg}\chi_e)^{\gamma}[\mathrm{tg}\theta_e + (A_1+1)\mathrm{tg}\chi_e] = 0 \qquad (9)$$

The stability analysis for this equation is shown in Figure 2. Point B is a critical point. The part of the curve below B is the stable branch, and the upper part is the unstable branch.

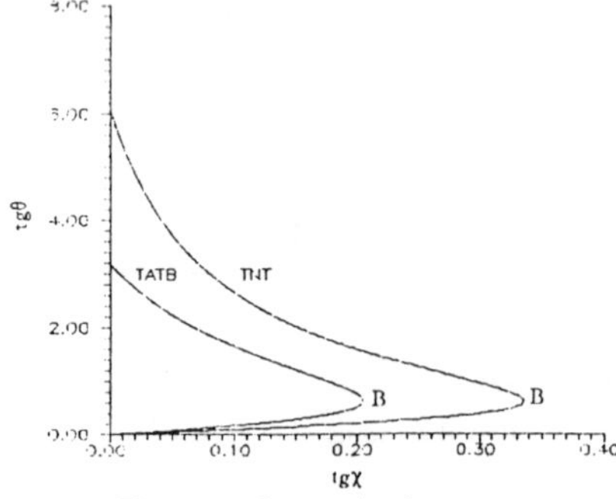

Figure 2. Curve of $\mathrm{tg}\theta_e$ vs $\mathrm{tg}\chi_e$

Since the slope is determined only by the detonation velocity D and is independent to the charge radius, point B corresponds to the vacuum boundary. The lower point on the stable branch corresponds to the heavier confinement and the smaller charge radius. Once the χ_e is determined, the shape of shock front is given.

For the cast TNT and the standard granular TATB the shape of detonation front is shown in Figure 3. The parameters used in calculation are shown in Table 1.

Table 1. The parameters for TNT and TATB[4]

	ρ_0 g/cm^3	A_0 GPa	γ	R mm	D mm/μs
TNT	1.575	0.013	6.8	5.01	6.760
TATB	1.800	0.019	7.2	25.00	7.621

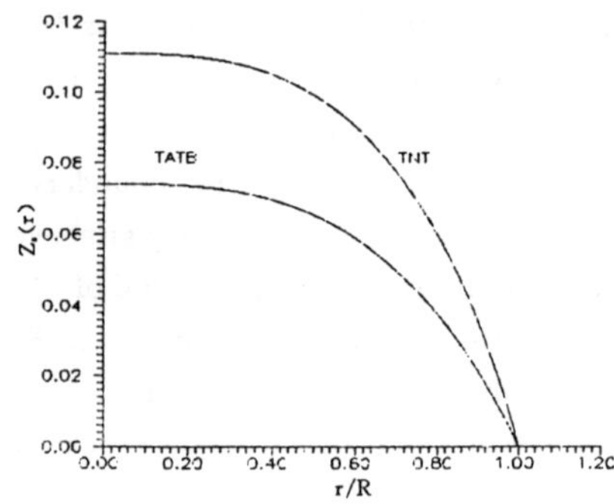

Figure 3. The shape of detonation front

CONCLUSION

When the deflection of streamline is taken as the equation (8), the shape of detonation front is determined only by parameter A_1. Since the detonation velocity is dependent on the flow variables and the confinement, it is a reasonable result that the shape of detonation front depends only on the detonation velocity. It is shown by the stability analysis that the boundary condition χ_e is not dependent on the form of the equation (8) but on the magnitude of D and R. The critical point will shift to right with the increase of D and R.

REFERENCES

[1] J. B. Bdzil, "Steady-state two-dimentional detonation", J. Fluid Mech. , 108, 1981, pp. 195—226.

[2]J. B. Bdzil and D. B. Stewart, " Modelling two-dimentional detonations with shock dynamics", Phys. Fluids A, 1 (7), 1989, pp. 1261—1267.

[3]F. Chaisse et al., "A theoretical analysis of the shape of a steady axisymmetrical reactive shock front in cylindrical charges of high explosive", in *Proceedings of the Eighth Symposium (International) on Detonation*, 1986, pp. 159—167.

[4]S. Huan, "Thesis on shock initiation and two-dimentional steady state detonation in heterogeneous explosive", April, 1988.

EFFECTS OF CRYSTAL ORIENTATION ON THE PROPERTIES OF A CHEMICALLY SUSTAINED SHOCK WAVE IN A MODEL ENERGETIC MATERIAL

D. H. Robertson
Department of Chemistry
Indiana University-Purdue University at Indianapolis
402 N. Blackford St., Indianapolis, IN 46202

D. W. Brenner and C.T. White
Chemistry Division
Naval Research Laboratory
Washington, DC 20375-5340

We have recently introduced a model energetic material based on a many-body empirical-bond-order potential that can be used in molecular dynamics (MD) simulations to study chemically sustained shock waves (CSSW) at the molecular level. This energetic model has been shown to produce a CSSW whose propagation is supported by the release of energy as it processes reactant molecules to form molecular products. The properties of this CSSW are consistent with experimental results and the classic continuum theory of planar detonations. In this paper, we compare the results of the properties of this CSSW for propagation in two perpendicular crystal directions. This model shows little differentiation in characteristics for these two propagation directions but the results do indicate a slight dependence of initiation on these crystal orientations.

INTRODUCTION

Energetic materials have the potential to release energy at enormous rates.[1] The initiation of an energetic material results in the rapid conversion of reactants to products with the formation of an associated high-pressure, high-velocity shock wave.[1-3] The destructive nature and fast processes involved in detonations have inhibited the experimental study of the shock-induced chemistry at the atomic scale. However, the time (sub-picosecond) and length (sub-nanometer) scales of these rapid processes associated with typical condensed-phase detonations make them ideal for simulation at the atomic scale using classical molecular dynamics (MD) techniques. Indeed, early MD simulations of shock waves in Lennard-Jones systems have shown that atomic-scale simulations can be of sufficient size to reproduce continuum results[4,5] as well as modeling such complex behavior as split shock waves resulting from a polymorphic phase transition.[6] However, to study the coupling of chemistry to shock waves present in detonations requires chemically reactive potentials capable of simulating thousands of atoms while including such chemical information as distinct reactants and products, reaction barriers, reaction pathways and transition states.

Recently, we have introduced a model for condensed phase detonations[7] based on an Abell-Tersoff formalism[8,9] that incorporates the possibility for chemical reactions in shock wave studies. The results from simulations using this reactive potential shows the formation of a chemically sustained shock wave with a constant detonation velocity that is intrinsic to the parameterization of

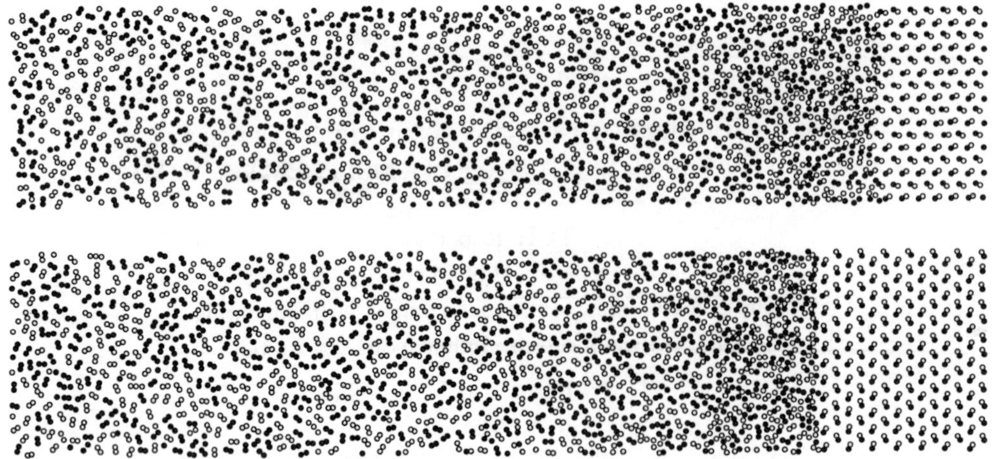

Figure 1. Snapshots of the atomic positions for chemically sustained shock waves at 12.6 ps. The shock wave is propagating from left to right. The upper snapshot is crystal orientation O1 and the lower is O2. The two atom types are denoted by light and dark circles.

the potential.[6] The shock profiles for this model show behavior that is consistent with the classic Zel'dovich–von Neumann–Doering model for planar detonations.[1-3] A careful study of the Rankine-Hugoniot[2,3] relations across the shock front shows that the simulations rapidly approach near steady-flow conditions over a successively wider region as the simulation progresses.[7] This shows that, on the time scale accessible to MD calculations, these simulations can approach continuum behavior and therefore have the potential to address macroscopic issues. MD simulations using this and future models for condensed phase detonations may uncover details of shock-induced chemistry at the atomic-scale that may facilitate the development of safer, more reliable explosives.

To further characterize the properties of this model, we performed simulations for two different shock propagation directions with respect to crystal orientation. Both orientations allowed the formation of a CSSW. The properties of the resulting CSSWs appear to be insensitive to the crystal orientation. However, the results indicate some dependence of initiation on the crystal orientation.

MODEL

These simulations are based on an AB model presented earlier.[7] This model has the potential to undergo reaction from the energetic AB reactant molecules to the more stable A_2 and B_2 product molecules with an associated energy release of 3 eV per AB reactant. The current simulations are performed in two dimensions using periodic boundary conditions perpendicular to the direction of shock propagation and material addition in front of the advancing shock wave. The periodic boundary conditions and material addition allow these calculations to simulate the propagation of the shock wave into a semi-infinite piece of the reactant molecular solid. The shock wave is initiated by impacting the free edge of the molecular solid with a flyer plate composed of the reactant material. The trajectories of the individual atoms are followed on the potential energy surface by integrating Newton's equation of motion with a high-order predictor-corrector strategy.[10]

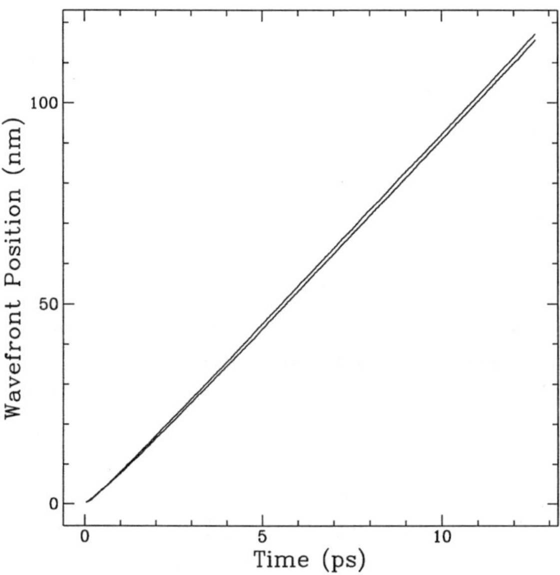

Figure 2. Wave front positions as a function of simulation time for orientation O1 (upper line) and O2 (lower line).

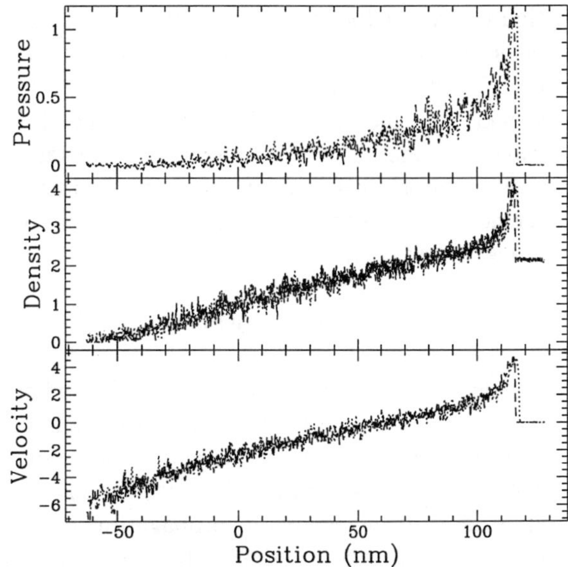

Figure 3. Profiles of the pressure (eV/Å^2), density (amu/Å^2), particle flow velocity (km/s) at 12.6 ps for O1 (dotted lines) and O2 (dashed lines).

Results and Discussion

Simulations were performed using the two different crystal orientations (O1 and O2) as seen in the far right of Figure 1. Each was initiated by impacting the free edge of the semi-infinite molecular solid with a 6 km/s 96-atom flyer plate. The trajectories were then monitored up to an elapsed time of 12.6 ps. Both of these simulations developed a chemically sustained shock wave which is depicted in Figure 1. The shock wave progresses through the molecular solid transforming the AB reactant molecules (on the far right) into the more stable A_2 and B_2 product molecules (to the far left). As seen from these snapshots, the shock front is very abrupt in these simulations with a width on the order of atomic dimensions. Besides the offset of the shock front positions, these two simulations show no qualitatively distinct behavior.

The positions of these shock waves as a function of the simulation time are plotted in Figure 2. The upper line is for O1 and the lower line is for O2. As can be seen from Figure 2, after an elapsed time of 5 ps these lines appear to be parallel. The parallel nature of the lines indicates that these CSSWs have similar shock velocities. A least-squares fit of the wave front position as a function of time in the range of 5 to 12.6 ps gives slopes of 9.478 and 9.451 km/s for O1 and O2, respectively, with correlation coefficients of 1.0000 for both fits. Therefore, these CSSWs, after initiation, are relaxing to indistinguishable shock velocities. This indicates that the shock wave velocity is independent of the crystal orientation in this model. However, these wave front positions are offset from one another (as noted above). The majority of the offset is introduced in the first 5 ps of the simulations—during initiation. This offset indicates some dependence of the initiation of these CSSWs on the crystal orientation.

Figure 3 shows the profiles of the pressure, density, and particle flow velocity for the resulting CSSWs at an elapsed time of 12.6 ps after flyer plate impact. Again, the shift of the shock front position of O1 with respect to O2 is visible in this figure. Except for the slight shift in shock front position, the profiles and peak values of the two CSSWs show no distinct differences. This is consistent with the lack of difference in the shock wave velocities. Therefore, the crystal orientations used in this study do not introduce any distinct differences in either the detonation velocities or properties of the CSSW.

CONCLUSIONS

The dependence of the detonation velocity and profiles of a CSSW in a model system was examined with respect to changes in the crystal orientation. This change in orientation did not introduce any significant changes in the propagation characteristics of the CSSW after initiation. However, there is evidence (the shifted wave front positions) that suggests that there may be a difference in the initiation characteristics with respect to these orientations. Although these studies show only a slight dependence on crystal orientation, this orientational dependence is consistent with experimental results that show a marked change in initiation behavior as a function of crystal orientation.[11] Further, study is necessary to determine if this dependence of initiation on crystal orientation is reproducible for other simulations and crystal structures. The dependence of the CSSW properties for different crystal structures also requires further study.

ACKNOWLEDGMENTS

This work was supported in part by the ONR through NRL and the ONR Physics Division.

REFERENCES

[1] W.C. Davis, *Sci. Am.*, **256**, 106 (1987).
[2] W. Fickett, *Introduction to Detonation Theory*, Berkeley: U. Calif. Press, 1985.
[3] I.B. Zel'dovich and A.S. Kompaneets, *Theory of Detonations*, New York: Academic Press, 1960.
[4] B.L. Holian, W.G. Hoover, W. Moran, and G.K. Straub, *Phys. Rev. A* **22**, 2798 (1980).
[5] A.N. Dremin and V.Yu Klimenko, *Prog. Astronaut. Aeronaut.* **75**,253 (1981).
[6] D.H. Robertson, D.W. Brenner, and C.T. White, *Phys. Rev. Lett.* **67**, 3132 (1991).
[7] D.W. Brenner, D.H. Robertson, M.L. Elert, and C.T. White, *Phys. Rev. Lett.* **70**, 2174 (1993).
[8] G.C. Abell, *Phys. Rev. B* **31**, 6184 (1985).
[9] J. Tersoff, *Phys. Rev. B* **37**, 6991 (1988).
[10] C.W. Gear, *Numerical Initial Value Problems in Ordinary Differential Equations*, Englewood Cliffs: Prentice-Hall, 1971.
[11] J.J. Dick, R.N. Mulford, W.J. Spencer, D.R. Pettit, E. Garcia, and D.C. Shaw, *J. Appl. Phys.* **70**, 3572 (1991).

CRYSTAL ORIENTATION DEPENDENCE OF ELASTIC PRECURSOR STRENGTH IN PENTAERYTHRITOL TETRANITRATE

J. J. Dick, M. C. Whitehead, and A. R. Martinez
Group M-7
Los Alamos National Laboratory
MS P952
Los Alamos, New Mexico 87545

Elastic precursor shock strengths were measured using VISAR instrumentation on pentaerythritol tetranitrate crystals 2.9 to 6.4 mm thick. Input shock strength was 1.2 GPa. A factor of 3 difference in elastic shock strength and a factor of 2 difference in critical resolved shear stress were observed depending on the crystal orientation. The order of increasing elastic shock strength was [100], [101], [110], and [001]. This is the same order as that obtained in our analysis for increasing steric hindrance to shear, indicating that the relative strength of different orientations of this molecular crystal under shock conditions is governed by steric hindrance to shear.

INTRODUCTION

In previous work we have shown that the shock initiation sensitivity of pentaerythritol tetranitrate (PETN) single crystals depends strongly on crystal orientation relative to the plane shock wave.[1,2] The effect has been explained in terms of a model at the molecular level for the steric hindrance to the shear induced by the uniaxial strain generated by a plane shock wave.[2,3] In a crystal the shear occurs on a crystallographic slip plane and direction as illustrated in Fig. 1. It takes place on a slip plane near 45° to the shock propagation direction, particularly on the slip system that has the maximum resolved shear stress (MRSS) generated by the longitudinal stress of the compressive shock.

The critical resolved shear stress is the shear stress that must be applied on the MRSS slip system to cause the onset of plastic or irreversible, inelastic flow. In a molecular crystal it is likely that this critical resolved shear stress determining the yield point for a given orientation is determined to some extent by the steric hindrance to shear. The sterically hindered shear has a dramatic effect on the shock sensitivity of PETN. Furthermore, the preferred slip system observed in quasistatic deformation of PETN crystals[4] is not the one with the shortest Burgers vector as is expected from the standpoint of energetics in simple atomic lattices. Rather, it is the one that our calculations show has the least steric hindrance to shear. Based on these observations we conclude that the elastic precursor shock strength should correlate with the amount of steric hindrance. The sterically hindered orientations should have large elastic precursors, and the unhindered orientations should have small precursors. We report on a series of VISAR interferometer experiments undertaken to verify this hypothesis.

VISAR EXPERIMENTS

A series of impact experiments was performed using a light-gas gun.. An aluminum projectile impacted a plus-x-cut quartz crystal 5 mm thick. The PETN crystal slab (3 to 6 mm thick) was bonded to the quartz with Sylgard 184 silicone elastomer. A mirrored polymethylmethacrylate (PMMA) window was bonded to the crystal with the elastomer. The motion of the PETN/PMMA interface was monitored with a VISAR laser interferometer. Transit time through the PETN was measured using a PZT pin on the quartz crystal and the VISAR signal. Impact velocities were about 0.3 mm/μs. The longitudinal stress for the plastic wave was estimated to be about 1.2 GPa. Experiments were performed on specimens about 3 and 6 mm thick for each of the four orientations, [100], [101], [110], and [001], given in order of increasing steric hindrance. Particle velocity histories for the thick

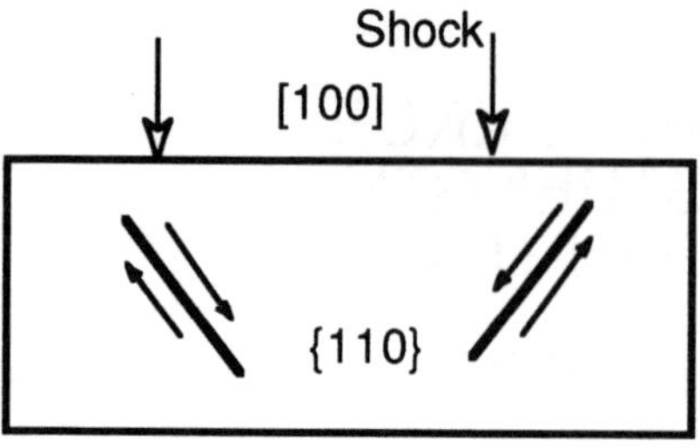

Unhindered shear, insensitive

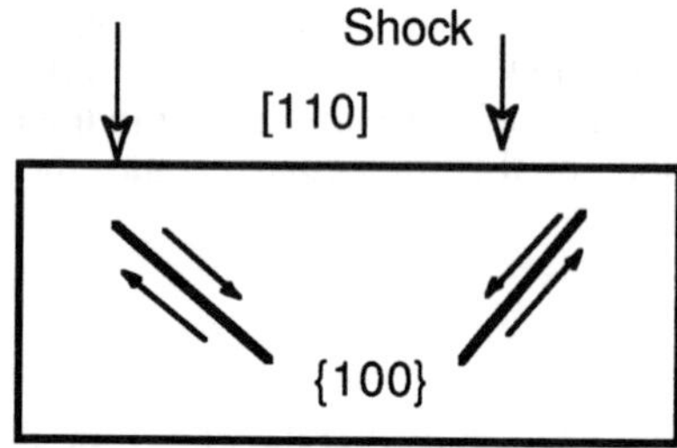

Hindered shear, sensitive

Figure 1. Schema of the relative orientations of shock and shear planes. When the sterically unhindered {110} plane is available for shear, the crystal is insensitive and has a small elastic precursor. When the slip system is hindered ({100} < 011 >, e.g.) the crystal is sensitive and has a large elastic precursor.

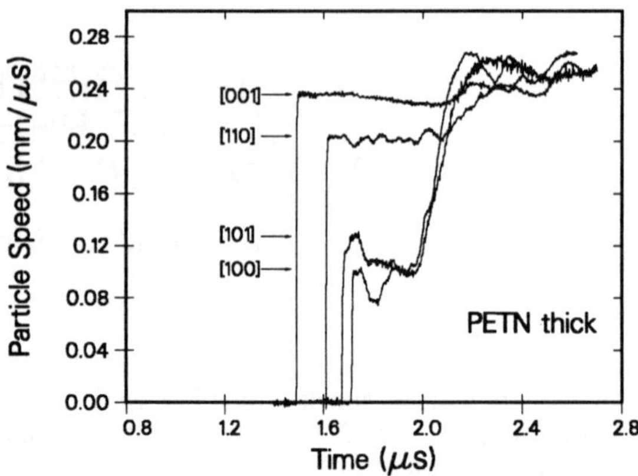

Figure 2. Elastic-plastic wave profiles at the PETN/PMMA interface for thick crystals of the four orientations. The strongly hindered orientations [001] and [110] have larger elastic precursor shocks than the weakly hindered orientations [101] and [100].

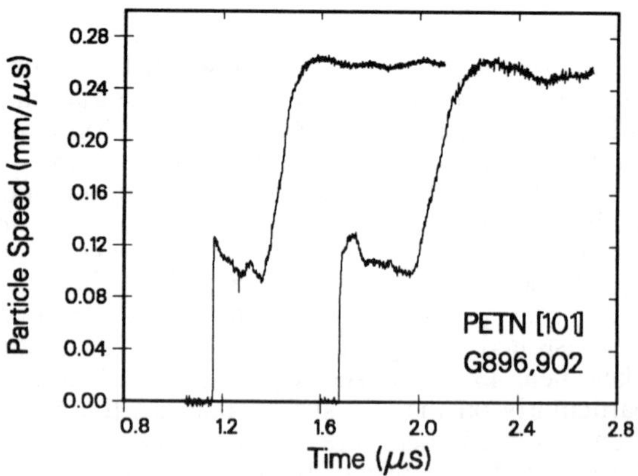

Figure 3. Elastic-plastic wave profiles at the PETN/PMMA interface for the [101] orientation for crystals 4.30 and 6.13 mm thick.

samples of all four orientations are displayed in Fig. 2. The results show that the the elastic precursor strength for a given input strength increases with increasing steric hindance as predicted. The results are consistent with the earlier results of P. Halleck and J. Wackerle[5] and L. Soulard[6] for the hindered orientations. No significant precursor decay was observed between 3 and 6 mm for all orientations. Results for the [101] orientation are shown in Fig. 3. Any decay must have occurred in less than 3 mm of run. Preliminary analysis of the longitudinal stresses has been performed. In order of increasing size, the longitudinal elastic stress in PETN is about 0.37 GPa for a [100] shock, 0.58 GPa for a [101] shock, 1.0 GPa for a [110] shock, and 1.2 GPa for [001] shock. The corresponding critical resolved shear stresses on the MRSS slip system are 1.1, 1.6, 2.1, and 2.2 GPa, respectively. These rankings are the same as the steric hindrance from least to most hindrance (see Table 1) providing convincing supporting evidence for the steric hindrance model.

The steric hindrance analysis given in Table 1 enumerates the number and types of close approaches closer than 1.70 Å for shear across the unit cell by rigid molecules. The closest approaches are clearly unphysical. The equilibrium, molecular-mechanics analysis of J. Ritchie[3] for flexible molecules shows that atomic groups on the molecules can rotate and bend out of each others way so

Table 1. Atom-Atom Interactions for PETN.

			Body-Centered Molecule		Corner Molecule	
Shock Direction	MRSS[a] Slip System	Atom Pair	Number of Interactions	Closest Approach (Å)	Number of Interactions	Closest Approach (Å)
[100]	$\{110\}\langle 1\bar{1}1\rangle$	O-O	3	1.05	1	1.65
	$\{110\}\langle 001\rangle$[b]	O-O	2	0.78	2	0.78
[101][c]	$\{100\}\langle 001\rangle$	O-O	4	0.78	4	0.78
[110][c]	$\{100\}\langle 011\rangle$	O-O	9	0.54	9	0.54
		N-O	5	1.01	5	1.01
		C-O	2	0.83	2	0.83
		O-H	6	0.31	6	0.31
		N-H	4	0.80	4	0.80
		H-H	2	0.99	2	0.99
		N-N	1	1.58	1	1.58
		C-N	1	1.60	1	1.60
			30		30	
[001]	$\{101\}\langle\bar{1}01\rangle$	O-O	3	0.86	12	0.86
		C-O	4	0.71	6	0.71
		O-H	6	0.11	10	0.11
		N-H	2	1.01	2	1.00
		C-N	1	1.52	1	1.52
		N-O	1	1.38	5	1.00
		N-N	0		2	1.58
			17		38	

[a]MRSS ≡ Maximum resolved shear stress.
[b]Slip system expected from the standpoint of the shortest Burgers vector and widest interplanar separation.
[c]Interactions are with the body-centered or the corner molecule but not both, for a given shear.

that the closest atom-atom approaches are greater than 2 Å, in general. Nonetheless, the correlation of the simple, geometric analysis using rigid molecules with experimental results for elastic precursor dependence and with the energy barrier to shear computed with molecular mechanics indicates that the geometric analysis captures the extent of physical hindrance to some degree.

In Ref. 2 we presented a table of geometric hindrance for only the interactions of the body-centered molecule. In Table 1 the complete analysis is given including the interactions for the corner molecule, the other molecule per unit cell. The major change is that now the slip system [001] shocks shows the most interactions even though [110] crystals are most sensitive, indicating the limitations of the geometric analysis in describing the physical and chemical behavior of the crystals under shock conditions. It is interesting to note that the $\{110\} < 001 >$ slip system which might be expected to be the preferred slip from the standpoint of having lower energy in atomic lattices from the standpoint of having a shorter Burgers vector[7] has the same number of interactions but closer interactions than the observed $\{110\} < 1\bar{1}1 >$ slip system, so that the geometric analysis as well as the molecular mechanics analysis[3] is in agreement with experimental observations. This indicates that that steric hindrance controls the preferred slip system even under quasistatic deformation.

The nature of the shear or slip process in PETN under shock conditions is not known with certainty. In quasistatic deformation in indenter tests deformation by generation and growth of dislocation loops is observed.[4] Since [100] shocks apparently use the same slip system as quasistatic deformation, it is possible that dislocation processes govern the plastic shear flow for this case under shock conditions, especially at low shock strengths. It was observed earlier[8] that for the strongly hindered [110] and [001] shocks that the resolved shear stress may exceed the estimated strength of the perfect crystal. In that case, supercritical or simultaneous shear may be occurring.

There are some results that indicate that the elastic precursor strength is strongly dependent on input shock strength for these orientations.[5,9]

ACKNOWLEDGMENTS

Thanks to Jim Ritchie for helpful conversations and interactions. This work was performed under the auspices of the U. S. Department of Energy and partially supported by the Office of Munitions Memo of Understanding between the Department of Energy and the Department of Defense.

REFERENCES

1. J. J. Dick, *Appl. Phys. Lett.* **44**, 859 (1984).

2. J. J. Dick, R. N. Mulford, W. J. Spencer, D. R. Pettit, E. Garcia, and D. C. Shaw, *J. Appl. Phys.* **70**, 3572 (1991).

3. J. T. Ritchie, "Computational Analysis of Slip in PETN," presented at the Tenth Symposium (International) on Detonation, Boston, MA, July 12-16, 1993.

4. H. P. Gallagher, P. J. Halfpenny, J. C. Miller, and J. N. Sherwood, *Phil. Trans. R. Soc. of Lond. A* **339**, 293 (1992).

5. P. M. Halleck and Jerry Wackerle, *J. Appl. Phys.* **47**, 976 (1976).

6. L. Soulard, Thesis, *Etude du Monocristal de Pentrite Soumis a un Choc Plan*, L'Universite de Haute Alsace, 1990, p. 30.

7. J. P. Hirth and J. Lothe, *Theory of Dislocations*, Malabar, Florida:Krieger Publishing Company, 1992, ch. 9, p. 271.

8. J. J. Dick, *Appl. Phys. Lett.* **60**, 2494 (1992).

9. J. J. Dick, to be published.

PARTICLE VELOCITY AND STRESS MEASUREMENTS IN LOW DENSITY HMX⁺

S. A. Sheffield, R. L. Gustavsen, and R. R. Alcon
Los Alamos National Laboratory
Group M-7, MS P952
Los Alamos, NM 87545

R. A. Graham and M. U. Anderson
Sandia National Laboratories
Department 1153
Albuquerque, NM 87185

Magnetic particle velocity gauges and PVDF stress rate gauges have been used to measure the shock response of low density HMX explosive (1.24 g/cm^3). In experiments done at LANL, magnetic particle velocity gauges were located on both sides of the explosive. In nearly identical experiments done at SNL, PVDF stress rate gauges were located at the same positions. Using these techniques both particle velocity and stress histories were obtained for a particular experimental condition. Loading and reaction paths were established in the stress-particle velocity plane for each input condition. This information was used to determine that compacted HMX has an impedance close to that of Kel-F and also that a global reaction rate of ≈ 0.13 μs^{-1} was observed in HMX shocked to about 0.8 GPa. At low input stresses the transmitted wave profiles had long rise times (up to 1 μs) due to the compaction processes.

INTRODUCTION

Porous octotetramethylene tetranitramine (HMX) at a density of 1.24 g/cm^3 has been shown to reproducibly undergo a deflagration-to-detonation transition (DDT) when suitably confined.[1] Small input energies, in the form of a flame or a slowly moving piston, precipitate the DDT process, illustrating that insensitive explosives can be made to detonate with small inputs under the right conditions. This gives rise to safety concerns which is the principal reason for studying porous HMX under low shock input conditions.

Two studies with direct application to this work have been done on low density HMX. Dick performed several explosively driven cutback tests in which he measured the average transit time through HMX compacts of different thicknesses (at a density of 1.24 g/cm^3) for inputs of 0.8 and 2.0 GPa.[2] By plotting transit time vs. compact thickness, he was able obtain some Hugoniot and initiation information. Elban and Chiarito subjected two different HMX powders to slow compaction conditions up to 0.2 GPa.[3] They found that the breakage of HMX crystals starts at stresses below 1 MPa and that widespread crystal fracture takes place between 62 and 75% of theoretical maximum density (TMD). At a stress of 0.2 GPa, 96% of TMD was obtained. The data from these studies are not sufficient to construct a reliable EOS so we embarked upon a study to make time-resolved measurements as an extension of Dick's work with manganin gauges.[4]

Magnetic particle velocity measurements were made at Los Alamos National Lab. (LANL) and polyvinylidene difluoride (PVDF) stress rate measurements[5,6] were done at Sandia National Labs. (SNL) in experiments that were nearly identical. Time resolved measurements of these two properties allows tracking of any process occurring (e.g. compaction or reaction) in the stress vs. particle velocity plane. This paper discusses some of the experiments completed and their interpretation.

EXPERIMENTAL DETAILS

Experiments at both labs utilized gas gun driven projectiles to obtain sustained-shock input conditions. Projectile velocities were nearly the same at both labs for a given experimental setup so that in separate, similar experiments, both stress and particle-velocity histories were measured.

HMX powder was confined in sample cells which had a polychlorotrifluoroethylene (Kel-F) front face (on which the projectile impacted) and a poly 4-methyl-1-pentene (TPX) cylindrical plug back. (TPX is a low impedance material and therefore a reasonable impedance match to the pressed HMX.) Gauges were epoxied on the HMX side of both pieces. The front face was

⁺ Work performed under the auspices of the U. S. Department of Energy.

screwed to a Kel-F confining cylinder with an outside diameter of 68.6 mm and an inside diameter of 40.6 mm. The pressed HMX (between the Kel-F and TPX) was ≈ 4 mm thick and had a density of 1.24 g/cm^3.

The HMX powder used in all the experiments was coarse HMX from Holston (Lot HOL 920-32) with a bulk density of ≈ 1.16 g/cm^3 (see Ref. 2). The material was screened to eliminate agglomerates and a few of the largest particles.

In the LANL experiments the magnetic particle-velocity gauges were 25 μ thick FEP Teflon with a 5 μ thick aluminum "stirrup" gauge on it. Active region of the gauge was 10 mm by 0.5 mm. In the SNL experiments PVDF stress-rate gauges were composed of 25 μ thick PVDF with plated electrodes on each side and a 12 μ thick FEP Teflon film on the HMX side. The active area of this gauge is 3 mm by 3 mm. The side next to the HMX was coated with aluminum to eliminate any pyroelectric effects in the PVDF. Although gauge conditions were not exactly identical, they were as close as possible to being the same.

RESULTS

Experiments were performed at projectile velocities ranging from 0.15 to 0.7 km/s with corresponding stress inputs to the HMX samples between 0.1 and 0.8 GPa. At the lower input stresses, the compaction process dominated and the transmitted waves as measured by the back gauges had long rise times; the lowest input experiments were over 1μs. At the higher projectile velocities, evidence of reaction was apparent at both the front and back gauges.

Figure 1 shows particle velocity and stress waveforms obtained in two experiments in which the projectile velocity was ≈ 0.29 km/s. In the front PVDF gauge measurement, there is a considerable overshoot in stress because of the Kel-F front plate (this overshoot was observed in all the front PVDF gauge measurements). The stress measurement in the HMX begins after this overshoot - about 40 ns into the record. Rounding at the top of both the front gauge waveforms results from the viscoelastic wave shaping that occurs in the shock as it moves through the Kel-F cell front. The back gauge waveforms show a very disperse wave with a risetime of ≈ 700 ns. This is due to the compaction process in the HMX that develops as the wave progresses through the sample. We do not know if the profile is steady but assume that it is not.

Figure 2 gives the particle velocity and stress waveforms obtained in two experiments in which the projectile velocity was ≈ 0.68 km/s. In these experiments there is evidence of reaction in both

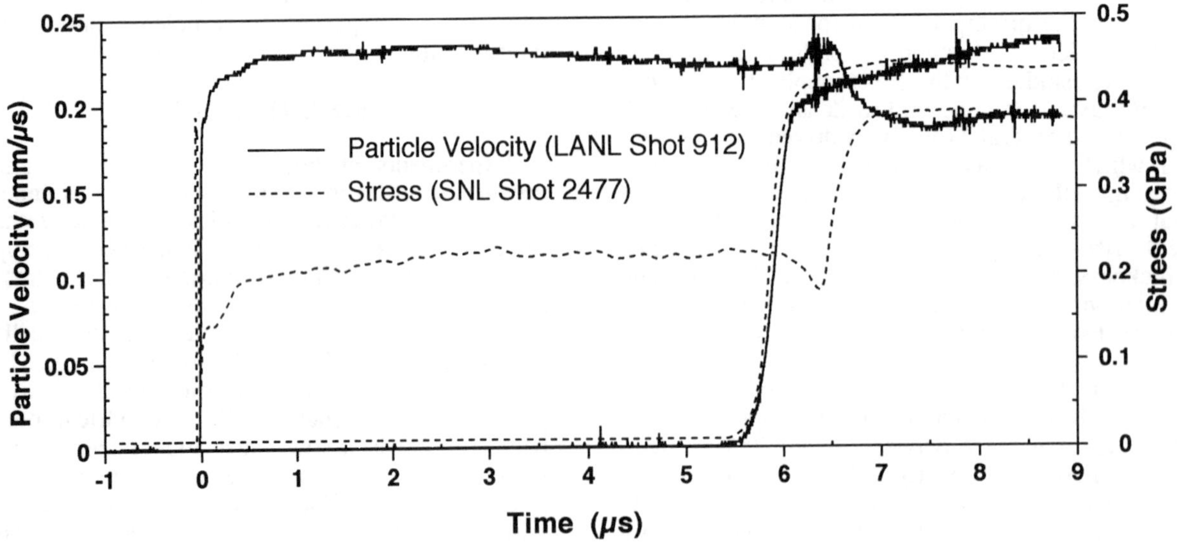

Figure 1 Particle velocity waveforms (LANL Shot 912, proj. vel. 0.288 km/s) and stress waveforms (SNL Shot 2477, proj. vel. 0.285 km/s) for two similar experiments involving a Kel-F faced projectile impacting the Kel-F sample cell front.

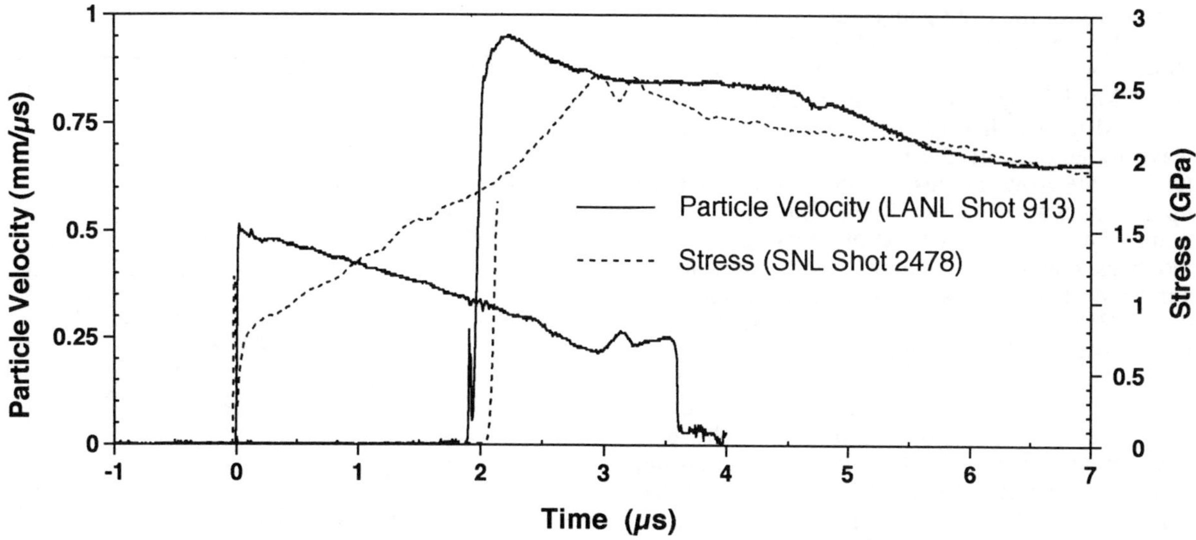

Figure 2 Particle velocity waveforms (LANL Shot 913, proj. vel. 0.696 km/s) and stress waveforms (SNL Shot 2478, proj. vel. 0.669 km/s) for two similar experiments involving a Kel-F faced projectile impacting the Kel-F sample cell front. The SNL projectile velocity was slightly lower so the arrival times at the back gauges do not coincide exactly.

the front and back gauge measurements. Reaction in the front gauge is manifested by a decrease in particle velocity (the reacting HMX is slowing down the cell front) and a corresponding increase in stress. The wave grows as it traverses the HMX sample because of reaction in the shock front so rather than the 0.5 km/s expected when a nonreactive wave interacts with the TPX back, a particle velocity of 0.95 km/s is measured. (The back PVDF gauge measurement was lost.) The risetime in the back particle velocity gauge was also considerably faster than in the lower input experiments (without reaction). However, it is still ≈ 50 ns, longer than expected for a sharp shock. There is apparently competition between the reaction (trying to sharpen up the wave) and the compaction (trying to smear it out).

The Hugoniot data obtained from the experiments, along with an equation of state development is discussed in a paper to be given later.[7]

DISCUSSION

Using the particle velocity and stress data from the experiments shown in Fig. 1, these two properties can be plotted against each other at the appropriate times in the stress vs. particle velocity plane. This plot can be superimposed on a Hugoniot cross plot to give some understanding of the processes that are occurring in the experiment. This plot is shown in Fig. 3 from the data of Fig. 1.

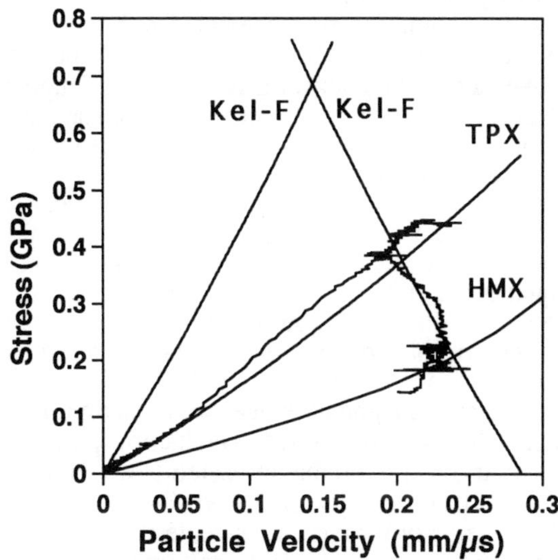

Figure 3 Stress vs. particle velocity plot obtained from the data of Figure 1. Plots are shown for both the front and back gauges; they are the wiggly curves. Appropriate Hugoniots are also shown.

The curve for the front gauge data starts somewhat low (due the viscoelastic wave shaping in the Kel-F) and moves up to and hovers near the HMX/Kel-F Hugoniot crossing, where it would be expected to be. It stays near this point until the wave reflected from the back face of the cell returns to the front gauges, at which time it moves up the backward facing Kel-F Hugoniot to the point where the TPX Hugoniot intersects it. This indicates that the compacted HMX Hugoniot is similar to that of Kel-F. If one looks at the fully dense HMX and the Kel-F Hugoniots, they are similar with the Kel-F being slightly softer.

In the same figure, the back gauge data starts out near the zero state and moves up along the TPX Hugoniot for a ways and then plots above it. It eventually gets near the TPX/Kel-F crossing, which is separate supporting evidence that the compacted HMX Hugoniot is close to that of Kel-F. This loading path is for the disperse wave which results from the compaction processes. It plots above the TPX Hugoniot where it would be expected to be if a ramp wave were loading the TPX. In this experiment there was no evidence of reaction in any of the waveforms.

The data shown in Fig. 2 are definitely in the regime where reaction is taking place. Using the front gauge data and plotting the stress vs. particle velocity results in the wiggly curve shown in Fig. 4. Again, it starts somewhat low in stress due to the viscoelastic effects in the Kel-F but then moves along the backward facing Kel-F Hugoniot clear off the figure. In other words, the state at the front gauge as the reaction occurs moves up along the Kel-F Hugoniot because this is what it is in contact with. In this experiment the maximum stress at the front gauge was about 2.5 GPa. Ritchie[8] has calculated the BKW reaction product equation of state for 1.24 g/cm^3 HMX and it can be shown that about 40% reaction has taken place by the end of the 3 μs record, leading to an estimated global reaction rate of $\approx 0.13\ \mu s^{-1}$.

The back magnetic gauge had a maximum particle velocity of 0.95 km/s, which corresponds to a stress of 2.8 GPa on the unreacted HMX Hugoniot and a shock velocity of 2.4 km/s. The average shock velocity through the sample was 1.96 km/s, considerably above the 1.36 km/s expected if there were no reaction. Considerable reaction is occurring in the shock front (as is normally the case for heterogeneous explosives) to strengthen the shock to this level. If the porous HMX were detonating, the detonation velocity would be 6.7 km/s.

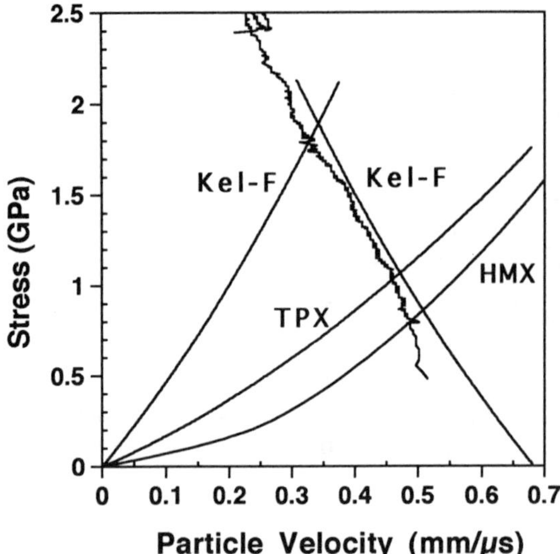

Figure 4 Stress vs. particle velocity plot obtained by plotting the stress and particle velocity against each other for the front gauge data shown in Fig. 2.

This set of experiments demonstrates the usefulness of making both stress and particle velocity measurements in near identical experiments. It is clear that to really understand the compaction and reaction processes in detail, computer modeling with accurate material, compaction, micromechanical, and reaction models will be required.

REFERENCES

[1] J. M. McAfee, B. W. Asay, A. W. Campbell, and J. B. Ramsay, Ninth Symposium (Intl.) on Detonation, Office of the Chief of Naval Research Report OCNR-113291-7, Arlington, VA (1989), p. 265.

[2] J. J. Dick, Combustion and Flame **54**, 121 (1983).

[3] W. L. Elban and M. A. Charito, Powder Tech., **46**, 181 (1986).

[4] J. J. Dick, Combustion and Flame **69**, 257 (1987).

[5] F. Bauer, in Shock Waves in Condensed Matter, Y. M. Gupta, ed. (Plenum Press, New York, 1986), p. 483.

[6] R. A. Graham, L. M. Lee, and F. Bauer, in Shock Waves in Condensed Matter 1987, S. C. Schmidt and N. C. Holmes, eds. (North-Holland, Amsterdam 1988), p. 619.

[7] S. A. Sheffield, R. L. Gustavsen, and R. R. Alcon, to be presented at the Tenth (International) Symposium on Detonation, July 12-16, 1993, Boston, Mass.

[8] J. P. Ritchie, Los Alamos National Lab., private communication.

MULTIPLE STRESS-TIME PROFILES IN A RDX/AP/Al/HTPB PLASTIC BONDED EXPLOSIVE

G.T. Sutherland, J.W. Forbes, E.R. Lemar,
K.D. Ashwell, and R.N. Baker

Naval Surface Warfare Center
Dahlgren Division, White Oak Detachment
10901 New Hampshire Avenue
Silver Spring, MD 20903-5640

PBXN-111 samples were shocked using light-gas guns. Six experiments were instrumented with insitu manganin or ytterbium gauges. Two experiments were instrumented with a rear surface quartz gauge. A linear relationship between shock velocity and particle velocity was obtained for stresses to 42 kbar. These results are compared with those from a wedge test study. Experimental stress-time profiles suggest a low level reaction occurs behind the shock front for stresses above about 16 kbar.

INTRODUCTION

The purpose of this study was to obtain an unreacted shock velocity-particle velocity relationship (Hugoniot) for PBXN-111. This Hugoniot will be used to help analyze results from other experiments such as corner turning and the modified gap test. An unreactive Hugoniot is also necessary for reactive rate modeling of this explosive.

EXPERIMENT

PBXN-111 (formerly PBXW-115) is a cast cured explosive with RDX, ammonium perchlorate (AP), aluminum (Al), and hydoxyl terminated polybutadiene binder (HTPB). PBXN-111 is similar to some propellants[1-2] except that PBXN-111 contains RDX instead of HMX. The initial density of PBXN-111 used in this work was 1.79 g/cm3. The median particle size (by weight) of the RDX was calculated to be 60 μm. Nominal particle sizes for AP and Al particles were 200 and 5 μm, respectively.

Schematic drawings of the targets and projectiles used in this study are shown in Figures 1 and 2. General experimental techniques for the ytterbium and manganin gauge experiments are given in a paper on PBXN-110.[3] Experimental techniques for the quartz gauge experiments are given in a paper on Composition B3.[4] In some experiments, part or all of the explosive behind the deepest gauge was replaced with a Teflon backer. The nominal thickness of each explosive layer was about 5 mm for experiments 2, and experiments 4-7. Sample diameters for the quartz gauge shots were nominally 51 mm; sample diameters for the ytterbium and manganin gauge experiments were 70 mm. Experiments were performed with either a 4 inch or 3.5 inch bore gas gun.

Table 1. Unreacted Hugoniot of PBXN-111.

Experiment	Projectile Velocity (mm/µsec)	Shock Velocity (mm/µsec)	Calculated Particle Velocity (mm/µsec)	Calculated Peak Stress (Kbar)
1	0.1886	2.469	0.149	6.7
2	0.2409	2.702	0.186	8.8
	0.2409	2.558	0.179	8.4
3	0.2947	2.741	0.226	11.1
4	0.3936	2.900	0.296	15.5
5	0.5990	3.355	0.432	25.6
	0.5990	3.371	0.420	24.6
6	0.6985	3.505	0.497	31.0
	0.6985	3.479	0.488	30.2
7	0.8512	3.763	0.592	39.7
	0.8512	3.653	0.591	39.6
8	0.8852	3.788	0.615	42.0

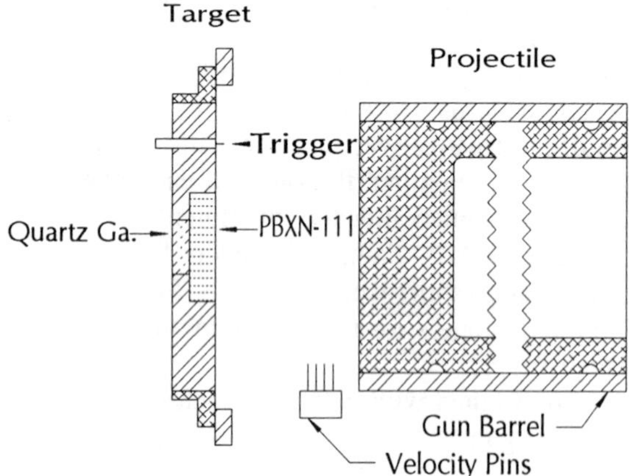

Figure 1. Schematic view of a light gas gun quartz gauge experiment.

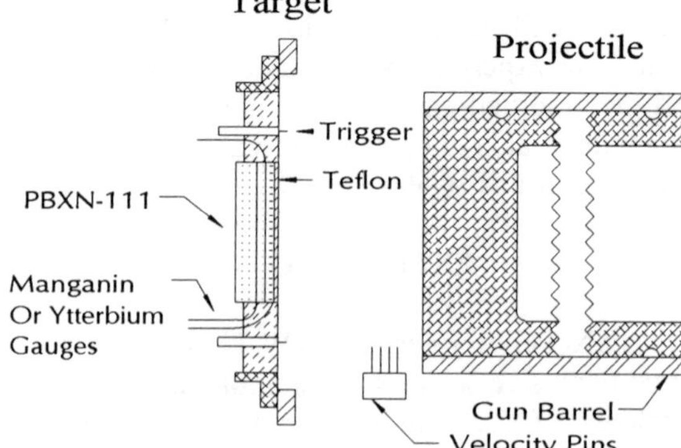

Figure 2. Schematic view of a light gas gun manganin gauge or ytterbium gauge experiment.

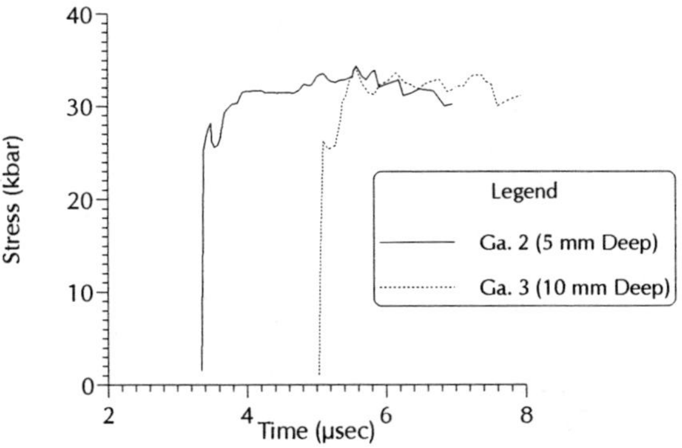

Figure 3. Stress-Time profiles from experiment 6.

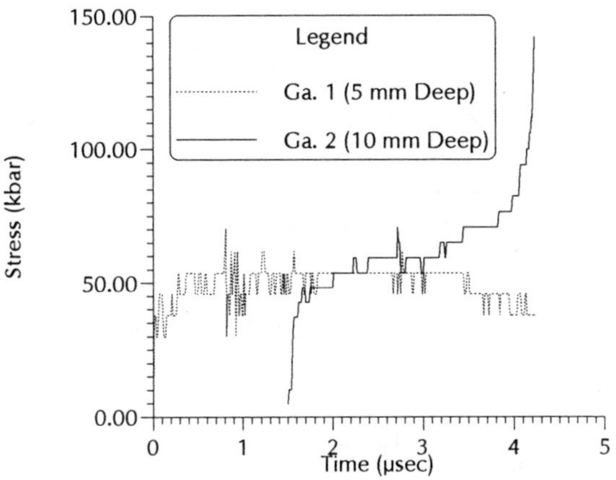

Figure 4. Stress-time profiles for experiment 8.

Impedance matching was used to obtain particle velocities and stress from the shock and projectile velocity data given in Table 1. Hugoniots of Teflon[5] and 6061-T6 aluminum[6-7] were used in this data analysis. For experiments instrumented with three gauges, shock velocities between the first two gauges and the last two gauges are given in Table 1. For the manganin gauge experiments (Teflon encapsulated), the transit times through the Teflon encapsulation were taken into account. Stress-time profiles for experiments 6 and 8 appear in Figures 3-4.

The shock velocity (U_s)-particle velocity (u_p) data were fitted to a linear Us-up expression resulting in Equation 1. This data is displayed in Figure 5. The density of PBXN-111 was 1.79 g cm^{-3}.

$$U_s = 2.117 \pm 0.034\ mm/\mu sec + (2.758 \pm 0.081)\ u_p \quad (1)$$

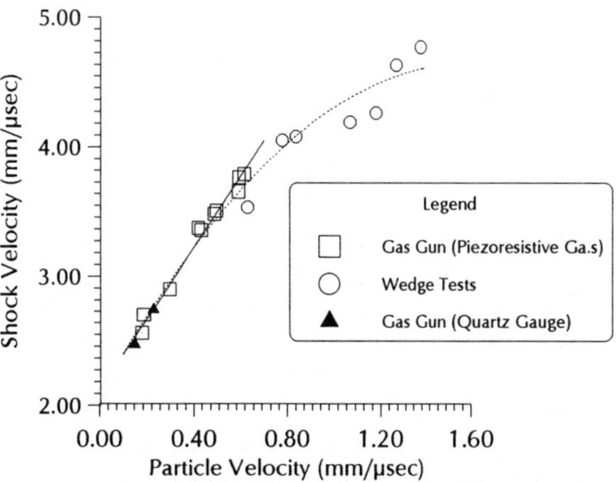

Figure 5. Shock velocity-particle velocity values from gas gun and wedge test experiments. The solid line is equation 1 plotted; the dotted line is equation 2 plotted.

DISCUSSION

Results from PBXN-111 wedge tests[8] are also displayed in Figure 5. A fit to the gas gun and wedge test data is given by Equation 2 (see dashed line in Figure 5).

$$U_s = 2.083 + 3.258\ u_p - 1.037\ u_p^2 \quad (2)$$

The wedge test data tends to fall below the gas gun data. There was evidence of reaction in the results of the wedge test[8] for the four highest pressures. The shock velocities reported are likely reactive shock velocities. Corresponding unreactive shock velocities for these stress levels would be smaller.

Inspections of Figures 3 and 4 reveals, that for gauges 2 and 3 of experiment 6 and gauge 1 of experiment 8, the near constant pressures in the plateau behind the shock fronts are higher than pressures calculated from measured shock velocities. This suggests that a least one of the components of the explosive is reacting slightly behind the shock front. This is consistent with the observation that reaction occurs in PBXN-111 in the modified gap test (MGT) for pressures above 24 kbar.[9-10]

In experiment 4, a reaction was observed 3 μsec after passage of the shock front, which raised the pressure in the explosive from about 15.5 to 17.5 kbar. A gauge 5 mm deep in the explosive observed this reaction. The critical energy fluence[11] of first reaction[9-10] is in agreement with that found from the MGT.[9-10] This energy fluence was calculated using data from Table 1 and a pulse width time of 3 μsec.

Substantial reactive stress growth was observed for gauge 2 in experiment 8. This was the only experiment where substantial stress growth was observed. Experiments are planned where the explosive will be impacted at a projectile velocity higher than 0.9 mm/μsec. Resulting reactive stress-time profiles will be used to obtain reactive rate parameters for the Lee-Tarver reaction rate model.[12] This reactive rate model will be used in modeling PBXN-111 corner turning,[13] wave curvature,[13] and modified gap test results.[9-10]

ACKNOWLEDGEMENTS

This work was sponsored by the Office of Naval Research (Technology Directorate) through the Explosives and Undersea Warheads Block Program. R. Doherty, L. Roslund, and C. Dickinson are thanked for encouraging this work. J. O'Connor, H. Dobbs, B.Watt, and A.D. Brown are thanked for assisting in the experiments.

REFERENCES

[1] J.J. Dick, *Comb. and Flame*, Vol. 37, 1980., pp. 95-99.

[2] D. Price and A.R. Clairmont, Jr., *Comb. and Flame*, Vol. 29, 1977, pp. 87-93.

[3] G.T. Sutherland, in *Shock Compression of Condensed Mater* -1989, S.C. Schmidt,J.N. Johnson, L.W. Davison (editors), Elsevier Science Publishers B.V., (1990), pp. 721-724.

[4] E.R. Lemar, J.W. Forbes, J.W. Watt, and Elban, J. Appl. Phys. **58** (9), pp. 3404-3408.

[5] A.R. Champion, J. Appl. Phys. **42**, 1971, pp. 5546-5550.

[6] C.D. Lundergan and W. Hermann, J. Appl. Phys. 34, 1963, pp. 2046-2052.

[7] J.R. Asay, Ph.D. thesis, Washington State University, 1971.

[8] J.C. Dallman, Los Alamos National Laboratory Letter Report on Wedge Test of PBXW-115, 17 February 1987.

[9] E.R. Lemar, T.P. Liddiard, J.W. Forbes, G.T. Sutherland, and W.H. Wilson, NAVSWC TR 89-290, 1993.

[10] E.R. Lemar, T.P. Liddiard, J.W. Forbes, G.T. Sutherland, *Proc. Tenth Symposium (International) on Detonation*, Boston, MA, July 1993.

[11] F.E. Walker and R.j. Wasley, "Critical Energy for the Shock Initiation of Heterogeneous Explosives," *Explosivestoff* 17, 9, 1969.

[12] E.L. Lee and C.M. Tarver, Phys. Fluids., **23**, No. 12, (1980), pp. 2362-2372.

[13] J.W. Forbes, E.R. Lemar, R.N. Baker, this proceedings.

DETONATION WAVE CURVATURE OF CAST COMP B AND PBXN-111

E. R. Lemar and J. W. Forbes

Naval Surface Warfare Center
Dahlgren Division, White Oak Detachment
Silver Spring, Maryland 20903-5640

Detonation wave profiles for cast Comp B and PBXN-111 have been fitted accurately over the entire wave fronts using a series expansion of the natural logarithm of a Bessel function. The fit equation has been used to obtain the angle of the detonation front as a function of position and the radii of curvature used in Wood-Kirkwood[1] zone length calculations. The results obtained from the fit equation agree with results obtained previously for PBXN-111.[2] Since the fit equation gives a functional form for the detonation wave across the whole charge diameter, it can be used to test the results obtained from detonation theories and code calculations.

INTRODUCTION

Detonation wave shape data were measured for cylindrical charges of cast Comp B (density = 1.67 g/cm^3) and PBXN-111 (formerly called PBXW-115, density = 1.79 g/cm^3). Tests were performed on a 50.86 mm diameter, 153 mm long, Comp B charge and five 305 mm long charges of PBN-111 with diameters of 40.90, 41.05, 48.02, 48.12, and 68.25 mm.

EXPERIMENTAL PROCEDURE

A streak camera was used to record the detonation wave arrival at the ends of cylindrical charges. The experimental setup used to obtain these breakout data is shown in Figure 1. A reflector of aluminized Mylar or Teflon tape was glued to the end of the charge. The alignment and/or reflectivity was destroyed when the shock arrived at the reflecting material. On some of the tests, lines were drawn on the Teflon tape at accurately measured distances from the edges of the charges. These marks appeared on the streak camera records and showed that the breakout data extended to the edges of the charges. The experimental methods are explained in detail in reference 2.

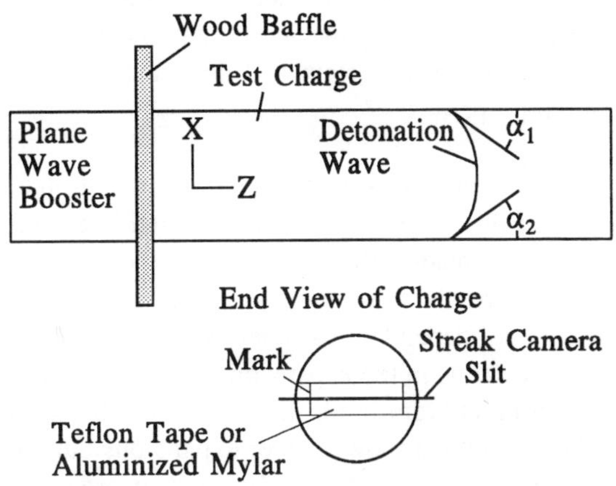

Figure 1. Experimental setup.

DATA ANALYSIS

The wave arrival distance-time data and detonation velocities were used to calculate the wave front shapes inside the charges. For the Comp B charge, a detonation velocity of 7.86 mm/μs was measured in the actual breakout experiment. For PBXN-111, the value of the detonation velocity for each charge diameter was obtained from the fit presented in Reference 3.

In the following discussion, the Z axis (wave propagation axis) is taken to be along the axis of the cylindrical charge and the X axis is taken to be along a charge diameter (see Figure 1).

Fit Over Entire Diameter

Chaissé and Oeconomos[4] have fitted wave front curvature data to the natural logarithm of a Bessel function. To obtain the full-diameter fit of our Comp B and PBXN-111 data, we have used the equation

$$Z = Z_o + B \ln [J_o(A \cdot (X-X_o))] \qquad (1)$$

where J_o is the Bessel function of zero order, Z is the wave position in the direction of the charge axis at a position X across the diameter of the charge (see Figure 1), and Z_o and X_o are parameters used only to translate the origin and do not depend on material properties.

Equation 1 was expanded in a series around $X-X_o$ and this series expansion was used in a nonlinear least squares fitting program to obtain the material dependent parameters, A and B, and the non-material dependent parameters, X_o and Z_o. In this work, terms in the expansion up to and including 14th order were used. In most cases, the data can be fit well with lower order expansions but the terms up to 14th order must be used in order for the series to approximate the Bessel function for the charge diameters in these particular tests. The values of A and B obtained from the fit depend on the order of the expansion used in the fit and approach limiting values as the order of the expansion is increased. If the values of A and B are used to discriminate between various wave curvature models as Chaissé and Oeconomos[4] have done, care must be taken to ensure not only that the expansion fits the data well, but also that the expansion is a good approximation to Equation 1 for the charge diameter.

The parameters obtained from these calculations are presented in Table 1. Figure 2 shows the data along with the calculated fit for a PBXN-111 shot. In all cases, the actual data are fit well. For some of the shots the detonation wave is not centered on the center of the explosive stick. This is probably the result of the plane wave booster being at a slight angle to the axis of the charge.

Table 1. Parameters obtained by fitting the data to a 14th order series expansion of Equation 1.

Material	Diameter (mm)	Fit Parameters A	B	X_o	Z_o
Comp B	50.86	0.0775	1.42	24.4	11.8
PBXN-111	40.90	0.0846	5.12	20.5	14.9
PBXN-111	41.05	0.0872	4.25	20.3	14.3
PBXN-111	48.02	0.0800	4.20	22.6	14.5
PBXN-111	48.12	0.0794	3.88	23.8	14.8
PBXN-111	68.25	0.0585	3.88	33.2	15.4

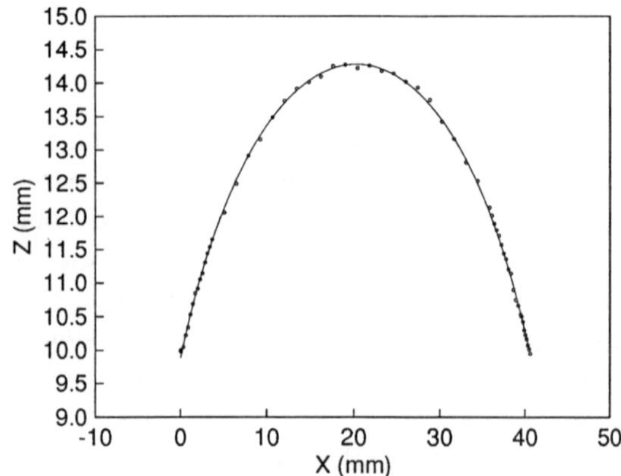

Figure 2. Wave front data plotted along with the fit (solid line) for 41.05 mm diameter PBXN-111.

Wave Front Angle

The wave front data were used to find the angle, α, (see Figure 1) that the detonation wave makes to the edge of the charge. The angle was determined by two methods. In the first method[2], the data at each edge of the charge was least squares fitted to a straight line to obtain the angles. In the second method, the derivative of the series expansion of Equation 1 was used to obtain the slope of the wave front, and from this, the angle, α, was calculated. The angles at the two edges of each charge, calculated by both methods, are presented in Table 2.

As shown in Table 2, the angles obtained by the two methods agree well. In general, the angles obtained by the second method are slightly smaller than those obtained by the linear fit. The reason for this is that the angle decreases as the edge is approached, and as a result, the angle obtained from a linear fit will be an average that is larger than the value at the actual edge.

Wood-Kirkwood Zone Length

The Wood-Kirkwood curved detonation front theory[1] was used to calculate the zone length at the center of the charge, L_{CJ}. It is obtained from the expression

$$L_{CJ} = \frac{R}{C} \cdot \frac{D_\infty - D}{D_\infty} \qquad (2)$$

where R is the spherical radius of curvature of the wave front, D_∞ is the infinite diameter detonation velocity, D is the detonation velocity, and C is a constant dependent on the equation of state of the material. Wood and Kirkwood used the properties of a liquid explosive to calculate a value of 3.5 for C. This value was used in our calculations.

Because the dependence of detonation velocity on charge diameter has not been measured for the cast Comp B used in this study, no value for D_∞ exists. To get an approximate value, D_∞ from Table 7-1 in Reference 5 was scaled by the amount necessary to predict our measured detonation velocity. This gives a value of D_∞ for Comp B of 7.889 mm/μs.

Two methods were used to obtain values for R. In the first method, the wave front data for each experiment were least squares fitted to circles over the center 50% of the charge diameters.[2]

Table 2. The angles of the detonation wave at the edge of the charges and the Wood-Kirkwood zone length for the tests in this work.

Material	Diameter (mm)	α_1* (Deg)	α_1** (Deg)	α_2* (Deg)	α_2** (Deg)	Zone Length (mm)†	(mm)††
Comp B	50.86	78.7	77.8	77.7	74.8	0.24	0.25
PBXN-111	40.90	61.4	56.9	61.1	58.1	2.6	2.6
PBXN-111	41.05	63.9	59.8	63.9	59.1	2.9	2.9
PBXN-111	48.02	63.8	60.2	62.2	56.9	2.7	3.0
PBXN-111	48.12	61.9	58.7	63.3	57.8	3.1	3.3
PBXN-111	68.25	62.1	60.7	63.0	63.9	4.1	4.3

* Obtained from a linear fit of the data at the edge. ** Obtained from ln Bessel function fit. † Radius in calculation obtained from fit of data to circle. †† Radius in calculation obtained from ln Bessel function fit.

In the second method, the series expansion of Equation 1 was used to obtain the radius of curvature as a function of position. The resulting function for one of the PBXN-111 charges is plotted in Figure 3. The peak value, which occurs at the center of the detonation wave, was used in Equation 2 to calculate the zone length.

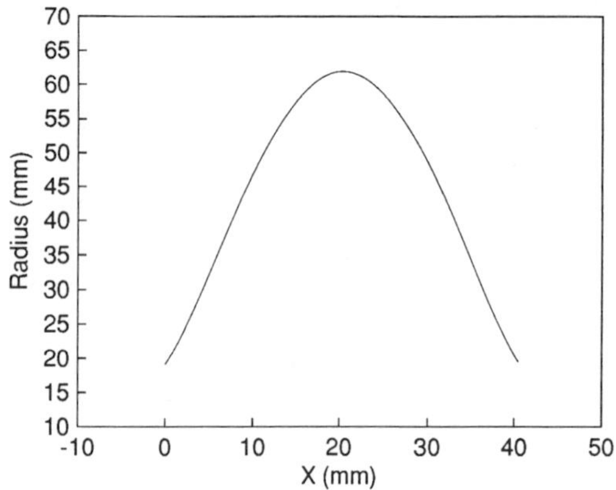

Figure 3. Radius of curvature across the charge for 41.05 mm diameter PBXN-111.

The zone lengths calculated by both methods are presented in Table 2. The results of the two methods agree well. The values obtained from the second method are slightly larger since the radius at the center of the detonation wave used in Equation 2 is the peak value which is, in all cases, larger than the average value calculated from a circular fit over 50% of the diameter.

SUMMARY

Detonation wave profiles have been fitted across the whole charge diameters for Comp B and PBXN-111. The fit equation has been used to obtain the angle of the detonation front as a function of position and the radii of curvature used in the Wood-Kirkwood zone length calculations. The results obtained from the fit equation agree with results obtained previously for PBXN-111. Since the fit equation gives a functional form for the detonation wave across the whole charge diameter, it can be used to test the results obtained from detonation theories and code calculations.

ACKNOWLEDGMENTS

This work was performed for and funded by the Office of Naval Research, Code 4525, as part of the Explosives and Undersea Warheads Technology Block Program PE602314N.

REFERENCES

[1] Wood, W. W. and Kirkwood, J. G., "Diameter Effect in Condensed Explosives. The Relation Between Velocity and Radius of Curvature of the Detonation Wave," J. Chem. Phys., Vol 22, Nov 1954, pp. 1920-1924.

[2] J. W. Forbes, E. R. Lemar, G. T. Sutherland, and R. N. Baker, "Detonation Wave Curvature, Corner Turning, and Unreacted Hugoniot of PBXN-111," NSWCDD TR-92/164, 19 Mar 1992.

[3] J. W. Forbes, E. R. Lemar, and R. N. Baker, "Detonation Wave Propagation in PBXW-115," in *Proceedings of the Ninth Symposium (International) on Detonation*, Portland, OR, Aug 1989, pp. 806-815.

[4] F. Chaissé and J. N. Oeconomos, "The Shape Analysis of a Steady Detonation Front in Right Circular Cylinders of High Density Explosive," in *Proceedings of the Tenth Symposium (International) on Detonation*, Boston, MA, July 1993.

[5] T. N. Hall and J. R. Holden, "Explosion Effects and Properties. Part III. Properties of Explosives and Explosive Compositions," *Navy Explosives Handbook*, NSWC MP 88-116, Oct 1988.

DETONATION WAVE CURVATURE OF PBXN-111

J. W. Forbes, E. R. Lemar, and R. N. Baker

Naval Surface Warfare Center
Dahlgren Division, White Oak Detachment
Silver Spring, Maryland 20903-5640

ABSTRACT

Spherical curvatures of detonation waves were measured by streak photography over the center 50 percent of PBXN-111 charges. These curvatures ranged from 54 to 143 mm for charge diameters of 41 to 68 mm and are not spherical near the edges of the charges. The wave fronts appear linear over about the last 3 mm at the charges'edges. The angle between the detonation wave front and the edge of the charge was about 62 degrees over this last 3 mm for all the charges. Detonation velocity and wave front curvature data of PBXN-111 were used to calculate CJ zone lengths of 2-4 mm using the Wood-Kirkwood theory.

BACKGROUND

PBXN-111 (formerly PBXW-115) is a cast cured explosive with RDX, AP, Al and an HTPB binder. The compositon of PBXN-111 is similar to some propellants[1,2] except that PBXN-111 contains RDX instead of HMX. The initial density of the PBXN-111 used in this work was 1.79 g/cm^3. The median RDX particle size was calculated[3] to be 60 μm. The nominal sizes for AP and Al particles were 200 and 5 μm, respectively. PBXN-111 cylinders have failure diameters of a few centimeters and curved wave fronts.[4,5]

DETONATION WAVE ARRIVAL AT END OF CHARGE

A streak camera was used to record the detonation wave arrival at the ends of unconfined cylindrical PBXN-111 charges. The experimental setup used to obtain these breakout data is shown in Figure 1. Aluminized Mylar or Teflon tape was glued to the end of the charge as a light reflector. Two of the experiments had lines drawn on the Teflon tape at accurately known distances from the charge edges. These lines appeared on the streak record and confirmed, within experimental error, that the records terminated right at the charges edge. The camera and exploding wire light source were positioned such that the alignment and/or reflectivity was destroyed when the shock arrived at the reflecting material. This greatly reduced the amount of light reaching the film.

DETONATION WAVE CURVATURE RESULTS FOR UNCONFINED CHARGES

Wave arrival distance-time data and detonation velocities are required to determine the wave front shape inside an explosive charge. The detonation velocity in the PBXN-111 charges was assumed to be steady. This assumption appears justifiable since the measured velocities were constant within experimental error over the last 30-40 mm of propagation distance. Wave front curvature measurements[6] on porous RDX and Tetryl explosives have shown that the length to diameter ratios of these materials need to be greater than five before constant curvature can be attained. It is possible that the wave curvature in

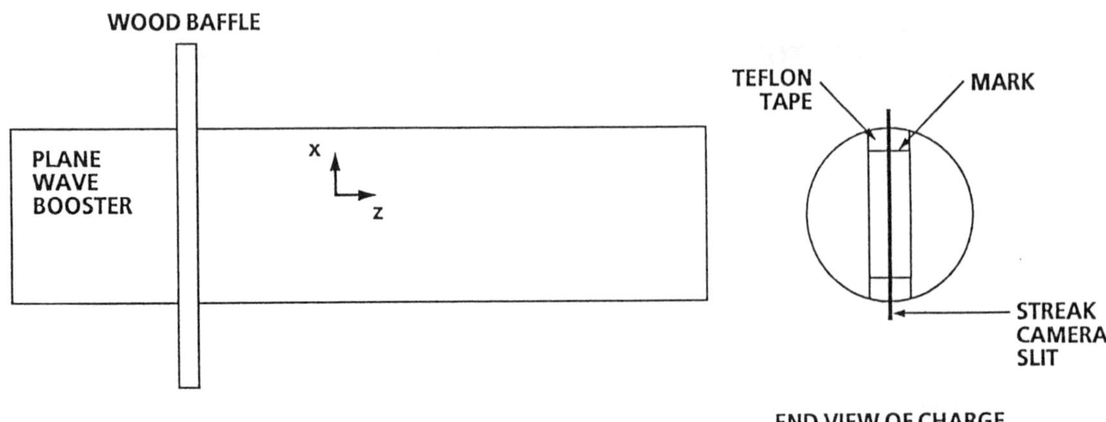

FIGURE 1. DETONATION WAVE BREAKOUT EXPERIMENTAL ARRANGEMENT

the PBXN-111 experiments would be slightly different than measured in this study if the detonation waves propagated for longer distances.

The wave fronts were not spherical over the entire diameter of the cylindrical PBXN-111 charges. This was particularly true near the edges of the cylinders. As a result, the best fit for the radius depended on how much of the data across the diameter of charge was used. In this work the data were fit over the center 50 percent of the charge diameter. Figure 2 shows a typical fit of curvature data for a 48.12 mm diameter charge.

The spherical radii of curvature for the unconfined breakout experiments, are given in Table 1. The spherical radii of the 41.05, 48.02, and 68.25 mm diameter charges are improved values over those previously published.[4] The results show that wave curvature increases with charge diameter. This is consistent with the findings of Campbell, et al.[7] Table 1 also gives the angles that the detonation waves make with the edges of the charges. The wave front appeared linear (i.e., not curved) over the last 3 mm at the charge edges.

Detonation velocity and wave front curvature data of PBXN-111 were used to calculate the CJ(i.e. sonic) zone lengths[8] given in Table 1 using the Wood-Kirkwood theory[9]. The calculated zone lengths are a few millimeters. These zone lengths are consistent with previously published calculations on ammoniuim perchlorate[6] and two plastic-bonded TATB explosives.[7,10] Recent improvements in the time resolution of zone length measurements[10] have provided data accurate enough to distinguish between various analytical curved wave front theories. D. Price[11] has pointed out that the limited number of accurately measured zone lengths are calculated well by the Wood-Kirkwood curved front theory. More recent curved front theories[12,13,14,15] have reduced the number of assumptions used in the Wood-Kirkwood treatment. Accuracy of these recent theories is unknown at present because of insufficient data to test them. The application of this detonation properties data base to these new theories is a subject of future work.

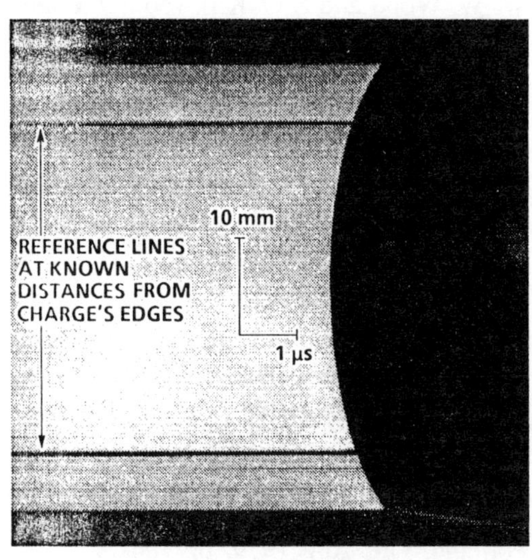

(A) STREAK CAMERA FILM RECORD

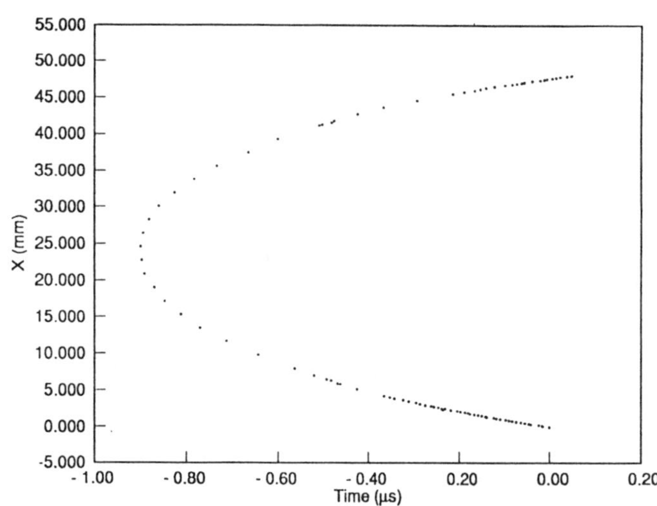

(B) BREAKOUT DISTANCE VERSUS TIME

FIGURE 2. DETONATION WAVE BREAKOUT FOR A 48.12 mm DIAMETER CYLINDRICAL PBXN-111 CHARGE

TABLE 1. PBXN-111 WAVE CURVATURES, ZONE LENGTHS, AND ANGLES AT CHARGE EDGE

CHARGE DIAMETER (mm)	SPHERICAL RADIUS* (mm)	ZONE LENGTH** (mm)	ANGLE AND DISTANCE FITTED AT EDGE OF CHARGE			
			RIGHT		LEFT	
			α (Deg)	S (mm)	α (Deg)	S (mm)
40.90+	53.7 ± 0.4	2.6	61.4 ± 1.1	3.2	61.1 ± 1.3	3.1
41.05+	61.2 ± 0.6	2.9	63.9 ± 0.9	3.4	63.9 ± 1.0	3.5
48.02	(66.5 ± 1.1)	(2.7)	63.8 ± 1.1	3.6	62.2 ± 1.4	2.5
48.12+	77.2 ± 0.5	3.1	61.9 ± 1.2	2.9	63.3 ± 1.1	3.1
68.25	143.1 ± 1.0	4.1	62.1 ± 1.3	3.0	63.0 ± 1.9	2.9

+ THESE EXPERIMENTS USED TEFLON TAPE AS A REFLECTOR WHILE OTHERS USED ALUMINIZED MYLAR.
* FITTED OVER THE CENTER 50%. PARENTHESIS INDICATES POOR CENTER OF RECORD.
**CALCULATED USING WOOD-KIRKWOOD THEORY WITH C = 3.5

ACKNOWLEDGEMENTS

This work was performed for and funded by the Office of Naval Research, Code 23, as part of the Explosives Project within the Explosives and Undersea Warheads Technology Block Program PE602314N. The authors wish to acknowledge many useful discussions on the contents of this paper with S. Jacobs, R. Bernecker, and D. Tasker. R. Doherty and L. Roslund have given technical and moral support for this work.

REFERENCES

[1] J. J. Dick, *Comb. and Flame*, Vol. 37, 1980., pp. 95-99.

[2] D. Price and A. R. Clairmont, Jr., *Comb. and Flame*, Vol. 29, 1977, pp. 87-93.

[3] J. W. Forbes and J. W. Watt, NAVSWC TR 90-168, 10 Aug 1990.

[4] J. W. Forbes, E. R. Lemar, and R. N. Baker, *Proc. Ninth Symposium (International) on Detonation*, Portland, OR, Aug 1989, pp. 806-815.

[5] J. W. Forbes, E. R. Lemar, G. T. Sutherland, and R. N. Baker, NSWCDD/TR-92/164, 19 March 1992.

[6] J. O. Erkman and D. Price, NOLTR 69-235, May 1970.

[7] A. W. Campbell and R. Engelke, *Proc. Sixth Symposium (International) on Detonation*, Coronado, CA, 24-27 Aug 1976, pp. 642-652.

[8] E. R. Lemar, J. W. Forbes, this proceedings.

[9] W. W. Wood and J. G. Kirkwood, *J. Chem. Phys.*, Vol 22, Nov 1954, pp. 1920-1924.

[10] S. A. Sheffield, D. Bloomquist, and C. M. Tarver, *J. Chem. Phys.*, Vol. 80, 1984, pp. 3831-3844.

[11] D. Price, Final Progress Report, ATR 88-0046, Nov 1988.

[12] D. S. Stewart, J. B. Bdzil, *Proc. Ninth Symposium (International) on Detonation*, Portland, OR, Aug 1989, pp 773-783.

[13] B. D. Lambourn, D. C. Swift, *Proc. Ninth Symposium (International) on Detonation*, Portland, OR, Aug 1989, pp 784-797.

[14] I. J. Kirby and G. A. Leiper, *Proc. Eighth Symposium (International) on Detonation*, Albuquerque, NM, July 1985, pp. 176-186.

[15] M. Cowperthwaite, Universite De Poitiers report Avril 1992.

[16] E. R. Lemar, J. W. Forbes, J. W. Watt, and W. L. Elban, J. Appl. Phys., 58, 1985, pp. 3404-3408.

[17] G. T. Sutherland, E. R. Lemar, P. Miller, J. W. Forbes, E. Anderson, K. D. Ashwell, and R. N. Baker, this proceedings.

[18] A. R. Champion, J. Appl. Phys., 42, 1971, pp. 5546-5550.

[19] C. D. Lundergan and W. Hermann, J. Appl. Phys., 34, 1963, pp. 2046-2052.

UNREACTED HUGONIOTS FOR POROUS AND LIQUID EXPLOSIVES†

R.L. Gustavsen and S.A. Sheffield
Los Alamos National Laboratory
Group M-7, MS P952

Numerous authors have measured the Hugoniots of a variety of granular explosives pressed to different densities. Each explosive at each density was typically then treated as a unique material having its own Hugoniot. By combining methods used by Hayes, Sheffield and Mitchell (for describing the Hugoniot of HNS at various densities) with Hermann's P-α model, it is only necessary to know some thermodynamic constants or the Hugoniot of the initially solid material and the porous material sound speed to obtain accurate unreacted Hugoniots for the porous explosive. We discuss application of this method to several materials including HMX, PETN, TNT, and Tetryl, as well as HNS. We also show that the "Universal Liquid Hugoniot" can be used to calculate the unreacted Hugoniot for liquid explosives. With this method only the ambient pressure sound speed and density are needed to predict the Hugoniot. Applications presented include nitromethane and liquid TNT.

INTRODUCTION

Equation of state (EOS) information is difficult to obtain on porous explosives as these materials are very sensitive to the shock initiation of detonation. Even at pressures of only a few kbar, shock velocities cannot be obtained from transit time measurements because the explosive is starting to react and accelerate the wave. In wedge tests, wave acceleration is often apparent well before the onset of detonation. Because of the early onset of reaction, measurements of pressure or particle velocity in transmitted waves provide unreliable equation of state information as well.

The best EOS information has been obtained in flying plate experiments using flyers made of well characterized materials whose velocities were accurately measured and when pressure or particle velocity was measured at the flyer/explosive interface. Data from these types of experiments is uncommon, as most researchers have been more interested in the initiation properties, and have hence used wedge experiments.

Because of the difficulties in making reliable EOS measurements on porous explosives it is often useful to construct a Hugoniot using thermodynamic constants obtained from static and hydrostatic measurements, the bulk sound speed of the porous explosive, and then to properly account for the porosity. If hydrostatic data is unavailable, the thermodynamic constants can be obtained by fitting to Hugoniot measurements on single crystals of explosives. These are generally much less sensitive to shock initiation.

POROUS EXPLOSIVE EQUATION OF STATE

The formalism for the equation of state which is used in this paper was developed by Hayes, and was first used to describe the porous explosive, HNS (hexanitrostilbene) by Sheffield, Mitchell and Hayes.[1] It was later amended by Setchell and Taylor[2] to be used in Hermann's P-α model.[3] Thus, the ideas are not new, but neither have they seen widespread application.

The method is based on constructing a complete thermodynamic potential function for the fully dense explosive, namely the Helmholtz Free Energy. The specific form which Hayes chose for the Helmholtz Free Energy is[1]

$$F(T,V)=C_V\left[(T-T_0)\left(1+\frac{\gamma}{V}(V_0-V)\right)+T\ln\left(\frac{T_0}{T}\right)\right]+\frac{K_{T_0}V_0}{N(N-1)}\left[\left(\frac{V_0}{V}\right)^{N-1}-(N-1)\left(1-\frac{V}{V_0}\right)-1\right] \quad (1)$$

† Work performed under the auspices of the U.S. Department of Energy.

where C_V is the specific heat at constant volume, γ is Gruneisen's parameter, V_0 is the specific volume of the fully dense explosive at zero pressure, $K_T$is the bulk modulus at constant temperature, and N is a constant. This construction assumes C_V and γ/V are constants, while the bulk modulus is

$$K_T = K_{T_0}\left(\frac{V_0}{V}\right)^N. \qquad (2)$$

These constants are readily obtained from static thermodynamic measurements and hydrostatic pressure - volume measurements.

In order to describe the compaction of the porous explosive in the framework of Hermann's P-α model,[3] Eq. (1) must be recast in the form $P(E,V)$ or $E(P,V)$. Setchell and Taylor[2] have shown that

$$E(P,V)=\frac{P}{\gamma/V}-\frac{\gamma}{V}C_V T_0(V_0-V) -\frac{K_{T_0}}{N\gamma/V}\left[\left(\frac{V_0}{V}\right)^N-1\right] +\frac{K_{T_0}V_0}{N(N-1)}\left[\left(\frac{V}{V_0}\right)^{1-N} -(N-1)\left(1-\frac{V}{V_0}\right)-1\right] \qquad (3)$$

Eq. (3) describes the behavior of the fully dense explosive. While Eq. (1) is a complete thermodynamic EOS, Eq. (3) is not.

Hermann's theory,[3] as modified by Carroll and Holt[4] states that in a porous material, Eq. (3) describes the solid portion. The distension of the porous material is

$$\alpha = V/V_s, \qquad (4)$$

where V is the specific volume of the porous explosive at a given pressure and energy, and V_s is the specific volume of the solid explosive at the same pressure and energy. If in the porous material the average pressure is P and the average specific volume V, then the pressure in the solid portion is $P\alpha$ and the specific volume of the solid portion is V/α. Equation (3) can thus be used to describe the energy at average pressure P and volume V in the porous explosive if modified to describe only the solid portion:

$$E = E(P\alpha, V/\alpha). \qquad (5)$$

Eqs. (3), (4), and (5) are now augmented by defining α as a function of the shock pressure P. A simple form for $\alpha(P)$, such as the following one suggested by Herman,[3] is sufficient.

$$\begin{aligned} \alpha &= 1+(\alpha_0-1)(1-P/P_s)^2 \cdots (P\le P_s) \\ \alpha &= 1 \qquad\qquad\qquad\quad \cdots (P\ge P_s) \end{aligned} \qquad (6)$$

In Eq. (6), α_0 is the original distension, $\alpha_0 = V_{00}/V_0$, and V_{00} is the initial specific volume of the porous explosive. P_s is the pressure at which the material crushes to solid density. Herman has also shown how P_s can be determined from measurements of the sound speed in the porous material.[3] Different values of P_s must be used for different initial porosities.

Given P and $\alpha(P)$, Eq. (5) is then itteratively solved for V such that the energy is the same as that given by the Hugoniot jump condition $E = P/2(V_{00}-V)$. Given the quality of much of the experimental EOS data, further sophistication in an EOS is unwarranted.

POROUS EXPLOSIVE DATA

Table 1. lists the thermodynamic constants for the explosives HMX, HNS, PETN, TNT, and Tetryl. Brief comments about where these constants were obtained, and how well they fit the data follow.

K_{T_0} and N for PETN were obtained by fitting the hydrostat obtained by Olinger and Cady.[5]

Table 1. Thermodynamic constants by explosive.

Explo-sive	ρ_0 g/cm^3	K_{T_0} Mbar	N	γ/V g/cm^3	C_V $cm^2/\mu s^2/K$
HMX	1.90	0.129	10.3	2.09	1.05(10-5)
HNS	1.74	0.146	3.5	2.82	0.89(10-5)
PETN	1.77	0.110	7.1	2.04	1.00(10-5)
TNT	1.65	0.082	7.3	1.51	1.08(10-5)
Tetryl	1.73	0.072	10.2	1.56	1.08(10-5)

We have also used the values of γ , and C_V contained in Ref. 5. Using these values and the crystal density of 1.775 g/cm^3 reproduces Shock Hugoniot measurements at 1.775, 1.75, and 1.71 g/cm^3 [6] fairly well, as shown in Figure 1 and 2. Using the P-α formalism with values of P_s = 15 and 3.5 kbar respectively, also reproduces the 1.60 and 1.40 g/cm^3 data shown, which were selected from the reports of Wackerle and coworkers.[7,8] These data were obtained using x-cut quartz and manganin pressure gauges. As porous explosive Hugoniot data go, these are excellent. As is typical there is more scatter in the P-V than the U_s - u_p plane.

K_{T_0} and N for HMX were obtained from fits to the hydrostatic pressure - volume data of Olinger, Roof and Cady.[9] γ and C_V are as reported in Ref. 9, as well. These constants, reproduce the 1.891 g/cc HMX Hugoniot[10] quite well up to pressures of about 100 kbar. Above 100 kbar, neither the 1.891 nor the single crystal HMX Hugoniot[11] is reproduced very well, possibly because of a phase transition in the HMX at a pressure near 100 kbar.[12] These constants with P_s set equal to 2.5 kbar nicely reproduce our Hugoniot measurements on 1.24 g/cc HMX.

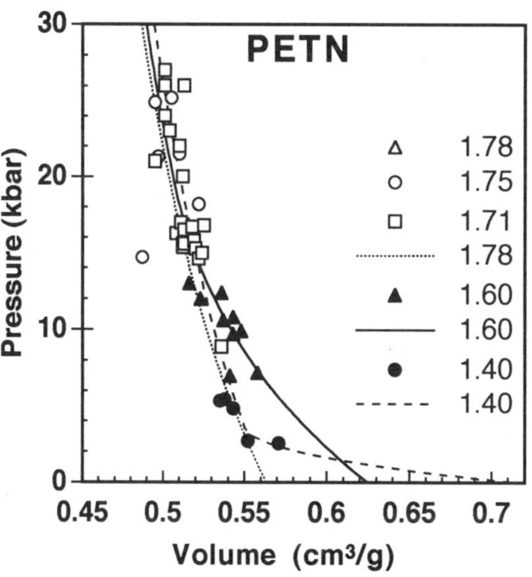

Figure 1. Hugoniots for PETN in the P-V plane. The initial density is noted beside each symbol. Smooth curves were calculated using the initial density noted beside the curve symbol. P_s was 3.5 kbar for the 1.40 g/cm^3 PETN and 15 kbar for the 1.60 g/cm^3 PETN.

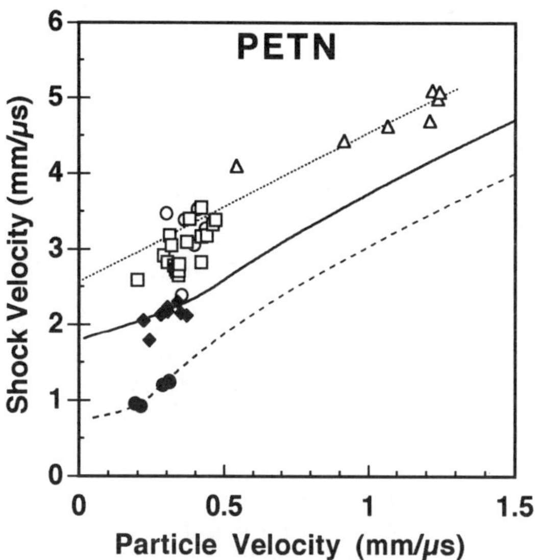

Figure 2. Hugoniots for PETN in the U_s - u_p plane. Symbols represent the same data sets as those in Figure 1. Solid curves are calculations. The data shown in this figure cover a wider pressure range than those in Figure 1.

The constants we show for the γ and C_V of HNS were obtained from Setchell and Taylor.[2] While Setchell and Taylor[2] also claimed to have improved estimates for K_{T_0} and N, we found that they do not reproduce the data of Ref. 1. as well as the original constants reported by Sheffield et. al.[1] Hence we list K_{T_0} and N from Ref. 1.

For TNT, γ and C_V, were obtained from values for the volume coefficient of thermal expansion and C_p [13] combined with values of K_{T_0} and N obtained from fitting to single crystal TNT Hugoniot data.[14] Relations among the thermodynamic constants were used with an iterative procedure to arrive at the final values.

For Tetryl, good values of the thermodynamic constants were not available in the literature. Because of its chemical similarity with TNT, we set γ and C_V equal to the TNT values. K_{T_0} and N were then obtained by least squares fitting to the 1.70 g/cc (98.3 % of crystal density) Hugoniot data of Lindstrom.[15] Lindstrom's data for lower densities of tetryl were obtained from wedge experiments and have significant scatter (in the P-V plane).[15]

LIQUID EXPLOSIVES EQUATION OF STATE

Liquid explosives and many other liquids have equations of state, which for the purpose of predicting shock states are well defined by the "Universal Liquid Hugoniot" first proposed by Woolfolk, Cowperthwaite, and Shaw.[16]

$$\frac{U_S}{C_0} = 1.37 - 0.37e^{-2u_p/C_0} + 1.62\frac{u_p}{C_0} \qquad (7)$$

In Eq. (7), U_s and u_p are, as usual, the shock and particle velocity, while C_0 is the sound velocity at zero pressure. Figure 3 shows measured shock and particle velocities for the explosives liquid TNT[17] and nitromethane.[18-20] The solid curves were calculated using Eq. (7) and C_0 = 1.55 mm/μs for liquid TNT[21] and C_0 = 1.30 mm/μs for nitromethane. Reproduction of the experimental data is excellent. Unfortunately, virtually no Hugoniot information exists for other liquid explosives. However, we have found that Eq. (7) works well for every other liquid we have tried.

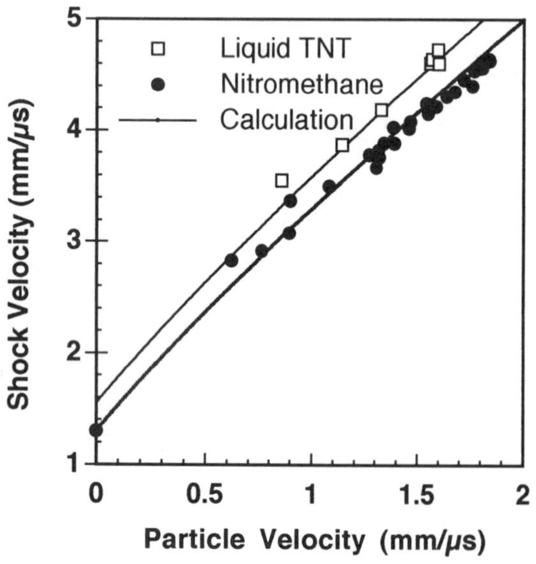

Figure 3. Hugoniots for liquid TNT and nitromethane in the U_S - u_p plane. Experimental data is from Garn[17] for liquid TNT and from Refs. (18-21) for nitromethane. Solid lines were calculated from Eq. (7).

ACKNOWLEDGMENTS

We would like to thank Ronald Rabie for useful discussions concerning the P-α model, and Jerry Dick and Jerry Wackerle for discussions concerning general properties of porous explosives.

REFERENCES

[1] S.A. Sheffield, D.E. Mitchell, and D.B. Hayes, in "Proceedings of the Sixth Symposium (International) on Detonation", Office of Naval Research, ACR-221, Arlington, VA, 1976, p. 748.
[2] R.E. Setchell and P.A. Taylor, J. Energetic Mat. 6,157 (1988).
[3] W. Hermann, J. Appl. Phys. 40, 2490 (1969).
[4] M.M. Carroll and A.C. Holt, J. Appl. Phys. 45,3864 (1974).
[5] B. Olinger and H. Cady, in "Proceedings of the Sixth Symposium (International) on Detonation", Office of Naval Research, ACR-221, Arlington, VA, 1976, p. 704.
[6] LASL Shock Hugoniot Data, S.P. Marsh Ed. U. of California Press, Berkeley, (1980) pg. 618-622.
[7] J. Wackerle and J.O. Johnson, Los Alamos Scientific Laboratory Report, LA-5131 (1973).
[8] J. Wackerle, J.O. Johnson, and P. M. Halleck, "Shock Compression and Initiation of Porous PETN" Submitted to the Anaheim meeting of the American Physical Society, Jan. 29-Feb. 1 (1975).
[9] B. Olinger, B. Roof, and H. Cady in "Symposium H.D.P. (Commissariat a l'Energie Atomique)", 1978. pg. 3.
[10] Ref. 6, pg. 596.
[11] Ref. 6, pg. 595.
[12] J.J. Dick, J. Energetic Mat. 1, 275 (1983).
[13] LASL Explosive Property Data, T.R. Gibbs and A. Popolato Eds., U. of California Press, Berkeley, (1980) pg. 599.
[14] Ref. 13 pg. 344.
[15] I.E. Lindstrom, J. Appl. Phys. 41, 337 (1970).
[16] R.W. Woolfolk, M. Cowperthwaite, and R. Shaw, Thermochim. Acta 5, 409 (1972).
[17] W.B. Garn, J. Chem. Phys. 30, 819 (1959).
[18] Ref. 6 pg. 595.
[19] V.S. Ilyukin, P.F. Pokhil,O.K. Rozanov, and N.S. Shvedova, Sov. Phys. Doklady, 5, 337 (1960).
[20] D.R. Hardesty, Comb. and Flame, 27,229 (1976).
[21] I.M. Voskoboinikov, V.M. Bogomolov, and A. Ya. Apin, Fizika Goreniya i Vzryva, 4,45 (1968).

UNREACTED HUGONIOT OF AMMONIUM NITRATE

R. Courchinoux and P. Lalle

CEA - Centre d'Etudes Scientifiques et Techniques d'Aquitaine B.P. N° 2 33114 LE BARP - FRANCE

The usual impedance mismatch method is prone to experimental difficulties when used with explosive samples to measure the unreacted Hugoniot : the samples have to be very thin to ensure that no reaction occurs. We describe a new experimental procedure which does not have such inconveniences, and use it to determine the unreacted Hugoniot of ammonium nitrate.

INTRODUCTION

The Hugoniot of explosive materials in the inert, unreacted state is an important quantity in a number of problems of explosive physics, for instance to know the location of VON NEUMANN's peak or the amount of energy produced by the decomposition of the explosive. When a pressure jump is suddenly applied to the back side of an explosive sample, the shock velocity across the sample varies continuously with the distance. The early shock velocity is the velocity in inert explosive, and after same distance of propagation, the shock reaches the detonation velocity D, as sketched in figure 1.

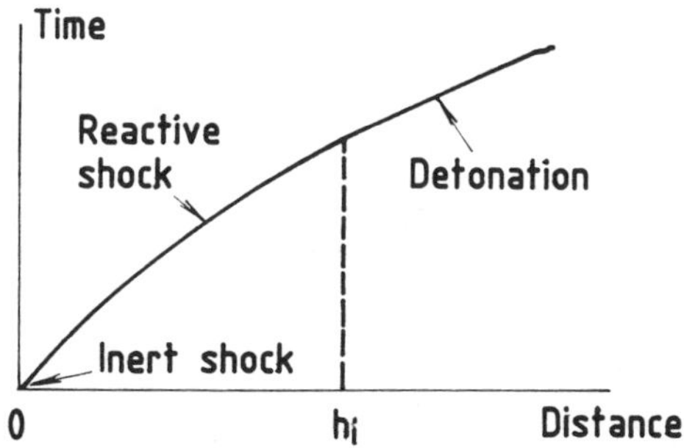

Figure 1 : Shock travel and run to detonation distance.

This explains why classical methods used to measure the Hugoniot state in inert materials are of difficult application to explosives. These methods, usually impedance mismatch, needs an accurate determination of the shock velocity Us. When these methods are used with explosives, two contradictory conditions appear. With very small sample thickness, the explosive remains unreacted, but the accuracy in the measured Us is poor. With greater sample thickness, the explosive reacts and the Us value thus measured is not the relevant one.

We have measured the inert Hugoniot of ammonium nitrate by means of a new method, suggested by PUJOLS [1] which is free of the above mentionned inconveniences, and allows us to determine the inert Hugoniot despite the explosive decomposition under the test conditions.

II PRINCIPLE OF THE INERT HUGONIOT DETERMINATION

II-1 In figure 1 the shock velocity reaches the detonation velocity D at the distance h_i from the back side of the explosive sample and h_i is called the run to detonation distance. The h_i value is measured in experiments where the explosive sample is impacted by a thick projectile with a constant velocity in order to apply a constant pressure P on the back side of the sample. The pressure is varied by varying the velocity or the shock impedance of the projectile and the run to detonation distance varies with the applied pressure. The experimental data show that the relation between P and h_i is usually a straight line when plotted in a $\ln(h_i)$-$\ln(P)$ diagram called the "pop-plot". The h_i value depends on the pressure P, but does not depend on the shock impedance of the projectile which has created this pressure.

II-2 The Hugoniot curve of an inert material can be determined without a shock velocity measurement in the following way (figure 2).

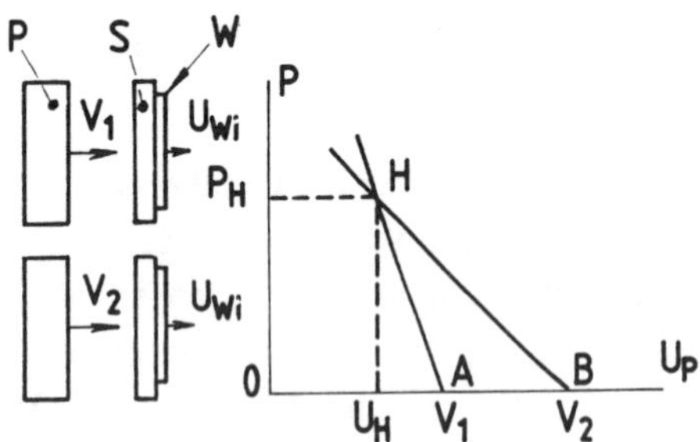

Figure 2 : Hugoniot measurement. P is the projectile, S is the sample, W is a thin metallic witness plate. In the pressure - material velocity diagram the curves AH and BH are the Hugoniots of the high and low impedance projectile, respectively.

Let us suppose that we get the same initial free surface velocity U_{wi} of the witness plate in two successive experiments, the first one when the projectile has high shock impedance and velocity V_1, the second one when the projectile has low shock impedance and velocity V_2. The same U_{wi} value means that the shocked state reached in the sample is the same in the two experiments, and this Hugoniot state (u_H, P_H) in pressure material velocity diagram is calculated as the intersection of the Hugoniot curves of the two projectile materials passing through the ($U_p = V_1$, $P = 0$) and ($U_P = V_2$, $P= 0$) points.

III-3 When this method is used with reactive sample, the shock wave travel is not the same as with an inert sample. We assume that the sample thickness is less than the run to detonation distance, but can be high enough so that some decomposition can occur in the tested material. This decomposition increases the pressure and the velocity in the shock front, and compressive waves are sent backwards. These waves are reflected frontward after reflexion on the projectile material (waves labelled CD in figure 3) and can reach the shock front. The amplitude of the compression changes induced by these waves depends on the projectile impedance. The existence of an unique pop-plot despite the use of different shock impedance impacting plates for its construction shows that these reflected wave have small influence on the building of the decomposition. Then the method of II-2, which needs no shock velocity measurement, can be used with explosive samples, leading to the inert Hugoniot. Successive experiments with a high impedance projectile material with different projectile velocities V_p allows us to draw a curve U_{wi} versus V_p. Another serie of experiments with a low impedance projectile material leads to another plot. Then, for each U_{wi} value, the calculation shown in figure 2 gives a point u_h, P_h lying on the inert Hugoniot of the sample. The corresponding shock velocity U_H in inert explosive obeys :

$$U_H = \frac{P_H}{\rho_o \cdot u_h}$$

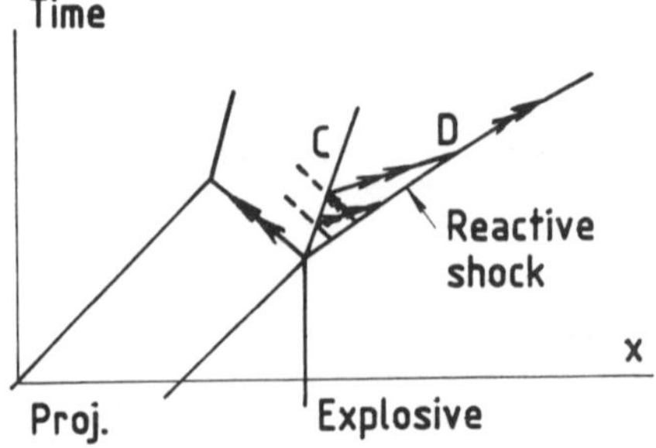

Figure 3 :Waves travels during the building of the reactive shock.

III REACTIVE AND UNREACTED HUGONIOT OF AMMONIUM NITRATE

III-1 EXPERIMENTS

The reactive material under study was ammonium nitrate NH_4NO_3 compressed to an initial density of 1,69 g/cm3 close to the density of compact material (1,72 g/cm3).

In a first series of five shots the reactive Hugoniot was measured by means of the usual impedance mismatch method. The shock entering the sample was produced by a stack made of an explosive, a buffer and a driver plate. The measured quantities were the mean shock velocity Us across the sample (to +/- 0.3 km/s) and the initial free surface velocity of the driver plate, to +/- 15 m/s.

The thickness of the samples was 4.00 mm (each value of the sample thickness leads to its own value of the reactive Hugoniot). The U_s-U_p states obtained in this way are shown as crosses in figure 6. This set of points is fitted to by the following linear relation in km/s:

$$U_S = 3 + 1.85\ U_P$$

for pressure less than 30 GPa.

A second series of six shots was made to measure the unreactive Hugoniot according to the above method. The experiments are sketched in figure 4.

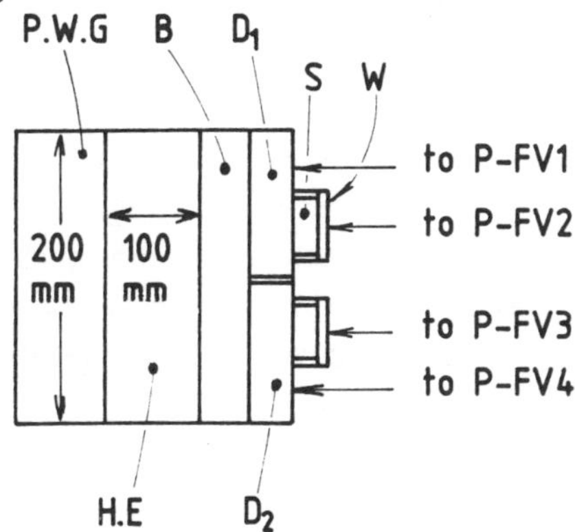

Figure 4 :P.W.G. is a plane wave generator, H.E is a cylinder of octogen, B is the buffer plate, D1 and D2 the tantalum and magnesium driver plates, S the sample and W the witness plate.

The high impedance driver material was tantalum, and the low impedance one was magnesium alloy GA3Z1. The ammonium nitrate samples (40 mm in diameter and 1.50 mm thickness) were put in a sealed box to avoid moisture.

The top of the box is a copper plate of 0.50 mm thickness which is used as witness plate. In each experiment a four beam PEROT-FABRY velocimeter was used to measure the velocities U_T and U_G versus time of the tantalum and magnesium alloy plates (initial values $U_T(0)$ and $U_G(0)$), and the velocities versus time of the two copper witness plates. The imput pressure was varied by using different buffer materials. For high pressure shots, a thick copper plate was thrown by an explosive system against the driver plates.

III-2 HUGONIOT DATA

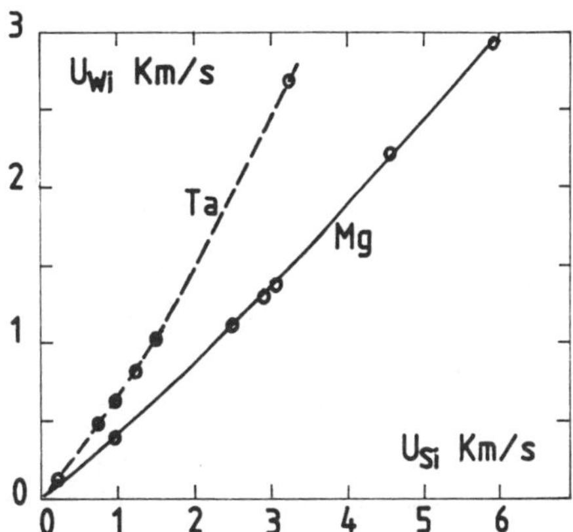

Figure 5 :Initial free surface velocity of the witness plate Uwi vs initial free surface velocity of the driver plate. The dashed and continuous lines are for tantalum and magnesium driver plate. The points are measurements .

Figure 5 shows the experimental curves U_{wi} vs. $U_t(0)$ and U_{wi} vs. $U_G(0)$ which were used to find the inert Hugoniot. The procedure illustrated in figure 2 was used, with the release curve of tantalum and magnesium alloy instead of Hugoniot curves of the projectile materials. For tantalum we have assumed that the isentropic release curve is the mirror image of the Hugoniot in pressure material velocity (P-U_p) plane. With respect to this last curve, thermal effects shift the true curve towards the right, and elastic effects toward the left. In the mirror image approximation we assume that elastic effects exactly cancel the thermal effects. For the magnesium alloy we have assumed a MIE-GRUNEISEN equation of state with constant specific heat C_v, and with the Gruneisen coefficient varying with density according to $\gamma\rho=\gamma_0\rho_0$.

The Hugoniot are depicted by a linear U_s-U_p relation :

$\rho o = 16.66$ g/cm^3- $U_s = 3.293+1.307\ U_p$
from [2] for tantalum,

$\rho o = 1.775$ g/cm^3- $U_s = 4.516+1.256\ U_p$
from [3] for the magnesium alloy.

The resulting unreacted Hugoniot of the ammonium nitrate is shown as the continuous line in figure 6. The equation of this line is :
$U_s = 1.8 + 1.8\ U_p$ (km/s)

The maximum pressure in the experiments was 35 GPa.These experiments give also points lying on the reactive Hugoniot for 1.50 mm thick samples, the accuracy in reactive shock velocity measurements being around 0.5 km/s. These points are shown as circles in figure 6. The close proximity of the reactive Hugoniot points with the unreacted Hugoniot shows that a very small amount of ammonium nitrate reacts in the first 1.5 mm of shock travel.

III-3 DISCUSSION

(i) The experimental conditions used here were not the ideal conditions for using PUJOL's method, for the shock entering the driver plates decreases slightly as a function of time, and the decrease in shock intensity depends on the shock impedance of the driver plate. It would be better to impact the driver plates with the thick projectile of a gun.

(ii) The larger the difference between the shock impedances of the two driver plates, the greater the accuracy in the determination of the intersection of their Hugoniot in figure 2. The choice of tantalum and magnesium appears as satisfactory in this respect, but infortunately their behavior during release is not accurately known. Thus the accuracy in the determination of the ammonium nitrate inert Hugoniot would be improved with respect to our data by a better choice of experimental conditions.

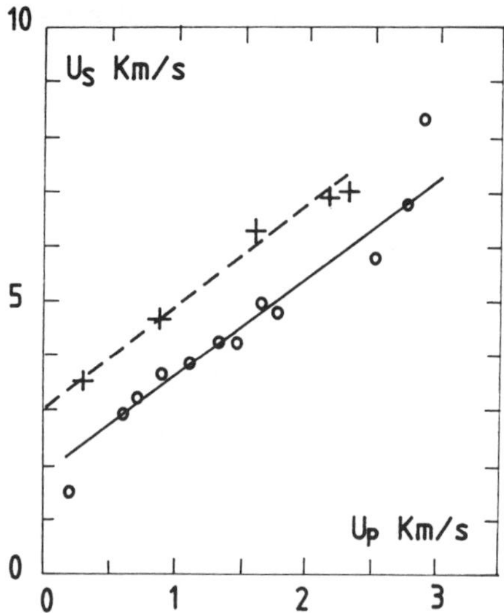

Figure 6 :Hugoniots of ammonium nitrate. The dashed curve is the reactive Hugoniot for samples with 4.00 mm thickness, Us is the mean value of the shock velocity. The continuous line is unreacted Hugoniot.

CONCLUSION

By using a new method which does not need shock velocity measurement, the Hugoniot of unreacted ammonium nitrate with initial density 1.69 g/cm3 has been measured. A linear relation holds between shock velocity and particle velocity (unit : km/s): $U_s = 1.8 + 1.8\ U_p$.

REFERENCES

[1])H.Ch. Pujols - CEA/CESTA - Int. Report (1986).

[2]A.C. Mitchell and W.J. Nellis - "Shock compression of aluminum, copper and tantalum", J; Appl. Phys. 52 (5), May 1981.

[3]LASL Shock Hugoniot Data, MARSH ed, University of California Press (1980).

SENSITIVITY STUDIES OF A NEW ENERGETIC FORMULATION

W. H. Wilson, J. W. Forbes, T. P. Liddiard, and R. M. Doherty
Naval Surface Warfare Center
Dahlgren Division, White Oak Detachment
10901 New Hampshire Avenue
Silver Spring, MD 20903-5640

ABSTRACT

The shock sensitivity of a new pressed formulation based upon CL-20 has been studied. Samples were made from a bimodal particle size distribution of the CL-20 ε-polymorph and an EVA binder, pressed to an average 97% of theoretical maximum density. The material exhibited an anomalous reversal in slope of shock sensitivity vs. input stress. Over a limited stress range near the first reaction threshold, the level of reaction decreased with increasing input stress. Within this range of input shock it was observed that break-out of reaction was delayed, and was concentrated near the sample centerline.

INTRODUCTION

CL-20 is a relatively new energetic ingredient which may prove useful as an alternative to traditional materials such as HMX in explosive or propellant applications. The explosive which has been studied here, PBXC-19, is a pressed material similar to LX-14, using CL-20 instead of HMX. Critical to eventual application of any formulation is a full appreciation of the safety implications of its use, and an ability to perform hazards analyses. It is thus imperative that a thorough understanding of the material's sensitivity, particularly its response to shock loading, be made available to potential users. Details of the shock response of PBXC-19, including sub-detonation reaction leading to detonation, are reported here. Two experimental methods were used: the Modified Gap Test (MGT)[1], and the Insensitive High Explosives (IHE) gap test.[2]

EXPERIMENTAL DESCRIPTION

The pressing powder for the samples consisted of ethylene vinyl acetate (EVA) binder and a bimodal distribution of ε-polymorph phase CL-20. The samples were pressed under controlled heat and vacuum conditions; FTIR spectroscopy confirmed that the phase remained unaltered after pressing. Sample densities ranged from 96.9% to 97.6% of theoretical maximum density (TMD).

The MGT and IHE gap tests both use the 51-mm diameter donor-gap system used in the NOL Large Scale Gap Test (LSGT)[3]. The donor is pentolite, 51-mm long, pressed to a density of 1.56 g/cm^3. The shock output is controlled by varying the length of a polymethyl methacrylate (PMMA) gap. This arrangement has been calibrated[4]; it produces a quasi-triangular shock pulse of 1 to 2 μs duration, with peak stress which can be varied from 5 to 80 kbar. MGT and IHE gap test configurations are shown in Figures 1 and 2. The 13-mm thick, 51-mm diameter acceptor in the MGT is unconfined. In the IHE test, the acceptor consists of four 13-mm diameter pellets, each 13-mm long, confined in a steel tube of 3-mm wall thickness. A 13 mm air gap separates the open output end of the tube from a steel witness block.

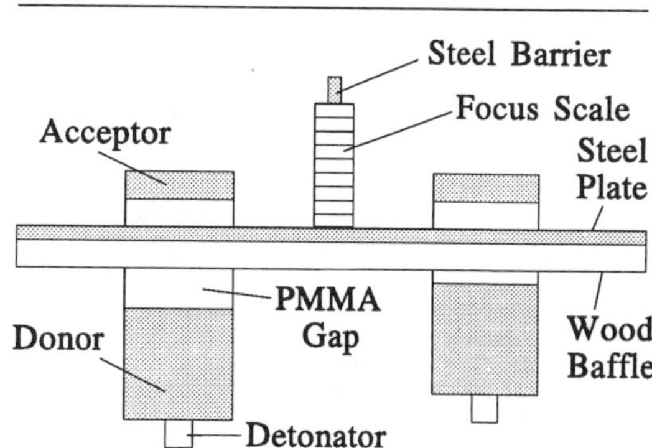

Figure 1. Modified Gap Test (MGT) experimental configuration.

In the MGT, motion of the acceptor's free rear surface, caused by shock transmitted through the sample plus any chemical reaction in the material, is recorded photographically. By comparing the observed motion to that predicted using an estimated or known Hugoniot for the unreacting material, the level of any chemical reaction in the acceptor can be quantified. The measured velocity minus that predicted by the unreacting Hugoniot is designated the "excess velocity." In the analysis, the excess velocity is plotted against the peak stress entering the sample material for a series of tests. Usually, six to ten tests are required to cover a response range from no reaction to detonation. The shape of MGT excess velocity plots typically found for pressed explosives is illustrated in Figure 3, showing points of first reaction, sustained ignition, and detonation.[5] It generally has been found, for all energetic materials previously tested, that for shock input above that causing first reaction the excess velocity increases monotonically with input stress.

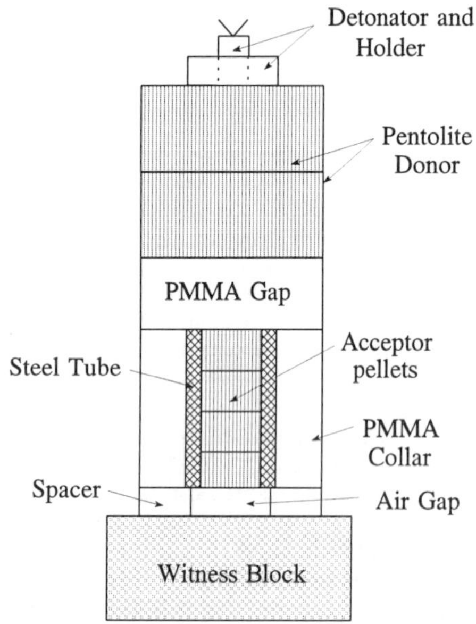

Figure 2. Insensitive High Explosives (IHE) gap test experimental configuration.

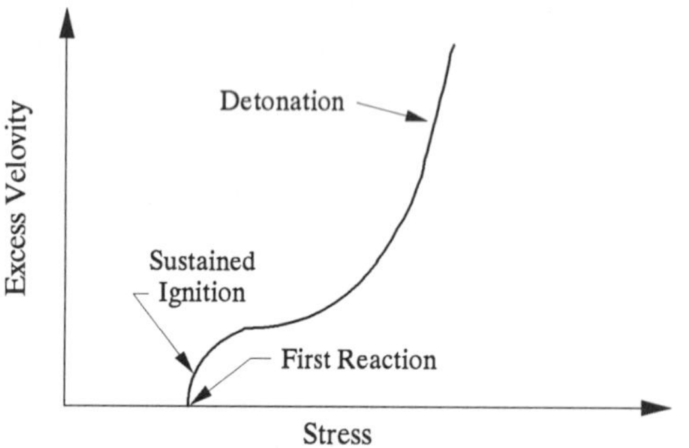

Figure 3. Typical MGT excess velocity vs. stress plot.

The IHE test was developed to provide shock sensitivity information when only limited amounts of sample material may be available. The test is uninstrumented, relying mainly on depth of a dent produced in the witness block as a measure of reaction level. It is a particularly advantageous test for obtaining a general estimate of shock sensitivity at an early stage in the development of an explosive. Stress in excess of 10 kbar is required to dent the witness block. Detonation in the sample is inferred by production of a dent of depth greater than 0.25 mm; the post-test condition of the confinement tube also gives an indication of the level of sample reaction. Generally, about seven tests are required in an IHE test series to characterize the shock sensitivity of a material.

EXPERIMENTAL RESULTS

IHE Gap Tests

Due to scarcity of PBXC-19 material, only five IHE tests were run. The dent depths produced are plotted in Figure 4, as a function of the shock input in the explosive samples. (Shock input levels in the samples were estimated by impedance matching the calibrated stress output from the PMMA gap used in each test. No shock Hugoniot is available for PBXC-19; thus, a linear shock vs. particle velocity (U_s-u_p) relation based upon similar materials was used. The calculated stress values were found to change only slightly with relatively large changes in estimates of the U_s-u_p parameters.) Detonation occurred in all but one of the IHE tests, based upon the dent depth criterion. The steel confinement tube was highly fragmented in each of the four tests which produced dents, also indicating that these specimens had detonated. By contrast, there was no dent produced in the test at 9.7 kbar; that sample was recovered almost fully intact.

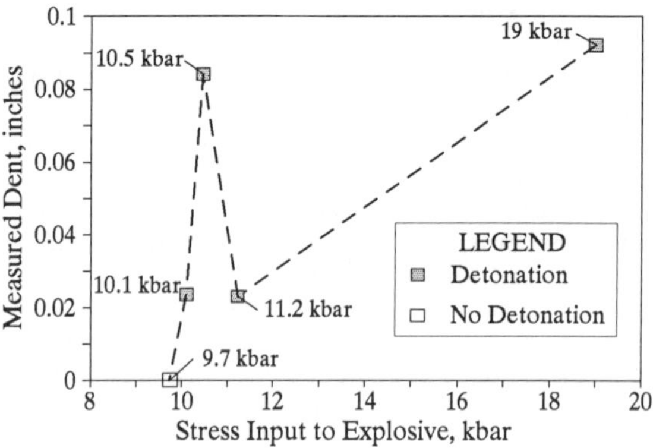

Figure 4. Dent depths in PBXC-19 IHE gap tests.

A general increase in the measured IHE test parameter (dent depth) with increasing shock input is expected from first reaction up to detonation. However, in an IHE series slight variations occur in the depth of dents produced, due to variations in strength of the steel witness block, sample density, etc. In general, one would not expect to find a dramatic reversal in dent depth as shock input is increased. However, as illustrated in Figure 4, a very significant reversal occurred in the PBXC-19 IHE tests, at a shock input of approximately 11 kbar. It is not clear how detonation due to a 10.5 kbar input stress could produce a dent more than three times deeper than that produced by the detonation due to an 11.2 kbar shock input.

Modified Gap Tests

Some insight into the anomalous sensitivity behavior observed in the IHE gap tests may be gained from the results of ten MGT experiments run for PBXC-19. Figure 5 shows the plot of excess velocity vs. shock input. As observed in the IHE series, reversal in slope of the MGT response occurs for reacting samples of PBXC-19. In this case, the reversal occurs as the shock input is increased from approximately 11 to 12 kbar, close to the range at which reversal was seen in the IHE tests.

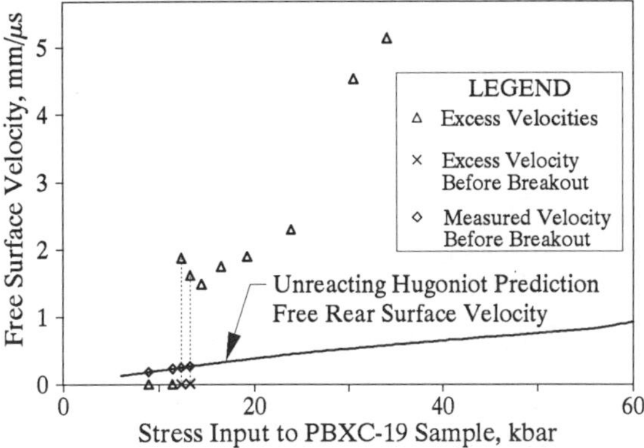

Figure 5. Excess velocities for PBXC-19 MGT series.

In general, a plot of excess velocity as a function of input stress is sufficient to summarize the results of a MGT series and to illustrate a material's shock sensitivity. However, this is not the case for PBXC-19, because the rear surface motion in the two tests which showed anomalous excess velocity was unlike that normally observed in a MGT. This difference is illustrated in Figure 6, which shows plots of the rear surface positions vs. time for each of the ten PBXC-19 MGT tests. Zero time corresponds to first motion of the rear surfaces. Motion of four general types can be described from these plots. For tests in which no sample reaction occurs, such as that at 8.8 kbar, the rear surface moves at low velocity, showing no apparent acceleration after it begins to move. The slope of a line fit to the observed positions for this motion is found to be essentially the velocity predicted by the unreacting Hugoniot, corresponding to a zero excess velocity point in Figure 5. For tests in which the sample detonates, such as the one at 34 kbar, the surface moves out at very high velocity. A short period of high acceleration may be observed just after first motion, but this is often too brief to be resolved in the high-speed photographs. For tests in which some intermediate level of reaction such as sustained ignition occurs, motion such as that of the test at 16.4 kbar typically is observed. In such cases, there is a longer period of steady acceleration after the free surface first begins to move; however, the velocity exceeds that predicted by the unreacting Hugoniot from the start. After a relatively short time, the velocity becomes steady; this linear region is then used to determine the excess velocity.

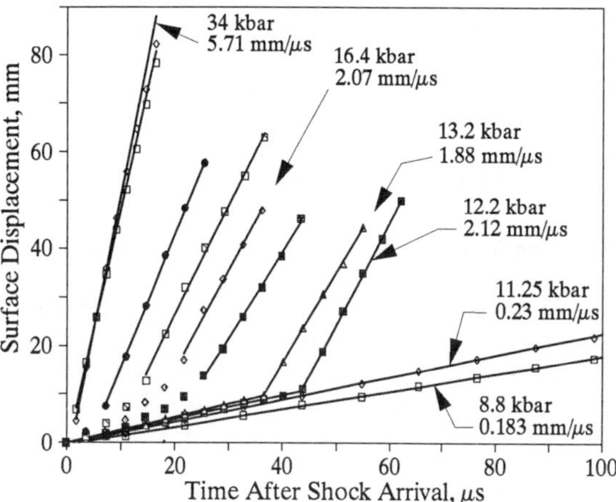

Figure 6. Rear surface motion for PBXC-19 MGT series.

For the tests at 12.2 and 13.2 kbar, the character of the motion was different than any of the three normally observed types described above. In these two tests, the motion was essentially like that of an unreacting material for relatively long times. Initially, the rear surfaces moved at low, steady velocity which was that predicted by the unreacting Hugoniot. But, at late time (37 μs and 44 μs, respectively) the motion suddenly accelerated to a much higher velocity. This late-time motion was used to calculate the excess velocities shown in Figure 5 for these tests. In the high-speed photographs, the sudden change in surface velocity is observed primarily in the central portion of the sample's expanding disk.

It is interesting to note that while the *initial* free surface motion for the test at 12.2 kbar was correspondingly slower than that for the test at 13.2 kbar, the velocity *after* break out of reaction at the rear surfaces was higher in the test which had the lower input stress. However, it took approximately 7 μs longer for the reaction to reach the rear surface in the test at 12.2 kbar, indicating that the strength of this intermediate type of reaction may have been more a function of time delay than of input stress.

DISCUSSION and CONCLUSION

Usually, when any sample reaction occurs in MGT or IHE gap tests, it occurs promptly. For a prompt reaction, the free surface velocity in the MGT exceeds the predicted unreacting velocity essentially from the start of motion. This implies that chemical reaction in the acceptor starts prior to motion of the rear free surface. By contrast, in the two PBXC-19 MGT tests which showed anomalistic excess velocities, the very long delays before sudden acceleration occurred imply that start of reaction was not prompt. Apparently, for shock input in the range of 10 to 12 kbar, delayed transition to sustained ignition, by a mechanism not yet identified, occurs for PBXC-19. Time dependence of this mechanism is further supported by the observation that the stronger reaction occurred for the case in which the delay before reaction was longer, even though the input stress in this case was lower.

This delayed reaction in PBXC-19 is sufficiently strong to transition to detonation given sufficient run length, as evidenced by the IHE results. Note that IHE gap test samples have a confined run length of 51 mm, in contrast to 12.7 mm in the MGT. Thus, detonation may be observed at lower input stress in IHE gap tests than in the MGT, as was found for PBXC-19 in this study.

The energetic constituent of PBXC-19, ε CL-20, undergoes various phase transitions under quasi-static pressure of approximately 6 to 7 kbar. At lower temperature, the high pressure ζ-polymorph occurs[6]; at higher temperatures, transition is to the α phase. In the α phase, several clathrates are known to occur[7]. How these phase transitions may occur in a shock is not yet known, but it is reasonable to speculate that any dynamic phase transition may occur over a broader, higher pressure range, and would be time dependent. If the α polymorph occurs with shock loading, it is possible that with time clathrate sites grow and provide hot spot initiation points, which would make the material more sensitive. Other possible causes for the delayed reaction which should be considered include shear effects due to non-planarity of the shock front, and shock focusing toward the sample centerline.

Because of the anomalous behavior in these gap tests, it is difficult to identify a conventional description of the shock sensitivity for PBXC-19 as a threshold shock stress which could be expected to produce detonation in service, the usual purpose of such tests. If the late time MGT data at 12.2 and 13.2 kbar are ignored, the excess velocity plot of Figure 5 then shows a conventional shape, with an abrupt jump from no reaction to sustained ignition at approximately 14.4 kbar. The hazards analysis picture is complicated by the unknown nature of the very vigorous late time reactions which occurred in the tests for which slope reversal of the sensitivity plots was observed. Regardless of such academic difficulties, from a practical viewpoint these results imply that a shock sensitivity threshold of about 10 kbar should be assumed for PBXC-19 safety and hazards analyses. As noted, at this shock input level, the sub-detonation reactions which occurred in the MGT were very strong, and transition to detonation always occurred in the IHE test configuration.

ACKNOWLEDGEMENTS

This work was sponsored by the Office of Naval Research, Code 4525, as part of the Explosives and Undersea Warheads Technology Block Program PE602314N. The authors gratefully acknowledge Mr. S. L. Collignon for providing the sample materials, and Messrs. K. D. Ashwell, A. D. Brown and R. N. Baker for conducting the tests.

REFERENCES

[1] T. P. Liddiard, Jr. and S. J. Jacobs, Initiation of Reaction in Explosives by Shocks, NOLTR 64-53, 1965.

[2] J. W. Forbes, J. W. Watt and H. G. Adolph, The Insensitive High Explosives (IHE) Gap Test, NSWC TR 86-58, 12 July 1986.

[3] D. Price, A. R. Clairmont, J. O. Erkman, The NOL Large Scale Gap Test. III. Compilation of Unclassified Data and Supplementary Information for Interpretation of Results, NOLTR 74-40, 8 Mar 1974.

[4] T. P. Liddiard and J. W. Forbes, A Summary Report of the Modified Gap Test and the Underwater Sensitivity Test, NSWC TR 86-350, 12 March 1987.

[5] T. P. Liddiard, J. W. Forbes and D. Price, " Physical Evidence of Different Chemical Reactions in Explosives as a Function of Stress," Proceedings, Ninth Symposium (International) on Detonation, 1989, pp 1235-1242.

[6] T. P. Russell, P. J. Miller, G. J. Piermarini and S. Block, "High-Pressure Phase Transition in γ-Hexanitrohexaazaisowurtzitane," *J. Phys. Chem.* 1992, *96*, 5509-5512.

[7] T. P. Russell, P. J. Miller, G. J. Piermarini and S. Block, "Pressure/Temperature Phase Diagram of Hexanitrohexaazaisowurtzitane," *J. Phys. Chem.* 1993, *97*, 1993-1997.

PRESHOCK DESENSITIZATION OF PBX EXPLOSIVES+

Roberta N. Mulford, Stephen A Sheffield, and Robert R. Alcon
Los Alamos National Laboratory
Group M-7, MS P952
Los Alamos, NM 87545

Preshocking delays initiation of PBX-9404 and PBX-9501, relative to unshocked material. In PBX-9404 preshock experiments, a first shock of 2.3 GPa was followed 0.65 μs later by a second shock of 5.6 GPa. Both PBX explosives show clear desensitization while the preshock persists. In PBX-9404, initiation of detonation occurs nearly as anticipated for the material, after coalescence of the preshock and main shock into a single wave. Multiple embedded magnetic gauges were used to measure the shock histories. Our data indicates a slightly longer run to detonation than expected, even though a single wave is initiating the material. A slight stress reduction at coalescence, as required by the shock dynamics, may be responsible for the overrun. A reactive wave is clearly evident while the preshock persists. The long run to detonation indicates that this reactive wave is not driving the initiation. A set of four preshock experiments were performed on PBX-9502, which is unreactive at these pressures, to investigate the shock dynamics of the two waves in the HE.

INTRODUCTION

Preshocking resulting in delayed initiation has been examined in PBX-9404 and PBX-9501, using multiple magnetic gauges embedded in the initiating explosive. These measurements of particle velocity enable us to follow the evolution of the reactive wave behind the shocks, and to observe the development of this wave into a detonation. Our observations address the previous idea that the material is completely desensitized while the preshock is active, but that the normal run-to-detonation (as given by the pop plot) for the material applies as soon as the two shocks coalesce into a single shock.

Previous work on preshock desensitization was done by Campbell and Travis.[1] In their experiments, a detonation wave was run into a preshocked region, where it was weakened and eventually extinguished. The critcal criterion for desensitization was given by $P^{2.2}\ \tau = 1140$ (kbar and μs), for both PBX-9404 and Comp B. The active region was interpreted as an induction time for hot spot deactivation in the material.

EXPERIMENTAL SETUP

Our experiments are performed using a light gas gun to generate well supported, planar shock waves of well-known pressure. The experiments are one-dimensional over the region and time of interest. The square pressure pulse generated by the projectile may eliminate some variables to simplify consideration of the time-dependent behavior of the growth of the reactive wave, and allows accurate manipulation of time and pressure parameters. The gas gun can reach projectile velocities of up to 1.4 mm/μs, corresponding to pressures to about 10.5 GPa in PBX materials when single crystal sapphire impactors are used. This pressure will detonate PBX-9404 and PBX-9501, but is not sufficient to promote prompt reaction in PBX-9502.

Embedded multiple magnetic gauges provide unique measurements, in the Lagrangian frame, of the time evolution of the shocks, for up to 3 μs. The gauge package consists of either 5 nested particle velocity gauges and 5 impulse gauges, or of 10 particle velocity gauges, to take data at 1/2 mm depth intervals when the gauges are placed at a 30° angle. Use of multiple gauges gives independent measurements of particle velocity (u_p) and shock velocity (U_s). These parameters are obtained directly from the data.

Preshock experiments are done using a composite projectile-mounted impactor consisting of a low impedance thin layer on the front surface of a high impedance backing material. The projectile impacts a precisely machined flat explosive cylinder, into which the gauge package is glued at a 30°

+ Work performed under the auspices of the U. S. Department of Energy.

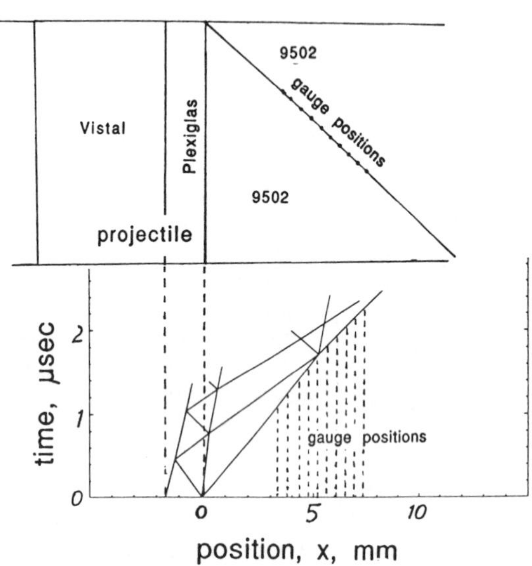

Figure 1. Experimental arrangement and x-t diagram showing preshock and main shock generation for a PBX-9502 experiment.

angle. The experimental setup and x-t diagram for a PBX-9502 experiment are shown in Fig. 1.

Experiments have been done on PBX-9404, PBX-9501, and PBX-9502. Data obtained from a shot on PBX-9502 are shown in Figure 2. The character of the input waves and time of coalescence are clearly evident, since the material behaves as an inert material at these pressures. Data from a pair of shots done on PBX-9404 is superimposed in Figure 3. Preshock and main shock pressures of 2.3 and 5.6 GPa and wave separation of 0.7 μs are accurately reproduced between the two shots. Growth of the reactive wave to near detonation is evident in Figure 3. The reactive wave emerging during the preshock is more clearly presented in Figure 4, in which maximum particle velocity vs location serves to show the approximate position of the reactive wave.

Detonation occurs after 9.4 mm of run, from impact of the first shock, or 8.7 mm after the second shock enters the explosive. The pop plot for PBX-9404 predicts[2] a run of 3.5 mm at the pressure of the second shock (5.6 GPa). Measured from the location of wave coalescence the run is 3.8 mm, slightly longer than the run predicted from the pop plot. The slight overrun is also observed by John Ramsay in plane wave lens experiments.[3]

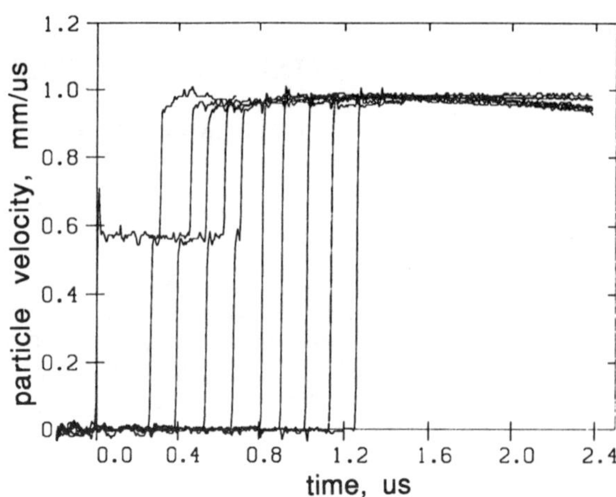

Figure 2. Data from experiment on PBX-9502 with P_1 = 3.71 GPa, t_1 = 0.32 μs, and P_2 = 8.19 GPa.

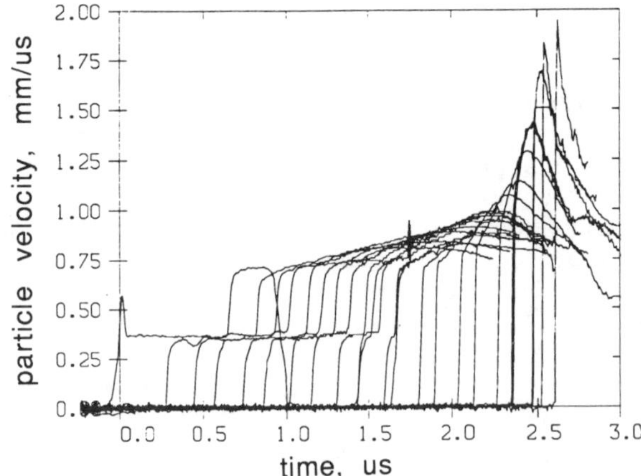

Figure 3. Data from two experiments on PBX-9404, showing growth of reactive wave in preshocked material: P_1 = 2.3 GPa, t_1 = 0.68 μs, P_2 = 5.6 GPa.

DISCUSSION

The Hugoniot crossing diagram in the t-x plane is shown in Figure 5. At wave coalescence, the return to a single shock in the material requires a switch from the second to the principal Hugoniot, with corresponding generation of a small rarefaction in the material. The magnitude of this pressure drop is calculated, using the MACRAME[4] code, to be at most 0.15 GPa (2.7%) in PBX-9502, and about 0.06 GPa (1.1%) in PBX-9404, if the PBX-9404 were inert. While the magnitude of this drop is not sufficient to alter the run obtained from the pop plot appreciably, it may

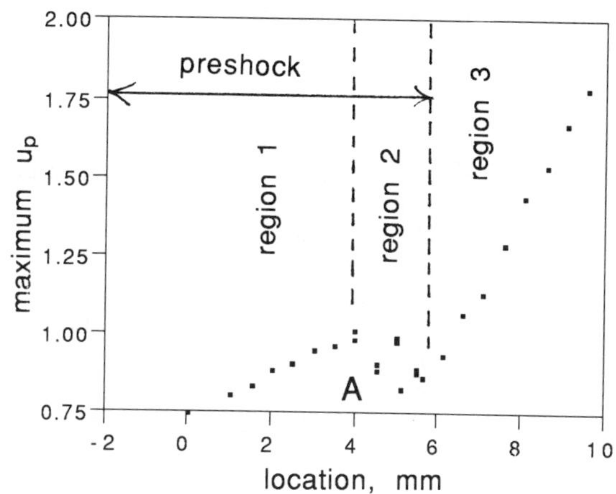

Figure 4. Maximum particle velocities of reactive waves in PBX-9404 experiments. Collision of reactive wave and small rarefaction occurs at point A.

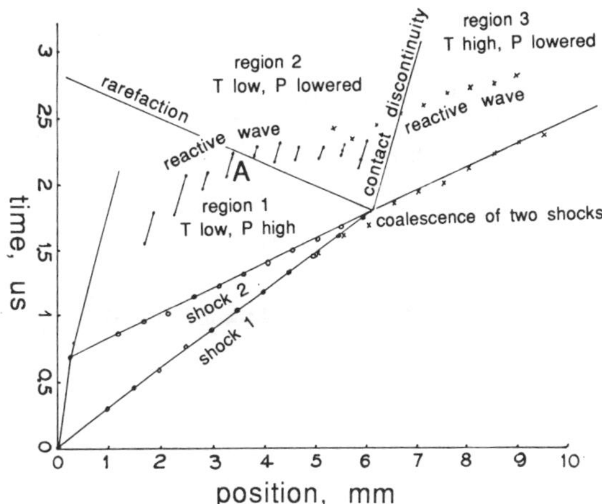

Figure 5. Complete x-t diagram for experiment on PBX-9404 showing reactive waves (from experimental data) and rarefaction.

lengthen the run by a small amount, within the margin of error of the pop plot.

The bulk temperature of the material is lowered substantially in the doubly shocked case at a given pressure, by up to 25% at 4 GPa. A contact discontinuity separates the cold region behind the two shocks from the hot single shock region, as shown in Figure 5.

The PBX-9502 data is expected to exhibit this pressure drop as a propagating perturbation on the flat region of the second wave. Careful examination of the record in the region where the rarefaction wave is calculated to be (velocity obtained from MACRAME calculation) reveals no perturbation on the flat top of the wave. The 1.7% rise calculated in u_p was expected to be large enough to detect, but this is apparently not the case. The uncertainty in particle velocity in these records is about 1 to 2%.

The PBX-9404 experiments exhibit the same particle velocity profiles as those observed for PBX-9502, with the addition of the reactive wave emerging after the second shock. This wave emerges almost as soon as the second shock pressure is established in the material, contradicting the idea that the material has been completely desensitized by the first shock. According to Campbell and Travis' criterion,[1] the first shock is too short to produce desensitization, with $P_1^{2.2}\tau$ = 644<1140.

However, the emergence of the reactive wave before coalescence apparently does not contribute to the development of the detonation once coalescence of the two waves has occurred. The run is, instead, extended slightly after establishment of a single shock.

The small rarefaction discussed earlier propagates back into the reacting material as shown in Figure 5. When the reactive wave encounters the rarefaction, a reduction in the maximum u_p reached by the wave occurs, as shown in Figure 4. The reactive wave is quenched at the point (marked "A") at which the rarefaction meets it. This drop is seen in individual waves as an early maximum in u_p and then a sharp drop off, a truncation of the reactive profile.

These observations lead to a model in which the preshock compresses the material, and then the second shock promotes a reaction. The second shock is propagating in a preshocked region of elevated T, P, and density. This second shock produces a state, off the principal Hugoniot, of lower temperature for the given final pressure. Thus the reactive wave propagates in a region of relatively low T, high P, and high density, which has been precompressed to a density around 2.08 g/cm^3, a density at which the run to detonation might be expected to be exceedingly long based on estimates made in Ref. 6. The elevated initial density in this region also is associated with the removal of some fraction of the hot spots in this material. This region is shown on the x-t diagram, Figure 5, as region 1, bounded by the input shock and the returning small rarefaction. Under these conditions, the reactive wave accelerates slowly,

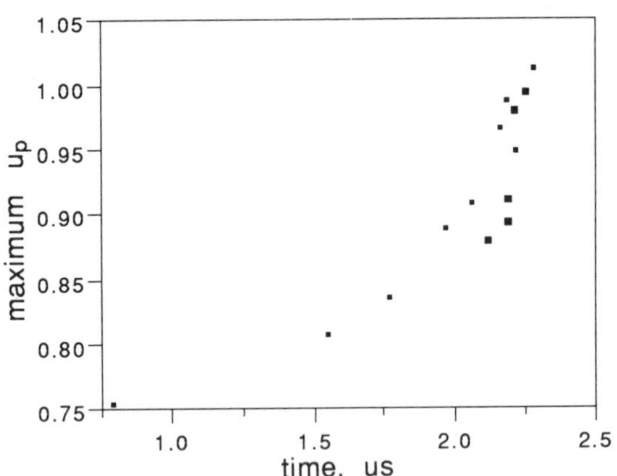

Figure 6. Maximum particle velocities of reactive waves in PBX-9404 experiments, in region of preshock. Heavy points are maxima of waves arising after collision with rarefaction, in region 2.

propagating at nearly the same velocity as the second shock which promotes it.

Encountering the rarefaction, the reactive wave is attenuated. The wave proceeds in a second region (Figure 5 region 2) in which P, T, and density are lowered slightly. The initial conditions are still dictated by the preshock. The reactive wave in this region exhibits a reduced particle velocity and also a wave velocity near zero, as shown in Figures 5 and 6.

The establishment of a single shock generates a contact discontinuity, which bounds a third region (Figure 5 region 3). Across this contact discontinuity, the temperature is raised to that prescribed by the principal Hugoniot. The single shock propagates into material with initial T and density again in the usual (1.84 g/cm^3, 230 K) range for development of a normal heterogeneous reactive wave. Neither Figure 4 nor Figure 5 indicates that the reactive wave in this region is unrelated to the reactive waves in the preshocked regions, but the long run to detonation supports this idea. This wave develops into detonation as expected. The run to detonation is extended slightly over that anticipated at the pressure of the second wave because of the slight pressure reduction at coalescence.

The $P_1^{2.2}\tau > 1140$ criterion[1] for desensitization may arise partly from the condition where the longer τ allows the reaction in region 1 to run nearer completion, chemically changing the remaining hot spots, either overpressuring them with reaction product gases or altering the local chemistry through partial reaction. We anticipate doing experiments in this regime.

CONCLUSIONS

A pressure drop is required by the shock dynamics of a double shock coalescing to a single shock. This pressure drop is not visible in PBX 9502 records, but may nonetheless be resulting in the extended run observed in PBX-9404 after coalescence of the two shocks.

A reactive wave is emerging in the preshocked material, but apparently does not contribute to the detonation, as indicated by an extended rather than truncated run after coalescence. The reactive wave is depleted by the small rarefaction at coalescence. The reactive wave in the preshocked region may indicate chemistry or "pre-burning" of the hotspots, as well as their compression, as a mechanism for desensitization.

REFERENCES

[1] A. W. Campbell and J. R. Travis, Proc. of the Eighth Symposium (International) on Detonation", (1985), NSWC MP 86-194, pp.1057.

[2] T. R. Gibbs and A. Popolato, "LASL Explosive Property Data," University of California Press, Berkeley (1980).

[3] John Ramsay, private communication.

[4] MACRAME Computer Program, J. Fritz, Los Alamos National Laboratory, Group M-6.

[5] J. J. Dick, C. A. Forest, J. B. Ramsay, and W. L. Seitz, J. Appl. Phys., **63**, 4884-4888 (1988).

[6] A. W. Campbell, W. C. Davis, J. B. Ramsay, and J. R. Travis, Physics of Fluids, **4**, 511-521 (1961).

ISOTHERMAL AND SHOCK COMPRESSION OF HIGH DENSITY AMMONIUM NITRATE AND AMMONIUM PERCHLORATE

F.W. Sandstrom and P.A. Persson
Research Center for Energetic Materials
New Mexico Institute of Mining and Technology
Socorro, NM 87801

B. Olinger
Los Alamos National Laboratory
Los Alamos, NM 87545

Bulk sound speed measurements, isothermal volume compression/X-ray diffraction experiments and shock loading experiments (maximum pressure $\approx$20 GPa) have been performed for high initial density ($\geq$94% TMD) ammonium nitrate (AN) and ammonium perchlorate (AP). The experimental data, and full density Hugoniots calculated from that data, suggest the presence of low pressure, shock induced phase transitions in both the AN and AP. The AP phase transition occurs at $\approx$4 GPa, and exhibits characteristics of a high density to low density phase transition, but the present data are not conclusive. The AN phase change occurs at a shock pressure of less than 3.5 GPa, but the associated volume change is relatively large, indicating the presence of a previously unidentified high pressure, high density phase.

INTRODUCTION

Given the extensive use of AN and AP in explosive and propellant applications, relatively little data has been reported pertaining to the static or shock loading of either material with regard to their shock Hugoniots or equations of state. Dremin et al.[1] have reported shock Hugoniot data for AN at an initial density of 0.86 g/cm^3, and estimated a Hugoniot for AN at solid density (1.73 g/cm^3) based on bulk sound speed measurements and a generalized Hugoniot formula proposed by Afanasenkov et al.[2] The resulting U_s, U_p fit for the solid AN Hugoniot was $U_s = 2.20 + 1.96U_p$. Sandusky et al.[3], in analyzing shock loading experiments on single crystals of AP, (TMD = 1.95 g/cm^3), considered the U_s, U_p fit estimated by Martynyuk et al.:[4] $U_s = 2.84 + 2.0\ U_p$. However, Sandusky et al. found that the relation $U_s = 2.84 + 1.6\ U_p$ best fit shock compression data for 1.92 g/cm^3 AP pressings at 15.5 and 17.8 GPa.[5]

The present study reports the results of sound speed measurements, isothermal compression/X-ray diffraction experiments, and shock loading experiments used to evaluate the shock Hugoniots of AN and AP at high initial density ($\geq$94% TMD) to pressures of approximately 20 GPa. From this data, full density Hugoniots have subsequently been calculated assuming a Mie-Grüneisen equation of state.

EXPERIMENTAL

The AN and AP samples used for the experiments were prepared by pressing. The AN starting material was a commercially available reagent grade in flake form. The AP starting material used was an ultra-high purity grade with a nominal grain size of 200 μm. The cylindrical (25 mm diameter) pressings were made at nominal thicknesses of 3, 4.5 and 6 mm. Samples used in the shock compression experiments were cut into 16 mm wide $\times$ 22 mm long rectangles to accommodate the experimental geometry. Individual sample densities were determined using gas pycnometry.

Bulk sound speeds were determined by measuring the longitudinal (c_l) and shear (c_s) wave velocities with pairs of X- and Y-cut quartz crystals, respectively, and the relation

$$c_b = (c_l^2 - 4/3\ c_s^2)^{1/2}. \qquad (1)$$

The isothermal compression experiments were performed using a high pressure X-ray diffraction technique developed by Halleck and Olinger.[6] The isothermal pressure and volume data can be conveniently expressed in a form similar to the shock Hugoniot

$$U_{st} = c_t + s_t U_{pt} + qU_{pt}^2, \qquad (2)$$

where the t subscript denotes isothermal conditions. The isothermal shock and particle velocity analogs, U_{st} and U_{pt}, respectively, are obtained from pressure and volume along the isotherm using the Hugoniot conservation relations that apply to shock loading:

$$U_{st} = (PV_o/(1 - V/V_o))^{1/2} \quad (3)$$

and

$$U_{pt} = (PV_o\,(1-V/V_o))^{1/2}. \quad (4)$$

In the isothermal Equation (2), c_t is related to the isothermal bulk sound speed at zero pressure in the same way that the adiabatic bulk sound speed is related to the c_o term in the Hugoniot equation.

The shock compression experiments utilized explosively generated plane shock waves to simultaneously drive shocks through small samples of 6061 Al and the AN and AP pressings mounted on 6061 Al base plates. Each experiment typically used three each 5 mm thick 6061 Al samples, and three each of the AN and AP samples at nominal thicknesses of 3, 4.5, and 6 mm. Transit times of shocks through the samples were recorded with flash gaps and a multiple slit streak camera. The shocked states of the AN and AP were obtained from impedance matching with the 6061 Al standard.[7]

RESULTS AND DISCUSSION

The results of the sound speed measurements on the AN and AP are summarized in Table 1. Each data point represents the average of four measurements on two different samples. Sound speed data reported by other workers[1,8,9] is shown for comparison. Our longitudinal sound velocities (c_l) for the AP pressings are consistent with the data reported by Reese et al. for AP pressings using various grain size starting materials, but also illustrates the effect that grain size can have on the measurements. The isothermal bulk sound speed (c_t) obtained from a linear fit to the U_{st}, U_{pt} isothermal compression data is also in good agreement with the bulk sound speed value reported for AP at TMD. On the other hand, our measured AN adiabatic sound speed is considerably higher than the value reported by Dremin et al. The discrepancy is even more pronounced in light of the differences in density. The reason for the discrepancy is not readily apparent, but could be the result of inhomogeneities and/or anisotropicity of the AN pressings used for our measurements. Similarly, the isothermal bulk sound speed obtained from a linear fit to the U_{st}, U_{pt} isothermal compression data is also significantly higher than the value reported by Dremin et al. The difference here is interesting in light of the fact that the values are both representative of AN at TMD.

The isothermal and shock compression data for the AN and AP are illustrated in Figures 1 and 2. In the isothermal compression experiments, no phase changes were observed in the AN up to the maximum pressure of 7.7 GPa. However, a diffraction pattern of the AP taken at 4.7 GPa indicates that a phase change had occurred. Unfortunately, we were unable to solve the diffraction pattern and therefore could not calculate the volumetric compression any further, although the pattern was characteristic of an asymmetrical crystal structure such as triclinic or monoclinic. This result is in sharp contrast to the cubic structure of AP(II), which occurs at temperatures above 240°C at atmospheric pressure. The linear fits to the U_{st}, U_{pt} data sets were chosen over a quadratic fit (Equation 2) due to the limited low pressure (<1 GPa) data. In the case of the AN, a quadratic fit to the U_{st}, U_{pt} data might give an intercept value in closer agreement to the bulk sound speed of Dremin et al., but attempts at forcing a fit through this value did not represent the current data accurately.

Each shock Hugoniot data point shown represents the average shocked states of the three AN and AP samples on each shot. At lower shock pressures (<12 GPa) the AN data exhibited considerable scatter, both for individual samples on a given shot as well as for the shot-to-shot averages. This scatter is presumably the result of sample inhomogeneity and/or anisotropicity, as was demonstrated by the erratic nature of the shock arrival traces. This result may also be related to our discrepancies in sound speeds for the AN. However, at this point we cannot definitively rule out non-equilibrium effects of a low pressure, shock induced phase transition.

In the absence of phase transitions, the experimental isotherms should be good approximations to the full

Table 1. Sound velocity measurements for AN and AP.

This Work

	TMD (g/cm^3)	ρ_o (g/cm^3)	c_l (mm/μs)	c_s (mm/μs)	c_b (mm/μs)	c_t^a (mm/μs)
AP	1.951	1.87	2.81	1.57	2.16	2.81
AN	1.728	1.60	4.06	1.81	3.48	3.01

Other Work

	TMD (g/cm^3)	ρ_o (g/cm^3)	c_l (mm/μs)	c_S (mm/μs)	c_b (mm/μs)	c_t^a (mm/μs)
AP[8]	1.951	1.90 (500 μm)	2.18	—	—	—
AP[8]	1.951	1.90 (76 μm)	2.97	—	—	—
AP[9]	1.951	1.95	—	—	2.84	—
AN[1]	1.728	1.73	—	—	2.20	—

[a] Isothermal bulk sound velocities shown are for AN and AP @ TMD

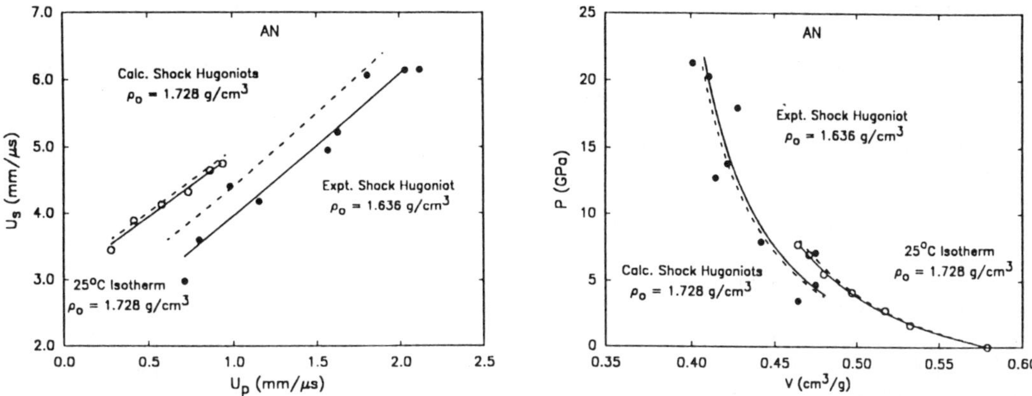

Figure 1. AN experimental isotherms and Hugoniots (solid lines), and calculated solid density Hugoniots (dashed lines). U_s, U_p fits: isotherm, $U_{st} = 3.01 + 1.87\ U_{pt}$; experimental Hugoniot, $U_s = 1.82 + 2.13\ U_p$; solid density Hugoniots, $U_s = 3.07 + 1.89\ U_p$ for $0.28 \leq U_p \leq 0.94$; $U_s = 2.23 + 2.18\ U_p$ for $0.72 \leq U_p \leq 2.12$.

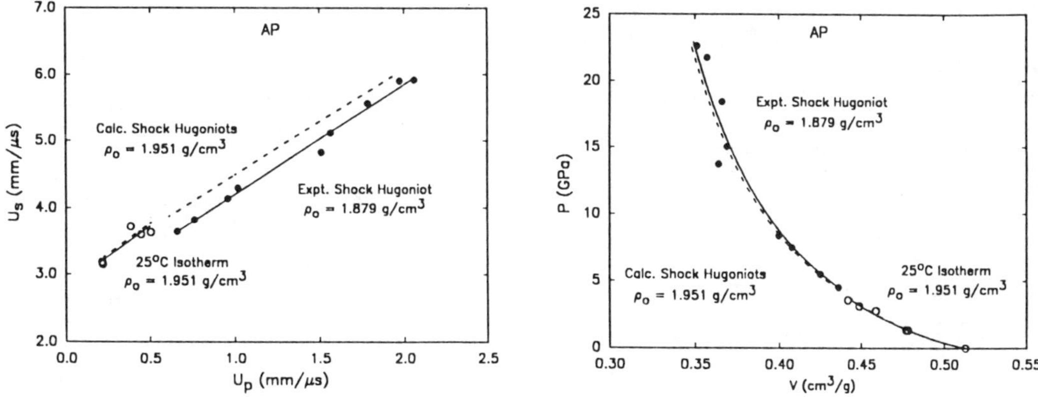

Figure 2. AP experimental isotherms and Hugoniots (solid lines), and calculated solid density Hugoniots (dashed lines). U_s, U_p fits: isotherm, $U_{st} = 2.81 + 1.84U_{pt}$; experimental Hugoniot, $U_s = 2.56 + 1.65\ U_p$; solid density Hugoniots, $U_s = 2.84 + 1.85\ U_p$ for $0.21 \leq U_p \leq 0.50$; $U_s = 2.90 + 1.59\ U_p$ for $0.66 \leq U_p \leq 2.10$.

density shock Hugoniots at lower pressures, while the measured shock Hugoniots are for slightly porous initial states. For AP, the positions of the U_s, U_p and P, V isotherms and Hugoniots (Figure 2) conform to the different initial densities. The porous Hugoniot lies below, and has the same or slightly steeper slope than the isotherm in the U_s, U_p plane, and is to the right of the isotherm in the P, V plane. For AN, while the porous U_s, U_p Hugoniot lies below, and is slightly steeper than the isotherm, the porous P, V Hugoniot lies to the left of the isotherm, which is characteristic of a material that undergoes a shock induced phase transition (Figure 1). This evidence for the existence of a low pressure (<3.5 GPa), shock induced phase change in the AN is interesting in light of the fact that no phase changes were observed in the isothermal compression experiments. One reason for this may be the absence of heating in the isothermal compression experiments. Bridgman[10] has reported a sixth phase of AN at pressures above 0.88 GPa and temperatures greater than 169°C in static compression experiments. Deal[11] has suggested that the shearing mechanisms present under shock loading may also be required to induce the phase transition. Visual extrapolation of the AN P, V shock Hugoniot to zero pressure also suggests that the transition goes to a higher density, metastable phase. In contrast, although a phase change in the AP was observed in the isothermal compression experiments, the P, V isotherm and shock Hugoniot data are essentially continuous, indicating that if a shock induced transition does exist, the volume change associated with it is very small.

The solid density Hugoniots for the AN and AP (dashed lines in Figures 1 and 2) were calculated from the isotherms and experimental Hugoniots using a Mie-Grüneisen EOS and assuming that ratios of the Grüneisen parameter, γ, to the specific volumes and the constant volume heat capacities were constant. These assumptions were maintained even though the experimental shock Hugoniots for the AN and AP are thought to be representative of different phases than the isothermal compression curves. The values of the Grüneisen parameters used for the calculations were 1.0 and 0.8 for the AN and AP respectively. It is interesting to note that our calculated high pressure Hugoniots for AN ($U_s = 2.23 + 2.18\ U_p$) and AP ($U_s = 2.90 + 1.59\ U_p$) agree very well with previous estimates (Dremin et al., AN ($U_s = 2.20 + 1.96\ U_p$), and Sandusky et al. AP ($U_s = 2.84 + 1.6\ U_p$).

The displacements between the calculated low and high pressure U_s, U_p and P, V AN Hugoniots continue to suggest the presence of a low pressure, shock induced phase transition to a new higher density phase for this material. In the case of the AP, both the calculated low and high pressure U_s, U_p and P, V Hugoniots are nearly continuous. The negative change in slope from the calculated low pressure to high pressure U_s, U_p Hugoniots could be the result of a shock induced phase transition from a high density to low density phase, but the present data are not conclusive.

CONCLUSION

The isothermal and shock compression of AN and AP at high initial density demonstrates evidence for the existence of low pressure ($\leq$4 GPa) shock induced phase transitions in both materials. For the AN, the presence of a new high density, high pressure phase is strongly suggested by the data, although the shocked state at which the transition occurs is not clearly defined. For the AP, aside from the fact that a phase change was observed to occur in the isothermal compression experiments, the evidence for a shock induced phase transition to is less conclusive, although the data illustrates characteristics of a high density to low density phase transition. Our limiting assumptions regarding the equation of state and calculation of solid density Hugoniots from the experimental isotherms and porous Hugoniots likely do not adequately address the complex thermodynamic properties associated with the shock loading of either the AN or the AP. For this reason, low pressure shock loading experiments using carefully prepared samples, and coupled with more sophisticated diagnostics (e.g., wave profile measurements) are in order. These experiments would presumably shed considerable light on the nature of the phase transitions.

ACKNOWLEDGEMENTS

We gratefully acknowledge the support of the members and staff of the Research Center for Energetic Materials, a National Science Foundation Industry/ University Cooperative Research Center. Special thanks to G. Faulks and K. Paisano, NAWC, China Lake, for preparing the AP pressings, L. Stretz and M. Barr, LANL, for preparing the AN pressings, and J.N. Fritz, LANL, for much discussion and constructive criticism.

REFERENCES

[1] A.N. Dremin, K.K. Shevdov and O.S. Avdonin, *Comb. Exp./Shock Waves* 6, p. 449 (1970).

[2] A.N. Afanasekov, V.M. Bogomolov and I.M. Voskobinikov, *Zh. Prikl. Mekh. Fiz.* 10, p. 660 (1970).

[3] H.W. Sandusky, B.C. Glancy, D.W. Carlson, W.L. Elban and R.W. Armstrong, "Deformation and Shock Loading Studies on Single Crystals of Ammonium Perchlorate," in *Proceedings of the Ninth Symposium (International) on Detonation*, Portland, OR, 1989, pp. 1260-1270.

[4] V.F. Martynyuk, B.A. Khasainov, A.A. Sulimov and M.K. Sukoyan, *Comb. Exp./Shock Waves* 23, p. 58 (1987).

[5] P.K. Salzman, O.R. Irwin, and W.H. Andersen, *AIAA Journal* 45, p. 2238 (1965).

[6] P.M. Halleck and B. Olinger, *Rev. Sci. Instrum.* 45, p. 1408 (1974).

[7] R.G. McQueen, S.P. Marsh, J.W. Taylor, J.N. Fritz and W.J. Carter, *High Velocity Impact Phenomena*, R. Kinslow, Ed., New York: Academic Press, 1970, pp. 293-417.

[8] B.O. Reese, J.H. Blackburn, L.B. Seely and M.W. Evans, *Comb. Flame* 11, p. 262 (1967).

[9] Dobratz, B.M.; and Crawford, P.C., "Properties of Chemical Explosives and Explosive Simulants," *LLNL Explosives Handbook*, UCRL-52997 Change 2, January 1985, LLNL, Livermore, CA.

[10] P.W. Bridgman, *Proceedings of the American Academy of Arts and Science* 51, p. 581 (1916).

[11] W.E. Deal, Personal Communication, October 27, 1992.

SHOCK WAVE AND DETONATION WAVE RESPONSE OF SELECTED HMX BASED RESEARCH EXPLOSIVES WITH HTPB BINDER SYSTEMS

G.T. Sutherland, E.R. Lemar, J.W. Forbes, E. Anderson, P. Miller,
K.D. Ashwell, R.N. Baker and T.P. Liddiard

Naval Surface Warfare Center
Dahlgren Division, White Oak Detachment
10901 New Hampshire Avenue
Silver Spring, MD 20903-5640

ABSTRACT

The sensitivity, detonation properties, and performance of selected HMX based explosives are compared. All explosives were manufactured using a hydroxyl-terminated polybutadiene (HTPB) binder system. IRX class explosives were manufactured to obtain explosives in which ingredients were systematically varied. The particle size range of the HMX particles was controlled by sieving. Sensitivity and performance experiments were conducted using the explosives IRX-1, and IRX-3A. These experiments measured: detonation pressure, detonation velocity, modified gap test shock sensitivity, and detonation wave curvature. Modified gap tests were also performed for SW-21 and PBXN-110. In addition, light gas gun experiments were performed in which reactive stress-time profiles were obtained for IRX-1 and PBXN-110.

INTRODUCTION

The Navy has an effort to develop composite explosives which encompass the simple formulation of a nitramine ingredient and HTPB to multi-component mixtures. Some of these explosives contain nitramine ingredients (RDX/HMX) and a fuel [aluminum (Al)]. Other explosives contain an explosive particle, a fuel, and an oxidizer [ammonium perchlorate (AP)]. To better understand the behavior of these composite explosives, we have undertaken a program to study the role of the above ingredients in explosive shock sensitivity, performance and detonation wave propagation. Shock sensitivity, performance and detonation property measurements are being made on three research explosives that contain different amounts of AP, HMX, Al, and HTPB binder. This approach is similar to previous studies.[1,2,3,4,5] Explosive properties are known to be affected by the amount of each ingredient and by each ingredients morphology. In particular, particle size,[3,4,5,6] particle shape,[7] and defect concentrations[8] alter the sensitivity of explosive crystals. Therefore, the distribution of ingredient particle sizes were controlled in these research explosives to reduce the number of variables affecting the explosive properties.

This paper is a summary paper, results of this study are further discussed in two existing publications[9,10] and will be discussed in two future publications.

MANUFACTURE OF EXPLOSIVES

The compositions of the research explosives[11] IRX-1, IRX-3A, and IRX-4 along with the SW-21 are listed in Table 1. The compositions are given in volume percentage to aid in subsequent comparisons of different compositions. IRX-1 was formulated to be an HMX analog to a composition studied by Moulard et al.[3] To assure uniformity in HMX particle morphology, the HMX was sieved from the same batch and lot for all experiments except the modified gap tests (MGTs). For the MGT, sieved HMX from a different batch and lot was used. HMX particle size distributions indicate particle sizes were between 60-210 μm. An average HMX diameter by volume of 142 μm was obtained from a particle size analysis.[11] The nominal particle size of the aluminum was 5 μm and the AP was 200 μm. These AP and Al particle sizes are used in many Navy composite explosives.

Two existing explosives were included in this study. PBXN-110 (PBXW-113)[12] is a bimodal mixture of Class 2 and Class 3 HMX particles. The loading is higher than the other explosives tested. No HMX particle size analysis was obtained for the PBXN-110 or the SW-21. There are specifications on the median particle size by weight for various classes of HMX.[12] For Class 5 HMX the median particle size (by weight) is under 15 μm; for Class 2 HMX, the median particle size is under 23 μm; for Class 3 HMX the median particle size is between 265 and 600 μm.

Table 1. Composition in volume percent of HMX based explosives.

Ingredient	SW-21	IRX-1	IRX-3A	IRX-4
Sieved HMX (60-210μm)		52.8	58.5	23.6
Very Fine HMX (Class 5)	58.3			
Aluminum (5μm)			5.9	8.9
AP (200μm)				18.4
HTPB Binder	41.7	47.2	35.6	49.2

SENSITIVITY EXPERIMENTS

Light Gas Gun Experiments

In the light gas gun experiments (see Figure 1), the explosive targets were impacted by flat ended projectiles. Gauges at various depths in the target measure stress as a function of time. The stress-time profiles are used to calibrate reactive rate models when reactive stress growth is observed in the results. In some experiments, the explosive behind the second gauge was replaced by a Teflon disk (backer).

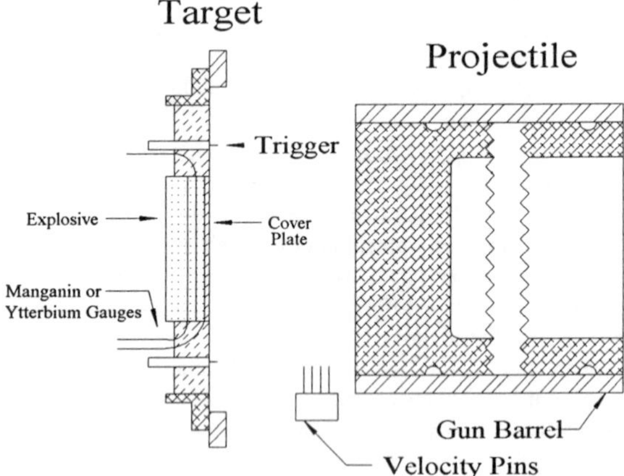

Figure 1. Schematic view of a Light Gas Gun Experiment.

Figures 2 and 3 show stress-time profiles for the explosives IRX-1 and PBXN-110 for impact velocities of 0.91 and 0.93 mm/μsec, respectively. Additional experiments have been performed at lower impact velocities for both explosives. Shown in Figure 3 is a simulation of the experiment using the Lee-Tarver reaction rate model.[10] Reactive stress growth at the shock front is observed for both explosives. This is in agreement with experiments by Simpson et al.[5] for course HMX/water compositions. The

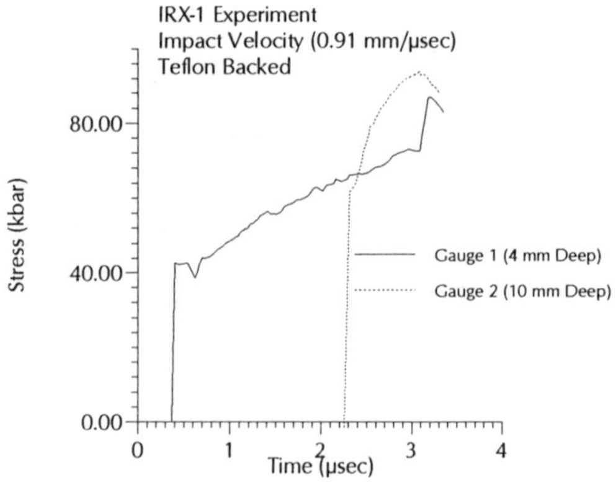

Figure 2. IRX-1 Stress-Time Profiles from a Light Gas Gun Experiment.

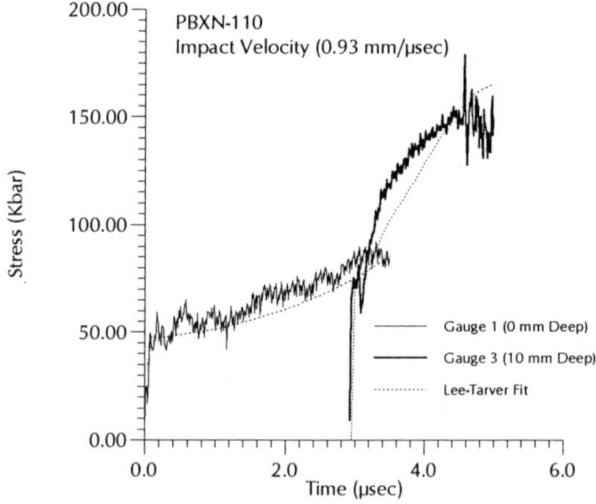

Figure 3. PBXN-110 Experimental Stress-Time Profiles from a Light Gas Gun Experiment.

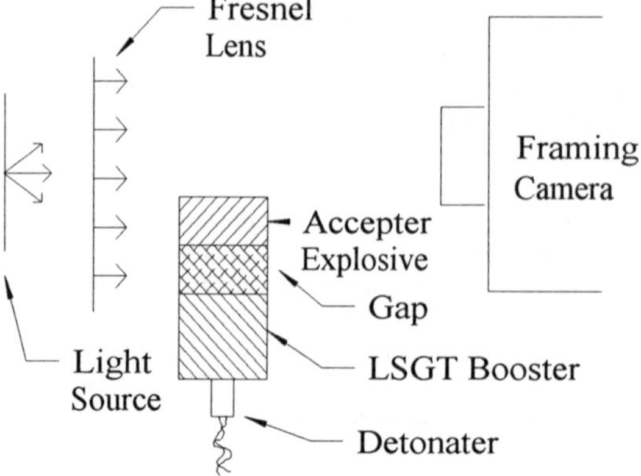

Figure 4. Schematic view of the MGT.

PBXN-110 has more reactive stress growth after the shock front than does IRX-1. This is expected because PBXN-110 has both a higher total volume percentage of HMX and a higher volume percentage of coarse HMX than does IRX-1.

Modified Gap Test

The MGT[13,14] is a useful screening test for comparing the sensitivity trends of different explosives. The MGT is schematically shown in Figure 4. The MGT measures the surface velocity of an explosive pellet. The difference between the measured and the calculated surface velocity (U_a - U_a^*) is plotted against the pressure (P_e) in the explosive for each experiment. The plots for IRX-1, IRX-3A, SW-21, and PBXN-110 are given in Figure 5.

For explosives made up of coarse particles (PBXN-110, IRX-1, IRX-3A) there is a roughly linear increase in final surface velocity with input pressure from 25 to 50 Kbar. For the explosive with fine particles (SW-21), there is a region which appears to show no increase in surface velocity for input pressures between 30-42 Kbar. Comparison of the curves of IRX-1 and SW-21 in Figure 5 shows that for an input pressure between 35 and 50 kbar, IRX-1 produces more reactive final surface velocity. This occurs even though IRX-1 has a lower HMX loading than SW-21. This implies that very fine HMX particles produce less reaction than coarse particles for this pressure range. SW-21 has a larger surface velocities than PBXN-110 for pressures between 52 and 60 Kbar. This implies that the small HMX particles result in more reaction than coarse particles for these input pressures. Comparison of the curves for IRX-1 and IRX-3A in Figure 5 may show some indications of an increase in surface velocity due to the aluminum in IRX-3A for a pressure of about 40 kbar. This indication should be checked by comparing existing IRX-1 experiments with planned IRX-3A gun experiments. The surface velocity curves in Figure 5 suggests similar particle size dependent sensitivity as found by Moulard et al[3-4] for RDX and Simpson et al.[5] for HMX.

In the MGT, the surface velocity is measured for tens of μsecs. Therefore, the details of how reactive stress growth occurs behind the shock front cannot be obtained from these experiments. To better understand the reactive contributions to the measured MGT surface velocities, the MGT will be modeled with a 2-D hydrocode.

PERFORMANCE AND DETONATION PROPERTY EXPERIMENTS

Detonation pressure (P_{cj}),[15] detonation velocity (D),[16] failure diameter,[16] and detonation wave curvature[16] experiments were conducted on IRX-1 and IRX-3A. Results from these experiments are listed in Table 2. The wave curvature experiments consisted of measuring the breakout of a detonation wave at the end of a long

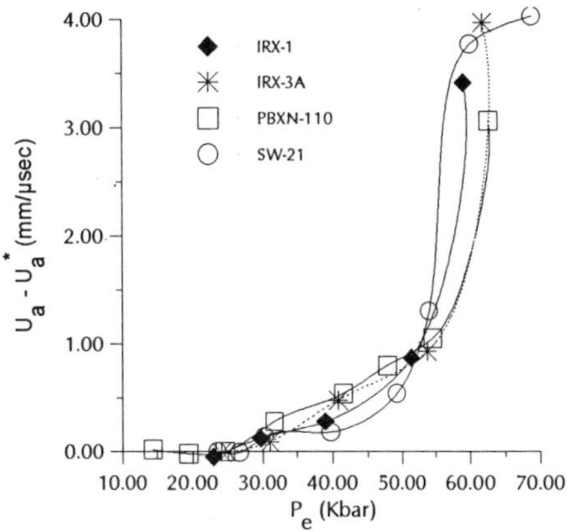

Figure 5. MGT Reactive Surface Velocity vs. Pressure for IRX-1, IRX-3A, PBXN-110 and SW-21.

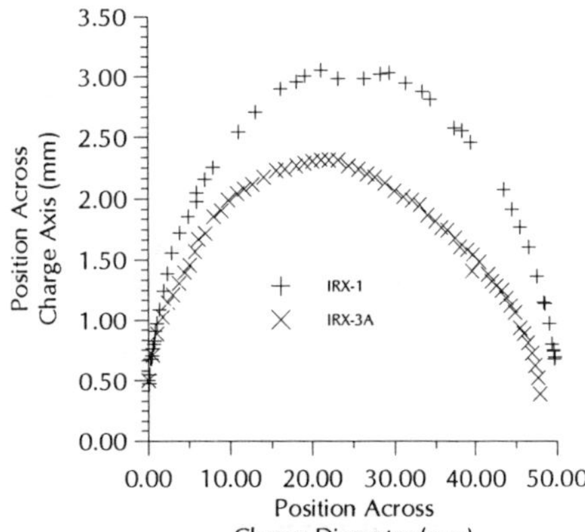

Figure 6. Wave Front Curvature Data from IRX-1 and IRX-3A Experiments.

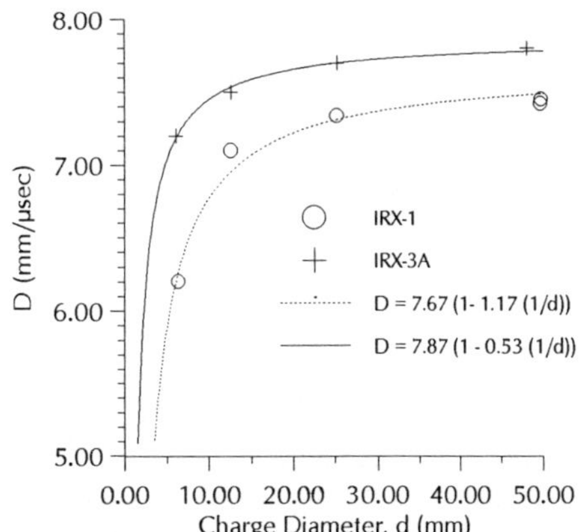

Figure 7. The Detonation Velocity (D) vs. the Charge Diameter (d) for IRX-1 and IRX-3A.

cylindrical explosive charge. Curvature data for IRX-1 and IRX-3A are given in Figure 6.

Table 2. Measured and calculated performance measurements on HMX based explosives.

Exp.	Meas. Pcj (Kbar)	Meas. D (mm/µsec)	Failure Diameter (mm)	Reaction Zone Thickness (mm)
IRX-1	200	7.67	4.95-6.20	1.16
IRX-3A	228	7.87	<6.13	0.61

The Wood-Kirkwood theory[17] was used to obtain the reaction zone thickness from the wave curvature and detonation velocity measurements. Figure 7 shows the relationship between detonation velocity (D) and charge diameter (d) for IRX-1, and IRX-3A. The results were fitted with the Eyring form[18] for velocity decrement ($D = D(\infty)\ (1 - k\ (1/d))$).

Results from the detonation velocity and detonation pressure experiments indicate that the detonation velocity and pressure can be expressed as a function of the volume loading of the HMX.[9]

Detonation velocity measurements of Figure 7 indicate that the critical diameter for IRX-3A is smaller than that for IRX-1. The smaller reaction zone thickness for IRX-3A as compared with IRX-1 is likely due to the higher HMX loading of IRX-3A. The wave curvature profiles provide useful data for investigators developing curved wave front theories.

ACKNOWLEDGEMENTS

This work was performed for the Independent Research Project at the Naval Surface Warfare Center and the Office of Naval Research (Technology Directorate) through the Explosive and Undersea Warheads Block Program. The authors thank R. Doherty, C. Dickinson, R. Bernecker, J. Leahy, C. Gotzmer, T. Fillman, V. Ringbloom, S. Prickett, L. Burke, and J. Kury (LLNL) for valuable suggestions. J. O'Connor, H. Dobbs, and A. Brown are thanked for assisting in the experiments.

REFERENCES

[1] M. Finger, H.C. Horning, E.L. Lee and J..W. Kury, in *Proceedings of the Fifth Symposium on Detonation*, Pasadena, CA, Aug, 1970, pp. 137-194.

[2] B. Chunhua and D. Jing, in *Proceedings of the Ninth Symposium (International) on Detonation*, Portland, OR, Aug 1989, pp. 879-885.

[3] H. Moulard, J.W. Kury, and A. Delchos, in *Proceedings of the Eighth Symposium (International) on Detonation*, Albuquerque, NM, July 1985, pp 902-914.

[4] H. Moulard, in *Proceedings of the Ninth Symposium (International) on Detonation*, Portland, OR, Aug 1989, pp. 18-24.

[5] R.L Simpson. F.H. Helm, P.C. Crawford, and J.W. Kury, in *Proceedings of the Ninth Symposium (International) on Detonation*, Portland, OR, Aug 1989, pp. 25-38.

[6] R.R. Bernecker, in *Shock Compression of Condensed Matter 1991*, S.C. Schmidt, R.D. Dick, J.W. Forbes, D.G. Tasker (editors), 1992 Elsevier Science Publishers B.V., pp. 695-698.

[7] A.C. van der Steen, J.J. Verbeek, and J.J. Meulenbrugge, in *Proceedings of the Ninth Symposium (International) on Detonation*, Portland, OR, Aug 1989, pp. 83-88.

[8] B.C. Beard and H.W. Sandusky, Identification of a Microstructural Mechanism for Variation in Explosive Sensitivity, NAVSWC DD MP 92-452, pp. 6-3 - 6-4.

[9] G.T. Sutherland, E.R. Lemar, J.W. Forbes, E. Anderson, K.D. Ashwell, and R.N. Baker, in *Proceedings of the JANNAF Propulsion Systems Hazards Subcommittee Meeting*, May 11-13, 1993, Fort Lewis, WA.

[10] P.J. Miller and G.T. Sutherland, in *Proceedings of the JANNAF Propulsion Systems Hazards Subcommittee Meeting*, May 11-13, 1993, Fort Lewis. WA.

[11] G. T. Sutherland, L. Burke, J. Leahy, S. Prickett, and S. Deiter, *Composition Choice and Formulation of Three HMX Based Research Explosives*, to be submitted to the Journal of Energetic Materials.

[12] E.W. Anderson, Explosive Performance of PBXW-113 and PBXW-114, NSWC TR 86-518, 1 July 1988.

[13] T.P. Liddiard, J.W. Forbes and D. Price, in *Proceedings of the Ninth Symposium (International) on Detonation*, Portland, OR, Aug 1989, pp. 1235-1242.

[14] E.R. Lemar, T.P Liddiard, J.W. Forbes, G.T. Sutherland, and W.H. Wilson, , NAVSWC TR 89-290, 1993).

[15] N.L. Coleburn, NOLTR 64-58, 25 June 1964.

[16] J.W. Forbes, E.R. Lemar, and R.N. Baker, in Proceedings of the Ninth Symposium on Detonation, Portland, OR, Aug 1989, pp. 806-815.

[17] W.W. Wood and J.G. Kirkwood, J. Chem. Physics, **22**, Nov 1954, pp. 1920-1924.

[18] H. Eyring, R.E. Powell, G.H. Duffy, and R.B. Parlin, Chem Rev. **45**, p. 1949.

EFFECTS OF LATE CHEMICAL REACTIONS ON THE ENERGY PARTITION IN NON-IDEAL UNDERWATER EXPLOSIONS

Philip J. Miller and Raafat H. Guirguis
Naval Surface Warfare Center, White Oak
10903 New Hampshire Avenue
Silver Spring, MD 20903-5640

The bubble oscillation and the pressure pulse induced in the water due to the underwater detonation of non-ideal explosives are calculated. In non-ideal explosives, a substantial amount of energy could be released after the Chapman-Jouguet surface, often after the bubble has expanded a few times the original charge size. The calculations were performed using a modified version of DYNA2D hydrocode in which a time-dependent Jones-Wilkins-Lee equation of state was introduced in order to account for this late energy release. The effect of delaying the energy release on how the explosive chemical energy is partitioned between water and bubble is obtained.

INTRODUCTION

The chemical energy released when an explosive charge is detonated underwater is generally distributed between the explosive products and the surrounding water [1]. In ideal explosives, most of the energy is released in a narrow reaction zone. The fraction of energy deposited in the water and the resulting hydrodynamic motion are mostly affected by the equation of state (EOS) of the detonation products. But new underwater explosives are non-ideal, formulated such as to release a substantial amount of their chemical energy late in the explosion process, after the Chapman-Jouguet (CJ) surface, and even after the bubble has expanded a few times the original charge size. Determining how delaying the energy release affects the energy distribution, and the flow in the surrounding water, is the subject of this paper.

For simplicity, let us consider a bare spherical explosive charge, initiated underwater at the center and consumed by a constant velocity detonation wave. Let us assume that there are no reflecting boundaries or obstacles in the vicinity of the charge, commonly known as a free-field condition. For example, when the charge is deep enough, the water-surface does not affect the behavior of the bubble significantly. Let us further ignore the effects of the vertical gradient in hydrostatic water pressure caused by gravity, responsible for the migration of the bubble upward and sometimes formation of a water jet if the bubble collapses, i.e., let us assume that the undisturbed (ambient) water is at uniform pressure. In practice, this condition is satisfied if the size of the bubble is much smaller than the depth. These conditions yield a spherically symmetric bubble and hydrodynamic flow. We can still admit ambient water pressures higher than atmospheric, in order to take into account the other effects of depth.

When the detonation wave reaches the surface of the explosive charge, it sends a shock wave into the water and rarefaction waves back into the exlosive products. Because the pressure decreases behind the CJ plane, the initial jump in the interface velocity quickly slows down, thus sending rarefaction waves forward into the water, as illustrated in Fig. 1. The pressure pulse observed in the water at a given point in space always exhibits a decaying profile with time, after the initial rise caused by the arrival of the shock, because of these rarefaction waves. They also weaken the shock until it eventually becomes a sound wave. From there on, the water behaves as an incompressible fluid, until the bubble collapses back to a minimum radius, where in its vicinity, the water becomes compressible again.

Because of the inertia the water acquires during bubble expansion, the bubble over-expands to pressures smaller than the ambient pressure of the surrounding water. The higher pressure outside eventually reverses the flow, the bubble starts collapsing, the pressure inside the bubble increases beyond the ambient water pressure, the bubble reverses its motion and starts expanding again, and so on. After a few oscillations, most of the energy is dissipated in heating the water. If buyoancy is included, the bubble migrates to the surface and vents, convecting its remaining energy into the atmosphere.

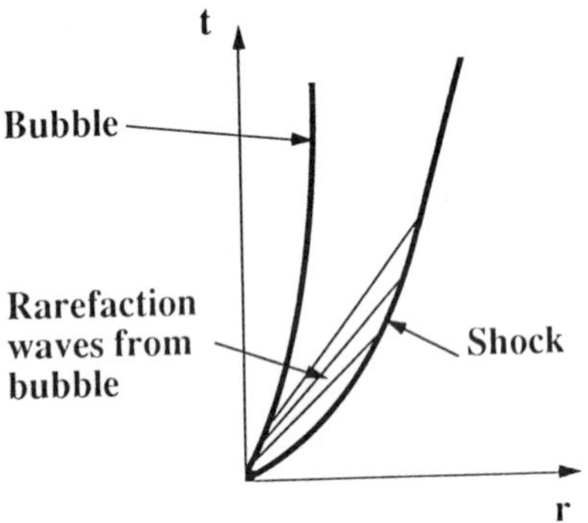

Figure 1. Early expansion of bubble.

The chemical energy of the explosive is divided between the water and detonation products. The energy is stored in the water in the form of internal and kinetic energies. The shock compresses the water and increases its internal energy. Some of this energy, manifested as increase in pressure, is useful. However, the shock also heats the water, and that is wasted energy. The turbulence created in the water, especially at the interface with the bubble during the collapse process, as well as heat transfer from the hot detonation products to the colder water, also add to the energy wasted in heating the water. But some of this heat evaporates the water near the interface, adding to the mass of gases inside the bubble, making it bigger, and contributing to the useful energy.

The energy stored in the products is in the form of internal and kinetic energies, in addition to the potential energy of the whole bubble as a system. The potential energy is the energy used to statically displace the water outwards against the ambient water pressure p_∞. It is equal to $p_\infty(V_b - V_b^o)$, where V_b is the volume of the bubble and V_b^o is the original charge size.

When the bubble reaches its maximum radius, the shock wave in the water is long gone, and the water behaves as an incompressible fluid. By definition, at the maximum radius, the radial velocity at the interface of the bubble is zero, and since the water behaves as incompressible fluid, the whole field of water is also stagnant. The kinetic energy of the water is zero. But the water near the bubble is hot, and since it is not compressed, its internal energy is just equal to the heat used to raise its temperature.

At the maximum radius, the detonation products are already over-expanded to low pressures. Their internal energy is small compared to the potential energy of the bubble. In principle, because they are compressible, the gases may be still moving inside the bubble when it reaches maximum radius, even though the radial velocity at the interface has to vanish. But after it expands, the bubble is nearly uniform, and the total kinetic energy of the gases inside is usually much smaller than the potential energy of the bubble.

Thus, when the bubble reaches its maximum radius, the distribution of energy is easily derived. The energy remaining in the bubble$\approx p_\infty(V_b^{max} - V_b^o) \approx p_\infty V_b^{max}$. The rest of the explosive energy is already wasted in heating the water. With each oscillation, more energy is lost in heating the water. In Cole's book [2], from measurements of the period of oscillation, 59% of the energy of a typical explosive is calculated wasted in heating the water at the first bubble maximum. In these calculations, it is assumed that the water is incompressible. As explained above, we can calculate the energy lost in the water by measuring the maximum bubble volume, without assuming that the water is incompressible throughout the whole cycle. But it is much easier to measure the time than the volume. Nevertheless, even if slighly exaggerated, 59% is large enough to make it worthwhile to try to reduce the fraction of energy wasted in heating the water by delaying the release of energy, such as to reduce the shock strength.

SIMILITUDE EQUATIONS

If the reaction time in the detonation wave consuming the underwater explosive is negligible compared to the other characteristic times of the problem, the underwater explosion problem can be scaled to the size of the charge, whether the water is considered compressible or not [3]. Assuming that the water behaves as incompressible fluid, one can easily derive similitude relations by solving the 1-D unsteady equations or by using dimensional analysis. For example, the period of oscillation τ

$$\tau = K_E \frac{\rho_o^{1/2} E^{1/3}}{p_\infty^{5/6}} = K_r \, r_{max} \frac{\rho_o^{1/2}}{p_\infty^{1/2}} \qquad (1)$$

where ρ_o is the water density, r_{max} the maximum bubble radius, and the constants K_E, K_r depend on the explosive. The second equality is obtained by equating the total energy remaining in the bubble E to $p_\infty V_b^{max}$. If the water is incompressible, and heat transfer is ignored, no energy can be wasted in heating it, and E is also the energy of the explosive. Although derived for incompressible surroundings, the similitude relation in Eq. 1 usually gives reasonable predictions, because the time-span during which the water behaves as a compressible fluid is small compared to the time of one oscillation. If the water is compressible, one can still formally derive similitude equations, but they will be more complicated than for incompressible.

NON-IDEAL EXPLOSIVES

Non-ideal explosives contain components which reaction times are comparable to hydrodynamic time scales. When detonated underwater, the detonation structure, the behavior of the bubble, and the flow properties of the surrounding water, all do not scale [3]. In addition, we cannot solve the problem without including the rate of late reactions, that release energy after the CJ surface, into the model. In the calculations presented below, a time-dependent JWL EOS, in which the late energy released λQ is added to the energy of the products, is used, where λ is the late reactions progress variable (at CJ, $\lambda \equiv 0$), and

$$\frac{d\lambda}{dt} = a \left(1 - \lambda\right)^{1/2} p^{1/6} \qquad (2)$$

The same CJ detonation pressure and velocity are used for all cases considered. The details of the derivation of the EOS of the products and the rate of late reactions are given in references 4 and 5. The EOS of the water takes its compressibility into account.

RESULTS

Figures 2 and 3 show the effects of delaying the release of the explosive energy. In Fig. 2a, two different values of the reaction rate parameter a in Eq. 2 were used. The value of a for the faster rate is 25 times larger than that for the slower one. At all three locations where the pressure pulse was sampled, the faster rate resulted in a stronger shock. In Fig. 2b, the slower rate yields a faster decay of the shock/peak pressure. As we go farther from the bubble, however, the pressure decay behind the shock seems to be slower when the rate of late energy release is reduced.

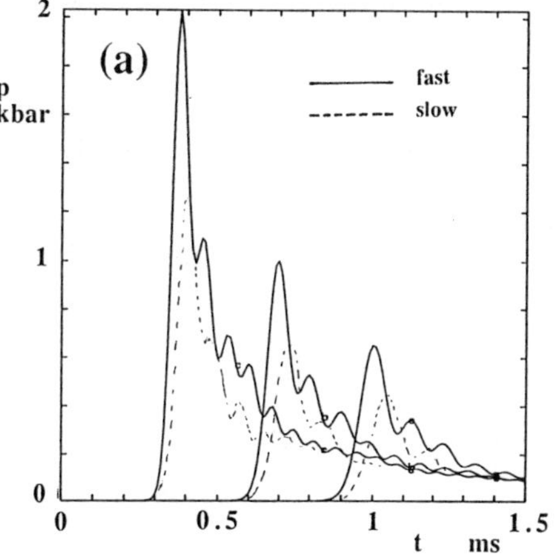

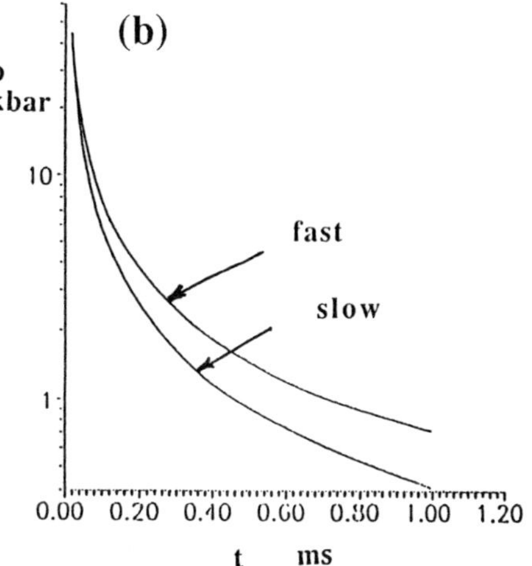

Figure 2. Pressure in water for two different rates; (a) pressure pulses; (b) peak pressures.

As indicated above in Fig. 1, the shock wave in the water decays as the rarefaction waves that emanate from the interface with the bubble reach it. These rarefaction waves are produced because the initial radial velocity at the bubble interface quickly decreases. The faster energy release keeps the pressure during the early expansion of the bubble higher, causing a slower decay in the bubble expansion velocity, thus yielding weaker rarefaction waves, and, in turn, a slower decay of the shock. But the stronger shock also increases the energy lost in heating the water.

In Fig. 3, the bubble oscillation is displayed for the same two values of the reaction parameter a in Fig. 2, as well as for an intermediate value, 5 times that of the slower rate. The slower energy release results in a longer period of oscillation and a larger bubble. As explained above, at each bubble maximum, the sum of the energy remaining in the bubble and that wasted in heating the water equals the total chemical energy released. More energy remains in the bubble when the energy release is slowed down, because less energy is wasted in heating the water. It is worth noticing that in each case, the late reactions, releasing energy after the CJ plane, were finished before the maximum bubble radius was reached.

DISCUSSION AND CONCLUSIONS

In all the calculations presented above, the CJ detonation pressure and velocity were kept the same. The early reactions, reponsible for sustaining the detonation wave itself are not modeled here.

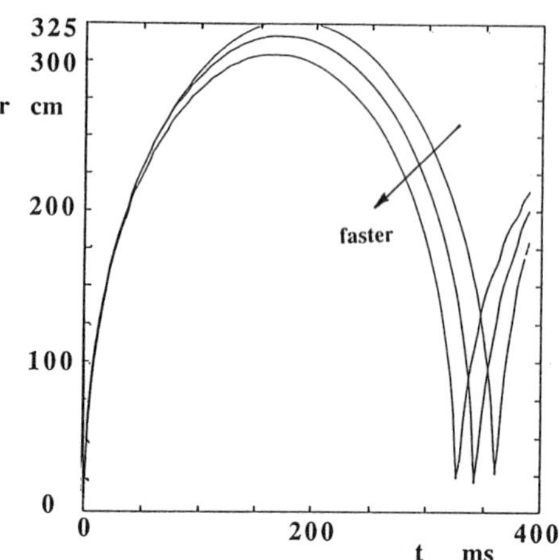

Figure 3. Bubble oscillation.

Only the effects of the late energy, released after the CJ surface, are investigated. In this case, the results indicate that the slower the late energy release, the faster the decay of the peak pressure of the pulse induced in the water. However, because the weaker the shock, the less energy is wasted in heating the water, the energy remaining in the bubble is larger, the slower the rate of late energy release. As a result, the bubble reaches a larger maximum size after expansion and the period of oscillation is lengthened for the same total energy released.

It is common practice to compare the energy of a test explosive to that of a standard explosive by comparing the periods of oscillation of these explosives. From Eq. 1, one can derive a relative bubble energy (RBE) for a test explosive as RBE ≡ $(k_{test} / k_{standard})^3$, where

$$k = \tau \frac{(\text{Depth} + 33\text{ ft})^{5/6}}{\text{Weight}^{1/3}}$$

But the RBE should be only considered a measure of how well the explosive produces a bubble, and not a measure of the energy released by that explosive, because as obvious from Fig. 3, the same total amount of energy can produce different periods of oscillation, depending on the rate of release of the late energy.

ACKNOWLEDGEMENTS

This work was supported by the Office of Naval Research, Code 3322.

REFERENCES

[1] A. B. Arons and D. R. Yennie, *Reviews of Modern Physics*, 20, 3, 519 (1948).

[2] R. H. Cole, *Underwater Explosions* (Princeton University Press, Princeton, New Jersey, 1948).

[3] R. H. Guirguis, "Modeling the Late Reactions in Aluminized Underwater Explosives," Proceedings of 1992 JANNAF PSHS meeting, (CPIA, Columbia, Maryland, 1993).

[4] P. J. Miller and R. H. Guirguis, "Experimental Study and Model Calculations of Metal Combustion in Al/AP Underwater Explosives," Proceedings of 1992 MRS meeting (MRS, Pittsburgh, Pennsylvania, 1993), vol. 296, pp. 299-303.

[5] R. H. Guirguis and P. J. Miller, "Time-Dependent Equations of State for Aluminized Underwater Explosives," Tenth Symposium (International) on Detonation, 1993 (NSWC, White Oak, Maryland, 1994).

AN INVESTIGATION OF THE RESPONSE OF SECONDARY EXPLOSIVES TO CONICAL-TIPPED PROJECTILES AND OBLIQUE IMPACTS

M D Cook, P J Haskins
DRA, Fort Halstead, Sevenoaks, Kent TN14 7BP, UK
&
H R James
AWE, Foulness, Essex SS3 9XE, UK

In this paper new results are reported for conical-tipped impacts onto covered RDX/TNT (59.5:39.5 + 1% beeswax), and the similarities between these results and those from earlier work on PE4 (RDX/grease, 88:12) are discussed. In addition a connection is made between the initiation thresholds for conical-tipped projectiles and flat-nosed rods impacting obliquely on bare explosive. Empirical relationships are established which describe the effects of both barrier thickness and impact angle on the initiation thresholds.

INTRODUCTION

In a previous paper [1] we described the results of a systematic study of the effect of projectile geometry on initiation thresholds for PE4 explosive. We interpreted the results of these experiments in terms of a divergent shock initiation mechanism. In the present paper we build upon the results of the previous work in two main respects. Firstly, we present new data for conical-tipped projectile impacts onto covered RDX/TNT, and compare these results with those for PE4. A simple empirical relationship is established which describes the effects of barrier thickness, for a fixed cone angle, on the initiation thresholds for both explosives. Secondly, by examining data for bare explosives impacted by conical-tipped projectiles and obliquely by flat-ended rods a connection is made between these data sets, and an empirical relationship established to describe the effect of the impact angle.

EXPERIMENTAL

The new experimental results reported here were performed using cylindrical (100mm long, 57mm diameter) cast RDX/TNT charges which were housed in a 9mm thick steel casing, open at one end. The charges were impacted on the flat open end, which was either left bare or covered by an aluminium barrier plate. The projectiles were 13.15mm diameter steel rods with various conical tips but of constant mass (27g). The projectiles were housed in a nylon sabot and fired from a 30mm RARDEN gun, with which it was possible to achieve velocities up to ca. 2000m/s. The projectile flight and impact were filmed using a Fastax camera fitted with a quarter height block and framing at ca. 30,000 fps. The film records were used to measure impact velocity, and as a check on projectile stability.

In a separate series of experiments, steel flat-nosed rods (13.15mm diameter) were impacted onto RDX/TNT charges. In these experiments the charge was inclined to the line of flight of the projectile, allowing an oblique impact at the charge surface. Charge dimensions were 93.5mm diameter by 141mm long; the explosive was cast into plastic piping designed to not give a shock reflection at the interface with the charge.

RESULTS

Conical-Tipped Projectile Impacts on Covered RDX/TNT

In figure 1 we show the detonation threshold curves for RDX/TNT covered by aluminium barrier plates. The results for flat-ended ($\Theta = 180^o$) and four conical-tipped ($\Theta = 165^o$, 150°, 135° and 120°) projectiles are shown, the error bars indicating the lowest velocity round which detonated and the highest velocity which did not. Projectiles with more acute cone angles failed to yield detonations at the maximum velocity obtainable with our gun.

The first thing to note about the data displayed in figure 1 is the strong similarity with that for PE4 reported in [1]. For the three most acutely tipped projectiles it can be seen that there is a near linear increase in threshold velocity with increasing barrier thickness. The different shape response curve for the flat-ended projectile has been described previously [1,2], and is believed to result from a 1-D shock mechanism operating for thin barriers, with a divergent shock process taking over for

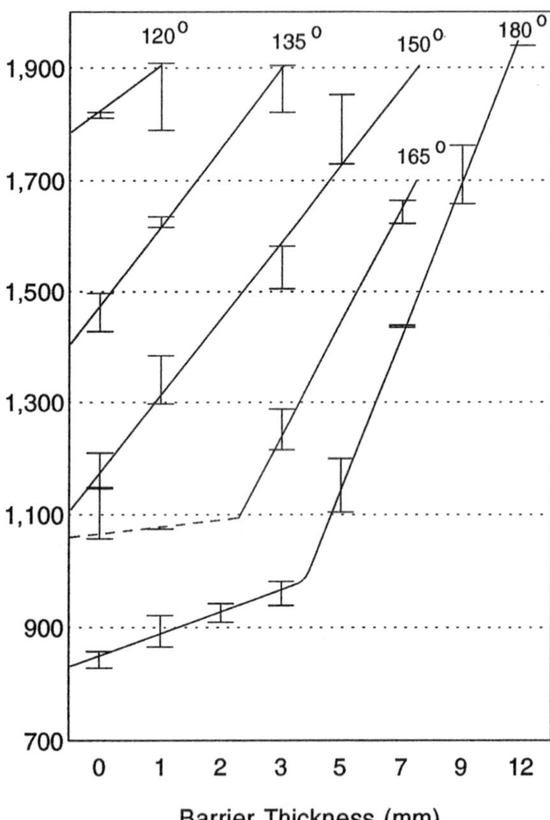

Figure 1. Detonation threshold curves for conical tipped impacts of RDX/TNT covered by aluminium barriers.

thicker barriers. Similar behaviour is shown by the 165° conical projectiles. This mechanistic transition occurs between 5 and 7mm for aluminium barriers.

Empirical Formula for Barrier Effects

As discussed above there appears, for the conical-tipped projectiles, to be an approximately linear dependence of threshold velocity with barrier thickness for both RDX/TNT and PE4. It is also noticeable that the slope of these response lines does not appear to depend on the cone angle or the target explosive. Naturally there are slight differences in overall sensitivity between the two explosives, but by dividing the critical velocity for a given cone angle and barrier ($Vc\{\Theta,d\}$) by that for a bare charge impacted by the same angle cone ($Vc\{\Theta,0\}$) it is possible to normalise the results and compare the two data sets. Following such a normalisation, linear regression analysis yields:

$$V(\Theta,d)/V(\Theta,0) = 0.998 + C.d \qquad (1)$$

where d is the aluminium barrier thickness in millimetres, and the constant C has the value 0.0768 for PE4 and 0.0753 for RDX/TNT. The extremely close agreement suggests that the data sets can be combined to give a general relationship of this form with C = 0.076. Whilst it is to be hoped that this relationship will hold reasonably well for a wide range of explosives it is highly likely that the constant C will depend markedly on the projectile and barrier material.

Oblique Impacts on RDX/TNT

The critical velocity was determined, for most of the impact angles (ϕ), by ten or more firings. These results are summarised in Table 1.

Table 1. Critical Velocities for Oblique Impact Experiments

ϕ^o	V_{crit} (m/s)
0	945 - 975
5	923 - 1027
10	1093 - 1104
15	1110 - 1149
20	1250 - 1261

Oblique and Conical-Tipped Results for Bare Explosives

In this section we analyse the dependence of critical velocities on the impact angle, for both conical projectiles and for flat-ended rods striking the target at an oblique angle. Data for impacts on bare charges has been collected from a number of sources and is displayed in figure 2. For clarity the threshold velocities are shown without error bars in this figure. We have again normalised the data, this time by dividing the critical velocity ($V\{\phi,0\}$) for a given impact angle by that for a normal impact from a flat rod of the same diameter ($V\{0,0\}$). The impact angle (ϕ) is defined here as the deviation from a normal impact; for cones this is related to the internal angle of the cone tip (Θ)

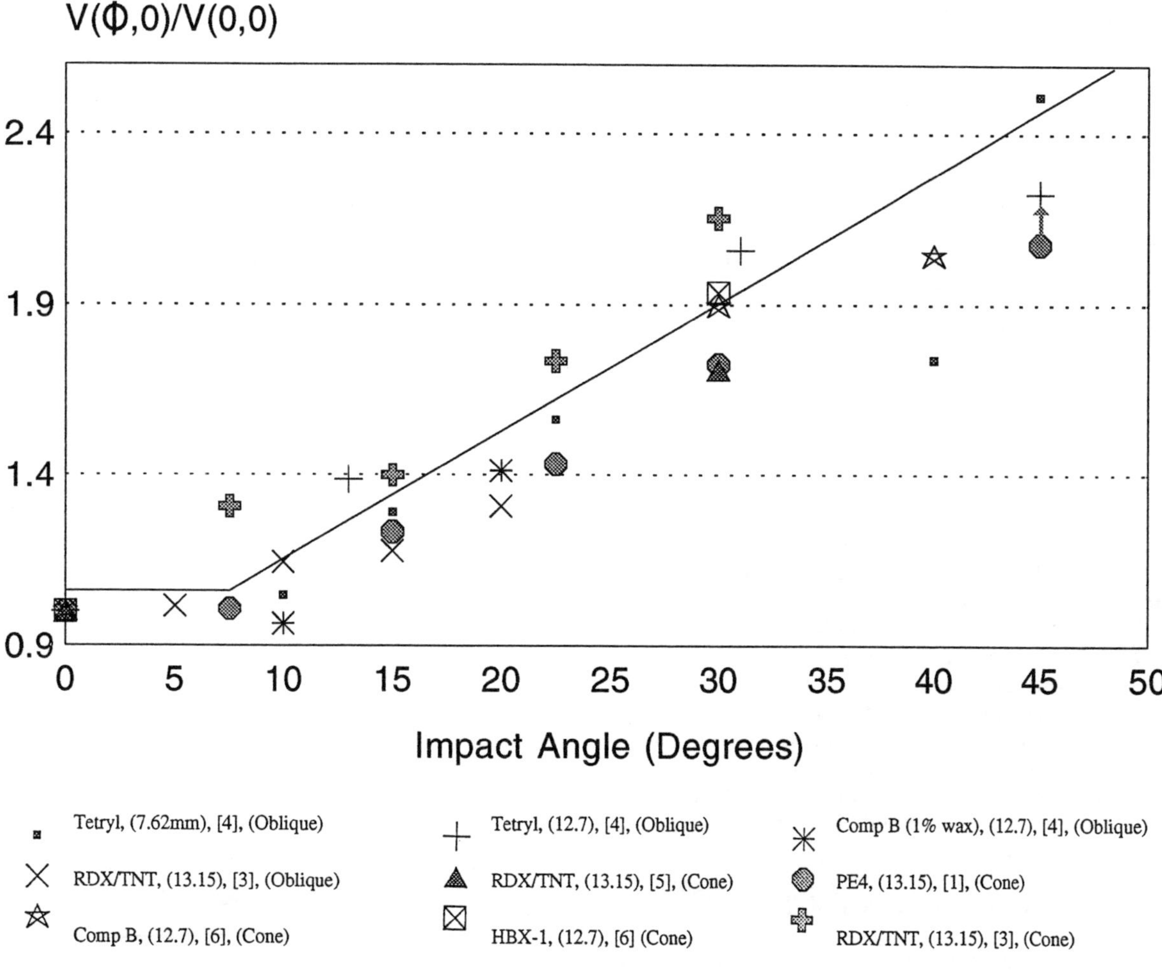

Figure 2. Threshold velocities for oblique and conical impacts of bare charges. {Projectile diameter in mm shown in ( ); references shown in [ ]}

by:

$$\phi = 90 - \Theta/2 \qquad (2)$$

Examination of figure 2 shows that for both conical projectiles and oblique impacts there appears to be an almost constant response threshold out to impact angles of ca. 10°. For impact angles greater than this there is an approximately linear increase in critical velocity with angle. All projectiles were either steel or brass.

Empirical Formula for Impact Angle Effects

For ϕ greater than 7.5^o it is possible to obtain a good linear fit to the data for both oblique and conical impacts. Linear regression analysis of the data yields:

$$V(\phi,0)/V(0,0) = A + B.\phi \qquad (3)$$

where for the oblique impacts A = 0.771 and B = 0.0325, and for the conical projectiles A = 0.860 and B = 0.0327. Considering the relatively small data sets available the closeness of these figures suggests that the conical and oblique results are, as might be expected, from the same population.

It is now possible to combine equations 1 and 3 to give the dependence of the threshold velocity on both impact angle and barrier thickness. Thus for the impact of steel cones onto aluminium barriers we have:

$$V(\phi,d) = V(0,0).[0.86 + 0.0327.\phi].[1 + 0.076.d] \quad (4)$$

This relationship enables the effect of barrier thickness and cone angle (for $\phi > 7.5^o$) to be predicted from a single determination of V(0,0) (the critical velocity for a bare impact with a flat-ended rod), which can in turn be predicted from a knowledge of the critical energy [2].

CONCLUSIONS

We have shown that there is a simple linear dependence of threshold velocity on barrier thickness for impacts by conical-tipped projectiles. In addition we have demonstrated a simple linear dependence of the threshold velocity on impact angle (above 7.5^o) for both conical-tipped projectiles and oblique impacts. By normalising this data with respect to the explosive we have obtained simple empirical relationships to describe the effects of barrier thickness and impact angle on initiation thresholds. For a given projectile and barrier material these relationships should enable approximate predictions of threshold velocities to be made from a single threshold velocity or critical energy.

ACKNOWLEDGEMENT

The authors wish to acknowledge the careful work performed by Mr D Hewitt, of AWE Foulness, in carrying out the oblique impact series of experiments.

REFERENCES

[1] M. D. Cook, P. J. Haskins and H. R. James, "An Investigation of Projectile and Barrier Geometry Effects on Impact Initiation of a Secondary Explosive", in *Proceedings of the American Physical Society Topical Conference on Shock Compression of Condensed Matter*, North Holland, 1991, pp. 675.

[2] M. D. Cook, P. J. Haskins and H. R. James, "Projectile Impact Initiation of Explosive Charges", in *Proceedings of the Ninth Symposium (International) on Detonation, Portland Oregon, USA,* 1989, pp 1441.

[3] This paper.

[4] D. C. Slade and J Dewey, "High Order Initiation of Two Military Explosives by Projectile Impact", *Ballistic Research Laboratory Report* No. 1021, July 1957.

[5] D Hewitt, Private Communication, 1988.

[6] T. P. Liddard, L. A. Roslund and J. W. Watt, "Destruction of On-Deck Torpedoes by Fragments from G P Bombs", *NSWC Report* WOL/TR 76-138, 1977.

CHAPTER XVIII

BIOLOGY

HIGH PRESSURE NMR STUDIES OF PROTEINS AND MEMBRANES

Jiri Jonas
Department of Chemistry
University of Illinois
600 South Mathews
Urbana, Illinois 61801

Advanced high resolution NMR spectroscopy, including two-dimensional NMR techniques, combined with the high pressure capability represents a powerful new tool in studies of proteins and membranes. Selected results taken from recent studies illustrate the high information content and the range of problems that can be investigated. Three specific studies dealing with proteins are mentioned: pressure-induced reversible unfolding of lysozyme; investigation of conformation of the pressure-dissociated monomer of Arc repressor, and cold denaturation of several proteins performed at high pressure by taking advantage of the phase diagram of water. A brief overview of the recent multinuclear NMR studies of 1,2-dipalmitoyl-sn-glycero-3-phosphocholine (DPPC) multilamellar aqueous dispersions and sonicated vesicles and DPPC bilayers containing the charged form of local anesthetic tetracaine (TTC) shows the type of unique information that can be obtained from high pressure NMR studies of model membranes.

INTRODUCTION

Both the progress in experimental techniques and the new developments in theoretical methods allow one to investigate complex problems, including biological systems. The use of pressure as an experimental variable in studies of biochemical systems has a distinct advantage, as it does not change the energy of the system nor its chemical composition. In recent years, one has witnessed a major increase in the number of high pressure studies of biochemical systems, and one may conclude that high pressure biochemistry [1,2] and biotechnology [3,4] have become well-established fields with great promise for the future. A recent NATO ASI on "High Pressure Chemistry, Biochemistry, and Materials Science" [2] has illustrated well this important development [5-13]. The large majority of nuclear magnetic resonance (NMR) applications to biochemistry deal with liquid solutions in which the NMR lines are narrowed by motional averaging to a natural line width of the order of 0.1 Hz to 1 Hz. High resolution NMR spectra of complex biochemical molecules in aqueous solutions usually exhibit a great deal of structure, and yield a wealth of information about the structure and dynamics of the biomolecule. The experimental capability [14,15] of recording high resolution NMR spectra on dilute spin systems opened an exciting new direction of high pressure NMR spectroscopy dealing with pressure effects on biochemical systems.

In this contribution, I shall concentrate on the use of high resolution NMR techniques [15] to investigate proteins and membranes at high pressure. Several specific examples of our recent high pressure NMR studies [16-20] will illustrate the high and unique information content.

PRESSURE-INDUCED UNFOLDING OF LYSOZYME

It is well known that reversible denaturation (unfolding) of a protein in solution can be caused not only by an increase in temperature or by changes in the composition of the medium, but also by application of high pressure [21,22]. Several studies reported in the literature provided the main motivation for the recent work [16]. First of all, the high pressure fluorescence study of lysozyme and lysozyme with bound tri-N-acetylglucosamine (tri-NAG) by Weber and co-workers [23] represents the main reason why we have chosen to investigate lysozyme. Second, the pioneering study of Kundrot and Richards [24] determined the crystal structure of hen egg white lysozyme at a hydrostatic pressure of 1 kbar, and found a differential compressibility in the different regions of the protein. Third, Dobson and co-workers [25] investigated the thermal denaturation of lysozyme using high resolution NMR by following NMR signals for various residues located in different regions of the protein, and concluded that unfolding can be represented by a cooperative, two-state process.

In our study [16], we used high resolution NMR to follow the effect of pressure on the equilibrium constant for the native and denatured forms of lysozyme by observing the proton resonances of the following residues: His-15$^{\varepsilon 1}$, Leu-17$^{\delta 2}$, Trp-28$^{\varepsilon 3}$, Cys-64$^{\alpha}$ and Trp-108$^{\varepsilon 3}$. Since these residues lie in the regions for which Kundrot and Richards [24] determined different compressibilities, we were interested to find out whether these differences are also reflected in the determined reaction volumes (ΔV) for the individual residues. Dobson and co-workers [25] proposed that thermal denaturation of lysozyme is a cooperative, two-state process, since all the observed resonances belonging to different residues gave equivalent ΔH and ΔS values for the unfolding process. Therefore, the determination of ΔV's for the same residues may contribute to resolving the fundamental question of how similar or different is pressure denaturation compared to thermal denaturation.

The experiments were performed at pH 3.9 and 68.5°C, in the pressure range from 1 bar to 5 kbar, both in the absence and presence of tri-NAG. From the pressure-induced changes of the equilibrium between the native and denatured forms of lysozyme, the reaction volumes (ΔV) were calculated for each residue. Small, but statistically significant, differences in ΔV were found for residues located in different regions of the protein. For example, ΔV for the disulfide bonded Cys-64^{α} is smaller than the ΔV's found for the other residues. In particular, the effect of tri-NAG binding to lysozyme was a change of ΔV from -10.3 ± 0.6 cm^3/mol to -18.1 ± 1.7 cm^3/mol for the Trp-$108^{\varepsilon 3}$ residue, which is located close to the active site. It is important to note that the Cys-64^{α} residue also senses the binding of the substrate analog. The ability to detect statistically significant differences for ΔV of individual residues located in different regions of lysozyme represents the main result of these experiments.

COLD DENATURATION OF PROTEINS

As a basic experimental variable, high pressure can be utilized not only to perturb the protein structure in a controllable way, but also to lower the freezing point of the protein aqueous solution. Therefore, one can investigate the cold denaturation of proteins working at high pressures. In our current study [18], we took advantage of the high pressure phase diagram of water, and investigated the reversible cold denaturation of Ribonuclease-A by high resolution, high pressure NMR techniques [15]. The main goal of our experiments was to find out whether cold denaturation is a general process [26], and whether the structures of cold-denatured proteins are different from heat-denatured proteins and/or pressure-denatured proteins. Our results, as given in Fig. 1, show that at pressures of 3-5 kbar and temperatures of -10 to -22°C, Ribonuclease-A undergoes a reversible cold denaturation, and its one-dimensional ^{1}H NMR spectrum resembles the pressure-denatured form, but it is different from the heat-denatured form obtained both at ambient pressure and at high pressure. A detailed, conformational characterization of these various denatured states is in progress using two-dimensional NMR techniques [18].

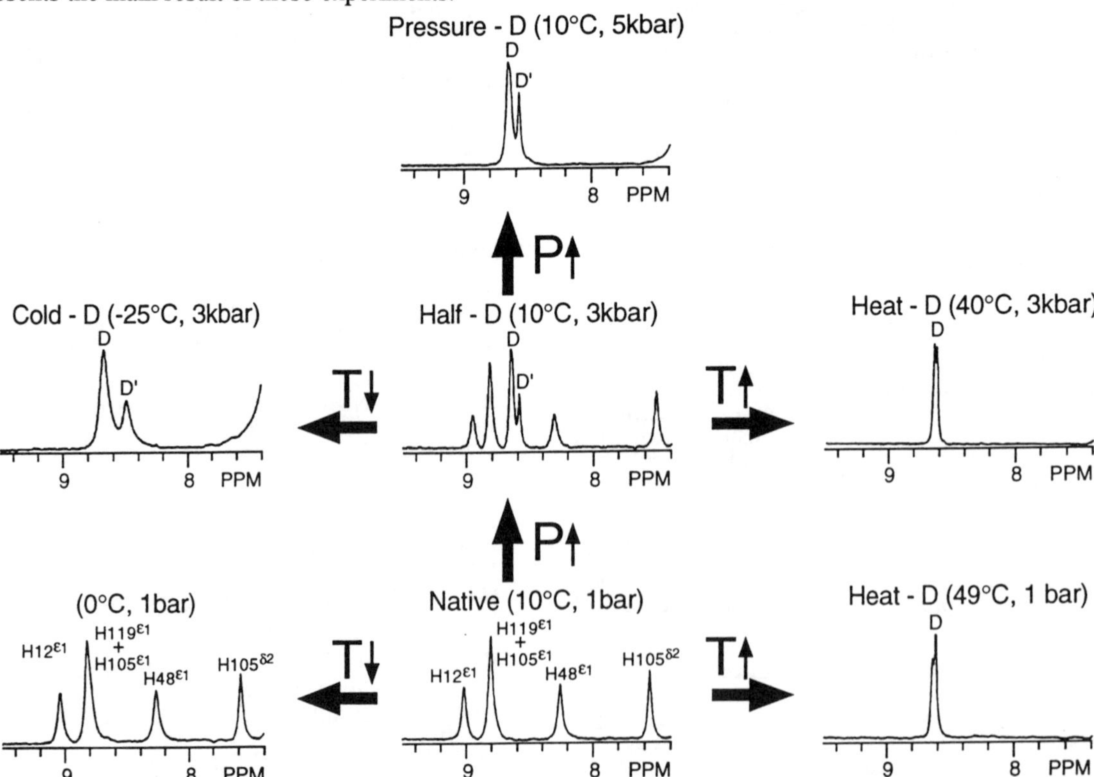

Figure 1. Comparison of the histidine region of the ^{1}H NMR spectra among native, pressure-denatured, and heat and cold-denatured states of Ribonuclease-A.

CONFORMATION OF THE PRESSURE-DISSOCIATED MONOMER OF ARC REPRESSOR

In our study [17], we described a unique approach, the use of hydrostatic pressure, to stabilize and characterize the intermediate states for the dissociation and denaturation of Arc repressor. Recent fluorescence experiments demonstrated that hydrostatic pressure induced reversible dissociation of Arc repressor [27]. The dissociated monomer has properties characteristic of a molten globule. For example, it is compact with its partially exposed nonpolar core that binds bis-ANS [27]. Nuclear magnetic resonance has been shown to be a powerful tool for the investigation of protein structure and dynamics of protein folding intermediates [28]. The complete ^{1}H NMR assignments for Arc repressor have been reported [29,30] and a tertiary and quaternary structure model for Arc repressor has been proposed [31].

In our study [17], we have used high pressure, high resolution NMR techniques to monitor the structural and dynamic changes of Arc repressor during the course of pressure dissociation and denaturation.

The NMR spectra of the monomer under pressure (up to 5.0 kbar) are typical of a molten globule, and they are considerably different from those of both the native dimer and the thermally-denatured monomer. The two-dimensional NOE spectra suggest that the pressure-induced molten globule retains some secondary structure. The presence of NOEs in the β-sheet region in the dissociated state suggests that the intermonomer β -sheet (residue 8-14) in the native dimer is replaced by an intramonomer β-sheet. Changes in one- and two-dimensional NMR spectra prior to pressure dissociation were found, and suggest the existence of a "pre-dissociated" state.

HIGH PRESSURE NMR STUDIES OF MODEL MEMBRANES

It is important to realize that, by applying pressure to membrane systems, one can observe not only volume effects, but one can also produce new pressure-induced phases [32]. We have initiated systematic high pressure NMR studies on model phospholipid membranes in our laboratory, and an overview of our results is given in Table 1.

Table 1. High Pressure NMR Studies of Model Phospholipid Membranes.

System	Experiment	Result	Reference
DPPC[a]	Natural Abundance ^{13}C,T_1,T_2	Phase Transitions	[33]
DMPC[b] POPC[c]	^{1}H 2D-NOESY	NOE Build-up Curves	[34]
DPPC-d_{62}	^{2}H Lineshapes	Phase Diagram; Order Parameter; Pressure Reversal of Anesthetic Effect of Tetracaine	[35,36]
DPPC(TTC)	^{31}P Lineshapes, T_1	Structure and Dynamics of the Head Group (Phase Diagram)	[19]
DPPC-d_2 (2,2)(9,9)(13,13)	^{2}H Lineshapes, T_1,T_2	Order Parameters; Cooperative Chain Motions	[37]
DPPC(TTC)	^{1}H T_1, 2D-NOESY	Dynamics; Location of TTC; Spin-Diffusion	[38]

[a]1,2-Dipalmitoyl-sn-glycero-3-phosphocholine;
[b]1,2-Dimyristoyl-sn-glycero-3-phosphocholine;
[c]1-Palmitoyl-2-oleoyl-sn-glycero-3-phosphocholine.

ACKNOWLEDGMENTS

This work was supported by the National Institutes of Health under grant PHS 5 RO1 GM42452-03, and by the National Science Foundation under grant NSF CHE 90-17649.

REFERENCES

[1] G. Weber, *Protein Interactions*, New York: Chapman and Hall, 1992.
[2] R. Winter and J. Jonas (Eds.), *High Pressure Chemistry, Biochemistry and Materials Science*, Dordrecht: Kluwer Academic Publishers, 1993, *NATO ASI, Series C*, 401.
[3] J. M. Ludlow and D. S. Clark, *Crit. Rev. Biotechn.* 10, pp. 321-345 (1991).
[4] C. Balny, R. Hayashi, K. Heremans, and P. Masson (Eds.), *High Pressure and Biotechnology*, France: Colloque INSERM/ Libbey, 1992, 224, pp. 123-127.
[5] K. Heremans, *NATO ASI, Series C*, 401, pp. 443-469 (1993).
[6] G. Weber, *NATO ASI, Series C*, 401, pp. 471-487 (1993).
[7] G. Weber, *NATO ASI, Series C*, 401, pp. 489-509 (1993).
[8] P.T.T. Wong, *NATO ASI, Series C*, 401, pp. 511-543 (1993).
[9] R. Winter and M. Böttner, *NATO ASI, Series C*, 401, pp. 545-560 (1993).
[10] J. Silva, *NATO ASI, Series C*, 401, pp. 561-578 (1993).
[11] M. Villas-Boas, J. L. Silva, and R. M. Clegg, *NATO ASI, Series C*, 401, pp. 579-602 (1993).
[12] D. Zakim and J. Kavecansky, *NATO ASI, Series C*, 401, pp. 603-617 (1993).
[13] G. Reinhart, E. Gratton, and W. W. Mantulin, *NATO ASI, Series C*, 401, pp. 619-626 (1993).
[14] J. Jonas, "NMR Basic Principles and Progress," in *High Pressure NMR*, P. Diehl, E. Fluck, H. Gunther, R. Kosfeld, and J. Seelig (Eds.); J. Jonas (Guest Ed.), New York: Springer-Verlag, 1991.
[15] J. Jonas, X. Peng, P. Koziol, C. Reiner, and D. Campbell, *J. Magn. Reson.*, in press (1993).
[16] S. Samarasinghe, D. M. Campbell, A. Jonas, and J. Jonas, *Biochem.* 31, pp. 7773-7778 (1992).
[17] X. Peng, J. Jonas, and J. Silva, *Proc. Natl. Acad. Sci. USA*, 90, pp. 1776-1780 (1993).
[18] X. Peng, J. Zhang, and J. Jonas, unpublished results.
[19] X. Peng and J. Jonas, *Biochem.* 31, pp. 6383-6390 (1992), and references cited therein.
[20] J. Jonas, *NATO ASI, Series C*, 401, pp. 393-441 (1993).
[21] A. Zipp and W. Kauzmann, *Biochem.* 12, pp. 4217-4228 (1973).
[22] G. Weber and H. G. Drickamer, *Quart. Rev. Biophys.* 16, pp. 89-112 (1983).
[23] T. M. Li, J. W. Hook III, H. G. Drickamer, and G. Weber, *Biochem.* 15, pp. 5572-5580 (1976).
[24] C. E. Kundrot and F. M. Richards, *J. Mol. Biol.* 193, pp. 157-170 (1987).
[25] R. E. Wedin, M. Delepierre, C. M. Dobson, and F. M. Poulsen, *Biochem.* 21, pp. 1098-1103 (1982).
[26] P. L. Privalov, *Crit. Rev. Biochem. Mol. Biol.* 25, 181-305 (1990).
[27] J. L. Silva, C. F. Silveira, A. Correia, Jr., and L. Pontes, *J. Mol. Biol.* 223, pp. 545-555 (1992).
[28] H. Roder, *Methods Enzymol.* 176, pp. 446-473 (1989).
[29] J. N. Breg, R. Boelens, A. V. E. George, and R. Kaptein, *Biochem.* 28, pp. 9826-9833 (1989).
[30] M. G. Zagorski, J. U. Bowie, A. K. Vershon, R. T. Sauer, and D. J. Patel, *Biochem.* 28, pp. 9813-9825 (1989).
[31] J. N. Breg, J. H. J. van Opheusden, M. J. M. Burgering, R. Boelens, and R. Kaptein, *Nature* 346, pp. 586-589 (1990).
[32] P. T. T. Wong, D. J. Siminovitch, and H. H. Mantsch, *Biochim. Biophys. Acta* 947, pp. 139-171 (1988).
[33] J. Jonas, C.-L. Xie, A. Jonas, P. J. Grandinetti, D. Campbell, and D. Driscoll, *Proc. Natl. Acad. Sci. USA* 85, pp. 4115-4117 (1988).
[34] J. Jonas, R. Winter, P. J. Grandinetti, and D. Driscoll, *J. Magn. Reson.* 87, pp. 536-547 (1990).
[35] D. A. Driscoll, S. Samarasinghe, S. Adamy, J. Jonas, and A. Jonas, *Biochem.* 30, pp. 3322-3327 (1991).
[36] D. A. Driscoll, J. Jonas, and A. Jonas, *Chem. Phys. Lipids* 58, pp. 97-104 (1991).
[37] X. Peng and J. Jonas, *Biochem.*, submitted.
[38] X. Peng and J. Jonas, *J. Am. Chem. Soc.*, submitted.

HIGH PRESSURE FT-IR SPECTROSCOPY FOR BIOMEDICAL AND CANCER RESEARCH

Patrick T. T. Wong
Steacie Institute for Molecular Sciences
National Research Council of Canada
Ottawa, Ontario, Canada K1A 0R6

By resolving technical and methodological problems, we are now able to obtain extremely high quality infrared spectra of animal and human tissues and cells as a function of pressure. This allows us to analyze the spectra in great details in terms of structural and dynamic properties at the molecular level in a wide range of biological and biomedical problems. For instance, in our cancer research we found that many structural modifications of cellular molecules in the malignant transformation are common to all the cancers that we have studied to date. Recently, large scale evaluation of the use of high-pressure FT-IR spectroscopy for the prescreening of cancer as well as preinvasive lesions of the cervix has been initiated in our laboratory. In order to optimize the specificity of the FT-IR technology for cervical screening, we have systematically studied and analyzed the high-pressure infrared spectra of individual abnormal lesions of the cervix. The results of one of these studies, differentiation between malignancy and inflammation in the human uterine cervix are given in this paper.

INTRODUCTION

The advances in the high-pressure infrared spectroscopic technique for intact biological tissues and whole cells in our laboratory allowed us to apply this technique to investigate the molecular bases of a wide range of biological and biomedical problems including various human cancers. In our cancer research, we have found that many structural changes at the molecular level are common to all cancers we have studies to date. We have also found that many features in the infrared spectra and their pressure dependences show clear cut differences between the normal, preinvasive and cancerous tissues and cells. These findings have prompted the consideration whether infrared spectroscopy has any value as a diagnostic tool in cancer and other diseases.

Cervical cancer is the third most prevalent cancer of the female genital tract. Papanicolaou smear test of the cervix is a major tool to identify women at risk for this cancer. However, studies show that the Pap smear test fails 25-40% of the time to spot cervical cancer or preinvasive anomalies (1). We have apply FT-IR spectroscopy in combination with high pressure for the evaluation of cancerous and preinvasive lesions in cervical tissues and exfoliated cells from more than 600 women (2-4 and unpublished results). Our data have demonstrated that FT-IR spectroscopy is a highly sensitive technique for detection of cervical anomalies and is a potential tool for prescreening of the malignant lesions as well as the preinvasive lesions of the cervix. Recently, large scale evaluation of the use of infrared spectroscopy in the screening of cervical smears has been initiated. While the sensitivity of the FT-IR technique for the screening of cervical anomalies is extremely high, its specificity for individual abnormal lesions needs to be developed. In our laboratory, infrared spectra of a series of cervical specimens with various diseases and other conditions have been systematically studied and analyzed in a great details in order to optimize the specificity of this FT-IR technology for the screening of malignant and preivasive lesions of the cervix. In this lecture, the results of one of these studies, the differentiation between inflammation and malignancy in the human uterine cervix is given.

RESULTS AND DISCUSSION

Figure 1 shows the representative infrared spectra in the frequency region of 950-1350 cm-1 of cervical cells with inflammatory changes, the normal and the malignant cervical cells. In both malignant cells and cells with inflammatory changes, the strong glycogen band at 1025 cm-1 and 1047 cm-1 decrease dramatically. The symmetric (1082 cm-1) and the antisymmetric (1240 cm-1) phosphate stretching bands of the phosphodiester groups in nucleic acids become very strong. However, considerable differences in many fine features in the spectra between the cells with inflammatory changes and the malignant cells are also evident from figure 1. Several structural changes at the molecular level, and other cellular changes in the cervical cells associated with inflammation, the normal cells and the malignant cells have been extracted from their infrared spectra.

The infrared spectra of the antisymmetric phosphate stretching mode of the malignant and cervical cells with inflammatory changes together with the one from the normal cervical cells are given in figure 2. This phosphate stretching band in the spectra of tissues and cells is mainly contributed by the phosphodiester groups in the DNA (2, 5-6). It is clear from figure 2 that the antisymmetric phosphate band of the normal cells is a single peak at 1241 cm^{-1}, whereas in both the cells with inflammatory changes and the malignant cells, it consists of two overlapping bands with peak positions near 1240 and 1222 cm^{-1}. The low frequency component band is from the hydrogen-bonded phosphodiester groups whereas the high-frequency component band is from the non-hydrogen-bonded phosphodiester groups (2, 5). The increase in the intensity of the low-frequency component band in malignant cells indicates that a large number of phosphodiester groups in the malignant cells are hydrogen-bonded to water (2, 6-7). The low-frequency component band of the cells with inflammatory changes is stronger than the high-frequency component band. This suggests that more phosphodiester groups of DNA form hydrogen-bonds with water in the cells with inflammatory changes than in the malignant cells.

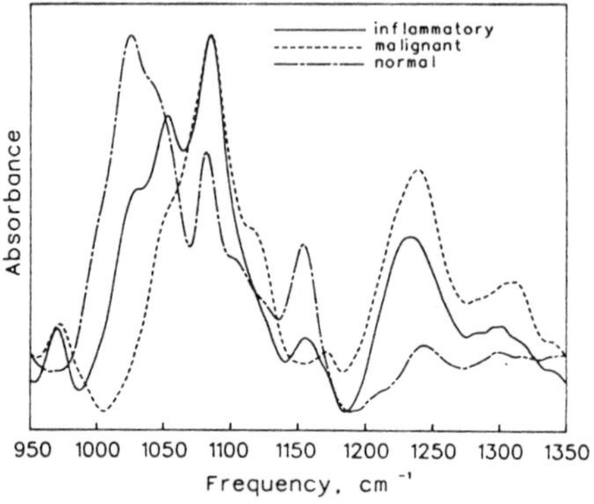

Figure 1. Infrared spectra of the cervical cells in the frequency region 950-1350 cm^{-1}.

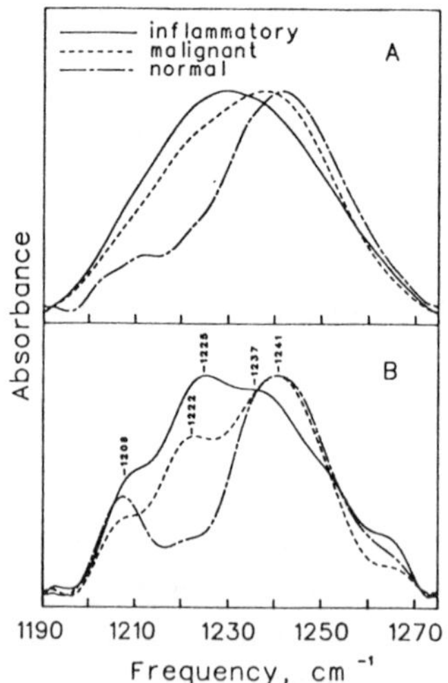

Figure 2. Infrared spectra of the cervical cells in the asymmetric phosphate stretching region. (A) Superimposed original spectra from three types of cervical cells. (B) Corresponding deconvolved spectra with an enhancement factor of 2 and band width of 20 cm^{-1}.

Pressure dependences of the symmetric phosphate stretching frequencies of the cells with inflammatory changes, the malignant and the normal cervical cells are shown in figure 3. This symmetric phosphate stretching band in the spectra of biological tissues and cells is mainly contributed from the vibrational mode of the phosphodiester groups in nucleic acids (2, 5-6). The higher frequency in the malignant cells and cells with inflammatory changes, as compared to the normal cells, has been attributed to the result of a tighter intermolecular packing of the nucleic acids in the malignant cells (3, 8). However, as indicated by the lower frequency of this band, the packing in the inflammation is not as tight as in the malignant cells.

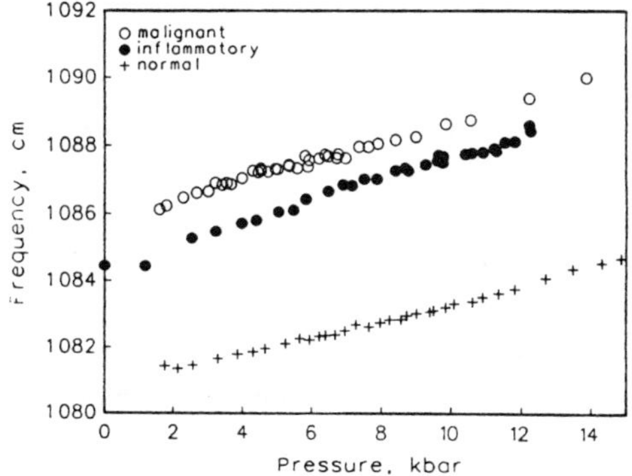

Figure 3. Pressure dependences of the symmetric phosphate stretching frequency of the cervical cells.

Infrared spectra in the C-O stretching mode region of the cervical cells are shown in figure 4. A total of three overlapping C-O stretching bands are observed in this region. It has been shown, previously (2, 9), that the 1155 cm^{-1} band is from the C-O groups in the carbohydrate moieties whereas those at 1162 cm^{-1} and 1172 cm^{-1} are from the C-OH groups of serine, threonine and tyrosine in proteins. Moreover, the component bands at 1155 cm^{-1} and 1162 cm^{-1} are due to the stretching modes of hydrogen-bonded C-O groups, whereas the band at 1172 cm^{-1} is due to the stretching mode of non-hydrogen bonded C-O groups (2, 9). In the cells with inflammatory

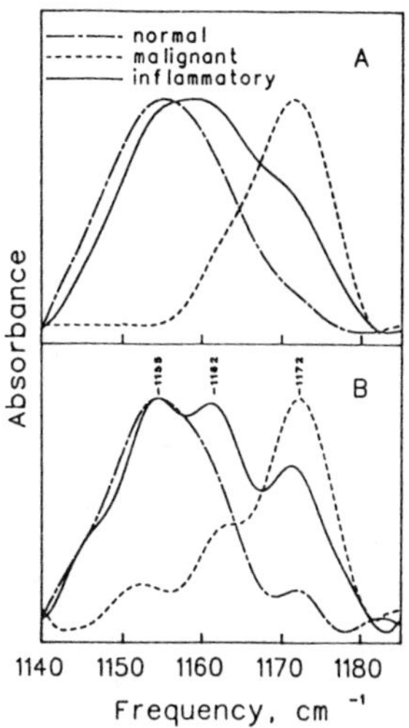

Figure 4. Infrared spectra of the cervical cells in the C-O stretching region. (A) Superimposed original spectra from three types of cervical cells. (B) Corresponding deconvolved spectra with an enhancement factor of 1.8 and band width of 10 cm^{-1}.

changes, the intensities of the hydrogen-bonded C-O bands predominate over that of the non-hydrogen-bonded C-O band. Therefore, unlike in the malignant cell, only very few C-O groups are non-hydrogen-bonded in inflammation. The characteristics of the C-O groups in the cells with inflammatory changes also differ significantly from those in the normal cells. There are more non-hydrogen-bonded C-OH groups and less hydrogen-bonded C-O groups in carbohydrate moieties in the cells with inflammatory changes than in the normal cells.

Figure 5 shows the pressure dependences of the CH_2 bending frequencies of the methylene chains in membrane lipids of the cervical cells with inflammatory changes, the malignant cells, and the normal cells. The pressure effects on the frequency of this vibrational mode has been widely used to study the packing structure and the order/disorder structure of lipids in aqueous bilayers (8, 10-12). In lipid bilayers, pressure

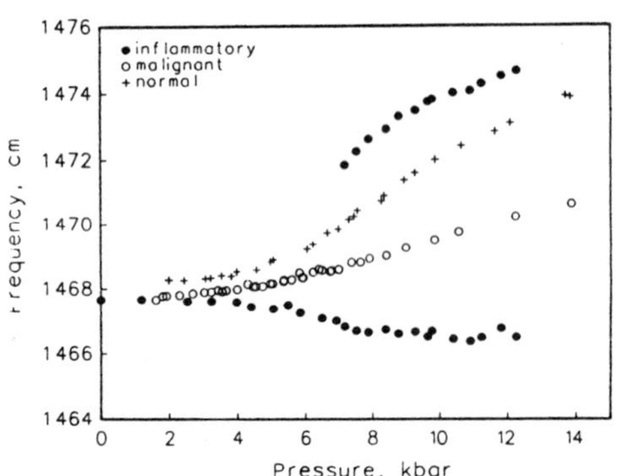

Figure 5. Pressure dependences of the CH_2 bending mode frequency of the methylene chains in lipids of the cervical cells.

always increases this frequency as a result of pressure-induced orientational and conformational ordering of the methylene chains, thereby increasing interchain interaction. Pressure induces a smaller frequency shift in the malignant cells as compared to the normal cells. Thus, the methylene chains of membrane lipids in the malignant cells are more disordered than those in the normal cells. The pressure effects on the CH_2 bending mode frequency of the membrane lipids in the cervical cells with inflammatory changes are entirely different from those in the malignant and the normal cells. In inflammation this band splits into two at about 7 kbar. The correlation field splitting at 7 kbar observed in the spectra of the cells with inflammatory changes indicates that the methylene chains in the membrane lipids are fully extended and well aligned with non-equivalent orientations of neighboring zig-zag planes at this pressure.

Cytologically, the changes associated with inflammation may only be seen in a small number of epithelial cells, and the majority of the cells may appear normal. However, as demonstrated in the present work, prominent changes occur in the infrared spectrum of the inflammatory lesions compared with the infrared spectrum of the normal cervical cells. This implies that the structural properties at the molecular level of these morphologically normal cells in the inflammatory specimens have already changed. These structural changes take place before the morphological changes in the inflammatory lesions and can be detected unambiguously by infrared spectroscopy.

REFERENCES

1. R. Peid, in "Practical Gynecologic Oncology", J. Berek and N. F. Hacker, eds., Williams and Wilkins, Baltimore, 199 (1989).
2. P. T. T. Wong, R. K. Wong, T. A. Caputo, T.A. Godwin and B. Rigas, Proc. Natl. Acad. Sci. USA, 88, 10988-10992 (1991).
3. P. T. T. Wong, R. K. Wong and M. Fung Kee Fung, Appl. Spectrosco. (1993) in press.
4. H. M. Yazdi, M. A. Bertrand, S. Lacelle and P. T. T. Wong, Proc. Amer. Soc. Cytology (1993) in press.
5. P. T. T. Wong, E. D. Papavassiliou and B. Rigas, Appl. Spectrosco., **4**, 1563 (1991).
6. F. S. Parker, Application of Infrared Spectroscopy in Biochemistry, Biology and Medicine (1971), Plenum Press, New York.
7. H. Susi, in "Structure and Stability of Biological Macromolecules", S. N. Timasheff and C. D. Fasman, Eds., (1969), pp. 641-659, Marcel Dekker, New York.
8. P. T. T. Wong, in "High Pressure Chemistry , Biochemistry and Materials Science", R. Winter and J. Jonas Eds., NATO series C, Kluwer Academic Publishers, Dordrecht, (1993). in press.
9. B. Rigas, S. Morgello, I. S. Goldman and P. T. T. Wong, Proc. Natl. Acad. Sci. USA, **87**, 8140 (1990).
10. P. T. T. Wong, in "Vibrational Spectra and Structure", ed. J. R. Durig (1987), Vol.16 pp. 357-445, Elsevier, Amsterdam.
11. P. T. T. Wong, in "High Pressure Chemistry and Biochemistry," R. van Eldik and J. Jonas, Eds., NATO series C. Vol. 197, D. Reidel, Dordreht, pp. 381-400 (1987).
12. P. T. T. Wong and H. H. Mantsch, Biophys. J., **54**, 781 (1988).

THE EFFECT OF HIGH PRESSURE ON MODEL MEMBRANES

A. Landwehr, M. Böttner, W. Hahn and R. Winter
Ruhr-University of Bochum, Universitätsstraße 150
D-44780 Bochum , F.R.G.

Phospholipids, which provide valuable model systems for lipid membranes, display a variety of polymorphic phases, depending on their molecular structure and environmental conditions. High hydrostatic pressure has been used as a physical parameter to study the thermodynamic properties and phase behavior of these systems, and because high pressure is a characteristic feature of certain natural membrane environments. By use of small-angle neutron scattering (SANS), differential scanning calorimetry (DSC), differential thermal analysis (DTA) and volumetric measurements, the temperature and pressure dependent phase behavior of several phospholipid systems, differing in lipid conformation and headgroup structure, have been studied. Possible biochemical implications of these studies are discussed.

INTRODUCTION

Aqueous dispersions of lipid bilayers, in particular the phosphatidylcholines, provide valuable models for the investigation of biophysical properties of membrane lipids, because they constitute the basic structural component of biological membranes. They exhibit a rich lyotropic and thermotropic phase behavior [1]. Most fully hydrated saturated phospholipid bilayers exhibit two principal thermotropic lamellar phase transitions, corresponding to a gel - gel ($L_{\beta'}$ - $P_{\beta'}$) transition and a gel - liquid-crystalline ($P_{\beta'}$ - L_α) main transition at a higher temperature T_m. In the physiological liquid-crystalline (L_α) phase, the hydrocarbon chains of the lipid bilayers are conformationally disordered ("melted"), whereas in the gel phases, the hydrocarbon chains are more extended and relatively ordered. The lipids can differ in bilayer surface structure and lipid chain packing, however. In addition to these thermotropic phase transitions, pressure-induced lamellar to lamellar phase transitions have been observed (see e.g. [2-6]). Besides the general interest in high pressure phase behavior of amphiphilic molecules, high pressure is also of considerable physiological interest. For example, pressure studies on lipid systems are of interest in understanding the physiology of deap sea organisms, the sensitivity of excitable cell membranes to pressure, and the antagonistic effect of pressure to anesthetic action. Most lipids exist in these lamellar bilayer phases, although certain lipids, such as phosphatidylethanolamines, can form non-bilayer phases, such as inverted hexagonal (H_{II}) or cubic structures, as well [7-9]. The H_{II} phase consists of inverted micellar rods with cylindrical water cores. Many natural membranes are rich in lipids which have strong tendencies to form H_{II} phases, and considerable effort is currently spent on trying to identify such structures in biological systems. They might play an important role during transient membrane processes, such as vesicle fusion, which occurs during endo- and exocytosis.

LIPID BILAYER PHASE TRANSITIONS

As an example of the thermodynamic properties of a saturated phospholipid, Fig. 1a shows the temperature dependence of the apparent specific lipid volume V_L of DMPC* in H_2O. The small change of V_L near 14 ^oC corresponds to a small volume change in course of the $L_{\beta'}$ - $P_{\beta'}$ transition. The main transition at T_m = 23.9 ^oC is accompanied by a well pronounced 3 % volume change [10], which is mainly due to changes of the chain cross-sectional area, because chain disorder increases drastically at the transition. Fig. 1b exhibits the pressure dependenc of V_L at e.g. 30 ^oC. Increasing pressure triggers the phase transformation from the L_α into the gel phase, as can be seen from the rather abrupt decrease of the lipid volume at 270 bar. The accompanying volume change ΔV_m at the main transition decreases only slightly with increasing temperature along the main transition line [10]. It appears that the compressiblity of the $P_{\beta'}$ gel phase is substantially lower than that of the liquid-crystalline phase (for T = 30 ^oC: $\chi_T(P_{\beta'}) \approx 5{\cdot}10^{-5}{\cdot}bar^{-1}$ and $\chi_T(L_\alpha) \approx 13{\cdot}10^{-5}$ bar^{-1}). From the compressibility data, the relative root mean square fluctuation $\delta V_{L,rel}$ of the lipid volume can be calulated. $\delta V_{L,rel}$ is about 7 % in the liquid-crystalline phase, increases up to about 30 % at the main transition and decreases to about 4 % in the gel phase. In comparison to $\delta V_{L,rel}$ of proteins, these volume fluctuations in lipid systems are large, they are smaller, in comparison to those of water, however. This fact may be of significant biological relevance, as in biological membranes many proteins are embedded in the lipid bilayer. The T-P-phase diagram for the main transition of DMPC-water is displayed in Fig. 2. Up to pressures around 1 kbar, a linear increase of the phase transition curve with 22 ^oC/kbar is observed, whereas for higher pressures, dT_m/dp decreases. Assuming a first-order phase transition for the main transition, the entropy and enthalpy changes at the main transition can be calculated, employing the Clausius-Clapeyron equation. An enthalpy change of ΔH_m = 26 kJ/mol and an entropy change of ΔS_m = 86 $Jmol^{-1}K^{-1}$ is obtained. Recent high pressure DTA experiments [11] on this system revealed, that ΔH_m does not change significantly up to about 1.5 kbar.

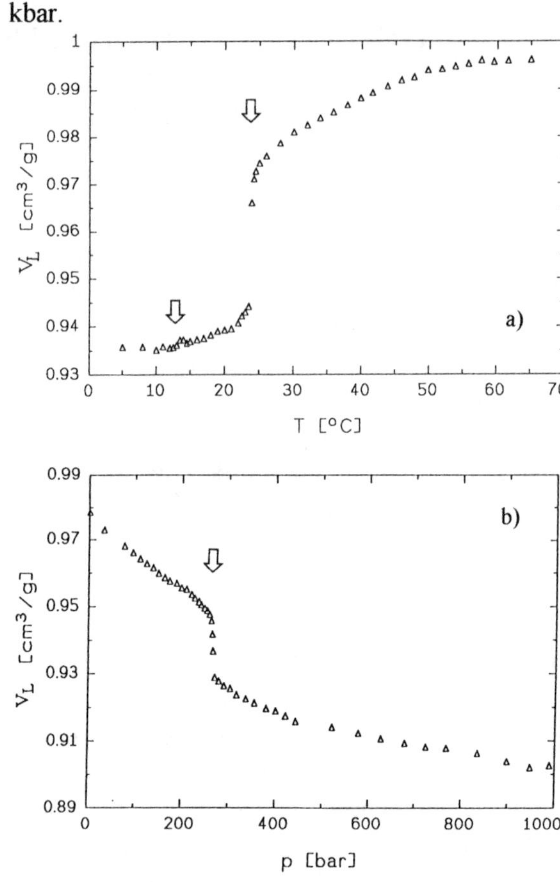

Fig. 1a,b. Apparent specific lipid volume of DMPC-water dispersions a) as a function of temperature at p = 1 bar, b) as a function of pressure at T = 30 ^oC.

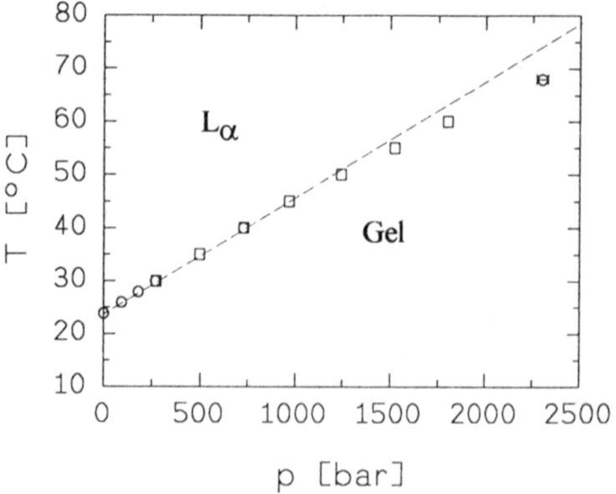

Fig. 2. Temperature-pressure phase diagram for the main transition of DMPC-water dispersions.

As an example of the temperature and pressure dependent structure of an unsaturated phospholipid, we focus on SANS results of the mixed chain phospholipid POPC*, which has a main transition temperature of $T_m(1bar) = -5\ ^oC$. Fig. 3 exhibits the SANS results for the bilayer repeat distance d, which consists of the bilayer thickness including the water layer around the lipid headgroup, for POPC at different temperatures as a function of pressure. With increasing pressure, the d-spacing increases as a result of the in-plane compression of the hydrocarbon chains and the order parameter of the acyl chains should increase upon pressurization. The transition from the L_α to the gel state is indicated by a significant increase in d-spacing. Also in POPC, increasing temperature shifts the L_α -gel transition to higher pressures. In both phases, the L_α and the gel phase, the d-spacing increases with increasing pressure, about 1-2 ^oC/kbar. This implies, that a considerable amount of disorder exists not only in the L_α phase, but also in the gel state, which contrasts the behavior observed for saturated phospholipids [4].

Interestingly, a common value for the L_α-gel transition slope dT_m/dp of about 21 ^oC/kbar has been obtained not only for saturated phospholipids, but also for POPC and the trans-unsaturated DEPC* [5]. However, for the di-cis-unsaturated lipids DOPC* and DOPE* (see below), dT_m/dp has been found to be significantly smaller [3,11,12]. Further pressure-induced gel phases have been observed, such as an interdigitated high pressure gel phase in long chain saturated phosphatidylcholines [4-6].

Thus, by regulating the lipid composition of the cell membranes through changes in lipid chain length and degree of unsaturation, biological organisms are provided with a mechanism for efficiently modulating the physical state of their membranes in response to changes in the external environment.

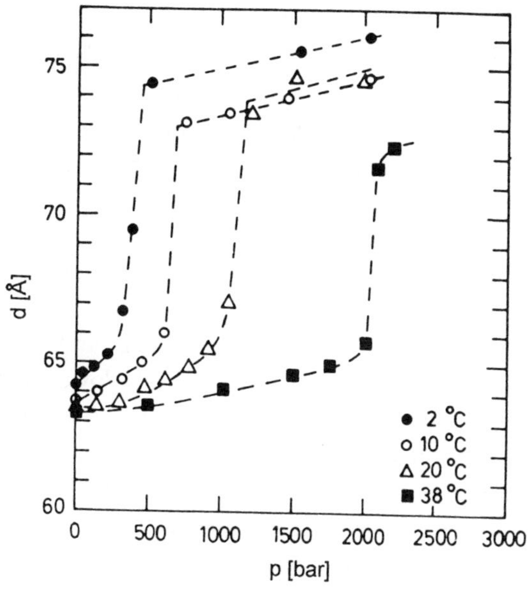

Fig. 3. The lamellar repeat distance d of POPC dispersions as a function of temperature and pressure.

NON-BILAYER PHASE TRANSITIONS

Certain lipids, such as phosphatidylethanolamines, cardiolipin and phosphatidic acid, can form non-bilayer phases as well. From DSC studies it is known, that e.g. DOPE* -water dispersions undergo a lamellar ($L_{\beta'}$) to lamellar (L_α) transition at $T_m \approx -6\ ^oC$ and a lamellar (L_α) to inverted hexagonal (H_{II}) thermotropic transition at $T_h \approx 13\ ^oC$ [13]. The driving force for the L_α-H_{II} transition is the drastic increase in hydrocarbon chain volume at higher temperatures, which is due to the increase in population of gauche conformers, past the point where the headgroups can "cover" a bilayer [7-9]. At the L_α-H_{II} - transition, no significant volume change has been found. Whereas the main transition at ambient pressure of DOPE - water dispersions is accompanied by an enthalpy change ΔH_m of about 20 kJ/mol, ΔH_h of the L_α-H_{II} transition is 2 kJ/mol [13], only. In view of the large topological structural changes that have to take place during the

L_α-H_{II} transition, it is surprising that the transition enthalpy is significantly lower than that of the gel to liquid-crystalline transition. However, since the lamellar to non-lamellar transition takes place wholly in a fluid-like state, both the transition enthalpies and transition entropies are probably so small. Fig. 4 displays the T-P - phase diagram for the two endothermic transitions of the system DOPE- water. As can be clearly seen, the transition slope of the lamellar chain-melting transition (dT_m/dp = 14 ^oC/kbar) is significantly lower than that of saturated phospholipids. For the smaller pressures, the slope of the L_α-H_{II} transition (dT_h/dp = 40 ^oC/kbar) is almost three times steeper as the slope of the lamellar chain-melting transition. At higher pressures, dT_h/dp slightly decreases. E. Shyamsunder et al. [14] reported, using small-angle X-ray diffraction, that at a pressure of 500 bar and T = 20 ^oC, DOPE - water dispersions have indeed transformed into the H_{II} phase. Using high pressure FTIR, Wong et al. found an indication of an additional lamellar to lamellar transition in DOPE-water at 9 kbar [15]. A similar steep slope for the L_α-H_{II} transition has been

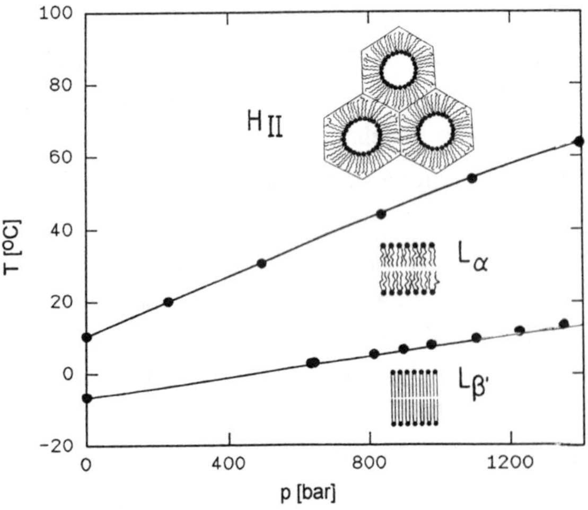

Fig. 4. Temperature-pressure phase diagram of DOPE - water dispersions as obtained from DTA experiments [11].

observed for egg-PE by turbidity measurements up to 320 bar [16] as well. This L_α-H_{II} transition is the most pressure-sensitive lipid phase transition found to date.

The data above clearly indicate, that the bilayer form is stabilized at high pressure for any temperature as a consequence of the smaller lipid volume. Therefore, biochemical processes involving the H_{II} phase as an intermediate state should be slowed down by application of hydrostatic pressure. The observations made may e.g. help to explain the inhibition of chemical transmission at neural synapses by pressure.

*)abbreviations: DMPC:1,2-dimyristoyl-sn-glycero-3-phos-phatidylcholine (di-C14:0), DOPC: 1,2-dioleoyl-sn-glycero-3-phosphatidylcholine (di-C18:1,cis), DOPE: 1,2-dioleoyl-sn-glycero-3-phosphatidylethanolamine (di-C18:1,cis), POPC: 1-palmitoyl-2-oleoyl-sn-glycero-3-phosphatidylcholine, (C16:0, C18:1, cis), DEPC: 1,2-dielaidoyl-sn-glycero-3-phosphatidylcholine (di-C18:1, trans).

REFERENCES

[1] G. Cevc and D. Marsh, *Phospholipid Bilayers*, New York: John Wiley & Sons, 1987
[2] P. L.-G. Chong and G. Weber, *Biochemistry* 22, 5544 (1983)
[3] P. T. T. Wong, D. J. Siminovitch, and H. H. Mantsch, *Biochim. Biophys. Acta* 947, 139 (1988)
[4] L. F. Braganza and D. L. Worcester, *Biochemistry* 25, 2591 and 7484 (1986)
[5] R. Winter and W.-C. Pilgrim, *Ber. Bunsenges. Phys. Chem.* 93, 708 (1989)
[6] D. A. Driscoll, J. Jonas, and A. Jonas, *Chem. Phys. of Lipids* 58, 97 (1991)
[7] D. Marsh, *Chem. Phys. of Lipids* 57, 109 (1991)
[8] S. M. Gruner, *Ann. Rev. Biophys. Biophys. Chem.* 14, 211 (1985)
[9] J. M. Seddon, *Biochim. Biophys. Acta* 1031, 1 (1990)
[10] M. Böttner, D. Ceh, U. Jacobs, and R. Winter, *Z. Phys. Chem.*, in press
[11] A. Landwehr and R. Winter, *Ber. Bunsenges. Phys. Chem.*, in press
[12] R. Winter and P. Thiyagarajan, *Progr. Colloid. Polym. Sci.* 81, 216 (1990)
[13] W. Hahn, Diploma-Thesis, Univ. of Marburg, 1993
[14] E. Shyamsunder, P. Botos, and S. M. Gruner, *J. Chem. Phys.* 90, 1293 (1989)
[15] P. T. T. Wong and H. H. Mantsch, *J. Chem. Phys.* 90, 1295 (1989)
[16] P. Yager and E. L. Chang, *Biochim. Biophys. Acta* 731, 491 (1983)

CHAPTER XIX

ELECTRICAL AND MAGNETIC PROPERTIES

PRESSURE EFFECT ON TRANSPORT PROPERTIES OF $Mn_{3-x}Co_xGaC$ (x<0.3)

T.Harada and T.Kanomata
Faculty of Engineering,Tohoku Gakuin University,
Tagajo 985,Japan
H.Yoshida and T.Kaneko
Institute for Materials Research, Tohoku University
Katahira, Sendai 980, Japan

In this paper,we have examined the pressure effect on the magnetic transitions of $Mn_{2.97}Co_{0.03}GaC$ and $Mn_{2.7}Co_{0.3}GaC$ by measurering the electrical resistivity.The Curie temperature T_C increased linearly with increasing pressure for both samples.For $Mn_{2.97}Co_{0.03}GaC$,magnetic transition temperature T_{t1} from the antiferromagnetic state to the intermediate one, which also appears by substituting Co for Mn, decrease rapidly with pressure.

INTRODUCTION

The cubic perovskite type Mn_3GaC is ferromagnetic (F) below the Curie temperature T_C= 255K and antiferromagnetic(AF) below the transition temperature T_t=165K[1].It shows a discontinuous volume contraction at the AF-F transition temperature T_t. According to the previous neutron diffraction studies[2], the magnetic moment of the Mn atom is 1.8 μ_B at 4.2 K in the AF state and 1.2μ_B at 170 K in the F state. The small value of magnetic moment of Mn suggests that Mn_3GaC is an itinerant magnet. Recently, Kaneko et.al.[3] have examined the effect of hydrostatic pressure on the magnetic properties of Mn_3GaC.They have reported that pressure increases T_C and decreases T_t for Mn_3GaC. They also have found that a new intermediate magnetic (I) phase appears between the AF phase and the F one at pressures higher than 0.3 GPa. Furthermore ,Kanomata et. al.[4][5] have reported that the similar I phase also appears by substituting Al and Zn for Ga and Co for Mn, and the AF-I transition temper-ature T_{t1} and the I-F transition temperature T_{t2} decrease with increase of substitution content. In the present paper, we investigate the pressure effect on T_{t1} ,T_{t2} and T_C of $Mn_{2.97}Co_{0.03}GaC$ and $Mn_{2.7}Co_{0.3}GaC$ by measuring the electrical resistivity ρ.

EXPERIMENTAL PROCEDURE

Sintered samples of $Mn_{2.97}Co_{0.03}GaC$ and $Mn_{2.7}Co_{0.3}GaC$ were prepared with the same procedure reported previously[5]. With X-ray diffraction, the lattice parameters of $Mn_{2.97}Co_{0.03}GaC$ and $Mn_{2.7}Co_{0.3}GaC$ were given as 3.893 A and 3.880 A, respectively, which are smaller than that of Mn_3GaC , 3.898 A.

The measurements of the ρ under various pressures as a function of temperature T were carried out by using the piston sylinder-type apparatus. Fluorinert was used as the pressure transmitting fluid. ρ was measured by a usual four-leads technique with a Chromel-Alumel thermocouple to monitor the temperature.

EXPERIMENTAL RESULTS AND DISCUSSION

Figure 1 shows the ρ-T curves in the range of temperature through T_C under various pressures for $Mn_{2.97}Co_{0.03}GaC$. As seen in the figure, ρ-T curve at normal pressure consists of two linear parts below and above ~248K. We defined T_C as an intersection point of both linear curves as seen with an arrow. T_C increases with pressure P. The pressure variation of T_C is shown in Fig.2. The T_C-P curve is linear over the range of pressure measured. The derivative of T_C, dT_C/dP, is evaluated as +12.8 K/GPa. Figure 3 shows the

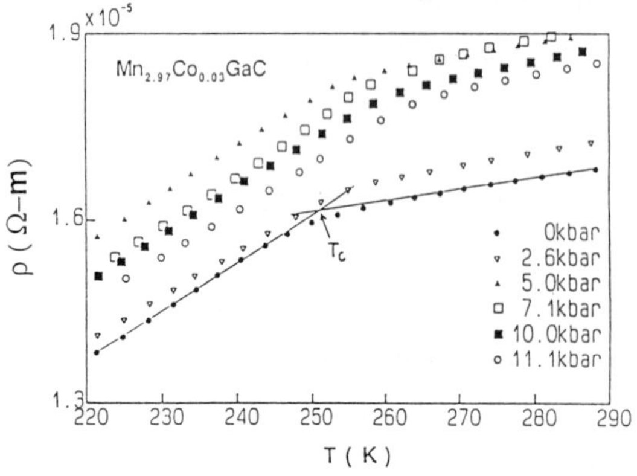

Figure 1. ρ vs. T near T_C under various pressures for $Mn_{2.97}Co_{0.03}GaC$.

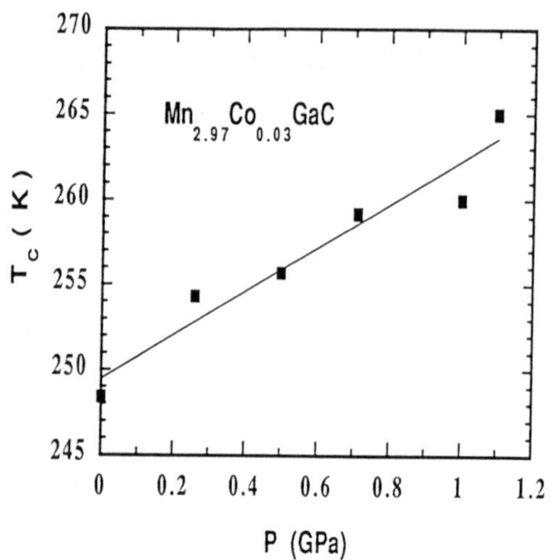

Figure 2. T_C as a function of pressre for $Mn_{2.97}Co_{0.03}GaC$.

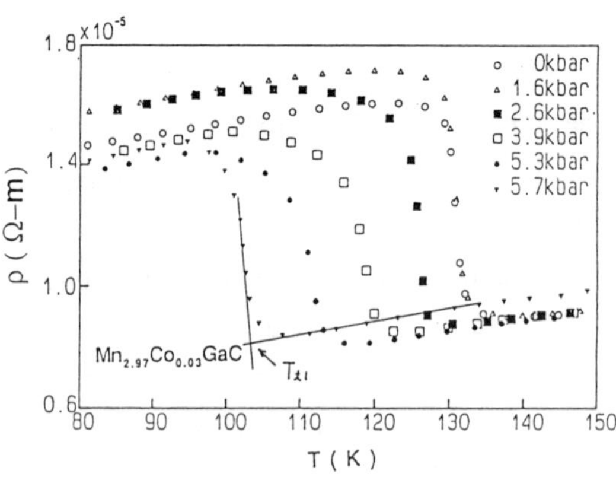

Figure 3. ρ vs. T near T_{t1} under various pressures for $Mn_{2.97}Co_{0.03}GaC$.

ρ-T curves between 80 K and 150 K under various pressures. As temperature increases, ρ increases almost linearly,decreases abruptly at T_{t1} and then increases again. We defined T_{t1} as shown with an arrow in the figure. Figure 4 shows the pressure variation of the first order AF-I transition temperature T_{t1}. T_{t1} decreases non-linearly with pressure. This decrease of T_{t1} with pressure is consistent with the experimental results by Kanomata et.al. that T_{t1} decreases with the decrease of volume by substituting Al and Zn for Ga or Co for Mn. Pressure dependence of the magnetic transition temperature T_{t2} was obtained similarly with measuring temperature dependence of ρ under pressure. The result is shown in Fig.5. T_{t2} also decrease with increasing pressure. The derivative of T_{t2},dT_{t2}/dP, is evaluated as -13.8K/GPa. The change of T_{t2} is small compared with that of T_{t1}. Thus, the region of the I state spreads with increasing pressure.

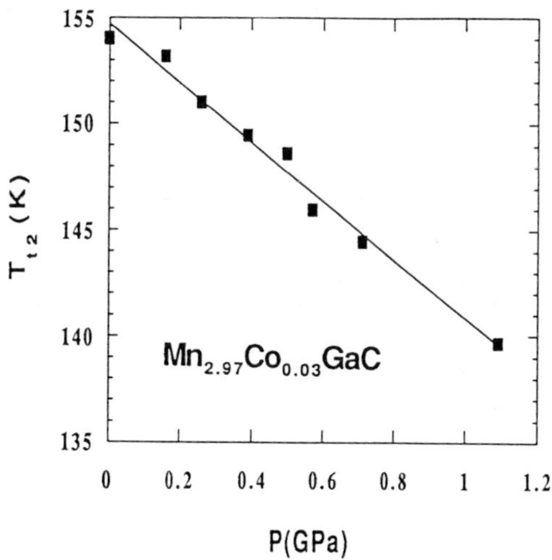

Figure 5. T_{t2} as a fuction of Pressure P for $Mn_{2.97}Co_{0.03}GaC$.

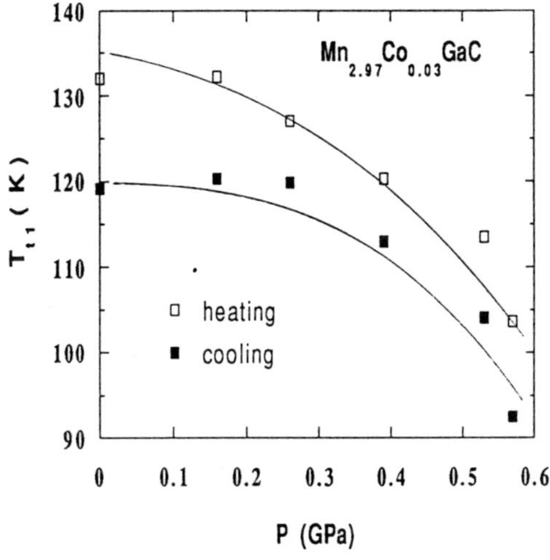

Figure 4. T_{t1} as a function of pressure P for $Mn_{2.97}Co_{0.03}GaC$.

Furthermore, for $Mn_{2.7}Co_{0.3}GaC$, we have measured the temperature dependence of ρ. For this sample,T_{t1} and $T_{t2}$are not seen over the range of temperature measured. The pressure dependence of T_C was obtained in the same way as that of T_{t1}. The result is shown in Fig. 6. As shown in figure, T_C increases linearly with P and dT_C/dP is evaluated as +12.3 K/GPa.

The results show that the first order magnetic transition is sensitive of slight change of pressure. Recently,Motizuki et.al.[6] and Ishida et.al.[7] have calculated the band structure of Mn_3GaC.They have reported that the electronic structure in the AF state is different from that in the F one and difference of magnetic moment between the AF and the F state can be explained on the basis of these band calculations.Therefore, the magneto volume effect obtained in this study also may be discussed on the itenerant magnetism.

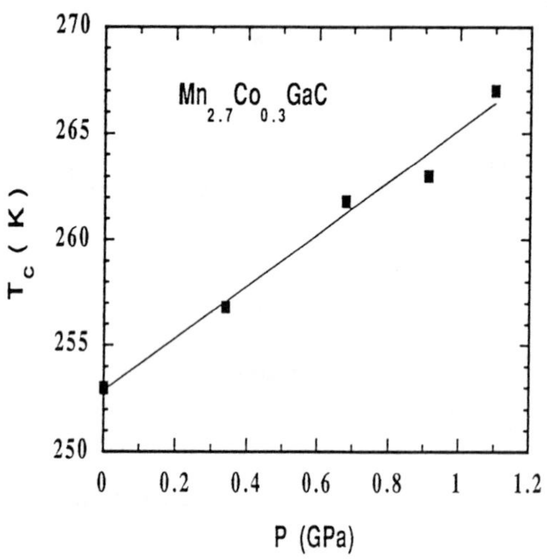

Figure 6. T_C as a function of pressre for $Mn_{2.7}Co_{0.3}GaC$.

A part of this work was carried out under Interuniversity Cooperative Research Program of the Institute for Materials Reseach,Tohoku University.

References

[1]J.P.Bouchaud,R.Fruchart,R.Pauthenet,M.Gillot, H.Bartholin and F.Casse, J.Appl.Phys.37, pp.971-(1966).

[2]D.Fruchart,E.F.Bertaut,B.L.Clerc,L.D.Khoi,P.Veillet, G.Lorthior,M.E.Fruchart and R.Fruchart, J.Solid Chem.8,pp.182-(1973).

[3]T.Kaneko,T.Kanomata and K.Shirakawa,J.Phys. Soc.Jpn.56,pp.4047-(1987).

[4]T.Kanomata,T.kawashima,H.YoshidaandT.Kaneko, Appl.Phys.67,pp.4824-(1990)

[5]T.Kanomata,T.Harada and T.Kaneko,physics of transition metals,world scientific,press,1992,pp.875 -878.

[6]K.Motizuki and H.Nagai,J.Phys.C.21, pp. 525-(1988)

[7]S.Ishida,S.Fujii,A.Sawabe and S.Asano, to be published.

INFLUENCE OF TEMPERATURE ON THE ELECTRICAL CONDUCTIVITY OF GLASS UNDER SHOCK EFFECT

A.N.Dremin, A. V. Orlov and A. M. Molodets
Institute of Chemical Physics (Chernogolovka)
Russian Academy of Sciences, Moscow Region
Chernogolovka, 142432, Russia

A study of electroconductivity change in Pyrex type glass under the effect of intense wave compression (13.8 Gpa) has been undertaken. Time correlations of the electroconductivity and the inelastic deformation rate of the glass have been revealed. The findings are interpreted in terms of "structural rearrangement" of the SiO_4 tetrahedron during the homogeneous process of glass densification.

INTRODUCTION

At present there are many publications on the response of silicate glasses to intense wave compression [1-17]. In spite of the large number of publications there is still no generally accepted concept of the materials high-rate inelastic deformation. All the same, two ideas are most often discussed. The first ideas has been elaborated on for high-strength materials with low thermoconductivity [18]. According to the idea the inelastic deformation kinetic process is heterogeneous in volume. The process is governed by some progress dynamics of adiabatic shear bands originating behind the elastic wave front. Almost all elastic energy is dissipated inside the shear bands. As a result of such local evolution of energy, partial melting of the materials takes place within the shear bands, that is, the monolithic material transforms into some conglomerates of initial structure fragments united by liquid interlayers. The liquid layer substance transforms into denser phase according to the thermo-activated mechanisms. However, according to a second idea [19], inelastic deformation of glass is supposed to proceed homogeneously throughout the material volume by the relaxation process of some structural rearrangement (transposition) at a microscopic level. At a stress above the Hugomot Elastic Limit (HEL), irreversible inclination of the SiO_4 tetrahedron takes place. The tetrahedron rearrangement begins when the inclination approaches some critical value. The rearrangement is the main mechanism of glass densification.

In this paper, a study of electroconductivity change in Pyrex type glass has been undertaken, the character of the change being assumed to provide an answer to the question - which idea is more plausible. Indeed, if the first idea is correct then the glass sample electroconductivity is governed by the electroconductivity of a small fraction of substance involved in adiabatic shear bands [20]. This is because the ion mobility of liquid interlayers is several orders of magnitude greater than that of the initial structure (non-melted) fragments [20]. The interlayers form a continuous spacial network. Current paths appear inside the network during the electroconductivity measurement. These paths allow current to flow between the electrodes.

If the second idea is correct, then the free carrier concentration will be proportional to the number of broken bands per unit volume, the electroconductivity of the material under deformation being uniform in volume since the rearrangement proceeds homogeneously. It has been shown in [17] that according to the first idea, the temperature of melted glass inside the shear bands will increase due to the increase of the glass HEL from the initial temperature decrease. On the other hand, according to the second idea, the shock compression glass temperature decreases. However, it is known from static investigations [21, 22] that the glass electroconductivity decreases markedly as the sample temperature decreases. Moreover a similar decrease has been revealed in the course of some shock wave experiments [11]. In these experiments, the electroconductivity of the glass has been related to its temperature behind the shock wave front. Consequently, one could expect that the shock wave electroconductivity of the glass would significantly depend on temperature. One could also hope that the character of the dependence would help to elucidate the most reliable idea of the two. Indeed, the adiabatic shear idea will be more plausible if the electroconductivity of the material increases as its initial temperature decreases. If it decreases the structural rearrangement idea will be more plausible.

EXPERIMENT

Samples of Pyrex type glass (Russian designation LK-105 [23]) have been investigated. The glass composition of wt % is the following: SiO_2 - 80.5; B_2O_3 - 12.5; AL_2O_3 - 1.48; $NaCl$ - 1.0; MgO - 0.51; and the remaining constituents - 4.21; its density is equal to 2.237 g/gm^3.

The samples consisted of flat parallel face plates of dimensions 110 X 80*mm* with thicknesses from 1 mm to 10 mm. The samples had no visible defects, and its roughness did not exceed 8 μm.. Aluminum flyer plates 7 mm thick accelerated by some explosive device to a velocity of 1.95 km/s were used to generate shocks of 13.8 GPa. The flat central part of the flyer plate was no smaller than 80 mm in diameter.

The experiments were performed at different initial temperatures, from 77 K (the boiling point of liquid nitrogen) to 300 K (room temperature). The samples were cooled to 77 K by immersing the experimental arrangement in liquid nitrogen.

Intermediate temperatures between 77 K and 300 K were achieve by allowing the liquid nitrogen to drain from the box containing the experimental arrangement. The temperature of the arrangement increased evenly until the desired temperature, which was monitored by a copper-constant thermo-coupler located between the samples (see Figure 1). The temperature gradient during both the cooling and warming did not exceed 0.5 K/mm. This was verified by separate experiments. The electric conductivity profiles were measured along the direction of propagation of the shock, i.e. the electric field vector was perpendicular to the shock front. The gauge assembly used in the measurements consisted of two copper strips 15 mm wide and 0.03 mm thick placed on either side of a 1 mm thick glass plate. The strips were positioned perpendicularly such that they crossed at the center of the plate. The assembly was placed between two glass samples and was isolated from the samples with Teflon films 0.05 mm thick. In all experiments the sample impacted by the flyer plate was 7 mm thick. The lower sample was more than 10 mm thick. A managing or constant pressure gauge was placed near the center of the electric conductivity gauge (see Figure 1 [25]). For the intermediate temperature experiments between 77 K and 300 K, a copper-constant was also placed near the center of the gauge.

The circuit used in the electric conductivity profile measurements is shown in Figure 2. The gauge in the differential resistance bridge was shunted by a 2.8 K Ω resistor. The bridge was then balanced. Just before the recording, a constant current was introduced into the bridge. The resistance of the glass decreases during shock compression. The bridge is unbalanced and a voltage U appears. The relation between U and the gauge resistance R was determined in separate calibration tests using a resistance bank. The calibration curve is shown in Figure 3. For sufficiently large values of R, the relation is linear. It should be noted that all experiments were performed in the linear region. The time dependence of the resistance æ(t) given by (t) = h/s showed the characteristic electric conductivity of glass behind the shock wave front. In the formula, h is the thickness of the gauge glass, S is the area of the intersection of the copper foil strips.

The thickness of the electroconductivity gauge used in this paper was 1 mm, which is substantially smaller than the compression wave front width evaluated at approximately 3-5 mm. The front crosses the gauge in 0.2 - 0.3 μS, and this time should be considered as some measure of the gauge inertia.

One can see from Figure 1 that loading of the gauge occurs as the technique and the charged condenser method [11,20,24]. In the charged condenser technique, the sample is located between two electrodes consisting of metallic plates which as a rule have a larger dynamic impedance than the sample. It shall also be noted that volume electroconductivity was measured in this paper since the gauge surface was large and edge effects were negligibly small.

It is known that [11,24] electroconductivity measurements can be complicated by spurious electrical signals generated during the passage of the shock through the gauge. In fact, shock polarization and high frequency capacity change were considered sources of electromagnetic noise. They were evaluated in the following way: certain experiments were conducted with copper strips isolated by Teflon films 0.05 mm thick. It was found that the noise amplitude was, on the average, an order of magnitude smaller than the useful signal and was within experimental error. They were therefore not taken into account.

RESULTS AND DISCUSSIONS

Electroconductivity profiles in glass were recorded at five different initial temperatures (77, 132, 187, 242 and 300 K). Longitudinal stress profiles were recorded simultaneously. Representative experimental oscillograms are shown in Figure 4 and the profiles in Figure 5.

It is shown that the close order position of the glass ions changes in the shock wave front [18, 19]. This structural change must manifest itself as a change in not only mechanical but electrical properties as well. Indeed, it is seen from Figure 5 that a notable increase of the electroconductivity occurs during the material inelastic deformation. One can also see that the electroconductivity at the same Lagrangian coordinates decreases as the sample temperature decreases

It should be noted that the electroconductivity profile also changes with temperature changes. At 77 K the profile consists of two spikes, and as the temperature increases, one of the two spikes decreases so that at 300 K, only one spike is observed. From the considerations mentioned in the introduction, the structural rearrangement idea appears to be more feasible for the interpretation of glass behavior in the shock wave front.

It has been shown in [17] that the glass-shock inelastic deformation rate decreases with decreasing initial temperature. On the other hand, it has been revealed in this paper that the electroconductivity of glass also decreases inside the deformation compression wave. The relation between the two profiles are shown in Figure 6 for initial temperatures of 300 K and 77 K. The deformation rate profiles were obtained by differentiation of the deformation profiles. The deformation profiles were determined by Lagrangian analysis of two sets of stress profiles recorded at some Lagrangian coordinates for each of the corresponding initial temperatures [16, 17]. Figure 6 shows not only temperature but also the time correlation of the electroconductivity and deformation rate in the region of inelastic shock deformation. Indeed, the electroconductivity and the deformation rate profiles change simultaneously in time at both initial temperatures of 77 and 300 K.

Time correlation of the electroconductivity and the inelastic deformation rate can be interpreted in terms of "structural rearrangement". A deformation rate increase causes the acceleration of the structure rearrangement, and consequently increases the rupture rate of the bonds. This leads to an increase in the number of free carriers, resulting in an increase of the electroconductivity. Conversely, a deformation rate decrease attenuates the process of structural rearrangement. It decreases the number of free carriers due to the recombination of broken bonds, hence decreasing electroconductivity.

The observed temperature and time correlations imply that the temperature dependence of the electroconductivity is in fact governed by a change of the shock compressibility regularities of the glass with temperature. On the whole, the data obtained in this paper allows for interpretation in terms of the assumption proposed in [17]. According to this assumption, homogeneous processes taking place in the shock compressed material volume are responsible for inelastic deformation of the glass.

REFERENCES

1. J. Wackerle, J. App. Phys., v. 33, 922 (1962).
2. A.N. Dremin and G.A. Adadurov, Fizika Tverdogo Tela (Russ.), v. 6, no. 6, 1756 (1964).
3. T.J. Ahrens and G.E. Duvall, J. Geophys. Res., v. 71, 4349 (1966).
4. L.M. Barker and R.E. Hollenbach, J. Appl. Phys., v. 41, 4208 (1970).
5. J. Arndt, U. Horneman and W.F. Muller, Phys. Chem. Glasses, v. 12, no. 1 (1971).
6. A.V. Anan'in, O.N. Brensov, A.N. Dremin, S.V. Pershin, A.I. Rogacheva and V.F. Tatsii, Fizika Gorenja i Vzriva (Russ.), no. 4, 578 (1974).
7. G.I. Kanel and A.M. Molodets, Zhurnal Technitsheskoi Fiziki (Russ.), no. 46, 398 (1976).
8. G.I. Kanel, A.M. Molodets and A.N. Dremin, Fizika Goreniya i Vzriva (Russ.), no. 6, 906 (1972).
9. J. Gagnoux, Shock Waves in Condensed Matter - 1981, ed. W. Nellis, L. Seaman, R. Graham's Academic Press, N.Y. 392 (1982).
10. H. Siguira, K. Kondo and A. Sawaoka, J. Appl. Phys., v. 52, 3375 (1981).
11. K. Kondo, A. Sawaoka and T.J. Ahrens, J. Appl. Phys., v. 52, 5084 (1981).
12. L.C. Chabildas and D.E. Grady, Shock Waves in Condensed Matter - 1983, ed. J.R. Asay., R. Graham, G.K. Straub, Elsevier Science Publishers B.V., Amsterdam (1984) 175.
13. Y. Yeshurun, G. Rosenberg and Z. Rosenberg, Shock Waves in Condensed Matter - 1985, Ed. Y.M. Gupta, Plenum Press, N.Y. (1985), 431.
14. S.J. Bless, N.S. Brar and A. Rosenberg, Shock Waves in Condensed Matter - 1987, ed. S.C. Schmidt, N.C. Holmes, N-H Physics Publishing Amsterdam (1988) 309.
15. C.M. Lopatin, S.J. Bless and N.S. Brar, Shock Compression of Condensed Matter - 1989, ed. S.C. Schmidt, J.N. Johnston, L.W. Davison, - Elsevier Science Publishers NY (1990) 633.
16. A.M. Molodets, A.V. Orlov and A.N. Dremin, Detonation - Proc. of IX All Union Symp. on Combustion and Explosion, Chernogolovka, (1989) 74.
17. A.N. Dremin, A.V. Orlov, and A.M. Molodets, Proceedings of the 2nd International symposium on intense dynamic loading and its effects, (1992) Chengdu, China, 415.
18. D.E. Grady, W.P. Murri and P.S. DeCarli, J. Geophys. Res., v. 80, 4857 (1975).
19. H. Siguira, K. Kondo and A. Sawaoka, High Pressure Res. Geophys., Dordrecht, e.a., Tokyo 551 (1982).
20. T. Mashimo, K. Nagayama and A. Sawaoka, Phys. Chem. Minerals, v. 9, 237 (1983).
21. I. Hoprins and K. Kerkjian, Fizitsheskaya Akustika (Russ.) v. 2, ed. U. Meson, Mir, Moscow (1969).
22. Chemical technology of glass and sitals, Teaching Book for Institute and Universities, ed. N.M. Pavlushin, Stroiizdat, Moscow (1983).
23. Inquiri book-optic, ed. S.M. Kusnetsov, M.A. Okatov, Mashinostroenie, Leningrad (1983).
24. T.J. Ahrens, J. Appl. Phys., v. 37 2532 (1966).
25. G.I. Kanel, Review VINITI, Science Department, no. 477, (28.11.1974).

FIGURES

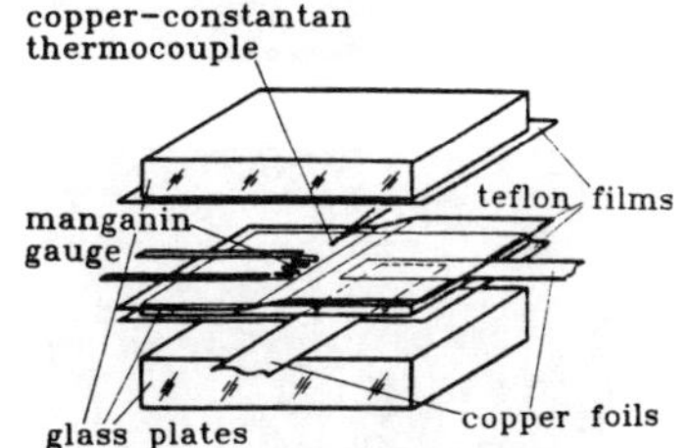

Figure 1. Experimental assembly to measure electroconductivity at different initial temperatures. 1 - glass plates, 2 - teflon films, 3 - copper foils, 4 - mangoanin gauge, 5 - copper-constantan thermocouple.

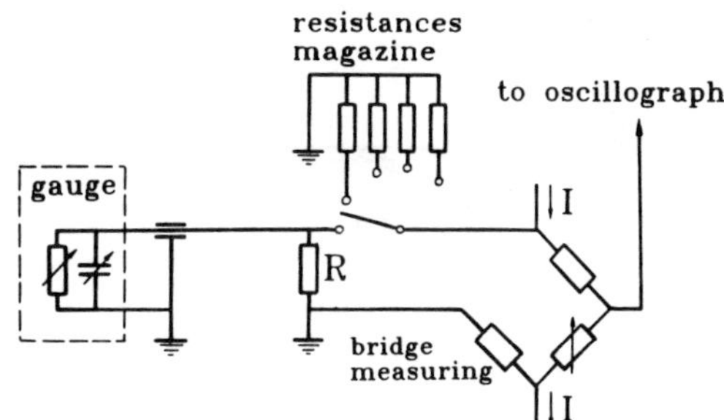

Figure 2. Schematic of the circuit for electroconductivity time profile recording.

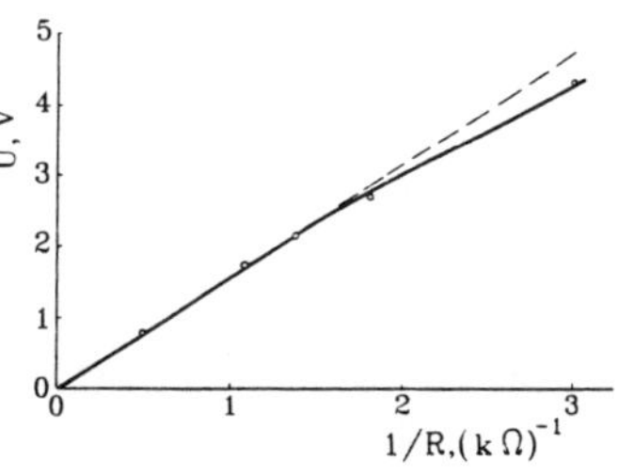

Figure 3. Dependence of the bridge unbalance voltage U on the inverse resistance of the gauge $1/R$.

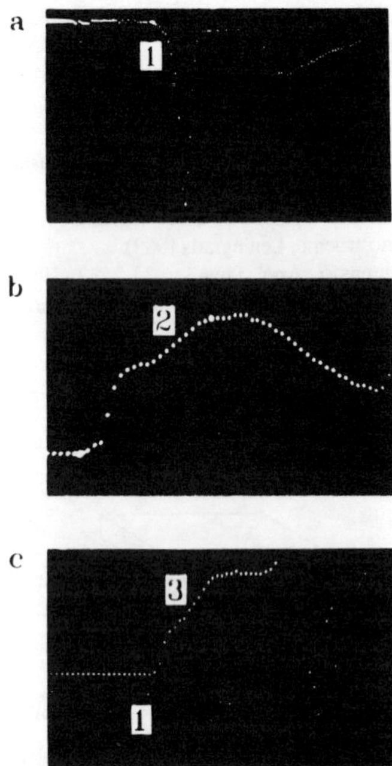

Figure 4. Representative oscillograms for the different gauges: 1 - electroconductivity, 2 - constantan, and 3 - manganin, recorded at different initial temperatures: a - 77 K, b - 300 K, c - 187 K. It is clear that the electroconductivity and pressure gauge signals begin simultaneously.

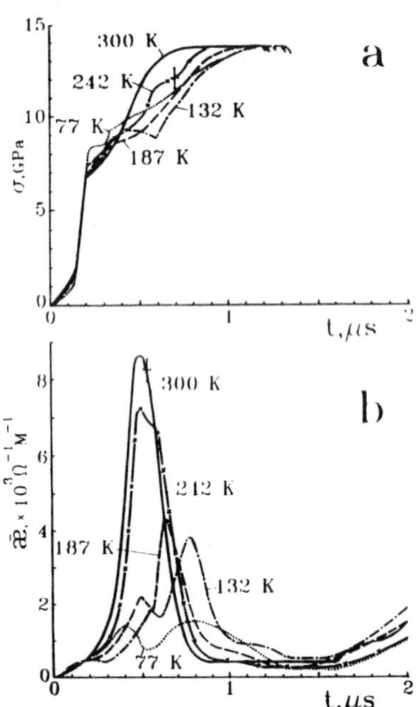

Figure 5. Stress (a) and electroconductivity (b) profiles recorded at different initial temperatures.

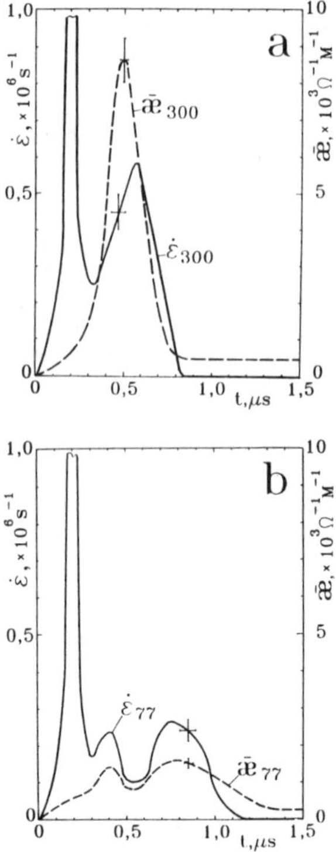

Figure 6. Glass electroconductivity x and strain rate ϵ profiles for a 7 mm Lagrangian coordinate at different initial temperatures: a) 300 K, b) 77 K

THE ELECTRICAL CONDUCTIVITY OF THE ORGANIC CONDUCTORS UNDER HIGH PRESSURE

V. Čelebonović

Institute of Physics, P. O. B. 57, 11001 Beograd, Yugoslavia

H. J. Schulz

Université Paris-Sud, Labor. Phys. Solides, Bat. 510, 91405 Orsay, France

Quasi one-dimensional (Q1D) organic conductors (the Bechgaard salts) were discovered in 1980. It was soon shown that their electrical conductivity cannot be calculated by using the standard theory of transport processes in metals. We have calculated the conductivity of the Q1D organic conductors due to electron-electron scattering. The calculation was performed for the 1D half-filled discrete Hubbard model, using the "memory function" method. The agreement with high-pressure, low temperature experiments is excellent.

The aim of this paper is to report on a calculation of the low temperature electrical conductivity of the quasi one-dimensional (Q1D) organic conductors. These materials were recently described as "almost a complete mystery" [2]. Experiments searching for the existence of possible conducting and superconducting phases in the organic materials received a strong boost in the sixties. It has then been suggested that superconductivity in these materials might be mediated by a non-phonon pairing mechanism [13]. Hopes were high at the time that such a mechanism could lead to high critical temperatures.

The first example of a Q1D organic superconductor was found in $(TMTSF)_2$ PF_6 [8]. This material belongs to the $(TMTSF)_2$ X family of organic salts, where $(TMTSF)_2$ is bistetramethyl-tetraselenafulvalene, and X is an anion; X = PF_6, ReO_4, FSO_3, ClO_4,.... Measurements of conductivity were performed on many Q1D organic conductors (for reviews of the field see [5,7,9,11] and references given there).

It was soon established [10] that the theory of the electrical conductivity of standard metals was not applicable to those materials. Following this, and a theoretical proposal by Anderson [1], Q1D organic conductors are studied within the Hubbard model of correlated electrons, which is exactly solvable in one dimension [12].

We have performed our calculation by the "memory-function" method [6]. The big advantage of this method is that the only input it demands is the Hamiltonian of the system under consideration. We have limited the calculation to the case of half filling, because this fixes the chemical potential (that is, $\mu = 0$) [12]. The electrons were assumed to behave as a normal Fermi liquid.

The algorithm of our calculation consists of the following equations:

$$\chi_{AB}(z) = \langle\langle A; B \rangle\rangle$$

$$= -i \int_0^\infty e^{izt} \langle [A(t), B(0)] \rangle dt \quad (1)$$

where z is the frequency and $A(t)$ is the Heisenberg representation of the operator A. This is a general definition of a correlation function of two operators, which can be applied to the current-current case by putting $A = B = [j, H]$. Once the current-current correlation function $\chi_{AB}(z)$ has been determined, the memory function is introduced as

$$M(z) = z\chi(z)/[\chi_0 - \chi(z)] \quad (2)$$

and the conductivity is given by

$$\sigma(z) = (i/4\pi)\omega_p^2/[z + M(z)] \quad (3)$$

where $\omega_p^2 = 4\pi ne^2/m$ denotes the square of the plasma frequency.

The Hubbard Hamiltonian, and the current operator have the following forms:

$$H = -t\sum_{l,\sigma}(c_{l,\sigma}^+ c_{l+1,\sigma} + (c_{l+1,\sigma}^+ c_{l,\sigma}) + U\sum_j n_{j,\uparrow} n_{j,\downarrow} \quad (4)$$

where the first term is due to electronic hopping, and the second one to the Coulomb interaction of electrons with opposite spins. The current operator is

$$j = -it\sum_{l,\sigma}(c_{l,\sigma}^+ c_{l+1,\sigma} - c_{l+1,\sigma}^+ c_{l,\sigma}) \quad (5)$$

and all the symbols in eqs. (4) and (5) have their usual meaning.

Skipping all the mathematical details, the final expression for the imaginary part of the conductivity of a Q1D organic conductor is:

$$\sigma(z,\beta) \cong i\{(\mathbf{X}/z)[1 - \mathbf{K}\beta/(1+\exp(2\beta))] + \mathbf{G}\beta/(1+\exp(2\beta))\} \quad (6)$$

In this expression, β denotes the inverse temperature, the hopping is equal to 1 and **X**, **G**, **K** are known functions containing parameters of the specimen.

The shape of the curve $\sigma(z,\beta)$ can be varied by changing the values of **X**, **G**, **K**. This means that our calculation gives the possibility of determining material parameters and their changes under pressure by fitting eq. (6) to experimental data on the conductivity. On the purely theoretical side, this calculation was performed in a discrete Hubbard model, and the correlation functions were determined by definition. This is a distinct advantage over recent work by Giamarchi [4], where the continuum formulation and bosonization techniques were employed. Work is now in progress to calculate the conductivity and the optical response functions for arbitrary band filling (which means for $\mu \neq 0$).

ACKNOWLEDGEMENTS

This work was started while the first author was a visitor in Orsay in 1989/1991 under a French Government scholarship.

REFERENCES

[1] P. W. Anderson, *Science* 235, pp. 1196–1198 (1987).

[2] P. W. Anderson and R. Schrieffer, *Physics Today* 44 (6), pp. 54–61 (1991).

[3] K. Bechgaard, C. S. Jacobsen, K. Mortensen *et al.*, *Solid State Commun.* 33, pp. 1119–1125 (1980).

[4] T. Giamarchi, *Phys. Rev.* B44, pp. 2905–2913 (1991).

[5] L. P. Gor'kov, *Sov. Phys. Usp.* 27, pp. 809–828 (1984).

[6] W. Gotze and P. Wolfle, *Phys. Rev.* B6, pp. 1226–1238 (1972).

[7] T. Ishiguro and K. Yamaji, *Organic Superconductors*, Berlin: Springer Verlag, 1990.

[8] D. Jérome, A. Muzaud, M. Ribault *et al.*, *J. Physique Lett.* 41, pp. L95–L98 (1980).

[9] D. Jérome, H. J. Schulz, *Adv. Phys.* 31, pp. 299–490 (1982).

[10] D. Jérome and F. Creuzet, (ed. by S. A. Wolf and V. Z. Kresin), in *Novel Superconductivity*, New York: Plenum Press, 1987, pp. 103–133.

[11] D. Jérome, K. Bechgaard, *Adv. Mater.* 4, pp. 461–463 (1992).

[12] E. H. Lieb and F. Y. Wu, *Phys. Rev. Lett.* 20, pp. 1445–1448 (1988).

[13] W. A. Little, *Phys. Rev.* A134, pp. 1416–1424 (1964).

PRESSURE INDUCED METALLIZATION OF THE MOTT INSULATOR VI_2*

Eran Sterer and Moshe P. Pasternak
School of Physics and Astronomy, Tel Aviv University, 69978 Tel Aviv, ISRAEL
and
R.Dean Taylor, Physics Division, Los Alamos National Laboratory, NM 87545, USA

Using diamond anvil cells, ^{129}I Mössbauer Spectroscopy (MS) and Resistivity measurements were carried out in the layered antiferromagnet VI_2 as a function of pressure ($0<P<45$ GPa) and temperature ($4<T<300$K). MS to 15 GPa reveals an impressive increase in the *Néel temperature* and a slight increase in the *Transferred Hyperfine Field*. The pressure behavior of R(P,T), in particular near the metal-insulator pressure P_c=44 GPa, is described. Being the lightest transition metal (TM) in the isostructural (TM)I_2 series of the iodides compounds, the V^{2+} (d^3 configuration) represents a typical candidate for a pure **Mott-Hubbard** gap closure. Results are compared with the *heavy* TM diiodides such as NiI_2 and CoI_2 where it is expected that the **Charge Transfer** regime prevails.

INTRODUCTION

The majority of the binary Transition-Metal (TM) compounds obey the fundamental phenomenology of *Mott Insulators*[1] namely, (*i*) they are antiferromagnetic insulators in which local moments persist unchanged above T_N, (*ii*) they have relatively large optical band gaps and (*iii*) excitons are present in their optical absorption spectrum. Among numerous binary *Mott Insulators* (MI) TM diiodides (TM = V, Cr, Mn, Fe, Co and Ni), as will be discussed later, constitute an interesting case for studying pressure-tuned electronic and magnetic properties.

The (TM)I_2 are structurally isomorphous and are all antiferromagnetic with the TM cations forming a ferromagnetic ordered layer separated by two adjacent iodine layers. The present studies deal with the lightest among the TM diiodides; $\mathbf{VI_2}$, an antiferromagnetic (T_N=15K) insulator. Measurements were carried out to determine the *Insulator-Metal* transition using Resistivity and ^{129}I Mössbauer Spectroscopy methods[2] . Of the latter, only preliminary findings will be reported.

Vanadium diiodide crystallizes with a CdI_2 structure (space group $C\bar{3}m$) in which the TM is surrounded by a nearly octahedral environment of six iodine ions, whereas each iodine is bound to three equivalent nearest neighbor metal ions. The spin direction in the antiferromagnetic state has been determined by Mössbauer Spectroscopy (Friedt et al.[3]) and found to be along the V-I bond direction; 54 degrees with respect to the *c*-axis.

EXPERIMENTAL

Sample Preparation

Samples in milligram amounts were prepared by direct solid-vapor reaction of high purity vanadium metal and elemental iodine. For the R(P,T) measurements, iodine in its natural abundance form was used. For MS measurements an absorber was prepared using $Pd^{129}I_2$ which decomposes to I_2 at 350 ^{0}C. Stoichiometric amounts of the elements were encapsulated under vacuum in a quartz tube and heated for 24 hours at 850 ^{0}C. The purple/pink VI_2 crystals were loaded under dry atmosphere inside a glove box.

Measurements

Mössbauer Spectroscopy spectra were recorded using a top-loaded variable temperature He cryostat. in conjunction with a $Mg_3{}^{129m}TeO_6$ source. A Merill-Bassett cell with $Ta_{0.9}W_{0.1}$ gasket alloy was used. Pressures[2] were determined by the ruby fluorescence method.

Resistivity measurements were carried out in a miniature Diamond Anvil Cell[4] (DAC) using a quasi four-point method. Gold wire electrodes, 10 μm diameter were applied to the culet of the diamond (400 μm diameter) facing the insulating layer. Up to pressures close to the Mott transition pressure (P_c), measurements were carried out solely at room temperature. At $P \sim P_c$ series of R(P,T) measurements were carried out.

RESULTS

Mössbauer Spectroscopy

Mössbauer Spectroscopy measurements were carried out to P = 15 GPa as function of pressure and temperature. Typical spectra recorded in the antiferromagnetic (4 K) and paramagnetic states (300 K) are shown in Fig. 1. The RT spectrum was fitted with a pure quadrupole splitting and the data at 4 K. with a magnetic and quadrupole interaction assuming the following *Hamiltonian*:

$$H = \mu H_{eff} I_z + \left\{ \frac{e^2 q_{zz} Q \,(3\cos\theta^2 - 1)}{8I(2I-1)} \right\} \left\{ 3I_z^2 - I(I-1) \right\}$$

where H_{eff} is the hyperfine field at the nucleus, $e^2q_{zz}Q$ is the quadrupole coupling and θ the angle between H_{eff} and the electric field gradient eq_{zz}.

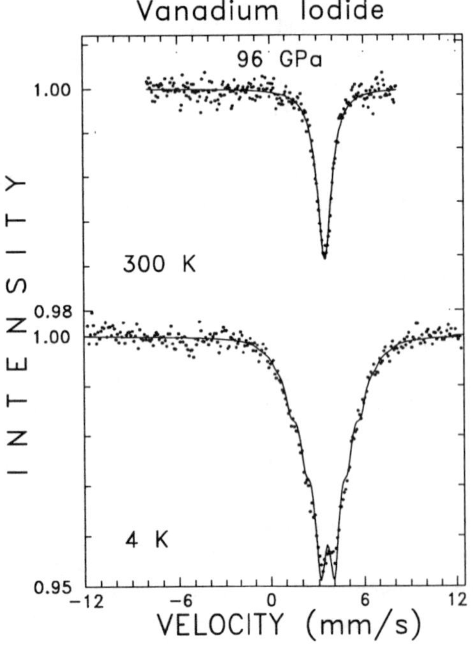

Figure 1. ^{129}I Mössbauer spectrum of VI_2 at 9.6 GPa recorded in the antiferromagnetic (4 K) and in the paramagnetic states (300 K) respectively. The solid line is a theoretical spectrum obtained from least-squares-fitting to the experimental points. The source was $Mg_3{}^{129m}TeO_6$.

Resistivity

The pressure dependence at 300 K of the sample resistance as a function of pressure is shown in Fig. 2. The log(R) levels off around 35-40 GPa and does not reach a plateau as would be expected if the whole sample metallizes.

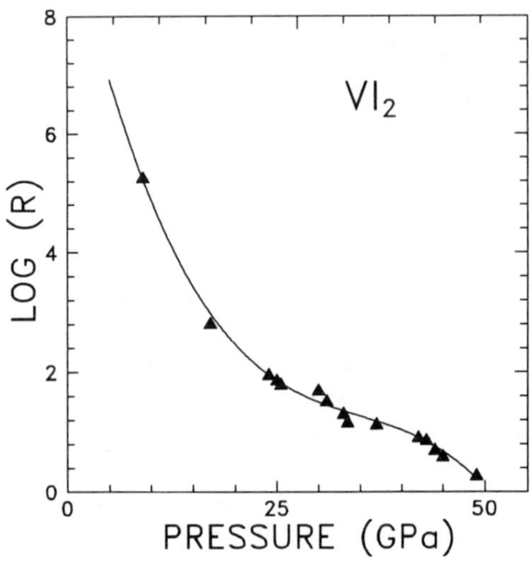

Figure 2. The pressure dependence of the Resistance of VI_2 at 300 K. The solid line is a guide to the eye. The error in pressure is ±0.4 GPa. Note the leveling off of log(R) near 35 GPa; an indication of possible metalization.

To measure the insulator-metal transition pressure, a series of R(T,P) data were recorded in the 200 - 350 K temperature range near 35 GPa. In this temperature range the R(T) functions displayed a linear behavior. The resistance derivative could be calculated using a least-squares-fitting program. A plot of $dR/dT(P)$ is shown in Fig. 3. There is clearly a change in sign, from negative to positive, at ~ 45 GPa. A value of P_c = 44±1 GPa is obtained from this analysis. No hysteresis was detected under decompression.

DISCUSSION

Vanadium diiodide is the lightest of the $(TM)I_2$ MI. It has the highest P_c (44 GPa) of all measured pressure-induced Mott transitions. For the *heavy* iodides, Ni, Co and Fe, values of P_c are: 19, 12 and 21 GPa respectively[5,6,7]. For Mott-Hubbard theory[8] in its simplest form it is proposed that charge fluctuations of the $d_i^n d_j^n \leftrightarrow d_i^{n-1} d_j^{n+1}$ results in an intra-band gap U. At ambient pressure it is now accepted that this mechanism is responsible for the electronic (optical) band gap in the Ti and V compounds. Zaanen et al.[9] proposed a different charge fluctuation scheme to explain the origin of the optical gap in the *heavy* TM compounds, namely, the *Charge-Transfer* mechanism. It involves the CT inter-band gap Δ and charge fluctuation of the form $d_i^n \leftrightarrow d_i^{n+1}\underline{L}$ where $\underline{L}$ denotes, in the present case, a 5*p*-hole in the iodine valence band.

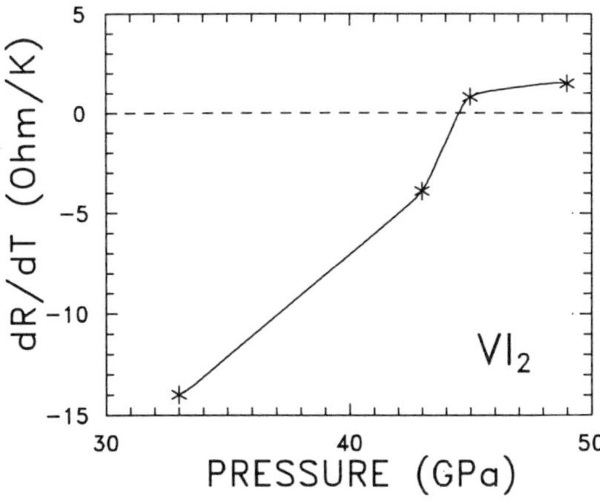

Figure 3. The pressure dependence of the resistance derivative of VI_2 at 300 K near 45 GPa. The solid line is to guide the eye. The transition from (-) to (+) values determines the pressure of the *insulator→metal* transition.

The CT mechanism, in which $E_{gap} \propto \Delta$, is explicitly proportional to the electronegativity of the anion via Δ . A pure Mott-Hubbard gap formulation does not include the ligand electronegativity, it uses a free-ion basis for the d^n configurations. Undoubtedly a better scheme would have been to incorporate *bonding and antibonding* basis functions so that much of the ground state 5*p*-3*d* hybridization is included from the outset. The exclusion of this factor in the basis functions results in intra-band gaps exceeding 5-8 eV. The relatively low experimental value of P_c for VI_2 is a clear evidence for such an extended basis function.

At this stage we assume the VI_2 gap closure to be of the Mott-Hubbard type. A better understanding of the mechanism of the gap closure will be available once the ^{129}I Mössbauer results near P_c will have been analyzed. The latter, via the Isomer Shift and magnetic interaction data will provide information[10] on the magnetic and electronic properties at and close to the Mott transition. The MS results will also permit one to check the possibility of the coexistence of the metallic and *"gapped"* states near P_c There is evidence of this coexistence in Fig. 2; namely, *R*(P) does not level off at $P \geq P_c$. A similar result was observed in CoI_2 (ref. 10) in which the metallic behavior near P_c as measured by *R*(T) was explained on the basis of a percolative system.

REFERENCES

* Partially supported by ISF grant 165/2 and by the DOE-IGPP.

[1] B. Brandow, *Int. J. Quantum Chem.* **26**, 417, (1977).

[2] Moshe P. Pasternak and R. Dean Taylor, *Hyperf. Interact.* **62**, 89, (1990).

[3] J.M. Friedt, J.P. Sanchez and G.K. Shenoy, *J. Chem. Phys.* **65**, 5093, (1977).

[4] E. Sterer, M.P. Pasternak and R.D. Taylor, *Rev. Sci. Instrum.* **61**, 1117, (1990).

[5] M.P. Pasternak, R.D. Taylor, A. Chen, C. Meade, L.M. Falicov, A. Giesekus, R. Jeanloz and P.Y. Yu, *Phys. Rev. Lett.* **65**, 790, (1990).

[6] Eran Sterer and Moshe P. Pasternak, *High Pressure Research* **10**, 457, (1992).

[7] E. Sterer, G. Hearne, M.P. Pasternak and R.D. Taylor, *to be published.* A. Chen, *private communication.*

[8] N.F. Mott, *Proc. Phys. Soc.* (London) A**62**, 416, (1949). J. Hubbard, *ibid.* A**277**, 237, 1964 and A**281**, 401, (1964).

[9] J. Zaanen, G.A. Sawatzky and J.W. Allen, *Phys. Rev. Lett.* **55**, 418, (1985).

[10] M.P. Pasternak, R.D. Taylor and R. Jeanloz, *Frontiers of High Pressure Research*, eds. H.D. Hochheimer and R.D. Etters, New York: Plenum Press, 1991, pp. 227-242.

HIGH PRESSURE STUDIES ON THE FERROMAGNETIC DENSE KONDO SYSTEMS $CeRh_3B_2$ AND UCu_2Ge_2

A.L. Cornelius and J.S. Schilling
Department of Physics
Washington University
Campus Box 1105, One Brookings Drive
St. Louis, MO 63130–4899, U.S.A.

T. Endstra and J.A. Mydosh
Kamerlingh Onnes Laboratorium
University of Leiden
P.O. Box 9506
2300 RA Leiden, The Netherlands

The dependence of the Curie temperature of the anomalous ferromagnets UCu_2Ge_2 and $CeRh_3B_2$ on hydrostatic pressure to 11 GPa is determined using a diamond–anvil cell loaded with dense helium as pressure medium. A sensitive primary/secondary coil system allows the detection of the ferromagnetic transition in the ac susceptibility for tiny samples with less than 1 μg mass. The Curie temperatures of the above two compounds, $T_c \approx 110$ K and 118 K, both increase initially under pressure but pass through maxima at 8 GPa and 2 GPa, respectively, before falling rapidly at higher pressures. We take this as evidence that both compounds behave as dense Kondo systems, where T_c depends on the exchange coupling J according to a magnetic phase diagram originally proposed by Doniach.

INTRODUCTION

High–pressure studies of magnetism in solids are of particular value for two principal reasons: (1) they allow a relatively well–defined test of theoretical models, and (2) they may induce structural phase transitions revealing new magnetic states of matter. Unfortunately, the variation of a given magnetic property in a typical high–pressure experiment to 1–2 GPa is quite small, normally amounting to ~ 1% or less. Considerably larger pressure–induced changes have become possible by the recent development of a diamond–anvil high–pressure cell (DAC) suitable for the determination of the Curie temperature of tiny ~ 1 μg ferromagnetic particles to hydrostatic pressures beyond 10 GPa [1].

One of the more interesting forms of magnetism is exhibited by the so–called Kondo–lattice or dense Kondo system where an array of individual Kondo ions are arranged on specific lattice sites. For Kondo impurities such as Fe, Mn, Ce, or U embedded in a nonmagnetic host metal, the negative exchange interaction J between the spins of these impurities and the host conduction electrons precipitates a many–body resonance which leads to strong anomalies in most solid state properties. Perhaps the most significant anomaly is the apparent demagnetization of the impurity moment at temperatures low compared to the characteristic Kondo temperature T_k. In a Kondo–lattice the interactions between the Kondo ions can lead to magnetic ordering below T_c if $|J|$ is not too large. Doniach has shown [2] that within a one–dimensional "Kondo necklace" model antiferromagnetic order can occur at a temperature T_c which is a function of $|JN(E_f)|$, as seen in Fig. 1, where $N(E_f)$ is the density of electron states at the Fermi energy. For sufficiently small values of $|JN(E_f)|$, T_c increases as the square of $|JN(E_f)|$. As $|JN(E_f)|$ increases further approaching the value 1, T_c passes through a maximum and then falls rapidly to zero. The low–temperature saturation moment μ_s would be expected to decrease monotonically as $|JN(E_f)|$ increases. Similar dependences of T_c and μ_s are anticipated for Kondo ions arranged in two– and three–dimensional arrays which may exhibit other than antiferromagnetic order.

For many Kondo impurities, including Fe, Mn, Ce, and U, $|JN(E_f)|$ has been shown to increase under the application of high pressure [3]. One way to map out the magnetic phase diagram in Fig. 1 experimentally would thus be to apply extremely high pressures to a Kondo–lattice system which has been selected to possess a small initial value of $|JN(E_f)|$.

The two intermetallic compounds $CeRh_3B_2$ and UCu_2Ge_2 are Kondo–lattice systems with reduced saturation moments $\mu_s \approx 0.31\ \mu_b$ [4] and 0.88 μ_b [5] which order ferromagnetically below $T_c \approx 115$ K [4] and 105 K [5,6], respectively. Both ordering temperatures are notably high, lying well above the Neel temperatures of the corresponding isostructural stable–moment compounds $GdRh_3B_2$ ($T_c \simeq 90$ K [7]) and $GdCu_2Ge_2$ ($T_c = 14$ K [8]). In fact, $CeRh_3B_2$ possesses the highest magnetic ordering temperature of *any* Cerium system with nonmagnetic constituents. A tentative assignment places both systems to the left of the maximum in T_c versus $|JN(E_f)|$, as seen in Fig. 1. For $CeRh_3B_2$ this assignment appears justified both from the results of chemical substitution [9] and high—pressure experiments to 1.1 GPa [10]; in the latter, T_c is found to increase under pressure at the rate +1.0 K/GPa, whereas μ_s decreases $d\ell n\mu_s/dP \simeq -6.6$ %/GPa. The placement of UCu_2Ge_2 to the left of T_c in Fig. 1 was suggested by Endstra et al. [11] after applying a hybridization model to a compound series where Cu is replaced by various transition metals. To our know-

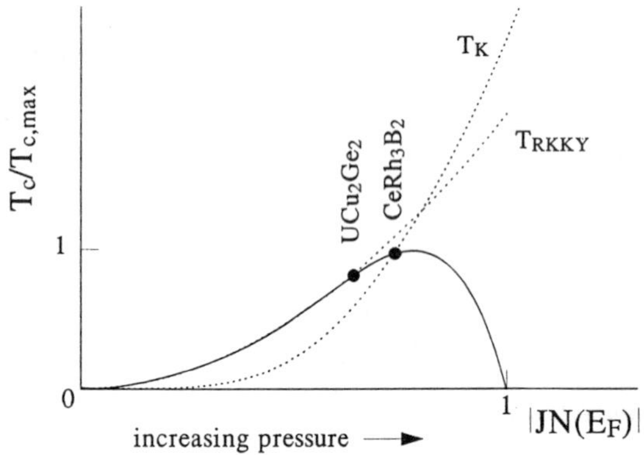

Figure 1. Solid line gives phase diagram of a Kondo lattice from Ref. 2. See text for parameter definitions.

ledge, UCu_2Ge_2 has yet to be studied under high–pressure conditions.

In view of the fact that for both Ce– and U–ions the quantity $|JN(E_f)|$ increases under pressure [3], a particularly direct way to test the present placement of $CeRh_3B_2$ and UCu_2Ge_2 in Fig. 1 would be to determine whether or not the pressure dependence of T_c passes through a maximum. It is clear that to test this prediction a considerable extension of the pressure range beyond the conventional 1–2 GPa would be highly desirable.

EXPERIMENT

The polycrystalline samples used in the present study were prepared from stoichiometric ratios of the pure starting materials by arc–melting under an argon atmosphere. Samples were turned and remelted five times to promote homogeneity; powder x–ray diffraction studies confirmed the anticipated hexagonal (P6/mmm) structure of the $CeRh_3B_2$ sample and the tetragonal (I4/mmm) structure of the UCu_2Ge_2 sample with no trace of secondary phases. For more details of the sample preparation procedures see Refs. 5 and 10.

The high–pressure apparatus used in the present experiments is displayed in Fig. 2 and consists of a copper–beryllium clamp [12] using two 1/6–carat type I diamond anvils with 0.5 mm dia. culets mounted on B_4C plates. The ~ 300 μm thick TaW gaskets with 3 mm dia. are preindented to ~ 120 μm before drilling a 250 μm dia. hole through the center of the gasket. Care is taken to place sufficiently small pieces of sample (60x60x30 μm^3) and ruby (20x20x20 μm^3) into the cell that the diamond anvils do not press directly onto either during an experiment. The pressure clamp is placed in a continuous flow cryostat and superfluid He is loaded into the gasket hole at 2 K to serve as pressure medium. The pressure in the gasket hole (pressure cell) is determined using the standard ruby fluorescence technique [13]. The pressure in the cell is changed at a temperature above the melting curve of He by varying the force between the diamond anvils by loading a membrane with He gas [14].

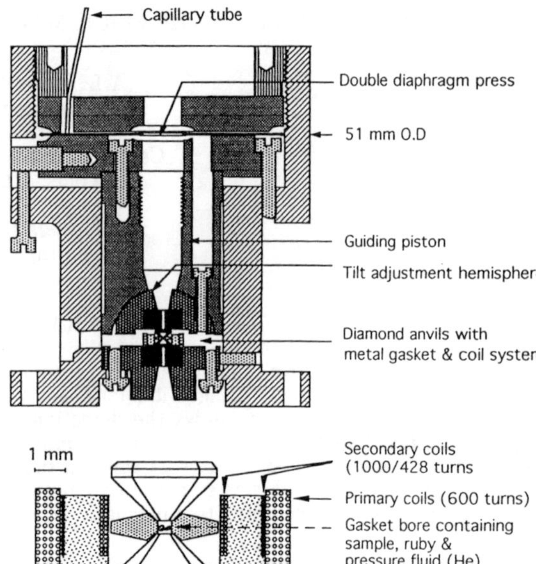

Figure 2. Diamond–anvil pressure clamp for magnetic studies from Ref. 1. Pressure medium is dense He.

The Curie temperature is detected inductively by a sensitive measurement of the ac susceptibility $\chi_{ac}(T)$ using a PAR 124 lock–in amplifier with an impedance–matched Model 119 preamplifier as a function of slowly varying temperature (0.3 – 0.5 K/min.). The temperature is determined using calibrated platinum and carbon resistors located near the sample. After the subtraction of a temperature dependent background from $\chi_{ac}(T)$, the ferromagnetic transition can be clearly resolved (see Fig. 3) and the onset used to define T_c, as indicated by the arrows. The effective sensitivity in the present experiment is not sufficient to detect weaker forms of magnetism such as antiferromagnetism, paramagnetism or diamagnetism. The coil system used for the susceptibility measurement is placed just outside the metal gasket and consists of primary (field) and secondary (pick–up) coils made of 30 and 16 μm dia. copper wire, respectively, and cast in epoxy. The primary field amplitude is ~ 20 Oe at a frequency of 820 Hertz.

In Fig. 3 it is also seen that for pressures above 4 GPa the magnitude of the ferromagnetic transition in $\chi_{ac}(T)$ is strongly diminished. We have observed a similar reduction in transition signal for pressures above 2–3 GPa in previous studies on both ferromagnetic [15] and superconducting [16] materials. At the present time it is not clear whether this reduction is intrinsic to the sample or arises from increased shielding of the sample by the metal gasket at higher pressures; for pressures above 10 GPa the diameter of the gasket hole is reduced to ~ 100 μm. The increase in transition magnitude between 0 and 4.1 GPa in Fig. 3 is not normally observed and probably arises from a

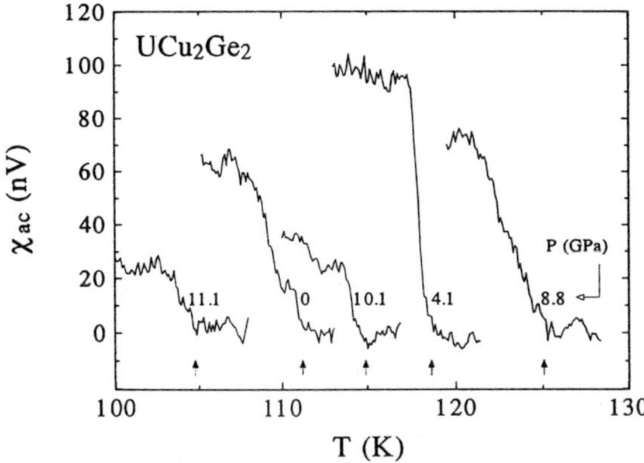

Figure 3. AC susceptibility signal (in nanovolts) versus temperature at various applied hydrostatic pressures.

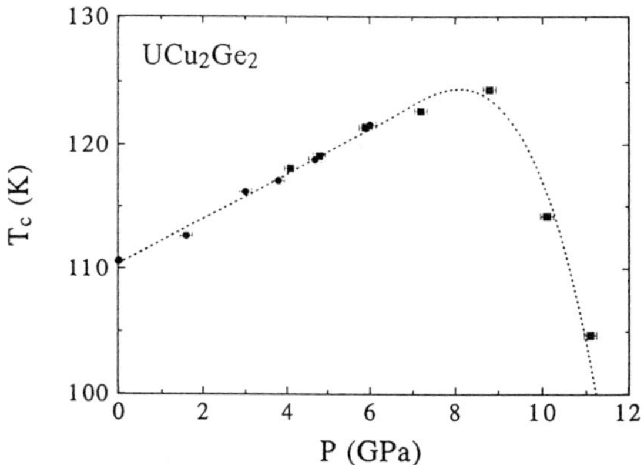

Figure 4. Curie temperature versus pressure.

demagnetization factor effect as the irregularly shaped sample turns with respect to the applied field as the pressure is changed. In the present DAC experiments it is thus not possible to obtain unequivocal information on the pressure dependence of the magnetic moment for either compound. Further details of the high–pressure techniques are given in Refs. 1 and 17.

RESULTS AND DISCUSSION

Results on UCu_2Ge_2

A sampling of the results of the present measurement of $\chi_{ac}(T)$ on the ternary uranium compound are shown in Fig. 3. It is seen that the Curie temperature T_c initially shifts to higher temperatures under pressure, but passes through a maximum near 8 GPa and falls rapidly at higher pressures. This dependence is clearly visible in Fig. 4, where T_c is plotted versus increasing pressure for two separate pressure experiments on different pieces of the same sample. Note that the initial dependence of T_c on pressure is approximately linear and $dT_c/dP \approx +1.9$ K/GPa. The $T_c(P)$ dependence for UCu_2Ge_2 in Fig. 4 obviously bears a close qualitative resemblence to Doniach's phase diagram for a Kondo lattice in Fig. 1. The present experiment thus strongly suggests that UCu_2Ge_2 is a dense Kondo system which should be positioned at ambient pressure somewhat to the left of the maximum in the T_c versus $|JN(E_f)|$ phase diagram. It would be interesting to extend the present studies to even higher pressures; however, the strongly diminished amplitude of the ferromagnetic signature in the higher pressure range make such experiments extremely difficult.

Results on $CeRh_3B_2$

In the right half of Fig. 5a we show the pressure dependence of the Curie temperature of $CeRh_3B_2$ to 7 GPa from four separate experiments on four distinct pieces of the same sample. After an initial increase with pressure at the rate $dT_c/dP \approx +1.0$ K/GPa, $T_c(P)$ passes through a maximum at ~ 2 GPa and falls rapidly at higher pressures; as seen in Fig. 5a, this dependence is reversible in pressure. In the upper pressure range, the change in the signal amplitude of $\chi_{ac}(T)$ at the ferromagnetic transition becomes progressively smaller (45 nV at 2.5 GPa, 30 nV at 3.5 GPa, 20 nV at 5.2 GPa, and 15 nV at 6.3 GPa). For pressures greater than 6.3 GPa no transition is observed; this means that either the transition amplitude is below our experimental resolution of 10 nV, or that the temperature of the transition has fallen below the lowest temperature studied 4 K.

The dependence of T_c on pressure for $CeRh_3B_2$ is in good qualitative agreement with Doniach's phase diagram in Fig. 1. This conclusion is further strengthened by the fact that earlier dc magnetization experiments by Shaheen et al. [10] to 1.1 GPa revealed that the saturation moment μ_s of $CeRh_3B_2$ decreases under pressure, as seen in Fig. 5b. The present experiments thus lend support to the identification of both UCu_2Ge_2 and $CeRh_3B_2$ as dense Kondo systems lying to the left of the maximum in the plot of T_c versus $|JN(E_f)|$, where the cerium compound lies somewhat closer to the T_c–maximum than the uranium compound.

To further support the identification of the above compounds as Kondo–lattice systems it would be desirable to apply *negative* pressure (i.e. dilate the lattice) and determine whether for both systems the Curie temperature T_c decreases whereas the saturation moment μ_s increases. Whereas negative pressure cannot be applied in a hydrostatic pressure experiment, it can be obtained by appropriate chemical substitution, for example, by substituting the larger Si for B in $CeRh_3(B_{1-y}Si_y)_2$. The results from Ref. 9 are displayed in the left half of Figs. 5a and 5b. The fact that T_c decreases and μ_s increases with lattice dilation lends further support to the conclusions of the present high–pressure experiments on $CeRh_3B_2$.

We emphasize here that the functional dependence of T_c on either the Si content or pressure in Fig. 5a should only be compared in a very rough qualitative way with the phase diagram in Fig. 1. The depen–

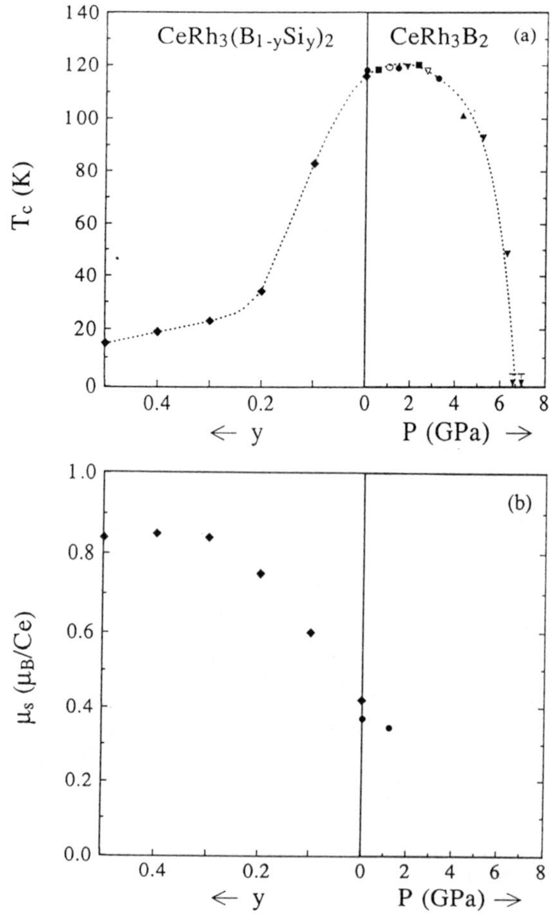

Figure 5. (a) Curie point and (b) saturation moment versus pressure (to right) and Si–content (to left).

dence of $|JN(E_f)|$ on pressure (or sample volume) is strongly nonlinear; in fact, a model calculation by Harrison and Straub [18] indicates that $|J|$ is proportional to the inverse *fourth* power of the relative sample volume. In addition, the sample volume of $CeRh_3(B_{1-y}Si_y)_2$ is a very nonlinear function of the Si content y. If T_c is plotted not versus y or pressure but versus the relative change in the coupling strength J, a very reasonable qualitative agreement with the phase diagram in Fig. 1 is obtained [15]. We refer the interested reader to Ref. 15 for a more detailed analysis of the results on $CeRh_3B_2$ and related Ce compounds.

REFERENCES

[1] S. Klotz, J.S. Schilling, and P. Müller, in *Frontiers of High Pressure Research*, edited by H.D. Hochheimer and E.D. Etters (Plenum Press, New York, 1991) p. 473.
[2] S. Doniach, in: *Valence Instability and Related Narrow Band Phenomena*, edited by R.D. Parks (Plenum Press, New York, 1977); S. Doniach, *Physica* 91B, 231 (1977).
[3] J.S. Schilling, *Advances in Physics* 28, 657 (1979).
[4] S.K. Dhar, S.K. Malik, and R. Vijayaraghavan, *J. Phys.* C 14, L321 (1981).
[5] A.J. Dirkmaat, T. Endstra, E.A. Knetsch, A.A. Menovsky, G.J. Nieuwenhuys, and J.A. Mydosh, *J. Magn. Magn. Mater.* 84, 143 (1990).
[6] J. Leciejewicz, L. Chelmicki, and A. Zygmunt, *Solid State Commun.* 41, 167 (1982).
[7] S. Malik, R. Vijayaraghavan, W.E. Wallace, and S.K. Dhar, *J. Magn. Magn. Mater.* 37, 303 (1983).
[8] A. Szytuta, in *Handbook of Magnetic Materials, Vol. 6*, edited by K.H.J. Buschow (North–Holland, Amsterdam, 1991) p. 85.
[9] S.K. Malik, G.K. Shenoy, S.K. Dhar, P.L. Paulose, and R. Vijayaraghavan, *Phys. Rev. B* 34, 8196 (1986).
[10] S. A. Shaheen, J.S. Schilling, P. Klavins, C.B. Vining, and R.N Shelton, *J. Magn. Magn. Mater.* 47&48, 285 (1985).
[11] T. Endstra, G.J. Nieuwenhuys, and J.A. Mydosh (to be published in *Phys. Rev. B*).
[12] J.S. Schilling, *Mat. Res. Soc. Symp. Proc.* 22, 79 (1984).
[13] G.J. Piermarini, S. Block, J.D. Barnett, and R.A. Forman, *J. Appl. Phys.* 46, 2774 (1975); A. Jayaraman, *Rev. Modern Phys.* 55, 65 (1983).
[14] W.B. Daniels and W. Ryschkewitsch, *Rev. Sci. Instr.* 54, 115 (1983).
[15] A.L. Cornelius and J.S. Schilling (submitted for publication).
[16] S. Klotz, *Ph.D. Thesis*, University of Munich (1992).
[17] S. Klotz and J.S. Schilling, *Physica C* 209, 499 (1993).
[18] W.A. Harrison and G.K. Straub, *Phys. Rev. B* 36, 2695 (1987).

PRESSURE DEPENDENCE OF THE ELECTRONIC AND MAGNETIC PROPERTIES OF THE LAYERED ANTIFERROMAGNETIC INSULATOR FeI_2

G R HEARNE, E STERER and M P PASTERNAK
School of Physics and Astronomy, Tel-Aviv University, Ramat-Aviv 69978, Tel-Aviv, Israel

R D TAYLOR
Physics Division, Los Alamos National Laboratory, Los Alamos, NM 87545, USA.

Nuclear hyperfine interaction parameters have been deduced from ^{57}Fe Mössbauer spectra recorded in the range of 0-26 GPa and at temperatures of 10 - 296 K in anhydrous ferrous iodide. X-ray diffraction data indicate that the compound is isostructural in the range 0 - 25 GPa. There is an abrupt change in the electronic state and spin dynamics of the transition-metal (*TM*) atom, and in the magnetic behavior of the compound at 20 GPa. In the range 0-19 GPa, antiferromagnetic ordering occurs below well-defined Néel temperatures T_N. T_N increases by more than ten-fold and static internal fields of up to 12 Tesla are generated at the *TM* nuclear site. At pressures higher than 20 GPa hyperfine structure associated with atomic-spin fluctuations are evident down to 10 K. An enhanced dynamic internal field of ~30 Tesla -- associated with the spin fluctuations -- is sensed by the iron nucleus. No static magnetic ordering due to cooperative exchange interactions is observed above 20 GPa, in contrast to the magnetism that occurs in the low pressure regime.

INTRODUCTION

Many electrical and magnetic properties of *TM* compounds -- including halides, chalcogenides and oxides -- are sensitively dependent on the electronic structure of the *TM* atom. The insulating properties and antiferromagnetism of most *3d TM* compounds stem from the strong electron correlations that introduces a gap in the lowest-lying metal conduction band. It has been observed that the pressure-induced isostructural transition from a correlated electronic state to a non-correlated state by means of band-gap closure may be accompanied by drastic changes in transport and magnetic properties of the compound [1]. An insulator-to-metal transition ensues and magnetism is lost. It is of obvious interest to "tune" the band-gap and to monitor the electronic structure of the *TM* cation as the band-gap varies until gap-closure ultimately occurs. ^{57}Fe Mössbauer Spectroscopy (MS) on a Fe-based insulator pressurized in a diamond-anvil cell (DAC) may be used to track the electronic structure of the *TM* atom as the interatomic spacing is reduced. It is anticipated that the ferrous dihalide FeI_2 would be amenable to band-gap closure within an accessible range of pressures. The preliminary results of ^{57}Fe MS studies on FeI_2 which has been subjected to high pressures, are reported on here.

CRYSTAL AND MAGNETIC STRUCTURE

FeI_2 crystallizes in the CdI_2 structure. Close-packed hexagonal layers of Fe^{2+} metal ions, which extend perpendicularly to the c-axis, are each sandwiched between two layers of I^- ions. Each ferrous ion is surrounded by an octahedral configuration of anions. Cation sheets have spins ferromagnetically aligned along the c-axis within each I^---Fe^{2+}--I^- slab. Adjacent slabs are coupled by van der Waals forces. Cations in adjacent slabs have antiparallel spins. The overall structure at ambient pressure is antiferromagnetic with $T_N = 9$ K.

EXPERIMENTAL

Samples of FeI_2 enriched to ~25 % in ^{57}Fe were synthesized by solid-vapor reaction in an evacuated quartz tube. Ferrous dihalides are extremely hygroscopic. The crimson-red flakes were loaded into a Merrill-Bassett-type miniature DAC [2] under exceptionally dry conditions in a glove bag with a relative humidity of ≤ 2 %. The ruby chips for ruby-fluorescence manometry and the anvils were oven-dried at ~120°C for at least an hour prior to loading the sample. Argon was loaded as the pressurizing medium. Pressure gradients were less than 5% of the recorded average pressure.

A 5 mCi $^{57}Co(Rh)$ "point" source in conjunction with a high-efficiency Ar-CH_4 proportional counter has been used in the conventional source-DAC-detector transmission geometry. A *Janis* cryostat with top-loading capabilities permits variable temperatures of 6 - 300 K to be obtained. There are severe constraints imposed upon ^{57}Fe MS in DACs because of the high attenuation ($\geq$ 75 %) of incident 14.4 keV gamma-radiation by the anvils and by the minute volume of the sample in the gasket. These problems are exacerbated in the case of FeI_2 because of additional attenuation by the Iodine and by the low mass-fraction , 18%, of iron in the sample. Nevertheless, a spectrum with a sufficiently good signal-to-noise ratio may be obtained in 20-30 hours . This has been achieved by making simple refinements to existing elements of high-pressure MS methodology. Details of the facility which has been used to record spectra at $0 < P < 26$ GPa and $10 < T < 300$ K in a miniature DAC will be published separately [3].

RESULTS AND DISCUSSION

At 296 K the spectrum is a doublet at all pressures in the range 0-26 GPa. The nuclear hyperfine interaction parameters are obtained from theoretical fits to the data. Theoretical spectra were derived from an application of the full Hamiltonian to obtain the nuclear transition energies and intensities [4]. The splitting of the doublet (quadrupole splitting QS) is proportional to the magnitude of the electric field gradient (EFG) at the ^{57}Fe site. The centroid of the spectrum is related to the isomer shift IS which is proportional to the s-electron density at the Fe nucleus .

At low temperatures (***T* « *T*$_N$**) in the range **0-19 GPa** , each absorption spectrum has features of combined magnetic/quadrupole interactions that have comparable magnitudes (***figure 1 (b)***). The absorption envelope extends over a range of ~ 5mm/s . These are typical features when a static magnetic hyperfine field is present in a high-spin ferrous compound. Least-squares-fits of the data yielded typical values of the saturation magnetic hyperfine field H_0 = 10 Tesla, $QS \approx 2$ mm/s and $\theta = 0 \pm 10°$ (θ specifies the direction of H_0 with respect to the principal axes of the EFG).

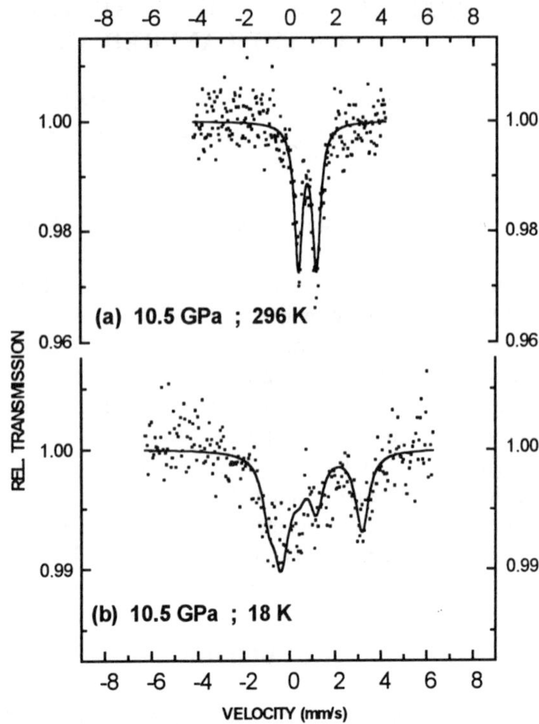

Figure 1. Examples of MS spectra recorded at 10.5 GPa. Solid lines are theoretical fits to the data by using a static spin Hamiltonian. (a) Paramagnetic state. (b) Magnetically ordered state.

There are drastic changes in features of the spectra recorded at low temperatures and high pressures $P \geq$ 20 GPa (***figure 2 (b)***). Each spectrum is **symmetric** with a characteristic **"sagging" baseline** . The absorption envelope extends over a range of ~10 mm/s corresponding to an internal magnetic field $H \approx 30$ Tesla. A pronounced central resonance is evident with additional weaker resonance dips symmetrically located on either side. The outer resonance dips gradually diminish in intensity as the temperature is raised. The spectrum collapses to a symmetric doublet with a flat baseline at high temperatures (*figure 2 (a)*). These temperature-dependent spectral features are characteristic of electron spin relaxation (fluctuations) in a **paramagnetic** iron compound. At 296 K the spin fluctuation frequency ω_S is greater than the nuclear-spin Larmor precession frequency ω_L and H will have a time-average of zero. As the temperature is lowered the intermediate possibility $\omega_S \approx \omega_L$ obtains and a complex spectrum occurs.

The spectrum involves an apparent superposition of spectral components and a "sagging" base-line .

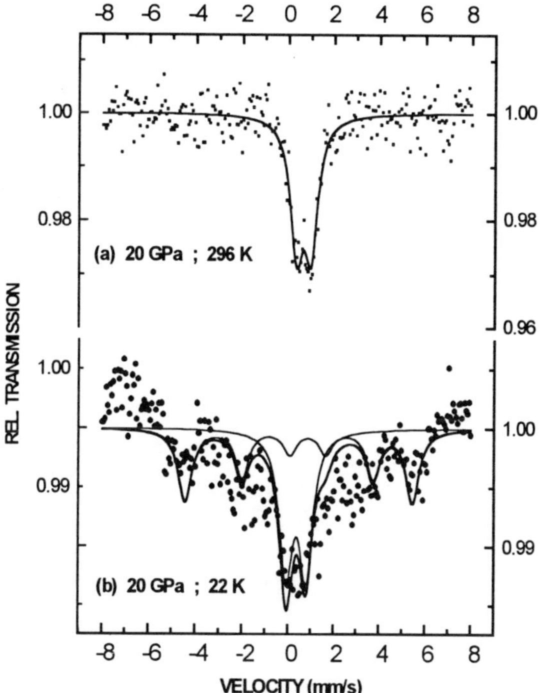

Figure 2. Examples of MS spectra recorded at 20 GPa. Solid lines are theoretical fits by using a static spin Hamiltonian. (a) Paramagnetic state. (b) Spin relaxation regime. The static spin Hamiltonian is, strictly speaking, not applicable in (b).

The pressure evolution of each of the hyperfine interaction parameters is briefly described below.

IS (figure 3(a)) : Values at 296 K decrease monotonically in the range 0 - 18 GPa followed by an abrupt discontinuous change of ≈15 % at 20 ± 1 GPa. The change corresponds to an increase in *s*-electron density at the Fe nucleus. Note that changes in the 3*d* valence-electron shell may also affect *IS* because of the shielding effect of *s*-electrons by *d*-electrons. There is no hysteresis in *IS* upon decompression.

QS at 296 K : Exhibits a broad maximum at 12 ± 1 GPa . The monotonic increase in the range 0-12 GPa is due to an increase in the trigonal crystal field. This affects the valence-electron contribution q_{el} of the EFG. There is a monotonic decrease of *QS* when *P* exceeds 12 GPa , partly because of the lattice contribution q_{latt} to the EFG.

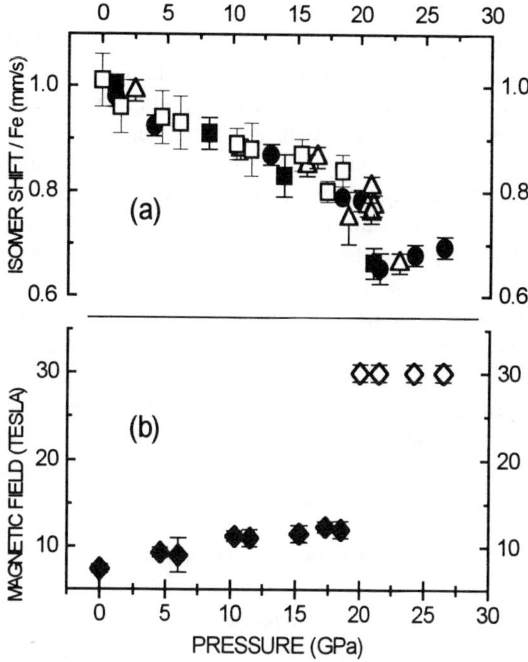

Figure 3. (a) Isomer shift at 296 K as a function of pressure. Each set of symbols correspond to a separate experimental run. (b) Internal magnetic field H_0 at $T << T_N$ (solid symbols) ; open symbols are estimates of the "dynamic" internal magnetic field.

Néel temperature : This is located at the temperature where *H* collapses to zero. T_N increases more than ten-fold from 9 K to 125 K in the range of 0 - 19 GPa. This is due to an enhanced interlayer magnetic exchange coupling as the *c/a* ratio is reduced under compression. There is no evidence of static magnetic hyperfine fields associated with magnetic ordering in the range 20-26 GPa.

Internal magnetic field and H_o (figure 3(b)) : H_0 exhibits a weak monotonic increase of **7.4 - 12 Tesla** in the range **0 - 19 GPa**. The temperature evolution of the spectra in the range of **20-26 GPa** exhibits paramagnetic hyperfine structure. Enhanced "dynamic" fields of up to **30 Tesla** are generated at the iron nuclear site.

SUMMARY

^{57}Fe Mössbauer spectroscopy reveals an abrupt change in the electronic state of the Fe cation at 20 GPa in FeI_2. A reduction or closure of an intra-band gap (involving *TM* cation sub-bands only) or of an inter-band gap (involving separate *TM* cation and anion sub-bands) will drastically alter the electronic state of the cation with a concomitant impact on the electrical and magnetic properties of the compound [1,5]. The dynamics of the magnetic moment (that is, of spin fluctuations) as manifested in the temperature dependence of the MS spectra at $P \geq 20$ GPa, may be indicative of a relaxation process which involves thermally excited intra-band or inter-band electronic transitions. Complementary ^{129}Iodine MS and conductivity measurements on FeI_2 as a function of pressure are currently in progress. This may help to identify the origin of both the change in the electronic structure of the *TM* atom in FeI_2 and the magnetic behavior of the compound at $P \geq 20$ GPa.

ACKNOWLEDGMENTS

One of us (GRH) acknowledges partial financial support, from De Beers DRL (Johannesburg, South Africa) and the FRD (Pretoria, South Africa), by way of travel-assistance funds to conduct post-doctoral research at TAU in Israel. This research has been partially supported by ISF grant 165/91-2.

REFERENCES

[1] M P Pasternak, R D Taylor and R Jeanloz, J. Appl. Phys. **70** , pp. 5956-5960 (1991).

[2] E Sterer, M P Pasternak and R D Taylor, Rev. Sci. Instr. **61**, pp. 1117-1119 (1990).

[3] G R Hearne, M P Pasternak and R D Taylor, *to be submitted to* Rev. Sci. Instr..

[4] W Hofmann, H Keller and W Kündig, Nucl. Instr. Meth. **143**, pp. 609-611 (1977).

[5] J B Torrance, P Lacorre, A I Nazzal, E J Ansaldo and Ch Niedermayer, Phys. Rev. **B45**, pp. 209-212 (1992).

ELECTRICAL CONDUCTIVITY OF PEROVSKITE-MAGNESIOWÜSTITE AS A FUNCTION OF PRESSURE AND TEMPERATURE

J Peyronneau and J.-P.Poirier
Département des Géomatériaux
Institut de Physique du Globe de Paris
75252 Paris Cedex 05
FRANCE

T. J. Shankland
Earth and Environmental Sciences Division,MS D443
Los Alamos National Laboratory
Los Alamos, New Mexico 84545
USA

The high pressure transformation products of olivine, $(Mg_{1-x},Fe_x)_2SiO_4$—the most abundant mineral in Earth's upper mantle—are perovskite $(Mg,Fe)SiO_3$ and magnesiowüstite (Mg,Fe)O. These materials are considered the principal components of the lower mantle, which comprises about 2/3 of Earth's volume. We measured the electrical conductivity σ of a perovskite–magnesiowüstite mixture transformed by laser heating in a diamond anvil cell. From a starting material of San Carlos olivine having x=0.16 the high pressure phases were $(Mg_{1-x},Fe_x)SiO_3$ with x=0.08 and $(Mg_{1-x},Fe_x)O$ with x=0.24. Iron-magnesium partitioning was determined by TEM and x-ray microanalysis. During conductivity measurements the sample was heated to 400°C by an external heater at different pressures to 40 GPa. To derive activation energy and activation volume the data were simultaneously fitted to an equation of the form $\sigma=\sigma_0\exp(-\Delta U-P\Delta V)/kT)$. Conductivities extrapolated with this formula to lower mantle conditions are of order 1-10 S/m, in remarkably good agreement with geophysical models.

INTRODUCTION

Because the lower mantle comprises the bulk of the Earth, its electrical conductivity σ is a property of great interest for propagation of geomagnetic disturbances from the core and possible electromagnetic coupling between core and mantle, as well as to problems of bulk composition, mineralogy, and temperature. We report on electrical conductivity measurements in the diamond anvil cell (DAC) of three starting materials from San Carlos, Arizona: an enstatite $(Mg_{0.89},Fe_{0.11})SiO_3$ having x_{Fe} = 0.11 and two olivines $(Mg_{1-x},Fe_x)_2SiO_4$ having x_{Fe} = 0.11 and 0.16.

APPROACH

As described earlier[1,2] the DAC was heated by a small external heater; temperatures were measured by a thermocouple in contact with the diamond. Samples were ground under alcohol in an agate mortar to a grain size less than 5 μm. We used either freshly ground samples dried at 120°C or powders that were heated to above 300°C, a procedure found necessary to remove the influence of adsorbed water[2]. Each sample was brought to about 40 GPa before being transformed to its high pressure phase by laser heating a strip of material between two tungsten electrodes[1]. Conductivities were measured by raising and lowering temperatures over the range 20 to 400°C at constant pressures between 1.2 and 40 GPa.

One purpose of this paper is to express σ in a manner that allows extrapolation and interpolation of the laboratory data to temperatures outside the conditions of the experiment. To accommodate effects of pressure P in the usual semiconduction equation activation energy should be replaced by activation enthalpy $\Delta H = \Delta U + P\Delta V$ so that

$$\sigma = \sigma_0 \, e^{-(\Delta U + P\Delta V)/kT}, \tag{1}$$

where k is Boltzmann's constant and T is absolute temperature. Strictly speaking, one should use an activation Gibbs free energy, but the temperature-independent entropy term can be included in the pre-exponential factor σ_0. ΔV can be obtained from (1) in three ways; the first is from the isothermal pressure shift

$$\frac{\Delta V}{kT} = -\left[\left(\frac{\partial(\ln\sigma)}{\partial P}\right)_T - \left(\frac{\partial(\ln\sigma_0)}{\partial P}\right)_T\right]. \tag{2}$$

This method has the disadvantage that it requires either good temperature stabilization or that measurements be made only at room temperature where leakage can introduce extra currents in cases of low sample conductivity. Neglect of the second term erroneously forces all pressure dependence into ΔV even when it is inappropriate, i.e., when zero intercepts $\sigma(T^{-1}=0)$ on a plot of $\ln\sigma$ vs. T^{-1} differ significantly at different pressures. If zero intercepts are not approximately equal, $(\partial\ln\sigma/\partial P)_T$ by itself is not a measure of ΔV, and it is even possible to calculate an apparent ΔV of the wrong sign.

A second method yields a true measure of ΔV independent of assumptions about pressure dependence of σ_0. It is necessary to have several pressure curves and to determine the effect of pressure on the slope $\Delta H/k = (\partial\ln\sigma/\partial T^{-1})_P$ on a plot of $\ln\sigma$ vs. T^{-1} such as Fig. 1; in this case

$$\Delta V = \left(\frac{\partial \Delta H}{\partial P}\right) = -\frac{\partial\left(\frac{\partial\ln\sigma}{k\partial T^{-1}}\right)_P}{\partial P} \tag{3}$$

We used this approach initially because it employs all the data from a given pressure run.

A third approach is to determine σ_0, ΔU, and ΔV in (1) by simultaneously fitting all the P, T data with a nonlinear Levenberg-Marquardt method[3]. As with equation (2) it is necessary to either establish that σ_0 is pressure–independent or take its pressure dependence into account. In these samples equation (3) and the simultaneous fit give the same result for ΔV, and it is not essential to assign a pressure dependence to σ_0. Table 1 summarizes results for the three compositions considered here.

RESULTS AND DISCUSSION

Results for the three materials have several common features. First, σ_0 values are of order 10 S/m. Zero-pressure activation energies ΔU are of the order of 0.4 eV, much lower than the values of order 1.6 eV for low pressure phases such as olivine[9]. Equally significantly, activation volumes ΔV are small, of magnitude 0.2 cm^3/mole, and *negative*. Because $\partial\ln\sigma/\partial P = -\Delta V/kT$ (σ_0 = constant), the effect of pressure on σ for finite ΔV is smaller at mantle temperatures than at room temperature. As a consequence, at mantle temperatures and pressures $\sigma \rightarrow \sigma_0$, and thus the parameters that govern σ_0, namely, iron content x_{Fe} and oxygen activity $\mathbf{a}_{O_2}$, should become as significant as temperature and pressure in the lower mantle[4]. We note that perovskite with $x_{Fe} = 0.11$ has slightly lower conductivity than that of the olivine starting material with the same bulk x_{Fe}, which actually

Table 1. Fitting Parameters to $\sigma=\sigma_0 e^{-(\Delta U + P\Delta V)/kT}$.

Bulk Composition	$\ln\sigma_0$	σ_0, S/m	ΔU, eV	ΔV, cm^3/mole
$(Mg_{0.84},Fe_{0.16})_2SiO_4$, Ol16	2.90 ± 0.24	18	0.40 ± 0.01	-0.18 ± 0.01
$(Mg_{0.89},Fe_{0.11})_2SiO_4$, Ol11	2.82 ± 0.56	17	0.42 ± 0.02	-0.10 ± 0.02
$(Mg_{0.89},Fe_{0.11})SiO_3$, NatEn11	1.92 ± 0.68	7	0.48 ± 0.02	-0.26 ± 0.03

Indicated errors are 95% confidence limits ($\pm 2 \times$ standard deviation) with no error assignment to the data.

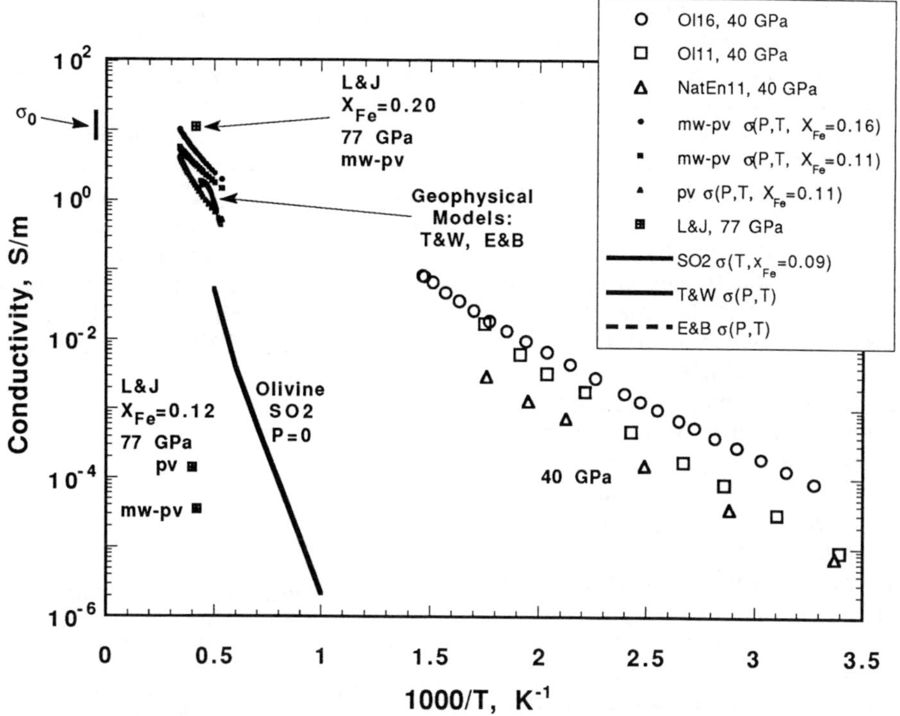

Figure 1. Electrical conductivity vs. reciprocal temperature for 3 laboratory samples at 40 GPa (large hollow points), experimental values extrapolated to lower mantle T and P (small hollow points densely spaced), and 2 sets of geophysical data: E&B[14] and T&W[15]. For comparison, data of Li & Jeanloz[6,7] with different compositions and iron fractions and of standard olivine SO2[9] at P = 0 are indicated. High temperature points are deliberately left bunched to indicate how small are the differences between them at mantle temperatures.

disproportionates into perovskite (x_{Fe} = 0.06) and magnesiowüstite (x_{Fe} = 0.16)[5]. The 40 GPa curves agree well with earlier values[1,2], but the disagreement with low values of Li & Jeanloz[6] persists.

The activation volume ΔV = -0.1 cm^3/mole of the olivine sample having x_{Fe} = 0.11 agrees with values from room temperature measurements[2] using the first term of (2) where $(\partial \log_{10}\sigma/\partial T^{-1})_P$ = 0.02 GPa^{-1}. [Other pressure derivatives[7,8] are given in the range 0.014 to 0.030 GPa^{-1}, but for the reasons given above, equation (2) cannot be used to calculate ΔV.] This ΔV could be assigned to hopping of the ferric valence state as a *3d*-band electronic (small polaron) charge carrier, although it is likely that any electronic mechanism could have a ΔV of this order.

Fig. 1 summarizes some thermal observations. Experimental curves of this work (40 GPa only) are indicated, as are zero pressure olivine data for comparison with a standard low pressure, upper mantle mineral (olivine SO2[9]) and representative low- and high-x_{Fe} data of Li & Jeanloz[6,7] for three compositions. Deliberately clustered are σ values calculated from (1) using the parameters of Table 1 together with pressures[10] P(z) and temperatures[11] T(z) as functions of depth z . With small ΔH and large T extrapolation of the experimental data in T^{-1} is not great, and temperature uncertainties do not appreciably affect the result. All these values are close together, probably within their errors of calculation. Further, they all approach the maximum $\sigma_0(T=\infty)$. Alhough temperature increases by about 50% and pressure by a factor of almost 6 across the lower mantle, there is simply very little range remaining for variations of T(z) and P(z) to have much effect. The bunching seen in these models is a consequence that depends very little on the values in Table 1.

There have been different hypotheses to explain lower mantle conductivities in the range shown in Fig. 1. One[1,2,4] is the small polaron hopping mechanism. Another might be an extrinsic mechanism in which Fe^{2+} acts as a donor for conduction band electrons or Fe^{3+} as an acceptor to produce valence band holes in an iron-enriched lower mantle (a variation on a suggested model[7]). A third[12,13] is to argue that interconnected magnesio-wüstite, which also conducts by polaron hopping, is the high conductivity phase in the lower mantle. The consistent explanation for laboratory measurements that give conductivities in this range have in common a probable electronic mechanism. Each explanation yields a lower mantle material that behaves in the manner observed in these experiments, i.e., has a ΔU of a few tenths of an eV and a ΔV of a negative few tenths of a cm^3/mole.

CONCLUSIONS

A geophysical consequence of these observations is that a smooth curve resembling that of Ol11, i.e., an olivine having x_{Fe} of order 10 at% could provide a good estimation of lower mantle conductivity to the base of the mantle—always excepting D", the anomalous 100–200 km thick layer just above the core which is likely to be compositionally heterogeneous. Also, conductivity of a convecting lower mantle may differ indetectably from radial symmetry. Over the entire lower mantle conductivity increases only by a factor of 5 so that lateral temperature variations of ± 200 K are not likely to produce observable changes. Further, should a lower mantle of higher conductivity be desired for reasons such as core-mantle coupling, then D" may be the only other place in which to locate a more conducting zone because of its differences in physical properties.

ACKNOWLEDGMENTS

We are grateful to Pascal Tarits for making data available in advance of publication. TJS thanks the Institut de Physique du Globe de Paris and the Centre National de la Recherche Scientifique for support and hospitality. Portions of this work were performed under the auspices of the Office of Basic Energy Research, U.S. Department of Energy under contract W-7405-ENG-36 with the University of California. This work was partly supported by CNRS (Unité de Recherches Associée 734).

REFERENCES

[1] J. Peyronneau and J. P. Poirier, *Nature* **342**, pp. 537-539 (1989).

[2] J. P. Poirier and J. Peyronneau, "Experimental determination of the electrical conductivity of the material of the Earth's lower mantle," *High-Pressure Research: Application to Earth and Planetary Sciences*, Y. Syono and M. H. Manghnani, eds., Washington, D.C.: American Geophysical Union, pp. 77-87 (1992).

[3] W. H. Press, B. P. Flannery, S. A. Teukolsky, and W. T. Vettering, *Numerical Recipes*, Cambridge: Cambridge University Press (1986).

[4] L. M. Hirsch and T. J. Shankland, *Geophys. Res. Letters*. **18**, pp. 1305-1308.(1991).

[5] F. Guyot, M. Madon, J. P. Poirier, and J. Peyronneau, *Earth Planet. Sci. Lett.* **90**, pp. 52-64 (1988).

[6] X. Li and R. Jeanloz, *J. Geophys. Res.* **95**, pp. 5067-5078 (1990).

[7] X. Li and R. Jeanloz, *J. Geophys. Res.* **96**, pp. 6113-6120 (1991).

[8] X. Li, L.-C. Ming, M. H. Manghnani, Y. Wang, and R. Jeanloz, *J. Geophys. Res.* **98**, pp. 501-508 (1993).

[9] S. Constable, T. J. Shankland, and A. G. Duba, *J. Geophys. Res.* **97**, pp. 3397-3404 (1992).

[10] A. M. Dziewonski and D. L. Anderson, *Phys. Earth Planet. Interiors* **25**, pp. 297-356 (1981).

[11] T. J. Shankland and J. M. Brown, *Phys. Earth Planet. Interiors* **38**, pp. 51-58 (1985).

[12] X. Li and R. Jeanloz, *J. Geophys. Res.* **95**, pp. 21609-21612 (1990).

[13] B. J. Wood and J. Nell, *Nature* **351**, pp. 309-311 (1989).

[14] G. D. Egbert and J. R. Booker, *J. Geophys. Res.* **97**, pp. 15099-15112 (1992).

[15] P. Tarits and J. Wahr, *Eos Trans AGU.* **73**, p. 523 (1992) and private communication (1992).

PRESSURE EFFECT ON THE CURIE TEMPERATURES OF MnRuAs, MnPdAs AND MnRhP

T.Kanomata and T.Kawashima*
Faculty of Engineering, Tohoku Gakuin University.
Tagajo,985,Japan
H.Yoshida and T.Kaneko
Institute of Materials Research, Tohoku University.
Katahira,980,Japan

The pressure derivative of the Curie temperature $\partial T_c/\partial p$ of MnRuAs, MnPdAs and MnRhP have been obtained from the results of temperature dependence of initial permeability under pressure up to 1.1 GPa. The values of $\partial T_c/\partial p$ are -3.6 K/GPa for MnRuAs , -37.5 K/GPa for MnPdAs and +11.6 K/GPa for MnRhP.

INTRODUCTION

The intermetallic compounds MnMX (M=Ru,Rh,Pd and X=P,As) crystallize in the hexagonal Fe_2P-type structure. In the Fe_2P-type crystal structure, shown in Fig.1 , non-metal atoms form tetrahedral and square-based pyramids both stacked in triangular channels along the hexagonal c-axis. The 4d atoms are located on the tetrahedral sites of the adjacent channels [1]. Therefore, compounds MnMX are pseudo two-dimentional magnets. The compounds MnRhAs and MnRuP have attracted considerable attention during the last few years, because of their interesting magnetic properties which have magnetic order-order transition from the antiferromagnetic (AF) state to the AF + F coexistent state of the antiferromagnetic and ferromagnetic (F) components of magnetic

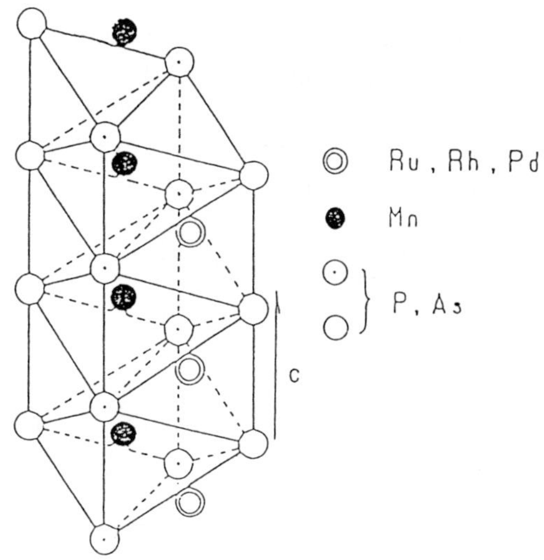

Figure 1. The Fe_2P-type crystal structure.

*Present address : Sony Magnetic Products Inc.
Tagajo, 985 Japan

from the AF1 state to the AF2 state for MnRuP [4]. MnRuAs and MnRhP are ferromagnets with the Curie temperature (T_c) of 496 K and 401 K , respectively [1]. The observed magnetic moments per molecule of MnRuAs and MnRhP are 3.9 μ_B and 3.0 μ_B , respectively [5]. On the basis of the results of the magnetization measurement, Kaneko et al have concluded that the magnetic structure of MnPdAs is in the canted state [5]. T_c of MnPdAs is 210 K.

In this paper, we report the pressure effect of the magnetic transition temperatures for the collinear ferromagnets MnRuAs and MnRhP, and the canted ferromagnet MnPdAs to understand the volume dependence of the magnetic exchange interactions of MnMX (M=4d metals, X=P,As)

EXPERIMENTAL

The samples were prepared with the same heat treatment as that reported previously [6]. The pressure dependence of the magnetic transition temperatures was determined by measuring the temperature variation of magnetic permeability under various pressures up to 1.1 GPa. The pressure was applied by using a piston-cylinder type apparatus, where the sample was placed in a Teflon cell filled with Fluorinert as a pressure transmitting liquid. The ac magnetic permeability was measured by a transformer method.

EXPERIMENTAL RESULTS AND DISCUSSIONS

For MnPdAs, initial permeability decreases rapidly just below T_c and then takes a nearly constant value with further rise in temperature. T_c was defined as the point of intersection of linear extrapolation from the high and low temperature ranges. The pressure dependence of T_c is shown in Fig.2 . It is found that T_c decreases

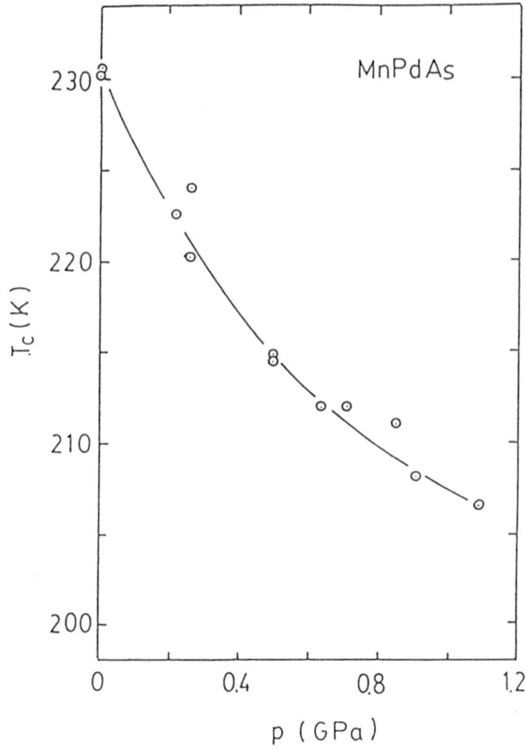

Figure 2. The Curie temperature vs. pressure curve for MnPdAs.

with increasing applied pressure and the pressure dependence of T_c is nonlinear. This dependence can be represented in the forms $T_c(p)=a+bp+cp^2$, where numerical values of coefficients are found by the least-squares method : a=230.6 K, b=-37.53 K/GPa, c=14.7 K/GPa^2 . The pressure derivative of T_c at p=0 is given by $\partial T_c/\partial p$ = -37.5 K/GPa. T_c at p=0 is somewhat larger than the value reported by Kanomata et al [1].

Figures 3 and 4 show the pressure change of T_c for MnRuAs and MnRhP, respectively. T_c of MnRuAs is found to decrease linearly with applied pressure in the pressure range investigated. The value of $\partial T_c/\partial p$ is -3.6 K/GPa. On the other hand, T_c of MnRhP is found to increase linearly with applied pressure in the pressure range investigated. The value of $\partial T_c/\partial p$

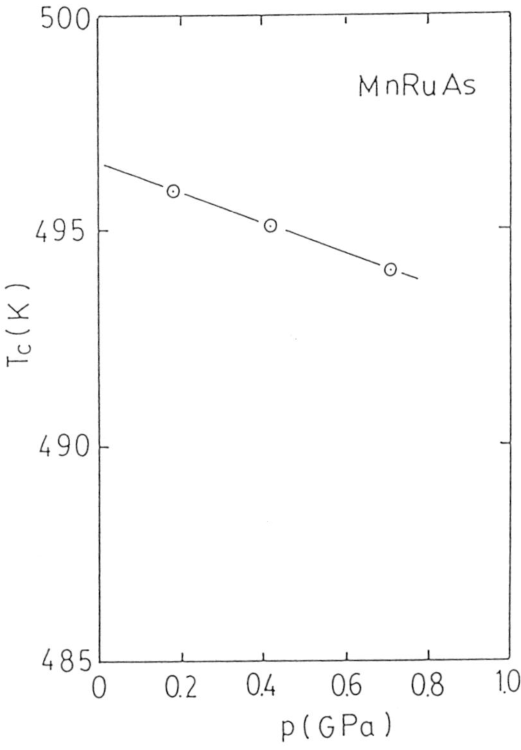

Figure 3. The Curie temperature vs. pressure curve for MnRuAs.

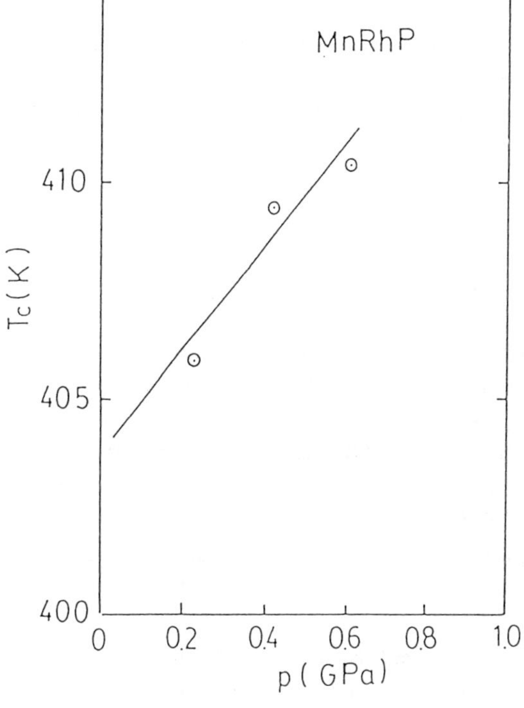

Figure 4. The Curie temperature vs. pressure curve for MnRhP.

is +11.6 K/GPa . Kanomata et al [6] reported that the compound MnRhAs has also the positive value of $\partial T_c / \partial p$ and the value is +7.1 K/GPa .

The magneto-volume effects of the manganese intermetallic compounds have been discussed qualitatively on the basis of emperical interaction curves, in which the interatomic exchange interactions between the localized moments is assumed to be strong function of interatomic spacing. Recently, Ishida et al [7] and Suzuki et al [8] calculated the band structures of manganese intermetallic compounds Mn_2P and MnMGe (M=Al, Ga), respectively. According to their calculations, the 3d bandwidth is fairly wide. These authors concluded that the d electrons should be treated not as localized electrons, but as itinerant electrons. Recent studies of the photoemission and inverse photoemission spectra of Mn_2Sb and MnAlGe show that the characteristic feature of the observed spectra is in good correspondence with the calculated total density of state for these compounds [9]. Thus, it is concluded that the magnetic properties of MnMX (M=Ru,Rh,Pd, X=P,As) should be discussed in terms of the itinerant-electron magnetism. The theory of the magneto-volume effect in an itinerant-electron system was derived by Wagner and Wohlfarth [10]. Their model suggests the large negative value of $\partial T_c / \partial p$ for the itinerant-electron system. The positive value of $\partial T_c / \partial p$ of MnRhP and MnRhAs are not explained by their model. The large positive values of $\partial T_c / \partial p$ may be due to the pseudo two-dimentional character, or the effect of spin fluctuation which plays a predominant role on magnetic properties in itinerant magnets.

ACKNOWLEDGMENTS

A part of this study was carried out under inter-university cooperative research program of the Institute for Materials Research, Tohoku University.

REFERENCES

[1] T.Kanomata, T.Kawashima, H.Utsugi, T.Goto, H.Hasegawa and T.Kaneko, *J.Appl.Phys.* 69, pp.4639-4641 (1991)

[2] B.Chenevier, M.Bacmann, D.Fruchart, J.P.Senateur and R.Fruchart, *Phys.Stat.Sol.* (a) 90, pp.331-341 (1985)

[3] B.Chenevier, J.Baruchel, M.Bacmann, D.Fruchart and R.Fruchart, *J.Alloys.Comp.*, 179, pp.147-156 (1992)

[4] J.Bartolome, J.Garcia, C.Rillo, E.Palacios, M.Bacmann, D.Fruchart and B.Chenevier, *J.Magn,Magn.Mater.* 54-57, pp.1499-1500 (1986)

[5] T.Kaneko, T.Kanomata, T.Kawashima, S.Mori, S.Miura, and Y.Nakagawa, *Physica* B 177, pp.123-126 (1992)

[6] T.Kanomata, K.Shirakawa, H.Yasui and T,Kaneko, *J.Magn.Magn.Mater*, 68, pp.286 - 290 (1987)

[7] S.Ishida, S.Asano and J.Ishida, *J.Phys.F* 17, pp.475 - 482 (1987)

[8] M.Suzuki, M.Shirai and K.Motizuki, *J.Phys.Condens.Matter* 4, pp.L33-36 (1992)

[9] A.Kimura, S.Suga, H.Matsubara, M.Matsushita, Y.Saitoh, H.Daimon, T.Kaneko and T.Kanomata, *Solid State Commun.* 81, pp.707-710 (1992)

[10] D.Wagner and E.P.Wohlfarth, *J.Phys.F* 11 pp.2417-2428 (1981)

PRESSURE EFFECT ON THE CURIE TEMPERATURE AND EXCHANGE STRICTION OF YMn_2Ge_2

T. Kaneko, T. Kanomata*, T. Kawashima* and H. Yasui
The Institute for Materials Research, Tohoku University,
Katahira, Sendai, 980 Japan,
*Department of Applied Physics, Faculty of Engineering,
Tohoku Gakuin University, Tagajo, 985 Japan

Pressure effect on the Neel temperature(T_N)is measured for the antiferromagnetic compound YMn_2Ge_2 with a $ThCr_2Si_2$-type crystal structure. T_N increases linearly with pressure with dT_N/dP = 23 K/GPa. Thermal expansion of lattice parameters a and c is in the temperature range through T_N. Exchange strictions along the a- and c-axis are obtained to be negative and positive, respectively. Volume exchange striction is estimated to be negative. The relation between the lattice parameters and magnetic order is discussed on the basis of the present results.

Intermetallic compounds RM_2X_2 (R is a rare earth metal, M a 3d or 4d metal and X germanium or silicon) have the crystal structure of a $ThCr_2Si_2$-type which can be described as a stacking of atomic layers in the direction of c-axis with the sequence of R-X-M-X-R as shown in Fig.1. In RMn_2Ge_2 compounds at temperature above 100 K, the magnetic moments of Mn atoms order ferromagnetically for light R and Y except for Sm and antiferromagnetically for heavy R, respectively. In the antiferromagnetic state, the Mn magnetic moments couple ferromagnetically in the same c-plane and ferromagnetic Mn layers couple antiferrogmanetically with adjacent c-planes. $SmMn_2Ge_2$ and $Y_{1-x}La_xMn_2Ge_2$(0.25<x<0.35) have an antiferromagnetic (AF) - ferromagnetic(F) transition at T_t below the Curie temperature (T_C)[1,2]. Fujii et al.[2] have pointed out that the Mn-Mn distance , R_{Mn-Mn}, in the Mn intralayer has a close relation for an appearance of AF or F states of the Mn magnetic moments on the basis of the interaction curves where the magnetic transition temperatures are plotted against the lattice parameter a as shown in Fig.2. In order to examine the Mn-Mn distance dependence of the magnetic transition, the pressure effect on the magnetic transiton temperatures and exchange striction have been studied for $DyMn_2Ge_2$[3], $Y_{0.7}La_{0.3}Mn_2G_2$[4],

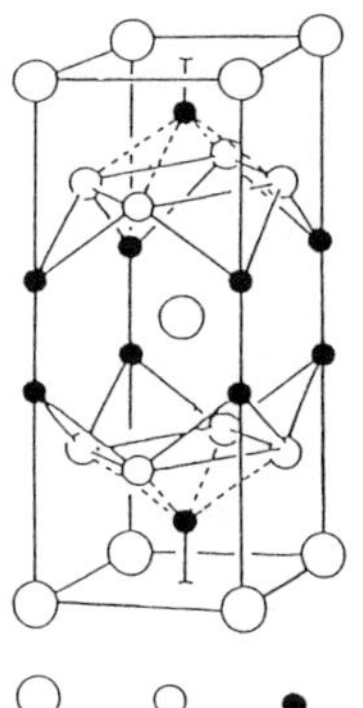

Fig.1 Crystal structure of a $ThCr_2Si_2$-type.

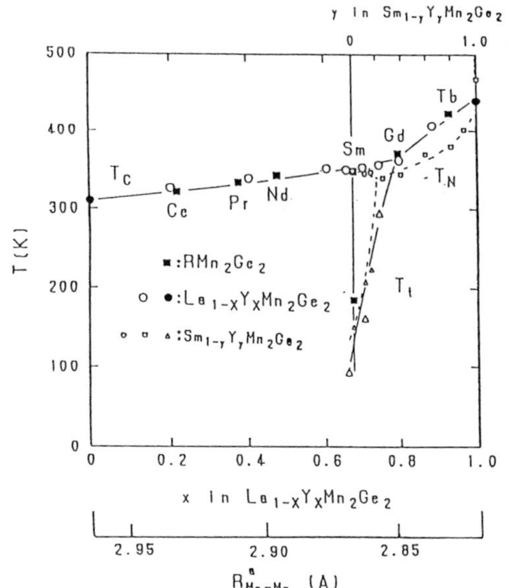

Fig.2 Magnetic phase diagrams [5] of $La_{1-x}Y_xMn_2Ge_2$[2] and $Sm_{1-y}Y_yMn_2Ge_2$[8].

$PrMn_2Ge_2$ and $NdMn_2Ge_2$[5] and $LaMn_2Ge_2$[6] by the present authors and for $SmMn_2Ge_2$[7], $Sm_{1-y}Y_yMn_2Ge_2$-[8], $Sm_{1-y}Gd_yMn_2Ge_2$[9] by Duraj et al.. In this paper, the pressure effect on the Neel temperature(T_N) and the thermal expansion of lattice parameters are studied for a antiferromagnetic compound YMn_2Ge_2.

The specimen was prepared by melting the mixture of constituent elements and annealing at 800 °C for 7 days. The pressure dependence of T_N was determined by measuring the temperature variation of electric resistance under various pressures which was applied by using a piston-cylinder type apparatus. The temperature variation of lattice parameter was measured by using high temperature X-ray diffractometer at temperatures from 300 K to 700 K.

Figure 3 shows the electric resistance(R) versus temperature(T) curves at pressures of 0.05 and 0.78 GPa. As temperature increases, R increases linearly just below T_N and after showing a break increases linearlly again above T_N. T_N was defined as the intersection temperature of linear curves below and above T_N as shown with an arrow in the figure. T_N thus determined for 0.05 GPa is 432 K. As seen in the figure, T_N is shifted to higherr temprature with pressure. In Fig. 4 is shown the Curie temperature versus pressure curve thus obtained. T_N increases linearly with pressure and its pressure derivative, dT_N/dP, is obtained to be 23 K/GPa. The positive dT_N/dP is also observed for $DyMn_2Ge_2$ and $La_{0.3}Y_{0.7}Mn_2Ge_2$(P > 0.4 GPa).

Figure 5 shows the lattice parameters a and c versus temperature curves. Since a contracts to the smooth extrapolation (dotted line) of its thermal expansion curve above T_N, a has a negative exchange striction. On the contrary, c has a positive exchange striction. Volume expansion curve is also shown in the figure and volume exchange striction is negative. The change of volume themal expansion coefficient at T_N, $\Delta\alpha_V = \alpha_V(T<T_N)-\alpha_V(T>T_N)$, is estimated to be 5×10^{-5} 1/K.

The negative sign of the volume exchange striction is consistent with that expected from the positive value of dT_N/dP obtained above. When we take J_a along the a-axis and J_c along the c-axis as exchange interactions, J_a and J_c are considered to be positvie and negative in the antiferromagnetic compound YMn_2Ge_2, respectively. The negative sign of exchange striction of a and the positive one of c obtained above mean $dJ_a/da < 0$ and $dJ_c/dc < 0$ ($J_c<0$),respectively, from the viewpoint of interaction curve which take Ja and Jc as a function of Mn-Mn distance.

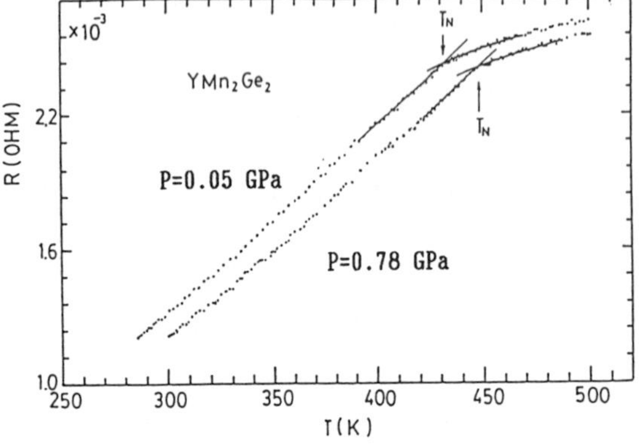

Fig.3 Temperature variation of resistance at pressures 0.05 GPa and 0.78 GPa.

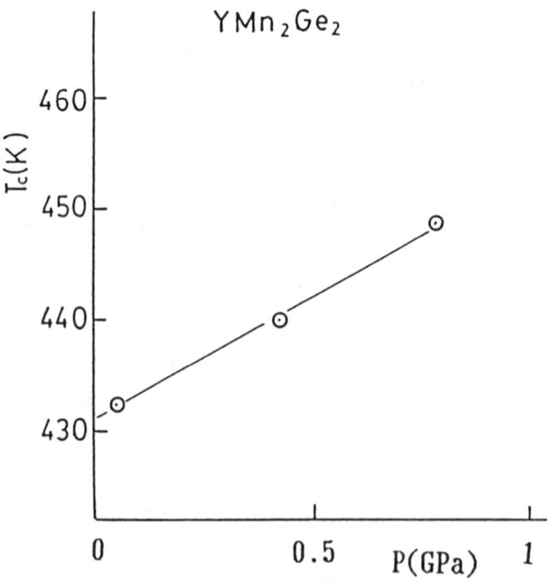

Fig.4 Pressure variation of T_N.

As mentioned above, dT_N/dP of $DyMn_2Ge_2$ is positive as well as YMn_2Ge_2. But its exchange strictions of a and c are negative and positive as shown schematically in Fig.6. These results imply $dJ_a/da < 0$ and $dJ_c/dc > 0$ ($J_c<0$), respectively. The distance dependence of J_c has an opposite sign to that of YMn_2Ge_2. Then it is considered that the positive dT_N/dP of YMn_2Ge_2 and $DyMn_2Ge_2$ is caused mainly from the distance dependence of the exchange interaction along the a axis. On the other hand, we have reported that for the ferromagnetic compounds $LaMn_2Ge_2$[6] and $La_{0.3}Y_{0.7}Mn_2Ge_2$ ($P<0.4$ GPa, $T>T_t$)[4] dT_C/dP is negative and both exchange strictions of a and c are positive, which imply $dJ_a/da > 0$ and $dJ_c/dc > 0$.

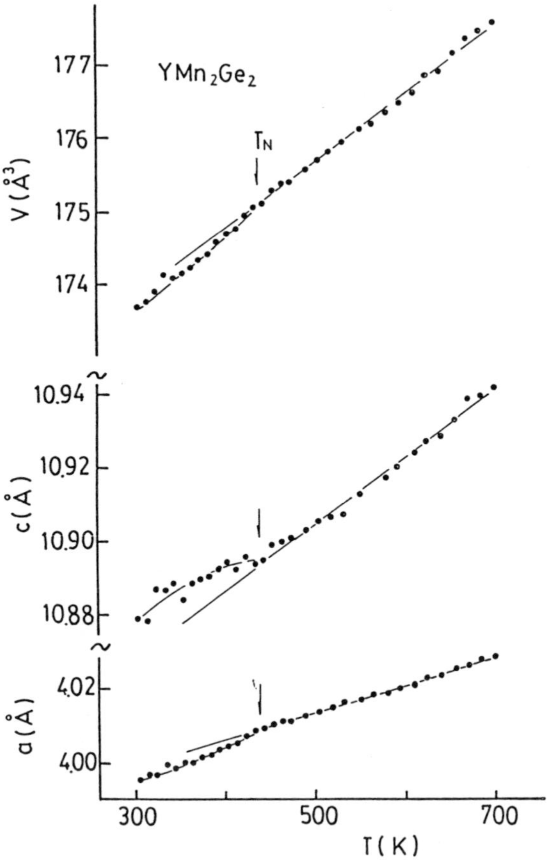

Fig.5 Thermal expansion curves of lattice parameters a and c, and volume.

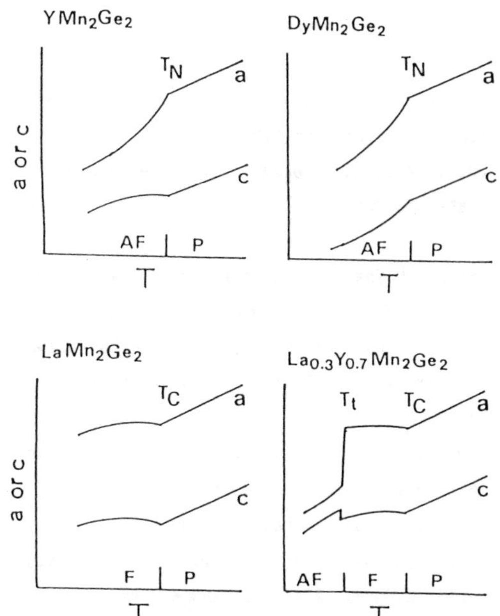

Fig.6 Schematic representations of thermal expansion of a and c for YMn_2Ge_2, $DyMn_2Ge_2$, $LaMn_2Ge_2$ and $La_{0.3}Y_{0.7}Mn_2Ge_2$.

These negative value of dT_C/dP and the positive exchange striction of a are inconsistent with those expected fron the curves in Fig.2. Furthermore, it is pointed out that the sign of discontinuous change of c at T_t is incosistent with that expected from Kittel model which assume the change of sign of J_c at a certain critical value of c for the AF-F transition[5]. Therefore, the appearance of AF and F states of Mn can not be discussed simply in terms of the interaction curve in Fig.2 based on the localized magnetic moment model.

Recently, Ishida et al.[10] have done the band structure calculations for YMn_2Ge_2 and $LaMn_2Ge_2$. They reported that the appearance of the AF state in YMn_2Ge_2 and the F state in $LaMn_2Ge_2$ is well understood on the basis of the results of band calculations. Therefore, the magnetic properties of RMn_2Ge_2 compounds are considered to be discussed in terms of itinerant electron magnetism.

A part of this work was carried out under the Inter-University Cooperative Research Program of the Institute for Materials Research, Tohoku University.

REFERENCES

1) S.Siek,A.Szytula and J.Leciejewics, Solid State Commun. 39 pp.863-866 (1981)
2) H.Fujii, M.Isoda, T.Okamoto, T.Shigeoka and N.Iwata, J. Mag. Mag. Mater. 54-57 pp.1345-1346 (1986)
3) T.Kaneko, H.Yasui, T.Kanomata, H.Kobayashi, and H.Onodera, J. de Phys. 49 pp. C8-441-442 (1988)
4) T.Kaneko, T.Kanomata,H.Yasui, T.Shigeoka, M.Iwata and Y.Nakagawa, J. Physs. Soc. Japan 61 PP.4164-4173 (1992)
5) T.Kawashima, T.Kanomata, H.Yoshida and T.Kaneko, J. Mag. Mag. Mater. 90 & 91 pp.721-722 (1990)
6) T.Kaneko, H.Yasui, T.Kanomata and T.Suzuki, J. Mag. Mag. Mater. 104-107 pp.1951-1952 (1992)
7) M.Duraj, R.Duraj, A.Szytula and R.Tomkowicz, J. Mag. Mag. Mater. 73 pp.240-246 (1988)
8) M.Duraj, R.Duraj and A.Szytula, J. Mag. Mag. Mater. 82 pp.319-321 (1989)
9) M.Duraj, R.Duraj and A.Szytula, J. Mag. Mag. Mater. 79 pp.61-66 (1989)
10) S.Ishida, S.Asano and J.Ishida, J. Phys. Soc. Japan 55 pp.936-945 (1986)

ELECTRICAL AND MAGNETIC PROPERTIES OF Ce MONOPNICTIDES

Nobuo Môri
Institute for Solid State Physics,
University of Tokyo,
Roppongi, Minato-ku, Tokyo 106, Japan

Recent investigations for the influence of pressure on the electrical and magnetic properties of single crystalline CeX (X=P, As, Sb and Bi) with NaCl structure are reviewed. The highly unusual behavior of these compounds has been revealed by the electrical resistivity and the Hall coefficient measurements under pressure using a newly designed high pressure apparatus.

INTRODUCTION

In recent years, there has been considerable interest in the study of the electrical and magnetic properties of rare-earth compounds. High pressure experiments have proved to be of great benefit to revealing the characteristic features of these materials. Of special interest are the so-called "anomalous" rare-earth systems which show a large pressure and temperature dependence of the transport and magnetic properties. Recent high pressure experiments on Ce monopnictides have yielded quite fruitful results which provide new insight into our understanding of the highly unusual electrical and magnetic properties observed at ambient pressure.

The Ce-monopnictides (CeX; X=P, As, Sb and Bi) having the NaCl-type crystal structure have received attention focusing on the anomalous behavior in connection with their extremely low carrier concentration. CeP and CeAs have a carrier number of only about 0.1% per Ce atom, and CeSb and CeBi have a few percent per Ce atom [1]. In addition to the low carrier concentration, the interplay of the interactions, such as the position and the width of 4f level with respect to the Fermi level, the crystal field effects, the Coulomb correlation effects, and the magnetic interaction, gives rise to the great diversity of physical properties observed in these compounds.

The result of photoelectron spectroscopy studies[2] indicates a systematic change in the spectral intensity ratio which suggests that the f level approaches the Fermi level from Bi to P, in order. The crystal field splitting of $4f_{5/2}$ are 150, 137, 37 and 8K for CeP, CeAs CeSb and CeBi, respectively[3], which are much less than those expected from extrapolation from other rare-earth monopnictides. CeP and CeAs clearly exhibit a dense Kondo like behavior with an antiferromagnetic ordering far below the temperature at which the resistivity goes through a maximum caused by a Kondo coherent scattering or the crystal field effects, while in CeSb and CeBi a characteristic decrease in resistivity due to the coherent scattering is not observed in spite of their having a high Kondo temperature of about 100K[1].

The NaCl-type crystal structure is maintained under pressures up to 19, 16, 10 and 13GPa for CeP, CeAs, CeSb and CeBi, respectively[4,5]. In CeP, however, there exists an isomorphous transition at a pressure of around 9-10GPa with a volume change of 3-8% [4,6]. Figure 1 shows the relation between the lattice constants of these compounds. The lattice constant at 10GPa is indicated by an arrow for each compound. From this figure, it can be seen that the application of pressure is a significantly useful tool to clarify the interrelations among the unusual behavior observed in the individual compounds.

In this paper some of the recent experimental results are reviewed. A part of this paper has been reported elsewhere[7-9].

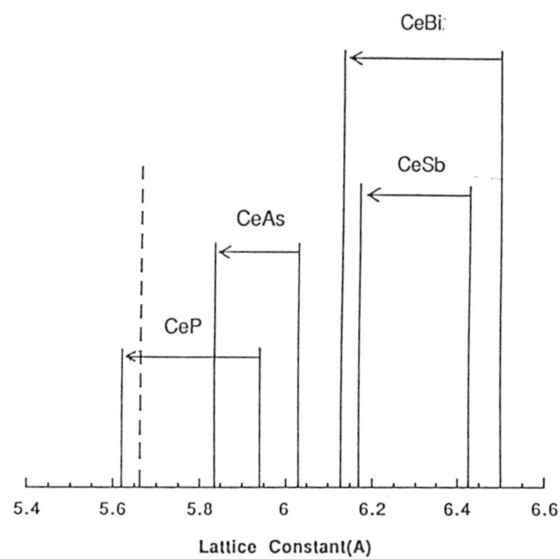

Figure 1. The relation between the lattice constants for CeP, CeAs, CeSb and CeBi. Lattice constant at 10GPa for each compound is shown by an arrow. Dotted line; electronic phase transition of CeP.

EXPERIMENTAL

The single crystalline samples used in this study were prepared by Suzuki et al. by a procedure described in detail elsewhere [1].

We have measured the Hall coefficient under the constant magnetic field of 4T and under the pressure up to 2.6GPa using a piston cylinder technique. The electrical resistivity was measured under the pressure up to 8GPa using a cubic anvil device which has been recently developed by us for precise electrical measurements at low temperature. A schematic cross-sectional view of the high pressure cryostat is shown in fig. 2, which has a similar geometry as one described earlier[10]. The cubic anvil dies were placed between the end of a pair of pressure transmitting columns consisting of fiber-reinforced plastic disks. Figures 3(a) and 3(b) show the top and side cross-sectional views of a compact cubic anvil device designed by Mori and Takahashi[11]. In fig. 4 is shown the internal configuration of a gasket with a Teflon cell in which the sample is immersed in fluid. As a pressure transmitting fluid, we used a mixture of Fluorinert No. FC70 and No. FC77.

Electrical resistivity was measured by means of a four-terminal method. The measurements were carried out at fixed pressure with variable temperature between 4.2 and 300K, the applied pressure being changed at room temperature after each low temperature run. The pressure was calibrated from the phase transition points of bismuth at 2.55(I-II), 2.7(II-III) and 7.7GPa(III'-V) at room temperature. It was also determined at low temperature from the pressure dependent superconducting transition temperature of lead using the pressure coefficient of dT_c/dP=-0.381K/GPa below 3GPa. Above 3GPa, the pressure was estimated from a pressure-load calibration curve at room temperature.

EXPERIMENTAL RESULTS AND DISCUSSIONS

Figures 5 and 6 show the temperature dependent resistivity and Hall coefficient of CeP at various pressures as a representative example. They exhibit a surprisingly pressure and temperature sensitive behavior. At ambient pressure, the resistivity behaves as a typical magnetic dense Kondo system. However, the value of Hall coefficient is much larger than that in typical dense Kondo substance[12] because of the low carrier concentration. There is a sharp pointed peak in both resistivity and Hall coefficient curves near 10K which is caused by the antiferromagnetic phase transition. With increasing temperature, the resistivity and Hall coefficient pass through a minimum at about 23K, and then the resistivity has a broad maximum at $T=T_{max}$ around 80K while the Hall coefficient becomes saturated near this temperature.

Under pressure, one observes at first that the sharp pointed peak in resistivity at T_N splits into two peaks at a pressure of 0.5GPa; one is a knee-like anomaly at higher temperature, T_H, and the other is a small peak

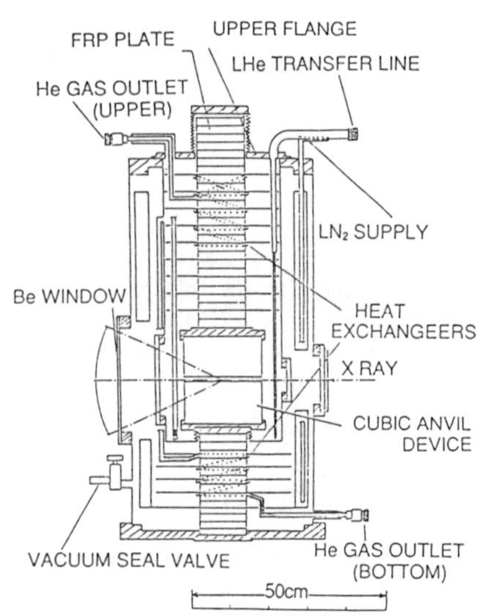

Figure 2. A cross-sectional view of a high pressure cryostat.

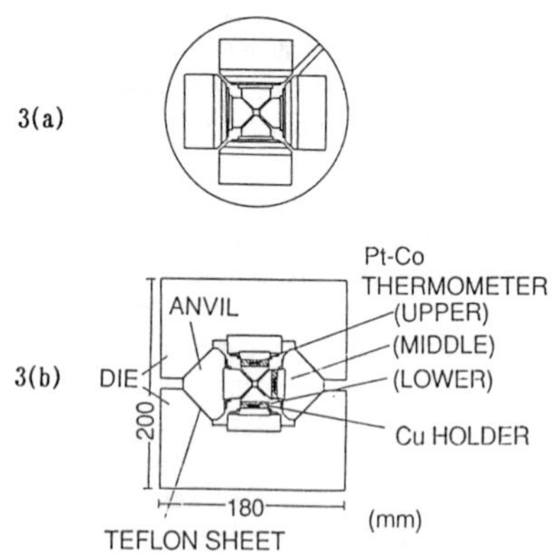

Figure 3. A cubic anvil device.

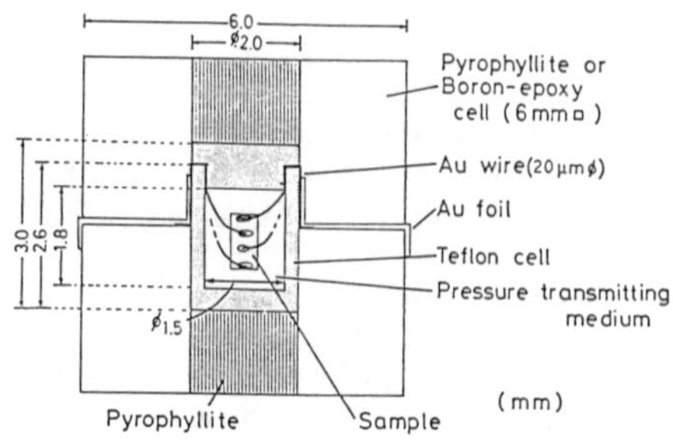

Figure 4. Configuration of a gasket with Teflon cell.

at lower temperature, T_L. Anomalies in Hall coefficient are also observed at these temperatures. The T_H is shifted towards higher temperatures rapidly up to 2GPa, becomes saturated around 3GPa and then moves downward with increasing pressure. The T_N and T_L depend very little on pressure, but T_L levels out at around 2.5GPa. The T_H and T_L have been confirmed by neutron diffraction experiments and magnetic susceptibility measurements to correspond to new magnetic phase transition temperatures induced by applying pressure[9,13]. The low temperature phase has an antiferromagnetic component, while the high temperature phase shows a ferromagnetic behavior as in the case of CeSb and CeBi[14,15].

The T_{max} moves rapidly towards lower temperatures as pressure is applied. The temperature where the saturation of the Hall coefficient takes places corresponds well to the T_{max}. This result indicates that the T_{max} is not caused by the coherent Kondo effect, but by the crystal field splitting effect. The decrease of T_{max} can be explained if the crystal field splitting between Γ_7 and Γ_8 decreases with applying pressure[9]. The rapid decrease of the Hall coefficient below the temperature near T_{max} also supports this idea. Because similar temperature dependent Hall coefficient was seen in UPd_3 [16] which has almost the same crystal field splitting [17] as in CeP. Indeed, recent inelastic neutron scattering experiments have revealed that the crystal field splitting of CeP and CeAs decreases with pressure[18].

At the pressure higher than 2GPa, the T_{max} of the resistivity disappears and the Hall coefficient changes the sign from negative to positive above the magnetic transition temperature T_H. The large temperature dependent Hall coefficient observed at 2.2GPa shows a typical behavior due to a magnetic skew scattering as observed in many dense Kondo substances[12]. However, it is noticeable findings that the temperature coefficient of the Hall coefficient changes its sign continuously from positive to negative with increasing pressure. Recent theoretical model proposed by Levy and Fert[19] may explain these results if the Kondo temperature T_K corresponds to T_{max}. From their theory, a large negative Hall constant is anticipated in the temperature range $T \ll T_K$ when the 4f j=2/5 state of Ce is split into doublet states.

As seen in fig. 5, the T_H decreases above 3GPa and is found to disappear at pressure about 5.5GPa. Considering the resistivity change at T_H, it is suggested that the magnetic moment residing on Ce atom becomes delocalized with applying pressure beyond 3GPa. Furthermore, the residual resistivity is found to decrease abruptly just at the pressure where the T_H approachs zero. This sudden change in resistivity corresponds well to the abrupt change in volume reported earlier[4,6] and has been confirmed as an electronic transition from the magnetic dense Kondo(MK) to normal metallic state(NM) [9].

A pressure-temperature phase diagram for CeP is shown in fig. 7 [9]. Figure 8 shows the resistivity of Ce mono-

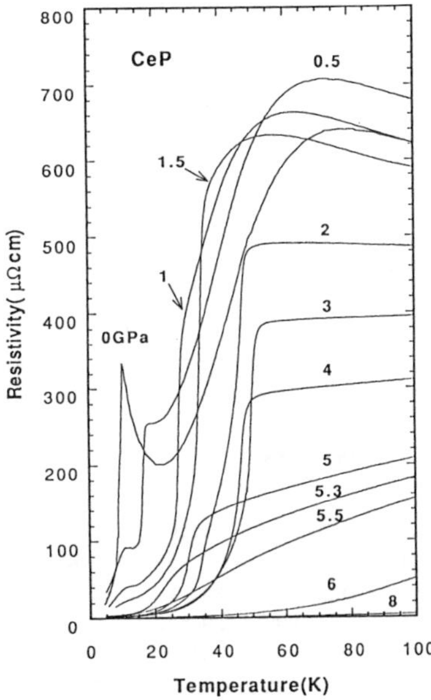

Figure 5. The resistivity of CeP as a function of temperature at various pressures.

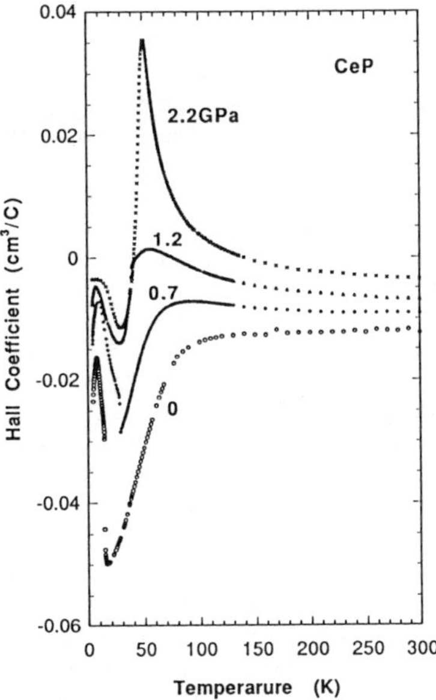

Figure 6. The Hall coefficient of CeP as a function of temperature at various pressures.

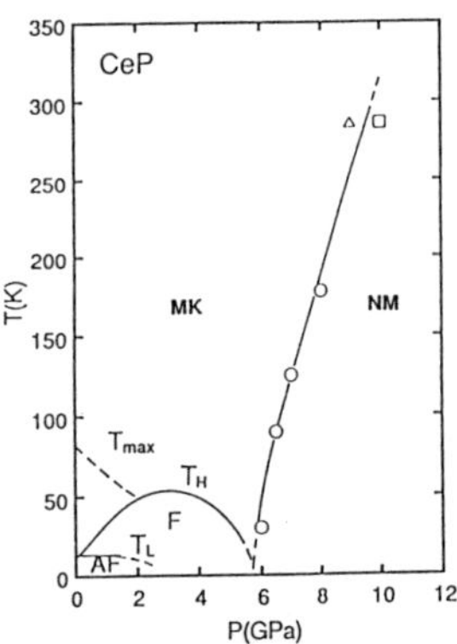

Figure 7. A pressure-temperature phase diagram of CeP.

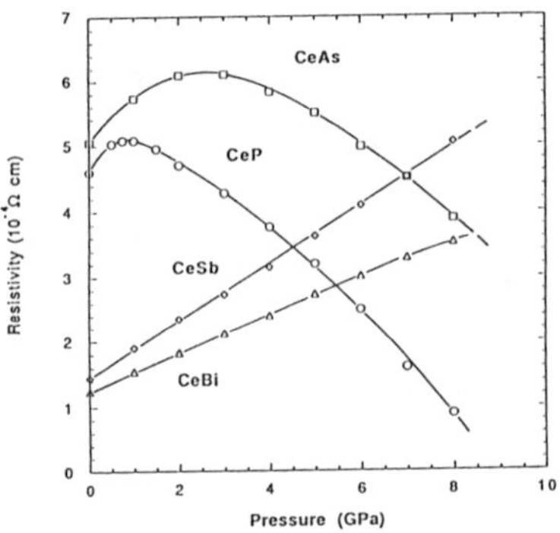

Figure 8. The resistivity of Ce monopnictides as a function of pressure at room temperature.

pnictides as a function of pressure at room temperature. The resistivity of CeP and CeAs increases initially under pressure, passes through a maximum and then decreases. On the other hand, the resistivity of CeSb and CeBi increases monotonously with pressure up to 8GPa. This behavior seems to correlate well from the point of view that the lattice constant is changed by applying pressure as shown in fig.1. Taking account of the systematic change in resistivity with pressure as shown in fig. 8, the phase diagram is thought to represent allover features in Ce monopnictides under pressure.

As pressure is increased, magnetic phase transitions take place with its highest transition temperature, T_H, passing through a maximum, and then decreasing to zero. This behavior can be interpreted by the interplay between the RKKY interaction and the Kondo spin fluctuations as described earlier[9]. The characteristic temperatures of these interactions, T_{RKKY} and T_K, have different pressure dependencies. For low pressure regions, the magnetic Kondo state is realized, $T_{RKKY} > T_K$. The large increase in T_H is due to the superlinier change in T_{RKKY} with pressure. Near the maximum temperature of T_H, however, a crossover, $T_{RKKY} < T_K$, takes places. After the crossover occurs, the magnetic moment is decreased rapidly due to Kondo coupling with strong hybridization between 4f level and the conduction band through the shift of the conduction bands with respect to the 4f level. And finally, the 4f electron changes with a first order transition from a localized to an itinerant state. This is the case just observed in CeP at 5.5GPa. The first order transition may be interpreted by the Kondo collapse model[20,21]. To confirm this point further experiments, especially measurements of the Fermi surface under pressure, are important.

In this paper, we have explained some main features of Ce monopnictides revealed under high pressure. However, as mentioned before[9], some phenomena, such as a huge enhancement of the resistivity induced by applying pressure in CeSb, still remain unexplained.

ACKNOWLEDGMENTS

The author wishes to acknowledge Drs. Y. Okayama, Y. Haga and H. Takahashi, and Professor T. Suzuki for collaboration and Professor T. Kasuya for valuable discussions. This work was supported partly by the Scientific Research Grant-in-Aid from Ministry of Education Japan.

REFERENCES

[1] Y.S.Kwon, Ph.D. Thesis, Tohoku University,(1991).
[2] A.Fransiosi et al., Phys. Rev. B24, 3651(1981).
[3] R.J.Birgenean et al., Phys. Rev. B8, 5345(1973).
[4] J-M.Leger et al.,J.Magn.Magn.Mater.63&64,4951(1987)
[5] J-M.Leger et al., J. Phys. C, 17,4983(1984).
[6] A.Jayaraman et al., Phys. Rev. Lett. 36, 366(1976)
[7] N.Mori et al., J. Appl. Phys. 69, 4696(1991).
[8] Y.Okayama et al., J.Magn.Magn.Mater.108, 113(1992).
[9] N.Mori et al., Jpn.J.Appl.Phys. 32,Suppl.32-1, 300 (1993); *Physical Properties of Actinide and Rare Earth Compounds*, Jpn. J. Appl. Phys. Series 8, 182 (1993); Physica B, in press.
[10] N.Mori et al., Proc.4th Int.Conf. on High Pressure, Kyoto, p295(1975).
[11] N.Mori and H.Takahashi, J. High Pressure Inst. Jpn. 28, 124(1990).
[12] Y.Onuki et al., J.Phys.Soc.Jpn.,58,2126-2134(1989).
[13] Y.Okayama et al., Physica B, in press.
[14] J.Rossad-Mignod et al., J. Magn. Magn. Mater.52,111 (1985)
[15] J.Rossad-Mignod et al., J. Magn. Magn. Mater.31&34, 398(1983).
[16] Y.Onuki et al., J. Phys. Soc. Jpn. 58, 2119(1989).
[17] N.Shamir et al., Physica 94B, 225(1978).
[18] M.Khogi et al., Physica B, in press.
[19] P.M.Levy and A.Fert, Phys. Rev. 39,12224(1989).
[20] J.W.Allen and R.M.Martin, Phys. Rev. Lett. 49, 1106 (1982).
[21] M.Lavagna et al., Phys. Lett. A92, 210(1982).

MOSSBAUER STUDY OF H_{STHF} FOR Sn^{119} IN $NdFeO_3$ UNDER PRESSURE

G.N. Stepanov and A.G. Gavriliuk, Institute for High Pressure Physics, Russian Academy of Science
IHPP, Troitsk, Moscow region, Russia, 142092

I.S. Lyubutin, Institute of Crystallography, Russian Academy of Science,
Inst. of Crystallography, Moscow, st. Butlerova 17, Russia, 117342

Dependance of magnitude of a "supertransferred hyperfine magnetic field" (STHF) on a nucleus of diamagnetic atom Sn^{119} upon pressure was investigated in rare earth orthoferrite $Nd_{0.9}Ca_{0.1}Fe_{0.9}Sn_{0.1}O_3$ using Mossbauer absorption spectroscopy. The diamond anvil cell (DAC) was used for high pressure generation up to 17.5 GPa at room temperature. It was found that the dependance is approximately linear with coefficient dH/dP=+(2±0.1) kOe/GPa. The growth of STHF can be explained by decreasing of Sn-O distance.

INTRODUCTION

A strong magnetic field H_{eff} on a nucleus of some diamagnetic ion D arises if D is implanted into a lattice of magnetic compound [1]. The greatest part of the H^D_{eff} results from the transference of a spin density from paramagnetic ions M to the ion D. The magnetic compounds may be metallic, semiconducting or dielectric. Moreover in some dielectric compounds the cations are separated by the anion A so that there is no direct mixing of the electron states of cations. The transference of spin density is realized by means of the ions chains M-A-M or M-A-D. These magnetic field is called "supertransferred hyperfine magnetic field" H_{STHF} [2]. Field H^D_{STHF} on the nucleus of the diamagnetic ion D as a whole arises as a result of the interaction with cations M because its own shell is compensated in the absence of a magnetic environment. That is why H^D_{STHF} is sensitive to local structure and to local magnetic environment. The theory H^D_{STHF} is in initial stage and it can only qualitatively interpret the experimental results [3,4,5,6]. In this paper we present the study of the influence of the high pressure on H^D_{STHF}.

EXPERIMENTAL METHOD AND SAMPLE

The measurement of H_{STHF} on nuclei Sn^{119} in the lattice orthoferrite $NdFeO_3$ at the high pressure was carried out by Mössbauer absorption spectroscopy. Ions Fe^{3+} in the sample were substituted partly with the ions Sn^{4+} and the ions Ca^{2+} were added for the charge compensation. The sample's formula was $Nd_{0.9}Ca_{0.1}Fe_{0.9}Sn_{0.1}O_3$. Tin in the sample was enriched with Sn^{119} to 90%. The diagram of the crystal structure of orthoferrite $NdFeO_3$ is presented on Fig 1. It is distorted perovskite [7].

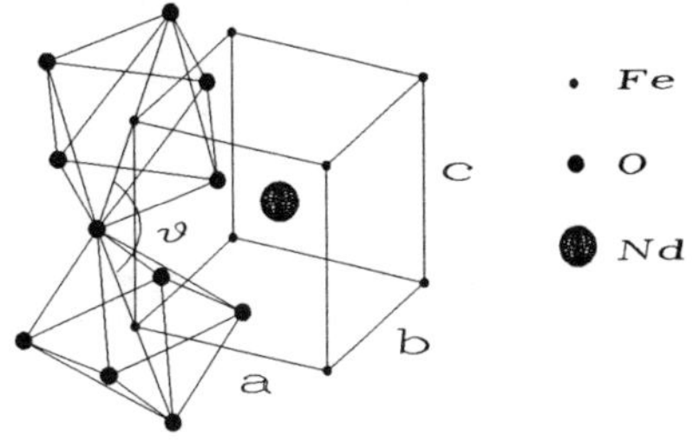

Figure 1. Lattice of orthoferrite

The sample was prepared by means of the ceramic method [8]. The lattice parameters of the sample were a=5.476A, b=5.608A, c=7.788A; Neel temperature was T_N=615K. High pressure was generated by means of the diamond anvil cell (DAC) [9]. The metal rhenium foil (initial thickness ~300 μm) was used as a gasket. To form the gasket the foil was placed between the anvils and the load was applied to the anvils many times. The maximum value of the load was increased gradually. Otherwise in the case of rapid loading the rhenium foil was cracked. The diameter of anvils was 600 μm, the diameter of hole in the gasket was 200 μm. The pressure was measured in the center of the sample and in 4 points on the edges of the sample. The spectrum line of the fluorescence of ruby was broadened because of no special medium for pressure transition was used. The difference in pressure values at the center and on the edges of the sample was ~10%. The pressure was measured before and after the exposure on Mössbauer spectrometer. The pressure was practically invariable. Mössbauer spectrometer was operated in constant acceleration mode. The intensity of the source radiation was ~3 mCu. The exposure at the spectrum measurement was ~120 h. The values H_{STHF} for different pressures were calculated by computer-fitting program based on the W.Kundig model [21]. All measurements were carried out at room temperatures.

EXPERIMENTAL RESULTS

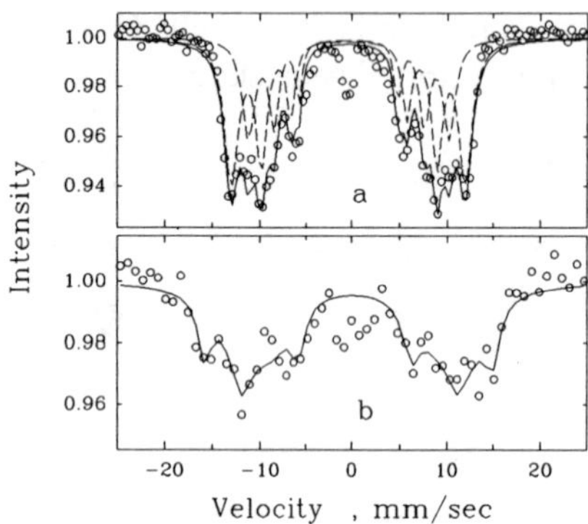

Figure 2. Mössbauer spectra: a- P=0 GPa, b- P=17.5 GPa

Figure 2 a, b show the Mössbauer spectrums obtained at normal conditions and at 17.5 GPa respectively. Low quality of the spectrum at high pressure was caused by small size of the sample (diameter ~200μm, thickness ~50μm and limited intensity of $CaSn^{119}O_3$ gamma-ray source. The spectrum of Sn^{119} in $NdFeO_3$ consists of more then one sextet. The composite spectrum reflects the distinction of local environments of Sn atoms in the lattice of orthoferrite. Most of the Sn atoms have 6 Fe atoms in the nearest environment. But there are Sn atoms with 5, 4 of Fe atoms in the nearest environment. The part of the Fe atoms are substituted by Sn. The existence of diamagnetic Sn atoms in nearest environment of resonance nucleus Sn^{119} lead to decrease the value H. We computed our results assuming the existence of two sextets. One can see these two sextets on the spectrum at P=0 (see fig.2, a). As a result of the experiment we consider only dependence of the H_{STHF} corresponding to presence of 6 atoms of the Fe in the nearest environment of resonance nucleus Sn^{119} upon the pressure. The figure 3 shows the variation of magnetic field H_{STHF} with pressure P.

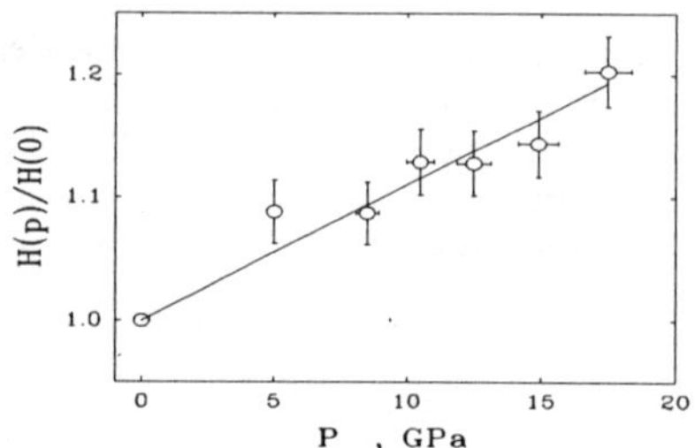

Figure 3. The dependence of H^{Sn}_{STHF} on the pressure

DISCUSSION

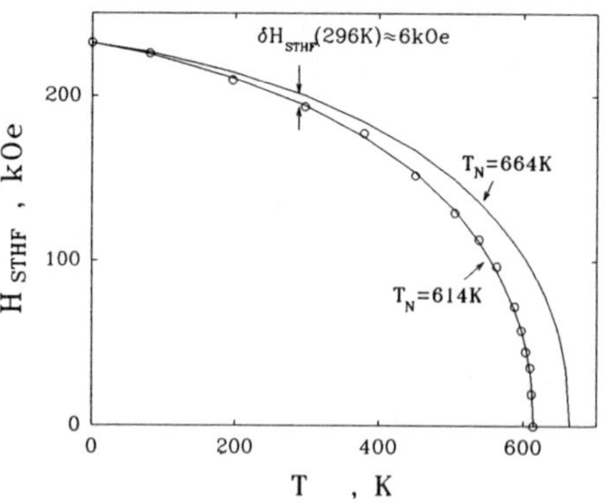

Figure 4. The temperature dependence H^{Sn}_{STHF} in $NdFeO_3$

The consideration of the experimental results we begin with the analyses of the temperature dependence of H^{Sn}_{STHF} in $NdFeO_3$ at P=0 [8] (see fig.4). The pressure can act on the both parameters $H^{Sn}_{STHF}(0K)$ and T_N. The change of both T_N and $H^{Sn}_{STHF}(0)$ may have influence on the value of $H^{Sn}_{STHF}(300K)$ that was measured in the study. The approximation of the effect of pressure on Neel temperature in orthoferrites gives dT_N/dP=0.4-0.7 K/kbar [10]. As it follows from experimental dependence $H^{Sn}_{STHF}(T)$ the increase of H^{Sn}_{STHF}(300 K) related with the rise of only T_N at high pressure may be about 6 kOe at 10 GPa (see fig.4). The increase of H^{Sn}_{STHF}(300 K) determined in the course of this study was ~20 kOe at 10 GPa (see fig.3). It is because one can conclude that the main part of the rise of H^{Sn}_{STHF}(300K) is conditioned by the effect of pressure on H^{Sn}_{STHF}(0 K). Below in the text H^{Sn}_{STHF}(0 K) is re-marked as H^{Sn}_{STHF}. Supertransfer hyperfine interaction may be defined as the interaction of nucleus with its own electron shell disturbed by the paramagnetic M-ions via the normally diamagnetic ligands A in a dielectric. Hyperfine field H_{STHF} is mainly a result of the Fermi contact interaction, we are concerned with determining the spin density. On the other hand superexchange that defines T_N may be defined as the exchange mechanism taking place in transition-metal compounds in which the paramagnetic M-ions are fairly well separated by normally diamagnetic groups A, and in which conduction is poor at all normal temperatures [11]. Superexchange is usually thought of as a transference from the *d*-orbital of one M-ion to the *d*-orbital of another M-ion, while the *d* orbital of one M-ion and the *s*-orbitals of the other M- or D-ion are involved in producing H_{STHF}. So both effects depend on transference from one metal ion to another metal ion via the ligand, and we expect that H_{STHF} and T_N will behave in the same way. In orthoferrites $RFeO_3$ where R is rare-earth in going from $LaFeO_3$ to $LuFeO_3$ the T_N and H^{Fe}_{hpf} and H^{Sn}_{STHF} gradually decrease, while the isomer shift (IS) remains constant [12,8]. X-ray measurements show that the Fe-O distance in orhoferrite remain almost constant (~2.01 A) while the bond angle decreases gradually from 157° in $LaFeO_3$ to 142 in $LuFeO_3$ [7]. Using LCAO T_N, H_{hpf} and IS may be expressed in terms of the covalency parameters and overlaps which is strongly dependent on the Fe-O distance and Fe-O-Fe bond angle [3-6]. Let us consider the simple model of arising H^{Sn}_{STHF}. In the ground nonexcited state the configuration of ions in the chain Fe-O-Sn have the form

Fe^{3+}	O^{2-}	Sn^{4+}
$3d^5\uparrow$	$2p^2\uparrow\downarrow$	$5s^0$

In excited state when the $2p\downarrow$ electron of O^{2-} partly transfers to the empty $3d\downarrow$ state of Fe^{3+}. Uncompensated spin density of 2p electrons appears on ligand O^{2-}. These unpaired 2p electrons by means of covalency transference to 5s-shall of Sn^{4+} and overlap with inner *ns*-states of Sn^{4+} cause the arising H^{Sn}_{STHF}. Since the isomer shift is only weakly dependent on the bond angle the X-ray data is exactly what is needed to explain the constancy of the isomer shift. H^{Fe}_{hpf} decreases from 564 kOe to 545 kOe [12] and H^{Sn}_{STHF} from 256 kOe to 160 kOe [8] in going from $LaFeO_3$ to $LuFeO_3$. Together with decrease of H_{hpf} it is observed the reduction of T_N. As it is well known in arguments, related to superexchange, the spin transference from one cation to another via an intermediate anion is the largest for a bond angle of 180° and the smallest for a 90 . Since the supertransferred hyperfine field depends on the spin transference in much the same way as superexchange the H_{STHF} also must be function of the Fe-O-Sn bond angle Θ. The expressions, relating the hyperfine field on Fe-57 nuclei and the T_N to the bond angle are in excellent agreement with the experimental results. It is evident that at high pressure we have the right to expect the diminution of Fe-O and Sn-O distances. But thanks to the fact that the bulk modules of the compounds are usually smaller then the bulk modules of the polyhedrons, at high pressure the bond angle may be altered too. H^{Sn}_{STHF} according to the dependence on bond angle for the row of orthoferrites must be decreased if the bound angle is decreased. The bulk modules of the oxide octahedron with Fe^{3+} in its center is ~2.8 Mbar, the bulk modules of ferrite ~1.8 Mbar [13]. The rough estimation of the bond angle change yields delta theta $\Delta\Theta$~-1.4° at P=10 GPa. The corresponding decrease of H^{Sn}_{STHF} that was to be expected at 10 GPa is ~10 kOe. Let us move on to consideration of H^{Sn}_{STHF} dependence on Fe-O and Sn-O distances. The rise of overlaps is expected with the decrease of the lattice parameter and, consequently, an increase in H_{STHF} and T_N. The dependence of overlaps on interatomic distance was calculated in [14]. From the calculation it follows that the decrease of Sn-O distances on 1% leads to increase of overlap to ~1% and increase of parameter covalency to ~3%. The increase of T_N in compounds with superexchange mechanism of magnetic ordering is observed at high pressure really [15]. However the information about the influence of the pressure on H_{STHF} have ambivalent disposition. Lister and Benedek have measured the pressure dependence of the hyperfine fields at Fe^{57} nuclei in A- and B-sites in yttrium iron garnet. They found that the hyperfine field are nearly independent on the lattice parameters [16]. Halasa, DePasquali and Drickamer have made high pressure studies to 15 GPa on four orthoferrites, on $NiFe_2O_4$ and on Fe_3O_4 [10]. The major feature observed for the orthoferrites include an increase in H^{Fe}_{hpf} which can be interpreted in terms of increase in T_N and constancy of $H_{hpf}(0K)$ under pressure. For NiFe2O4 the results could best be interpreted in terms of decrease $H^{Fe}_{hpf}(0K)$ but at the same time $dT_N/dP=+1.16$ K/kbar [17]. For Fe_3O_4 H^{Fe}_{hpf} was decreased too. Geschwind and Locher have pointed out that the $H^{Fe}_{hpf}(0K)$ is quite independent of the Fe-O distance as confirmed by the EPR data of Fe^{3+} on various hosts [18]. On the other hand the considerable rise of H^{Sn}_{STHF} in $MnFe_2O_4$ was recorded under pressure to 1.2 GPa ($dH_{STHF}/dP=+0.03$ kOe/GPa) [19]. For discussion of the dependence H_{STHF} on the Fe-O, Sn-O distances it is necessary to consider the simplest model of H_{STHF} [20]. According to this model

$$H_{STHF} \sim A^2_{\sigma,\pi}[-\sum_{n=1}^{4} S_{ns}\Phi_{ns}(0)+a_{5s}\Phi_{5s}(0)]^2 \quad (1)$$

Where $A_{\sigma,\pi}$, a_{5s} - covalency parameters of $2p\downarrow\rightarrow 3d\downarrow$ and $2p\rightarrow 5s$; S_{ns} - overlap $<2p|\Phi_n>$, Φ_n - *s*- functions of Sn. If we take into account that the largest contribution in H^{Sn}_{STHF} is caused by covalent transference from *2p*-shell of O^{2-} to *5s*-shell of Sn^{4+} the field on Sn^{119} nuclei is determined by

$$H_{STHF} \sim A^2_{\sigma,\pi} a^2_{5s} \Phi^2_{5s}(0) \quad (2)$$

If we neglect the influence of the pressure on $A_{\sigma,\pi}$ [10] we are able to do the rough estimation of dependence H_{STHF} on the pressure

$$\Delta H_{STHF}(10GPa) \sim \frac{dH_{STHF}}{dr_{Sn-O}} \cdot \frac{dr_{Sn-O}}{dP}\Delta P = 12kOe \quad (3)$$

On the other hand let us estimate the contribution of the decrease Fe-O, Sn-O distances to rise of H_{STHF} as it follows from experimental data. We had observed the change of H_{STHF} at 10 GPa on 20 kOe. The rise up to ~6 kOe is may be connected with the increase of T_N upon pressure (see fig. 4). But it should be born in mind that the decrease of bond angle under pressure can bring about the diminution of H^{Sn}_{STHF} on ~10 kOe at 10 GPa. So the rise of H_{STHF} at 10 GPa owing to decrease of Fe-O, Sn-O distances may be about 24 kOe. The rough estimation coincides with experimental changing of H^{Sn}_{STHF} under pressure in the sign and the order of the value.

REFERENCES

[1] K.P.Belov, I.S.Lubutin, *JETP Let. (USSR)*, 1, pp. 26-31 (1965).; V.I.Goldansky, M.N.Devisheva, *JETP Let (USSR)*, 1, pp. 31-36. (1965).

[2] L.Huang, R.Orbach, E.Simanek, J.Owen and D.R.Taylor, *Phys.Rev.*, 156, pp. 383-390 (1967).

[3] F.van der Woude and G.A.Sawatzky, *Phys.Rev.B 4*, pp. 3159-3165 (1971).

[4] Bokema, F.van der Woude, G.A.Sawatzky, *Int.J.Magnetism,*, 3, pp. 341-348 (1972).

[5] A.S.Moskvin, N.S.Ovanecyan, V.A.Trukhtanov, *Hyp. Indern.*, , 3, pp. 429-447 (1977).

[6] A.S.Moskvin, N.S.Ovanecyan, V.A.Trukhtanov, *Ibid.* , 1, pp. 265-281 (1975).

[7] M.Marezio,J.P.Remeika, P.D.Dernier., *Acta Cryst.B*, 26, pp. 2008-2015 (1970)

[8] I.S.Lubutin, Yu.S.Vishnyakov, *JETP (USSR)*, , 61, pp. 1962-1969 (1971).

[9] A.Jayaraman, *Rev.Mod.Phys.*, 55, pp 65-83 (1983).

[10] N.A.Halasa, G.De Pasquali and H.G.Drickamer, *Phys.Rev. B*, 10, pp. 154-164 (1974).

[11] P.W.Anderson, *Phys.Rev.*, 115, pp.2-13 (1959)

[12] M.Eibschutz.S.Shtriknan and D.Treves, *Phys.Rev.*, 156, pp.562-571 (1967).

[13] R.M.Hazen, L.W.Finger, *Comparative Crystal Chemistry* Wiley

[14] Y.Miyahara, S.Iida, *J.Phys.Soc.Jap.* ,37, pp. 1248-1256 (1974).

[15] H.G.Drickamer, C.W.Frank, *Electronic transition and the high pressure chemistry and physics of solids.* Chapman and Hall. London.1973; C.L.Foiles, C.T.Tomizuka, *J.Appl.Phys.*, 36, pp. 3839-3843 (1965).

[16] J.D.Litster, G.B.Benedek, *J.Appl.Phys.*, 37, pp. 1320-1333 (1966)

[17] G.A.Samara, A.A.Giardini, *Phys.Rev.*, 186, pp. 577-562 (1969).

[18] S.Geschwind,P.P.Locher, *Phys.Rev.*, 139, pp. A991-A999 (1965).

[19] I.N.Nikolaev, V.P.Potapov, I.S.Lubutin, *Fiz.Tverd.Tela* ,20, pp. 3585-3587 (1978).

[20] G.A.Sawatzky, F.Van der Woude,*J.Phys.*,35, N C6. pp. 47-65 (1974).

[21] W.Kundig, *NIM (Nuclear instruments and method)*, 48, pp.219-225 (1967).

CHAPTER XX

OPTICAL STUDIES

INFLUENCE OF A RARE GAS ON THE VIBRATIONAL SPECTRUM OF A DIATOMIC SYSTEM AT HIGH PRESSURE

J.A. Schouten and M.I.M. Scheerboom
Van der Waals-Zeeman laboratory
University of Amsterdam
Valckenierstraat 65
1018 XE Amsterdam, The Netherlands

Vibrational Raman spectroscopy is a useful technique for investigating the behaviour and properties of systems at high pressures. Recently, some interesting studies have been reported in literature about the influence of the surrounding medium on the vibrational properties of diatomic molecules. We will discuss the shift in the peak position as well as the broadening of the line due to the admixture of a second component.

INTRODUCTION

Vibrational Raman spectroscopy is one of the most useful tools for studying fluids at high density. Mostly due to the anharmonicity of the intramolecular potential the intermolecular forces can cause a change in the frequency of the molecular vibration [1], but also in the profile of the spectrum [2,3]. So this technique not only probes the intermolecular forces, but also the fluctuations and the dynamics of the system. Other possible broadening mechanisms like resonance transfer and clustering processes can also be investigated.

The environment of a molecule is, of course, not only influenced by pressure and temperature. The addition of a second component generally changes the forces on a particular molecule even more. As is well known, due to the unlike interactions the behaviour is much more complicated and several new phenoma might occur. As an example we refer to fluid-fluid phase separation, in particular the fluid-fluid critical point, and molecular charisma. At high pressure large density fluctuations will not easily occur. However, near a critical point in a mixture the behaviour of the system is dominated by **concentration** fluctuations, which might have influence on the spectra. Supercritical fluid mixtures show unique properties, e.g. an enormous enhancement of the solubility. This is a manifestation of the fact that the local properties of the system might be essentially different from the bulk properties leading to the concept of molecular charisma [4] The Raman shift gives insight in the change in the environment due to the unlike interaction while the spectrum profile gives information on clustering in H_2 mixtures and probably critical effects in N_2 mixtures. For our purpose the most important feature of the profile is the full width at half maximum, which we will refer to as FWHM.

In this survey we will discuss the vibrational Raman measurements on simple binary fluid mixtures at high density. Experimental results at room temperature and pressures up to 100 kbar have been published for N_2-O_2 [5] and H_2 in Ar, He, Ne, or D_2 [6-10]. Moreover, we have investigated the system N_2-He in a range of temperatures.

EXPERIMENTAL METHODS

All of the measurements discussed in this paper have been performed in a diamond anvil cell. The pressure has been determined by means of the usual ruby fluorescence technique. It

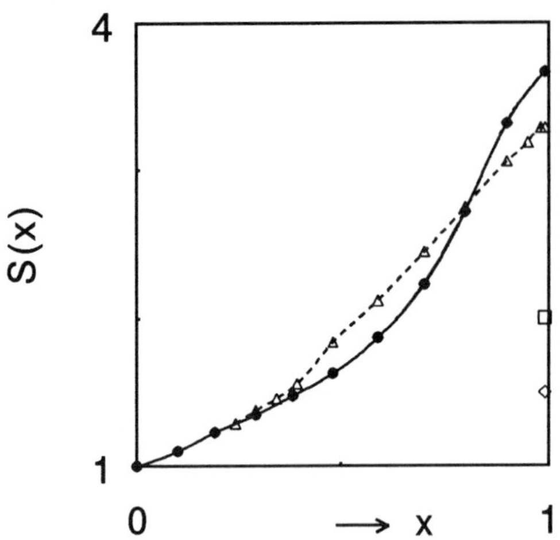

Figure 1. Relative Raman shift of H_2 at room temperature as a function of mole fraction of the second component[8]. ● He; ▲ Ne; □ Ar; ◊ D_2.

should be noted that the phenomena described below are not very sensitive to uncertainties in the pressure or temperature measurements. More important is the accurate determination of the composition and care should be taken in the loading procedure [6,11]. After preparation of the mixture the system should be given sufficient time to become homogeneous before the diamond anvil cell is loaded. For calculating the composition low pressure p-V-T data of the mixture have to be known. The uncertainty in the composition for the systems reported in literature is 0.3 mole percent, except for N_2-O_2 where it is 3 mole percent. The uncertainty in the composition of the nitrogen-helium system for the measurements reported in this paper range from 0.3 mole percent in a 50-50 mixture to 0.1 mole percent in a 10-90 mixture.

RESULTS AND DISCUSSION

a) H_2 in Ar, He, Ne and D_2 :

The influence of various simple molecules on the Raman peak position and halfwidth of hydrogen has been investigated by Loubeyre et al. [6-10]. These investigators expressed the change in Raman shift of the mixture with respect to that of the pure component by the function S(x), which is defined as: $S(x) = [Q(x,p)-Q(0,0)]/[Q(0,p)-Q(0,0)]$. Here Q(x,p) is the vibrational Raman shift of hydrogen in the mixture at pressure p and mole fraction x. S(x) turned out to be independent of p in the high density fluid mixtures. A room temperature plot of S(x) for the various H_2 mixtures is shown in fig.1. It is interesting to look at the value of S for x=1, when the hydrogen molecules are completely surrounded by other molecules, since this provides the best probe for the unlike interaction. The large S(1) values for H_2 in He and Ne (±3.5) and the sequence of the magnitude of S(1) for H_2 in the rare gases are remarkable. On the basis of the relative differences in the molecular potentials one would expect the value for Ar to be larger than for He and Ne. The smallest value of S(1) in fig.1 is for H_2 in D_2 and indeed in this case the interaction potentials are very similar.

At high densities the FWHM of H_2 increases as a function of the mole fraction of helium. For a mole fraction of 0.5 the width is about five times that of pure H_2 and remains constant for higher mole fractions of helium [7]. It should be noted that the mole fractions have been corrected in a later article [6] but this revision will not change the considerable increase of the width and the constant value at high helium contents. Remarkable is the occurrence of a low frequency tail, which also has been observed in the mixtures with Ar, Ne and D_2. In these systems the increase of the FWHM is about a factor of two [8] These effects have been interpreted as partly due to an clustering process, which indeed has been reported previously for H_2 in rare gas mixtures at ambient pressure [12]. The broadening due to clustering has been calculated to be enhanced at increasing density [13].

b) N_2 in He and O_2

We have investigated the system N_2-He for a number of concentrations in a range of temperatures. In fig.2 a plot is shown of the Raman shift of N_2 versus mole fraction (x) of He in the fluid mixture at a pressure of 45 kbar. The results

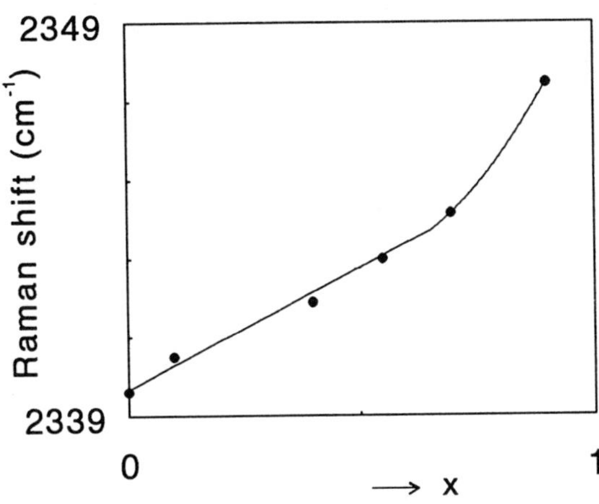

Figure 2. Raman shift of N_2 as a function of the molefraction of He at p=45 kbar [this work].

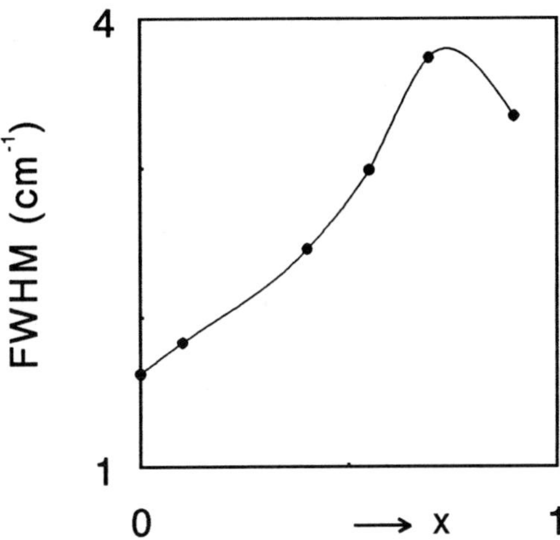

Figure 3. Deconvoluted FWHM of N_2 at room temperature as a function of the mole fraction of helium [this work].

turned out to be independent of temperature from the coexistence surface up to 400 K. Extrapolation to x=1 gives a value for S(1) between 1.6 and 2, which is remarkably low compared to that for H_2 in He. Very recently the change in Raman shift due to the intermolecular forces at high densities has been calculated accurately for pure fluid nitrogen [14]. It has been shown that a separation of the intermolecular interaction according to Weeks, Chandler and Anderson, namely purely repulsive and purely attractive forces, leads to good agreement between calculations and experiment. An important contribution to the shift shown in fig.2 is due to the fact that the unlike attractive He-N_2 interaction is very much smaller than that of the N2-N2.

In fig.3 a plot of the FWHM versus x is presented for p=45 kbar and room temperature. It is shown that the width increases with a factor of 2 compared to that of pure N2. It is remarkable, however, that at 80 mole percent helium it has a distinct maximum. Such a clear maximum has not been reported previously. What is the explanation for the occurrence of this maximum?

Recently it has been shown that for N_2 at high density the broadening due to the repulsive interaction becomes much larger than that due to the attractive interaction and the vibration-rotation coupling [15]. Since in pure components all other possible broadening mechanisms are negligible [2,3] it is not to be expected that in a mixture a competition exists between different mechanisms, in contrast with the situation at ambient pressure [16]

As mentioned before, concentration fluctuations lead to a broadening of the line width. Recently the phase diagram of N_2-He at high pressures has been studied extensively in our laboratory and it turned out that a fluid-fluid phase separation is present up to more than 100 kbar. The critical composition hardly varies between 10 and 100 kbar and is roughly 80 mole percent helium. The maximum in the width (fig.3) is also at about 80 mole percent. Although one might argue that the system is far from critical conditions, the influence of the critical point might extend over a considerable range in temperature and pressure [19]. In order to show decisively whether this is a critical effect measurements of the line width as a function of pressure and temperature, starting near the critical point, are in progress. Also larger mole fractions of He have to be studied, because it is to be expected that a critical effect will completely vanish for a single N_2 molecule in a He bath. At ambient pressure an extensive Raman spectroscopic study of the system N_2-Ar has been performed [16,17]. It has been shown that a

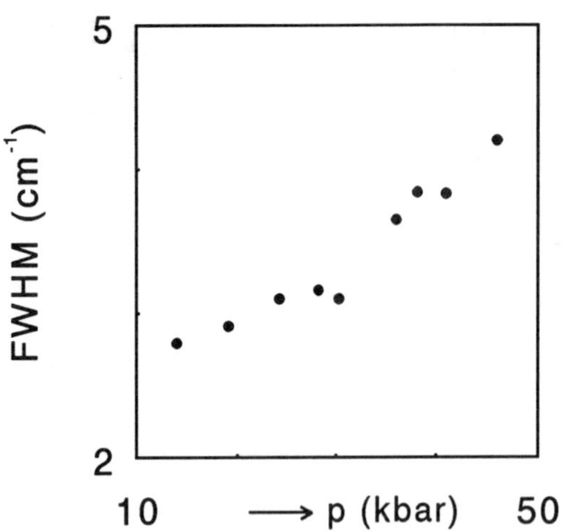

Figure 4. FHWN of N_2 at room temperature as a function of pressure for the system N_2-O_2 (45% O_2) [5].

critical enhancement is present, but a quantitative analysis is difficult because of the many competing broadening mechanisms involved [16].

Unlike the previous systems, which show fluid-fluid demixing, the system N_2-O_2 is completely miscible in the fluid phase and does not show a critical point at high pressure. Also the high density solids appear to be highly miscible. This is due to the fact that the intermolecular potentials of both molecules are similar. It is, therefore, not to be expected that the addition of O_2 will give rise to a broadening of the N_2 peak. The system has been investigated at room temperature by Baer and Nicol [5]. In fig.4 the line width of N_2 at room temperature is plotted as a function of pressure for a mixture containing 45 mole percent O_2. At other compositions this plot is essentially the same [5]. Indeed a broadening of the line due to the admixture of O_2 has not been detected. This result is the same as obtained for the liquids at ambient pressure [17].

It is well known that in the pure components N_2 and O_2 at moderate densities the contribution to the line width of population relaxation [2,3], resonance transfer[2,3] or clustering [13] is negligible and therefore these systems are the best candidates for studying critical effects [18,19]. In a mixture the contribution of resonance transfer and clustering might change. However, the above mentioned experiment shows that these mechanisms are also negligible at high densities.

REFERENCES:

[1] D. Schiferl, R. LeSar and D. S. Moore in *Simple Molecular Systems at Very High Density*, pp.303 ed. by A.Polian, P.Loubeyre, and N.Boccara (Plenum, NY, 1989).

[2] M.J.Clouter, *Ann. Rev. Phys. Chem.* 39, pp. 69 (1988).

[3] J.Chesnoy, and G.M.Gale, *Adv. Chem. Phys.* 70, pp. 297 (1988).

[4] C.A. Eckert and B.L. Knutson, *Fluid Phase Equilibria*, 83, pp. 93 (1993)

[5] B.J.Baer, and M.Nicol, *J. Phys. Chem.* 94, pp. 1073 (1990).

[6] P.Loubeyre, R.LeToullec, and J.P.Pinceaux, J. *Phys: Condens. Matter*, 3, pp. 3183 (1991).

[7] P.Loubeyre, R.LeToullec, and J.P.Pinceaux, *Phys. Rev.* B36, pp. 3723 (1987).

[8] P.Loubeyre, R.LeToullec, and J.P.Pinceaux, *Phys. Rev.* B45, pp. 12844 (1992).

[9] P.Loubeyre in *Molecular Systems under High Pressure* ed. by R.Pucci, and G.Piccitto (Elsevier, Amsterdam, 1991).

[10] P.Loubeyre, R.LeToullec, and J.P.Pinceaux, *Phys. Rev. Lett.* 67, pp. 3271 (1991).

[11] J.A.Schouten, N.J.Trappeniers, and L.C. van den Bergh, *Rev. Sci. Instrum.* 54, pp. 120 (1983).

[12] J.A. Beswick, and J. Jortner, *Adv. Chem. Phys.* 47, pp. 363 (1981).

[13] G.Ewing, *Chem.Phys.* 29, pp. 253 (1978).

[14] G.S.Devendorf and D.Ben-Amotz, *J. Phys. Chem.* 97, pp. 2307 (1993).

[15] R.Kroon, M.Baggen,and A.Lagendijk, *J. Chem. Phys.* 91, pp. 74(1989).

[16] H.J.van Elburg,and J.D.W.van Voorst, *J.Chem.Phys.* 113, pp. 463 (1987).

[17] S.A. Akhmanov, F.N.Gadzhiev, N.I.Koroteev, R.Yu. Orlov and I.L.Shumay, *JETP Lett.* 27, pp. 243 (1978).

[18] M.J.Clouter,H.Kiefte, and N.Ali, *Phys.Rev.Lett.* 40, pp. 1170 (1978).

[19] J.Chesnoy, *Chem. Phys. Lett.* 125, pp. 267 (1986).

RECENT HIGH PRESSURE PHOTOLUMINESCENCE STUDIES

H. G. Drickamer, J. M. Lang and Z. A. Dreger
Department of Chemical Engineering
University of Illinois
1209 W. California Street
Urbana, Illinois 61801

In this paper we discuss two studies involving the effect of pressure on luminescent properties of organic molecules in polymeric media. (1) The efficiency of energy transfer from Coumarine 138 to Rhodamine B in polyacrylic acid (PAA) is measured by both steady state and time dependent methods. The "Forster efficiency" obtained by these two methods is consistent and shows the same pressure dependence as efficiencies derived from relative peak intensities. The non-monotonic pressure dependence of the efficiency is accounted for in terms of the properties of the molecules and the media. (2) The effect of pressure on the luminescent efficiency of molecules with two or more possible excited state geometrics has been measured. The efficiency is described in terms of the non radiative dissipation of energy from a planar excited state and the rates of crossing to and from the possible twisted states as well as non-radiative decay from these states. The processes involved in these two studies are pertinent to a number of technologically and biologically important processes.

INTRODUCTION

We discuss here two examples of high pressure luminescence studies of molecules in dilute solution in polymeric matrices. This is, in essence, an extension of the technique of matrix isolation spectroscopy to high pressure and polymeric media.

ENERGY TRANSFER

In the first example [1] we discuss energy transfer between two organic molecules (coumarin 138 and Rhodamine B) in the matrix polyacrylic acid (PAA).

Coumarin 138 has a broad absorption peak in the UV which can absorb the 365 nm line of a Hg arc lamp. Its emission is centered at ~ 22 x 10^3 cm^{-1} at one atmosphere. Its low energy tail overlaps significantly the high energy tail of the RbB absorption. This provides the possibility for comparing various forms of the Förster-Dexter theory [2-3] of energy transfer. The theory is applied in many aspects of science from photosynthesis to fluorescent lighting.

In an isotropic medium the rate of donor-acceptor transfer is given by

$$k_{DA} = \frac{1}{\tau_D}\left(\frac{R_o}{r}\right)^6 \qquad (1)$$

where τ_D is the excited donor lifetime, r is the donor-acceptor distance, which may have a range of values in a given medium, and R_0 is the Förster distance" i.e., the distance at which there is a 50% chance of Förster energy transfer. The transfer efficiency can be extracted from either time dependent or steady state measurements. Here we compare three different ways of extracting this efficiency along with a fourth method not necessarily related to the Förster mechanism and show semiquantitative agreement among all four methods.

From time dependence measurements one can obtain a quantity γ:

$$I(t) = I_O \exp\left[-\frac{t}{\tau_D} - 2\gamma\left(\frac{t}{\tau_D}\right)^{1/2}\right], \qquad (2)$$

where γ is the value of reduced concentration, given by

$$\gamma = \frac{2}{3}\pi^{3/2} n_A R_O^3 . \qquad (3)$$

Here τ_D is the donor lifetime and n_A is the number diversity of acceptors.

One can then express the efficiency directly in terms of γ.

$$E = \pi^{1/2}\gamma \exp(\gamma^2)\left[1 - erf(\gamma)\right], \qquad (4)$$

We call this method I. Alternatively one can extract R_o from the measured γ and eq. 3. The efficiency is then given by:

$$E = \frac{R_0^6}{R_0^6 + r^6} \qquad (5)$$

where in a random mixture one assumes one can use a single mean value of $r = \bar{r}$ which should vary with compression as the cube root of the density. This we call method II. A third possibility is to use eq. (5) but to extract R_o from steady state measurements and then use eq. 5.

$$R_0^6 = \frac{9000 \ln 10\, \Phi_D k^2}{128\, \pi^5 n^4 N}\int_o^\infty \frac{f_D(\nu)\,\varepsilon_A(\nu)}{\nu^4}\, d\nu , \qquad (6)$$

where Φ_D is the absolute fluorescence quantum yield of donor in the absence of an acceptor and quencher, n is the refractive index of the medium, N is Avogadro's number, $f_D(\nu)$ is the emission spectra of the donor with the area (intensity) normalized to unity, $\varepsilon_A(\nu)$ is the adsorption spectra of the acceptor in the units $M^{-1}cm^{-1}$, and ν is the wavenumber in cm^{-1}. This involves extracting the overlap integral from donor emission and acceptor absorption spectra, the donor quantum yield from donor lifetime as a function of pressure and n^4 from the Lorenz-Lorentz relationship, so there are multiple possibilities of error in method III.

A fourth possibility, not necessarily related to any of the above, is to use the expression:

$$E = 1 - \frac{I_{DA}}{I_D}, \qquad (7)$$

where I_D and I_{DA} are the relative intensities of the donor emission in the absence and presence of the acceptor, respectively.

The efficiency extracted by method 1 (eq. 4) exhibits one atmosphere value of 0.69, maximizes at ~ 45 kbar at ~ 0.8 and then falls to 0.76 at 80 kbar. To apply either method II or III requires that one extract R_0 from time dependent or steady state data via eq (3) or (6). Although the time dependent and steady state techniques are obtained from the properties of the system in entirely different ways, they give remarkably similar changes in R_0. There is a drop of a few percent in the first 10-12 kbar, a rise to a maximum and then a drop back below the one atmosphere value at high pressure. For the time dependent measurements the maximum is at ~ 40 kbar while for the steady state measurements it is near 45-50 kbar. The efficiencies correspond to an initial value of 67-72% with a maximum in the range 78-84% very much like the results of method I. From method IV, which has no direct connection with the Förster theory the initial efficiency is ~ 66%, the maximum at 45 kbar of about 80-83% and has a value of ~ 75% at 80 kbar.

The non-monotonic behavior depends on four factors. The overlap at first increases rapidly with pressure, then levels and drops slightly at the highest pressures, due to changes in peak shift and peak shape for donor emission and acceptor absorption. The quantum efficiency of the donor drops by ~ 20% in 80 kbar while the value of $\left[\frac{\bar{\nu}(o)}{\bar{\nu}(p)}\right]^4$ increases by ~ 20% so these cancel. n^4 is superlinear with density. Since the compressibility decreases with increasing pressure, $\left[\frac{n(o)}{n(p)}\right]^4$ decreases rapidly at low pressure and becomes essentially linear above ~ 40 kbar. The balancing of these parameters provides the observed behavior. This study illustrates how pressure can vary both molecular and bulk properties to validate various theories of a given phenomenon.

EXCITED STATE GEOMETRY

The second phenomenon presented involves molecules which are planar in the ground state and can have either a planar or twisted excited state. The twisted state involves an electron transfer within the molecule so the interactions of the two excited states with the environment are different. We present here data on two molecules jolulidine malononitrile (JDMN) and p N-N[1] dimethylamino malononitrile (DMABMN) [4]. JDMN can exhibit a twist of the malononitrile group only, while DMABMN can show either that twist or one by the dimethylamino group. These molecules were studied in four polymers (polymethyl methacrylate (PMMA) polyvinylacetate (PVAC), polyvinylchloride (PVCl) and polystyrene (PS)). The behavior in the first three media were rather similar. In PS there were some anomalies which later (unpublished) work have been able to systematize. We shall not dwell on these here. In general the quantum efficiencies for JDMN were a factor of 8-10 higher than for DMABMN in all media. The quantum yields increase rapidly with pressure by a factor of 10-200 in 30-40 kbar depending on the molecule and the medium and then drop off at a slower rate at higher pressures. The emission efficiency can be expressed in the following terms

$$\Phi = \frac{k_r^P}{k_r^P + k_{nr}^P + k_{nr}^l} \quad \textbf{(8)}$$

where k_r^P and k_{nr}^P are the rates of radiative and non-radiative dissipation of energy from the excited planar state and

$$k_{nr}^l = \frac{k_{PT}}{1 + \frac{k_{TP}}{k_T}} \quad \textbf{(9)}$$

where k_{PT} and k_{TP} are the rates of crossing from planar to twisted state and vise versa, $k_T = k_T^{nr}$ is the rate of thermal dissipation of energy from the twisted state. A little analysis shows one can evaluate k_{nr}^l, which is the focus of our interest from the quantum efficiencies at any pressure p, at p = 0 and at the maximum.

For JDMN a plot of $\ln k_{nr}^l$ vs pressure is linear for all polymers over a pressure range below p_{max} which indicates a generalized relationship from k_{nr}^l of the form

$$k_{nr}^l = \alpha \exp\left(-\frac{"\Delta G"}{k_B T}\right) \quad \textbf{(10)}$$

and

$$\frac{\partial \ln k_{nr}^l}{\partial P} = -\frac{"\nabla V"}{k_B T} \quad \textbf{(11)}$$

Two limiting cases are of physical interest. If a single rate process controls $\alpha = \frac{k_B T}{h}$ and $"\nabla G" = \Delta G\neq$, the activation free energy of Eyring. Then $"\Delta V" = \Delta V^{\neq}$ the volume change on going from reactants to the transition state. If an equilibrium process controls them $\alpha = 1$ and "ΔV" is the volume charge between reactants and products.

For JDMN a plot of $\ln k_{nr}^l$ vs the peak energy is linear with a slope of approximately $(k_B T)^{-1}$ which indicates that the second term in the denominator of eq (9) is negligible and $k_{nr}^l \cong k_{PT}$. Thus "ΔV" = $\Delta V^{\neq}$ which has a value of 4.5 to 6.7 cc/mol in different polymers.

For DMABMN the situation is more complex.

A plot of $\ln k_{nr}^{l}$ vs pressure can be fit with two straight lines in all polymers. The line of lower slope which is dominant at pressures above 5-8 kbar has the characteristics of the JDMN data when plotted against peak energy and evidently represents k_{PT} for the twist of the malononitrile group. The $\Delta V^{\neq}$ values were slightly lower than those in JDMN.

The line dominant at lower pressures is evidently associated with the twist of the dimethylamino group. It is harder to characterize definitively. One possibility is that the second term in the denominator of eq. 9 is large compared with one.

Then

$$\ln k_{nr}^{l} = \ln \frac{k_{PT}}{k_{TP}} + \ln k_{T}^{nr} \qquad (12a)$$

$$= \ln K_{eq}^{TP} + \ln k_{T}^{nr} \qquad (12b)$$

It is reasonable to assume the pressure dependence of the first term in (12b) is dominant. Thus

$$\frac{\partial \ln k_{nr}^{l}}{\partial P} = \Delta V_{eq} \ , \qquad (13)$$

For DMABMN ΔV_{eq} is ~ 7% of the molar volume, a not unreasonable value. It should, however be pointed out that there are other possible scenarios.

The decrease in quantum yield in the high pressure region is apparently associated with an increase in k_{P}^{hr} with the red shift of the emission peak and an increase in k_{T}^{nr} as the twisted excited state is stabilized with increased interaction between the molecule and the matrix.

These molecules have been widely used as probes of polymer free volume and as potential light harvesting media. This pressure study illustrates how high pressure luminescence can sort out the properties of complex systems in a way not possible with atmosphere pressure work alone.

The examples here represent only two of the multiple possibilities of combining matrix isolation studies in polymers with high pressure luminescence.

ACKNOWLEDGEMENT

The authors are pleased to acknowledge the continuing support of the Materials Science Division of the Dept. of Energy under contract DEFG02-91ER45439.

REFERENCES

(1) J. M. Lang and H. G. Drickamer
J. Phys. Chem 97 5058 (1993)

(2) T. Förster Ann. Physik 55 6 (1948)

(3) D. L. Dexter J. Chem. Phys. 21 836 (1953)

(4) Z. A. Dreger, J. M. Lang and H. G. Drickamer
Chem. Phys. 166 193 (1992), Chem. Phys. 169 351, 360, 369 (1993).

References (1) and (4) contain surveys of all relevant literature)

PRESSURE DEPENDENCE OF PHOTOLUMINESCENCE IN GaInP GROWN ON MISORIENTED (100) GaAs BY METALORGANIC VAPOR PHASE EPITAXY

T. Kobayashi and M. Shoji
Department of Electrical and Electronics Engineering,
Kobe University, Kobe 657, Japan

R.S. Deol
Optoelectronics Research Centre, University of Southampton,
Southampton SO9 5NH, United Kingdom

N. Buchan*, W. Heuberger, A. Jakubowicz and P. Roentgen
IBM Research Division, Zurich Research Laboratory,
8803 Rüschlikon, Switzerland

Photoluminescence (PL) measurements on MOVPE-grown $Ga_{0.52}In_{0.48}P$ have been made as a function of pressure up to about 4.5 GPa at 77 K. The PL peak energy shows a sublinear shift up to 3.8-4.0 GPa but a weakly negative pressure shift above 4.0 GPa. The pressure coefficient of the PL peak energy obtained below 3 GPa and the maximum pressure for the observation of PL emission are found to be sensitive to substrate misorientation, reflecting the degree of ordering in this alloy system. This can be partly explained in terms of the repulsion between the Γ-folded energy states in the CuPt-type partially ordered structure.

INTRODUCTION

In recent years, it has been found that the optical properties of GaInP alloys, grown lattice matched to GaAs substrates using metalorganic vapor phase epitaxy (MOVPE), strongly depends on atomic ordering of the group III atoms. The most well known of these effects is the anomalous reduction of the direct band-gap energy by 50-100 meV as compared with that of the disordered (bulk) material. The degree of ordering, and therefore the photoluminescence (PL) emission energy, has been found to depend strongly on numerous growth conditions such as growth temperature, growth rate, V/III ratio, impurity concentration, and substrate misorientation[1–5].

This structure, caused by the ordering of group III atoms with doubling of periodicity in the (111) planes, corresponds to the CuPt-type $(AC)_1(BC)_1$ (111) superlattice structure. The mechanism for this band-gap reduction is theoretically explained as band folding from L-point to Γ-point, followed by repulsion between the Γ-folded states absent in disordered alloys[6]. Recently, high-pressure PL measurements on MOVPE-grown GaInP grown at

* Present address: Advanced Technology Materials, Inc. Danbury, CT 06810

various growth temperatures have been made with the intention of investigating effects of repulsion on the PL spectra[7,8]. The PL behavior under high pressure has been found to be closely related to the growth temperature and hence to the degree of ordering in this alloy system. In this paper we report on a comprehensive study of the dependence of the high-pressure PL properties on a wide range of substrate misorientations. We discuss possible explanations for some of the trends and the complexities involved in high-pressure PL properties in GaInP alloys having different degrees of ordering.

EXPERIMENTAL RESULTS AND DISCUSSION

PL spectra at atmospheric pressure

The series of $Ga_{0.52}In_{0.48}P$ used in this study were grown, in one growth run for comparative purposes, by MOVPE. The GaAs substrates of various orientations on and off the (100) plane toward [011] and [01$\bar{1}$] up to 25° were used[4].

Prior to high-pressure PL measurements on each sample at 77 K, anomalous reductions in band-gap energy were obtained from atmospheric pressure measurements. The PL spectrum for each sample shows a dominant single peak, which is located almost near the E_0 band gap. In Figure 1, the PL peak energy at 77 K is plotted as a function of the substrate off-angle from the (100). As the substrate is tilted toward [011], the energy increases with increasing off-angle and gradually approaches a "normal" band gap of 1.98eV at large angles beyond 10°, this indicating that long-range ordering vanishes at higher angles[3]. However, as the substrate is tilted toward [01$\bar{1}$], at first the energy decreases, then shows a minimum value at around 5°, and approaches nearly the same value as that at orientations of greater

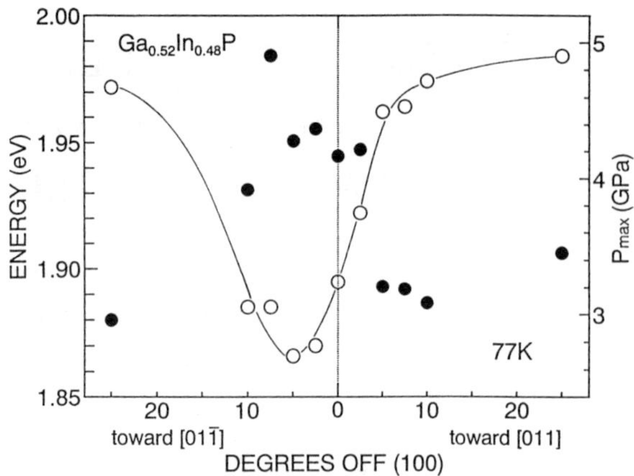

Figure 1. PL peak energy (open circles) and maximum pressure (closed circle), beyond which the PL emission disappears, as a function of substrate off-angle from (100).

than 10° toward [011]. The maximum band-gap variation of ~120 meV is obtained, which is similar to that obtain by Buchan *et al* [4]., and significantly larger than the value of 55 meV obtained by Suzuki *et al* [5].

Effects of repulsion at high pressures

Recent theory has shown that in the CuPt-type ordered $Ga_{0.5}In_{0.5}P$ alloys, the states of different symmetry, Γ and L, of the binary constituents can fold into the same symmetry, Γ, interact and hence repel each other[6]. The amount of such repulsion between Γ-folded energy states is inversely proportional to the energy separation in disordered alloys. The application of hydrostatic pressure decreases the energy separation between Γ_{1c} and L_{1c} conduction-band minima, and hence increases the amount of repulsion between two energy states. This will lower the rate at which the $\overline{\Gamma}_{1c}$ state shifts to higher energies as compared with that for disordered alloys. Above a certain pressure we can also expect to find its shift saturated or even to lower energies. This simple model enables us to interpret the observed PL behavior at high pressure[7,8].

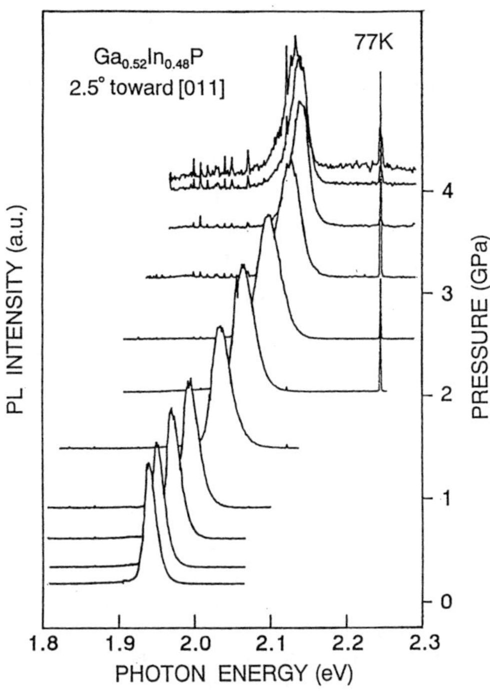

Figure 2. Typical spectra for the sample grown on substrate misoriented 2.5° toward [011] for a series of pressures. The PL intensity units are normalized to the main PL emission for all spectra.

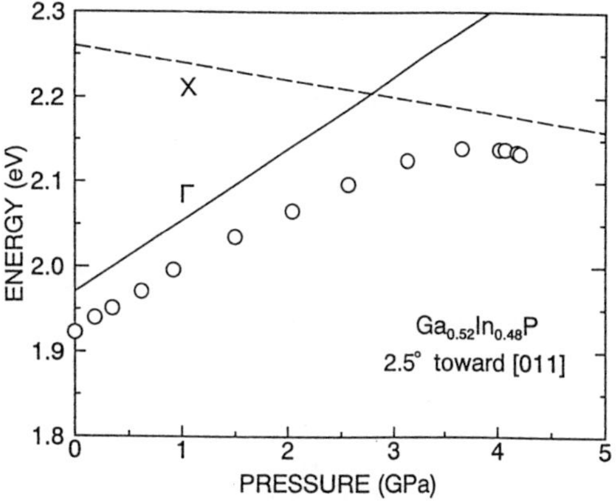

Figure 3. Pressure dependence of the PL peak energy for the sample grown on substrate misoriented 2.5° toward [011]. The Γ_{1c} (solid line) and X_{1c} (dashed line) states are the results for the bulk GaInP in Ref. 9.

Pressure Dependence of PL Spectrum

Figure 2 shows typical PL spectra for the sample grown on (100) GaAs substrate misoriented 2.5° toward [011] for a series of pressures up to about 4.2 GPa at 77 K. The entire spectrum exhibits a rapid shift to higher energies with increasing pressure, indicating the increase in the direct E_0 band gap. At a certain pressure 3.8-4.0 GPa the upward shift of PL spectra saturates, and there appears to be a decrease in the PL peak energy, followed by complete disappearance of this emission at pressures beyond 4.2 GPa. No significant change in the PL intensity is noticed for pressures up to about 2.5-3.0 GPa, while an order of magnitude decrease in the intensity is observed for higher pressures near 4.0 GPa. Figure 3 shows the pressure dependence of the PL peak energy. This shows a sublinearity in the dependence of E_0 in the pressure range 0-3.8 GPa. In addition, the variation of the PL peak energy is found to be located below that in the sample having the lowest degree of ordering (i.e., 25° toward [011]). These results agree well with those obtained for the ordered GaInP alloys grown at various growth temperatures between 600 and 700°C[7,8], and can be partly described by the simple model of repulsion.

For the samples grown on (100) GaAs substrates oriented 7.5, 10, 25° toward [011] and 25° toward [01$\bar{1}$], we have also noticed that the shift of PL spectra shows neither saturation nor decrease in energy and the PL emission tends to disappear at lower pressures below 3.5 GPa. The maximum pressure P_{max} beyond which the PL emission disappears, is strongly dependent on the substrate off-angle and hence on the degree of ordering as shown in Figure 1.

We performed least-squares fits to the data up to ~3 GPa using a quadratic dependence of E_0 on pressure. We note that the linear pressure coefficient for the samples grown on GaAs substrates oriented toward [01$\bar{1}$] is systematically smaller than that for the samples grown on substrates oriented toward [011].

These results can be compared with those obtained for bulk GaInP alloy at 25 K[9]. The PL peak arising from the direct transition across the E_0 band gap show a very linear shift up to ~2.6 GPa with a pressure coefficient of 84 meV/GPa. Beyond this pressure it disappears and a new peak, whose energy decreases with pressure, emerges and remains visible up to 6 GPa. This is due to the pressure-induced Γ-X crossover. But the pressure needed for this band-edge crossover is significantly lower than the pressure region 3.8-4.4 GPa for the saturation or decrease in the PL peak energy observed in the ordered GaInP alloys grown at substrate misorientations other than 7.5, 10, 25° toward [011] and 25° toward [01$\bar{1}$].

If the pressure shift of X minima is not affected with ordering but the variation of X minima with pressure is located ~50 meV below that of the bulk GaInP in Figure 3, there would be some possible explanations of the observed decrease in the PL peak energy beyond ~3.8 GPa and the off-angle dependence of P_{max}. The variation of the band gap E_0 (or the $\bar{\Gamma}_{1c}$ state) in the highly ordered GaInP with pressure is sufficiently below that in the disordered (bulk) GaInP, due to the effect of the repulsion between the Γ-folded states. We would expect that the $\bar{\Gamma}$ -X crossover could occur at pressures higher than 2.6 GPa for the "ordinary" Γ-X crossover. However, in the less ordered GaInP, the resultant $\bar{\Gamma}$-X crossover should take place at pressures near 2.6 GPa, since the variation of the band gap E_0 is closer to that in the bulk GaInP. In addition, it is probable that the PL emission attributed to indirect transition from descending X conduction-band minima, which is typical in the bulk GaInP alloys at 25 K, is not so efficient to be observed at 77 K in the samples grown at substrate misorientations 7.5, 10, 25° toward [011] and 25° toward [01$\bar{1}$]. The only indication of the $\bar{\Gamma}$-X crossover will come from the falling its intensity and the disappearance at lower pressures around 3.0-3.4 GPa as shown in Figure 1.

The situation is therefore quite complicated. Nevertheless, the variations of the PL peak energy with pressure observed here demonstrate the importance of the effects of repulsion on the optical spectra in the ordered GaInP alloys, depending on various substrate orientations and hence on the degree of ordering.

REFERENCES

[1] A. Gomyo, K. Kobayashi, S. Kawata, I. Hono, T. Suzuki, and T. Yuasa, "Studies of $Ga_xIn_{1-x}P$ layers grown by metalorganic vapor phase epitaxy; effects of V/III ratio and growth temperature," *J. Cryst. Growth* 77, pp.367-373 (1986).

[2] A. Gomyo, S. Kawata, T. Suzuki, S. Iijima, and I. Hino, "Large (6°) off-angle effects on sublattice ordering and band-gap energy in $Ga_{0.5}In_{0.5}P$ grown on (001) GaAs substrates," *Jpn. J. Appl. Phys.* 28, pp.L1728-L1730 (1989).

[3] S. Minagawa and M. Kondow, "Dependence of photoluminescence peak energy of MOVPE-grown AlGaInP on substrate orientation," *Electron. Lett.* 25, pp.758-759 (1989).

[4] N. Buchan, W. Heuberger, A. Jakubowicz, and P. Roentgen, "The growth of $Ga_{0.52}In_{0.48}P$ and $Al_{0.18}Ga_{0.34}In_{0.48}P$ on lens-shaped GaAs substrates by metalorganic vapor phase epitaxy," *Inst. Phys. Conf. Ser.* 120, pp.529-534 (1991).

[5] M. Suzuki, Y. Nishikawa, M. Ishikawa, and Y. Kokubun, "Effects of substrate misorientation on doping characteristics and band gap energy for InGaAlP crystals grown by metalorganic chemical vapor deposition," *J. Cryst. Growth* 113, pp.127-130 (1991).

[6] S. -H. Wei, and A. Zunger, "Band-gap narrowing in ordered and disordered semiconductor alloys," *Appl. Phys. Lett.* 56, pp.662-664 (1990).

[7] T. Kobayashi, and R. S. Deol, "High-pressure photoluminescence study of ordered $Ga_{0.5}In_{0.5}P$ alloys grown on GaAs by organometallic vapor phase epitaxy," *Appl. Phys. Lett.* 58, pp.1289-1291 (1991).

[8] T. Kobayashi, M. Ohtsuji and R.S. Deol, "Pressure dependence of photoluminescence in ordered $Ga_{0.5}In_{0.5}P$ grown on (001) GaAs by organometallic vapor phase epitaxy," *J. Appl. Phys.* (to be published).

[9] J. Chen, J. R. Site, I. L. Spain, M. J. Hafich, and G. Y. Robinson, "Band offset of $GaAs/In_{0.48}Ga_{0.52}P$ measured under hydrostatic pressure," *Appl. Phys. Lett.* 58, pp.744-746 (1991).

NON-LINEAR OPTICS PROBES OF ULTRA-VIOLET ENERGY LEVELS OF SOLIDS AT HIGH PRESSURES

William B. Daniels, M. Lipp, D. Strachan, C. Yoo, H.M. Zhang, Department of Physics and Astronomy, University of Delaware, Newark, DE 19716 USA

Zu-he Yu, Institute of Physics, Academy of Sciences, P.O. Box 603, Beijing, 100080 CHINA

In general, one photon absorption and reflectivity spectroscopies are limited to study of excited states having energies for which pressure cell windows are transparent to the probing photons. This provides a serious barrier to making measurements of excited states having energies greater than about 5.5 eV using *uv* grade Type II diamond windows, 3.5 eV in common type I diamond, or about 7.5 eV using sapphire windows. Non-linear optical processes on the other hand, can probe states having energies which are sums and or differences of photon energies in beams illuminating the sample. For example, coherent two photon resonances have been used to seek electronic excited states at greater than 6 eV in hydrogen within a type I diamond anvil cell at 37 GPa. In addition to the above mentioned fundamental gain in energy space which can be probed optically, there are a number of secondary advantages in the multiphoton resonance techniques. These have been used to probe details of the exciton polariton levels in alkali halides and xenon at high pressures yielding a number of straightforward results such as pressure dependence of band gaps and self energies as well as several unusual phenomena in exciton dynamics near level crossings at high pressures.

INTRODUCTION

Interaction of electromagnetic radiation with solids has provided one of the most powerful probes of electronic structure and dynamics of atoms, molecules and solids. Even the pre-laser period, an enormous body of knowledge of electron bands, excitons, etc., developed and contributed a great deal to the quantitative state of understanding of electrons in solids. In that period, because of the relatively low intensities of conventional light sources, only the familiar **linear** optical spectroscopy of electronic states could be done, e.g., one-photon absorption, etc. In these linear spectroscopies, one probed states which were resonant in energy with single photons of the probing light, i.e., $E_i = h\nu_i \rightarrow \nu_i$ is the frequency of the light h is Planck's constant and E_i is energy of some excited state of the system under study.

The availability of intense, tunable light sources, specifically pulsed dye lasers has changed the picture by making it possible to examine quantitatively phenomena which depend **non-linearly** on the intensity of the optical fields applied. This gives rise to a large number of new effects ranging from a "simplest," multi-photon absorption, through coherent spectroscopies such as CARS (coherent anti-Stokes Raman scattering) to complex time dependent "echo" effects isomorphous to those observed in Magnetic Resonance spectroscopies. Each of these has its own characteristics. For example, multi-photon absorption is capable of uncovering transitions between states of the same parity, while CARS may be nine orders of magnitude more intense than conventional Raman scattering (COORS) together with substantially zero background, while photon echo techniques can eliminate effects of inhomogeneous broadening of spectral lines. All of these have potential application to systems at high pressure, but the "surface has only been scratched" by high pressure observations to date. A number of experiments have been done by Brown and collaborators [1] using impulse stimulated Brillouin scattering to obtain pressure dependence of macroscopic parameters such as acoustic velocities and thermal conductivity. Also, there have been CARS measurements in shocked materials by the Los Alamos group [2] stimulated Raman gain (SRG) by Baggen et al. [3], broad band CARS measurements in a DAC by Costantino et al. [4] and our own measurements of CARS together with two and three photon absorption in several systems at high pressures [5].

The responses of crystals to multi-photon excitation is highly variable, and usually quite different than in single photon processes, and the sample "geometry" involved is quite different. For example, single photons resonant with the lowest energy exciton in alkali halides have a penetration length about 10^{-5} cm whence the surface conditions are significant, but the absorption of photons having one third this energy is small, rendering three-photon absorption a **bulk** crystal process.

SPECTRAL WINDOWS

For any photon-based spectroscopy to be applicable at high pressures, the pressure cell "windows" must be reasonably transparent to the photons used. Referring

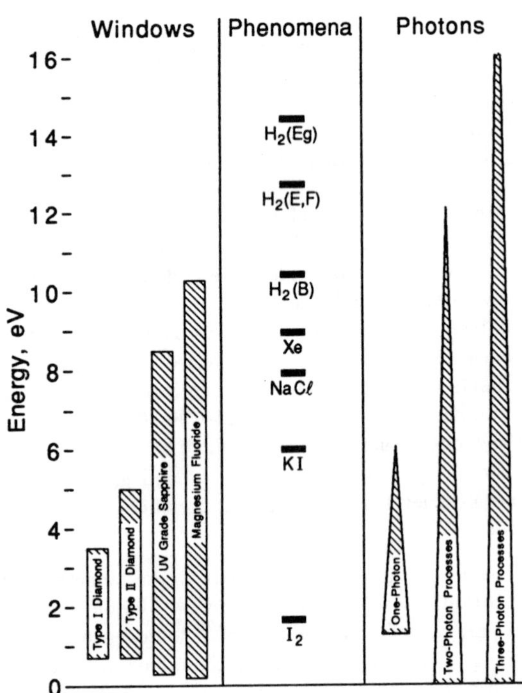

Figure 1: Relevant Energy Scales

to Fig. 1, the left column indicates ranges of transmission of various materials. The center column indicates energies of some interesting excited states. The final column indicates energy limits of conventional tunable dye laser based sources. With these, one can construct some limits attainable using particular combinations of window and photon-order, e.g., a one photon absorption cannot probe excited states of Xe using a diamond or sapphire windowed cell, but a two-photon absorption process with a sapphire or type II diamond could reach the Xe levels.

NON-LINEAR OPTICS PHENOMENOLOGY AND NOTATION

Conventionally, it is convenient to develop the non-linear optical response as a series representing the dielectric polarization P in increasing powers of components of the optical electric field as

$$P_\alpha = \sum_\beta \chi_{\alpha\beta} E_\beta + \sum_{\beta\gamma} \chi^{(2)}_{\alpha\beta\gamma} E_\beta E_\gamma + \sum_{\beta\gamma\delta} \chi^{(3)}_{\alpha\beta\gamma\delta} E_\beta E_\gamma E_\delta + \cdots \qquad (1)$$

The polarization is expanded in a Fourier series, and becomes a frequency dependent source in Maxwell's equations, yielding a signal proportional to $|\chi^{(n)}|^2$. For example, where probing frequencies ν_1, ν_2 are used such that the system is near a CARS resonance and a two-photon electronic state resonance with ν_1, the signal intensity I signal $\propto |\chi^{(3)}|^2$

$$\propto |\chi^{(3)}_{NR} + \frac{A_{\text{Raman}}/h}{\nu_{\text{Raman}} - (\nu_1 - \nu_2) + i\Gamma_{\text{Raman}}} + \frac{A_t/h}{\nu_t - 2\nu_1 + i\Gamma_t}|^2 \qquad (2)$$

In this expression, $\chi^{(3)}_{NR}$ is a non-resonant background contribution, the second and third terms represent Raman and two-photon resonant contributions to $\chi^{(3)}$. Interference among these terms in $|\chi^{(3)}|^2$ gives rise to characteristic lineshapes such as the typical CARS lineshape.

Probably the simplest manifestation of non-linear optics is the occurrence of multi-photon absorption. An example of this process shown schematically in Figure 2a for absorption of two photons having frequencies ν_1 and ν_2, to an excited state at $E = h\nu_1 + h\nu_2$. That is, the system can be excited to a state represented by the sum of two of the incident photon energies, without having an intermediate real state of the system. Also indicated is a possible scheme for detecting the resonance, in which the excitation process is followed by a non-radiative decay followed by emission of a fluorescent photon. More generally, an n-photon process involves energy sums and/or differences among n-photons adding up to an excited state energy of the system. Not surprisingly, a variety of processes resonant with real intermediate states can also occur. Figures 2b, 2c and 2d indicate some possibilities for a four-photon transition between a ground state G and a particular excited state E. In 2c, there are no intermediate state resonances while 2d might be described as a "three photon resonant four photon process." In general, an n-photon excitation process is proportional to the product of intensities of the photon fields involved, e.g., if three photons of the same frequency excite a transition, the transition rate will be proportional to the cube of the intensity of the beam incident on the system. This relationship between the order of the process and its intensity dependence provides practical limits on the order of processes employable to probe particular states because optical intensities must not only be kept below the optical breakdown limit of the material under study (and of windows, anvils, etc.) but at values small enough that, e.g., Stark shifting of the levels shall not be important. Selection rules for multi-photon transitions differ from single photon transition rules. For simple geometries, e.g., all photons having the same frequency and polar-

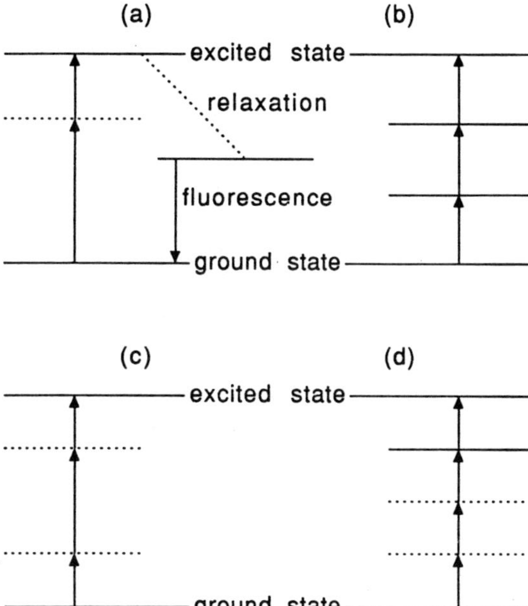

Figure 2: Types of multi-photon resonances (see text).

ization and wave vector, the rule that odd numbers of photons connect states of opposite parities, even photon number processes connect states of the same parity. Other selection rules enter for more general cases [6].

The examples considered here will be three-photon absorption in compressed Xenon and the search for two-photon resonances near the vibron CARS resonance in compressed hydrogen plus a comment on thermal effects.

EXCITON - PHONON COUPLING - THERMAL EFFECTS ON Eg

Extensive measurements were made of both the pressure and temperature dependence of the exciton energies in KI and RbI [5]. Having both of these dependencies, together with an equation of state enables calculation the temperature dependence at constant volumes as well as a limited identification of which phonon branches are most strongly coupled to the excitons. Inasmuch as the excitons nearly track the bandgap (in KI the exciton binding energies about 450 meV and only weakly pressure dependent), the value of the derivative provides a measure of isochoric temperature dependence of Eg, $(\partial E/\partial T)_V$. This derivative of course vanishes at $T = 0$ and follows roughly a Bose-Einstein function. In the high temperature regime, where E varies nearly linearly with temperature, $(\partial E/\partial T)_V$ has values near $-.6$ meV per Kelvin in both KI and RbI. That is, a 1000 K temperature increase would shift the band edge in these materials downward by about 0.6 eV if the crystals were maintained at constant volume. Such a shift may be significant in inferring electronic band gaps using thermally activated processes.

XENON

Xenon has been an object of interest and controversy since early optical measurements of optical absorption [7] and reports of insulator-metal transitions at high pressures [8]. At low pressures, the electronic structure lies at energies greater than 8 eV precluding one photon studies until pressures ($\approx$ 32 GPa) such that an absorption edge appears below the type II diamond cut-off near 5 eV, and may be followed to higher pressures. The edge structure measured in [7] is inferred from the weakness of the absorption process, and its spectral form, to represent an indirect transition across the bandgap.

At zero pressure, the large excited state energies suggested use of a three-photon excitation process. Fortunately, there is a fairly strongly Stokes shifted fluorescence near 7 eV which could be used to detect three photon resonances with near-edge exciton structure. The Xe samples were grown within compressible gasket sapphire ball cells [9]. The charging was done from the liquid phase of Xe using a temperature controlled cryostat. Two systems were used to detect the VUV fluorescence. The first of these incorporated a single crystal shim of potassium iodide external to the cell to act as an ultraviolet down converter, permitting use of filters to prevent the pump beam from reaching the photomultiplier tube. The signals obtained were less intense than expected because the sapphire windows of the cell were strongly attenuating the VUV fluorescence from the Xe. To overcome this window problem we constructed a CsI intra-cell UV converter. The resultant down-converted fluorescence was near 3.7 eV which was easily transmitted by the window to the filters-photomultiplier combination. The result is a blue shift of 89 meV/kB in this pressure range. A blue shift of the direct gap excitons at low pressure followed by a red shift as initially higher levels push their way downward is a not uncommon occurrence. What is perhaps more unusual about the result is that the shift, 89 meV/kB, is substantially larger than corresponding values in the alkali halides. On the other hand, the dimensionless quantity $d\ln E/d\ln V$ equals about $-.38$ in Xe vs. $-.34$ in KI which is comparable. Band structure calculations covering this pressure range in solid Xe do no appear to exist at this time. The data would provide a quantitative test of their validity.

HYDROGEN-COHERENT FOUR WAVE MIXING

There is a paucity of experimental measurement energies of electronic excited states of compressed solid hydrogen in spite of the strong emphasis on study of this material. The principal reason for this situation is that the relevant energies lie deep in the ultraviolet, far above the limits of transmission of diamond or sapphire pressure cell windows. At least that is the situation at low pressures where there is a reasonable understanding of the H_2 levels. Quantitatively at zero pressure, the experimentally observed absorption edge of H_2 lies near 11.1 eV and the conduction band gap is estimated to lie near 14.4 eV. Measurements of the band gap have been made by using electrical conductivity data under high pressure-high temperature shock wave conditions [10]. Their measurements generated a conduction band gap value 11.7 eV in D_2 at a molar volume of 7.6 cm^3 and elevated temperatures. Frequency dependent dielectric constants have also been measured to infer electronic energy levels [11]. The measurements reported here are the result of a non-degenerate four wave mixing experiment probing both a two-photon resonance (second term of eq. (2)) and in the same scan, a nearby CARS resonance. Figure 3 shows a typical scan near the upper end of the accessible two-photon energy range, in H_2 at a pressure of 37.5 GPa. The upper energy limit of the study was set by the requirement that the cell windows (type I diamond) pass photons of energy $\sim \hbar(\omega_1 + \Omega_R)$ where Ω_R is the vibron energy ~ 0.5 eV. Thus limited, the experiments probed the two-photon resonance region up to 6.12 eV. Although the signal-to-background ratio was fairly good at about 1000:1 as may be noted in Figure 3, we did not detect any two-photon resonances below the 6.12 eV limit. It is quite possible that a weak resonance could have been missed in the experiments but experience in other systems suggests that the 6.12 eV is probably a lower bound on the absorption edge of H_2 at 37.5 GPa and 300 K.

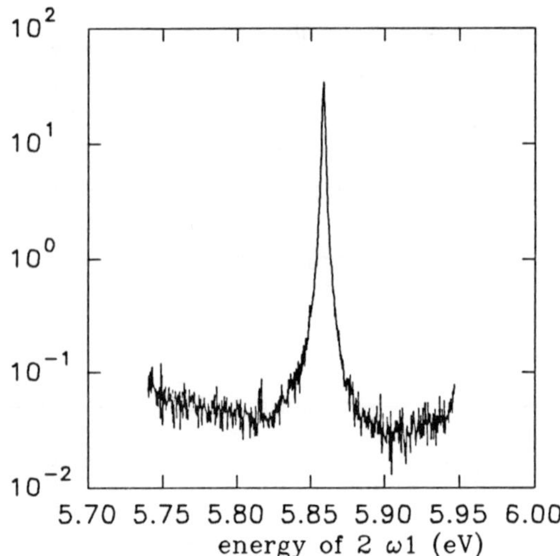

Figure 3: Coherent four wave mixing in hydrogen at 37.5 GPa.

ACKNOWLEDGEMENTS

The authors would like to thank the Unidel Foundation of the University of Delaware and the National Science Foundation for its support under Grants DMR 8822639 and DMR 9208517.

REFERENCES

[1] J. M. Zaug, E. H. Abramson, J. M. Brown and L. J. Slutsky, Science, 260, 1487 (1993) and references therein.

[2] D. S. Moore, S. C. Schmidt, M. S. Shaw and J. D. Johnson, J. Chem. Phys., 95, 5603 (1991).

[3] R. Kroon, M. Baggen and Ad Lagendijk, J. Chem. Phys. 91, 74 (1989).

[4] M. Costantino, private communication.

[5] M. J. Lipp, J. Blechschmidt and W. B. Daniels, Phys. Rev. 48, 1, July (1993); M. J. Lipp and W. B. Daniels, Phys. Rev. Lett., 67, 2810 (1991).

[6] A. Pasquarillo and L. Andriani, Phys. Rev. B 41, 12230 (1990).

[7] K. Syassen, Phys. Rev. B (Rapid Communications) 25, 6548 (1982).

[8] D. A. Nelson, Jr. and A. L. Ruoff, Phys. Rev. Lett., 42, 383 (1979); R. Reichlin, K. Brister, McMahan, M. Ross, S. Martin, and Y. K. Vohra, Phys. Rev. Lett., 62, 669 (1989); K. A. Goettel, J. H. Eggert, I. F. Silvera and W. C. Moss, Phys. Rev. Lett., 62, 665 (1989).

[9] W. B. Daniels, M. Lipp, D. Strachan, D. Winters and Z-H Yu in "Recent Trends in High Pressure Research," Proceedings for the XIII AIRAPT Conference, ed. A. K. Singh (Oxford and IBH, New Delhi, 1991), p. 809.

[10] W. J. Nellis, A. C. Mitchell, P. C. McCandless, D. J. Erskine and S. T. Weir, Phys. Rev. Lett., 68, 2937 (1992).

[11] A. García, M. L. Cohen, J. H. Eggert, F. Moshary, W. J. Evans, K. A. Goettel and I. F. Silvera, Phys. Rev. B 45, 9709 (1992), and references therein.

NEAR-IR ABSORPTION MEASUREMENTS OF THE TRANSITION-METAL IODIDES UNDER PRESSURE

Anthony L. Chen and Peter Y. Yu

Physics Department of the University of California at Berkeley
and
Materials Sciences Division of Lawrence Berkeley Laboratory
Berkeley, CA 94720

We have performed near-IR absorption measurements between 0.5 and 2.0 eV on NiI_2, CoI_2 and FeI_2 under pressure. All three compounds show a charge-transfer absorption edge that decreases linearly with increasing pressure. Extrapolation of the edge yields gap-closure pressures of 21, 17, and 22 GPa for NiI_2, CoI_2, and FeI_2 respectively, in good agreement with available resistivity measurements. This result strongly suggests that these materials metallize by closure of the charge-transfer energy gap.

INTRODUCTION

Pressure-induced insulator-to-metal transitions (IM) have long been the subject of fervent research. An interesting IM transition that has been discovered in recent years is the phase transition in NiI_2 at a pressure of about 17 GPa [1-3]. Resistivity measurements imply that this IM transition is caused by the gradual closure of a transport energy gap [1,3]. Mössbauer measurements have shown that the IM transition is accompanied by a simultaneous magnetic transition characterized by the disappearance of antiferromagnetic ordering [1,2]. Since then, studies on CoI_2 and FeI_2 have shown that both compounds exhibit similar magnetic and IM transitions [3,4].

Despite the research on these materials, there is little understanding of the underlying cause of the IM transitions and their relation to the magnetic transitions. It has been suggested that the cause is the closure of the energy gap between filled anion $5p$ states and transition-metal $3d$ states, the so-called charge-transfer energy gap (E_{CTG}) [5,6]. However, there is no experimental verification of this suggestion. Furthermore, there is a dearth of experimental studies on IM transitions of simple transition-metal compounds.

The ambient-pressure electronic properties of bulk transition-metal compounds are themselves of considerable interest. Recent theoretical and experimental studies of the transition-metal compounds [7,8] have shown that the Ni dihalides all have E_{CTG} smaller than their Mott-Hubbard energy gaps. Thus, these materials should be correctly classified as charge-transfer insulators rather than Mott-Hubbard insulators.

In this paper we present near-IR absorption measurements of NiI_2, CoI_2, and FeI_2 under pressure. From these absorption measurements we determine the pressure dependence of E_{CTG}. We are able to show that the metallization of these iodides under pressure is caused by the closure of E_{CTG}.

SAMPLE PROPERTIES

NiI_2, CoI_2, and FeI_2 are antiferromagnetic

insulators at ambient pressure [9]. All three compounds crystallize in hexagonal layered structures [10]. Recent studies indicate a density of electronic states qualitatively similar to that shown in Fig. 1. The salient features are (i) a manifold of occupied valence bands composed mainly of the I^- $5p$ states, (ii) narrow upper and lower Hubbard bands formed from the transition metal $3d$ states and split by the Mott-Hubbard, on-site, Coulomb repulsion (U), and (iii) a high-energy, unoccupied conduction band made up of Ni^{2+} $4s$ states. The Fermi level lies in between the top of the iodine $5p$ band and the upper Hubbard band. The charge-transfer energy (Δ) is the energy between the middle of the I^- $5p$ band and the middle of the upper Hubbard band. The Mott-Hubbard gap (E_{MHG}) and the charge-transfer gap (E_{CTG}) are respectively defined as U and Δ minus the relevant bandwidths (see Fig. 1).

For NiI_2 photoemission studies [8] show that U and Δ are about 4.5 eV and 1.5 eV respectively, suggesting that NiI_2 is a charge-transfer insulator. Although photoemission data on CoI_2 and FeI_2 are unavailable, optical reflectivity experiments [11] show Δ to be about 4 eV for all three iodides. The discrepancy between the two values of Δ obtained by the two measurements in NiI_2 can be attributed to the I^- $5p$ bandwidth. The photoemission experiment measures the exciton associated with the charge-transfer transition and is probably a better estimate of E_{CTG} than Δ. The I^- $5p$ bandwidth has been calculated to be about 5 eV [12]. The value of Δ as determined by photoemission (1.5 eV) plus half the I^- $5p$ bandwidth equals 4.0 eV, in agreement with the reflectivity measurement. The value of U determined by photoemission probably should also be corrected by the $3d$ bandwidth. The correction is not as important since the $3d$ bandwidth is about 0.5 eV. Thus all these iodides are charge-transfer insulators.

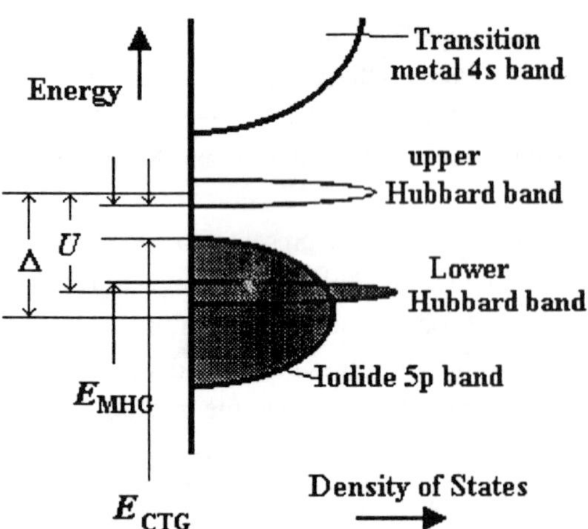

Fig. 1. Probable electronic density of states for the transition-metal iodides. Symbols are explained in the text.

EXPERIMENTAL PROCEDURE

The crystals were grown inside an evacuated quartz ampoule by the vapor transport method. The resultant crystals are black, shiny platelets about 1 cm in diameter. These platelets were cleaved perpendicular to the c-axis into thin sheets ~10μm thick. These shiny thin sheets were used in the absorption measurements without further treatment. The sample was loaded into a diamond-anvil high-pressure cell with liquid nitrogen as the pressure medium. The pressure was determined by the ruby fluorescence technique. Pressure inhomogeneity was better than ±3%.

Near-IR measurements (0.8 to 2.5 μm) were performed at room temperature using a 1/4 meter grating monochromator with a tungsten halogen lamp. Mirror optics were used throughout the experiment to minimize chromatic aberration. The light transmitted by the sample was detected by a PbS photoconductor and a lock-in amplifier. The spectral resolution of this system was estimated to be 20 meV. No correction was made for the reflectivity of the sample since such a correction should not change the position of the absorption edge.

DATA AND RESULTS

Absorbance spectra for NiI_2 at several pressures are shown in Fig. 2. The absolute absorption coefficient could not be easily determined from the absorbance because of uncertainty in the thickness of the sample. One division on the y-scale corresponds roughly to 10^3 cm^{-1}. The spectra are spaced vertically for clarity. They show two conspicuous features: (i) a steeply rising absorption edge that decreases with increasing pressure; (ii) one or two broad peaks between 0.9 and 1.0 eV. The latter features have been assigned to intra-*d* transitions [13,14] within the Ni^{2+} ion and will not be discussed here. We assign the absorption edge to the charge-transfer edge based on comparison with previous ambient pressure measurements [13,14].

To extract a value of E_{CTG} we simply take the intersection of a straight line through the absorption edge with a horizontal line through the residual absorption below the gap as illustrated in Fig. 2. The values of E_{CTG} obtained in this way for all three iodides are plotted in Fig.3. The data points can be fitted rather well by a straight line. Although we could not follow the gap below 0.5 eV, extrapolation of the fitted line to zero gap gives a gap-closure pressure of 21, 17 and 22 GPa for NiI_2, CoI_2, and FeI_2 respectively. The corresponding pressure coefficients $d(E_{CTG})/dP$ are -62, -82, and -90 meV/ GPa.

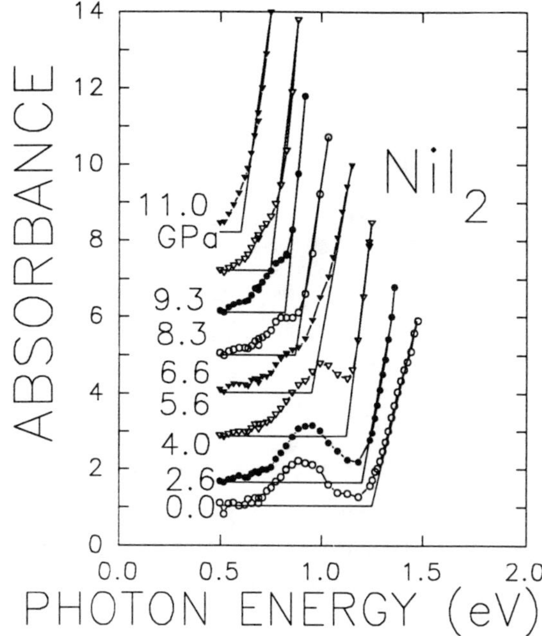

Fig. 2. Absorbance spectra of NiI_2 as a function of pressure. Spectra are spaced vertically.

DISCUSSIONS AND CONCLUSIONS

Resistivity measurements on NiI_2, CoI_2, and FeI_2 have shown that they become metallic at pressures of 17, 10, and 23 GPa [3,4] respectively. Furthermore, temperature dependence of the resistivity as the metallization pressure is approached suggests that the IM transitions are caused by gradual closure of a transport energy gap [3]. The lack of any structural changes or discontinuities in the lattice constants in NiI_2 and FeI_2 near the transition point [1,15] suggests that the transitions are purely electronic.

Our optical measurements of the extrapolated gap-closure pressures show good agreement with the metallization pressures, especially for FeI_2. For NiI_2 and CoI_2, the extrapolated E_{CTG}-closure pressures exceed the metallization pressures by roughly 24% and 70% respectively. The good agreement between the E_{CTG}-closure pressures and the metallization pressures, at least for NiI_2 and FeI_2, strongly suggests that metallization is caused by closure of E_{CTG}. Our conclusion is consistent with a Mössbauer study of CoI_2 that shows a transfer of charge from the I^- ion to the Co^{2+} ion between 10 and 13 GPa [2].

For NiI_2 and CoI_2, a possible explanation for the discrepancy between the gap-closure pressure determined by resistivity measurements is a discontinuous closure of E_{CTG} in these two compounds. Discontinuous gap closures caused

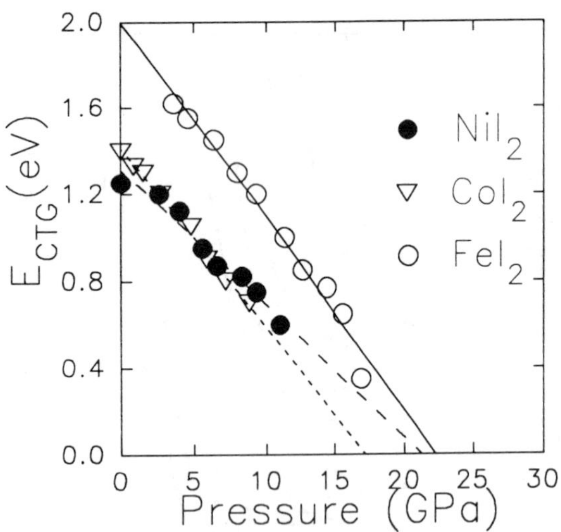

Fig. 3. Charge-transfer energy gap vs. pressure for NiI_2, CoI_2, and FeI_2. Straight lines are first-order least-squares fits to the data.

by excitonic effects have been predicted by several authors [6,16]. For CoI_2, E_{CTG} is about 0.6 eV just before the metallization pressure of 10 GPa. For NiI_2, the required discontinuity would be about 0.3 eV at 17 GPa.

In conclusion the closure of the charge-transfer energy gap in the late-transition-metal iodides is the cause of the IM transition.

ACKNOWLEDGMENTS

The authors would like to thank Raymond Jeanloz, Leo M. Falicov, Moshe P. Pasternak, and R. Dean Taylor for stimulating discussions concerning this work. This research was supported in part by the National Science Foundation under Grant No. DMR-8718228 and by the Director, Office of Energy Research, Office of Basic Energy Sciences, Material Sciences Division of the U.S. Department of Energy under Contract No. DE-AC03-76SF00098.

REFERENCES

[1] M.P. Pasternak, R.D. Taylor, A. Chen, C. Meade, L.M. Falicov, A. Giesekus, R. Jeanloz, and P. Y. Yu, Phys. Rev. Lett. **65**, 790 (1990).

[2] M. P. Pasternak, R. D. Taylor, R. Jeanloz, J. Appl. Phys.**70**, 5956 (1992).

[3] A.L. Chen and P.Y. Yu, to be published.

[4] E. Stener and M. P. Pasternak, *High Pressure Research 1992* (Gordon and Breach Science Publishers S.A., United Kingdom, 1992).

[5] A. Giesekus and L.M. Falicov, Phys. Rev. B **44**, 10449 (1991).

[6] J.K. Freericks and L.M. Falicov, Phys. Rev. B **45**, 1896 (1992).

[7] J. Zaanen, G.A. Sawatzky, J.W. Allen, Phys. Rev. Lett. **55**, 418 (1985).

[8] J. Zaanen, C. Westra, and G.A. Sawatzky, Phys. Rev. B **33**, 8060 (1986).

[9] L.G. van Uitert, H. J. Williams, R.C. Sherwood, and J.J. Rubin, J. Appl. Phys. **36**, 1029 (1965); H. Bizette, C. Terrier, and B. Tsai, C.R. Acad. Sci. **246**, 250 (1958); J.B. Goodenough, *Magnetism and the Chemical Bond* (Interscience, New York, 1963).

[10] R.W.G. Wyckoff, *Crystal Structures*, Vol I (Interscience, New York, 1963).

[11] I. Pollini, J. Thomas, and A. Lenselink, Phys. Rev. B **30,** 2140 (1984).

[12] S. Antoci and L. Mihich, Phys. Rev. B **14**, 5768 (1978); **21**, 3383 (1980).

[13] S.R. Kuindersma, P.R. Boudewijn, and C. Haas, Phys. Stat. Sol. B **108**, 187 (1981).

[14] M. Kozielski, I. Pollini, G. Spinolo, J. Phys. C **5**, 1253 (1972).

[15] M. Kruger and R. Jeanloz, private communication.

[16] B.I. Halperin and T.M. Rice, Revs. of Mod. Phys. **40**, 755 (1968).

AN OPTICAL STUDY OF PENTACENE IN P-TERPHENYL AT HIGH PRESSURE AND LOW TEMPERATURE

Eric L. Chronister* and Bruce J. Baer
Department of Chemistry
University of California at Riverside
Riverside, California 92521

A low temperature (2-15 K) optical study of pentacene doped p-terphenyl at high pressure (0-7 kbar). Absorption spectra, time-resolved fluorescence, and photon echo measurements at high pressure are presented.

INTRODUCTION

High resolution spectroscopic measurements in high pressure molecular solids are typically obscured by strain effects. Even a spectral resolution of a few wavenumbers can be several orders of magnitude greater than the homogeneous optical linewidth. We present photon echo measurements of the homogeneous linewidth at high pressure.

Pentacene doped p-terphenyl is of particular interest [1,2,7-15] since four photosites (labeled O_1, O_2, O_3, and O_4) are observed in the absorption spectrum, each with unique vibrational and electronic dynamics [10-14]. In contrast, the monoclinic host crystal phase yields only a single pentacene absorption origin. Crystalline para-terphenyl has two known solid phases: a monoclinic crystal phase (Space group $P2_1/a$) with two equivalent molecules per unit cell [3], and a triclinic phase (space group $P\bar{1}$) with four inequivalent molecules per unit cell [4]. The triclinic phase is stable at low temperatures and low pressures [5,6].

Previous fluorescence lifetime studies at ambient pressure suggest that the first excited singlet state (S_1) lies above the second excited triplet state (T_2) for the two bluer photosites (O_3 and O_4), while the singlet levels corresponding to the redder photosites (O_1 and O_2) lie below their corresponding T_2 states [1,13]. This state ordering is consistent with the intersystem crossing/fluorescence ratio of about 0.6 for O_3 and O_4 and <0.005 for O_1 and O_2, at low temperature and low pressure [10,11,13]. We present photosite specific changes in intersystem crossing at high pressure.

EXPERIMENTAL

High Pressure Mixed Crystals

Pentacene doped para-terphenyl ($<10^{-5}$ mol/mol) crystals were grown from the melt at ambient pressure and subsequently loaded into the gasket aperture of a Merrill-Bassett diamond anvil cell (DAC) [16]. The hole diameter of the gasket was approximately 0.4 mm and the sample thickness was 0.1-0.2 mm. This material was remelted under pressure and crystals were grown under nearly constant pressure conditions by slow compression of the cell. Pressures were measured with the ruby luminescence method [17] and by spectral shifts of the O_1 photosite [6].

High Pressure Spectroscopy at Low Temperature

The samples were cooled using either closed cycle (15 K) or helium flow cryostats (2-10 K). Absorption spectra were obtained by scanning the output of a 75 W xenon arc lamp with a 0.75 meter monochromator, with an instrumental resolution of $2 cm^{-1}$. The light was directed through the low temperature sample by fiber optic light guides and detected with a photomultiplier tube (PMT).

Time resolved fluorescence lifetime measurements were obtained by selectively exciting the different pentacene photosites using the tunable output ($1 cm^{-1}$ bandwidth) of a high

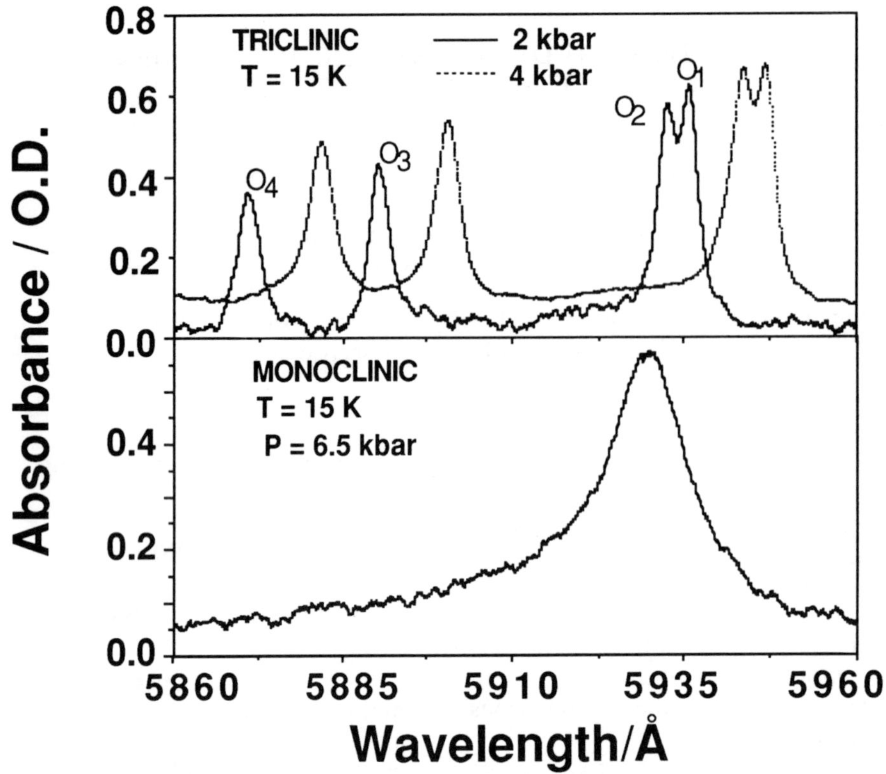

Figure. 1. The low temperature (15 K) absorption spectrum of pentacene in p-terphenyl. a) At P= 2.0 and 4.0 kbar the spectrum is characteristic of the triclinic p-terphenyl phase. b) The absorption spectrum of pentacene in the monoclinic para-terphenyl crystal phase at P= 6.5 kbar.

repetition rate (1 kHz) short pulse (30ps) cavity dumped dye laser. The time-resolved decay of the fluorescence intensity was averaged using a 400MHz digitizing oscilloscope. The output of the cavity dumped dye laser was also used to perform picosecond photon echo measurements. For these experiments, a fixed and a variable time-delay laser pulse were crossed in the DAC, which was immersed in a helium flow cryostat.

RESULTS and DISCUSSION

High Pressure Spectroscopy

Spectral Shifts

At low temperature and at pressures below 5.5 kbar, the pentacene impurity spectrum in para-terphenyl yields four photosites, O_1, O_2, O_3, and O_4, characteristic of the triclinic para-terphenyl crystal structure, as shown in Fig. 1. The absorption frequencies of these four origins red shift with increasing pressure, as is typical for π-π^* transitions in many hydrocarbons. The shift in the pentacene absorption band(s) is found to be ~15 cm^{-1}/kbar for the triclinic and 19±2 cm^{-1}/kbar for the monoclinic p-terphenyl crystal phases. These pressure shifts are considerably lower than the 37 and 40 cm^{-1}/kbar shifts observed for anthracene and tetracene in the same host crystal at ambient temperature [18]. This difference may be due to the close fit of the pentacene molecule in the p-terphenyl lattice, resulting in a local compressibility similar to that of the pure crystal, with a correspondingly small pressure shift.

Crystal Strain

Pressure induced strain can arise due to the different compressibility and thermal expansion coefficients of the three unique axis of the host crystal. Although the experimental resolution in

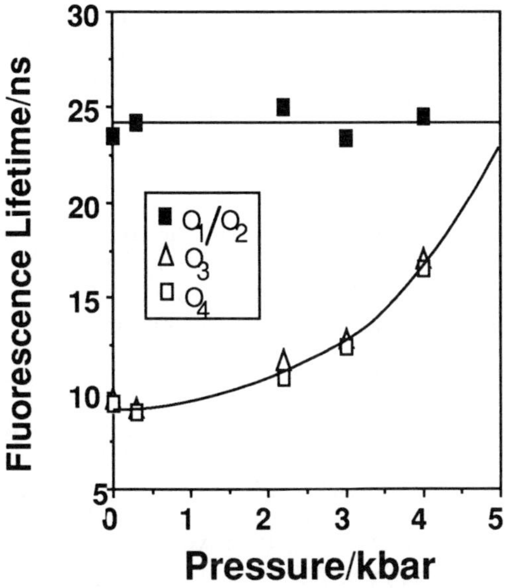

Figure. 2. The effect of pressure on the fluorescence lifetimes of the O_1, O_2, O_3, and O_4 photosites of pentacene in p-terphenyl. The increase in the fluorescence lifetime of O_3 and O_4 at high pressure is attributed to the singlet energy level falling below the energy of the nearest triplet level.

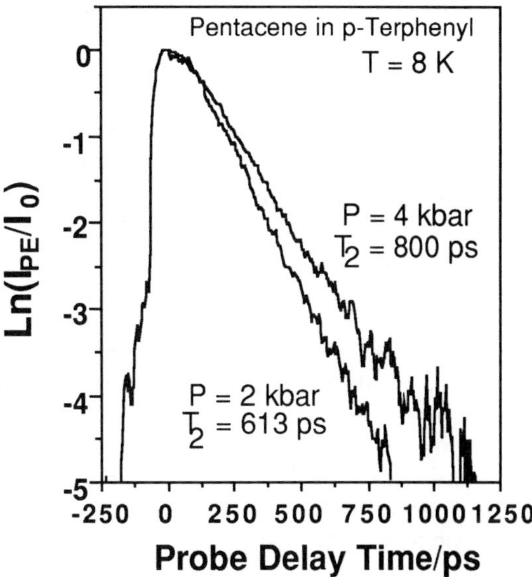

Figure. 3. A semilog plot of the normalized photon echo intensity I_{PE}/I_0 versus probe delay time for pentacene in p-terphenyl at T = 8 K and P = 0 and 4 kbar.

Fig. 1a can resolve structural changes in the host p-terphenyl lattice, it is still several orders of magnitude larger than the homogeneous width of this transition at low temperature.

Solid State Phase Change of p-Terphenyl

At high pressures and/or high temperatures the absorption spectrum of pentacene in p-terphenyl is characteristic of the monoclinic crystal phase, yielding only one photosite, as shown in Fig. 1b. The pronounced changes in the pentacene impurity spectrum have been used as a sensitive probe of pressure or temperature induced changes in the local crystal structure [6].

High Pressure Dynamics

Fluorescence Lifetimes

Site specific fluorescence lifetime measurements at ambient pressure yield values of 8ns for O_3 and O_4, versus 23ns for O_1 and O_2 [6]. This difference has been attributed to different intersystem crossing rates [10,11,13]. The effect of pressure on the fluorescence lifetimes of the different photosites is presented in Fig. 2. A significant increase in the fluorescence lifetimes of O_3 and O_4 is evident, however, no significant change in the fluorescence lifetime of the O_1/O_2 photosite was observed.

The energy of the O_1/O_2 triplet level (T_2) is believed to be ~75 cm^{-1} above the first excited singlet level (S_1) at ambient pressure, resulting in a small intersystem crossing ratio, and a correspondingly long fluorescence lifetime of 23ns at low temperature (20K). In comparison, the lifetime of O_3 and O_4 photosites are much shorter at ambient pressure, but approach the lifetime of the O_1/O_2 sites at pressures near 5 kbar, as shown in Fig. 2. Since the pressure shift of S_1 is expected to be several times that of T_2 [19], the increase in the fluorescence lifetimes of the O_3 and O_4 photosites at high pressure is attributed to a relative lowering of the S_1 energy level below that of the closest triplet state (T_2). A similar increase in fluorescence lifetimes due to a pressure induced decrease in intersystem crossing has been seen in anthracene [20] and 9-anthraldehyde [21].

Photon Echo Measurements: Homogeneous Dephasing at High Pressure

The high pressure absorption spectra shown in Fig. 1. are considerably broadened by inhomogeneous pressure strain effects. In order to resolve the homogeneous lineshape at high pressures we have performed photon echo measurements on the O_1 photosite of pentacene in p-terphenyl. The effect of pressure on the homogeneous dephasing time (T_2) at a temperature of 8K is shown in Fig. 3. The homogeneous dephasing time is observed to decrease at high pressure, i.e. pressure induced spectral line *narrowing* is observed. Experimentally it is useful to characterize the temperature dependence of the homogeneous dephasing rate as an activated process of the form,

$$\frac{1}{T_2} = \frac{1}{2T_1} + \frac{1}{T_2^*} \qquad (1a)$$

$$= \frac{1}{2T_1} + \frac{1}{T_2^*(\infty)} \exp\left(\frac{-\Delta E}{kT}\right) \qquad (1b)$$

where T_2^* is the pure homogeneous dephasing time, T_1 is the lifetime of the excited electronic state, and ΔE characterizes the pseudolocal phonon mode frequency.

In general, pressure induced changes in the dephasing rate, such as those illustrated in Fig. 3., can arise due to changes in both $T_2^*(\infty)$ and ΔE. Temperature dependent measurements at high pressure (not shown) indicate that the pressure induced increase in the dephasing time at 8 K occurs primarily due to a change in the prefactor $[T_2^*(\infty)]^{-1}$ (i.e. a change in the pseudolocal phonon lifetime).

CONCLUSION

We have presented the results of optical studies of pressure induced (0-7 kbar) dynamic and structural changes associated with a pentacene guest chromophore in a p-terphenyl host crystal at low temperature (5-15 K). Pressure induced changes in the low temperature absorption spectrum are sensitive to structural phase changes of the host matrix. In addition, the observed increase in the fluorescence lifetime of O_3 and O_4 photosites is attributed to a decrease in intersystem crossing at high pressure. Finally, picosecond photon echo measurements have been used to observe the *narrowing* of the homogeneous lineshape at high pressure.

ACKNOWLEDGMENTS

We acknowledge the National Science Foundation (CHE-9008551) and the Los Alamos Center for Nonlinear Studies INCOR Program for financial support of this research.

REFERENCES

[1] J. O. Williams, A. C. Jones and M. J. Davies, J. Chem. Soc. Farad. Trans. 2 79, 263 (1983)

[2] H.-C. Fleischhauer, C. Kryschi, B. Wagner and H. Kupka, J. Chem. Phys. 97, 1742 (1992)

[3] H. M. Rietveld, E. N. Maslen and C.J. B. Clews, Acta. Cryst. B26, 693 (1970)

[4] P. J. L. Baudour, Y. Delugeard and H. Cailleau, Acta. Cryst. B32, 150 (1976)

[5] B. Toudic, P. Launois, F. Moussa, A. Girard and H. Cailleau, Ferroelectrics 80, 241 (1988)

[6] B.J. Baer and E. L. Chronister, J. Chem. Phys. 99, xxx (1993)

[7] J. H. Meyling and D. A. Wiersma, Chem. Phys. Lett. 20, 383 (1973)

[8] J.-M. Donnini, J. de Chim. Phys. 71, 1543 (1974)

[9] W. H. Hesselink and D. A. Wiersma, Chem. Phys. Lett. 56, 227 (1978)

[10] T. E. Orlowski and A. H. Zewail, J. Chem. Phys. 70, 1390 (1979)

[11] H. de Vries and D. A. Wiersma, J. Chem. Phys. 70, 5807(1979)

[12] R. W. Olson and M. D. Fayer, J. Phys. Chem. 84, 2001 (1980)

[13] F. G. Patterson, H. W. H. Lee, W. L. Wilson and M. D. Fayer, Chem. Phys. 84, 51 (1984)

[14] C. Kryschi, H.-C. Fleischhauer, and B. Wagner, Chem. Phys. 161, 485 (1992)

[15] E. L. Chronister and R. A. Crowell, Mol. Cryst. Liq. Cryst. 211, 361 (1992)

[16] L. Merrill and W. A. Bassett, Rev. Sci. Instrum., 45, 290 (1974).

[17] S. Buchsbaum, R. Mills and D. Schiferl, J. Phys. Chem., 88, 2522 (1984)

[18] P.F. Jones, J. Chem. Phys. 48, 5448 (1968)

[19] M. Nicol and J. Somekh, J. Opt. Soc. Am. 58, 233 (1968)

[20] P. C. Johnson and H. W. Offen, Chem. Phys. Lett. 6, 505 (1970)

[21] D. J. Mitchell, G. B. Schuster and H. G. Drickamer, J. Am. Chem. Soc. 99, 1145 (1977)

OPTICAL ABSORPTION OF ISOLATED SELENIUM CHAINS UNDER PRESSURE

Yoshinori KATAYAMA, Naoe KOYAMA[(a)] and Kazuhiko TSUJI
Department of Physics, Keio University
3–14–1 Hiyoshi, Yokohama 223, Japan

In order to study the effect of the intrachain interaction on the electronic structure of Se chains, isolated Se chains confined in mordenite channels (M–Se) were uniaxially compressed using smaller molecules than the diameter of the mordenite(M) channel as a pressure transmitting medium. Optical transmission spectra of M–Se were measured up to 10 GPa using a diamond anvil cell. The absorption edge of M–Se shifts to lower energy with increasing pressure. The pressure coefficient of optical gap of M–Se is –0.03eV/GPa, which is about one fifth of that of bulk trigonal Se. A simple tight–binding calculation suggests that the gap narrowing is attributable to the increase of a second neighbor lone–pair to lone–pair interaction.

INTRODUCTION

Crystalline trigonal selenium (t–Se) consists of infinite spiral chains arranged parallel in a hexagonal array. The electronic configuration of the Se atom is $4s^2 4p^4$. Of the four p electrons per atom, two p electrons enter bonding p–states (σ–states) and the remaining two p electrons enter non–bonding lone–pair (LP) states. The LP states are the highest filled states and form the valence band. The Fermi level falls between LP states and the anti–bonding p–states (σ^*–states). The optical gap of t–Se is 1.85eV at atmospheric pressure.

The optical gap of t–Se decreases under pressure[1]. The band gap depends on both the positions of the valence and conduction band center and the band widths. The position of the band center mainly depends on the strength of covalent bonds and the band width depends on both intra– and interchain interactions. These interactions results from the overlap of the orbitals, hence are determined by the structure. A single crystal x–ray diffraction study of t–Se revealed that the bond length and the bond angle are almost constant under pressure, while the interchain distance is significantly decreased with pressure[2]. The closer packing of the chains increases the overlap of the orbitals of neighboring atoms in adjacent chains. Increasing interchain interaction broadens both valence and conduction bands, so that the band gap becomes narrower[3,4].

On the contrary, the optical gap increases when the Se chain is isolated in a mordenite crystal(M) matrix which has one–dimensional straight channels of 6.7 A in diameter. Recent studies of the properties of isolated Se chains in mordenite (M–Se) revealed unique features of this material[5–11]. (1)Extended X–ray Absorption Fine Structure (EXAFS) measurements and electron microscopy studies show that the chain structure is preserved in the channel and only one Se chain is confined in each channel. (2)The bond length of M–Se obtained from EXAFS measurements is 1.5% shorter than that of t–Se. (3)The optical gap of M–Se is estimated to be 2.3 eV at room temperature, which is much larger than that of t–Se (1.85 eV). (4)At low temperature, illumination with light induces new absorption bands. Theoretical studies were also carried out on isolated Se chains[12–16]. The results of calculations for the chain and electronic structure agreed with experiments.

Utilizing M–Se, we can investigate the effect of the intrachain interaction on chain and electronic structure without interference of the interchain interaction. Interestingly a theoretical study suggests that stretching the chain results in a planar zigzag geometry with overlapping conduction bands[13]. In order to modify the intrachain interaction, the isolated Se chains in mordenite are uniaxially compressed using smaller molecules than the diameter of mordenite channel as a pressure transmitting medium. Optical transmission spectra under uniaxial compression were measured. The change of the band structure is deduced from the results and discussed in terms of a simple tight-binding calculation by taking into account EXAFS data.

EXPERIMENTAL

Sample preparation

We used synthetic mordenite powder (TSZ-640, $Na_2OAl_2O_320SiO_2$) supplied by Tosoh manufacturing Co., Ltd. Mordenite has one-dimensional channels, surrounded by 12-membered oxygen ring, 6.7 A in diameter[17]. The size of the particle was about 1 μm. Mordenite has no light absorption in the wavelength range of the present experiment. The M powder was washed by distilled water and dehydrated at 500 °C for 6 hours under vacuum (10^{-4} Pa). Dehydrated M, sealed in a Pyrex tube with Se, was exposed to vapor of Se at 500 °C for 24 hours. Then it was cooled down slowly to room temperature. The color of the M powder changed from white to orange when it absorbed Se vapor.

Optical measurements

Optical transmission spectra were measured using a diamond anvil cell and a micro-optical system. We used 4:1 methanol-ethanol mixture as a pressure transmitting fluid. The diameter of methanol and ethanol molecules is about 4.0 A, which is smaller than that of the mordenite channel. Therefore, both molecules are easily absorbed in mordenite. The measurements were carried out up to about 10 GPa, the hydrostatic limit of the mixture[18]. Since a thick layer of the powder sample was not transparent due to light scattering with the sample, the total thickness of the sample was controlled using a thin stainless steel gasket, 0.03 mm in thickness. A halogen lamp was used as a light source. The transmitted light was monochromatized and then detected by a photomultiplier. The wavelength range was from 460 nm to 800 nm, corresponding to photon energies from 1.6 eV to 2.7 eV. All measurements were carried out at room temperature. Pressure was determined using the ruby fluorescence method.

RESULTS

Figure 2(a) shows optical transmission spectra of M-Se at various pressures up to 11 GPa as a function of photon energy for increasing pressure. At 1.6 GPa, the intensity of the transmitted light decreases with increasing photon energy and become zero above 2.2 eV. With increasing pressure the absorption edge

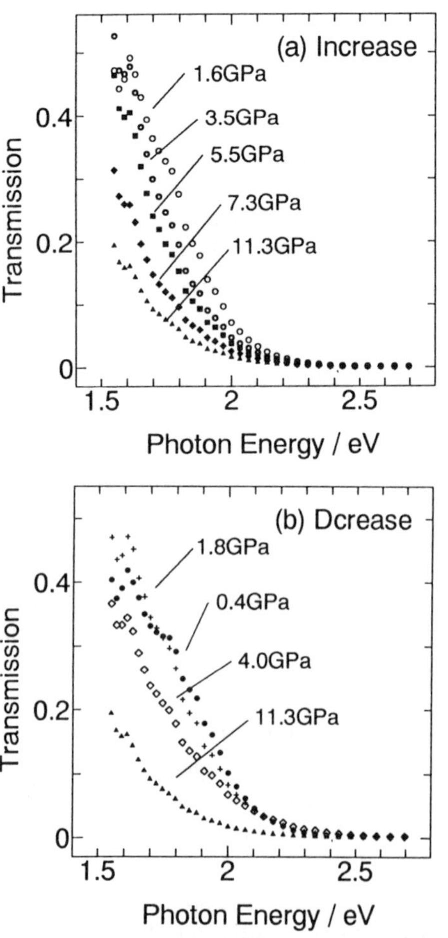

Figure 1. Optical transmission spectra of M-Se at varous pressures as a function of photon energy; (a) increasing pressre, (b) decreasing pressure.

shifts toward lower energy, which implies that the optical gap decreases with increasing pressure. The slope of the absorption edge does not change under pressure.

Figure 2 (b) shows the optical transmission spectra of M–Se for decreasing pressure. The optical absorption edge returns to higher energy with decreasing pressure. The spectra observed at 1.8 GPa after the compression is same as that before the compression. This fact indicates that no irreversible changes such as collapse of the mordenite crystal or desorption of Se has occurred.

We deduced the optical gap (Eg) of M–Se under pressure from the shift of the absorption edge. In Figure 2 we show Eg of M–Se as a function of pressure. We adopted 2.3 eV as Eg at 0 GPa, which was obtained from photoacoustic measurements[11]. The Eg of t–Se is also plotted as a reference[1]. The optical gap of M–Se decreases linearly with increasing pressure up to 11 GPa.

DISCUSSION

The pressure coefficient of the optical gap of M–Se is about –0.03 eV/GPa. This value is roughly one fifth of that of t–Se. The small value of the pressure coefficient is attributable to the absence of interchain interactions. This is a direct evidence that the gap narrowing in t–Se is caused by the band broadening due to the strengthening of interchain interactions.

The reduction of the band gap in M–Se is then ascribed to the strengthening of the intrachain interaction. We carried out EXAFS experiments on M–Se under pressure and obtained the variation of the covalent bond length[19]. The bond length of M–Se decreased linearly with increasing pressure. The decrease was 1% at 10 GPa. Unfortunately the pressure dependence of the bond angle can not be obtained from the present EXAFS experiments.

In order to estimate the relation between the chain structure and the band structure, we use a simple tight–binding calculation presented by Robertson[12]. He calculated the band structure of a single Se chain using a basis of s and p orbitals and provided analytic expressions for the band dispersion. The interactions which have been included in the calculation are interactions between orbitals on adjacent atoms and second nearest LP–LP interaction. These interactions are shown in Figure 3. We evaluated the strength of interactions using the values and formulas presented in the text of Harrison[20]. Let us consider the situation at 10 GPa. The bond length shortened by 1% at this pressure. This shortening increases the bonding

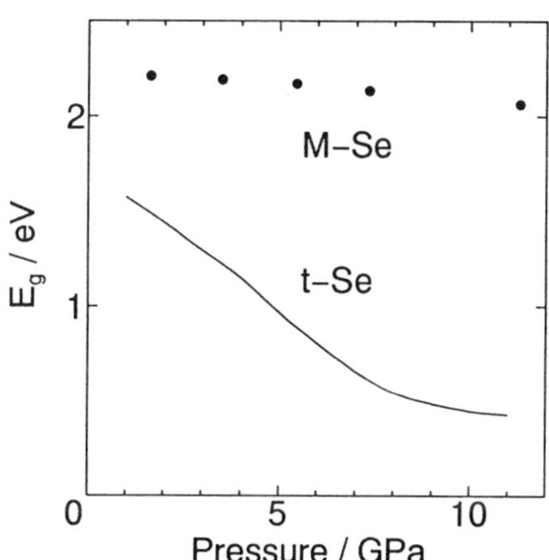

Figure 2. Pressure dependence of the optical gap of M–Se. Optical gap of t–Se is also shown as a reference[1].

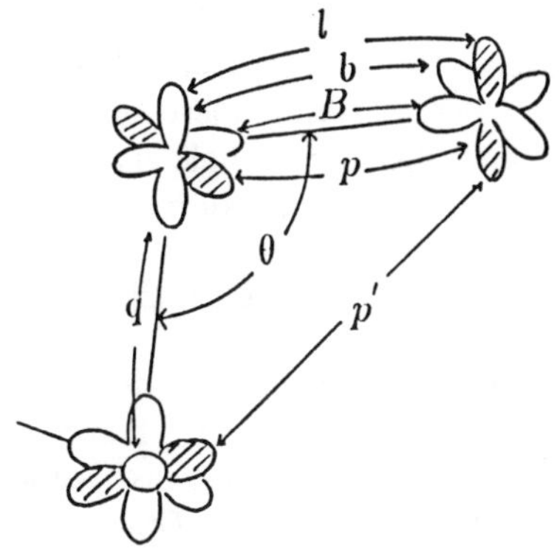

Figure 3. The interactions between orbitals which have been included in the thight–binding calculation presented by Robertson[12].

anti–bonding splitting, thus increases the gap. The increase is estimated to be 0.07 eV. Therefore broadening of the bands is required to explain the reduction of the gap. We calculated the gap as a function of the bond angle and the dihedral angle and found that the reduction of the bond angle notably broadens the LP band. If the bond angle is reduced, the second nearest neighbor distance is decreased and the LP–LP interaction is strengthened. Increasing LP–LP interaction broadens the LP band, thus reduces the optical gap. From this calculation, an estimation of the bond angle at 10 GPa is 90°. Of course the results of this calculation is rather qualitative than quantitative because of the rough approximations. There is an additional contribution to the reduction of the gap due to the increasing interaction between Se chain and mordenite under pressure. However, this contribution is supposed to be small because the electronic level of p electron of Se atom is much higher than that of O atom, which is the main constituent of the inner surface of the channel.

The relative change of bond angle estimated from this calculation is an order of magnitude larger than that of the bond length. This result is consistent with the fact that the potential curvature for bond bending is smaller than that for bond stretching[14]. The EXAFS experiments suggest the possibility that the Se atoms approach O atoms of the inner surface of the channels. This is achieved when the bond angle is reduced. With these evidences we conclude that the bond angle is significantly reduced under uniaxial pressure.

ACKNOWLEDGEMENT

We would like to thank Professors H.Endo and F. Yonezawa, Drs. A. Ikawa and T. Yamaguchi for their valuable discussions. This study is partly supported by Grant in Aid for Scientific Research, Ministry of Education.

REFERENCES

(a) Present address: NTT LSI Laboratories, Atsugi, 243–01 Japan.

[1] B. M. Riggleman and H. G. Drickamer: J. Chem. Phys. 38 (1963) 2721.

[2] R. Keller, W. B. Holzapfel and H. Schulz: Phys. Rev. B16 (1977) 4404.

[3] Th. Starkloff and J. D. Joannopoulos: J. Chem. Phys. 68 (1978) 579.

[4] J. von Boehm and H. Isomaki: J. Phys. C: Solid State Phys. 13 (1980) 4953.

[5] V. N. Bogomolov, S. V. Kholodkevich, S. G. Romanov and L. S. Agroskin: Solid State Commun. 47 (1983) 181.

[6] K. Tamura, S. Hosokawa, H. Endo, S. Yamasaki and H. Oyanagi: J. Phys. Soc. Jpn. 55 (1986) 528.

[7] Y. Katayama, M. Yao, Y. Ajiro, M. Inui and H. Endo: J. Phys. Soc. Jpn. 58 (1989) 1811.

[8] Y. Katayama, K. Maruyama, M. Yao and H. Endo: J. Phys. Soc. Jpn. 60 (1991) 2229.

[9] J. B. Parise, J. E. MacDougall, N. Herron, R. Farlee, A. W. Sleight, Y. Wang, T. Bein, K. Moller and L. M. Moroney: Inorg. Chem. 27 (1988) 221.

[10] Y. Nozue, K. Kodaira, O. Terasaki, K. Yamazaki, T. Goto, D. Watanabe and J. M. Thomas: J. Phys.: Condens. Matter 2 (1990) 5209.

[11] O. Terasaki, K. Yamazaki, J. M. Thomas, T. Ohsuna, D. Watanabe, J. V. Sandersand J. C. Berry: J. Solid State Chem. 77 (1988) 72.

[12] J. D. Robertson: Phil.Mag., 34 (1976) 13.

[13] M. Springborg and R. O. Jones: J. Chem. Phys., 88 (1988) 2652

[14] A. Ikawa and H. Fukutome: J. Phys. Soc. Jpn., 58 (1989) 4517.

[15] A. Ikawa and H. Fukutome: J. Phys. Soc. Jpn., 59 (1990) 1002.

[16] T. Yamaguchi and F. Yonezawa: J. Non–Crys. Solids, 156–158 (1993) 268.

[17] W. M. Meier: Z. Kristallographie 115 (1961) 439.

[18] G. J. Piermarini, S. Block and J. D. Barnet: J. Appl. Phys. 44 (1973) 5377.

[19] Y. Katayama, N. Koyama, K.Tsuji, H. Oyanagi and O. Shimomura, this volume.

[20] W. A. Harrison: "Electronic Structure and the Properties of Solids", (W. H. Freeman and Company, 1980)

OPTICAL EFFECTS OF FINE CERAMIC POWDER IN SOLIDIFIED GASES

Raymond G. Greene and Arthur L. Ruoff
Department of Materials Science and Engineering
Cornell University,
Ithaca, New York 14853

Effective medium theory has been applied to an idealized model of a ceramic powder in a solidified gas. The composite is optically equivalent to a graded index of refraction on the scale of the particle size. This produces dispersion in the reflectance spectrum for wavelengths greater than the particle size. These results have direct application to the practice of using fine ruby powder to achieve higher pressure in the diamond anvil cell. Ruby powder with a particle size of approximately $\frac{1}{2}\mu$m is shown to give dispersion in the infrared reflectance spectrum that resembles a plasma edge. Recent experiments from the literature are examined from this perspective.

INTRODUCTION

The standard interpretation of DAC optical absorption and reflectivity experiments is based on the twin assumptions of planar diamond-sample interfaces and a single component sample system. In practice, small deviations from this ideal are considered to have negligible contribution to the optical spectra. The prescence of ruby in the sample chamber is such a deviation.

The ceramic material ruby is the pressure marker of choice in optical DAC experiments. The ruby pressure gauge has become a standard; the measurement technique and equipment are widespread in high pressure laboratories (there are four such setups at Cornell!) It has been empirically determined that the optimal size for ruby powder chips is 0.5 to 1μm diameter [1]. This volume of ruby is much less than 0.01% of the typical sample chamber volume. For redundancy a few small chips are often used.

What are the consequences of increasing the volume of the ruby powder from $\sim$ 0.01% to $\sim$ 5%? It has been suggested that for the special case of solidified gases loaded in DAC's the extra ruby powder could "improve" the reflectivity spectra in the sense of eliminating the characteristic Fabry-Perot (F.P.) pattern [2]. It is the purpose of this study to develop an idealized model of this situation, analyze the resultant optical system, and determine the characteristic features. Some illustrative work from the literature will then be checked for these features.

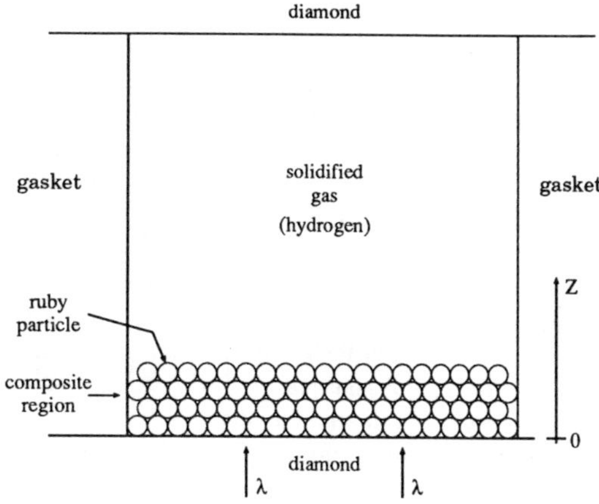

Figure 1: DAC sample chamber for graded index effect.

IDEALIZED MODEL

For the standard gas or liquid loading system the final configuration of the loaded DAC sample chamber is shown schematically in figure 1. All the extra ruby powder is at the bottom of the chamber and is trapped there because the sample above is now solid. The test of whether this has actually been achieved is if the F.P. pattern is spoiled or not. The diamond surface must be covered with the particles to spoil the pattern.

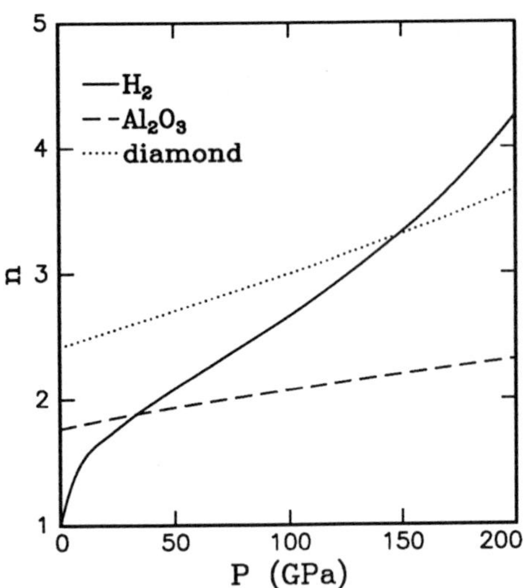

Figure 2: Clausius-Mossotti n vs pressure.

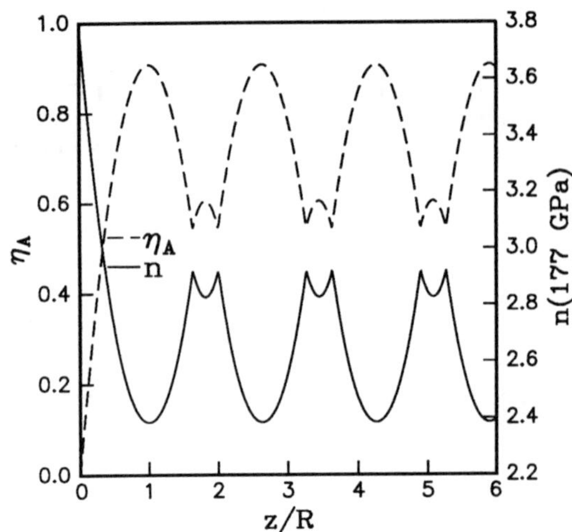

Figure 3: Volume fraction of ruby, η_A, vs distance from diamond interface. Also refactive index based on Clausius-Mossotti eqn. and effective medium theory.

A consequence of this layer being a fine powder vs a solid slab of ruby and the sample being a solidified gas is that all the voids between the particles are filled with sample. There now exists a composite region. The composite region must be considered as a zone where the refractive index is modulated between some fractions of the sample and Al_2O_3 indices, excepting one (at most a couple) of pressure(s) where $n_{sample} = n_{ruby}$.

If the composite region consisted of alternating layers of ruby and sample the modulation would be 100%. To make the model as simple as possible the particles are taken as spheres of identical size with radius R, and the composite region consists of closest packed spheres. The only result of relaxing these model assumptions is to change the the amplitude of the modulation by some percentage. There will still be modulation of the refractive index in the composite region and the characteristic length scale will still be the average particle size.

To model optical phenomena as a function of pressure a relation between refractive index and pressure is needed for diamond, Al_2O_3, and the sample. Assuming a theoretical or measured EOS exists this becomes equivalent to a relation between refractive index and density. Limiting the model to non-metalized samples, and in the low frequency limit, the Clausius-Mossotti relation,

$$\frac{\epsilon/\epsilon_0 - 1}{\epsilon/\epsilon_0 + 2} = \rho P_M \qquad (1)$$

is used. The constant P_M is the molar polarizability and ρ is the density in $moles/cm^3$. Although this relation cannot be expected to give quantitatively correct results, it provides a consistent qualitatively correct framework for the model.

For diamond and ruby the measured parameters B_0 and B_0' are fit to the Birch EOS. Hydrogen is used as an example of a solidified gas sample and Ashcroft's model data is fit to an EOS [3]. These values of density are used in the Clausius-Mossotti eqn. (1) to estimate the refractive indices vs pressure of hydrogen, ruby, and diamond. The results are are plotted in Figure 2. For future reference note that at 177 GPa: $n_{H_2} = 3.78$, $n_{Al_2O_3} = 2.26$, and $n_{diamond} = 3.49$.

OPTICAL ANALYSIS

Figure 3. shows the relative volume of Al_2O_3 vs distance from the diamond-composite interface based on the close-packed spheres model. The bounds on the dielectric constant of the composite are given by the Maxwell-Garnett relations [4]

$$\bar{\epsilon} = \epsilon_H \left[\frac{2\epsilon_H + \epsilon_A + 2\eta_H(\epsilon_H - \epsilon_A)}{2\epsilon_H + \epsilon_A - \eta_H(\epsilon_H - \epsilon_A)}\right] \qquad (2)$$

and

$$\bar{\epsilon} = \epsilon_A \left[\frac{2\epsilon_A + \epsilon_H + 2(1-\eta_H)(\epsilon_A - \epsilon_H)}{2\epsilon_A + \epsilon_H - (1-\eta_H)(\epsilon_A - \epsilon_H)}\right], \qquad (3)$$

where ϵ_H and ϵ_A are the real dielectric constants of hydrogen and Al_2O_3, respectively.

The effective medium result of Bruggeman [4] given by

$$\frac{3(1-\eta_A)}{2 + \epsilon_H/\bar{\epsilon}} + \frac{3\eta_A}{2 + \epsilon_A/\bar{\epsilon}} = 1 \qquad (4)$$

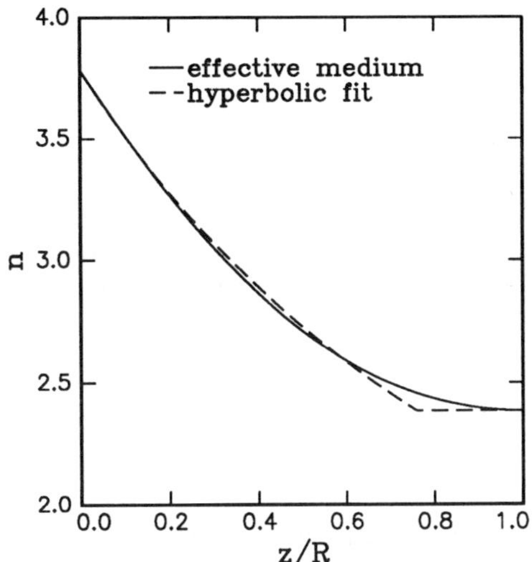

Figure 4: The calculated refractive index in Figure 3 to z/R= 1, and the least-squares fitted hyperbolic plus constant profile. Here $n_H = 3.78$, $n_m = 2.38$, and d/R= 0.76.

falls between these two nearly overlapping curves and is used in this analysis. The results for n (where $n^2 = \bar{\epsilon}$) of the composite region at 177 GPa are also shown in Figure 3.

Although optical reflectance at the diamond-composite interface can readily be calculated using well established computer programs, some physical insight can be gained by considering an approximation to the function n(z/R) of Figure 2 in the region between $0 \leq z/R \leq 1$. Let

$$n(z/R) = \frac{n_H n_m}{n_m - (n_m - n_H)\frac{z/R}{d/R}} \quad ,0 \leq \frac{z}{R} < \frac{d}{R} \quad (5)$$

$$= n_m \quad ,\frac{d}{R} \leq \frac{z}{R} \quad (6)$$

$$= n_H \quad ,0 > \frac{z}{R}, \quad (7)$$

where n_H is the refractive index at z/R= 0 and n_m is the index at z/R= 1. This function is least squares fitted to the n(z/R) data of Figure 3. for the parameter d/R, and the result is plotted in Figure 4.

For the hyperbolic profile the reflectivity is given by [5]

$$R = \left(\frac{n_H - n_m}{n_H + n_m}\right)^2 \left(\frac{sin\sigma}{\sigma}\right)^2 \quad (8)$$

where

$$\sigma = \frac{2\pi}{1.24} E(eV) d(\mu m) \frac{n_H n_m}{n_H - n_m} ln\left(\frac{n_H}{n_m}\right) \quad (9)$$

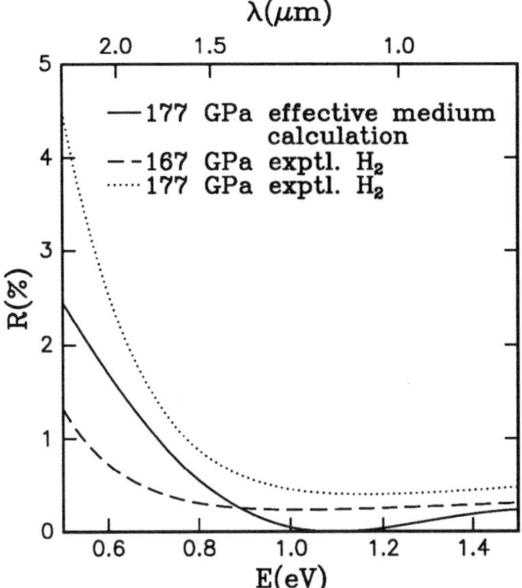

Figure 5: Reflectivity vs energy and wavelength: results of effective medium simulation and computed curves from the experimental data of Mao et al [2] (assuming a modified Drude model).

Note that n_H and $n_{Al_2O_3}$ and hence n_m are assumed to be real and to not depend on ω. Also E is the photon energy and d is the layer thickness. Substituting R= 0.25μm and using the values of n_H, n_m, and d from the previous paragraphs the resulting reflectivity curve is plotted in Figure 5. This curve is very similar in shape to that of the plasma edge associated with Drude type behavior.

The calculated reflectivity curve of Figure 5. is the optical response to the hyperbolic refractive index profile from the leading edge of the composite region. The reflectivity due to the sample-diamond Δn is a constant and will give a small positive offset estimated to be $\approx 0.15\%$.

With particle diameters of 0.5μm, $R = 0.25\mu$m, and there is a change in the refractive index of $\Delta n \approx 1.4$ over a distance of 0.25μm. High-energy (small wavelength) waves move through the index gradient without being reflected, while low-energy (large wavelength) waves behave as if they have arrived at a sharp discontinuity.

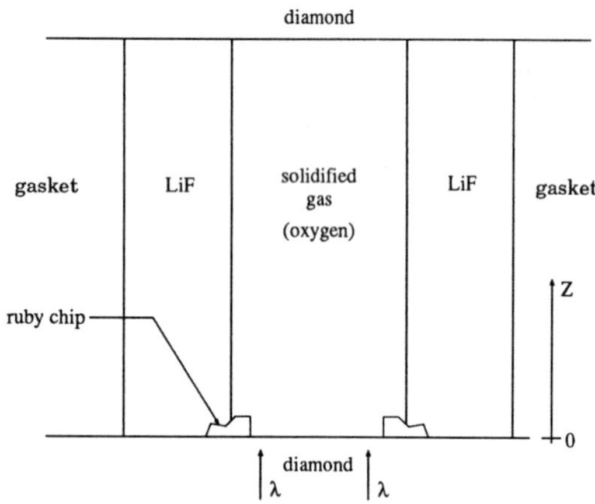

Figure 6: Schematic of DAC sample chamber for no graded index effect.

APPLICATIONS

Hydrogen

Since hydrogen was used as the sample material in the optical analysis of the preceding two sections the results can now be compared to the experimental results. In the hydrogen work of Mao *et al* [2], $\approx 5\%$ fine ruby powder was used and so the results developed here are directly applicable. This comparison is presented in Figure 5. Clearly the graded index analysis presented here is a possible explanation for the experimental observations.

Oxygen

An alternative approach is presented in the work of Desgreniers [6]. A schematic of the DAC sample chamber is presented in Figure 6. Only a few small ruby chips are used. They are placed at the boundary between a LiF region and the sample. There is no possibility of the graded index effect. The reflectivity curves taken to 135 GPa and associated plasma edges may then be analyzed solely in terms of applying the Drude model to the sample [7].

SUMMARY

The practice of using fine ruby powder in solidified gas samples to more easily reach high pressures or to spoil the interferometry in DAC reflectivity studies should be discouraged. The large amount of ruby powder forms a composite region with the sample. Refractive index gradients of $\Delta n > 1$ on the scale of the ruby particle size may give artifacts in the reflectivity spectra that appear like plasma edges in the near infrared region.

ACKNOWLEDGMENTS

We would like to thank the National Science Foundation for its support through Grant No. DMR–89178831. A. L. Ruoff also appreciates very useful discussions with David E. Aspnes and Neil W. Ashcroft.

REFERENCES

[1] H. K. Mao, R. J. Hemley, and M. Hanfland, *Phys. Rev. B* **45**, 8108 (1992)

[2] H. K. Mao, R. J. Hemley, and M. Hanfland, *Phys. Rev. Lett.* **65**, 484 (1990)

[3] N. W. Ashcroft, *Phys. Rev. B* **41**, 10963 (1990)

[4] W. Lamb, D. Wood, and N. W. Ashcroft, *Phys. Rev. B* **21**, 2248 (1980)

[5] R. Jacobsson, *Progress in Optics*, edited by E. Wolf, **V**, 247 (1966)

[6] S. Desgrenier, "Physical Properties of Pressure-Densified Solid Oxygen", Ph.D. thesis, Cornell Univ. (1991)

[7] S. Desgrenier, Y. K. Vohra, and A. L. Ruoff, *J. Phys. Chem* **94**, 1117 (1990)

ESTIMATION OF REFRACTIVE INDEX AND DENSITY OF LUBRICANTS UNDER HIGH PRESSURE BY BRILLOUIN SCATTERING

Y. Nakamura, I. Fujishiro and H. Kawakami
Faculty of Engineering
Mie University
1515 Kamihama-cho, Tsu, Mie 514, Japan

Employing a diamond-anvil cell, Brillouin scattering spectra of 90° and 180° angles for synthetic lubricants (paraffinic and naphthenic oils) were measured and sound velocity, density and refractive index under high pressure were obtained. The density obtained from the thermodynamic relation was compared with that from Lorentz-Lorenz's formula. The density was also compared with Dowson's density-pressure equation of lubricants, and density-pressure characteristics of the paraffinic oil and naphthenic oil were described considering the molecular structure for solidified lubricants. The effect of such physical properties of lubricants on the elastohydrodynamic lubrication of ball bearings, gears and traction drives was considered.

INTRODUCTION

The mechanical properties of lubricants under high pressure, such as refractive index, density, elastic constant and viscosity, play an important role in the elastohydrodynamic lubrication (EHL) [1] of ball bearings, gears and traction drives. At a pressure over 1 GPa, the usual lubricant does not behave as Newtonian liquid. For example, the lubricant in traction drive elicits a viscoelastic behavior, and a traction coefficient is estimated by applying the viscoelastic model. Density and shear strength of lubricant are also important in evaluating friction and pressure spike of EHL under high pressure. Furthermore variation of the refractive index due to high pressure must be considered for the evaluation of oil film thickness of EHL by optical interference method using a glass (or sapphire) disk and a steel ball in rolling contact under high pressure [2]. On the other hand, a diamond-anvil cell was used for the Brillouin scattering measurement in order to study elastic properties and crystal structures of simple molecules under high pressure [3].

In the present study, employing a diamond-anvil cell, Brillouin scattering spectra of 90° and 180° angles for synthetic lubricants (a paraffinic oil and a naphthenic oil) were measured and sound velocity, refractive index and density under high pressure were obtained. The density under high pressure was obtained from both the thermodynamic relation and Lorentz-Lorenz's formula, and then density-pressure relations were compared between them. The obtained density was also compared with Dowson's density-pressure equation, which is usually employed in the field of tribology, and density-pressure characteristics of the paraffinic oil and naphthenic oil were described considering the molecular structure of solidified lubricants.

FUNDAMENTAL RELATIONS OF BRILLOUIN SCATTERING IN DAC

Brillouin shifts ($\Delta\nu_{90}$, $\Delta\nu_{180}$) of the lubricant in DAC are expressed as follows, based on the interaction between phonons and photons considering Bragg–reflection law and momentum conservation [4].

$$\Delta\nu_{90} = \sqrt{2}\ \nu_i \frac{V}{C}, \quad \Delta\nu_{180} = 2\ n\ \nu_i \frac{V}{C} \qquad (1)$$

where ν_i, n, V and C are frequency of incident photons, refractive index, sound velocity of the medium (lubricant) and the light velocity in vacuum, respectively. From Eq. (1), the refractive index n of the lubricant is expressed by the ratio of Brillouin shifts ($\Delta\nu_{90}$, $\Delta\nu_{180}$) as follows.

$$n = \frac{\Delta\nu_{180}}{\sqrt{2}\ \Delta\nu_{90}}\ . \qquad (2)$$

The relation between density and refractive index is expressed by Lorentz–Lorenz's formula as,

$$\frac{4}{3}\pi N_0 \alpha = \frac{M}{\rho}\frac{n^2-1}{n^2+2} \qquad (3)$$

where α and ρ are polarizability and density, and N_0 and M are Avogadro's number and molar weight, respectively. Assuming α is constant with increase of pressure, density $\rho(P)$ under high pressure P is obtained from density, refractive index at atmospheric pressure, and refractive index of the pressure P. The density under high pressure is also derived from the following thermodynamic relation by substituting the obtained sound velocity under high pressure,

$$\rho(P) - \rho_0 = \int_{P_0}^{P} \frac{\gamma}{V^2}\, dP \qquad (4)$$

where P_0, ρ_0 and γ are atmospheric pressure, density at atmospheric pressure, and ratio of heat capacities, respectively.

EXPERIMENTAL DETAILS

An optical system employing the PZT scanning multi–pass Fabry–Perot interferometer (Burleigh RC–110) was used. Figure 1 shows a schematic diagram of the optical system. In the optical system, An argon ion laser (Spectra–Physics Lasers, BeamLok 2060, 514.5 nm, 5W) with air–spaced temperature–controlled etalon (Model 586) was newly established in the previously reported optical system [5]. The incident laser beam was split into two optical paths, the one for 90° Brillouin scattering measurement, and the other for 180° measurement, which facilitates immediate exchange of the incident light path for each scattering angle by a light block. A Bassett type DAC (cubic shape) was used for high pressure generation. For the light scattering, two holes with angles ±45° symmetric to the piston axis in the axial plane, were drilled to allow light to pass through. The slit for the optical path was made through the tilting diamond mount hemisphere. Tested synthetic lubricants were a paraffinic oil PAO68 (polyalphaolefine) and a naphthenic oil TN68 (tar naphthenic oil).

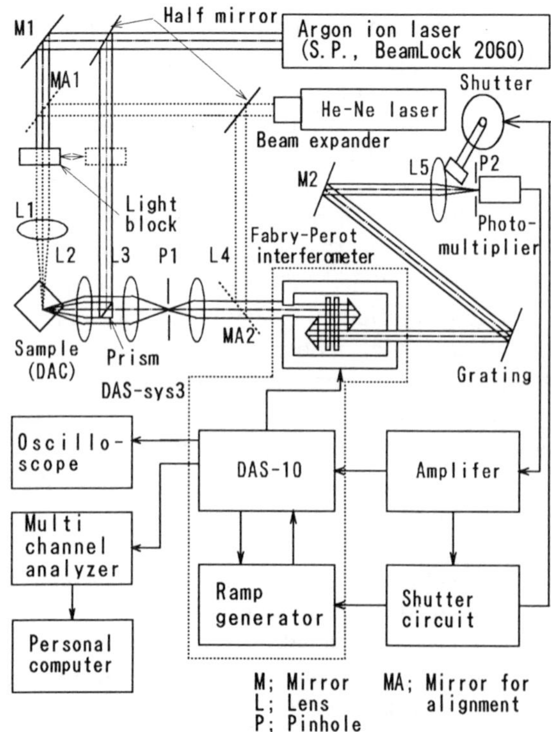

Figure 1. Optical system for Brillouin Scattering.

RESULTS AND DISCUSSION

Figure 2 depicts the sound velocity–pressure relation for a paraffinic oil PAO68 and a naphthenic oil TN68 obtained from 90° Brillouin scattering measurement and Eq. (1). The sound velocity for both oils increase with pressure with small dispersion of the data points. More detailed observation revealed that the sound velocity varies in a convex fashion toward the axis of ordinate up to 3 GPa. Figure 3 depicts the refractive index–pressure relation for PAO68 and TN68 obtained from both 90° and 180° Brillouin scattering measurement and Eq. (2). The refractive index for both oils increase with pressure despite of some dispersion of the data points, and the slope became small gradually with pressure. The data points were expressed by a regression curve shown in the figure. The density under high pressure was derived from both a thermodynamic relation (Eq. (4)) with the obtained sound velocity and from Lorentz–Lorenz's formula (Eq. (3)) with the obtained refractive index. Figure 4 shows the results for PAO68 and TN68 in a pressure–relative density relation. As for the thermodynamic equation, the ratio of heat capacities was estimated to be 1.2 for paraffinic oils and 1 for naphthenic oils from the former report [6]. The coincidence between the density from the thermodynamic relation and that from Lorentz–Lorenz's formula can be seen up to 1GPa for PAO68 and 3 GPa for TN68. Dowson's density–pressure equation is also drawn in the figure, which is usually employed in the field of tribology and is expressed as follows [1],

$$\frac{\rho(P)}{\rho_0} = 1 + \frac{0.581P}{1+1.67P} \tag{5}$$

From comparing the results with Dowson's equation, the density–pressure relations for paraffinic oil PAO68 can be expressed by this equation up to 1 GPa. However, the variation of density due to pressure for the naphthenic oil TN68 is two–thirds that for Dowson's

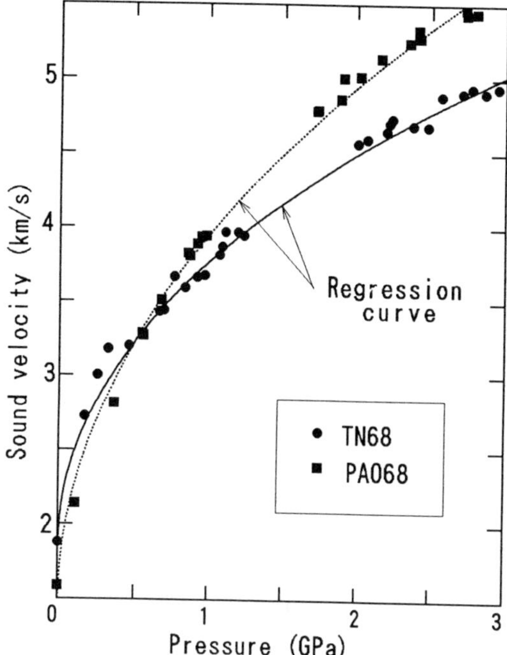

Figure 2. Pressure dependence of sound velocity.

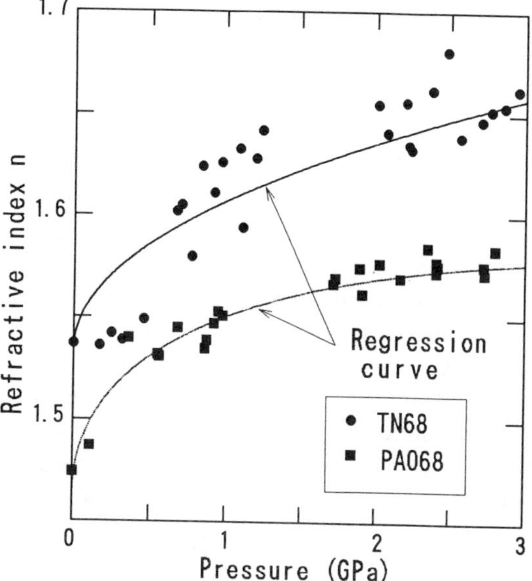

Figure 3. Pressure dependence of refractive index.

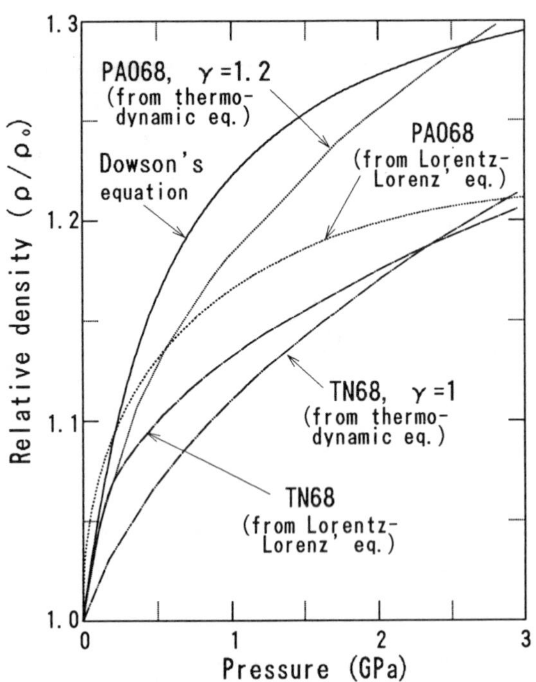

Figure 4. Relative density vs. pressure relation.

equation. This small variation in density may be concerned with the pressure-sensitive viscosity variation which assures high performance of lubricants in the traction drive of the machine.

CONCLUDING REMARKS

Brillouin scattering spectra of 90° and 180° angles for a synthetic lubricant paraffinic oil PAO68 and a naphthenic oil TN68 were measured under high pressure employing a diamond-anvil cell, and sound velocity, density and refractive index were obtained. The density under high pressure was derived from both the thermodynamic relation with the obtained sound velocity data and from Lorentz-Lorenz's formula with the obtained refractive index data. A coincidence between the density from both derivations was observed. The results were compared with Dowson's equation, and the density-pressure relations for PAO68 could be expressed by this equation up to 1 GPa. However, the variation of density due to pressure for TN68 was found to be two-thirds that for Dowson's equation.

ACKNOWLEDGMENTS

This study was supported by Grants- in-Aid for Science Research (03402027 and 03555031) from the Ministry of Education, Science and Culture of Japan. The technical assistance of Mr. K. Murai (Mie University) is acknowledged.

REFERENCES

[1] D. Dowson and G.R. Higginson, *Elasto-hydrodynamic Lubrication*, Pergamon, 1966, ch. 6-7, pp.65-105.

[2] B. O. Jacobson, *Rheology and Elasto-hydrodynamic Lubrication*, Amsterdam: Elsevier, 1991, ch. 11, pp.165-196.

[3] Y. Shimizu, S. Sasaki, and T. Ishidate, "Brillouin Scattering of Carbon Disulfide at Pressures up to 70 kbar," J. Chem. Phys., 86-15 pp.7189-7193 (1987).

[4] M.H. Manghnani and S. Akimoto, ed., *High-Pressure Research*, (W.A. Bassett and E.M. Brody) New York: Academic Press, 1977, Session IV, pp.519-532.

[5] I. Fujishiro, Y. Nakamura, K.Tanaka, and L. Hou, "Laser Light Scattering of Lubricating Oils at High Pressure and Evaluation of Mechanical Properties (1st Report, Experimental Apparatus and Rayleigh and Brillouin Scattering under High Pressure)," Trans. of JSME, (in Japanese) Ser. C, 58-552, pp.2527-2532 (1992).

[6] I. Fujishiro, Y. Nakamura, and T.Tamura, "Brillouin Scattering of Lubricating Oils under High Pressure," in Proceedings of XIII AIRAPT Conference on High Pressure Science and Technology, 1991, pp.532-534.

REFRACTIVE INDEX OF DIAMOND ANVILS AT HIGH PRESSURE

Arthur L. Ruoff and Kouros Ghandehari
Department of Materials Science and Engineering
Cornell University,
Ithaca, New York 14853

The variation of the refractive index at the tip of a diamond anvil based upon the computed stress state there is shown to be a slowly decreasing function of sample pressure. The expression is obtained using a description for the variation of refractive index with density which is consistent with available shock data. The relation of refractive index with density is also used to show consistency between Brillouin scattering results and direct measurements of the refractive index of diamond to 40 GPa under hydrostatic pressure.

INTRODUCTION

An extremely good description of the density dependence of the refractive index of an isotropic dielectric is given by

$$n = n_0 + A\frac{\Delta\rho}{\rho_0} \tag{1}$$

where $\Delta\rho = \rho - \rho_0$ is the change in density. Wise and Chhabildas [1] have made extensive studies on LiF. Their data when fit by Eq. (1) gives an excellent fit as shown in Figure 1 with $A = 0.108$. Wackerle and Stacey [2] obtain excellent straight fits on LiF with $A = 0.11$ up to $\Delta\rho/\rho_0 = 0.75$ If we were to otherwise consider n as a function of pressure, it would be highly nonlinear. The experimental evidence is that with normal solids for a fractional density change $\Delta\rho/\rho_0 \leq 0.75$, the index of refraction, n, varies linearly.

Available data for diamond is used to obtain an expression of the above form for diamond under hydrostatic pressure. This is compared to theoretical calculations. The state of stress at the center of the tip of a diamond anvil is considered and this is used to find an expression for the refractive index of the diamond anvil at the tip-center having the form of Eq. (1).

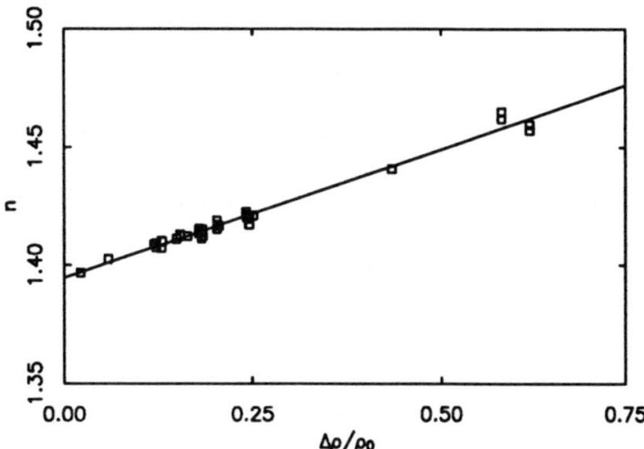

Figure 1: Refractive index vs fractional density increase for LiF [1].

STRESS STATE AT THE DIAMOND ANVIL TIP

We assume a normal pressure distribution on the surface of the diamond anvil tip which is radially symmetric and represented by P(r). The shear distribution on the surface is about two orders of magnitude smaller and is neglected. At the center of the tip, the stress state is

$$\begin{pmatrix} -1 & & \\ & -\alpha & \\ & & -\alpha \end{pmatrix} P \tag{2}$$

where $0 < \alpha < 1$.

To get a good approximation for α, Ruoff and Luo [3] considered a pressure distribution P(r) acting on a semi-infinite slab. The result is

$$\begin{pmatrix} -1 & & \\ & -(0.5+\nu) & \\ & & -(0.5+\nu) \end{pmatrix} P \tag{3}$$

where ν is Poisson's ratio and P is the maximum pressure at the center of the pressure profile. When considered a random polycrystalline isotropic elastic solid, diamond has a Poisson ratio [3],

$$\nu = 0.11 + 8.4 \times 10^{-4} P(GPa). \tag{4}$$

Although different pressure distributions with the same maximum pressure P can have very different stress distributions in the bulk of the semi-infinite slab [3], the stress state on the surface at the center of the tip is about the same.

HYDROSTATIC PRESSURE VARIATION OF THE REFRACTIVE INDEX

The stress dependence of the refractive index [4] is given by

$$n = n_0 - \frac{n_0^3}{2} \sum_j \pi_{ij} \sigma_j. \tag{5}$$

The values for π_{ij} can be obtained from the data of Grimsditch and Ramdas [5] using the elastic constants of McSkimmin and Andreatch [6]. The result is $\pi_{11} = -2.28 \times 10^{-4}$ GPa and $\pi_{12} = 0.609 \times 10^{-4}$ GPa. If we evaluate Eq. (5), for hydrostatic pressure the index of refraction varies as:

$$n = 2.415 - 7.479 \times 10^{-4} P. \tag{6}$$

Since

$$dP = B\frac{d\rho}{\rho} \tag{7}$$

we have for small pressures

$$P = B_0 \frac{\Delta\rho}{\rho_0} \tag{8}$$

and with $B_0 = 442$ GPa [6]

$$n = 2.415 - 0.331\frac{\Delta\rho}{\rho_0}. \tag{9}$$

The coefficients π_{ij} were obtained from Brillouin scattering at atmospheric pressure [5] and it is necessary to determine if they can be extrapolated to high pressure. Eremets *et al* [7] have measured n directly to 40 GPa by studying interference fringes in a thin sample of diamond surrounded by a NaCl pressure medium. Their results were fitted by us to obtain

$$n = 2.415 - 6.7 \times 10^{-4} P - 0.83 \times 10^{-6} P^2 \tag{10}$$

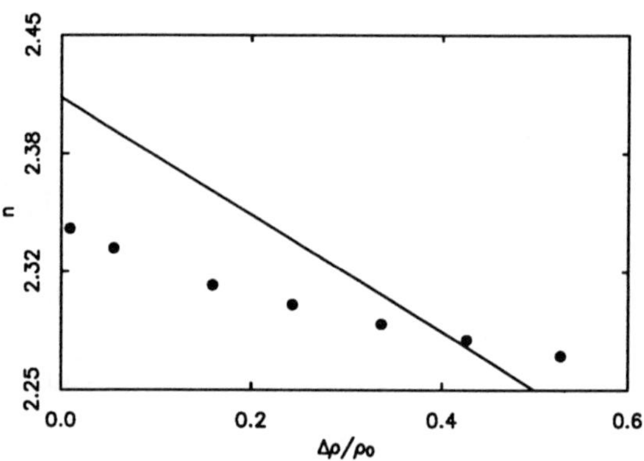

Figure 2: The data of Surh et al [10] for diamond is shown using solid circles plotted as n vs $\Delta\rho/\rho_0$. The line represents the index of refraction vs fractional density increase for diamond calculated in Eq. (9) based upon low pressure data [5,6].

where P is in GPa. The Birch equation of state [8] with $B_0 = 442$ GPa and $B_0' = 4$ [6] is used to relate P and ρ/ρ_0 according to

$$P = 663 \left[\left(\frac{\rho}{\rho_0}\right)^{7/3} - \left(\frac{\rho}{\rho_0}\right)^{5/3} \right]. \tag{11}$$

At 40 GPa, where $\rho/\rho_0 = 1.0806$ the measured value according to Eremets is 2.387 while Equation (9) gives 2.388. Thus the data of Grimsditch *et al* extrapolates nicely to 40 GPa. Because we are using a representation for n (Eq. (9)) which is consistent with typical shock compression data good to a much higher fractional density increase, we can with reasonable confidence extrapolate to $\Delta\rho/\rho_0 = 0.43$ which corresponds to 250 GPa in diamond.

COMPARISON WITH THEORETICAL CALCULATIONS

Theoretical calculations of the refractive index versus pressure have been made by Surh *et al* using the GW method [9]. Their results [10] are plotted as n vs $\Delta\rho/\rho_0$ in Figure 2.

Also shown is the line for Eq. (9). The theoretical results differ in two respects. The value of n_0 is low and the magnitude of the value of n_0' is low. They do show that n_0' is negative and that n' is negative on the entire range studied. We would not expect more than qualitative agreement. Surh *et al* also compute the value of n for the stress state

$$\begin{pmatrix} -0.89 & & \\ & -0.29 & \\ & & -0.29 \end{pmatrix} P \quad (12)$$

at P = 250 GPa, obtaining $n(250GPa) = 2.27$ compared to their computed $n(0) = 2.34$; thus $\Delta n = -0.07$. From Eqs. (5) and (8) we obtain $n = 2.415 - 0.311\Delta\rho/\rho_0$ and from Eq. (11), $\Delta\rho/\rho_0 = 0.358$ at P = 250 GPa, so $n(250GPa) = 2.304$; thus $\Delta n = -0.11$. For n in the x_2 direction with the stress state of Eq. (12) we obtain an increase in n as does Surh *et al.*

REFRACTIVE INDEX AT THE CENTER OF A DIAMOND ANVIL TIP

From the results above, we have

$$n = 2.415 - 7.042 \times 10^{-4}[2.28 - 2(0.609)(0.5 + \nu)]P(GPa). \quad (13)$$

Using Eq. (8) we obtain

$$n = 2.415 - 0.311[2.28 - 1.218(0.5 + \nu)]\frac{\Delta\rho}{\rho_0}. \quad (14)$$

When combined with Eq. (4), this represents a good approximation for the value of n at the center of the surface of the diamond anvil tip and until precise measurements are made at high pressure, Eq. (14) can be used with reasonable confidence to 250 GPa.

ACKNOWLEDGEMENT

The authors wish to thank the National Science Foundation for support by Grant No. DMR-9218249. We would also like to thank Huan Luo as well as M.P. Surh, S.G. Louie, and M.L. Cohen.

References

[1] J.L. Wise and L.C. Chhabildas, *Shock Waves in Condensed Matter*, ed. by Y.M. Gupta, Plenum Press, New York, 1986, p. 441.

[2] J. Wackerle and H.L. Stacy, *Shock Waves in Condensed Matter*, ed. by S.C. Schmidt and N.C. Holmes, Elsevier Science Publishers, BV, 1988, p. 699.

[3] A.L. Ruoff and H. Luo, J. Appl. Phys. **70**, 2066 (1991).

[4] J.F. Nye, *Physical Properties of Crystals*, Oxford University Press, New York, 1960, p. 252.

[5] M.H. Grimsditch and A.K. Ramdas, Phys. Rev **B 11**, 3139 (1975).

[6] H.J. Mc Skimmin and P. Andreatch Jr., J. Appl. Phys. **43**, 2944 (1972).

[7] M.I. Eremets, V.V. Struzhkin, Ju.A. Timofeev, A.N. Utjuzh, and A.M. Shirokov, *Recent Trends in High Pressure Research*, Oxford and IBH Publishing Co., New Delhi, 1992, p. 362.

[8] F. Birch, J. Geophys. Res. **83**, 1257 (1978).

[9] M.P. Surh, S.G. Louie, and M.L. Cohen, Phys. Rev. **B 45**, 8239 (1992).

[10] M.P. Surh, personal communication.

HIGH-PRESSURE RAMAN SCATTERING STUDY OF SULFUR

Huan Luo and Arthur L. Ruoff

Department of Materials Science and Engineering, Cornell University
Ithaca, New York 14853

Most of the recent high-pressure Raman measurements of sulfur by different groups have exposed the sample to a laser power of at least 20 mW. This was found strong enough to cause darkening or permanent damage of the sample under pressure when examined under the microscope and hence cause changes in the Raman spectra. Having this problem in mind, we have performed Raman measurements on sulfur in a diamond anvil cell with a laser power of no more than 4 mW on the sample up to 12 GPa. Three excitation laser wavelengths were used. The differences in the Raman spectra from the previous results of other groups are addressed and the consistency with our pervious optical absorption and x-ray diffraction results are discussed.

INTRODUCTION

Properties of sulfur, a classic elemental molecular system, under high pressure and room or low temperature have been extensively studied over the past 20 years, especially by the Raman spectroscopic method after the initial work of Zallen in 1974 [1] and Wang et al. in 1987 [2] using the DAC technique. Recent work by Häfner et al. [3] and Possmanith et al. [4] have made studies to 45 GPa and found two phase transitions above 10 GPa and the laser heating caused the phase transitions. It was later reported by Wolf et al. [5] that a photochemical reaction of solid sulfur could be excited by certain laser wavelengths. The latest Raman studies by Nagata et al. detected a phase transition at 5.2 GPa [6]. However, the previous Raman results are inconsistent and even controversial in several aspects. For instance, significant differences existed among the Raman spectra obtained by different groups under similar pressure and temperature.

It was found that most of the earlier Raman work used a laser power of 20 mW or more at the sample, which is typical for most of materials but may be too strong for sulfur under pressure. Although sulfur (S_8) is traditionally considered as a molecular system, its internal and external phonon modes overlap in the frequency range 70 - 100 cm^{-1}, indicating relatively weak intermolecular bonds in solid sulfur. There are two things which could cause bond breaking in sulfur under the effects of compression similar to what happened in solid benzene [7]: (1) the single S-S bond has a bonding energy of 2.7 at ambient conditions, which corresponds to 460 nm in wavelength. But the energy needed to break a bond could become less when pressure is applied; (2) the initial band gap, $E_g = 2.9$ eV of an indirect type, decreases with increasing pressure with a slope of 0.074 eV/GPa until 25 GPa [8]. Thus, strong absorption to the 488 nm radiation with an optical density greater than 2 is expected to occur in sulfur at $P \geq 4.8$ GPa.

In our earlier optical and x-ray diffraction studies on sulfur up to 120 GPa [8,9], we have found an orthorhombic to monoclinic transition at 5.3 GPa, a crystalline to amorphous transition completed at 25 GPa and an insulator to metal transition at 95 GPa. To continue our interest on the behavior of sulfur under high pressure, especially the phase transition sequence viewed by vibrational spectra, we present the Raman spectroscopic results of sulfur under pressures to 12 GPa. To minimize the laser heating problem during the Raman measurements, the laser power was kept low (only 3-4 mW at the sample) throughout the entire measurements. The emphasis of this paper is on the phase transition and its dependence, if any, on the excitation source. Only the internal Raman modes are presented and discussed in this paper. Details on the lattice vibrational modes and their pressure dependences will be presented elsewhere.

EXPERIMENTAL

Orthorhombic sulfur powder with a purity of 99.9995% was placed with a few small ruby chips into a hole, 150 µm in diameter, drilled on a spring steel gasket in a diamond anvil cell. The incident laser had focusing spots 5-10 µm in diameter at the sample. The non-linear ruby calibration method [10] was used to determine the pressure. The back scattered Raman signals were collected on a triple monochromator (Spex model 1877C) equipped with a cooled optical multichannel detector. Three excitation laser wavelengths, the 488 and 514.5 nm lines from an Ar^+ laser and the 632.8 nm line from a He-Ne laser, were used. With an improvement on the entrance optical part of the Raman setup and the use of low groove density gratings (600 gr/mm) in the spectrometer, we were able to record good Raman signals with a laser power no more than 4 mW at the sample.

RESULTS AND DISCUSSION

Figure 1 shows the Raman spectra of sulfur at five selected pressures involving different laser wavelengths. With the 632.8 nm excitation and a power of 3-4 mW at the sample, the Raman signals could be detected up to 12 GPa on our setup. The pressure dependences of the observed internal modes are plotted in Figure 2, which shows a discontinuity at about 6±1 GPa. This is consistent with the earlier x-ray diffraction data [9] that indicated an orthorhombic to monoclinic phase transition at 5.3 GPa. The Raman results showed that the molecular unit, i.e. the 8-atom ring type S molecule, remains intact under pressure

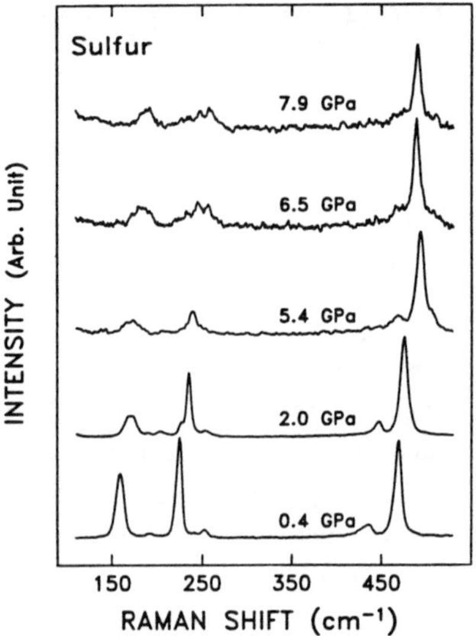

FIG.1. Raman spectra of sulfur under pressures.

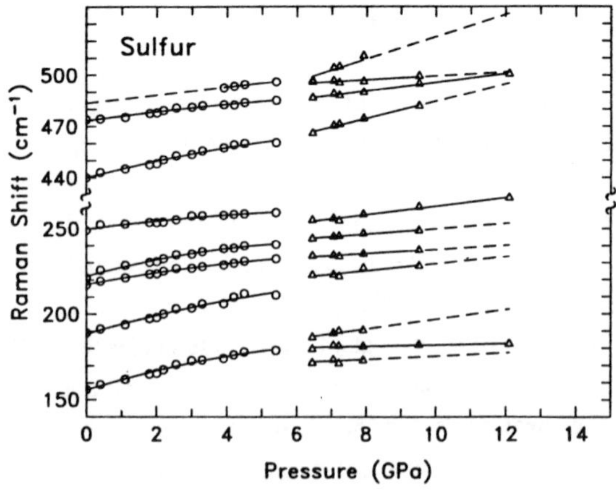

FIG.2. Observed internal Raman-active modes of sulfur as a function of pressure with discontinuities shown at about 6 GPa.

up to, at least, 12 GPa. The extra modes (see Figure 1) appearing above 6 GPa may come from degeneracy caused by the phase change and lattice field splitting.

Under low laser power, we had to switch to longer wavelength at higher pressures in order to record the Raman signals. For the three excitation wavelengths used in the present work, we found a linear relationship between the laser wavelength (in eV) and the corresponding highest pressure at which no signal was measurable. This result is shown in Figure 3 along with our earlier transmission data. Good agreement between the two data sets indicates that sample absorption caused by band gap closing is the key reason for the observed disappearance of the Raman signal above certain pressure .

In order to examine previously reported laser heating phenomena [3,4] and photo reaction [5] in sulfur under pressure, tiny regions of the sample above 3 GPa were deliberately exposed to a laser power of 20-25 mW with either 488 nm or 514.5 nm line for 2-3 minutes. Significant differences showed at around $\Delta\nu = 470$ cm^{-1}. Those overexposed sample regions appeared slightly, but permanently, darker under a microscope. Figure 4 shows three spectra all under the same pressure of 6.5 GPa. Figure 4 (a) was taken with the 514.5 nm line under a low power (≤ 4 mW). Figure 4 (b) was taken from a previously darkened region also with the 514.5 line and low power. Figure 4 (c) was taken from the same region as in Figure 4 (a) but with the 632.8 nm line. Figure 4 (c) is basically similar to the other spectra shown in Figure. 1, presenting pure compression effects. Apparently, the overexposed region has a different molecular structure from the original S_8. The Figure 4 (b) type Raman spectrum has been observed in Refs. 3-6 but explained in different ways. It should be noted that for a given laser wavelength the Figure 4 (b) type spectrum only appears above certain pressure, below which laser power has very little or no effects to the feature of the Raman spectra. For instance, at P=0 and with 488 nm radiation, the Raman spectrum stays the same no matter what the laser power is. Therefore, it may be concluded that the sample absorption as a result of pressure-induced band gap closing provides energy to dissociate the S_8 unit and plays a key role in the resulting Raman spectra.

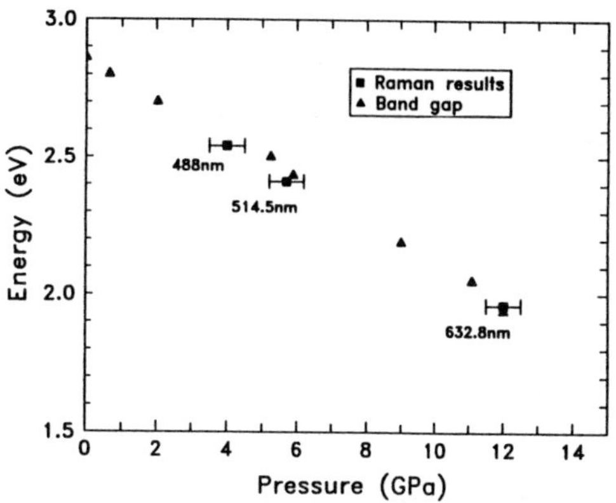

FIG. 3. The relationship between the laser wavelength (in eV) and the pressure at which the Raman signal became too weak to be measured on our setup using a low laser power ($\leq$4 mW), along with the band gap (E_g) vs pressure data from Ref. 8.

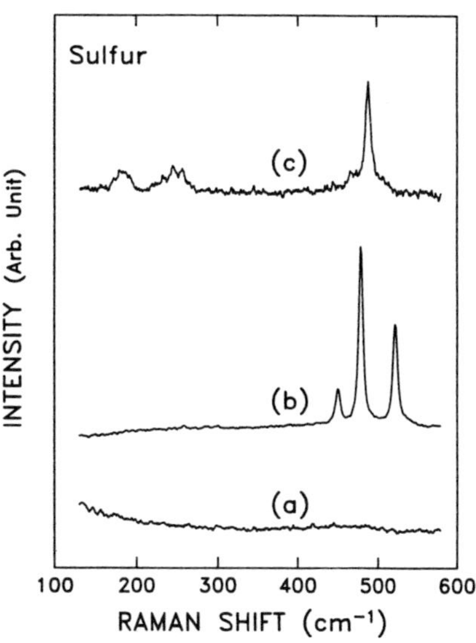

FIG. 4. The Raman spectra of sulfur at 6.5 GPa. (a) with the 514.5 nm line and a low laser power; (b) with the 514.5 nm line on an overexposed darker sample region; (c) with the 632.8 line and a low laser power.

ACKNOWLEDGMENTS

This work was supported by the MRL Program of the NSF through the Cornell Materials Science Center under Award No. DMR-9121654.

REFERENCES

[1] R. Zallen, Phys. Rev. **B9**, 4485 (1974).

[2] L. Wang, Y. Zhao, R. Lu, Y. Meng, Y. Fan, H. Luo, Q. Cui, and G.Zou, in *High-Pressure Research in Mineral Physics*, edited by M.H. Manghnani and Y. Syono, (Terra Sci. Pub., Washington, D.C., 1987), pp. 299-304.

[3] W. Häfner, J. Kritzenberger, H. Olijnyk, and A. Wokaun, High

[4] P. Rossmanith, W. Häfner, A. Wokaun, and H. Olijnyk, High Pressure Research, (to be published).

[5] P. Wolf, B. Bear, M. Nicol, and H. Cynn, in *Molecular System Under High Pressure*, edited by R. Pucci and G, Piccitto, (Elsevier Science Pub. B.V. North-Holland, Amsterdam, 1991), pp 263-271.

[6] K. Nagata, T. Nishio, H. Taguchi, and Y. Miyamoto, Jpn. J. Appl. Phys. Vol. 31, 1078 (1992).

[7] J. M. Besson, M.M. Thiery, and Ph. Pruzan, in *Molecular System Under High Pressure*, ed. by R. Pucci and G, Piccitt0, (Elsevier Sci. Pub. B.V. North-Holland, 1991), pp 341-359.

[8] H. Luo, S. Desgreniers, Y. K. Vohra, and A. L. Ruoff, Phys. Rev. Lett., 67, 2998 (1991).

[9] H. Luo and A. L. Ruoff, Phys. Rev. B 48, 569 (1993).

[10] H. K. Mao, J. Xu, and P. M. Bell, J. Geophys. Res., 91, 4673 (1986).

HIGH PRESSURE RAMAN STUDIES ON p-DICHLOROBENZENE.

S.K. Deb[1], S. Meenakshi[2] and B.K. Godwal[2]

[1] Solid State Physics Division,

[2] High Pressure Physics Division,
Bhabha Atomic Research Centre,
Bombay 400 085, India.

We report the results of Raman measurements on p- dichlorobenzene up to the pressure range of 80 kbar much higher than the limit of 20 kbar reached in the past. The ambient α phase remains stable up to 80 kbar when the pressure is changed rapidly (≈ every 2 hours). However, at low pressure (≈ 5 kbar) it transforms to γ phase very slowly (after ≈ 16 hours) and continues to retain this phase till about 80 kbar. The Raman frequency variation with pressure does not show any drastic change in value or slope, indicative of any further phase change.

INTRODUCTION

p-dichlorobenzene ($C_6H_4Cl_2$) is a halogen substituted benzene derivative which is solid at ambient temperature and pressure. It exists in different structural phases at different pressures and temperatures due to the competition between the C-C, C-Cl and Cl-Cl interactions between the neighbouring molecules. So far, it is known to exist in three different phases [1] It transforms from its ambient α phase to β phase at 304 K and changes to γ phase at 273 K. The space groups and the number of molecular units (Z) per unit cell in α, β, and γ phases are $P2_1/a$, Z = 2; $P\bar{1}$, Z = 1; and $P2_1/c$, Z = 2 respectively [1]. The temperature dependent phase transitions were studied by X-ray diffraction [1], Raman [2] , IR [3] and NQR spectroscopy [4]. The structure of all these phases have been determined at 100 K by X-ray diffraction on supercooling the different phases [1].

Pressure is a better parameter to modulate the interactions between molecules by changing the intermolecular distances. High pressure X-ray diffraction studies suggest a transition at 3 kbar to an orthorhombic phase [5]. However NQR [6] and Raman investigations [7] indicate α to γ transition at about 1.5 kbar with indication of a transition to δ phase at about 9 kbar from Raman data [7]. A phase diagram in the P-T plane has already been reported [8].

Here we present high pressure Raman scattering results from lattice modes of p- dichlorobenzene up to 80 kbar which is much higher than the maximum pressure (17 kbar) in the previous study. Our motivation was to investigate the kinetic effects and to look for further phase transitions at higher pressures. We were also interested in exploring the possibility of crystal to amorphous transition at high pressure as observed by us recently in an analogous compound resorcinol [9], around 40 kbar.

EXPERIMENTAL DETAILS

A good optical quality commercial grade p- dichlorobenzene sample was loaded in a diamond anvil cell with a tiny ruby chip for pressure calibration in a pre-indented Inconel gasket with a 250 μm hole. Water was used as a pressure transmitting fluid because the conventional ethanol- methanol mixture was found to dissolve the sample. Raman spectra were excited using 5145 A line from an Innova-70, Ar^+ laser with power less than 10 mW focussed on to a 40 μm spot. The scattered light was collected in the exact backscattering geometry and analysed with a home made grating double monochromator with photon counting [10]. The power density had to be kept low to prevent sample melting, particularly at low pressure. The pressure was determined from shift of ruby flourescence line.

RESULTS

At ambient conditions, p-$C_6H_4Cl_2$ exists in α phase with point group C_{2h} and Z = 2 and there are six external Raman active modes - 3 belonging to A_g and 3 belonging to B_g mode and all librational in nature. The Raman spectrum at ambient pressure is shown in Fig.1 which agrees with the spectra available in the literature [11]. We see five clear librational modes with probably another one accidently degenerate with the 53 cm^{-1} mode, as noted previously [7]. The spectra recorded with increasing pressures are also shown in the same figure. The most interesting feature is that all the spectra upto 70 kbar show the characteristic features of the α phase. This implies that p-$C_6H_4Cl_2$ has not transformed from the α to γ phase even though the pressure has been increased up to 70 kbar. All the Raman lines belonging to the α phase increase in frequency and the broad line at 90 cm^{-1} at 1 bar shows clear splitting into doublets at pressures beyond 30 kbar. The pressures were changed quite rapidly and spectra recorded at intervals of two hours. The variation in frequency of different modes as a function of pressure is shown in Fig.2. It is clearly seen that within the

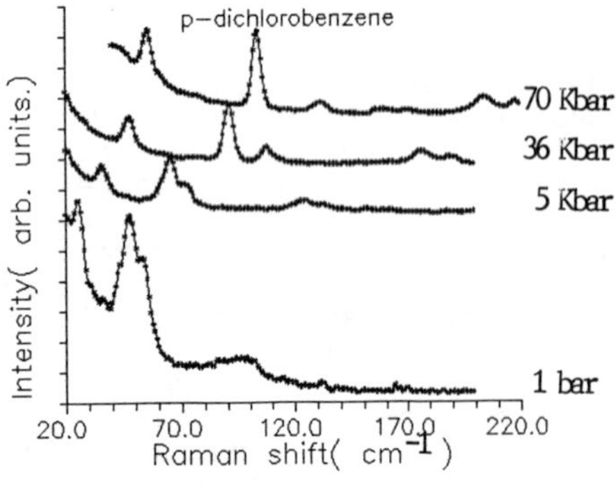

Figure 1 Raman spectra of p-dichlorobenzene in the α phase at different pressures.

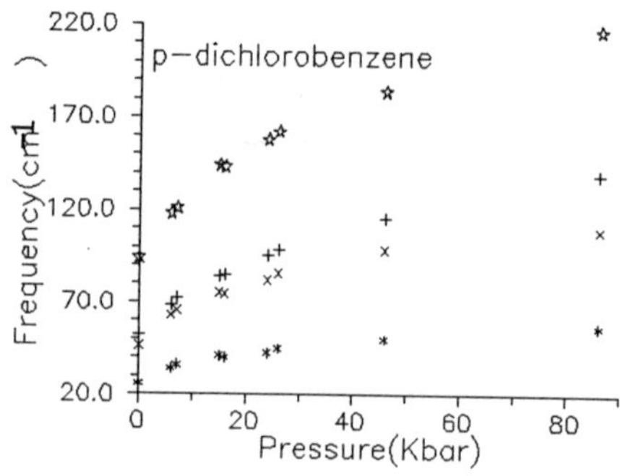

Figure 2 Variation in frequency of different modes with pressure in the α phase.

experimental errors in frequency (+ 1 cm^{-1}) and pressure (+ 1 kbar) there is no abrupt discontinuity in slope or in values of the frequencies. In particular, at low pressure (< 5 kbar) the uncertainty in frequency and pressure can be more. Further, as has been observed earlier, there is a discontinuity in frequency of modes across the α to γ transition. Thus, the α phase is retained till 90 kbar with a non-linear variation in frequency with pressure. The pressure was then released from 90 kbar to about 5 kbar and after an interval of about 16 hours, the spectrum recorded is characteristic of the γ phase [11] and shows that the crystal has transformed from α to γ phase.

In the γ phase the pressure has been gradually increased with time interval similar to what was for the α phase between the two pressures. The Raman spectra recorded at some typical pressures are shown in Fig.3. The

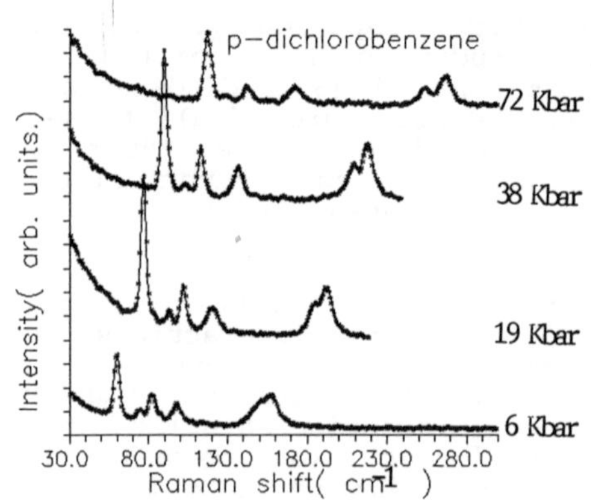

Figure 3. Raman spectra of p-dichlorobenzene in the γ phase at different pressures.

frequencies of all the modes increase together with increasing separation between closely spaced lines. In particular, two lines at ≈ 155 cm^{-1} has been clearly resolved at ≈ 70 kbar. The variation in frequency of all the modes shown in Fig.4 do not exhibit any abrupt discontinuity typical of any phase transition. Thus we do not observe any transition from the γ to δ phase as has been suggested by earlier Raman scattering result [7].

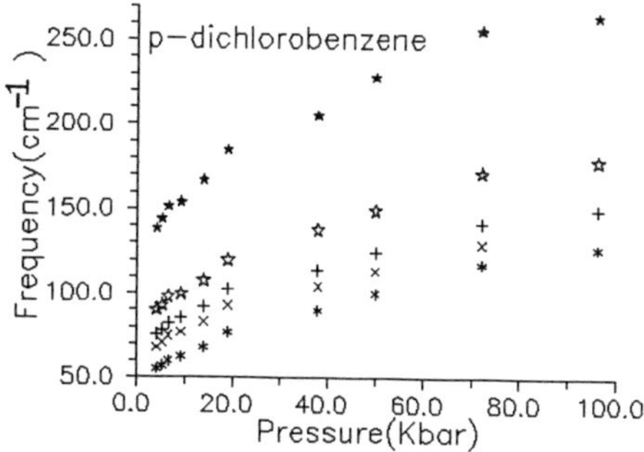

Figure 4. Variation in frequency of different modes with pressures in the γ phase.

On releasing the pressure completely the γ phase slowly changes back to the α phase.

CONCLUSION

Our study on p-dichlorobenzene from Raman scattering as a function of pressure shows that good quality spectra can be obtained up to about 100 kbar. This is much more than the previous study up to 17 kbar beyond which a degradation of sample was observed which prevented recording of spectra at higher pressure [7].

Our results differ from earlier works in certain respects. We do not observe any indication of γ to δ transition, as suggested by earlier Raman study. Our results also do not seem to agree with the high pressure X-ray diffraction study [5] where the phase above 3 kbar could be indexed with orthorhombic Pbca; Z = 4 structure. Factor group analysis indicates 12 external Raman active libration modes for this point group and our spectra show that the maximum number of Raman external modes observed are six. Thus we do not observe this transition to the orthorhombic phase.

ACKNOWLEDGEMENT

We acknowledge fruitful discussions with Dr. A.P. Roy and Dr S.K. Sikka. We are also grateful to Dr. K.R. Rao for encouraging us during the course of this work.

REFERENCES

[1] L. Wheeler and S.D. Colson, *J. Chem. Phys.* 65, 1227 (1976) and references there in.

[2] M. Gherferstein and H. Szwarc, *Molecular Crystals and Liquid Crystals* 14, 283 (1971).

[3] S. Ganguly, J.B. Fernandes, D. Bahadur and C.N.R. Rao, *J. Chem. Soc. Faraday Trans.* 2, 75, 923 (1979).

[4] C. Dean and E. Lindstrand, *J. Chem. Phys.* 24, 1114 (1956).

[5] H. Sankaran, S.M. Sharma, S.K. Sikka and R. Chidambaram, *Pramana - J. Phys.* 27, 835 (1986).

[6] T. Kushida, G.B. Benedek and N. Bloembergen, *Phys. Rev.* 104, 1364 (1956).

[7] D.M. Adams and J.O.C. Ekejiuba, *J. Chem. Soc. Faraday Trans.* 2, 77,851 (1981).

[8] P. Figuiere and H. Szwarc, *Molecular Crystals and Liquid Crystals* 27, 305 (1974)

[9] S.K. Deb, M.A. Rekha, A.P. Roy, V. Vijayakumar, S. Meenakshi and B.K. Godwal, *Phys. Rev.* B47, 11491 (1993).

[10] A.P. Roy and M.L. Bansal, *Ind. J. Pure and Appl. Phys.* 27, 407 (1989).

[11] P. Figuiere, M. Ghelfenstein and H. Szware, *High Temp. High Pressure* 6,61 (1974).

HIGH PRESSURE RAMAN AND EDXD STUDY OF DIASPORE

Raymond G. Greene, Huan Luo, and Arthur L. Ruoff
Department of Materials Science and Engineering
Cornell University,
Ithaca, New York 14853

Diaspore (AlOOH) has been proposed as a high pressure product of the reaction of ruby and hydrogen [1]. To improve the accuracy of this calculation the EOS of diaspore has been measured from 0 to 65 GPa using EDXD. A fit of this data to the Birch eqn. gives the parameters $B_0 = 170.3 \pm 6$ GPa, and $B_0' = 4.40 \pm 0.3$. This result does not favor the hydrogen reduction of ruby. It has also been suggested that the OH stretching Raman mode could be used as a signal for the prescence of diaspore at Mbar pressures [2]. Raman spectroscopy on diaspore suggests that the OH vibron is a poor marker for diaspore due to sensitivity and fluorescence.

INTRODUCTION

There are two motivations for studying the high pressure properties of diaspore: as a product of the postulated Mbar chemical reaction of the hydrogen reduction of ruby and use of the (OH vibron) Raman signal of diaspore as a marker for the prescence of diaspore at Mbar pressures [1, 2].

Ruoff and Vanderborgh [1] proposed that at room temperature and pressures ≥ 136 GPa hydrogen could reduce ruby based on the chemical reaction

$$Al_2O_3 + \frac{3}{4}H_2 \rightarrow \frac{3}{2}AlOOH + \frac{1}{2}Al \qquad (1)$$

The calculation of the free energy, ΔG, of the above reaction is based on the EOS's of the components, of which two, hydrogen and diaspore, were estimated. Thus the reaction should be considered as plausible but unproven.

If this reaction occurs it could serve as a prototype for Mbar chemistry. It also implies that ruby powder could chemically interact with a hydrogen sample at Mbar pressures in DAC experiments [3, 4, 5]. At room temperature the reaction would proceed very near to the surface of the Al_2O_3 particle by a tunneling mechanism. After several atomic layers of Al were formed this process will end. Any further reaction would be diffusion controlled. Diffusion at room temperature is expected to be very slow, i.e. the reaction stops. Since the Al layer thickness is small compared to the skin depth (at 177 GPa it is calculated to be 290Å) there will be little effect on ruby measurements.

Mao *et al* [2] state that their inability to observe the OH vibron in hydrogen loaded DAC's with ruby powder at Mbar pressures is inconsistent with prescence of diaspore. However there is no evidence presented as to the ability to measure the diaspore OH vibron with pressure. Here again the argument is plausible but unproven.

The purpose of this study is to measure both the EOS, and the Raman spectra vs pressure, of diaspore. This new physical information will then be applied to the arguments of the preceding paragraphs.

EXPERIMENTAL

Sample

The crystal structure of diaspore at 1 atm is orthorhombic (*Pbnm*) with a tetramolecular unit cell: $a_0 = 4.396Å$, $b_0 = 9.426Å$, and $c_0 = 2.844Å$ [6].

A sample of natural diaspore was purchased from Ward's Natural Science Establishment, Inc. Sample purity was checked by powder diffraction and FTIR. The powder diffraction was performed at the Cornell MSC X-Ray Facility and was in excellent agreement with the ASTM card for diaspore. FTIR was performed in the laboratory of Prof. A. J. Sievers of the Cornell Univ. Physics Dept. and the spectrum was a good match with spectra in the literature [7, 8]. In neither case were there any apparent impurity phases or artifacts in the spectra.

General

All Raman and EDXD experiments were performed with a DAC at room temperature. Some small ruby chips were always present in the sample chamber as a pressure marker. All pressure measurements were made with the non-linear ruby scale [9] with the spectrometer to be described below.

Raman Spectrometer

Micro-Raman spectroscopy was performed on a system whose major components were: Ar^+ laser, microscope, SPEX model 1877 spectrometer with a 600 grooves/mm grating, and EG&G model 1422 cooled intensified diode-array detector. The 488 nm line of the laser was used and the collection time for each spectrum varied from ten minutes to a couple of hours. Ar-Hg and Ne lamps were used for spectrometer calibration.

Raman runs were made with powder samples, chip sample with indium pressure medium, chip sample with gold pressure medium, and chip sample with powder sample as pressure medium.

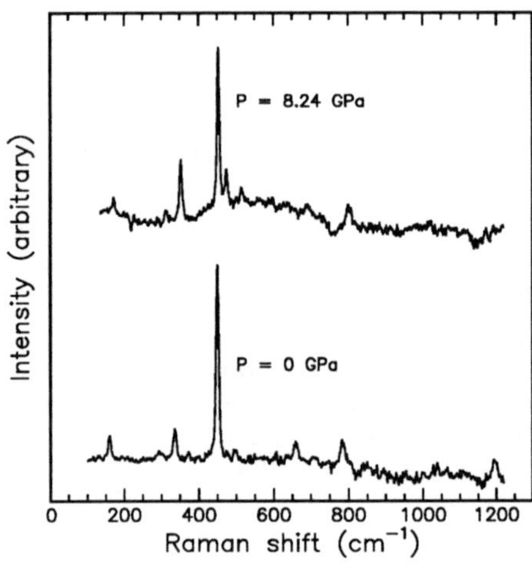

Figure 1: Raman shift - typical low cm^{-1} region spectra.

Energy Dispersive X-Ray Diffraction

EDXD was performed at the CHESS B1 station. The diffraction geometry was calibrated with a gold foil and the collection time was typically one hour per spectrum. Diffraction angles, 2θ, of 7.4, and 10.0 deg were used. The sample was a finely ground powder, and a 4:1 methanol/ethanol mixture was used as a pressure medium.

RAMAN RESULTS

Low Wave Number Region

Figure 1 shows typical DAC Raman spectra for the low wave number (100 – 1200 cm^{-1}) region at pressures of 0 and 8.2 GPa. Nine lines were observed in the zero pressure spectrum eight of which were followed with increasing pressure. Figure 2 shows the Raman shift vs pressure for the low wave number region. In all cases the Raman shift was $< 5\ cm^{-1}/GPa$. *Due to strong fluorescence no Raman was observable above* 8.2 *GPa.* The highest pressure that a systematic search was made for Raman signal was 13 GPa. The small slope of the Raman shift with pressure is indicative of a stiff crystal.

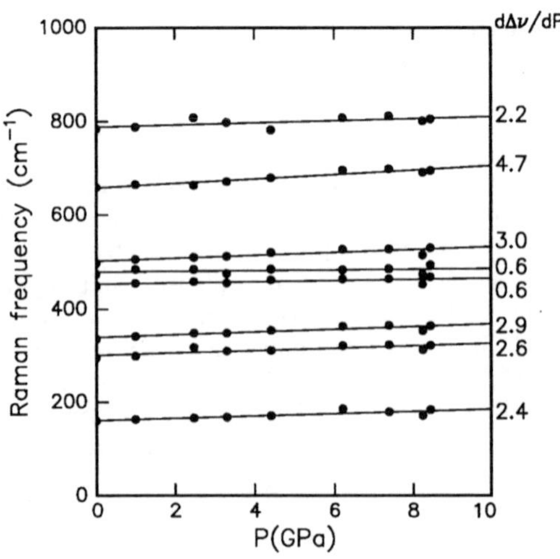

Figure 2: Raman shift - low cm^{-1} region vs pressure.

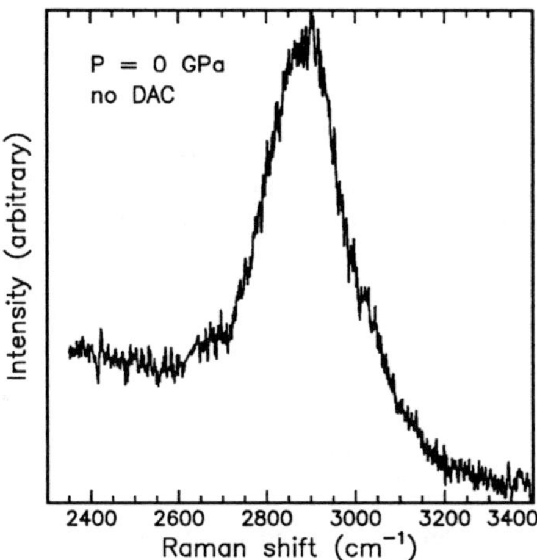

Figure 3: Raman shift - OH vibron spectrum.

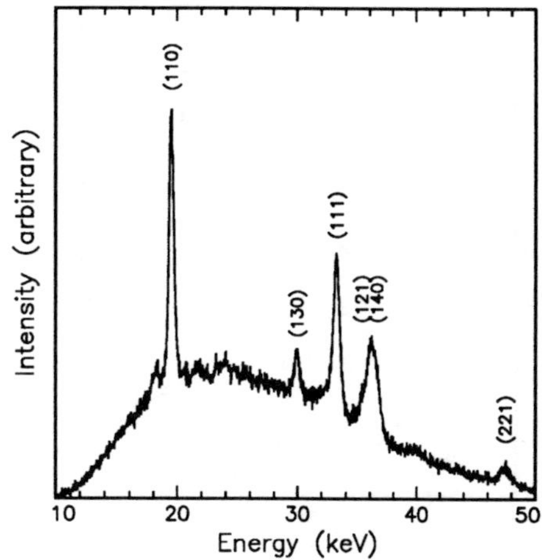

Figure 4: Diaspore EDXD spectrum at 65 GPa.

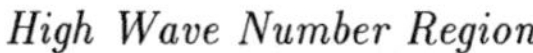

High Wave Number Region

Figure 3 shows a 1 atm Raman spectrum of the diaspore OH vibron for a sample not in a DAC. The broad OH vibron is at ≈ 2900 cm^{-1}. This position and width for the OH vibron are quite reasonable in comparison to other OH compounds. The strength of this peak was reduced by approximately a 3X with respect to the background when the sample was placed in the DAC. *The OH vibron was not able to be followed with increasing pressure due to strong fluorescence to even 3 GPa.*

Discussion

Various schemes were attempted to overcome the fluorescence and sensitivity problem. These included use of gasket, defocused sample, pressure medium, and even powder sample backgrounds. None of these proved satisfactory. Also the other strong lines of the Ar^+ laser were tried with no apparent difference in fluorescence.

Additionally a synthetic powder sample was acquired [10], its spectrum matched the natural sample for peak positions but the fluorescence was even worse. A FT-Raman spectrum taken at STP with a 1.06 μm Nd:YAG laser was also supplied with the synthetic sample [10]. The Raman peak to background levels indicate that fluorescence is quite strong with this wavelength laser too.

EDXD RESULTS

Figure 4 is the EDXD spectrum of diaspore at 65 GPa, the highest pressure achieved in this study. Figure 5 is the EOS of diaspore from 0 to 65 GPa. A fit of this data to the Birch eqn. gives the parameters $B_0 = 170.3 \pm 6$ GPa, and $B_0' = 4.40 \pm 0.3$. No phase transformations were observed from the original structure. The value of B_0 and B_0' used by Ruoff and Vanderborgh [1] were 85 GPa and 5.2. *This large change, all other things being equal makes the hydrogen reduction of ruby unlikely.* All other things being equal includes no phase transformations of diaspore.

To address the issue of whether diaspore is likely to have a phase transformation at some pressure P_t, it can be compared to CaO ($B_0 = 117$ GPa, $P_t < 70$ GPa) [11], and $Ca(OH)_2$ ($B_0 = 37.8$ GPa, $P_t \approx 7.9$ GPa [12].

The equilibrium transformation for CaO may be substantially lower. The estimate of the equilibrium transformation pressure for $Ca(OH)_2$ is the average pressure at which transformation begins on loading (10.7 GPa) and at which the reverse transformation (from the fully transformed material) begins on unloading (5.1 GPa). In other words sizeable overpressures are needed to drive the reaction.

For both the oxide and hydroxide P_t is a fraction of B_0. It is likely that in the mixed oxide-hydroxide $AlOOH$ the P_t would be a fraction of B_0.

The reaction (1), when thermodynamically favored, will occur by a tunneling mechanism as noted earlier. However, if diaspore itself is to have a polymorphic transformation a sizeable overpressure is likely to be required.

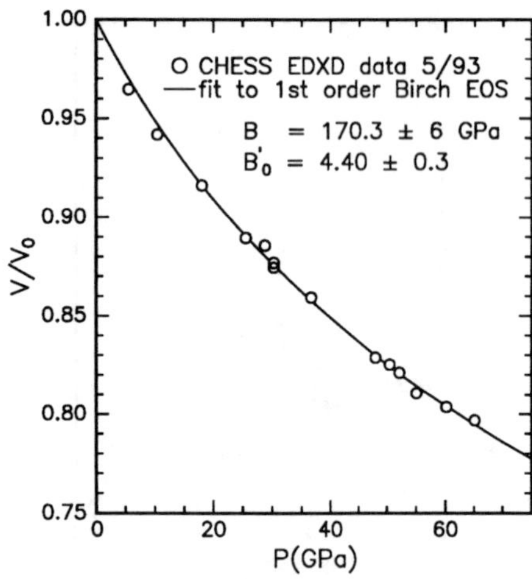

Figure 5: Diaspore EOS.

As an example $NaCl$ whose bulk modulus is only 25 GPa required an overpressure of 3.5 GPa at 298^0K and involves a thermally activated process with an activation energy of 0.055 eV [13].

If the activation energy required for the polymorphic transformation of diaspore scales with the bulk modulus, then the activation energy is estimated to be 0.37 eV and a very large overpressure would be required. Thus the equilibrium pressure could be at 60 GPa or lower.

If $AlOOH$ undergoes a transformation at 60 GPa to a phase which is 13% more dense and whose EOS is parallel to that of the extended diaspore EOS, the Gibbs free energy for the reaction (1) to this new polymorph will become negative at 155 GPa.

The conclusion is that further studies are needed before it is known whether the reaction in equation (1) can occur at high pressure.

SUMMARY

- No phase transformations to 65 GPa.
- Birch EOS parameters: B_0 = 170.3 ± 6 GPa, and $B'_0 = 4.40 \pm 0.3$.
- The hydrogen reduction of ruby at Mbar pressures requires a polymorphic transformation of diaspore to a denser phase.
- Raman and the OH vibron in particular are unsuitable as a diaspore marker at Mbar pressures.

ACKNOWLEDGMENTS

We would like to thank the National Science Foundation for its support through Grant No. DMR–89178831. Thanks also to A. J. Sievers for use of FTIR spectrometer, Maura S. Weathers of the MSC X-Ray Facility, Keith Brister of CHESS, and Angela M Ahern of ALCOA ATC.

REFERENCES

[1] A. L. Ruoff and C. A. Vanderborgh, *Phys. Rev. Lett.* **66**, 754 (1991).

[2] H. K. Mao, R. J. Hemley, and, M. Hanfland, *Phys. Rev. B* **45**, 8108 (1992).

[3] H. K. Mao, R. J. Hemley, and, M. Hanfland, *Phys. Rev. Lett.* **65**, 484 (1990).

[4] M. Hanfland, R. J. Hemley, and H. K. Mao, *Phys. Rev. B* **43**, 8767 (1991).

[5] R. J. Hemley, M. Hanfland, and H. K. Mao, *Nature* **350**, 488 (1991).

[6] Wyckoff, Crystal Structures vol. 1, pp 290

[7] W. B. White and R. Roy, *American Mineralogist* **49**, 1670 (1964)

[8] M. C. Stegmann, D. Vivien, and C. Mazieres, *Spectrochemica Acta* **29A**, 1653 (1973)

[9] H. K. Mao, J. Xu, and P. M. Bell, *J. Geophys. Res.* **91**, 4673 (1986)

[10] Dr. A. M. Ahern, ALCOA ATC

[11] R. Jeanloz and T. J. Aherns, *Geophys. J. R. astr. Soc.* **62**, 505 (1980)

[12] C. Meade and R. Jeanloz, *Geophys. Res. Lett.* **17**, 1157 (1990)

[13] X. Li and R. Jeanloz, *Phys Rev. B* **36**, 474 (1987)

PRESSURE-RAMAN STUDIES OF LAYERED ALUMINO-SILICATE COMPOUNDS

M. Holtz [1], S.A. Solin [2], and T.J. Pinnavaia [3]

[1] *Department of Physics, Texas Tech University, Lubbock, Texas 79409*
[2] *NEC Research Institute, 4 Independence Way, Princeton, New Jersey 08540*
[3] *Department of Chemistry, Michigan State University, East Lansing, Michigan 48823*

We have conducted pressure-Raman studies in order to understand the effects of structure on the vibrational properties of layered silicate materials. The basal oxygen torsional mode up-shifts with pressure at a rate which agrees with that expected from a van der Waals force model. The pressure coefficient of the hydroxyl stretching mode near 3600 cm^{-1} is found to have a structurally dependent *sign*, stiffening for trioctahedral structures, softening for dioctahedral silicates. This is found to be associated with hydroxyl orientation and coulombic repulsion between the hydroxyl proton and the interlayer cation.

INTRODUCTION

Layered silicates, or clays, possess structures in which multiple layers of cationic guests can intercalate relatively rigid monolayer hosts.[1,2] The complexity of the layered silicates is seen in Fig. 1, where we show a cut from a typical 2:1 layered silicate studied here. The 2:1 notation signifies that there are two layers which consist of tetrahedral silicate sheets sandwiching one octahedral sheet. Central to the tetrahedral layers are silicon or aluminum atoms, tetrahedrally bonded to four oxygens. Those oxygens which form the tetrahedral bases border the interlamellar gallery and are arranged in hexagonal rings which form a Kagomé lattice. In the central plane of each silicate layer resides an atom octahedrally coordinated to the oxygens which comprise the tetrahedron tips. In trioctahedral (*T*) silicates, all octahedral sites are filled, primarily with Mg^{++}. Dioctahedral (*D*) materials have only 2/3 of the octahedral sites filled, usually with Al^{3+}. The vacant octahedral sites of the *D* layer are situated above the hexagonal pocket in the basal Kagomé lattice. The oxygen situated above the hexagonal ring (*D* and T) is not shared with the tetrahedral layer. This oxygen is terminated with a proton, resulting in a hydroxyl group above Kagomé ring. The net negative charge on each unit cell (0 or $1e^-$) is balanced by the gallery cation in that cell. In the simplest picture, this cation nests below and above the hexagonal cavities and is surrounded by six basal oxygens and the hydroxyl group of each layer. The layers are typically 10-Å thick.

Only slow progress has been made in understanding the vibrational spectra of clays.[1,3,4] This is clearly due to the extreme complexity of the unit cell (22 and 23 atoms in the unit cell for *D* and *T* structures, respectively). We discuss here the application of pressure-Raman as a means of systematically studying key vibrational modes in clays.

EXPERIMENTAL DETAILS

The layered silicates reported on here are listed in Table I. All specimens were natural. Room temperature Raman spectra were generated using the 514.5-nm or 488.0-nm line of an argon ion laser. Scattered light was collected in the backscattering geometry and not polarization analyzed. Low-wavenumber spectra were collected using a triple-additive-dispersive Raman system. Light is detected using a cooled GaAs photocathode photomultiplier in the photon counting mode. High pressures were generated using conventional diamond anvil cell techniques[5]. Because the layered silicate Raman signals are weak, and to avoid confusion with the hydroxyl vibrations present in alcohols, we used KCl as pressure transmitting medium. Conditions within the cell remained nearly hydrostatic to over 30 kbar. Ruby fluorescence was used to measure the pressure.

TORSIONAL MODES

Raman spectra of dioctahedral margarite and muscovite are displayed from 0 to 150 cm^{-1} in Fig. 2. The 100-cm^{-1} lines, which are common to all these silicates, correspond to the torsional mode of the SiO_4 basal tetrahedra vibrating about the Si-O bond parallel to the c axis.[6] Neighboring tetrahedra in the hexagonal ring oscillate out of phase. Torsional mode frequencies and their pressure coefficients are presented in Table I for several compounds.

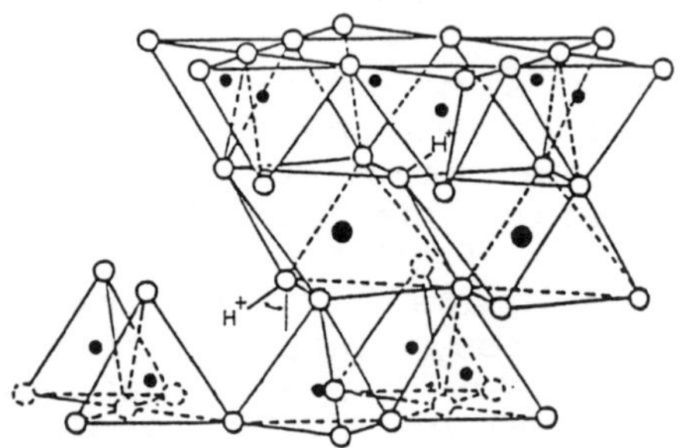

Figure 1. Typical structure of a 2:1 layered alumino-silicate compound.

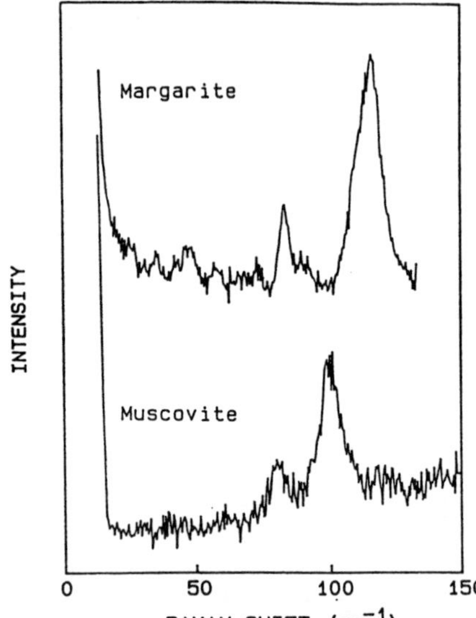

Figure 2. Detailed Raman spectra at 1 bar for margarite and muscovite.

Hydrostatic pressure provides a fairly complex deformation in these materials due to the variety of bond strengths present. The effect of compression along the ab directions will be to deform the weakest bonds (primarily), and alter the *orientations* of the molecular units. The static torsional angle of the SiO_4 tetrahedra, and their orientations relative to the crystalline c axis, will vary as pressure is applied. Despite these complexities, the effect of pressure on the torsional-mode frequency can be estimated using the model of Jiang, *et al.* [7]. This model accounts for van der Waals forces ($F \sim R^n$, $n = -7$) between neighboring oxygens in the basal Kagomé lattice, and between the cation and these same oxygen atoms. The lattice parameters are b, relevant to the basal O spacing, and h, the vertical distance from the cation center to the basal oxygen plane.

For muscovite, one of the best characterized silicates, h = 1.70 Å and b = 2.60 Å (Ref.8). Further, the elastic stiffness coefficients of muscovite have been measured using Brillouin scattering.[9] The expression for the vibrational energy ν(cm^{-1}) of the torsional mode is

$$\bar{\nu}^2_{TOR} = -\frac{2b^{n-1}}{m}\left(\frac{\alpha}{4\pi^2c^2}\right)\left[3+\gamma\left(1+\frac{h^2}{b^2}\right)^{\frac{n-3}{2}}\left(n+\frac{h^2}{b^2}\right)\right] \quad (1)$$

where m is the oxygen mass. α and β (< 0) are the attractive force constants between the oxygens and the oxygen-cation, respectively. $\gamma \equiv \alpha/\beta$, and n = 7 is the force-separation exponent.

Hydrostatic pressure will not simply alter the bond lengths in these systems. As the ab plane is compressed and the cation is simultaneously pushed up into the hexagonal pocket, the tetrahedra will rotate about the axis which is nearly parallel to the c axis (at P=0 this angle is approximately 11°, Ref.8). Furthermore, the tetrahedra will tilt. Taking these two effects to be small, the

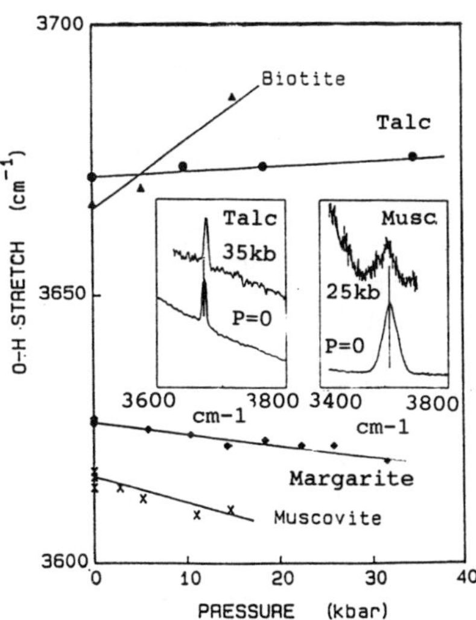

Figure 3. Pressure shifts for the OH stretching mode for four materials. Inset are spectra for the two structures.

relative pressure coefficient of the torsional mode can be expressed

$$\frac{1}{\bar{\nu}}\frac{d\bar{\nu}}{dP} = \frac{1}{\bar{\nu}}\frac{\partial\bar{\nu}}{\partial h}\frac{\partial h}{\partial P} + \frac{1}{\bar{\nu}}\frac{\partial\bar{\nu}}{\partial b}\frac{\partial b}{\partial P} \quad (2)$$

Using a c-axis compression modulus of 586 kbar,[9] the first term in Eq. 1 is -2 x 10^{-3} kbar^{-1}. The value of γ = 0.25 used here was found to be quite good in the case of vermiculite, which possesses a similar structure.[10] The second term in Eq. 2 is overall positive and estimated to be 5 x 10^{-3} kbar^{-1} using a Young's modulus of 90 kbar.[9] The net relative pressure shift of the torsional mode in muscovite is calculated to be 3 x 10^{-3} kbar^{-1}. This is to be compared with the experimental value of 8.6±2.0 x 10^{-3} kbar^{-1} from Table I. The agreement is acceptable, given the factors mentioned.

HYDROXYL STRETCHING MODE

In Fig. 3 we show Raman spectra of the O-H stretching mode for four silicates: talc and biotite (both *T*), and muscovite and margarite (both *D*). Representative spectra are shown under ambient conditions and under pressure. The hydroxyl stretching mode of both talc and biotite show weak, positive pressure shifts. Fits to our Raman-shift vs. pressure data are summarized in Table I. Stiffening under pressure is typical; the small magnitude is reasonable since the hydroxyl proton must be oriented toward the gallery in the direction of (but not directly toward) the cation.

The situation is surprisingly different for the two *D* micas, muscovite and margarite, where we observe weak *negative* pressure shifts. For these structures, the cations are nested deep into the hexagonal cavity with the oxygen atoms adjacent to the gallery in near contact. A plausible explanation for this pressure induced bond softening is arrived at by

TABLE I: Minerals studied, cation, and torsional and hydroxyl stretching mode frequencies.

Compound	ν_{TOR} (cm^{-1})	$d\nu_{TOR}/dP$ (cm^{-1}/kbar)	ν_{OH} (cm^{-1})	$d\nu_{OH}/dP$ (cm^{-1}/kbar)
Talc	111 ± 3	0.86 ± 0.05	3672 ± 1	0.11 ± 0.02
Biotite	-	-	3666 ± 5	1.3 ± 0.2
Phlogopite	104 ± 6	0.14 ± 6	3700 ± 2	-
Margarite	115 ± 5	0.07 ± 0.04	3625 ± 3	0.19 ± 0.03
Muscovite	100 ± 2	0.86 ± 0.20	3616 ± 2	-0.49 ± 0.09

supposing that the proton extends away from the cation, pointing instead toward the unoccupied octahedral site. This site is filled in *T* silicates, typically by Mg, which prevents the proton from orienting far from the c axis. Cation-proton coulombic repulsion would weakly soften the hydroxyl bond as pressure is applied to a *D* structure, stiffening it for the *T* systems.

The possibility of the hydroxyl orienting away from the interlamellar gallery has been discussed by several authors.[8] Infrared absorption measurements on single crystals of muscovite have yielded conflicting conclusions;[11] in all cases, the O-H transition moment makes a small angle with the ab plane, but the exact orientation of the hydroxyl group is difficult to determine. Giese performed electrostatic energy minimization calculations to predict the O-H orientation in muscovite.[11] This work relies on coulombic interaction of fixed lattice point charges to arrive at a bond angle of 8° from the ab plane. Using this, the cation-proton-oxygen angle (proton and oxygen of the hydroxyl) is acute (~82°). Compressing the cation-oxygen separation (along the c axis) would tend to repel the proton further from the oxygen for this *D* structure, supporting our interpretation of the pressure induced bond softening.

A detailed account of this work has been submitted to Phys. Rev. B.

ACKNOWLEDGMENTS: Work conducted at Michigan State University has been supported by NSF-MRG grant DMR 8903579, by the Michigan State University Center for Fundamental Materials Research, and by the NEC Research Institute.

REFERENCES

1. R.E. Grim, Clay Mineralogy, (McGraw-Hill, New York, 1968).
2. G.W. Brindley and G. Brown, eds., Crystal Structures of Clay Minerals and their X-Ray Identifaction, (Mineralogical Society, London, 1980).
3. M. Ishii, T. Shimanouchi, and M. Nakahira, Inorganica Chimica Acta **1:3**, 387 (1967).
4. S.A. Solin in Intercalation in Layered Materials, ed. by M.S. Dresselhaus (Plenum, NY, 1987).
5. B.A. Weinstein and R. Zallen in Light Scattering in Solids, ed. by M. Cardona and G. Guntherodt (Springer, Berlin, 1984), p. 463.
6. B.R. York, S.A. Solin, N. Wada, R.H. Raythatha, I.D. Johnson, and T.J. Pinnavaia, Sol. State Comm. **54**, 475 (1985).
7. H.X. Jiang, S.A. Solin, H. Kim, and T.J. Pinnavaia, Proc. Mat. Res. Soc., **111**, 225 (1988).
8. S.W. Bailey in Ref. 2, Ch. 12.
9. M. T. Vaughan and S. Guggenheim, J. Geophys. Res. **91**, 4657 (1986).
10. S.A. Solin, H.X. Jiang, H. Kim, and T.J. Pinnavaia, J. Raman Spect. **21**, 103 (1990).
11. R.F. Giese, Science **172**, 263 (1971).

ULTRAFAST SPECTROSCOPY OF TEMPERATURE AND PRESSURE JUMP AND SHOCK WAVES IN MOLECULAR MATERIALS

I-Yin Sandy Lee, Xiaoning Wen, and Dana D. Dlott
School of Chemical Sciences
University of Illinois at Urbana Champaign
Box 37-1 Noyes Lab
505 S. Mathews Avenue
Urbana, Illinois 61801

This paper discusses some dynamical aspects of shock wave excitation and shock wave induced chemical reactions in molecular materials. Just behind the shock front lies a zone of nonequilibrium material which is not in mechanical, thermal or chemical equilibrium. The thickness of this zone depends on the nature of the material. In order to obtain picosecond time resolution of the nonequilibrium dynamics, it is necessary to probe the behavior of the material behind the shock front with nanometer spatial resolution. Progress in understanding these issues and in fabricating and characterizing optical shock nanogauges is described here.

INTRODUCTION

Consider the shock wave shown in Fig. 1, passing through material at equilibrium, described by composition variable(s) χ_i, with pressure P_0, temperature T_0, and specific volume V_0. Far behind the front, the material is again in equilibrium, described by variables P_1, T_1, V_1, and χ_j. Behind the front lies a thin layer which is far from equilibrium[1,2]. Investigations of the properties of this interesting region constitute the field of *shock wave dynamics*.

In this paper we describe theoretical and experimental methods to study shock wave dynamics in molecular materials. The initiation of secondary explosives, which ordinarily consist of grains of organic molecular crystals and polymeric binders, is one specific practical application where the study of shock wave dynamics would be useful in understanding and controlling the sensitivity of energetic materials to shock excitation.

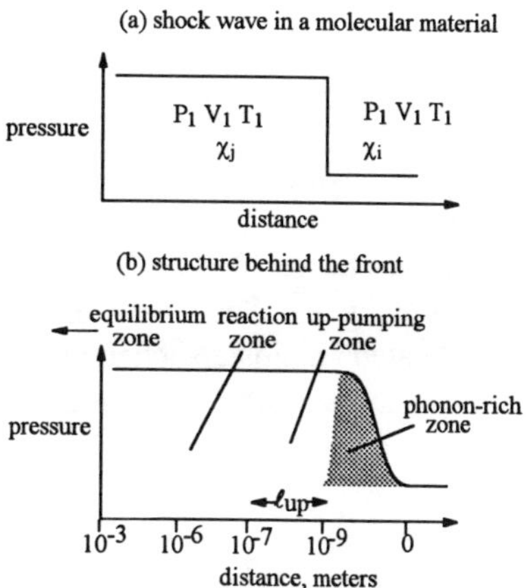

Figure 1. Structure of the nonequilibrium zone behind the front (adapted from [1]).

NONEQUILIBRIUM SHOCK LAYER

Pressure rise

When the shock front crosses a line of molecules, the pressure does not rise instantaneously. The finite rise time has been attributed to the finite viscosity of the material[3]. Here viscosity is used in an abstract sense[3] to mean the flow stress rate depends on the strain rate, as when, for example, plastic deformation occurs. Molecular dynamics simulations give a pressure rise time of picoseconds, corresponding to a layer a few nanometers thick, as shown in Fig. 1.

Temperature rise

The internal energy increase behind the front follows the pressure rise, but a thermal distribution is not obtained instantly. The shock wave excites phonons first[1], and later molecular vibrations become excited by multiphonon up pumping[1] (see Fig. 2). Up pumping occurs on the 10-100 psec time scale in large organic molecules in solids, corresponding to an up pumping zone thickness ℓ_{up} of a few hundred nm (e.g. see Fig. 3). Behind this zone, the material has a well defined temperature.

Chemical equilibrium

In systems which undergo chemical reactions, the attainment of chemical equilibrium behind the front can be far slower than the pressure or temperature rise. Secondary explosives undergo complicated multistep chemical reactions. The initial unimolecular bond breaking re-

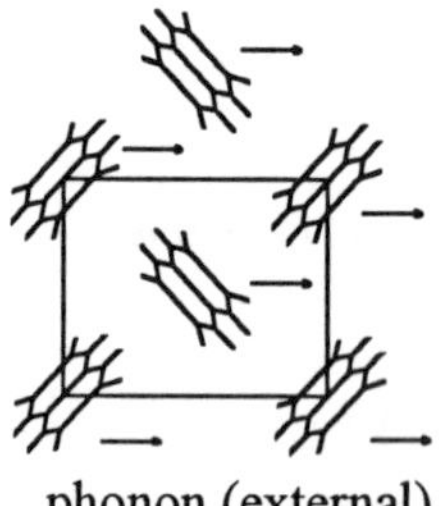

phonon (external) excitation

vibration (internal) excitation

Figure 2. Schematic diagram for multiphonon up pumping in a prototype molecule, naphthalene ($C_{10}H_8$). The shock wave initially excites lower frequency (0-140 cm^{-1}) modes termed phonons (left), which involve motions of whole molecules. Multiphonon up pumping subsequently excites molecular vibrations (right), which involve deformations of individual molecules. Vibrations must be excited before chemical reactions can occur.

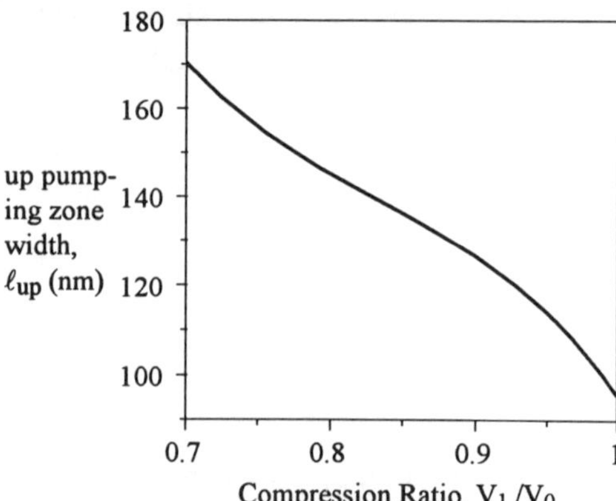

Figure 3. Computed width of up pumping zone versus compression ratio for crystalline naphthalene versus compression ratio, from ref. [1].

actions may be quite fast, but they are highly endothermic. Only a few of the subsequent bond making reactions are strongly exothermic. These provide the energy to drive sustained detonation waves. The exothermic reactions are the rate-limiting steps in detonations. These bimolecular, diffusion controlled reactions occur on the 10^{-8}-10^{-6} sec time scale, corresponding to a reaction zone of a few tens of μm to a few tens of mm, as shown in Fig. 1. (See [1] and references therein).

NANOSCALE SHOCK EXPERIMENTS

This discussion provides the motivation for developing techniques to probe shock wave dynamics with nanometer spatial resolution and picosecond time resolution. Unfortunately conventional optical probes of the shock wave are inadequate, since diffraction limits the attainable spatial resolution to a few μm. Our novel approach involves the use of optical nanogauges. A nanogauge is a nm-thick layer of material whose optical properties are sensitive to temperature and pressure.

Our system was designed with the following considerations:

(1) A planar shock wave should be reproducibly initiated by a picosecond optical pulse and

subsequently interrogated by a second optical pulse with variable delay.

(2) High repetition rate (ten per second) to obtain accurate time resolved data

(3) Shock target assembly readily and reproducibly fabricated with nanometer accuracy, from inexpensive materials which must be discarded after the experiment.

The system we have developed is shown in Fig. 4. The pressure window is a large (8" x 8" x 3/8") slab of float glass on a motorized assembly, which moves the target while the laser is pulsed. The shock wave is launched by optical heating of a confined metal foil[4]. The remainder of the target consists of several layers of polymers which are closely impedance matched.

Above the foil is a layer of 6.35 μm thick Mylar™ with an evaporated mirror layer of 500Å aluminum. On the Al mirror, we coat a 100 nm layer of polymer containing a substantial concentration of dye which acts as an optical thermometer and pressure transducer. A second layer of Mylar without aluminum is coated with another 100 nm layer containing a different dye. The assembly is covered with a 1/2" thick optical polymer pressure plate, and is tightly clamped by vacuum contacting.

The essential elements of this assembly are a pair of nanogauges backed by a thin mirror, with an accurately known 6.35 μm spacing, each containing a dye which absorbs in a different region of the visible spectrum. The progress of the shock wave between the two gauges is monitored by sending a picosecond white light pulse through a microscope, and reflecting it off the mirror, as shown in Fig. 4. After a double pass through the dye layers, the white light can be imaged into a video camera, or into a spectrograph, where shock-induced effects on the nanogauge spectrum can be analyzed.

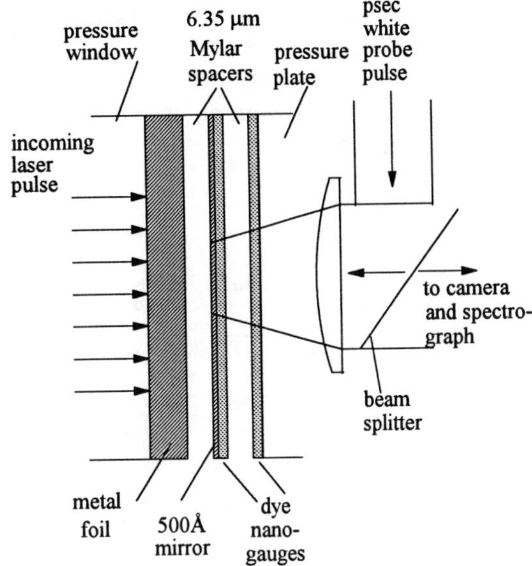

Figure 4. Schematic diagram (not to scale) of shock target assembly incorporating a pair of nanogauges with an accurately known separation of 6.35 μm.

PROPERTIES OF NANOGAUGES

We have used ultrafast spectroscopy to investigate some of the dynamical behavior of nanogauges consisting of a polymer, *poly*-(methyl methacrylate) (PMMA), doped with various dyes, including Rhodamine 6G (R6G). Pressure causes the R6G spectrum to red shift[5]. Temperature causes the spectrum to develop a hot band absorption on the red edge[6].

We find the PMMA and the dye in the nanogauge have a different response to instantaneous temperature and pressure jumps. For these studies, the PMMA was doped with a dye denoted IR-165, which functions as a molecular heater and a thermometer[6]. The dye is rapidly heated by the laser pulse. When the dye concentration is low, the dye cooling has little effect on the bulk material and the ultimate temperature jump $\Delta T \approx 0$. When the dye concentration is large, $\Delta T = 115°C$ and $\Delta P = 1.4$ kBar. In a detailed study (to be published in J. Chem. Phys.), we showed that the PMMA heats up in two stages. First the phonons, which account for 1/4 of the total heat capacity heat up, and then the vibrations, accounting for the remaining 3/4, heat up with an up pumping time constant of about 50 psec.

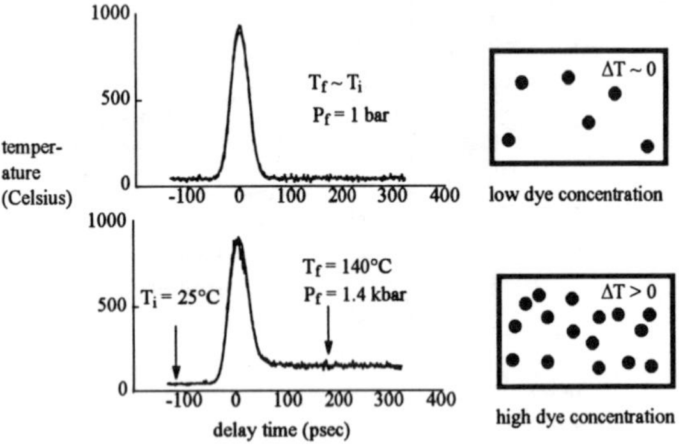

Figure 5. A dye in PMMA is heated by a 25 psec laser pulse and its temperature is optically monitored. At low dye concentration, the bulk temperature jump $\Delta T \approx 0$. At high dye concentration there is a large bulk temperature and pressure jump. The PMMA heats up in two stages...first phonons and then vibrations in 50 psec.

The behavior of the R6G dye in PMMA was also studied[6]. Figure 6 shows some data. The two solid curves represent the spectrum of the dye hot band absorption at the initial and final temperatures. This experiment provides informa-

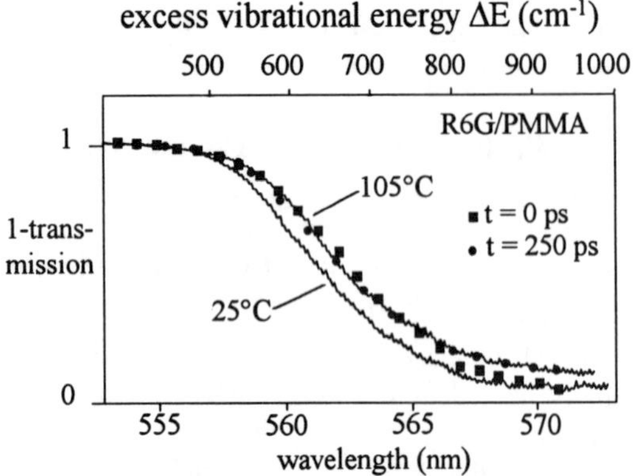

Figure 6. Time dependence of the R6G absorption in a PMMA nanogauge with an ultrafast temperature and pressure jump, compared to calibration curves obtained at the indicated temperatures (from ref. [6]).

tion about the time dependent populations of the R6G internal vibrations in the 500-1000 cm^{-1} range[6]. At time t = 0 (the peak of the heating pulse) the dye does not have a temperature. Instead there is an excess of vibrational excitation below 700 cm^{-1} and an excitation deficit above 700 cm^{-1}. The dye equilibrates at the new temperature of 105°C within about 250 psec. This type of experiment provides clear evidence for multiphonon up pumping in temperature and pressure jumped materials[6].

ACKNOWLEDGMENTS

Our research was supported by US Army Research Office grant DAAH04-93-G-0016, and National Science Foundation grant DMR-91-04130.

REFERENCES

[1] A. Tokmakoff, M. D. Fayer and D. D. Dlott, *J. Phys. Chem.*, 97, 1901 (1993).

[2] D. D. Dlott, "Ultrafast Vibrational Energy Transfer in Molecular Solids", in *Shock Compression of Condensed Matter 1991*, pp. 709-716.

[3] J. W. Swegle and D. E. Grady, *J. Appl. Phys.*, 58, pp. 692-701 (1985).

[4] P. E. Schoen and A. J. Campillo, *Appl. Phys. Lett.*, 45, pp. 1049-1051 (1984).

[5] X. A. Shen and Y. M. Gupta, J. Appl. Phys. 70, pp. 7549-7553 (1991).

[6] S. Chen, I-Y. S. Lee, W. A. Tolbert, X. Wen, and D. D. Dlott, *J. Phys. Chem.*, 96, pp. 7178-7186 (1992).

THE EFFECT OF LOW VELOCITY IMPACT ON VARIOUS INERT CRYSTALLINE SAMPLES

Diana L. Woody
Naval Surface Warfare Center
Silver Spring, MD 20903-5000
Jeffery J. Davis
The American University
Department of Physics
Washington, DC 20016

In this experiment, alkalide halide crystalline samples were subjected to low velocity impacts provided by a drop weight machine. A fast responding two color infrared detector system was used to image the light emissions from the impacted crystals. This information was used to approximate the temperature profiles of the impacted crystalline samples.

INTRODUCTION

Small scale impact tests were performed on three crystals to observe the result of low level impacts on crystals of varying material properties. The samples were subjected to similar impact velocities and therefore similar impact stresses. The crystals used were NaCl, KCl, and LiF. A two color infrared detector was used in this experiment to obtain a temperature profile of the crushing of the crystals during impact. The emittance from the impacted crystalline samples was analyzed with the InSb and HgCdTe detector elements. The detectors were calibrated before impact and this data of temperature vs emission for the detectors was used to determine the determine the temperature profile of the impacted crystals. The emission data and relative temperature profiles for the three crystalline samples are compared in this paper to the characteristic properties of the individual crystals. A correlation appears to exist between the energy release shown in the temperature profile of the sample and the shear modulus indigenous to the crystal. The impact stress experienced by each crystal was .034 GPa. Given a similar shear stress for each crystal, each crystals should undergo differing shear strains dependent upon their individual characteristics and modulus. Therefore, it appears that the temperature profiles observed by the two color detectors can give a ranking, at the very least, of the strain experienced by the crystal over the duration of the impact, heating of the solid, and relaxation of the crystal.

EXPERIMENT

The impact of the crystals was obtained with the use of an accelerated drop weight and impact machine. The impact machine consisted of an anvil, drop weight, base, and release triggering device. The impact machine is described in detail in another publication.[1] The drop weight used was .377 kg. The distance from the bottom of the drop weight to the anvil of the impact machine was 157 cm. This height corresponded to the free fall velocity of 5.5 m/s.

The drop weight was designed to allow it to be accelerated to high velocities. It was a hollowed out tube with an inner diameter of 2.99 cm, possessing two holes on the outer rim through which the guide rails were run. This allowed for guided impacts in which the face of the drop weight was flat against the sample face upon impact. The tilt of the drop weight was less than 2 mrads.

The sample was placed on a silicon anvil. The silicon anvil was capable of transmitting infrared emissions out to nine microns in the mid-infrared spectrum. The infrared transmission from the sample on the anvil was reflected by an Edmund Scientific gold front faced mirror, model # f32085 placed underneath the anvil, in the base, at a 45 degree angle to the anvil. The focusing lens was a Janos #A0707-112 barium fluoride infrared transmitting lens of diameter 2.5 cm. A two color infrared sensitive detector received the focused light. The experimental set up is shown in Fig. 1.

The Infrared Associates two color infrared detector consisted of a HgCdTe element and an InSb element. The InSb element was situated in front of the HgCdTe element so that the same area of flux of radiation was observed per element. Each element had dimensions of 0.101 cm by 0.101 cm with an active area of .010201 cm^2. The detectors were housed in a liquid nitrogen cooled dewar and kept at an operating temperature of 77 K. The InSb element's spectral response was from 1 μm to 5 μm. The HgCdTe element was capable of detecting wavelengths from 5.5 μm to 12 μm but was wavelength limited to 9 μm by the use of the silicon anvil.

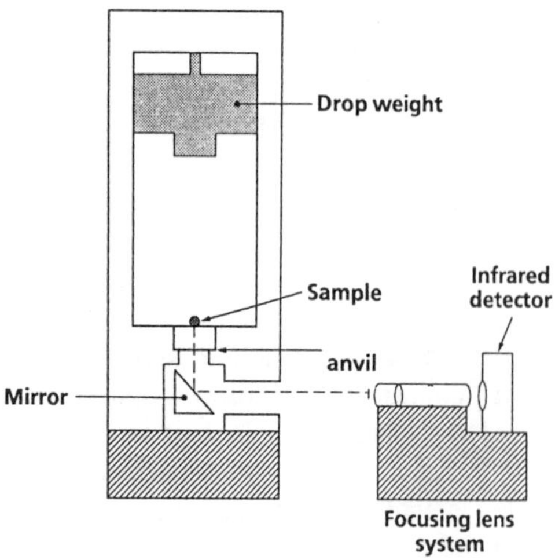

Figure 1. Experimental Setup

The signal from each infrared detector was transmitted in the form of a voltage through an initial voltage amplifier and transferred to a 9424 LeCroy digital oscilloscope to be stored and transferred to a computer for further analysis and image reconstruction.

RESULTS AND DISCUSSION

Figure 2 show the traces of the infrared emission measured as voltage vs time for the impact of the crystals. The ratio of the two emittance values observed by the InSb and the HgCdTe was used to obtain approximate temperatures over time for the impacted samples. Using the ratio of the two emissions eliminated the dimension factors since I = flux of radiation per unit area of source in Watts/cm^2.

A plot of temperature vs time for the three samples is shown in Figure 3. This gives an approximate temperature profile over time of the three crystals impacted at the same initial pressure of .034 GPa. The infrared emissions measured on the microsecond timescale represent the energy release history of the impacted crystal as the crystal is crushed. The temperature profile shows that the KCl crystal is generating more heat than either the NaCl or LiF impacted crystals. Ranking these crystals according to the temperature profiles would have KCl releasing more energy than NaCl and NaCl releasing more energy than than LiF. The ranking of the temperature profiles of the crystals appears to be inversely related to the shear modulus for each crystal as shown in Table 1.[2] The stress applied to each crystal during impact was similar. The temperature profiles appear to show a relationship between energy released upon impact and strain on the crystal and hence the strain energy in the crystal due to loading.

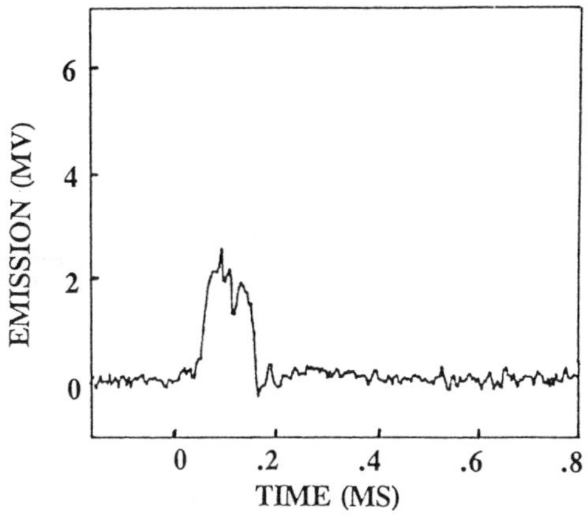

Figure 2a. Emission from KCl on HgCdTe

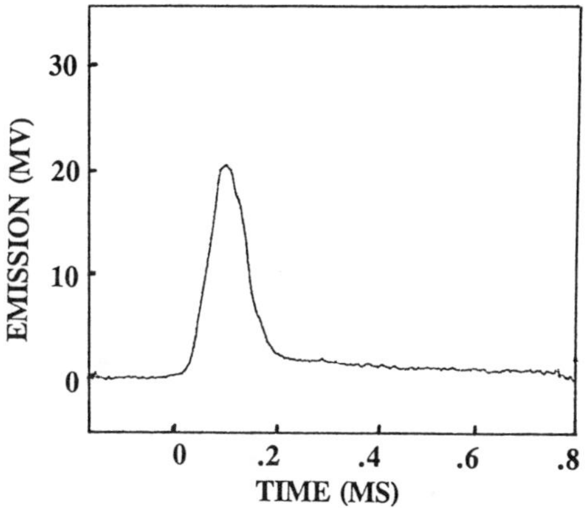

Figure 2b. Emission from KCl on InSb

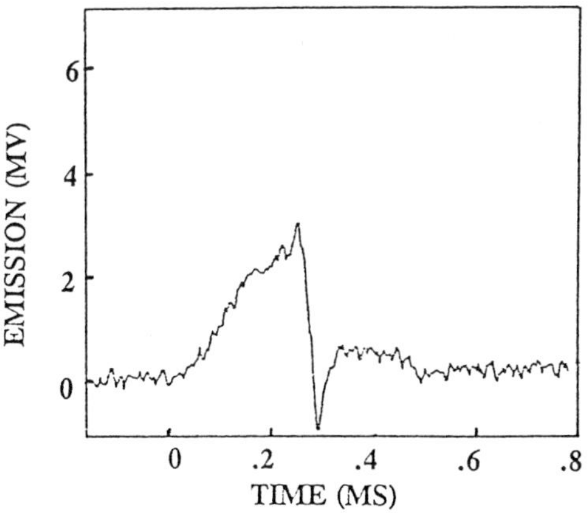

Figure 2c. Emission from NaCl on HgCdTe

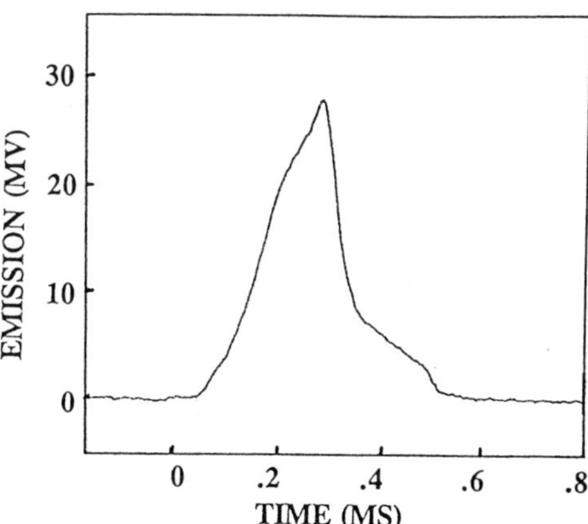

Figure 2d. Emission from NaCl on InSb

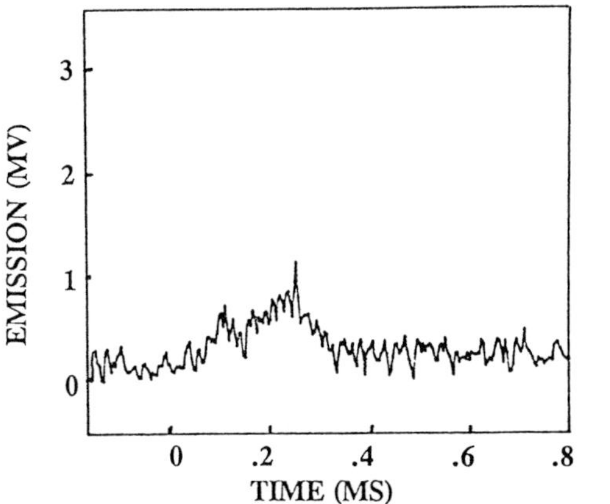

Figure 2e. Emission from LiF on HgCdTe

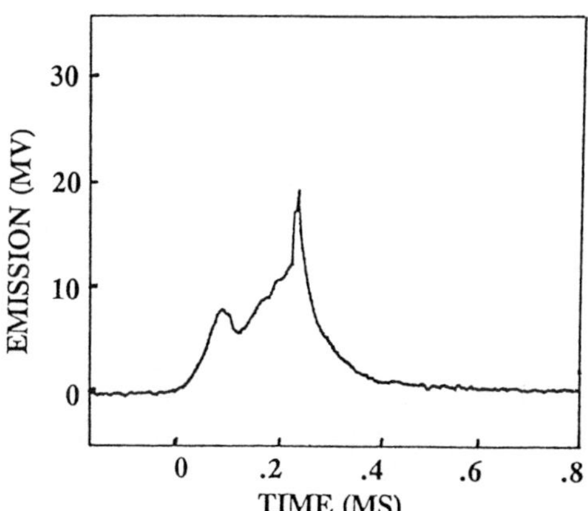

Figure 2f. Emission from LiF on InSb

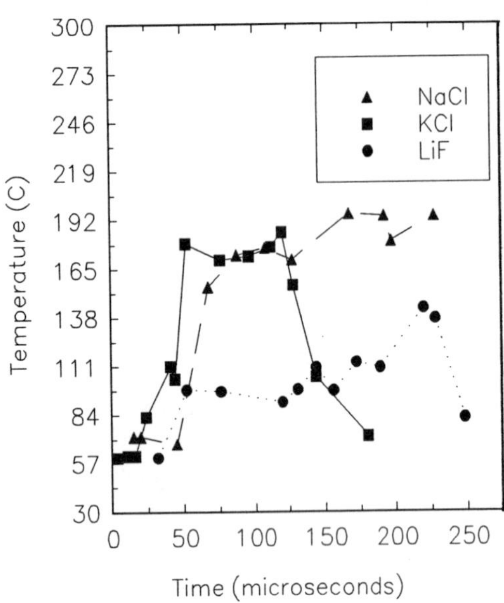

Figure 3. Temperature profile for impacted crystals

Table 1. Shear moduli of Crystals.

Crystal	G (10^{10} N/m^2)
LiF	5.3
NaCl	1.28
KCl	.62

CONCLUSIONS

The small scale impact test and two color detector system appears to be a possible means of obtaining information on the material properties of crystalline materials subjected to similar stresses. The temperature profile of the impacted energetic materials gives an indication of the behavior of the materials during impact. A relationship between the heating of the crystal and the strain in the crystal was observed. Further experiements will be performed in the future using the two color detector and Hopkinson bar apparatus to follow up on the relationship between strain and the temperature profiles.

ACKNOWLEDGMENTS

This research was performed under the sponsorship of the Independent Research program at the Naval Surface Warfare Center, Silver Spring Md.

REFERENCES

[1] C. S. Coffey; V. F. Devost; and D. L. Woody, "Towards Developing the Capability to predict the Hazard Response of Energetic Materials Subjected to Impact," in *Proceedings of the Ninth International Symposium on Detonation, 1989, pp 1243-1252.*

[2] C. Kittel, *Introduction to Solid State Physics*, New York:John Wiley & Sons,1956, ch. 4,pp. 93.

FREE-SURFACE LIGHT EMISSION FROM SHOCKED TEFLON

Kathleen G. Gallagher, Wenbo Yang, and Thomas J. Ahrens
Lindhurst Laboratory of Experimental Geophysics
Seismological Laboratory
California Institute of Technology
Pasadena, CA 91125

Shock initiated light emission experiments were performed on Teflon shock loaded to pressures up to ~17 GPa. Radiances up to 600 x 10^6W · m^{-2}/(ster · nm), were measured over a range of 390 to 820 nm. We have measured the spectra of light emitted upon reflection of the shock at the free surface and observed it to be distinctly non-thermal in nature. The light emission appears to result from bond destruction such as observed in shock recovery experiments on Teflon and in quasistatic experiments conducted on other polymers.

INTRODUCTION

Although shock wave propagation in polymers has been well studied [1-5], the light emission from shocked polymers has not. The equation of state of polytetrafluoroethylene (teflon) has been studied to 80 GPa by Morris et al. [2] and there is some evidence that other polymers exhibit breakdown into radicals upon shock loading and subsequent isentropic release. The present series of experiments was an exploratory study to try to understand the nature of the radiation emitted by shock loading a polymer. Three types of experiments were conducted.

The first type used high speed framing camera photography, to determine if photons were emitted as a result of shock-induced cracking or shear processes. This type of light emission was previously observed upon driving shock waves, with amplitudes in the ~ 10 GPa range, into crystalline and amorphous dielectric materials (e.g. NaCl, $CaCO_3$, and SiO_2 (amorphous and crystalline)) [6-10]. These experiments demonstrated that resulting irreversible deformation is largely localized about defects, giving rise to heterogenous optical radiation. The zones of high deformation which induce optical thermal radiation are called shear bands. These typically radiate as black bodies with temperatures constrained by the local melting point at the shock pressure achieved.

The second type of experiment was to determine when and where the radiation came from within the sample. The opacity of the sample at high pressure and the spectral radiance of the light emission were difficult to predict á priori, therefore, time-resolved streak camera imaging was conducted. Specifically, we wished to determine how close to the front surface of the sample the shock wave had to be before a measurable amount of light was emitted. We noted from one experiment that the absorption coefficient in the visible range for teflon was $\lesssim$10 mm^{-1}. The third type of experiment determined the nature of the spectrum of the emitted light. For this the spectrum was averaged in time over the entire light emitting event. However, we will show that the event was at most ~24 ns, so the average time was much smaller than the thermal diffusion time in teflon. Emission spectra can be used to determine whether or not radiation is thermal in origin, and if so, the temperature of the thermal radiation. For non-thermal radiation such spectra may be useful in identifying the source of characteristic radiation.

EXPERIMENT

The teflon (polytetrafluoroethylene) 12mm diameter extruded rod (Furon Corp., Anaheim, Ca.) had a bulk density of 2.171 ± 0.009 g/cm^3. The Archemedian density was 2.1678 ± 0.0074 g/cm^3.

Shock loading was conducted using impact of gun-launched 18 mm diameter 2.5 mm thick 304 stainless steel, tantalum and tungsten flyer plates at 1.25 to 1.74 km/sec inducing shock pressures of 8 to 17 GPa (Figure 1). Morris et al.'s data were used to calculate shock pressures using the impedance match method.

Three types of measurements were conducted to characterize light emission:

1. Framing camera imaging of light emission during shock propagation through samples 3 mm thick, was attempted. However, because of the ≤10 mm^{-1} absorbance (Figure 2) of samples, the duration of the observable flash was too short to easily capture it with 20 nsec exposures.

2. Streak camera imagery (Figure 3) conducted demonstrated that a highly visible flash occurred when shock arrived at the free surface. The 4.0 mm diameter circular image of the target observed was smeared in time by only ~0.5 mm. Using the 21 mm/μsec streak camera writing rate, implies a light flash duration of only ~24 nsec. Because the total shock propagation in the sample is 700-800 nsec, depending on shock pressure, the lack of observed imagery with the framing camera is explained

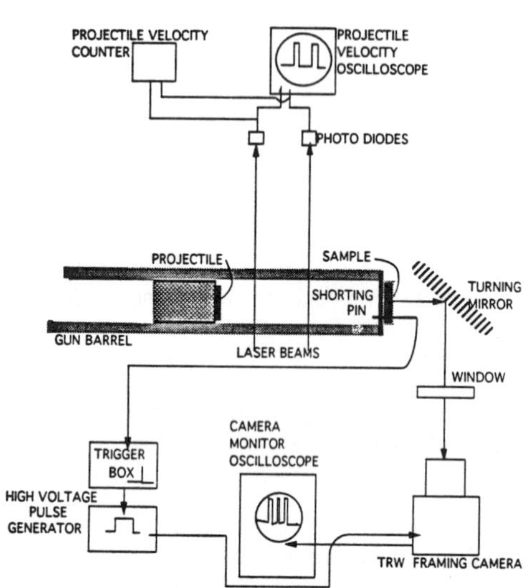

Figure 1. Experimental configuration for framing or streak camera recording of light emission from shocked teflon.

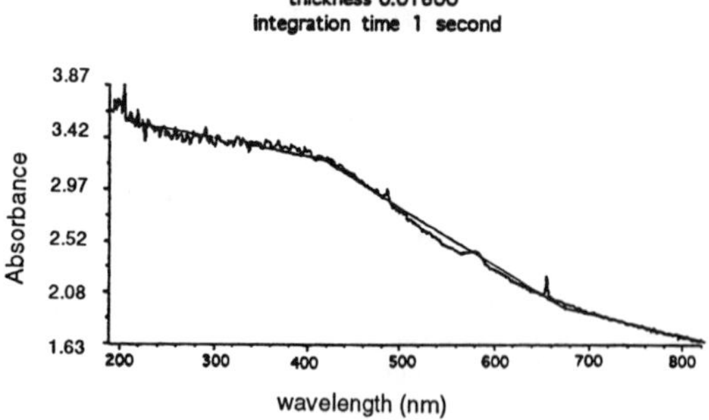

Figure 2. Absorbance versus wavelength for 0.34 mm thick teflon sample. Solid curve represents approximation used in calculations.

by the short light flash duration.

3. Optical multichannel analyzer recording of the spectra of the light emitted close to the time shock waves were internally reflected within the teflon samples. Notably, for one shot, when a steel shim was placed on the free surface of sample, essentially no light was recorded, demonstrating that the source of light was the sample and not shocked residual air in the vacuum chamber.

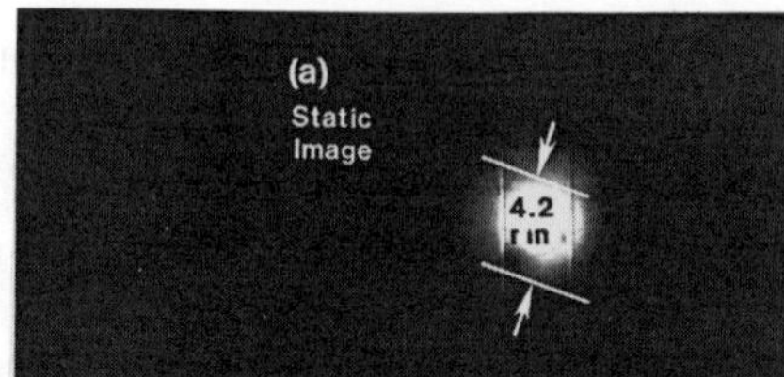

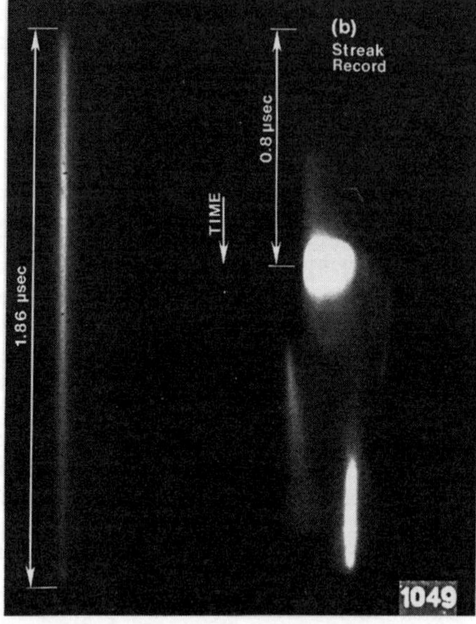

Figure 3. (a) Streak camera static image of 7.5 mm aperture in teflon shock experiment. (b) Streak camera record from Shot #1049 showing flash, corresponding to arrival of shock @ ~0.8 µsec.

RESULTS

In conducting the spectral analysis, we set the ~300 nsec time window of the pulse controlling the PARC optical multichannel analyzer instrument to be centered on the expected time of the shock arrival at the teflon free surface. The spectral analysis of the light emitted at the free surface was corrected for the attenuation of light due to the absorptivity of teflon, and then was fit to the Planck radiation law of the form:

$$R = \frac{\varepsilon C_1}{\lambda^5 \left(e^{C_2 / \lambda T} - 1 \right)}$$

where R is the spectral radiance, ε is emittance, T is temperature, λ is wavelength, and C_1 and C_2 are constants with values 1.191 x 10^{-6}Wm^2/ster and 0.01438mK. For shot number #1052 (Fig. 4) the best fit temperatures and emissivities are T = 5857K and ε = 1.17 x 10^{-6}.

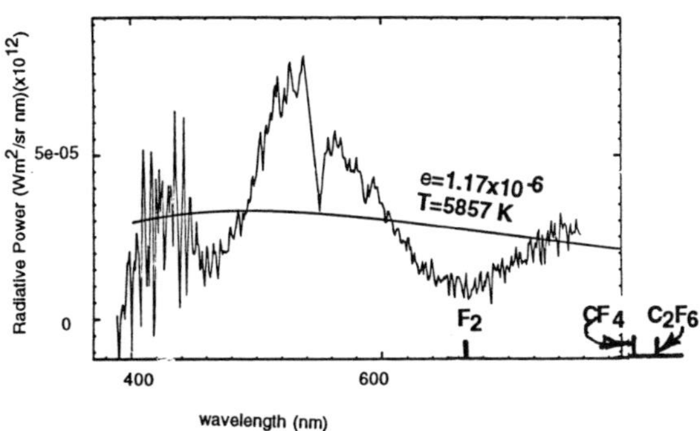

Figure 4. Absolute emission spectra from shot #1052, 15GPa. Parameters of fitted greybody curve is shown. The downward spike at 450nm is an artifact of the vidicon gating system. Vertical lines at lower axis represent expecter positions of spectral peaks from gaseous species.

For these values we assume that the emissivity is occurring over the entire 300 ns of the gate pulse of the PARC optical multichannel analyzer. This is an overestimate because the flash duration was shown in the streak experiment to be on the order of 30 nsec. Hence, the above values of ε should be corrected upward to as much as a factor of 10. Even allowing for this, the values of ε are still much less than unity. In addition, Morris et al. [2] estimated the values of the continuum shock temperatures in teflon shocked to 17 GPa to be only 800 K to 900 K, which is less than one sixth that inferred here even allowing the extremely untenable values of ε observed. For these reasons and the fact that the curve is not shaped so as to fit well to a Planck function lead us to the conclusion that the radiation is non-thermal.

DISCUSSION

Charged particle emissions from a wide variety of materials under a wide variety of conditions have been previously observed in both metallic and insulating elements, and both organic and inorganic, as well as polymeric dielectrics [11-13]. The conditions of observation were both plastic and brittle deformation, as well as both quasistatic and dynamic loading. The emissions have included both electrons and positive ions as well as photons ranging in energy from the optical (1 ev) range up to x-rays at 10^4ev.

In the case of teflon, dissociation appears likely as under quasistatic conditions, photodissociation has been observed upon heating to 10^3K. Shock recovery experiments reported by Morris et al. [2] indicate carbon is a residual phase with evidence of gaseous products including CF_4 and C_2F_6, as well as more complex species. Reactions among these species may induce some or all of the photons observed in the present experiments. Moreover, radiation from recombination of electron states in the solid state is observed upon quasistatic loading of polymeric substances such as polyethylenes. However, the gaseous species of elements and fluorine carbides all have ~5mm wide radiation bands, much narrower than ~50 - 100mm bands observed as in Figure 4. Also, none of the emission lines are consistant with the wavelengths of the observed radiation. Therefore, it is more probable that the radiation comes from the depolymerization of teflon into radicals. However, virtually all previous measurements of photon emission of deforming solids are less quantitative than the present study regarding both the photon flux and the energies of the photons.

ACKNOWLEDGMENTS

The experimental assistance of M. Long and D. Wickes and the helpful technical comments of Dr. L. Zernow are appreciated. The teflon sample material was donated by the Furon Corp., Anaheim, CA. Research was supported under ZSC-90-001-(3005), ARO-DAAL03-89-C-0005.

REFERENCES

[1] R.G. McQueen, S.P. Marsh, J.W. Taylor, J.N. Fritz and W.J. Carter, in *High-Velocity Impact Phenomena*, R. Kinslow (eds.), Academic Press, New York, 1970, p 249-419.

[2] C.E. Morris, J.N. Fritz and R.G. McQueen, *J. Chem. Phys.*, 80, p 5203-5218 (1984).

[3] A.R. Champion, *J. Appl. Phys.*, 43, p 2216-2220 (1972).

[4] L. Davison and R.A. Graham, *Phys. Rep.*, 55, p 255-379 (1979).

[5] R.A. Graham, *J. Phys. Chem .*, 83, p 3048-3056 (1979).

[6] D.E. Grady, *J. Geophys. Res.*, 85, p 913-924 (1980).

[7] K.-I. Kondo and T.J. Ahrens, *Phys. Chem. Minerals*, 9, p 173-181 (1983).

[8] D.R. Schmitt and T.J. Ahrens, *J. Geophys. Res.*, 94, p 5851-5871 (1989).

[9] D.R. Schmitt, T.J. Ahrens and B. Svendsen, *J. Appl. Phys.*, 63, p 99-106 (1988).

[10] D.R. Schmitt and T.J. Ahrens, *Geophys. Res. Lett.*, 10, p 1077-1080 (1983).

[11] S.C. Langford, J.T. Dickinson and L.C. Jensen, *J. Appl. Phys.*, 62, p 1437-1449 (1987).

[12] V.A. Zakrevskii and V.A. Pakhotin, *Sov. Phys. Solid State*, 20, p 214-218 (1978).

[13] A.G. Lipson, V.I. Berkov, V.A. Klyuev and Y.P. Toporov, *Sov. Tech. Phys.*, 12, p 536-537 (1987).

WINDOW PROBLEM AND COMPLEMENTARY METHOD FOR SHOCK-TEMPERATURE MEASUREMENTS OF IRON

Ken-Ichi Kondo
Research Laboratory of Engineering Materials
Tokyo Institute of Technology
4259 Nagatsuta, Midori,
Yokohama 227, Japan

Emission from the window material of sapphire was determined by a 512-channel pyrometer and a single channel photo-diode from 15.6 to 84.7 GPa. The data reveal a constant emission temperature of 4930 + 470 K with an emissivity which changes monotonically with the increase of pressure and are attributed to triboluminescence with a long decay time. The characteristics of sapphire are applied to both the absorptive and the emissive corrections of the published shock temperatures of iron.

INTRODUCTION

Experimental determination of the shock temperature of materials is one of the important tasks to confirm the equation of state (EOS) of solids at high pressures and high temperatures, because most of the EOS parameters are based on the steady-flow equation and the heat equation of some models. We must, therefore, attempt to obtain independently shock temperatures as well as the other efforts, e.g. flash X-ray diffraction for specific volume under shock loading [1,2].

Shock-temperature measurements have been carried out mainly by time-resolved or short-period-integrated spectral radiance pyrometry of which data are fitted to a grey-body spectrum. The fitting is based on the assumptions that an emission temperature is in equilibrium with a shock temperature and that an emissivity is independent of wavelength. Kirchhoff's low is applied to partially transparent reflecting bodies, and, for opaque bodies, an indispensable window requires additional assumptions and supporting physical data for both the analyses of the spectrum and the interface condition.

Since the shock temperatures and the melting temperatures of iron and iron alloys are essentially important for earth science, many investigators have tried to measure those temperatures and to resolve many problems which were fairly addressed by Nellis and Yoo [3]. The purpose of this paper is to propose the additional complementary method for shock temperature of opaque materials such as iron on the basis of the shock-induced emission spectra from sapphire which is often used as a window.

EMISSION FROM SAPPHIRE

Experimental arrangement was the same as the previous experiments for minerals or fused quartz [2,4-6]. Shock-induced radiance was dispersed from 400-nm to 700-nm wavelength by a spectrometer and was accumulated for 300 ns as 512 channel discrete signals by a spectral multichannel analyzer. Sensitivity for spectral radiance was calibrated for both of wavelength and gating time by using a calibrated standard lamp. A single channel of the avalanche photodiode (APD) circuit was used for obtaining a time-resolved intensity change of emission without filter.

The sapphire samples used were of stock commercial grade for optical elements, having a diameter of 20 mm and a thickness of 3 mm. The sample and a copper-driver plate were cemented by epoxy resin. The cemented side of the sample surfaces had been coated by evaporated silver in advance, in order to prevent a strong emission at the interface from superimposing into the emission from the sapphire [4]. The sample assembly was impacted by a tungsten or copper flyer plate accelerated by a two-stage light-gas gun. Emission from the aggregate of sapphire powder was also determined by the sample assembly similar to the diamond powder experiments [6].

Figure 1 shows a typical example of the emission spectrum and the intensity change at a pressure of 84.7 GPa. The spectral radiance is in good agreement with the greybody spectrum at a temperature of 5060 K and a emissivity of 0.074. All of the other data are fitted to a greybody very well and result in the high color-temperatures with low emissivity in contrast to the continuum temperatures, as shown in Figure 2. The brightness temperatures shown are obtained by integrating the spectral radiance over the observed region of wavelength with the emissivity of unity. The color temperatures obtained are almost constant in spite of the increase of pressure and are averaged to be 4930 ± 470 K, while the brightness temperatures monotonously increase with the increase of pressure and are different from the case of fused quartz in which shock-induced triboluminescence quickly falls in the local thermodynamic equilibrium in the hot shear bands [5].

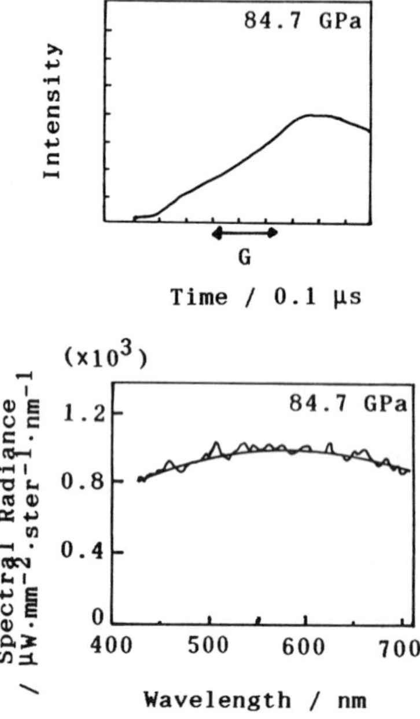

Figure 1. Emission Spectrum and intensity change for the sapphire at a shock pressure of 84.7 GPa.

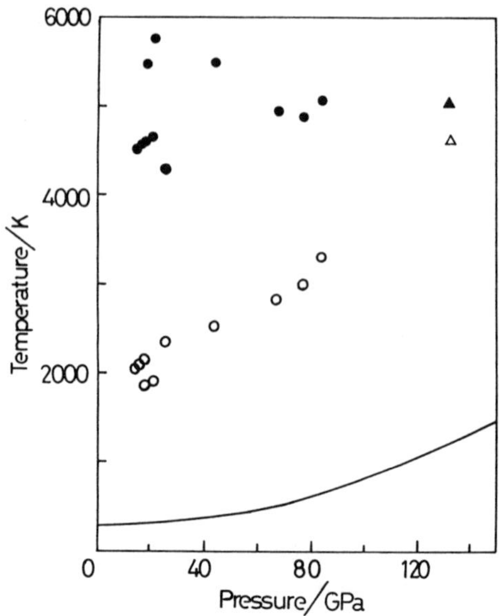

Figure 2. Color temperature (solid circle) by fitting of the emission to the greybody and brightness temperature (open circle) for the sapphire as a function of shock pressure. Triangle denotes the published data with the same meaning for Ag film with sapphire window [9].

All the data of intensity change are likely to be linear or concave with the increase of time and clearly shows no interface contribution. When the elastic and plastic arrives at the free surface, no fluctuation happens, and the emission still increases along the same tendency for a certain duration after that time. The shock temperatures of silver are low enough not to contribute to the observed. The pattern is in good agreement with the case of a sufficient absorptivity in the shocked region and a finite absorptivity in the unshocked region, or the case of a sufficiently small absorptivity in the shocked region [7]. However, the former case can be excluded in case of sapphire, and the latter is inconsistent with the concave pattern. The pattern can be explained *via* a hot shear band model whose width slightly increases with time, but the color temperatures are much higher than the melting temperature of sapphire. These imply that the emission occurs neither in thermal equilibrium at the shear band nor spontaneously at a shock-wave front. Another possibility is triboluminescence with a long decay time and is supported by the increase of emission at the post shock state.

Figure 3 shows the spectrum from the powder sample at a shock pressure of 23 GPa and is consistent with 4790 K-greybody radiation. However, many band-type spectra are evidently superimposed. This implies that the defect and trap levels are formed between the bad gap and intensified by crushing of particles. In conclusion, the emission from sapphire attributes to triboluminescence having a long decay time.

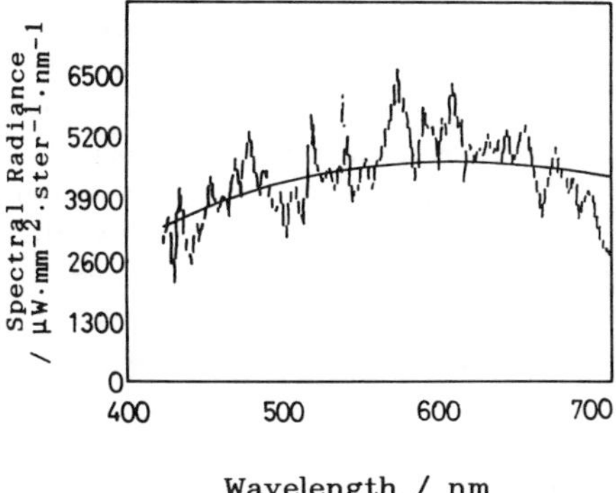

Figure 3. Emission Spectrum from sapphire powder at a shock pressure of 23 GPa.

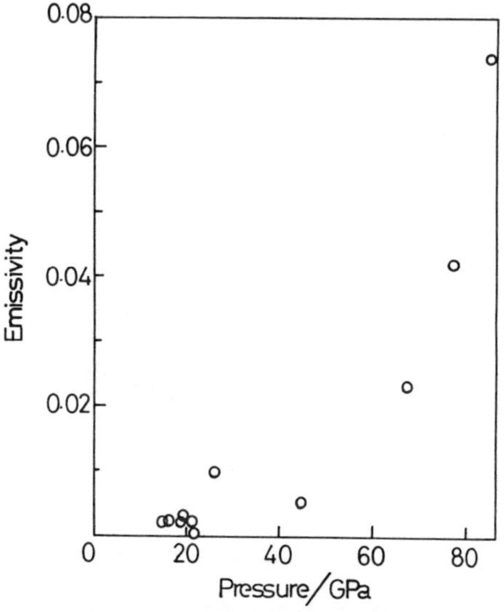

Figure 4. Changes in emissivity of sapphire as a function of shock pressure.

The emissivity obtained by the greybody fitting of the spectrum is shown in Figure 4 as a function of shock pressure and is extrapolated along some fitted curves into the higher pressure region, as shown in Figure 5. The parabolic function has the best correlation coefficient of 0.944 and is expressed as follows:

$$e = -2.48 \times 10^{-3} + 8.50 \times 10^{-6} P^2 \text{ (in GPa)}.$$

Although the emission data obtained are in the limited pressure region, the characteristics of sapphire can be extrapolated to a certain region because of both the unchangeable spectrum and the monotonous change in emissivity.

COMPLEMENT OF IRON DATA

Optical properties of window materials at megabar shock pressures have not been investigated in details,* but both optical opacity and nonthermal emission in the window can introduce systematic errors into the temperature determined by emission spectra. As shown above, a many kinds of defect and trap levels by which continuous spectrum is emitted are apparently created in the intrinsic band gap of sapphire under shock loading even in case of window. The excited electrons screening of thermal photon from the interface between a metal film and a window would result in lower estimation of the radiative brightness (i.e., emission temperature). However, since the ob-

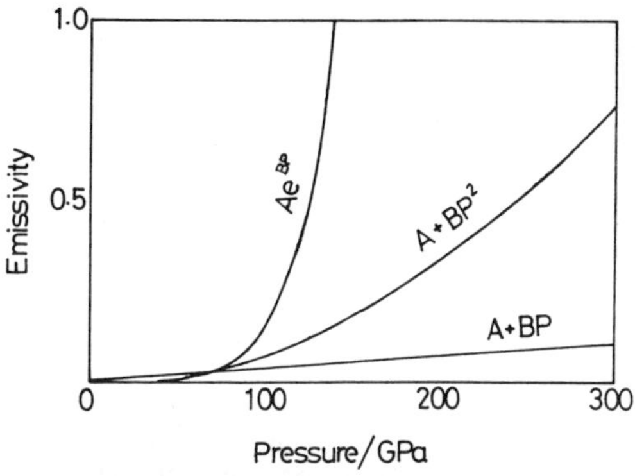

Figure 5. Extrapolated changes in emissivity of sapphire as the functions of shock pressure fitted to the observed.

served emission temperature strongly depends on the spectrum form rather than brightness, wavelength dependence of the screening leads to an serious error which results in a higher or lower estimation dependent on absorption spectrum. If we can tentatively assume that the wavelength-dependent absorption coefficients of sapphire are the same as those of the emission, the published iron data [8], for an example, an emission temperature of 6240 K with an emissivity of 0.33 can be compensated to be 5940 K with an emissivity of 0.52 as shown by the absorption correction spectrum in Figure 6. In the case, the electrons should be excited to and trapped at the defect levels in the observed time.

On the other hand, if sapphire can emit nonthermal radiation without interaction with thermal photons from the interface, this luminescence increases the radiative intensity and also modifies the spectrum form. Subtracting the radiance simply from the observed spectrum, the published emission temperature can be compensated to be 7030 K with an emissivity of 0.15. In the case of the interface temperature lower than or comparable to the emission temperature of sapphire, the temperature, 4750 K with an emissivity of 0.29 [8], is inversely corrected to be 4840 K with an emissivity of 0.49 and 3850 K with an emissivity of 0.13 for the absorptive correction and the emissive one, respectively.

In conclusion, even though the temperature of a window is low enough, optical properties of a window under shock loading strongly modify not only the brightness but also the spectrum and seriously decrease the reliability of the shock temperature determined. The continuous emission from sapphire like a greybody radiation implies that there exist both the numerous defect and trap levels and the complicated relaxation process of the excited electron. It is, therefore, that the absorptive process may be dominant in a sapphire window, though it is necessary to measure magnitude of the absorptivity which may be larger. To increase the reliability of the shock temperature, a theoretical model for emissivity is essentially required.

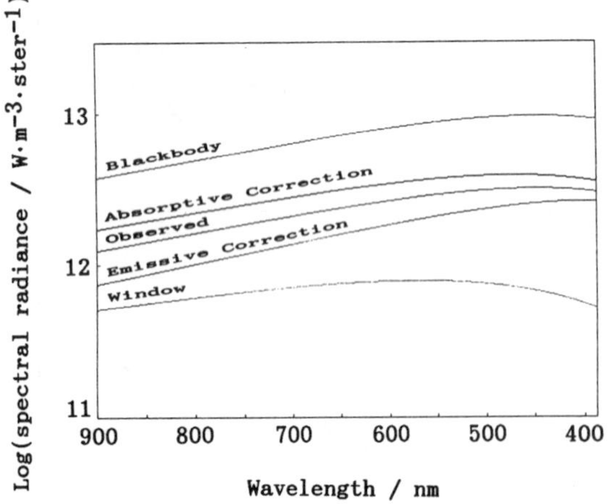

Figure 6. Spectral radiances from the sapphire window and the interface between the iron film and the window versus wavelength. The observed spectrum can be modified by the blackbody and the both of absorptive and emissive corrections of window.

ACKNOWLEDGMENTS

The author are grateful to Mr. T. Hiramatsu of Asahi Glass Co., and Dr. T. Taniguchi of Nat. Inst. Lab. Inorganic Materials for their help.

REFERENCES

[1] K.Kondo, A.Sawaoka, and S.Saito, in *High Pressure Science and Technology, vol 2* , New York, Plenum, 1979, pp.281-284.

[2] K.Kondo and T.J.Ahrens, *Phys. Chem. Minerals*, 9, 173-181 (1983).

[3] W.J.Nellis and C.S.Yoo, *J. Geophys. Res.*, 21, 749-752 (1990).

[4] K.Kondo, T.J.Ahrens, and A.Sawaoka, *J. Appl. Phys.*, 52, 4382-4385 (1983).

[5] K.Kondo and T.Hiramatsu, in *Recent Trends in High Pressure Research*, New Delhi, Oxford & IBH Publ., 1991, pp.863-865.

[6] K.Kondo, *High Pressure Res.*, 10, 747-757 (1992).

[7] M.B.Boslough, *J. Appl. Phys.*, 58, 3394-3399 (1985).

[8] T.J.Ahrens, H.Tan, and J.D.Bass, *High Pressure Res.*, 2, 145-157 (1990).

[9] G.A.Lyzenga, in *Shock Waves in Condensed Matter-1981*, New York, Am. Inst. Phys., 1982, pp.268-276.

THE UV / VISIBLE ABSORPTION SPECTRA OF SHOCKED NITROMETHANE - AMINE MIXTURES

C. P. Constantinou and Y. M. Gupta
Shock Dynamics Centre
Washington State University
Pullman WA 99164-2814
USA

Time-resolved optical absorption spectroscopy has been used to examine the response of a mixture of nitromethane with ethylenediamine (0.1% by weight) to stepwise shock compression up to a pressure of 14 GPa. Unlike pure nitromethane, the mixture shows an irreversible time-dependent shift in the absorption edge of up to 100 nm towards longer wavelengths. This provides evidence for the chemical nature of the mechanism by which nitromethane is sensitized in the presence of amines.

INTRODUCTION

Time resolved spectroscopy provides a direct probe for obtaining information on shock induced chemical changes in condensed phase materials.[1] Among energetic materials, nitromethane is well suited for achieving this goal. It is liquid and therefore largely homogeneous. Its physical state consequently makes it possible to isolate chemical effects in the interaction of a shock wave with condensed matter; it also has the added advantage of variable sensitivity in the presence of amines.[2]

The decomposition of nitromethane in the gaseous phase is known to involve unimolecular breakage of the C-N bond.[3] Constantinou[4] has previously obtained evidence that the decomposition of liquid nitromethane at ambient pressures follows a cubic autocatalytic process that involves a nitromethane molecule reacting with a methyl radical and nitrogen dioxide.

The sensitization of nitromethane by amines has been a subject of study for many years.[2,5,6] The decomposition of nitromethane-amine mixtures has been examined under ambient conditions.[4] It was found that the reaction proceeds in two stages; the relative exothermicity of these reaction stages depends on the amine concentration. The first stage in the reaction was determined to be governed by unimolecular decay of a charge-transfer complex formed between nitromethane and the amine.

In our work, we seek to obtain information on the chemical behaviour of pure and sensitized nitromethane under shock conditions and relate these, if possible, to decomposition studies under ambient conditions.[4] In this paper we report on measurements of the near-UV and visible absorption spectrum of a mixture of nitromethane with ethylenediamine (0.1% wt.) during dynamic compression up to pressures of 14 GPa. We discuss our findings in comparison with the corresponding measurements on pure nitromethane.[7]

EXPERIMENTAL METHODS

Spectrophotometric grade nitromethane and ethylenediamine, both of 99+% purity, were supplied by Aldrich Chemical Company. Nitromethane was used as received. The amine was purified in the laboratory by double distillation and was always used freshly distilled.

The experimental arrangement is described elsewhere.[7] Essentially in every experiment, we are obtaining a series of 50 absorption spectra, each separated by a 50 ns time interval, while the sample undergoes stepwise shock compression.

The sample is loaded in a liquid cell through a stainless-steel capillary tube. The cell consists of two optical windows and a cylindrical brass housing. C-cut or a-cut sapphire disks,[8] supplied by Union Carbide, are used for the front and the back window. Two different types of liquid cells were used in the work reported here. In the reverberation experiment, the back sapphire window is 12.5 mm thick. This ensures that the pressure in the portion of the sample that is under observation will remain constant until the experiment is terminated by rarefaction waves originating from the lateral boundaries of the cell. In the pressure reversal experiment, the back window is made thin (1.5 or 2mm) so that the plane rarefaction wave arising from the free interface at the rear, can travel back to the sample and rapidly reduce its pressure prior to the arrival of lateral rarefraction waves.

During shockup, and also pressure release in the unloading experiment, the variation of pressure with time can be calculated by successive applications of the shock jump conditions or with a one-dimensional wave propagation code. All such calculations used an equation of state for nitromethane that is still under development in our laboratory,[9] and a material model describing the elastic response of sapphire.[8] The calculated peak pressures should be accurate to within 1-2%. Using the same equation of state, sample temperature values could also be calculated, as a function of time, during shockup. Because reliable methods do not exist to measure shock temperatures at these pressures, it is difficult to ascertain the accuracy of the temperature calculations.

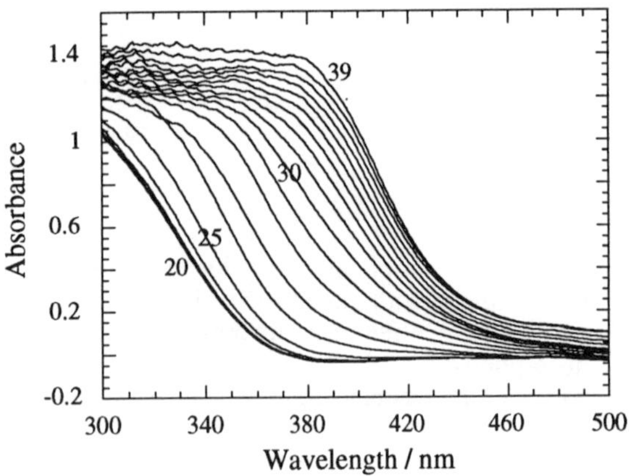

Figure 1. The absorption spectrum of nitromethane - ethylenediamine (0.1 %wt.) while it is being shocked to 13.5 GPa. Only tracks 20-39 are shown.

RESULTS

The UV / visible absorption spectrum in nitromethane consists of two broad bands: a π-π^* transition centred around 220 nm and an n-π^* transition around 275 nm. In this work only the latter band could be probed.

In a series of thin cell experiments the sample thickness was limited to below 20 µm in order to enable monitoring of the whole of the absorption band. These experiments showed that during shock compression the band appears to broaden and extend towards longer wavelengths. No newly appearing bands could be resolved. These data support the procedure used to analyse the thick cell experiments discussed here.

The thick cell experiments employed a sample thickness of around 150 µm. Such experiments were carried out at peak pressures in the range 10 - 14 GPa. In these thick cell shots only the long wavelength band edge of the 275 nm band could be resolved. Figure 1 depicts the behaviour of this band edge as a sample of nitromethane - ethylenediamine (0.1% wt.) was shocked to a peak pressure of 13.5 GPa. Successive spectra are separated by 50 ns time intervals. In this experiment, seventeen transmission spectra were taken prior to impact and another six spectra were recorded while the shockwave traversed the front window and before it entered the liquid sample. These twenty-three transmission spectra (tracks 1-23) gave identical absorbance spectra.

Among them, only tracks 20-23 are shown in Figure 1. The shockwave entered the liquid between tracks 23 and 24. As seen from Figure 1, once the shockwave started to propagate in the liquid, the absorption edge shifted consistently towards longer wavelengths and continued to shift until the experiment was terminated.

A relative shift in the absorption edge was calculated for each of the thick cell experiments as follows. For each track, the absorption edge and the background absorbance were fitted with a straight line. The intersection of these two lines was taken as an indication of the relative position of the absorption edge. A plot of the measured absorption edge shift as a function of time, for the shot discussed above, is shown in Figure 2. When the shockwave enters the liquid, the absorption edge begins to shift slowly towards longer wavelengths. The shift subsequently accelerates and finally reaches a plateau, all during the observation time window of the experiment. Figure 3 shows the corresponding shift in the absorption edge for a sample of pure nitromethane being shocked to a peak pressure of 14.3 GPa. On each of these two plots we have also shown the calculated variation in the sample pressure. It is important to note that as the pressure rings up with each reflection of the shock wave, so does the sample temperature. The peak temperatures achieved in these two experiments were calculated as 592 and 605 K, respectively.

It is clear from Figures 2 and 3 that there is a significant difference in the behaviour of the nitromethane - ethylenediamine (0.1% wt.) mixture as

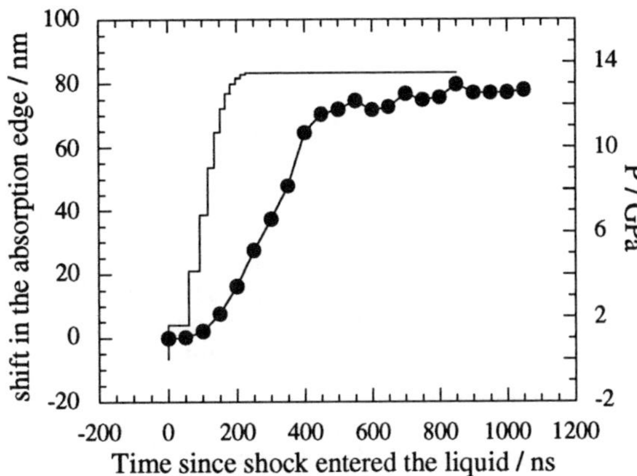

Figure 2. The variation with time of the shift in the absorption edge (points) and the sample pressure for nitromethane - ethylenediamine (0.1% wt.) shocked to a final pressure of 13.5 GPa. The calculated peak temperature was 592 K.

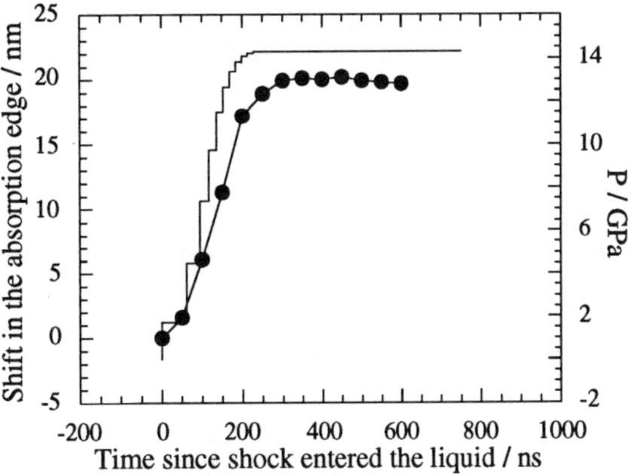

Figure 3. The variation with time of the shift in the absorption edge (points) and the sample pressure for pure nitromethane shocked to a final pressure of 14.3 GPa. The calculated peak temperature was 605 K.

compared to that of neat nitromethane. In nitromethane there is a total shift in the absorption edge of 19.5 nm at 14.3 GPa. This appears to be pressure induced and is expected to be completely reversible upon unloading.[7] Once peak pressure is reached, there is no further shift in the absorption edge. In contrast, the nitromethane-amine mixture shows a substantially larger shift (80 nm at 13.5 GPa), most of which takes place after maximum pressure is reached (at approximately 200 ns in Figure 2). The nitromethane-amine mixture displayed this type of time-dependent behaviour down to a peak pressure of 10 GPa. This time dependence in the absorption edge shift exhibited by the nitromethane-amine mixture, is attributed to a chemical change. Under these conditions, pure nitromethane appears to remain chemically stable when shocked up to a pressure of 14 GPa.[7]

Pressure reversal experiments have also been carried out on the nitromethane-amine mixture at peak stresses of 13.8 and 9.8 GPa in order to determine whether the time dependent shifts in the absorption edge are reversible. It is evident from these experiments that stresses above 10 GPa cause irreversible changes in the UV/visible absorption spectrum of the nitromethane-amine mixture. In contrast, stresses up to 14 GPa cause no permanent changes to the absorption spectrum of pure nitromethane.

DISCUSSION

Despite the small amine concentration employed in this work, profound differences are observed between the absorption spectra of pure and sensitized nitromethane. Unlike pure nitromethane, the mixture shows an irreversible time-dependent shift in the absorption edge of up to 80 nm towards longer wavelengths. A substantial component of the shift takes place after the sample has reached a peak pressure greater than 10 GPa. This time dependent red-shift is indicative of a chemical change and it confirms the chemical nature of the mechanism by which nitromethane is sensitized in the presence of amines.[2]

For both pure and sensitized nitromethane, the thick cell experiments show a shift in the absorption edge which is sigmoid in shape as a function of time. The final absorption edge shift is dependent on the maximum pressure. In the case of pure nitromethane the whole of the shift is induced by the change in thermodynamic state which is caused by the reverberation of the shockwave inside the sample cell. The final plateau in the shift in the absorption edge is obtained when and because the sample pressure and temperature have arrived at their constant final values. This plateau is reliably observed for around 500 ns in these experiments. This places a lower limit on any induction time for chemical reactions in nitromethane under stepwise loading to 14 GPa.

In the case of the nitromethane-ethylenediamine (0.1% wt.) mixture, the shift in the absorption edge is dependent on pressure, temperature and time, and its final value is much higher than that displayed by pure nitromethane under the same loading conditions. The time-dependent part of the shift results from a chemical change. This is supported by the pressure reversal thick cell experiments which show that the shift is partially irreversible. The fact that the shift reaches a plateau towards the end of the experiment indicates that the observed chemical change comes to an end within the time window of the experiment.

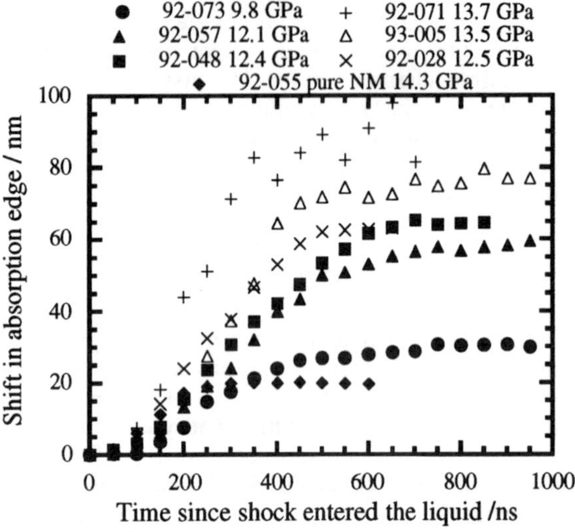

Figure 4. The variation with time of the shift in the absorption edge from six reverberation experiments on nitromethane - ethylenediamine (0.1% wt.) and one experiment on pure nitromethane(NM). The peak pressure for each experiment is indicated.

The final value of the shift is again pressure dependent. Figure 4 shows the shifts in the absorption edge obtained in five separate experiments on sensitized nitromethane and one experiment on nitromethane. It will be seen that in all cases sensitized nitromethane gave rise to a larger final shift than pure nitromethane shocked to 14.3 GPa. In the sensitized nitromethane, as the final pressure is changed from 9.8 GPa to 13.5 GPa the final shift in the absorption edge changes from 30 to 80 nm, in each case reaching a plateau well before the experiment is terminated but a considerable time after peak pressure is reached. The variation in the final shift in the absorption edge with maximum pressure constitutes evidence that the reaction under observation remains incomplete.

CONCLUSION

A time-dependent irreversible change has been observed in the absorption spectrum of a mixture of nitromethane with ethylenediamine (0.1% wt.) when it is shocked to a pressure of at least 10.0 GPa. In contrast, pure nitromethane shows only completely reversible changes in its spectrum when shocked to 14.0 GPa. The spectral changes in the nitromethane-amine mixture were attributed to a chemical change. The observation confirms the sensitization of nitromethane in the presence of amines.

ACKNOWLEDGEMENTS

We thank G. I. Pangilinan and M. Winey for discussions. D. Savage and K. Zimmerman are gratefully acknowledged for expert technical assistance with the experiments. This work was supported by ONR Grants N00014-90-J-1400 and N00014-93-1-0369.

REFERENCES

[1] Y. M. Gupta, High Pressure Research 10, pp. 717-732 (1992).

[2] C. P. Constantinou, T. Mukundan and M. M. Chaudhri, Phil. Trans. R. Soc. Lond. A 339, pp. 403-417 (1992).

[3] P. Gray, A. D. Yoffe and L. Roselaar, Trans. Faraday Soc. 51, pp. 1489-1497 (1955).

[4] C. P. Constantinou, Ph.D. Thesis, University of Cambridge (1992).

[5] R. Engelke, Phys. Fluids 23, pp. 875-879 (1980).

[6] M. D. Cook and P. J. Haskins, "Chemical Sensitization of Nitrocompounds," in Proceedings of the 19th International Annual Conference of ICT on Combustion and Detonation Phenomena, 1988, pp. 85.1-85.8, Karlsruhe, Germany.

[7] J. M. Winey, Y. M. Gupta and K. G. Casey, "Shock-induced changes in the absorption spectrum of nitromethane," in these Proceedings.

[8] L. M. Barker and R. E. Hollenbach, J. Appl. Phys. 41, pp. 4208-4226 (1970).

[9] G. Duvall, Washington State University, unpublished.

SHOCK-INDUCED CHANGES IN THE ABSORPTION SPECTRUM OF NITROMETHANE

J. M. Winey, Y. M. Gupta, and K. G. Casey
Shock Dynamics Center
Washington State University
Pullman, WA 99164-2814

Electronic changes in pure nitromethane under shock compression have been examined using UV/VIS absorption spectroscopy. The redshift of the band edge located near 300 nm was measured in multiple-shock experiments for peak pressures to 14 GPa. At this pressure, all observed changes are fully reversible. Lithium fluoride has been introduced as an optical window, producing a higher shock temperature for a given pressure. This configuration exhibited an increased band edge shift when compared to an all-sapphire cell.

INTRODUCTION

Spectroscopic techniques have been shown to be a useful method for probing molecular-level changes in shock-compressed materials [1,2]. This paper describes the application of one of these techniques, UV/VIS absorption spectroscopy, to study the behavior of energetic materials under shock compression. It is part of a larger effort involving both absorption and Raman spectroscopy.

As a prototype material, we have chosen nitromethane (NM) because of its relative structural and chemical simplicity, its accessible electronic [3] and vibrational [4] transitions, and its insensitivity to mild shocks [5] (i.e. safety in handling). Our objectives in this work were to determine the threshold pressure at which we could observe chemical reaction, to observe the electronic behavior prior to the reaction, and to observe the effects of shocking to different pressure-temperature states.

EXPERIMENTAL METHODS

The experimental configuration used in this work is similar to that used to study carbon disulfide [6]. Therefore the experimental details will be discussed only briefly.

Figure 1 shows the impactor and the cell assembly. The impactor was c-cut or a-cut sapphire [7]. The NM sample was contained between two optical windows. The back window was sapphire of the same crystal orientation as the impactor. The front (impact side) window was either sapphire or [100] oriented LiF [8]. Typical thicknesses were 1.27 cm for the impactor and back window, 3.175 mm for a sapphire front window, 3.0 mm for a LiF front window, and .15 mm for the NM sample. The NM thickness was kept small to provide good spatial resolution.

Upon impact, a shock wave is launched into the front window. After the shock enters the liquid, peak pressure is attained through a reverberation process as shown in Figure 2. The final pressure and temperature depend on the

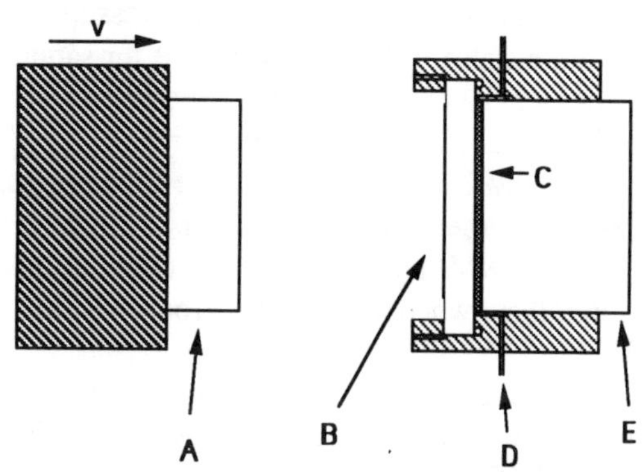

Figure 1. Sample cell and impactor assembly. A) sapphire impactor, B) sapphire or LiF front window, C) NM sample, D) fill tubes, E) sapphire back window

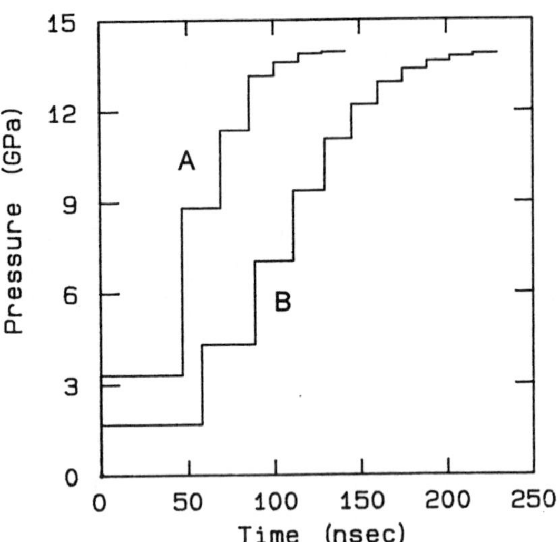

Figure 2. Calculated pressure-time history for a 150 micron thick cell. Time zero is when the shock first enters the liquid. Curve A has a LiF front window and reaches a final state of P=14 GPa and T=695K. Curve B has a sapphire front window and reaches a final state of P=14 GPa and T=586K.

projectile velocity and the material properties of the windows.

In order to access different pressure and temperature states, LiF was substituted for sapphire as a front window in some of the experiments. Due to its low impedance relative to sapphire, the LiF causes the NM to ring up to the same final pressure in fewer reverberation steps. This results in a higher final NM temperature, for a given peak pressure, than when a sapphire front window is used.

The pressure and temperature histories for both front windows of the cell were calculated using SHOCKUP [9], a program which does impedance-matching calculations using the shock jump conditions. This code uses an equation of state for NM which is still under development in our laboratory [10]. Early results of these calculations are shown in Figure 2. Note that the temperature of the LiF cell relative to the sapphire cell is the significant result rather than the absolute temperature of either one.

Calculations using the same equation of state were also performed using COPS [11], a 1-D wave propagation code. These calculations were used to account for wave interactions in the design of cells for unloading experiments. These cells were similar to the previously mentioned cells except that the back window was thin (typically 1.588 mm). Thus, the shock wave would reflect off the sapphire free surface and propagate back into the NM, resulting in a release of pressure.

The shock-induced changes in the absorption spectrum were recorded by sending the light from a xenon flash lamp through the shocked liquid. The collected light was dispersed in wavelength by a spectrometer, dispersed in time by an electronic streak camera, and recorded on a vidicon detector. The result was a set of transmission spectra, each taken 50 ns apart.

The experiments focused on the 270 nm band of NM which is the $n\pi^*$ transition on the nitro group [3]. Because of the thickness of the cell and the limited dynamic range of our detector, the absorption measurements saturated for wavelengths in the vicinity of the peak. Our analysis was therefore restricted to the band edge on the red side of the peak.

In collecting data, a reference spectrum, a background spectrum, and a shot spectrum were recorded. These were then used to calculate absorbance through a simple application of the Beer-Lambert law. The band edge location was then determined by fitting straight lines to the band edge and to the baseline. The intersection of these two lines was taken to be the position of the band edge.

RESULTS

Five samples of NM were shocked to peak pressures ranging from 10 GPa to 14 GPa. The effect of the pressure increase was to shift the absorption band edge toward the red. Figure 3 shows the results of these experiments for both LiF

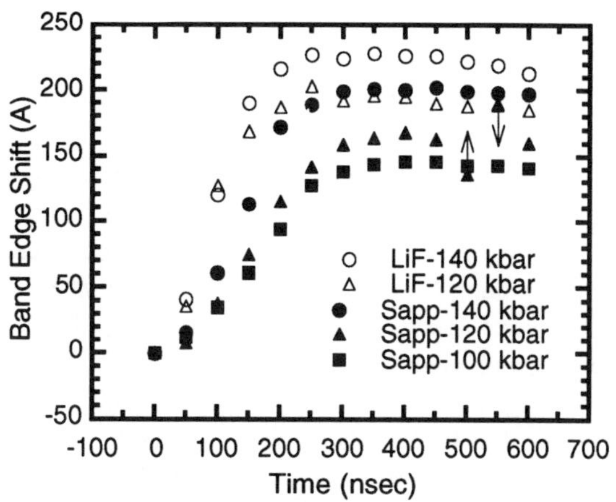

Figure 3. Band edge shift as a function of time. Time zero is when the shock enters the liquid. In the 120 kbar sapphire experiment, the two data points (solid triangles) marked with arrows are out of position due to detector artifacts.

and sapphire front windows. No data are shown for times later than 600 ns after the shock enters the liquid. After this time, the impactor becomes opaque due to the arrival of waves from the edges of the sapphire.

The experiments with the LiF window showed a larger rate of shift with time than those with the sapphire window. This is to be expected since the rate of pressure increase is also higher in the LiF cell. The LiF cell also reached a higher final value of edge shift. This is presumably due to the higher final temperature.

The data for all five experiments show that the edge shift reached a plateau when the pressure and temperature reached their final values. This suggests that no irreversible chemical change was occurring since that would lead to changes in the spectrum even after the final pressure and temperature were reached.

To further examine the reversible nature of the band edge shift, an unloading experiment was performed. If the shift was of a physical origin (a pressure effect only), then the band would return to its original shape and position upon unloading. If it was a chemical change, then the changes in shape and position of the band would be irreversible.

The unloading experiment was carried out with a NM sample that was 22 microns thick to allow a shorter ring-up time. The sample would then be at peak pressure for a longer time before the arrival of the release wave from the back window. Figure 4 shows three absorption spectra corresponding to several times during the experiment. The data clearly show that the spectral changes are indeed reversible.

SUMMARY

We have introduced LiF as a window material in absorption spectroscopy experiments under shock conditions. This has allowed us to access different regions of pressure-temperature space by making only minor changes in the experimental configuration.

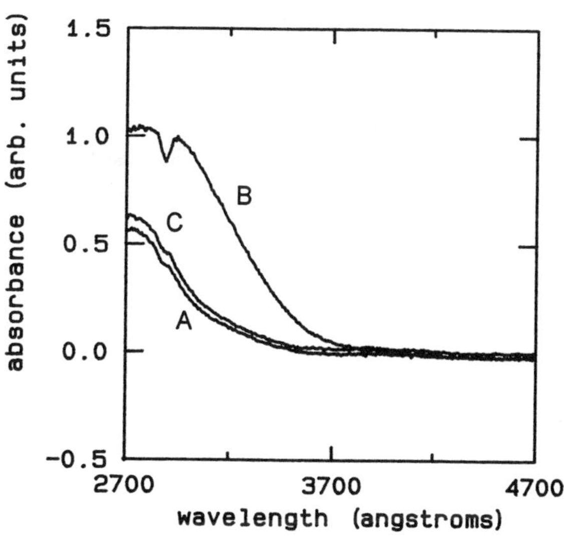

Figure 4. Absorbance spectra for different times during the experiment. Spectrum A: before the shock enters the liquid. Spectrum B: while the NM is at peak pressure. Spectrum C: after the NM has unloaded to ambient pressure. The sharp feature at 3000 angstroms in spectrum B is an artifact from the xenon flash lamp.

The five experiments shown in Figure 3 have demonstrated that the shift of the band edge is a function of shock pressure. Specifically, the data show that higher pressures produce larger shifts. However the fact that the LiF cells produced a larger shift than the sapphire cells, for a given pressure, leads to the conclusion that the shift is a function of shock temperature as well.

We have also shown that NM displays no evidence of chemical reaction under stepwise loading to 14 GPa. This is indicated by the fact that the absorption spectrum showed no change after the final pressure and temperature were reached. Confirmation is provided by the unloading experiment which showed that the band edge shift was fully reversible at 14 GPa.

We are presently performing experiments at higher peak pressures to determine the threshold pressure and temperature for reaction in NM and to probe the early stages of reaction.

ACKNOWLEDGMENTS

Dave Savage, Paul Bellamy, and Kurt Zimmerman are all thanked for their able assistance in performing these experiments. This research was supported by ONR Grants N00014-90-J-1400 and N00014-93-1-0369.

REFERENCES

1. Y. M. Gupta, *High Press. Res.*, 10, pp. 717-732 (1992)

2. Y. M. Gupta, "Progress in Understanding Shock Deformation in Condensed Materials at the Atomic/Molecular Level: Recent Experimental Developments", in *Shock Compression of Condensed Matter 1991*, Amsterdam, Elsevier Science Publishers B. V., 1992, pp. 15-26

3. S. Nagakura, *Mol. Phys.*, 3, pp. 152-162 (1960)

4. J. R. Hill, D. S. Moore, S. C. Schmidt, and C. B. Storm, *J. Phys. Chem.*, 95, pp. 3037-3044 (1991)

5. M. D. Cook and P. J. Haskins, "Chemical Sensitization of Nitrocompounds", in *Proceedings of the 19th International Annual Conference of ICT on Combustion and Detonation Phenomena*, 1988, pp. 85.1-85.8

6. C. S. Yoo and Y. M. Gupta, *J. Phys. Chem.*, 94, pp. 2857-2865 (1990)

7. Union Carbide, Inc., Washougal, WA

8. Solon Technologies, Inc./Harshaw, Solon, OH

9. Ogilvie, K. M., G. E. Duvall, and R. Collins, (Washington State University, 1984), unpublished

10. Duvall, G. E., unpublished

11. Gupta, Y. M., (Stanford Research Institute, Menlo Park, CA, 1978), unpublished

SHOCK INITIATION OF NITROMETHANE

C.S. Yoo and N.C. Holmes
Lawrence Livermore National Laboratory
Livermore, California 94551

The shock initiation processes of nitromethane have been examined by using a fast time-resolved emission spectroscopy at a two-stage gas gun. A broad, but strong emission has been observed in a spectral range between 350 nm and 700 nm from the shocked nitromethane above 9 GPa. The temporal profile suggests that the shocked nitromethane detonates through three characteristic periods, namely an induction period, a shock initiation period, and a thermal explosion period. In this paper we will discuss the temporal and chemical characteristics of these periods and present the temperature of the shock-detonating nitromethane at pressures between 9 and 15 GPa.

INTRODUCTION

In homogeneous high explosives like nitromethane the detonation is believed to occur by thermal explosion at the rear boundary;[1-3] that is, rapid exothermic reactions which feed the energy into the shock front and increase the temperature and pressure. This chemical energy brings the unreacted high explosive at the shock front to a substantially higher thermodynamic state, the von-Neumann spike, from which the chemical reaction takes place to a steady detonation state, the C-J state. The energetics of these processes are relatively well known in many explosives, including the spike and C-J conditions, detonation wave velocity, and material velocity. However, the chemistry of these processes is not well known at the molecular level. For example, it has not been understood how the shock compressed explosive initiates the chemical reaction and evolves into the detonation products like graphite, H_2O, CO, CO_2, etc.

A reasonable approach to obtain an insight of the shock initiation and detonation of high explosives is time-resolved spectroscopy which can directly probe the chemical species and their changes in time. In this paper we report the results of emission studies of shock compressed nitromethane.

EXPERIMENTS

Figure 1 depicts three schematics of the emission experiments of shock-detonating nitromethane showing the target design and various shock states. The nitromethane is contained in a 6 mm-thick cavity between an Al base plate and a sapphire window. The impactor is also made of aluminum and is accelerated to a velocity 2-3.2 Km/s using a 2-stage gas gun. The impedance matching technique using the Hugoniot of Al[4] and Mie-Gruneisen equation of state for nitromethane[5] was used to obtain the thermodynamic state of shock compressed nitromethane.

Emission from the shocked and detonating nitromethane is time-resolved in a direction parallel to the shock propagation. An optical fiber bundle is used to collect the emission from a small central area of the sample where the shocked state is well defined in one-dimension and, thus, provides fast time resolution that primarily depends on the rise time of the recording electronics. Time and spectral resolution of the system are approximately 1 ns and 2 nm, respectively. The detailed description of the system can be

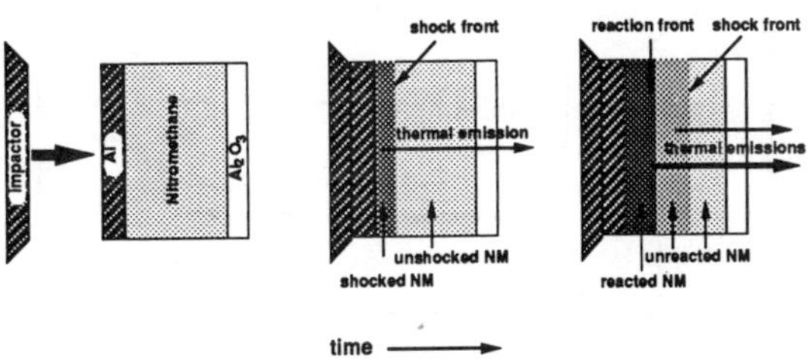

Fig 1. Schematics of the emission experiment of shocked nitromethane showing a target design and shock states.

found elsewhere.[6]

Three instances are shown in the figure: (a) prior to the instant of impact, (b) after the impact but prior to thermal explosion, and (c) after thermal explosion. The shock temperature of nitromethane at 10 GPa is estimated to be approximately 1000 K. The thermal explosion temperature of nitromethane is estimated to be over 3000 K. Based on black-body radiation the emission intensity at 1000 K is roughly six orders of magnitude less than that at 3000 K in the spectral region between 350 nm and 700 nm where the emission spectrum is recorded in this study. Therefore, thermal emission of shocked, but unreacted nitromethane is negligible.

Nitromethane has an absorption band above 300 nm, peaking at 270 nm. The pressure dependent shift of this band is estimated to be rather small, less than ~2 nm/GPa.[7] This means that both shocked and unshocked nitromethane are optically clear in a spectral range between 350 nm and 700 nm, as far as they remain unreacted. On the other hand, the reaction products of shocked nitromethane such as carbon particles and graphite are believed to be optically thick due to absorption and scattering.[8] Assuming no reactions of the shocked nitromethane prior to thermal explosion this experiment should monitor the emission coming from a thin layer at the reaction front, and its temporal change should represent the chemical evolution of shocked nitromethane at the reaction front. However, we will see that neither is the reaction front optically thick, nor the shocked nitromethane is chemically inert or optically transparent. The emission characteristics are rather complicated by the initiation process of shocked nitromethane, which occurs prior to the thermal explosion and strongly depends on time and pressure.

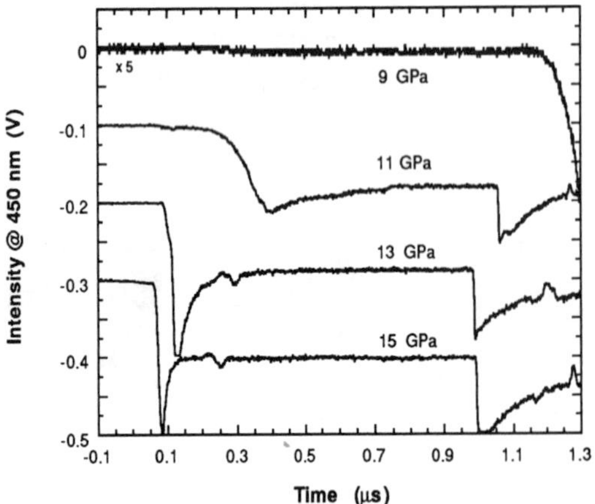

Fig 2. Time-resolved emission intensity changes of shocked nitromethane at several pressures.

RESULTS AND DISCUSSION

Figure 2 shows the temporal characteristics of emission obtained from shock detonating nitromethane at several pressures. The emission intensity peaks at some time after nitromethane is shocked and then, levels off to a steady value. The spike of the emission intensity change clearly represents a rapid exothermic chemical reaction of shocked nitromethane. This explosion time (t_e) strongly depends on pressure. It occurs at 1.2 μs after the shock wave enters nitromethane at 9 GPa and at 60 ns at 15 GPa. It is also evident at the 15, 13, 11 GPa experiments that there is a small jump in the emission intensity just before it reaches a steady level. This likely represents that the reaction front catches up the shock front (t_c). From this time on, the thermal explosion takes place directly from the unshocked nitromethane. A small rise in the emission intensity is also evident prior to the rapid rise by thermal explosion (t_i; for example, see the 264 ns jump at 9 GPa). We attribute this to the initiation of shocked nitromethane before the explosion takes place. The initiation process has also been observed in the previous measurements.[2] This shock-initiation may result in two consequences: smearing the explosion front and increasing the opacity of the shock-initiated nitromethane in time. The intensity decrease after the peak value may reflect those.

The chemical processes occurring in shocked nitromethane can be classified into three regions based on the temporal behavior of the emission intensity. (1) An induction period (before t_i) during which shocked nitromethane remains unreacted and transparent at relatively low temperature of 1000 K, (2) a shock initiation period (from t_i to t_e) in which the shocked nitromethane initiates the reaction, and finally (3) a thermal explosion period (after t_e) during which rapid exothermic reactions take place to produce the stable detonation products. Figure 3 shows the pressure dependence of the initiation and thermal explosion times, together with that of the catch-up time. While t_e and t_c agree well with the previous ones, this work shows that nitromethane starts the initial reaction at substantially earlier time than that reported previously. This is probably due to higher sensitivity of the current recording system.

The spectral characteristics of shocked nitromethane were also obtained after the thermal explosion occurred. However, the spectral characteristics in the initiation time period were not resolved due to the extremely low intensity (see Fig 2). Therefore, at the present time we know nothing about the spectral characteristics of thermal emission at the initiation period. In the explosion period no emission

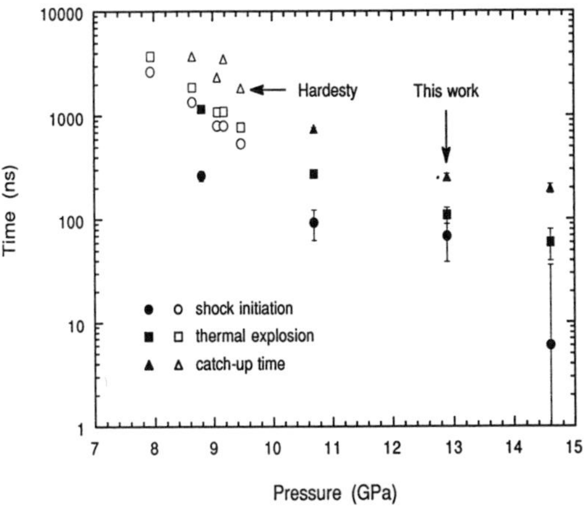

Fig 3. The pressure dependence of the initiation time, thermal explosion time, and catch-up time.

features are apparent to characterize the transients or reaction products, but there is only a broad emission band between 350 nm and 700 nm. Assuming thermal emission, the temperature of shocked nitromethane can be obtained from a gray-body radiation fit. Figure 4 shows the temperatures at the spike and the steady-state, which could represent the temperatures of the reaction front of shock-compressed nitromethane (superdetonation) and of nitromethane (normal detonation), respectively. Notice that the superdetonation temperature is higher than the normal detonation temperature by 200-500 K, which is in contrast to the previous observations.[1] The steady temperature is nearly independent of pressure, 3960 ± 40 K, whereas the spike temperature strongly depends on pressure ~ 60 K/GPa. This may be due to the fact that the normal detonation front is very sharp, whereas the superdetonation front is smeared by the initiation reactions occurring behind the shock front. Therefore, the reaction zone after the von-Neumann spike is extremely narrow at these pressures, and the steady temperature may represent the temperature at a condition similar to the CJ temperature. On the other hand, the superdetonation front is relatively smeared by the initiation reactions and, therefore, the emission is obtained in a relatively thick chemical region, where the temperature strongly varies with pressure.

The emission spectrum is best fit with the emissivity value 1.0 for all the experiments, representing black-body radiation. This would mean that the thermal emission likely comes from the carboneous species such as graphite. If so, the carbon nucleation and growth kinetics should be important processes occurring in this thermal explosion period.

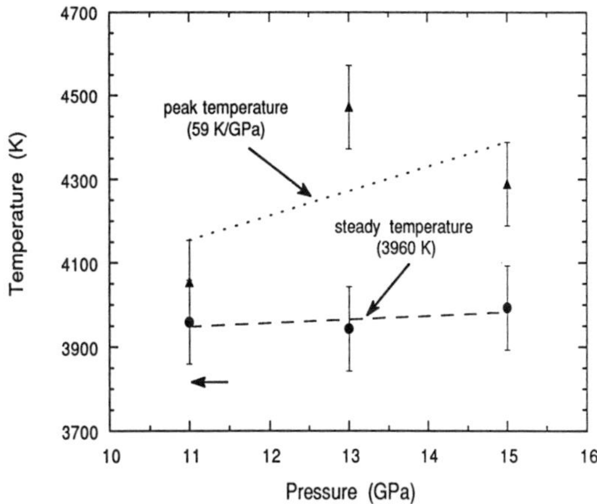

Fig 4. The temperatures of shock detonating nitromethane at several pressures.

ACKNOWLEDGMENTS

We thank Ervin See, Jim Crawford and Sam Weaver at LLNL for their technical assistance. Discussions with Clark Souers, Mat van Thiel, Francis Ree at LLNL and Steve Sheffield at LANL were extremely valuable to this study. This work was performed under auspices of the U.S. DOE by the LLNL.

REFERENCES

[1] A.W. Campbell, W.C. Davis, and J.R. Travis, Phys. Fluids **4**, 498 (1961).

[2] D.R. Hardesty, Combustion and Flame **27**, 229 (1976).

[3] S.A. Sheffield, R. Engelke, and R.R. Alcon, "*In-situ study of the chemically driven flow field in initiating homogeneous and heterogeneous nitromethane explosives*" in *Proceedings of the Ninth International Symposium on Detonation*, pp 39, Portland, Oregon (1989).

[4] A.C. Mitchell and W.J. Nellis, J. Appl. Phys. **52**, 3363 (1981).

[5] R.W. Woolfolk, M. Cowperthwaite, and R. Shaw, Thermochimica Acta **5**, 409 (1973).

[6] C.S. Yoo, N.C. Holmes, and E. See, in *Shock Waves in Condensed Matter -1991,* edited by S.C. Schmidt, R.D. Dick, J.W. Forbes, D.G. Tasker, pp733 (North-Holland, Amsterdam, 1992).

[7] J.M. Winey, Y.M. Gupta, and K.G. Casey, in this proceeding.

[8] N.C. Holmes, Rev. Sci. Instrum. **64**, 357 (1993); N.C. Holmes, G. Otani, P. McCandless, and S.F. Rice, in *Proceedings of the Ninth International Symposium on Detonation*, pp 88, Portland, Oregon (1989).

TIME-RESOLVED RAMAN MEASUREMENTS IN SHOCKED Z-CUT, α-QUARTZ SUBJECTED TO TENSION

S. M. Wood, Y. M. Gupta, and G.I. Pangilinan
Shock Dynamics Center
Physics Department
Washington State University
Pullman, Washington 99164-2814

An experimental method has been developed to use time-resolved Raman measurements as a microscopic probe of shock-induced tensile deformation in crystals. Rarefaction waves from sample boundaries interact to produce uniaxial tensile strain in the center of the sample. Optical fibers are used to transmit 514.5 nm light from a pulsed laser to the sample and then to transmit the scattered light from the sample to a recording system with a time resolution of 50 nsec. Experiments have been carried out on z-cut quartz to build on earlier work [1]. The A_1 (464 cm^{-1}) line of quartz exhibits a blue-shift in compression followed by a return to the ambient position upon unloading followed by a red-shift in tension. Experimental results are analyzed to gain insight into structural changes by comparing the measured Raman shifts in tension with the compression data.

INTRODUCTION

In recent years there has been a growing interest in the investigation of structural and symmetry changes of materials in the shocked state [1]. Time-resolved, Raman spectroscopy is a particularly attractive method for observing such temporal changes because it allows them to be viewed in real time. Experiments revealing the compression shift of the 464 cm^{-1} line of α–quartz [2] and the splitting of the 1333 cm^{-1} line of diamond [3] have already proven the effectiveness of this method for microscopic characterization of the shocked state. In the present work, an experimental method for using Raman spectroscopy as a microscopic probe of tensile deformation in crystals has been developed. Studies of shock-induced tension provide information about the effects of tensile strain within the sample interior without generating the surface effects associated with static tension. Although this work is still in progress, we report here the results of three experiments performed on α–quartz resulting in tension along the z-axis. Results are compared with compression data for both static and dynamic loading to gain insight into the microscopic mechanisms of expansion for this material.

EXPERIMENTAL PROCEDURE

Experiments were carried out on optically polished discs, 19 mm in diameter, obtained from Valpey Fisher. Shock waves were generated by impacting a 1.5 mm thick quartz impactor on a 3.0 mm thick target sample. The impactor was mounted on a projectile which was accelerated to velocities of 0.34 to 0.67 mm/μsec using a compressed gas gun. Longitudinal stresses produced were in the range of –55 (tension) to 60 (compression) kbar. Tension was created in the shocked sample by allowing rarefaction waves to interact in the center of the sample, thereby producing uniaxial tensile strain (Figure 1).

The overall experimental configuration is shown in Figure 2. A flash lamp pumped, pulsed dye laser provides 514.5 nm monochromatic light which is transmitted by an optical fiber to the sample. Incident light is focused on the center of the sample at 45 degrees to the axis of compression. Scattered light is collected along the axis and transmitted by another optical fiber to a recording system configured for 50 nsec time resolution. The recording system consists primarily of the single stage of a triple-spectrometer (SPEX 1877), a streak camera (Hadland Imacon 790), an image

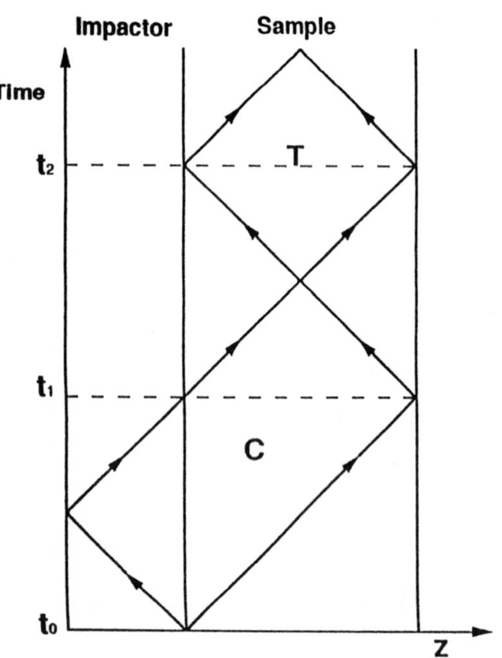

Figure 1. Position along z-axis versus time (C - compression , T - tension).

intensifier (ITT F4113), a Vidicon detector (EG&G 1254), and an optical multichannel analyzer (OMA). A holographic edge filter is used to block the Rayleigh scattered light from reaching the detector. The final output consists of Raman intensity versus wavelength versus time. The laser and recording system are triggered at appropriate times by a charged coaxial pin, which is shorted by the face of the projectile prior to sample impact, and a delay generator. Futher experimental details may be seen in Refs. [2] and [3].

RESULTS AND DISCUSSION

Quartz is composed of a network of almost regular tetrahedra consisting of oxygen atoms located at the corners and a silicon atom in the center. Tetrahedra are connected by a common oxygen with a bond angle of 144 degrees. Changes in this intertetrahedral Si-O-Si bond angle have been shown to be the primary compression mechanism in quartz [4-6]. As quartz is compressed, the intertetrahedral angle decreases such that the nearly rigid tetrahedra tilt or fold into the molecular structure.

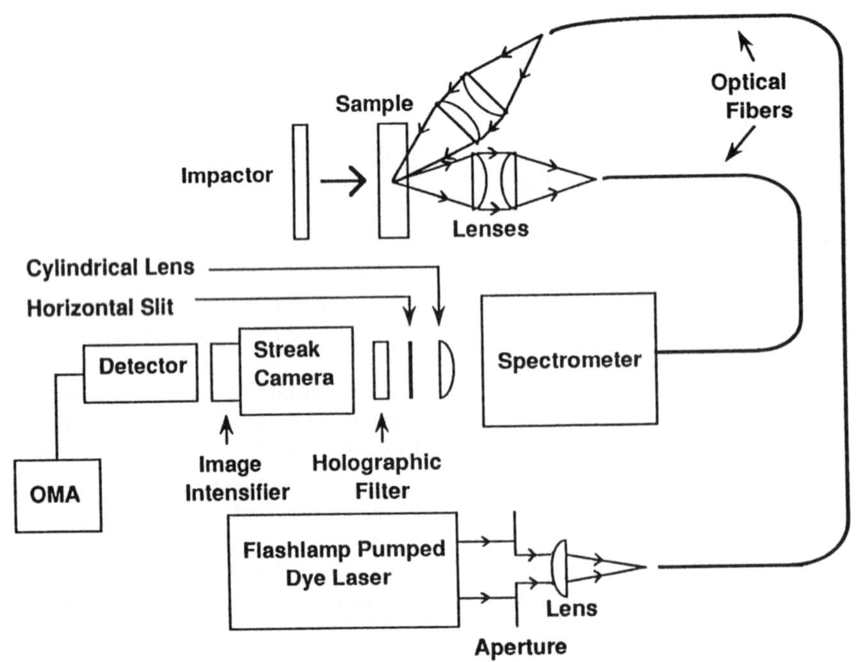

Figure 2. Overall experimental configuration.

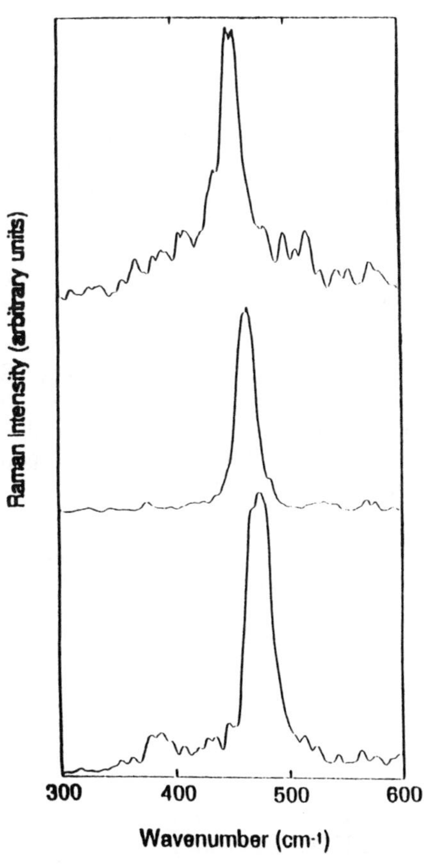

Figure 3. Sample raw data for quartz.

According to theoretical studies, the A_1 Raman line of quartz is associated with the symmetric bending of the Si-O-Si bond [7-10]. The oxygen atom moves in the Si-O-Si plane along the bisector of the Si-O-Si angle. When quartz is compressed and the Si-O-Si angle decreases, an increase in A_1 mode frequency results which can readily be observed as a blue-shift in the associated Raman line.

Figure 3 shows raw data obtained with the experimental arrangement described in the previous section. The ambient, 464 cm^{-1} Raman line of quartz exhibits a blue-shift to the right upon compression to 31 kbar (bottom), followed by a return to the ambient position upon unloading (middle), as expected for elastic deformation, followed by a red-shift under tension to –29 kbar (top). The small difference in the absolute values in compression and tension is the result of anharmonic forces in the crystal lattice. The appearance of a curved background during tension is being investigated and may signify a partial break-up of the quartz crystal.

Figure 4 shows the change in the Raman frequency with density compression for the present work in tension and compression compared with the experimental data of Gustavsen [1] and the hydrostatic compression curve for quartz [4, 11]. Density compression is defined as $(\rho - \rho_0) / \rho_0$ where ρ is the density of the shocked quartz, obtained from Rankine-Hugoniot relations [1], and ρ_0 is the ambient density of quartz of 2.650 g/cm^3. The hydrostatic curve was calculated using the

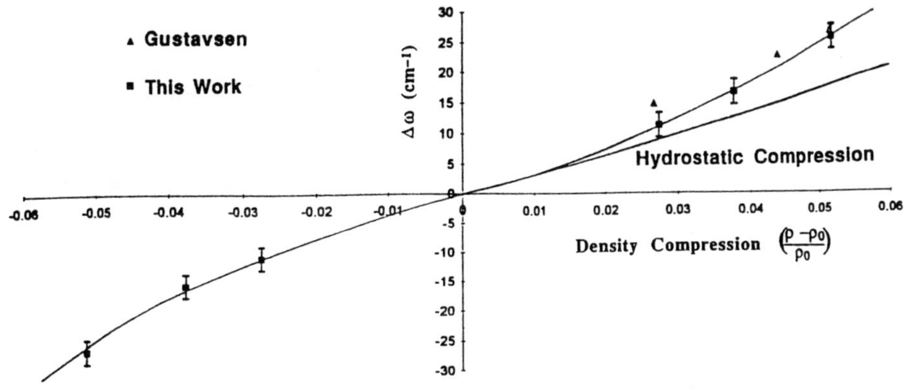

Figure 4. Change in Raman shift as a function of density compression.

Birch-Murnaghan equation of state [4] and a line shift of 0.8 cm^{-1} / kbar for quartz [11]. The fitted data show that the Raman frequency increases with compression, while it decreases with tension. These results strongly support the hypothesis that uniaxial tensile strain in quartz causes an increase in intertetrahedral angle resulting in a decrease in A_1 mode frequency. Experiments are planned for higher stresses to provide further data needed to verify the shape of the experimental curve.

SUMMARY

An experimental method has been developed for microscopically probing shock-induced tensile deformation in crystals using time-resolved Raman spectroscopy. Tension experiments have been carried out on z-cut, α-quartz which exhibit shifts in the A_1 Raman line of quartz toward lower wavenumbers, revealing a marked increase in the intertetrahedral angle of quartz under tension. Additional experiments are planned to help establish the shape of the Raman shift versus density compression curve and further characterize the detailed expansion mechanisms of quartz.

ACKNOWLEDGEMENTS

This work was supported by the Northwest College and University Association for Science (NORCUS). The authors would like to thank Dave Savage and Kurt Zimmerman for their assistance with the experiments.

REFERENCES

[1] Y. M. Gupta, "Progress in Understanding Shock Deformation in Condensed Materials at the Atomic Molecular Level: Recent Experimental Developments," Proceedings of the APS Topical Conference on Shock Compression of Condensed Matter, 1991, 15-26.

[2] R. L. Gustavsen and Y. M. Gupta, submitted to J. Appl. Phys.

[3] J. M. Boteler, "Time Resolved Raman Spectroscopy in Diamonds Shock Compressed Along [110] and [100] Orientations," Ph. D. Thesis, Washington State University, (1993).

[4] L. Levien, C. T. Prewitt, and D. J. Weidner, Am. Mineralogist, 65, 920 (1980).

[5] J. D. Jorgensen, J. Appl. Phys., 49(11), 5473 (1978).

[6] H. Grimm and B. Dorner, J. Phys. Chem. Solids, 36, 407-413 (1975).

[7] D. A. Kleinman and W. G. Spitzer, Phys. Rev., 125(1), 16 (1962).

[8] J. Etchepare, M. Merian, and L. Smetankine, J. Chem. Phys., 60(5), 1873 (1974).

[9] M. E. Striefler and G. E. Barsch, Phys. Rev. B, 12(10), 4553 (1975).

[10] T. H. K. Barron, C. C. Huang, and A. Pasternak, J. Phys. C, 9, 3925 (1976).

[11] R. J. Hemley, edited by M. H. Manghnani and Y. Syono, High Pressure Research in Mineral Physics, Tokyo, Terra Scientific Publishing Company, 1987, 347.

CHAPTER XXI

EXPERIMENTAL METHODS: Static

CRYSTAL STRUCTURE STUDIES TO 10 GPa WITH THE PARIS-EDINBURGH CELL : HIGH PRESSURE ASPECTS

S. Klotz[1], J.M. Besson[1], G. Hamel[2],
[1] Physique des Milieux Condensés, (CNRS URA 782),
[2] Département des Hautes Pressions
Université Pierre et Marie Curie, B 77,
4, place Jussieu, F.-75252 PARIS Cedex 05, France
R.J. Nelmes, J.S. Loveday, R.M. Wilson
Department of Physics, Univ. Edinburgh, Edinburgh EH9 3JZ, U.K.
and S. Hull
The ISIS facility, Rutherford Appleton Lab., Chilton OXII 0QX U.K.

We review two versions of a low weight (50 kg) press of 250 tonnes capacity, enabling us for the first time to perform neutron diffraction on powder samples of 40 to 100 mm^3 volume by time-of-flight spectroscopy over 20 GPa. The assembly consists of a hydraulic ram compressing two opposed toroidal anvils, made of tungsten carbide or sintered diamond dies supported by steel binding rings and backed by WC-seats. We discuss specific features of this device such as gasketing, pressure load characteristics, pressure gradients and loading techniques for solid powder samples, fluids and gases. The low temperature performance of the cell is reported as well as recent developments towards a further reduction in size and mass.

INTRODUCTION

Neutron diffraction experiments on powder samples require in general samples at least 50 mm^3 in volume in order to collect patterns on which full profile refinement can be performed in a reasonable amount of time. Since the development of the McWhan cell[1] in the late 1960's, however, little progress has been made in the construction of standard user devices for pressures beyond 3 GPa, although presses and multianvil assemblies for compression to 10-20 GPa are commercially available. The reason for that is evident: diffraction experiments impose rather severe restrictions on the geometry of the anvils and the weight (size) of the press, rendering standard devices either useless or extremely cumbersome.

The problem of constructing a portable high pressure cell with the required performance is thus twofold: first to chose the right anvil geometry and second to design a press with minimal weight and size. Toroidal anvils[2] have been used in the ex-USSR and other east european countries in the past decades for material syntheses but their geometry is also adequate for diffraction experiments. Concerning the press, a simple estimation and experiment show that a thrust of 100 to 150 tonnes is required to deform a metallic gasket of 20 mm diameter containing a sample of 100 mm^3 at 10 GPa. Standard hydraulic presses of this capacity have a mass of typically several hundred kg. However, as shown below, it is indeed possible to reduce the weight considerably by choosing a particular shape of the ram which minimizes the deformations at critical levels. The Paris-Edinburgh cell is a high pressure device which combines a toroidal anvil assembly with an optimized low weight (50 kg) 250 tonnes hydraulic ram. The anvil geometry requires measurements of the diffracted beam at a fixed angle $2\Theta \approx 90°$ and suits experiments on pulsed sources by time-of-flight spectroscopy. The cell has been designed specifically for use at the POLARIS-station at the U.K. pulsed source ISIS.

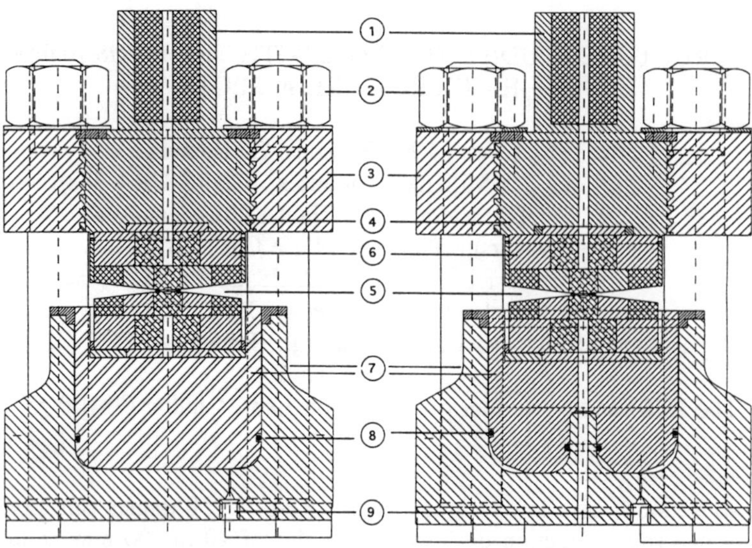

Figure 1: Cross cut of two versions of high pressure cells V3 (left) and V2 (right). (1) collimator, (2) nuts and tie rods, (3) top platen, (4) breech, (5) anvils, (6) anvil seats, (7) piston-cylinder assembly, (8) hydraulic fluid seal, (9) high pressure fluid inlet.

DESIGN AND PERFORMANCE

Description of the cell

Figure 1 shows two versions (V2 and V3) of the Paris-Edinburgh cell, which differ mainly in the shape of the hydraulic press: V2 is equipped with an axial bore at the back of the ram allowing transmission measurements, which is not present in V3. The thrust on the anvils (5) and seats (6) is generated by the piston-cylinder (7) assembly which is shown here with the piston fully recessed. With a 250 MPa (2500 bar) pressure in the hydraulic fluid which is fed in through the inlet (9) a 250 tonnes (2.5 MN) thrust is generated by the 100 cm^2 piston. The tie rods with their corresponding nuts (2) connect the ram body to the top platen (3). The press is almost entirely made of high performance steel 819A by Aubert et Duval (35NCD16).

Finite element calculations were used in order to find the optimal shape and dimensions of the ram. This leads to the unusual shape shown in Fig. 1, where the deformations at the level of the O-ring seal as well as the centering ring are almost zero although some parts of the cylinder deform by 0.45 mm at 200 tonnes load. Maximum stresses of ca. 1 GPa occur at the bottom of the ram. The inlet for the hydraulic fluid was placed in a region of minimal stress.

Toroidal anvil and gasket assembly

Figure 2 shows an enlarged view of standard WC anvils including the gasket, consisting of a washer and a toroidal part. The high pressure chamber (sample volume V) is situated in the center of the drawing, limited laterally by the washer and vertically by the two spheroidal surfaces of the anvils.The washer is laterally supported by the toroidal gasket. High pressure is created by applying load onto the anvils which causes the sample volume to decrease both by the decrease of the gasket thickness as well as theintrusion of the washer into V. For such a profile the upper limit for the volume reduction V_0/V is roughly 2. This causes no restriction for experiments on solids and liquids, where V_0/V is between 1 (NaCl : 1.2) to 2 (NH_3, CH_4), between loading and ~ 10 GPa but excludes measurements on gaseous samples

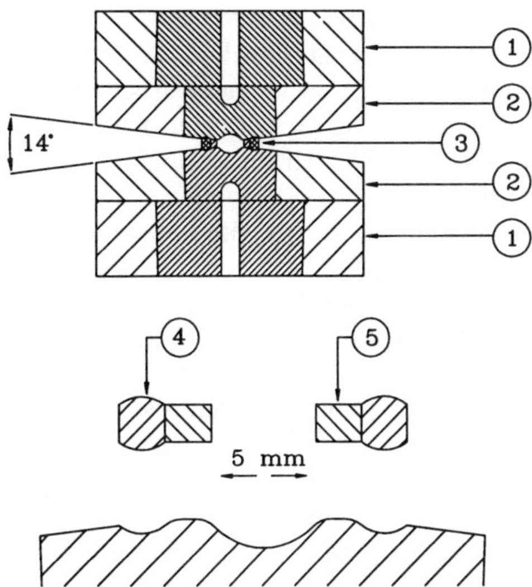

Figure 2: Toroidal anvil assembly (top) with enlarged view of the gasket and anvil profile (bottom). (1) Seats (CW), (2) anvils, (3) sealing assembly consisting of (4) toroidal gasket and (5) flat washer. Anvils are made of CW (standard) or diamond dies, supported by steel binding ring.

(H_2, He) if they are loaded at ambient pressure above the current low temperature limit of 100 K.

The standard anvils are made of slightly conical WC kernels (overall cone angle 3°) of 25 mm diameter and 14 mm height. They are supported by pressing them into a steel binding ring (819A by Aubert et Duval) at ambient temperature, producing a tangential stress of ca. 1 GPa. At the back they are provided with a recess of 6 mm depth and 5 mm diameter to reduce the attenuation of the incident neutron beam.

The compressive strength of WC is approximately 60 tonnes/cm^2, which means for gaskets of 18 mm diameter a maximal load of ca. 150 tonnes. According to the empirical load/pressure characteristic of the cell (see below) this results in a maximal pressure of 12 GPa. For pressures beyond this limit, there seems at the moment to be only one feasible solution, namely compacted diamond dies. These are provided by General Electric under the commercial name COMPAX and have to be shaped to the specific anvil profile by spark erosion. Our experience at the present time is limited to a few experiments beyond 10 GPa, among them one on Ni above 20 GPa and another on D_2O (ice VIII) to 13 GPa.

Gasket materials

Pyrophyllite and Cu:Be, were initially used as gasket materials, but are now replaced by null-scattering TiZr (52% Ti, 48% Zr by weight) to eliminate wavelength dependent absorption due to Bragg edges. Despite a much lower yield strength (900 MPa) compared to 1300 MPa for hardened CuBe the performances of the two materials in a given configuration are very similar. This indicates that the performance of the cell is determined by the geometry rather than the mechanical properties of the gasket material.

Pressure gradients

Anvils with spheroidal pressure chambers are expected to produce less pressure gradients and biaxial strains than flat anvils, but detailed data have not been available so far. The transparency of COMPAX diamond anvils to high energy x-rays (>50 keV) makes it possible to map out in detail the pressure distribution within the sample by sending an x-ray beam along the cell axis across the anvils and observing the diffracted beam at a fixed angle 2Θ in the energy dispersive mode. Recent results[3] of an experiment at the new European Synchrotron Source ESRF (Grenoble) with $2\Theta \approx 6°$ at energies between 60 and 220 keV show that the central 1/3 of the NaCl pellet is within $\pm$ 0.05 GPa of the nominal pressure of 6 GPa and the pressure variation across the whole sample is not larger than 0.3 GPa.

Load-pressure characteristic

After sealing the high pressure chamber under a load L of ca. 20 tonnes, P increases linearly with L to approximately 8 GPa and 90 tonnes, followed by a levelling off at 12 GPa and 130 tonnes. This holds for both solid and initially liquid samples, if the starting volume is chosen according to the specific elastic properties by using gaskets of different dimensions. The pressure/load characteristics for TiZr and CuBe gaskets are almost identical.

Loading procedures

To alleviate pressure broadening effects, which are commonly observed in solid powder samples at high pressures, the following procedure proved to be effective. As much as possible of the powder sample is placed into the bore of the gasket, glued to the bottom anvil. The sample is then soaked with Fluorinert and the pressure chamber is quickly sealed off by applying a load of ca. 20 tonnes.

Liquid samples are loaded directly in the cell, with no need for encapsulation: the cell is placed into its "measuring position", i.e. with its axis horizontally. Then a rubber ring is placed between the anvils, before applying a few hundred N onto them, which creates a sealed cavity around the gasket assembly. Then the sample is injected by a syringe, while a second one ensures that no air bubbles remain in the cavity. Again, 20 tonnes are applied to seal off the high pressure chamber before finally the rubber is cut off.

Gaseous samples are loaded by condensing them at sufficiently low temperatures into a loading chamber around the gaskets as in the previous case. This can be a rubber ring, or, for temperatures below 200 K a PTFE-ring, supported by a metal bracket. Such a set-up holds pressures to well beyond 50 bars, which means that some gases (Ar, CH_4) can be loaded close to their critical point at relatively elevated temperatures. This again is an original feature of this large volume cell.

Low temperature experiments

Being able to cool the cell down to moderately low temperatures (100 K) is important for structural studies (phase transitions, especially magnetic), but also for loading gaseous samples (NH_3, CH_4) and for improving the quality of powder patterns by collecting them at low temperature.

To vary the temperature the cell and its support are placed into a thermally insulating container which fits into the existing POLARIS tank. By filling the bottom of the container with ca. 10 cm of liquid nitrogen, the cell cools down to 150 K within 2 1/2 hours and to 100 K in 5 hours.

Future developments

At the moment, development is focussed on two issues: first, development of smaller presses for standard use to 10 GPa and possibly for low temperature work. All dimensions can be scaled down by a factor 0.8, leaving the anvils as they are and leading to a cell with a mass of ca. 30 kg instead of 50 kg.

A second development concerns the use of the cell for inelastic work on single crystals. The measurement of phonon dispersion curves under pressure for example has been restricted so far to only a few systems[4] like black phosphorus, SmS and RbI, showing significant effects in the 1 or 2 GPa range. A tenfold increase in pressure would dramatically increase the number of accessible systems. The Paris-Edinburgh cell is in principle adaptable for such experiments if the fixed angle geometry is abandoned and the incident and diffracted beam go through the metallic gasket in the equatorial plane between the two anvils. By mounting the single crystal in different orientations phonon dispersion measurements along all principal symmetry axes should be possible. Preliminary measurements in this geometry have shown that it is indeed possible to obtain a reasonable good diffraction signal even on powder samples.

Acknowledgments This work was supported in parts by the U.K. Science and Engineering Research Council, the French Commissariat à l'Energie Atomique under contract n° W 00319/3255 and the Commission of the European Community under SCIENCE contract SC1*CT 91 0692. COMPAX diamond dies were provided by General Electric.

REFERENCES

[1] D.B. McWhan, D. Bloch and G. Parisot, *Rev. Sci. Instrum.* **45**, 634 (1974).

[2] L.G. Khvostantsev, L.F. Vershchagin and A.P. Novikov, *High Temperatures-High Pressure* **9**, 637 (1977); L.G. Khvostantsev, *High Temp.-High Pr.* **16**, 171 (1984).

[3] S. Klotz, J.M. Besson, G. Hamel and D. Häusermann, to be published.

[4] O. Blaschko, *European Workshop on Neutron scattering at High Pressure,* Abingdon, U.K., 19-21.3.1992.

GAS-CHARGED PISTON-CYLINDER APPARATUS FOR PRESSURES TO 4 GPa.

Ivan C. Getting and Hartmut A. Spetzler
CIRES and Department of Geological Sciences
University of Colorado at Boulder
Boulder, Colorado 80309-0216, USA

An end-loaded piston-cylinder high pressure apparatus which utilizes an argon pressure medium has been developed. This device has a pressurized volume in excess of 3 cm^3 and offers the absolute pressure calibration of the piston-cylinder apparatus with the truly hydrostatic and chemically inert environment of argon. The vessel is precharged to 0.5 GPa through a port and valve system built into the end-load hardware. No port is required in the wall of the vessel. After precharge, the piston is advanced into the chamber to generate pressures to 4 GPa.

Solid argon, at pressures greater than ~1.3 GPa, is so weak that it requires gas sealing techniques to contain it. The seals consist entirely of unsupported area mitre rings in chamfers. No O-rings or other soft seal components are used. This configuration permits extensive cycling through the melting-freezing pressure of argon without failure. Leak rates are exceedingly low over the entire pressure range. A safety barrier has been constructed which comfortably contains the shock wave and any ejecta associated with failure.

At slightly elevated temperatures, argon remains a true fluid. With an internal heater and internal temperature and pressure sensors, this apparatus is intended for high precision, ultrasonic velocity measurements. It will also be useful for truly hydrostatic studies of phase equilibria, diffusion, and partial melts. Deformation studies with truly hydrostatic confining pressure are also planned with the addition of an internal piston to generate differential stress.

APPARATUS DESIGN

The design of the gas piston-cylinder is based on the extended range piston-cylinder devices developed by Ivan Getting both at UCLA and for commercial diamond synthesis. With solid media, these devices have been used routinely to 6.5 GPa with some excursions to 8.0 GPa.

The adaptation of the extended range piston-cylinder from solid media to a gas medium motivated a substantial review of this device. Many design issues related to safety and reliability have been addressed. A partial lists includes 1.) the shock wave and projectile hazard which would accompany a mechanical failure, 2.) a strategy for the introduction of precharge gas into the vessel without violating the structural design features required for 4-6 GPa operation, and 3.) a suitable method for sealing the argon at high pressures.

Hazards

Failures are likely in the course of this work. With a gas pressure medium this results in two hazards: 1.) an energetic shock wave created by the rapidly expanding gas and 2.) possible high velocity projectiles accelerated by the escaping gas. Protection has been established for both .

Shock energy is contained and dissipated by a special containment structure around the press. The upper limit to the energy contained in the shock wave is the work done by the gas expanding adiabatically and irreversibly against one atmosphere. For an ideal gas this is

$$-w = \frac{3}{5}nRT,$$

where n is the number of moles of gas, R is the gas constant, and T is the initial temperature. This expression has a value of ~40% of the internal energy of the gas. It is suitable for calculations on highly compressed, non-ideal gas as the contribution to the work done against the constant external pressure is very small at high pressures where the change in volume is very small. The number of moles of gas, n, however, must be determined from the equation of state of the gas and its initial pressure, temperature, and volume.

A containment structure design was developed empirically. Test shocks were produced by the intentional failure of a closure plug on a 150 ml, gas-charged vessel at pressures up to 400 MPa. The pressurized gas was vented suddenly through a 13 mm diameter nozzle producing shocks with energies from 0.5 to 6.0 kJ. The maximum anticipated shock from the gas piston-cylinder apparatus is ~2 kJ for a 12.7 mm diameter chamber and ~6 kJ for a 19 mm diameter chamber.

Test shocks were successfully contained and attenuated in an air-tight 600 mm plywood box lined with 50 mm thick, open cell acoustic foam. The foam provides a dissipative, compliant surface with which the shock wave can interact without applying large forces to the walls of the box. The 6 kJ expansions produced a reasonably comfortable peak sound level of 120 dB in a small laboratory room. This set of tests has resulted in the design and construction of an air-tight shock containment structure around the press used for the gas piston-cylinder apparatus. It consists of a steel, angle iron frame with 19 mm plywood panels. The inside is lined with 75 mm of open-cell acoustic foam. Failures in an abandoned seal design from above 4 GPa are inaudible in the adjacent room.

The second source of hazard from a failure of this apparatus is projectiles. The kinetic energy of a projectile can be determined by estimating the fraction of the work done by the expanding gas which might be transferred to the projectile. This fraction for a rifle is typically around 25-30%. Failure of this apparatus would result in the escape of gas and projectiles outward from the source in all directions without the "benefit" of a constraining barrel to accelerate projectiles. We estimate that a single projectile would contain no more than 5% of the total energy released, typically much less.

The primary armor in the press consists of four alternating layers of 6 mm thick polycarbonate plastic and Astralloy-V ballistic armor steel. This design would stop a projectile with more than 10 times the maximum kinetic energy we expect. It is fully expected that the worst case failure would produce no risk or discomfort to persons in the room from either projectiles or shock waves.

Apparatus Layout

Figure 1 shows a cross section of the gas piston-cylinder configuration. The pressurized cylindrical volume is just above the primary piston in the figure. The pressure vessel consists of a tungsten carbide core surrounded by interference fit binding rings. The entire vessel is wrapped in annealed stainless steel ribbon for a safety ring. End-load force is applied to the ends of the vessel core through the bottom end-load plate and through the top end-load plate core. Precharge gas is introduced through a port in the top end-load hardware as described below. Cooling is provided by circulating a heat transfer fluid, hydrocarbon oil, across the ends of the vessel and through axial holes in the adapter shim around the vessel core.

Precharge Gas Port

The design of this device retains the uninterrupted pressure vessel walls and short piston geometry of the extended range, solid medium piston-cylinder apparatus. A novel path through which to precharge the vessel has been developed. Gas is introduced and sealed with a valve mechanism built into the end-load tooling at the end of the vessel opposite the piston. The top end-load plate core, see Figure 1, fits into its binding ring with a modest interference on a large taper. It slides in and out in response to changes in end-load force. To precharge the vessel, approximately one half of the design end-load force is applied. This creates sufficient normal stress on the taper and between the binding ring and the vessel core to seal 0.5 GPa. Argon is introduced through the gas port and flows across a slight gap on the end of the vessel core into the bore. Application of additional end-load force closes the gap, engages the static seal mitre ring, and applies end-load to the core. The piston is then advanced to generate higher pressures.

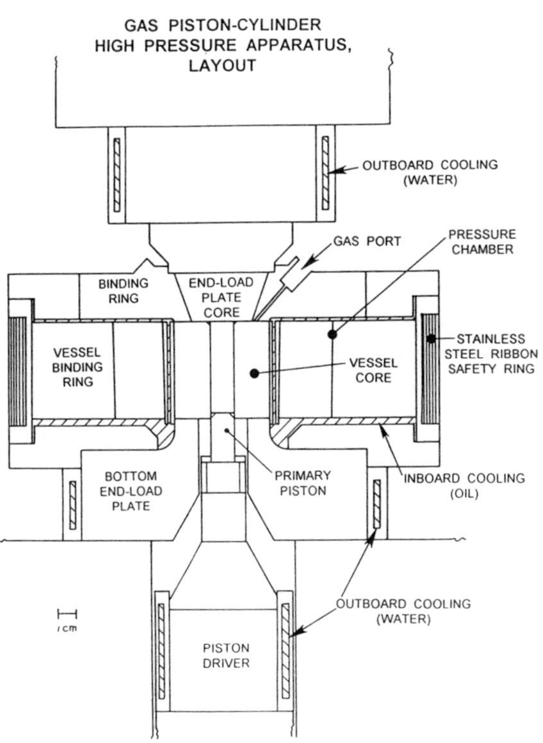

Figure 1. The layout of the gas piston-cylinder apparatus. Details are described in the text.

High Pressure Seals

A static seal is required at the end of the vessel opposite from the piston. This seal must admit precharge gas to 0.5 GPa and then establish a seal. A simple steel mitre ring installed in a chamfer in the I.D. corner of the vessel bore has proven completely successful. The dynamic seal on the piston is also a simple steel mitre ring on a chamfer on the piston. The initial seal is established by advancing the piston slowly against the mitre ring, which has a slight interference fit into the bore of the vessel, as the argon gas is introduced into the vessel. Neither of these seals has ever failed in dozens of runs.

PERFORMANCE

Several excursions to the design pressure of 4 GPa and many tests to 3 GPa have been made. The leakage of argon past the seals is undetectable in both the fluid phase, below 1.3 GPa, and in the solid phase. The piston insertion of ~15 mm at 3 GPa typically repeats to 5 μm on subsequent cycles. Over 3 days at 3 GPa spontaneous piston advance was less than 2 μm. No deterioration of the tungsten carbide core of the pressure vessel or carbide piston has been detected after many cycles to 3 GPa. This stability bodes well for high precision runs of long duration.

Absolute pressure is determined from the piston force, seal area, and friction correction. Piston force is measured directly by a calibrated force gage in series with the piston. This is much more accurate than relying on the measurement of hydraulic pressure in the piston ram. The effective area of the seal is well defined by the diameter of the dilated vessel bore. This can be calculated quite accurately by finite elements using the stress strain curve of the core carbide. The simple piston seal has resulted in quite low friction. Figure 2 shows a hysteresis loop of piston displacement versus nominal pressure calculated from the force on the piston and the seal area. The width of this loop is about 5% at the freezing pressure of argon.

This implies a friction correction of ~2.5%. The width of the hysteresis loop increases very slowly with pressure. The friction correction at 4 GPa is anticipated to be less than 2%.

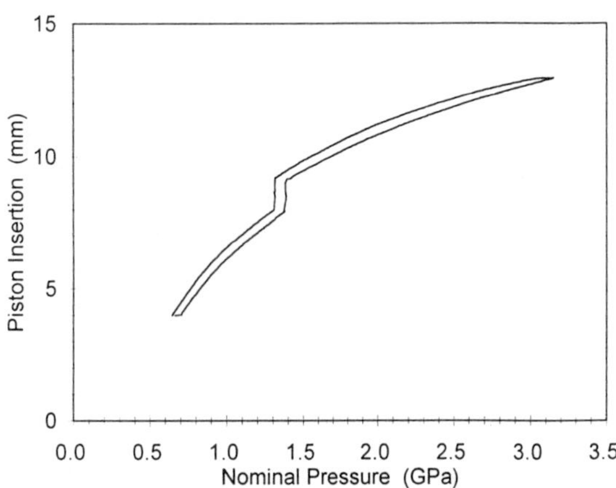

Figure 2. Piston displacement hysteresis loop. Piston position is plotted versus nominal pressure for one complete pressure cycle from 0.6 to 3.2 GPa and back. The piston velocity was ~1 μm/s. The freezing and melting of argon occurs abruptly with only a few percent friction.

This instrument also exhibits extremely high precision in pressure. The freezing pressure of argon repeats to 0.2% at ~1.3 GPa. With a hydrostatic pressure medium, this apparatus offers unprecedented absolute accuracy in pressure to 4 and possibly 6 GPa. This capability will be used to make extremely accurate ultrasonic equation of state determinations for materials of interest as pressure standards such as NaCl.

Electric feedthroughs have been built and operated successfully. Manganin coils are currently under test as internal pressure sensors. Internal heaters and instrumentation are under development. A prototype heater has achieved 1200 K with dramatically less power than is typically required in solid media devices.

ACKNOWLEDGMENTS

This work was supported by the National Science Foundation, Division of Earth Sciences, Instrumentation and Facilities under grant number EAR 89-16327 and by the University of Colorado.

PISTON - CYLINDER APPARATUS FOR HIGH PRESSURE AND HIGH TEMPERATURE STUDIES

K.Anbukumaran, C.Venkateswaran
N.Victor Jaya and S.Natarajan
Department of Physics, Anna University
Madras - 600 025, India

A simple Piston-Cylinder apparatus has been designed and developed for high pressure and high temperature studies. The maximum pressure obtained is 10 kbar and temperature is 1200° C. The device has a larger sample volume. Pyrophillite and graphite is used as the pressure medium and heater respectively.

Introduction

Since the discovery of high temperature superconductivity in the La-Ba-Cu-O system [1], many superconducting copper oxides have been found. In general the superconducting materials are synthesised by ordinary solid state reaction at atmospheric pressure . These superconductors when subjected to pressure undergo a change in T_c value. Some of the compounds which are nonsuperconductors at normal pressure becomes superconducting under high pressure [2]. But if the pressure is released the compound goes to the normal state. By the simultaneous application of pressure and temperature, stability of the superconducting state may be achieved.

Smith et al reported an infinite layer compound $Nd_{0.16}Sr_{0.84}CuO_{2.8}$ having T_c=40K, synthesised by high pressure technique [3]. Later Ba-Sr-Cu-O infinite layer superconductor with T_c=90K have been synthesised [4]. The layered copper oxides $ACuO_2$ (A: Alkaline earths), which are composed of 2D sheets of Cu-O squares sandwiching the A ions has been synthesised under high pressure [5]. Superconductivity at 110K in the infinite- layer compound $(Sr_{1-x}Ca_x)_{1-y}CuO_2$ is synthesised by high pressure technique[6]. H.Okada et al reported the synthesis of Nd_2CuO_4 type R_2CuO_4(R=Y,Dy,Ho,Er,Tm), using high pressure technique [7].

High pressure and High temperature technique has been employed not only to synthesise the superconducting compounds but also for synthesising new, hard,crystalline materials. The synthesis of single crystals under pressure finds direct application in numerous semiconducting and optical devices throughout the industry [8].

In broad perspective, there are a limited number of basic apparatus types that have been developed for simultaneous use of high pressure and high temperature. Piston-Cylinder, Bridgmann Anvil, Belt and Mulltiple Anvil apparatus are generally used for synthesising the materials at high pressure.

Bridgmann Anvil apparatus is the least expensive device in all of the apparatus mentioned above. Highest static pressures can be achieved by Bridgmanns device. But it has a small "two dimensional" volume and attainable steady state temperatures are lower than in any of the other devices. The Belt and Multiple anvil apparatus are comparatively expensive than Piston-Cylinder apparatus.

In this paper we report a simple Piston-Cylinder apparatus which is less expensive and easy to handle. Samples of larger volume can be synthesised using this apparatus in the pressure range upto 10 kbar.

Apparatus Design

The ordinary form taken by a high pressure apparatus is that of a cylinder provided with a closure on one end and a movable piston on the other. The specimen to be subjected to pressure is placed in the cylinder and is compressed by the moving piston, usually driven by the ram of the hydraulic press. Figure (1) shows the Piston- Cylinder apparatus and it is constructed by using EN24 alloy steel.

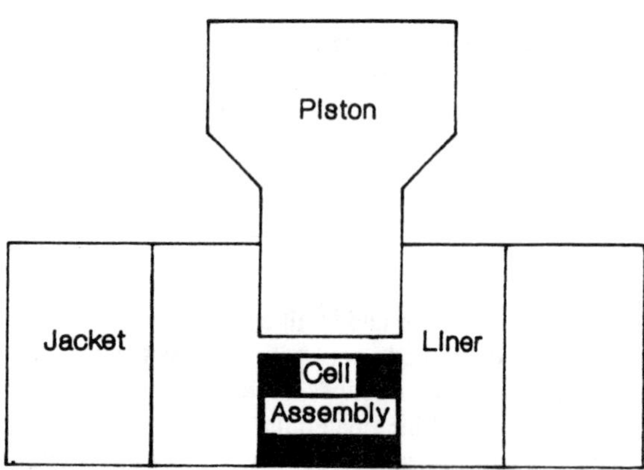

Fig. 1 Cross section of Piston Cylinder Apparatus

CYLINDER

In order to increase the pressure capability of a cylinder, generally two methods are employed. One is by shrink fitting two or more cylinders together and other is by Autofrettaging a monobloc cylinder. Here the shrink fitting method is employed. Mild steel is used as the Jacket and Liner is of EN24 alloy steel hardened to RC52. The bore of the inner cylinder is 25mm diameter and height is 34mm. The diameter of the Jacket and Liner is 195 and 80 mm respectively. The interference wedge is 1\2°.

PISTON

The piston is also made up of EN24 alloy steel hardened to RC54. The top of the piston has a 46 mm diameter. The tapering angle is choosen to be 35°.

Cell Assembly

The cell assembly is shown in figure (2). Talc is used as the gasket material and pyrophillite as the pressure transmitter. Graphite sleeve of thickness 0.6mm is used to heat the sample. A backing block made of EN24 (RC54) is inserted at the bottom of the cell. Talc being a bad conductor of heat, it prevents the cylinder while heating.

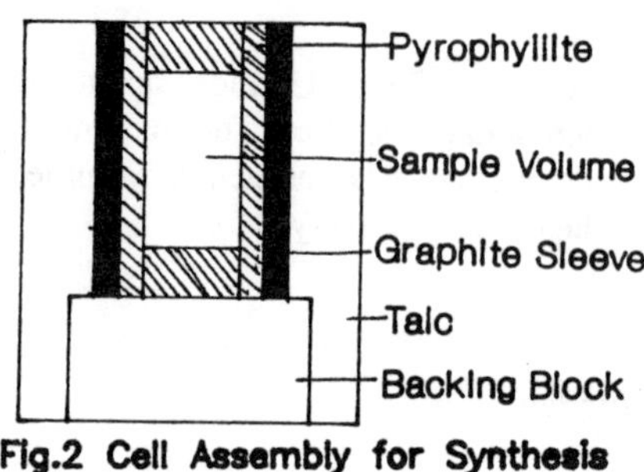

Fig.2 Cell Assembly for Synthesis

Pressure Calibration

When an assembly such that of figure (2) is compressed, there is certain "frictional holdup", that is certain percentage of the pressure at the piston tip,which is not transmitted to the sample. With pyrophyllite cylinders the frictional holdup is usually 10 to 20 % . Hence, the cell must be calibrated (that is at the sample site).

Certain elements undergo phase transition by the application of pressure. Thus Cerium shows a very large abrupt drop in resistance at about 7 kbar. Which is believed to be caused by a shift of outer shell electrons to one of the inner, unfilled, shells [9]. Electrically deposited chromium shows an abrupt transition at about 4 kbar[9].

We made use of these known transitions in Ce and Cr to calibrate our Piston-Cylinder apparatus. Figure (3) shows the resistivity cell assembly used for calibration. The central hole (9mm) in the gasket material accommodates the calibrant, which is sandwiched between pyrophyllite pressure

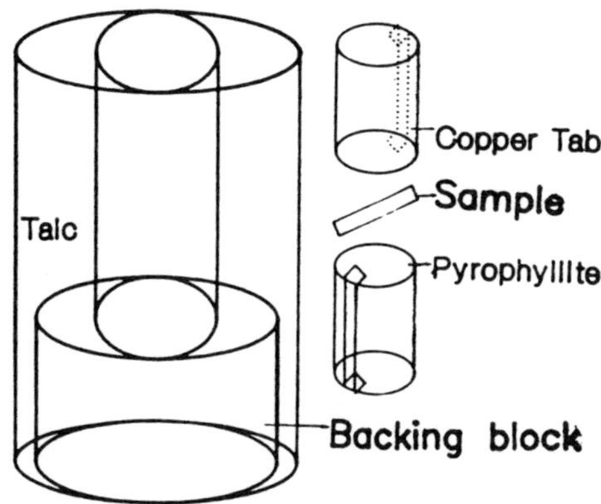

Fig.3 Cell Assembly for Calibration

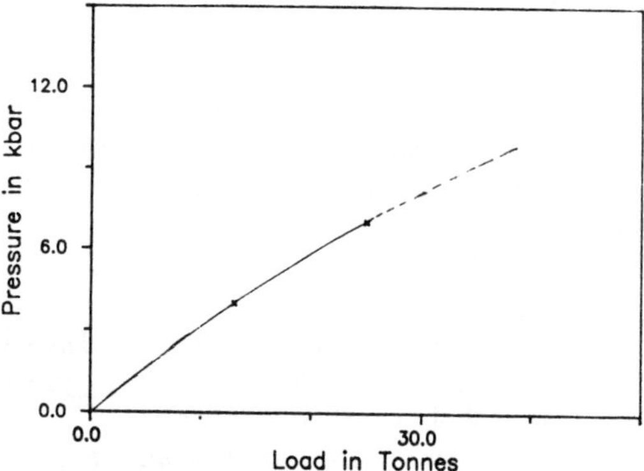

Fig. 6 Calibration Chart

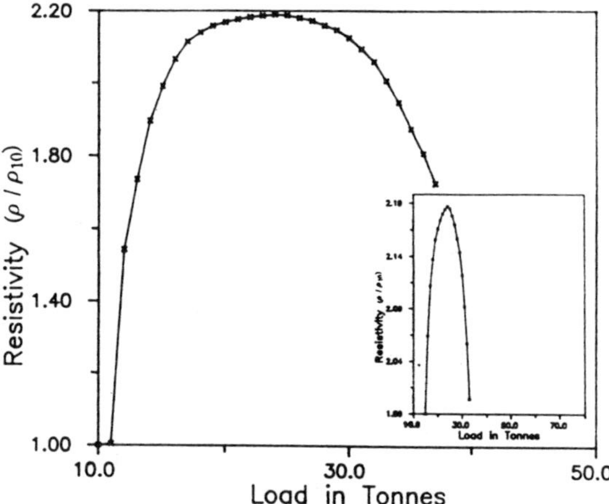

FIG. 4 Load Vs Resistivity for Cerium

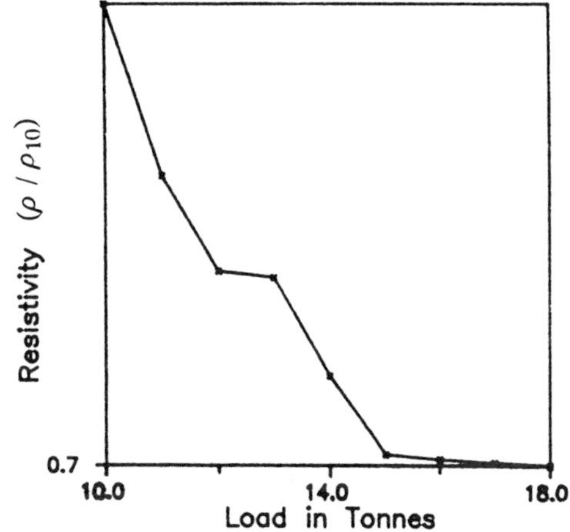

FIG. 5 Load Vs Resistivity for Chromium

transmitters. The ends of the samples are connected to the piston and the backing block by means of copper strips. The calibrant is made very thin and the length is about 7mm to increase the effective resistance. Figures (4)and (5) show the Load versus Normalised resistivity of cerium and chromium respectively. To ensure better contact between the sample and copper tabs, the cell is initially clamped at 10 tonnes load. The calibration graph is shown in figure(6).

Experiment

A thin sheet of mica is placed on the bottom of the cylinder and at the top of the piston to provide electrical insulation. Piston and the backing block serves as the electrode for passing high current. A transformer of 10V,1000A capacity is used. A 100 tonnes hydraulic press is employed to pressurise the cell assembly. Temperature of the sample is measured by using Chromel-Alumel thermocouple, which is kept nearer to the sample. It should be mentioned here that a thermal pressure of 0.3kbar is generated during the process of synthesis.

Conclusion

A simple Piston-Cylinder apparatus has been designed and fabricated for the synthesis of high T_c superconductor and other new materials. The apparatus is simple in construction and less expensive. It has been found to be successful upto 10 kbar and 1200° C. R_2CuO_4 (R-rare earths) type of compounds are being synthesised using this device.

ACKNOWLEDGEMENT

The authors **K.A.** and **C.V.** are grateful to **K. Govindarajan, P.Ch. Sahu** and his colleagues at MSD, IGCAR, Kalpakkam, India for their help and useful discussions. Thanks are due to DST for funding.

REFERENCES

[1] J.G.Bednorz and K.A.Muller, Possible High T_c Superconductivity in the Ba-La-Cu-O system, *Z.Phys.* **B64**, pp.189-193, (1986).

[2] John.W.Stewart, *The world of high pressure* Princeton, New Jersey, D.Van Nostrand company, Inc., pp.152-159, (1967).

[3] M.G.Smith, A.Manthiram, J.Zhou, J.B.Goodenough and J.T.Markert, Electron-doped superconductivity at 40K in the infinite-layer. *Nature*, **359**, pp.549-551, (1991).

[4] M.Takano, M.Azuma, Z.Hiroi, Y.Bando and Y.Takeda, Superconductivity in the Ba-Sr-Cu-O system, *Physica C* **176**, pp.441-443, (1991).

[5] M.Takano, Y.Takeda, H.Okada, M.Miyamoto and T.Kusaka $ACuO_2$ (A-Alkaline Earth) crystallizing in a layered Structure. *Physica C*, **159**, pp.375-378, (1989).

[6] M.Azuma, Z.Hiroi, M.Takano, Y.Bando & Y.Takeda Superconductivity at 110K in the infinite-layer compound $(Sr_{1-x}Ca_x)_{1-y}CuO_2$" *Nature*, vol-356, pp.775-776, (1992).

[7] H.Okada, M.Takano, Y.Takeda- Synthesis of Nd_2CuO_4 type R_2CuO_4 (R=Y,Dy,Ho,Er,Tm) under high pressure. *Physica C* **166**, pp.111-114, (1990).

[8] L.Spain and Jac.Paauwe *High Pressure Technology Vol.II* New York and Basel - Marcel Dekker. Inc., Chap-7, pp.293-317, (1977).

[9] F.P.Bundy and H.M.Strong, *Solid State Physics 13* New York and London, Academic Press, pp.81-146, (1962).

ELASTIC DISTORTIONS OF A MULTI-MODE PISTON-CYLINDER UNIT UP TO 28 MPa

G.F. Molinar(*), C. Ehrlich(†), J. Houck(†), and P.C. Cresto(*)
(*) Istituto di Metrologia "G. Colonnetti" - IMGC-CNR
Torino (Italy)
(†) Thermophysics Division
National Institute of Standards and Technology
Technology Administration
United States Department of Commerce
Gaithersburg, MD 20899 (USA)

The elastic distortions of a special hydraulic piston gauge (PG27) operating to 28 MPa in the simple, re-entrant and controlled-clearance configurations were calculated by application of an analytical iterative technique. With these calculations one can determine the radial displacements of the piston and the cylinder at any pressure and with different fluids, the pressure distribution in the clearance, and the pressure distortion coefficient of the piston-cylinder unit under conditions of use. The effective areas based on the calculated value of the pressure distortion coefficient in each of the three configurations show agreement with the experimentally determined effective areas well inside 11 parts per million (ppm).

INTRODUCTION

A special piston gauge, called PG27, for liquid media up to 28 MPa was designed and tested at the National Institute of Standards and Technology (NIST) in the USA. The main novelty of this piston gauge is that it can be operated in "simple", "re-entrant" and "controlled-clearance" configurations with the same piston-cylinder unit [1]. The Istituto di Metrologia "G. Colonnetti" (IMGC) in Italy has developed an analytical iterative method to compute, for any piston-cylinder geometry, the elastic distortions of the piston-cylinder unit, the pressure distribution in the piston-cylinder clearance and the pressure distortion coefficient. This method of calculation can also be applied to compute the effects of imposed force, torque or pressure boundary conditions on the piston-cylinder unit, and the effects of different pressurizing fluids and of the different materials used for piston-cylinder fabrication [2,3]. The present paper gives some data on the calculated variations in piston-cylinder clearance versus pressure for the PG27 unit, values of pressure distribution in the clearance, and a comparison of the experimental and calculated values of the pressure distortion coefficients for the three configurations.

ELASTIC DISTORTION

The PG27 piston-cylinder unit is made of tungsten carbide. The nominal piston diameter is 7.9 mm, the average piston area at 23 °C and atmospheric pressure is 49.02139 mm^2 (its 1σ uncertainty being ± 6.5 ppm), and the mean radial undistorted clearance is 0.527 μm. Other data of the PG27 unit can be found in paper [1] or [4]. Experimental determinations were made of elastic pressure distortion coefficients (λ) for the three basic configurations, and the following results were obtained:

λ (simple config.) = 1.15 10^{-6} MPa^{-1}

λ (re-entrant config.) = -1.96 10^{-6} MPa^{-1}

λ (controlled-clearance config.) = 0.075 10^{-6} MPa^{-1}

The above values are based on measurements which were then fitted to give a linear dependence of the effective area versus pressure. That is, the effective area at pressure P is given by the equation:

$$A_e(P) = A_0(1 + \lambda P),$$

where A_0 is the zero-pressure effective area. This linear fitting agrees to within 1 ppm with the experimental data.

Calculations of the piston and cylinder elastic distortions were made with the same iterative methods previously described [3], for the three PG27 configurations and for pressures up to 28 MPa. In all calculations convergence was obtained within four to seven iterations. The number of iterations increases (which means that the convergence is more difficult to achieve) with smaller clearances (e.g., in the case of the PG27 "re-entrant" configuration).

Fig. 1 gives the calculated values of the radial distortions of the inner surface of the PG27 cylinder at 28 MPa for each of the three configurations, versus the piston-cylinder engagement length. The length z is measured from the bottom (z=0 mm) to the top (z=27 mm) of the cylinder. The bottom of the piston cannot extend below 12 mm. The same figure also indicates the constant 0.527 μm value of the initial undistorted piston-cylinder radial clearance. It is in the "simple" configuration that the largest radial clearance (0.928 μm) occurs, while the smallest radial clearance (0.282 μm) occurs in the "re-entrant" configuration. The "controlled-clearance" configuration has radial clearance values ranging from 0.49 μm to 0.7 μm. The average radial clearance is 0.57 μm, only 0.043 μm larger than the 0.527 μm initial undistorted clearance value. This is an indication that in the present controlled-clearance configuration the distortions of the cylinder are kept relatively small, a desirable feature of a piston gauge. It should be noted that for the controlled-clearance configuration, the same experimentally-determined jacket pressure versus applied pressure relationship, $P_j = 3x10^6 + 0.36xP$, where P_j and P are in pascals, was used for both the measurements and calculations.

Calculations were made for mineral oil (m.o.) as well as for a synthetic oil (s.o.). Calculations of elastic distortions and of the pressure distribution in the clearance up to 28 MPa showed no differences due to the two different fluids, even though they are quite different, particularly their densities.

From the calculated elastic distortions we are able to draw the following conclusions:

- the cylinder undergoes larger distortions in the "simple" and "re-entrant" configurations than in the "controlled-clearance" configuration;
- the piston, in all configurations, undergoes very small (from 0.05 μm to 0.1 μm) distortions of the compression (negative) type.

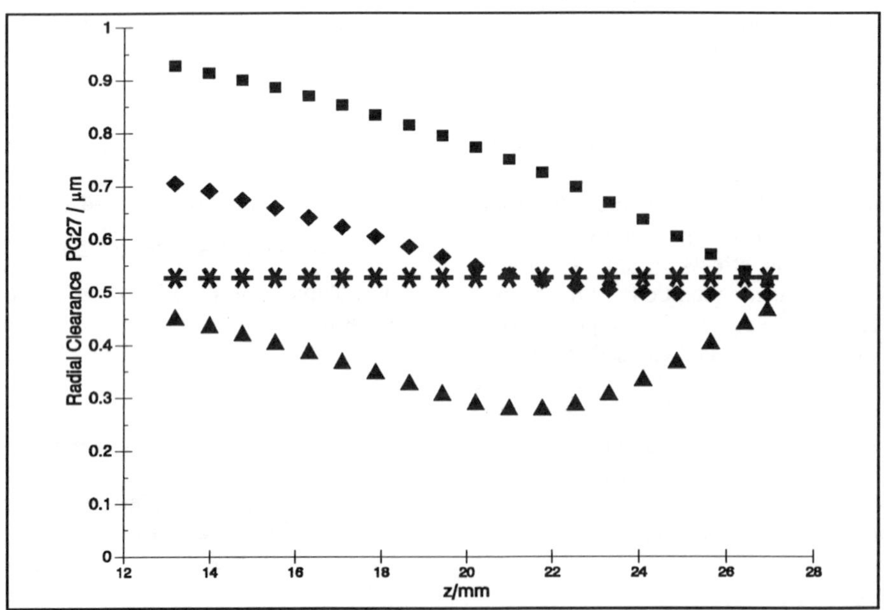

Figure 1. Calculated values of radial clearance at 28 MPa for the PG27 piston-cylinder assembly in its three basic configurations. (■) simple; (▲) re-entrant; (♦) controlled clearance; (*) 0.527 μm initial undistorted radial clearance.

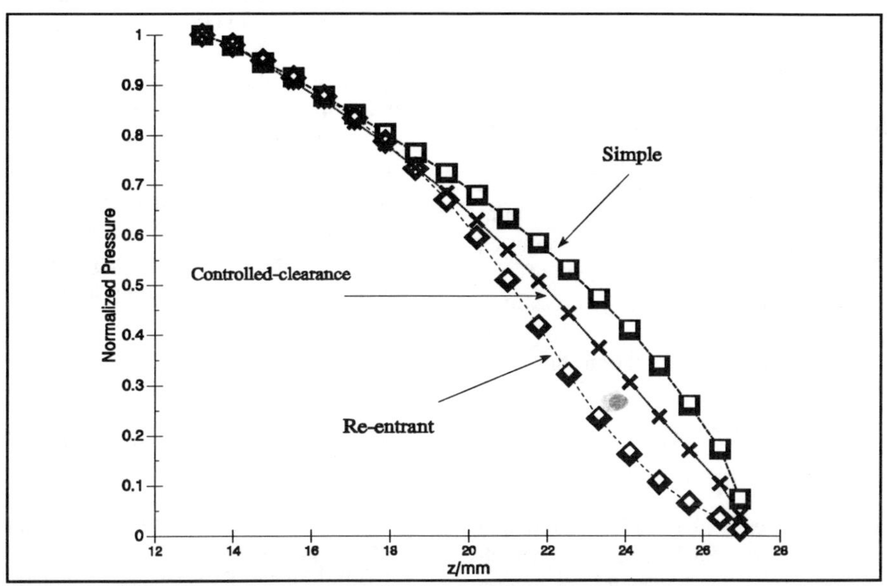

Figure 2. Normalized pressure distribution in PG27 clearance as a function of piston-cylinder engagement length. (□,■) simple (mineral oil, synthetic oil); (◊,♦) re-entrant (mineral oil, synthetic oil); (×) controlled clearance

PRESSURE DISTRIBUTION CALCULATION

Fig. 2 illustrates the normalized pressure distribution in the clearance of the PG27 piston-cylinder versus the piston-cylinder engagement length (from z=12.7 mm representing the zone of the initial piston-cylinder engagement at the measurement pressure value, to z=26.95 mm which is the top end of the cylinder). Fig. 2 shows that the pressure distribution in the clearance is not linear and its behavior largely depends on the type of piston-cylinder configuration. With the "simple" configuration, a markedly parabolic behaviour is obtained, whereas with the "re-entrant" the behaviour is "S-shaped" and represents the effect of the small and irregular clearance (see Fig. 1). The "controlled-clearance" configuration ensures the highest linearity of pressure distribution in the clearance, but even here the behavior exhibits marked nonlinear effects. It is interesting to note that the fluid does not affect the pressure distribution in the clearance for the two fluids used in the calculations.

COMPARISON OF THE PRESSURE DISTORTION COEFFICIENTS

The calculated radial distortions of the piston and cylinder (data similar to Fig. 1) and the corresponding calculated pressure distributions in the clearance (data similar to Fig. 2), at any of the pressures for which the calculations are made, can be used to compute the pressure distortion coefficient (λ) for the three configurations; such values are compared with the values obtained experimentally (see section on Elastic Distortion Calculations and [1]).

For the "simple" configuration, the λ values obtained (4 iterations) are:

λ(14 MPa, m.o.) = 1.128 10^{-6} MPa^{-1}

λ(28 MPa, m.o.) = 1.134 10^{-6} MPa^{-1}

λ(28 MPa, s.o.) = 1.132 10^{-6} MPa^{-1}

The largest difference between the experimental and the calculated values, equal to 1.9 %, (equivalent to 0.64 ppm in area at 28 MPa) indicates a very good agreement. The calculated λ values are pressure and fluid-independent.

For the "re-entrant" configuration, the λ values obtained (from 3 to 7 iterations) are:

λ(14 MPa, m.o.) = -2.23 10^{-6} MPa^{-1}

λ(28 MPa, m.o.) = -2.25 10^{-6} MPa^{-1}

λ(28 MPa, s.o.) = -2.241 10^{-6} MPa^{-1}

The largest difference between the experimental and the calculated values is 14.5 % (equivalent to 8 ppm in area at 28 MPa); also in this case the λ values proved to be pressure and fluid independent. The 8 ppm difference is still acceptable if compared, for example, with the 6 ppm three standard deviation of the experimental effective area obtained during a crossfloat.

For the "controlled-clearance" configuration, the λ values (4 iterations) are:

λ(14 MPa, m.o.) = -0.691 10^{-6} MPa^{-1}

λ(28 MPa, m.o.) = -0.279 10^{-6} MPa^{-1}

These values yield a difference of 10 to 11 ppm in area from the experimental values. Such differences, which are larger than expected, may depend on some phenomena (e.g., a reaction force on the upper cylinder due to the jacket pressure application) not taken into account in the calculations. Evidence exists as well that the radial clearance inversion observed in Figure 1 for the controlled-clearance and re-entrant configurations at the position z = 22 mm may depend on the position of the upper jacket pressure seal, which is very close to the upper end of the cylinder.

CONCLUSIONS AND DISCUSSION

- The calculated distortions of the piston and cylinder and the pressure distribution in the clearance are shown to be independent of the fluid used.
- The effective areas based upon the calculated pressure distortion coefficients at 14 and 28 MPa agree to within 1 ppm.
- The **"simple"** PG27 configuration gave very satisfactory calculated results; the agreement between the effective areas using either the calculated or experimental values of λ is within 1 ppm over the entire experimental pressure range.
- The calculation of λ for the **"re-entrant"** configuration also compares satisfactorily with the experimental value. However, because of the small radial clearance (0.282 μm at 28 MPa), the reproducibility of the experimentally-obtained effective area is not as good as that of the simple or controlled-clearance configurations [1].
- The **"controlled-clearance"** configuration has the smallest cylinder distortion and the pressure distribution with the least deviation from linearity in the clearance. At pressure values of 14 and 28 MPa the calculations agreed with the experimental results for the effective area within 11 ppm. Further, the calculations predict the anticipated advantages of controlled-clearance methods.
- There is a need for extension of the experimental and calculational investigations performed here to gauges having the same typical design as the PG27 system presented here, but operating at higher pressures.

REFERENCES

[1] K. Jain, C. Ehrlich and J. Houck, *Rev. Sci. Instrum.* 63 (5), 3127-3135 (1992).
[2] G.F. Molinar, P.C. Cresto and R. Maghenzani, *BIPM Monographie 89/1*, G.F. Molinar Editor, pp. 12-21 (1989).
[3] G.F. Molinar, R. Maghenzani, P.C. Cresto and L. Bianchi, *Metrologia* 29, pp. 425-440 (1992).
[4] G.F. Molinar, P.C. Cresto, C. Ehrlich and J. Houck, "Elastic distortion calculations on a special piston gauge (PG27) up to 28 MPa in different operational modes," presented at the Second CCM International Seminar "Pressure Metrology from 1 kPa to 1 GPa", Paris(F), June 2-4, 1993.

LOAD CYCLING AND PRESSURE EFFICIENCY IN A LARGE VOLUME CUBIC PRESS

R.A. Secco
Dept. of Geophysics
University of Western Ontario
London, Ontario, Canada N6A 5B7

Pressure efficiency is investigated as a function of load cycling for a pyrophyllite pressure medium in a cubic press. Pressure efficiency is determined by the cycle dependent applied load at the I→II and the I→III phase transitions in Bi and Tl standards, respectively. For up to five cycles, the pressure efficiency increases significantly with each cycle.

INTRODUCTION

In most high pressure experimentation, deviatoric stresses are undesirable and result mainly from the finite shear strength of the pressure transmitting medium. Soft solids such as alkali halides, pyrophyllite, graphite and boron nitride, are therefore normally chosen for pressure media to transmit uniaxial load (e.g. piston cylinder, belt, girdle, DIA-type, split sphere presses) or multi-axial load (e.g. cubic, tetrahedral presses) quasi-hydrostatically to a sample. Since the resultant 3-dimensional compression is not truly hydrostatic, as in the case of fluid pressure medium experiments[1], it must be treated in terms of the three principal stresses, σ_x, σ_y, and σ_z, acting on the sample.

The yield condition for multi-axial stress states can be formally expressed by the von Mises criterion[2]

$$\frac{1}{2^{\frac{1}{2}}}\left[(\sigma_x-\sigma_y)^2 + (\sigma_x-\sigma_z)^2 + (\sigma_y-\sigma_z)^2\right]^{\frac{1}{2}} > \sigma_c \tag{1}$$

where the combination of stresses on the lefthand side must be greater than the critical stress, σ_c, in order for flow to take place. The 3-dimensional yield surface for triaxial compression, representing the interface between elastic states of stress inside and plastic states of stress outside, is a circular cylinder as shown in Figure 1. The geometric axis of the cylinder lies along the line $\sigma_x = \sigma_y = \sigma_z$ and with a width of zero, it represents the loci of possible states of an ideal pressure transmitting material (i.e. a fluid) which has no rigidity.

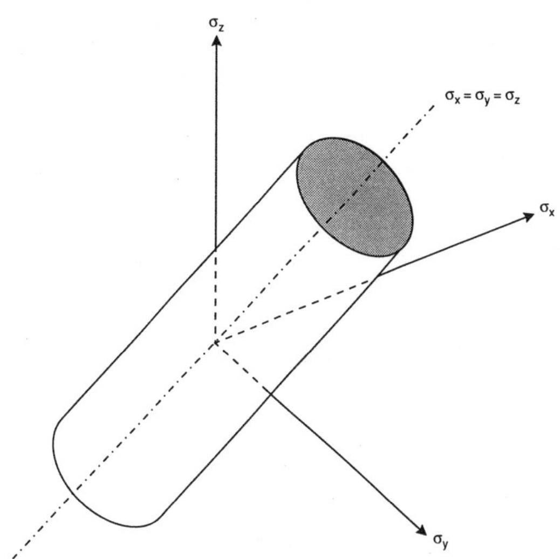

Figure 1. 3-dimensional yield envelope according to the von Mises yield criterion (after Fenner, 1989).

Internal cell pressure (i.e. sample pressure) is often determined via the load applied by the rams. Based on prior calibrations, using structure transformations in pressure standards such as Hg, Bi, Tl, Ba, SiO_2 and Fe_2SiO_4, a pressure vs. load curve can be confidently employed in experiments designed for a single excursion to high pressure. That is, the efficiency of pressure generated by the applied load is reproducible from one experiment to the next (assuming other factors that affect the shear strength of the pressure medium, including temperature[3,4] and humidity[5] are held constant). However, in experiments involving cyclic loading to the same or different maximum loads, as in equilibrium studies of, or physical property measurements through, large |dp/dT| valued phase boundaries, internal calibrants are required in each experiment. Due to work hardening of the pressure medium and the cell components, the pressure efficiency increases with each new cycle. This is illustrated for constant plastic strain cycling in Figure 2 where the area of the stress-strain

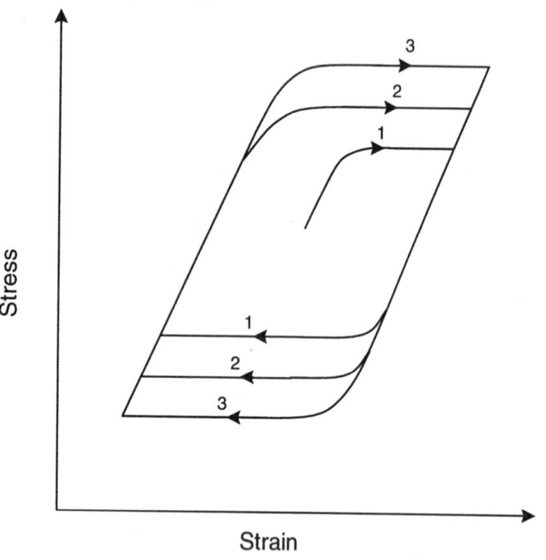

Figure 2. Cyclic stress-strain behaviour for a material that cyclically hardens (after Courtney, 1990).

hysteresis loop increases with the number of cycles. Concomitant with the increase in stress for each new cycle is a reduction in hydrostaticity. Therefore, the increase in deviatoric stress in the pressure medium resulting from work hardening and the increase in pressure efficiency are directly related. The investigation of these two effects is the purpose of this study.

EXPERIMENTAL

The experiments were carried out in a 1,000-ton cubic anvil press using 1 inch cubes of pyrophyllite. The pyrophyllite used was the natural material as mined in South Africa and supplied by AlSiMag Technical Ceramics, Inc., Laurens, S.C., U.S.A. as Grade "A" lava. A single strip of either Bi or Tl (purity 99.999%), of approximate l x w x t dimensions of 1.0 x 0.5 x 0.1 mm was placed in the centre of a pyrophyllite half-cube as shown in Figure 3. Two Cu foil

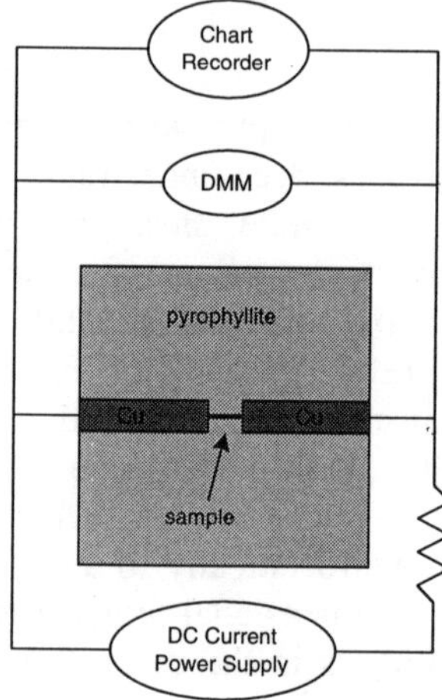

Figure 3. Schematic diagram of the pressure cell (in cross-sectional view) and measurement system.

electrodes were overlain on the ends of the sample strip before the other half-cube was put in place. The metal strips were handled under Ar atmosphere to avoid sample oxidation. Each cube was loaded in the press and brought to a starting load of approximately 1500 psi not longer than 3 minutes after it was prepared. All experiments were at room temperature. Measurements and chart recordings of the voltage drop across the sample were made with increasing and decreasing pressure while the dc current was held constant by means of a large series resistor. The load was increased in 200 psi steps (our present pumping system does not allow controllable, slow, continuous loading) and the load was released continuously at rates varying between 380-730 psi/min.

RESULTS AND DISCUSSION

Examples of loading and unloading chart recorder traces for Tl and Bi are shown in Figures 4a and 4b, respectively. These two sets of traces have two common features. Firstly, the load at which the transition occurs in each sample is significantly reduced on subsequent cycles. This increase in pressure efficiency can be explained by work hardening in the pyrophyllite caused by load cycling. Since the pressure medium becomes work hardened, the confining pressure must also become less hydrostatic. Although these experiments were not designed to measure quantitatively the magnitude of deviatoric stresses within the cell, as for example was done by measurements of dislocation density in MgO and San Carlos olivine single crystals[7] or by geometrical measurements of compressed cylindrical specimens[8], the traces in Figure 4 do qualitatively indicate an increase in deviatoric stress by the sluggishness in the transition region for the higher cycle runs.

a)

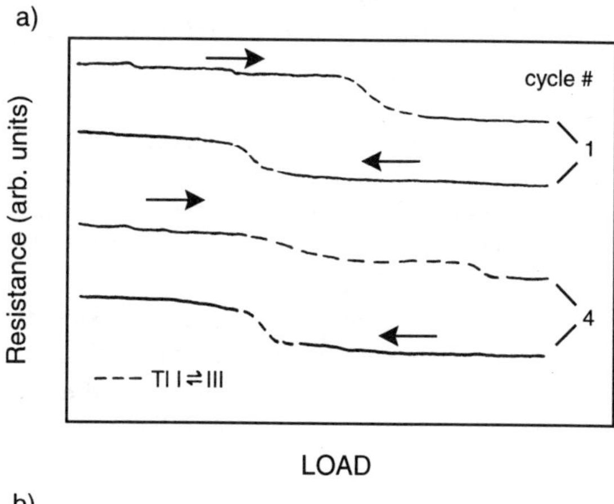

b)

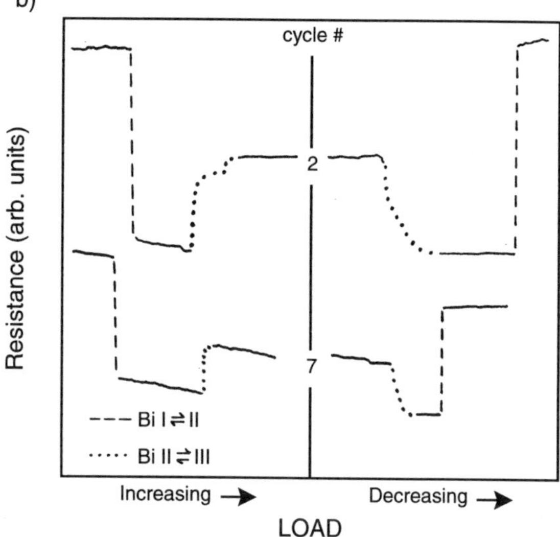

Figure 4. Examples of loading and unloading chart recorder traces for (a) Tl and (b) Bi in a pyrophillite pressure medium at room temperature showing the Bi I⇌II and Tl I⇌III transitions, respectively.

The results of applied load at the Bi I→II and Tl I→III transitions as a function of cycle number are plotted in Figure 5. They self-consistently and clearly indicate that cyclic loading increases the pressure efficiency. The Bi data suggest a constant pressure efficiency after 5 loading cycles for pyrophyllite. The change in strength of the pressure medium with cyclic loading demands a pressure vs. load calibration curve for each cycle, as illustrated in Figure 6. The error in pressure at 37 kbar amounts to 6 kbar or approximately 16% for a 3 cycle loading.

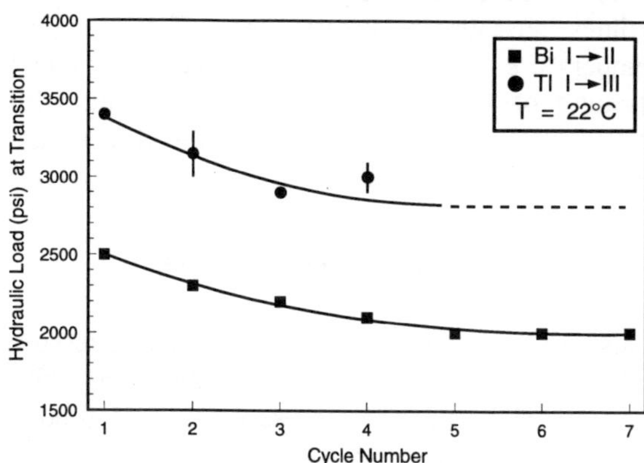

Figure 5. Ram loads at the Bi I→II and Tl I→III transitions (on-loading) for repeated cycles.

The results of this preliminary investigation point to the need for the characterization of the mechanical properties of the pressure medium if cyclic loading is to be carried out on a single pressure cell. Work-hardening in other pressure

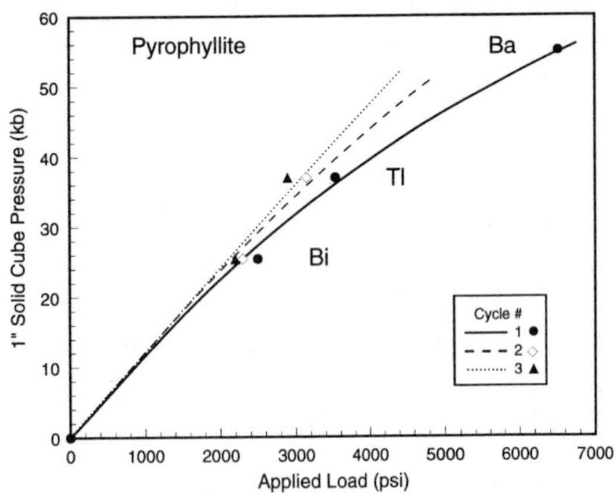

Figure 6. Cell pressure vs. applied load calibration curves for three cycles.

medium materials like BN, graphite, and alkali halides must also be investigated. The effects of temperature and grain size on the mechanical strength of these materials in combination with cyclic loading must also be known if accurate pressures are to be determined for any given cycle.

ACKNOWLEDGEMENTS

This work resulted from a detailed pressure calibration of our cubic press following a major mechanical repair. The press repair was funded by the University of Western Ontario. I thank H.H. Schloessin for commenting on the manuscript, R. Tucker for technical help, M. Rice for typing the manuscript and A. Bukata for help with preparation of the figures.

REFERENCES

[1] R.A. Secco and H.H. Schloessin, "On-line p,T calibration based on well-known phase transitions", *J. Appl. Phys.* 60(5), pp.1626-1633 (1986).

[2] R.T. Fenner, *Mechanics of Solids*, Oxford, Blackwell Scientific Publications, 1989, ch.9, pp.516-519.

[3] I. Sigalas, J.B. Clark and S. Hart, "Shear strength measurements at high temperatures and pressures", *High Temp. High Press.* 15, pp.553-564 (1983).

[4] R.B. Graf and C.O. Hulse, "Effect of temperature on the mechanical properties of solid pressure-transmitting media. I: Talc", *J. Appl. Phys.*, 35 no.12, pp.3466-3468 (1964).

[5] I. Sigalas, A. Vlachos and G. Vekinis, "Shear strength of pyrophyllite and talc as a function of pressure, temperature and relative humidity", *High Temp. High Press.* 18, pp.293-300 (1986).

[6] T.H. Courtney, *Mechanical Behaviour of Materials*, New York, McGraw-Hill, 1990, ch.12, p.588.

[7] J. Ingrin and R.C. Liebermann, "Deviatoric stress in a girdle-anvil type high-pressure apparatus: Effect on the quartz-coesite phase transformation", *Phys.Earth Planet.Int.*, 54, pp.378-385 (1989).

[8] J.M. Edmond and M.S. Paterson, "Strength of solid pressure media and implications for high pressure apparatus", *Contr. Mineral. and Petrol.* 30, pp.141-160 (1971).

OPTICAL NONMAGNETIC LOW-TEMPERATURE HYDROSTATIC PRESSURE CELLS UP TO 3 GPa

Eremets, M.I.*, Utjuzh, A.N.

High Pressure Physics Institute, Academy of Sciences of Russia, Troitsk, Russia, 142092.
*Physique des Milieux Condensés, CNRS (URA 0782) Université P. et M. Curie, T 13, E 4, B 77, place Jussieu, F-75252 Paris, France

Two kinds of sealing for optical windows are proposed: a) modified Poulter sealing with a metallic gasket between the window and the support and b) sealing on the cylindrical surface of the window with the help of a Teflon cell. The pressure distribution in the gasket is calculated for a window and a diamond anvil. Three small non-magnetic low-temperature optical clamped cells with electrical leads are described with outer diameters of 32, 27 and 20 mm, operating up to 3 GPa (the smallest one was tested up to 2 GPa).

INTRODUCTION

For the majority of physical applications a hydrostatic cell has to have both electrical and optical inputs, it has to be non-magnetic, resist low-temperatures and be rather miniature. Such cells are useful for the investigation of semiconductor and superconductor physics. Cells were developed for pressures up to 2 GPa [1,2]. In the 2-3 GPa region transport cells [3-6] and pure optical cells, up to 4.5 GPa, [7,8] are known. The methods proposed in [7,8] have some restrictions. The unsupported area is very small and a very good optical contact between surfaces is required to create reliable sealing.

We present the combined miniature optical - transport hydrostatic cells which are working up to 3 GPa. Two new methods for the sealing of optical windows are proposed. In the first a metallic gasket between window and support is used, in another sealing is achieved on the cylindrical surface of the Teflon cell. Application to a diamond anvil cell is proposed.

SEALING OF WINDOW

We used a small aperture to achieve high pressures, as in [7,8]. An aperture of diameter 0.9 mm corresponds to a rather large angle aperture of 30° when the light is focused through a sapphire window of thickness 3 mm. But the unsupported area principle does not work in the case of the small aperture. To avoid this difficulty we used the arrangement shown in fig.1. An indium ring was placed between window and seat. The ring is slightly pressed by the window to form the initial sealing. Afterwards the sealing is effective during pressure generation due to the large initial unsupported area. Under pressure, the indium ring is extruded in both directions maintaining the seal. The required window seal surface quality is low, it can be used directly even after a lathe cutting. Well polished windows (sapphire) were used. We did not round the edge of aperture as in [7-9]. In our opinion the main reason for successful operation of the window up to the highest pressures is the favorable pressure distribution under the window.

Pressure distribution in the gasket

Consider a gasket as a disk of a material with compressive yield strength σ_0, which is pressed between two rigid planes, and calculate a force balance on a small volume element of height h located between radii r and r+δr inside an angle $\delta\Theta$, fig.1. It can be shown that equation of equilibrium is very simple:

$$d\sigma_r/dr=\sigma_0/h \qquad (1)$$

when the "sticking condition" ("gluing" the gasket

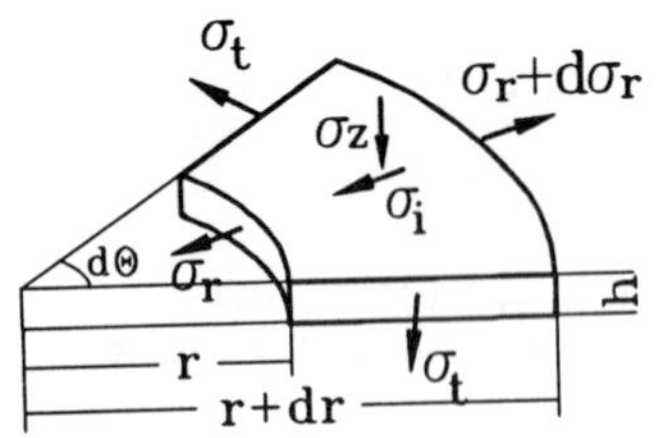

Fig.1a. Force balance on a volume element of the gasket.

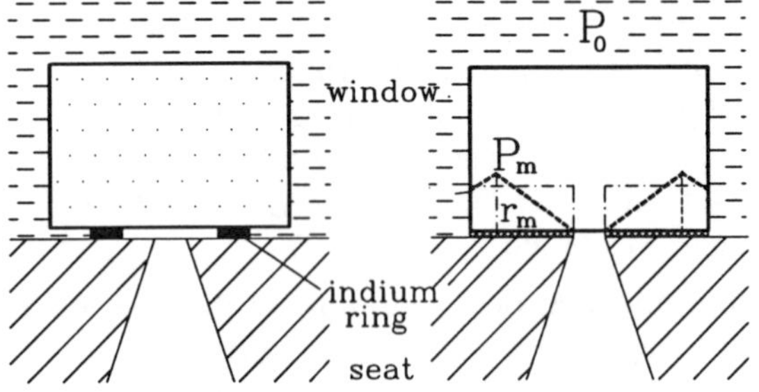

Fig.1b. Sealing of window with the help of indium ring placed between window and seat.

Fig.1c. Pressure distribution on the gasket (dashed line), dash-dot line - pressure distribution when the dry contact.

to the plane) is fulfilled: $2\mu\sigma_z \geq \sigma_0$, where μ is the friction coefficient between the disk and plane. This condition is easily fulfilled for soft materials like indium (σ_0 = 2.6 MPa). The normal stress σ_z is approximately equal to the radial component σ_r because $\sigma_r = \sigma_z + \sigma_0 \approx \sigma_z$. Boundary conditions are: $\sigma_r(b)=0$ and $\sigma_r(a) = P_0$ - pressure in medium surrounding the window, a is outer diameter and b is the inner diameter of the disk. An additional condition is that the force applied to the window by the hydrostatic medium is equal to the integral of the pressure distribution on the gasket. So, the pressure distribution σ_z on the radius of the gasket is

$$\sigma_z=\sigma_0(r-b)/h \text{ at } r\leq r_m; \quad \sigma_z=\sigma_0(a-r)/h+P_0 \text{ at } r\geq r_m \tag{2}$$

$$r_m^3=(a^3+b^3)/2;$$

$$\sigma_{max}=P_0[1+(a-b)/\{-a-b+\sqrt[3]{4(a^3+b^3)}\}]/2$$

where r_m is the radius when the maximum pressure σ_m is achieved. The pressure distribution in the gasket is plotted in fig.1 by dashed line. The gasket completely changes the pressure distribution in comparison to the dry contact (dash-dot line in fig.1) and makes the pressure distribution much more smooth.

This consideration can be applied also to diamond anvils. It is known that large stresses appear at the edge of the aperture under loading [10-12] and sometimes anvils are broken down for this reason. Metallic films made of soft material which create "conical " pressure distribution as shown in fig.1 make stresses distribution in anvils more favorable. In particular, depolarization by hydrostatic windows and diamond anvils has to be sufficiently decreased, because the depolarization is maximal in the places of maximum shear stress, typically at the edge of the aperture.

Teflon sealing of window

Here we describe an even more simple method of window sealing by using a Teflon cell, fig.2. The window is not sealed by the contact with the plug, but on the Be-Cu ring around the window. Therefore the quality of the window contact surface and the plug is also minimal, it has to be only flat. We used Staycast epoxy in the contact area or else direct dry contact, with the same success. The sealing is achieved on the top of the teflon tube where the contact pressure is higher than the hydrostatic pressure inside the cell due to the yield strength of teflon.

CONSTRUCTION OF CELLS

Even without optical input the achievement of 3 GPa region is a difficult problem for non-magnetic cells. There is a strong limitation to the material, in most cases Be - Cu was used. A pressure of 3 GPa is an upper practical limit even for a double-walled cylinder [4]. The non-magnetic low-temperature alloy NiCrAl (hardness up to 60 HRC) allows 3 GPa to be approached more regularly [5,6]. In our construction a double-walled cylinder was used with NiCrAl alloy (hardness 55HRC) as the insert. The body was made of Be-Cu, of hardness HRC38. Both the body and the insert were autofretaged.

The feature of our cells is that the Teflon

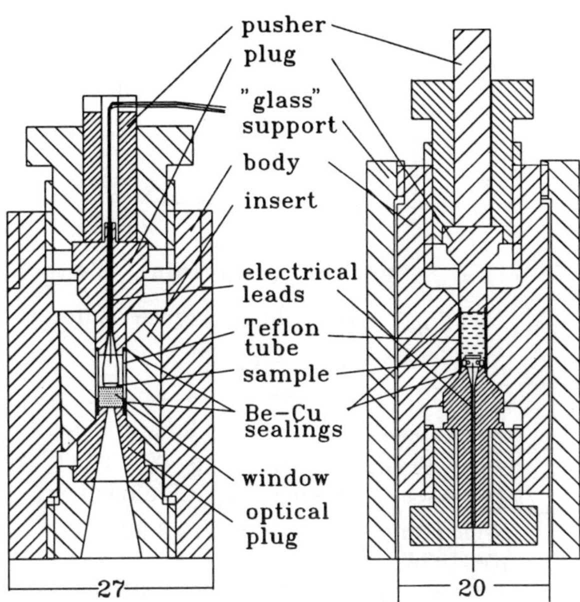

Fig.2. The optical cell. The window is sealed on the contact of a Teflon cell with a Be-Cu ring around the window.

Fig.3. The miniature hydrostatic cell of Ø20 mm.

used. Another feature of the cell interior is the using a short cylinder. Because the sample thickness is small the height of the pressure volume, under highest pressures is ≤ 4 mm with the sample holder and a pressure gauge (manganin wire), which was constructed as short as possible, less than 2 mm. In this case there is a sufficient massive support of the loaded piece of the cylinder and, consequently, higher pressures than with a long cylinder can be achieved. With this approach the cell was built very small, exterier diameter 27 mm, inner Ø4 mm, fig.2. The cell of Ø32, inner Ø6,5 mm has a similar construction. The cell of Ø20 mm, inner Ø3.4 mm has a one-body construction, fig.3.

In these constructions the weakest part in the cell is the neck of the optical plug, which is made of NiCrAl alloy. At pressures above 2.6 - 2.8 GPa small cracks sometimes appeared. Above these pressures we can use a plug made of tungsten carbide.

The electrical leads are also working at the highest pressures. In the cell Ø32 mm we used the leads [13], fig.4, as it takes a small space and

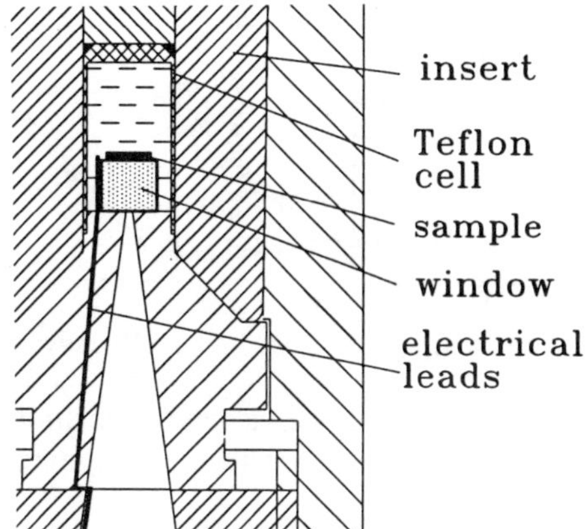

Fig.4. Optical end electrical inputs in the cell of Ø32 mm.

therefore it is possible to make a combination with the optical input in the same plug. To extend the pressure limit a long and small diameter (15 - 25 mm, Ø0,4 - 0.7 mm) channel for electrical leads was made. Staycast epoxy with a filler of hard material was used for gluing the pillar of the leads: more than 20 copper wires of diameter 0.04 - 0.07 mm.

Operation and testing of the cells

To maintain pressure after generation under press the "glass" support was used, fig.3. The cell is in the strained state during loading and therefore the loss of pressure during clamping is small, 0.03 to 0.05 GPa. During the cooling the lost of pressure is 0.2-0.4 GPa. The cells of Ø32 mm and Ø27 mm were tested up to 2.5 GPa at helium temperature. The first two cells were tested at 300 K repeatedly without damage up to 2.8 GPa with combined optical - electrical inputs and the cell, and the cell of Ø27 mm up to 3.15 GPa, in the version when the electrical plug instead of the optical one was used. A load curve and phase transitions in bismuth are shown in fig.5,6. The 20 mm cell, fig.3 was tested up to 2 GPa. For demonstration, the dependence of the ruby shift under pressure was recorded on a manganin gauge, fig.7. In this particular experiment pressure was limited by allowing displacement of the plug.

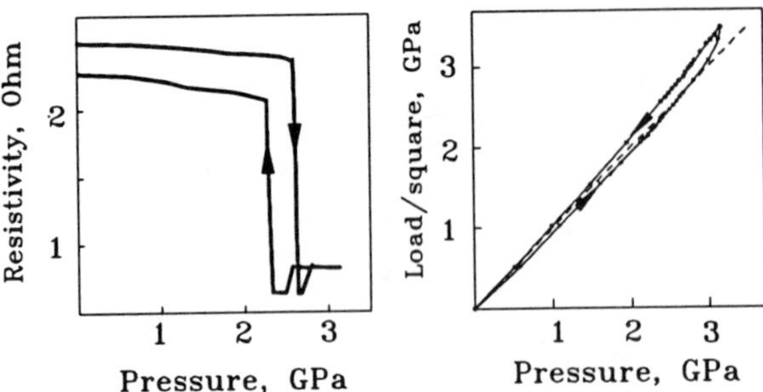

Fig.5,6. The loaded curve and transitions in bismuth recorded with manganin gauge for the cell shown in fig.2.

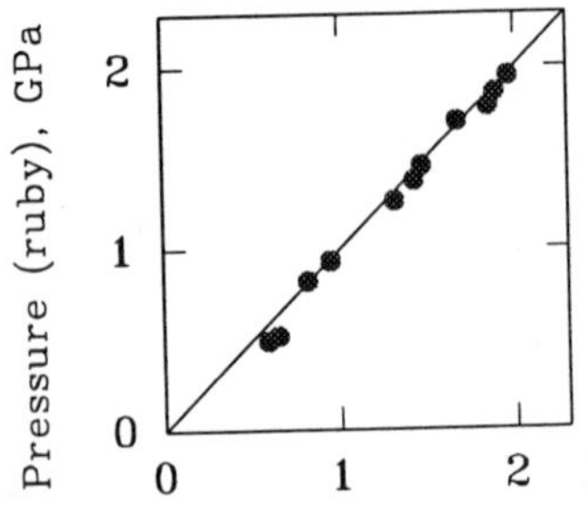

Fig.7. Ruby luminescence shift

Conclusions.

New methods of sealing of optical window in a hydrostatic cell are proposed. In first a metallic gasket between a window and a support is used. The gasket completely changes the pressure distribution under window and eliminates stress concentrations at the edge of aperture. In the second method sealing is achieved with a Teflon cell at the cylindrical surface of a window. Both methods were tested up to 2.8 GPa with a sapphire window.

The Teflon cell principle has been applied successively to the construction of the cell to simplify and miniaturize it. Three cells of outer diameter 32, 27, 20 mm were developed. The cell of ∅27 mm was tested up to 3.15 GPa with electrical leads. The cells were tested up to 2.5 GPa at helium temperature.

Acknowledgements

We are grateful to prof. E.S.Itskevich, A.N.Voronovskij, A.G.Gapotchenko, L.M.Kashirskaja for discussions and for the detail acquaintance with their cells and V.A.Kudrjashov and V.A.Guzov for the technical assistance.

References

[1] Z.Wasilewski, S.Porowski, R.A.Stradling, *J. Phys. E: Sci. Instrum.* 19, pp. 480-482 (1986).

[2] J.M.Besson, J.P.Pinceaux, R.Piotrzkowski, *High Temp. - High Pressures* 6 pp. 101 - 106(1974).

[3] R.E.Jones Jr., G.C.Anderson,W.J.Keeler, *Rev. Sci. Instrum.* 46 pp. 1025-1027 (1975).

[4] H.Fujiwara, H.Kadomatsu, K.Tohma, *Rev. Sci. Instrum.* 51, pp. 1345- 1348 (1980).

[5] A.N.Voronovskij, Ye.M.Dizhur, Ye.S.Itskevich, *Sov. JETP* 77 pp. 161-164 (1979).

[6] S.L.Budko, A.G.Gapotchenko, Ye.S.Itskevich, Fisika Metallov Metallovedenie 62 pp. 76-78 (1986).

[7] E.Whalley, A.Lavergne, P.T.T.Wong *Rev. Sci. Instrum.* 47 pp. 845-848 (1976).

[8] A.Lavergne, E.Whalley, *Rev. Sci. Instrum.* 50 pp. 962-963 (1979).

[9] W.F.Sherman, A.A.Stadtmuller, *Experimental techniques in high-pressure research*, John Wiley & Sons Ltd, 1987.

[10] D.M.Adams, A.C.Show, J.Phys.D:Appl.Phys. 15 pp. 1609-1635 (1981).

[11] H.C.Alt, J.Kalus, *Rev. Sci. Instrum.* 53 pp. 1235-1239 (1982).

[12] D.P.Shelton, *Rev. Sci. Instrum.* 63 pp. 3978-3982 (1992).

[13] M.I.Eremets, J.S.Itskevich, Yu.V.Kosichkin, V.B.Anzin, A.M.Shirokov, *Instr. Exp. Tech.* 2, (1978).

THE APPARATUS FOR MECHANICAL TESTING OF MATERIALS UNDER HIGH HYDROSTATIC PRESSURE WITH THE IN-SITU ACOUSTIC EMISSION ANALYZER

Z. Witczak, R. Jemielniak, J. Szczepek
High Pressure Research Center, Polish Academy of Sciences
Sokołowska 29/37
01-142 Warszawa, Poland

The universal (liquid or gas as pressure medium) apparatus for mechanical testing of materials under constant hydrostatic pressure (up to 1.5 GPa) is presented. Main characteristics — load range: 0–20 kN; cross-head displacement range: 0–30 mm; cross-head speed range: 0.01–0.15 μm/s. Both tension and compression tests can be performed. The apparatus is equipped with the piezoelectric sensors made out of monocrystalline lithium niobate to enable the in-situ registration of the acoustic emission (AE) signals from the tested specimens. The sensors co-work with the AE signals analizer GACEK within the frequency range from 50 kHz to 2 MHz and 90 dB dynamic range. The analyzer digitizes AE signals and prepares the energy and amplitude spectra of AE events. The tests of the apparatus are described.

INTRODUCTION

Acoustic emission (AE) techniques are used for monitoring the process of plastic deformation and fracture of materials being mechanically tested. They ware applied in high pressure investigations of rocks (e.g. [1,2]) which are acoustically very active. In case of metals there is a problem of detection the small acoustic activity of the material over the noise made by the high pressure apparatus itself. We propose the usage of AE sensors made of monocrystalline piezoelectric materials that can be placed near the sample and that can operate in high pressure conditions.

DESCRIPTION OF APPARATUS

A schematic view of the high pressure apparatus is presented in Figure 1. After generation a required pressure with a piston or an outer compressor (the piston is replaced by the plug with a capillary) the two-layer high pressure vessel can move with a constant speed (0.01–0.15 μm/s). The distance between the piston and the plug is constant so the pressure remains constant too. The samples can be tested in compression (Fig. 2) or tension (yokes are needed) up to the 20 kN load.

A piezoelectric sensor cut out of a single crystal of $LiNbO_3$ (Y-35^0) is used as a dynamometer and an AE sensor (resonance at 3 MHz), simultaneously. Both electric signals are separated in an electronic equipment. The load is measured with the 3 % accuracy. The AE signal is amplified (100 dB) and analized (amplitude and energy) at 15 levels (every 6 dB up to 90 dB) by an acoustic signal analyzer GACEK.

A LVDT sensor is used for measuring the displacement of the pressure vessel (upper anvil) against the outer chamber (lower anvil) with the 1 μm accuracy. The elastic compliance of the loading system is taken into acount (0.15 μm/N).

All data from the experimental setup are preacqusited by GACEK and sent to the computer. The results are displayed at the screen during tests (tables or graphs) and stored for further acquisition.
The yoke system for tensile tests is equipped with an additional AE sensor placed on the face of the specimen, while the dynamometer sensor is of a sandwich type to raise its sensitivity.

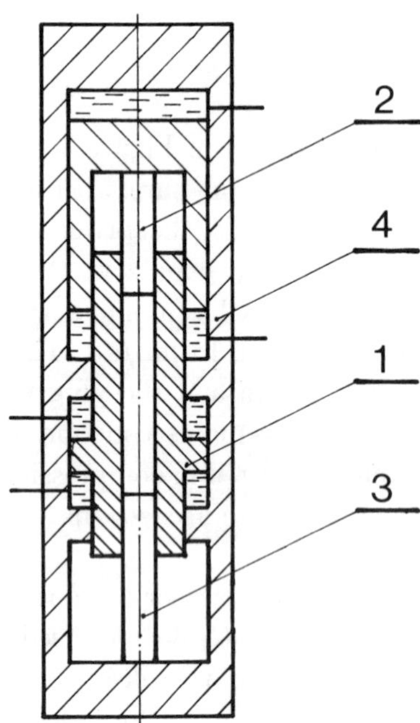

Figure 1. Schematic view of apparatus for mechanical testing of materials under high hydrostatic pressure; 1 - high pressure vessel, 2 - piston, 3 - plug, 4 - outer chamber.

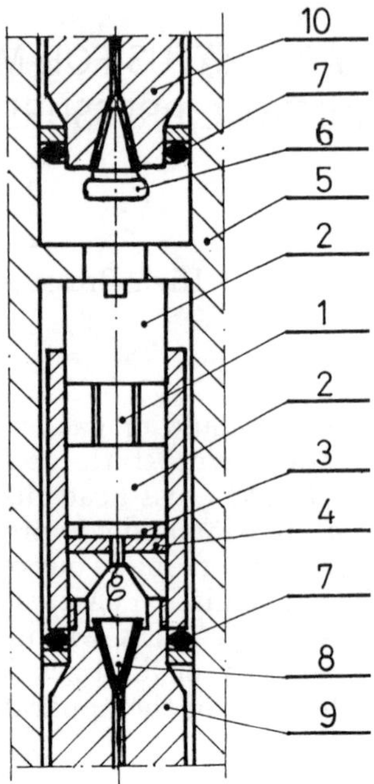

Figure 2. Setup for the compression tests: 1 - sample, 2 - anvils, 3 - piezoelectric sensor, 4 - insulator, 5 - pressure vessel, 6 - manganin coil, 7 - seals, 8 - electric fit-through, 9 - plug, 10 - piston.

TESTS

Compression tests on annealed copper were performed to estimate the capability of the system. Copper has already been investigated under pressure (tension tests) and no effect of the pressure [3], or very small one [4], on the flow stress of this material was found. Theoretically an increase of the flow stress under pressure can be expected because of its effect on dislocations [5], while for tough pitch copper some decrease under pressure was observed [4]. That was because of the elastic heterogeneity of the material [6].

In our tests (Fig. 3) there was the same effect, as the material contained numerous oxide inclusions (Fig. 4). At the same time an AE activity changed dramatically (Fig. 5), which indicates a high sensitivity of AE method to the state of dislocations in the material.

The same effect is distinctly visible in the distribution curves of AE signals for various conditions of deformation of the material (Fig. 6). In this case the depinning effect of high hydrostatic pressure on dislocations results in decreasing the number of higher energy AE signals.

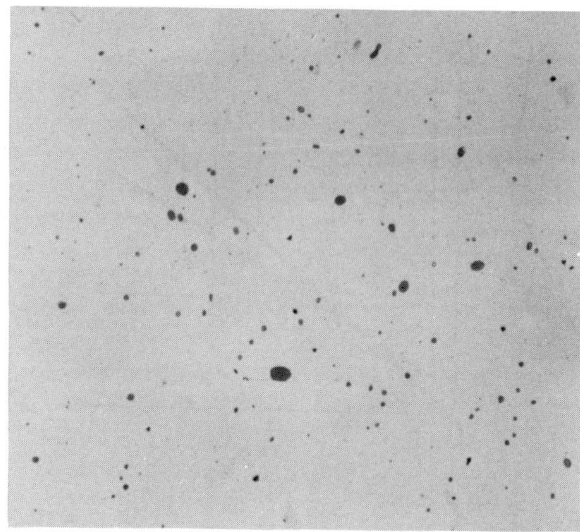

Figure 4. Optical micrograph of the annealed copper.

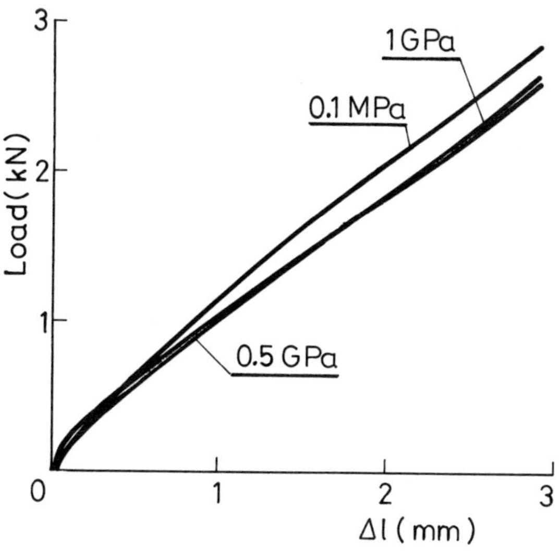

Figure 3. Compression diagrams for copper under various hydrostatic pressures.

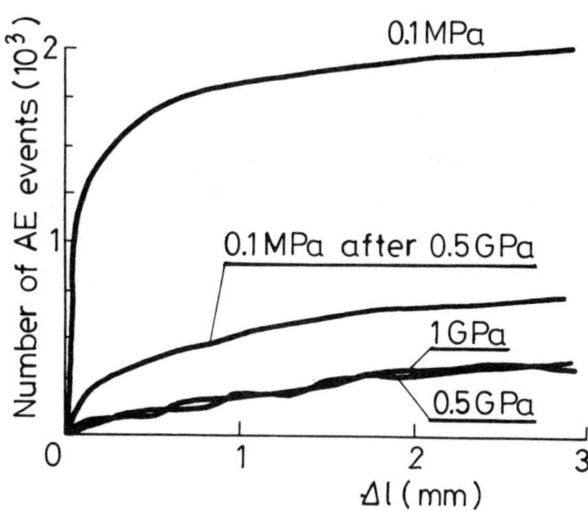

Figure 5. Acoustic activity of the annealed copper during compression tests under various hydrostatic pressures. The sample pressurized at 0.5 GPa was aged for 26 h at room temperature before testing.

CONCLUSION

An application of acoustic emission techniques for monitoring the mechanical tests of metals under pressure gives additional, very clear information about the real structure of the material under high pressure circumstances.

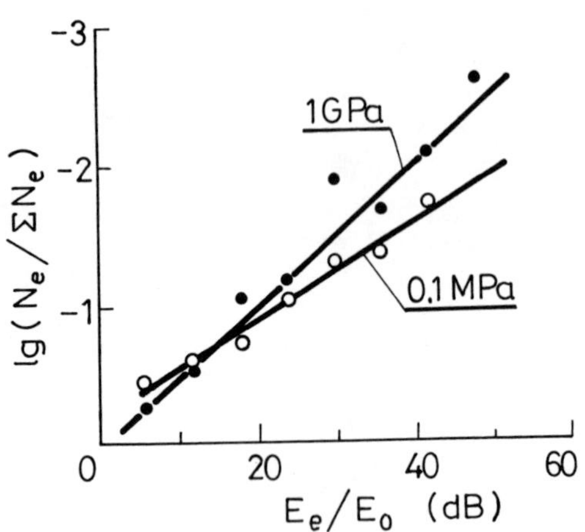

Figure 6. Energy distribution of AE signals for copper being deformed under various pressures.

ACKNOWLEDGEMENTS

The authors thank the State Committee for Scientific Research in Poland for support of this work (grant 3-P407-071-04).

REFERENCES

[1] C.H. Scholz, *J. Geophys. Res.* 73, pp. 1417–1432 (1968).

[2] H. Yukutake, *J. Seismol. Soc. Jpn.* 35, pp. 223–235 (1982).

[3] M. Brandes, Mechanical Properties of Materials under Hydrostatic Pressure, in The Mechanical Behaviour of Materials under Pressure, ed. H.Ll.D. Pugh,Elsevier, Amsterdam, 1970.

[4] S. Yoshida, A. Oguchi and M. Nobuki, *Trans. JIM* 12, pp. 238–242 (1971).

[5] W.A. Spitzig and O. Richmond, *Acta Metall. Mater.* 32, 3, pp. 457–463 (1984).

[6] S.V. Radcliffe, Pressure-Induced Effects on Direct Structure and Properties, in The Mechanical Behaviour of Materials under Pressure, ed. H.Ll.D. Pugh, Elsevier, Amsterdam, 1970.

INVESTIGATION OF ANNULAR FORCES USING AN OSCILLATING, GAS-OPERATED PISTON GAUGE

T. Lettieri, J. Kelley, and C. Ehrlich
National Institute of Standards and Technology
Thermophysics Division
Met-A55
Gaithersburg, MD 20899

We attempt to understand and measure the frictional forces in the annulus between the piston and the cylinder of a gas-operated piston gauge by measuring the damping of a vertically oscillating piston. For all gases used, thermal losses in the volume beneath the piston dominate the damping.

INTRODUCTION

To improve the calibration accuracy of gas-operated (pneumatic) piston gauges as primary standards, it is important to understand the forces that act on the piston and, thereby, influence the effective area of the piston. One of the least-quantified of these forces is the (frictional) force on the piston that occurs due to the flowing gas in the narrow annulus between the piston and the cylinder. In an attempt to measure this annular force, the experiments reported here look at the damped vertical oscillation of a piston/weight stack after it is excited by a delta-function impulse. Since the piston is moving during these measurements, the system is called the dynamic piston gauge apparatus, or DPGA.

THEORY OF THE OSCILLATING PISTON GAUGE

If the piston/weight stack of a gas-operated piston gauge is given a vertical impulsive force, then the vertical displacement of the piston as a function of time is that of a damped harmonic oscillator:

$$z(t) = z_o + z_m e^{-\Gamma t}\cos(\omega_o t + \phi) \qquad (1)$$

where z_o is the equilibrium position, z_m is the amplitude of the oscillations, ω_o is the oscillation frequency, t is time, Γ is the damping coefficient, and ϕ is an arbitrary phase angle. The experiment reported here involves two measurable quantities, ω_o and $Q = \omega_o/2\Gamma$. If there were no damping in Equation 1, then the frequency of oscillation, under adiabatic conditions, would be given by the Ruchhardt formula, $\omega_o = (\gamma A^2 P_o/MV_o)^{1/2}$, in which γ is the ratio of the specific heat capacities of the gas (C_p/C_v), A is the geometrical area of the piston, P_o is the pressure at the bottom of the piston, M is the mass of the piston plus the weight stack, and V_o is the volume beneath the piston [1]. For isothermal oscillations, the frequency is given by the same expression, except with γ set equal to 1.

Annular Friction Losses

The viscous force (or "friction") on the oscillating piston due to the gas in the annulus has two components, a static one (f_s) and a dynamic one (f_d). The static force on the piston is due to the constant flow of gas past the piston as it falls slowly or remains at a fixed height, while the dynamic component is due to viscous damping by the gas as the piston oscillates up and down. Although it is the static component of the force which influences the effective area of the piston, the dynamic component is the one that can be measured with the DPGA. However, the two quantities are related, especially at low frequencies.

It can be shown that the (upward) static annular force, assuming viscous flow for calculational simplicity, is given approximately by

$$f_s = \pi r_o h \Delta P, \quad (2)$$

where r_o is the piston radius, h is the gap width, and ΔP is the pressure differential between the top and the bottom of the piston.

The dynamic force, f_d, is given approximately by

$$f_d = (2\pi r_o L\eta/h)\dot{z} \quad (3)$$

in which L is the contact length between the piston and the cylinder, $\dot{z}$ is the instantaneous velocity of the piston, and η is the viscosity of the gas.

If we assume that there are no other losses in the system, then it can be shown using Eqs. 2 and 3 that the expressions for ω_o and the viscous damping coefficient, Γ_v, are approximately:

$$\omega_o^2 = \gamma P_o(A + \pi r_o h)^2/MV_o \quad \text{and} \quad (4)$$

$$\Gamma_v = \pi r_o L\eta/Mh. \quad (5)$$

Note that the expression for frequency is the same as that for adiabatic (Ruchhardt) oscillations with the geometrical area, A, replaced by $A + \pi r_o h$. This is just another way of saying that the static annular force increases the effective area of the piston.

Thermal Losses

In addition to the annular friction, there is also thermal loss, through the walls of the volume beneath the piston, of the heat generated by compression and expansion of the gas in the volume. Equations 4 and 5 must be modified to account for these losses. Clark and Katz [2] give the following expression for the corrected oscillation frequency (ω_m):

$$\omega_m^2 = \omega_o^2/\{(1 + G + G^2)\} - 2\Gamma^2 \quad (6)$$

where the ω_o in these equations is the same as the adiabatic frequency for undamped motion; $G = (3/R_o)(\gamma - 1)(1 - \xi)/(\alpha\sqrt{2})$; R_o is the radius of the (assumed) spherical volume beneath the piston; $3/R_o = s$ is the surface-to-volume ratio of this sphere; $\alpha^2 = \omega_m C_p \rho/k$; C_p is the heat capacity at constant pressure; ρ is the gas density; and k is the thermal conductivity of the gas. The ξ parameter is an empirical measure of how adiabatic the oscillations are: if $\xi = 1$, then the oscillations are completely adiabatic, and if $\xi = 0$ they are completely isothermal. In general, $0 < \xi < 1$.

The damping coefficient due to thermal losses can be derived from Clark and Katz's results as

$$\Gamma_T \approx \omega_o G/2$$
$$= \omega_o(3/2R_o)(\gamma - 1)(1 - \xi)/(\alpha\sqrt{2}) \quad (7)$$

in the absolute mode (assumed for calculational simplicity). We would like to maximize the ratio of the annular forces to the thermal losses i.e., maximize f_d/f_T or, equivalently, Γ_v/Γ_T. Taking the ratio of Equations 5 and 7, and using some substitutions, results in

$$\Gamma_v/\Gamma_T = [(2\sqrt{2}/\sqrt{RT})(\pi g)^{1/4}] \times [(\eta\sqrt{C_p})/(\gamma\text{-}1)\gamma^{1/4}\sqrt{k}] \times [LR_o^{7/4}/r_o^{1/2}h\sqrt{M}] \quad (8a)$$

$$\equiv [\text{constant}] \times [FOM_g] \times [FOM_a] \quad (8b)$$

where R is the universal gas constant, T is the temperature, and FOM_a is the apparatus figure-of-merit. Of the four gases considered here (helium, nitrogen, argon, and SF_6), the gas figure-of-merit (FOM_g) ranges from 2.7×10^{-4} for hydrogen to 0.014 for SF_6. Thus, SF_6 would be the best gas of the four to maximize Γ_v/Γ_T.

EXPERIMENTAL DPGA SYSTEM

To test the above model, we assembled the DPGA shown schematically in Figure 1. The piston gauge in this system was a gas-operated (pneumatic) gauge with a pressure range of 10.5 to 350 kPa (1.5 to 50 psi), a piston diameter of 10.2 mm, a geometrical piston area of 81.1 mm^2, and a gap (annular) width of about 1.5 μm (determined by measurement of the fall rate). Helium, argon, SF_6, and nitrogen were used in the gauge, with all measurements being made in the gauge mode.

The prototype version of the DPGA used an automobile fuel injector to keep the weight stack floating at a fixed height, but the constant pulsing of the gas added unacceptable noise to the data. To correct this and other problems, several modifications were made to the prototype system. In the newer design, the fuel injector was replaced by a needle valve that was smoothly controlled by a stepper motor and an electronic feedback circuit such that gas flowed into the annulus at the same rate it escaped, thus keeping the piston/weight stack at constant height. To better define the geometry beneath the piston, a volume controller was employed in the DPGA to give a predominately cylindrical volume. The volume controller also made it easy to adjust the volume beneath the piston (V_o) in a precise, known manner. It also reduced thermal losses since the volume controller had a relatively small surface-to-volume ratio compared to the copper tubing that it replaced. A final improvement over the prototype DPGA system was the use of pulsed electromagnets to initiate the piston oscillations, yielding a much better defined delta-function impulse.

EXPERIMENTAL RESULTS AND DATA ANALYSIS

The first round of experiments with the improved DPGA used helium, nitrogen, and argon as the operating gases. Oscillation data taken with helium for two different volumes (110 ml and 208 ml) are shown in Figure 2. To get ω_o and Γ, the piston displacement vs. time data in Figure 1 were fit with an expression of the form given in Equation 1. The fits to ω_o were good to 1 part in 10^4 and the fits to Q were good to 1 part in 10^3. These represent factors of 70 and 10, respectively, improvements in the data from the prototype DPGA design.

A second round of experiments used SF_6 to minimize thermal losses in the DPGA. The sizable increase in the Q of the oscillations, from 7.1 for He to 63.4 for SF_6 (Figure 3), verify that thermal losses have indeed been reduced with SF_6, but they are still about an order of magnitude or so greater than the calculated annular frictional losses.

CONCLUSIONS

Although the data from the new DPGA has improved markedly, and thermal losses have been reduced significantly, over that from the prototype system, the oscillation data (ω_o and Q) do not lend themselves to simple interpretations in terms of the desired piston-gauge annular forces. The major problem is the excessive thermal loss in the volume beneath the piston, which is at least an order of magnitude greater than the annular forces. Even if thermal losses were completely eliminated (i.e., an adiabatic system), we still need to investigate further the connection between the measured oscillation parameters and the static annular forces that influence the effective area. Thus, improved modelling and/or an improved design for the DPGA are needed to get an accurate measurement of the desired annular forces. Nevertheless, this work has been a positive step in that we have shown what factors are important in this measurement and how to increase annular frictional forces, while minimizing thermal losses.

ACKNOWLEDGEMENTS

This work was supported by the US Air Force under contract number CCG-910A038, Task 319. We acknowledge the initial work on this project by Dr. A. Ratnam, as well as assistance on the theory by R. Kayser, M. Moldover, and K. Gillis.

REFERENCES

[1] M. Zemansky, *Heat and Thermodynamics*, New York: Addison-Wesley, p. 128 (1968).

[2] A. Clark and L. Katz, "Resonance Method for Measuring the Ratio of the Specific Heats of a Gas, C_p/C_v, Part IV" **Can. J. Res. 21**, p. 1 (1943).

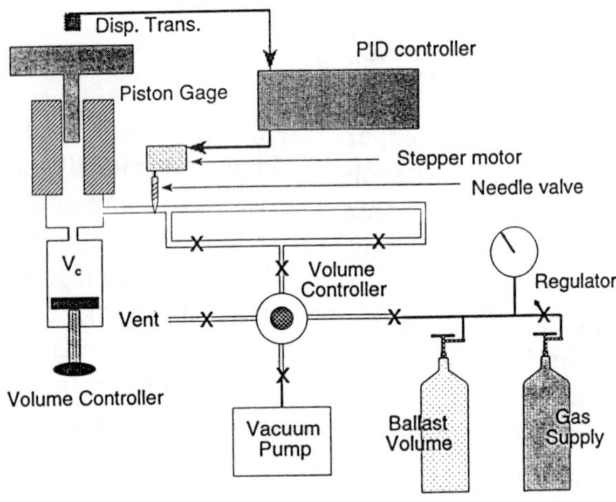

Figure 1. Schematic diagram of the DPGA.

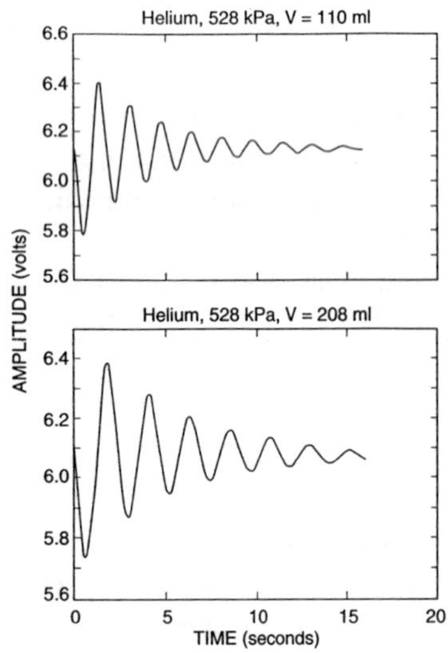

Figure 2. Oscillation data for He for two different volumes (110 ml and 208 ml).

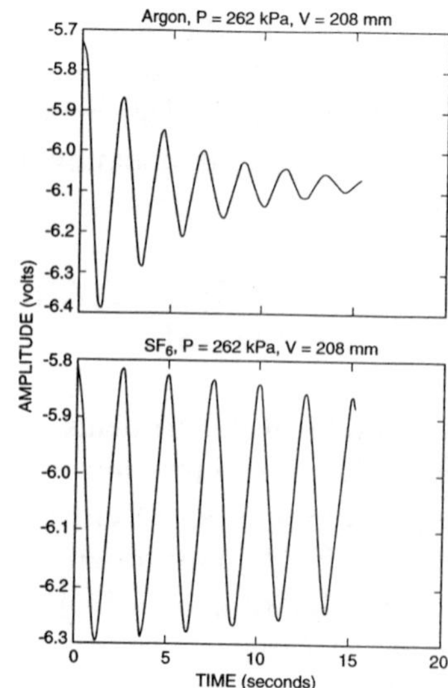

Figure 3. Oscillation data for Ar and SF_6.

IMPLICATION OF THE COMPLETE TRAVEL TIME EQUATION OF STATE FOR A NEW PRESSURE SCALE

Akira Yoneda, Hartmut Spetzler*, and Ivan Getting
CIRES (*also at Dept. of Geol. Scien.), Univ. of Colorado at Boulder
Boulder, Colorado 80309-0216, USA

A complete equation of state results from ultrasonic travel time measurements at simultaneous temperature and pressure, and thermal expansion and heat capacity measurements as a function of temperature at zero pressure. When unit cell dimensions are measured simultaneously (by X-ray methods) a second determination of the equation of state is obtained. It is possible to eliminate the pressure as a dependent variable between the two EOSs and thus determine it from the other equation of state parameters. Present accuracy obtainable by X-ray and ultrasonic methods suggests a new pressure scale which is more accurate than present absolute scales based on the dead-weight tester.

Introduction

Pressure, P, can be obtained from density, ρ, and isothermal bulk modulus, K_T, as

$$dP = K_T (d\rho/\rho)_T . \qquad (1)$$

Applying this principle, Ruoff et al. [1] determined the mercury freezing pressure (~0.757 GPa) with 0.02% accuracy. In this method, K_T is obtained from the adiabatic bulk modulus, K_S. Independent length measurements, ultrasonic travel times and some thermodynamic approximations yield K_T as a function of pressure.

We show that the Complete Travel Time Equation of State, CT-EOS, enables us to obtain all adiabatic and isothermal thermodynamic parameters without any assumptions. A new absolute pressure scale with unprecedented accuracy results from combining ultrasonic and X-ray measurements at simultaneous high pressure and high temperature.

Complete travel time EOS

Spetzler and Yoneda [2] showed that a complete equation of state can be obtained by combining sound travel times at T and P with thermal expansivity, α, and heat capacity at constant pressure, C_P, measurements at T (temperature) and at zero pressure (CT-EOS). Since this EOS is not well known we provide an outline.

Assume that C_P and α are given as functions of temperature at zero pressure $(T,0)$ and data for $t_p(T,P)$ and $t_s(T,P)$ (t_p and t_s: travel times for P and S waves, respectively) have been obtained at simultaneous temperature and pressure. Here we assume an isotropic material for simplicity. The principle holds for any symmetry. Furthermore the sample dimensions l_0 and density ρ_0 are known at ambient conditions (0,0). From $\rho(0,0)$ and $l(0,0)$, and $\alpha(T,0)$ we calculate $\rho(T,0)$ and $l(T,0)$.

$$\rho = \rho_0 \, exp\left(-\int_{T_0}^{T} \alpha dT \right), \qquad l = l_0 \left(\frac{\rho_0}{\rho} \right)^{1/3} \qquad (2)$$

The velocities, v, and the adiabatic bulk modulus, K_S, are readily calculated at $(T,0)$ as

$$v_p = \frac{l}{t_p}, \quad v_s = \frac{l}{t_s}, \quad K_S = \rho\left(v_p^2 - \frac{4}{3} v_s^2 \right). \qquad (3)$$

The definition of the Thermal Gruneisen Parameter $\gamma = \alpha K_S / (\rho C_P)$ and the thermodynamic identity $K_T = K_S (1 + \alpha\gamma T)^{-1}$ allow the calculation of all required parameters at $(T,0)$. We now extend the calculation into the pressure regime by a pressure increment ΔP, and obtain $\rho(T,\Delta P)$ and $l(T,\Delta P)$ and thus also $\alpha(T,\Delta P)$. $K_S(T,\Delta P)$ can be calculated. To extend the calculation by the next pressure interval requires the conversion from K_S to K_T, and thus C_P at (T,ΔP), and therefore $\left(\partial C_P/\partial P\right)_T$. Differentiating $C_P = T(\partial S/\partial T)_P$ with respect to P yields

$$\left(\partial C_P/\partial P\right)_T = -T\rho^{-1}\left[\alpha^2 + (\partial\alpha/\partial T)_P\right] \qquad (4)$$

Thus all parameters can be calculated for every new interval in pressure and all thermodynamic parameters can be calculated over the entire range in temperature and pressure over which the travel times are measured.

The proposed new pressure scale is based on making measurements for two equations of state (CT-EOS and P-ρ relation by X-ray method) simultaneously and thus over determining the measured parameters. By eliminating the pressure as a dependent variable, it can be determined uniquely, provided the two EOSs used do not require thermodynamic approximations.

Current status of high pressure scale

The very definition of pressure, as the normal force divided by the area on which the force is acting, is used in the piston cylinder apparatus and provides the primary standard for pressure determinations. However, the finite strengths of cylinders and pistons limit the applicability of this method to below 8 GPa [3]. An uncertainty of several percent at the highest pressures results from a lack of knowledge of where to chose the pressure within the hysteresis loop caused by the friction between piston and cylinder.

A newly developed piston-cylinder device which uses argon as a pressure medium (Getting and Spetzler, this meeting) offers improved absolute pressure accuracy. Stress gradients within the pressure medium are exceedingly small, even within solid argon. Seal friction has been reduced to the ~2% range. Thus, the entire friction correction is now comparable to pressure uncertainties in previous piston cylinder devices.

The highest absolute pressure calibration which does not suffer from the hysteresis problem has been made with a dead-weight tester with a freely rotating piston. The highest pressure reached was 2.5 GPa and the accuracy after corrections for dimensional changes of the piston and cylinder is ~0.2% [4].

Measurements of shock- and particle-velocities during shock compression and the application of conservation laws of mass and momentum yield values for pressure and density along the shock Hugoniot. Some phase transitions detected in shock experiments have been used as reference fixed points of pressure. Furthermore, temperature corrections applied to Hugoniots have yielded isothermal equations of state. However uncertainties in the temperature corrections and the dynamic effects on the kinetics of phase transitions lead to large uncertainties in the absolute pressures. For instance, different temperature corrections could yield ~10% discrepancy in pressure at ~100 GPa [5].

Continuous pressure scales are based on pressure-volume relations of certain materials at constant temperatures, i.e., isothermal equation of state. Decker [6] established the NaCl pressure scale, which has been used as the most reliable pressure scale up to 30 GPa. He assumed a semi-theoretical functional form for the equation of state, and adjusted the input parameters to fit the experimental pressure-volume relations obtained by the free piston cylinder method and the shock compression data. When extrapolated to 30 GPa the uncertainty in the input parameters and the uncertainty in the functional form of the EOS result in estimates of the pressure uncertainty of ± 3%. Thus the NaCl scale, above the free piston range, is a theoretical compromise among various experimental results rather than an absolute pressure scale (we use the term *"absolute pressure scale"* for an experimentally determined pressure scale which does not rely on thermodynamic assumptions). Further, the ruby-pressure scale widely used in diamond anvil cell could have a significant uncertainty at higher pressure, because it is based on the NaCl scale and other EOSs derived from shock Hugoniot [7, 8].

Procedure of the Performance Test of the New Pressure Scale

Basically the present method (we call it the **$K\rho$** method) should be applicable in any pressure range within which there is no phase change. However, taking into account the present experimental technology, we assume 4 GPa as the experimental range, and examine the expected uncertainty in this range and semi-theoretical extrapolation to higher pressures. We made the performance test by using analogs of MgO (periclase) and NaCl (halite); MgO is one of the most suitable materials for a pressure scale up to 100 GPa, while NaCl, which change to the CsCl structure at ~30 GPa, is worth examining for comparison with the current NaCl scale [6].

We generated internally consistent data (substitute of experimental data) for t_p, t_s and density as a function of pressure and temperature (0 to 4 GPa with 0.1 GPa intervals and 300 to 400 K with 10 K intervals) and for C_P at P=0 between 300 and 400K by using the expanded Birch-Murnaghan EOS [2]. Table 1 is the list of the parameters used for MgO and NaCl. Note that by specifying all of these parameters they become redundant. We assumed random noise consistent with present experimental capabilities, i.e. 10^{-4} for t_p, t_s, ρ, and l_o, and 10^{-2} for α and C_P at P=0. Using these random noise figures, we calculate the uncertainty in pressure consistent with the over determined EOS. Within the experimental range the new pressure scale gives much better constrained pressure values than previous methods (Fig. 1). When estimating uncertainties beyond the experimental range, both the uncertainties of the data and the choice of the EOS for extrapolation contribute to the uncertainty. Our estimation of uncertainty due to the selection of EOS in the extrapolated region is based on the discrepancies between the Birch-Murnaghan and the Murnaghan EOSs.

Note that the absolute pressure scale requires data as a function of both temperature and pressure, otherwise t_p and t_s will not absolutely constrain the EOS and thermodynamic assumptions have to be made in converting from adiabatic and isothermal parameters. However the above calculations are based on a small temperature excursion (100 K), which in most cases can be easily accomplished with external heating, thus avoiding emf pressure corrections to thermocouple readings.

Table 1 List of input parameters. These values are quite similar to those of real MgO (periclase) [5, 9, 10, 11] and NaCl (halite) [12]. Note that T'=(T-300 K)/100 K (T'=0 at T=300 K; T'=1 at T=400 K); $\xi_C = K_T C'/C$, where C is any elastic constant, and C' the pressure derivative of C [2, 5].

	MgO	NaCl
ρ_0	3585 kg/m^3	2165 kg/m^3
$\alpha(T') = a_1 + a_2T'$		
a_1	3.0E-5 K^{-1}	11.8E-5 K^{-1}
a_2	1.7E-6 K^{-1}	1.0E-5 K-1
$C_P(T') = b_1 + b_2T'$		
b_1	900 J/kgK	841 J/kgK
b_2	25 J/kgK	25.2 J/kgK
$K_{S_0}(T') = c_1 - c_2T' - c_3T'^2$		
c_1	160 GPa,	30 GPa
c_2	1.0 GPa,	0.4 GPa
c_3	0.017 GPa	0 GPa
$\mu_0(T') = d_1 - d_2T' - d_3T'^2$		
d_1	130 GPa,	12.8 GPa
d_2	1.5 GPa,	0.35 GPa
d_3	0.017 GPa	0 GPa
$\xi_{Ks}(T') = \frac{K_{T_0}}{K_{S_0}}(e_1 + e_2T') - 4.0$		
e_1	4.3,	5.25
e_2	0.02,	0.02
$\xi_\mu(T') = \frac{K_{T_0}}{\mu_0}(f_1 + f_2T') - 4.0$		
f_1	2.0	4.0
f_2	0.02	0.002

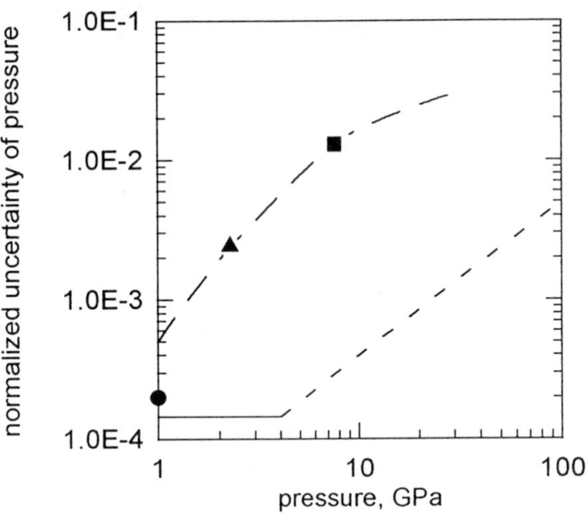

Figure 1. Relative uncertainty of pressure versus pressure. The lower curve shows the uncertainty (normalized standard deviation of pressure for ten recalculations of pressure) of the present method. The solid line covers the expected experimental range. The dashed line corresponds to extrapolating data as well as assuming differences between the Birch-Murnaghan and the Murnaghan EOSs.

The upper curve shows the uncertainty of the NaCl scale [6] which terminates at ~30 GPa because of a phase change. The triangle and square represent the uncertainty in pressure determined by the piston cylinder apparatus [3, 4]. The circle represents the uncertainty from the simultaneous ultrasonic velocities and density measurements [1].

Acknowledgments

This work was supported by the NSF through grant EAR-8916327 and a matching grant from the Univ. of Col. One of us (AY) receives additional support form the Yamada Science Foundation and the Seism. Soc. of Japan while visiting CIRES at the Univ. of Col.

References

[1] A. L. Ruoff, R. C. Lincoln, and Y. C. Chen, "High-pressure calibration with a new absolute-pressure gauge," *Appl. Phys. Lett.* 22, pp. 310-311 (1973).

[2] H. Spetzler and A. Yoneda, "Performance of the complete travel time equation of state at simultaneous high pressure and temperature," *Pure and Applied Geophys.*, in print.

[3] J. C. Haygarth, H. D. Luedmann, I. C. Getting, and G. C. Kennedy, "Determination of portions of the bismuth III-V and IV-V equilibrium boundaries in single-stage piston-cylinder apparatus," *J. Phys. Chem. Solids* 30, pp. 1417-1424 (1969).

[4] P. L. M. Heydemann, "The Bi I-II transition pressure measured with a dead-weight piston gauge", *J. Appl. Phys.* 38, pp. 2640-2644 (1967).

[5] A. Yoneda, "Pressure derivatives of elastic constants of single crystal MgO and $MgAl_2O_4$," *J. Phys. Earth* 38, pp. 19-55 (1990).

[6] D. L. Decker, "High-pressure equation of state for NaCl, KCl and CsCl," *J. Appl. Phys.* 42, pp. 3239-3244 (1971).

[7] G. J. Piermarini, S. Block, J. D. Barnett, R. A. Forman, "Calibration of the pressure dependence of the R1 ruby fluorescence line to 195 kbar," *J. Appl. Phys.* 46, pp. 2774-2780 (1975).

[8] H. K. Mao, P. M. Bell, J. W. Shaner, and D. J. Steinberg, "Specific volume measurements of Cu, Mo, Pd, and Ag and calibration of the ruby R1 fluorescence pressure gauge from 0.06 to 1 Mbar," *J. Appl. Phys.* 49, pp. 3276-3283 (1978).

[9] I. Jackson and H. Niesler, "The elasticity of periclase to 3 GPa and some geophysical implications," in *High Pressure Research in Geophysics*, ed. S. Akimoto and M. H. Manghnani, Tokyo, Center for Academic Publications Japan, 1982, pp. 93-113.

[10] H. Spetzler, "Equation of state of polycrystalline and single-crystal MgO to 8 kilobars and 800 K," *J. Geophys. Res.* 75, pp. 2073-2087 (1970).

[11] I. Suzuki, "Thermal expansion of periclase and olivine, and their anharmonic properties," *J. Phys. Earth* 23, pp. 145-159 (1975).

[12] H. Spetzler, C. G. Sammis, R. J. O'Connell, "Equation of state of NaCl: ultrasonic measurements to 8 kbar and 800 C and static lattice theory," *J. Chem. Phys. Solid* 33, pp. 1727-1750 (1972).

RECENT DESIGN OF ULTRAHIGH-PRESSURE DIAMOND CELL

Ho-kwang Mao, Russell J. Hemley
Geophysical Laboratory and Center for High Pressure Research, Carnegie Institution of Washington
5251 Broad Branch Road, N.W., Washington, D.C. 20015, U.S.A.

Agnes L. Mao
George Mason University, Fairfax, VA 22030 U.S.A.

We present a modification of the piston-cylinder design of diamond cells which has been developed to achieve more precise alignment of diamond anvils with beveled culets. A two-stage lever arm device is also used for high-loading conditions. The modified diamond cell is superior to the previous megabar cell for ultrahigh pressure experiments above 150 GPa.

INTRODUCTION

In 1976, Mao and Bell [1, 2] reported a mechanical design of diamond cell with which pressures above 100 GPa was reached for the first time. This design and its variation have been used widely for ultrahigh-pressure research. The main improvements of this design over previous ones was the precise and stable diamond anvil alignment at high pressures. The alignment is achieved by two half-cylindrical diamond seats (rockers), and is maintained at high-loading conditions by the rigidity of rockers (tungsten carbide) and the long, closely-fitted piston and cylinder. The hardened steel piston and cylinder are each made of a single piece to assure rigidity.

Modification of the diamond by adding bevel to the culet (Fig. 1) led to another major advancement [3]. The beveled diamond formed the configuration of the second-stage anvils which allowed ultrahigh pressures far beyond 150 GPa to be reached routinely [4]. Even though the rocker-type diamond cell has been used successfully with beveled anvils, some disadvantages became apparent, particularly with very small anvil culets. We have developed the following modified mechanical design of diamond cells, and have used it since 1988. The performance at ultrahigh pressures is superior to the previous design.

DIAMOND SEATS AND PISTON-CYLINDER

A major concern in diamond-cell design is the alignment mechanism for parallelism and concentricity of the two diamond culets (Fig. 1). In most current designs, the culet alignment is achieved either by a pair of half-cylindrical seats, each for rotational and translational adjustment of one of the two orthogonal axes in the plane of the culet, or by the combination of a hemispherical seat for 2-axis rotation and a disk seat for 2-axis translation. These devices function well for large culets with diameter above 300 μm. The deviation from concentricity is detected by viewing through the culets with a microscope, and is corrected by adjusting set screws holding the half cylinders or the disk to match the culets within 5-10% of the diameter of the culet. The deviation from parallelism is detected by bringing the two culets into contact and observing Fabry-Perot interference fringes caused by multiple reflections between the two culets [5]. Deviations are corrected by rotational adjustment of the hemispherical or half-cylindrical seats down to the detection limit which is approximately half a fringe with white light, or a 0.15 μm difference in distance between the two culets at various points across the diameter. For culet sizes of 300 μm, the difference amounts to 0.5 mrad deviation from parallelism.

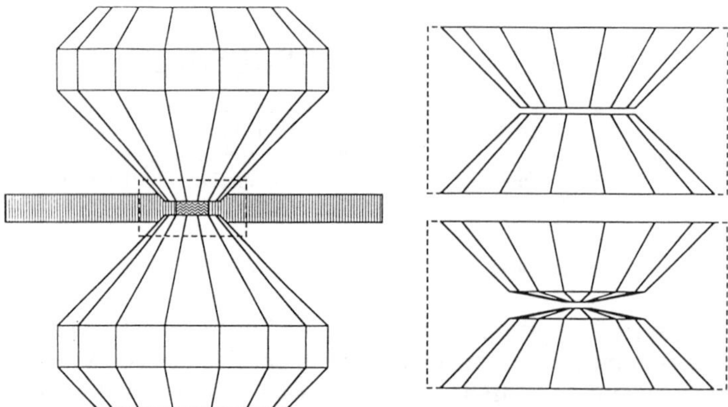

Figure 1. Configuration of diamond anvils. Right top, flat anvils; right bottom, beveled anvils.

This technique functions poorly as the culets get smaller with the bevel design; culet sizes of 50 to 20 μm are used routinely for experiments above 150 GPa [6, 7]. There is a great danger of damaging diamonds by bringing the two diamonds into contact without the sample and gasket during the alignment process, while inevitably some force will be exerted. A small force of 1 N is sufficient to produce ring cracks on a beveled diamond with 20 μm culet. For comparison, unaligned 300 μm culets can tolerate a force up to 200 N. The detection limit of 0.15 μm by the interference fringe method implies 3 to 7.5 mrad uncertainty in parallelism, which is rather poor. Without an adequate method to measure parallelism, the rotational adjustment is useless.

The problem is resolved by making each component parallel at the fabrication stage, thus assuring parallelism of the assembled diamond cell and eliminating the need for rotational adjustment. In the modified design in Fig. 2, diamond anvils are mounted on two flat disk-shaped tungsten-carbide seats, each is held at the center of a counterbore in the piston or the cylinder. Bottom flats of the counterbores are machined to be perpendicular to the axis of the piston and cylinder within 0.5 mrad accuracy. The sliding surfaces of the hardened steel piston and cylinder are ground precisely to a 5-μm fitting tolerance. The two flat sides of each tungsten carbide seat are ground to 0.5 mrad parallelism. For beveled diamonds, a large culet (>500 μm) is needed for measuring parallelism to the table facet within 0.5 mrad with laser interferometer. After the parallelism has been established, the culet diameter was reduced by adding the bevel facets and closing the pavillion facets. The parallelism of the culets in the final assemblage is within 0.5-1 mrad.

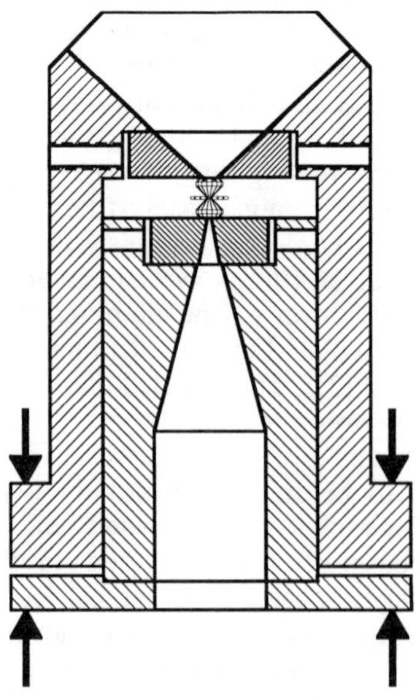

Figure 2. Flat-seat diamond cell. NE-SW cross hatch, cylinder; NW-SE cross hatch piston; dense cross hatch, disk-shaped tungsten carbide seats.

The flat-seat design has the following additional advantages. Since only the concentricity of the two culets needs to be adjusted, the alignment procedure is simplified. With each disk adjustable in two directions, one can bring both diamond culets to the center of the piston-cylinder axis. In contrast, the rocker design allows the matching of the two culets, but not necessary at the center of the axis, thus intrinsically less stable. In the rocker design, the translational and rotational adjustments are not totally independent. Adjustment of set screws for culet concentricity also causes rotation of the rocker. Because the culet is usually not at the center of the rotation axis of a rocker, rotational adjustment also leads to translational displacement. The alignment procedures are iterative and tedious, particularly when high precision is required for very small culets. For the flat seat design, every adjustment is independent. Higher concentricity can be achieved in shorter time.

With its more stringent requirements of machining accuracy, the flat-seat cell is still easier to construct, because it only contains flat cuts of the counterbore. Seats with the support of the entire flat surface area are more stable than the rockers, which have a tendency to rotate slightly with a component of non-central loading at high pressures.

The flat-seat diamond cells have been used for all experiments above 120 GPa reported by this laboratory in the past four years. For the lower pressure range with large culets, it works equally well as the rocker design.

LEVER ARMS

The piston-cylinder assemblage, as in Fig. 2, constitutes a complete unit for the high-pressure cell. Force can be exerted by various means, including lever arm, hydraulic pressure, pressurized membrane, or simply several screws in the arrow direction in Fig. 2. The lever arm device is noted for its convenience and extreme stability for days and even years.

Diamond cells compressed by lever arms with mechanical advantage of 5:1. have been used extensively. At ultrahigh pressures above 150 GPa, the load on the force-exerting bolt and springs is typically 2000 N for generating 10^4 N on the diamond anvils. Very high torque is needed to turn the bolts, causing the system to be difficult to operate. To reduce the torque by simply increasing the length of the lever arm would result in a large and bulky instrument. We resolve the problem by using a two-stage lever arm device. As shown in Fig. 3, the first stage lever has the mechanical advantage of $\underline{BE}$: $\underline{DE}$ = 3:1, and the second stage, $\underline{AC}$:$\underline{BC}$= 5:1. The net

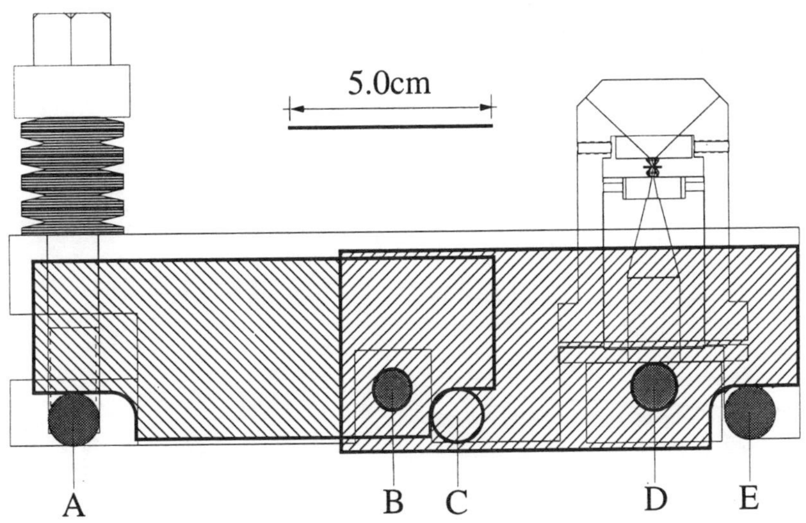

Figure 3. Two-stage lever arm device.

advantage is 15:1. With this design, pressures at high load can be applied with ease. When the diamond cell is mounted on a delicate instrument such as a cryogenic dewar or on a microscope stage, the application of pressure will not disturb the accurate alignment. Finally, finer steps of pressure increment can be achieved with the higher mechanical advantage.

ACKNOWLEDGMENTS

We thank Andy Antoszyk, Steve Coley, Mark Wah, and Bobbie Brown for constructing the cells, Wendy Mao for help with the paper, and NASA and NSF for financial support.

REFERENCES

[1] H. K. Mao and P. M. Bell, *Carnegie Inst. Washington Yearb.*, 75, 824 (1976).
[2] H. K. Mao and P. M. Bell, *Science* 191, 851 (1976).
[3] H. K. Mao and P. M. Bell, *Science* 200, 1145 (1978).
[4] R. J. Hemley and H. K. Mao, in *Shock Compression of Condensed Matter*, (Elsevier, New York, 1992), 27-38.
[5] A. P. Jephcoat, H. K. Mao, and P. M. Bell, in *Hydrothermal Experimental Techniques*, (John Wiley & Sons, New York, 1987), 469-506
[6] H. K. Mao and R. J. Hemley, *Nature* 351, 721 (1991).
[7] H. K. Mao and R. J. Hemley, *Science* 244, 1462 (1989).

USER- AND DIAMOND-FRIENDLY METHOD OF ROUNDING DIAMOND ANVIL EDGES

William B. Daniels, Department of Physics and Astronomy, University of Delaware, Newark, DE 19716 USA

We describe a very simple and effective method of rounding the edges of culets (or other edges) on diamond anvils. The method is based upon principles developed in lapping other hard and brittle materials using abrasive powders.

INTRODUCTION

Some years ago while having difficulties with chipping of the sharp edges near the culets of diamond anvils, we wondered whether some simple lapping principles would permit us to "round" the sharp edges. If successful, this would not only reduce the chances of accidental damage, but would certainly make the electrical lead through problem easier, and might also permit higher pressures to be reached by reducing stress concentrations. Possibly a compromise could be struck between the conventional flat or beveled culets and the Ruoff indenter. In the course of making high pressure cells to operate with He gas as a pressure medium, at cryogenic temperatures we gained substantial experience in using lapping techniques to super-finish pressure seals, optical window "seats," etc. This work had somewhat of a menial aspect, but a number of principles or at least procedures emerged as being important. It was relatively easy to bring some shapes to a smooth, regular, polished form by lapping two pieces together. Flat surfaces, spheres and cylinders worked well. Cones on the other hand were never easy. Trying to lap one cone to fit another using abrasive powders etc. almost invariably left irregular grooves in circles around the work piece, perpendicular to the cone axis. There seemed to be some instability developing as the process went on, lumping up material and abrasive so as to create those circumferential grooves which became deeper as time went on. The problem of course was that with the two cones in contact, each rotation or oscillation moved the same elements of the two past one another, whereas in spheres and cylinders, in principle all elements of each piece pass one another, rather than a limited set as in the case of the cones. An additional principle which appeared, in lapping brittle materials was in trying to round a sharp edge, it was advantageous to begin with a very fine abrasive (approximately the initial radius of the "sharp" edge?), then go sequentially into coarser grits to remove material, then back to fine grits to reach a regular and polished final form. If too coarse a grit was initially used, the edges almost invariably became chipped. It then required significant additional effort to generate a smooth rounded contour without irregularities seemingly inevitably induced by the chipped edges. Thus, when we considered putting one of our anvils "at risk," we had some guidelines based on experience–admittedly in objects very different from diamonds in their hardness. We also had to overcome a prejudgment–I do not know where it was impressed on me–that it is not possible to form a curved surface on a diamond material object. That is, that one could cut numerous facets, or bevels (except very near certain crystallographic directions) approximately forming a curved surface but could not form an actually curved surface.

It also seemed advisable at first in any case, to use a lap which was not massive. In this way it was hoped that impacts between existing edges or points on the diamond and the lap would not be severe enough to crack off pieces of the diamond. Approximately .25 mm thick brass shim stock was selected for the purpose, and a fine diamond paste, 8000 grit was chosen initially and found to be satisfactory to initiate the process. Currently we use the even finer 14500 grit diamond paste. A description of the procedures used is given below as a set of steps:

PROCEDURE

1. Mount the diamond anvil so that it can be rotated about its symmetry axis. We do this by epoxy cementing it into a mandrel consisting of a 6 mm diameter brass rod with a shallow depression in one end. The diamond should be mounted such that the culet is centered on the mandrel axis and perpendicular to that axis.

2. Place the mandrel and diamond in the culet of a rotating machine, e.g. a lathe, or better a commercial high speed die grinder with a speed controller.

3. Prepare a lap. A piece of brass shim stock 1.5 cm $\times$ 16 cm $\times$ .25 mm will be satisfactory. Smear a thin layer of 14500 grit diamond paste over an area covering $\sim$ 5 cm of one end.

4. With the diamond rotating in the die grinder, hand hold the lap and outwardly "stroke" the diamond with the lap very nearly tangent to the culet. The direction of stroking motion should be radially outward from the edge. After a few minutes of this, the stroking motion can be at an increasingly steeper angle relative to the culets, in such a way as to generate a rounded edge form.

5. Inspect the edge under a microscope to examine the edge. If significant rounding is visible, one can go in steps to coarser diamond grits, 8000 and 3000. These can be used to produce the desired degree of rounding, followed by a return (using a fresh lap for each grade) to finer grits for generating a more highly polished surface.

6. The operation can be done completely using hand-held laps, but the process is tedious. We have made an automatic "shuttling" lap holder which uses the fact that the lap is flexible to cause the lap to address the rounding edge at different angles as the shuttle moves. This has permitted us to carry out a process of deeper rounding without attending to the machine–except to smear a bit more diamond paste onto it at $\sim$ 30 minute intervals.

ACKNOWLEDGEMENTS

The author would like to thank the National Science Foundation for its support of this work under Grants DMR 8822639 and DMP 9208517, and the Unidel Foundation for salary and material support. The author would also like to thank David Schiferl for helpful discussions of this and many other processes.

HIGH-PRECISION GRINDING OF DIAMOND ANVILS

R. Boehler
Hochdruck-Mineralphysik
Max-Planck-Institut für Chemie
Postfach 3060
55020 Mainz, Germany

A new method to grind diamond anvils for high pressure research is introduced. The essential advantages over conventional grinding are cost, speed, and precision and has proven extremely helpful for ultrahigh pressure, and laser heating experiments where diamond anvils are frequently damaged. The cost of the essential parts of the grinding apparatus is less than one standard diamond anvil. Resurfacing culet and facets can be achieved within minutes and tolerances of a few μm can be easily achieved. Surface quality is comparable to super-fine conventional grinding.

Ultrahigh-pressure experiment above one Mbar require precisely ground diamond anvils to avoid stress concentrations. These anvils often develop shallow microcracks upon pressure release. When used in conjunction with laser-heating small pits and cracks form in the high temperture region or in the presence of chemical reactions.

The present method shows a fast, easy, and economical technique to manufacture and repair diamond-anvils. The apparatus is shown in figure 1. The diamond anvil is mounted in a collet with it's large table exactly parallel to the base plate. This collet should allow light passage through the diamond. The collet can be rotated stepwise. The amount of steps is optional but 16 was chosen in the present apparatus. The grinding wheel is a (stock item) polycrystalline diamond disc (COMPAX, General Electric Co. or SYND, De Beers) with a grain size of 10 μm. A disc with a diameter of approximately 13 mm. is well suited for very high-precision grinding of small facets at shallow angles. A larger disc (~ 30 mm diameter) is used for large facets and culets. The grinding discs are mounted on miniature, high-precision, DC-motors (ESCAP or Faulhaber) with about 3 and 30 Watts of power, respectively, running between about 6000 and 9000 RPM. The motors are mounted on handheld rectangular bars which, during grinding, rest on an adjustable guide block. Motor mount- and guide block- adjustments allow grinding angles between 0 and about 40 degrees.

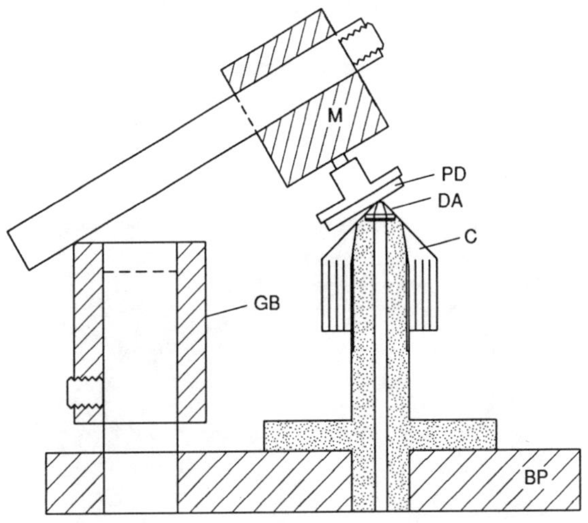

Fig. 1. Diamond grinding apparatus: BP = base plate (L=100mm); C = collet; DA = diamond anvil; PD = polycrystalline diamond disc; M = high-speed DC-motor; GB = guide block.

The grinding apparatus can be mounted on a X-Y translation stage under a stereo, or standard microscope with suitable working distance to allow frequent measurement of dimensions and surface quality. New grinding discs will have to be 'dressed' simply by grinding until its surface becomes smooth enough to yield microscopically clean facets. Because of its anisotropic behaviour, the position of the grinding disc must be changed until grinding becomes most effective. For best results, the grinding disc should be kept in an oscillating motion during grinding to avoid grinding marks.

Culets and facets can be easily ground with a precision of a few μm. No grinding marks have been observed under a microscope with 800 X magnification. With some skill and practice culet and 16 facets can be ground in less than 15 minutes. The quality of the polycrystalline diamond disc does not diminish even after extensive grinding and the discs do not require any treatment other than 'dressing' described above. Figure 2 shows several examples of routine manufacturing of standard brilliant cut jewelry diamond and repair of anvils.

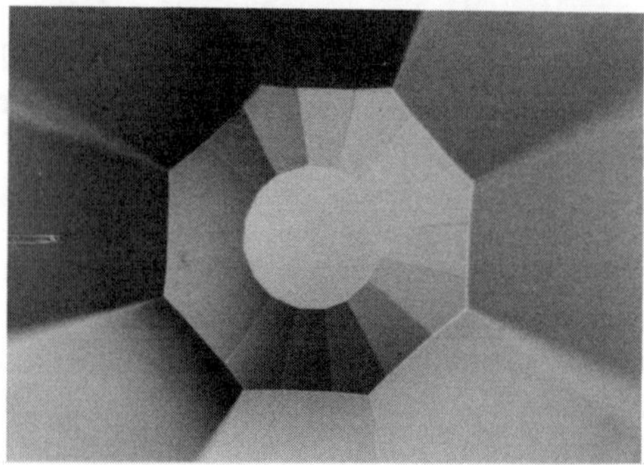

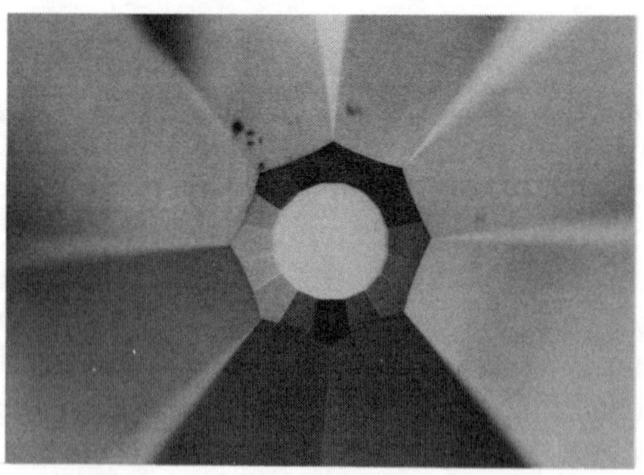

Fig. 2. Examples of precision ground diamond anvils.

RECENT ADVANCES IN HIGH PRESSURE AND HIGH TEMPERATURE *IN-SITU* X-RAY STUDIES USING SINTERED DIAMOND AND SYNCHROTRON RADIATION

Takehiko Yagi
Institute for Solid State Physics, University of Tokyo
Roppongi, Minato-ku, Tokyo 106, Japan

Combination of a newly developed high pressure apparatuses employing sintered diamond as an anvil material and very strong x-ray from a synchrotron radiation enables us to extend the P-T range of an *in-situ* x-ray diffraction studies considerably. Characteristic features of the modified Drickamer-type apparatus, which works up to at least 50 GPa, are described.

INTRODUCTION

The quality of high pressure and high temperature *in situ* X-ray diffraction study has been improved dramatically by using synchrotron radiation as an X-ray source. Combination with a large-volume type high pressure apparatus enables us to study the behavior of materials under well characterized high pressure and high temperature conditions[1]. More than that, various improvements of the sample assembly made it possible to control fugacity in the sample chamber, and studies such as high hydrogen pressure were successfully made[2]. Compared to the diamond anvil apparatus, however, the limited pressure range was a great disadvantage of this large volume-type apparatus. In order to overcome this weakness, many efforts were made to extend the pressure range utilizing sintered diamond as an anvil material. Three different types of apparatus, a single-stage cubic anvil[3], double-stage cubic-octahedral anvil[4], and a modified Drickamer-type[5], were developed.

Fig. 1 shows the pressure and temperature range so far achieved by each of these apparatuses and it is evident that the P-T range of the *in situ* x-ray study has extended considerably by these apparatus. In this paper, the detailed characteristic features of the modified Drickamer-type apparatus are described.

APPARATUS

Fig.2 shows the schematic diagram of the modified Drickamer-type apparatus developed in the present study. The raw material of the sintered diamond had a cylindrical shape, 15mm in diameter and 15mm high, surrounded by a tungsten-carbide ring. This sintered diamond was machined into an anvil shape with a circular top flat face of 3 mm, surrounded by a slope of 30° from the top face. This dimension was selected after many trials to get a large sample volume without sacrificing the efficiency of pressure generation. The pressure transmitting medium were made of three parts, all of which were made of a mixture of amorphous boron and epoxy resin or water glass. A small resistance furnace was developed using a mixture of TiC and diamond, which works stably up to at least 1900K and 36 GPa[6]. This material has low absorption for high energy x-rays and has relatively small number of diffraction lines which always appears with that of the sample.

Incident x-ray was collimated to a thin beam (0.05 mm high and 0.1 mm wide) and was introduced to the sample chamber perpendicular to the compression axis of this apparatus. The diffracted x-ray can be detected in two different orientations. One is in a vertical plain containing the compression axis and the other is in a horizontal plain perpendicular to it. An energy dispersive technique was employed and the 2θ angle was fixed to 6°. Crystallographic plains of the sample observed by the diffractions in the horizontal plane are always parallel to the compression axis, while those in the vertical plane are almost (only 3° off) perpendicular to it. When the sample is randomly oriented or the pressure is purely hydrostatic, diffractions in these two different orientations are identical. However, when the sample has preferred orientation or when the applied pressure has uniaxial stress component, these two diffractions provide different information, which are very difficult to get using a diamond anvil apparatus. The advantage of the present apparatus over diamond anvil apparatus can be summarized as follows:

1. The sample chamber is much larger and consequently even the samples with small scattering power, such as carbon, gives high quality x-ray diffraction patterns.
2. Uniform and well controlled heating of the sample can be made up to at least 1900 K.
3. Crystallographic information under uniaxial compression can be obtained, which helps a lot to understand the crystal structure and elastic property of the samples under pressure.

Examples of the experiment using each characteristic features are given below.

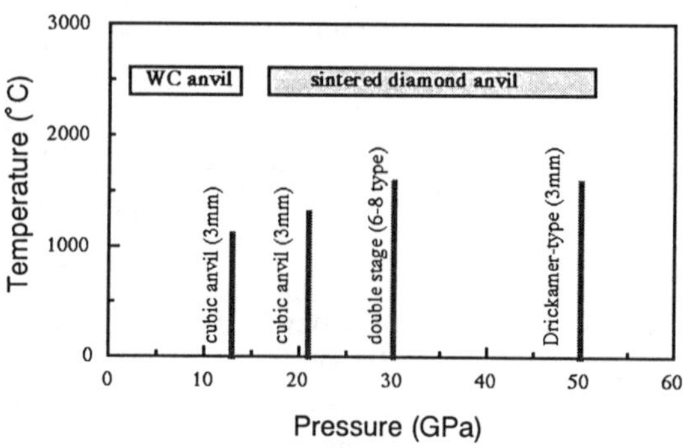

Figure 1. Pressure range of the high pressure and high temperature *in situ* x-ray diffraction studies using large volume apparatus. Each line represents the current pressure limit of each apparatus. Use of the sintered diamond extended the pressure limit considerably.

RESULTS

This modified Drickamer-type apparatus were successfully applied to the studies of the graphite-"hexagonal diamond" transition[5,7] and the enstatite-perovskite transition in $MgSiO_3$[6]. Stress field analysis were also made using NaCl as a standard material.

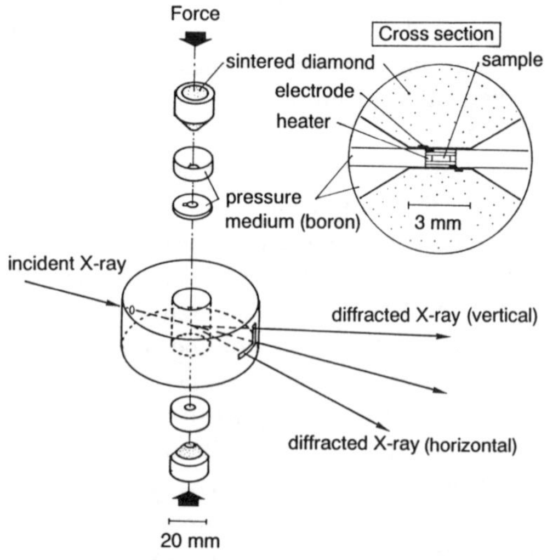

Figure 2. Schematic diagram of Drickamer-type apparatus developed in the present study and an enlarged cross section of the sample chamber. X-ray diffraction can be measured in two different orientations relative to the uniaxial compression axis.

Graphite-Hexagonal Diamond Transition

It has been know that when a well crystallized graphite is compressed at room temperature, a dramatic change of the optical properties occurs at around 18 GPa[8]. However, its nature remain unclear because x-ray diffraction study using diamond anvil apparatus gave only very poor pattern on the high pressure phase of graphite. As is clear from Fig.3, using present apparatus, almost two orders of magnitude more graphite can be placed in the sample chamber, which improved the signal to noise ratio of the x-ray diffraction patterns considerably.

Moreover, strong preferred orientation is inevitable when graphite is compressed in diamond anvil, and only very limited diffraction lines were observed. On the other hand, in the present apparatus, diffractions in two different orientations (Fig.3) provide much more information on the crystal structure of the high pressure phase and it was clarified that the nature of the dramatic change of the optical property is a phase transformation from graphite to hexagonal diamond[5,6,7].

Enstatite-Perovskite Transition in $MgSiO_3$

Perovskite-type $MgSiO_3$ is believed to be a dominant mineral in the lower mantle which occupies more than 50 % of the total volume of the Earth. Therefore its property plays key role to understand the structure and composition of our planet. Since the quenched perovskite transforms back to low pressure phase quickly on heating, its behavior under high temperature remains unclear. Although various attempts were made to observe it under its stable condition, that is, above 26 GPa and 1000℃, it was impossible to do it.

We have concentrated our efforts to develop small resistance furnace which works stably in such condition, and have finally succeed making *in situ* observation under lower mantle condition[6]. Fig. 4 shows an example of the diffraction pattern of $MgSiO_3$ perovskite observed at 36 GPa and 1900 K, the condition well within the lower mantle. In spite of the low symmetry (orthorhombic) of this sample, unit cell demension could be determine precisely from such diffraction pattern[6].

Based on these observations, it became clear that the orthorhombic-perovskite type of $MgSiO_3$ is a stable phase of $MgSiO_3$ under most of the lower mantle[9]. Besides, the thermal expansion coefficient was measured reliably, which contributes a lot to give constraints for the chemical

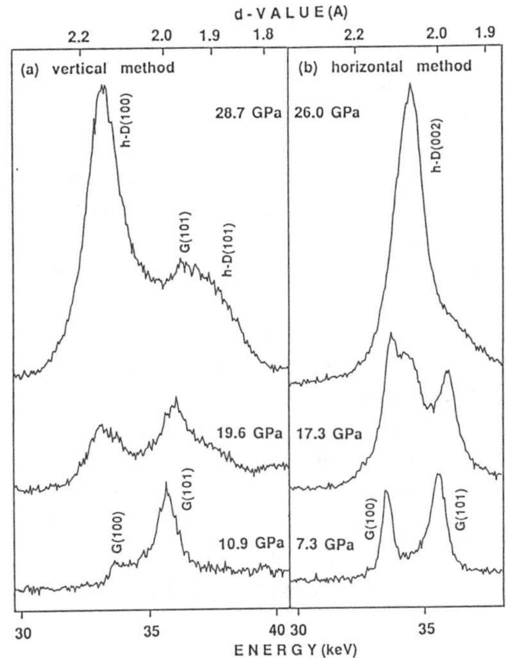

Figure 3. X-ray diffraction patterns of hexagonal diamond observed in two different orientations. Because of the strong preferred orientation, observed diffractions are quite different [7].

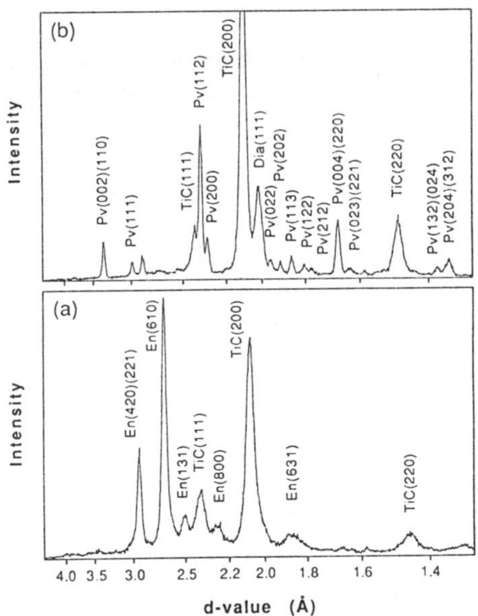

Figure 4. In situ observation of enstatite - perovskite transition in $MgSiO_3$. (a) at 35 GPa and room T. (b) at 36 GPa and 1600K[6].

composition of the lower mantle.

Stress Field Analysis

In opposed-anvil type apparatus like diamond-anvil and present apparatus, direct compression of the solid sample results uniaxial compression, rather than the hydrostatic or isotropic compression. However, the effect of uniaxial stress component was difficult to observe. In the present apparatus, two sets of d-values observed in two different orientations, relative to the compression axis, provides mean to analyze the stress field applied to the sample. Fig. 5 is an example of this kind of measurement, which shows systematic difference of the lattice parameters determined from the diffraction lines in two different orientations. These data, together with the knowledge of elastic constants c_{ij} of the sample, provides various information of the stress state and the strength of the sample[10].

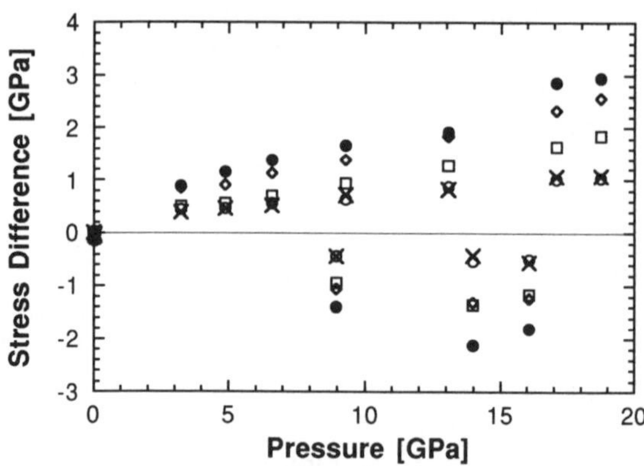

Figure 5. Differential stress of NaCl under uniaxial compression calculated from the d-values of each diffraction lines. : ○200, ◇220, ●222, ×400, □420. Upper and lower half are for pressure increasing and decreasing cycle, respectively[10].

CONCLUSION

An improved Drickamer-type apparatus employing sintered diamond was combined with a synchrotron radiation. Using this apparatus, the P-T range of simultaneous high pressure and temperature *in situ* x-ray diffraction study was extended considerably. The highest pressure so far tested is about 50 GPa, but the principle of this apparatus is very similar to that of the diamond-anvil apparatus, and further extension of the pressure and temperature range is expected. A large sample volume and diffraction measurements in two different orientation are additional advantages of this apparatus. These advantages makes it possible to study various materials which was difficult to study before.

ACKNOWLEDGMENTS

All the x-ray studies were carried out at the Photon Factory, KEK, and the author is grateful to T. Kikegawa and O. Shimomura for their continuous supports for the experiments.

REFERENCES

[1] T. Yagi, *EOS (Transactions, American Geophysical Union)*, 69, 18-19 and 27-28 (1988).

[2] M.Yamakata, T. Yagi, W. Utsumi, and Y.Fukai, *Proc. Jpn. Acad.*, 68B, 172-176 (1992).

[3] W. Utsumi, T. Yagi, K. Leinenweber, O.Shimomura, and T. Taniguchi, in "High Pressure Research: application to Earth and Planetary Sciences" TERRAPUB/ AGU,Tokyo/ Washington (1992).

[4] T. Irifune, W. Utsumi, and T. Yagi, *Proc. Jpn. Acad.*, 68B, 161-166 (1992).

[5] T. Yagi, W. Utsumi, M. Yamakata, T. Kikegawa and O. Shimomura, *Phys. Rev. B.*, 46, 6031-6039 (1992).

[6] N. Fuanamori and T. Yagi, *Geophys. Res. Lett.*, 20, 387-390 (1993).

[7] W. Utsumi and T. Yagi, *Proc. Jpn, Acad.*, 67B, 159-164 (1991).

[8]W. Utsumi and T. Yagi, *Science*, 252, 1542-1544 (1991).

[9] N. Funamori, T. Yagi, and W. Utsumi, Proc. AIRAPT Conf. (1993)

[10] N. Funamori et al. , in preparation.

MEASURING DEVIATORIC STRESS IN THE DIAMOND ANVIL CELL USING TWO X-RAY DIFFRACTION GEOMETRIES

T.-C. Wu & W. A. Bassett
Mineral Physics Laboratory, Department of Geological Sciences,
Snee Hall, Cornell University,
Ithaca, New York 14853

Two methods using synchrotron radiation are employed to measure deviatoric stress in a diamond anvil cell. Polycrystalline gold is used as both a pressure and a stress indicator. In the first method a white beam parallel to the load axis is diffracted at a low 2θ angle and analyzed by the energy dispersive method. We measure the elastic strain of two crystal planes oriented normal to the diffraction vector. Stresses nearly parallel and perpendicular to the load axis can be calculated by stress-strain tensor relationship. In the other method the diamond anvil cell is oriented so that an incident monochromatic beam from a wiggler is perpendicular to the load axis. The diffraction pattern recorded on an image plate area detector is used to measure elastic strains responding to stresses perpendicular and parallel to the load axis. Stresses of the same orientations are calculated from the strain data. Away from the center of the sample chamber, these measurements provide a lower bound of the actual differential stresses in a diamond cell. We also measured stress distribution in a less deviatoric gasketed sample at room and high temperatures.

INTRODUCTION

When the Diamond Anvil Cell (DAC) is used without a gasket or hydrostatic pressure medium, it is basically a uniaxial loading device that is capable of producing one of the largest non-hydrostatic stresses available (Fig. 1). Knowing the deviatoric stress distribution which is material-dependent, is important for analyzing uncertainties in pressure measurement in the DAC[1], for understanding shear-induced phenomena such as phase transitions[2], and for measuring the yield strength of materials [3,4,5,6]

Deviatoric elastic strain measured from *in-situ* X-ray diffraction can be combined with elastic constants of the material to give stress components. This method was used by Kinsland and Bassett[3] to measure the yield strength of MgO and NaCl at high pressure and room temperature. In that study, the incident X-ray beam was perpendicular to the load axis of the DAC (cross axial geometry (Fig. 2a) and a specially designed cross-axis diamond anvil cell (XPDAC) was used. The advantage of cross axial geometry is that diffraction data produced by planes having normals perpendicular and parallel to the load axis can be collected simultaneously and elastic strains of both orientations can be measured. However, the application of XPDAC at high temperature is difficult.

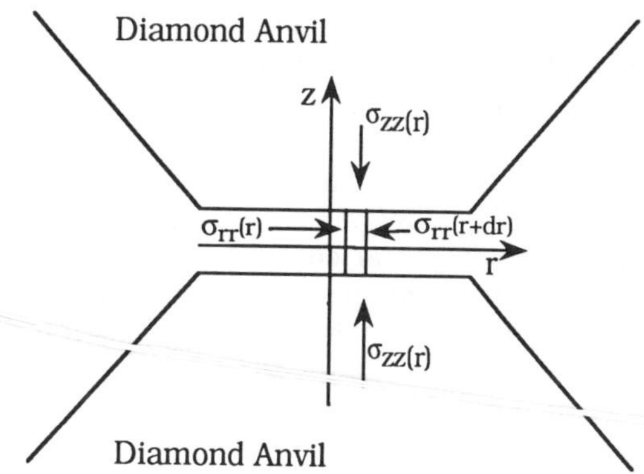

Figure 1. The cross section of a Diamond Anvil Cell (DAC) sample chamber. A cylindrical coordinate system is used, although the azimuth, θ, is not shown in the diagram. σ_{zz} and σ_{rr} are axial stress and radial stress, respectively.

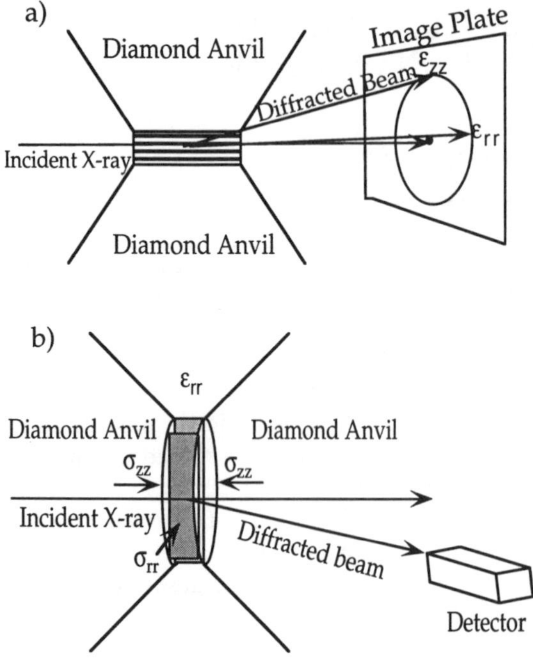

Figure 2. a) Cross axial X-ray diffraction geometry and b) coaxial X-ray diffraction geometry in DAC experiments and their relationship with the stress and strain orientations. ε_{zz} and ε_{rr} are elastic strains of lattice planes perpendicular to the loading and radial axes, respectively.

A coaxial geometry in which the X-ray beam travels along the load axis is normally used for a DAC with an energy dispersive X-ray diffraction (EDXRD) set-up. With this arrangement, a high-temperature DAC can be used without further modification. However, when combining the EDXRD method and coaxial geometry, only those crystal planes with their plane normals essentially perpendicular to the load axis can be measured (Fig. 2b). Elastic strain measured from two lattice planes can be used to derive stress components.

Cross axial geometry has the benefit of producing complete diffraction rings. Elastic strains from all orientations between radial and axial strain can be measured from a single ring. However, coaxial is the normal geometry used in most DAC's and is the only geometry used to date for high temperature studies. A comparison between the results from these two methods can show if high temperature studies can be successfully carried out using the more standard coaxial geometry. In this paper we describe some preliminary results of a comparative study of stress measurement in DAC using these two geometries at room temperature. We also measured different stress histories in the same material with and without gasket using the coaxial method. The effect of high temperature on the stress has also been observed.

EXPERIMENTAL METHOD

All the X-ray diffraction work, including white beam and monochromatic beam, were done at the Cornell High Energy Synchrotron Source (CHESS). In experiments with both geometries, samples consisting of gold powder embedded in fayalite (Fe_2SiO_4) were compressed up to ~20 - 25 GPa in a DAC. Gold was used as a pressure and stress indicator. Using coaxial geometry, we also compressed NaCl mixed with gold powder with and without rhenium gasket around the sample. We also heated the gasketed sample up to 200°C. The volume ratio between both samples and gold was approximately 10:1.

In experiments with coaxial geometry, the EDXRD method was used. A white incident synchrotron radiation beam at CHESS B-1 beamline was collimated to a size of 15 μm. The diffracted beam was collected at $2\theta=10°$ with an intrinsic Ge solid-state detector. With this small angle, the lattice planes corresponding to the collected diffraction signal are nearly perpendicular to the radial stress, thus their strain can be treated as radial strain ε_{rr} (Fig. 2b). A piston type of DAC was used[7].

The diamond anvil cell designed for cross axial diffraction geometry (XPDAC)[3] was placed on a monochromatic synchrotron radiation beam (17 kev,~0.73Å) at CHESS with an image plate area detector set up to record complete diffraction rings[8]. The incident X-rays were collimated by a 40 μm pinhole and the anvil faces were 450 μm across. An external standard of NaCl placed in the beam down stream of the sample provided camera length calibration. The variation of camera length was less than 0.01 mm even when the DAC was removed and replaced. A fragment of polycrystalline gold was placed at the sample location to confirm the sample-detector distsance and to provide information on the natural line width.

The dimensional stability of image plate also eliminates problems that exist in photographic film[3] The only data correction necessary is for tilting due to the plate holder. The diffraction pattern was measured and intensity for each individual pixel was read out on the display program IPVIEW

DATA ANALYSIS

Because of the symmetry of our sample, we assume cylindrical coordinates for the sample chamber. In coaxial diffraction geometry, only radial elastic strain is measured. However, because of the anisotropy of gold, different lattice planes have different elastic strains under non-hydrostatic stress. Therefore, combining measured strains of two lattice planes and the relationship between stress and strain tensors in cubic material, one can calculate deviatoric stress by solving a pair of simultaneous equations[8]. Elastic constants of gold taken from[9] were linearly extrapolated to high pressure.

In cross-axial geometry the X-ray beam traverses the sample from one side of the anvil face to the other side. A diffraction ring, therefore, is produced by material under a range of pressures. The center of the diffraction line produced by the highest pressure portion of the sample was determined by subtracting half of the natural line width (based on the gold diffraction pattern obtained at ambient pressure) from the outer edge (smallest d-spacing) of the line taken at high pressure. The tilting of the plate calculated from the shifting center of the diffraction ring is ~0.5° - 1°, and a correction is made for each individual plate. Different stains in gold were measured at two diameters of the diffraction ring. Using the strain data and the compliance tensor for a single lattice plane, one can solve for deviatoric stress from a pair of equations[8].

RESULTS AND DISCUSSION

Distribution of deviatoric stress measured from gold embedded in fayalite by the two experimental geometries at comparable pressures are shown in Figure 3. Both geometries gave a deviatoric stress of ~0.7 GPa at the center of the fayalite sample. This value gradually decreased toward the edge. At lower pressures (<10 GPa), data taken at the center of the sample using coaxial geometry indicated a smaller stress of ~0.1 GPa at a pressure of ~1 GPa but a comparable stress of ~0.7 GPa at a pressure of ~10 GPa. The deviatoric stress in gold seems to increase with the pressure up to ~10 GPa and to stop increasing above ~10 GPa. Therefore, this small stress may represent yield strength of gold and only a minimum value for that of fayalite. This is in agreement with observations of Weidner[10] and yield strength measurements of fayalite by Sung et al[4].

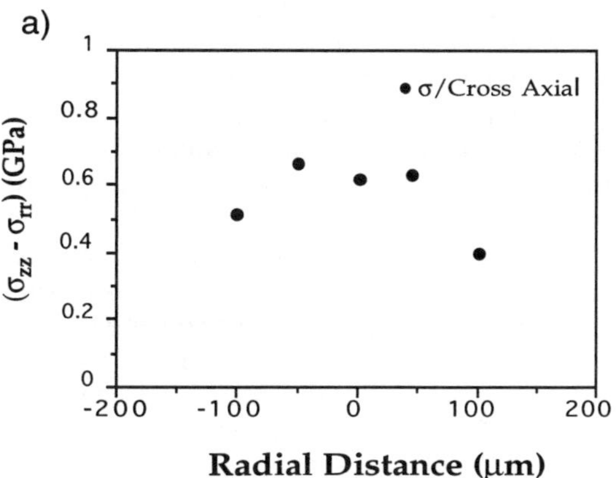

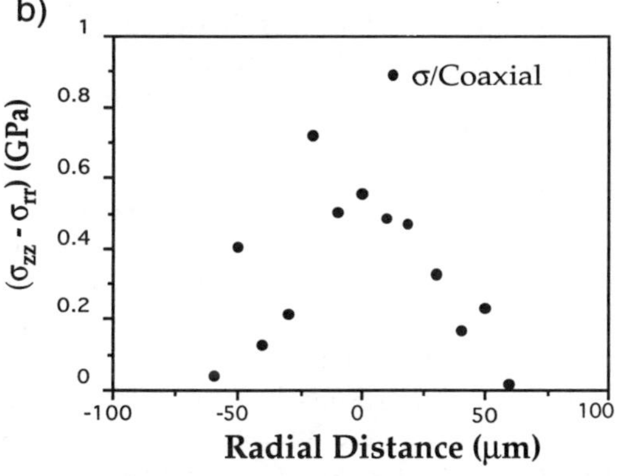

Figure 3. Distribution of deviatoric stress $(\sigma_{zz}\text{-}\sigma_{rr})$ measured from gold embedded in fayalite by a) cross axial geometry and b) coaxial geometry.

In the compression of NaCl, deviatoric stress measured from gold at the center in both gasketed and non-gasketed samples was ~0.5 GPa at a pressure of ~20 GPa. However, data from the sample at a pressure of ~8 GPa without gasket showed the stress was already as high as ~0.5 GPa. On the other hand, the sample with a rhenium gasket clearly showed increasing deviatoric stress with increasing pressure. The deviatoric stress increases from ~0.15 GPa at a pressure of ~3.5 GPa to ~0.5 GPa at a pressure of ~20 GPa at room temperature. Upon heating , the deviatoric stress of this gasketed sample dropped to ~0.3 GPa when the temperature was raised to 200°C. These measurements are consistent with the fact that the stress environment in a gasketed sample is less deviatoric and therefore shows a slower increase of deviatoric stress with pressure. The dropping of deviatoric stress when the sample was heated is also consistent with the expected lowering of yield stress with increasing temperature.

Note that in Figure 3, it shows that the deviatoric stress drops more rapidly along the radius in the coaxial geometry run (Fig. 3b). This could be due to the smaller anvil face used in this run. There are some other differences between the two methods that worth considering. First, the 2θ angle used in the two geometries is different. It is fixed at 10° for all lattice planes in coaxial geometry while in cross axial geometry, it is 17.83° for the (111) plane of gold. Since stresses s_{zz} and s_{rr} are approximatly equal to the principal stresses close to the center, they are simply the stresses we measured divided by cos q. Calculated differences between the two geometries caused by the different 2θ values is less than one percent. The difference is even smaller if differential stresses (σ_{zz} - σ_{rr}) are compared. Secondly, the natural half line width used to determine the high-pressure line position in the cross axial geometry was based on the gold diffraction pattern collected at ambient pressure and may underestimate the real half line width at high pressure since high stress may cause line broadening. This results in an overestimate of the elastic strain and therefore of the stress because too small a correction is made. Since this effect is similar at all points along a diffraction ring, it is expected to be negligible in differential stress (σ_{zz} - σ_{rr}).

Strictly speaking, the stress components measured in the sample can represent the maximum and minimum stresses only when the strains are measured at the center of the sample. Away from the center, the stress ellipsoid may be at a different orientation and therefore the maximum and minimum stresses may be at different orientations from perpendicular and parallel to the loading axis in DAC. For this reason, the stress measured for the part of the sample away from the center can only be treated as a lower bound of the deviatoric stress at those positions. From our measurements, we think that at least within a quarter of the anvil radius from the center, the deviatoric stress is comparable to and possibly even larger than the that at the center. This has a profound effect on shear-sensitive processes at high pressure (e.g., Wu et al., in press).

ACKNOWLEDGMENTS

We want to thank Don Weidner of SUNY Stony Brook for providing computer programs and for his encouragement. We also wish to thank the staff at CHESS for their valuable help. This research is supported by NSF grant EAR-9206004

REFERENCES

[1] Y.Meng, D.Weidner, and Y.Fei, *Geophys Res. Lett.*, in press

[2]T.-C.Wu, W.A.Bassett, P.C.Burnley and M.S.Weathers, *J.Geophy. Res.*, in press.

[3]G.L. Kinsland and W.A. Bassett, *J. Appl. Phys.*, 48, 978-985.(1976)

[4]C.-M. Sung, C. Goetze, and H.-K. Mao, H.-K. *Rev. Sci. Ins.*, 48, 1386-1391.(1977)

[5]H. Kimura, D.G. Ast, and W.A. Bassett, *J. Appl. Phy.*, 53, pp. 3523-3528.(1982)

[6]C. Meade and R. Jeanloz, *J. Geophy. Res.*, 93, 3261-3269.(1988)

[7]M.D. Furnish, and W. A. Bassett, *J. Geophys. Res.*, 88, 10333-10341, (1983).

[8]T.-C.Wu and W.A.Bassett, *Pure Appl.Geophys,* in press

[9]Y. Hiki and A.V.Granato, *Phy. Rev.* 144, p. 411 (1967)

[10]D. Weidner, Personal communication.

THE EFFECT OF STRESS ANISOTROPY ON THE LATTICE STRAINS MEASURED WITH AN X-RAY DIFFRACTION OPPOSED ANVIL SETUP

Anil K. Singh
Materials Science Division
National Aerospace Laboratories
Bangalore 560 017, India

This article discusses the general equation derived recently for the lattice strains which correspond to the strains measured by a diffraction method on a solid polycrystalline specimen compressed nonhydrostatically in an opposed anvil setup. The equations for the various diffraction geometries used in high pressure work emerge as the special cases of this equation. The expressions for the strain based on isotropic elasticity theory (IET) available in the literature can be obtained by invoking the condition of elastic isotropy in the general equation. The equations based on IET give macroscopic strain in a specified direction, and this strain, in general, differs from the x-ray measured lattice strain in the same direction. The predictions of the general equation have been compared with those of the equation based on IET.

INTRODUCTION

The stress state at the center of a solid polycrystalline specimen compressed in an opposed anvil setup is nonhydrostatic. The resulting lattice strain can be measured by the x-ray diffraction technique. In the past, attempts were made to calculate the strain which corresponds to x-ray measurement. Basically, two approaches were followed. In the first approach[1-3], anisotropic elasticity theory (AET) was used to derive the equations for the lattice strain in a cubic case, for the different diffraction geometries used in high pressure work. These equations predict that the lattice strains depend on the Miller indices (*hkl*). This prediction was subsequently verified in a number of independent experiments[1,4-10]. In the second approach[11-18], isotropic elasticity theory (IET) was used to calculate the strain produced by nonhydrostatic pressure. For a long time, the two approaches have remained distinct in the literature, with no attempts made for an intercomparison.

GENERAL CONSIDERATIONS

IET versus AET

The strain derived from the diffraction angle, θ, measured at a point O (point of observation), is in a direction N which lies in the plane containing the incident and the diffracted x-ray beams, and bisects the angle XSO (Fig.1). The use of IET to calculate the strain along N gives the macroscopic strain [19] which corresponds to the measurement by a macroscopic method such as the strain gauge method.

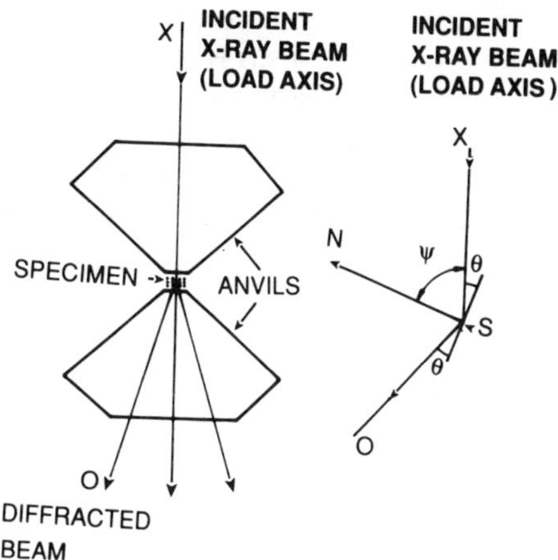

Figure 1. The diffraction geometry in a DAC.

It may be noted that all the crystallites in the specimen do not contribute to the diffracted intensity at O. Only those crystallites which have the diffracting plane normals pointing along N, contribute to the diffracted intensity at O; the orientations of all such crystallites are related by rotation φ about N. (These crystallites are termed φ-group of crystallites). The x-ray measured strain is the average of the strains in the φ-group of crystallites only. For this reason, the x-ray measured strain (lattice strain), in general, differs from the macroscopic strain in the same direction.

Diffraction geometries

The various diffraction geometries used in high pressure x-ray work can be uniquely defined, for the purposes of the lattice strain calculations, with the help of the angle, ψ, which the diffracting plane normal, N, makes with the direction of the applied load. For the diamond anvil cell (DAC) geometry, $\psi = \pm\{(\pi/2)-\theta\}$, and $\psi = \pm\pi/2$ for the tungsten carbide anvil geometry. In the Kinsland-Bassett geometry[13,14], wherein the x-ray beam passes perpendicular to the direction of the applied load in a DAC, and the diffraction ring is recorded on a flat film placed normal to the direction of the incident x-ray beam, the ψ value depends on the point of observation. For the diffraction ring diameters perpendicular and parallel to the direction of the load, $\psi = \pm\pi/2$ and $\psi = \pm\theta$ respectively.

Stress state

The stress state at the center of the solid specimen compressed between the anvils is referred to the right handed system of co-ordinates, x_i (i =1,2,3), such that x_3 is in the direction of applied load, and x_1 and x_2 parallel to the anvil face. Since, there exists a cylindrical symmetry about the direction of the load, the stress state is given by,

$$\sigma_{ij} = \begin{bmatrix} \sigma_1 & 0 & 0 \\ 0 & \sigma_1 & 0 \\ 0 & 0 & \sigma_3 \end{bmatrix}$$

$$= \begin{bmatrix} \sigma_p & 0 & 0 \\ 0 & \sigma_p & 0 \\ 0 & 0 & \sigma_p \end{bmatrix} + \begin{bmatrix} -t/3 & 0 & 0 \\ 0 & -t/3 & 0 \\ 0 & 0 & +2t/3 \end{bmatrix} \tag{1}$$

where the first and second terms represent mean normal stress (hydrostatic pressure) and the deviatoric stress component respectively. Further, $t = (\sigma_3 - \sigma_1)$ is termed uniaxial stress component and equals twice the shear strength of the specimen material. It can be shown that $\sigma_p = (2\sigma_1 + \sigma_3)/3 = (\sigma_1 + t/3)$.

EQUATIONS FOR THE LATTICE STRAIN

The calculation of lattice strains for a given stress state in a polycrystalline specimen consisting of elastically anisotropic crystallites requires certain assumptions regarding the stress and strain continuity across the grain boundaries. The Voigt[20] and the Reuss[21] limits, which assume respectively the strain and the stress continuity across the grain boundaries, represent the two extremes, and the real situation lies in between. As shown earlier[19], the strain produced by the deviatoric stress component, expressed as the average of the strains calculated under the Voigt and the Reuss limits, is given by,

$$\Delta\varepsilon(hkl) = \alpha\varepsilon_R(hkl) + (1-\alpha)\varepsilon_V \tag{2}$$

where,

$$\varepsilon_R(hkl) = -(t/3)(1-3\cos^2\psi)(S_{11} - S_{12} - 3\Gamma S)$$

$$S = (S_{11} - S_{12} - S_{44}/2)$$

$$\Gamma = (h^2k^2 + k^2l^2 + l^2h^2)/(h^2+k^2+l^2)^2$$

$$\varepsilon_V = -(t/3)(1-3\cos^2\psi)/(2G_V)$$

S_{ij} are single crystal elastic compliances, G_V is the shear modulus of the polycrystalline specimen material under Voigt limit, and α is a number lying between 0 and 1. If the crystallites are isotropic, i.e., S =0, then Eq.(2) reduces to

$$\Delta\varepsilon(iso) = -(t/3)(1-3\cos^2\psi)/2G \tag{3}$$

where G is the shear modulus of the polycrystalline specimen material. Since the shear modulus of a polycrystal is close to the average of the shear moduli under the Voigt and Reuss limits[22], it can be shown[19] that,

$$R = \Delta\varepsilon(hkl)/\Delta\varepsilon(iso) = \alpha f_R + (1-\alpha)f_V \tag{4}$$

where

$$f_R = F_1 + F_2$$

$$F_1 = (5/2)(3 + 2x)^{-1}[(1-3\Gamma)x + 3\Gamma]$$

$$F_2 = (1/10x)(2 + 3x)[(1-3\Gamma)x + 3\Gamma]$$

$$f_V = (1+F_1/F_2)/2$$

$$x = 2(S_{11} - S_{12})/S_{44}.$$

In practice, the d-spacings of a number of reflections are measured, and the reported lattice strain is an average (simple or weighted) over all the measured reflections. In such a case,

$$\langle R \rangle = \alpha \langle f_R \rangle_\Gamma + (1-\alpha)f_V.$$

The symbol $\langle\,\rangle$ denotes the type of average (simple or weighted) used to calculate the average strain from the measured d-spacings. The second term is independent of (hkl).

DISCUSSION

The equation discussed here (Eq.2) is general in that the equations for the various geometries can be obtained by inserting appropriate values of ψ. The equations for the tungsten carbide anvil[1] and the DAC [2] geometries derived earlier[1,2] can be obtained from Eq.(2) by letting $\psi = \pi/2$ and $\psi = \{(\pi/2) - \theta\}$ respectively. Further, the equations derived earlier using IET (e.g., ref 18) can be obtained from Eq.(2) by letting $S = 0$, the condition of elastic isotropy.

The Kinsland-Bassett geometry[13,14] is interesting, as it is possible, with this geometry, to record data with a wide range of ψ -values (between θ and $\pi/2$). However, the main drawback of this method stems from the fact that the incident x-ray beam passes through a region of large pressure differential ranging from one atmosphere at the edges of the anvil face to the highest pressure at the center. This makes the interpretation of the data difficult, though a method to overcome this difficulty was suggested[13]. In principle, an x-ray transparent gasket (e.g. Be gasket) can be used to confine the specimen at the center of the anvil face.

An obvious but unique situation arises if $\cos\psi = 1/\sqrt{3}$ because the strain produced by the deviatoric stress component vanishes, and the strain measured under this condition is the strain produced by σ_p alone. Because of the various experimental constraints, this condition is difficult to achieve in the DAC geometry, but is certainly possible in the Kinsland-Bassett geometry. Eq.(2) can provide a more comprehensive discussion of the data obtained under the Kinsland-Bassett geometry than was possible earlier.

The value of α is central to the calculation of the lattice strain. It is seen from Eq.(2) that the (hkl)-dependence of $\Delta\varepsilon(hkl)$ arises from the strain calculation under the Reuss limit. The observations of the (hkl)-dependence of the measured strain [1,4-10] indicate that $\alpha \neq 0$. In earlier discussions[5,10], $\alpha = 1$ was assumed. The view was expressed that $\alpha = 1$ is relevant to high pressure measurement[14]. However, no direct evidence for this assumption exists. The measured strains produced by the macro-residual stresses agree well with the average of the strains calculated under the Voigt and Reuss limits[23]. This can be taken to suggest that $\alpha = 1/2$ in the present case also. A comparison of the data from two independent measurements gives an estimate of the value of α. The analysis of the diffraction data (assuming $\alpha = 1$) on NaCl compressed to various pressures up to 10 GPa gave $t = (0.24+0.01p)$ GPa [15]. This suggests that at 9 GPa, $t = 0.35$ GPa. The measurement of the pressure gradient in NaCl compressed in a DAC gave $t = 0.54$ at 9 GPa [24]. This value of t can be obtained from the diffraction data [5] if $\alpha = 0.65$ is taken. While attempting such a comparison one should keep in

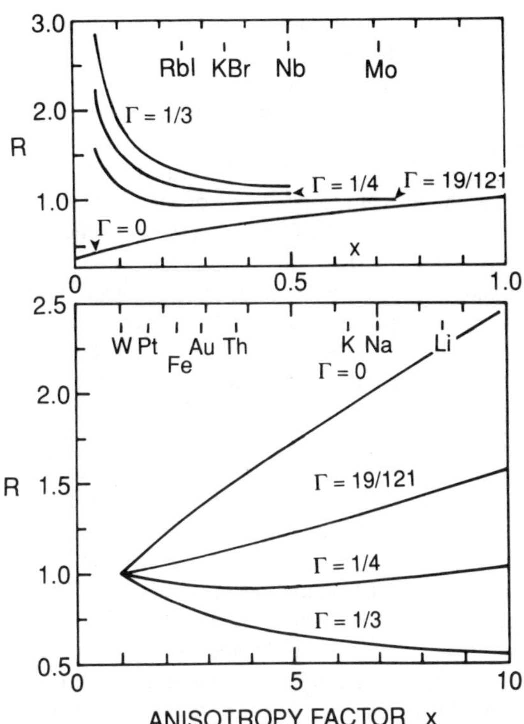

Figure 2. The ratio of the strains calucated using AET and IET as a function of x.

mind the fact that t depends on the extent of deformation the specimen undergoes during pressurization[24].

The ratio R given by Eq.(4) can be used to compare the strains along a common direction (hkl), calculated using AET and IET. This provides a direct estimate of the error introduced in the calculation of lattice strain if IET is used in the case wherein the crystallites are elastically anisotropic. Fig.2 gives a plot of R (with $\alpha = 0.5$) as a function of anisotropy factor x for the first five reflections of the face and body centered cubic structures. It is to be noted that the Γ-value is zero for (200), 19/121 for (311), 1/4 for (110), (220) and (211), and 1/3 for (111) and (222) reflections. The distinction between AET and IET vanishes if $x = 1$, and in this case, $R = 1$. The R -value increases as x deviates from unity. For a given value of x (<1), the R -value increases with increasing Γ, while the trend is reversed in the region $x > 1$. To illustrate the Γ -dependence of R in an actual case, we consider the example of gold (x =2.9). The R -values are 1.4, 1.1, 0.9 and 0.8 for Γ -values 0, 19/121, 1/4 and 1/3 respectively. However, the average value of R for the first five reflections of gold is 1, eventhough R -values for the extreme Γ -values differ widely. It may be noted that the variation of x with pressure is to be considered while estimating the R-values in the high pressure region.

The theoretical considerations[25] and a limited number of experiments[26,27] suggest that the shear strength ($=t/2$) scales with the shear modulus G. In such a case, the pressure-dependence of the shear strength reflects the variation of G with pressure. In the recent experiments on MgO and a few metals [28,29], the pressure-dependences of the shear strength were found to be much larger than what could be accounted for by the pressure-dependence of G. This enhanced pressure-dependence of the shear strength arises because the Peierls-Nabarro stress acting on the dislocations increases strongly with increasing pressure [30,31].

All the theoretical treatments of this topic are based on the assumption that the crystallites in the specimen are randomly oriented. In the present discussion, this assumption is made to calculate the average values of some trigonometric functions [19]. This assumption is seldom valid in a real situation because the flow, which occurs when the specimen is compressed between the anvils, introduces texture (preferred orientation). Since the degree of texture depends on the extent of flow, it is likely to differ for the specimens of the same material compressed to a given pressure in different high pressure setups. In principle, the effect of texture can be taken into account by the procedure suggested earlier [19]. This requires a complete knowledge of the orientation distribution function in the specimen region illuminated by the incident x-ray beam. The small size of the illuminated specimen area (10-100 μm diameter) poses serious practical problems if one attempts to determine the orientation distribution function in this region.

CONCLUSIONS

(1) The equation discussed in this article is general. The equations for the different diffraction geometries used in high pressure work emerge as the special cases of this equation. **(2)** The equations derived using IET can be obtained from this equation by letting $S = 0$, and using the relevant values of ψ. **(3)** The error introduced, if the strain produced by the deviatoric stress component is calculated using IET, can be estimated. **(4)** There exists an uncertainty in the value of α (though it is expected to be close to 0.5); a direct measurement of α is highly desirable. **(5)** The use of the present equation in the complete interpretation of the diffraction data requires a knowledge of the pressure-dependences of the elastic compliances; for some limited discussions, the pressure-dependence of the anisotropy factor only is required. **(6)** This analysis can be used to interpret the compression data obtained under nonhydrostatic pressure [32].

REFERENCES

[1] A.K.Singh and G.C.Kennedy, *J.Appl.Phys.*, **45**, 4686 (1974)

[2] A.K.Singh and C.Balasingh, *J.Appl.Phys.*, **48**, 5338 (1977)

[3] A.K.Singh, *High Temp-High Pressures*, **10**, 641 (1978)

[4] J.C.Jamieson, Private Communication, (1975)

[5] A.K.Singh and G.C.Kennedy, *J.Appl.Phys.*, **47**, 3337 (1976)

[6] K.Syassen and W.B.Holzapfel, *Rev.Sci.Instrum.*, **49**, 1107 (1978)

[7] S.N.Vaidya, W.A.Grosshans, and W.B.Holzapfel, *High Temp-High Pressures*, **16**, 491 (1984)

[8] W.A.Grosshans, E.F.Duesing, and W.B.Holzapfel, *High Temp-High Pressures*, **16**, 539 (1984)

[9] S.Usha Devi and A.K.Singh, *Physica*, **139-140B**, 922 (1986)

[10] A.K.Singh, Kalyani Vijayan, H.Xia, Y.K.Vohra and A.L.Ruoff, in *Recent Trends in High Pressure Research*, Edited by A.K.Singh, (Oxford & IBH, New Delhi, 1992) p782

[11] A.L.Ruoff, *Scripta Metall.*, **8**, 1161 (1974)

[12] A.L.Ruoff, *J.Appl.Phys.*, **46**, 1389 (1975)

[13] G.L.Kinsland and W.A.Bassett, *Rev.Sci.Instrum.*, **47**, 130 (1976)

[14] G.L.Kinsland and W.A.Bassett, *J.Appl.Phys.*, **48**, 978 (1977)

[15] G.L.Kinsland, *High Temp-High Pressures*, **10**, 627 (1978)

[16] H.K.Mao, P.M.Bell, J.W.Shaner and D.J.Steinberg, *J.Appl.Phys.*, **49**, 3276 (1978)

[17] A.L.Ruoff, H.Xia, H.Luo and Y.K.Vohra, *Rev.Sci.Instrum.*, **61**, 3830 (1990)

[18] A.L.Ruoff, H.Luo, H.Xia and Y.K.Vohra, *High Pressure Res.*, **6**, 183 (1991)

[19] A.K.Singh, *J.Appl.Phys.*, **73**, (in press) (1993)

[20] W.Voigt, *Lehrbuch der Kristalphysik* (Teubner, Liepzig, 1928)

[21] A.Reuss, *Z.Angew, Math.Mech.*, **9**, 49 (1929)

[22] R.Hill, *Proc.Phys.Soc. (London)*, **A65**, 349 (1952)

[23] G.B.Greenough, in *Progress in Metal Physics*, Edited by B.Chalmers (Pergamon Press, 1952) vol.3, p176

[24] C.Mead and R.Jeanloz, *J.Geo.Phys.Res.*, **93**. 3261 (1988)

[25] M.F.Ashby and R.A.Verrall., *Philos.Trans.Royal Soc.(London) Ser A*, **288**, 59 (1977)

[26] J.O.Chua and A.L.Ruoff., *J.Appl.Phys.* **46**, 4659 (1975)

[27] J.P.Poirier., *Creep of Crystals*, (Cambridge University Press, New York, 1985) p 260

[28] R.E.Reicker, L.C.Towle and T.P.Rooney, *Air Force Cambridge Res.Lab.Rep.* 67-0475 (1967)

[29] D.Kuhlmann-Wilsdorf, B.C.Cai and R.B.Nelson, *J.Mater.Res.* **6**, 2547 (1991)

[30] L.C.Towle and R.E.Reicker, *Appl.Phys.Letters*, **13**, 159 (1968)

[31] W.A.Jesser and D.Kuhlmann-Wilsdorf, *Mater.Sci.Eng.* **9**, 111 (1972)

[32] A.K.Singh, *Phil.Mag.Letters*. (in press) (1993).

5 μm X-RAY APERTURES AND THEIR METROLOGY

Arthur L. Ruoff, Huan Luo, Hui Xia and Craig Vanderborgh

Department of Materials Science and Engineering
Cornell University
Ithaca, NY 14853

To obtain multimegabar pressures, microminiaturization is necessary. The use of diamond anvil tips less than 20 μm in diameter, and the accompanying steep pressure gradients, require x-ray beams of small cross-section for x-ray diffraction studies. We describe here the production of 5 μm x-ray apertures for diffraction studies to 100 keV, and the metrology for characterizing these apertures.

INTRODUCTION

The use of diamond anvils with both tips only 20 μm in diameter has made possible the attainment for the first time of static pressures in excess of the pressure at the center of the earth; we have reported pressures of 416 GPa [1] and 560 GPa [2]. Pressures of this magnitude are measured by x-ray diffraction using equations of state obtained from shock data as described elsewhere [3], since the ruby pressure scale fails above 250 GPa [4]. Small-diameter x-ray beams are needed in these studies, and as tips with even smaller diameters come to be used, even tinier x-ray beams will be needed. It is necessary to provide apertures that are small enough and that can slide into the diamond anvil cell, fitting close to the diamonds to avoid beam divergence.

APERTURES

Figure 1 shows a schematic of the tungsten aperture we have fabricated by the following procedure.

Two tungsten rods, 3.175 mm in diameter and 25.4 mm long, are ground to half-cylinders in a special fixture. Then a clearance cut 1.59 mm long and 0.4 mm deep is made at both ends of each piece. A 5 μm groove is cut along the center of one of the pieces, and then both pieces are cut in half. The four half-cylinders are ground to

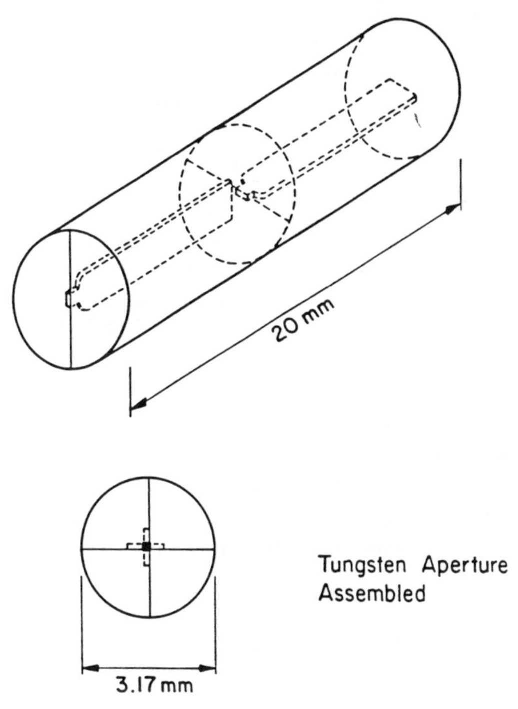

Figure 1. Schematic of slit assembly of four half-cylinders, with the slit of one pair at 90° to the slit of the other pair.

a length of 10 mm each. The small portion of the groove is 2.6 mm long. One pair of the half-cylinders is clamped and pushed into a section of thin-walled tubing and then the other pair is inserted with the slits at 90° to the first. The result is an aperture 50 μm square.

METROLOGY

To characterize the aperture, affirming its size and shape, we use a taut fixed tungsten wire and move the aperture past it, as indicated in Figure 2. We study the L fluorescence that is emitted from the tungsten wire at an angle similar to that used in our energy-dispersive diffraction studies, so that when we switch to diffraction studies, no change in the aperture orientation will occur. After a scan is made across the wire in one direction, the wire holder is rotated by 90° and another scan is made across the wire. Figure 3(a) shows a segment of the wire whose axis lies along the z direction. The x-ray input is in the y direction, the detector is at an angle 2θ relative to the y direction and the path to the detector is normal to the x direction. In order to measure S_x, the slit of width S_z is moved in the x direction during scanning.

Consider now the element of thickness dx, which has length $2Y = 2\sqrt{R^2-x^2}$ and width S_z and which is located between x and x+dx, as shown in Figure 3(a). Now take the portion of this element with length dy located between y and y+dy, as shown in Figure 3(b).

It can be shown that the number of photons per second entering the detector, I_D, is given by [5]

$$I_D = \int_x \int_E \int_y \left\{ J_o(E) S_z g \mu_p(E) \; e^{-\mu(E)(Y+y)} \; e^{-\mu_L (Y-y)/\cos\theta} \right\} dy dE dx \qquad (1)$$

Here $J_o(E)$ is the flux of photons having energy between E and E+dE that are entering and leaving the aperture in the y direction (J_o has units of photons/cm^2-sec-keV); $\mu_p(E)$ is the photoelectric

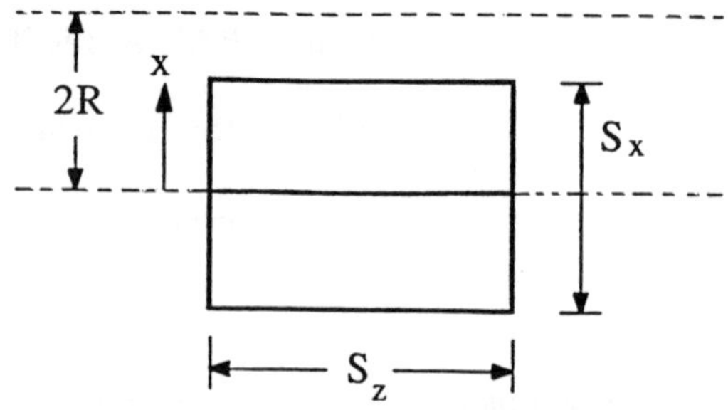

Figure 2. Diagram showing the rectangular aperture of dimensions S_x by S_z in front of the fixed tungsten wire. The incident x-ray beam is in the y direction. The aperture moves in the x direction during the scanning.

absorption coefficient, $\mu(E)$ is the total absorption coefficient; μ_L is the absorption coefficient at the energy of the L fluorescence at the energy E_L; g is the geometrical fraction of fluorescent radiation (emitted over 4π) which reaches the detector; and 2Y is the length of the element of thickness dx. This equation can be integrated on y, holding x and E constant to obtain

$$I_D = \int_x \int_E \left\{ J_o(E) S_z g \, \mu_p(E) \left[e^{-2\mu_L R q(x)} - e^{-2\mu(E) R q(x)} \right] \right\} dE dx \qquad (2)$$

where $q(x) = (1-x^2/R^2)^{1/2}$. The experiment is carried out at the fixed angle 2θ. We then integrate numerically on E at one specific value of x and repeat at other values of x to obtain the function F(x) in the expression

$$I_D = \int_x F(x) dx \qquad (3)$$

The integration on E goes from the appropriate E_L up to some large value of E, say E_K, above which

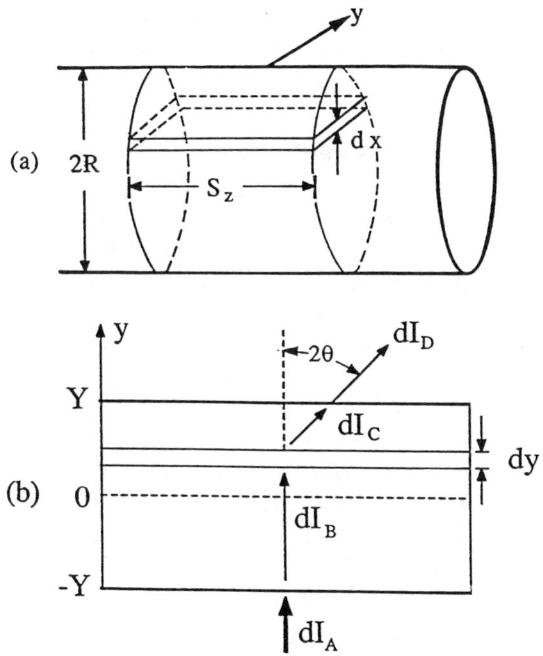

Figure 3. (a) Tungsten wire being irradiated along the slit length S_z and in part along the slit height S_x. The incident radiation is in the y direction. (b) The slab of thickness dx in (a) shown normal to the paper. The unscattered portion of the incident beam passes a distance 2Y through the wire. The actual path to the detector is shown by arrows.

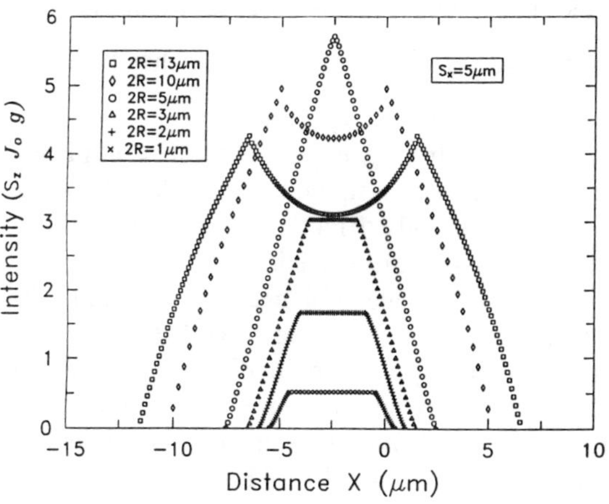

Figure 4. Calculated intensity profiles for S_x < 2R, S_x = 2R, and S_x > 2R.

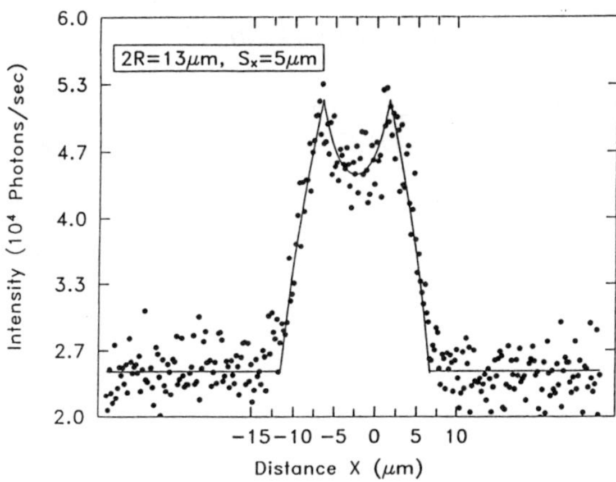

Figure 5. Experimental intensity profile data and calculated curve for 2R = 13 μm and S_x = 5 μm. The intensity at x=0 was fitted.

the contribution to the integral becomes negligible. The different fluorescences L_1, L_2, and L_3 must each be considered, and transition probabilities must be used when two or three transitions are possible. Once F(x) is determined, the final integration on F(x) follows. We use the absorption coefficients from Veigle [6].

Calculated intensity profiles are shown in Figure 4 for the case S_x = 5 μm with tungsten wires of different diameters. Figure 5 shows an experimental profile obtained with a tungsten wire with 2R = 13.00 ± 0.05 μm. The energy range of the detector was set to accept all the L fluorescence and the angle 2θ was chosen so that no diffraction peaks were present in this energy range. Also shown is a simulated curve for S_x = 5.0 μm. From the fit to curves with S_x = 5.0, 5.1 and 4.9 μm, we deduced that S_x = 5.0 ± 0.1 μm. A similar procedure was followed to obtain S_z. We note that the width of the peak when I approaches zero is $2R + S_x$, that the distance between the two peaks at I_{MAX} is $2R - S_x - \beta$ and that β is calculated to be nearly negligible.

Once the metrology experiments are completed, the wire holder is removed and replaced by the pressure vessel and diffraction experiments follow.

The 5-μm slits are sufficient for most research to 200 GPa, but we will need smaller slits for higher pressures. Since we have estimated that with diamond tips 5 μm in diameter, pressures above 1 TPa may be reached, we may need 2 μm apertures. (Such pressures may be sufficient to make metallic diamond.) Most of the loss in number of photons striking the sample in unit time due to the smaller aperture would be made up by the higher x-ray flux that will become available when the six pole wiggler at the Cornell High-Energy Synchrotron Source is replaced with a 24-pole wiggler.

ACKNOWLEDGMENTS

We acknowledge support as follows. H. Luo: NSF grant, DMR-9121654, through the Cornell Materials Science Center. Craig Vanderborgh: DOE-DE-FG02-87-ER-45320. H. Xia: NSF grant, DMR-88178831.

REFERENCES

[1] A. R. Ruoff, H. Xia, H. Luo and Y. K. Vohra, *Rev. Sci. Instrum.* 61, 3830 (1990).

[2] A. R. Ruoff, H. Xia and Q. Xia, *Rev. Sci. Instrum.* 63, 4342 (1992).

[3] N. C. Holmes, J. A. Moriarty, G. R. Gathers and W. J. Nellis, *J. Appl. Phys.* 66, 2962 (1989).

[4] A. L. Ruoff in *Recent Trends in High Pressure Research*, New Delhi: Oxford and IBH Pub. Co., 1992, p. 798.

[5] A. L. Ruoff, H. Luo, C. Vanderborgh, H. Xia and V. Arnold, Cornell Materials Science Center Report #7580, submitted for publication.

[6] W. J. Veigle, *Atomic Data Tables* 5, 51 (1973).

CHAPTER XXII

EXPERIMENTAL METHODS: Shock

Calculations Supporting Hypervelocity Launcher Development

Timothy G. Trucano and Lalit C. Chhabildas
Sandia National Laboratories
Albuquerque, New Mexico, USA 87185-5800

Sandia National Laboratories has developed a HyperVelocity Launcher (also referred to as HVL) in which a thin flier plate (nominally 1 mm thick) is launched to velocities in excess of 12 km/s. The length-to-diameter ratio of these launched flier plates varies from 0.02 to 0.06. The launch technique is based upon using structured, time-dependent, high-pressure, high-acceleration pulses to drive the flier plates. Such pulses are achieved by using a graded-density material to impact a stationary flier. A computational and experimental program at Sandia seeks to extend this technique to allow launching thick plates whose length-to-diameter ratio is 10 to 20 times larger than thin plates. Hydrodynamic codes are used to design modifications to the basic impact technique to allow this extension. Two-dimensional effects become more important for launching chunks with this technique. We have controlled and used these effects to successfully launch a chunk-flier, consisting of 0.33 gm of titanium alloy, 0.3 cm thick by 0.6 cm in diameter, to a velocity of 10.2 km/s. This is the largest chunky size ever launched at this velocity from a gas gun configuration.

This work performed at Sandia National Laboratories supported by the U. S. Department of Energy under contract number DE-AC04-76DP00789. Partial funding from the U.S. Defense Nuclear Agency is also acknowledged.

INTRODUCTION

Sandia has developed a HyperVelocity Launcher, HVL, which is capable of launching gram-size plates to velocities not to date accessible on smooth-bore guns such as the two-stage light-gas gun. The interest in increased velocity launch capabilities in part was motivated by Strategic Defense Initiative research, and concern regarding impact of orbital debris particles on space voyagers. This has led to the development of an impact technique [1,2] in which a time-dependent structured pressure pulse is generated to launch 0.5 mm to1.0 mm thick flier plates to velocities up to 12.2 km/s.

There are two main requirements in order to launch thin flier plates to hypervelocities. First, very high loading pressures are required. Second, this loading must be nearly *shockless* and *uniform* over the entire impact surface. To achieve both these requirements, a multi-layer, graded-density material [3] is used to impact the thin flier plate. With this graded-density impactor nearly shockless 100 GPa pressure pulses [4] are created in the flier. Since the loading on the flier is shockless, excessive heating is minimized, preventing melting of the flier. The method has been used [5] to launch a 0.5 mm thick titanium alloy (Ti-6Al-4V) plate intact to 12.2 km/s. With further improvements to this technique we expect that launch velocities approaching 14 km/s can be achieved.

As indicated above, the loading that is necessary to launch flier plates must be nearly ***shockless*** (***i.e., ramp***) and ***uniform*** during the acceleration process. When a material is subjected to ramp loading, constitutive behavior causes the compressive ramp wave to steepen as it traverses the material. This, in effect, increases the loading rate within the sample until the compression wave achieves a steady "high-pressure shock" profile. This shock produces high temperatures that can lead to melting. We thus require the flier plate to be *thin* in order to prevent shock up and melting. The current aspect ratio *i.e.*, the length to diameter ratio, of thin fliers launched on the Sandia HVL is approximately 0.05 to 0.1 It is the purpose of this report to describe a technique that has been developed to launch an intact "chunk", *i.e.* a 0.3 cm thick by 0.6 cm diameter cylindrical titanium alloy (Ti-6Al-4V) flyer, to approximately 10.2 km/s. The experimental techniques used to accomplish this launch were similar but not identical to techniques developed for the Sandia HyperVelocity Launcher (HVL). One key to the success of this experiment was pretest design work that was performed using the **CTH** [6] multi-dimensional hydrodynamic code. Although, many pretest calculations were necessary to achieve the final design, only a subset of these will be reported here to highlight the technical issues associated with the launch of a chunk flier. In particular, the calculations presented in this paper have been tailored to indicate the path that led to the experimental conditions that were finally selected. These **CTH** calculations are reported in the next section, while the experimental results are discussed in the final section.

TECHNICAL ISSUES

As indicated earlier, to launch plates to hypervelocities a high-pressure quasi-isentropic loading wave is necessary to prevent the flier plate from melting. To achieve this criterion, a multi-layer graded-density material is used to impact the thin flier plate. When this graded-density material is used to impact a thin flier plate at high velocities of over 6 km/s on a two-stage light-gas gun, nearly shockless 100 GPa pressure pulses are introduced into the flier plate.

If one wants to launch a thicker flier, then it is clearly necessary for the graded-density impactor to be scaled proportionately to produce loading of the thick *chunk* by a scaled time-dependent high-pressure pulse. This cannot be arbitrarily accomplished for the following reasons. Thickening the graded-density impactor will add considerable mass to the two-stage light-gas gun projectile, lowering the possible impact velocity to less than 6 km/s. This will reduce the high pressures that are necessary to launch the larger mass. Also, the loading pressure pulse resulting from a thicker impactor will scale proportionately and will be of a *longer* duration. Two-dimensional effects emanating from the edges of the thick chunk will become important and possibly create a severe velocity gradient over a larger radius of the flier. This may cause the flier to bend and even fragment.

From previous experience, we know that 2-D axisymmetric **CTH** calculations accurately simulate the impact of a multi-layer impactor and subsequent acceleration of a thin flier plate. We have therefore used **CTH** to simulate and evaluate the technical issues related to launching thicker flier plates. This approach is quite important to the experimental program, because it allows us to reduce the need to perform parameter variations in the laboratory in order to optimize the experimental configuration.

In all the calculations discussed here, a graded-density impactor which is approximately three times thicker than that used in a conventional HVL experiment is assumed. The exact dimensions of the graded-density impactor layers used in the experiment described in this report is indicated in Table 1. In all the calculations reported in this paper an impact velocity of 5.8 km/s for the graded-density impactor is used. This is the impact velocity at which the reported experiment was performed.

Table 1: Graded-Density Impactor Dimensions

Material Layer	Thickness (mm)	Diameter (mm)
TPX	3.00	12.7
Magnesium	1.803	12.7
Aluminum	1.499	12.7
Titanium	1.194	12.7
Copper	6.375	12.7
Titanium*	0.792	26.97

We report four different **CTH** calculations here. In all the calculations (as well as the experiment) a TPX (plastic) buffer ~4 mm thick lies on the impact side of the flier. The flier consists of a central portion, isolated from the barrel by a guard ring assembly. (See Figure 1 for the configuration used in the experiment and in calculation **#4**.) The term “flier” in the following discussion **ALWAYS** refers to the central portion. The use of guard rings with fliers is standard in our previous HVL experiments.

First, we performed a 1-D **CTH** calculation (**#1**) to confirm that the impactor assembly tabulated in Table1 will launch a flier without melting or fracturing it during the acceleration phase, and also to predict the final velocity. The velocity *vs* time of a 3 mm thick titanium alloy flier is presented in Figure 2. The predicted terminal velocity is ~ 8.8 km/s. The driving pulse in the simulation is observed not to melt or fracture the flier. This experiment cannot be performed because the resulting two-stage gun projectile would be too heavy to obtain the required impact velocity of 5.8 km/s.

The calculation **#2** is a two-dimensional simulation (see Figure 3) in which the barrel and radial response of the impactor and flier are modeled. The impactor and the flier have the same diameter as the tungsten barrel (~ 29 mm) that is generally used in Sandia HVL experiments. This experiment is still not feasible because of the impactor mass, but it is interesting to see the differences that the simulated 2-D effects create. The loading pulse is three times longer than in the usual thin flier case. A velocity gradient over the face of the flier is created by the resulting 2-D effects. The flier is predicted to bend and fracture in the simulation in response to this non-uniform loading. The velocity *vs* time of the center of the flier is plotted in Figure 2. The peak velocity is only 8 km/s, a reduction of 9% in velocity from the 1-D calculation.

This is directly due to 2-D effects.

In calculation **#3** the graded-density impactor diameter is reduced to 12.7 mm to reduce its mass. This makes it possible to achieve an impact velocity of 5.8 km/s in an experiment. The barrel and flier diameters are left unchanged (see Figure 3). The loading pulse has the same duration as that of **#2**. It is observed in calculation **#3** that 2-D edge effects are even more severe in this geometry This causes increased bending of the flier, as compared to **#2**, and a further reduction of the peak velocity in Figure 2 to ~ 6 km/s (70% of the 1-D calculation).

Our final calculation, **#4**, replicates the conditions of the experiment that was performed. See Figure 4. Our reasoning behind this calculation is as follows. One reason 2-D effects cause reduction of the flier velocity is because edge effects emanating from the impactor/flier boundary are *release waves*. The high pressure drive therefore decays too quickly. If we could maintain the driving pressure, even with 2-D distortions in the impact region, then we would not suffer the observed velocity reductions.

This can be achieved by using a step-down barrel of 10 mm diameter as indicated in Figure 4. An equal diameter flier is inserted in the barrel. The diameter of the impactor is 12.7 mm to maintain the 5.8 km/s impact velocity. Tungsten is used as a barrel material because of its high-impedance and relatively low sound speed. Upon impact, the stress states at the tungsten/flier boundary are higher than those in the sample itself. This prevents the release of the driving pressure, creating a longer duration acceleration phase for the flier. We also find that flier bending is reduced by maintenance of the high pressures. A potential trade-off is the radial "squeezing" that the flier and impactor undergo.

Optimizing this final configuration is obviously what a joint experimental/computational program is really about. That our insight is correct is seen in Figure 2, where the peak velocity observed for **#4** is 9.4 km/s (actually, it is still increasing at the final time of the calculation). This is an increase of 7% over the ideal 1-D behavior. This is dramatic evidence that 2-D effects actually work in our favor now, and create accelerations that are greater than we could achieve in idealized 1-D geometries. This is quite different from the thin flier situation. The calculation suggests that bending of the flier is minimal and that melting does not occur. (We show an illustration of the predicted deformation of the flyer past peak acceleration in Figure 4.) Thus, we predict an intact flier for **#4**.

Conclusion - A Successful Experiment

The geometry of calculation #4 was shot in an experiment at the Sandia two-stage light gas gun. An impact velocity of 5.8 ± 0.1 km/s was estimated for the experiment. The mass of the central flier (not including the guard ring) is 0.33 g, while the mass of the guard ring is 0.7 g.

Radiographic measurements of the flier and the guard ring are taken along their flight path after exit from the tungsten barrel and up to a flight distance of ~ 1.4 meters. These measurements yield an average flier velocity of 10.2 km/s, 16% greater than the 1-D simulation. The chunky projectile appears to be tumbling as it traverses, rotating approximately half a turn over this flight distance. These radiographic measurements are shown in Figure 5.

In conclusion, we observe that the interior ballistics for a chunk-flier HVL launch are considerably different than for a thin flier HVL experiment. Calculations have proven to be important for design and interpretation of experiments. Results of these calculations provide understanding of the behavior of the launch system that would be difficult to achieve in other ways. They are also effective in reducing the number of experiments in the program.

REFERENCES

[1] L. C. Chhabildas, L. M. Barker, J. R. Asay, and T. G. Trucano, "Sandia's New Hypervelocity Launcher - HVL," Sandia National Laboratories, SAND91-0675, 1991.

[2] L. C. Chhabildas, "Hypervelocity Launch Capabilities to Over 10 km/s," in *Recent Trends in High Pressure Research*, pp. 739-746, 1992.

[3] L. C. Chhabildas and L. M. Barker, "Dynamic Quasi-Isentropic Compression of Tungsten," in *Proceedings of the 1987 APS Topical Conference on Shock Waves in Condensed Matter*, pp. 111-114, 1988.

[4] L. C. Chhabildas, L. M. Barker, J. R. Asay, and T. G. Trucano, *Int. J. Impact Engng.*, 10, pp. 107-124, 1990.

[5] L. C. Chhabildas, W. D. Reinhart, and J. M. Miller, "An Impact Technique to Accelerate Flier Plates to Over 12 km/s", *Int. J. Impact Engng.*, 14, 1993. (To Be Published)

[6] J. M. McGlaun, S. L. Thompson, and M. G. Elrick, "A Brief Description of the Three-Dimensional Shock Wave Physics Code CTH," Sandia National Laboratories, SAND89-0607, 1989.

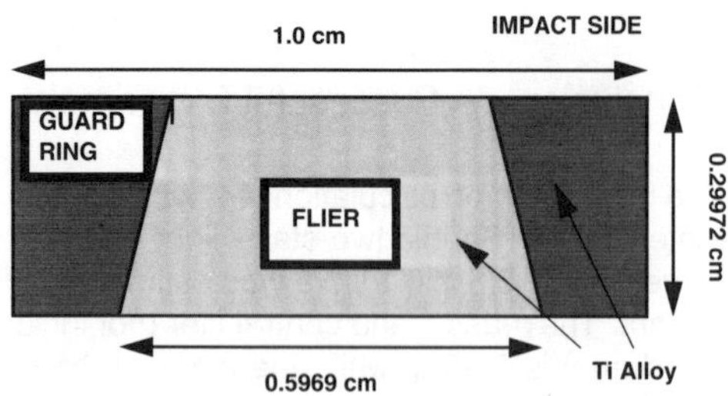

Figure 1. Guard ring used in experiment.

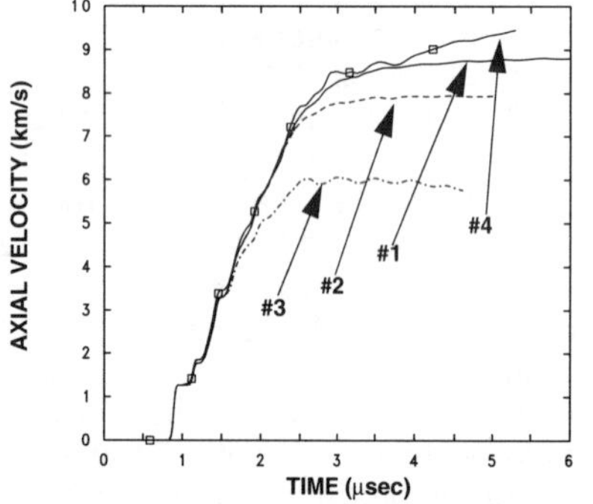

Figure 2. Flier velocity histories for calculations #1 - #4.

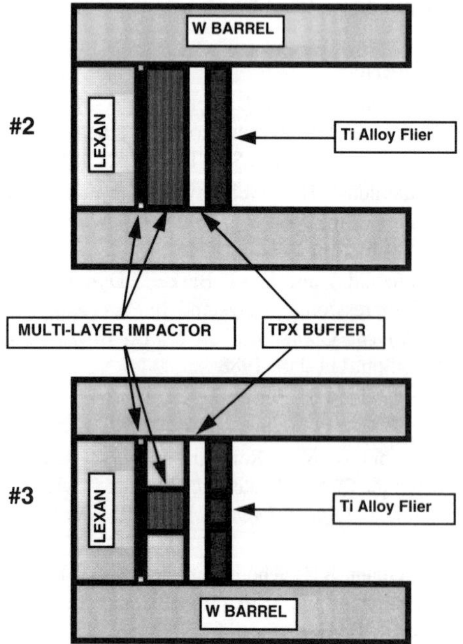

Figure 3. Schematics for #2 and #3 (not to scale).

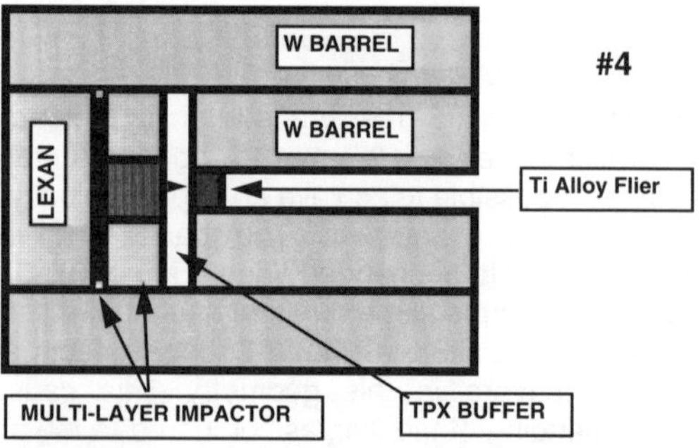

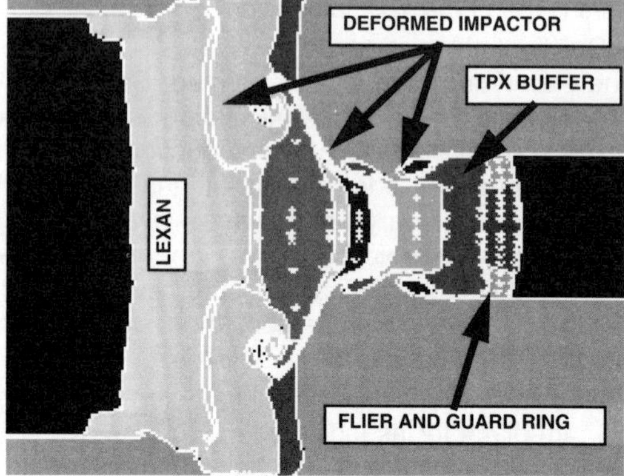

Figure 4. Schematic of #4 and a representative calculated configuration at t=3.5 μsec.

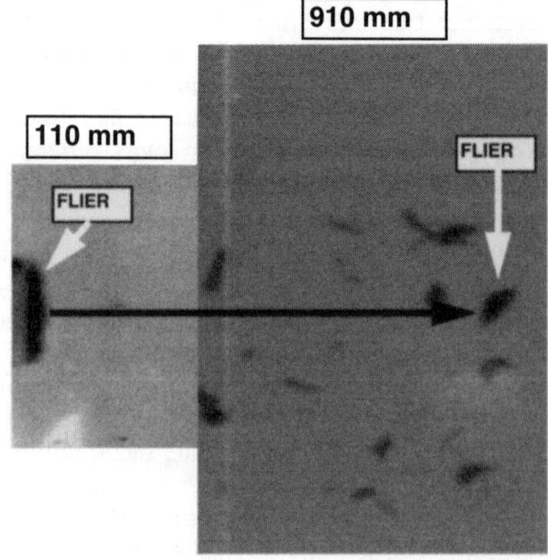

Figure 5. Experimental radiographs at 110 mm and 910 mm from the impact location. The scale is not the same in the two radiographs.

NEW LANL GAS DRIVEN TWO-STAGE GUN*

A. R. Martinez, S. A. Sheffield, M. C. Whitehead, H. D. Olivas, and J. J. Dick
Los Alamos National Laboratory
Group M-7, MS P952
Los Alamos, NM 87545

A new compressed-helium driven two-stage light gas gun has been installed at LANL to study shock initiated reaction in insensitive high explosives. The gun (based on a design at Ernst Mach Institute) has a 100-mm diameter by 7.6 long pump tube and a 50-mm diameter by 7.6-m long launch tube. The gas breech, capable of pressures up to 15,000 psi, has a volume of 42.5 liters and can be used in either a wrap-around or double-diaphragm mode. This breech was designed so we could use helium rather than powder combustion gases to drive the pump piston, eliminating the safety and cleanup problems associated with gun powder. Large hydraulic clamps (pressurized to 10,000 psi) are used to clamp the breech to the pump tube, the pump tube to the transition section, and the transition section to the launch tube. The target chamber was designed to allow the necessary room to do multiple magnetic gauging experiments. Gun control is accomplished using a MAC computer and LabVIEW control software.

INTRODUCTION

A new two-stage (TS) gas gun has been installed at the high explosive gun facility located at DF-Site at the Los Alamos National Laboratory. The primary purpose for this new gun is to perform research and characterization studies relating to the initiation and detonation of insensitive high explosive (IHE) materials. Our single-stage (SS) gas gun is not capable of producing the projectile velocities required to initiate IHE's (such as 1, 3, 5-triamino-2, 4, 6-trinitrobenzene--TATB) or homogeneous liquid explosives (such as nitromethane). Several years ago a program was undertaken to design and install a TS gun capable of providing the higher projectile velocities required. After visits to many gun facilities, we decided to use the gun design developed by Alois Stilp at the Ernst Mach Institut (EMI) in Freiburg, Germany.[1,2]

The Stilp design employs two large hydraulic clamps to clamp the transition section to both the pump tube and launch tube during a shot. Large interlocking "bayonet" arrangements on each end of the transition section (external) and inside the hydraulic clamp (internal) allow for interlocking the two pieces before the clamps are pressurized to about 10,000 psi when preparing to shoot. This design was used as the baseline for our new gun but a number of design changes were made to render it better suited to our needs.

GUN CALCULATIONS AND DESIGN

Several unique features were designed into our gun including: a gas breech (to eliminate the problems of using gun powder) capable of either wrap-around or double-diaphragm operation, a hydraulic clamp joint at the breech/pump tube interface, and a large launch tube bore (to maximize the experimental area available for 1-D experiments) so that multiple magnetic gauging experiments can be done. To determine whether or not these and other design changes would lead to a workable gun and also to help determine the final gun dimensions, a number of computer calculations to simulate gun performance were done using the gas gun code of Charters and Sangster.[3] The Stilp design was used as the baseline and changes were made to the various parameters to assess expected gun performance.

Initially, calculations were made for the original Stilp design with the powder breech. Then a helium filled gas breech was substituted for the powder breech to allow a comparison. In addition, only helium was used for the pump tube gas (eliminating the problems associated with using hydrogen in the new gun). A maximum pressure of 15,000 psi was chosen for the breech because we already have a breech and the supporting pressurization equipment with this capability on our single-stage gun. It became immediately apparent that some drop in maximum projectile velocity would result from this change

* Work performed under the auspices of the U. S. Department of Energy.

but since high velocities were not of prime importance to us, this was deemed acceptable. Calculations were done to determine an optimum breech volume by varying the volume while holding all other parameters constant. These calculations indicated that above a volume of about 42.5 liters (1.5 ft^3), gains in projectile velocity were minimal.

By varying the breech pressure the performance curve shown in Fig. 1 was calculated. An attempt to optimize some of the parameters (such as transition section pressure and piston mass) produced a calculated maximum projectile velocity of about 4 km/s. Comparing the optimized gas breech data to that of the powder breech indicates that the gas breech gives a lower projectile velocity by about 13%.

A number of calculations were done for a smaller bore (33-mm) to estimate the maximum projectile velocities that might be attained with our gun. The data are plotted in Fig. 2; the projectile velocity is shown as a function of maximum transition section pressure. Several parameters were varied to produce this data so some scatter is expected. (In practice the gun parameters will be controlled so maximum transition section pressures stay below 190,000 psi.) The data indicate that, with a projectile mass of 50 g, velocities between 4 and 7 km/s could be possible.

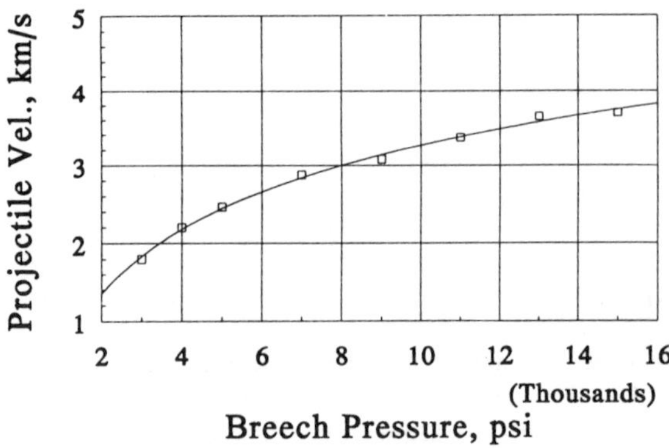

Figure 1. Plot of projectile velocity versus gas breech pressure for the gas breech (volume 42.5 liters) driven gun described in this paper. The launch tube was 50-mm diameter and the projectile mass was 200 g.

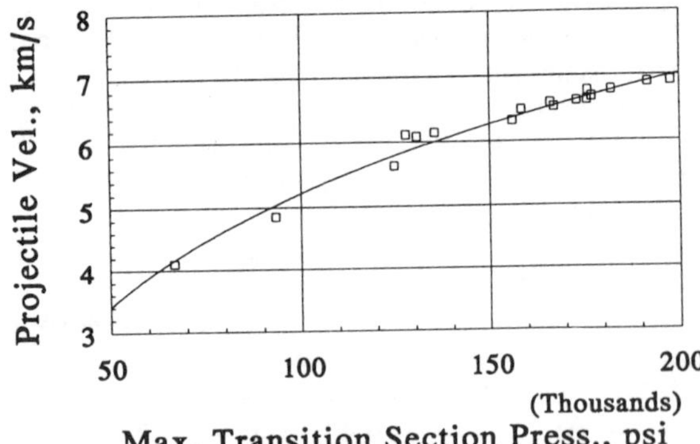

Figure 2. Plot of projectile velocity versus gas breech pressure for the gas breech (volume 42.5 liters) gun described in this paper. The launch tube was 33-mm diameter and the projectile mass was 50 g.

Final Gun Configuration

These and other calculations helped considerably in setting the final gun design. A schematic of the new TS gun with the gas breech attached is shown in Fig. 3. The figure shows a third hydraulic clamp at the breech/pump tube joint. This clamp is a redesigned pump tube/transition section joint clamp. The gun support structure was fabricated locally but the large gun pieces including the launch tubes, pump tube, breech, hydraulic clamps, and transition sections were fabricated by Honematic Machine Corp.[4]

Barrel & Transition Section

The pump tube ID was set a 100 mm and the length at 7.6 m. Two launch tubes were made with 33- and 50-mm IDs and the length was set at 7.6 m. These lengths represent an increase from 4.9 m in the Stilp gun.

We have some concern about the pump tube to launch tube diameter ratio being only 2 (rather than 2.5 or larger as normally is the case). This may lead to pump piston extrusion into the launch tube during a shot, a problem that has been experienced by others in the past. Two transition sections were designed, one with a ten-degree and the other with a twenty-degree included angle transition. It is hoped that the larger angle unit may help alleviate this problem if it occurs.

Gas Breech

A gas breech was designed with a volume of 42.5 liters and a 15,000 psi pressure capability. The design was based on the 15,000 psi double diaphragm breech routinely used on our SS gun and also on a design that includes interchangeable inserts for wrap-around and double-diaphragm operation.[5] The data of Fig. 1 show that breech pressures between 3000 and 8000 psi produce projectile velocities between about 1.5 and 3.0 km/s, the range where we expect to do most of our shots. Since a wrap-around breech could be operated in this pressure regime at a considerable savings, we designed the interchangeable wrap-around insert. A cross-sectional view of the breech/barrel/ hydraulic clamp arrangement is shown in Fig. 4.

In the wrap-around mode the back of the pump piston acts as the breech valve so an aluminum piston back with o-ring seals was designed. The front of the piston will be polyethylene as is normally the case. Firing the gun in this mode is accomplished by injecting gas behind the piston to start it moving and uncover the breech gas channels that connect the barrel to the breech volume.

In double-diaphragm mode two diaphragms are used with half the breech pressure across each one. Firing the gun in this mode is accomplished by venting the gas between the diaphragms, causing the breech gas to overpressure the first diaphragm, then the second diaphragm, and then accelerate the pump piston. Pure nickel diaphragms approximately 5-mm thick will be used.

Target Chamber and Catch Tank

A target chamber/catch tank system was not part of the Stilp design so we slightly modified our single-stage gun system to accommodate the larger launch tube. The inside diameter is 1 m and the joined together length is about 4 m. This system was fabricated[6] of 19-mm thick pressure vessel steel and is capable of containing 150 psi after a shot. The inside diameter of the target chamber provides ample room to install an electromagnet assembly so that magnetic gauging experiments can be done.

Gun Control System

Control of the gun will be accomplished using a MAC computer and LabVIEW control software[7] in the same manner that it is now being used to control our single-stage gun. The computer is the interface between the operator and the gun so that the gun is pressurized and controlled manually using a mouse to click on the icons that represent the valves and firing control buttons.

GUN COMPLETION SCHEDULE

All the gun parts, including the support structure, the breech, barrels, transition section, hydraulic clamps, and target chamber and catch tank are installed and aligned. The hydraulic systems to operate the hydraulic clamps are operational. Gun and building interlocks, observation equipment, and control points are being installed and wired to the control system at the present time. We are setting up to do a 25,000 psi hydraulic pressure test of the gun system with the hydraulic clamps holding the system together and an appropriate plug at the end of the launch tube. This represents a 1.5 times over test of the breech and will also demonstrate the integrity of the other gun components. After this test, the control system and gas pressurization system must be completed. We expect to begin preliminary testing in late summer 1993 with experiments on IHE materials following in the fall.

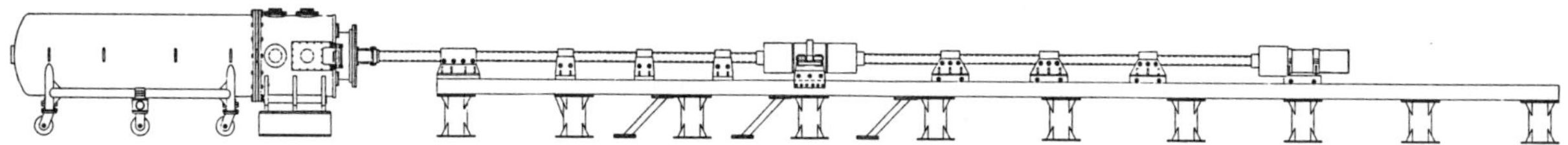

Figure 3. Schematic of the new two-stage gun at LANL, including the support structure and the target chamber and catch tank. The support structure is 18-m long with each of the barrels 7.6-m long. The target chamber/catch tank assembly is 1-m diameter and 4.7-m long with the walls 19-mm thick pressure vessel steel.

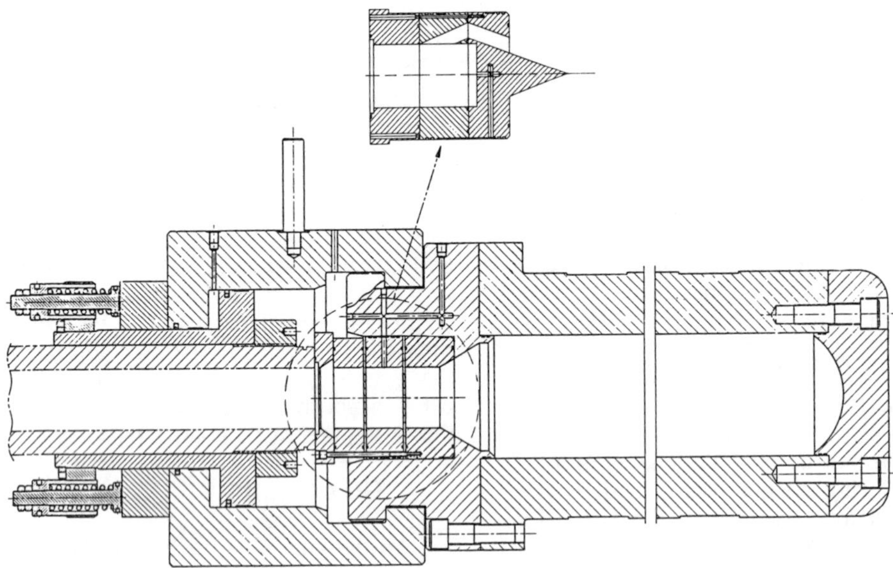

Figure 4 Cross-section of the gas breech/pump tube joint with the double-diaphragm package in place. A cross-section of the wrap-around insert is also shown. These two inserts are interchangeable.

ACKNOWLEDGMENTS

Alois Stilp of EMI helped a great deal in German/English translations of the gun design and provided operational data on his gun. Mike Williams redrew and helped modify many of the gun parts. George Friedman and the late Allan Glazer of Honematic Machine Corporation made sure the gun fabrication went as planned. Doug Dugan of Sandia National Labs. designed the first interchangeable double-diaphragm and wrap-around breech system.

REFERENCES

[1] Hypervelocity Impact Range," unpublished report, Ernst Mach Institut, Freiburg, Germany, August 1987.

[2] PTS is an abbreviation for Physikalisch-Technische-Studien GmbH, Leinenweberstr. 16, D-7800 Freiburg, Germany. Peter Seidl was the contact.

[3] A. C. Charters and David K. Sangster, "Fortran Computer Program for the Interior Ballistic Analysis of Light-Gas Guns," July 1973, unpublished report, Santa Barbara, CA.

[4] Honematic Machine Corporation is located at 22 Shrewsbury Street, Boylston, MA 01505.

[5] S. A. Sheffield and D. W. Dugan, "Description of a New 63-mm Diameter Gas Gun Facility", in Shock Waves in Condensed Matter, Ed. Y. M. Gupta, Plenum Press, New York, 1986, p. 565.

[6] The target chamber/catch tank system was manufactured by Terminal Manufacturing Co., Berkeley, CA.

[7] LabVIEW is a computer program developed by National Instruments, 6504 Bridge Point Parkway, Austin, TX. It was designed to allow MAC computer control of equipment.

EXPERIMENTAL TECHNIQUE TO OBTAIN MATERIAL RESPONSE AT STRAIN RATES TO $10^5 s^{-1}$

Robert Young
Southwest Research Institute
San Antonio, TX 78238

Stewart Silling
Sandia National Laboratories
Albuquerque, NM 87185

An experimental technique is under development to probe high strain rate pressure volume material response. The experimental domain consists of strain rates to 10^5 s^{-1}, pressures to 2.2 GPa, and dwell times around 50 μs. The development is focused on providing a standardized testing technique to acquire data for conditions that are difficult to explore using present methods. This technique uses direct projectile impact to pressurize the sample, and radial confinement to maintain the specimen in a known volume for the duration of the experiment. Varying the projectile length controls the dwell time and projectile velocity controls the peak pressure. This technique bridges the gap between planar impact experiments commonly yielding strain rates of 10^6 s^{-1} and split Hopkinson bar experiments normally performed at strain rates of 10^3 s^{-1}. This testing technique is expected to be beneficial in determining material properties used in numerical simulations, and in probing transient deformational processes in the time domain of 50 μs. Examples of such processes include heat conduction from heterogeneous sources, mass diffusion, some types of phase change phenomena, large void collapse, crack and/or damage evolution, and some types of chemical kinetics. This discussion centers around the use of numerical experiments to understand how accurately the pressure volume material response can be extracted from this experiment.

INTRODUCTION

A numerical analysis is used to explore the ability of this test to yield the desired data. This is accomplished by numerically simulating an experiment and extracting the type of data from the simulation which would normally be obtained under test conditions. This numerical data is reduced and analyzed in the same manner as if it were actual test data.

PROPOSED APPARATUS

The overall configuration of the Love Radial Constraint (LORC) apparatus is contained in Figure 1. A direct impacting projectile is used to pressurize a sample sandwiched between the projectile and back-up plug. The amplitude and duration of the pressure pulse is directly related to projectile velocity and length. The sample is constrained radially during pressurization by a confining ring. The strain rate in the sample is related to the sample thickness and projectile velocity. The force imparted by the projectile to the sample is transmitted through the back-up plug to a back-up disk where a pressure gage is mounted. The entire assembly is confined in a massive back-up piece which serves as a rigid barrier against translation.

The projectile diameter is slightly smaller than the inside diameter of the confinement ring. The reduced projectile diameter ensures that it will not strike the confinement ring during the experiment, which would

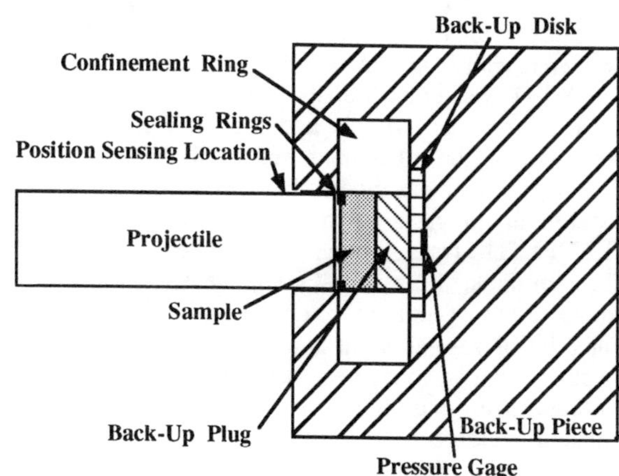

Fig. 1. Proposed Apparatus.

transmit load through the confinement ring rather than the test specimen. Specimen extrusion between the projectile and the confinement ring is inhibited by a small copper sealing ring. Both the copper ring and the back-up plug have an interference fit with the confinement ring. The amount of axial load transmitted to the confinement ring by the movement of these pieces is insignificant. The pressure diagnostic gage is mounted to the back-up disk. When the gage is placed directly on the back-up plug, the gage leads are cut early in the test by the edge of the plug. The projectile, confinement ring, back-up plug, and back-up disk are made of Vascomax 350 heat treated steel which has a yield strength of 2.4 GPa and possesses some ductility at failure.

A second diagnostic is used to time resolve the projectile position. A groove in the projectile passes between a transmitting and receiving fiber optic pair in a manner causing the transmitted light intensity to vary with projectile position. This technique is being developed and will be reported on at a later time. The use of two time-resolved diagnostics enables independent acquisition of pressure and volume.

NUMERICAL EXPERIMENTS

Numerical experiments were used to understand the dynamic interactions associated with the experiment and assess the experiment's ability to resolve the desired pressure volume response of the test specimen. To determine the ability of this experiment to yield pressure volume material response, the pressure and displacement associated with the diagnostic locations were obtained from the numerical analysis. These numerical data were reduced to yield the pressure-volume response, which was compared to the known response used in the original simulation.

A 2-D axisymmetric analysis was used to simulate a LORC experiment with the hydrocode CTH. The mesh size was on the order of .1 mm. The high strength Vascomax steel was modeled using the Johnson-Cook steel library properties with the yield strength altered to 2.2 GPa. The test specimen was modeled as Plexiglas, 2.2-mm thick. Between all components was placed a zone, .2- to .4-mm thick, containing a hypothetical material of zero strength and density of steel. This enabled relative movement between the components without major interference in the interface's ability to transmit pressure.

Simulation parameters included projectile velocities of .02, .04, .06, and .08 km/s which induced specimen pressure on the order of .7, 1.4, 2.1, and greater than 2.2 GPa, respectively. Various projectile lengths were used to vary the dwell time at pressure. The analysis of a projectile velocity at .06 km/s and projectile length of 10 cm is reported herein as a representative simulation. The dwell time (double the transit time of the elastic wave in the projectile) in this simulation is .44 μs. The duration of the simulation is 60 μs. The initial induced strain rate in the sample is $2.4 \times 10^{-4}\ s^{-1}$.

ANALYSIS AND DISCUSSION

A comparison of time-resolved pressure at the middle of the Plexiglas specimen and the diagnostic location on the back-up disk is contained in Figure 2. The top curve represents the true numerical pressure in the Plexiglas and the bottom curve represents the numerical axial stress sensed at the back-up disk. This is the stress value sensed by the pressure gages. From theory, a shift in both time and magnitude between these curves is expected. The time shift in the back-up disk signal corresponds to the time it takes the pressure wave to travel through half of the specimen, the back-up plug, and back-up disk. The theoretical time correction is less than 2 μs. The axial stress at the back-up disk should be less than the specimen intensity due to the divergence in the pressure field as a function of the back-up disk thickness. Analysis indicates the intensity at the back-up disk is 70% of the Plexiglas value. A correction is applied to the back-up disk stress yielding the specimen pressure.

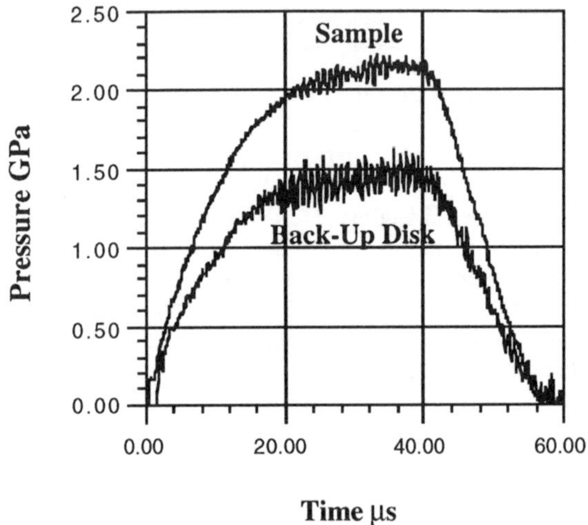

Fig. 2. Sample and Gage Pressure Comparison (back-up disk stress not corrected).

Figure 3 contains the two pressure traces where the back-up disk pressure is properly scaled. The two curves virtually lie on each other indicating that a good relationship exists. There is significant ringing at the maximum amplitudes on both curves, with the back-up disk ringing being more prominent. The cause of this ringing is not fully understood. It does seem to be influenced by the material interfaces.

The change in projectile position and the change in specimen thickness is plotted in Figure 4. The projectile position will be used as an indicator of the Plexiglas sample thickness which in turn is used to calculate test specimen volume. The difference between the two curves is related to the elastic compression of the projectile and back-up plug assembly. When the elastic deformations are taken into account and scaled appropriately, the projectile position accurately predicts

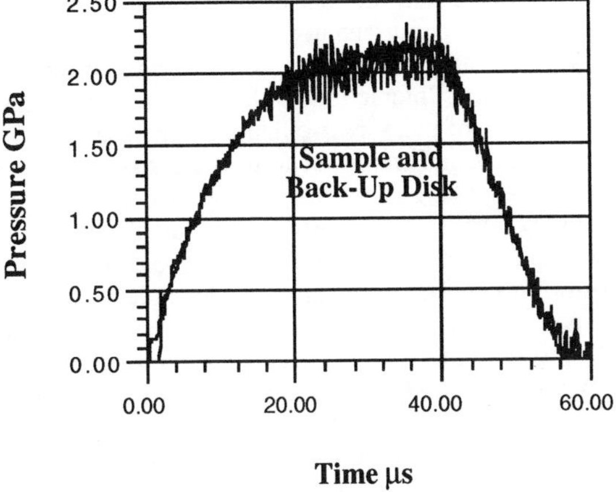

Fig. 3. Sample and Modified Gage Pressure Comparison (back-up disk stress corrected).

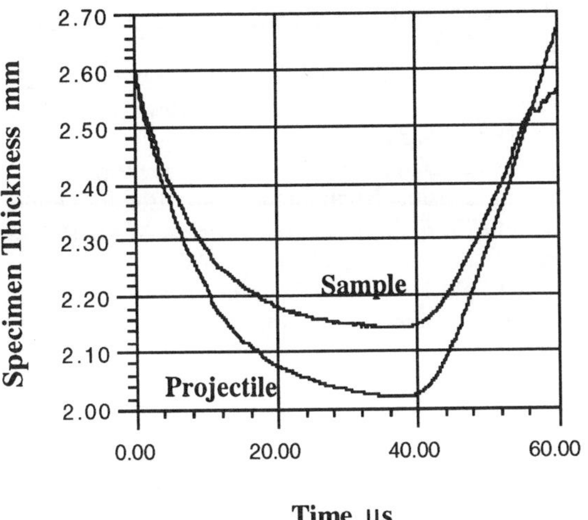

Fig. 4. Comparison of Time-Resolved Specimen Thickness Measurements (with elastic corrections not made to the projectile position).

the specimen thickness. The scaled projectile position and specimen thickness curves are plotted in Figure 5. The two curves are no longer distinguishable in the plot.

In analyzing the data, the specimen volume is calculated from the predicted specimen thickness and specimen radius. However, the radius undergoes significant elastic expansion for which corrections are required. The correction for elastic radial expansion of the confinement ring used herein is based on thick wall pressure vessel theory. A curve for specimen volume obtained from the sample density is plotted over the specimen volume curve predicted using the projectile position in Figure 6. The inability to distinguish the two curves shows the fidelity with which the volume can be predicted.

The pressure and volume relationships obtained using simulated diagnostic signals can now be reduced to obtain the pressure-volume material response. This relationship, along with the numerical response from the sample are plotted in Figure 7.

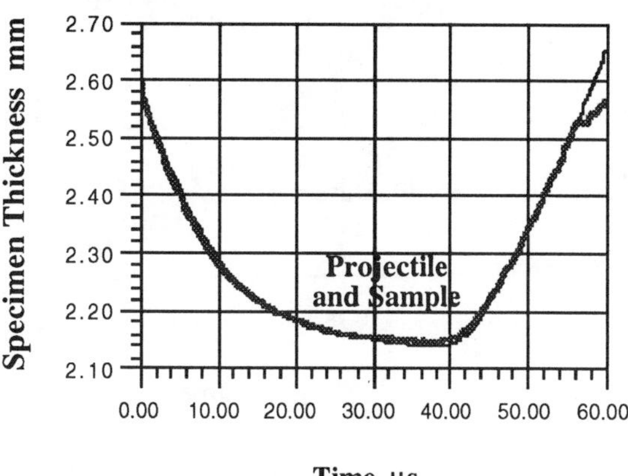

Fig. 5. Comparison of Time-Resolved Specimen Thickness Measurements (with elastic corrections made to the projectile position).

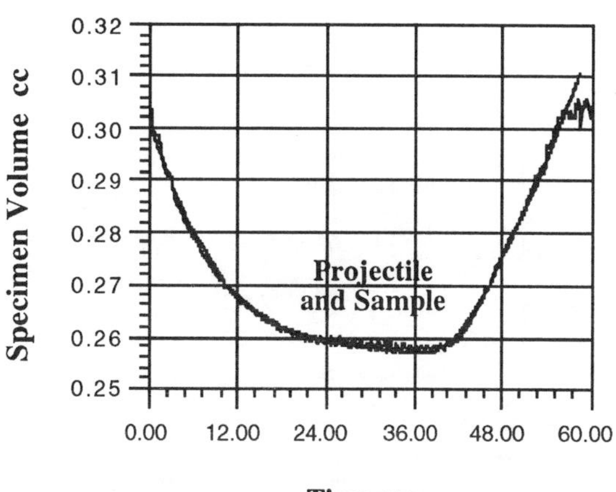

Fig. 6. Calculated and Actual Time-Resolved Volume.

There is a considerable amount of noise in the data. This is primarily due to the ringing in the pressure signal. Once the cause of this ringing is identified and eliminated, the overall correlation will be very good.

The pressure experienced by the Plexiglas sample is fairly uniform. Figure 8 contains a pressure contour plot from the CTH calculation. The square location where pressure gradients are absent is the location of the sample. It is important to note that the pressure gradients are sustained in samples possessing significant strength.

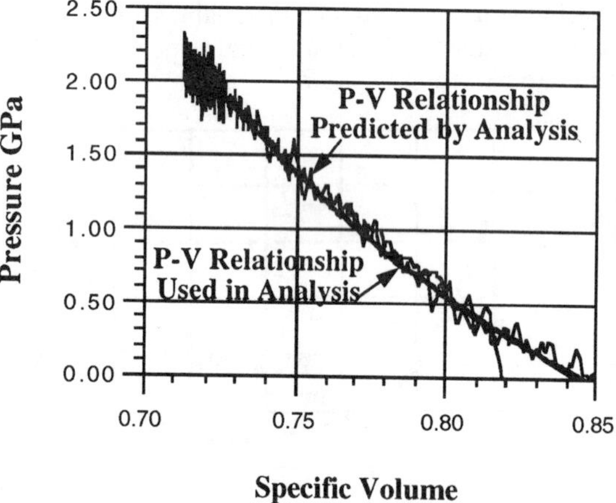

Fig. 7. Comparison of Pressure—Volume Relationships.

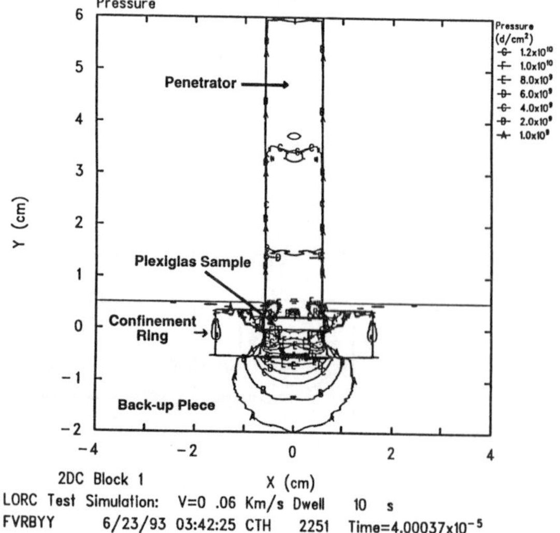

Fig. 8. Pressure Contours from Hydrocode Analysis.

CONCLUSIONS

It seems feasible to obtain both the pressure volume relationship of the test specimen from pressure measurements on the back-up disk and projectile displacement measurements. The data can be reduced to yield the sample's pressure-volume relationship with good accuracy. Interactions with the test apparatus may be the cause of pressure oscillations which are seen by the specimen and amplified at the back-up disk. These pressure oscillations are detrimental in obtaining high accuracy results. The ability to correlate the measured back-up disk pressure to sample pressure and projectile position to specimen thickness is dependent upon the fixture stresses remaining elastic throughout the analysis. This limits the upper bound pressure to between 2.5 to 3.0 GPa for materials currently available. Initial strain rates, which are dependent on sample thickness and projectile velocity, are achievable in the range of 10^3 to $10^5 s^{-1}$

REFERENCES

1. W. J. Murri, D. R. Curran, C. F. Peterson, and R. C. Crewdson, Advances in High Pressure Research, Vol. 4, Academic Press, 1974, pp. 1-163.
2. U. S. Lindholm, "Some Experiments with the Split Hopkinson Pressure Bar," *J. Mech. Phys. Solids*, Vol. 12, 1964, pp. 317-335.
3. U. S. Lindholm and K. D. Doshi, "Wave Propagation in an Elastic Nonhomogeneous Bar of Finite Length," *J. of Applied Mechanics*, 64-WA/APM-18
4. P. S. Follansbee and C. Frantz, "Wave Propagation in the Split Hopkinson Pressure Bar," *J. of Engng. Materials and Technology*, 1983, Vol. 105, pp. 61-66.

SIX-MM, PLANE-WAVE SHOCK DRIVER

Alan M. Frank
Henry H. Chau
Lawrence Livermore National Laboratory
P. O. Box 808, Livermore, CA, 94551, USA

A 6-mm-diameter, plane-wave shock generation system has been developed and characterized as a laboratory bench driver for small scale experiments. The driver is based on an exploding-foil-driven slapper used either directly or to initiate an HE pellet. The slapper is driven by a low-inductance fireset with burst currents on the order of 30 kA and burst times of about 250 ns, with a time-to-burst jitter under 10 ns. Both the slapper impact and the detonation breakout of the pellet have been measured to be flat to within 10 ns over a 6-mm diameter. Fabry-Perot velocimetry of impacts with LiF crystals were used to characterize shock pressures and durations. Attenuator plates and flyers driven by the HE were also measured, which provided a variety of available pulse shapes and data for modeling efforts.

INTRODUCTION

A well characterized, 6-mm-diameter plane-wave shock generator was developed as a tool for the small scale examination of equation of state, material shock response, and initiation and propagation of energetic materials. Of particular interest are materials of short scale length that are typically too fast for normal testing techniques. Advances in high speed microscopic techniques in the Micro Detonics Facility (μDF)[1] have spurred interest in small scale experiments.

DESIGN

The concept of the generator is that a thin flyer plate (slapper) launched by an electrically exploded foil (electric gun) can simultaneously initiate a high explosive (HE) pellet over its entire diameter.[2] If the explosive has a short run-to-detonation (RTD) distance, the pellet can be kept thin and the effects of the edge rarefaction minimized. This provides a planar shock wave over a reasonably large fraction of the diameter. The shock pressure is determined by the HE detonation pressure and can be attenuated using a suitably mismatched layer. The system can also be used to launch a dense slapper (attenuator) to provide impact pressures well above the detonation pressure (Fig. 1).

The choice of a 6-mm system was guided by the nominal scale sizes of μDF experiments as well as component availability. The maximum field of view at full resolution (2 μm) is about 2 mm for the μDF frame and streak cameras. To maintain a planar experiment, the driver should be flat over a significantly larger diameter. With our low-inductance, 12 kV/1 μF capacitive discharge unit (fireset), we could launch a 7- to 8-mm-diam flyer at a sufficient velocity (2.5 to 3 km/s) to initiate an HE pellet. With the availability of a 1/4-in. (6.34-mm) HE pellet press, a 6-mm system became the obvious choice.

The electric gun was optimized using R. S. Lee's models, which predict flyer velocity as a function of fireset parameters and gun construction parameters.[3] The resulting gun consists of a copper foil bridge, 4.5-μm thick and 6.4-mm square, deposited on Kapton (polyimide). As the copper is vaporized, a 50-μm Kapton over layer becomes the slapper and is accelerated through a 400-μm-long barrel. The foil and barrel thicknesses were chosen to provide a 3-km/s flyer velocity at the exit of the barrel. The barrel is simply an 18-mm-square sheet of tantalum (Ta), with a 6.4-mm hole, bonded to the flyer layer of the gun. Backing the bridge are three 50-μm Kapton layers that provide a 12-kV standoff from the 50-μm-thick ground plane. Three additional 50-μm Kapton layers isolate the

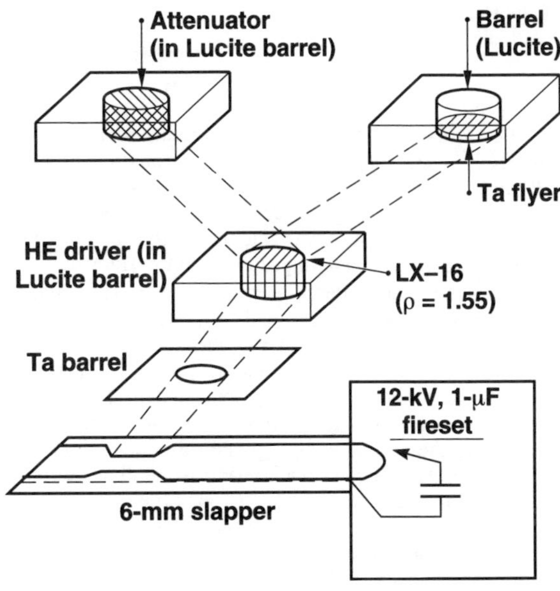

Figure 1. Six-mm plane-wave generator system.

ground plane from the tool steel reaction mass and mounting plate. The connecting cable is integral to the bridge assembly, which consists of two 50-μm by 18-mm copper layers insulated with 32-mm-wide Kapton as above. The entire Kapton-copper, gun-cable assembly is hot pressed into a single, 300-mm-long planar ribbon, which is then clamped to the mounting plate.

With the fireset charged to 12 kV, the guns draw 30 to 32 kA. The foils burst in just under 250 ns after the closing of the spark-gap switch. The spark gap is driven with a Krytron switch at 6 kV through a voltage tripler. The resulting ~18-kV spark-gap trigger pulse reduces jitter in the gun system to about 10 ns.

The HE pellet is LX-16, which is 96% PETN (propanediol dinitrate) and 4% copolymer vinyl chloride binder (OXY-461). LX-16 was chosen for its rapid run to detonation characteristics, good mechanical properties, and ease of pressing and handling. The pellets are pressed for 3 min at 30 ksi, in a die heated to 60°C, to a density of 1.55 g/cm^3. They are 6.4-mm in diameter by 3.2-mm thick and weigh 155 ± 2 mg. The pellet is both confined and mounted in a Lucite (polymethyl methacrylate) barrel. The barrel is an 18-mm-square sheet of stock 3.2-mm material with a 6.4-mm hole into which the pellet is pressed. The pellet/barrel assembly is bonded to the gun barrel before use.

Similarly, attenuators or dense slappers are also mounted in Lucite barrels. These barrels are appropriately milled to the thickness of the attenuator or the combined thickness of the slapper and flight path. The final result is a bonded stack with an 18-mm-square top surface, which is the test reference surface to which an experiment can be mated.

TESTING AND DATA

Performance verification experiments were of three different types. Slapper impact and detonation breakout flatness were measured with the streak microscope observing a reflecting surface bonded to the reference surface. Shock pressure was calculated from the measured particle velocity in an impacted lithium fluoride (LiF) crystal using a Fabry-Perot interferometer (FPI).[4] Slapper velocity measurements were made directly with the FPI.[5]

The impact and breakout measurements use an aluminized 0.15-mm-thick microscope cover glass. The aluminized surface is placed in contact with the reference surface. A reference grid with a 250-μm wire spacing was bonded to the back side as a spatial reference. A one-watt argon laser was focused to a line across the diameter of the experiment. The experiment is arranged so that the aluminized surface is at the focal plane of the streak microscope and the laser line is viewed in specular reflection. Temporal calibration is provided by a short pulse YAG laser through fiberoptic delay line stack.

The impact record of the electric gun flyer shown in Fig. 2(a) revealed only small scale perturbations of about 7 ns across the 6-mm diameter. With a flyer velocity of 3 km/s, the observed perturbations are consistent with the surface variations of a few microns in the rolled Kapton material. Thus further improvement in the electric gun flyer flatness will require entirely different fabrication techniques.

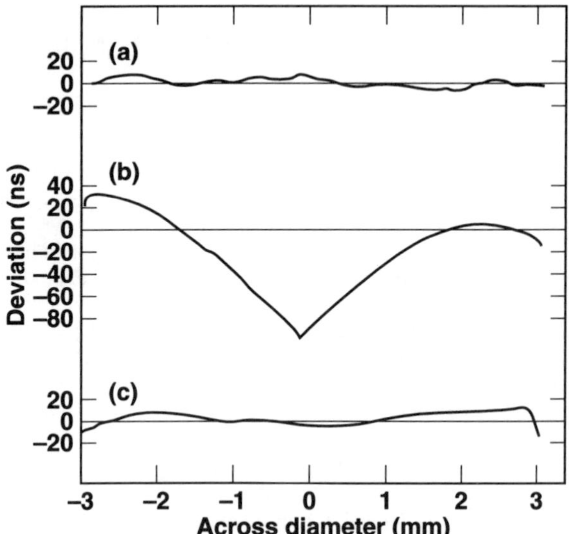

Figure 2. Impact and breakout planarity for (a) electric gun flyer, (b) initial LX-16 pellet, and (c) modified LX-16 pellet.

The breakout of the detonation wave from the initial LX-16 pellet resulted in a large scale delay (~125 ns) at the center [Fig. 2(b)]. This result was a clear indication of a radial density gradient often seen in pressed pellets. The initial pellets were pressed to a density of 1.7 g/cm^3 or 96% of theoretical maximum density. Although the RTD distance is not well characterized for this regime, it is known that both the variation and the slope of the variation of the RTD increase with density.[6] As the sensitivity to shock initiation increases with decreasing density, it was decided to decrease the pellet density to 1.55 g/cm^3. Furthermore, the pressing procedure was modified to require an initial leveling of the molding powder and heating the die. A single acting press also produces an axial gradient of increasing density from the anvil to the ram. Thus we also oriented the pellet so that the flyer impacted the low-density (anvil) end. The resulting pellet breakout was planar to within 10 ns [Fig. 2(c)].

The shock and impact pressure measurements are made in a LiF crystal that is in contact with the reference plane. What is actually measured is the particle velocity in the LiF at the interface to a thin aluminum foil pressed to the surface of the crystal. The foil is necessary to provide a reflective surface for the FPI. The shock pressure is then computed through the Hugoniot equations. LiF is used because its shock impedance is matched to many explosive products and its Hugoniot is well known.[7]

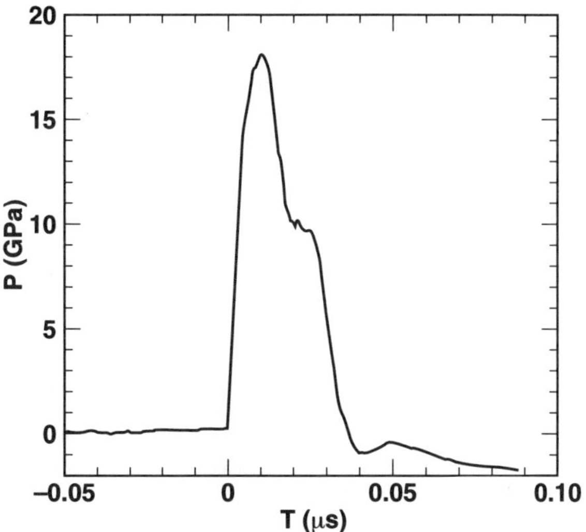

Figure 3. Impact of a 51-μm-thick Kapton flyer into LiF with 12-μm Al.

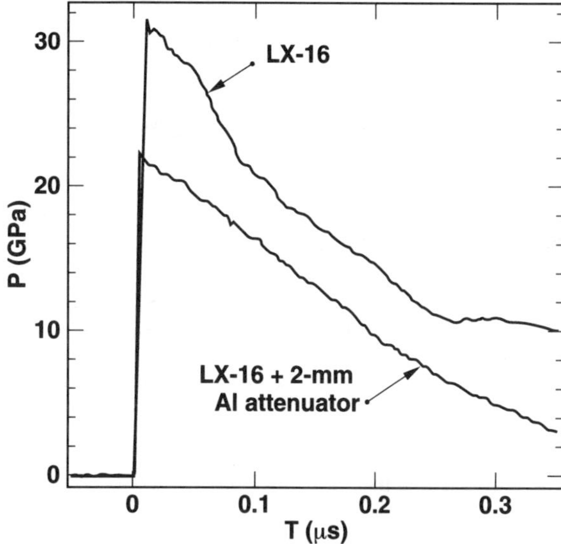

Figure 4. Pressure in LiF in contact with sample.

The pressure pulse caused by the impact of the electric gun flyer peaked at about 18 GPa in an 8 ±1-ns pulse (Fig. 3). The step in the decay of the pulse was caused by the aluminum layer on the LiF, which at 12 μm is significant with respect to the 50-μm Kapton flyer. This experiment should be repeated with an evaporated layer on the LiF. The 8-ns pulse width also stressed the temporal resolution capabilities of the FPI. Shock pressure produced by the HE pellet peaked at 32 GPa and was reduced to 22 GPa through a 2-mm aluminum moderator (Fig. 4).

Before measuring the impact pressures for the Ta flyers, flyer velocities were measured. This was accomplished by directly viewing the Ta surface with the FPI. The Ta flyers, 100- and 240-μm thick, respectively, were flown in 3-mm Lucite barrels. They were followed from the bottom of the barrel for as long as the FPI could keep them in focus, between 2 and 3 mm (Fig. 5). The magnitude of the observed internal ringing, or the surface pull back, caused considerable consternation in that it exceeded the predictions for spall. Yet there was no evidence of spall in either shot.

Measuring the impact pressures created by a Ta flyer was complicated by the sudden loss of reflectivity at the Al/LiF interface upon impact. It was concluded that although the computed impact pressure was well below the 65-GPa impact melt threshold in aluminum,[8] melting was indeed occurring. This is because the flyer is traveling through the strong magnetic field (est. 20 kG) of the electric gun. As the flyer approaches the foil, field compression causes eddy current heating of the foil, thus lowering the threshold for shock melting. By increasing the foil thickness to 100 μm and adding a shield around the foil, the impact melting was eliminated. However, a pre-impact velocity of the foil of 0.1 to 0.2 km/s was observed.

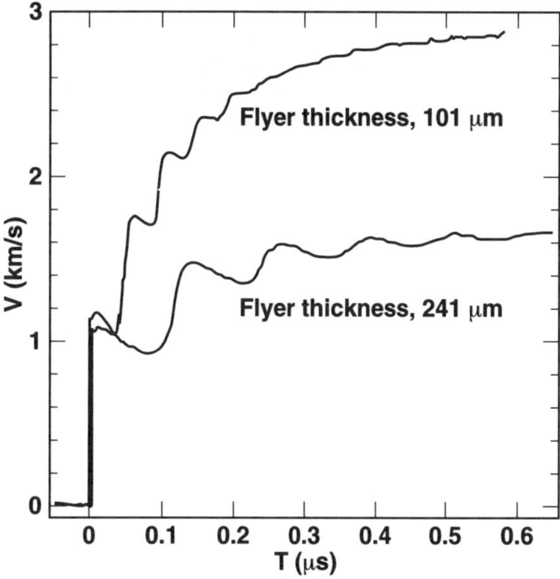

Figure 5. Tantalum flyer velocity.

The impact pressures of the 100- and 240-μm Ta flyers were measured to peak at 43 and 21 GPa, respectively (Fig. 6). Both flyers were mounted in 2.4-mm Lucite barrels so that the flight path was just over 2 mm. This distance was chosen to allow damping of the internal ringing and to allow the flyer to approach maximum velocity. In both shots, the step in the decaying pressure pulse is attributed to the aluminum foil.

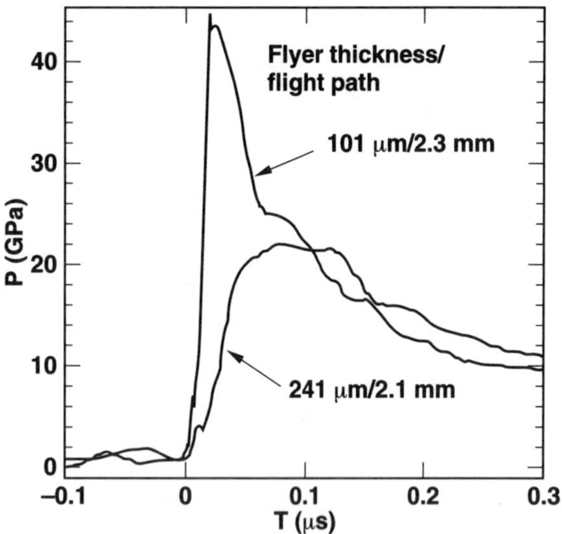

Figure 6. Tantalum flyer impacts into LiF.

ACKNOWLEDGMENTS

The authors wish to acknowledge the contributions of Ronald Lee, Harold Zimmerman, Ralph Hodgin, Ralph Boberg, and Jeff Davis. Work performed under the auspices of the U.S. Department of Energy by the Lawrence Livermore National Laboratory under Contract W-7405-Eng-48.

REFERENCES

[1] A. M. Frank, "High Speed Microphotographic Laboratory," *Proc. 18th Int. Congress, High Speed Photography & Photonics*, Xian, China, 1988.

[2] H. H. Chau, G. R. Ditbenner, W. W. Hofer, C. A. Honodel, D. J. Steinberg, J. R. Stroud, R. C. Weingart, and R. S. Lee, "The Electric Gun: A Versatile Tool for High Pressure Shock Wave Research," *Rev. Sci. Instr.* 51, p. 1676 (1980).

[3] R. S. Lee, "Simple Models for Electric Gun Operating Characteristics," *Proc. 3rd Int. Symp. on High Dynamic Pressure*, Paris, France, 1989, p. 297.

[4] D. J. Steinberg and H. H. Chau, "A New Approach for Studying the Expansion of Detonation Products," *The 8th Int. Symp. on Detonation*, 1985, Reprints vol. 3, p. 1009.

[5] H. H. Chau, C. F. McMillan, and J. E. Osher, "Application of Fabry-Perot Velocimeter to High Speed Experiments," *High Speed Photography & Photonics*, 1988, SPIE, vol. 1032, p. 540.

[6] B. M. Dobratz and P. C. Crawford, *LLNL Explosives Handbook*, Lawrence Livermore National Laboratory, Livermore, CA, UCRL-52997 (Rev. 2), pp. 9-55 (1985).

[7] S. P. Marsh, *LASL Shock Hugoniot Data,* Berkeley, CA: University of California Press, 1980.

[8] R. Kinslow, *High-Velocity Impact Phenomena,* New York, NY: Academic Press, 1970.

INVESTIGATION OF THE DYNAMIC BEHAVIOR OF LASER-DRIVEN FLYERS*

Wayne M. Trott
Energetic Materials and Fluid Mechanics Dept. 1512
Sandia National Laboratories, Albuquerque,NM, 87185-5800

Various aspects of the dynamic behavior of laser-accelerated flyer plates (e.g., planarity, cohesion, thickness, etc.) have been examined using several high-speed optical techniques. Images of accelerating flyers have been obtained by means of fast-framing photography and with an electronic image converter streak camera operated in an image motion configuration. These data are compared to records of flyer velocity vs. time as a function of laser fluence as well as impact particle velocity measurements on lithium fluoride "witness plates." Flyer materials examined include pure aluminum and a composite material containing a thin layer of aluminum oxide. Composite flyers exhibit superior performance due to better planarity and cohesion, increased thickness vs. displacement, and significantly higher velocity for a given driving energy. With proper tailoring of flyer properties and driving laser parameters, laser-driven acceleration of thin flyer plates offers a promising, laboratory-scale approach to quantitative studies requiring well-controlled, short-pulse shock compression.

INTRODUCTION

In recent years, the generation, characterization and use of laser-accelerated flyers have been subjects of active investigation.[1-12] One promising application of this experimental method is its use as a well-controlled, short-pulse shock driver in quantitative laboratory-scale experiments (e.g., in studies of shock-induced chemistry). Ideally, laser-driven flyers should provide a miniature version of impacting projectiles used in gas-gun experiments and, at a minimum, offer such features as (1) readily variable and reliably obtained velocity, (2) acceptable planarity on impact, and (3) well-characterized dynamic physical properties. The use of step-index, multimode optical fibers for coupling laser energy to the flyer target is a valuable technique in this regard.[3] In addition to providing a flexible and relatively safe delivery system for flyer acceleration, optical fiber coupling allows facile control of the illumination area and offers convenient means to homogenize the optical energy, resulting in a geometrically simple, well-conditioned driving process.

Flyer generation using optical fiber coupling has been exploited in detailed studies of both peak flyer velocities and flyer velocity-time histories as a function of incident fluence, optical pulse duration, target area and thickness, etc.[8] These measurements have focused on aluminum targets but other materials have been examined as well. A time-independent analytical model has been developed and compared to the data, accurately predicting final flyer velocities for a broad range of flyer target properties and laser parameters.[9,11,12] Computational simulations have also been successful in describing many of the time-dependent aspects of energy coupling and flyer acceleration.[9] These experimental and theoretical studies demonstrate that a modest laser-driver can deliver precise and continuously variable flyer impactor velocities over an reasonable range of flyer target mass, areas, etc.

Early work on the dynamic behavior of laser-driven flyers has been encouraging as well. In particular, both pulsed-laser stereo photography and electronic streak camera imaging techniques have shown that nearly planar impacts can be generated from laser-driven plates.[7] However, much additional characterization of the laser-acceleration process and a detailed understanding of the dynamic physical properties of flyers are needed before they can be employed as impactors in quantitative shock compression studies.

In this paper, we describe recent observations of laser-accelerated flyers with a variety of high-speed optical techniques, including velocity interferometry, fast-framing photography and the use of an electronic streak camera operated in an image motion configuration. Records of flyer impact have also been obtained from particle velocity measurements on lithium fluoride "witness plates." The various experiments have focused on comparing the performance and dynamic integrity of pure aluminum flyers vs. composite materials[4] containing a thin (i.e., submicron) layer of aluminum oxide that acts as an efficient thermal barrier.

* This work performed at Sandia National Laboratories supported by the U.S. Department of Energy under contract DE-A-CO4-76DP00789

EXPERIMENTAL

Many details of the experimental design have been described previously.[3,5,8] The driving laser used in this work was a Q-switched Nd:Glass oscillator (Lasermetrics Model 9380). The laser output ($\lambda = 1.054 \mu m$) was horizontally polarized and multimode. Coarse spectral analysis indicated that the output was relatively broadband (~ 1.3 nm). Flyer targets were prepared by physical vapor deposition on polished output ends of 0.4-mm-diameter multimode optical fibers. With the laser source used here, the spatial profile exiting an optical fiber should contain only relatively small intensity fluctuations due to modal noise propagation. These conditions were confirmed by measurements on uncoated fibers using a solid-state array camera and a beam profiling analysis system. All tests were performed with driving laser pulse durations near 18 ns (FWHM).

As before, a laser-based optically recording velocity interferometer system (ORVIS)[13] was used to determine velocity-time histories and final flyer velocities for various samples. The interferometer fringe displacement (linearly proportional to velocity) was viewed by an electronic image-converter streak camera (Hadland Photonics, Ltd., IMACON 675), recorded on high-speed film and analyzed using digital image processing techniques.[14] "Face-on" images of accelerating flyers were also obtained by the above camera operated in framing mode at 75,000,000 frames per second. For these tests, a microscope objective was used to obtain the desired magnification and the target was illuminated by a synchronized electronic flash.

Nearly "edge-on" views of flyers in motion were obtained with the image motion camera technique. In this set-up, a microscope objective was used to image the field of interest onto the slit of an IMACON 790 electronic image converter camera operated in streak mode. Differential micrometers were employed to obtain precise stand-off distances from the slit plane. As the accelerating flyer and driving plasma crossed this plane, a corresponding image was obtained on the sweep. The sweep speed was typically 10 ns-mm^{-1}. In these tests, back illumination was provided by the electronic flash unit.

In the witness plate tests, ORVIS was used for particle velocity measurements on flyer-impacted lithium fluoride windows. Acceptor windows were equipped with a very thin (50 nm) coating of sputtered aluminum. This coating provided both adequate fringe brightness in the interferometer and sufficient opacity to light generated in the flyer acceleration process. Accurate spacing between the coated fiber faces (flyer targets) and the Al-coated windows was provided by shim stock of known thickness. The very short impact events were viewed at streak rates of 1 ns-mm^{-1} or faster.

RESULTS AND DISCUSSION

The relative performance (in terms of peak flyer velocity) of aluminum targets vs. a composite material (both 0.004-mm-thick) has been obtained for incident fluences ranging from 2.5 J-cm^{-2} (near the threshold for flyer motion) to > 25 J-cm^{-2}. These data are illustrated in Fig. 1. Throughout the entire range, the composite flyers attain a higher final velocity for a given driving fluence. This effect is quite pronounced at fluences < 6 J-cm^{-2} but becomes much less obvious at the higher fluences. Also shown for comparison are predictions of the time-independent analytical ("effective properties") model. The calculated curve for the composite flyers represents an extension of the model to include the effect of the aluminum oxide thermal barrier (i.e., limited deposition depth).[15] In this case, the agreement between the experimental data and the model is excellent. Reasonable agreement is also obtained in the case of pure aluminum flyers; however, the experimental peak velocities appear to exceed slightly the model prediction at high fluences and fall well below the calculated values near threshold.

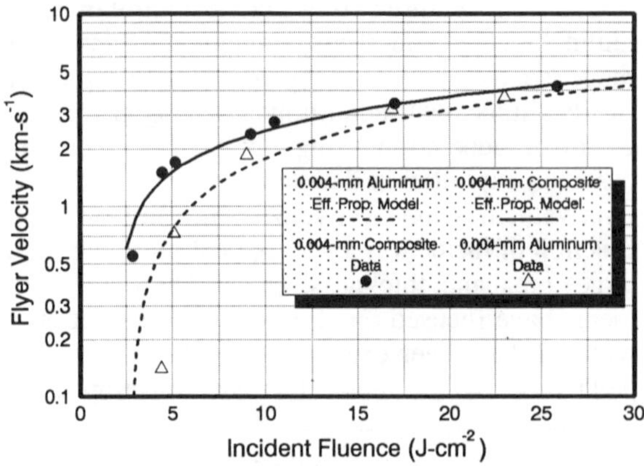

Figure 1. Peak flyer velocities as a function of incident fluence. Comparison of data with analytical model.

In the high-fluence regime, thermal diffusion can be expected to lead to a significant "thinning" of the solid density flyer material through phase transformations to a fluid state as well as ablation. Significant "blowoff" is in fact predicted by the analytical model. The tendency for the experimental data to "outperform" the model at higher fluences may indicate that thinning becomes quite substantial under these conditions. Slightly above threshold, on the other hand, deep thermal diffusion appears to deprive the driving plasma of much of the energy needed to push the flyer, resulting in very low values for the pure aluminum material.

Additional evidence for the superior performance of the composite material is provided by records obtained with the image motion camera. Figure 2a contains a record of an aluminum flyer observed at a displacement of 75 μm. In this case, a thin, opaque object crosses the slit plane first. This object is clearly associated with the flyer since its apparent width is near that of the fiber core diameter. An extended luminous region, undoubtedly associated with the driving plasma, is observed behind the flyer. Composite flyers produce a similar result at this standoff distance. At longer displacements, however, the images are quite different. Figures 2b and 2c show records obtained at a standoff distance of 300 μm for aluminum and composite materials, respectively. In the case of the composite material, the objects (flyer plus opaque residual driving plasma) crossing the slit plane are compact with a nearly planar leading edge. In contrast, the pure aluminum target produces an extended, diffuse image with a distinctly non-planar leading edge. Similar data at other displacements consistently indicate that composite flyers provide better planarity and cohesion.

A fast-framing photograph of an aluminum flyer viewed "face-on" is shown in Fig. 3. The magnification was adjusted to match the frame width to the 0.4-mm core diameter. The record is dominated by the luminous plasma which emerges at the edge the flyer and undergoes rapid radial expansion, leading to a series of overlapping images. Analysis of the timing between the laser and the framing camera shows that the plasma begins to emerge within one interframe time (i.e., 13 ns) of pulse arrival at the flyer target plane. The electronic flash used in these tests was not sufficiently bright to provide a good image of the flyer face. Illumination with a flashlamp-pumped dye laser would provide the requisite intensity and permit source discrimination with narrowband interference filters.

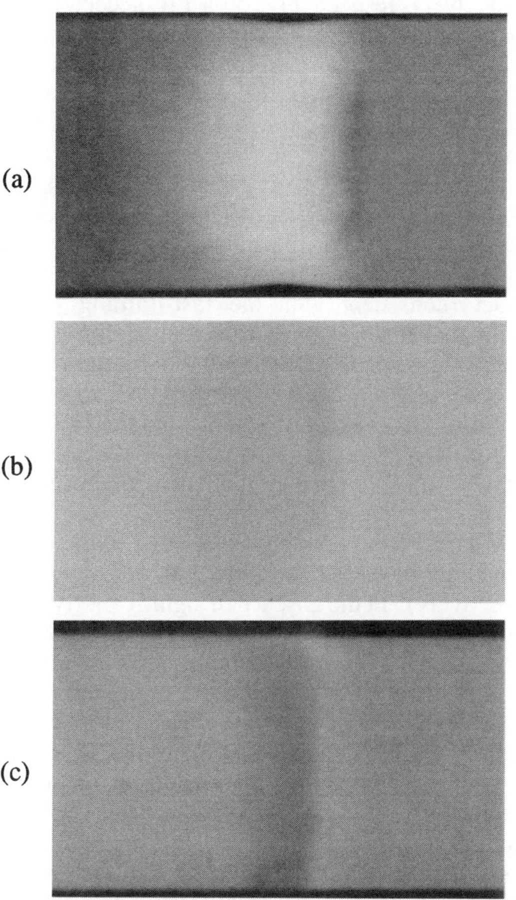

Figure 2. Image motion camera records of flyers viewed "edge-on." (a) Aluminum--75μm displacement; (b) Aluminum--300 μm; Composite--300 μm

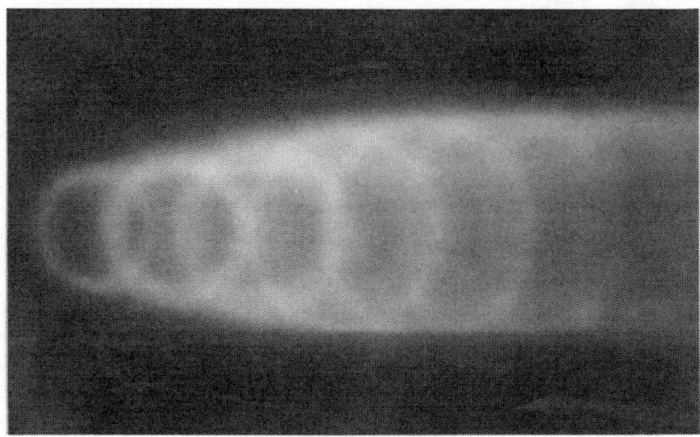

Figure 3. Fast-framing photograph of aluminum flyer viewed "face-on"--13.3 ns interframe time.

Particle velocity vs. time records generated by the impact of 0.008-mm-thick aluminum and composite flyers, respectively, on a LiF acceptor window are shown in Fig. 4. These tests were conducted with a 0.005" (127 μm) spacing between the flyer target material and the acceptor. Measured velocities have been corrected for index of refraction effects in LiF.[16] The witness plate records exhibit rapid rise times (consistent with the temporal resolution of the interferometer). The results indicate relatively planar impacts (on axis) as well as negligible effects due to gas compression ahead of impact (consistent with the fast-framing photographs that show expansion of the driving plasma occurring primarily in the radial direction).

From analysis of flyer velocity-time records at 27.5 mJ incident energy together with the Hugoniot relationships for aluminum and LiF[16], the peak particle velocities for the aluminum and composite impact events were expected to be 1.23 $km\text{-}s^{-1}$ and 1.298 $km\text{-}s^{-1}$, respectively. Observed values were only slightly lower (1.219 $km\text{-}s^{-1}$ and 1.268 $km\text{-}s^{-1}$, respectively). In the absence of significant flyer ablation or thinning, pulse durations near 2.4 ns should be obtained. The observed pulse duration was essentially identical to the expected value in the case of the composite flyer; however, the aluminum flyer produced a pulse that was >10% shorter. This trend has been confirmed with data taken at other displacements. At spacings greater than 200 μm, "thinning" of the pulse produced by aluminum flyer impacts becomes very significant. The presence of a thin Al_2O_3 layer in the flyer clearly attenuates the deleterious effects of deep thermal diffusion.

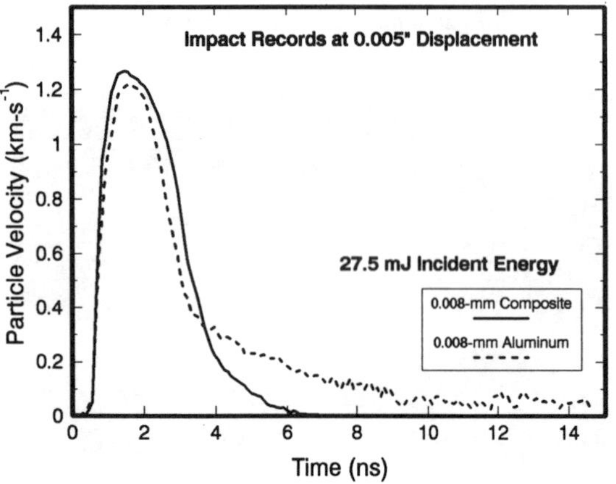

Figure 4. Particle velocity records from aluminum and and composite flyers impacting LiF.

ACKNOWLEDGMENTS

The technical assistance of J. N. Castaneda is gratefully acknowledged. The image motion camera tests were suggested by personnel in the Photometrics and Optics Department at Sandia National Laboratories and these tests were skillfully implemented by M. R. Nissen.

REFERENCES

1 S.A. Sheffield and G. A. Fisk, "Particle Velocity Measurements in Laser Irradiated Foils Using ORVIS," in *Shock Waves in Condensed Matter--1983,* eds. J. R. Asay, R. A. Graham and G. K. Straub, New York: Elsevier Science Publishers, 1984, pp. 243-246.

2 S. A. Sheffield, J. W. Rogers, Jr., and J. N. Castaneda, "Velocity Measurements of Laser-Driven Flyers Backed by High Impedance Windows," in *Shock Waves in Condensed Matter--1985*, ed. Y. M. Gupta, New York: Plenum Press, 1986, pp. 541-546.

3 W. M. Trott and K. D. Meeks, "Acceleration of Thin Foil Targets Using Fiber-Coupled Optical Pulses," in *Shock Waves in Condensed Matter--1989*, eds. S. C. Schmidt, J. N. Johnson, and L. W. Davison, New York: Elsevier Science Publishers, 1990, pp. 997-1000.

4 D. L. Paisley, "Laser-Driven Miniature Flyer Plates for Shock Initiation of Secondary Explosives," in *Shock Waves in Condensed Matter--1989*, eds. S. C. Schmidt, J. N. Johnson, and L. W. Davison, New York: Elsevier Science Publishers, 1990, pp. 733-736.

5 W. M. Trott and K. D. Meeks, "High-power Nd:Glass Laser Transmission Through Optical Fibers and its Use in Acceleration of Thin Foil Targets," *J. Appl. Phys.* 67, pp. 3297-3301 (1990).

6 D. L. Paisley, N. I. Montoya, D. B. Stahl, I. A. Garcia, and W. F. Hemsing, "Velocity Interferometry of Miniature Flyer Plates with Sub-nanosecond Time Resolution," in *SPIE Proceedings No. 1346,* San Diego, CA, 1990, pp. 172-178.

7 D. L. Paisley, N. I. Montoya, D. B. Stahl, and I. A. Garcia, "Interferometry, Streak Photography, and Stereo Photography of Laser-Driven Miniature Flying Plates," in *SPIE Proceedings No. 1358,* Cambridge, UK, 1990, pp. 760-765.

8 W. M. Trott, "Studies of Laser-Driven Flyer Acceleration Using Optical Fiber Coupling", in *Shock Waves in Condensed Matter--1991*, eds. S. C. Schmidt, R. D. Dick, J. W. Forbes, and D. G. Tasker, New York: Elsevier Science Publishers, 1992, pp. 829-832.

9 A. V. Farnsworth, Jr. and R. J. Lawrence, "Numerical and Analytical Analysis of Thin Laser-Driven Flyer Plates," in *Shock Waves in Condensed Matter--1991*, eds. S. C. Schmidt, R. D. Dick, J. W. Forbes, and D. G. Tasker, New York: Elsevier Science Publishers, 1992, pp. 821-824.

10 D. L. Paisley, R. H, Warnes, and R. A. Kopp, "Laser-Driven Flat Plate Impacts to 100 GPa with Sub-Nanosecond Pulse Duration and Resolution for Material Property Studies," in *Shock Waves in Condensed Matter--1991*, eds. S. C. Schmidt, R. D. Dick, J. W. Forbes, and D. G. Tasker, New York: Elsevier Science Publishers, 1992, pp. 825-828.

11 R. J. Lawrence and W. M. Trott, "A Simple Model for the Motion of Pulsed-Laser-Driven Thin Flyers," *J. de Physique IV, Colloque C3*, pp. 453-458 (1991).

12 R. J. Lawrence and W. M. Trott, "Theoretical Analysis of a Pulsed-Laser-Driven Hypervelocity Flyer Launcher," *Int. J. Impact Engineering* 14 (in press).

13 D. D. Bloomquist and S. A. Sheffield, "Optically Recording Interferometer for Velocity Measurements with Subnanosecond Resolution," *J. Appl. Phys.* 54, pp. 1717-1722 (1983).

14 G. A. Fisk, G. A. Mastin, and S. A. Sheffield, "Digital Image Processing of Velocity-Interferometer Data Obtained from Laser-Driven Shock Experiments," *J. Appl. Phys.* 60, pp. 2266-2271 (1986).

15 R. J. Lawrence (private communication).

16 J. L. Wise and L. C. Chhabildas, "Laser Interferometer Measurements of Refractive Index in Shock Compressed Materials," in *Shock Waves in Condensed Matter--1985*, ed. Y. M. Gupta, New York: Plenum Press, 1986, pp. 441-454.

WEAR RESISTANCE COATINGS OF STEEL MADE WITH SHOCK WAVE TECHNIQUE

A. A. Kiiski, P. R. Ruuskanen
Technical Research Centre of Finland, Metals Laboratory
P. O. Box 776
FIN-33101 Tampere, Finland

Wear resistant composite material coatings were made by the shock wave technique on the surface of a low alloyed steel. Shock waves were generated by high explosives. The experiments were done inside a vacuum chamber. As a coating material, we used Tungsten Carbide (WC) or Chromium Carbide (Cr_3C_2) powders mixed with Titanium (Ti) powder as a binder material. Microstructures of the coatings, substrate materials and the interfaces between the carbides, binder material and the substrate material were studied with optical and scanning electron microscopy, EDS analysis and microhardness measurements. Coatings with a thickness of 2 mm with no porosity were obtained. In the coatings the carbide particles were completely embedded in the binder material and no fractures or holes in the interface between the carbides, binder material and substrate material were found. A good adhesion between the coating and the steel was obtained.

INTRODUCTION

There is an increasing need for thick (more than 1 mm) wear resistant coatings in many industrial applications. In many cases thin coatings made by CVD or PVC do not offer sufficient protection against wear. Thus a thick hard metal type of coating on a surface of a steel is required, this being cheaper than making the whole piece from hard metal.

To get a uniform distribution of carbides in a metal matrix, powder technology must be used. The compaction and joining of thick layers of carbide and metal powders on a steel require high pressure. The explosive shock wave technique is a convenient way to obtain pressures high enough with low temperature changes [1,2]. The explosive working of metals has been under investigation for long time [3].

EXPERIMENTAL

The wear resistant coatings on a steel substrate were made by high explosive shock waves. The shock waves were generated by an ammonium nitrate based explosive with a detonation velocity about 4000 m/s for a diameter of 40 mm in open air. As a substrate material, a low-alloyed tool steel is used. The explosion experiments were done in a vacuum chamber. Coatings were made from Tungsten Carbide (WC) or Chromium Carbide (Cr_3C_2) powders mixed with Titanium (Ti) powder as a binder material. The average particle sizes of the powders were approximately the following: WC 70 μm; Cr_3C_2 120 μm; Ti 50 μm. The carbide to binder ratio was 50/50 vol.-%. The initial density of both of the carbide and binder mixtures was 50 % of the calculated theoretical density. Titanium was used as a binder material as it has a hexagonal crystal structure with a low work hardening.

The compaction experiments were done in two different ways. In the first case the coating powder was on the upper surface of the steel and the explosive was above the coating powder, as shown in Fig. 1a. The powder and the explosive were separated by a 0.1 mm steel foil. The coating powder was pre-pressed with a hydraulic press to 750 kg/cm^2. In the second case the coating powder was on the upper surface the steel. Explosive was placed on the flyer plate and there was an air-gap of 3 mm between the powder and the 1.5 mm flyer plate, as shown in Fig. 1b. The airgap allows the flyer to accelerate before it hits the powder. In both cases the charge was initiated from one end so that the detonation was moving with a grazing incidence. In the first case the thickness of the charge was varied, and in the second case the mass of the charge (C) to the mass of the flyer (M) ratio C/M was varied. In both cases the surface of the steel was ground with SiC paper number 800. The initial thickness of the coating powder before explosion was 1.0, 2.0 and 3.0 mm.

The effect of the roughness of the steel surface was studied by grinding the surface of the steel also with SiC paper numbers 80, 180, 500 and 1200. In this test the second explosive setup was used with a 1.5 mm steel flyer and 30 mm explosive. Powder thickness was 2 mm.

The microstructures of the coatings and steels were studied with optical and scanning electron microscopy. Microhardness measurements were made for the coating and the steel.

RESULTS AND DISCUSSION

Explosive setup

With the first method shown in Fig. 1a successful coatings were made with Cr_3C_2 + Ti powder with all three powder thicknesses 1.0, 2.0 and 3.0 mm. The thickness of the explosive was 30 mm. With the WC + Ti powder thicknesses 1.0 and 2.0 mm were successful. The 3.0 mm thickness was well compacted, but it did not stick on the steel.

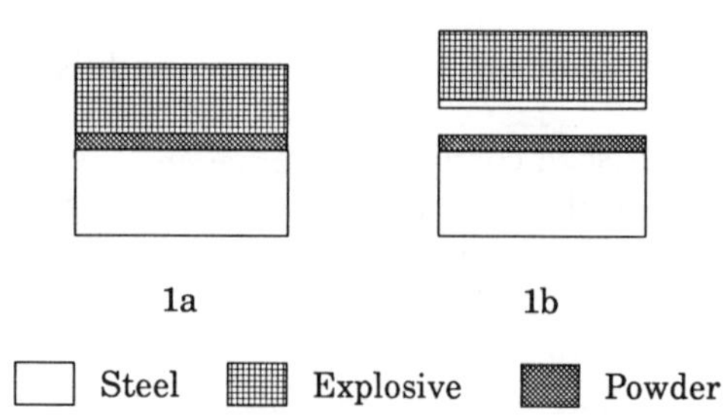

Figure 1. Experimental setup

The 3.0 mm powder was also tested with 40 and 45 mm explosive thicknesses. In both experiments the adhesion was not better than with the 30 mm explosive. The reason for this is that the pressure was not high enough. Moreover, the higher time duration of the pressure that was achieved with the higher explosive thickness [1] did not change the situation. The pressure is not changed by the different thickness of the explosive if the detonation velocity is not changed, because the pressure is related to the square of the detonation velocity. With this explosive it is possible that the detonation velocity increases a little when the thickness is increased from 30 to 45 mm, but the velocity change is less than 10%.

The second method illustrated in Fig. 1b was more successful than the first. Coating with the powder thickness of 3.0 mm was achieved by using WC + Ti powder. This was done with the 1.5 mm steel flyer and with 30 mm explosive thickness giving for the C/M ratio 2.3. The air-gap used was 3 mm. With the flyer plate a higher pressure is generated on the powder and hence the sticking between the coating and the steel is achieved.

Optical microscopy

In Fig. 2 there is an optical micrograph of the WC + Ti coating. As the figure illustrates the coating has been formed with no porosity. Titanium has formed a complete matrix and filled all of the space between the carbide particles. A good adhesion between carbides and titanium and between the coating and steel is achieved.

In the chromium carbide coating there is a loss of pieces from inside many carbide particles. This happens during the sample preparation. The obvious reason for this is that the shock wave has caused cracking in the carbide particles.

In the tungsten carbide coatings there are fewer pieces missing from the carbides, but still some indications of crack formation occur.

The effect of the roughness of the steel surface on the sticking of the coating was studied with optical microscopy. All of the coatings on the substrate with different surface treatments were attached to the steel. No noticeable differences were observed between the different surface treatments. The effect of the roughness of the surface of the steel is not critical for the formation of the coating.

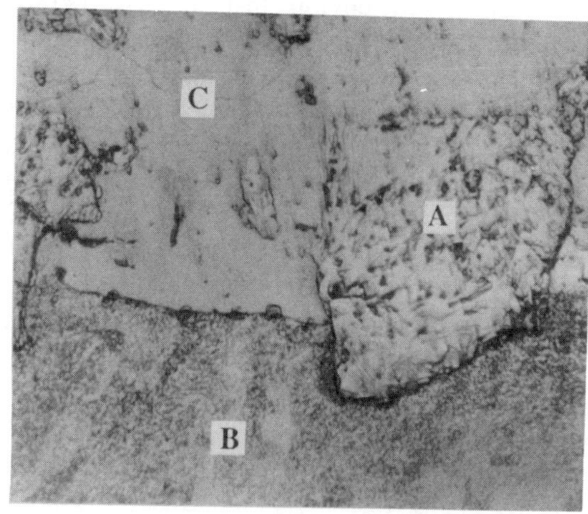

Figure 2. Boundary region of the WC+Ti coating on a steel. A is WC, B is steel and C is Ti. 725 x.

Scanning electron microscopy

The observations made by optical microscopy can be confirmed by SEM. The boundary area between the steel and coating is good also with higher magnifications. SEM confirms that the carbides are cracked during compaction. Carbide particles were investigated by SEM before compaction and no cracks were observed.

All the chromium carbides are full of cracks and some of them are badly broken. Tungsten carbides also have cracking, but they are not badly broken.

When using the first explosive setup (Fig. 1a) and the WC + Ti powder with a thickness of 2 mm and the explosive thickness of 30 mm, a new phase seems to appear on the boundary region between the coating and the steel. This new phase is illustrated in Fig. 3.

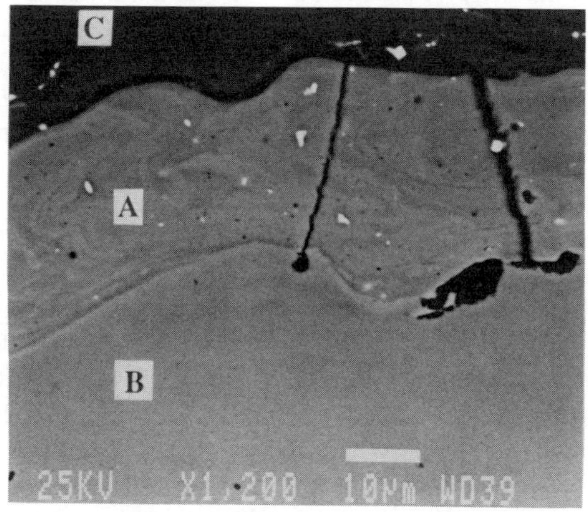

Figure 3. Back scatter image of the new phase A at the boundary region. B is steel and C is the coating.

The EDS analysis of this phase gives the following composition: Fe 40 w-%, Ti 30 w-%, W 30 w-%. It is obvious that the phase is formed by melting of the steel and titanium during compaction. This melt can partly dissolve the tungsten carbide particles. The crystal structure of the new phase was not analyzed. It is obvious that iron and titanium form a brittle intermetallic alloy with dissolved tungsten and carbon. Evidence of the brittleness of the interface phase is seen in Fig. 3. There are several perpendicular cracks in this phase. These cracks could have been formed by the shrinkage of the solidified brittle alloy.

Hardness measurements

The microhardness of the steel as delivered was 200 HV. The steel work hardened during compaction so that the final hardness is 280 - 290 HV at the boundary region. The hardness of the steel decreases as a function of the distance from the boundary region. At a distance of 10 mm, the hardness is 230 HV. The hardness of the titanium matrix varies from 130 HV to 200 HV. This is caused by the carbides nearby. Pure titanium has a hardness of around 90 HV. The hardness of the carbides is difficult to measure, because of the cracking. We measured the average hardness of the carbides to be around 1700 HV. The normal Macro Vicker hardness of the coatings is around 300 HV.

CONCLUSIONS

With explosive shock wave technology wear resistant coatings on steel were made. Chromium and tungsten carbide powders with titanium powder as a binder were used. The coatings had no porosity and good adhesion between the coating and the substrate steel was achieved. Wearing tests and tests for the adhesion of the coatings on the substrate are in progress. Equipment to measure the detonation velocity during the experiment is beeing installed. The particle size of the carbides is lowered to avoid the cracking.

REFERENCES

[1] O.E. Jones, Metal Response Under Explosive Loading, *Behavior and Utilization of Explosives in Engineering Design*, A.S.M.E. New Mexico, NM, 1972, p. 125-147.

[2] J.E. Kennedy, *Ref. [1]*, p. 109-124.

[3] J.S. Rinehart, J. Person, *Explosive Working of Metals,* London, Pergamon Press, 1963.

A SIMPLE RECOVERY TECHNIQUE FOR SHOCK WAVE STUDIES OF BRITTLE MATERIALS

Wolf-Dieter Winkler and Hartwig Nahme
Fraunhofer-Institut für Kurzzeitdynamik, Ernst-Mach-Institut (EMI)
Eckerstr. 4, 79104 Freiburg, Germany

Taking advantage of the wave propagation properties of planar shock waves and shock-induced shear stress allows planar plate impact experiments with brittle materials without the need of complicated sample geometries (star flyer). An appropriate shape of the sabot (flyer carrier) and the use of a brittle flyer plate are sufficient to induce shear stress in both plates, separating the plate edges from the central regions. So an influence of rarefaction waves emanating from the edges towards the central regions is avoided. This recovery technique has been successfully used during the investigation of the microstructural response of shock-loaded TiB_2, with VISAR measurements carried out simultaneously. Recent recovery experiments with Al_2O_3 confirm these results.

INTRODUCTION

The flyer plate technique is an appropriate tool to generate uniaxial compressive and tensile waves in a target. Softly recovered target fragments examinated by electron microscopy give information about the dynamic material behavior as well as the shape of the wave profile recorded at the target rearside by a velocity interferometer because details of the wave profile are connected with certain damage mechanisms within the target. So a correlation of macro- and micromechanical phenomena by examining both in a common experiment may yield a better understanding of the processes occurring during impact. Nevertheless, it is usual to separate both because the experimental setups are different and affect each other. For recovery experiments the plates are often provided with complicated shapes to prevent lateral rarefaction waves from affecting the target center.

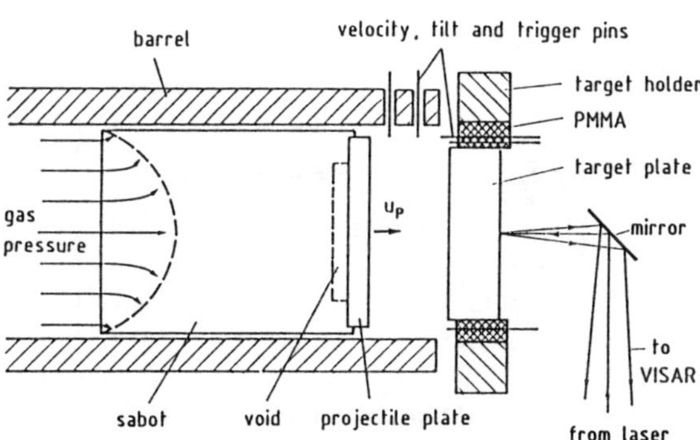

Figure 1. Flyer plate experiment.

EXPERIMENTAL TECHNIQUES

The ceramics used were produced by hot pressing. The TiB_2 and Al_2O_3 plates had a diameter of 50 mm and 61 mm, respectively. In the asymmetrical TiB_2 experiments projectile plates of PMMA, 1050 Al and Armco iron with a diameter of 58 mm have been used.

To get a free surface at the rearside, the projectile plate was supported only around its perimeter. Its center was backed by a void of 30 mm diameter cut in the polycarbonate sabot (Fig. 1). Target and projectile thicknesses were chosen to generate spallation inside the target (Tab. 1). The experiments have been carried out with a 70 mm bore diameter compressed gas accelerator.

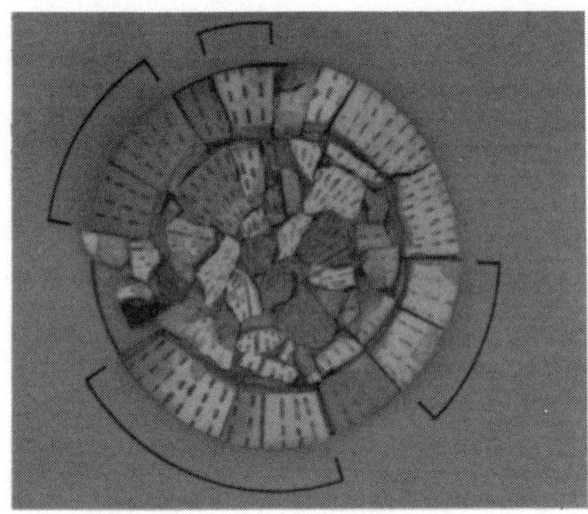

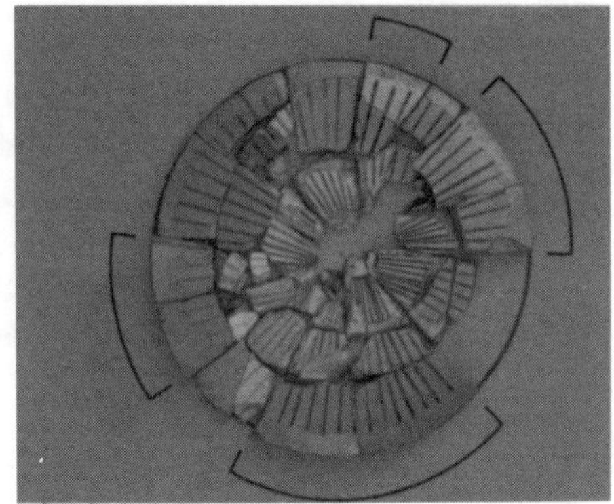

Figure 2. Reconstructed TiB_2 target (S948) with view on the front- (left) and on the rearside (right). Attached pieces from the edge are emphasized by brackets.

For the TiB_2 experiments the free surface velocity of a target rearside was recorded by means of a VISAR velocity interferometer. A catcher box filled with low-density material to achieve a soft recovery of the target was placed behind the mirror deflecting the VISAR laser beam. The impact of the target with the mirror before reaching the catcher box was taken into the bargain. Using the described technique, it was possible to get both macro- and micro-mechanical results [1,2,3].

The Al_2O_3 experiments with the catcher box placed immediately behind the target served to review the results of the TiB_2 recovery experiments.

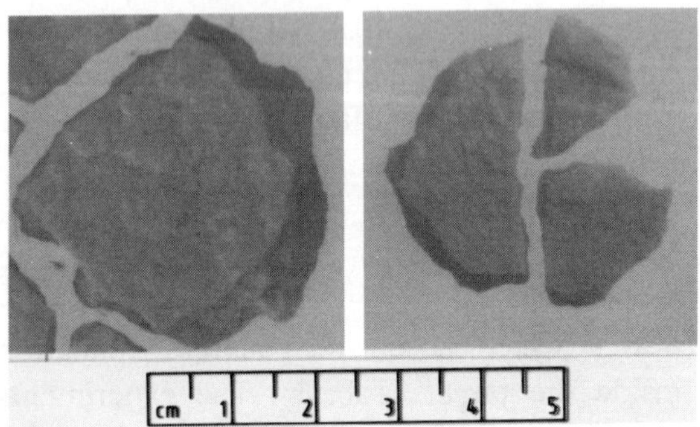

Figure 3. Rear centers of Al_2O_3 targets from experiments S1275 (left) and S1274 (right).

EXPERIMENTAL RESULTS

The TiB_2 targets were impacted up to 14.2 GPa. The HEL was ascertained to 4.2 - 4.9 GPa [1,3]. In the symmetric recovery experiments with Al_2O_3 the targets were impacted up to 3.5 GPa. In both ceramics spallation was induced. Surprisingly, fragments of at least some millimeter size could be recovered in all TiB_2 experiments. Different fracture processes have been identified (Figs. 2,3):

a) **Spallation** occurred in a plane, if the spall threshold was exactly met. At higher impact velocities, the spall plane broadened to a spall zone [2,3]. TiB_2 began to spall at 0.4 GPa. In

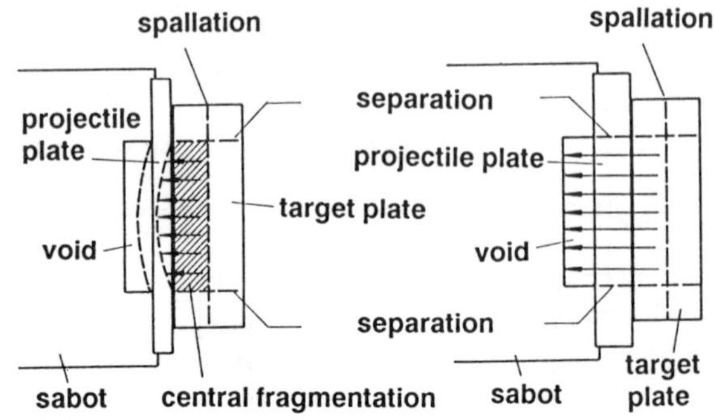

Figure 4. Effects of a ductile (left) and a brittle projectile plate (right) on the fracture processes in a brittle target plate.

symmetrical experiments its spall zone thickness d_{SP} increased to 2 mm at a tensile stress of about 12 GPa. In Al_2O_3 d_{SP} changed from 0 mm to about 10 mm for a stress variation from 1.9 GPa to 3.5 GPa (Tab. 1). In the spall zone the ceramics are totally pulverized. d_{SP} can be calculated from the target thickness d_T minus the thicknesses d_F and d_R of the recovered fragments from the target front- and rearside, respectively.

b) A ring-shaped fracture in extension of the lateral void surfaces separated the outer region from the central part of a target as well as of a ceramic projectile (Fig. 4). Based on this property this fracture process was named **separation.**

c) Lateral rarefaction waves cause **radial fragmentation.** To avoid this fracture, usually star-shape geometries of the plates are used. From Fig. 2 it can be seen that already at stresses near the spall threshold about a dozen radial cracks have been generated in TiB_2 all propagating from the edge up to the center. The more surprising is the successful recovery of fragments in the size of some millimeter at far higher stresses similar to recovery experiments using the star flyer technique [4]. The high fragmentation of the TiB_2 target center at low impact stresses is additionally in contrast to the results obtained from Al_2O_3. In comparison with the TiB_2 target of S948 (Fig. 2) the edges of the higher impacted Al_2O_3 targets of S1275 and S1274 are of course more strongly interlaced by radial cracks. But their centers are nearly intact (Fig. 3).

d) **Central fragmentation** destroyed the central part of the target between frontside and front spallation surface in the asymmetrical TiB_2 experiments (Fig. 4). Already at low impact velocities no pieces from the target frontside have been recovered [3]. Especially it was noticed that this central fragmentation did not appear in symmetrical experiments.

DISCUSSION

In planar impact experiments normally the spallation is the process to be examined. All fragmentation processes only disturb these investigations because they may superpose the effects due to spallation.

It has been found that both separation and central fragmentation are caused by the sabot void. The reason is that the compression wave propagating from the impact plane to the projectile rear surface is reflected at a free surface in the central region only. Along the support the reflection is governed by the impedances of projectile and sabot material. The resulting different tensile stress amplitudes are obviously from the target fragments of experiment S948 (Fig. 2): The center is completely spalled by many macro- and microcracks, the edge is only partly spalled by some macrocracks. Some pieces of the edge are still attached.

The different stress amplitudes inside the inner and outer parts of the plates produce different particle velocities in the two regions. Consequently shear stress is generated in the area between center and edge. It causes the separation of both regions.

As the projectile plate is supported only at the edges, its central part can yield into the sabot void. The type of yielding is different for ductile and brittle plates (Fig. 4):

In a ductile plate the shear stress does not separate the two regions because of the plate's possibility to deform. The result is a spatial dispersion of the shear stress and a beating out of the center into the sabot void depending on impact stress, plate ductility and plate thickness. Corresponding to the deformations of the projectile plate, non-uniform shear stresses are applied to the center of the target frontside. However, the brittleness of the target prevents its own deformation. Instead, the

Table 1. Experimental data: u_P = projectile velocity, σ = impact stress, d_P = projectile thickness, d_T = target thickness, d_F = fragment thickness (target frontside), d_R = fragment thickness (target rearside), d_{SP} = spall zone thickness. The sound velocities of both ceramics were determined to 10.79 mm/μs, their densities to 4.36 Mg/m^3 (TiB_2) and 3.95 Mg/m^3 (Al_2O_3). For further TiB_2 experiments see [2,3].

experiment	projectile material	target material	u_P [mm/μs]	σ [GPa]	d_P [mm]	d_T [mm]	d_F [mm]	d_R [mm]	d_{SP} [mm]
S948	1050 Al	TiB_2	52.8	0.6	1.5	5.5	3.0	2.5	0
S1275	Al_2O_3	Al_2O_3	90.1	1.9	8.8	10.2	1.2	9.0	0
S1274	Al_2O_3	Al_2O_3	118.3	2.5	6.8	9.3	(0.1)	4.4	(4.8)
S1273	Al_2O_3	Al_2O_3	166.6	3.5	7.0	11.5	0	2.4	$\geq$ 9.1

center of the frontside fragmentates.
On the contrary a ceramic plate cannot deform because of its brittleness. The shear stress proceeding from the edge of the sabot void does not disperse and the two regions of the projectile plate will be separated. Both parts retain their shapes and remain undestroyed. The shear stress will pass over into the target repeating the separation. Both plates do not offer a point of attack for the shear stress after the separation. The effects of the shear stress are confined to the separation. No central fragmentation occurs.

The shear stress is directly generated by the plane rarefaction wave reflected at the projectile rearside. Because of the longer distance to be travelled the cracks of the radial fragmentation cannot penetrate into the central region relieved by the plane wave. They will be stopped at the cracks, generated by the separation process. The uncritical separation process protects the central regions of both plates from the disagreeable radial fragmentation. Only low tensile stresses close to the spall threshold and an additional use of a ductile projectile plate pretend the protection, as can be seen in Fig. 2. In this case, the shear stress amplitude was diminished by spatial dispersion. A critical amplitude will only be reached after the waves are reflected several times there and back in the plates.

The large spall zone thickness d_{SP} of Al_2O_3 resulted in a small or zero fragment thickness d_F (Tab. 1). Consequently these experiments do not furnish a convincing proof of preventing central fragmentation.

It may be useful to start a second separation process emanating from the target rearside. For this a ring with an outer diameter similar to the target diameter and with an inner diameter corresponding to the sabot void diameter can be glued on the target rearside. The two kinds of circular separation cracks will then meet in the spall start plane.

SUMMARY

By the use of a brittle projectile plate in combination with a void in the sabot face, shear stress is generated in both projectile and target plate resulting in a separation of the edge from the center regions. This fracture process prevents propagation of lateral rarefaction cracks into the central regions preserving them for microscopic examinations. Consequently this technique allows in a simple manner the recovery of brittle materials.

REFERENCES

[1] W.-D. Winkler and A. J. Stilp, "Pressure induced macro- and micromechanical phenomena in planar impacted TiB_2", in Proceedings "Shock Compression of Condensed Matter - 1991", pp. 555-558.

[2] W.-D. Winkler and A. J. Stilp, "Spallation behaviour of TiB_2, SiC and B_4C under planar impact tensile stresses", in Proceedings see [1], pp. 475-478.

[3] W.-D. Winkler, Ph.D. Thesis, in press.

[4] F. Longy, Thèse De Docteur De L'Université De Limoges (Materiaux Ceramiques), France, 1987

A PRODUCTION OF CYLINDRICAL IMPLODING SHOCKS IN SOLID BY EXPLODING WIRE ROWS

T. Hiroe,* H. Matsuo,* K. Fujiwara,* T. Tanoue,* M. Yoshida,** and S. Fujiwara**
*Department of Materials Science & Resource Engineering, Kumamoto University, Kumamoto 860, Japan
**Department of Advanced Chemical Technology, High Energy Density Laboratory,
National Institute of Materials and Chemical Research, Ibaraki 305, Japan

One-dimensional cylindrical imploding shock waves have been produced in solid by the instantaneous detonation of cylindrical explosive shells. The detonation is initiated by simultaneous explosion of fine copper wire rows attached circumferentially to the outer surface of the explosive, using a high voltage impulsive current. At first, it is observed that the detonation front reaches the inner surface of cylindrical PETN shell (outer dia.: 100 mm, thickness: 6, 15 mm, effective length: 132 mm, density: 0.6 g/cc) within the longitudinal time jitter of ±170 ns, using 22 rows of copper wires (dia.: 100 μm, row interval: 6 mm). Next, PMMA cylinders (dia.: 42, 50 mm) are compressed radially by the cylindrical charge assembly (PETN, PETN/Silicon rubber) using the developed cylindrical initiation techniques. The shadowgraphs of cylindrical imploding shock waves in PMMA are taken using argon flash by high-speed framing camera and streak camera. These photos show that the axisymmetry of the imploding shocks has been maintained in the focusing stage. Finally the observed shock trajectories in use of PETN only have been successfully reproduced by the one-dimensional numerical simulations.

INTRODUCTION

The various methods have been successfully applied to produce focusing shocks in gases by many researchers [1,2]. On the other hand, there have been only a few experimental studies [3,4] on imploding shocks in solids. This is due to the difficulty encountered in producing strictly one-dimensional flow in solids. For example, it only appear in a middle section of a sufficiently long cylinder simultaneously compressed radially at the periphery. It is also difficult to monitor the generation and propagation of shocks in solids. Matsuo et. al. [1,2] produced cylindrical imploding shocks in air by detonating cylindrical explosive shells. The explosive was initiated around the periphery simultaneously by several fine copper wires exploded electrically. The authors [5] have developed a plane detonation generator, using the wire-rows explosion technique.

In this study, the technique is applied to produce one-dimensional cylindrical imploding shock waves in a transparent solid, PMMA. The fitting conditions of wires are investigated for instantaneous detonation of long cylindrical explosive shells. The imploding shocks in PMMA produced by the cylindrical charge assembly are monitored observing shadowgraphs by framing or streak camera. The observed shock trajectories are compared with numerical results by the one-dimensional random choice code (RCM) for solids and gases [6].

DETONATION TESTS OF PETN SHELLS

Figure 1 shows the experimental setup to investigate the conditions of wire-rows for simultaneous detonation of long cylindrical explosive shells. The low-density PETN is charged as uniformly as possible but no special pressing is used. The explosive was loaded as a cylindrical explosive shell with the thickness d: 6 (or 15) mm and at the density: 0.58 ~ 0.60 g/cc throughout the experiments. The rows of 100 μm-dia. copper wires are cemented over the inner surface (100 mm dia.) of the outer cylinder of PETN container. Various kinds of wire-rows are tested for the number of rows N: 2 ~ 22 and the intervals W: 6 or 12 mm. In addition to such continuous wire-row type, meshed wire-row type is provided for n = 22, where pairs of two thin copper tapes width of 6 mm are attached longitudinally with the interval of 6 mm sandwiching wire-rows between them. The wires are connected to the capacitor bank of 12.5 μF, max. 40 kV as an impulsive electrical current generator. The detona-

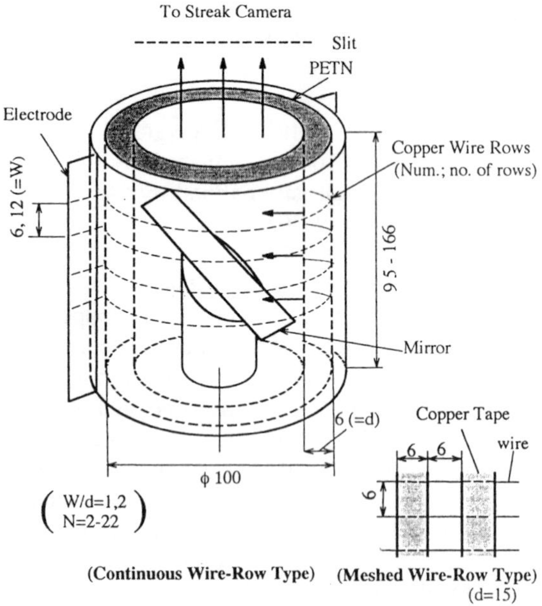

Figure 1. Sketch of experimental setup for detonation tests of cylindrical PETN shells; dimensional unit: mm.

tion arrival at the inner surface of the explosive shell is recorded with the streak camera (streak velocity: 8 mm/μs).

Typical streak camera records are shown in Figure 2. The records for W/d = 2 (N = 2, 4) indicate that the detonation fronts at the wire position arrive considerably sooner than those at the middle points between wires. However other records show such time jitter becomes negligible small for W/d = 1 or less. These phenomena suggest that the interferences of the initial detonation waves from the neighboring wire explosions play an important role in the buildup process of smooth surface detonation. The time jitters have been kept within ±170 ns throughout the experiments. This value seems passable under consideration of inevitable charge multiformity of explosive. For the meshed wire-row type, the reduction of the time jitter was expected, where exploded length of wire is reduced to a half of that for the continuous type. The streak camera records showed that it deserves practical use.

PRODUCTION OF IMPLODING SHOCKS

The experimental setup for the production of cylindrical imploding shocks in PMMA is shown

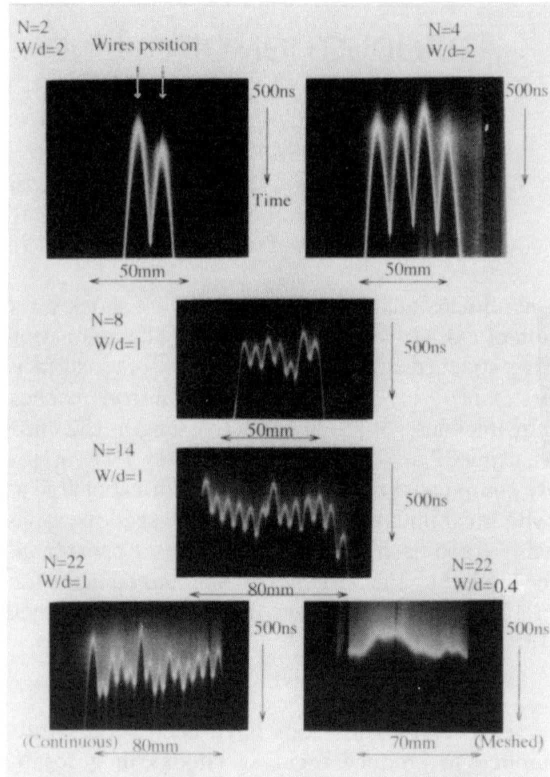

Figure 2. Typical streak camera records; N: number of wire rows, W: interval of rows, d: thickness of explosive shell.

in Figure 3. D, t1 and t2 represent dia. of PMMA and thickness of explosive shells. The outer explosive shell has the dia. of 100 mm and the effective length of 135 mm, and the two types of wire-rows (continuous and meshed) are employed for N = 22 and W = 6 mm. The cylindrical explosive assembly consists of outer PETN (density: 0.54 g/cc) and inner mixture (density: 1.32 g/cc) of 70 wt.% PETN and 30 wt% silicon rubber. The shadowgraphy using an argon flash

Table 1. Test cases and conditions; type of wire-rows, thickness of explosives t1 (PETN), t2 (PETN/Silicon rubber), dia. D of PMMA , used cameras for the measurement of shocks.

CASE	Type of wire rows	t1 (mm)	t2 (mm)	D (mm)	Cameras for shocks
A	Meshed	25	0	50	Framing
B	Continuous	8	21	42	Framing
C	Continuous	8	21	42	Streak

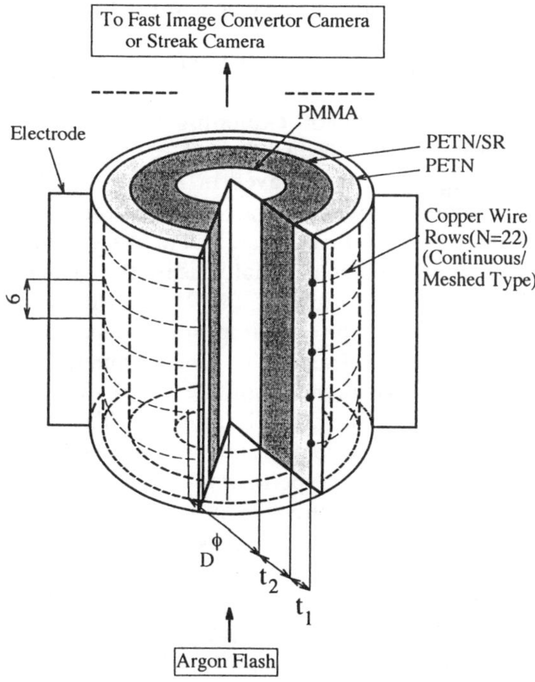

Figure 3. Sketch of experimental setup for the production of the cylindrical imploding shocks in PMMA.

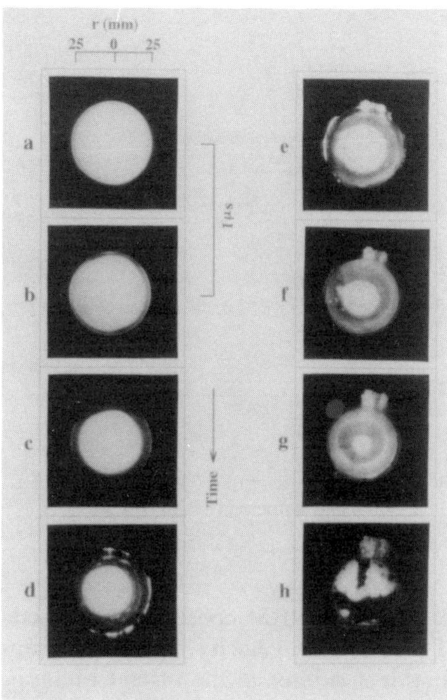

Figure 4. Typical series of sequential framing camera shadowgraphs taken at intervals of 1 μs (case A)

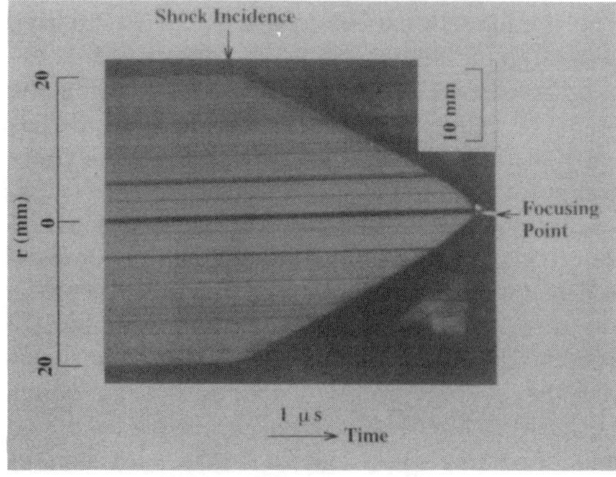

Figure 5. Streak camera record of shadowgraph (case C)

as a light source is adopted to monitor the produced imploding shock waves in PMMA with framing and streak cameras. Table 1 shows the test cases and conditions. Typical series of sequential framing camera shadowgraphs taken at intervals of 1 μs are shown in Figure 4 for case A. The good axisymmetry of imploding shocks can be seen even near the focusing stages. The light emitted surround the shock fronts seems the dispersion of light in PMMA. It seems that the shocks have focused between photos g and h. The imploding shock velocity driven by PETN/SR (case B) was 1.2 ~1.3 times larger than that by PETN only (case A). Figure 5 shows the streak camera shadowgraph (case C). Two symmetrical shock trajectories are recorded and the acceleration of imploding shocks can be seen near the focusing point.

NUMERICAL RESULTS AND DISCUSSIONS

It is known that the RCM is most suitable for treating flow discontinuity in the implosion problem. Recently one-dimensional RCM code for solids with Grüneisen-type equation of state has been developed [6] and extended to the medium of layered structure including gases and solids, which can be applied to the explosive-driven cylindrical imploding shock problems for solids. Numerical simulations are performed us-

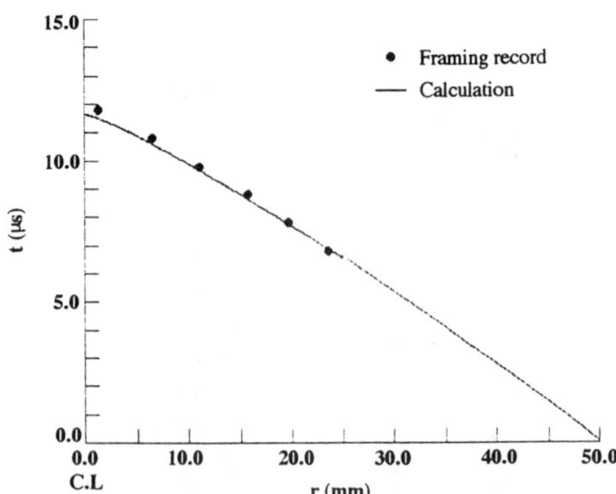

Figure 6. Shock trajectories in PETN and PMMA of experimental and numerical results (case A)

ing the developed RCM code. It is assumed that the C-J propagation velocity suddenly appear on the cylindrical surface at the instant of initiation by wire-row explosion and the combustion gas of PETN can be treated as a perfect gas with the ratio of specific heat of 1.59. These assumption has been successfully adopted for previous study [2]. The numerical analysis by the RCM has started just after the detonation wave has arrived at the contact surface of PMMA and PETN using the result of detonation analysis by the finite difference method (FDM) based on C-J volume burn technique [7]. C-J values are estimated as; density: 0.880 g/cc, pressure: 3.05 GPa, detonation velocity: 3.83 km/s. Figure 6 shows the comparison of the shock trajectory in PETN and PMMA for case A between experimental and numerical results. Experimental data are plotted by measuring the average radii of the imploding shock fronts in Figure 4. Numerical trajectory is drawn by connecting the result of FDM with that of RCM. The agreement of both results is good. A simple equation for the lateral unloading angle was adopted at every time steps of computation by the RCM. As the results, it was known that the cylinder length in this study was sufficiently long enough to produce one-dimensional imploding shock in a middle section. For the cases B or C, the calculated shock converged about 1.3 times faster than that observed. It seems that the difference is caused by the distance to detonation for PETN/SR, which can be neglected for PETN.

CONCLUDING REMARKS

The technique of exploding wire rows instantaneously has been adopted to produce the imploding detonation waves in PETN cylinders. Time jitters of the generated detonation fronts are small for practical use. The PMMA cylinders have been compressed radially using the cylindrical explosive assembly of PETN and PETN/SR. The shadowgraphs of imploding shocks in PMMA taken by framing or streak camera have showed the axisymmetry of the shock fronts is maintained during the implosion. The one-dimensional numerical results by the RCM are compared with the experimental shock trajectory for the case where only PETN is used as a driving explosive, showing a good agreement. The numerical analysis of the buildup process to detonation from wire-row explosion is left unsolved. The present technique could be applied also to the expansion of solids such as the work by Forrestal et al.[8] with use of explosion of etched copper bridge wires.

REFERENCES

[1] H.Matsuo and Y. Nakamura, "Experiments on cylindrically converging blast waves in atmospheric air," *J. Appl. Phys.* 51, pp. 3126-3129 (1980).

[2] H. Matsuo and K. Fujiwara, "Explosive-driven cylindrical imploding shocks," *Phys. Fluids* A 2, pp. 266-273 (1990).

[3] M.Yoshida, "Cylindrical implosion fixtures for high pressure generation and recovery," in *Proc. of 2nd Workshop on Industrial Application Feasibility of Dynamic Compaction Technology,*1988, pp. 263-264.

[4] M. R. Wixon, W. B. Fechner, R. L. Maynard, N. W. Schmerberg, and F. J. Mayer, "Shock processing in spherical geometry," in *Proc. of Shock Waves Condensed Matter 1987,* 1988, pp. 403-406.

[5] T. Hiroe, H. Matsuo, K. Fujiwara, M. Yoshida, S. Fujiwara, M. Miyata and T. Akazawa, "A production of plane detonation waves by wire-array explosion and its application," *J. Industrial Explosives Society* 53, pp. 219-226 (1992).

[6] T. Hiroe, H. Matsuo and K. Fujiwara, "Numerical simulation of cylindrical converging shocks in solids," *J. Appl. Phys.* 72, pp. 2605-2611 (1992).

[7] C. C. Maider, "*Numerical Modeling of Detonation,*" Berkeley: University of California press, 1979.

[8] M. J. Forrestal, B. W. Duggin and R. I. Butler, "An explosive loading technique for the uniform expansion of 304 stainless steel cylinders at high strain rates," *J. Appl. Mech.* 47, pp.17-20 (1980).

SOURCE CONDITIONS FOR EXPLODING WIRE STRESS WAVE IMPACT EXPERIMENTS

R. P. Swift and C. M. Snell
Geoanalysis Group, MS F665
Los Alamos National Laboratory, Los Alamos, New Mexico 87545

The exploding wire technique has been used to create flyer impact loading on the inner boundary of hollow cylinders [1,2]. This paper examines the dynamic performance for expanding cylindrical flyers driven by two types of line source conditions: (1) an exploding wire (EW), and (2) a high explosive (HE) PBX 9404-3. Calculations are performed to establish the velocity and kinetic energy imparted to flyers of varying mass in terms of energy and mass of the source. The differences in performance observed between the EW and HE sources are attributed to differences in their equation-of-state adiabatic expansion behavior. The calculated velocities are close to the data variation observed in the EW experiments. The results presented allow one to specify the energy conditions required to perform cylindrical impact experiments at different scales.

INTRODUCTION

The exploding wire technique applied to dynamic material behavior and stress wave studies provides a medley of pulse shapes tailored over a broad range of stress levels and strain rates. Specifically, in the experiments [1-5], explosive loading, blast wave loading, and impact loading were used to study the constitutive behavior of metals, polymers, and rocks; spallation of metals; and fracture of rocks in cylindrical geometry. Energy stored in a capacitor bank is rapidly deposited in a wire to vaporize it. By placing the wire along the axis of a borehole in a material sample, an axisymmetric disturbance is generated that propagates through the medium surrounding the wire to impinge uniformly on the borehole wall. Wire length may vary from several millimeters to the order of a meter. The strength of the cylindrical loading pulse can be varied over a broad range by altering the electrical energy, the type and/or diameter and/or length of the wire, and the borehole radius. The borehole can be filled with any of various gases, fluids, polymers, foams, etc., to tailor the shape of the loading pulse. The exploding wire can also be used to uniformly initiate detonable gases, high explosives, or propellants if more intense loading is desired. Loading stresses from a few MPa up to tens of GPa can be achieved with these methods, the latter level comparable to other high explosive and velocity impact experimental techniques.

In the exploding wire experiments [1,2], the rapid acceleration of a cylindrical "flyer", i.e., a sleeve surrounding the wire to impact on the inner wall of a metal cylinder, created stress levels of up to 3.2 GPa and pulse durations on the order of a microsecond. The polyethylene flyer impactors had thicknesses and masses ranging from 0.1 to 0.2 cm and from 0.06 to 0.2 g/cm, respectively. The kinetic energy (KE) imparted to these expanding flyers ranged from 500 to 3500 J for a 6000-J capacitor discharge system. This was achieved using 10 cm long copper wires, 0.064 cm to 0.084 cm in diameter.

The purpose of this paper is to define the dynamic performance that may be possible for cylindrical flyers for various flyer-mass to source-mass ratios that extend the physical scale to dimensions beyond the previous experiments. This performance, determined from one-dimensional cylindrical calculations, is defined in terms of the velocity and KE of the flyer as a function of the source mass and energy. A sleeve of mass M_F is assumed in uniform contact with a source of mass M_S that is initiated simultaneously along its length. The sources are an exploding wire (EW) and a high explosive (HE) that could be initiated by the EW. The EW-source is modeled as having an initial density and energy distributed uniformly through its cross-section.

The HE is modeled to detonate from the center axis outward, designated as a HE-det source, or to have an initial energy density analogous to the EW-source, designated as a HE-pill source. The energy density for the EW-source can vary greatly depending on the electrical characteristics of the discharge system and the wire material, diameter, and length. Energy densities for HE are all nearly the same, and a value of 5.5 KJ/g for PBX 9404-3 is used here. The flyer is modeled as a solid material with no strength. Strength effects are not significant until the mass of the flyer is considerably larger than the source mass.

The results show that the KE to source-energy ratio increases for increasing flyer-mass to source-mass ratio. Above a mass ratio of 0.5, the energy ratios begin to level off at values that are higher for higher initial energies. For mass ratios less than 0.5, the EW-source is less efficient than the HE, a feature that is attributed to differences in their adiabatic behavior as internal energy is converted into kinetic energy while expanding the flyer. As the mass ratio decreases to a sufficiently small value, the exponent for the energy ratio approaches unity, and the velocity of expansion approaches a theoretical limit that is proportional to the square root of the energy density of the source. The energy ratios, combined with ratios of the flyer velocity to the limit velocity, allow one to estimate impact velocities and the source energies required for cylindrical flyer impact conditions at different scales.

DYNAMIC PERFORMANCE OF FLYERS

Estimates of the velocity and kinetic energy associated with the cylindrical flyers are obtained from one-dimensional calculations in cylindrical geometry using the finite-difference code SOC [6]. The EW-source was modeled as a cylindrical "pill" of initial density and initial internal energy per unit length distributed uniformly through its cross-section, with a tabular pressure-energy-density equation of state to represent the metal wire [7]. Nominally, 100 zones were spaced equally across the source radius, which for most cases was the original wire radius. The HE source was modeled with the JWL equation of state [8]. Calculations were performed for the cases of a detonation burn from the center axis outward and for uniform volume burn conditions. The latter is analogous to the uniform pill initial conditions set up for the wire. The flyer material was modeled with a minimum of 10 zones and usually more if the thickness warranted it. It was treated as a strengthless solid material with a bulk modulus of about 100 GPa. The effect of bulk modulus was inconsequential for the regime of these calculations, and the influence of the flyer strength is negligible unless the thickness or mass is large relative to the source or the material has a very high strength. In all cases the flyer was assumed to be expanding into a vacuum.

Velocity Ratio

To establish the velocity performance in non-dimensional terms, the maximum velocity associated with the isentropic expansion of a cylindrical source into a vacuum is used to normalize the flyer velocity. For an ideal perfect gas, the relation for the source-vacuum boundary maximum velocity is from [9]

$$U_{max} = \frac{2}{\gamma-1}\left(\frac{\gamma p_0}{\rho_0}\right)^{1/2} = \left(\frac{4\gamma}{\gamma-1}\frac{E_0}{M}\right)^{1/2}, \qquad (1)$$

where γ is the constant specific heat ratio, and p_0, ρ_0, E_0, and M are the initial pressure, density, energy and mass of the source. Figure 1 shows the maximum expansion velocity for the non-ideal copper pill sources (i.e., where γ varies with pressure and density) versus E_0 / M for high and low initial densities. In comparison to the constant γ condition of Eq.(1), the exponent is about 0.55 for the high density sources and 0.52 for the low density sources. These velocity values were obtained in the following way. The pressure and density for specific energy source conditions, obtained from the tabular equation of state, were used in the ideal gamma-law gas relationship to obtain an effective specific heat ratio, γ_{eff}, for the initial state of the source. Then Eq.(1) was used to calculate U_{max}. Maximum

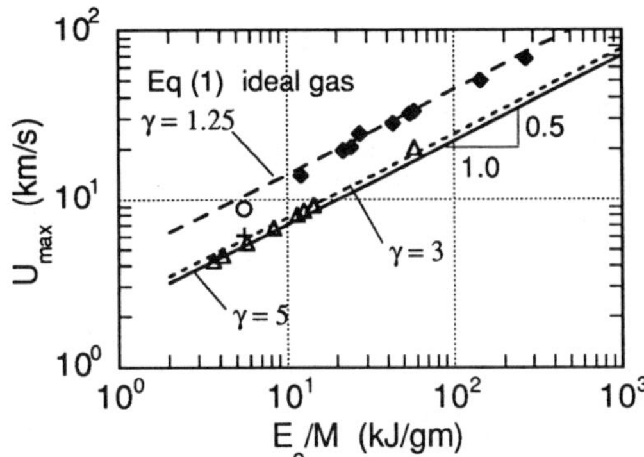

Figure 1. Maximum boundary velocity expansion into a vacuum versus energy/mass for various sources: ◆ EW low density, Δ EW high density, O HE-det, and + HE-pill. Lines refer to Eq(1) for different values of specific heat ratio.

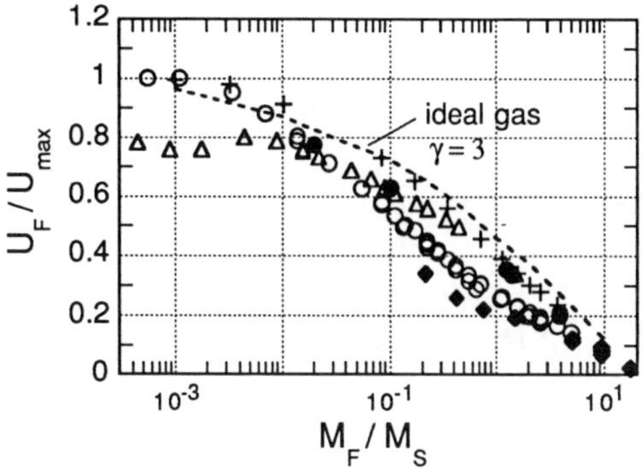

Figure 2. Velocity ratio versus mass ratio for flyers driven by various sources: ◆ high energy-EW low density, Δ high energy-EW high density, ● low energy-EW, O HE-det, and + HE-pill. Dashed line refers to an ideal gas pill-source for specific heat ratio = 3.

velocities for the PBX 9404-3 HE-det and the HE-pill conditions are also shown, with values of 0.88 cm/μs and 0.61 cm/μs, respectively. The higher value for HE-det is related to the Chapman-Jouguet (CJ) effect, which allows thin flyers with thicknesses of the order of the width of the CJ-pulse to attain velocities higher than those achieved by isentropic expansion.

The calculated ratio of flyer velocity to the maximum limit velocities, U_F/U_{max}, determined above versus the flyer-mass to source-mass ratio M_F/M_S, is given in Figure 2. Results for an ideal gas pill source with $\gamma = 3$ are given by the dashed line. Noteworthy is that the velocity ratio for the EW-source appears to be peaked out and fairly constant for mass ratios less than 0.01. For the other source conditions, however, the velocity ratio continues to increase and approaches unity in the range of mass ratios 0.0005 for the $\gamma = 3$ source to 0.003 for the HE-pill source. For mass ratios between 0.05 and 10, the velocity ratio for the high density EW source lies between the HE-det source and the HE-pill source. The low density EW source velocity ratio falls below that for the HE-det. At mass ratios above 10 all cases appear to be converging to nearly the same small velocity ratios.

The reason for the noted differences is unclear at present, but it is definitely related to the adiabatic expansion coupling of energy associated with the equation of state representations for the wire and the explosive. A dependence on γ_{eff} is noted, in that its initial value is 1.25 for low density EW and varies between 3 and 5 for high density EW. For the HE sources the initial value is about 3 and decreases to about 1.2 during the expansion process. The velocity ratio for the ideal gas pill with ($\gamma = 3$) acts as an upper bound in the 1 to 10 mass ratio range.

Energy Ratio

The KE to source-energy ratio versus flyer-mass to source-mass is shown in Figure 3. The KE coupled to the flyer increases with an increase in mass ratio, with marked differences observed at high and low mass ratios. The coupling is dependent on the initial source energy for mass ratios greater than 0.02, as well as on the type of source. For lower mass ratios, the EW source coupling is least efficient and the HE-det source is most efficient, which is consistent with the behavior for the velocity ratio. The additional KE

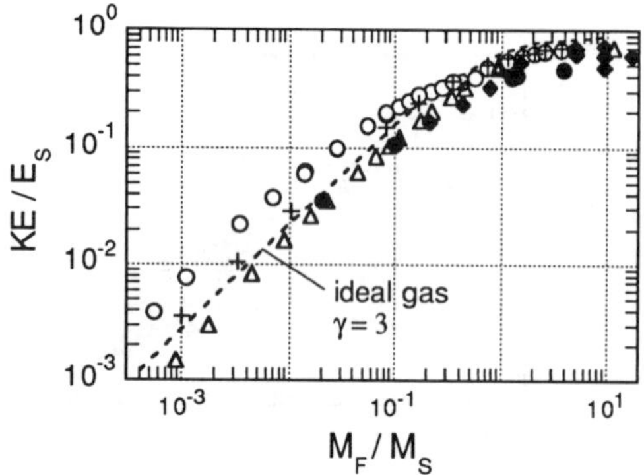

Figure 3. Energy ratio versus mass ratio for flyers driven by various sources: ♦ high energy-EW low density, Δ high energy-EW high density, ● low energy-EW, O HE-det, and + HE-pill. Dashed line refers to an ideal gas pill-source for specific heat ratio = 3.

boost for thin low-mass flyers in the HE-det case is attributed to the extra CJ impulse imparted to the flyer in addition to the normal adiabatic expansion coupling. In all cases, as the mass ratio becomes sufficiently small, the exponent for the energy ratio approaches unity. This corresponds to the flyer velocity approaching the maximum expansion boundary velocity. The efficiency levels off at mass ratios greater than 0.5 to 1, with a higher value associated with higher initial energy. Similar to the velocity ratio behavior in this range, the $\gamma = 3$ case acts as an upper bound.

DATA AND DISCUSSION

The velocity data obtained in [1,2] was for mass ratios of 1.245, 3.65, 3.88, and 4.4. Estimates for corresponding velocity ratios and energy ratios range from 0.11 to 0.57, and from 0.1 to 0.7, respectively. For clarity of Figures 2 and 3, this data range is not plotted. The ranges are based on the amount of EW-source energy coupled into the flyer, with the uncertainty being from 1800 to 6000 J The maximum expansion velocities are 0.43 cm/μs and 0.85 cm/μs. The higher energy is unrealistic because it represents the total energy in the discharge system. The lower value was estimated in [4] to match the blast wave time-of-arrival in air, for identical sleeveless wires and discharge energy, in terms of self-similar theory. The performance for the EW source may be suspect because of our simplified model. More realistic modeling would have to account for the time- and spatial-dependent deposition of the discharge energy in the wire and its surroundings. HE coupling has been successfully modeled in many areas using the above approach. Hence, flyer performance for the HE cases is considered quite reasonable. Nevertheless, the uniform source representation employed here allows one to get a first order estimate of the energy required to obtain a variety of impact conditions over various scales.

REFERENCES

[1] R. P. Swift and I. M. Fyfe, Elastic/Viscoplastic Theory Examined Using Radial Cylindrical Stress Waves, *J. Appl. Mech.*, **37**, 1134-1140 (1970).

[2] R. M. Schmidt and I. M. Fyfe, "Dynamic Fracture in Metals Under Biaxial Strain Conditions," University of Washington, College of Engineering Report 70-3 (1970).

[3] I. M. Fyfe, R. R. Ensminger and R. P. Swift, "The Effects of Shear on Stress Wave Propagation," Air Force Weapons Laboratory Technical Report AFWL TR-65-12 (1965).

[4] R. R. Ensminger and I. M. Fyfe, Constitutive Model Evaluation Using Cylindrical Stress Wave Propagation, *J. Mech. Phys. Solids,* **14,** 231-238 (1966).

[5] J. E. Reaugh, I. O. Huebsch, and R. P. Swift, "Fracture and Comminution of Rock," Physics International Co. Final Report PIFR-310 (1972).

[6] J. F. Schatz, "SOC, A One-Dimensional Wave Propagation Code for Rock Media," Lawrence Livermore National Lab., UCRL-51689 (1974).

[7] T. R. Butkovich, "Gas Equation of State for Natural Materials," Lawrence Livermore National Laboratory, UCRL-14729 (1967).

[8] E. L. Lee, H. C. Hornig, J. W. Kury, "Adiabatic Expansion of High-Explosive Detonation Products," Lawrence Livermore National Laboratory, UCRL-50422 (1968).

[9] Y. B. Zel'dovich and Y. P. Raizer, *Physics of Shock Waves and High-Temperature Phenomena*, Academic Press, 1966, ch. 1, pp.101-104.

CONTAINED HIGH EXPLOSIVE FIRING FACILITY (CHEFF)+

H. L. Stacy, W. L. Seitz and Jerry Wackerle
Los Alamos National Laboratory
Group M-7, MS P952
Los Alamos, NM 87545
Michael Polcyn and Edward Esparza
Southwest Research Institute
P. O. Drawer 28510
San Antonio, Texas 78209-1128

A cylindrical vessel capable of totally containing the products and shrapnel resulting from the detonation of 10 kg of TNT (or equivalent) has been designed and built by Southwest Research Institute for and according to the requirements of the Detonation Systems Group (M-7) of Los Alamos National Laboratory. The vessel is 6.0-m long by 3.6-m diameter and is manufactured of 50-mm (elliptical end caps) and 38-mm (cylindrical walls) thick high-strength steel (HY-100). The cylindrical walls of the vessel are lined with 13-mm thick replaceable steel plates for shrapnel protection. The floor is made of steel-covered concrete. Ten large-aperture (254 mm) optical ports are available for instrumentation and four ports are provided for cabling and plumbing. Two qualifying detonation tests of 8.8 kg of C-4 explosive (equivalent to 10 kg TNT) have shown that the maximum strain produced is less than 78% of the elastic limit. The vessel is installed in a converted outdoor firing facility that has been modified to include an insulated and heated metal building to house the vessel and additional instrumentation. A computer-based system for data acquisition, firing control, and the monitoring of vessel response is described.

INTRODUCTION

With the increasing cost of firing explosive experiments, an efficient method of gathering more data from a single experiment is needed. It seems logical that if the experiment can be placed in the center of a room and surrounded with diagnostics, rather than looking through a single port window, that more data can be obtained from each experiment. The center-of-the-room idea led to the containment vessel concept. The containment vessel provides a configuration suitable for surrounding the experiment with diagnostics and lends itself more easily to experiments that must have tight environmental controls than does outdoor firing. The contained approach to firing is environmentally friendly but is not the answer to all explosive testing. These concepts are the governing ideas behind the Contained High Explosive Firing Facility (CHEFF). A photograph of CHEFF is shown in Figure 1.

+Work performed under the auspices of the U.S.Department of Energy.

Figure 1. M-7's Contained High Explosive Firing Facility (CHEFF).

VESSEL DESIGN AND FABRICATION

In 1990, the Detonation Systems Group (M-7) of Los Alamos National Laboratory contracted with Southwest Research Institute to design and fabricate a cylindrical vessel capable of totally containing the products and shrapnel resulting from the detonation of 10 kg of TNT (or equivalent). Certain requirements were specified by M-7, such as ten large-aperture (254 mm) optical ports, four ports for cabling and plumbing, and limitations on the physical size and weight. Southwest Research Institute designed a 68 metric-ton vessel that is 6.0-m long by 3.6-m diameter manufactured of 50-mm (elliptical end caps) and 38-mm (cylindrical walls) thick high-strength steel (HY-100). The cylindrical walls are lined with 305-mm square tiles that are made of 13-mm thick neoprene covered with 13-mm thick steel for shrapnel protection, as seen in Figure 2. The tiles are bolted to the inside walls of the vessel and are designed to be replaced when necessary. A 2.1-m by 1.2-m door located in one of the elliptical end caps provides for easy access. The large physical size of the door prevents the vessel from being considered a confined space. Air circulation in and out of the vessel is provided through two 152-mm diameter tubes with butterfly valves on each tube. An 8.5-m^3/min fan on the exhaust tube provides circulation of fresh air through the vessel and removes particulate matter from exhausting gases by using HEPA filters.

Figure 2. Interior view of the containment vessel showing the replaceable tiles, the end cap containing the door frame, and gusset supports.

Blast loads in the vessel consist of both a shock loading phase and a quasi-static gas loading phase. The quasi-static load is predicted with confidence using empirically-based data [1]. The shock loading phase is much more difficult to predict because of the reverberation of shock waves within the vessel. Therefore, the shock loading was predicted using a combination of blast predictive methodologies and explosion test data from a similar vessel. Similarly, the response of most of the structural components to the blast loads was calculated using simple single-degree-of-freedom dynamic response methods. However, the response of the door, door frame, elliptical end cap, and cylinder (in the axial direction) are coupled and, thus, required a more complicated multi-degree-of-freedom dynamic analysis to predict the response.

TESTING

M-7 required that three air leak tests and two 10-kg TNT-equivalent explosive tests be conducted to qualify the vessel for acceptance. To confirm the design parameters and check the manufacturing process, Southwest Research Institute implemented additional tests that included a hydrostatic, several low pressure air, and additional small-scale explosive tests. All the testing, thus far, has taken place at the Southwest Research Institute facility in San Antonio, Texas. All tests were monitored using strain gauges, pressure gauges, displacement gauges, and thermocouples.

The explosive tests were divided into two distinct categories. The first category was the preliminary tests, which included two 2.27-kg and one 4.54-kg TNT-equivalent explosive experiments, that were used to calibrate the instrumentation, check reproducibility, and check design calculations. The second category was the qualifying tests, which included two 10-kg TNT-equivalent (8.8 kg C-4) explosive experiments each followed by the air leak test mentioned above. All explosive charges were spherical in shape and positioned at the geometrical center of the vessel when detonated.

Thirty three strain gauges, one static pressure gauge, two quasi-static pressure gauges, four blast pressure gauges, three displacement gauges, and two thermocouples were used for each test. Three of the blast pressure gauges were located in areas where high pressure was indicated by standard blast pressure calculations [2]. One gauge was located in the center of the elliptical end cap (opposite the door) and the other two gauges were in the cylindrical wall, on opposite sides of the vessel and in a vertical plane with the explosive charge. The last blast pressure gauge was located in a low pressure area and used for comparison with the other blast pressure gauges. Strain gauges were located in areas that included most of the geometrically different regions of the vessel, with a high concentration of gauging in areas of greatest calculational uncertainties, such as the area where the door frame intersects the elliptical end cap (see Figure 2).

The hydrostatic test involved filling the vessel with approximately 50 m^3 of water and then gradually pressurizing it to the 5.4-MPa design pressure. Measurements of strain for several previously determined pressures were compared to the predicted values. The hydrostatic test also checked the integrity of the vessel's construction before the steel-covered concrete floor was installed.

The air leak tests consisted of pressurizing the vessel to 1.1 MPa and verifying, over a four hour period, that all observed pressure changes were temperature induced. A total of three air leak tests were performed, one before any of the explosive tests and one after each of the two qualifying explosive tests.

All experimental measurements were in good agreement with calculated values. Table 1 gives a summary of measured peak amplitudes obtained from the explosive testing. Considering each specific geometry, the highest stress calculated from the measured strains was less then 78% of the elastic limit (690 MPa) of the steel used. The fact that there were no air leaks after the large

Table 1. Summary of Measured Peak Amplitudes for Explosive Tests

	Location*	2.27 kg TNT Test	2.27 kg TNT Test	4.54 kg TNT Test	10 kg TNT Test	10 kg TNT Test
Strain (μm/m)	A	527	522	1133	2222	2282
	B	>-400 Δ	-580 Δ	-886 Δ	1429	1388
	C	411	415	811	1118	1037
Peak Stress (MPa)	A	136	134	271	521	532
	B	>-110 Δ	-176 Δ	299	439	430
	C	108	103	127	242	216
Blast Pressure (MPa)	B	1.19	1.62	3.28	4.46	6.55
	C	3.17	3.38	6.00	11.6	14.5
Quasi-static Pressure (MPa)	D	0.23	0.24	0.43	0.78	0.79
Gas Temperature(°C)	D	-	244	490	-	>638
Displacement (mm)	A	1.85	-	4.01	6.76	6.58
	E	0.94	-	1.83	2.46	3.07
	F	0.30	-	0.68	1.29	1.24

*A= Door Center, B= Cylindrical Head, C= Circumference at Center of Cylinder, D= Internal to the Vessel, E= Edge of the Door on the Horizonal Center Line, F= Door Frame on the Horizonal Center Line

Δ Negitive Values Indicate Compression

test demonstrated that the seals, gaskets, and the port glass will withstand the pressures and shocks of multiple full-scale experiments.

FACILITY

The vessel is installed in a converted outdoor firing facility that has been modified to include an insulated and heated metal building to house the vessel and additional instrumentation. The outdoor firing site was built in the mid 1950s and had a small load limit of 2 kg, dictated by the proximity of other inhabited structures [3]. With the addition of the vessel to the firing site, the load limit was increased from 2 kg to 10 kg without endangering the other inhabited structures and actually decreasing the sound level at these structures. As a part of the renovation the electrical service was brought up to modern code by a complete rewiring of the firing site. This renovation has made CHEFF a clean modern facility in which to conduct explosive experiments.

A computer-based control system is currently under development. This system will not only monitor the vessel performance and operating controls, but it will also be an integral part of the data-gathering capabilities of the firing site and interlock-monitoring system for the firing controls. The data-gathering capabilities of CHEFF include, but are not limited to, laser velocimetry capabilities [4], digital oscilloscopes, streak cameras, image intensifier cameras, framing cameras, and digitizers. The operation of the instrumentation will be controlled and/or monitored by the computer system. Digitizers and digital oscilloscopes not used on any given experiment will be used to monitor the performance of the vessel by measuring strains. The measured strains will be analyzed and placed into a data base so that any long term deterioration of the vessel integrity can be detected.

CONCLUSIONS

Contained firing provides a practical solution to the increasing cost of performing explosive experiments and the encroachment of civilization on what were once remote firing sites. When CHEFF comes on line in late 1993, it will give the Detonation Systems Group (M-7) an invaluable tool for explosive experimentation that will not only be cost effective but also environmentally friendly.

ACKNOWLEDGMENTS

The authors acknowledge the hard work and cooperative attitudes displayed by both the Los Alamos team and the Southwest Research Institute team in bringing the vessel and renovation together in a timely manner. Without their hard work, dedication, and cooperation the merging of these two tasks would have been difficult, if not impossible. The people involved in this project are too numerous to mention individually, but a special thank you goes to: Ronald L. Rabie whose foresight and dedication made CHEFF possible, Thomas O. Davis for his untiring effort in preparing the statement of work, Doyle D. Simes for his major role in the facility design, Gary L. Green for his invaluable help in understanding the welding, steel selection, and mechanical processes, and Francis Caroline for his oversight and control of the fabrication effort.

REFERENCES

[1] M. A. Polcyn, E. D. Esparza and M. G. Whitney, *Minutes of the 25th Explosives Safety Seminar,* 1992.

[2] W. E. Baker, P. A. Cox, P. S. Westine, J. J. Kulesz and R. A. Strehlow, *Explosive Hazards and Evaluation*, Elsevier Press, Amsterdam, 1983.

[3] A. R. Martinez, S. A. Sheffield, M. C. Whitehead and H. D. Olivas, *New LANL Gas Driven Two-stage Gun,* This Conference, 1993.

[4] W. L. Seitz, H. L. Stacy and Jerry Wackerle, in *Proceedings of the Ninth Symposium (International) on Detonation,* ONCR Report 113291-7 pp. 157-169 (1989).

CHAPTER XXIII

DIAGNOSTICS

CALIBRATION AND FLUORESCENCE INTENSITIES OF SM:DOPED YAG TO ULTRA HIGH PRESSURES

Jun Liu and Yogesh K.Vohra

Department of Physics
University of Alabama at Birmingham
310 Campbell Hall, University Blvd.
Birmingham, AL 35294-1170, USA

Sm:doped YAG optical pressure sensor is calibrated against ruby in the diamond anvil cell up to 73 GPa. The Y_2 band fluorescence excited by 514.5 nm laser shows a linear pressure dependence of 0.322 nm/GPa to 73 GPa. The relative intensity of Y_2 sub-band compared to Y_1 shows a significant increase with increasing pressure. At high pressures, the overall integrated intensity of Y band increases by an order of magnitude which is in contrast to ruby R_1 line whose intensity decreases under identical conditions. x-ray diffraction studies show that the cubic phase of YAG crystal is stable to 69 GPa and has a volume compression of 17.9%. Our experiments indicate that Sm:YAG is a promising optical sensor for high pressure / high temperature (Hess et al[6-8]) research in the diamond anvil cell.

INTRODUCTION

Diamond Anvil Cell (DAC) devices can generate calibrated static pressures of several million atmospheres. The calibration of pressure in the DAC is a crucial issue for high pressure research. The conventional optical pressure sensor is the R_1 fluorescence line of ruby crystal[1,2]. However several factors limit this application of ruby as a pressure sensor to below $500^\circ C$ and 200 GPa: (1) R_1-R_2 doublet decreases in intensity and is broadened under high pressure, and this affects the accurate pressure reading. (2) Although R_1 peak position has a pressure dependence of about 0.36 nm/GPa, it also has a temperature dependence of 0.007 nm/$^\circ C$. In addition, the intensity decreases rapidly with temperature, and when the temperature is above $500^\circ C$, it is difficult to detect the ruby signal. (3) Under high pressure the diamond shows intensive absorption in the visible spectral range with increasing pressure above 100 GPa[3,4]. The optical density for the best chosen diamond will reach 3.0 for 514.5 nm Argon laser line at 400 GPa, which implies that only 0.1% of the incident laser can get through the diamond and excite the sample, so that only long wavelength light (i.e., the deep red region) is favored for pumping fluorescence under high pressures in the diamond anvil cell. On the contrary, the most efficient pumping wavelength of ruby R_1 line corresponding to the T-absorption band has a blue shift with pressure, falling into the range of deep blue, and so is obstructed by the diamond optical absorption. All these effects make ruby signal difficult to obtain above 200 GPa and thus several new optical sensors need to be investigated for this pressure range (200-400 GPa).

Several materials such as $Al_2O_3:Eu^{3+}$, $YAlO_3:Eu^{3+}$, $Gd_2O_3:Eu^{3+}$, $YAG:Eu^{3+}$, $YbAG:Eu^{3+}$, and $GdAG:Eu^{3+}$ were considered as optical pressure sensors[5]. In this early study, the YAG doped with Eu^{3+} was found to be most promising because of the large pressure shift (0.2 nm/GPa) and small negative temperature shift (-0.00054 nm/$^\circ C$). This led to the interest in these laser materials for optical sensor applications. Subsequent work by Hess et al[6-8] showed that Sm-doped (4 wt.% Sm) YAG ($Y_3Al_5O_{12}$) has negligible temperature dependence to $700^\circ C$, making it an ideal candidate for pressure calibration of diamond anvil cell at elevated temperatures. Bi et al[9] carried out calibration of Sm:YAG to 26 GPa at room temperature, which shows a roughly 0.307 nm/GPa change with pressure. However it was noticed in these earlier studies to 26 GPa that the Sm:YAG fluorescence intensity is 1-2 order of magnitude lower than that of the ruby R_1 line. In this paper we report our calibration and fluorescence intensity of Sm:YAG to 73 GPa at room temperature and compare our results with those of the ruby pressure sensor.

EXPERIMENTAL TECHNIQUES

Several Sm:YAG powdered crystals (4 wt% Sm, around several microns in size) and only one small piece (<2 microns) of ruby were placed inside a 50 micron diameter hole drilled in a spring steel gasket. CsCl was spread inside the hole as the soft medium to insure near hydrostatic conditions. Type Ia natural diamonds with central flat of 300 micron diameters were used in this set of experiments. Pressure was then gradually increased to 73 GPa with fluorescence data collected in small increment of pressure. Pressures were calculated from the non-hydrostatic calibration of ruby[2].

An Argon ion laser operated at 514.5 nm was used to excite fluorescence from both ruby and YAG. At each pressure, identical laser power and data acquisition conditions were intentionally kept for quantitative comparison of fluorescence intensities. Micro-raman and fluorescence spectrometer at the University of Alabama described elsewhere[10] was employed in the present experiments. The fluorescence data were collected from 20 micron diameter region in the sample chamber. Both ruby and YAG signals were obtained from the same spatial region to minimize the effects of pressure inhomogeneity. Spectral parameters like peak positions, full width at half maximum (FWHM), and integrated intensities were obtained by fitting Lorentzian line shape with linear background.

RESULTS AND DISCUSSIONS

Fig.1 is the fluorescence spectra from Sm:YAG in the diamond anvil cell at various pressures. All the spectra are normalized to the data collection time of 1 second so that the relative intensities of various spectra can be compared.

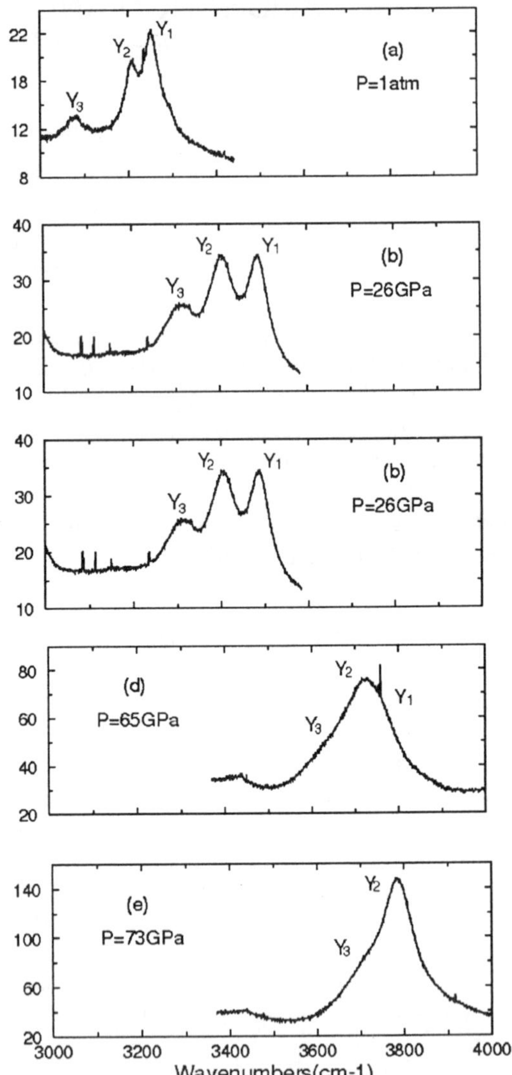

Fig.1: Sm:YAG fluorescence at various pressures indicated. Excited by 514.5 nm laser line, the data are shown as shifts from the laser line in wavenumbers. Note the increase in intensity of the fluorescence lines which are normalized to the collection time of 1 second with increasing pressure.

Fig.1 shows that both Y_1 and Y_2 lines move to higher wavelength with increasing pressure. Fig.2(a) and (b) show the pressure dependence of the Y_1 band to 65 GPa and Y_2 band to 73 GPa, respectively. The data points of the Y_1

and Y_2 bands were least squared fitted and the linear pressure coefficients were found to be 0.332 nm/GPa and 0.322 nm/GPa, respectively. We can not rule out the possibility of slight quadratic pressure coefficients due to the scattering in the data points in Fig.2. These results are comparable with ruby's R_1 line shift (0.36 nm/GPa), and are consistent with the slope of 0.307 nm/GPa obtained to 26 GPa in the earlier work[9].

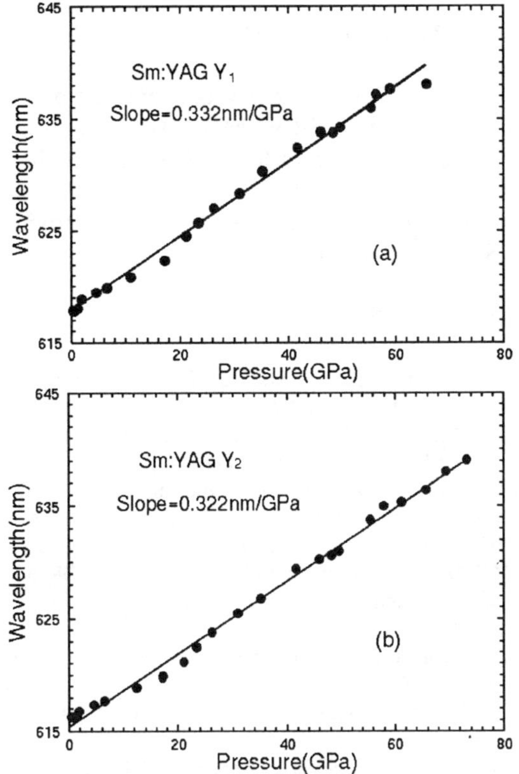

Fig.2: Pressure dependence of the fluorescence wavelengths of Sm:YAG: (a)Y_1 and (b)Y_2. The solid lines are the linear fits to the data.

The other interesting feature of the spectra in Fig.1 is the intensity change of Y band of Sm:YAG fluorescence. At ambient pressure, the Y_1 fluorescence band is the most intense one in the Sm:YAG and the Y_2- band is about 60% of the Y_1 intensity. However we found that at high pressures the relative intensity of Y_1 to Y_2 shows dramatic changes. The intensity ratio of Y_2 to Y_1 increases rapidly and above 70 GPa we observed that only the Y_2 band survives.

Fig.3 shows the integrated intensity of Sm:YAG Y band varying with pressure. The intensities are normalized to 100 second data collection time and plotted in linear-log form. The Y band gradually picks up its intensity with increasing pressures. At 73 GPa it has a factor of 15 in magnitude greater than that at ambient pressure. This is in contrast to the behavior of ruby's R_1 peak whose intensity will decrease with increasing pressure even at room temperature (in our experiments we noticed an factor of 10 decrease with increasing pressure). Our experiments indicate that 514.5 nm laser is more efficient to pump the Y band fluorescence of Sm:YAG at higher pressures than at lower pressures. Considering the red shift of the absorption band of diamond at high pressures, we suggest Sm:YAG Y band a candidate as an optical pressure sensor at megabar pressures. The strong Y_2 band fluorescence signal combined with its large pressure coefficient at high pressure are promising properties for accurate measurement of pressures.

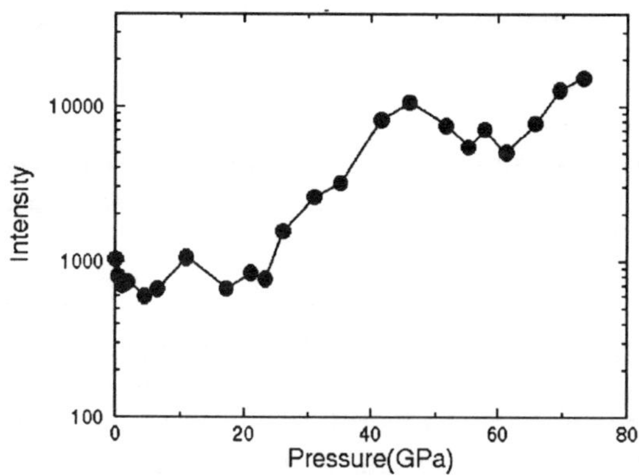

Fig.3: Comparison of the integrated intensities of the Sm:YAG Y band at different pressures. The intensities for all the data points have been normalized to collection time of 100 seconds.

We have also investigated the possibility of structural phase transition in the Sm:YAG at high pressures to explain the observed dramatic changes in its fluorescence intensity. Energy dispersive x-ray diffraction experiment on polycrystalline Sm:YAG power in the diamond anvil cell at 69 GPa was carried out at the superconducting wiggler white beam line X-17C at NSLS (Fig.4). Fig.4 is the diffraction pattern which is indexed based on a cubic unit cell with lattice parameter a=11.216 Å. This implies a volume compression of 17.9% at 69 GPa using our ambient pressure lattice parameter of 11.976 Å measured by x-ray diffraction. This value is close to the accepted lattice parameter (12.01 Å) for YAG crystal[11]. In addition to the thermal and chemical stabilities of Sm:YAG material[6-8], the stability of cubic structure under ultra high pressure is another promising property for its application as an optical pressure sensor.

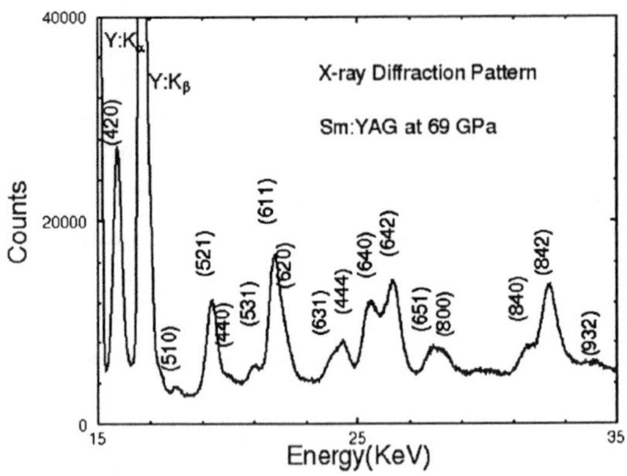

Fig.4: X-ray diffraction pattern of Sm:YAG at 69 GPa in the cubic phase. The product of energy and interplaner spacing Ed=39.576 keVÅ.

The absence of any structural rearrangement in Sm:YAG to 69 GPa indicates that the observed relative intensity changes in the Y band must be attributed to the changes in the electronic structures due to the compression of the cubic phase.

CONCLUSIONS

We offer the following conclusions:

(1) The integrated Y band intensity of Sm:YAG shows at least an order of magnitude increase with increasing pressures between ambient and 73 GPa;

(2) The Y_1 and Y_2 sub-bands shift at the rates of 0.332 nm/GPa to 65 GPa and 0.322 nm/GPa to 73 GPa, respectively;

(3) X-ray diffraction studies indicate that the cubic phase of Sm:YAG is stable to 69 GPa.

Future studies will concentrate on the Sm:YAG pressure calibration in the megabar pressure range. Reliable equation of state data exists for Cu and Pt to 500 GPa should form the basis of an accurate pressure scale. Sm:YAG appears to be a promising pressure sensor for diamond anvil cell research at ultra high pressure/high temperature regime[6-8].

ACKNOWLEDGEMENTS

This research was supported by NSF under grant No. DMR-9296212. We acknowledge the use of X-17C beam line at NSLS, Brookhaven National Lab supported by Department of Energy. Authors also thank N.J.Hess for kindly providing the Sm:Doped YAG sample.

REFERENCES

[1] J.D.Barnett, S.Block and G.J.Piermarini, *Rev. Sci. Instrum.* 44, pp.1-9 (1973).
[2] H.K.Mao, P.M.Bell, J.W.Shaner and D.J.Steinberg, *J.Appl.Phys.*49, pp.3276-3283 (1978).
[3] Y.K.Vohra, "Spectroscopic Studies of Diamond Anvil Under Extreme Static Stresses", in *Recent Trends in High Pressure Research: Proceedings of the XII AIRAPT International Conference*,1991, pp.349-358.
[4] H.K.Mao and R.J.Hemley, *Nature* 351, pp.721-724, (1991).
[5] H.Arashi and M.Ishigame, *Jap.J.Appl.Phys.* 21, pp.1647-1649 (1982).
[6] N.J.Hess and G.J.Exarhos, *High Pres.Res.* 2, pp.57-64, (1989).
[7] N.J.Hess and D.Schiferl, *J.Appl.Phys.* 68, pp.1953-1959 (1990).
[8] N.J.Hess and D.Schiferl, *J.Appl.Phys.* 71, pp.2082-2085 (1992).
[9] Q.Bi, J.M.Brown, and Y.Sato-Sorensen, *J.Appl.Phys.* 68, pp.5357-5359 (1990).
[10] Y.K.Vohra and S.S.Vagarali, *Appl.Phys.Lett.* 61, pp.2680-2862 (1992).
[11] H.S.Yoder and M.L.Keith, *J.Min.Soc.Am.* 36, pp.519-533 (1951).

HIGH PRESSURE TRANSDUCER WITH CERAMIC FREE ROD AS ACTIVE ELEMENT

R. Wiśniewski, GF. Molinar*,

INSTITUTE OF PHYSICS, WARSAW UNIVERSITY OF TECHNOLOGY, KOSZYKOWA 75, 00-662 WARSZAWA, POLAND
*ISTITUTO di METROLOGIA "G. Colonnetti", TORINO, ITALY.

Strain gauge pressure transducer for hydrostatic pressure measurements up to 0.5 GPa with free ceramic rod element in which pressure acts on its open ends is presented. Operating principles and main metrological properties of the device are also described.

INTRODUCTION

In previous papers [1],[2] a strain gauge dilating - cylinder pressure transducers in which pressure acts inside cylinder and on their open ends as well was described. In the transducer described in the second paper the inner diameter of cylinder was very small and played only the role of a transmitting pressure medium canal. That makes this transducer, in principle, a strain gauge free rod type. Both types of transducers have some metrological advantages in comparison to classical ones. Further investigations with this types of transducers was connected first of all with the elimination in bonding the strain gauge foil and in decreasing of the maximal value of strain to level of 1000 - 1500 μm/m for pressure up to 1 GPa. Materials of the non conducting of electrical current types with large value of Young's modulus and with large compression stress limits should be applied. The following ceramic materials have been taken under consideration: silicon carbide, aluminium oxide, boron carbide and diamond-borazon composites.

Firstly a Al_2O_3 ceramic material (alumina) of 99,7 % purity was used. Properties of alumina depend to the considerable degree on purity and porosity. Representative data can be given as follow: maximum work temperature 1800^{0}C, tensile strength (20^{0}C) 0.5-1.0 GPa. compressive strength 2.5-4.0 GPa, Charpy impact strength 0.1-0.15 J/cm^2, Young's modulus 300-450 GPa, Poissone ratio 0.24, Knoop hardness 1295-2050, electrical resistivity 10^{14} - 10^{15} Ohm cm, specific gravity 3.65 g/cm^3, thermal coefficient of linear expansion TCE = 8.5×10^{-6} deg^{-1}.

PRINCIPLE OF OPERATION

The construction of the free deforming ceramic rod pressure transducer in its the cross-section is presented in fig. 1.

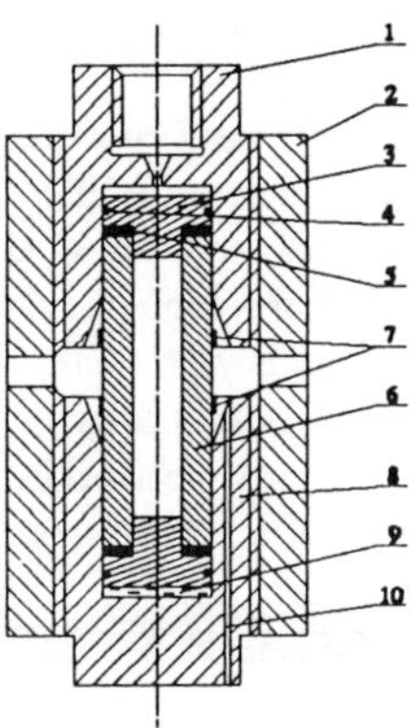

Figure 1. Cross section of the strain-gauge pressure transducer.

1 - part of the high pressure vessel, with left thread screw and with fitting for pressure connection,
2 - closing nut with left and right screw threading,
3 - closing plug of active element,
4 - Viton O ring,
5 - adaptation foil,
6 - Al_2O_3 active elements (thick-walled cylinder),
7 - strain gauge,
8 - part of the high pressure vessel, with right thread screw,
9 - transmitting liquid medium put in before mounting.
10- electrical leads hole.

The active element has thick-walled cylinder form (6) closed at the ends by plugs (3) both sealed by O rings (4). This version gives possibilities to increase by about 25% value the sensitivity of device. Parts (1), (2) and (8) constitute the pressure vessel with two separated but with good approximation the same pressure value, cavities. In our initial experiment a constantan wire of diameter 0.01 mm wrapped circumferentially on outer cylinder surface has been used. Wire was wrapped under definite tension and then covered with celluloid glue. To the points, distanced at about 5 mm from the ends of constantan wire, thin copper leads were connected. In this way it was possible to avoid an undetermined influence of "the ends effect". When pressure acts only on open ends of active element one can easy obtain the following formula for relative output voltage ΔV/V, for two active arms of Wheatstone bridge, as a function of pressure:

$$\frac{\Delta V}{V} = \alpha \mu p \frac{K}{2E} \quad (1)$$

where: E - Young's modulus and μ - Poisson coefficient of active elements material, K - the gauge factor of the strain gauges, α - multiplication factor equal to $W^2/(W^2-1)$, where W is a ratio outer to inner diameters of ceramic active element, V - input supply voltage of the bridge.

If required accuracy is not better than ±3 % Eq.(1) can be directly used to determine pressure p from the measurements values of all other physical quantities as it was described in [1]. For higher accuracy a testing procedure using high accuracy pressure standard must be done. The use of simple Viton O rings give conditions of almost free rod (cylinder) system working at pressure up to 0.5 GPa at nearly room temperatures.

METROLOGICAL PROPERTIES

The all main metrological characteristics of described pressure transducer (i.e. repeatability, hysteresis, creep and resolution) were determined by comparison with a dead - weight manometer of accuracy 0.05% and 0.5 GPa capacity.

Preliminary tests at temperature of (20 ± 1)°C showed the following results:

1) the observed zero drift was negligible,
2) the hysteresis was not observed,
3) repeatability in all pressure range, including the zero value (atmospheric pressure) was ± 0.10 MPa,
4) resolution of the pressure transducer at pressure of 300 MPa was estimated to be 50 kPa,
5) creep at upper values of applied pressure was not observed by half an hour.

So, the accuracy of this prototype transducer was estimated to be ±0.05% of f.s. (±0.25 MPa).

DISCUSSION

At this preliminary stage for this type pressure transducer three main conclusions can be drown:
- the repeatability of this transducer is the same or even better than these for dilating free cylinder described in [1] where cylinder was made from tool type steel.
- hysteresis do not exist. In the paper [3] there was described a similar device but strain gauges classical transducer foil type Micro Measurement N2A-06-TOO7M-350 was used. Some hysteresis was observed there.
- The measured value of strain at maximum pressure p = 0.5 GPa is less then 1500 μm/m what is a limit of measured strain recommended by the producers strain gauge (transducer type).

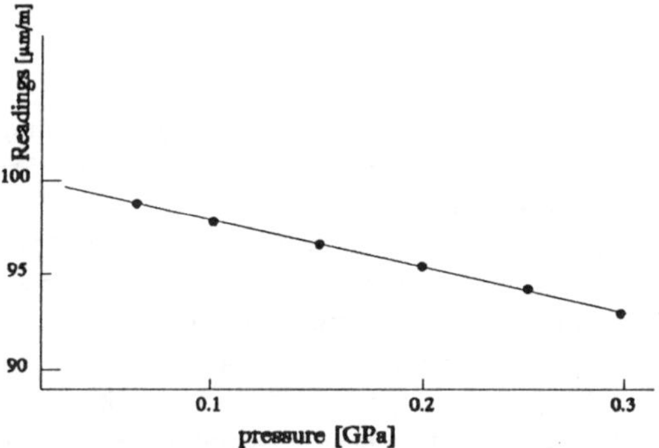

Figure 2. Reading equivalent strain Δε for Δp = 50 MPa as a function of applied standard pressure of transducer.

In fig. 2 there is shown a dependence of readings used by us strain indicator for Δp = 50 MPa on applied standard pressure. From this data results that sensitivity of transducer defined by:
$\alpha_p = \Delta\varepsilon_{READINGS}/\Delta p$ being about 2 μm/m/MPa, decrease with pressure with a rate less then 4.10^{-5} MPa μm/m/MPa^2.

REFERENCES

[1] R. Wiśniewski, GF. Molinar, *Rev. Sci. Instrum.* 63, pp. 3983-3884 (1992).

[2] GF. Molinar, R. Wiśniewski, L. Bianchi, " A Free-Rod Strain-Gauge Pressure Transducer of 1 GPa Capacity" presented at the Second CCM International Seminar "Pressure Metrology from 1 kPa to 1 GPa", LNE, Paris, France, 2-6 June,(1992).

[3] R. Wiśniewski and GF. Molinar,"Pressure transducer with ceramic free rod as active element", presented at the Second CCM International Seminar "Pressure Metrology from 1 Pa to 1 GPa", LNE, Paris, France, 2-6 June, (1993).

FIBER-OPTIC PRESSURE SENSOR USING AN ELECTRONICALLY SCANNED WHITE-LIGHT INTERFEROMETER

Wojtek J. Bock, Waclaw Urbanczyk[1], and Roland Wiśniewski[2])
Laboratoire d'optoélectronique, Département d'informatique,
Université du Québec à Hull,
P.O.Box 1250, Station B, Hull, Québec J8X 3X7, Canada
[1]on leave from the Institute of Physics, Technical University of Wroclaw,
50-370 Wroclaw, Wybrzeze Wyspianskiego 27, Poland
[2]Institute of Physics, Technical University of Warsaw,
00-662 Warszawa, Koszykowa 75, Poland

A novel fiber-optic sensing method allowing for improved measurement of hydrostatic pressure up to 40 MPa is presented in the paper. The sensor is temperature-compensated, independent of laser intensity fluctuations and unlike other interferometers enables absolute measurement of pressure. The accuracy of this device at room temperature is at least 0.5% and temperature stability in the range ±26°C is ±1.5% of the operation range.

I. INTRODUCTION

Advances in optical fiber telecommunication technology coupled with the availability and decreasing cost of active and passive optical fiber components have led to significant progress during the last few years in developing and implementing fiber-optic sensors [1]. Potential advantages in applying this technology for pressure measurement in geotechnical applications, especially in noisy or harsh environments such as those encountered in civil engineering while evaluating loads and stresses in structures are quite impressive: immunity to electromagnetic interference, compatibility with optical fiber data transmission systems and a better state of survival in adverse environments (electrical transducers for stress measurement in such structures as hydroelectric dams or bridges are often destroyed by lightning).

Several fiber-optic sensing methods for ranges of pressure up to 100MPa have recently been explored [2], [3]. The new approach involving white-light interferometry, presented in this paper is particularly interesting since the sensor output signal is immune to light intensity fluctuations (which is not the case with conventional polarimetric sensors).

II. DESCRIPTION OF THE SENSOR

To date, only a few discrete and quasi-distributed white-light interferometric sensor employing highly birefringent (HB) fibers have been developed to perform absolute measurement of strain and hydrostatic pressure and temperature simultaneously [4,5]. The idea of electronic scanning has recently been proposed [6,7,8,9,10] for single-mode and multi-mode white-light sensors in order to avoid the need for moving parts and to improve the mechanical stability of the receiving interferometer. The pressure sensor proposed in this paper is based entirely on HB fiber and enjoys the advantages of electronic scanning.

Configuration of the sensor is schematically shown in Fig.1. A laser diode LD served as a light source. It was driven by a low current, ensuring its broad-band operation mode with a central wavelength of λ_0 = 826nm and a coherence length of about 25 μm. The laser diode was pigtailed with the polarization preserving lead-up fiber (York bow-tie) and all the light was coupled into one of its polarization modes. The sensing part of the device, located inside a specially designed sensor head, was spliced with the lead-up and the lead-down fibers

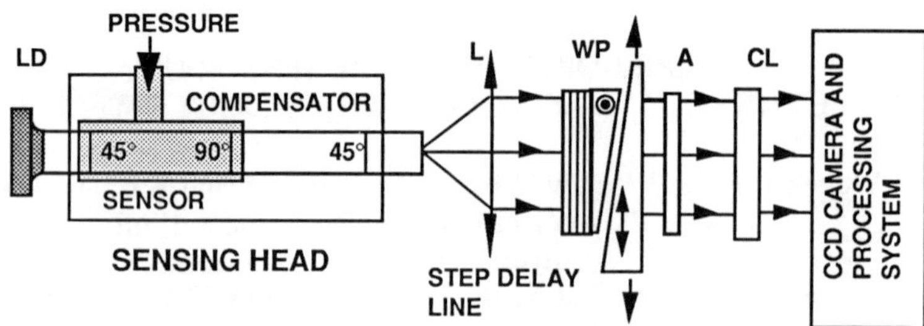

Figure 1. Configuration of white-light interferometric pressure sensor.

at an angle of 45°. The light from the output of the lead-down fiber was collimated by the lens L and passed through the step delay line and the Wollaston prism WP (both made of crystalline quartz), the analyser A, and the cylindrical lens CL. Polarization axes at the output of the lead-down fiber were aligned to be at 45° to the polarization axes of the step delay line, composed of three quartz retardation plates (each about 4 mm thick), which served to increase the operation range of the receiving interferometer up to 180λ.

The sensing part of the device was composed of two almost equal lengths of York bow-tie fiber spliced at 90° to achieve temperature compensation by ensuring that both fibers remained at the same temperature. The length of both parts was about 3.10 m while the difference in length was equal to 0.02 m. The sensing and compensating fibers were placed inside the respective chambers of the sensing head, Fig.2. The pressure chamber of the sensing head is attachable to any pressure inlet while the other chamber is separated from pressure and serves only for temperature compensation. To assure equal temperatures, the two chambers are located as close to each other as possible and both are filled with oil to achieve identical temperature conductivity.

It has been established [11] that hydrostatic pressure increases the difference in propagation constants as well as the polarization mode dispersion of HB fibers. Thus, an increase in pressure ΔP results in a transversal shift Δy of the white-light interference pattern (WLIP) registered by the CCD camera, which may be expressed as

$$\Delta y = K\, L_0 \frac{\partial \tau}{\partial P} \Delta P \ , \qquad (1)$$

where τ is the polarization mode dispersion of the HB fiber, L0 is the length of the sensing fiber, and K is the proportionality coefficient related to the geometry of the receiving interferometer. The processing performed on the signal digitized by the CCD camera should therefore establish the location of the center of the WLIP determined by the symmetry axis of the coherence function γ(y) Fig. 3. The details of our processing method are described in [12]. This method determines the symmetry axis of the WLIP with an accuracy better than one interference fringe. Since the width of our scanning area corresponds to 70 fringes, the achievable accuracy of measurement would be about 1.4%. To improve the low operation range, which is the greatest drawback of all electronically scanned white-light interferometric sensors, we proposed application of what we call the step delay line. Two quartz plates about 4 mm thick, each of them

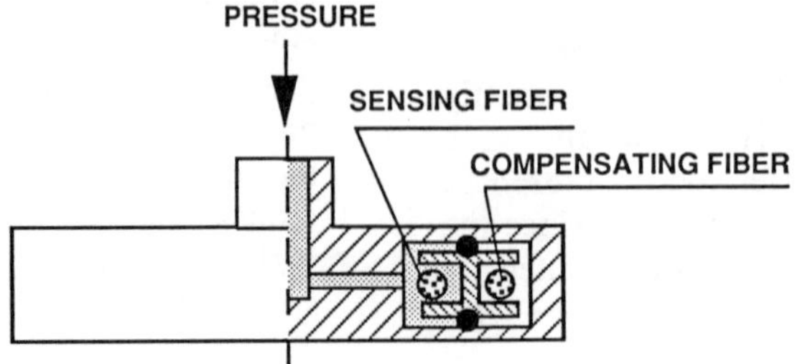

Figure 2. Configuration of the sensing head.

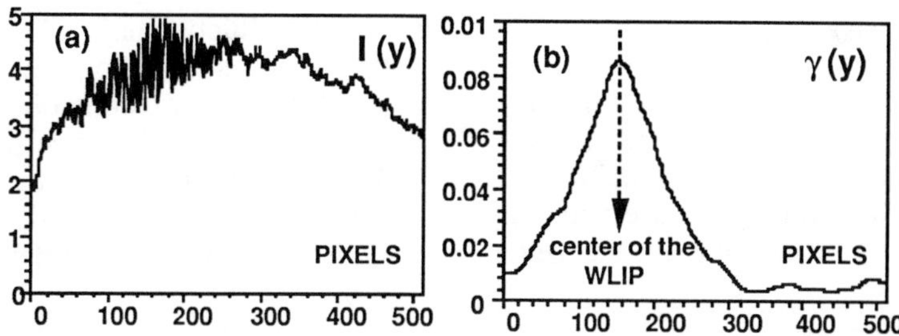

Figure 3. Interference pattern I(y) registered by the CCD camera (a) and the symmetry axis of the coherence function γ(y) determined by numerical processing of I(y).

compensating about 60λ were glued to the Wollaston prism, (Fig.4). In this way we divided the scanning area of our CCD camera into three scanning strips. The operation range of a single strip is about 70λ, while the step increase in group retardation between successive scanning strips is about 60λ. Thus, for pressures corresponding to 60-70λ, and 120–130λ the WLIP may be observed in the upper and lower strips simultaneously which allows for precise determination of the step increase in the group retardation between successive scanning strips. Application of the step delay lines triples the measurement resolution, which is now equal to 0.5%.

The sensor was calibrated for increasing and decreasing pressure for the range 0-40MPa using a Harwood DWT-35 Deadweight Tester generating the desired pressure with accuracy better than 0.1%. In order to determine the response of the sensor to ambient temperature changes we placed the sensor head inside the thermostat and carried out the pressure calibration at different temperatures T_1=10°C, T_2=23°C, T_3=36°C. We observed a very good repeatability of the order of 0.5% for tests of short as well as long (a few days) duration. The results shown in Fig.5 indicate, in addition to the linear pressure characteristics of the sensor, the existence of a residual response to the temperature changes which also depends on pressure. At atmospheric pressure, the temperature change ΔT=26°C shifts the WLIP by 0.4 interference fringe while at P=37.5MPa identical temperature change produces the response of the sensor equal to 2 interference fringes. This effect is most probably related to the temperature-hydrostatic pressure cross-sensitivity in York bow-tie fibers. It can be clearly seen from Fig.5 that at higher temperatures York bow-tie fiber becomes less sensitive to hydrostatic pressure. From our calibration data, the cross-sensitivity of York bow-tie fiber can be estimated as equal to -6.1×10^{-4}fringe/°C MPa m. Although the temperature-hydrostatic pressure cross-sensitivity worsens the compensation, this sensor demonstrates remarkable temperature stability . The temperature changes equal to ±26°C induced a systematic measurement error of ±1.5% of the operation range of the sensor.

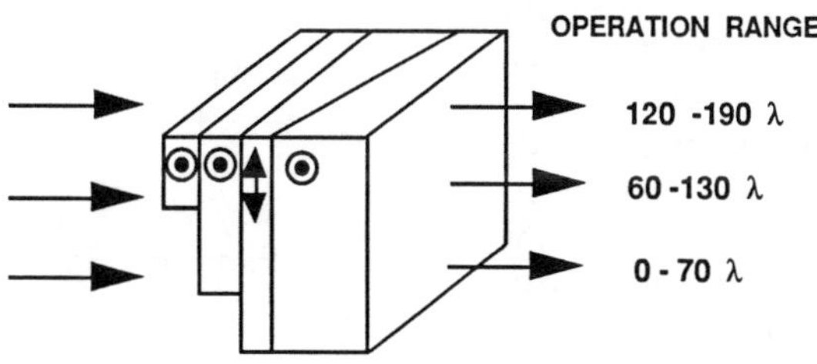

Figure 4. Step delay line for improvement of operation range of electronically scanned sensor.

III. SUMMARY

The novel white-light electronically scanned high hydrostatic pressure sensor presented here has no moving mechanical elements, enables absolute measurement of pressure and is truly insensitive to the light intensity fluctuations in laser source and leading fibers. It is also immune to electromagnetic interference and compatible with industrial data transfer systems that use optical fibers. Due to its satisfactory accuracy and demonstrated temperature stability it will be further tested for application in load evaluation in concrete civil structures.

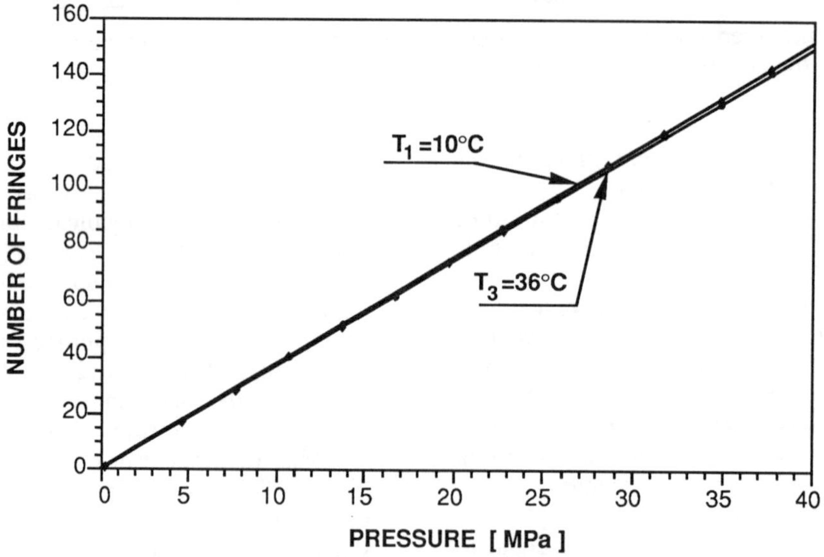

Figure 5. Position of the center of the WLIP as a function of applied pressure. Selected results of calibration carried out for increasing and decreasing pressure at two different temperatures T_1 = 10°C and T_3 = 36°C.

REFERENCES

[1] E. Udd, *Fiber Optic Sensors,* New York: John Wiley & Sons, 1991.

[2] W. J. Bock, M. Beaulieu and A. W. Domanski, IEEE Trans.Instrum.Meas.41, pp. 68-71 (1992).

[3] W. J. Bock, T. R. Wolinski and A. Barwicz, IEEE Trans.Instrum.Meas.39, pp. 715-721 (1990).

[4] V. Gusmeroli, P. Vavassori and M. Martinelli, in *Proceedings of the 6th International Conference OFS'89,* Paris, September 18-20, 1989, pp. 513-518.

[5] W. J. Bock, W. Urbanczyk and M. B. Zaremba, Opt. Comm.(to appear in 1993).

[6] M. Turpin, M. Brevignon, J. P .Le Pesant and O.Gaouditz, in *Proceedings of the 8th International Conference OFS'92,* Monterey, January 29-31, 1992, pp. 362-365.

[7] S. Chen, A. J. Rogers and B. T. Meggitt, Opt.Lett. 16, pp.761-763, (1991).

[8] S. Chen, B. T. Meggitt and A. J. Rogers, Electron. Lett. 26, pp.1367-1368, (1990).

[9] A. Koch and R. Urlich, Sensors and Actuators A25-27, pp.201- (1991).

[10] R. Dandliker, E. Zimmermann, and G. Frosio, in *Proceedings of the 8th International Conference OFS'92,* Monterey, January 29-31, 1992, pp. 53-56.

[11] W. J. Bock, A. W. Domanski and T. R. Wolinski, Appl.Opt. 29, pp. 3484-3488 (1990).

[12] W. J. Bock and W. Urbanczyk, in *Proceedings of the 9th International Conference OFS'93*, Florence, May 4-6, 1993, pp. 135-139.

HIGH PRESSURE DSC SIGNAL AMPLIFICATION USING THERMOPILES

R.A. Secco
Dept. of Geophysics
University of Western Ontario
London, Canada N6A 5B7.

A high pressure DSC method is described. The method is based on the *in-situ* amplification of the thermal signal by means of a thermopile and has been applied to Hg and Bi melting at pressures up to 3.25 GPa in a cubic anvil press.

INTRODUCTION

Enthalpy change, ΔH, is a fundamental thermodynamic quantity of any phase transition. In high temperature (T) calorimetric studies, an absolute measurement of ΔH requires both a thorough knowledge of the thermal properties of the calorimeter components, especially those in direct contact with the sample, and a well-defined and accurately measured T-field. At high pressures (p), however, these requirements are not only intrinsically more difficult to meet, but they are compounded by the pressure (p) dependence of thermal properties in addition to the restrictions on sample and probe sizes imposed by a particular high pressure cell geometry. In high p,T differential thermal analysis, where only the detection of a reaction or transformation as function of p and T is required[1,2], there are less restrictions on sample size than in quantitative high p,T calorimetric studies. In high p,T calorimetry[3,4], in order to ensure the entire sample is subjected to a single set of p,T conditions, the sample size must be reduced. This reduction in size causes a diminution in the endo/exothermic signal produced during a transition since the actual amount of heat, q, entering/leaving the sample is dependent on the sample mass (i.e. q is an extensive property). Determinations of ΔH(p,T) are therefore most frequently obtained using the well known Clapeyron equation

$$\frac{dp}{dT} = \frac{\Delta H}{T\Delta V}$$

since the slope of the phase boundary, dp/dT, can be readily determined by measurement of some physical property or parameter change across the transition and ΔV, the volume change, can be directly measured by x-ray diffraction.

In this report, the differential scanning calorimetry (DSC) method commonly employed at 1 atm is used for measurement of ΔH at high pressures. The thermal signal is amplified *in-situ* by means of a thermopile detector.

EXPERIMENTAL

The experiments were carried out in a cubic anvil press using pyrophyllite as the pressure transmitting medium. A cross-sectional view of the central plane of the pressure cell is shown in Figure 1. As in conventional DSC measurements at 1 atm, a ΔH calibrant is required. The calibrant and sample are contained in separate cavities milled out of a BN disk. A graphite rod through the centre of the disk acts as a heater to produce a radially symmetric T-field in the plane perpendicular to the graphite furnace[5]. The detector is a multi-junctioned differential chromel-alumel (Cr/Al) thermocouple (thermopile) arranged such that half of the junctions lie on a common inner (hot) radius and touch the BN container, while the other half of the junctions lie on a common outer (cold) radius. With n junctions, the detected thermal signal is thereby amplified *in-situ*by a factor of $n/2$. *In-situ* amplification has the distinct advantage over external amplification in

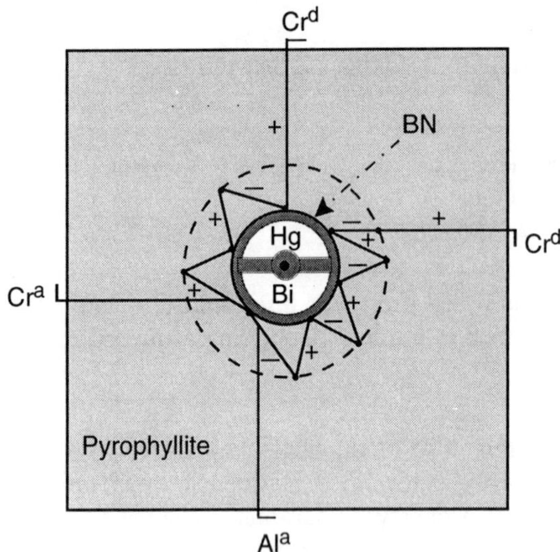

Figure 1. Cross-sectional view of a cubic pressure cell (•graphite rod furnace, Cr^a/Al^a ambient thermocouple, Cr^d/Cr^d thermopile).

that the relative amplitude of noise arising from parasitic potentials on the thermal emf is significantly reduced. The best amplification of the thermal signal is achieved by exploiting the symmetry of the temperature field.

RESULTS AND DISCUSSION

Thermal signals are recorded as differential T and ambient T vs. time for p-induced and T-induced transitions. Comparisons of the thermal signals recorded by a single junction Cr/Al thermocouple and a Cr/Al thermopile are shown for Hg and Bi melting in Figures 2a and 2b respectively. Differential T vs. ambient T plots display a characteristic transition loop, as shown in Figure 3, signifying the higher sensitivity of the thermopile (T_d) compared to the ambient thermocouple (T_a) to incremental or decremental changes in temperature (i.e. dT_d/dT_a is always greater than 1). The well pronounced stationary thermopile response just before the transition, is not clearly indicated by the ambient thermocouple. This is interpreted as a premonitory melting phenomenon.

The analysis involves area measurements of the endo/exotherms by a planimetry or by computer integration methods. The measured

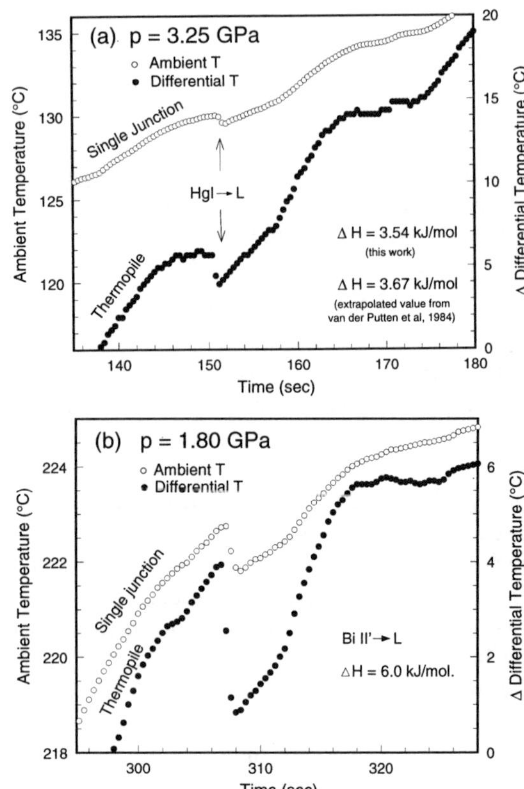

Figure 2. Ambient and differential (thermopile) T records of (a) Hg I melting at p = 3.25 GPa, and (b) Bi II' melting at p = 1.80 GPa.

areas are converted to ΔH values by a scaling factor determined by the transition signal area for a known mass of calibrant whose ΔH value is known either from measurements or from calculations using the Clapeyron equation. The latent heat signal shape and area depends not only on the amount of sample but also on the thermal conductivities as well as their pressure dependences of the BN and pyrophyllite surrounding media through which the heat pulse travels. Although there are some data on these materials[6-8], they are not required if calibration is made at p,T conditions similar to those of investigation (i.e. if appropriate calibrants are chosen).

The method was initially applied to the HgI→L at 3.25 GPa and to BiII'→L at 1.80 GPa based on ΔH measurements of Hg melting by van der Putten et al[9]. The linear fit to their data up to 1.0 GPa

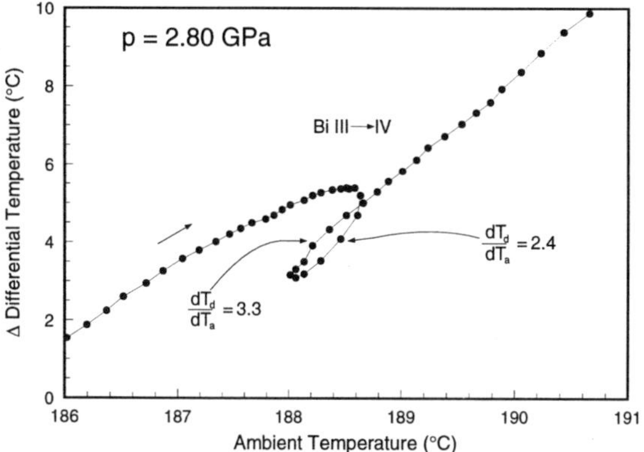

Figure 3. Characteristic transition loop of a differential (thermopile) T versus ambient T plot through the Bi IV melting transition at p = 2.80 GPa.

(i.e. their equation (3)) is extrapolated for comparison with the measurement of ΔH at 3.25 GPa from this work and shown in Figure 4 along

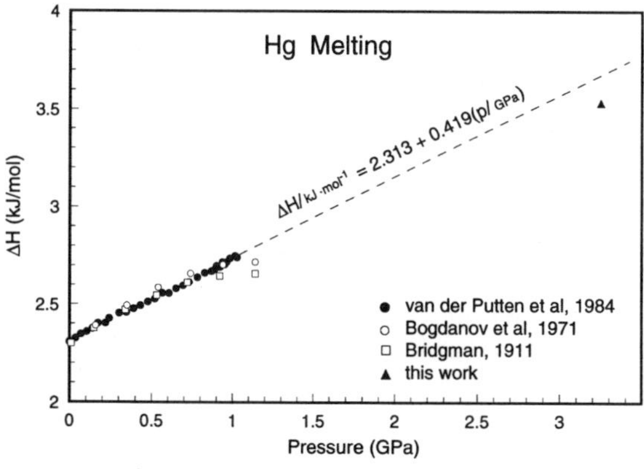

Figure 4. Pressure dependence of the transition enthalpy of Hg melting. The dashed line is an extrapolation of the linear fit to van der Putten et al[9] data only (i.e. their equation (3)).

with results from previous studies[10,11]. Based on the same calibration, $\Delta H_{BiII' \to L}$ has been determined to be 6.0 kJ/mol at p = 1.80 GPa.

The high pressure DSC method described here can be applied to much higher p and T than in this study and, in principle, to a variety of different high pressure apparatus provided the thermopile junction distribution exploits the symmetry of the temperature field to maximize the amplification of the thermal signal. The *in-situ* amplification of the heat pulse from a transforming sample is particularly well-suited to very small sample quantities which are often used to improve the sample p and T homogeneity or when limited quantities of synthesized high pressure phases are available.

ACKNOWLEDGEMENTS

This work was supported by a Natural Sciences and Engineering Research Council of Canada operating grant. I thank H.H. Schloessin for commenting on the manuscript, R. Tucker for technical help, M. Rice for typing the manuscript; and A. Bukata for help with preparation of the figures.

REFERENCES

[1] Z. Wang, H. Xie, Y. Chang and H. Xu, "Ultra-high Pressure Differential Thermal Analysis of Diasporite", *Chinese Sci. Bull.* 36, no. 18, pp.1545-1548 (1991).

[2] M. Kanzaki,"Dehydration of Brucite ($Mg(OH)_2$) at High Pressures Detected by Differential Thermal Analysis", *Geophys. Res. Letts.* 18, no. 12, pp.2189-2192 (1991).

[3] R.A. Secco, "Geophysical Property Studies at Upper Mantle Pressures and Temperatures" presented at the Cdn. Wkshp. on High Pressure Science and Technology, Vancouver, B.C., Sept. 28-29, 1992.

[4] R.P. Rapp and A. Navrotsky, "Differential Scanning Calorimeter in a Piston-Cylinder Apparatus", presented at Amer. Geophys.

Union Mtg., San Francisco, CA, Dec. 7-11, 1992.

[5] H.H. Schloessin and P.F. Lenson, "Measurement and Modelling of the Temperature Field in high p,T Experiments Assembled in Cubes with Internal Heating", *High Temp. High Press.* 21, pp.275-285 (1989).

[6] A.E. Carte, "Thermal Constants of Pyrophyllite and Their Change on Heating", *Brit. J. Appl. Phys.* 6, pp.326-328 (1955).

[7] Y.S. Touloukian, ed. *Thermophysical Properties of High Temperature Solid Materials*, New York, MacMillan Co., 1967, v.5, p.505.

[8] K-I. Horai and J-I. Susaki, "The Effects of Pressure on the Thermal Conductivity of Silicate Rocks up to 12 kbar", *Phys. Earth Planet. Int.* 55, pp.292-305 (1989).

[9] L. van der Putten, J.A. Schouten and N.J. Trappeniers, "Determination of the Heat of Transition of Mercury up to 10 kbar by Means of Differential Scanning Calorimetry", *High Temp. High Press.* 16, pp.281-288 (1984).

[10] V.S. Bogdanov, Y.L. Levin, S.S. Sekoyan, and Y.I. Shmin, "On Application of Mercury Melting Curve for Accurate High-Pressure Measurements", in NBS Spec.Pub. *Accurate Characterization of the High Pressure Environment*, ed. E.C. Lloyd, 1971, pp.297-302.

[11] P.W. Bridgman, "Mercury, Liquid and Solid, Under Pressure", *Proc. Am. Acad. Sci.* 47, pp.347-438 (1911).

REAL-TIME EVALUATION OF PRESSURE USING THE PRESSURE EFFECT ON EMF OF THERMOCOUPLES

M.Wakatsuki, K.J.Takano, H.Kagi, T.Yuino and S.Kumagai
Institute of Materials Science
University of Tsukuba
Tsukuba, Ibaraki 305, Japan

Evaluation of pressure based on the pressure effect on EMF of thermocouples has a great potential for monitoring the pressure within a high pressure apparatus during synthesis of materials in high temperature-high pressure environments. A trial has been made to realize a real-time sensing system of pressure, on the basis of precise measurement of thermal EMF and rapid processing of the data with a personal computer. The K-type (chromel/alumel) and the S-type (Pt/Pt10%Rh) thermocouples are employed. A quadratic formula is constructed by fitting it to available data of the pressure effects, and used to generate the pressure from two apparent temperatures, Tk and Ts, measured on a common junction embedded in the pressure space. Systematic errors in ΔT (= Tk - Ts), originated from the combination of the measuring instruments and the thermocouple wires used, are corrected, and random errors are eliminated by a statistical treatment of the pressure outputs. The present trial results in output of pressure with a period of a few seconds to a few minutes, and a sensitivity of 0.03GPa for detecting pressure change, when it is evaluated at a constant temperature in a particular sample.

INTRODUCTION

In material synthesis at high-temperature high pressure, the reaction pressure is only estimated through the hydraulic pressure loaded on the apparatus. The pressure inside of an apparatus changes gradually during the material-forming reaction. On the other hand, there are many cases in which the reactions are pressure-sensitive. A seeded growth of diamond with a carbon source of graphite pretreated for suppressing spontaneous nucleation, and crystallization of metastable graphite together with a diamond crystal under growth by the temperature-gradient process are typical examples, in which the main reactions are seriously affected by a rather small change in pressure[1,2].

Bundy[3], Hanneman and Strong[4,5], and Hanneman, Strong and Bundy[6] reported the pressure effects on EMF's in details for several kinds of thermocouples, and showed the possibility of simaltaneous and continuous in situ measurement of pressure and temperature on the basis of the pressure effect on EMF's of thermocouples.

In the present study, we try to construct a pressure-sensing system. The system should have a "real-time" nature, which is accomplished by the use of a personal computer to process measured data automatically and rapidly. Type-K (chromel/alumel) and type-S (Pt/Pt10%Rh) thermocouples are used because detailed data are reported on their behaviors at high pressure. A pressure standard, expressed with a simple formula to enable the computer-processing, is formed with its coefficients determined according to the data reported by Hanneman et al. The accuracy of evaluating pressure is also an important factor for such a system, because the pressure effect on the EMF is small. Efforts are also made to keep reasonable accuracy in temperature measurement. Possibility of a real-time sensing is confirmed in the present study, and the sensitivity of detecting change in pressure is also examined.

METHODS

Pressure Standard

The absolute pressure effects on the thermocouples employed here are given by Hanneman et al[6] as relations of δTk versus Tk at several pressures, and δTs versus Ts at several pressures, as well. δTk is difference between the true temperature, T, and the apparent temperature, Tk (δTk = T - Tk). And the same, for the type-S thermocouple. Those data are reconstructed into a relation easy for use.

$$\Delta T = Tk - Ts = \delta Ts - \delta Tk \quad (1)$$

The reconstructed relations are shown in Fig. 1. These curves are fitted by a quadratic form,

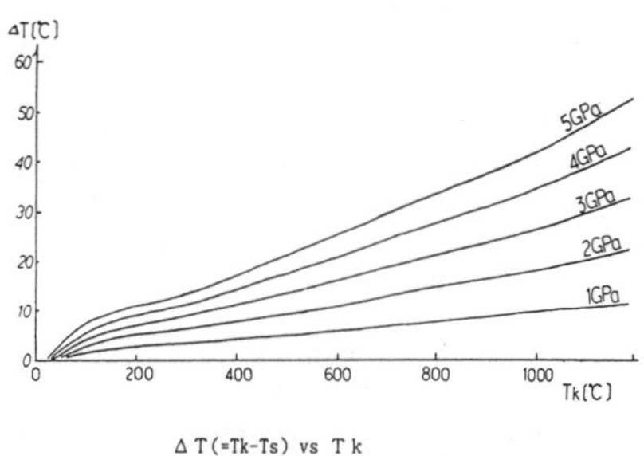

Figure 1. The pressure standard constructed from the available data on the type-K and the type-S thermocouples.

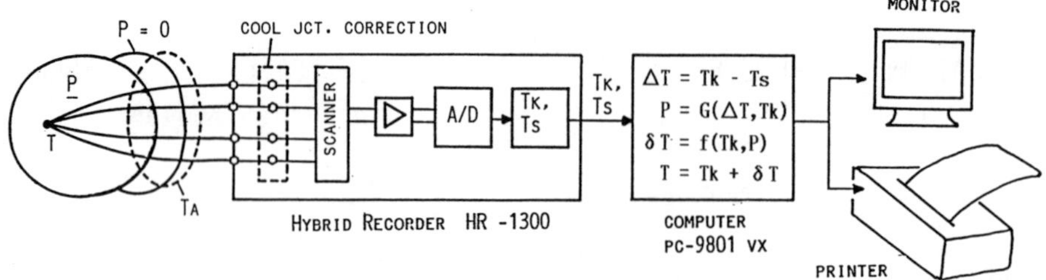

Figure 2. Construction of a real-time, pressure-sensing system.

$$\Delta T = F(Tk, P) = U(Tk)\cdot P^2 + V(Tk)\cdot P + W(Tk) \quad (2)$$

where,

$$U(Tk) = u2\cdot Tk^2 + u1\cdot Tk + u0$$
$$V(Tk) = v2\cdot Tk^2 + v1\cdot Tk + v0 \quad (3)$$
$$W(Tk) = w2\cdot Tk^2 + w1\cdot Tk + w0$$

The temperatute, Tk, is devided into seven regions, and nine coefficients in the equation (3) are determined for each of the devided regions, by the least square method for the best fit between the equation (2) and the data of Fig. 1. Then an inverse function of the equation (2),

$$P = G(\Delta T, Tk) = A(Tk)\cdot \Delta T^2 + B(Tk)\cdot \Delta T + C(Tk) \quad (4)$$

is derived, where

$$A(Tk) = a2\cdot Tk^2 + a1\cdot Tk + a0$$
$$B(Tk) = b2\cdot Tk^2 + b1\cdot Tk + b0 \quad (5)$$
$$C(Tk) = c2\cdot Tk^2 + c1\cdot Tk + c0$$

The nine coefficients in the equation (5) are derived from the nine coefficients in the equation (3), for each of the devided region of Tk.

The computer selects values of the nine coefficients in the equation (5), according to the input value of Tk. It also genarates ΔT, and the pressure,P, is calculated.

δTk, as a function of Tk and P, can also be expressed and calculated in the same manner as described above. The absolute correction, δTk, however, is very small (less than 4°C), and Tk can stand for the true temperature, for a practical purpose.

Degradation of the thermocouple material will result in change of the EMF, which can not be dis tinguished from a true change in pressure. Especially, chromel and alumel wires require to be used at temperatures below 1000°C. It is planned, in the present study, to use them at temperatures up to about 800°C with a margin of 200°C. The hot junction may be embedded in the solid pressure-medium, but apart from the heater, if a practical synthesis requires a higher temperature.

Construction of The System

The pressure-sensing system is composed of a temperature-measuring element and a data-processing part. Figure 2 shows its construction. Two thermo couples, having a common hot junction and lead out of a high pressure apparatus, are connected to Hybrid Recorder, HR-1300. It can evaluate Tk and Ts, and transfer them as digital quantities to the computer, through a GPIB interface. The computer calculate the pressure, P, according to the equations (5) and (4).

The calculated results are put out with a period. The minimum of the period was limited to six seconds by Hybrid Recorder. However, pressure drift in a high pressure apparatus, or correction of the press load may take a much longer time, compared to this period. Thus, an effectively real-time sensing is realized.

Another roll of the computer is to reduce errors of a random nature. Calculated pressure values are stored in RAM, and a number, n (one hundred, for ex ample) of the values in the past are used to predict a most plausible value (Pm) for that instant. The prediction is based on the least square fitting of a parabolic curve to the number (n) of P's in the past Thus, two series of pressure values, P and Pm, are put out in each of the period. Pm's showed a scattering width much smaller than that of P's.

A spurious ΔT at atmospheric pressure, caused by the temperature-measuring part including thermocouple wires used, was observed as seen in Figure 3, and was cancelled in calculating (Tk - Ts).

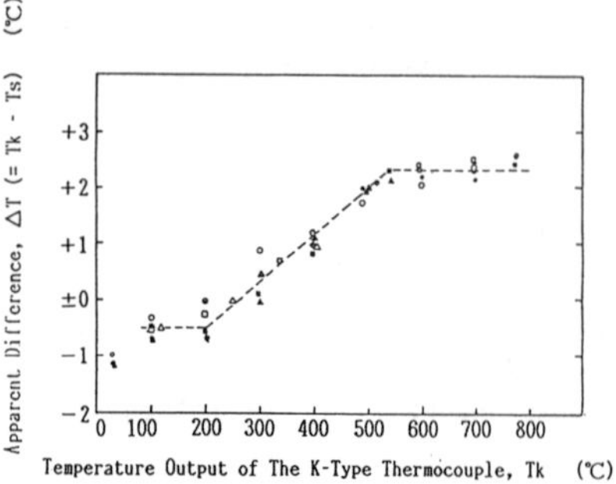

Figure 3. A spurious ΔT.

EXPERIMENTS AND RESULTS

Experiments with A Cubic Anvil Apparatus

Figure 4 shows the central part of a typical arrangement of samples, used with a cubic anvil apparatus[1]. This part was contained in a graphite tube heater. The common junction is embedded in hBN, and the thermocouple wires, 0,35mm thick, are insulated from the heater by alumina tubes (1ϕx0.4ϕ). The wires are lead out through edges of the cubic sample holder, to the atmospheric space.

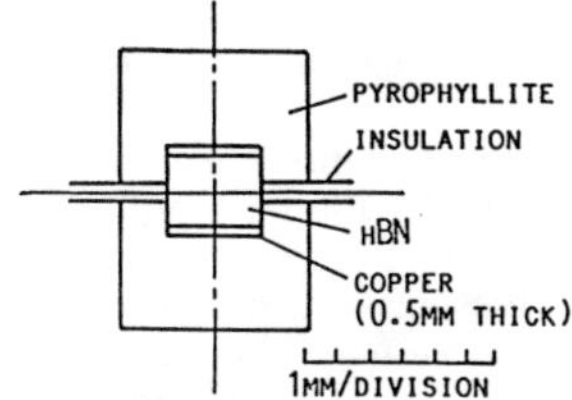

Figure 4. Sample arrangement.

A sample was pressurized to a press load which corresponded to a pressure around 2.7GPa. Then, it is heated to a temperature, for example, of 6oo°C, and the pressure was evaluated at this condition. After it, the press load was raised to another level and the pressure evaluation was repeated, while the heating condition was kept unchanged. The evaluated pressure values were put out repeatedly with a period of 6 seconds, and illustrated on the monitor as a graph of pressure versus time. Such a graph were printed out on a printer, when needed. Measured data of Tk, Ts and calculated pressures were stored, once in each period, into a hard-disk file.

The evaluated pressure showed a random scatter with a width of about 0.2GPa. But observing them for a few minutes allowed determination of an averaged value. In Figure 5 are shown typical results with the cubic anvil apparatus. A broken line is a calibration curve based on the conventional method.

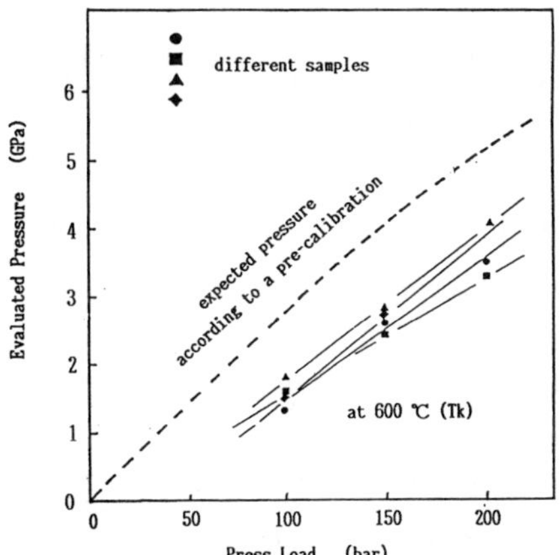

Figure 5. Experimental results with a cubic anvil apparatus.

Figure 5 shows, at first, that there are scattering of the evaluated pressure from sample to sample with a rather large width (as much as about 1GPa). On the other hand, within each of particular samples, the evaluated pressure showed reasonable response according to the press load change. Another problem is that the evaluated pressures were only from 60 to 70 % of those expected by pre-calibration. Experiments were also made at 500°C and 700°C, with results essentially the same as those at 600°C.

Although there are problems left in determining pressure absolutely, results of Figure 5 clearly show a possibility of detecting a small change of pressure within one sample, with temperature kept constant. An application, at this poit of view, of the present technique was made, in which Tk was raised in two minutes to 750°C after being kept at 600°C, and the pressure was recorded. The press load was kept at 150 bars, which corresponded to an expected pressure of 4.2GPa. The result is shown in Figure 6.

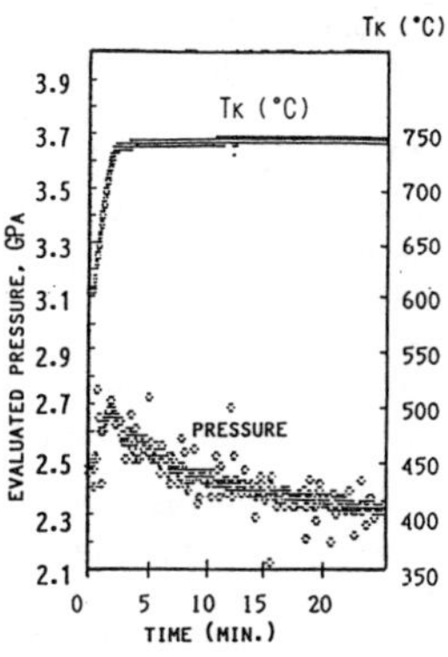

Figure 6. Change of the evaluated pressure after Tk is changed.

The pressure increased at first, and then it decreased slowly. This change may partly be apparent, being caused by the temperature change. However, rearrangement of the temperature distribution in a sample assembly for this apparatus, with water-cooled anvils, is expected to be accomplished at least within ten minutes. Therefore, the long-tailing small change of the evaluated pressure corresponds, possibly, to an actual change of pressure. For example, change of 0.07GPa can be read in the figure between 10 and 20 minutes, though the scattering width of 0.2GPa is much larger than the change.

Experiments with A Piston-Cylinder Apparatus

Similar experiments were made using a piston-cylinder apparatus with a bore of 19mm in diameter, up to a pressure of 2GPa. The thermocouple wires of 0.2mm thick were used. Results obtained were qualitatively the same as those described above. In this case, however, the evaluated pressures, averaged of their scatter, were in improved agreement with the expected pressure.

The reduction of the random errors (scatter) of the evaluated pressure were tried in experiments with the piston-cylinder apparatus. The last one hundred data of the evaluated pressures were stored in RAM, the oldest value being expired at storage of the newest one. The most plausible value of the pressure, Pm, was calculated for the newest instant, using those one hundred data as described previously. Such a statistical process took a time of about one second or shorter. The values of pressure, P's, each evaluated from only one set of Tk and Ts, showed a random scatter of a width of about 0.2GPa. The similar pattern is shown in Figure 6. On the other hand, Pm's showed a scattering width of only 0.03GPa.

DISCUSSIONS

The put-out period of six seconds enables response to change of pressure within a usual high pressure apparatus during the material-forming reaction. The calculation process for eliminating the random errors does not affect this real-time, or virtual real-time nature.

Problems of the accuracy in evaluating pressure can be divided into two categories. In the first, absolute determination of pressure is affected by the spurious ΔT and correction for the temperature (Ta in Figure 2) at which thermocouple wires are lead out to the atmospheric space. The spurious ΔT may most likely be caused by a temperature gradient at the common hot junction. According to the pressure standard adopted in this study, a spurious ΔT of 1 degree generates a spurious pressure of around 0.2GPa in a region of Tk from 600°C to 800°C. ing the common junction using thermocouple wires as thin as possible, The sample used with the piston-cylinder apparatus should be better in this point.

Correction for Ta, being not 0°C, has not yet been accomplished in the present study. But it is expected to be a decrease of the evaluated value by around 20%, according to measurement of an effective value for Ta.

Secondly, relative determination of pressure also has a great meaning for practical application, even though the absolute determination is not accomplished. That is, if a small change or drift in pressure is detected with a sufficient reproducibility, the change can be corrected and stable keeping of the pressure and temperature condition is realized. High relative accuracy should be essentially based on constant heating condition, to avoid the influence of the spurious ΔT. Data in the present study show stable sensitivity for pressure change. There is no experimental sign of factors negative for the reproducibility, at present, although it should be confirmed by comparing the evaluated pressure to some reliable, and independently obtained value of the pressure.

The most effective factor for the real-time, and high sensitivity detection is the narrowed width of the random scattering in evaluated pressure, because a change can be recognized only when it is exceeds the scattering width.

In application of the present technique to a case of actual synthesis, the common junction should be located outside of the heater, where a large temperature gradient exists and may result in disadvantage of a large spurious ΔT. On the other hand, degradation of thermocouple wires can be avoided by the lowered maximum temperature.

CONCLUSIONS

A real-time technique was realized for evaluating pressure generated within a high pressure apparatus, on the basis of the dual thermocouple method. Absolutely determined pressure valued showed large discrepancies from expected values, though possibility of future development is kept. On the other hand, the evaluated pressure showed a reasonable response to change of the press load, which makes one expect the technique to be used in detecting relative change of the pressure. A real-time or "predictive" smoothing of the scattered output of pressure was also tried and resulted in substantial suppress of the scattering width. It is possible to detect a pressure change of 0.03GPa, at present.

Acknowledgments

The present study was supported by Grant-in-Aid for Scientific Research on Priority Area, The Ministry of Education, Science and Culture, 03204003 and 04204002.

REFERENCES

[1] M. Wakatsuki and K. J. Takano, High Pressure Research in Mineral Physics, ed. by M. H. Manghnani and Y. Syono, Tokyo, TERRAPUB, 1987, pp. 203-207

[2] M. Wakatsuki, Recent Trends in High Pressure Researches, ed. by A. K. Singh, New Delhi, Oxford & IBH, 1992, pp. 671-675

[3] F. P. Bundy, J. Appl. Phys., 33, pp. 483-488 (1961)

[4] R. E. Hanneman and H. M. Strong, J. Appl. Phys., 36, pp. 523-526 (1965)

[5] R. E. Hanneman and H. M. Strong, J. Appl. Phys., 37, pp. 612-614 (1966)

[6] R. E. Hanneman, H. M. Strong and F. P. Bundy, Accurate Characterization of The High-Pressure Environment, ed. by E. C. Lloyd, Washington, D. C., NBS Spec. Publ. 326, 1969, pp. 53-62

COMPARATIVE STUDIES OF ROTATING ANODE AND SYNCHROTRON-BASED IMAGE PLATE SYSTEMS

P.D. Hatton and J. Crain

Department of Physics, The University of Edinburgh, James Clerk Maxwell Building, King's Buildings, Edinburgh, EH9 3JZ, UK.

and

H.Kawamura and Y.Akahama

Department of Materials Science, Himeji Institute of Technology, Himeji, Japan.

A series of experiments have been performed on a rotating anode x-ray source using Mo Ka radiation and an image plate area detector. The results are compared to those obtained on a synchrotron source. It is found that the performance of the image plate in conjunction with the rotating anode and conical aperture diamond-anvil-cells yields data quality which is comparable to that obtained on the synchrotron. The samples studied included La_2CuO_4, $SrTi0_3$ and InSb. Very weak features of the diffraction patterns of these samples were observable both in and out of pressure cells without the need for substantial increase in exposure time.

INTRODUCTION

The application of an image plate (IP) system in conjunction with a synchrotron radiation source for high-pressure x-ray powder diffraction has been the subject of much recent attention [1,2,3,4]. In particular, the potential benefits of such a system over conventional scanning detectors have been exploited in recent investigations of pressure-induced structural phase transitions in several III-V semiconductors [5]. In those experiments, extremely weak and subtle features of the diffraction patterns in the high-pressure phases of these materials were observed for the first time in a diamond-anvil pressure cell (DAC). In addition to making definitive structural solutions of high-pressure phases, long-range site ordering of the atoms in several high-pressure forms was investigated even in the semiconductor InSb which contains nearly isoelectronic constituent atoms. These studies led to renewed motivation for density functional total energy calculations on previously unreported phases [6] and a detailed investigation of defect formation at structural phase transitions [7].

In principle, a synchrotron-based IP system would be preferred to any conventional laboratory system such as a rotating anode for reasons such as beam intensity and the capability to tune wavelength. In practice, however, the advantages of a synchrotron source lead to intensecompetition for experimental time on central facilities and a severely restricted operating schedule. In addition, the complexity of synchrotron maintenance may result in unpredictable beamline shutdowns for indefinite periods. In light of these considerations it would be of great interest to determine exactly what can be achieved on a conventional laboratory-based rotating anode source (RAS) and whether for at least some applications it would be a viable alternative to a central synchrotron facility.

In this work, the diffraction patterns of several materials have been collected using angle-dispersive powder diffraction at high or ambient pressure on the Synchrotron Radiation Source (SRS) at Daresbury Laboratory and using Mo-Kα radiation of a RAS. In addition, several studies are performed on InSb using a RAS which extend the results and conclusions obtained previously at the SRS.

EXPERIMENTAL

The details of the experimental arrangement have been discussed elsewhere but a brief description of the essential points is given in this section. For the RAS experiments, a MAC Science rotating anode was used with a 0.3×3 mm focal spot size viewed at 6 degrees. Typical settings for operating voltage and current were 60 KV and 90 mA (5.4 KW) respectively. The beamline optics design incorporates a flat pyrolytic graphite monochromator (rocking curve approximately 0.3 degrees) and two-slit collimation which defines exiting beam size of between 80 and 125 μm. A commercial image plate scanner was located approximately 200mm from the sample.

The synchrotron experiments were performed on the powder diffraction station 9.1 of the SRS which uses radiation from a 5-Tesla wiggler magnet. Wavelength selection was made with a Si($1\bar{1}1$) water-cooled, channel-cut monochromator which allows wavelengths to be chosen between 0.4Å and 2Å. The intrinsic peak width of the synchrotron data is limited neither by the Si-monochromator rocking curve width nor the beam divergence, but by the IP scanning process. This process is common to both the SRS and RAS techniques and involves tracking a focussed laser beam across the IP surface to create photostimulated luminescence of x-ray induced colour centres. The Gaussian width of the focussed laser beam defines the pixel size of the image. This is approximately 88 μm^2 for the Molecular Dynamics 400A reader used for the SRS data and 125 μm^2 for the MAC Science DIP 100 used at Himeji. The colour centres are formed during exposure of the plates to x-ray radiation and represent a latent image of the diffraction pattern. The photons which are released during the scanning process are collected by a fibre-optic bundle and passed to a photomultiplier. The resulting spatial resolution is limited by bleed which is caused by stray laser light contacting adjoining pixels. It can be masked effectively except in the direction of the scan. The measured intrinsic peak width for SRS diffraction profiles is typically 5-7 pixels (FWHM) and is independent of the distance between sample and IP. A diagram of the IP scanning process is shown in Figure 1.

Due to the high intensity and low divergence of synchrotron radiation it is possible to employ perfect Si(111) monochromators with rocking curve widths of only a few millidegrees. This provides the basis for the extremely high resolution experiments undertaken there, which are difficult in the laboratory. However, the intrinsic resolution of the image plate detector means that we can considerably increase the incident flux by employing wider band pass monochromators without pattern degradation. This accounts for the success of the experiments at Himeji. The graphite monochromator has a rocking curve width approximately 100 times that of Si(111) and thus is better matched to the source divergence and the image plate resolution. In practice, the graphite (0001) monochromator resolution is slightly poorer than optimal, resulting in a slight increase of peak width. The graphite monochromator passes both $K\alpha_1$ and $K\alpha_2$ and this results in a slightly distorted peak profile. This is most evident at the highest scattering angles in which they are better separated. Nevertheless, the data obtained at Himeji are excellent and they represent a considerable advance for high-pressure crystallography.

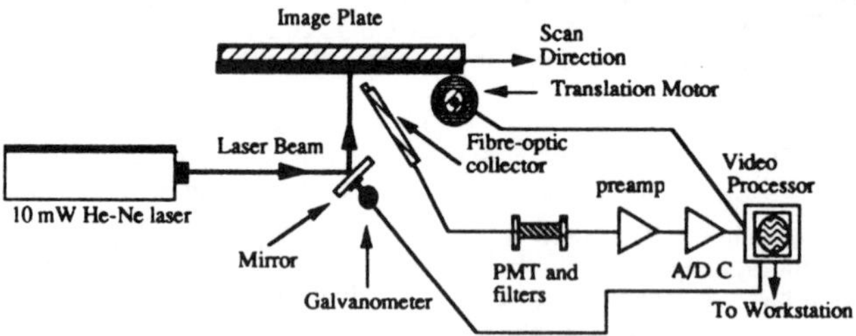

Figure 1. The image plate scanning process 20×25 cm image plates are scanned with a 10 mW He-Ne laser by means of a galvanometer-controlled mirror assembly. The Gaussian beam is focused to a spot of 88 μm at the plane of the phosphor plate which defines the "pixel size" of the image. It takes approximately 50 μsec for the laser to traverse one pixel. A DEC-5200 workstation is used for image manipulation and data analysis.

RESULTS AND DISCUSSION

General

Before discussion of the results obtained for specific materials several general observations can be made. It is found that the overall background level of the RAS datasets is lower than that obtained from the SRS. This is presumably due to the higher levels of hard ambient radiation at a synchrotron which requires more extensive shielding to attenuate. The accurate determination of lattice parameters using the IP method is also found to be more straightforward when used with a RAS. The use of a fixed, known wavelength simplifies the situation encountered at a synchrotron in which both the wavelength and sample to IP distance are variable. At a synchrotron, the wavelength calibration has to be checked regularly as it is dependent on the angle that the photons of the white beam strike the monochromator and hence is susceptible to electron beam movements in the storage ring.

The pattern quality is far superior to that obtained by energy-dispersive techniques and is sufficient for crystallographic refinement even in large and complex structures.

La_2CuO_4

Figure 2 is the diffraction pattern q from a sample of La_2CuO_4. The crystal structure of this material is orthorhombically distorted below T=533 K. The structural transition to the high-temperature tetragonal phase is characterised by two order parameters which describe the tilt of the CuO_6 octahedra and the distortion from tetragonal. The diffraction pattern of the orthorhombic phase differs from that of the tetragonal phase in only subtle features. Orthorhombic superstructure reflections have an intensity only 0.2% of that of the strongest reflection. A 30 minute exposure using the RAS and an IP allowed for clear observation of this reflection. The peaks split by the orthorhombic distortion could not be resolved though they have a measured width 55% greater than that of singlet reflections.

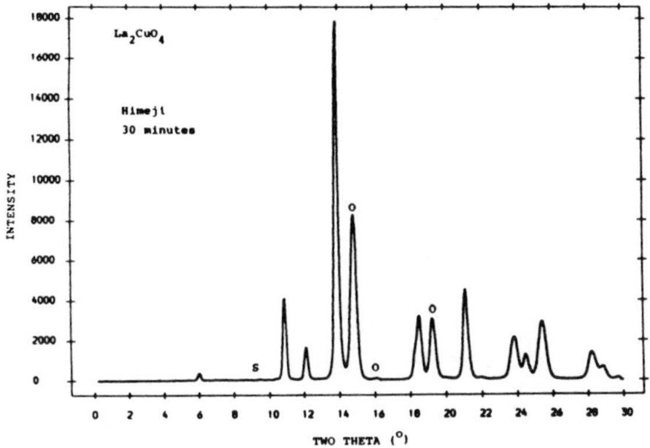

Figure 2. A diffraction pattern obtained from La_2CuO_4 at ambient pressure in a gasketted Merill-Bassett diamond anvil cell. The pattern was obtained in 30 minutes using Mo Kα x-rays from a laboratory-based rotating anode generator. The peaks marked 'O' are split due to the orthorhombic distortion. Although the splitting cannot be directly observed such peaks are ~55% wider than singlet peaks. The peak marked 's' is a weak superstructure reflection which is further evidence of the orthorhombic distortion.

Figure 3. A comparison of diffraction patterns obtained from InSb using a synchrotron and a laboratory-based x-ray source. The sample (in the P4 orthorhombic structure) is a 3-5 GPa in a gasketted Merill-Bassett diamond anvil cell. The top trace was obtained in 2.5 hours at the SRS using a wavelength of 0.71 Å. The lower profile was obtained in 45 minutes at Himeji. The insert shows the weak difference reflection caused by the residual difference in atomic scattering factors between In and Sb.

InSb

Figure 3 shows a comparison between SRS and RAS data obtained on the same sample of InSb in a conical aperture DAC at 3.5 GPa. The top trace was obtained in 2.5 hours on the SRS. The lower profile was obtained in 45 minutes using the RAS. The resolution and signal to noise ratios are clearly sufficient and the RAS data displays only a slightly increased peak width and signal to noise ratio. The inset of Figure 2 shows a weak reflection arising from the difference in atomic scattering factors between the nearly isoelectronic In and Sb atoms.

Motivated by the fact that recent ab initio density functional calculations underestimated the observed transition pressure (P_t) [6] for the zincblende to body-centred orthorhombic structural phase transition [5] by over 50%, a study of the reverse transition back to the zincblende structure was made using the IP-RAS method to investigate hysteresis effects. On the upstroke, P_t was measured to be approximately 23 kbar ± 2 kbar however reconversion to the zincblende structure was not observed to begin until 15 kbar. The reverse transition was not complete until pressure was reduced to approximately 12 kbar. The theoretical value of P_t was reported to be 11.5 kbar, a result gratifyingly close to that experimentally obtained.

Finally, the image from which Figure 3 is obtained is shown in Figure 4. It is composed ofspots from large crystallites. Our ability to secure accurate relative intensities for the individual reflections relied on having a sufficient number of spots in each ring. The increased source divergence of a rotating-anode generator results in a far larger number of crystallites being in the reflection condition - hence improving the powder averaging. This is particularly important for experiments at the highest pressures, that is in excess of 100 GPa, where the sample size is necessarily extremely small.

$SrTiO_3$

Figure 5 shows an integration of an image of strontium titanate $SrTiO_3$. This material represents a 'worst case' specimen for the RAS system. Strontium is strongly fluorescent at the wavelength of MoKα radiation. This causes a high but uniform background. Also, $SrTiO_3$ is susceptible to severe pressure broadening caused by powder particles bridging across the DAC. This results in nonhydrostatic shear stresses. Nevertheless it is still

Figure 4. The two-dimensional image obtained from InSb at 3.5 GPa. Azimuthal integration around the Debye-Scherrer rings leads to a one-dimensional profile similar to that of Figure 3. The spotty nature of the image is evidence of the existence of large crystallites.

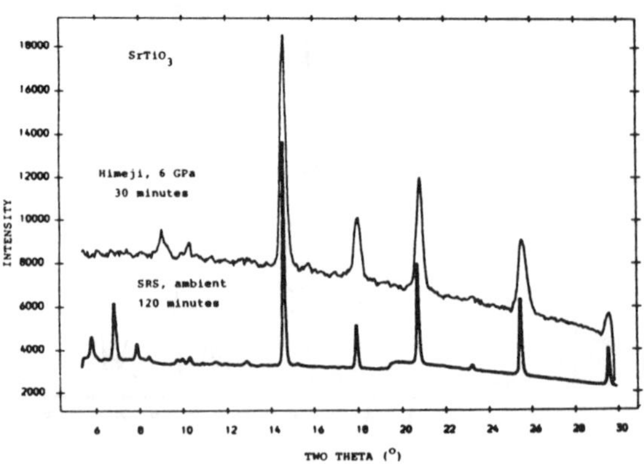

Figure 5. Diffraction patterns obtained from $SrTiO_3$ using a laboratory RAS (top trace) and a synchrotron source. The peak broadening at 6 GPa is evidence of severe bridging between particles resulting in non-hydrostaticity.

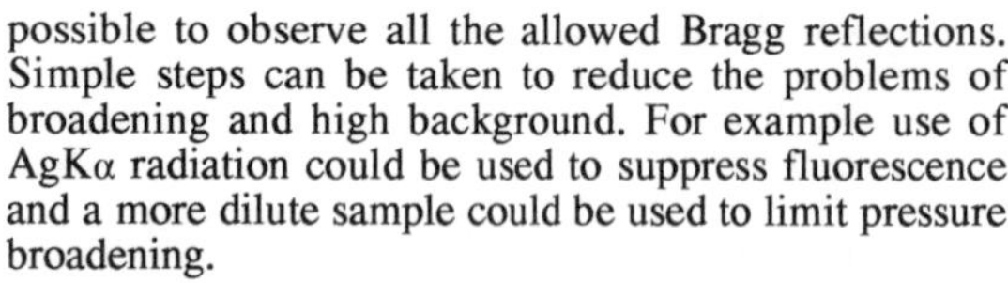

possible to observe all the allowed Bragg reflections. Simple steps can be taken to reduce the problems of broadening and high background. For example use of $AgK\alpha$ radiation could be used to suppress fluorescence and a more dilute sample could be used to limit pressure broadening.

SUMMARY AND CONCLUSIONS

Clearly, a synchrotron radiation source has many advantages over a laboratory-based rotating anode source. In addition to collimation and intensity, synchrotron radiation is tuneable which is essential for anomalous scattering experiments. The purpose of these experiments was to estimate the usefulness of a RAS system - both as a testing and development adjunct to a synchrotron based programme, but also as an alternative for preliminary studies on crystallographically simple materials. Our results clearly demonstrate that image plate detectors can be employed with laboratory based x-ray sources to provide high quality angle-dispersive data suitable for Rietveld refinement.

Recent results such as a study of C_{70} using a sealed source [8]; experiments on silicon up to 47 GPa [9] and studies of sulphur up to 90 GPa [10] demonstrate that angle-dispersive studies need not be restricted to synchrotrons but can be far more widely applied.

REFERENCES

[1] R J Nelmes, P D Hatton, M I McMahon, R O Piltz, J Crain, R J Cernik and G Bushnell-Wye, Rev. Sci. Instrum., **63**, 1039 (1992)

[2] R O Piltz, M I McMahon, J Crain, P D Hatton, R J Nelmes, R J Cernik and G Bushnell-Wye, Rev. Sci. Instrum., **63**, 700 (1992)

[3] Y Akahama, M Kobayashi and H Kawamura, Phys Rev **B47** 20 (1993)

[4] Y Fujii, K Hose, Y Ohishi, H Fujihisa, N Hamaya, K Kikegawa, Y Amemiya and T Matsushita, Phys. Rev. Lett., **63**, 536 (1989)

[5] R J Nelmes, M I McMahon, P D Hatton, J Crain and R O Piltz, Phys. Rev. B**47**, 35 (1993)

[6] G Y Guo, J Crain, P Blaha and W M Temmerman, Phys Rev B**47**, 4841, (1993)

[7] J Crain, G J Ackland, R O Piltz and P D Hatton, Phys. Rev. Lett. **70** 814 (1993)

[8] H Kawamura, M Kobayashi, Y Akahama, H Shinohara, H Sato and Y Saito, Solid St. Commun. **83**, 563 (1992)

[9] P D Hatton, J Crain, R O Piltz, H Kawamura and Y Akahama, to be published.

[10] Y Akahama, M Kobayashi and H Kawamura, Phys Rev B. In Press (1993)

RESPONSE OF INCLINED ELECTROMAGNETIC PARTICLE VELOCITY GAUGES IN SHOCKED LIQUIDS†

R.L. Gustavsen, S.A. Sheffield, and R.R. Alcon
Los Alamos National Laboratory
Group M-7, MS P952
Los Alamos, NM 87545

Multi-element electromagnetic particle velocity gauges are made by sandwiching aluminum conductive elements between sheets of Teflon. The 60 µm thick membrane is then placed in the liquid sample at an angle so that particle velocities are measured at multiple depths. In this paper we report particle velocity measurements in the liquids nitromethane, bromoform and diiodomethane using Teflon gauges inclined to the shock front by 0, 10, 20, and 30 degrees. The particle velocity measured by the inclined gauges was either higher or lower than the "correct" particle velocity measured by non inclined gauges. The error in the measured particle velocity is a function both of the relative impedance of the liquid and Teflon membrane, and of the angle of the gauge to the shock front. Measured velocities can be in error by ± 10% for gauges inclined 30°. Analysis shows that some of the error is caused by the liquid slipping past the Teflon membrane.

INTRODUCTION

Since its introduction by Vorthman and Wackerle[1] in the early 1980s, the inclined multi-element electromagnetic particle velocity (EMV) gauge has provided a convenient way to measure particle velocity at as many as 10 Lagrangian positions in a single gas gun driven shock experiment. These gauges are robust enough that they are often used to study the initiation of explosives.

Sheffield, Engelke, and Alcon[2] were the first to use inclined multi-element EMV gauges in liquids. While studying the initiation properties of liquid nitromethane (NM), they noticed that in the non reacting "inert" part of the NM flow, the particle velocities measured by the inclined gauges were about 10% lower than expected.

Concern that the gauges were not measuring particle velocity properly in liquids, and hence might also be in error in solids has prompted the present study. Our goals were to calibrate the errors in the measured particle velocity as a function of gauge angle and of the relative gauge/liquid impedance. While it is likely that other factors, such as the liquids' viscosity, are important, we felt that in the first stages of this study, it would be better to vary quantities over which we had good control.

EXPERIMENTAL SETUP

The multi-element EMV gauge packages were made for us by RdF Corp. (Hudson, NH) as follows. First a 25 µm thick sheet of FEP Teflon forms the base. To this base is epoxied a 5 µm layer of aluminum foil. Next, using photo etching techniques, aluminum is removed, leaving a series of nested, square cornered, "U" shaped conducting elements. The bottom of each conducting element is 6 - 10 mm long, depending on its location in the nest, and forms the active portion of the gauge. The active portions are typically spaced ~ 2 mm apart, and when placed at an angle, this spacing will convert to depth according to the sine of the wedge angle. Finally, a second sheet of 25 µm thick FEP Teflon is epoxied on top of the base sheet and active elements. The completed gauge package is typically ~ 60 µm thick.

The plastic targets containing the liquids were similar to those used by Sheffield, Engelke, and Alcon,[2] and were constructed as shown in the exploded view of Figure 1. Hollow PMMA cylinders

† Work performed under the auspices of the U.S. Department of Energy.

~70 mm O.D., with a liquid cavity 40 mm in diameter and 10 mm deep, were sliced to form wedges. The EMV gauge membrane was epoxied to the lower wedge while under tension. Next, the upper wedge was epoxied to the lower,

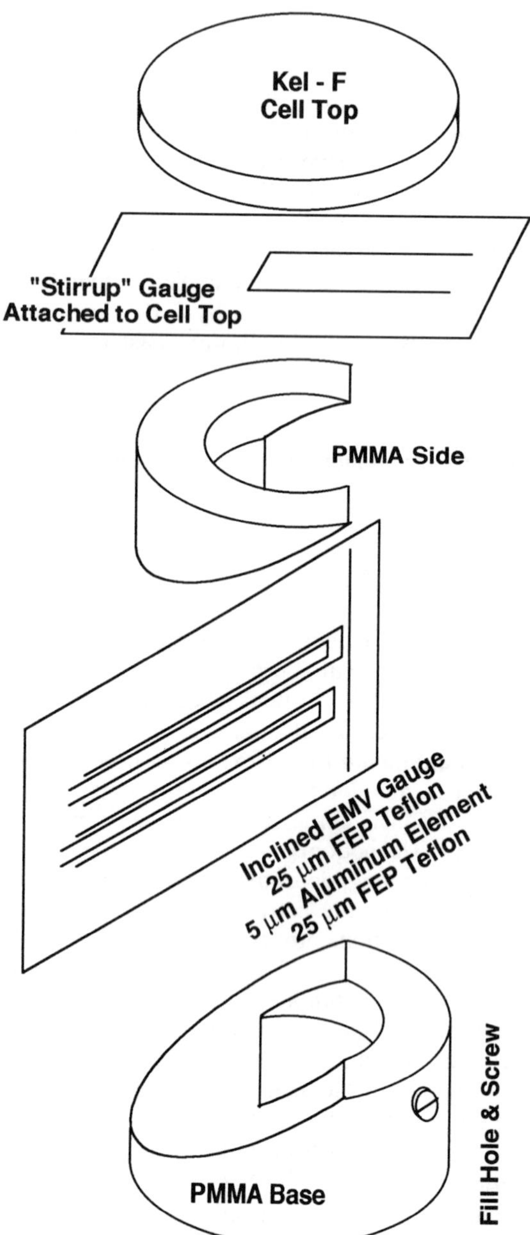

Figure 1. Exploded view of liquid cell and gauge.

reconstructing the complete hollow cylinder. In most experiments, PMMA surfaces were painted with epoxy to prevent the liquid from dissolving the PMMA. When the epoxy had cured, excess Teflon from the EMV gauge was trimmed, and excess PMMA from the upper wedge machined off. Except for the first few mm, which often ended slightly curled up, the gauge membranes were smooth and flat. Axial gauge positions (depths) and active element lengths were then measured using a computer controlled scanning and depth microscope.

Cell tops were made of ~ 6 mm thick Kel-F and had a single element EMV gauge bonded to the surface contacting the liquid. These single element gauges, which we call "stirrup gauges" were made by bonding an aluminum conductive element to a sheet of Teflon. The "stirrup gauge" was always oriented flat to the shock. It had not been used in Sheffield, Engelke and Alcon's early shots.[2]

To complete the assembly, the Kel-F cell top was epoxied and screwed (using nylon screws) to the lower hollow cylinder. The completed target was mounted on an aluminum plate containing fixtures for connecting coaxial cables to the electromagnetic gauge elements.

"Zero degree" experiments were constructed in a manner similar to that developed by Sheffield for studying the equation of state and shock induced reaction in liquid carbon disulfide.[3] "Stirrup" gauges were stretched and mounted on flat, parallel PMMA rings, as well as on Kel-F disks forming the cell top and bottom. These assemblies were completed by screwing and gluing the cell top, rings, and bottom together. Small holes were cut in the gauge membranes to allow the liquid to flow between rings.

Liquid was introduced into the cells through 6 mm screw holes, which were then capped with nylon screws and sealed using o-rings and epoxy. In all cases, the liquid was introduced into the cell less than three hours prior to the impact experiment.

All experiments were performed on an 8 m long, 72 mm bore light gas gun, capable of projectile velocities greater than 1.4 km/s. An electromagnet was installed in the gun's target chamber to provide the magnetic field (~ 750 gauss) for the electromagnetic velocity gauging. The magnetic field was calibrated prior to each shot using an F.W. Bell model 9200 gauss meter and HTB 92-0608 Hall probe. It was uniform to within ≤1% throughout the volume containing the gauges and of reproducible magnitude within ≤1% from experiment to experiment.

Voltage traces from the electromagnetic particle velocity gauges were recorded using Tektronix 7612 digitizers. These were voltage calibrated within 30 minutes after every experiment using a Tektronix CG 5001 programmable calibration generator. When converting gauge voltages to particle velocities, corrections were made for the aluminum conducting element resistance and the termination resistance.

Shock input to the liquid was obtained using lexan projectiles faced with 57 mm diameter by 12.7 mm thick z-cut sapphire impactors. Impact velocities ranged from ~ 1.2 to ~ 1.4 km/s and were recorded with a precision of ~ 0.3% using charged pins.

RESULTS

As it was our goal to measure the velocity error as a function of both the EMV gauge angle and the relative impedances of the gauge and liquid, we chose the following liquids: nitromethane, with lower impedance than the Teflon membrane. diiodomethane, with higher impedance than the Teflon membrane, and bromoform (CH_3Br) with approximately the same impedance as the Teflon membrane.

Shock states in the liquids were assumed to be predicted by the "Universal Liquid Hugoniot"[4]

$$\frac{U_S}{C_0} = 1.37 - 0.37e^{-2u_p/C_0} + 1.62\frac{u_p}{C_0} . \qquad (1)$$

Constants for the liquids are as follows: nitromethane; C_0 = 1.30 mm/μs, ρ_0 = 1.123 g/cm^3, diiodomethane; C_0 = 0.973 mm/μs, ρ_0 = 3.33 g/cm^3, bromoform; C_0 = 0.931 mm/μs, ρ_0 = 2.849 g/cm^3. To obtain shock states in the liquid from impedance matching, we also used the z-cut sapphire Hugoniot of Barker and Hollenbach[5] and the Kel-F Hugoniot of Sheffield and Alcon.[6]

Figure 2. shows results of an experiment in NM using a 30° inclined gauge and a 0° "stirrup" gauge at the Kel-F/NM interface. The "stirrup" gauge at the Kel-F/NM interface is recording the particle velocity of ~1.50 mm/μs predicted from an impedance matching calculation. The inclined gauges, meanwhile, register a value of ~ 1.35 mm/μs or about 10% lower than expected.

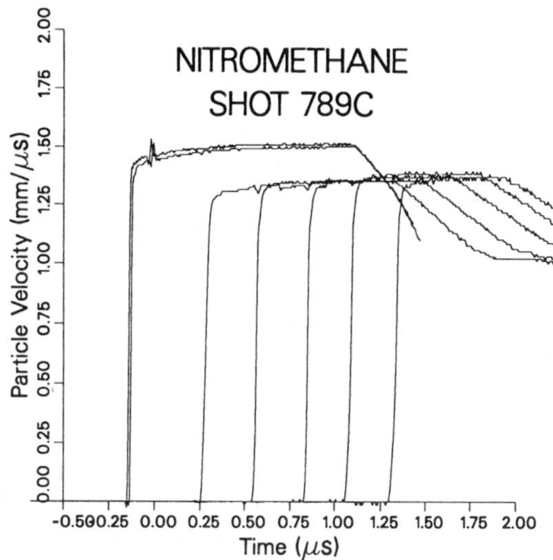

Figure 2. Observed particle velocity traces in nitromethane obtained with a 30° gauge.

We also did an experiment in NM in which flat to the shock "stirrup" gauges were embedded in the liquid. All three flat gauges in this experiment registered the expected particle velocity, indicating that the liquid did not somehow slow down after the Kel-F/NM interface.

Figure 3. shows results of an experiment in which a 30° gauge was embedded in diiodomethane, the liquid with higher impedance than the Teflon membrane. The particle velocity expected from impedance match calculations for this experiment was 0.99 mm/μs, and is shown by the horizontal dashed line. The inclined gauges are reporting a particle velocity of ~ 1.10 mm/μs which is about 10% higher than expected. (The flat "stirrup" gauge and one of the five inclined elements did not work in this experiment).

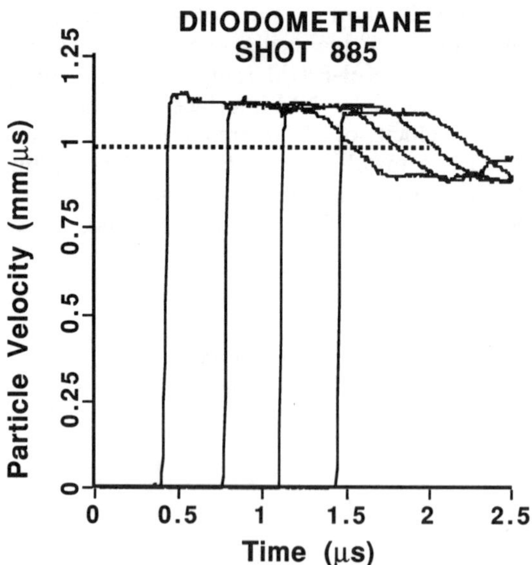

Figure 3.Observed particle velocity traces in diiodomethane obtained with a 30° gauge. The dashed line indicates the expected velocity of 0.99 mm/µs.

An experiment on bromoform, which has a shock impedance well matched to that of the Teflon gauge membrane, was also carried out using a 30° gauge. The gauges reported the expected particle velocity.

Table 1. shows the percentage error in measured particle velocity for all the experiments performed in this study. Inclined gauges in NM, for which lower than expected velocities are observed have a negative error, while inclined gauges in diiodomethane, for which higher than expected velocities are observed, have a positive error. Both the sign and magnitude of the error depend on the sign and magnitude of the relative impedance mismatch between the liquid and the Teflon gauge. For both overmatched and undermatched impedance conditions, the magnitude of the error increases with increasing gauge angle. Gauges oriented flat to the shock always produced the expected velocity.

Table 1. Error in measured particle velocity.

Liquid	NM	CH_3Br	CH_2I_2
Liquid/ Gauge Impedance	Undermatch	Match	Overmatch
0° Gauge	± 2 %		
10° Gauge	- (2 - 4) %		+ (1 - 2) %
20° Gauge	- (5 - 6) %		+ (3 - 4) %
30° Gauge	- (8 - 10) %	± 2 %	+ (9 -10)%

CONCLUSIONS

It should be noted at this point that the phenomenon of inclined gauges reporting a velocity which is not that of the surrounding material appears to be unique to liquids. After completing the experiments shown in Table 1, we used the gauges in a plastic having much lower impedance than the Teflon gauge membrane. The expected velocity was observed. It also seems unlikely that these gauges, being only 60 µm thick and hence having little mass, could change the velocity of the liquid by as much as 10%.

The likely difference between the solid and liquids is that in the solid, the gauge must move with the material because of friction between the solid and gauge. In liquids, by contrast, there is only viscous friction, and the present experiments indicate that this is inadequate to force the gauge to move with the material. The liquid, through shock interactions, must perturb the gauge velocity. There is an ongoing study of these effects in our group.

REFERENCES

[1] J. Vorthman and J. Wackerle in "Shock Waves in Condensed Matter 1983", North-Holland, Amsterdam, (1983) pg. 613. J. Vorthman, J. Andrews, and J. Wackerle, in "Proceedings of the Eighth Symposium (International) on Detonation" pg. 99

[2] S.A. Sheffield, R.P. Engelke, and R.R. Alcon, in "Proceedings of the Ninth Symposium (International) on Detonation" pg. 39

[3] S.A. Sheffield, J. Chem. Phys. 81, 3048 (1984)

[4] R.W. Woolfolk, M. Cowperthwaite, and R. Shaw, Thermochim. Acta 5, 409 (1972).

[5] L.M. Barker and R.E. Hollenbach, J. Appl. Phys. 41, 4208 (1970)

[6] S.A. Sheffield and R.R. Alcon in "Shock Compression of Condensed Matter 1991", S.C. Schmidt, R.D. Dick, J.W. Forbes, and D.G. Tasker eds. North Holland, Amsterdam (1992) pg. 909.

HYSTERESIS OF LATERAL PIEZORESISTIVE GAUGES

Z. Rosenberg
RAFAEL, P.O. Box 2250, Haifa, Israel
N.S. Brar
University of Dayton Research Institute, 300 College Park, Dayton, OH 45469-0182, USA

The response of embedded piezoresistance gauges to shock loading and unloading experiments is strongly dependent on the elasto-plastic of properties of gauge material. We extend our analytical model to account for the resistive hysteresis of the lateral gauges on unloading. It is shown that the hysteresis is different than that of the longitudinal gauge and this can lead to a negative resistance change on complete release to zero stress.

INTRODUCTION

The introduction of the lateral stress gauge concept by Bernstein et al [1] in order to completely determine the stress matrix has advanced the understanding of the response of shock loaded solids. During the last decade a number of workers have analytically modeled the response of piezoresistance gauges to planar shock loading [2-6]. In a recent paper [7] we extended our analytical approach to determine the lateral gauge response at low shock stresses. We found that in the elastic range of gauge material (manganin) its resistance change is not a unique function of the matrix lateral stress. Rather, the response depends on the elastic modulii of the matrix material. In the present paper we extend the analysis to account for the hysteresis in the lateral gauge response due to the elasto-plastic properties of the gauge material.

SUMMARY OF THE PREVIOUS RESULTS

In order to follow our analytical approach we summarize briefly the main findings of Reference 7. We have shown that the lateral gauge response is unique for high shock stresses. However, for shock stresses in the elastic range of the lateral gauge material, the response depends on the type of matrix. The onset of yielding of the lateral gauge is also matrix dependent as given by the folllowing expression for critical longitudinal stress (σ_x^c):

$$\sigma_x^c = \frac{Y_g}{A}; \qquad A = \frac{3G^g}{M_m} - \frac{\nu_m}{2(1-\nu_m)} \tag{1}$$

Where subscripts g and m refer to gauge and matrix and Y, G, and M are yield stress, shear modulus and longitudinal modulus, respectively. Inserting the appropriate values for elastic constants for matrix and manganin gauge, we find σ_x^c = 0.05, 0.45 and 4.0 GPa for plexiglass, soda-lime glass and alumina, respectively. In terms of critical lateral stresses in the matrix, these values are σ_y^c = 0.03, 0.15 and 1.0 GPa for these materials.

We have also shown that in the plastic range of the lateral gauge response ($\sigma_y>\sigma_y^c$) there exists a single calibration curve for all matrix materials. For manganin gauges we found that the slope of this curve is given by:

$$\frac{\Delta R/R_o}{\sigma_y} = 2.97x10^{-2}\frac{\Omega/\Omega}{GPa} \tag{2}$$

On the other hand, for stresses below σ_y^c (within the elastic range of gauge response), the calibration of the lateral gauge is not unique. Rather, the piezoresistance coefficient has a matrix-dependent term (ß) which is determined by the gauge and matrix elastic modulii. For manganin we have:

$$\frac{\Delta R}{R_o} = 1.98x10^{-2}.\beta.\sigma_y^m;$$

$$\beta = 1 + 2\frac{G^g}{M_m} \cdot \frac{(1 - \nu_m)}{\nu_m} \qquad (3)$$

ß varies between 17 (plexiglass) and 2.0 (alumina). Thus, the piezoresistance coefficient for lateral manganin gauges (below the elastic limit) is 34×10^{-2} for plexiglass, 8.8×10^{-2} for soda lime glass and $3.7x10^{-2}$ for alumina. This is a serious disadvantage in the lateral stress gauge concept. Ideally the gauge response is not expected to be dependent on the type of matrix material. However, the elastic range of the lateral gauge response is relatively low and the main usage of the gauge is to measure high stresses. The highest σ_y^c that can be measured in ceramics are 4.0 GPa for alumina and 6 GPa for titanium diboride. One should be aware of these limitations of the lateral piezoresistance stress gauge, which can be reduced by annealing the gauge to obtain much lower Y_g values. We used manganin gauge manufactured by Micro-Measurements in our studies and its yield strength Y_g = 0.75 GPA (see [4]). There are other types of gauges available with Y_g = 0.23 GPa (see [9]) for which the elastic range of the lateral gauges should be limited to $\sigma_x^c \approx 2$ GPa. In addition to these problems with the lateral gauge, the phenomenon of gauge hysteresis upon stress release is very important and is discussed next.

THE RESISTIVE HYSTERESIS OF LATERAL GAUGES

In order to understand the problems encountered with the response of lateral stress gauges we have to examine the structure of their calibration curves as shown in Figure 1 for the manganin gauges used by us. We have drawn the three elastic branches which correspond to lateral gauges embedded in plexigalss, soda-lime glass and alumina. Note the single curve for stresses in the plastic range of gauge material. We have also drawn the hydrostat, which is the calibration curve for gauge without strength (Y_g = 0).

Assuming elasto-plastic behavior for the gauge material we assign its resistive hysteresis to the mechanical hysteresis in stress-strain plane, as we have done previously for the longitudinal gauge [8]. Thus, the first part of gauge response to stress release should be

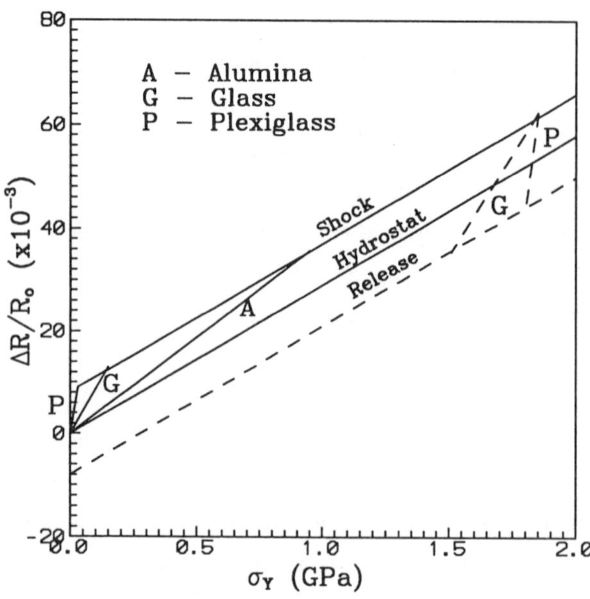

Figure 1. Manganin gauge resistance change during loading and unloading in PMMA, glass, and alumina

elastic, crossing the hydrostat and ending on a line below the hydrostat, which is a mirror image of the plastic calibration curve. These curves are shown as dashed lines in Figure 1 and since each matrix material has a different elastic line we have to draw three different elastic release curves. They result in very different hysteresis patterns for the three matrix materials. While the hysteresis for lateral gauges embedded in plexiglass is very pronounced, for practically any stress level, we should have a relatively small hysteresis for gauges embedded in alumina even at relatively high pressures. This is even more true for TiB_2 where the elastic calibration line is almost coincident with the hydrostatic curve.

In order to test these assertions, we performed several experiments with lateral manganin gauges embedded in different matrix materials. We have also reanalyzed some of our earlier data where shock and release levels are well defined for both lateral and longitudinal stresses. Table 1 lists the relevant data for these experiment together with the resulting resistance changes of the lateral gauge upon unloading. These are compared with the calculated values using Figure 1, as explained above and, as one can see, the agreement is quite good. One should note the fact that the unloading path in Figure 1 leads to a negative resistance change in the lateral gauge when unloading is complete. This phenomenon was actually observed by us in experiment with manganin gauges embedded in plexiglass [4].

One should also note that, contrary to the longitudinal stress gauge, the hysteresis of the lateral gauge reduces its resistance below the hydrostat during the release process. This is the result of the relative position of loading and unloading curves shown in Figure 1. The opposite happens with the longitudinal gauge (see [8]). One can clearly see this opposite behavior in Figure 2, where the profiles of the longitudinal and the lateral gauges embedded in plexiglass and impacted by a 6 mm copper disk, are shown. The shock and release stresses are 2.4 and 1.8 GPa respectively and, to a good approximation, one can assume the plexiglass behaves hydrodynamically so that lateral and longitudinal stresses are almost the same for both shock and release states. The two gauges show very different release patterns in that the differences between ΔR values in the shock and release states are very pronounced.

Table 1 Measured and calculated $\Delta R/R_o$ release values of lateral gauges

Shot #	Impactor Velocity (m/s)	Matrix	Long. and Lateral Release ($\Delta R/R_o$)			
			Shock (GPa)	Release	Measured	Calculated
R-ADA	Cu (6mm) 676	Plexi glass	σ_x= 2.4 σ_y= 2.4	σ_x= 1.8 σ_y= 1.8	0.046	0.044
7-0901	Cu (4mm) 295	Soda lime glass	σ_x= 2.9 σ_y= 0.92	σ_x= 1.3 σ_y= 0.43	0.005	0.004
7-1712	Alumina AD85 (5mm) 264	Alumina AD85	σ_x= 3.9 σ_y= 1.1	0	0	0

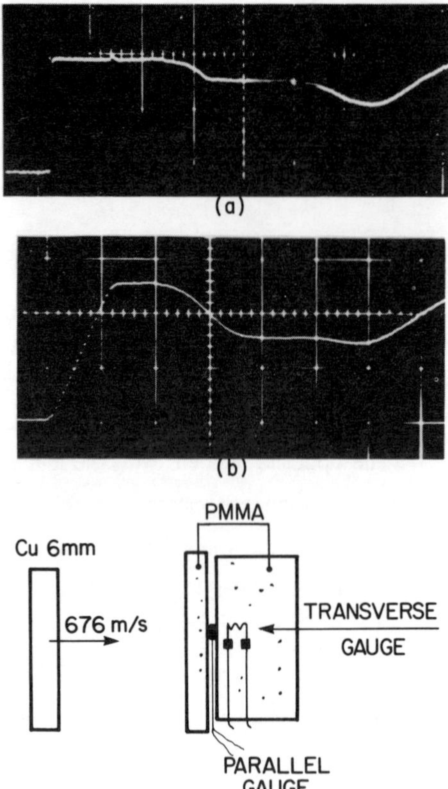

Figure 2. Longitudinal and lateral gauge profiles in PMMA

DIRECT MEASUREMENT OF THE MEAN PRESSURE

According to our analytical model for longitudinal [10] and lateral gauge [4], we can write their response in terms of their volumetric strain (pressure). Thus, to a first order (for our manganin gauges):

$$\left(\frac{\Delta R}{R_o}\right)_{long.} \cong 2.97x10^{-2}\ (\sigma_x^m - \frac{2}{3}Y_g) \qquad (4a)$$

$$\left(\frac{\Delta R}{R_o}\right)_{lat.} \cong 2.97x10^{-2}(\sigma_y^m + \frac{1}{3}Y_g) \qquad (4b)$$

Where σ_x^m and σ_y^m are the principal stresses in the matrix.

Multiplying Equation 4b by 2 and adding it to Equation 4a results in the following:

$$\left(\frac{\Delta R}{R_o}\right)_{mean} = \Delta_{long.} + 2\Delta_{lat.} = (2.97x10^{-2}).3P^m \quad (5)$$

where $P^m = (\sigma_x^m + 2\sigma_y^m)/3$ is the mean pressure (GPa) in the matrix. Thus, P^m is obtained directly from the measured resistance changes of longitudinal and lateral gauges, without the need to account for strength of the gauge material. Equation 5 can be expressed as

$$P^m(GPa) = 11.2x(\Delta_{long.} + 2\Delta_{lat.}) \qquad (6)$$

As long as we use gauges from the same batch we do not need to know their yield strength in order to find P^m, because it cancels out in the calculations.

CONCLUSIONS

We extended our analytical model for the elastic-plastic response of piezoresistance gauges to account for the resistive hysteresis of lateral gauges upon stress release. We found that this hysteresis lowers the resistance of the gauge and can result in even negative resistance changes upon complete release. Agreement between experimental results and the model is good, which enhances the validity of our model. In order to avoid complications arising from wrong interpretations of data, it is recommended to use annealed gauges for lateral stress measurements.

REFERENCES

[1] D. Bernstein, C. Godfrey, C. Klein, and A. Shimin, In Behavior of Dense Media Under High Dynamic Pressures, Gordon and Breech New York, 461 (1968).

[2] Z. Rosenberg, Y. Partom, and D. Yaziv, J. Appl. Phys., 52, 755 (1981).

[3] Y. M. Gupta, J. Appl. Phys., 54, 6256 (1983).

[4] Z. Rosenberg and Y. Partom, J. Appl. Phys., 58, 3072 (1985).

[5] S. C. Gupta and Y. M. Gupta, J. Appl. Phys., 57, 2464 (1985).

[6] Z. Rosenberg and N. S. Brar, J. Appl. Phys., 63, 349 (1988).

[7] Z. Rosenberg and N. S. Brar,"The Elasto-Plastic Response of Lateral Piezoresistance Gauges," To appear in App. Acoustics, 1993.

[8] Z. Rosenberg, J. Appl. Phys., 60, 3369 (1986).

[9] Z. Rosenberg and J. A. Charest, J. Appl. Phys., 60, 2641 (1986).

[10] Z. Rosenberg and Y. Partom, J. Appl. Phys., 58, 1814 (1985).

CHARACTERISTICS AND PULSED RADIATION RESPONSE OF NON-IDEAL QUARTZ SHOCK STRESS GAUGES

R.P. REED and J.I. GREENWOLL
Sandia National Laboratories/NM, Albuquerque, NM 87185-5800

This cautionary paper reminds users of quartz shock stress gauges that sensors that ignore the design rules of the "Sandia quartz gauge" may produce substantial and unrecognized deviations from normal sensitivity, waveform distortion, and anomalous conduction. Each deviant design must be extensively characterized. The consequence of non-standard gauge designs, like the "shorted quartz gauge" designs, are given for prompt response to pulsed radiation while stressed.

INTRODUCTION

The Sandia Quartz Shock Stress Gauge was invented by Nielson, Graham, and Benedick.[1] Its technology was developed by R. A. Graham and many associates at Sandia.[2] The Sandia Quartz Gauge allows accurate, finely time-resolved, and reliable measurement of brief stress pulses. Both normal behavior and many limitations are well understood and are documented in a collected set of original papers.[2] Properly applied, the widely used "quartz gauge" has produced shock stress data that has allowed keen experimental insights into the actual shock behavior of diverse real materials and so has profoundly influenced both theoretical and experimental gains in many related fields.[3]

The Sandia Quartz Gauge design was systematically developed by many meticulous projectile impact experiments that examined diverse gauge geometries and application conditions, by theoretical modeling, and by complementary analysis of the observed normal and anomalous behavior. The thorough work is definitive of the technology of a universal class of sensor specific to short duration time-resolved stress pulse measurement.[2]

However, commonplace quartz gauges that do not follow the design protocol are subject to many significant errors that are not generally understood. Errors may not be recognized because, even when misused, the sensor output often "looks good" so invalid data may be misinterpreted or not questioned. We review some of the problems of non-ideal designs and report new data concerning aggravated anomalous behavior of one such gauge form at high stress combined with pulsed radiation.

THE SANDIA QUARTZ GAUGE DESIGN DEFINITION

The shock stress sensing element is a right-circular cylindrical disk of diameter **D**. The stress input face is fully electroded. The opposing face is electroded with a centered circular signal electrode, of diameter, **E**, surrounded by a concentric guard ring electrode, of radial width **G**, that extends to the disk diameter. The center and guard electrodes are separated by a crucial insulating gap of uniform narrow width, **g**. The cylindrical surface must be entirely free of any conducting material. It must be remote from surrounding conducting surfaces.

Critically, for **X**-cut quartz the guard ratio, **G/H**, must be no less than 1.5 to assure one-dimensional field behavior throughout the full gauge transit time within the central region defined by the inner electrode.

The ratio of disk diameter to thickness, **D/H**, is not stated but experimental data were developed over a broad range. Values of **D/H** often are near 4 or 5:1.

The piezoelectric material must be of alpha quartz, synthetically grown. It must be free of significant acmite (sodium-iron silicate) inclusions and other defects within the axial cylindrical region defined by diameter **E** of the inner electrode. Imperfections in the entire disk volume must be few.

The disk faces must be of plate glass finish, normal to the **X** crystallographic axis within 1 degree, parallel within 500 mradians, and flat within 3 fringes of **He** monochromatic light.

Electrodes may be of vacuum deposited gold over chromium or of aluminum. The guard ring gap must be formed by sand blasting (rather than by laser machining) through the electrode material and electrically insulated by epoxy coating immediately after cutting to avoid conduction by contamination across the gap. Lead attachment must not damage the crystal disk.

Stress must be input to the negative electrode face (A properly electroded gauge produces a positive voltage signal at the rear electrode in response to transient compression.) The electrical signal is observed between the input electrode and the opposing inner positive electrode as a voltage across (or current through) an accurate purely resistive load R_L. The internal electric fields in the active and guarding volumes are partially balanced by electrically shunting the guard ring electrode to the input electrode through a balancing,

Funded by DOE Contract DE-AC04-76-DP00789

guard resistor, $R_G = R_L(A_E/A_G)$-- the ratio between active and guard areas.

The use temperature must be near 293K (20°C). Data over the range from 79K to 743K demonstrate usability but with variations of response of several percent.

For this authentic Sandia Quartz Gauge, the initial signal response to a step stress jump at the input electrode with the signal electrode essentially unstressed is simply:

$$V(\sigma) = [R_L \cdot A_E/t_t] \cdot [a \cdot \sigma^2 + b \cdot \sigma], \text{ where:}$$

R_L = effective load resistance, ohms,
$A_E = \pi[(E+g)^2]/4$ cm^2
(the effective electrode area),
$t_t = [(0.572 \cdot 10^5$, cm/s) / H, cm]
(the disk wave transit time),
$a = 9.7 \cdot 10^{-9}$ C cm^{-2} GPa^{-2}, and
$b = 2.0 \cdot 10^{-7}$ C cm^{-2} GPa^{-1}. [2]

The 2 GPa signal from a gauge of E=H=1cm into a 50 ohm load is about 9.9 volts.

Below 2.6 GPa, the response to a simultaneous planar jump of stress is an abrupt jump to an initial signal value, then a shallow upward linear ramp for the duration of the transit time. The few percent slope of the response depends on the stress. It occurs because of stress dependent deformation and material properties. Though the response to an ideal stress step is not a perfect step, the response is simple, reproducible, and correctable (if necessary) for stresses below 2.6 GPa and the gauge is usable and well understood for stresses even in excess of 4 GPa.[2]

Application limits are well defined. Under high stresses, the electrical fields within the quartz disks assume values of MV/cm order. This makes the gauge vulnerable to electrical conduction that tends, improperly, to increase the sensor output progressively as the wavefront progresses through the disk. Associated with this situation, there are several well known "anomalous" responses that accompany definite identified conditions of application.

The **"-X anomaly"** involves internal electrical conduction that distorts the waveform unpredictably above a stress threshold near 0.6 GPa when the disk is employed with the stress improperly first incident on the -X face. Similar conduction also occurs, but above a much higher stress threshold (3 GPa), when the stress is properly incident on the +X face.

The **"Short Pulse Anomaly"** is the onset of waveform distorting conduction that occurs on application within certain well-mapped regions in the pulse-duration-versus-stress plane. The anomaly can depend on pulse shape.

The tendency of pulsed X-ray or neutron radiation to trigger conduction is recognized but has not been systematically studied.[4] This paper illustrates that tendency.

THE NON-IDEAL QUARTZ GAUGE

The Sandia Quartz Gauge was carefully studied to comprehensively define design limits within which behavior is universal. Thus, it should be expected that **any** quartz gauge that departs significantly from this careful protocol may produce significantly deviant response and so cannot rely on the extensive characterization of Sandia Quartz Gauges for accurate measurement.

In other gauge configurations, the recognized anomalies of the ideal Sandia Quartz Gauge are exaggerated in magnitude, reduced in stress threshold, and distorted in form. Each distinct deviant design must be specially characterized for both normal and anomalous behavior.

Despite this consequence many arbitrary gauge designs in present use do not follow the known design rules. They are known to have different responses that affect initial jump sensitivity, waveform distortion, and anomalous behavior. Often, the consequences are not understood because the pitfalls are not recognized.

Motivations for departing from the ideal are several. They may be compelling. Sometimes the overall diameter of the sensor must be limited. The signal from the gauge depends on the geometric ratio (E^2/H). The noise environment is severe so enhanced output is required. Thus, the sensing electrode is enlarged to increase output. Measurement duration is limited by disk thickness. Extended measurement time may be essential. Thickness is increased to extend recording time (but reduces signal.)

The front electrode often is shorted to the rear guard ring by fully conductive plating the disk perimeter to allow direct access from the rear face.[5] To reduce noise, the gage is shrouded within a close-fitting conductive case.

Some designs wrap both input and guard electrodes around the periphery interleafed in a toothed pattern with electrodes separated by a narrow insulating gap of "saw-tooth" pattern.

Consequences of these well motivated changes are that the nearly-ideal characteristic step response of the Sandia Quartz Gauge may be substantially degraded, the desirable one-dimensional electrical field distribution within the disk is modified resulting in a distorted waveform and conduction susceptibility, and anomalous behavior is exaggerated.

Three pitfalls are: 1) characteristic distortion of the waveform for the arbitrary design may not be recognized, if recognized, may not be quantitatively defined, and even if known may not allow correction; 2) limits for use of the non-ideal gauge are different from those of the ideal gauge; and 3) anomalous behavior of the arbitrary gauge may be very different from that carefully studied for the ideal gauge. To assure that none of these pitfalls is important for an arbitrary gauge implementation requires an inordinate expenditure of resource.

Table 1. Sandia Field Test Quartz Gauges (FTQG)

Mod>	11-xxx	10-xxx	12-xxx	15-150	15-200	15-250
G/H	1.500	1.333	1.000	0.333	0.250	0.200
E/H	1.000	1.333	2.000	3.333	3.500	3.600
D,in	--*--	--*--	--*--	1.500	2.000	2.500

* D's are like Mod 15. D/H=4 for all gauges.[6]

THE SANDIA FIELD TEST QUARTZ GAUGE

The deviant Sandia Field Test Quartz Gauge (FTQG) family, Table 1, is characterized and is useful, though non-ideal. The set has a 4:1 disk aspect ratio. Guard and input electrodes are common. For any E/H, at low stress there is a characteristic relative step response, S/S_1, that defines the signal response $S(E/H,t/t_t)$ of the FTQG member relative to ideal response $S_1(\sigma)$ of the Sandia Quartz Gauge, Fig. 1.[6]

Relative to the Sandia Quartz Gauge, each has:

1. reduced initial response to a stress jump (The initial relative signal is reduced as much as 25% where E is enlarged for sensitivity (The net sensitivity gain is less than as E^2/H),
2. large waveform distortion (The step response inflates the signal at late times. The geometrically caused waveform distortion is reproducible. It results from the non-one-dimensional field. It is not conduction.),
3. enhanced sensitivity to stress conduction anomalies (lowered stress thresholds, more severe than for the Sandia Quartz Gauge),
4. enhanced sensitivity to conduction triggered by radiation insult.

Over the low stress range for which the relative response is independent of stress, distorted signals resulting from non-ideal response can be predicted by convolution from known input stress waveforms. Unknown stress waveforms are deduced by deconvolution from gauge-distorted output voltage waveforms.[6]

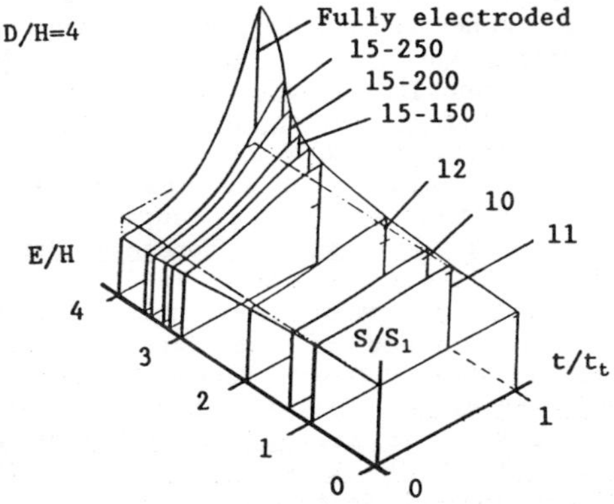

Figure 1. Relative response of the non-ideal Sandia Field Test Quartz Gauge design set.

The **FTQG** has not been recommended for use above **0.8** GPa as characteristics are not known adequately. Shorted electrode gauges like the FTQG MOD **11** reportedly have stress-independent response to **2.8** GPa and some like the FTQG MOD 10 had a nearly-linear ramping but of greater slope and dependence on stress than the Sandia Quartz Gauge.[7,8] Anomalous behavior, such as conduction under very short or arbitrary pulse shape loading, or radiation is not well studied.

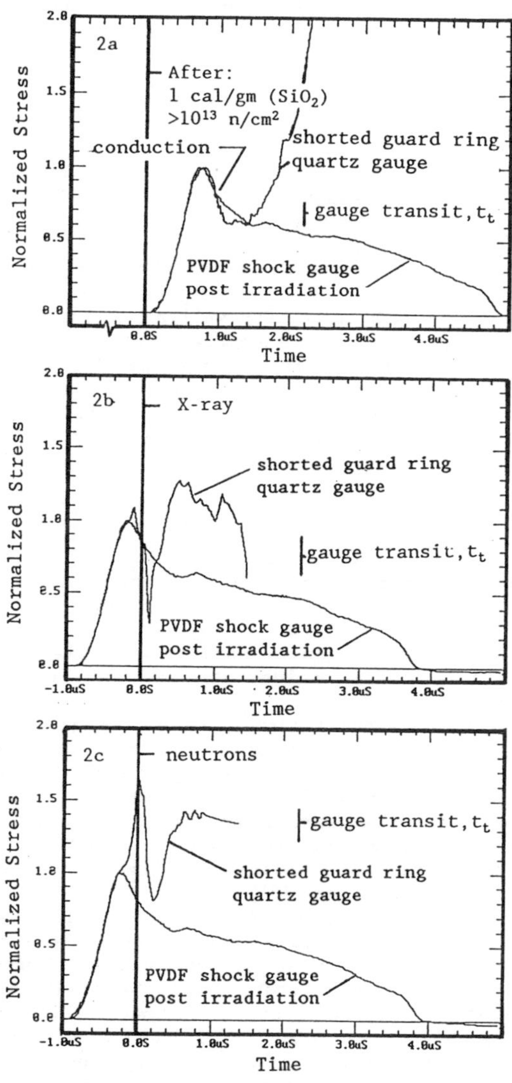

Figure 2. Response of shorted guard ring Mod 11 (D/H=4,G/H=1.5) Quartz Gauge to: a) excessive (>2 GPa) stress alone, and b) to excessive stress plus 1.4 cal/gm X-ray, and c) neutrons, $>10^{13}$ n/cm² fluence. Comparison to PVDF gauge.

RADIATION RESPONSE

Carriers radiation-induced into marginal electric fields of the gauge are expected to trigger anomalous conduction.[4] This pitfall is well illustrated by recent results observed in a field test environment. In that set of experiments, responses of Mod 11-200 Field Test Quartz Gauges were compared with the radiation response of PVDF shock stress gauges that were situated at the same interface.[9] The quartz gauges were deliberately subjected to excessive stress values (>2 GPa) while irradiated by pulsed X-rays or by $>10^{13}$ n/cm^2 neutron fluence.[9]

Figures 2a-c compare the responses of the FTQG Mod 11 quartz gauges exposed to: a) excessive stress only (following irradiation), b) excessive stress concurrent with moderate X-ray deposition, and c) pulsed neutron fluence superposed on excessive stress. The PVDF shock stress gauge tolerated the stress and radiation conditions and recovered fully.[9]

Amplitudes are normalized for comparison of shapes. Notably, the rise portion of waveforms from all gauges agree very well and actual peak values are in good agreement even at the stress level (>2 GPa) excessive for the Mod 11 FTQG.

Excessive stress alone causes the non-ideal quartz gage to experience +X conduction when irradiated early in the transit time. The magnitude of the conduction distortion also is larger than at lower stress levels.

Coincident with the 1½ cal/gm (SiO_2) X-ray deposition, distorting conduction is triggered, Fig. 2b. The conduction distortion is erratic and of aggravated amplitude. Likewise, promptly at the onset of $>10^{13}$ n/cm^2 neutron fluence conduction is precipitated, Fig. 2c.

These results, in comparison with the PVDF reference pulse, illustrate the anticipated adverse conduction response of this commonplace geometry of shorted guard ring quartz gauge as triggered by pulsed radiation. It confirms that the conduction anomaly is aggravated in the presence of stress above the recommended limit. Rule of thumb recommendations based on few prior measurements has suggested that the FTQG of Mod 11 design was usable within the limits 0.8 GPa, <5 cal/gm (SiO_2), and 10^{13} n/cm^2.

Significantly, the MOD 11-200 Field Test Quartz Gauges of this experiment have the same proportions as those of the Sandia Quartz Gauge. However, the ideal Sandia Quartz Gauge without radiation should respond normally without conduction at this stress of 2.2 GPa level. The proportions are also like those of many of the shorted guard ring gauges that are in routine use by many experimenters. The response of the FTQG and similar commonplace shorted guard ring gauges at excessive stress is anomalous and exaggerated even without radiation.

CONCLUSIONS

Shorted guard ring quartz gauges exposed to 2 GPa stress simultaneously with 1 cal/gm (SiO_2) X-ray deposition or $>10^{13}$ n/cm^2 neutrons experienced a premature and exaggerated conduction anomaly. Bauer-process Al-electroded PVDF shock stress gauges, less affected in the same experiment, extend the measurement realm of the Sandia Field Test Quartz Gauge.

Any quartz shock stress gauge that violates the design regimen of the Sandia Quartz Gauge cannot safely rely on published data for that ideal sensor to apply to a gauge of deviant design. A gauge of different material, non-standard proportion, with shorted guard ring, used at high stress, extreme temperatures, or in a radiation environment must be specifically and extensively characterized for stress-jump sensitivity, waveform distortion, and for thresholds of anomalous behavior.

ACKNOWLEDGEMENTS

Several colleagues influenced development, characterization, field application, and special data analysis for the non-ideal Sandia Field Test Quartz Gauge. R.A. Graham, Nathan Brown, W.B. Benedick, G.E. Ingram, and L.W. Bickle stimulated many key concepts. The indispensable contributions of many other associates and co-authors acknowledged elsewhere, made the radiation experiment successful.[9]

REFERENCES

1. F.W.Nielson,R.A.Graham,and W.P.Benedick, U.S.Patent No. 3,307,052, February 28, 1967.

2. R.A.Graham and R.P.Reed(Eds.),Selected Papers on Piezoelectricity and Impulsive "Pressure" Measurement, SAND78-1911, Sandia National Labs, Albuquerque, NM, 1978.('88 Print)

3. R.A.Graham, Solids Under High Pressure Shock Compression,Springer-Verlag,New York,1993.

4. R.A.Graham,"Conductivity in Shock-Loaded X-Cut Quartz" (Reproduced in SAND78-1911)

5. G.A.Jones and W.J.Halpin, "Shorted Guard-Ring Quartz Gauge,"Rev Sci.Instr.,39,258,(1968.)

6. R.P.Reed,The Sandia Field Test Quartz Gauge--Its Characteristics and Data Reduction, 1971 (Reproduced in SAND78-1911.)

7. A. Birnboim and Z. Rosenberg,"The Response of Shorted Quartz Gauge To Impact Loading,"Shock Compression of Condensed Matter," pp.833-836, Elsevier, New York, 1990.

8. Z.P.Tang,P.M.Bellamy,and Y.M.Gupta, "Stress Dependence of the Current Ramping Observed in Shorted Quartz Gauges," Shock Waves in Condensed Matter, Elsevier, New York, 1988.

9. R.P.Reed et al, Radiation Response of Stressed PVDF Shock Stress Gauges, Joint AIRAPT/APS Topical Conference on High Pressure Science and Technology, June 28-July 2, 1993.

INTERPRETATION OF QUARTZ-GAGE RESPONSE IN RADIATION PROBLEMS

Robert E. Tokheim
Poulter Laboratory
SRI International
333 Ravenswood Avenue
Menlo Park, California 94025-3493

The quartz gage is usually thought of as a piezoelectric gage responding to the difference in stresses at the front and rear surfaces, assuming stress wave loading from one direction. However, in radiation problems where there is energy deposition in the quartz gage and adjacent layers, it is simplest to interpret the gage response with respect to the difference between front and rear particle velocities of the quartz layer. The Grüneisen stress generated is positive, whereas the front surface particle velocity is negative and will show up as a negative apparent stress with the usual interpretation. However, the correct Grüneisen stress can be recovered from the measurement. These features are illustrated computationally for an X-ray blackbody source exposing an alumina target in front of a fused-silica buffer and quartz gage.

INTRODUCTION

The usual interpretation of the quartz gage is that a stress difference between front and rear surfaces, assuming uniaxial strain loading directed at the front of the quartz gage (with propagation constant equal to x- $v_q t$), generates a piezoelectric-induced current to flow in the gage circuit through an output load resistance. For this simple case the observed quartz-gage output voltage V(t) is given by[1]

$$V(t) = \frac{A v_q R\, k}{H}(\sigma(0,t) - \sigma(H,t)) \qquad (1)$$

where A, v_q, H, R and σ are the effective area (cm^2) of the electrode, absolute magnitude of the quartz sound speed (cm/s), gage thickness (cm), the gage load resistance (ohm), and the stress (kbar), respectively. The piezoelectric factor (below 5 kbar) is given by k = 2.004*E-8 coul/cm^2-kbar.[2]

There is a need for handling radiation problems where there is energy deposition in the quartz gage and adjacent layers and where there are multiple stress waves from different directions. Even with the usual stress loading, there may be multiple reflections from different layers, particularly for times greater than the gage transit time.

COMPLICATED RESPONSE

The steady wave assumption for a wave propagating through the quartz layer described above has a propagation constant equal to x - v_qt. For a wave propagating the opposite direction, the propagation constant is equal to x+ v_qt. Consequently, for the general wave case x - Sv_qt, where S is the sign corresponding to the direction of the propagation vector, the induced current results in the following voltage arising from individual stress-wave contributions:

$$V(t) = \frac{A v_q R\, k}{H}\left(\sum_{j=1}^{n} S_j \sigma_j(0,t) - \sum_{k=1}^{m} S_k \sigma_k(H,t)\right) \qquad (2)$$

where the signs S_j and S_k correspond to the propagation direction of each wave passing through the front and rear interface, respectively, and where we have assumed linear superposition of the piezoelectric-induced currents.

Now consider the jump condition for each steady wave in linear quartz

$$\sigma_j = \rho_o S_j v_q u_j \qquad (3)$$

where we have included the S_j to account explicitly for the direction of the wave propagation, and where u_j is the particle velocity increment associated with the j wave. Inserting Equation (3) into Equation (2) gives

$$V(t) = \frac{A (v_q)^2 \rho_o R\, k}{H}\left(\sum_{j=1}^{n} u_j(0,t) - \sum_{k=1}^{m} u_k(H,t)\right) \qquad (4)$$

where S_j and S_k have vanished because $(S_j)^2 = 1$. Because

$$\sum_{j=1}^{n} u_j(0,t) - \sum_{k=1}^{m} u_k(H,t) = u(0,t) - u(H,t) \qquad (5)$$

we then have for the voltage, simply

$$V(t) = \frac{A (v_q)^2 \rho_o R\, k}{H}[u(0,t) - u(H,t)] \qquad (6)$$

which is independent of the direction of propagating waves. This means that for a complicated response, the gage is more properly defined as a particle-velocity gage. Thus, it is easy to compare computed PUFF code results with Equation (6), either on the basis of voltage or difference in front and rear quartz crystal particle velocities. An alternative, often default, way of comparing code results with data is to find the apparent stress "σ" we obtained by using only the simplest relation derived from Equation (1) while ignoring the rear-surface stress term:

$$"\sigma" = \frac{HV(t)}{Av_q R\ k} \tag{7}$$

By comparison with Equation. 6, we find this equivalent to

$$"\sigma" = \rho_o v_q\,(u(0,t) - u(H,t)) \tag{8}$$

Hence, even the use of Equation 7 gives a usable result for code comparison. In our computations, then we compute the difference in particle velocities. But as we have implied above, the voltage will not correspond to differences in stresses except for a simple wave passing through the quartz.

BLACKBODY RADIATION EXAMPLE

Figure 1 shows an X-ray blackbody-irradiated configuration comprising porous alumina (ρ = 2.78) over a fused-silica buffer over a quartz gage, backed with epoxy. Figure 1 also shows the dose that is sufficient to generate the significant Grüneisen stresses, especially in the quartz layer.

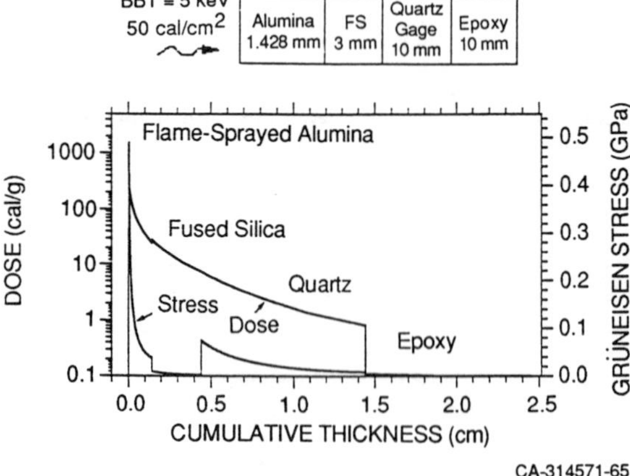

Figure 1. Computed dose and resulting Grüneisen pressure for near instantaneous (1 ns) energy deposition time in alumina quartz-gage configuration.

Computational model parameters for porous alumina[3] are given in Table 1. Standard model parameters for quartz, fused silica, and epoxy were used similar to literature values.[4,5] Equilibrium interface stresses and particle velocities derivable from Figure 2 are, for the front interface

Table 1. Material Model Parameters Used for Porous Alumina

```
ALUMINA-FLS(2.78)   RHOS =     3.969E+00 CFP = 003 DPY = 005
     NVAR = 45
EQST =     2.655E+12 4.200E+12 6.318E+10 1.320E+00 8.000E-02
     2.090E+12 1.670E+00
RHO =      2.780E+00
KCS,TS,RS      1 1 0 KCD,TD,RD      1 1 0
AK =       1.000E+12 MUP =      4.000E+11 Y0 =       1.000E+07
     RHOP1 =   2.910E+00
NREG =             4
RHOP =     2.780E+00 2.890E+00 3.333E+00 3.917E+00
COSQ =     4.000E+00 4.000E+00 4.000E+00 4.000E+00 4.000E+00
C1 =       5.000E-02 5.000E-02 5.000E-02 5.000E-02 5.000E-02
0 P1 =     1.000E+08
1 P2 =     1.000E+10 DELP =   -1.200E+09 YADDP =   1.000E+09
2 P2 =     6.100E+10 DELP =   -2.400E+09 YADDP =   1.000E+09
3 P2 =     1.400E+11 DELP =   -1.500E+10 YADDP =   3.000E+09
4 P2 =     3.350E+11 DELP =   -2.200E+10 YADDP =   1.000E+10
TER5 =    -1.000E+11 TER7 =     5.000E-01
MELT =     2.630E+10 1.350E+10 2.000E-02 9.000E-01-2.000E-01
SPH =      2.960E-01
YIELD =    6.600E+10 1.600E+12 0.000E+00 0.000E+00
VISC =     4.000E+00 5.000E-02 5.000E-02
TENS =    -3.000E+09-1.000E+10-0.100E+09
```

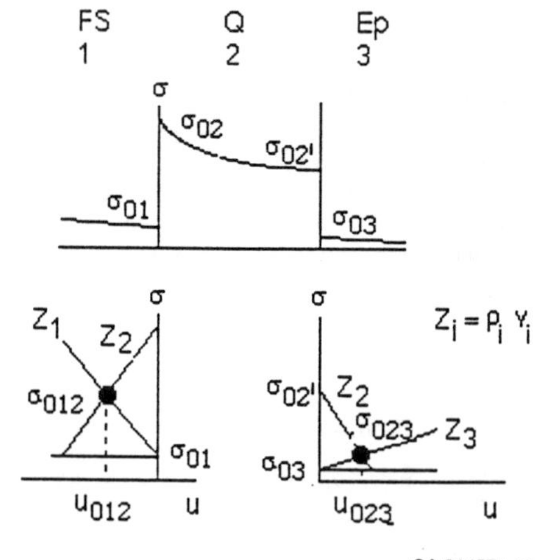

Figure 2. Grüneisen stress and stress-particle velocity plots for finding relationships between initial quartz interface stresses and particle velocities and Grüneisen stresses.

$$\sigma_{012} = \frac{\sigma_{01}Z_2 + \sigma_{02}Z_1}{Z_1 + Z_2}$$

$$u_{012} = \frac{-\sigma_{02}' + \sigma_{01}}{Z_1 + Z_2} \tag{9}$$

and for the rear interface

$$\sigma_{023} = \frac{\sigma_{03}Z_2 + \sigma_{02'}Z_3}{Z_2 + Z_3}$$

$$u_{023} = \frac{\sigma_{012'} - \sigma_{03}}{Z_2 + Z_3} \tag{10}$$

For our material model parameters with the Grüneisen stress given by $\sigma = \Gamma\rho e$ (Grüneisen ratio, density, energy density) we obtain $\sigma_{01} = 2.37$ MPa, $\sigma_{02} = 74.4$ MPa, $\sigma_{012'} = 8.45$ MPa, $\sigma_{03} = 0.66$ MPa. Inserting these into Equations (9) and (10) gives $\sigma_{012} = 36$ MPa, $u_{012} = -255$ cm/s, $\sigma_{023} = 1.7$ MPa, $u_{023} = 42.4$ cm/s, which agree with PUFF computations shown in Figures 3 and 4 for particle velocity and stress. The converse procedure enables the estimate of the Grüneisen for quartz from $u_{012} - u_{023}$, which is observed, either as particle velocity or apparent stress shown in Figure 5.

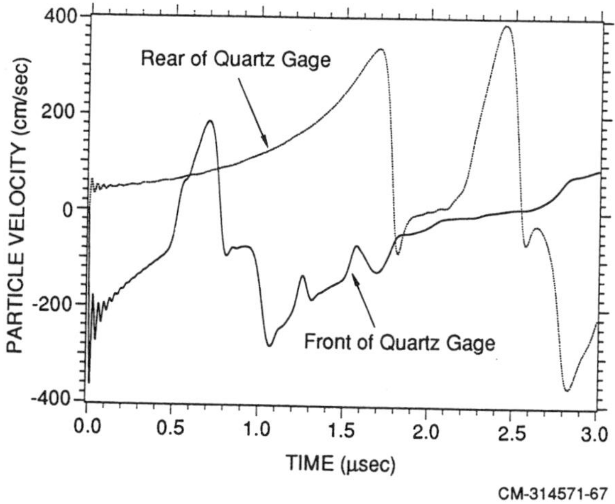

Figure 3. Computed particle velocities at front and rear of quartz gage.

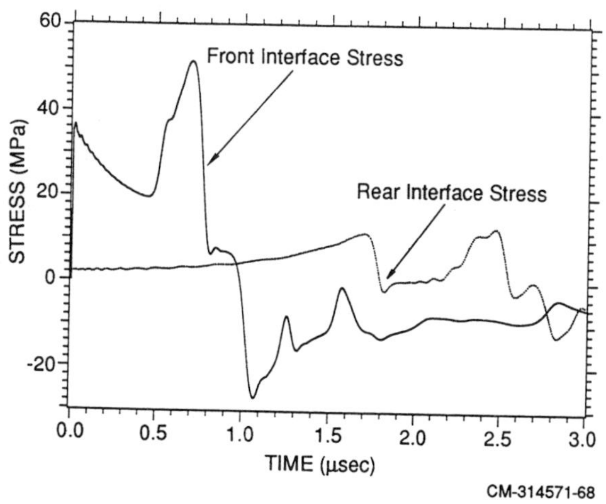

Figure 4. Computed stresses at front and rear of quartz gage.

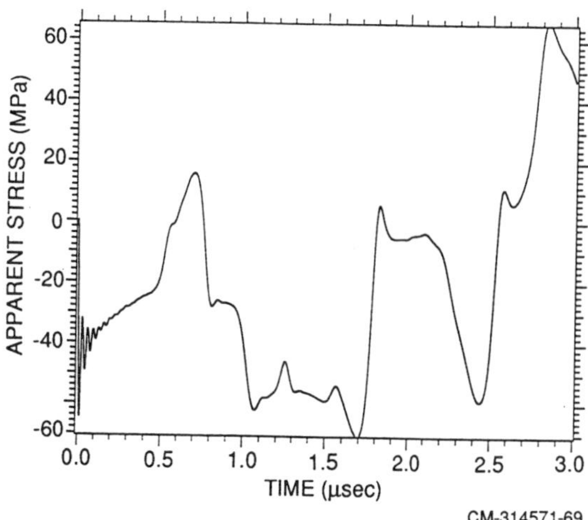

Figure 5. Computed apparent stress for quartz gage.

CONCLUSIONS

For radiation problems with significant in-depth energy deposition and configurations with multiple reflections, it is simplest to interpret the quartz gage as a particle-velocity gage.

ACKNOWLEDGMENTS

The author benefitted from discussions with D. Seitz and his description of work by T. Allen. Thanks also go to B. Lew for computational support.

REFERENCES

1. O. E. Jones, F. W. Neilson, and W. B. Benedick, "Dynamic Yield Behavior of Explosively Loaded Metals Determined by a Quartz Transducer Technique," J. Appl. Phys., **33**, 3324-3232 (1962).

2. R. P. Reed, "The Sandia Field Test Quartz Gage, It's Characteristics and Data Reduction," presented at "Underground Nuclear Test Measurements Symposium I," Sandia Laboratories, Albuquerque, NM, 7-9 December 1971.

3. L. Seaman and D. R. Curran, "SRI PUFF 8 Computer Program for One-Dimensional Stress Wave Propagation," Vol. II, US Army Ballistics Research Laboratory, MD (August 1978).

4. R. A. Graham, "Strain Dependence of Longitudinal Piezoelectric, Elastic, and Dielectric Constants of X-cut Quartz," Phys. Rev. B, Vol. 6, No. 12 (1972).

5. L. M. Barker and L. M. Hollenbach, "Shock-Wave Studies of PMMA, Fused Silica, and Sapphire," J. Appl. Phys., Vol. 41, No. 10 (1970).

APPLICATION OF PIEZOELECTRIC STRESS GAUGES TO THE MEASUREMENT OF FAST-RISE-TIME MULTIMEGAMPERE ELECTRIC CURRENTS

D. L. Hanson, K. W. Struve+, R. B. Spielman, and J. F. Seamen
Pulsed Power Sciences Center
Sandia National Laboratories
Albuquerque, New Mexico USA 87185-5800

Modeling of load behavior in Z-pinch plasma radiation sources driven by high current generators requires accurate measurement of fast-rise-time multimegampere electrical currents close to the load. Using a novel application of high pressure technology, we have demonstrated that fast-response piezoelectric stress transducers can measure such currents under conditions of extremely high current density, induced electric fields, and bremsstrahlung radiation where conventional current diagnostics fail. Large signal, nanosecond-time-resolution lithium niobate piezoelectric stress gauges are employed to directly measure the magnetic pressure $B^2/2\mu_0 = \mu_0 I^2/8\pi^2 r^2$ generated at radius r by a current I flowing in a radial transmission line near the load of a pulsed power current source. With a current diagnostic consisting of a pure tungsten electrode on a Y-cut lithium niobate stress gauge, current densities up to $I/2\pi r$ = 78MA/m can be measured before the electrode yield strength and piezoelectric operating stress limit are exceeded. Based on this work, we have developed a compact modular current probe for use on the high current (20-25 MA) DECADE simulator being constructed for the Defense Nuclear Agency. We also describe recent work extending this measurement technique to higher current densities (125 MA/m) using a copper-sapphire electrode impedance stack on an X-cut quartz piezoelectric element.

INTRODUCTION

In recent years, intense pulsed x-ray sources have been developed [1] which utilize pulsed power drivers delivering multimegampere electric currents to radially implode a hollow cylinder of ionized gas, a cylindrical foil, or wire array. Accurate current measurements close to the load are required to model the implosion dynamics and radiation production physics of the source. Standard Rogowski coil and B-dot loop current monitors are unreliable when used closer than about 5 cm to the load on large accelerators because of electrical failure resulting from large electric fields induced across the monitor housing when a conducting plasma is present.

To avoid these difficulties, we have developed a noninductive, nonperturbing current diagnostic [2] consisting of a miniature piezoelectric stress gauge which directly measures the magnetic pressure generated by the load current in the transmission line wall. We have extended this technique originally suggested by Williams et al. [3], by using high yield strength W electrode disks and sensitive lithium niobate ($LiNbO_3$) piezoelectric elements to provide sufficient signal amplitude for accurate current measurements up to current densities of $I/2\pi r$ = 78 MA/m in the harsh electrical noise environment of PROTO-II (5.5 MA peak current) and the much larger

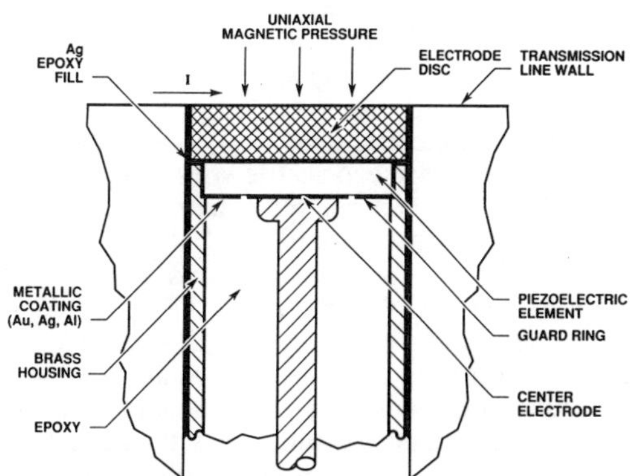

Figure 1. Schematic of the miniature piezoelectric stress gauge assembly mounted in a transmission line.

SATURN accelerator (10 MA peak current) at Sandia National Laboratories. We have also recently developed modular stress gauge current probes to permit rapid, accurate current measurements on the DECADE weapons effects simulator (20-25 MA peak current) now under construction for DNA. With a different combination of electrode and transducer materials, we have extended this measurement technique to a higher current density limit of 125 MA/m.

CURRENT MEASUREMENT TECHNIQUE

The current flowing in a magnetically insulated transmission line (MITL) can be determined directly from the magnetic pressure generated by the load current. The magnetic field for a total current I flowing at radius r in a radially symmetric feed is $B=\mu_0 I/2\pi r$. The magnetic pressure exerted on the transmission line wall is then given by:

$$P_M = \frac{B^2}{2\mu_0} = \frac{\mu_0 I^2}{8\pi^2 r^2} \tag{1}$$

At high current density and dI/dt, where inductive current monitors fail, this pressure pulse can be easily measured with nanosecond time resolution using an appropriate piezoelectric stress gauge.

We have demonstrated the effectiveness of this concept by performing a series of current measurements very near the load on the PROTO-II and SATURN accelerators, using compact stress gauges of high sensitivity [2]. The basic construction of the stress gauge current diagnostic is shown in Fig.1. A piezoelectric stress gauge is bonded to a metal electrode disk which forms an integral part of the transmission line wall. Thus, the stress gauge is mounted behind a continuous conducting surface several times the electrical skin depth in thickness and does not perturb the current flow. Dimensions of the piezoelectric element are chosen so that the active instrumented area of the gauge sees only a uniaxial stress wave during the transit time of the wave through the piezoelectric disk.

The response of piezoelectric stress gauges of this type has been characterized for a number of electrode configurations and impulsive shock loading conditions [4]. For a uniaxial stress wave σ_T(Pa) applied to the front surface of the piezoelectric element, the transducer responds with subnanosecond time resolution by generating a current i_T(A) in the load circuit which is directly proportional to the stress at the front electrode for times less than the transit time of the element. The resulting voltage across the load resistor R(Ω) is given by:

$$V_T = Ri_T = \frac{RkA\sigma_T}{t_0} \quad \text{for } t<t_0 \tag{2}$$

where k($C\ m^{-2}\ Pa^{-1}$, $C\ m^{-2}\ Pa^{-2}$) is the piezoelectric constant of the gauge material relating induced polarization to the applied stress, A(m^2) is the gauge active area, σ_T(Pa) is the stress on the front surface of the piezoelectric element, and t_0 is the transit time of the stress wave through the gauge. An impedance mismatch exists at the electrode-piezoelectric interface. The stress σ_E of the incident wave at the back of the metal electrode is related to the stress σ_T at the front of the piezoelectric transducer by:

$$\frac{\sigma_E}{\sigma_T} = \frac{Z_E + Z_T}{2 Z_T} \tag{3}$$

where Z_E and Z_T are the mechanical shock impedances of the metal electrode and piezoelectric disk, respectively. If an electrode material is chosen whose yield strength is greater than the peak applied pressure, then the current-generated stress wave will propagate elastically, and we can equate the magnetic pressure P_M with σ_E at the back of the electrode. Under these conditions, the current line density I/2πr(A/m) flowing in the transmission line at radius r(m) is given in terms of the measured stress gauge voltage V_T(V) as:

$$\frac{I}{2\pi r} = \left[\frac{2}{\mu_0}\left(\frac{Z_E+Z_T}{2Z_T}\right)\left(\frac{t_0}{RkA}\right)\right]^{1/2} V_T^{1/2} \tag{4}$$

A problem of particular concern for all current measurements on a high-current driver such as SATURN is the interaction of prompt high energy (>100 keV) bremsstrahlung radiation from the load region with the current diagnostic and signal cable. The stress gauge current diagnostic is unique in the sense that interference from source-generated bremsstrahlung noise can be eliminated in a straightforward way by providing adequate propagation time delay in the electrode layer to separate the prompt bremsstrahlung noise from the current-induced stress wave to be measured.

Piezoelectric materials tested included X-cut quartz, and Z-cut, Y-cut, and positive-36°-rotated Y-cut lithium niobate ($LiNbO_3$), with Ni and W electrode layers. Piezoelectric constants and other relevant parameters for these materials are summarized in Ref. 2. The most effective current stress gauge developed from this family of materials consisted of a pure W electrode, with a Hugoniot elastic limit of 3.77 GPa [5], on a Y-cut $LiNbO_3$ piezoelectric element. The primary advantage of $LiNbO_3$ over X-cut quartz for measurements with compact gauges at moderate current densities (< 50 MA/m) is the much higher sensitivity (10-20) of $LiNbO_3$ and the improved impedance matching of $LiNbO_3$ with electrode materials of higher yield strength than Al [6]. Y-cut $LiNbO_3$ has a relatively high sensitivity and the highest operating stress limit (1.8 GPa) of the three crystal orientations of $LiNbO_3$. Both the yield strength of W and the limiting operating stress of Y-cut $LiNbO_3$ impose a limitation on the maximum current density which can be measured of I/2πr = 78 MA/m [2].

The accuracy of the $LiNbO_3$ gauge current measurements was evaluated by comparison with other current diagnostics at large radius on shots where feed losses between diagnostics were judged to be small. Fig. 2 shows the results of a current measurement on a SATURN shot with a low-inductance short-circuit load. The agreement between current waveforms derived from the $LiNbO_3$ stress

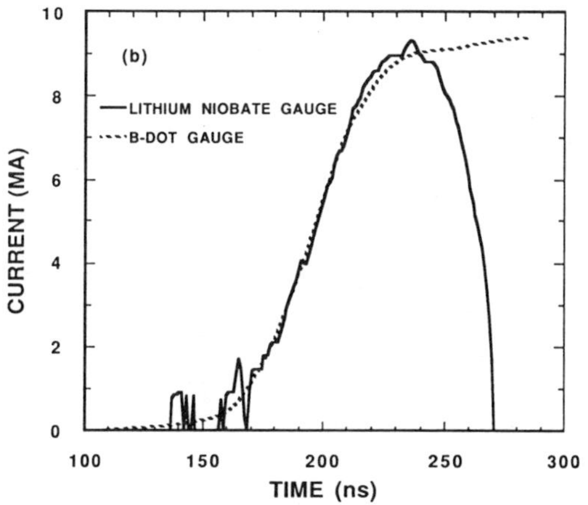

Figure 2. Comparison of current measurements with a $LiNbO_3$ gauge at r = 2.13 cm and a calibrated B-dot at r = 5.24 cm on a SATURN short circuit shot.

gauge current measurement at r = 2.13 cm and calibrated B-dot current monitor measurements at r = 5.24 cm is excellent. The reflection of the stress wave at the back surface of the piezoelectric element is marked by a sharp drop in the stress gauge signal, defining the end of the gauge recording time.

MODULAR CURRENT PROBES FOR DECADE

We have developed a compact modular piezoelectric current probe [7] to provide routine high-current density measurements on the DNA DECADE simulator (20-25 MA peak current) now under construction. The basic probe design again uses a W overlayer on a Y-cut $LiNbO_3$ piezoelectric element. The linear current density limit of 78 MA/m for this configuration restricts current measurements to r ≥ 5.1 cm for I = 25 MA. The recording time of the gauge is 250 ns to accommodate a 200 ns long current pulse. The transit time delay in the W electrode is 292 ns, about twice the expected implosion time of 150 ns for a Z-pinch load on DECADE.

The DECADE modular current probe is designed in a compact package that can be easily installed. The probe body (Fig. 3) is screwed into the transmission line wall and an indium gasket is extruded into the gap between the overlayer and wall to form a continuous electrical connection. Signal and shield cables can then be directly attached to threaded connectors. During development, these modular probes were tested on the SATURN accelerator. Probes were mounted at r = 3.8-4.8 cm and generated good signals under all conditions. Signal waveforms and derived feed currents from a typical shot are shown in Fig. 4. The large negative signal near the beginning of the trace is prompt-bremsstrahlung-induced noise which is isolated from the positive polarity current-induced pressure pulse by propagation delay in the W electrode. Work is in progress on methods to calibrate the individual gauges. A pulsed laser system is being used to measure the acoustic delay in the overlayer and the recording time of each probe.

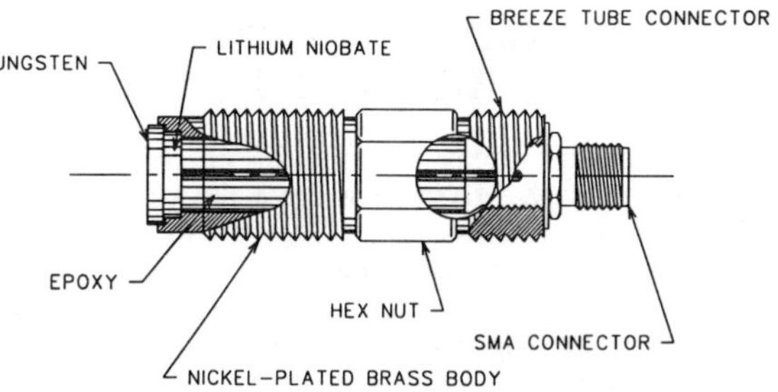

Figure 3. Design of DECADE stress gauge current probe.

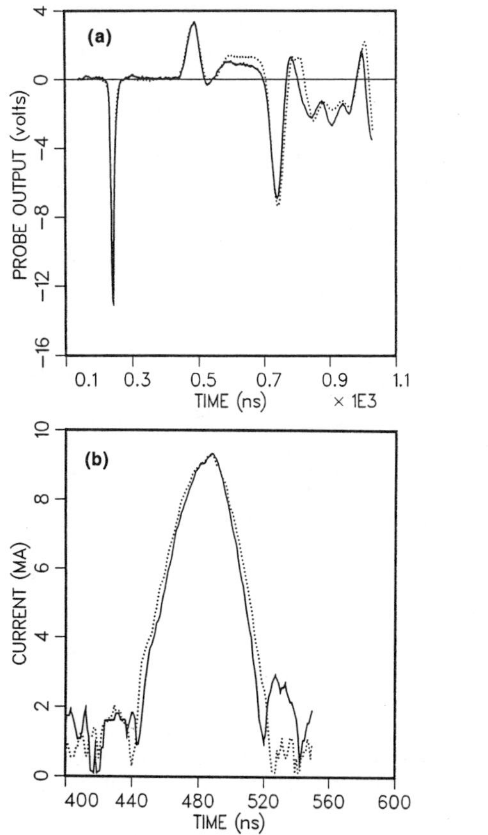

Figure 4. (a) Comparison of signals produced on a typical SATURN shot by two DECADE stress gauge current probes located 180° apart at r = 4.4 cm. (b) Total SATURN current derived from the stress gauge waveforms in 4(a).

EXTENSION TO HIGHER CURRENT DENSITIES

To permit measurements of current densities greater than 78 MA/m, we have designed a stress gauge configuration with a 50 μm (skin-depth-thick) Cu conducting layer bonded to a thicker layer of sapphire (Al_2O_3) on an X-cut quartz piezoelectric element. The Hugoniot elastic limit of 60°-rotated Z-cut single-crystal sapphire may be as high as 20 GPa with a lower limit of 12 GPa [4,5], so that stress waves of much higher peak stress can propagate elastically in this overlayer than in W. X-cut quartz has a limiting operating stress of 4-5 GPa and low sensitivity is no longer a problem at high stress levels. Fig. 5 shows a TITAN hydrocode calculation of stress-time profiles in a Cu-sapphire electrode. Attenuation and distortion of the input stress wave in the thin Cu conducting layer is minimized because negligible plastic work is required to shock-load this very low-yield-strength material. A 9.8-GPa peak surface stress is required to produce a 5.0-GPa (limiting) stress at the front of the X-cut quartz gauge. The peak-current-density limit for the Cu-sapphire electrode on X-cut quartz is 125 MA/m, or 20 MA peak current at r = 2.54 cm [2].

These copper-sapphire-quartz (CSQ) current monitors have been tested on foil implosion experiments on the SATURN accelerator. Fig. 6 shows a comparison of the MITL current derived from the signal of a CSQ gauge mounted at r = 1.65 cm (96 MA/m peak current) in a cylindrical wall immediately after a sharp bend in the MITL and the current from a W-$LiNbO_3$ gauge signal at r = 3.61 cm (42 MA/m peak current) measured on a smooth radial section of the feed. Typical of most measurements in this series, the two current waveforms show comparable peak currents, suggesting that the CSQ gauge is operating properly. However, the current from the CSQ gauge at small radius consistently shows a much faster risetime than the current from the gauge at large radius (25 ns vs. 65 ns), suggesting that current losses may be occuring early in the power pulse somewhere between the two gauges, probably at the sharp bend in the power feed.

At current densities above about 100 MA/m, the contribution to the transmission line surface pressure from heating and vaporization of the thin metal conducting layer can be significant and must be evaluated. For the range of current densities studied in the work described here, limits for transmission line surface ablation are not exceeded.

ACKNOWLEDGMENTS

This work was supported by the U. S. Department of Energy under Contract No. AC04-76DP00789 and by the Defense Nuclear Agency.

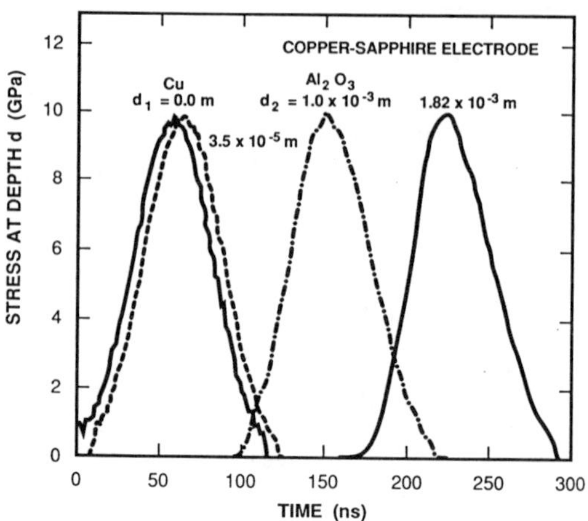

Figure 5. TITAN calculation of stress-time profiles in a Cu-sapphire electrode.

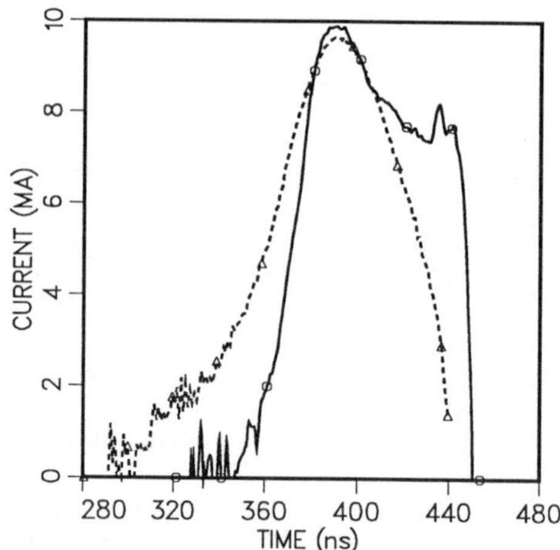

Figure 6. Comparison of MITL feed currents derived from a Cu-sapphire-quartz gauge measurement at r = 1.65 cm (solid line) and a W-$LiNbO_3$ gauge measurement at r = 3.61 cm (dashed line).

REFERENCES

+ Mission Research Corporation

[1] N. R. Pereira and J. Davis, *J. Appl. Phys.* 64 (1988).

[2] D. L. Hanson et al., *J. Appl. Phys.* 68, pp. 4917-4928 (1990).

[3] R. R. Williams et al., in *Proceedings of the IEEE 14TH Pulse Power Modulator Symposium, Orlando FL, June 3-5, 1980*, New York: IEEE Press, 1980, pp. 227-229.

[4] R. A. Graham and J. R. Asay, *High Temperatures - High Pressures* 10, pp. 355-390 (1978).

[5] R. W. Rohde, *J. Appl. Phys.* 40, pp. 2988-2993 (1969).

[6] R. A. Graham, *J. Appl. Phys.* 48, pp. 2153-2163 (1977).

[7] K. W. Struve et al., DNA Report, IACRO Number 92-850, Albuquerque, NM, September 30, 1992.

STUDY OF PRESSURE TRANSDUCERS AND ELECTRODES FOR UNDERWATER SHOCK WAVE GENERATORS

Fernando E. Prieto and Achim M. Loske
Departamento de Fisica Aplicada y Tecnologia Avanzada
Instituto de Fisica, UNAM
A.P. 20-364, 01000 Mexico D.F., Mexico

Frederick L. Yarger
Department of Physics
New Mexico Highlands University
Las Vegas, New Mexico, U.S.A.

This paper describes the results obtained using different pressure transducers and electrodes to measure the pressure obtained from an experimental electrohydraulic shock wave generator.

INTRODUCTION

In the last ten years non-invasive shock wave techniques have been the standard therapy for about 90% of all patients with kidney or ureteral stones [1,2]. Shock waves are produced by electrical breakdown of water, electromagnetically pulsed membranes and piezoelectric arrays [3]. Stone fragmentation results from the repeated administration of focused shock waves. A comparison of the capabilities of the systems is quite difficult and the results of the use of hydrophones for measuring focal pressures of shock waves normally change when using different gauges. Accurate reproduction of the waveforms require gauges with a very large bandwidth. Many problems arise when measuring the pressure generated by an underwater shock wave generator. Reflections created in the transducer due to the entrance and exit of the wave produce interference, small alignment errors affect the measurements and manufacturers normally do not calibrate their gauges in the same environment.

It is the aim of this work to compare different commercially available pressure gauges under the same conditions using a new type of electrodes to produce the shock waves. Due to the fact that the geometry of the ellipsoidal reflector destined to concentrate the shock waves, the discharge energy, the inductance of the electrical circuit and other parameters change from one manufacturer to the other, it is useless to compare measurements made on different clinical devices. It is because of this that for the purpose of comparison all our measurements were made using a highly versatile experimental facility of our own design (MEXILIT I) [4,5].

EXPERIMENTAL SETUP AND METHODS

The MEXILIT I consists of a pulsed power circuit operating between 10 and 1000 Joules, providing single or multiple pulses to a spark gap immersed in tap water. The spark gap electrode assembly is mounted at the focal point (F1) of an ellipsoidal stainless steel mirror mounted in the bottom of a fiberglass water tank. Application of high voltage (7 - 30 kV) across the electrodes induces a spark, creating the sudden ionization of the water. The fast expansion of the gas bubble generates a shock wave propagating into the surrounding water and reflecting off the ellipsoidal mirror, increasing the efficiency by creating a high energy region at the second focus (F2). The amount of energy reflected depends on the reflector material and on its geometry. The device has a fiberglass water tank mounted on an iron frame. A three dimensional position control system is placed on top of the water tank. The position of the spark gap and its length are adjustable. Basically the circuit consists of two parts: a capacitor charging system and a discharge control system. Once the capacitors are charged to the desired voltage, an oscillator sends an optical pulse, through a fiber optic, to a spark gap driver and the energy is discharged through the electrodes in the water tank producing low intensity shock waves (1 - 100 MPa). A detailed description of the MEXILIT I is given elsewhere [6].

In this work a stainless steel rotationally symmetric ellipsoidal reflector with 24 cm major axis, 17.2 cm minor axis and 12 cm depth was used. All gauges are positioned at the dynamic focus (region of maximum pressure) of the ellipsoidal reflector. Signals coming from the gauges were sent to the input channels of a Tektronics 2430A digital oscilloscope, triggered at the moment of the discharge.

Currently there are two different shapes of electrodes in clinical devices: flat and conical. In this study a new shape of electrodes was used (truncated cone), which has shown to be more reliable and suitable for lithotripsy than the conventional geometries [7]. One hundred consecutive pressure profiles were recorded for each pair of electrodes, using a 50 nF capacitor charged to 20 kV. For the pressure gauge comparison the shock waves were generated by a 100 nF capacitor charged to 19 kV. Spark gaps were adjusted to 2.5 mm. Tap water having a conductivity of 400 microS/cm and a temperature of 17°C was used. Electrodes were allowed to burn in for 100 discharges. The main characteristics of the pressure gauges used in this study are listed in Table 1.

RESULTS

Data corresponding to all three shapes of electrodes are given in Table 2. Pressure amplitudes obtained using the Kistler gauge were measured directly from the oscilloscope and therefore are expressed in volts. Amplitudes, widths and rise times are the averages of the total number of measurements. Variation coefficients appear in brackets

Table 1. Specifications of the pressure transducers.

TRANSDUCER	MODEL	RISE TIME (nsec)	ACTIVE AREA (mm^2)	CAPACITANCE (pF)
Dynasen	special 6EK	about 15	1.00	30.0
Dynasen	2107 6EK	about 15	10.08	57.0
Imotec	80-0.5-4.0	65	0.18	238.0
Kistler	603 B1	1000	17.40	12.0
Ktech	KP 117	15	9.30	58.9

Table 2. Data corresponding to the three different shapes of electrodes, obtained using the Kistler gauge. Variation coefficients appear in brackets below each average, indicating the reproducibility.

	FLAT	CONICAL	TRUNCATED
AMPLITUDE	1.770	3.904	4.444
(volts)	(0.337)	(0.154)	(0.193)
WIDTH	5.950	6.693	3.416
(microsec)	(0.182)	(0.168)	(0.097)
RISE TIME	3.150	3.122	1.844
(microsec)	(0.180)	(0.130)	(0.109)

below each average, indicating the reproducibility. Rise times were defined as the time required for the wave to rise from the base line to the maximum amplitude. Widths were measured at the baseline from the point where the pulse rises, to the point where it crosses the baseline again.

During the measurement of the shock wave pressure generated by an underwater spark discharge system, one finds some difficulties which are generally not a problem in many other experiments. The Kistler is a quartz piezoelectric unit and the others use the PVDF material. The shielding of the transducers against the electromagnetic pulse from the electrodes varies from one to another making comparison of the measured pressures more difficult. The signals produced by the pressure transducers listed in Table 1, located near the secondary focal point of the mirror (about 17 cm from the spark gap) are listed in Table 3. The direct wave goes directly from the spark gap to the transducer while the reflected wave is focused by the ellipsoidal mirror at the secondary focal point. The increased amplitude of the focused wave is very apparent.

DISCUSSION AND CONCLUSIONS

As far as we know, the best shock wave profile for lithotripsy has a fast rise time, a very short duration, a large compressional pressure and a tensile wave which is not too large, since this is a source of tissue damage. The new electrodes (truncated) seem to have the advantages of conical electrodes combined with a slower erosion and a longer lifetime. These electrodes produce the largest average compressional amplitudes, the smallest average widths and the smallest rise times with a good reproducibility. Due to the slow response time of the Kistler gauge, the rise times are shorter than reported here. The data of Table 2 should not be compared directly with that obtained with other pressure gauges. These data are useful only for comparison purposes, since electrodes were used under the same conditions.

The shock wave pressures in the water depend on several parameters, some of which can be controlled and some can not. The size of the focused wave is small enough so that a few millimeters error in the positioning of the transducer can produce a pressure signal more than ten percent less than that at the focus. The variations in pressure measurements may result from the positioning error, the variation in the electrode discharge, the electromagnetic pulse interference and internal

Table 3. Transducer measurements of shock waves

	SHOCK WAVE PRESSURE (bars)	
TRANSDUCER	DIRECT	REFLECTED
Dynasen special	11.8	118
Dynasen 2107	6.0	93
Imotec	-	99
Ktech	9.7	113
Kistler	10.3	90

reflections in the transducers.

REFERENCES

[1] Ch. Chaussy, E. Schmiedt, D. Jocham, W. Brendel, B. Forssmann and V. Walter, J. Urol. 127, p. 417 (1982).

[2] F. E. Prieto and A. M. Loske, Eds., Underwater Shock Waves and Extracorporeal Lithotripsy, an Introduction to the Bibliography, Mexico: Coordinación de la Investigación Científica UNAM, 1991.

[3] M. J. Coptcoat, R. A. Miller and J. E. A. Wickham, Eds., The End of the Stone Age, London: B.D.I. Publishing, 1987.

[4] F. E. Prieto, A. M. Loske and F. L. Yarger, Rev. Sci. Instrum. 62, p. 1849 (1991).

[5] F. L. Yarger, F. E. Prieto and A. M. Loske, Underwater Shock Waves in Medical Applications, in Proceedings of the Conference on Shock Compression of Condensed Matter, Elsevier Sciences Publishers, 1992, p. 843.

[6] A. M. Loske, Generación de Ondas de Choque Débiles en Agua por Rompimiento Eléctrico, Master's Thesis, Mexico: Facultad de Ciencias UNAM, 1990.

[7] A. M. Loske and F. E. Prieto, J. of Lithotripsy and Stone Disease, to be published.

HIGH PRESSURE APPLICATIONS OF FERROELECTRIC POLYMERS

F. Bauer
Institut Franco-Allemand de Recherches
5, rue du Général Cassagnou
68301 Saint-Louis, France

Ferroelectric polymers are the most recent class piezoelectric and pyroelectric materials developed. The most common piezoelectric polymers are PVDF, based on the monomer CH_2-CF_2 and copolymers PVDF with C_2F_3H. Techniques to process PVDF and P(VDF-TrFE) copolymers such that their physical properties exhibit reproducibility approaching that of piezoelectric single crystals are presented. Intrinsic piezoelectric properties of such materials are presented in this paper. Under high hydrostatic pressure, piezoelectric polymers exhibit well defined piezoelectric response. Piezoelectric response of shock compressed PVDF film prepared with attention to mechanical and electrical processing exhibits precise, well defined reproducible behavior to 35 GPa. P(VDF-TrFE) copolymers exhibit unique piezoelectric properties over a wide range of temperature depending on the compositions. Under high shock pressure loading, unique piezoelectric response is also observed. In particular, thickness can range from one micron up to more than one mm. Small and large area sensors can be prepared. Charge mode and current mode sensors are presented. These copolymers have the potential for new shock wave sensors with unique characteristics.

INTRODUCTION

The polar polymer polyvinylidene fluoride (PVDF) and its copolymers with 20 mol % - 50 mol % trifluoroethylene (TrFE) posses a variety of scientifically interesting and technologically important properties which have made them among the most widely investigated polymers[1,2].They exhibit large dielectric, piezoelectric and pyroelectric constants and were the first known ferroelectric polymers. Nylon polymers (Nylon 11, 7 etc...) has been reported to exhibit relatively large piezoelectric and pyroelectric activities. In particular J. Scheinbeim[4] confirmed that Nylon 11 stretched film exhibited ferroelectric behaviour above, at or below room temperature.

PVDF is a partially crystalline linear polymer with a carbon backbone in which each monomer [-CH_2-CF_2-] unit has two dipole moments, one associated with CF_2 and the other with CH_2. In the crystalline phase, PVDF exhibits a variety of molecular conformations and crystal structures depending on the method of preparation[1]. Melt cast films have the helical α form in which the molecular conformation is transgauche (TGTG), and the chains are packed in an antipolar unit cell. By stretching, the α phase in the film transforms to the β phase in which the molecular conformation in the all-trans (TT) planar zigzag with the dipole moments perpendicular to the chain axis. This β form exhibits reversible spontaneous polarization and is therefore the most useful ferroelectric and strongly piezoelectric phase.

An unusual property of PVDF is that the forces responsible for ordering the dipoles in the ferroelectric phase are sufficiently strong that the polymer melts before it undergoes a ferroelectric paraelectric transition. It is known, however, that copolymers of VDF and TrFE, [CHF-CF_2], with 20-50 mol % TrFE favour the β phase, and these copolymers exhibit ferroelectric transitions below the melting point (T_m). Poling of PVDF and the copolymers in the ferroelectric (FE) phase results in well ordered molecular conformation of the crystalline phase with a well defined remanent polarization[3]. This is also true for Nylon polymers and copolymers[4].

Previously conducted studies have shown that polyvinylidene fluoride films can serve as the active material in a piezoelectric shock wave stress gauge[3]. Today there are reproductible materials which make it possible to study the material's piezoelectric properties and to evaluate the potential application for these ferroelectric polymers under high pressure and shock wave action.

In the present paper, background information will be presented on PVDF, P(VDF-TrFE) copolymers and Nylon. Intrinsic piezoelectric properties of such prepared materials are pointed out.

Under high hydrostatic pressure, the piezoelectric response of PVDF and copolymers is reported. Piezoelectric behavior of PVDF as well as of P(VDF-TrFE) copolymers under shock wave action will be outlined. Review of thin, thick, small and large area sensors will be assessed.

FERROELECTRIC POLYMERS

PVDF : An orientation of the film is activated by stretching it just below the polymer's softening point with subsequent stretching and annealing. This process changes the crystalline structure of the film to the desired β polar phase. The PVDF material of the present work was biaxially stretched by Rhône Poulenc Films. Biaxially orientation leads to a more uniform thickness distribution (25 μm) and no wrinking effect. Such prepared films are isotropic in mechanical properties as well as in piezoelectric properties.

VDF/TrFE copolymers : The structure, ferroelectric properties and melting temperature of VDF/TrFE copolymers are known to depend on composition[1]. We have chosen for the present work the P($VDF_{0.7}$ -$TrFE_{0.3}$) composition because (i) it has the same crystalline β phase as PVDF at room temperature, (ii) it exhibits well defined and widely separated Tc and Tm and (iii) it has potential for applications. The samples, 1 to 25 μm thick, were deposited by spin coating of the VDF/TrFE copolymers under a liquid form on a glass substrate. Then the film was removed from the substrate and annealed, in order to eliminate the solvant and to enhance crystallisation of the copolymer. The resin was available from Solvay. The samples 25μm to 1mm thick, were prepared by compression molding of the melt followed by quench into either water or air. The samples were annealed at 413 K.

Nylon : A film of Nylon 7 film was obtained from J.Scheinbeim[4] who has prepared the sample by compression molding of the melt followed by quench into water, and then uniaxially stretched to a draw ratio 3:1 at room temperature. The thickness of the sample was 35 μm.

Poling process : In the preparation of piezoelectric polymers and copolymers it is in general necessary to apply a high poling electric field to an essentially insulating material. The poling process is the same as that established for PVDF[5,6], and provides a

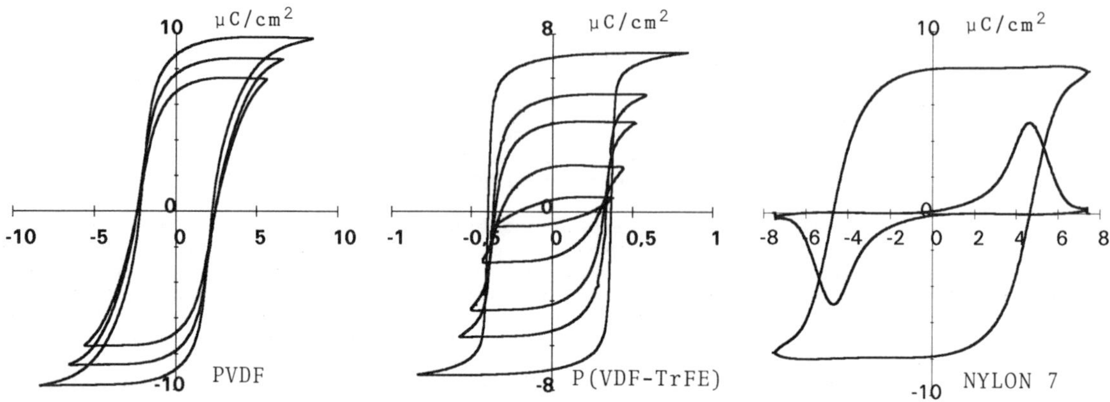

Figure 1. Hysteresis curves versus voltage : PVDF 25 µm thick, 9mm² area, P(VDF-TrFE) 70/30 8µm thick, 4.10^{-2} mm² area, NYLON 7 35µm thick, 4 mm² area.

means for achieving a homogeneous polarization at a predetermined level. Histories of hysteresis loops on 23 µm thick biaxially stretched PVDF films as well as on 8 µm spin coated P(VDF-TrFE) (70/30) film and on Nylon 7 are given Figure 1. Active area, displacement current and remanent polarization are precisely determined for each PVDF (9 µC/cm²) or P(VDF-TrFE) (7.5µC/cm²) films prepared. It should be pointed out that for the P(VDF-TrFE) copolymers, reproductible remanent polarization of 7.5 µC/cm² can be obtained for thicknesses ranging from 2 µm up to 1 mm. For Nylon 7, the remanent polarization reaches the value of 8 µC/cm².

Intrinsic piezoelectric properties : Direct evaluation of intrinsic thickness-mode characteristics is impossible in very lossy piezoelectric PVDF polymer and P(VDF-TrFE) copolymers. A characterisation method has been developed by R. Heintz[7] and H. Lefebvre[8] at ISL. In particular, they have studied an intrinsic characterisation of thickness-mode samples made from P(VDF-TrFE) piezoelectric copolymers as well as PVDF, based on an entirely automatic fitting of the simulated and measured electrical impedance frequency curves. Some intrinsic parameters of the PVDF and P(VDF-TrFE) 70/30 copolymer are given :

	resonance frequency	coupling factor	permittivity
PVDF	39.6 MHz	16.1%	6.2
VDF/TrFE	2.5 MHz	23.6 %	5.5

The measured characteristics are the signature of the quality and reproducibility of the materials prepared and poled.

PIEZOELECTRIC HYDROSTATIC PRESSURE RESPONSE OF PVDF AND P(VDF-TRFE) COPOLYMERS.

Prior works have shown that the piezoelectric response of ferroelectric polymers under hydrostatic compression was reversible at low pressure level. In most cases, experimentations were conducted in a quasi isothermal regime[9]. Study of the adiabatic piezoelectric response has been investigated by inducing hydrostatic compression pressure. In order to have an adiabatic phenomenon, the compression pulses must be generated rapidly[8]. Toward this end, a high pressure chamber has been designed and built in which hydrostatic compression pulses above 1.5 GPa can be generated on the polymer sample and with a total pulse-length of 10 ms. The electric charge released is measured through a charge amplifier or via digitally integration of the delivered current versus time as a function of the measured hydrostatic compression pulse induced. Thus it is possible to plot the "electrical charge released" diagram in a quasi adiabatic regime (Figure 2). This diagram shows that the response of both PVDF and P(VDF-TrFE) copolymers is reversible until and above 0.76 Pa. Higher activity is observed with P(VDF-TrFE) copolymers. In both cases the delivered charge follows exactly the hydrostatic pulse and upon unloading to zero stress, the charge is observed to return to zero.

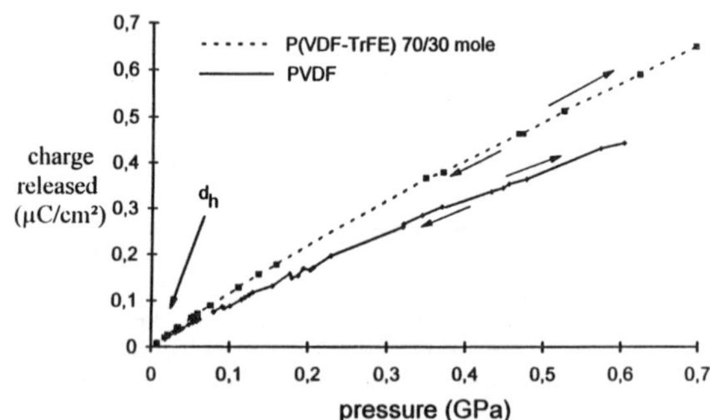

Figure 2. Electrical charge released versus hydrostatic pressure

PIEZOELECTRIC RESPONSE OF PVDF AND P(VDF-TrFE) UNDER SHOCK LOADING.

Background Studies of shock compression response of PVDF[3,13] and P(VDF-TrFE) copolymer[10] in a "standard" configuration have been especially a continuing effort of ISL, Sandia National Laboratories to develop high quality, reproductible sensors material and to determine their physical characteristics under high pressure shock compression. In fact, shock-compression gauges cannot be "calibrated". Even in the direct shock experiment, the controlled shock-compression experiment serves as a shock-calibration only if the reproducibility of the piezoelectric polymer is evaluated quantitatively and a persistent reproductible material is available.

At Sandia National Laboratories the principal experimental tool used to study the shock response is the compressed-gas gun which subjects the piezoelectric samples to precise, controlled shock loading with impactors and targets of well defined standard materials to control the stress input. Impact velocities are measured to accuracies and precisions of 0.1%. At the Institute of Saint-Louis, the experimental measures of electrical response of shock compressed piezoelectric polymer films are carried out on new impact-loading facility which is a powder gun 20 mm in diameter. The accuracy and precision are about 0.3%. In both laboratories, low loss coaxial cables and 1 GHz digitizers provide the high-frequency recording capability required to properly interpret the sensor responses. The responses are measured in the "current mode" to provide both a simple circuit and the most revealing electrical behavior.

Previous observations[6] of the PVDF piezoelectric charge response data to 50 GPa show significant deviations from idealized, continuous behavior between about 12 and 20 GPa. These differences were observed for both sapphire and copper standard impactors. Above about 16 GPa, the observed behavior appears to follow a well-defined relationship, but more scatter is observed than at pressures less than 10 GPa. Various PVDF film materials have been investigated and the difference in response does not appear to be related to the starting film.

It should be recalled that initial current data obtained for conditions in which the signal rise time is less than the transit time, the so called "thick gauge mode" follow a linear relation until 10 GPa[3].

PVDF HIGH PRESSURE RESPONSE

Considerations[6] of the effects of shock properties of standard materials, electronic circuit, the PVDF material and the gauge package have lead to PVDF polymer gauges as well as low inductance gauges with a new poling procedure, in order to identify the origin of the deviations observed (preceding section).

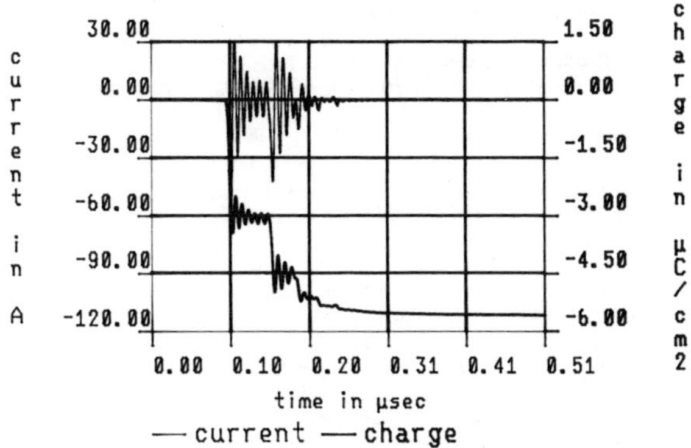

Figure 3. Current pulse and electrical charge versus time for a precisely-poled standard PVDF gauge (shock pressure 25.5 GPa). This standard gauge exhibits non-negligible inductance due to the spacing between the leads.

Impact loading is produced by controlled impact in a powder gun (caliber 20 mm) at ISL, or compressed gas gun (SNLA). The symmetrical impact of an impactor and target copper provides the loading. The gauge element is placed on the impact surface of the target material. The PVDF gauge is insulated on both sides with a Kel-F film of 110 µm in thickness. Kel-F matches the shock impedance of the PVDF. In this configuration the initial stress wave produced by impact is that typical of the impact of the copper impactor on the PVDF gauge. This wave then, reverberates between the impactor and target until stress is reached equal to that for the standard impactor and target.

The electrical signal from the shock-compressed PVDF gauge is recorded in the current mode : the gauge provides a signal dependent on the stress rate called here "multiple shock". Upon integration of the current pulse, the electrical charge- versus -time is obtained (Figure 3 and Figure 4).

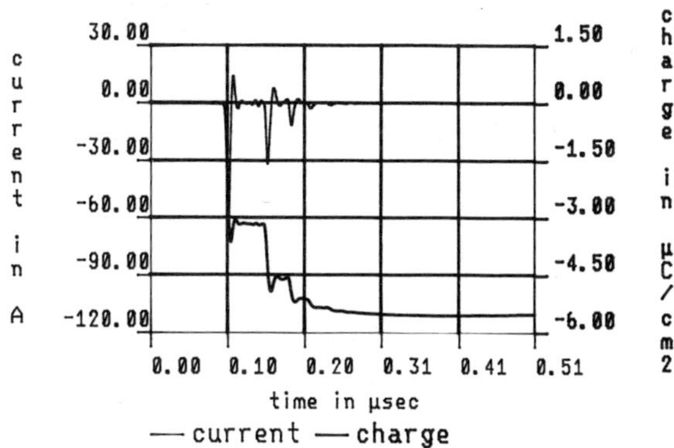

Figure 4. Current pulse and electrical charge of a low inductance PVDF gauge versus time (shock pressure 27 GPa).

The precisely poled PVDF gauges were subjected to shock loading between 10 and 35 GPa and have presented following characteristics: area ranges from 9.1 to 9.15 mm^2 after poling, maximum value of displacement current ranges from 7.5 to 7.7 µA, remanent polarization is between 9.1 and 9.2µC/cm^2. It should be pointed out that these two last values were measured for 7.7 kV sine wave high voltage applied during poling at a frequency equal to 0.08 Hz. The piezoelectric response of such precisely poled PVDF gauges is depicted on Figure 5.

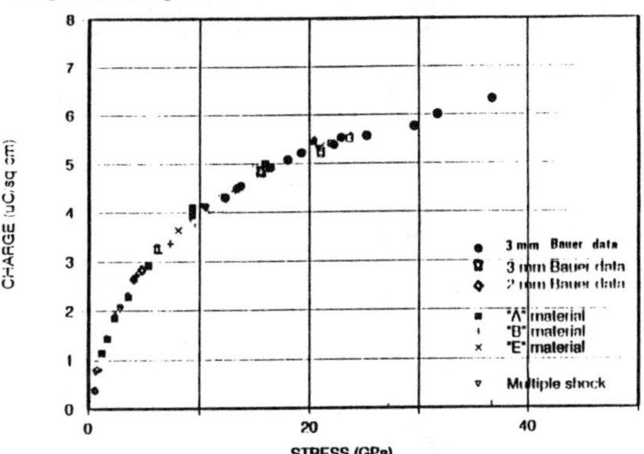

Figure 5: Piezoelectric polarization data for precisely-poled Bauer PVDF from 10 MPa to 35 GPa. Data below 10 GPa are from references 12 and 13.

It is observed that PVDF stress rate gauges show continuous response to pressures approaching 40 GPa. In particular, we do not observe deviation in the shock pressure range 10 to 16 GPa. The results included copper impactors and targets.

P(VDF-TrFE) BEHAVIOR

Piezoelectric response under shock compression The piezoelectric response of P(VDF-TrFE) copolymers under shock loading has been reported in a previous paper[10]. All these results show that in first approximation, the response of the P(VDF-TrFE) gauge is a continuous function of the shock pressure until 28 GPa. The data obtained, Figure 6, were obtained from a laboratory resin. The piezoelectric response is observed to be higher than that of PVDF.

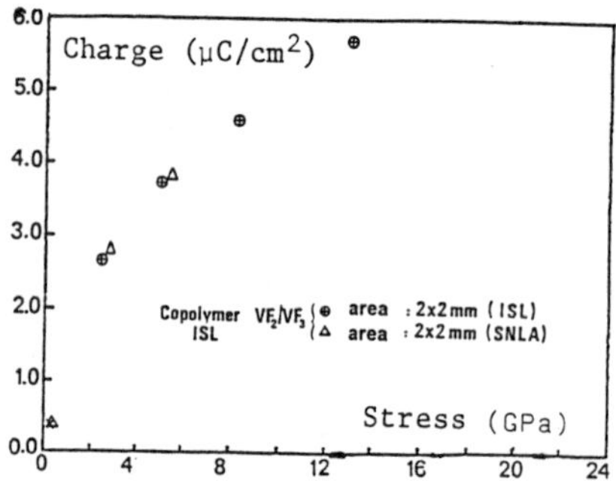

Figure 6. Piezoelectric polarization data for P(VDF-TrFE) from 0.2 GPa to 16 GPa. Data are from reference 10.

The precise determination of the response of reproducible copolymers $P(VDF_{0.7}\text{-}TrFE_{0.3})$ in a gauge configuration similar to that of PVDF is of fundamental interest. Thin copolymer gauges of 8 μm in thickness and with an active area of 4.10^{-2} mm^2 prepared with a new poling procedure have been subjected to a shock wave action. At a pressure level of 9 GPa rise ?? times of the current are of the order of 2 ns and the precision of the delivered charge is comparable to that of PVDF with 9 mm^2 areas. Further studies are needed to explore this new potential. Thick copolymers (thickness of 1 mm), poles at the same level are strong candidates for current shock gauges. As shown[10] and presented in a companion paper[11] thick piezoelectric copolymer seems to work like piezoelectric X-cut quartz.

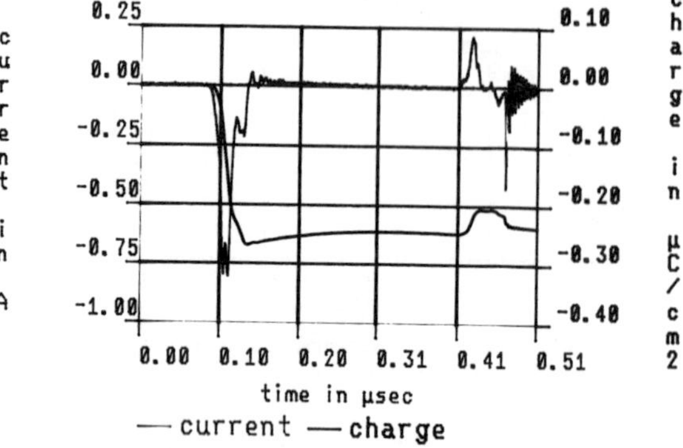

Figure 7. Current pulse and electrical charge versus time for a Nylon 7 sample. (Shock pressure 1.9 GPa).

NYLON

At ISL, first responses on the Nylon 7 poled and electroded in a gauge configuration under shock wave action, are shown in figure 7. As we can observe, the response of Nylon differs from that of PVDF and P(VDF-TrFE) copolymers. The electrical charge released is lower and the rise time of the current correspond to the transit time of the shock wave through the 35 μm sample thick (area: 5.4 mm^2). Understanding of the behavior of these particular ferroelectric polymer is a subject of future work.

CONCLUSIONS

Some high pressure applications of ferroelectric polymers has been presented.

PVDF stress rate gauges show continuous response with high reproducibility to pressure approaching 35 GPa. It appears that low inductance electrode lead designs and reproductible remanent polarization are (significantly) improving the precision of the piezoelectric response of the PVDF gauges under shock loading, especially for the 3 x 3 mm gauges.

It appears there is considerable potential for use of PVDF gauges as will as of P(VDF-TrFE) copolymer in very high pressure materials investigations.

This is true especially today, because a persistent reproductible source is available.

REFERENCES

[1] A.J. Lovinger, *Jap J. Appl. Phys.* 24, Supplement 24-2, 18 (1985)

[2] *Ferroelectrics* 32 Nos 1-4 (1981) and 115 N°4 (1991).

[3] R.A. Graham, *Solids under High Pressure Shock Compression*, New York: Springer Verlag, 1993, ch 5.2, pp 103-113.

[4] J. Scheinbeim, "New Ferroelectric and Piezoelectric Polymers" in *Proceedings ISAF '92*, 1992, pp. 248-249.

[5] F. Bauer, *Ferroelectrics*, 49, 231 (1983), 115, (1991).

[6] F. Bauer, R.A. Graham, M.U. Anderson, H. Lefebvre, L.M. Lee and R.P. Reed, "Piezoelectric Response of Precisely Poled PVDF to Shock Compression greater than 10 GPa", in *Proceedings of the ISAF 92*, 1992, pp. 273-276.

[7] R. Heintz, *Thesis*, University Paris VII, 1990.

[8] H. Lefebvre, *Thesis*, University Lyon N°93-0048, 1993.

[9] A. Dereggi, "Transduction Phenomena in Ferroelectric Polymers and their Role in Pressure Transducers" in *Ferroelectrics*, 1983, vol.50 pp. 21-26.

[10] F. Bauer, R.A. Graham, L.M. Lee, "Properties of VF_2/ VF_3 Ferroelectric Copolymers; Electrical Response under High Pressure Shock Loading", in *Proceedings of the ISAF'90*, 1990, pp.288-291.

[11] J.P. Romain, F. Bauer, D. Zagouri, M. Boustié, "Measurements of Laser Induced Shock Pressures using PVDF Gauges" to be published *APS Shock Wave Meeting , Colorado Spring* 1993.

[12] L.M. Lee, R.A. Graham, F. Bauer, R.P. Reed, "Standardized Bauer PVDF Piezoelectric Polymer Shock Gauge" in *Journal de Physique*, 1988, pp. 651-657.

[13] R.A. Graham, M.U. Anderson, F. Bauer, R.E. Setchell, "Piezoelectric Polarization of the Ferroelectric Polymer PVDF from 10 MPa to 10 GPa: Studies of Loading - Path Dependence," in *shock Waves in Condensed Matter-1991*, 1992, pp. 883-886.

PFV2 STRESS GAUGES FOR NON-PLANAR WAVE APPLICATIONS. PART I

J.A. CHAREST, M.D. LILLY

Dynasen, Inc. 20 Arnold Place, Goleta, Ca. 93117

A superimposed dual-sensor package, consisting in one biaxially-stretched PVF_2 stress gauge and one bidirectional constantan strain gauge, was developed and tested in controlled non-planar wave environments. The in-plane biaxial strain factors were found to be consistent and symmetrical for both gauges when exposed to compressive in-plane strain effects. In a test that combined compressive stresses and tension in-plane strains in the range of 0-6 % strain and 0-6 Kbars, the output of the PVF_2 gauge was successfully corrected for strain effects using a simple model and was shown to yield highly accurate profiles of net stresses.

1. INTRODUCTION

Over the past few years, many experimenters have been attracted into using PVF_2 (PVDF) stress gauges for their extended capability and simplicity in producing wave profiles using the charge integrator method [1,2,3,4,5]. However, as gauges were often exposed to non planar waves, difficulties arose in data interpretation due to lack of simultaneous in-plane strain measurements and knowledge of their effects on gauges' outputs. By in-plane strains, ε_y and ε_z , (See Fig. 1), we mean unit deformations that affect the areal dimensions of the sensing element.

The first systematic study aimed at investigating the effects of in-plane strains on PVF_2 stress gauges mounted in solids was undertaken by Charest and Lynch [6] using combinations of uniaxially-stretched PVF_2 and mono-directional constantan strain gauges. The results of their investigation were successfully interpreted using a simple model that linearly combines two physical effects, one being a normal stress, σ_G, and the other being an in-plane strain ε_z acting on the element along the leads direction. Having previously found the constantan strain gauge to respond only to in-plane strains [7], and assuming that the plane wave stress proportionality factor for PVF_2 applied equally to non-planar interaction, their model was formulated using Eqs. 1 and 2

$$\frac{Q}{A}=\left(\frac{Q}{A}\right)_{\sigma_G}+\left(\frac{Q}{A}\right)_{\varepsilon_G}=k\sigma_G+\pi_z\varepsilon_z \tag{1}$$

$$\frac{\Delta R}{R}=G_z\varepsilon_z \tag{2}$$

where (Q/A) is the total charge output per unit area of the PVF_2 gauge, $(Q/A)_{\sigma_G}$ is the unit charge release due to stress acting normally upon the element, $(Q/A)_{\varepsilon_G}$ is unit charge release due to in-plane strain effects, k and π_z are proportionality plane stress wave and lateral strain factors, and ΔR/R and G are relative change of resistance and strain proportionality factors of the constantan strain gauge. Conversely, Equations 1 and 2 allow one to infer a net state of normal stresses acting upon the PVF_2 gauge from two sets of measurements.

Following Charest and Lynch's work, the use of a second strain gauge was suggested to account for the other strain effect, ε_y, not measured in their tests but deemed necessary to improve modeling. As one knows, the use of two strain gauges for every PVF_2 gauge can be very complex and prohibitive for many applications. Thus was born the concept of the combination gauge package shown on Fig. 1 consisting of one superimposed biaxially-stretched PVF_2 and one bidirectional constantan strain gauge. Assuming that the effects of strain ε_y and ε_z are symmetrical for both gauges and the states of stresses and strains are the same for both sensors by virtue of their close proximity, one can therefore express our currently proposed bidirectional stress/strain effect model using Eqs. 3 and 4.

$$\frac{Q}{A}=k\sigma_G+\pi_{y,z}\left(\varepsilon_y+\varepsilon_z\right) \tag{3}$$

$$\frac{\Delta R}{R}=G_{y,z}\left(\varepsilon_y+\varepsilon_z\right) \tag{4}$$

where $\pi_{y,z}$ and $G_{y,z}$ are the biaxial in-plane strain factors for the PVF_2 and constantan strain gauge respectively. As one can see, the total strain effects (ε_y+ε_z) can be measured using a single bidirectional strain gauge.

The purpose of this investigation is therefore twofold. First, it is to derive values of in-plane strain coefficient for both biaxially stretched PVF_2 and bi-directional constantan gauges using compression plane wave gas gun tests. Second, it is to evaluate the usefulness of our proposed biaxial model to apply strain corrections when gauges are subjected to combined normal stresses and tension strains.

2. EXPERIMENTAL APPROACH AND RESULTS

2.1 Stress/Strain Gauge Package

Figure 1 shows the superimposed stress/strain gauge concept developed and used in this investigation. It basically consisted in a 25μm biaxially stretched PVF2 stress gauge that is superimposed to a bidirectional 10μm constantan strain gauge. Both gauges had a 3.18 x 3.18 mm element using 25μm polyimide film as a base support. They were laminated on top of one another using low viscosity epoxy resin, the base of the strain gauge serving as the electrical insulation between the two elements. A third layer of 25μm polyimide was added on top of the strain gauge to form a 115μm thick stress/strain gauge package.

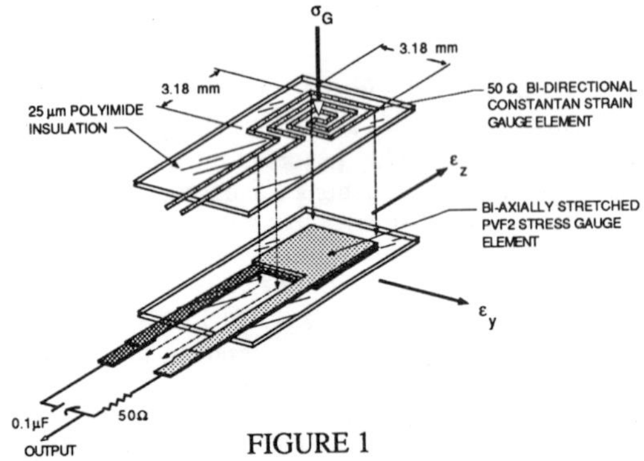

FIGURE 1

Superimposed Dual Gauge Arrangement

From direct experience and also from the observations of others, strain gauge signals have often been marred in past work by electrical noises when used concurrently with PVF2 gauges. This undesirable effect, which we currently attribute to capacitive and/or inductive coupling, is accentuated by rapid risetime wave interactions or when gauges are used in metal test objects. A satisfactory solution that eliminates the above noise problem remains yet to be formulated, but is believed to rest on the use of a thin film Faraday cage around the PVF2 gauge's element. In this current effort, we used maximum lateral separations between the gauge's leads to minimize cross talk effects. We also highly recommend pulse excitations of strain gauges when dealing with PVF2 gauges to improve signal to noise ratios.

The gauges produced for this investigation were made from Dynasen's stock of 25μm biaxially stretched (450%) PVF2 film produced by Solvay of Belgium [8] and 10μm constantan foils produced by Hamilton Technology [9] of U.S.A.. The PVF2 gauges used here were produced and calibrated in accordance to current Dynasen gauge manufacturing and their outputs were recorded using the charge integrator method developed earlier by this organization [2]. The bidirectional strain gauges were also fabricated at Dynasen using its current 50Ω foil gauges laminating and photo etching processes. They were activated using a 50Ω piezoresistive pulse power supply of the type Dynasen CK1-50-300.

2.2 Plane Wave Compression Tests

Figure 2 shows the experimental arrangement used to derive values of the biaxial strain factors $\pi_{y,z}$ and $G_{y,z}$ for the two biaxial gauges investigated. Essentially, it consisted of mounting gauges in the center of a PMMA target and subjecting them to the normal stresses (normal mode) or to combined stresses and in-plane strains (orthogonal mode) in symmetrical plane wave gas gun impact tests. Assuming that stresses and in-plane strains produced in the target were those experienced by the gauges, their values could therefore be inferred making use of the impact velocity, V_F, of the flyer, and the fundamental relationships expressed by Eqs. 5 through 9.

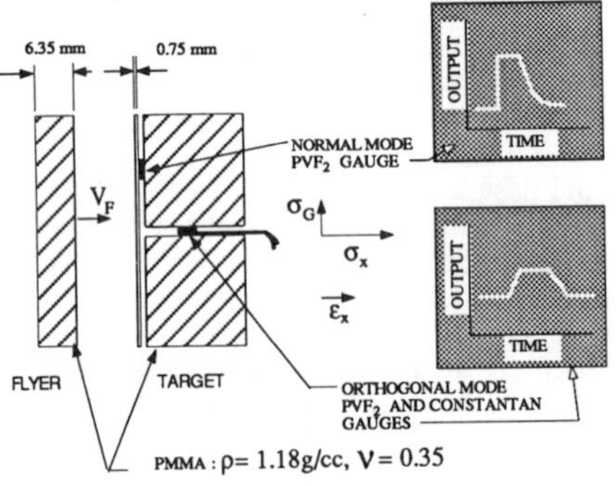

FIGURE 2

Compression Stress and Strain Test

$$\sigma_x = (34.1)U_P + (13.1)U_P^2 + (1.3)U_P^3 \quad (5)$$

$$U_P = \frac{V_F}{2} \quad (6)$$

$$\sigma_x = \rho_o U_s U_p \quad (7)$$

$$\sigma_G = \sigma_x\left(\frac{\nu}{1-\nu}\right) \quad (8)$$

$$\varepsilon_x = \left(\frac{U_p}{U_s}\right) \quad (9)$$

where σ_x is stress in PMMA in Kbar, U_p and U_s are particle and shock velocity in mm/μsec and ε_x is the uniaxial strain induced in the target.

The normal mode arrangement was used primarily to verify that the output of each PVF2 gauge was consistent with its 0.1 Kbar quasi-static calibration, a method shown earlier by this organization to directly reflect its plane wave calibration. Indeed, as in-plane strain coefficients are directly linked to gauges initial piezoactivity, it is necessary to normalize individual outputs to account for gauge-to-gauge variation and thus make it possible to use the universal PVF2 stress calibration developed earlier at around .0180μc/cm^2/0.1 Kbar. See Fig. 5.

Two tests were conducted in accordance to Fig. 2 at impact velocities of 0.0662 and 0.119 mm/µsec respectively involving each time two combination gauge packages. Calculations of the relevant impact parameters of the tests were made using Eq. 5 through 9 and are shown in Table 1. Also shown in Table 1 are biaxial strain factor values inferred from the individual gauge's outputs using Eqs. 3 and 4.

TABLE 1. Compression Stress and Strain Test Results

Test #	Imp. Vel V_F mm/µsec	Imp. Stress σ_x Kbar	Strain ε_x %	Lat. Stress σ_G Kbar	Strain Coeff. $\pi_{y,z}$ µC/cm^2/%	Strain Coeff. $G_{y,z}$	Gauge Package #
1	0.0662	1.14	1.13	0.64	0.08	1.05	1
1					0.083	1.36?	2
2	0.119	2.08	2	1.12	0.081	0.94	1
2					0.079	0.95	2

Since our experiment could only produce one state of in-plane strain (ε_Y or ε_Z) at a time on a given gauge, we mounted the second package of our Test #1 at 90° orientation with respect to the first set of gauges to verify symmetry of in-plane strain response. As one can see in Table 1, a substantially higher value of biaxial strain factor was found for the second constantan gauge. Although this discrepancy remains to be further investigated, we believe it to be the result of preferential etching of the gauge. Indeed, by virtue of its construction, one would expect a strain factor for our bi-directional strain gauge to be around 1.0 in order to be consistent with a gauge factor of 2.0 for the mono-directional constantan strain gauge. Otherwise, all the other biaxial strain coefficient factors produced by the tests appear to be reasonably consistent with one another.

2.3 Compression/Stress /Tension/Strain Test

Figure 3 shows the approach used to subject our superimposed stress/strain gauge packages to states of compression stresses and tension strains and hence to evaluate the usefulness of our proposed biaxial stress/strain model. As one can see, a free rear-surface PMMA flyer was propelled against a PMMA target of same diameter that was instrumented with near-edge mounted PVF_2/Constantan gauges and single carbon stress gauges of same element size. Upon impact, the above arrangement produced a momentary state of plane wave on gauges that was followed shortly thereafter by states of continuously changing compression stresses and in-plane tensions strains. The tension strains ε_Y and ε_Z ($\varepsilon_Y = \varepsilon_Z$) are induced by the radial and circumferential expansion of the target and flyer from the action of unloading waves that can be seen traveling inward toward the axis of symmetry of the arrangement. The test is completed when the compression stress on gauges is reduced to zero upon the return of the unloading wave from the rear face of the flyer. The main purpose of this experiment was to produce strain-corrected net-stress profiles from PVF_2 and constantan gauges' outputs using Eqs. 3 and 4 and the biaxial strain factors derived from our compression tests of Fig. 2 and compare them to the profiles obtained from the carbon gauge outputs.

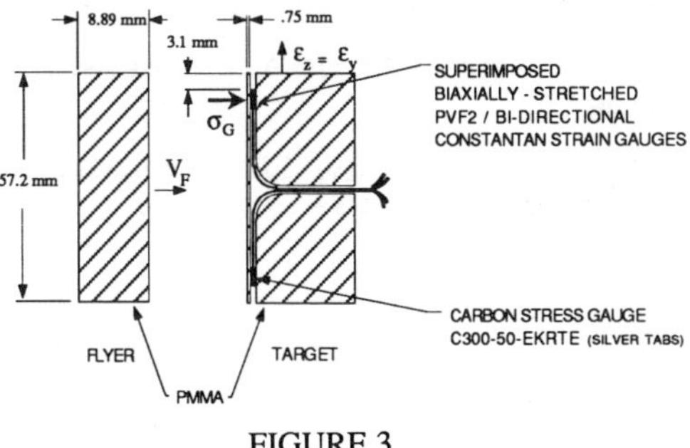

FIGURE 3

Compression Stress/Tension Strain Test

Figure 4 shows the partially analyzed data for our three gauges for our test #3 conducted in accordance to Fig. 3 at .316 mm/µsec of impact velocity (5.72 Kb impact stress). As one can see, the PVF_2 and carbon

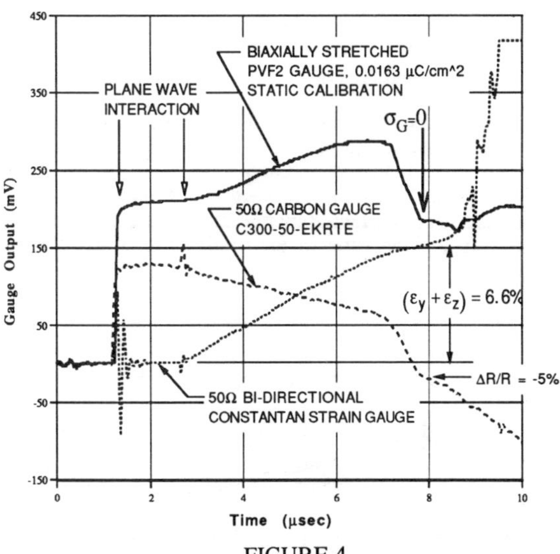

FIGURE 4

Uncorrected Gauge Outputs for Compression Stress /Tension Strain Test

stress gauges' outputs show an abrupt jump reaching first the Hugoniot plateau of the impact test and thereafter drifting positively or negatively from the effects of in-plane tensions strains of the expanding target. One must remember here that the effects on PVF_2 of compression stress and tension strains are in the same direction where they are opposite for the case of the carbon stress gauge. On the other hand the output of the bidirectional strain gauge can be seen to be actually insensitive to the impact stress, as we mentioned earlier, its output showing a continuous increased state of tension strain until the end of the test. The apparent residual stress indicated at 7.8μsec by both PVF_2 and carbon stress gauges is clearly the result of net tension strains as shown by the constantan gauge.

Using the calibrations shown of Fig. 5 for PVF_2 and carbon stress gauges, net states of compression stresses were derived from their recorded outputs, making use of Eqs. 3 and 4 and the in-plane biaxial strain factors

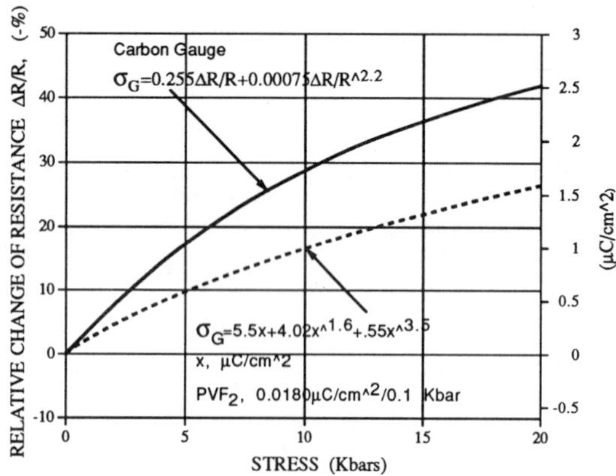

FIGURE 5

PVF_2 and Carbon Stress Gauges' Calibrations

derived earlier. The results of our calculations, which we have called strain-corrected stress profiles are presented in Fig. 6 showing very good agreement between the PVF_2 and carbon gauge. The output of the carbon gauge was also strain-corrected by linearly scaling the measured strain at a given time to the total strain effect seen at 7.8μsec (σ_G=0).

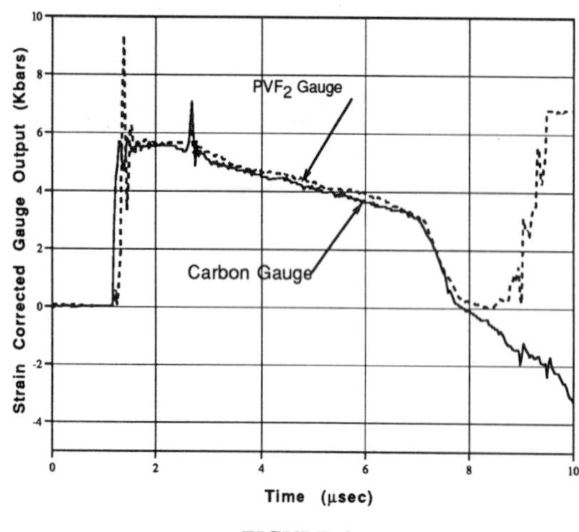

FIGURE 6

Strain Corrected PVF_2 and Carbon Gauge Outputs

3. CONCLUSIONS

The results of this investigation are very encouraging as they clearly show the potential for the biaxially stretched PVF_2 and bidirectional strain gauge combination to be used in non-planar wave environments and to be capable of yielding states of net stresses . There is of course the need to further refine the strain factor values defined by this work and also to further validate our stress/strain model over a wider range of stresses. Finally, techniques must be developed so that electrical noise generated on strain gauges' outputs by PVF_2 gauges are reduced to an acceptable level, ultimately allowing continuous DC excitations of strain gauges.

4. REFERENCES

1. J.A. Charest and C.S. Lynch. Comparative Study of Commercial Piezofilm Stress Gauges, 39th ARA Meeting, Albuquerque, N.M. (Oct. 10-13, 1988).

2. J.A. Charest and C.S. Lynch. The Response of PVF2 Stress Gauges to Shock Wave Loading. Proceedings of the American Physical Society Topical Conference on Shock Compression of Condensed Matter, (1989).

3. J.A. Charest and C.S. Lynch. The Use of the Piezofilm Stress Gauge Technique. 41st ARA Meeting, San Diego, Ca., USA , (1990).

4. J.A. Charest and C.S. Lynch. A Simple Approach to Piezofilm Stress Gauges. Proceedings of the American Physical Society Topical Conference on Shock Compression of Condensed Matter, (1991).

5. C.S. Lynch and J.A. Charest. Practical Considerations on the Piezofilm Gauge Technique. Proceedings of the American Physical Society Topical Conference on Shock Compression of Condensed Matter, (1991).

6. J.A. Charest and C.S. Lynch. Effects of Lateral Strains on PVF2 Stress Gauges. 42nd ARA Meeting, Adelaide, Australia, (1991).

7. J.A. Charest. Development of a Strain Compensated Shock Pressure Gauge. Dynasen Inc., TR-005, Feb. 1979.

8. Solvay, S.A. 33 Prince Albert, Brussel, B1050 Belgium.

9. Hamilton Technology, 1780 Rohrerstown Rd., Lancaster, Penn. 17604, USA.

Experiments and Analysis of Lateral Piezoresistance Gauges

Michael K. W. Wong
Computational Physics Research and Development Department
Sandia National Laboratories
Albuquerque, New Mexico, USA 87185-5800

The response of lateral piezoresistance gauges to shock wave uniaxial strain loading has been examined in a combined experimental and calculational effort. Plate impact experiments provided lateral gauge data which were analyzed using quasi-static and dynamic inclusion analyses. Experimental data showed that the response of the lateral gauge output depended upon the matrix material and gauge emplacement method. The calculations indicated that these differences were due to complex gauge-matrix interactions, These were influenced by the stress and strain distributions in and around the gauge, plasticity effects, material properties, and emplacement conditions.

INTRODUCTION

The work presented in this paper is part of a comprehensive effort [1-5] to understand and characterize the response of piezoresistance foil gauges under shock compression, uniaxial strain loads. This particular work examines the response of lateral piezoresistance gauges under such loads. A lateral gauge has the major surface of the foil parallel to the direction of wave propagation.

This work has been motivated by the need to be able to specify the lateral stress in shocked materials. However, for uniaxial strain experiments, two major issues make the interpretation of lateral gauge data difficult. The first is that the lateral stress in a material cannot be determined solely from the conservation equations for wave propagation in uniaxial strain [2]. Thus, a lateral stress measurement cannot be validated. Second, the lateral stress in the gauge is not, in general, uniquely related to the lateral stress in the material [3] (or matrix). Rather, the foil gauge must be considered as an inclusion in the matrix, requiring solution of the resulting boundary value problem in order to properly resolve the stress fields in and around the gauge. Other approaches and points of view regarding lateral stress gauge response may be found in the literature [6-8].

In this work experiments and analyses were used to gain an understanding of lateral gauge response. A series of plate impact experiments were performed in which targets of fused silica or aluminum oxide (alumina), containing lateral gauges of manganin or ytterbium piezoresistance foil were subjected to shock wave loading. Quasi-static and dynamic analyses were performed to interpret the resistance change data in terms of gauge-matrix interaction. These analyses were used to examine and understand differences in lateral gauge data obtained in the experiments.

EXPERIMENTAL TECHNIQUE

The experiments used designs similar to previous work reported by Gupta and coworkers [1-5]. The gauges were stamped from manganin or ytterbium foil and embedded in carefully machined grooves in the matrix which closely matched the shape and depth of the gauge. Thus, as closely as possible, the gauge was fully embedded and in contact with the matrix.

The matrix consisted of 5.7 cm diameter disks of fused silica or alumina. Many of these disks were cut in half to permit insertion of lateral gauges. A typical configuration is shown in Figure 1.

Both the gauge and matrix materials had been well characterized to permit accurate analysis of the gauge response. The ytterbium and manganin foils were characterized using methods described by Chen, et al. [12]. The fused silica and alumina had been characterized by Connor [13] and Gupta [14], respectively using compression-shear methods.

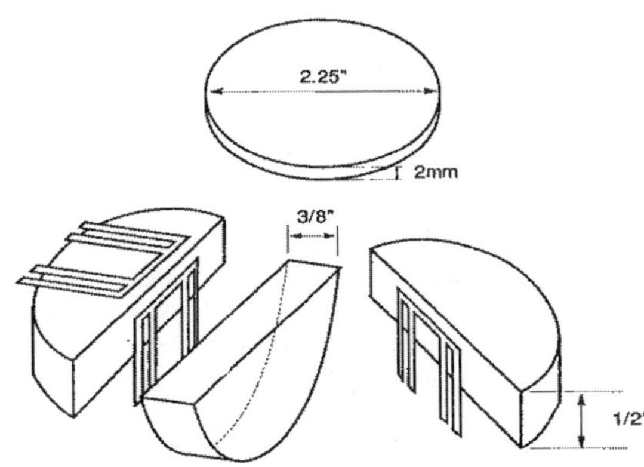

Figure 1. Typical experimental configuration.

A set of 19 experiments were performed, 17 in fused silica and 2 in alumina. These data were supplemented with data from a previous set of experiments of manganin gauges in alumina performed by Gupta and Gupta [5]. These data spanned a stress range of 5 - 90 kbar, matrix longitudinal stress.

Figure 2 shows the steady state resistance change values for ytterbium lateral gauges in both fused silica and alumina matrices. Similarly, Figure 3 shows the steady state resistance change values for manganin lateral gauges in both matrices. Additionally, both figures compare the experimental data with quasi-static and dynamic inclusion analyses.

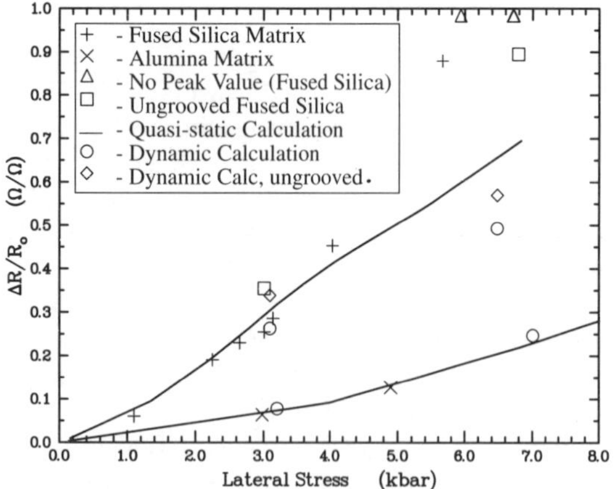

Figure 2. Ytterbium lateral gauge data, quasi-static and dynamic calculation results.

For both ytterbium and manganin lateral gauges, the steady state resistance change clearly reveals a dependence upon matrix material. The data in fused silica matrices is higher than in alumina matrices. The difference is also indicated in both the quasi-static and dynamic inclusion analyses. This trend indicates that the resistance change and lateral stress cannot be expressed as a unique relationship.

Additional experiments, plotted in Figure 2, were performed with ytterbium gauges in ungrooved matrices (the two data points denoted by squares). This configuration produced steady state resistance change values which differed from the data for gauges in grooved matrices at the same stress. These results indicate that the gauge response is sensitive to the emplacement method.

Experiments at the highest matrix lateral stresses in fused silica produced highly time dependent lateral gauge response with no steady state value. These observations are discussed in [9] and [11].

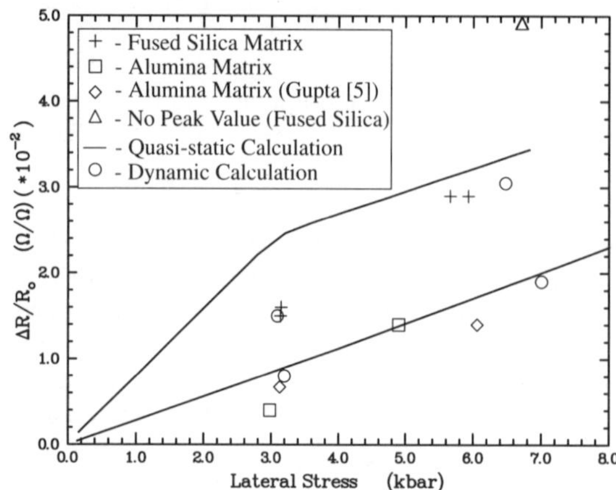

Figure 3. Manganin lateral gauge data, quasi-static and dynamic calculation results.

To further illustrate the differences in lateral gauge response, Figure 4 shows the records of three ytterbium lateral gauge outputs: one each in a grooved fused silica matrix, ungrooved fused silica matrix, and grooved alumina matrix. The ytterbium gauges were identical in geometry and from the same batch of foil. All three gauges were subjected to matrix lateral stresses of 3.0 kbar. However, each record indicates unique gauge response. In particular, the steady state resistance change values are different in each case.

QUASI-STATIC INCLUSION ANALYSES

Quasi-static solutions to the gauge-matrix interaction and electromechanical problems were obtained using methods developed by Gupta [1]. As shown in

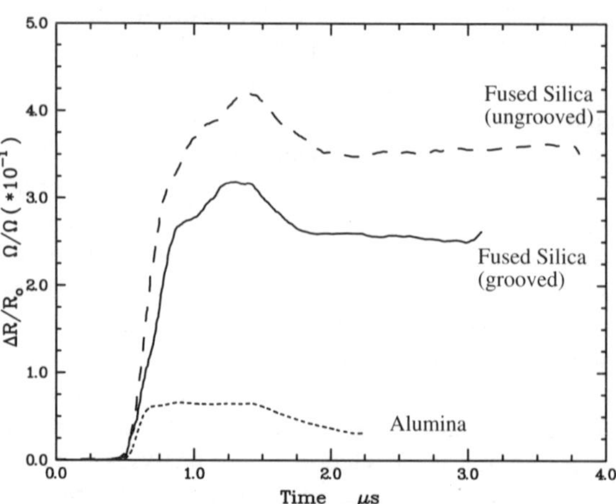

Figure 4. Comparison of ytterbium lateral gauge output at 3 kbar lateral stress.

Figure 2 and Figure 3, these analyses were able to predict measured resistance changes with reasonable accuracy. Furthermore, these calculations demonstrate that the lateral gauge response depends on the matrix and gauge materials and is not a unique measure of matrix lateral stress. However, the limitations of this approach (see [11]) do not allow it to properly analyze the ungrooved gauge case nor the nonequilibrium cases.

DYNAMIC INCLUSION ANALYSES

Dynamic finite element calculations were performed to examine the response of the lateral gauges from impact through equilibration to the steady state resistance change. The EXCALIBUR finite element program [15] was used for the analyses.

The simulations were performed in plane strain. The cross section of the sensing element of the gauge was in the plane of calculation and the flow of current through the gauge was perpendicular to the plane. Simulations of the three experiments shown in Figure 4 are discussed.

For calculations in the grooved fused silica and alumina matrices, the gauge was modeled as an inclusion, completely surrounded by the matrix material. For the calculation of the gauge in the ungrooved fused silica matrix, material in the plane of the gauge foil was modeled as epoxy. Details of the calculational method may be found in [10] and [11].

The most significant finding of the dynamic calculations is that the distribution of stress and strain in the gauge is highly nonuniform. Figure 5 shows the highly nonlinear stress and strain distributions through the width of the gauge for the case of the ytterbium gauge in the grooved fused silica matrix. The zero position is the upstream edge of the piezoresistance foil. Both stress and strains are largest at the upstream edge. Also, the longitudinal and lateral stresses in the gauge are nearly equal. Furthermore, the strains are of similar magnitudes, but opposite sense. The interpretation of these two graphs is that the shock, propagating through the matrix, loads the upstream edge of the foil and induces plastic deformation. This plastic response increases the lateral stress in the gauge. The gauge expands laterally in the upstream region, pressing upon the surrounding matrix.

In the fused silica matrix, a lateral stress of 3 kbar corresponded to a longitudinal stress 23 kbar. Thus, a relatively large longitudinal stress loaded the edge of the gauge while a smaller lateral stress provided limited containment of the expanding foil. As a result, the lateral strain in the upstream region of the gauge indicates expansion.

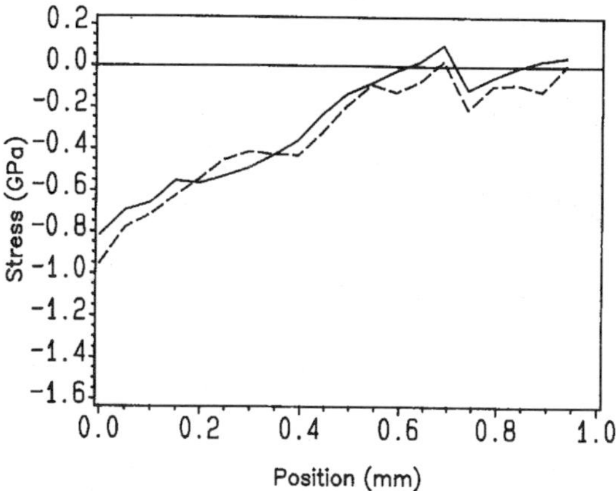

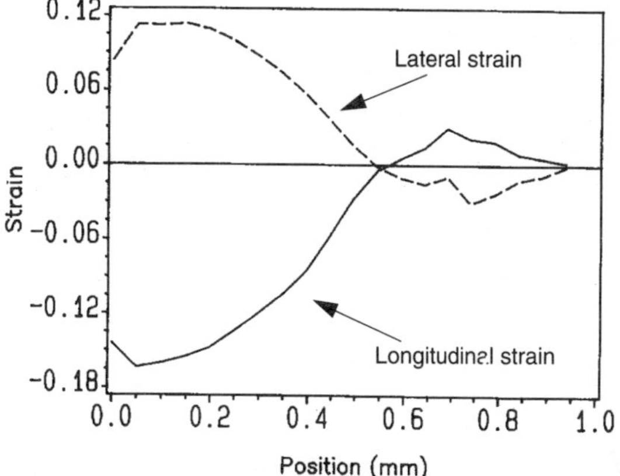

Figure 5. Steady state stress (top) and strain (bottom) distributions through gauge width for grooved fused silica.

By comparison, Figure 6 shows the stress distributions for the ytterbium gauge in the alumina matrix. In this case, the matrix longitudinal stress was 9.8 kbar while the matrix lateral stress was 3.0 kbar. The stress and strain distributions are quite different from those of the fused silica case. The stress distribution is more uniform. The effect of the matrix longitudinal stress does not dominate the stress distribution. Furthermore, the lateral stress in the gauge is close to the matrix lateral stress.

The stress distribution in the gauge for the ungrooved fused silica case is shown in Figure 7. The stresses in this case are more uniform than for the grooved case with the most nonuniformity occurring at upstream end of the gauge. Because, the gauge was surrounded by epoxy in the plane of the foil, the loading

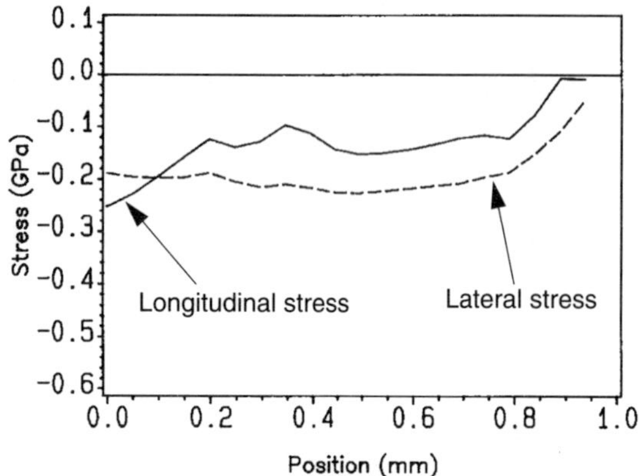

Figure 6. Steady state stress distribution through gauge width for grooved alumina matrix calculation.

due to the longitudinal wave was less than for the grooved case. Furthermore, because the gauge material was stiffer than the surrounding epoxy, the gauge experienced larger compression than for the grooved case. The larger lateral compression contributed to the higher resistance change shown in Figure 4.

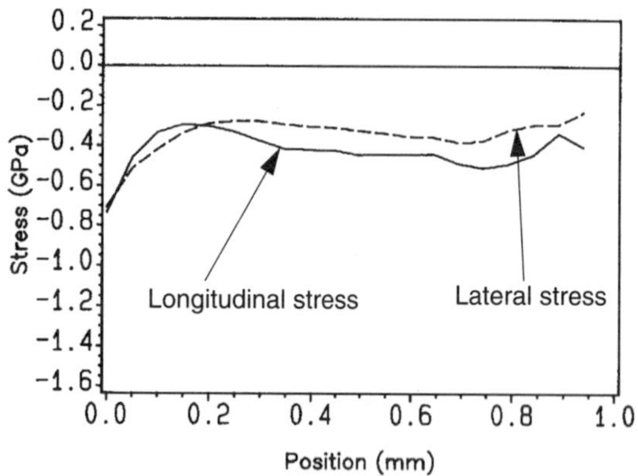

Figure 7. Steady state stress distribution through gauge wi for ungrooved fused silica matrix calculation.

CONCLUSIONS

This combined experimental and calculational effort has been used to gain an understanding of lateral gauge response under dynamic loading. The experimental data show that the response of lateral piezoresistance gauges is dependent upon matrix material and emplacement method, not simply the matrix lateral stress. Furthermore, the calculations show that the response is a complex gauge-matrix interaction. The effects of gauge plasticity and longitudinal loading must be considered when examining the interaction. The approach and general understanding of lateral piezoresistance gauges from this work can be the basis for examining gauge response under more complicated loading conditions and more practical gauge designs.

ACKNOWLEDGEMENTS

This work was performed with Dr. Y.M. Gupta of the Shock Dynamics Laboratory, Washington State University. Paul Bellamy and Jerry Thompson provided substantial experimental support. Dr. Y.M. Ito and Y. Muki provided the EXCALIBUR program and invaluable guidance with the dynamic calculations.

REFERENCES

[1] Gupta, Y.M., *J. Appl. Phys.,* 54, p. 6256 (1983).

[2] Gupta, Y.M. et al., *Appl. Phys. Lett.,* 37, p. 395 (1983).

[3] Gupta, S.C. and Y.M. Gupta, *J. Appl. Phys.,* 57, p. 2464 (1985).

[4] Brar, N.S. and Y.M. Gupta, *J. Appl. Phys.,* 61, p. 1304 (1987).

[5] Gupta, S.C. and Y.M. Gupta, *J. Appl. Phys.,* 62, p. 2603 (1987).

[6] Bernstein, D. et al., *Behavior of Dense Media Under High Dynamic Pressures,* Gordon and Breach, New York, p. 461, 1968.

[7] Kanel, G. I., A. M. Molodets, and A. N. Dremin, *Combust. Explos. Shock Waves,* 13, p. 772, 1978.

[8] Rosenberg, Z., and Y. Partom, *J. Appl. Phys.,* 58, p. 3072, 1985.

[9] Wong, M.K.W. and Y.M. Gupta, "Response of Lateral Piezoresistance Gauges in Fused Silica Shocked to 60 kbar," *Proceedings of Shock Compression of Condensed Matter - 1989,* pp. 829-832.

[10] Wong, M.K.W. and Y.M. Gupta, "Dynamic Inclusion Analyses of Lateral Piezoresistance Gauges Under Shock Wave Loading," *Proceedings of Shock Compression of Condensed Matter - 1991,* pp. 871-874.

[11] Wong, M.K.W., "Experiments and Analysis to Understand the Response of Lateral Piezoresistance Gauges Under Dynamic Loading," Ph.D. thesis, Washington State University, 1991.

[12] Chen, D. Y., et al., *J. Appl. Phys.,* 55, p. 3984 (1984).

[13] Connor, M.P., "Shear Wave Measurements to Determine the Nonlinear Elastic Response of Fused Silica Under Shock Loading," M.S. thesis, Washington State University, 1988.

[14] Gupta, Y.M., *J. Geophys. Res.,* 88, p. 4304 (1983).

[15] EXCALIBUR is a dynamic finite element program of California Research and Technology, Chatsworth, California.

DETERMINATION OF EQUIVALENT CIRCUIT FOR PVDF SHOCK-PRESSURE GAUGES

J. D. Kotulski, M. U. Anderson, B. C. Brock, J. Gomez, R. A. Graham, and C. N. Vittitoe
Sandia National Laboratories
Albuquerque, New Mexico 87185-5800

Broadband impedance measurements of a PVDF shock-pressure gauge are used to build an equivalent circuit for the gauge. The essential components are a gauge capacitance and a low-loss transmission line. Component features are consistent with the physical characteristics. With knowledge of this circuit, troublesome oscillations can be anticipated and prevented.

INTRODUCTION

Polyvinylidene fluoride (PVDF) shock-pressure gauges are an interesting subset of piezoelectric devices because of applications as electromechanical transducers.[1] In some applications, an equivalent circuit helps clarify the device operation and extend its range of operation. For piezoelectric devices, such equivalent circuits may be complicated, with multiple stray capacitances and associated inductances required to explain the system response.[2] Building an equivalent circuit for the PVDF devices used to record shock-pressure waves is a critical step toward understanding electrical resonances that interfere with accurate measurements. We outline our use of the pressure gauges, review the measurement difficulty, develop the equivalent circuit, and show how the circuit accounts for the behavior.

GAUGE BEHAVIOR

Figure 1 shows a PVDF gauge. The two 44-mm-long (after cut to length for use) sputtered Au-over-Pt leads form a lossy transmission line. The two leads are deposited on opposite sides of the 23.1-μm-thick PVDF polymer film. Each lead is 3 mm wide and >0.2 μm thick. At one end the leads form a capacitor with crossover area 9.2 mm^2 and capacitance 44.1 pF at low frequencies. This region is the active area that drives the gauge. As manufactured, the lead resistances add to 9.2 Ω. Each gauge has a serial number (E530H10 here). These data are provided by the manufacturer, Metravib RDS, France.

In a typical application, a shock wave passes from the front to the rear electrode of the capacitor, displacing charge through the piezoelectric effect.[3] Increases in the shock stress increase the displaced charge. The charge propagates down the leads forming the strip transmission line and induces a voltage across a current-viewing resistor (CVR) connected across the open end of the leads in Figure 1. A 50-Ω coax carries this signal to the recorder. The CVR has an accurately measured resistance near 0.01 Ω. Figure 2 shows the record of a typical shock wave and the resulting current in the CVR. The current reaches a 97-A peak, with a 4-ns full-width-at-half-maximum.

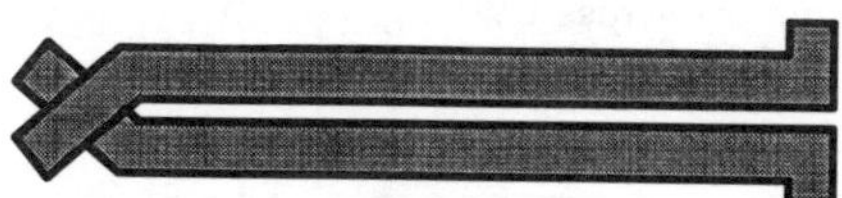

Fig. 1. Projected view of PVDF gauge.

Even though the current from the gauge typically maintains the general characteristics in Figure 2, at times the current pulse is quite different. Figure 3 shows spurious oscillations from the electrical-circuit response that interfere with analysis of the pressure data. A Fourier transform of the data in Figure 3 shows a spectral peak near 200 MHz.

EQUIVALENT CIRCUIT FOR PVDF GAUGE

Figure 4 shows an equivalent circuit.[4] The current produced by the mechanical stress is modeled by a current source in parallel with the capacitance of the gauge active area. The R_m and L_m allow for a large resistance and inductance that may also appear across the active portion. The electrode section is characterized by an inductance L_e, capacitance C_e, and resistance R_e per unit length for the strip transmission line.

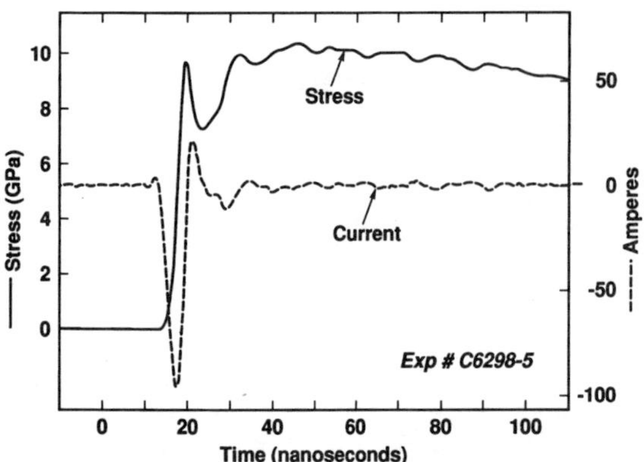

Fig. 2. Pressure wave incident on PVDF gauge and resulting current across CVR. R_{CVR}= 0.01016 Ω, gauge area 9.095 mm^2.

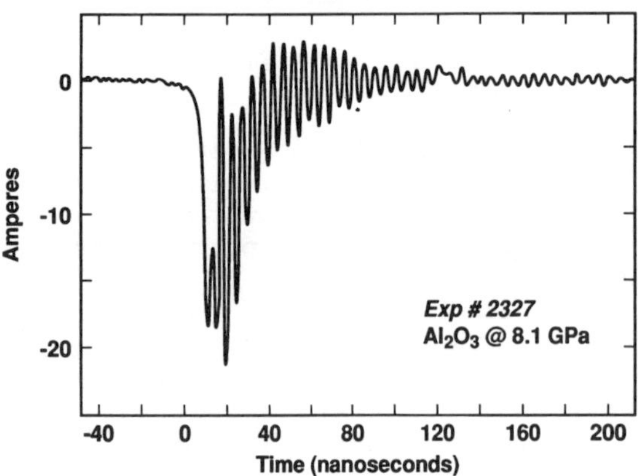

Fig. 3. Oscillatory current induced into CVR. R_{CVR}=0.01986 Ω, gauge area 9.050 mm^2.

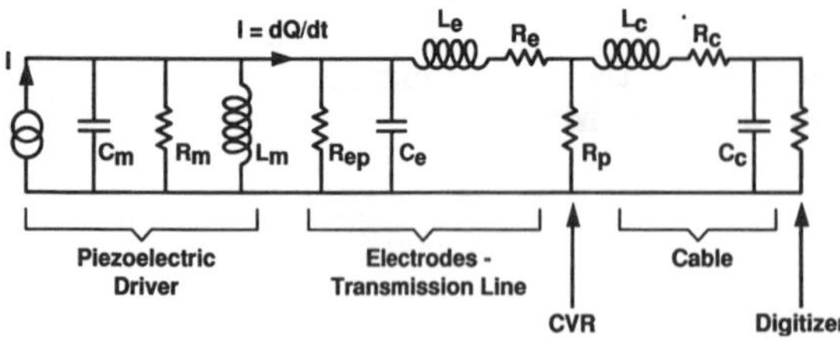

Fig. 4. Lumped parameter model for PVDF gauge and associated circuitry.

The R_{ep} allows for the possibility of a small conductivity in the PVDF material between the electrodes forming a resistive shunt path. The CVR resistance is R_p. The L_c, R_c, and C_c are lumped parameters representing the 42-ft-long cable transmitting the signal to a 50-Ω load at the digitizer. In many cases, especially for long cables, these lumped parameters are better represented as a transmission line. Here our emphasis is on the components shown in Figure 1.

Several parameters in Figure 4 can be assigned approximate values. From cable characteristics, C_c=1 nF, L_c=25 μH, R_c is negligible, R_p=0.01 Ω. Termination impedance at the digitizer is 50 Ω. Remaining parameters characterize the basic gauge in Figure 1.

A coax test lead (connector) was soldered to the open gauge leads in Figure 1, and this configuration was probed by an impedance analyzer over the range 1 MHz to 1 GHz. To ensure that the results represent the geometry, separate measurements were made for the connector, the connector plus gauge strip leads, and the connector, gauge leads, and the gauge capacitor all assembled. The connector behaves as a 1-pF capacitor.

The gauge leads are represented by a coplanar-strip parallel-wire transmission line with leads of width w=3 mm separated by distance b=1 mm, embedded in a material with effective relative dielectric constant $\epsilon_r(f)$. The leads have a characteristic impedance (Reference 5)

$$Z_0 = 120\pi \frac{K(k)}{K(\sqrt{1-k^2})} \frac{1}{\sqrt{\epsilon_r}},$$

where K is the complete elliptic integral of the first kind, ϵ_r is the relative dielectric constant of the surrounding medium, and $k = b/(b+2w) = 1/7$.

When the connector and lead measurements are made, the connector is in parallel with the input impedance of the transmission line. For a line of length l with an open-circuit termination (for the leads alone) and with characteristic impedance Z_0, the input impedance is[6]

$$Z(l) = Z_0 \left(\frac{1 + e^{-j2\beta l}}{1 - e^{-j2\beta l}} \right).$$

The $j\beta$ is the imaginary portion of the propagation constant. At low frequency, $\beta l \ll 1$, and $Z(l) = Z_0/(j\beta l)$ for a lossless line and for $2\beta l < 0.05$. Assuming quasi-TEM propagation,

$$\beta = 2\pi f \sqrt{\epsilon_r}/c,$$

where c is the speed of light in free space. Removing the connector contribution from the connector and leads measurement gives data for $Z(l)$. Using the low-frequency $Z(l)$ and neglecting losses, the expression for Z_0 allows the effective relative dielectric constant, ϵ_r, to be evaluated: $\epsilon_r = 1.53$. This gives the gauge strip transmission line a characteristic impedance $Z_0 = 141.8\ \Omega$ and a phase velocity $c/(\epsilon_r)^{1/2} = 2.43 \times 10^8$ m/s. These values provide estimates for the transmission line parameters, C/l and L/l. From $Z_0 = \sqrt{L/C}$ and phase velocity$= 1/\sqrt{LC/l^2}$, we find $L/l = 0.583\ \mu H/m$ and $C/l = 29.0$ pF/m.

Figure 5 shows measurements for the three connected components (gauge active region, gauge strip leads, and connector). At low frequency, the circuit reacts as a 1-pF connector in parallel with 21 pF from the gauge capacitance. At 230 MHz, the gauge strip-lead inductance contributes to form an impedance minimum, characteristic of a series RLC network. As in Figure 4, a lumped-parameter model can account for this resonance, but the model would be valid only in a narrow frequency band centered at the resonance. Additional elements would be needed to generate the parallel-circuit resonance near 800 MHz. As we will see, **the only components needed to match the measurements are the connector capacitance, gauge strip transmission line, and gauge capacitance.** With analysis, circuit parameters are identified that are consistent with the problem geometry and the measurements. Stray elements are not required to represent the gauge (because it is sufficiently isolated from surrounding connectors).

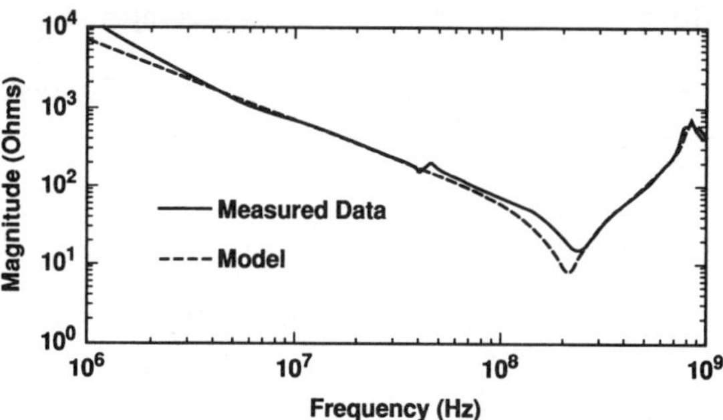

Fig. 5. Measured and calculated impedances for the connector, leads, and driving capacitor of Sample E530H10.

Circuit Resistance, Losses

Figure 5 shows an impedance minimum near 15 Ω. For a series RLC network at resonance, this value is the resistance, R. Gauge data suggest 9.2 Ω for the total gauge-lead resistance. The circuit losses are modeled by including loss in the propagation constant ($j\beta$ is replaced by $\alpha + j\beta$). The attenuation constant, α, is the sum of two contributions—conductor loss and dielectric loss.

Conductor loss is caused by lead resistance and by the reduced effective cross-sectional area resulting from the skin effect. The skin depth of Au is 2.5 μm at 1 GHz, a factor of 10 greater than the lead thickness, consistent with the earlier thin-lead approximation. However, the 3-mm width, which is significant relative to a skin depth, causes current concentration at the edges as frequency increases. When the skin effect dominates, this increases the resistance by a factor proportional to $\sqrt{f}$.

Because the dielectric loss is not explicitly known, $Z(l)$ data are used to generate α. Results are shown in Figure 6. The unit Np (neper) is the natural logarithm of the attenuation factor. At 10^8 Hz, attenuation of the 44-mm transmission line is $\exp(-0.4\ \text{Np/m} \times 0.044\ \text{m}) = 0.9826$. Because losses are small at low frequencies, the previous analysis assuming lossless dielectric behavior of the strip line is still valid.

At low frequencies, the slope in Figure 6 suggests that α is proportional to f^n. A value of $n = 1/2$ is an obvious effect of skin depth. However, the exponent is closer to 5/3. Dielectric loss of the strip transmission line dominates, even at the lower frequencies in Figure 6.

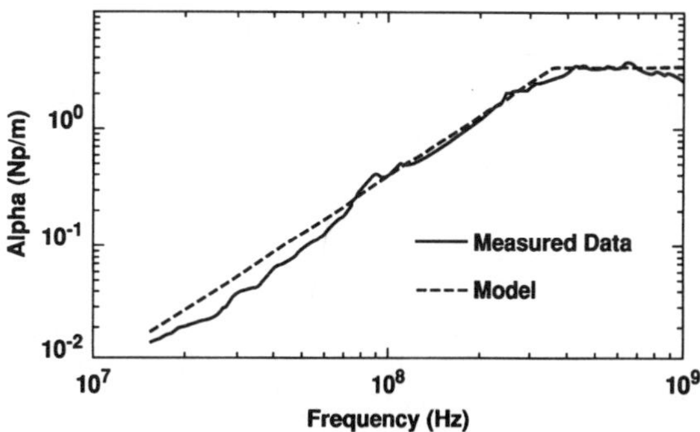

Fig. 6. Frequency variation of attenuation coefficient for transmission-line leads, S/N E530H10.

Gauge Capacitance

The final problem is to identify an equivalent circuit for the PVDF gauge active area. The device geometry suggests modeling simply as a parallel-plate capacitor. This capacitance is extracted from the measurements of the overall system while compensating for the impedance of the strip transmission line and the connector. $C_m = 20.0$ pF gives a reasonable match to data for

$1 \times 10^6 \leq f \leq 1 \times 10^9$ Hz. The change in slope of the impedance at ~5 MHz in Figure 5 suggests that dielectric constant decreases as frequency increases. Reference 7 verifies this behavior for poled PVDF at constant pressure in frequency range $1 \leq f \leq 20$ MHz. The ratio of dielectric constant at 1 kHz to its value at 10 MHz is 2.2,[7] the same as that of the low-frequency capacitance, 44 pF, to the 20 pF we found appropriate for our high-frequency model.

Complete Model of Gauge Measurements

The essential components are identified in Figure 7: a capacitor for the active area, a transmission line for the strip leads, and a capacitor for the connector. Figure 5 shows good agreement between the modeled and measured impedance. Some discrepancy does exist in resonant frequency and shape of the resonance. A more appropriate model would include frequency variation of the PVDF film between the capacitor plates.

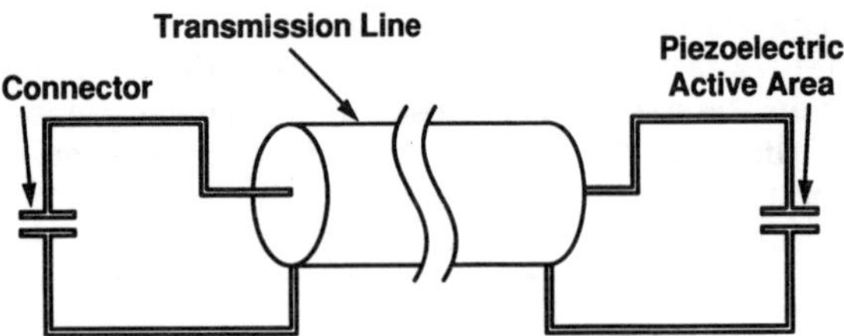

Fig. 7. Schematic model for PVDF gauge, its strip transmission line leads, and the connector needed for impedance measurements.

The presented model is appropriate for the initial state of the gauge, while stresses remain low. During actual use, the capacitance is time dependent as the shock wave compresses the active dielectric and reduces the plate separation. Shock pressures of 20 GPa, with shock velocities ~5 km/s, compress the 23.1-μm PVDF to 60% of its original thickness within a few nanoseconds. The dielectric constant also increases as the shock pressure increases.[8] Thus, the compression increases the capacitance and reduces the resonant frequency as time progresses. But a dynamic model awaits another report.

CONCLUSIONS

A technique is presented to model a PVDF shock-pressure gauge in a realistic manner over a large frequency range. This is realized by identifying the appropriate subcomponents and extracting their parameters from measurements consistent with their physical characteristics. The three components are the connector, strip-line leads, and PVDF active area. The model estimates agree with the measurements and predict device resonances. We presented data for a 9-mm^2 gauge. PVDF gauges with areas ~1 mm^2 have also been analyzed, with the same model agreement. Different PVDF geometries can be analyzed by inserting the appropriate subcomponent parameters and model into the overall model. Design tradeoffs then allow optimization of the response for applications. In particular, circuit alterations (such as a simple 100-Ω resistor in series with strip-line leads) can prevent a deep minimum in impedance variation with frequency and inhibit troublesome oscillations from interfering with measurements.

ACKNOWLEDGMENTS

This work, performed at Sandia National Laboratories, was supported by US DOE under contract DE-AC04-76DP00789. R.P. Reed of SNL/NM furnished helpful discussions and manuscript review.

REFERENCES

[1]H.R. Gallantree, "Review of transducer applications of polyvinylidene fluoride," IEEE Proc **130**, pp 219-224 (1983). This article is reprinted by C.Z. Rosen, B.V. Hiremath, R. Newham, *Piezoelectricity,* New York: Am Inst of Physics (AIP), 1992, Sec II-11, pp 189-194. This AIP ref is the source for a series of associated articles.

[2]R.C. Smythe, "Some recent advances in integrated crystal filters," IEEE Proc **67**, pp 119-129 (1979), reprinted on pp 438-448, AIP Ref 1.

[3]R.A. Graham, *Solids Under High Pressure Shock Compression,* New York: Springer Verlag, 1993, ch 5.2, pp 103-113.

[4]F. Bauer, Institut franco-allemande de recherches de Saint-Louis, France, private communication, 1992.

[5]R. Chadha, R. Garg, K.C. Gupta, *Computer-Aided Design of Microwave Circuits,* Dedham, MA: Artech House, 1981, ch 3, pp 67-72.

[6]R.E. Collin, *Foundations for Microwave Engineering,* New York: McGraw-Hill, 1992, ch 3, pp 93, 178-180.

[7]F. Bauer, *Ferroelectrics* **115**, pp 247-266 (1991).

[8]G.A. Samara, *J Polym Sci, Polym Phys Ed* **27**, pp 39-51 (1989).

PULSED RADIATION RESPONSE OF STRESSED PVDF SHOCK STRESS GAUGES

R.P. Reed*, J.I. Greenwoll*, F. Bauer**, L.M. Lee***, F.W. Davies*** and D.J. Johnson***

* Sandia National Laboratories/NM, Albuquerque, NM 87185-5800
** Instut Saint-Louis, Saint-Louis, France 68310
*** Ktech Corporation, Albuquerque, NM 87110

PVDF shock stress sensors were subjected to X-ray deposition at nominal absorbed levels of 1, 1½, 3, and 5 cal/gm (SiO_2 equiv.) and to neutron fluence above 10^{13} n/cm^2 while stressed at a peak level of about 2 GPa. Moderate transitory electrical noise that occurred briefly during the radiation did not persist. PVDF shock sensors with aluminum electrodes appear satisfactory for measurement within these exposure limits. Reference quartz gauges were severely affected.

INTRODUCTION

The PVDF (polyvinylidene difluoride) piezoelectric polymer shock stress sensor [1] has seemed well suited to stress wave measurement where subjected to significant nuclear radiation. The PVDF composition includes only components of low atomic number [H(Z=1), C(Z=6), and F(Z=9)] therefore absorption by PVDF of X-radiation energy is small relative to that of metallic or semiconductor sensors. On the other hand, the low-Z composition tends to make the PVDF susceptible to damage by neutrons.

Though PVDF is not heated excessively by direct energy deposition, commercially available Bauer-process PVDF shock stress gauges use 0.3 μm thick sputtered high-Z electrodes [0.05 μm Pt(Z=78) and 0.25 μm Au(Z=79).] Though the electrodes are very thin, calculation has shown that the high-Z thin film electrodes, heated by X-ray absorption, rapidly diffuse and radiate this heat into the 26 μm thick PVDF film on a time scale that can be short enough to thermally affect shock stress measurement.[2]

Despite these possible limitations, commercial PVDF shock sensors have measured stress with apparent success in several field experiments involving high levels of neutron or X-ray exposure. The prompt response of the PVDF polymer gauge to severe pulsed radiation while simultaneously subjected to high stress has not previously been reported.

Four possibilities exist. Radiation might 1) produce no significant response, 2) it might cause a merely momentary electrical noise response that is not sustained significantly after the brief interval of exposure, 3) it might produce a transitory effect that would interfere with measurement over an interval of several microseconds following exposure during which stress measurement is desired, or 4), permanent damage might persist. The radiation could either cause a change in sensitivity or introduce a biased indication. A transient change of sensitivity can only be detected while a gauge is in the stressed state. Any transitory change of behavior must be observed actively during radiation exposure. Any of the effects might be rate dependent. Therefore, it is essential to examine radiation response during measurement under stressed conditions that are representative of intended application. Experiments were conducted to examine the prompt and transitory radiation response of PVDF shock stress gauges to γ/X-ray exposure and separately to neutron insult during stress peak loading to 1.5 to 2.5 GPa.

Funded by DOE Contract DE-AC04-76-DP00789

THE EXPERIMENT DESIGN

Five experiments explosively imposed a stress pulse that was sustained at a level greater than 0.5 GPa for about 4 μs. The onset of the stress and its peak were timed to occur just prior to the local arrival of either γ/X-rays or else neutrons. Incident times of X-rays and neutrons were separated sufficiently to observe the prompt effects independently.

The effect of pulsed radiation was observed as a deviation from the separately characterized nominal gauge response to the reproducible explosive stress pulse. Standard, but non-ideal, Sandia Field Test Quartz Gauges (FTQG) were fielded in the same package for comparison of response.[3] The test matrix in Table 1 summarizes the radiation conditions imposed. The levels of X-ray absorption were adjusted by filtering the fluence. To relate the deposition to historic limits stated for quartz gauges, absorptions are expressed throughout in terms of equivalent deposited value for quartz (SiO_2.)

The shock stress was imposed by a single-point initiated explosive assembly that had an explosive train of slender elements treed within a LEXAN matrix to simultaneously emerge at 52 points of 1 mm diameter that were equally spaced

Table 1. Response Experiment Parameters

Observed Insult	X-ray cal/gm	Neutron n/cm²	Gauge Type	Elements	Electrode Material
X-ray	1	--	PVDF	Dual	Al
	1	--	FTQG	----	Al
X-ray	1½*	--	PVDF	Dual	Al
X-ray	3	--	PVDF	Single**	Au/Pt
X-ray	3	--	PVDF	Dual	Al
X-ray	3	--	FTQG	----	Al
X-ray	5	--	PVDF	Twin**,***	Au/Pt
X-ray	5	--	PVDF	Dual	Al
X-ray	5	--	FTQG	----	Al
Neutron	1½*	$>10^{13}$	PVDF	Dual	Al
Neutron	1	$>10^{13}$	PVDF	Dual	Al
Neutron	1	$>10^{13}$	FTQG	----	Al
Post rad	1½*	$>10^{13}$	PVDF	Dual	Al
Post rad	1	$>10^{13}$	PVDF.	Dual	Al
Post rad	1	$>10^{13}$	FTQG	----	Al

* Gauges embedded in the buffer. They were not at the quartz gauge interface.
** Metravib(France)/Ktech M25-09-PL **PVDF** gauge.
*** Two in series and symmetric with ground.

over an approximately circular pattern. The stress generator consisted of the explosive assembly and a laminated stress buffer that separated the stress gauges from the explosive lens. The buffer smoothed the wavefront from the emergent points so that the area-averaged stress history was similar for the sensing regions of gauges of two very different areas. The PVDF stress gauges had an active sensing area of 3x3 mm. The quartz gauge had a much larger active area of 12.7 mm diameter. Buffers on different experiments had laminations of different materials and thicknesses to produce essential precise wave propagation delays and X-ray depositions.

A pair of **PVDF** sensors was mounted near the axis of the buffer and a standard Sandia Field Test Quartz Gauge, **FTQG MOD 11-200 [3]**, was then applied axially centered on the same buffer surface so that on most experiments a pair of **PVDF** gauges and a quartz gauge simultaneously experienced similar stress histories at the same interface. The quartz gauge was used for peak stress comparison and was also the subject of separately reported experiments to examine the radiation response of the quartz gauge under stress levels above its normal **0.8** GPa recommended use limit.[3]

PVDF sensors were of two kinds. To address the issue of the effect of energy absorption in the thin film gauge leads, the responses of commercial Bauer-process gauges with **Au/Pt** leads were compared with those of custom gauges with aluminum thin film leads. The aluminum-electroded gauges were specially fabricated at the **ISL** also using the proprietary Bauer process. They were of special Sandia balanced dual element design that provides improved rejection of common-mode noise and simplifies electro-mechanical assembly.

Incidental electrical noise was recognized as an obstacle to accurate interpretation. Because noise reducing techniques require demonstration under actual conditions of use, several different recording circuits were employed as a secondary aspect of the experiments. All circuits were balanced to enhance rejection of common-mode noise. A typical balanced recording circuit is shown in Fig. 1. Signals from all PVDF sensors were transmitted via **RG22** twinax cable. To balance the system, the gauges (via the source shunting resistors), were all symmetrically connected to the twinax cable shield and through it to the remote single-point ground at the recorder.

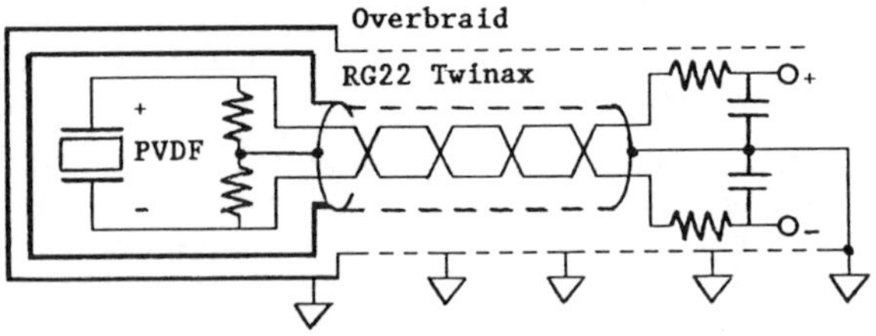

Figure 1. Balanced recording circuit for PVDF

To allow active pre-event simulation of the self-generating **PVDF** sensor signals and also to facilitate system characterization, the **PVDF** gauges were all shunted at the source by **100** ohm resistance. That shunt resistance corresponded to the nominal characteristic impedance of the twinax cable and also to the effective internal resistance of the step pulsed voltage source that was used for system characterization. In this shunted-gauge circuit mode, the observed voltage output is proportional to the time derivative of the stress-produced charge.[1] The peak voltage amplitude from such stress derivatives is difficult to accurately predict to allow well-resolved recording in field experiments. Therefore, the sensor voltage was hardware integrated at the balanced input of the differential recording system. The step response of the recording system, including the 350m length of twisted-pair shielded and overbraided cable and integrator, was characterized for each sensor. The waveform of the recorded voltage signal was significantly distorted by non-ideal cable response, the imperfect integrator, and by the nonlinear sensitivity of the **PVDF** gauges. However, distortion was accurately corrected, using those individual characterizations, by validated convolutional techniques before non-linear conversion to the stress equivalent.[1]

The stress experiment package was entirely enclosed within a sealed steel canister. The PVDF and quartz gauges were exposed to deposition through a radiation filter that moderated the deposition, a LEXAN window/closure plug, and the LEXAN body of the explosive stress generator. The outer canister was electrically grounded locally to the experiment bulkhead and was connected to the overbraid shield that was grounded at many points en route to the distant recording station. The gauges within the canister were enclosed within an inner Faraday cage. An aluminum plate of the stress buffer, electrically isolated from the outer canister, served as a portion of the inner Faraday cage.

Stress pulses differ in amplitude and shape because buffer designs varied. At the lower deposition levels, gauges were at two different locations. One gauge was at the quartz gauge interface. The other was separated by 3 mm by a fused quartz buffer layer so that stress arrival times were separated by about 0.2 μs. All gauges tested at the lower levels were of the dual element Al electrode design.

RESULTS

Figures 2a-d show some of the waveforms. The irrelevant common-mode electrical noise was very well suppressed by the balanced-circuit single-point ground arrangement. Distinct deviations from the nominal waveform of the stress-induced voltage (those not due to superposed stress reflected from within the buffer stack) are therefore correctly interpreted as 1) a relevant prompt direct electrical noise response, 2) a thermal effect on the gauges indirectly from contiguous elements such as the high-Z thin film electrodes, or else 3) a damage effect of radiation on the gauges

Similar assemblies were laboratory tested for normal waveform, critical timing, and

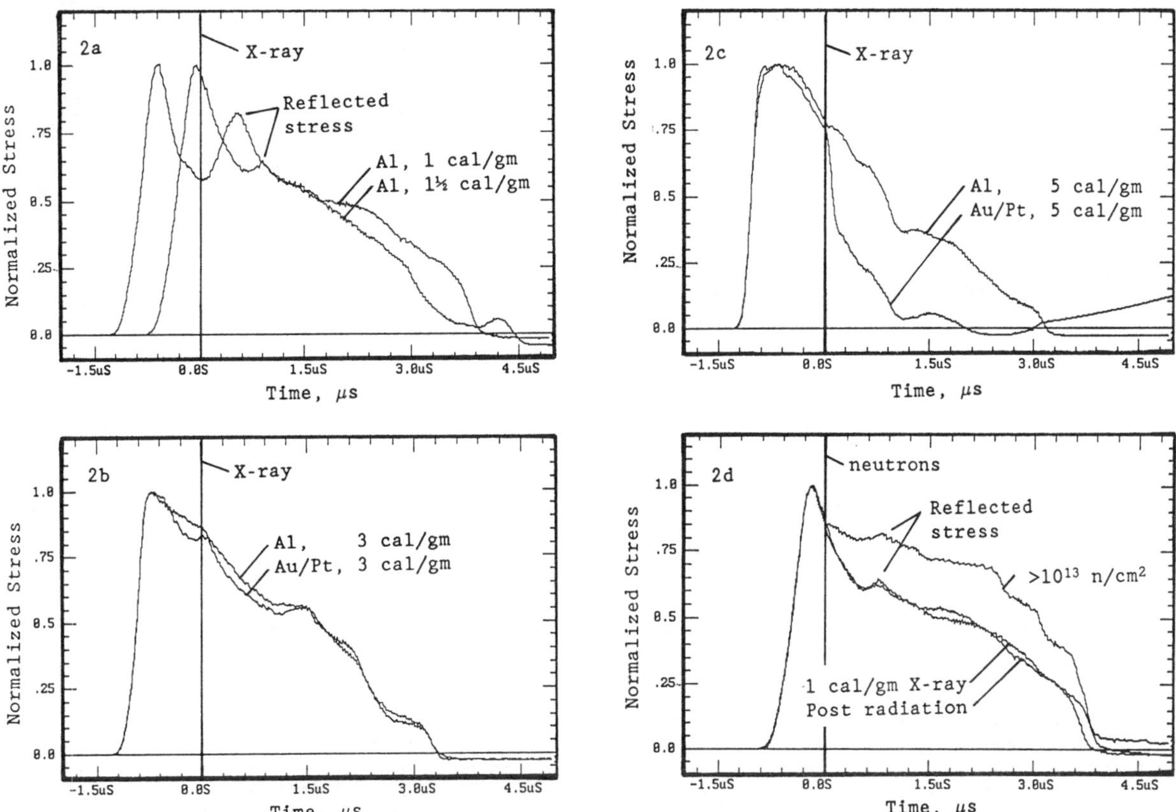

Figure 2. Response of PVDF shock stress gauges to pulsed radiation, a) 1 and 1½ cal/gm(SiO_2), b) X-rays at 3 cal/gm, c) X-rays at 5 cal/gm, d) >10^{13} n/cm^2 neutrons after X-ray deposition at 1 cal/gm (SiO_2). Stress amplitudes normalized to 1. Times zeroed at radiation arrival.

containment of explosive products before fielding. Adverse radiation response is sensed as significant deviations from normal pre-test or post exposure waveforms.

Figures **2a-c** show the response of gauges to nominal levels of 1, 1½ , 3, and 5 cal/gm (SiO_2) X-ray deposition. The most notable feature on the 1½ **cal/gm** trace is a buffer-reflected stress pulse that appears in coincidence with X-ray deposition time. a corresponding pulse, delayed and attenuated by the buffer is seen in the deeper 1 cal/gm gauge record, as well. It is seen only on neutron and post irradiation experiments with the same buffer design in Fig. 2d. There is no definite effect of the X-radiation at either deposition level.

The response of **Au/Pt** electroded gauges is compared to that of **Al** electroded gauges only at the 3 and 5 cal/gm levels. In Fig. **2b** at the 3 cal/gm level, both **PVDF** gauges are at the same **FTQG** interface and the traces strongly resemble. Coincident with **X**-ray arrival time both experience a noticeable negative perturbation. The **Au/Pt** electroded gauge appears slightly more affected than the **Al** electroded gauge.

At the 5 cal/gm deposition level there is a distinctive difference between the response of the gauges with low-**Z** and high-**Z** electrodes. The slight effect on the **Au/Pt** gauge that is marginally evident in Fig. **2b** has become readily evident at the **5** cal/gm level. This definitely different observed response between gauges of different electroding, and supporting thin-film thermal calculations,[2] indicate that deposition heating of the **Au/Pt** electrodes (below melt) is sufficient to affect, by thermal diffusion, the response of the contiguous PVDF material that lies between contact and only 13 μm distant from the **Pt** electrode interface.

Figure **2d** shows the gauge response during a neutron fluence at a level above 10^{13} n/cm^2. The actual neutron fluence is typical of levels commonly encountered in application. In this instance (immediately preceding the stress onset) the gauges have already experienced a transient episode of **X**-ray exposure at a level of 1 or of 1½ cal/gm (SiO_2) absorption at the gauge locations. The deviation of the pulse is prompt, significant, and persistent for at least 2 μs. But, the effect was not evident in the trace following neutron exposure by **5** μs nor in a companion trace not reported here. As in Fig. **2a**, the prominent perturbation near mid neutron arrival time is actually a stress pulse reflected within the buffer. The time between the stress features and their relation to neutron and X-ray arrival distinguishes them as not radiation produced. Stresses measured during such a brief neutron arrival interval might be slightly affected but those occurring immediately before (but after X-ray exposure) or after such a neutron exposure interval should be unaffected by the radiation.

CONCLUSIONS

The small data set suggests some tentative conclusions. For **X**-ray deposition less than **5** cal/gm (SiO_2) with stress levels below 2.5 GPa, **Al** electroded **PVDF** sensors appear to be usable for accurate stress wave measurement. **PVDF** gauges with high-Z electrodes, such as of **Au/Pt**, should not be employed with **X**-ray depositions greater than 3 cal/gm (SiO_2). However, it appears prudent to avoid crucial measurement during a neutron fluence of >10^{13} n/cm^2 without further study. **PVDF** extends the range of the FTQG quartz shock stress gauge.[3]

Waveforms, recorded with the electrically balanced and single-point grounded circuits, were all exceptionally free from the usually severe electrical noise introduced apart from the sensor. However, the balanced system with hardware integration reduces system bandwidth compared to the usual recording of stress wave data. Nevertheless, in these experiments that involve stress pulses with 0.25-0.4 μs risetimes that are typical of many field stress wave experiments, careful system response characterization and numerical compensation allowed accurate correction of waveform and amplitude. The benefit of improved signal-to-noise ratio by balanced recording is thus available for field stress wave measurements with realistic risetimes.

Extended radiation tolerance, fidelity, and noise reduction of the Sandia balanced dual-element aluminum-electroded shock stress gauge was demonstrated.

ACKNOWLEDGEMENTS

We appreciate the crucial contributions to the success of this experiment made by R.L. Peabody, P.W. Cooper and their associates, the laboratory and fielding staffs of Sandia, Joyce Sikora and Mark Wing of Ktech, and the staff of the ISL who fabricated special gauges.

REFERENCES

1. R.P. Reed and J. I. Greenwoll, The PVDF Piezoelectric Polymer Shock Stress Sensor -- Signal Conditioning and Analysis for Field Test Application SAND88-2907 UC-37, Sandia National Laboratories, Albuquerque, NM, May 1989.

2. A.J. Watts, et al., Thin Film Transport (PUFF-TFT) Computer Code Development, (Ktech Corporation,) AFWL-TR-88-66, Air Force Weapons Laboratory, Albuquerque, NM, June 1988.

3. R. P. Reed and J.I. Greenwoll, Characteristics and Response to Pulsed Radiation of Non-Ideal Quartz Gauges, 1993 AIRPT/APS Joint Topical Conference on High Pressure Science and Technology, Colorado Springs, CO, June 28-July 2, 1993.

MEASUREMENT OF LARGE GROUND MOTIONS WITH THE ASM GAGE*

B. L. Wright, K. R. Alrick, and J. N. Fritz
P15 MS D406, P15 MS D406, and M6 MS C970
Los Alamos National Laboratory
Los Alamos, New Mexico 87545 USA

Conversion of the energy from underground explosions to distant seismic signals involves hydrodynamic flows sampling a wide range of pressures. For lower pressures a larger portion of the initial wave motion must be measured to obtain definitive results. The intermediate pressure range, where the initial wave is strong enough to destroy most instrumentation but does not contain definitive information in its initial amplitude, presents special difficulties. We present design considerations for an experiment implementing the ASM gage principle (induction of eddy currents in a moving conducting plate) that can sample wave motion for many milliseconds. In essence we hang a large metal plate (large in area) on a wall and watch the free-surface release. This is not an in-situ measurement of the wave profile because the incoming wave is modified by the release propagating backward from the wall. However, this is a relatively clean modification of the incoming wave and is a situation commonly handled in many shock-wave experiments.

INTRODUCTION

The ASM (axially-symmetric magnetic) gage principle[1] (induction of a signal in a pick-up coil by induced eddy currents in a moving plate) has been used successfully[2] in the measurement of motion from underground explosions. For a strong shock, the initial amplitude of the wave can determine the energy of the explosion. Previous gages used a plate run of 6.35 mm and varying time intervals of the order of microseconds (depends on the strength of the shock) to measure the initial amplitude and rise time of the wave. At late times and large scaled distances the wave will evolve and have structure (elastic leads, two wave structures due to phase transitions, dispersion due to heterogeneity, etc.). A longer look at the wave profile is indicated. To this end we have constructed an ASM gage with a free-surface plate run of roughly 300 mm, corresponding to a measurement time of several milliseconds. All gage dimensions have been scaled up accordingly. Because of its size we do not intend to imbed the instrument in grout. Instead, the gage is to be mounted in a wall normal to the wave vector.

EXPECTED SIGNALS

The essential "levitated" geometry of an ASM gage is show in Fig. 1. For no diffusion of the field

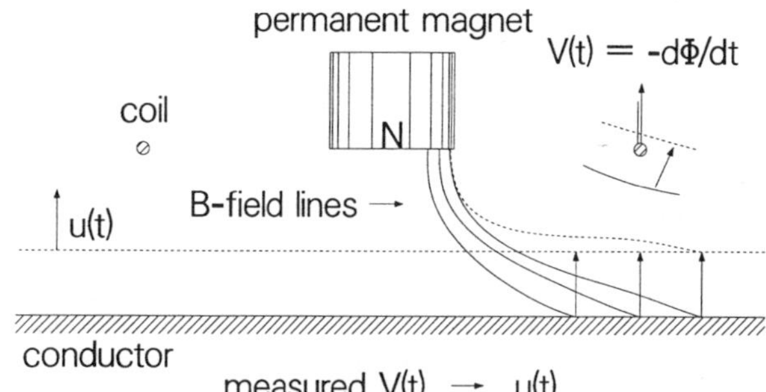

Figure 1. ASM gage elements. The B-field lines from a permanent magnet are "pinned" by a conductor. Motion of the conductor results in motion of the B-field lines and a change in flux Φ in the pick-up coil. For this large aspect ratio (lateral dimensions larger than vertical) only the dipole moment of the magnet contributes to the signal. Important dimensions are the radius of the coil ρ_c, the vertical distance of the coil from the conductor z_c, and the distance of the dipole from the conductor z_s.

the E.M.F. in a single turn is given by[1]

$$E = u[2F(z_c + z_s - 2z_f) - F(z_c + z_s - z_f - z_f(0))]$$

where $u(t) = dz_f(t)/dt$, $F(\zeta) = 2\pi\rho_c B_\rho(\rho_c, \zeta)$, and ρ_c, ζ are measured from the location of the moments describing the initial magnetic field. Again for no diffusion, $E(t)/u(t)$ is a sensitivity curve, volts/velocity, that does not depend explicitly on time. It only depends on the location of the moving conductor $z_f(t)$. We can increase the sensitivity by using as strong a magnetic field as

*This work supported by the US Department of Energy.

possible. We use a 2 inch cube Nd_2BFe_{12} magnet with a dipole moment of 1.6×10^6 G-cm^3. The sensitivity can also be increased by using multiple turns. The cost is an increased gage rise time ($\tau_{90} = 2.3L/50\,\Omega$). Because we are looking over such a long time scale we can afford more turns. The inductance of a single turn of radius 152.4 mm is 3.7 μH. If we require $\tau_{90} \leq 0.1$ ms, then $2.3n^2L_1/50 \leq 0.1$ ms implies $n \leq 24.4$. We have chosen a 25-turn coil for our gage. We give up looking at the detailed behavior of the initial wave motion in exchange for a more robust amplitude.

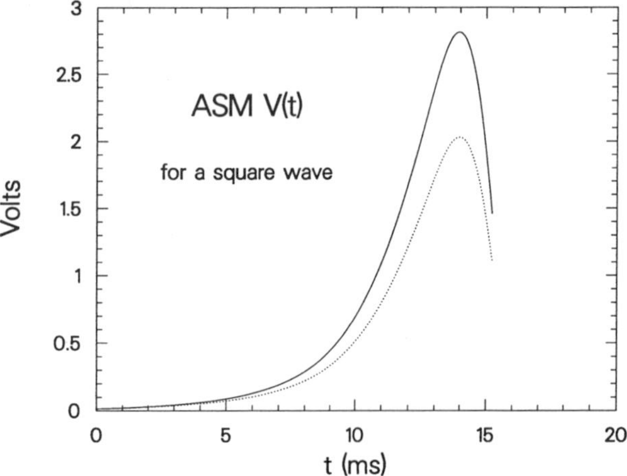

Figure 2. The expected E.M.F. from our gage for a constant $u(t)$. A square wave of 0.02 mm/μs will produce this E.M.F. across the 25 turns in our gage. The solid line is for no diffusion and the dotted line shows the effect of magnetic field diffusion through a 6.35 mm plate of aluminum. The voltage passing to the cable from the gage will be slightly modified by the resistance and inductance associated with the gage.

We show $E(t)$ for a 25-turn coil in Fig. 2. The solid line is essentially the sensitivity curve. The low initial sensitivity is an inherent problem with a dipole field. The effect of diffusion for a 6.35 mm aluminum plate is not negligible, and is also shown. This effect *is* time dependent; however, exact solutions are available[1] for handling this case. An actual record will deviate from the curve shown here, and when analyzed, will yield the $u(t)$ for the aluminum plate.

MECHANICAL DESIGN CONSIDERATIONS

In the present instance, the conductor indicated in Fig. 1 consists of a 914 x 914 x 6.3 mm aluminum plate. For a proposed underground test, this plate is mounted, in a vertical plane, on the rib of a side drift at approximately the elevation of the center of explosion. The volume between the plane of the plate and the rock surface is filled with grout. In order to measure the plate's free-surface motion using the ASM principle, a core structure is required on which the permanent magnet, pickup coil, auxiliary shock pins, and associated circuitry are rigidly mounted. Before the measurement, the position and orientation of the core with respect to the plate must be well established. But during the measurement, the core must be "levitated" with no substantive mechanical connection to the moving plate. These requirements are met with the string suspension system described below.

The design of the core structure is illustrated in Fig. 3. It consists of two 330 x 330 x 6.3 mm

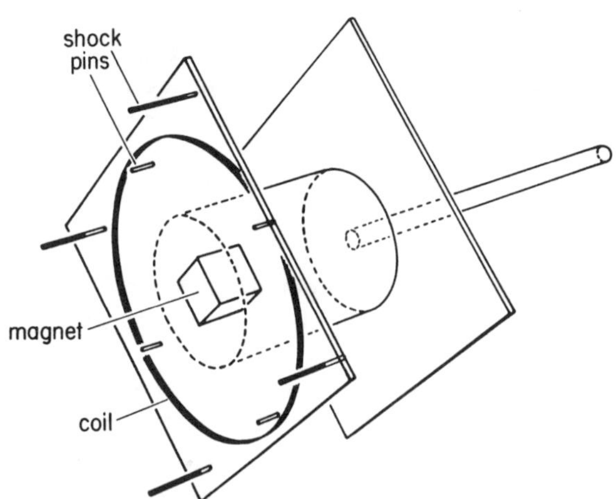

Figure 3. The gage core-structure assembly.

square plastic plates separated by a 197 mm long, 152 mm o.d. plastic cylinder. Eight piezoelectric shock pins are mounted in a 279 mm square array on the front plate. The four pins at the corners extend, alternately, 64 mm and 51 mm forward; the four pins at the edges are flush with the front surface. The magnet cube is cemented flush with the rear surface of the plate, along with a 305 mm o.d., 6.3 mm thick plastic annulus on which the 25-turn pickup coil is wound. Circuitry for filtering and mixing the pin signals is housed in the cylinder. The rigid stalk extending further to the rear supports two signal cables for the pins and the coil. The total mass of this assembly is about 3.0 kg.

The design of the housing and suspension system is illustrated in Fig. 4. The housing consists of

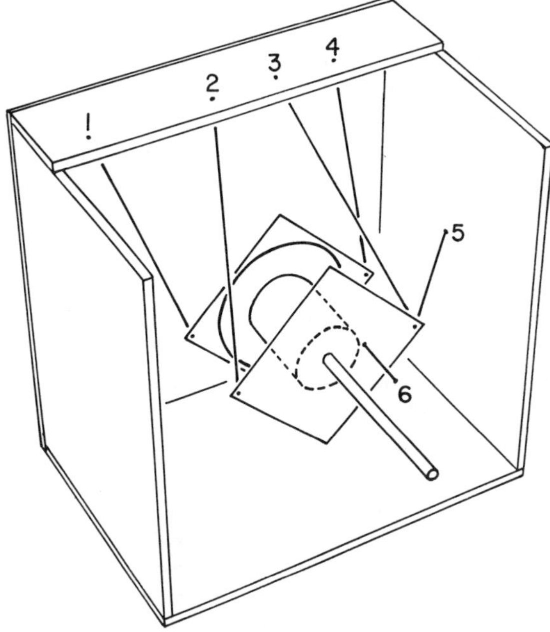

Figure 4. Illustrating the use of 6 strings for suspension and alignment of the core assembly relative to the aluminum plate. Release of string tension "levitates" the core during data acquisition.

a simple box made of 19 mm thick, fire-retardant plywood with the mounted aluminum plate forming the front side. Not shown in the figure are the rear side (610 mm from the plate) and a removable lid section. Suitable cutouts in the sides and rear of the box allow additional access to the interior and ample clearance for the stalk.

The core is suspended at four corners by the numbered strings indicated in the figure. Strings 1, 2, 3, and 4 pass through holes in the forward top section. String 5 passes horizontally through the side wall, and string 6 (off center in the rear plastic plate) comes straight out through a hole in the rear wall. Because a rigid object in 3-dimensional space has six degrees of freedom, the location and orientation of the core, relative to the housing, is uniquely determined by the lengths of these strings. Therefore, providing the strings are all under positive tension, the core is rigidly positioned prior to the explosion. Upon arrival of the shock wave, tension is released on strings 1 through 5 which angle forward. Because the stalk is well separated from the housing, the only mechanical link between the core and rest of the world, prior to arrival of the aluminum plate, is via string 6. This string contains a section with a static breaking strength of about 90 Newtons. Thus the maximum acceleration experienced by the core during the approximately 10 ms measurement interval is at most a few g's—corresponding to a net possible displacement of a millimeter or so.

There is considerable choice in how the six strings may be configured to provide the functions described above. Our choice was constrained by field conditions which prevented access to the left side wall of the box. Beyond this, an effort was made to keep the string tensions within reasonable bounds—neither too large nor too small—and to minimize the sensitivity of key alignment parameters to the string lengths.

Alignment of the system is not difficult. It is a straightforward matter to generate a matrix relating the differential translations and rotations of the core to differential changes in the lengths of the strings. (Through the principle of virtual work, this matrix is also used to determine the string tensions.) A similar matrix can be developed for any set of six canonical measurements specifying the alignment of the core relative to the aluminum plate. Thus, for any six measured increments of misalignment, these matrices can be used to calculate adjustments to the six string lengths that provide the necessary correction. Because the gauge is accessible, the final alignment can be determined just prior to the test.

SIGNAL EXTRACTION

Like the smaller version, the large ASM gage produces two types of electrical signals: 1) a signal from the coil induced by eddy currents in the moving plate and 2) a set of sharp impulses generated by the piezoelectric pins as they are sequentially impacted by the plate near the end of its travel. Both of these signals are available via 50 Ohm RG-174 coaxial cables passed through the stalk at the rear of the gage. The coil signal is used to determine the velocity of the moving plate and the pin signals are used to determine the tilt of the plate relative to the axis of the gage. The eight pins are longitudinally staggered such that if the plate velocity is aligned with the axis of the gage the pins will generate signals with an anticipated temporal pattern. A deviation from this pattern implies a tilt in the plate. The temporal separation of the signals also allows the pulses from the eight pins to be multiplexed into a single output. The low plate velocity and long travel distance lead to several differences in the output signals when compared to the those of the smaller gage. First, the coil signal is smaller in amplitude, has a lower frequency content, but covers a much higher dynamic range. Second, the temporal separation of the pin signals is much larger.

A diagram of the pin multiplexing circuit is shown in Fig. 5. As shown in the diagram, the

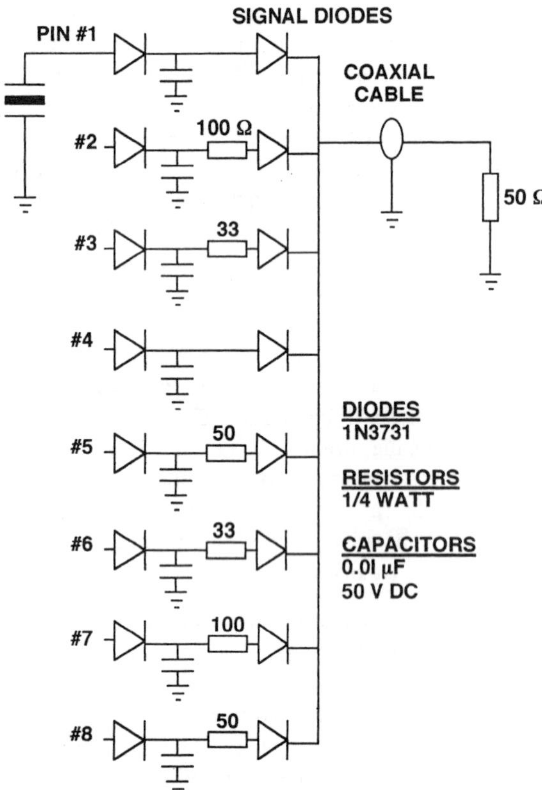

Figure 5. Circuit for stretching and multiplexing the 8 shock-pin pulses. The use of different series resistances aids in the interpretation of the output signal.

output from each pin is used to charge a capacitor which then discharges through a resistor and a diode into a common 50 Ohm load. Except for the 0.01 μF capacitor this circuit is similar to the one used to multiplex the pin signals in the smaller ASM gage. Because of the larger temporal separation between pin signals it is possible to stretch the time duration and reduce the amplitude of the signals before multiplexing, allowing the use of lower bandwidth recording equipment. Since both the amplitude and the discharge time constant of the resulting signal depend upon the size of the resistor, the individual pin signals in the multiplexed pattern can be recognized once the resistor values are known.

DISCUSSION

In the study of energy flow from underground explosions, the ASM gage provides a versatile means for recording shock-wave motion in the inelastic region between the hydrodynamic zone and the region of seismic wave propagation. The aim of the present work has been to extend the application of the ASM gage to cases in which motion must be recorded over time scales of the order of 10 ms. The result is an instrument in which linear dimensions have been increased by roughly an order of magnitude, but which otherwise consists of the same elements as the smaller model. The most significant changes in design resulting from this change in scale are: wall mounting instead of borehole installation, a "levitating" suspension system, the use of a stronger magnet and a multi-turn coil, less relative sensitivity to motion at earlier times, reduced bandwidth requirements, and additional conditioning for shock-pin signals. A field test of two identical units built from this design is planned for the near future.

REFERENCES

1. J. N. Fritz and J. A. Morgan. An electromagnetic technique for measuring material velocity. *Rev. Scient. Instr.*, 44(2):215–221, February 1973.
2. W. C. Moss, A. C. Mitchell, R. Heinle, and J. N. Fritz. Particle velocity measurements near underground nuclear explosions using axially symmetric magnetic gages. In S. C. Schmidt, R. D. Dick, J. W. Forbes, and D. G. Tasker, editors, *Shock Waves in Condensed Matter—1991*, pages 867–870. North-Holland, Amsterdam, 1992.

EIGHT BEAM PEROT-FABRY VELOCIMETER

M. Durand, P. Lalle and P. Andriot

CEA - Centre d'Etudes Scientifiques et Techniques d'Aquitaine B.P. n° 2 - 33114 - LE BARP - FRANCE -

GIDON and BEHAR demonstrated the feasibility of interferometric velocity measurements with a dye laser as light source. We have extended this principle and we describe here a new eight beam PEROT-FABRY velocimeter and we give examples of the results obtained in shock waves studies.

INTRODUCTION

Since the early measurements of velocity by use of PEROT-FABRY velocimeters (PFV) numerous attemps have been made to increase the amount of light entering the recording system. This was done to extend the applicability of laser velocimetry to poorly reflecting surfaces and to perform multiple-location measurements in the same shot. One way is to amplify the intensity of the laser source, e. g. a single mode c.w. argon ion laser [1], and this was shown to be quite efficient in a number of situations where the bare source did not give a recordable signal [2]. A converse way is to amplify the output of the interferometer. Doing so, SEITZ and STACY [3]were able to record the fringes with a mecano-optical camera. More recently, GIDON and BEHAR[4] showed that a powerful wide spectrum dye laser could be used as PFV light source when using a special configuration of the interferometer. In this paper we describe a new version of this last device which allows us to perform eight simultaneous measurements of velocity.

PRINCIPLE

GIDON and BEHAR [4] and later MERCIER, VEAUX, BEHAR and CAVAILLER [5] studied the theory of the PEROT-FABRY interferometer (PFI) lighted by a multiline laser. The principle of this operation is sketched in figure 1.

The nearly parallel beam of light produced by a flash pumped dye laser goes through a PFI. At the exit side of this PFI the light spectrum, intensity vs wavelength, appears as a number of lines separated by $\lambda^2/2e$, where e is the distance between the PFI plates and λ the wavelength of the dye laser. This light is sent through an other PFI (analyzer) having exactly the same plate separation as the first one. The line labelled i (Fig. 1), with wavelength λ, gives bright rings in directions whose angles $\theta_{i,k}$ with respect to the axis are given by :

$$2e \cos\theta_{i,k} = k\lambda$$

where k is the integer value of $2e/\lambda$.

For the line i+1 one gets :

$$2e \cos\theta_{i+1,k-1} = (k-1)(\lambda + \frac{\lambda^2}{2e}) \cong k\lambda$$

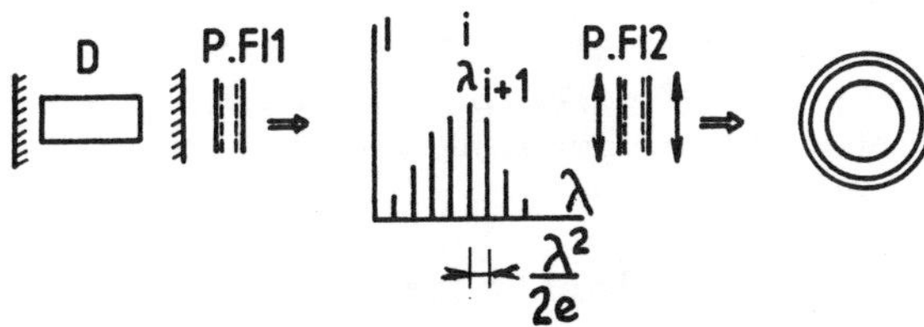

Figure 1 :D is a dye laser. The plates of the PFIs n° 1 and 2 have a coefficient of reflexion of 0.3 and 0.92 respectively.

The light out of the second PFI is focused by a lens. In the focal plane of this lens, the line i will produce rings of order k having the same diameters as those produced by the line i+1 and corresponding to order k-1. Strictly speaking, this coincidence is true for only one ring and approximate for the other ones [5]. But in practice deviations from coincidence are negligibly small.

EIGHT BEAMS VELOCIMETER

The laser used in our experiments (see Fig. 2) was built by B.M.I. (B.M. Industries, Z.I. du Bois Chaland, LISSES, FRANCE).

The two dye are pumped by electric flash lamps sharing the same power supply. The lasing dye is Rhodamine 6G and the mean value of the wavelength is 602 nm.The light power out of the filtering interferometers PFI1 and PFI2 is about 1 kW and the pulse duration ~50 μs. A Helium-Neon Laser is used for alignment of the dyes lasers

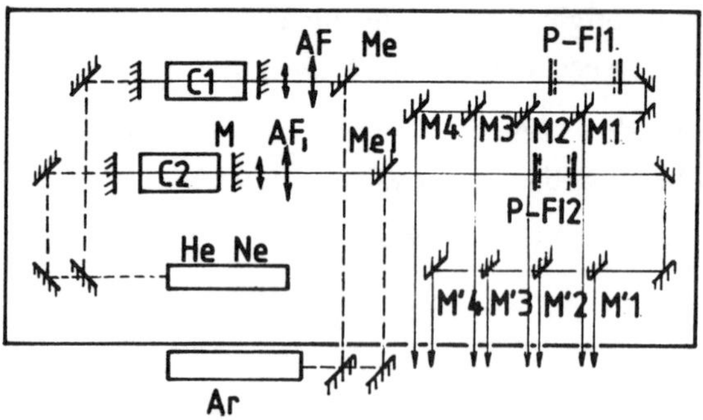

Figure 2 :Laser and beam layout. C1 and C2 : dye lasers. M1, M2, M3 and M4 : mirrors with coefficients of reflexion 0.3, 0.3, 0.5 and Rmax respectively
PFI1 and PFI2 : PFIs with a R=0.3 coefficient of reflexion of the plates, and 49.947 and 19.997 mm mirror separation, respectively.
Me and Me1 : moving mirrors. AF and AF1 : beam expanders (x4).

and an argon ion laser for alignment of the set-up, from the sources to the target and return.

Starting from the set-up sketched in Fig. 2, each beam goes to the target and from the target to the analyzing PFI through a same optical fiber, as described by DURAND [6.]

In a conventional set-up where an Ar^+ laser is the light source, optical fibers having a 200 μm core diameter are convenient. Because the beam divergence of the dye laser is greater than that of Ar^+ laser, a conical optical fiber is used for the first meters of light travel. The core diameter of this fiber (ORIEL SFT 600T 200V) vary from 600 μm to 200 μm. The eight light beams reflected from the target are analyzed by eight PFIs having exactly the same distance between plates as the filtering PFIs, and the corresponding eight interferograms are recorded by four streak cameras (two interferograms per camera). The whole system is depicted in Fig. 3.

EXAMPLE OF RESULTS

Figure 4 shows an example of eight simultaneous velocity records obtained in a single experiment, with the following experimental conditions : slit width equal to 0.3 mm ; the time markers were separated by 0.4 or 0.8 μs ; the light power of the beams out of the filtering PFIs was attenuated by neutral filters and the power was divided by 20, 20, 33, 10, 0, 10, 10, 10 for the beams1 to 8 respectively. Beams1 to 4 correspond to a PFI spacing equal to 19.997 mm and the others to 49.947 mm.

In other experiment we observed that with a polished target illuminated by the full power from one of the dye lasers, the output from the analyzing PFI was high enough to be recordable by a mecanooptical camera with a sweeping rate equal to 3.125 mm/μs.

COMMENTS

The velocity is calculated from the measurements of three diameters Do, D1 and D' in the interferograms according to :

$$V = \frac{\lambda c}{4e}\left(n + \frac{D'^2 - D_o^2}{D_1^2 - D_o^2}\right)$$

Do and D1 are the diameters of two successive "static" rings, D' is the diameter of a "dynamic" ring at the instant of measurement, n is an

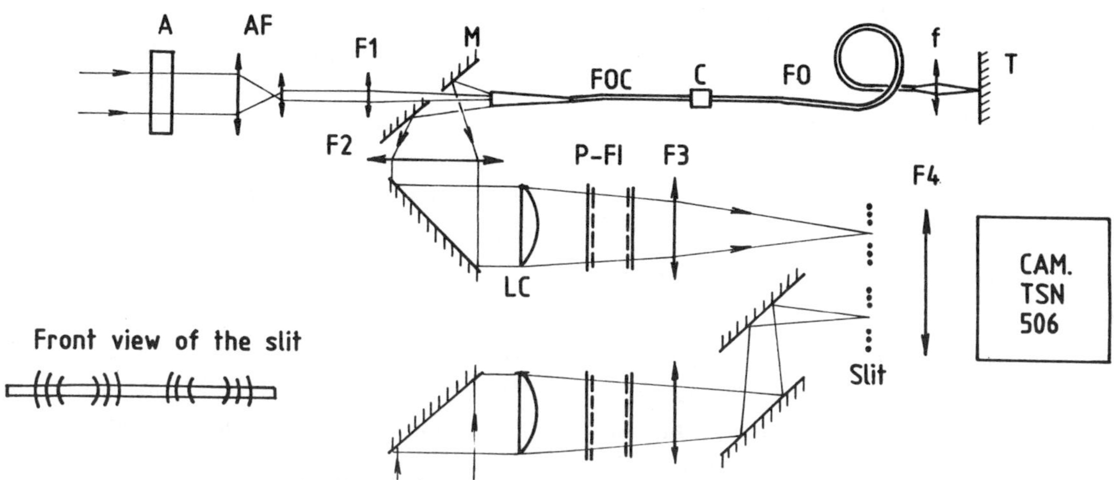

Figure 3 :Top view A : neutral filter - AF : beam reducer (/4). - F1, F2, F3, F4, F : spherical lenses with focal lengths equal to 50, 120, 1000, 160 and 50 nm, respectively.- M : mirror with a centered hole - FOC : conical optical fiber - C : optical fiber connexion LC cylindrical lens - T : target.

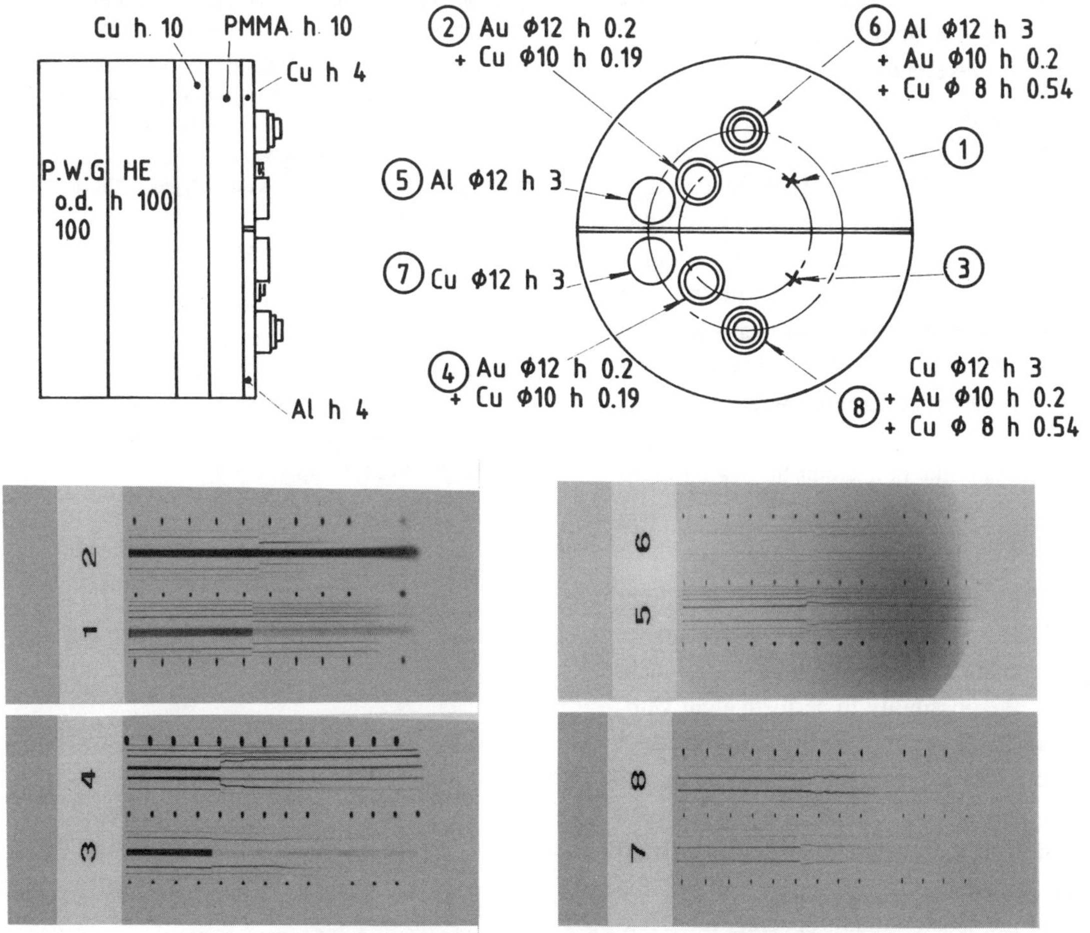

Figure 4 :Schematic diagram of the experiment and a photographic reproduction of the real records. The number on the curves refers to the number on the target. is the diameter and h the thickness of the samples (Unit : mm).

integer,λ the wavelength of the laser and c the velocity of light. In the error calculation, one can neglect the uncertainty in the distance e between the plates of the PFI. Then :

$$\Delta V \leq \frac{\lambda c}{4e}\left[(n+1)\frac{\Delta\lambda}{\lambda}+2\Delta D\frac{D1\left|D'^2-Do^2\right|+Do\left|D_1^2-D'^2\right|+D'(D_1^2-D_o^2)}{(D_1^2-D_o^2)^2}\right]$$

where ΔD is the error in the diameter measurement.

Statistically we have found that the standard deviation in a diameter measurement is the same as with Ar^+ laser light, namely 7 μm, leading to ΔD~0,02mm. $\Delta\lambda$ is the uncertainly in wavelength measurement due to the multiline laser : it depends on the width of the wavelength spectrum of the dye laser, which is around 5 nm, leading to a 1% relative error in wavelength.

Further, some experiments carried out with rather large values of the sweep duration (15-30 μs) have shown that the diameters of the "static" fringes produced by this kind of laser vary with time. Due to our system of light transmission through a single optical fiber, some part of the light (without Doppler shift) is reflected from the entrance face of the fiber to the analyzing PFI. In this way, "static" fringes are recorded together with the "dynamic" ones, so, with some extra work in the data reduction, we can take in account this variation of the static fringes with time.

CONCLUSION

This new PFV, using a multiline laser as a light source, features advantages and inconveniences with respect to the usual argon ion laser. The main advantage is the possibility to perform eight velocity measurements during each shot, the main drawback the loss of accuracy due to the uncertainty in wavelength. The fixed spacing between the PFI plates has the advantage of straightforward alignment procedure, but of course has not the flexibility of the usual, variable spacing, interferometers.

We are now studying a slightly different configuration, where the same PFI is used to filter the dye laser output and to analyze the light reflected from the target. The PFI plates are of varying reflectivity, with a central area of moderate reflectivity for filtering and a high reflectivity outer part for analyzing.

ACKNOWLEDGMENTS

We are greatly indebted with Claude SEGARD and Jean-Hugues QUESSADA for their clever solutions to a number of technical problems.

REFERENCES

[1]L. Steinmetz- "New laser amplifier improves Doppler interferometry" -Energy and Technology Review (Feb. 1986).

[2]D.R. Goosman, A.M. Frank, H.H. Chau and N.L. Parker "Proceedings on High Speed Photography, Videography and Photonics",- Soc. Photo-opt. Instrum. Eng. 427, 186 (1983).

[3]W.L. Seitz, H.L. Stacy -" Fabry-Perot interferometry using an image intensified rotating mirror streak camera", proc. SPIE vol. 427 (1983).

[4]S. Gidon, G. Behar - "Multiple line laser Doppler velocimetry" - Applied Optics, Vol. 27, n° 11, 2315 (1 june 1988).

[5]Mercier, Veaux, Behar, Cavailler - "Laser multiraies appliqué à l'interférométrie Doppler Laser" - 40° rencontre A.R.A. - Sept. 1989 - PARIS.

[6]M. Durand - "Proceedings of the 16th International Congress on Highspeed photography and photonics" - Soc. Photo Opt. Instrum. Eng. 491, 650 (1984).

MICROWAVE INTERFEROMETRY TO ELUCIDATE SHOCK PROPERTIES

Gabriel G. LUTHER

Los Alamos National Laboratory, Los Alamos, New Mexico, USA, 87545

Barry J. WARTHEN

EG&G/EM, Los Alamos, New Mexico, USA, 87544

A series of measurements have been performed using a simple, lightweight, inexpensive, compact K-Band (SLICK) interferometer to measure the shock properties of passive (Teflon, grout) and energetic (HE) materials. Shock and particle velocity measurements are made simultaneously along the same path. This path is determined by either a thin walled (1/2 mil aluminum foil) waveguide embedded in the material or the caustic of a Teflon axicon. Typically the velocities are determined to about a percent. The measurements will be described and data presented.

INTRODUCTION

A simple K-band microwave interferometer, based on our X-band interferometer [1] has been developed at the Los Alamos National Laboratory to measure various transient properties in both energetic (high explosive) and passive (grout and Teflon) materials. The interferometer measures the position as a function of time of either a dielectric discontinuity, i.e., a shock front, or the position as a function of time of a conducting surface such as the detonation wave in a high explosive. By embedding a reflector in a dielectric material, both the particle velocity and the shock velocity may be measured at the same time and in the same place.

INSTRUMENTATION

The interferometer (Fig. 1) is based on a 24 GHz Gunn diode oscillator, normally found in automatic door openers, etc., and a mixer diode pair obtained from the same company [2]. The two mixer diodes, electrically one-quarter wave apart, yield quadrature components of the signal (sine and cosine) which are typically recorded on LeCroy 8818 CAMAC digitizers. In order to prevent frequency pulling of the Gunn diode by this reflector signal so as to resolve subwavelength position details, the mixer diode and the oscillator are separated by an isolator, sometimes using a commercial K-band isolator and sometimes using a three-port circulator and a dummy load; in some cases, a simple attenuator may be substituted to isolate the Gunn diode from the reflected signal. Usually, six to ten db of attenuation is inserted in the waveguide between the mixer diode and the reflecting surface to be measured to balance the amplitudes of the transmitted and reflected signal.

The phase of the reflection is determined by two things: 1) The distance between the reflecting surface and the mixer diode, and 2) the index of refraction of the material between the reflecting surface and the mixer diode. In particle velocity measurements, the amount of refracting material between the reflecting surface and the mixer diodes is a constant and hence in the Gladstone-Dale

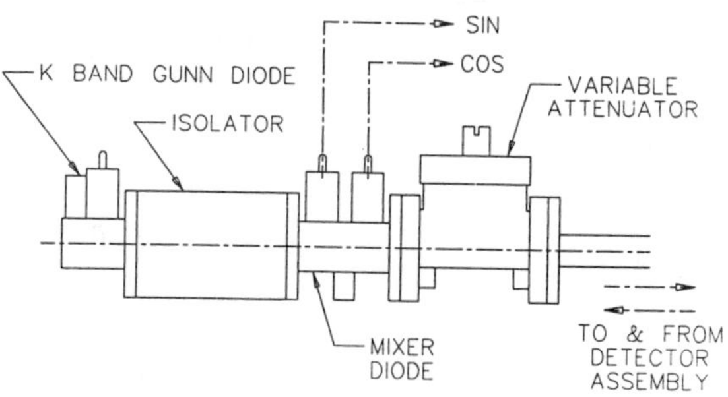

Figure 1. The interferometer showing the Gunn diode, the isolator, the attenuator and the waveguide leading to the detector.

approximation [3] (n-1 is proportional to the density), the travel necessary to give a 2 π phase change at the mixer diode is the same as in vacuum (approximately 0.77 cm in a WR-42 waveguide). However, shock velocity measurements consist of a wave front (dielectric discontinuity) moving *through* a material medium and so the index of refraction needs to be considered. The measured value in Teflon in a WR-42 waveguide for the length required to give the same 2 π phase change is 0.45 cm. Since the shock wave is faster than the particle wave and the distance necessary to produce in some 2 π phase shift is shorter, the two signals are characterized by very different frequencies. The two signals may be separated by either analog or digital filtering. As examples of the range of uses of the interferometer, three measurements will be described. It has been used to measure the shock properties of grout, the deflagration-to-detonation transition in a compacted powder explosive (both inside a waveguide) and an unconfined measurement of the detonation velocity in solid HE, the velocity of the explosion products at the interface of the explosive shock and air and the pressure at a Teflon surface upon which the explosive products impinge.

First Example

As a first example, a pressure measurement was performed. A waveguide detector was constructed of one-half mil household aluminum foil the size of the inside of the WR-42 waveguide (0.170 x 0.420 in.), having Teflon inside and outside of the waveguide. An aluminum plate, one-eighth in. thick terminated the waveguide and was immersed in the grout. As the shock passed from the grout through the aluminum plate into the Teflon, the shock front produced the high-frequency signal seen in the data, i.e., the shock velocity, and the motion of the aluminum plate (and hence the grout and Teflon between which it was sandwiched) the low-frequency component in the data gave the particle velocity (Fig. 2). Analysis of these two signals fitted the Marsh Handbook [4] data, showing that the Gladstone-Dale model is appropriate.

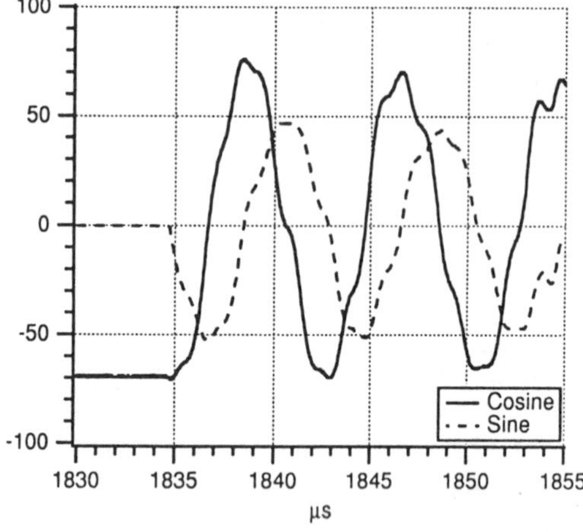

Figure 2. The quadrature signals, sine and cosine, of the particle and shock velocity motions in the grout.

Second Example

Another experiment done inside a waveguide is a measurement of the process by which deflagration transitions to detonation in a compacted powdered HE. A one-half-in. inside-diameter heavy-walled brass tube, which acted both to confine the explosive and as a circular waveguide, was packed with the powdered HE to a density of 1.25 gm/cm^3. A Teflon plug covered with copper foil was shaped to form a reflectionless transition between the WR-42 waveguide and the brass tube and acted as a tamper on the powdered HE (Fig. 3). The HE was ignited with a pyrofuse so as to initiate a slow burn. The burn, the compaction wave produced by the burning HE, the deflagration-to-detonation transition and the detonation wave can be clearly seen (Fig. 4). In addition, the analysis of the shock and particle velocity signals in the Teflon plug give the pressure.

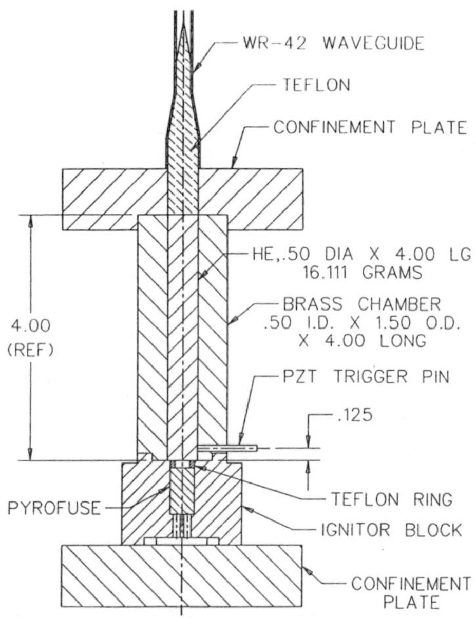

Figure 3. Shows the WR-42-to-one-half-in. transition, the compacted HE, the pyrofuse that sets it off and the containment pieces.

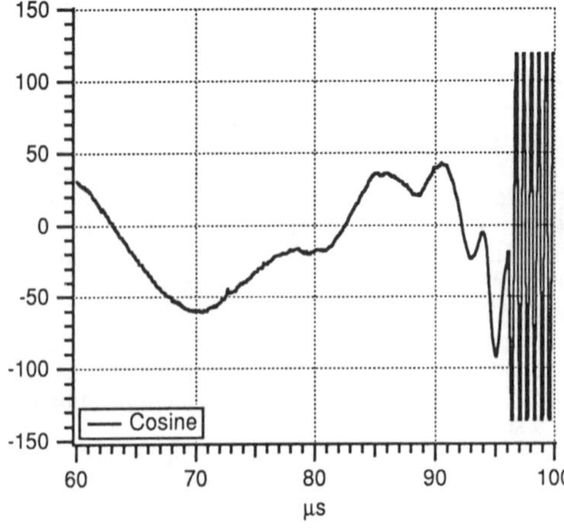

Figure 4. Deflagration to detonation transition showing the slow burn initiated by the pyrofuse, the compaction wave generated by the slow burn, the instant of the onset of detonation and the detonation wave.

Third Example

In this example, a free space measurement, a Teflon axicon [5] was used to focus the microwaves from a horn through a 2-in. air gap and hence into a 2-in.-thick piece of solid HE (Fig. 5). A sheet of aluminum foil between the lens and the HE was the initial reflector. Figure 6 clearly shows the detonation front moving through the HE, the shock front generated as the HE products travel through the air gap, and the shock and particle velocities in the Teflon when the HE products impinge upon the Teflon. Since the equation of state of Teflon is well known, the pressure at the air-Teflon interface can be determined as in the First Example. The time of the initiation of the detonation in the solid HE and the time of the transition of the shock from the HE to the air could be accurately determined. Using these times and the length of the HE (2 in.), the velocity of detonation was determined with an accuracy of about one percent.

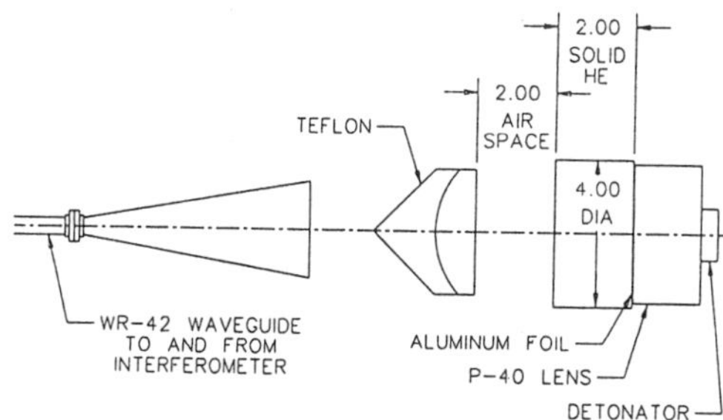

Figure 5. Third example instrumentation showing the axicon used to focus the microwaves, the horn, the air gap and the solid HE.

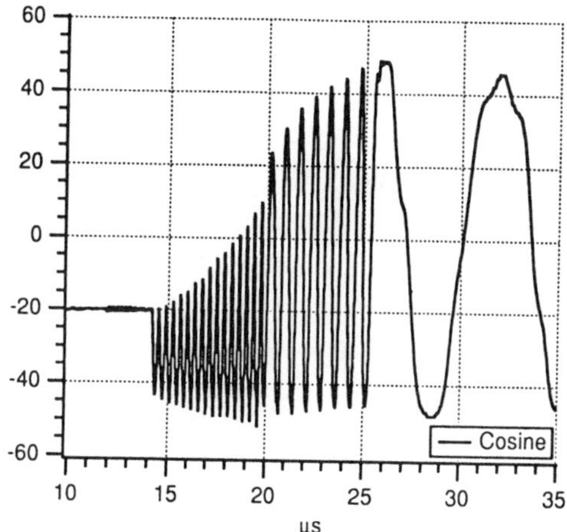

Figure 6. The data from the third example showing the passage of the detonation through the HE. It is possible to determine accurately the time it takes to transit the two inches and, from that, the velocity to within 1%.

CONCLUSION

These techniques are still under development. It is possible (limited by the signal-to-noise ratio) to use the ratio of the amplitude of the shock signal to the amplitude of the particle signal to determine the index of refraction change at the shock front and hence to determine the change in density. This feature has not been fully explored. Frequency agile measurements are currently being made which give not only the velocity but the position from which the reflection emanates. Knowledgeable experimenters in this field can obviously find other uses for this SLICK apparatus.

ACKNOWLEDGMENTS

We would be very pleased to acknowledge information from and conversations with Frank Harlow, George Nichol, John Moses, Blaine Asay, Gil Miranda, Stan Marsh, Joe Fritz and the technicians in the P-3 Group, Los Alamos National Laboratory.

REFERENCES

1. G. Luther, L. Veeser, B. Warthen, "A Microwave Interferometer to Measure Particle and Shock Velocities Simultaneously", Shock Compression of Condensed Matter-1991, S.C. Schmidt, R.D. Dick, J.W. Forbs, D.G. Tasker, Eds., Williamsburg, Virginia, June 17-20, 1991 (Elsevier Science Publishers B. V., 1992),pp. 775,778.

2. Alpha Industries, 20 Sylvan Road, Woburn, Massachusetts, 01801. This doesn't constitute an endorsement of this companies product but merely gives an indication of the type of apparatus used.

3. J. Wackerle, H. L. Stacy, J. C. Dallman, Proceedings of the SPIE, v. 832, August 17 - 19, 1987, San Diego, CA, p. 76 (SPIE, 1988)

4. S. P. Marsh, LASL Shock Hugoniot Data (University of California Press, Berkeley, CA, 1980), pp.467-468.

5. J. McLeod, "The Axicon: A New Type of Optical Element", Journal of the Optical Society of America, v. 44, 8, (1954), pp.592-597.

ON THE POSSIBILITY OF FRACTO-EMISSION IN CERAMICS DURING SHOCK COMPRESSION

N. S. Brar
University of Dayton Research Institute,
300 College Park, Dayton OH 45469-0182, USA
Zvi Rosenberg
RAFAEL, P.O. Box 2240 (24), Haifa, Israel

We use commercially available manganin grid gauges to measure Hugoniot stresses in materials. We find that the gauge response (resistance change versus time) is normal in ceramic targets for shock stress below 110 kbar. For stresses above 110 kbar, gauge profile shows a dramatic short-circuiting across gauge leads during shock loading to peak stress. The gauge remains short-circuited until the arrival of the release wave. On arrival of the release wave the gauge response returned to the base line, suggesting that the gauge is not physically damaged during loading. The threshold peak shock stress at which the short-circuiting begins to happen is raised to 170 kbar by embedding the special gauge between thicker (50 μm) mylar sheets. No short-circuiting of the thin (25 μm) mylar encapsulated gauges in metal and alloy targets is observed for stresses to 190 kbar. The short-circuiting of the gauge in ceramic targets is conjectured to take place due to the strong electric field generated by the charged particles emitted from the fracturing of ceramic during shock compression[1].

INTRODUCTION

The phenomenon of emission of electrons and positive ions from materials during and following fracture is known as fracto-emission (FE). Dickinson et al. have reviewed the subject on FE for a number of materials including crystalline insulators, glass, graphite, polymers and fiber-reinforced epoxy systems[1]. According to this study FE is caused by the high concentration of energy deposited into a small volume of a material during a short period of time (microseconds or less). The energy deposition can result in creation of excitations and defects giving rise to separation of charges on crack walls and production of dangling bonds in materials.

The process of shock compression of materials results in the deposition of a large amount of energy in a few microseconds. There have been a number of investigations on the failure of various types of alumina ceramics under shock compression. Louro studied shock wave induced damage in alumina based ceramics by carrying out scanning electron microscopy of the soft recovered specimens[2]. He concluded that the ceramic failed through transcrystalline and intercrystalline fractures. Espinosa has made similar observations on recovered polycrystalline alumina ceramics subjected to well defined shock compression pulses[3]. In general, these studies conclude that the ceramic failure under shock compression takes place with microfracturing initiated on the specimen surface.

We embed piezoresistive manganin gauges in between two ceramic plates in order to monitor shock stress during loading and unloading. The gauges in direct contact with the ceramic surface in the target exhibit short circuiting at stresses above 110 kbar[4-5]. Whereas in the case of metal targets no short circuiting takes place for stresses to 190 kbar[6]. The objective of the present work is to investigate the possible correlation of the short circuiting of the embedded manganin gauge in ceramic targets with the FE as a result of the failure of ceramic by fracturing under shock compression.

EXPERIMENTAL METHOD AND RESULTS

Manganin gauges were purchased from Micro-measurements. Four different types of manganin gauges were used in the present study. The gauges were embedded in ceramics target plates with 25 or 50 μm thick mylar encapsulation. Details of the target assembly are given in Reference 4. Eight experiments were performed with manganin gauges embedded in AlN targets[4], two with Coors AD-85 targets and one with a copper target. All experiments were performed at University of Dayton Research Institute using a 50 mm gas/powder gun. The data on the impactor, impactor velocity, and target configuration in all the experiments are summarized in Table 1.

We experienced the normal gauge response in measuring Hugonoit stresses in AlN and AD-85 ceramic targets to 110 kbar. In experiments above 110 kbar the standard manganin gauge (1) exhibited symptoms of short circuiting[4]. For example, gauge profile in shot 7-1348 on AlN target using the standard gauge at a peak stress of about 134 kbar (Figure 1a) displays short-circuiting at point A, but recovers at point B to just above base line on arrival of the release wave from the back of the impactor. In shot 7-1362 we used a special gauge (2), in which gauge grid and leads are fully encapsulated between 40 μm thick fiber reinforced epoxy sheets, along with a thicker mylar package in order to overcome this short-circuiting of the gauge. The gauge

Table 1. Summary of shot data

Shot #	Impactor(mm)/ Velocity(m/s)	Target	σ_{peak} (kbar)	Gauge short circuiting
7-1348	Cu(8)/730	6.96 mm AlN+50 μm mylar+gauge (1)+ 50 μm mylar+ 6.97 mm AlN	134	Yes
7-1362	cu(8)/1010	9.2 mm AlN+50 μm mylar+gauge (2)+ 25 μm mylar+9.2 mm AlN	170	Yes
7-1528	Cu(8)/742	6 mm AlN+gauge (3)+25 μm mylar+6 mm AlN	135	Yes
7-1530	Cu(6)/950	4 mm AD-85+gauge (1)+12 μm mylar+4 mm AD-85	152#	Yes
7-1532	Cu(6)/687	6 mm AlN+gauge (1)+12 μm mylar+6 mm AlN	121#	Yes
7-1534	Cu(6)/706	5.5 mm AlN+gauge (4)+5.5 mm AlN	125	Yes
7-1540	Cu(8)/780	4 mm AD-85+25 μm mylar+gauge (1)+ 25 μm mylar+6 mm AD-85	123	Yes
7-1569	Cu(6)/649	3.23 mm AlN+50 μm mylar+gauge (2)+50 μm mylar+ 5.46 mm AlN	117	No*
7-1572	Cu(6)/859	same as 7-1569	147	No*
7-1575	Cu(8)/1015	same as 7-1569	172	Yes**
7-1650	AD-995(6)/904	2 mm Cu+25 μm mylar+gauge (1)+25 μm mylar+ 12.5 mm Cu	180	No

Standard gauge (1)-LM-SS-125CH-048 (grid 5x5 mm and grid+ backing=50 μm)
Special gauge (2)-LM-SS-210FD-050-SP60 (grid 6.3x6.3 mm and grid+backing+cover=100 μm)
Special gauge (3)-LM-SS-210FD-050 (grid 6.3x6.3 mm and grid+backing=75 μm)
Special gauge (4)-C-880113-B (grid 2x4 mm and grid+backing+cover=75μm)
Estimated   * Thick gauge package   ** Impact velocity high

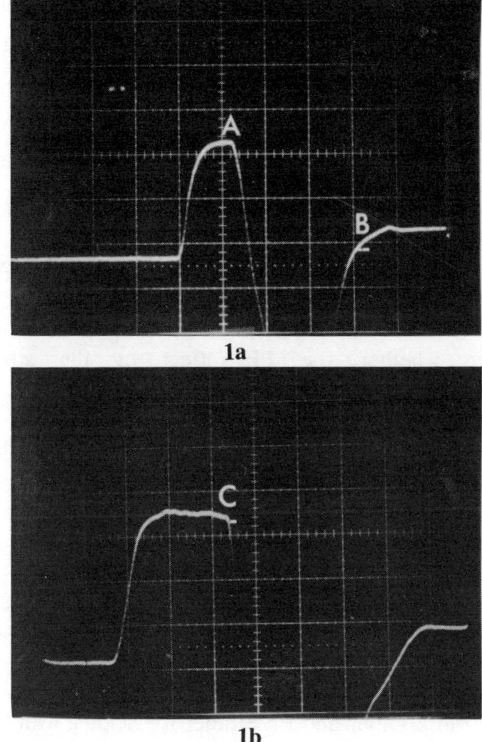

Figure 1. Gauge profiles (a) 7-1348 and (b) 7-1362; scales (2 v/div, 0.5 μs/div)

profile (Figure 1b) in this shot is almost flat top until point C, when the gauge short-circuits but recovers as in shot 7-1348. Stress-time profiles from other experiments on AlN (7-1532, 7-1534, and 7-1540) and on alumina AD-85 targets (7-1530, 7-1540) were similar to those shown in Figure 1. Gauge profiles in two shots on AD-85 ceramic targets were also similar to those shown in Figure 1.

We repeated shot 7-1362 with the special gauge (2) and adding another 25 μm thick mylar on the back of the gauge at a lower impact velocity of 649 m/s. The gauge profile in this shot (7-1569) did not show any short circuiting. No short-circuiting of the same gauge was observed in shot 7-1572 with the same target configuration as shot 7-1569 at an impact velocity of 859 m/s (Figure 2a, σ=147 kbar). Thus the threshold for short-circuiting of this gauge configuration has been raised to about 150 kbar. As we increased the impact velocity to 1015 m/s (σ=172 kbar) in shot 7-1575, the gauge profile was similar to that obtained in shot 7-1362 showing short-circuiting during the shock phase and recovering as the release wave arrives at the gauge location (Figure 2b).

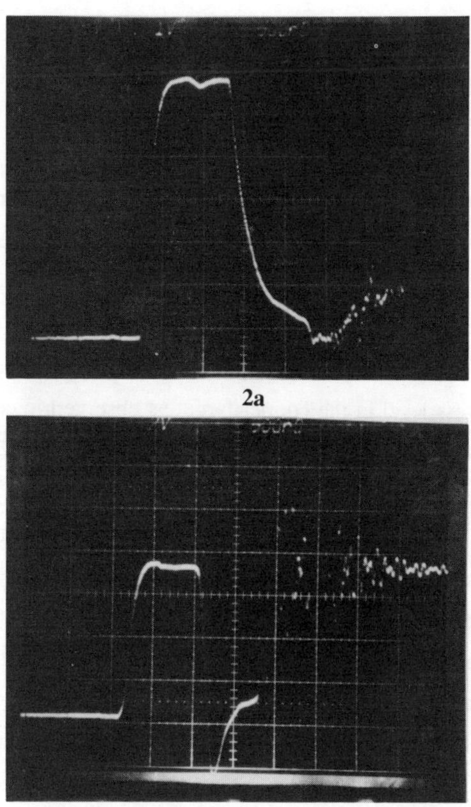

Figure 2. Gauge profiles (a) 7-1572 (1 v/div, 0.5 μs/div) (b) 7-1575 (2 v/div, 0.5 μs/div)

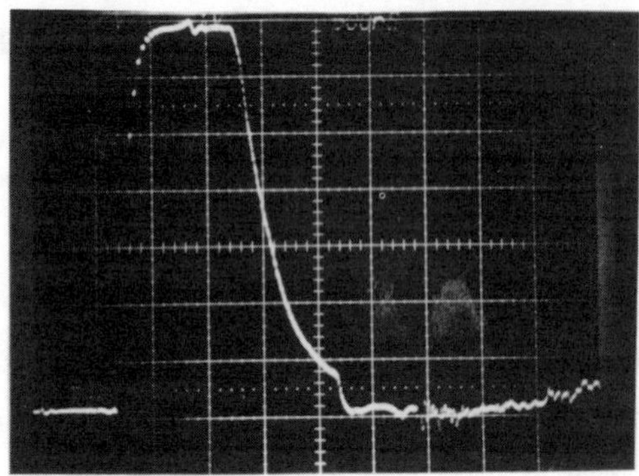

Figure 3. Gauge profile 7-1650 (1 v/div, 0.5 μs/div)

In shot 7-1650 we prepared a target by embedding the standard manganin gauge with 25 μm thick mylar sheets on both sides in between two copper disks. This target was impacted by a Coors AD-995 impactor plate at 904 m/s producing a peak stress of about 180 kbar. The gauge profile shown in Figure 3 is almost flat topped and releases to just above the base line, because of the hysteresis on unloading in piezoresistace gauges. The profile does not show any short-circuiting at 180 kbar stress level in the copper target as observed in ceramic targets.

CONCLUSIONS

The short-circuiting of the gauge takes place when embedded in ceramic targets without any encapsulation during the shock phase at peak stress above 110 kbar and recovers to normal response on arrival of the release wave. The peak shock stress at which short-circuiting takes place is increased by embedding the gauge in thicker encapsulation. This observation suggest that when the gauge grid is in direct contact with the ceramic surface or insulated with less than 25 μm thick mylar sheet, FE from fracturing ceramic during shock compression affects the gauge response. Our conjecture is supported by the fact that when the gauge is embedded in the metal (copper) target, gauge profile at comparable shock stress levels does not show any short-circuiting. We attribute the short circuiting of the gauge in ceramic targets is due to the FE generated on the ceramic surface due to the fracturing of the ceramic under shock compression.

We plan to perform more experiments on ceramics by grounding the vapor deposited metallic coating on ceramic surfaces or by using a Faraday cage around the gauge package. These experiments are expected to resolve whether the FE effect or the stress concentrations due to ceramic fracturing, proposed in Reference 4, cause the short circuiting of the gauge. More work is also required to quantify the time and the extent of FE in different ceramics.

ACKNOWLEDGEMENTS

The work was supported in part by U. S. Army Research Office Contract No. DAAL03-88-K-0203. We thank Mark Laber and Ed Strader for helping with the experiments.

REFERENCES

[1] J. T. Dickinson, E. E. Donaldson, and M. K. Park, J. Mater. Sc., 16, 2897 (1981).

[2] L. H. Lauro, "Stress Wave Induced Damage in Alumina-Based Ceramics," Ph.D. Thesis, New Mexico Inst. of Min. and Tech., July 1991.

[3] H. D. Espinosa, "Micromechanics of the Dynamic Response of Ceramics and Ceramic Composites," Ph.D. Thesis, Brown University, May 1992.

[4] Z. Rosenberg, N. S. Brar, and S. J. Bless, J. Appl. Phys., 70, 167 (1991).

[5] Z. Rosenberg, N. S. Brar and S. J. Bless, "The Dynamic Responses of AlN," The University of Dayton Research Institute Report UDR-TR-89-74 (1989).

[6] N. S. Brar and Z. Rosenberg, "Dynamic Response of 1210 Steel," Interim Report, The University of Dayton Research Institute Report UDR-TR-87-117 (1987).

A FLASH X-RAY RADIOGRAPHY DIAGNOSTIC FOR STUDYING SURFACE PHENOMENA UNDER SHOCK LOADING

Christian REMIOT, Pierre CHAPRON, Bruno DEMAY

Commissariat à l'Energie Atomique
Centre d'Etudes de Vaujours-Moronvilliers
77181 COURTRY - FRANCE

These experimental studies are mainly concerned with the matter ejection from the free surface and the bulk microspalling of the sample near the free surface. We describe an experimental technique using flash X-ray radiography in order to study the shock-induced ejection and microspalling. Experiments have been achieved with tin shocked at different pressures 15 to 40 GPa by an explosive generator or by a powder gun. We show that microspalling depends on tin sample melting in release and also on other parameters such as the incident shock profile level.

INTRODUCTION

When a shock wave emerges from a solid metallic sample, it often happens that the expanding free surface is actually moving behind a cloud of so-called ejected mass [1,2,3,4] and, as we now know, sometimes between this cloud and the free surface a dynamic decoherence area called microspalling also happens. In this paper, we describe our experimental technique using flash X-ray radiography in order to study the shock-induced ejection and, in particular, microspalling, and we give the experimental results on the tin sample.

EXPERIMENTAL SET-UP AND DIAGNOSTICS

An explosive generator induces a 40 GPa shock level inside a tin sample whose free surface has two different preparations : one half of the surface is polished and the other half is roughly machined with wedge-shaped parallel grooves (300 µm wide and 100 µm in depth). The target is composed of a copper plate 3 mm thick and a tin plate 3 mm thick (Fig. 1).

We also used a powder gun of 60 mm diameter (Fig. 2). The shock level, depending on projectile velocity, is determined by varying the flying plate thickness of the projectile. The range of the shock is from 15 to 40 GPa. In this case, electrical probes measure the projectile velocity in order to determine the shock level by using the equation of state of target samples.

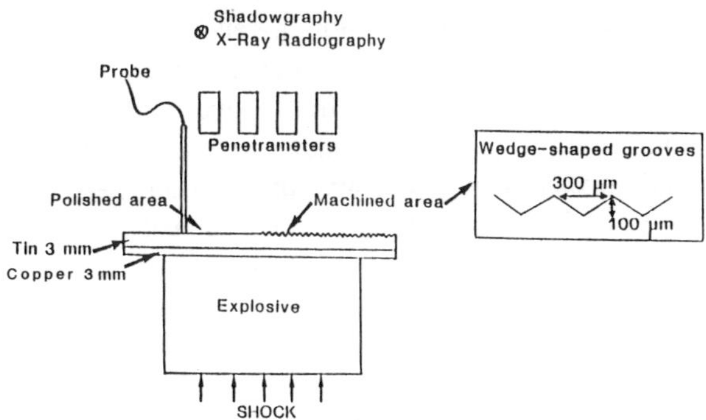

Figure 1. Experimental set-up

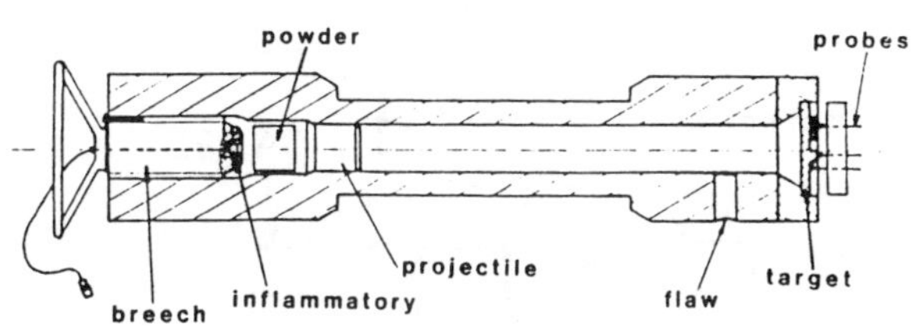

Figure 2. Powder-gun, 60 mm in diameter

In all cases, other electrical probes detect the time of the shock reflection arrival on the metallic sample free surface and trigger the X-ray flash generator through a delay generator. The delay generator allowed us to study the expansion of the ejected mass and the microspalling.

The measurement technique uses a 600 kV X-ray pulse generator (Scandiflash 600) providing a 20 mrad exposure at 1 meter during 20 ns (FWHM) with a 1.2 mm focal spot diameter. This generator can penetrate about 15 g/cm^2 in tin. An ultra short X-ray pulse is necessary to reduce the dynamic blurring and a small focal spot minimizes the geometrical blurring. One X-ray flash, taken parallel to the shocked free surface a few microseconds after the shock arrival, gives a picture coded in optical density on the film. A flying cassette in lexan, initially positioned at 400 mm from the metallic samples, contains the KODAK TMAT G film coupled with LANEX FAST intensifying screens. For distributed ejected mass measurement, assuming an uniform spatial distribution in the direction parallel to the free surface and using suitable penetrameters which give the relation between film optical density and thickness of penetrated matter, ejected material and microspalling density distribution can be simply derived from an optical density record perpendicular to the free surface (Fig. 3). Image processing is made with a Joyce and Loebl microdensitometer driven by a personal computer.

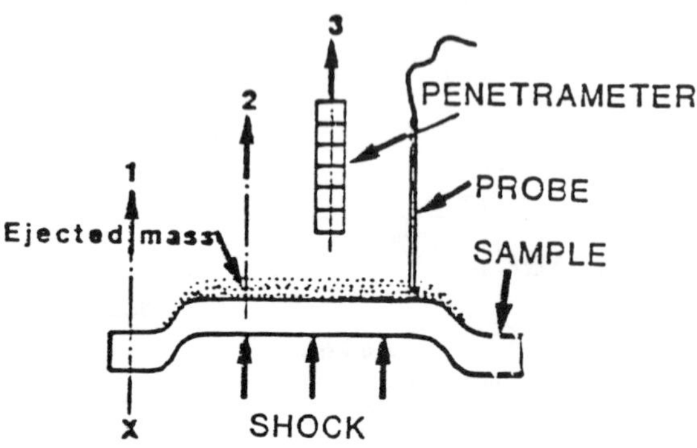

Figure 3. Distributed ejected mass

The experimental set-up, in the firing chamber is shown in figure 4.

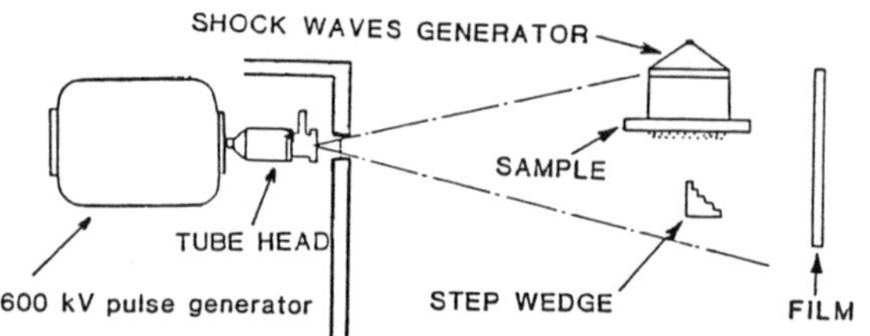

Figure 4. Experimental device for radiography investigation

EXPERIMENTAL RESULTS

Four experiments have been accomplished, the first with an explosive generator and the three others with the launcher. Tables 1 and 2 give the initial conditions of the experiments. Zero on the time corresponds to shock arrival at the tin free surface. We defined the free surface to be the boundary between the microspalling area and the dense material. Figure 5 shows the X-ray radiographs obtained for the four experiments and the type and the amplitude of the shock profile obtained by a monodimensional hydrodynamic code.

Table 1. With explosive

Exp. numb.	Shock pressure in tin GPa	Shock profile	With explosive	radio. flash instant (µs)
1	40	◹	High energy explosive	14.0

Table 2. With powder gun

Exp. numb.	Shock pressure in tin GPa	Shock profile	Flying plate thickness (mm)	Powder mass (g)	radio. flash instant (µs)
2	28	⊓	3 Cu	150	9.74
3	15	◹	0.5 Ta	80	9.98
4	30	◹	0.5 Ta	150	9.48

In the first experiment, we observe a different behaviour between the polished surface area (without any ejection) and the roughly machined area. Furthermore, we can notice another zone behind the initial polished surface area and the

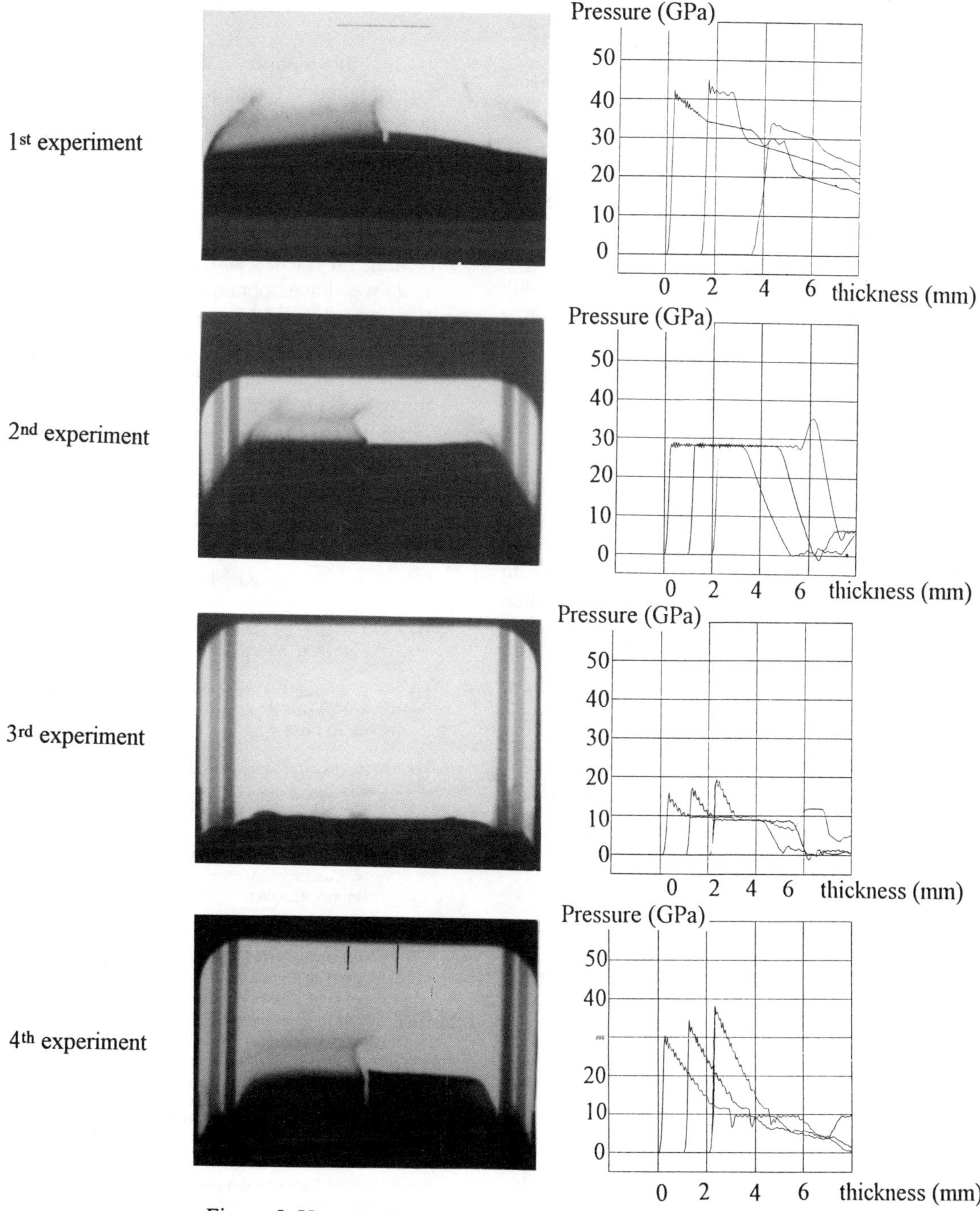

Figure 5. X-ray radiographs and shock profiles

roughly machined area, this zone is due to microspalling [5, 6]. The density of ejected mass is about one hundreth of the tin density (7.31 g/cm3) and for microspalling is about one tenth of the tin density (Fig. 6).

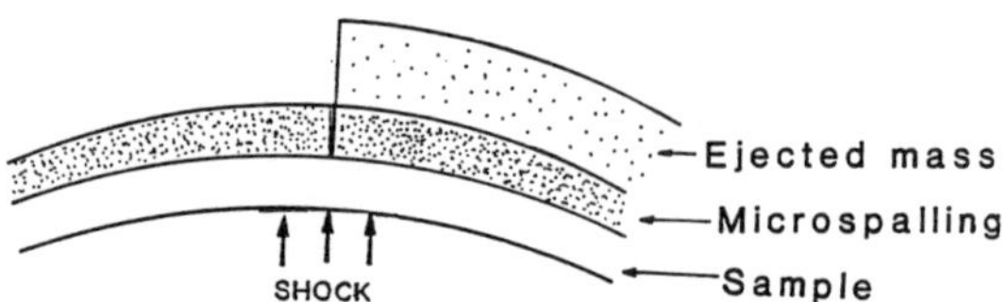

Figure 6. Discrimination between ejected mass and microspalling

In the second experiment, we observe only ejected mass in front of the roughly machined area and no microspalling zone.

In the third experiment, we observe no ejected mass and no microspalling zone. The shock level is under 23.5 GPa in tin which is the pressure inducing melting in release [7].

In the fourth experiment, we observe exactly the same as in the first experiment.

So we have observed a microspalling zone only near or above the pressure of melting in release and we also observed microspalling when two release waves cross each other, the first wave coming from the reflection of the shock wave at the free surface and the second wave coming from the shock profile. There is no connection between the free surface preparation and microspalling zone appearance.

Table 3 summarizes the densities and thickness obtained of both ejecta and microspalling.

Table 3.

Exp. num.	Ejecta thickness (mm)	Ejecta density	Microsp. thickness (mm)	Microsp. density
1	6,5	$\rho_o/70$	1,6	$\rho_o/10$
2	5,4	$\rho_o/80$	0	-
3	0	-	0	-
4	8,1	$\rho_o/80$	7,0	$\rho_o/9$

ρ_o is the initial tin density (7.31 g/cm^3)

CONCLUSION

In this paper, we have described our experimental technique using flash X-ray radiography in order to analyse appearance of microspalling zone near the free surface and the connection with ejecta.

We have provided evidence that the main cause of surface deterioration by microspalling is melting on release and the incident shock profile, and we have obtained no significant relation between these two surface phenomena (ejected mass and microspalling).

In future experiments we plan to study microspalling effect at different shock pressures in order to try to carry out a scaling law regarding this phenomenon and another experimental to study the microspalling behavior when a dense gas is put ahead of the sample free surface.

REFERENCES

[1] J.R. Asay, L.P. Mix, and F.C. Perry. *Applied Physics Letters*, Vol. 29, n° 5 (September 1976), pp.284-287.

[2] R. Chéret, P. Chapron, P. Elias,J. Martineau, *Shock Waves in Condensed Matter 1985*, ed. Y. Gupta. Plenum, (1986), pp. 651-654.

[3] R. Couch, L. Shaw, R. Barlett, L. Steinmetz, W. Behrendt, C. Firpo, *Journal de Physique. Supplément au n° 8*, tome 46, (1985), pp.C5-385. DYMAT 85.

[4] V. Frachet, P. Elias, J. Martineau, *Shock Waves in Condensed Matter 1987*, eds. S.C. Schmidt and N.C. Holmes. Elsevier

[5] P. Andriot, P. Chapron, V. Lambert, F. Olive, Influence of free surface behaviour using doppler laser interferometry and X-ray densitometry, J.R. Asay, R.A. Graham, Stranb GK (eds), *Shock waves in condensed matter 83*. (1983), Elsevier, pp. 277-280.

[6] P. Chapron, P. Elias, Surface phenomena of shock loaded metallic samples, *Shock Waves Proceedings*, Sendai, Japon, (1991), Vol. 1, pp. 435-440.

[7] P. Elias, P. Chapron, B. Laurent, Detection of melting in release for a shocked loaded tin sample using the reflectivity measurement method, Optics Communications, (04.15.1988), Vol. 66, number 2-3, pp. 100-106.

CHAPTER XXIV

IMPACT PHENOMENA AND HYPERVELOCITY STUDIES

A STUDY USING MOLECULAR DYNAMICS OF THE SHOCK WAVES PRODUCED IN AN ALUMINUM THIN FILM VIA HYPERVELOCITY IMPACTS

R. McDonald, W. G. Tanner and W. M. Alexander
Baylor University Space Science Laboratory

Thin films form an essential part of in-situ detectors used in the study of micrometeroids. With the development of sensor arrays using thin films with thicknesses between 500 and 1000 Å an investigation of the response of the films to hypervelocity impacts was undertaken using Molecular Dynamics. A projectile of 256 particles and a film with a surface area forty-nine times greater than the projectile are equilibriated using a Lennard-Jones potential. The film is subdivided into forty-nine equal volume elements whose dimensions are equal to the projectile's initial volume. The thermodynamic response of these volume elements are used to analyze the propagation of the shockwave in the thin film as a function of impact speed, radial distance from the impact site, and the elasped time from the moment of impact.

INTRODUCTION

In-Situ measurements of micrometeoroids and orbital debris in Low Earth Orbit (LEO) have been the subject of renewed interest for the space community. For space scientists one of the principle problems is the designing of instruments capable of determining the origin of a detected particle. The impact plasma created by a hypervelocity impact with a thin film is a means for ascertaining the velocity vector of the impacting particle and thereby its origin. When passive sensors are utilized as in the Long Duration Exposure Facility (LDEF) and the European Retrieval Carrier (EuReCa), thin films are still a significant part of the experiments. Both types of sensor are useful in studying the problem of orbital debris and micrometeoroid fluxes. For both classifications of experiments it is necessary to understand the physics of a hypervelocity impact with a thin film. For these reasons Baylor University Space Science Laboratory (BUSSL) has been engaged in the study of hypervelocity impacts with thin films using both Hydrocodes and Molecular Dynamics (MD) for the last four years . Some of these results obtained through MD are presented in this paper. The work described below uses procedures described by Holian[1] who modeled a lead sphere hitting a lead plate. In this paper MD is used to study impacts of an aluminum particle on an aluminum film at speeds ranging from 7 to 28 km/s. The density, pressure, and temperature were calculated at various points in the thin film. The first section describes the procedures used to simulate the hypervelocity impacts, and the techniques employed to study the thermodynamic response of the thin film. The second section discusses the results of the computer experiments with a particular emphasis on the arrival and magnitude of the shock front created by the impact.

PROCEDURES

The procedure used to study the impacts through the use of MD first required the equilibration of a system of 256 particles interacting under a Lennard-Jones potential that was truncated at 1.78σ in a volume of $(6.35\sigma)^3$ at approximately 200K with a density of $\rho\sigma^3/m = 1$ A thin film of 12544 particles was equilibrated under the same conditions with the dimensions being changed so that the thickness of the film was the same length as the length of any side of the projectile, while the length and width of the film were seven times larger than those of the projectile. The projectile was placed at an initial distance of 2σ from the center of the thin film, and then given an initial velocity normal to the face of the thin film. The computer simulation was allowed to run for 23 Time Scaling Elements (TSEs), where a TSE is the time obtained by dividing the thickness of the thin film by the normal velocity of the projectile. The thin film was divided into forty-nine equal volume elements with a volume of each equal to the initial volume of the projectile. Since the impact occurs at the center of the film it is possible to employ radial symmetry in analyzing the response of the thin film to the hypervelocity event. Three of these volume elements at an initial radial distance of 0σ, 6.35σ and 14.20σ were selected to maintain a record of the time evolution of the density, pressure, and temperature. To determine the values of these thermodynamic variables the following five steps were employed: For the first step the equations of motion were solved using a Gear-Predictor Corrector with a time step of one femtosecond for all of the impacts. Second the density was found by counting the number of particles inside the boundary of the volume element. Third the macroscopic velocity was calculated for each volume element. Fourth the macroscopic velocity was subtracted from the individual velocities of the particles to find the temperature and pressure. Finally the position of the volume element was changed using the macroscopic velocity. From the fact that the volume elements were free to move they are denoted as Lagrange Points (LPs) corresponding to the usage common in hydrocodes. It was originally for the purpose of comparing the results of MD to hydrocodes that this procedure was employed by McDonald[2].

RESULTS

The behavior of the three LPs defined above was studied for velocities from the range of 7-28 km/s. The primary object for study is the time evolution of the density, pressure, and temperature. In particular the arrival and magnitude of the shock front associated with each of these quantities created by the hypervelocity impact are two features of interest. The data of interest here is found between one and six TSE's The first LP considered is the center of the film, whose response is shown in Fig. 1. The density curves are similar with a small variation for the 10 km/s impact. One particular feature of interest in the behavior of the temperature is the two peak nature of the pulse associated with the impact. The second peak for each of the impacts occurs at 2 TSE's. The origin of this peak, which is not seen in hydrocode simulation[2], is a subject that requires further investigation into whether this peak is a physical phenomena or a numerical artifact. The same four velocities are used for the LP that was a distance of 6.35σ from the impact are shown in Fig. 2. Two effects are of note in this plot: The first concerns the 10 km/s impact which shows lower values for the density immediately after the impact, while retaining a higher value at the end of the six TSE's than the other three impacts. The second feature of interest is the second peak associated with the 25 km/s impact. This peak occurring between 2.5 and 3.0 TSE's is probably due to reflection from the edge of the film which has free boundary conditions. The response in terms of temperature shows that the slope increases for higher velocity impacts so that the peak occurs at roughly the same value of time normalized for the velocity. This is also true for the behavior of the pressure whose decay from the maximum values is slower than seen for the center of the thin film. It is of interest to note that the maximums that occur vary with the quantity being measured. For this LP the maximum values for the density occur the earliest, while the temperature is the slowest of the variables to reach its maximum. The final LP to be considered here was at an original distance of 14.20σ from the impact. The most immediate result from this greater distance is the separation of the peaks associated with the shock front as shown in Fig. 3. This variation is apparent for each of the three quantities shown, with the shocks arriving later in terms of TSE's with increasing velocity. In examining the plot of the density one finds that the 10 km/s impact has a first peak slightly higher than 2.8 gm/cm^3, then a dip below 2.8 gm/cm^3, followed by a rise to its maximum value over 2.9 gm/cm^3. This behavior is not observed for the other three velocities shown. The plot of the temperature shows that for 10 km/s impact the absolute maximum of the temperature is not coincident with the shock front. Another item of interest is that in contrast to Fig. 2 the slopes are quite similar while the time of the peak that corresponds to the shock front

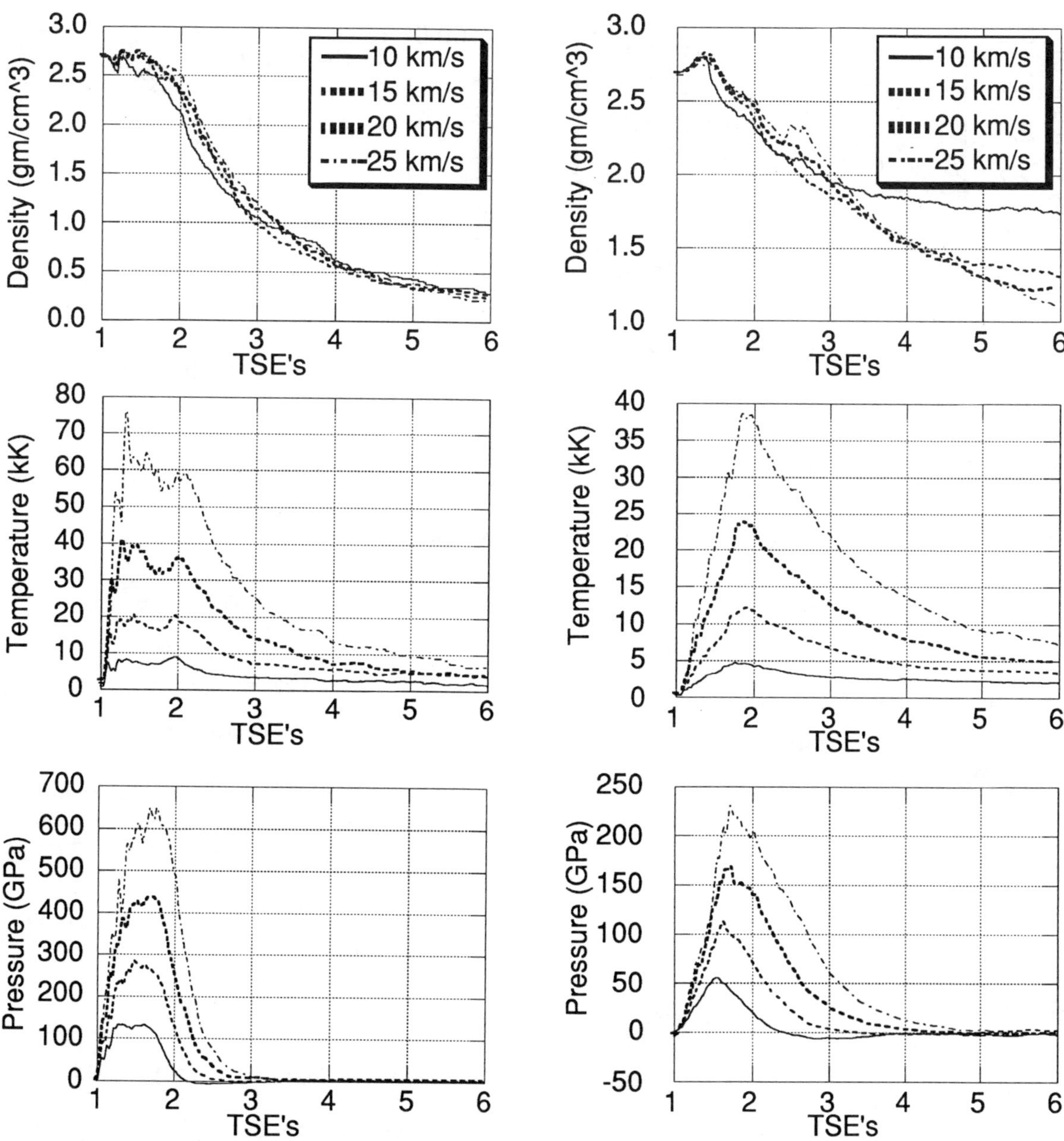

Figure 1. Plots of the density, temperature, and pressure for r = 0σ.

Figure 2. Plots of the density, temperature, and pressure for r = 6.35σ.

occurs later. The pressure shows a similar behavior in this regard as the temperature.

From Figs. 1-3 it is possible to see that the shape of the curves are similar with the primary variation in the curves being the expected differences of magnitude associated with the velocity of the impact. To classify the relationship of the magnitude of the shock wave with the impact velocity the maximum value of the shock front for the pressure and temperature was

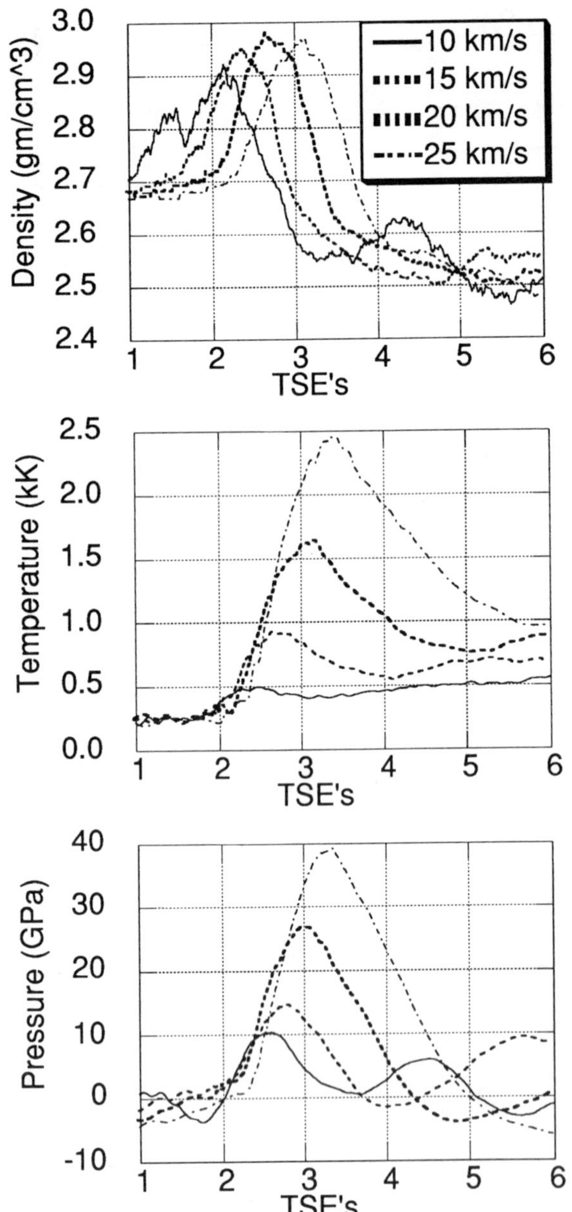

Figure 3. Plots of the density, temperature, and pressure for r = 14.20σ.

plotted against the impact velocity. These two graphs are shown in Fig. 4. The plot of the temperature vs. velocity does show a clear power law relationship for two LPs at 0σ and 6.35σ. The LP at 14.20σ deviates from the power law description at the lower velocities

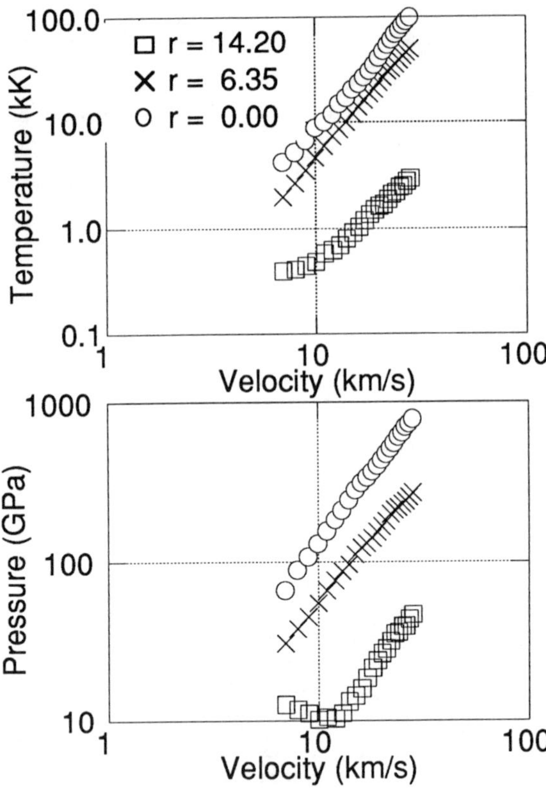

Figure 4. Plots of the maximum values for the temperature and pressure at three different positions in the thin film.

Further study is required to determine the origin of this phenomena.

REFERENCES

[1] B. L Holian, Phys. Rev. A 36, pp. 3943-3946 (1987).

[2] R. A. McDonald, "A Comparison of Hole Size Formation caused by a Hypervelocity Impact with a Thin Film using Molecular Dynamics and CTH," in Proceedings of the 1992 meeting of the Hyper*velocity Impact Society*, (in press)

MULTI-MATERIAL VELOCITIES FOR MIXED CELLS

James D. Walker and Charles E. Anderson, Jr.
Engineering and Materials Sciences
Southwest Research Institute
6220 Culebra Road
San Antonio, TX 78238

The treatment of mixed cells (computational cells containing multiple materials) has always been a great source of error in Eulerian and Arbitrary Lagrangian-Eulerian (ALE) calculations. In an effort to improve the interface treatment between materials in a mixed cell, multi-material velocities have been introduced. This allows each material within the cell to have its own velocity. This enables materials to slip by each other within a cell, and material is allowed to flow in both directions through cell faces. The treatment of these velocities within the cell is examined, and an algorithm is presented for their calculation.

INTRODUCTION

In Eulerian and Arbitrary Lagrangian-Eulerian (ALE) calculations, the most complicated coding occurs in dealing with computational cells which are simultaneously occupied by many materials. These cells are referred to as mixed cells. When this occurs, the material state must be stored for each material, and it is necessary to treat the time evolution of the materials in a sub-cell fashion.

Traditionally, the material in a mixed cell has been viewed as moving as a block, with no internal slip. In order to maintain material boundaries, complex *interface trackers* have been designed to limit material diffusion. These interface trackers build a geometric picture of where material is located in a cell by looking at material volume fractions in contiguous cells. The Simple Line Interface Tracker (SLIC) of Noh and Woodward [1] uses straight lines for material boundaries which align with the indexing coordinates. More recent interface trackers have been based on work of Youngs [2], which again use straight lines for material boundaries, but the lines may cross the cell in any fashion. Usually the direction of the interface line is determined by calculating a normal to it (Fig. 1),

$$\vec{n} = -\nabla\phi \quad (1)$$

where ϕ is the volume fraction of the material. The gradient is estimated based on volume fractions of the material in contiguous cells. The actual value of ϕ within the cell is then used to fix the location of the interface. More than two materials in a cell are handled by ordering the materials and performing these calculations for exclusive sets of materials. These methods maintain well defined material boundaries as material moves through an Eulerian mesh.

However, these methods all suffer from difficulties at material interfaces if materials are moving relative to each other. Since the material in a mixed cell moves as a block, the implied boundary condition is a no-slip boundary condition. In the physical problems considered with these types of codes, the boundary condition is rarely no-slip on the zoning scale used: solids are sliding over solids, and gases are flowing over solid surfaces. (Lagrangian calculations have been plagued by these interface problems too, and their coding response is the *slide line*. Slide lines are the most complex parts of Lagrangian codes.)

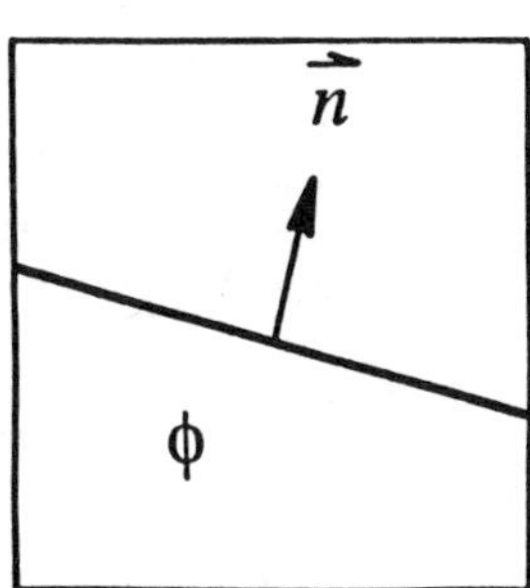

Figure 1. Mixed cell with interface between materials.

The difficulty clearly shows itself in the inability of an Eulerian code to treat the penetration of a metal target by a much stronger, and hence essentially rigid, projectile. Special coding to allow slip has been examined [3], but the most natural solution would be to allow material to flow in both directions within a mixed cell.

CELL CENTERED VELOCITIES

In most calculational settings, the velocities are either at the faces of cells or the vertices of cells. However, in the pursuit of a multi-material velocity, it is desirable to have a value associated with the cell, as it is the cell which is mixed and contains multiple materials. To this end, a cell centered material velocity is defined. In this paper, *all multi-material velocities are cell centered.*

The geometric definition of the cell-centered velocity for a cell is

$$\vec{v}_{cc} = \frac{1}{4}\sum_{\text{vertices}} \vec{v} \tag{2}$$

where the sum is taken over the cell vertices or the cell faces, depending on how the velocity is defined. For clean cells (that is, cells that are not mixed and so contain only one material) this average of the vertex or face velocities is the material cell-centered velocity.

For a mixed cell, not only the geometric definition of cell-centered velocity holds, but it also equals an average velocity based on the multi-material velocities within the cell:

$$\vec{v}_{cc} = \sum \tilde{\phi}_m \vec{v}_m \tag{3}$$

Both summations are over the number of materials in the mixed cell, the $\tilde{\phi}_m$ are the volume fractions of the materials in the cell which have been normalized with respect to the void content (that is, $\tilde{\phi}_m = \phi_m/(1-\phi_{void})$), and the subscript m refers to the material.

The cell-centered velocity is treated as an internal state variable for the material. In particular, it is advected based on material mass at each time step. The time evolution of the multi-material velocity is handled as follows. After the advection is complete, the material cell-centered velocity must be updated. These multi-material velocities produce an "old" cell-centered velocity from Eq. (3). The "new" cell centered velocity is provided geometrically by Eq. (2). The cell centered velocities of each of the materials are then updated by

$$\vec{v}_m^{\,new} = \vec{v}_m^{\,old} + \vec{v}_{cc}^{\,new} - \vec{v}_{cc}^{\,old} \tag{4}$$

This update is performed for every material in the cell. The updated value of the cell-centered velocities are consistent with the face-centered velocities, on which the computational step (mass, momentum, and energy conservation) is based. It will be noted that the update of the velocity is completely geometrical, and no subcell physics has been used. Perhaps better updating schemes exist which would use the cell physics. However, what is done here is consistent with what is done in CTH (the code we were using for this work [4]), where it is assumed that the deformation rate of all materials in a mixed cell is the same for purposes of calculating the energy change. Such behavior actually occurs if the materials are in parallel or their compressibilities are the same.

DIFFERENTIAL FLOW

The interface tracking coding is very complex, as it is difficult to keep track of materials within a cell and to ensure that the material being moved from a cell is not more than was previously there. Thus, an algorithm which fit easily into the current framework of existing codes and used the already existing interface trackers was desired [5]. The method presented here relies on a Youngs' interface tracker and makes three passes through it for a genuinely mixed cell (one with at least two non-void materials in it).

The Lagrangian and grid-motion parts of the code provide a flow volume ΔV through a cell face which is advected. The following discussion, as well as Fig. 2, assumes ΔV is positive. From the advected volume change, a flow velocity through the face of the cell is calculated, which in Cartesian coordinates is given by

$$v_f = \Delta V/(A\Delta t) \tag{5}$$

where Δt is the time step and A is the area of the cell face through which material is flowing.

The first pass through the interface tracker is solely to produce cell-face fractions. The interface tracker provides volumes of materials ΔV_m to be moved. Using these volumes, the donating cell determines the cell face fractions of the materials:

$$\mu_m = \Delta V_m/\Delta V \tag{6}$$

Using the multi-material velocities, these fractions are used to compute a forward flow volume through the cell face. (If less than two non-void materials touch a cell face, the initial pass provides the advection information. This helps limit material diffusion.) With v_m as the material flow velocity, then the forward flow volume is

$$\Delta V^F = \sum_{v_m \geq 0} v_m \mu_m A \Delta t \tag{7}$$

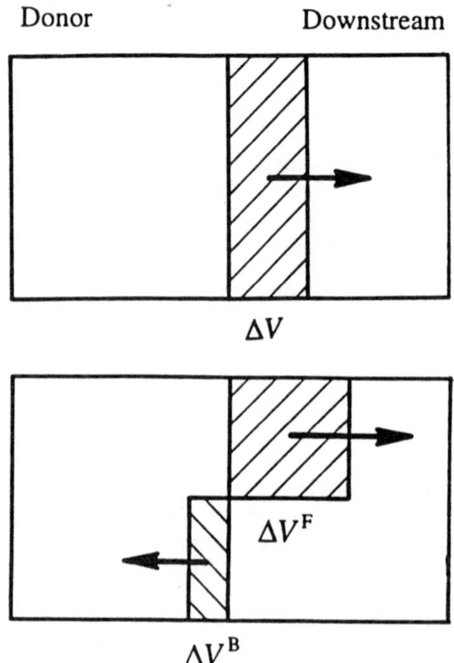

Figure 2. Volume flux through a face divided into forward and backward components.

In the calculation, it is assumed that void moves with the face velocity v_f. If $\Delta V^F < \Delta V$, then ΔV^F is set equal to ΔV, as it is necessary to match the total advected volume of the cell. Given the forward flow volume, a back flow volume is determined by

$$\Delta V^B = -(\Delta V^F - \Delta V) \tag{8}$$

This back flow volume is negative, and the donating cell is the downstream (or downwind) cell.

Now, a pass is done through the interface tracker for both the forward volume and backward volume. At this stage, the interface between the materials within the mixed cell is rotated based on the relative flow (Fig. 3). The rotation angle

$$\tan(\theta) = -\frac{1}{4}\frac{(\Delta y)^2}{\Delta x}\frac{\partial v_x/\partial y}{|(v_{cc})_x|}\frac{1}{\min(\phi_m, 1-\phi_m)} \tag{9}$$

is computed (this formula is for flow in the x direction, where Δx and Δy are the cell edge lengths). The velocity derivative is calculated using the divergence theorem based on the multi-material velocities and the cell boundary information obtained from $\vec{n}$ and ϕ_m. In the limit as $\Delta t \to 0$, the above expression gives the correct amount of rotation for a cell evenly divided down the middle with both multi-material velocities in the same direction. It is assumed that $-\pi/2 \le \theta \le \pi/2$. With the calculation of the angle, $\vec{n}$ is rotated to reflect which material will predominantly be at the interface:

$$\vec{n}^{new} = \begin{pmatrix} \cos(\theta) & -\sin(\theta) \\ \sin(\theta) & \cos(\theta) \end{pmatrix} \vec{n} \tag{10}$$

This allows the volumes to reflect the relative flow within the cell.

The final advection volumes for a material are given by

$$\Delta V_m = \Delta V_m^F + \Delta V_m^B \tag{11}$$

and the sign of ΔV_m determines whether the material comes from the donor cell or the downstream cell.

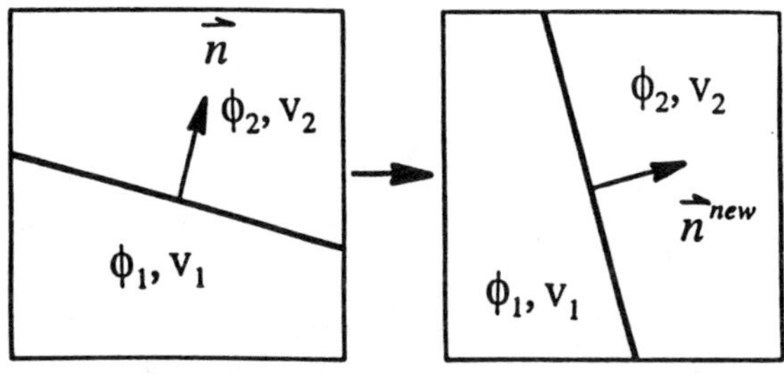

Figure 3. Material interface rotated to reflect relative material velocities within cell.

MIXED CELL STRESS STATE

The stress state of the mixed cell has a great effect on the results of a calculation. Ideally, the multi-material velocities should allow the calculation of the stress tensor independently for each material. However, at the present time, the stress state is adjusted in a more direct fashion.

It is assumed that the surface between the materials is frictionless. This implies that, at the surface, the material cannot support shear stresses in the tangent plane of the surface. Thus, the tangent plane shear stresses are removed:

$$\sigma^{new} = \sigma - (\sigma - \vec{n}^T\sigma\vec{n}I)\vec{n}\,\vec{n}^T - \vec{n}\,\vec{n}^T(\sigma - \vec{n}^T\sigma\vec{n}I) \tag{12}$$

In this expression, σ is the stress, I the identity matrix, and the superscript T stands for transpose. Numerous computations have demonstrated that it is not sufficient to adjust the stress in the mixed cell itself. Rather, it is also necessary to adjust the stresses in the cells contiguous to mixed cells in order to allow surfaces to slide over each other without producing shear stresses further away in the material. The need to do this is due to the choice of calculating stresses from the deformation gradients based on the cell vertex or face velocities.

Since the stresses are being calculated from the cell vertex or face velocities, it is necessary to have one flow stress for the whole mixed cell. Currently, the flow stress is taken as the average of the materials in the mixed cell:

$$Y = \sum \tilde{\phi}_m Y_m \tag{13}$$

("MIX=3" in CTH).

PRELIMINARY RESULTS

The above algorithm was placed in the Eulerian wavecode CTH. As an initial example problem, we consider the case of a 3.55 cm long tungsten projectile impacting an aluminum target at 810 m/s. The geometry and the material properties can be found in [3] and [6] (though the calculations reported here do not include thermal softening in the aluminum). Experimentally, the projectile perforates the 5.08 cm thick aluminum plate virtually undeformed, and has a residual velocity of 595 m/s [6]. If the problem is run with the standard assumptions that work well in eroding penetration, in particular that the flow stress of a mixed cell is given by Eq. (13), then the projectile comes to rest 3.7 cm into the plate, well short of the back surface. As a comparison, the same problem was run using the multi-material velocity algorithm. The results of this calculation are shown in Figs. 4 and 5. The projectile erodes at early times, as can be seen by the front end velocity being less than the back end velocity (Fig. 4) as well as the fact that the pointed nose of the projectile is gone by 150 μs (Fig. 5). At later times the projectile travels through the plate as a rigid body, and perforates the plate with a residual velocity of 240 m/s. At early

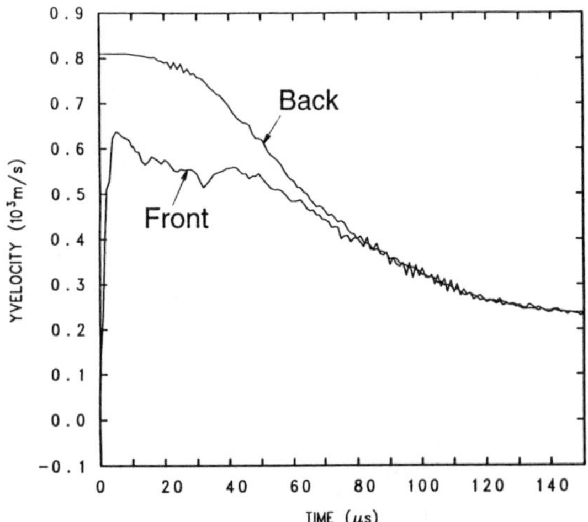

Figure 4. Projectile front end and back end velocity versus time.

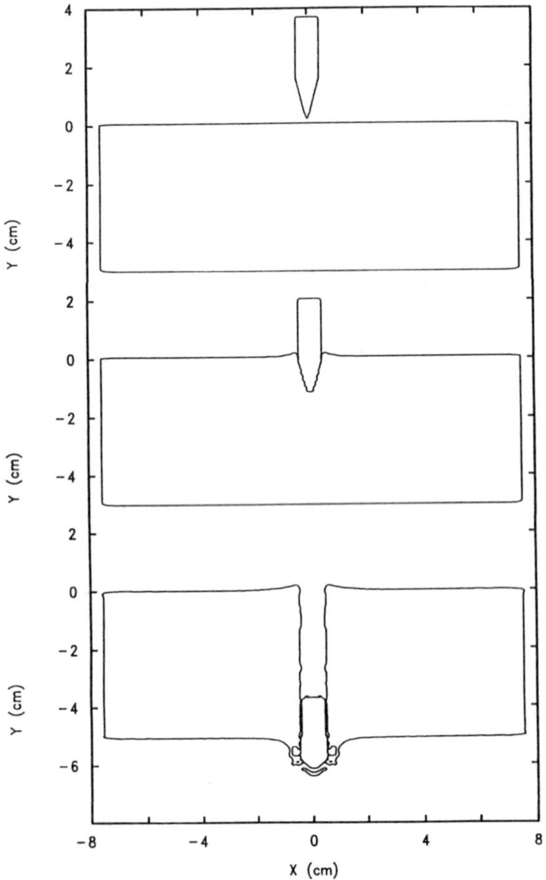

Figure 5. Material interfaces at 0, 20, and 150 μs.

times the differential flow algorithm helps maintain the original nose shape, although it is clear that more work needs to be done on the algorithm in this regard. For much of the penetration, however, the improved behavior is due to the adjustment of the stress state of the mixed cells and their neighbors.

CONCLUSIONS

An approach to handling multi-material velocities has been presented. This approach treats the subcell velocity behavior in a geometric fashion. It allows use of current interface trackers which simplifies its implementation. Each material has a cell-centered velocity, which is treated as if it were an internal state variable: the cell-centered velocity is advected. The method allows materials to flow in both directions through an interface. Also, the stress is adjusted to reflect the fact that the interface between materials cannot support shear stresses. The method has been placed in the wavecode CTH, and preliminary calculations indicate improved results in some problems.

ACKNOWLEDGMENTS

We would like to acknowledge helpful discussions with Mike McGlaun of Sandia National Laboratories, and Tom Adams and James Painter of Los Alamos National Laboratory. This work was funded by the U. S. Army Research Office Contract DAAL03-92-K-0001.

REFERENCES

[1] W. F. Noh and P. Woodward, "SLIC (Simple Line Interface Calculation)," *Lecture Notes in Physics*, V. 59, Springer-Verlag, Berlin, 1976.

[2] D. L. Youngs, "Time-Dependent Multi-Material Flow with Large Fluid Distortion," in *Numerical Methods for Fluid Dynamics*, ed. K. W. Morton and M. J. Baines, Academic Press, London, 1982.

[3] S. A. Silling, "Eulerian Simulation of the Perforation of Aluminum Plates by Nondeforming Projectiles," Sandia Report SAND92-0493 UC-405, Sandia National Laboratories, Albuquerque, NM, 1992.

[4] J. M. McGlaun, S. L. Thompson, and M. G. Elrick, "CTH: A Three-Dimensional Shock Wave Physics Code," *Int. J. Impact Engng.*, **10**, pp. 351-360 (1990).

[5] R. L. Bell and E. S. Hertel, Jr., "An Improved Material Interface Reconstruction Algorithm for Eulerian Codes," Sandia Report SAND92-1716 UC-410, Sandia National Laboratories, Albuquerque, NM, 1992.

[6] M. J. Forrestal, V. K. Luk, and N. S. Brar, "Perforation of Aluminum Armor Plates with Conical-Nose Projectiles," *Mech. of Mat.*, **10**, pp. 97-105 (1990).

SECOND ORDER DISCRETE REZONING

Gabi Luttwak

Rafael Ballistics Center
P.O.Box 2250,[24],Haifa 31021,Israel

The efficient solution of many fluid dynamic problems depends on the capability to change the computational mesh during the calculation.Discrete rezoning is customarily used in Lagrangian calculations to prevent grid distortions. We consider a second order accurate, discrete rezoning of multimaterial Euler and ALE calculations.While remapping zones containing more than one single fluid,special attention must be given to properly resolve the material boundaries cutting through the mesh.In a second order scheme,a piecewisely linear density distribution is assumed.We specifically consider here the case of a two dimensional structured grid, but it is straightforward to apply this method to a general connectivity mesh in either two or three dimensions.

INTRODUCTION

In numerical simulations, the problem is solved over a discrete mesh. The field variables like mass, momentum, energy or deviatoric stress have to be interpolated to the computational zones. The size and the shape of these zones determines the spatial resolution and the accuracy of the solution.

In Lagrangian codes, the grid points move with the material velocity. Thus the zones deform with the material. Eventually, the grid distortion may reduce the accuracy of the calculation, while the stability condition may decrease the time step, effectively stopping the computation. During discrete rezoning, or relagrangization[1−4], the field variables are reinterpolated into a new mesh in which it is possible to carry on the calculation.

In Eulerian coordinates the zones are fixed in space and the materials flow through the mesh, thus there is no grid distortion. Still, if we want to change the spatial resolution during the calculation, then we may have to pass to a new grid. In the Arbitrary Lagrangian Eulerian (ALE) technique[6,3,7−11], the grid motion can be prescribed so as to prevent grid distortion[7−10].The ALE grid motion can be also utilized to dynamically increase the resolution in regions of interest[10], or as a cost effective way to describe fluid-structure interaction[11]. However,even in this case,it may be sometimes beneficial to pass over, during the ALE calculation, to a new mesh with more zones, or with a different connectivity.

The equations of fluid dynamics result from the conservation laws of mass,momentum and energy and it appears that the best numerical schemes are those which make a form preserving analog of these conservation equations[5]. The recently published schemes [2−4] for second order, conservative, discrete rezoning have been applied only to a structured grid with quadrilateral zones, each containing a single material. We want to treat the discrete rezoning of multimaterial Euler and ALE calculations. In these cases,the material boundaries cut through the mesh. Thus, there may be more than one material in a zone, and we have to consistently define the subzones occupied by a specific material[7−8]. Even if the original zones are quadrilateral, these subzones may be bounded by a polygon with a different number of sides. In the code MMALE[8] we have applied the algorithm of D. S. Mason [1], to compute the common volume between two polygons. This was used to compute the fluxes during the advection phase of the ALE calculation. This approach had the advantage that corner fluxing could be properly taken into account. Moreover, we got second order accuracy, by computing the densities in the fluxed volume, as a proper interpolation of their values, in the donor and acceptor zones.

Later, we have applied this method also for the discrete remapping of a multimaterial ALE mesh. However, for a discrete remap, this will result in a first order scheme. In this work, we generalize this algorithm to second order accuracy.

THEORY

In a multimaterial Euler or ALE calculation, the material boundaries may cut the zone sizes. To prevent a catastrophic mixing of the materials during a remap we must keep a consistent picture of the locations of the separate materials in the cell. In a discrete remap, we cannot apply any simple donor-acceptor scheme, like preferential transport. We will have to divide the cells into disjoint subzones. To locate the subzone covered with a certain material, we look at the relative volume $\alpha_i = V_i/V$ of this fluid in the neighbouring cells. We assume the boundary of the fluid i to be normal to the gradient of the relative partial volume, $\nabla\alpha_i$.We approximate the interface in the zone by a straight line cutting the yet uncovered part of the cell. The knowledge of the fluid partial volume V_i and the direction of the interface exactly determines its position.[7,8](see fig.1).

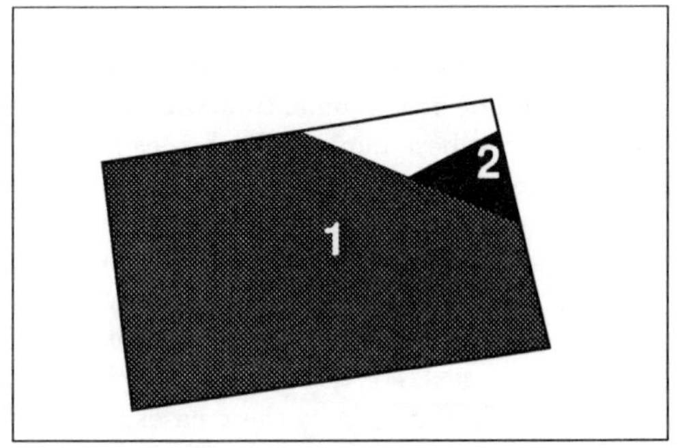

Figure 1. A multimaterial zone.

We pass over the materials, in order of their relative partial volume. This scheme has been successfully used in the code MMALE[7-10] in the advection phase of the ALE calculation, but unlike the donor-acceptor schemes,such high resolution interface schemes[13,7,8] can be readily employed also for a discrete remap.

For a first order scheme, the densities are constant over a zone. We need only to compute the common volumes δV_j^i between the zones of the new and the old mesh. In two dimensions the computational zones are usually defined by quadrilaterals or triangles. There is a simple yet ingenious way[1] to compute the volume common to two polygons, as the algebric sum of the common volumes below pairs of sides of these polygons. To get these, we need only to compute the volume contained below one or two segments as shown in fig.2. In this work we consider a piecewisely linear density distribution over the computational zones in the old mesh. Thus in a given zone:

$$\rho(\vec{\mathbf{r}}) = \rho_0 + (\vec{\mathbf{r}} - \vec{\mathbf{r}}_0) \cdot \vec{\nabla}\rho \qquad (1)$$

If we take $\vec{\mathbf{r}}_0 = (\mathbf{x_0}, \mathbf{y_0})$ at the zone centroid,than $\rho_0 = m/V$ is the average density of the cell[3]. We note that both $\nabla\rho$ and $\nabla\alpha_i$ in a zone can be calculated,as a line integral over the zone boundary, the same way a zone centered gradient of the pressure is computed in Eulerian codes. However, the slope of the density gradient must be limited to prevent the formation of new extrema during the remap[3,12]. Following Van Leer[3,12], we ask that the value of the density at any point in our zone should remain in between the smallest value ρ_{min} and the biggest value ρ_{max} of the average density in the neighboring cells. Let $\Delta\rho_{max} = \min(\rho_{max} - \rho_0, \rho_0 - \rho_{min})$ be the maximum permitted change in the zone density, while $\delta\rho = |\delta\vec{\mathbf{r}} \cdot \vec{\nabla}\rho|$ is the density change resulting from the unlimited gradient with $\delta\vec{\mathbf{r}}$ being half the zone size in the direction of $\nabla\rho$. Then, we multiply $\nabla\rho$ by a factor f:

$$f = \frac{\Delta\rho_{max}}{\max(\Delta\rho_{max}, \delta\rho)}$$
$$(\nabla\rho)' = f\,\nabla\rho \qquad (2)$$

To compute the mass common to two polygons. we again express it,as the algebric sum of the masses in the common volume below pairs of the segments bounding them.As before,to get an element in the sum we only need to compute, the mass in the volume below one or two of the resulting segments shaded in fig.2. For cylindrical symmetry,the mass per unit radian below a segment $\vec{\mathbf{r}}_{12}$ is:

$$m_{12} = \int_{y_1}^{y_2} \int_0^{x(y)} \rho(x,y) x \, dx \, dy \qquad (3)$$

Substituting (1) and carrying out the integration yields

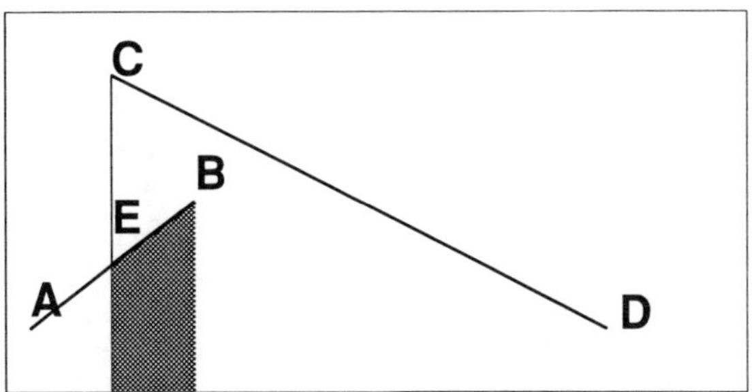

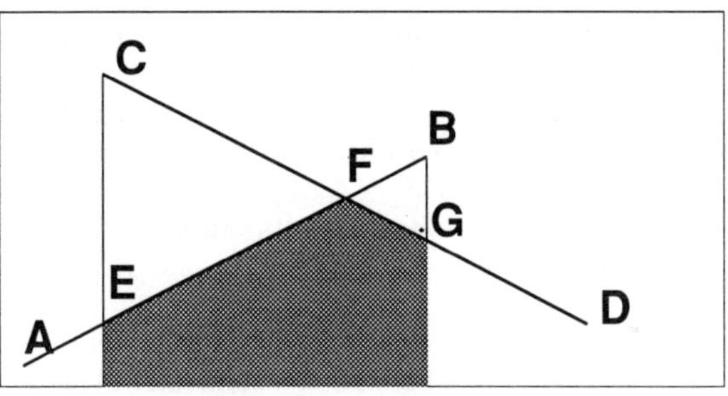

Figure 2. The common volume (or mass) under a pair of segments.

after some manipulation:

$$m_{12} = \frac{1}{2}\rho_0 \Delta y_{12}\left(\left(1 - x_0\frac{\partial \rho}{\partial x} - (y_0 - y_1)\frac{\partial \rho}{\partial y}\right)\langle x_{12}^2\rangle + \frac{2}{3}\frac{\partial \rho}{\partial x}\overline{x_{12}}\,\overline{x_{12}^2} + \frac{1}{6}\frac{\partial \rho}{\partial y}\Delta y_{12}(2\overline{x_{12}}^2 + x_2^2)\right) \tag{4}$$

Where we have used the notations:

$$\begin{aligned} \Delta y_{12} &= y_2 - y_1, \\ \overline{x_{12}} &= (1/2)(x_1 + x_2), \\ \overline{x_{12}^2} &= (1/2)(x_1^2 + x_2^2), \\ \langle x_{12}^2\rangle &= (1/3)(x_1^2 + x_1 x_2 + x_2^2) \end{aligned} \tag{5}$$

For two dimensional plane symmetry,the mass under the segment $\vec{\mathbf{r}}_{12}$, per unit width will be:

$$m_{12} = \int_{y_1}^{y_2}\int_0^{x(y)} \rho(x,y)dx\,dy \tag{6}$$

And this will yield with a similar notation:

$$m_{12} = \rho_0 \Delta y_{12}\left(\left(1 - x_0\frac{\partial \rho}{\partial x} - (y_0 - y_1)\frac{\partial \rho}{\partial y}\right)\overline{x_{12}} + \frac{1}{2}\frac{\partial \rho}{\partial x}\langle x_{12}^2\rangle + \frac{1}{6}\frac{\partial \rho}{\partial y}\Delta y_{12}(x_1 + 2x_2)\right) \tag{7}$$

We proceed the same way for remap of the other conservative variables. For the remap of the momenta we consider the momentum densities $\rho\vec{\mathbf{u}}$,and we compute the new momenta. To conserve the total energy, we have to take the energy densities ρe_T with $e_T = e + (1/2)\vec{\mathbf{u}}^2$ being the specific total energy of the zone. Stability requires the remap schemes to be diffusive. Thus the conservation of momentum will result in a loss of kinetic energy,and the conservation of total energy may thus lead to an increase in the internal energy. In a second order scheme this will be quite small, third order effect. However for high speed impact problems, the kinetic energy may be much bigger than the internal energy. Thus, to prevent an artificial heating it is still better to conserve separately the internal energy. In this case we consider the density of the specific internal energy ρe. For the remap of other intensive Lagrangian variables like the deviatoric stress $\mathbf{s}$ or the equivalent plastic strain ϵ_p we assume a volume weighted average. That is we regard the intensive variables as a volumetric density and use the same scheme.

CONCLUSIONS

We have presented a second order accurate scheme for the discrete rezoning, of multimaterial Euler and ALE calculations. We note that the algorithm is not restricted to an $i - j$ type of finite difference structured grid, but applies as well for a general connectivity mesh. It is also straightforward to generalize this approach to three dimensional calculations. We have used a variant of this method to evaluate the fluxes in the advection phase of Euler and ALE calculations. It could be also used , to compute the variables after reconnecting the nodes in a finite element or free Lagrangian codes.

For a discrete remap, there are two additional topics not disscussed in these work. One is the related problem of grid generation. The other is how to find efficient ways to preliminary asses the zones of the old mesh which may overlap with a given new cell.

REFERENCES

[1] B. J. Thorne, D. B. Holdridge, "The TOOREZ Lagrangian rezoning code", Sandia National Laboratory, report, SLA-73-1057(1974)

[2] J. K. Dukowicz, "Conservative rezoning (remapping) for general quadrilateral meshes", J. Comp. Phys. 54, pp. 411- 424,(1984)

[3] J.K.Dukowicz, J.W.Kodis, Accurate conservative remapping (rezoning) for Arbitrary Lagrangian-Eulerian Computations, SIAM J. Sci. Stat. Comput. 8, (3), pp. 305-321, (1987)

[4] J.D.Ramshaw, "Simplified Second Order Rezoning Algorithm for Generalized Two-Dimensional Meshes", J. Comp. Phys. 67, pp. 214-222, (1986)

[5] J.G.Trulio, K.R.Trigger, "Numerical Solution of the One Dimensional Hydrodynamic equations in an Arbitrary Time dependent Coordinate System", Lawrence Livermore Laboratory report, UCRL-6522(1961)

[6] C. W. Hirt, A. A. Amsden, J. L. Cook, " An Arbitrary Lagrangian Eulerian Calculation Method for Fluid Flows at All Speeds", J. Comp. Phys., 14, pp. 227-253, (1974)

[7] G.Luttwak, "Numerical Simulation of Water Jet Penetration", Shock Waves in Condensed Matter-1983 , J.R.Asay, R.A.Graham, G.K.Straub (editors), Elsevier Science Publishers B.V. , (1984) pp.191-194

[8] G.Luttwak, R.L.Rabie,"The Multimaterial Arbitrary Lagrangian Eulerian Method in Fluid Flow Simulations",unpublished 1984,to be submitted to the J.Comp.Phys

[9] G.Luttwak, Y.Kivity, A.A.Betser, "Effects of a Hypervelocity jet on a Layered Target", Int. J. Eng. Sci. 20, p947, (1982)

[10] G.Luttwak, "Numerical Simulation of Jet Formation Using an Adaptive Grid in the Multimaterial A.L.E. Code MMALE", Proc. of the 3^d High Dynamic Pressure Symposium,La Grande-Motte,France,(June 1989),pp. 45-52

[11] G.Luttwak, C.Florie, A.Venis, "Numerical Simulation of Soft Body Impact", Shock Compression of Condensed Matter-1991, S.C.Schmidt, R.D.Dick, J.W.Forbes, D.G.Tasker (editors) , North Holland (1992) pp.999,1002

[12] B. van Leer, "Towards the ultimate conservative difference scheme", J. Comp. Phys., 32, pp. 101-136, (1974)

[13] D.L.Youngs,"Time-Dependent Multimaterial Flow with Large Fluid Distortion", in Numerical Methods for Fluid Dynamics,(K.W.Morton and M.J.Baines editors) Academic Press(1982)

DIFFERENTIAL SENSITIVITY THEORY APPLIED TO THE MESA CODE

R. J. Henninger
Group X-3, MS F663
P. J. Maudlin and E. N. Harstad
Group T-3, MS B216
Los Alamos National Laboratory
Los Alamos, New Mexico 87545

A technique called Differential Sensitivity Theory (DST) is applied to the system of equations solved by the MESA continuum mechanics code. DST uses adjoint techniques to determine exact sensitivity derivatives, i.e., if R is a calculational result of interest (response R) and α_i is a calculational input (parameter α_i), then $\partial R/\partial\alpha_i$ is defined as the sensitivity. The advantage of using DST is that for an n-parameter problem *all* n sensitivities can be obtained by integrating the solutions from only *two* calculations, a MESA calculation and its corresponding adjoint calculation using an Adjoint Continuum Mechanics (ACM) code. This work presents the derivation and solution of the appropriate set of adjoint equations for the purpose of computing sensitivities for high-rate two-dimensional, multi-component, high-deformation problems. As an example, results for a flyer plate impact problem are given.

INTRODUCTION

A sensitivity technique[1-3] used successfully in the early eighties[4-6] called Differential Sensitivity Theory (DST) is applied to a system of time-dependent continuum mechanics equations.[7] DST uses adjoint techniques to determine exact sensitivity derivatives, i.e., if R is a calculational result of interest (response R) and α is a calculational input (parameter α_i where the subscript is usually not indicated for convenience), then $\partial R/\partial\alpha_i$ is defined as the sensitivity. The advantage of using DST over other sensitivity analysis techniques is mainly economic: for an n-parameter problem *all* n sensitivities can be obtained by integrating the solutions from only *two* calculations, a so-called forward (physical) calculation and its corresponding adjoint calculation. This work describes the derivation and solution of the appropriate set of adjoint and sensitivity equations for the ultimate purpose of computing sensitivities for high-rate two-dimensional, multi-component, high-deformation problems.

Following Cacuci et al.,[2] consider a system of nonlinear equations written in symbolic form as

$$N[\bar{y}(\bar{x}),\bar{\alpha}] = O(\bar{x},\bar{\alpha}), \tag{1}$$

where $\bar{y}$ is a dependent variable vector, $\bar{x}$ is an independent variable vector, and $\bar{\alpha}$ is a parameter vector. Also we assume a response function having the general form:

$$R = \iint_{t\ \bar{r}} F(\bar{y},\bar{x})\,d\bar{r}\,dt \equiv \langle F(\bar{y},\bar{x})\rangle\ , \tag{2}$$

where the angle brackets denote space-time integration. If Eq. 1 is differentiated with respect to an arbitrary parameter α, then the resulting system of equations is linear with respect to the new differentiated dependent variable vector, and has the form:

$$\mathbf{L}\frac{\partial\bar{y}}{\partial\alpha} = \bar{s}, \tag{3}$$

where $\mathbf{L}$ is a linear operator operating on the dependent variable vector and $\bar{s}$ represents a vector source term that contains the problem parameters differentiated with respect to α. Taking the partial with respect to α of the response (Eq. 2) gives

$$\frac{\partial R}{\partial\alpha} = \iint_{t\ \bar{r}} \frac{\partial\bar{F}}{\partial\bar{y}}\bullet\frac{\partial\bar{y}}{\partial\alpha}\,d\bar{r}dt \equiv \left\langle\frac{\partial\bar{F}}{\partial\bar{y}},\frac{\partial\bar{y}}{\partial\alpha}\right\rangle\ . \tag{4}$$

Taking the inner product of the left-hand side of Eq. 3 with an arbitrary vector function $\bar{y}^*$ and invoking a property of inner-product spaces gives

$$\left\langle\bar{y}^*,\mathbf{L}\frac{\partial\bar{y}}{\partial\alpha}\right\rangle = \left\langle\frac{\partial\bar{y}}{\partial\alpha},\mathbf{L}^*\bar{y}^*\right\rangle + B\left(\bar{y}^*,\frac{\partial\bar{y}}{\partial\alpha}\right), \tag{5}$$

where the function B represents the appropriate boundary terms. This equation can be used to derive a linear operator adjoint to $\mathbf{L}$ (i.e., $\mathbf{L}^*$) that operates on $\bar{y}^*$; and, when set equal to the differentiated response function from the integrand of Eq. 4, this system of equations can be solved for the so-called adjoint solution:

$$\mathbf{L}^*\bar{y}^* = \frac{\partial\bar{F}}{\partial\bar{y}}\ . \tag{6}$$

Substituting Eq. 6 into the right-hand side of Eq. 4, using the inner product property given by Eq. 5 and substituting again with Eq. 3, gives

$$\frac{\partial R}{\partial \alpha} = \left\langle \mathbf{L}^* \bar{y}^*, \frac{\partial \bar{y}}{\partial \alpha} \right\rangle = \left\langle \bar{y}^*, \mathbf{L} \frac{\partial \bar{y}}{\partial \alpha} \right\rangle - B\left(\bar{y}^*, \frac{\partial \bar{y}}{\partial \alpha} \right)$$
$$= \left\langle \bar{y}^*, \bar{s} \right\rangle - B\left(\bar{y}^*, \frac{\partial \bar{y}}{\partial \alpha} \right) \quad (7)$$

The rightmost right-hand side of this equation represents the final integral form of the sensitivity $\partial R/\partial \alpha$.

Practical application of DST requires the solution of the adjoint system represented by Eq. 6 and the sensitivity integration represented by Eq. 7.

PHYSICAL EQUATION SET

In this effort the physical system of equations represented by Eq. 1 is the one-dimensional set of Eulerian conservation equations for mass, momentum and internal energy, an isotropic elastoplastic strength description using a von Mises yield surface, and an equation-of-state (EOS) expressed here using the substantial (or material) derivative D/Dt:

$$\frac{D\rho}{Dt} = -\rho \frac{\partial u_z}{\partial z} \quad (8a)$$

$$\rho \frac{Du_z}{Dt} = \frac{\partial (s_{zz} - P')}{\partial z} + \rho g \quad (8b)$$

$$\rho \frac{Di}{Dt} = (s_{zz} - P') \frac{\partial u_z}{\partial z} \quad (8c)$$

$$\frac{Ds_{zz}}{Dt} = 2G(\dot{e}_{zz} - u\langle d \rangle \dot{\lambda} s_{zz}) \quad (8d)$$

$$P' = P(\rho, i) + Q(\rho, \dot{\varepsilon}) \quad (8e)$$

$$\text{where } d = \frac{3}{2\sigma^2} s_{ij}s_{ij} - 1 \text{ and } \dot{\lambda} = \frac{3}{2\sigma^2} \dot{e}_{ij}s_{ij} \,. \quad (8f)$$

In this equation set the independent variables are time t and space coordinate z, the dependent variable vector $\bar{y}$ has as components the density ρ, velocity u_z, internal energy i, the deviatoric stress s_{zz}, and the pressure P', i.e., the sum of an EOS pressure P and an artificial viscosity Q. The stress deviator s_{zz} is defined as $\sigma_{zz} - P'$, where σ_{zz} is the total stress. The total strain rate $\dot{\varepsilon}$ is equal to the velocity gradient $\partial u_z/\partial z$, and a body force has been included in Eq. 8b using an acceleration g. Note that, since Q is a function of the velocity gradient, substitution of P' into Eq. 8b formally results in the second derivative $\partial^2 u_z/\partial z^2$. The unit step function $u\langle d \rangle$ in Eq. 8d is zero during elastic flow and unity during plastic flow. An elastic-perfectly plastic solid with yield stress σ and shear modulus G is assumed. Repeated indices in Eqs. 8f and below imply a summation over the range of the index (i.e., standard indicial notation).

In this work a solid phase Mie-Gruneisen[8] EOS is used having the form

$$P = P_H + \Gamma\left(\rho_o i - \frac{1}{2} P_H \frac{\mu}{1+\mu} \right) \,, \quad (9a)$$

where the Hugoniot pressure is

$$P_H = \frac{\rho_o c_o^2 \mu (1+\mu)}{[1 - \mu(s-1)]^2} \,, \quad (9b)$$

and μ is defined as the compression $\rho/\rho_o - 1$. The form of the artificial viscosity used in this work is

$$Q = -c_L \rho c_o \Delta z \dot{\varepsilon} + c_Q \rho \Delta z^2 \dot{\varepsilon}^2 \,, \quad (9c)$$

where Δz is the mesh cell dimension. The other parameters appearing in Eqs. 9 are defined in Table I.

System 8 is next differentiated with respect to α to form a linear system of forward equations represented by Eq. 3. The new differentiated dependent variable vector is

$$\frac{\partial \bar{y}}{\partial \alpha} = \left(\frac{\partial \rho}{\partial \alpha}, \frac{\partial u_z}{\partial \alpha}, \frac{\partial i}{\partial \alpha}, \frac{\partial s_{zz}}{\partial \alpha}, \frac{\partial P'}{\partial \alpha} \right)^T \equiv (\Psi, \Phi_z, I, \tau_{zz}, \Pi)^T \,, \quad (10)$$

and the source vector needed as part of the general relationship for $\partial R/\partial \alpha$ given by Eq. 7 is

$$\bar{s} = \Bigg[0, \; \rho \frac{\partial g}{\partial \alpha}, \; 0,$$
$$\left(\frac{u\langle d \rangle 4G s_{zz} \dot{\lambda}}{\sigma} + \delta\langle d \rangle 2\beta \dot{\lambda} s_{zz} \frac{s_{ij}s_{ij}}{\sigma} \right) \frac{\partial \sigma}{\partial \alpha}$$
$$+ 2\left(\dot{e}_{zz} - u\langle d \rangle \dot{\lambda} s_{zz} \right) \frac{\partial G}{\partial \alpha}, \quad \frac{\partial P}{\partial \rho_o} \frac{\partial \rho_o}{\partial \alpha} + \frac{\partial P}{\partial s} \frac{\partial s}{\partial \alpha} \quad (11)$$
$$+ \frac{\partial P}{\partial \Gamma} \frac{\partial \Gamma}{\partial \alpha} + \frac{\partial P'}{\partial c_o} \frac{\partial c_o}{\partial \alpha} + \frac{\partial Q}{\partial c_L} \frac{\partial c_L}{\partial \alpha} + \frac{\partial Q}{\partial c_Q} \frac{\partial c_Q}{\partial \alpha} \Bigg]^T$$

The parameter β in Eq. 11 is $3G/\sigma^2$.

DST EQUATION SET

Adjoint Equations

Deriving the adjoint system as prescribed by Eqs. 5 and 6 results in the following equations:

$$-\frac{D\Psi^*}{Dt} + \frac{Du_z}{Dt} \Phi_z^* - g\Phi_z^* + \frac{Di}{Dt} I^* - \frac{\partial P'}{\partial \rho} \Pi^* = \frac{\partial F}{\partial \rho} \quad (12a)$$

$$
\begin{aligned}
&-\rho\frac{\partial\Psi^*}{\partial z}-\rho\frac{D\Phi_z^*}{Dt}+\rho\frac{\partial u_z}{\partial z}\Phi_z^*+\sigma_{zz}\frac{\partial I^*}{\partial z}+\frac{\partial\sigma_{zz}}{\partial z}I^*\\
&+\rho\frac{\partial i}{\partial z}I^*+\frac{\partial}{\partial z}\left(\frac{\partial Q}{\partial\dot\varepsilon}\right)\Pi^*+\left(\frac{\partial Q}{\partial\dot\varepsilon}\right)\frac{\partial\Pi^*}{\partial z}\\
&+\left[\frac{\partial s_{zz}}{\partial z}-u\langle d\rangle\frac{\partial}{\partial z}\left(\beta s_{zz}^2\right)-\delta\langle d\rangle\beta s_{zz}^2\frac{\partial d}{\partial z}\right]\tau_{zz}^*\\
&-\left(-\tfrac{4}{3}G+u\langle d\rangle\beta s_{zz}^2\right)\frac{\partial\tau_{zz}^*}{\partial z}=\frac{\partial F}{\partial u_z}
\end{aligned}
\tag{12b}
$$

$$
-\rho\frac{DI^*}{Dt}-\frac{\partial P'}{\partial i}\Pi^*=\frac{\partial F}{\partial i}
\tag{12c}
$$

$$
\begin{aligned}
&\frac{\partial\Phi_z^*}{\partial z}-\tfrac{3}{2}\dot e_{zz}I^*-\frac{D\tau_{zz}^*}{Dt}\\
&+\left(-\dot e_{zz}+u\langle d\rangle 4G\dot\lambda+\delta\langle d\rangle 3\beta\dot\lambda s_{zz}^2\right)\tau_{zz}^*=\frac{\partial F}{\partial s_{zz}}
\end{aligned}
\tag{12d}
$$

$$
\Pi^*-\frac{\partial\Phi_z^*}{\partial z}+\dot\varepsilon I^*=\frac{\partial F}{\partial P'}\ ,
\tag{12e}
$$

where the dependent variables (with SI units given in parentheses, [R] indicating units of the response), are the adjoint density Ψ^* ([R]/kg), the adjoint velocity Φ_z^* ([R]/N-s), the adjoint energy I^* ([R]/J), the adjoint deviatoric stress τ_{zz}^* ([R]/Pa-m^3), and the adjoint pressure Π^* ([R]/Pa-m^3-s) giving the adjoint dependent variable vector:

$$
\bar y^*=\left(\Psi^*,\Phi_z{}^*,I^*,\tau_{zz}^*,\Pi^*\right)^T .
\tag{13}
$$

Boundary Terms

Derivation of the adjoint System 12 also determines the boundary terms B, as indicated in Eq. 5. For a specified set of physical initial and boundary conditions for System 8, the boundary terms are used to derive the adjoint initial and boundary conditions and the sensitivity coefficients to the physical initial and boundary conditions. As an example, say that $\rho(z{=}0)$ is a specified boundary condition and $\rho(z{=}L)$ is unknown in that it must be calculated from the solution of System 8. With the objective of eliminating all unknown quantities from the boundary terms so that it only contains sensitivity coefficients to initial and boundary conditions, we proceed as follows. Since $\rho(z{=}L)$ is an unknown, then $\Psi(z{=}L)$ is also an unknown and can be eliminated from B by specifying the adjoint boundary condition $\Psi^*(z{=}L)$ to be zero. In similar fashion, if we further specify $u_z(z{=}0)$, $i(z{=}0)$, $s_{zz}(z{=}0)$, and $u_z(z{=}L)$ as the remaining forward boundary conditions and specify $\rho(t{=}0)$, $u_z(t{=}0)$, $i(t{=}0)$, and $s_{zz}(t{=}0)$ as initial conditions, then it can be verified that $\Phi_z^*(z{=}0)$, $I^*(z{=}L)$, $\tau_{zz}^*(z{=}L)$, $\Phi_z^*(z{=}L)$, $\Psi^*(t{=}t_f)$, $\Phi_z^*(t{=}t_f)$, $I^*(t{=}t_f)$, and $\tau_{zz}^*(t{=}t_f)$ must all be equal to zero in order to eliminate the unknown variables $\partial\Phi_z/\partial z(z{=}0)$, $I(z{=}L)$, $\tau_{zz}(z{=}L)$, $\partial\Phi_z/\partial z(z{=}L)$, $\Psi(t{=}t_f)$, $\Phi_z(t{=}t_f)$, $I(t{=}t_f)$, and $\tau_{zz}(t{=}t_f)$, respectively. Note that the adjoint initial and boundary conditions are conveniently homogeneous for the our selection of forward initial and boundary conditions. Other selections of forward initial or boundary conditions, for example a zero velocity gradient at a boundary in space or time, can lead to non-homogeneous adjoint conditions. Typically, adjoint initial conditions are homogeneous.

Sensitivity Coefficients

Substituting Eq. 11 and the expanded form of the boundary terms from Eq. 5 into Eq. 7 gives the sensitivity integrals for the boundary conditions, initial conditions and other problem parameters associated with the original physical equation set. These sensitivities contain parts of the forward solution weighted by the adjoint functions. As an example say we want the sensitivity of R to the sound speed c_0. This specific sensitivity coefficient where $\alpha = c_0$ is derived to be:

$$
\frac{\partial R}{\partial c_o}=\iint\limits_{t\,z}\left(\frac{\partial P'}{\partial c_o}\right)\Pi^* dz\,dt\ .
\tag{14}
$$

PLATE IMPACT PROBLEM

Consider the one-dimensional impact of a copper plate with a rigid boundary where the plate has an initial velocity of 500 m/s, an initial density of 8930 kg/m^3, a sound speed of 3940 m/s, a yield stress of 5 GPa, and a shear modulus of 50 GPa. Upon impact the plate experiences a right going shock that compresses the material to the Hugoniot pressure of 20.89 GPa (density of 9961 kg/m^3). The plate is 2 cm in thickness and is divided into forty 0.5 mm cells for the numerical computations. The impact problem was simulated out to a final time of 2.0 µs.

The response for this problem was arbitrarily chosen to be the time-averaged density at the spatial location z_o = 0.6 cm, i.e.,

$$
R=\iint\limits_{t\,z}\rho\,\delta\langle z-z_o\rangle\frac{1}{t_f}dz\,dt=\bar\rho(z_o)
\tag{15a}
$$

so that the adjoint source for Eqs. 12 is

$$
\frac{\partial\bar F}{\partial\bar y}=\left(\delta\langle z-z_o\rangle/t_f,0,0,0\right)^T .
\tag{15b}
$$

Sensitivity results for this impact problem are given in Table I for the time-average density located at 0.6 cm

(ρ_0 = 9236.74 kg/m^3). This Table lists the parameters of interest in columns one through three, the DST sensitivities $\partial R/\partial\alpha$ in column four, and the "direct method" sensitivities $\Delta R/\Delta\alpha$ in column five (obtained via finite perturbations of each parameter appearing in the physical equation set) for validation purposes. Constructing the 17 direct method sensitivities in column five required 18 forward calculations, as compared to the 2 calculations (i.e., one forward and one adjoint) needed for the 17 DST sensitivities in column four.

SUMMARY AND CONCLUSIONS

Differential Sensitivity Theory was applied to a one-dimensional set of continuum mechanics equations with a realistic solid phase equation-of-state (i.e., compressible flow) and elastoplastic strength of materials for the purpose of sensitivity analysis. Equations adjoint to a differentiated set of physical equations (differentiated with respect to an arbitrary parameter α) were derived. The resulting DST equation set was illustrated using a simple one-dimensional plate impact problem, computing reasonably accurate sensitivity coefficients as validated with the Direct Method (forward perturbations to the forward solution). A table comparing DST $\partial R/\partial\alpha$ to Direct Method $\Delta R/\Delta\alpha$ was constructed for 17 sensitivities associated with the plate impact problem at a cost of 2 calculations versus 18 calculations, respectively, a saving of 88.9% in computational time. These low-cost DST sensitivity coefficients can then be used in a subsequent uncertainty analysis, response surface construction or optimization analysis.

REFERENCES

[1] E. M. Oblow, "Sensitivity Theory for Reactor Thermal-Hydraulics Problems," *Nucl. Sci. Eng.*, **68**, 322 (1978).

[2] D. G. Cacuci, C. F. Weber, E. M. Oblow, and J. H. Marable, "Sensitivity Theory for General Systems of Nonlinear Equations," *Nucl. Sci. Eng.*, **75**, 88 (1980).

[3] D. G. Cacuci, P. J. Maudlin, and C. V. Parks, "Adjoint Sensitivity Analysis of Extremum-Type Responses in Reactor Safety," *Nucl. Sci. Eng.*, **83**, 112 (1983).

[4] P. J. Maudlin, C. V. Parks, and C. F. Weber, "Thermal-Hydraulic Differential Sensitivity Theory," ASME paper No. 80-WA/HT-56, presented at the ASME Annual Winter Conference (1980).

[5] C. V. Parks and P. J. Maudlin, "Application of Differential Sensitivity Theory to a Neutronic/Thermal Hydraulic Reactor Safety Code," *Nucl. Technol.*, **54**, 38 (1981).

[6] C. V. Parks, "Adjoint-Based Sensitivity Analysis for Reactor Applications," ORNL/CSD/TM-231, Oak Ridge National Laboratory, 1986.

[7] Y. C. Fung, *Foundations of Solid Mechanics*, Prentice-Hall, Inc., Englewood Cliffs, N.J., 1965.

[8] F. H. Harlow and A. A. Amsden, "Fluid Dynamics," LA-4700, Los Alamos Scientific Laboratory, 1971.

Table I: Comparison of Plate Impact Sensitivities

α	**Description**	**Value**	$\partial R/\partial\alpha$ *	$\Delta R/\Delta\alpha$ *
$\rho(t=0)$	Initial Density (kg/m^3)	8930	1.090	1.085
$u_z(t=0)$	Initial Velocity (m/s)	-500	-0.626	-0.628
$i(t=0)$	Initial Internal Energy (J/kg-K)	0	2.85×10^{-5}	2.75×10^{-5}
$s_{zz}(t=0)$	Initial Stress Deviator (GPa)	0	7.49	6.75
s	Shock Velocity Constant	1.489	36.4	34.4
c_0	Sound Speed (m/s)	3940	0.0720	0.0716
ρ_0	Nominal EOS Density (kg/m^3)	8930	-5.44×10^{-2}	-5.09×10^{-2}
Γ	Second Gruneisen Ratio	2.002	7.8	7.9
c_l	Linear Artificial Viscosity Constant	0.8	-11.6	-8.2
c_Q	Quadratic Artificial Viscosity Constant	16.0	0.134	0.184
$u_z(z=0)$	"Outflow" Velocity (m/s)	0	0.628	0.760
$\rho(z=L)$	Inflow Density (kg/m^3)	8930	1.38×10^{-4}	
$i(z=L)$	Inflow Internal Energy (J/kg-K)	0	1.59×10^{-7}	
$u_z(z=L)$	Inflow Velocity (m/s)	-500	-3.90×10^{-3}	-5.84×10^{-3}
$s_{zz}(z=L)$	Inflow Deviatoric Stress (GPa)	0	0.444	
σ	Yield Stress (GPa)	5	5.72	5.23
G	Shear Modulus (GPa)	50	-1.85	1.48

*R = time-averaged density at z=0.6 cm over 2×10^{-6} s, R_o = 9236.74 kg/m^3

INFLUENCE OF PLASTICITY MODELS UPON THE OUTCOME OF SIMULATED HYPERVELOCITY IMPACTS

John N. Thomas
Space Kinetic Impact and Debris Branch
Air Force Phillips Laboratory
PL/WSSD
Kirtland AFB, NM 87117

This paper describes the results of numerical simulations of aluminum upon aluminum impacts which were performed with the CTH hydrocode to determine the effect of different plasticity formulations upon the final perforation size in the targets. The targets were 1 mm and 5 mm thick plates and the projectiles were 10 mm by 10 mm right circular cylinders. Both targets and projectiles were represented as 2024 aluminum alloy. The hydrocode simulations were run in a two-dimensional cylindrical geometry. Normal impacts at velocities between 5 and 15 km/s were simulated. Three isotropic yield stress models were explored in the simulations: an elastic-perfectly plastic model and the Johnson-Cook and Steinberg-Guinan-Lund viscoplastic models. The fracture behavior was modeled by a simple tensile pressure criterion. The simulations show that using the three strength models resulted in only minor differences in the final perforation diameter. The simulation results were used to construct an equation to predict the final hole size resulting from impacts on thin targets.

INTRODUCTION

The use of hydrocodes in analyzing high velocity impact events is now commonplace. Hydrocodes are used for many purposes such as engineering design, the design and analysis of impact experiments, and the extrapolation of experimental results to different conditions, e.g., higher velocities. There is a wealth of codes available to users [1]. There have been steady improvements in the solution techniques employed in the codes. Examples are higher order differencing schemes, more general or accurate representations of the equation of state, and detailed yield strength and fracture models. Yield strength models generally available include the elastic-perfectly plastic model, and the Bodner-Partom, Zerelli-Armstrong, Johnson-Cook, and Steinberg-Guinan-Lund models [2 - 5].

The purpose of this paper is to describe the results of simulations of hypervelocity impacts upon thin, flat plates made with the CTH Eulerian hydrocode [6], using three different yield strength models. The impact geometry was limited to several target thicknesses and a single impactor configuration. The impact velocity was varied between 5 and 15 km/s. Both the projectile and the targets were composed of 2024 aluminum alloy, and the projectile was compact, i.e., the aspect ratio was near unity. The results of the simulations were compared to each other to determine the influence of the plasticity model upon the final perforation size. In addition, the results were compared to empirical equations for perforation size [7,8] and an alternative prediction equation for aluminum was developed.

NUMERICAL EXPERIMENTS

A series of simulations of hypervelocity impacts was performed with the CTH hydrocode. The outcome of interest was the final perforation size. The projectiles were right circular cylinders 10 mm in diameter and 10 mm long. They struck the targets normally. Two target thicknesses (1 mm and 5 mm) and three impact velocities (5, 10, and 15 km/s) were used in the simulations. Three yield strength models were used: an elastic-perfectly plastic (EPP) model, the Johnson-Cook (JC) model and the Steinberg-Guinan-Lund (SGL) model. These models were selected because of their availability in CTH and the availability of the necessary material constants for 2024 aluminum alloy. (In contrast, the Zerelli-Armstrong material constants are available for only two metals.) Recommended or handbook values for these constants were used in all cases. A summary of the calculations is given in Table 1.

CTH was run in the cylindrical geometry mode for the impact simulations. Different grids were used, one for the 1 mm targets and another for the 5 mm targets. The simulations with the 5 mm targets employed a computational space (Figure 1) that was 65 mm radially and 55 mm axially. The cell size was .5 mm by .5 mm resulting in ten cells across the target thickness. The simulations with the 1 mm targets had a computational space which was 50 mm radially and 35 mm axially. The cells were .125 mm by .125 mm in the vicinity of the impact and were larger elsewhere. In both cases, the problems were set up so that the expected perforations were less than ten per cent of the target areas.

Table 1. Summary of CTH Simulations Performed

Target Thickness (mm)	Impact Velocity (km/s)	Strength Model
5	5, 10, 15	EPP,Yo = 324MPa
5	5, 10, 15	Johnson-Cook
5	5, 10, 15	Steinberg-Guinan-Lund
1	5, 10, 15	EPP,Yo = 324MPa
1	5, 10, 15	Johnson-Cook
1	5, 10, 15	Steinberg-Guinan-Lund

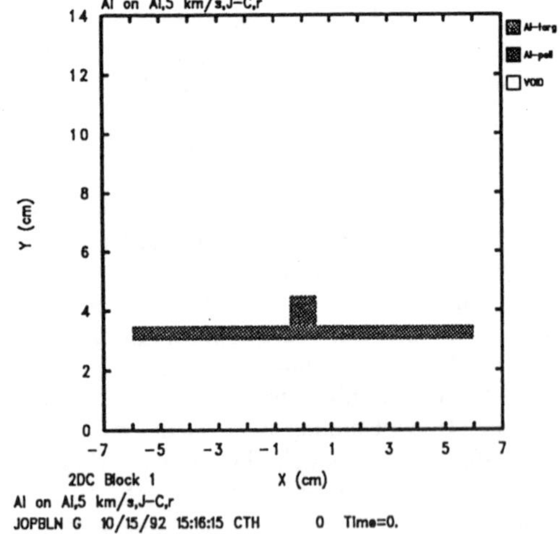

Figure 1. Geometry of 10 mm by 10 mm projectile striking a 5 mm thick target in CTH simulations.

The CTH code solves the finite difference forms of the conservation laws and incorporates into the solution equation of state (EOS), plasticity and fracture models. The EOS used in the simulations was the SESAME tabular EOS [9] for 2024 aluminum. In this scheme, the pressure is determined from the density and temperature. Generally, this tabular EOS is valid over a wide range of densities and temperatures and can account for melting, vaporization and ionization. The reference density for this alloy is 2.793 gcm^{-3}; the Poisson's ratio is 0.330.

The plasticity formulation for metals in CTH [5,10] is based upon the von Mises theory of yielding combined with a flow rule, i.e., a prescription for defining plastic strains. The assumption in the von Mises theory is that yielding (the onset of plastic strains) occurs when the magnitude of **S**, the deviatoric stress tensor, reaches a constant value:

$$S = \sqrt{\frac{2}{3}}\, Y \tag{1}$$

where S is the magnitude of **S**, defined by

$$S = \sqrt{S_{ij}\, S_{ij}} \tag{2}$$

and Y is a material constant called the yield stress. The yield point may also be expressed in terms of J_2, the second invariant of the deviatoric stress tensor. Physically meaningful variations on the von Mises theory have been constructed by making the yield stress a function of variables such as strain, strain rate, temperature, and pressure. In addition to a criterion for defining the yield point, a flow rule is necessary to calculate plastic strains. The flow rule used in CTH is an associated flow rule of the Prandtl-Reuss form:

$$\dot{\mathbf{e}}^{P} = \lambda\, \mathbf{S} \tag{3}$$

where $\dot{\mathbf{e}}^{P}$ is the plastic portion of the deviatoric strain rate tensor and λ is a scalar proportionality factor.

The three strength models tested were the EPP, JC and SGL models. In the EPP model the yield strength is a constant, designated Y_0. For the baseline simulations, Y_0 was held at 324 MPa, which is a typical (static) yield strength of 2024-T4 or 2024-T351 aluminum at 297 deg K [11]. No attempt to account for strain hardening was made.

The yield strength in the Johnson-Cook [4] viscoplastic model is determined by:

$$Y = \left[A + B(\epsilon^{P})^{N}\right]\left[1 + C\ \ln\dot{\epsilon}^{P}\right]\left[1 - \theta_h^{M}\right] \tag{4}$$

where A, B, C, M and N are material constants and ϵ^P and $\dot{\epsilon}^P$ are the equivalent plastic strain and the equivalent plastic strain rate. ϑ_h is the homologous temperature defined by :

$$\theta_h = \frac{T - T_R}{T_M - T_R} \tag{5}$$

where T_M and T_R are the melt temperature and ambient temperatures, respectively. In the calculation of Y, the homologous temperature is not allowed to exceed unity. In the simulations the values for A, B, C, M, N, T_M and T_R were 265 MPa, 426 MPa, 0.015, 1.0, 0.34, 800 deg K and 300 deg K.

The SGL model [12] in its most general form is a viscoplastic model. However, for fcc metals such as aluminum, Steinberg does not at this time include strain rate effects in the yield strength and it takes the form:

$$Y = Y_0 \, f(\epsilon^P) \, G\,(P,T)/\, G_0 \qquad (6)$$

where $f(\epsilon^P) = [1 + \beta\,(\epsilon^P + \epsilon_i)]^n$ (7)

and $G(P,T) = G_0\,[1 + \frac{AP}{\eta^{1/3}} - B(T\text{-}300\text{degK})]$ (8)

Y_0 is the initial yield stress and G_0 is the initial shear modulus. $f(\epsilon^P)$ is a strain hardening term and the shear modulus G(P,T) is used to account for both pressure strengthening and thermal softening. The variables ϵ^P, ϵ_i, P, T, and η are the equivalent plastic strain, its initial value, the pressure, temperature, and compression. Y_0, G_0, β, n, A and B are material constants. The SGL model has an option for introducing Bauschinger effects into the material response through the shear modulus but this option is not available in CTH. The SGL model sets limits on Y and G as the temperature approaches the melt temperature and there is also a limit on the strain hardening. In the simulations Y_0, G_0, β, n, A and B had the values 260 MPa, 28.6 GPa, 310.0, 0.185, 0.0652 GPa^{-1}, and 6.16e-04 deg K^{-1}. Y was limited to a maximum value of 760 MPa.

A simple minimum tensile pressure ("P_{min}") fracture model was used in all the calculations with the dynamic fracture strength set to 1.32 GPa. This compares to a 1.2 GPa dynamic fracture strength recommended by Steinberg [12] for 6061 aluminum. Davison and Graham [13] recommended 1.25 GPa for 2024-T4 aluminum.

RESULTS

The CTH simulations shown in Table 1 were run until the final perforation was attained. This was at about 20 μs for the 5 mm targets and at about 10 μs for the 1 mm targets. The calculated perforation diameters are shown in Table 2 for the 5 mm targets and Table 3 for the 1 mm targets.

Table 2. Perforation diameters (in mm) for 5 mm thick 2024 Aluminum Targets

Strength Model	Dia at 5 km/s	Dia at 10 km/s	Dia at 15 km/s
EPP, Yo = 324MPa	28.3	35.4	38.6
Johnson-Cook	26.2	33.3	35.8
Steinberg-Guinan-Lund	25.8	32.5	34.9

Table 3. Perforation diameters (in mm) for 1 mm thick 2024 Aluminum Targets

Strength Model	Dia at 5 km/s	Dia at 10 km/s	Dia at 15 km/s
EPP, Yo = 324MPa	15.2	16.3	16.9
Johnson-Cook	14.5	15.8	16.2
Steinberg-Guinan-Lund	14.8	15.9	16.3

DISCUSSION

Use of the three strength formulations resulted in only minor variations in the final perforation size. For the 5 mm targets, the final hole diameters from the simulations were all within 6% of the mean at any impact velocity. The differences produced by the strength models in the 1 mm targets were within 3% of the mean. The more elaborate JC and SGL models resulted in hole sizes slightly smaller the those from the EPP model.

There are several empirical equations for the final hole size produced in thin targets by compact projectiles. Maiden and McMillan [14] report:

$$D/d = 0.45V\,(t/d)^{2/3} + 0.9 \qquad (9)$$

and McHugh [15]:

$$D/d = .658V\,(t/d)^{0.14} \exp\,[0.63\,(t/d)^{0.43}] \qquad (10)$$

where D is the final perforation diameter, d is the projectile diameter, V is the impact velocity (km/s) and t is the target thickness. Equation 9 is a fit to aluminum impacts with velocities between 2 and 7.5 km/s. Herrmann [7] states that an extensive collection of hole data could not be fitted successfully by these equations and that they predict very large hole sizes at very high velocities. Hill [8] suggests another fit based upon data from micrometer sized iron particles impacting gold and aluminum foils at velocities from 2 to 25 km/s.

$$\frac{D}{d} = 1.0 + \frac{2.9\left(\frac{\rho_T}{\rho_p}\right)^{0.6}\left(\frac{t}{d}\right)V^{0.3}}{1.0 + 2.9\left(\frac{\rho_T}{\rho_p}\right)\left(\frac{t}{d}\right)^2 V^{-n}} \tag{11}$$

where

$$n = 1.02 - 4.0\exp(-9.0V^{0.9}) - 0.003\,(20.0 - V) \tag{12}$$

and ρ_T and ρ_P are the target and projectile densities.

The CTH results are roughly consistent with Equation (9) for velocities up to 10 km/s. They are within several percent of Equation (11) for 1 mm targets and are about 12% lower than Equation (11) for the 5 mm targets. A comparison of the simulation results to the empirical fits is shown in Figure 2.

A fit to an average of the CTH results was devised by assuming that the form of D/d was similar to Equation [11] but with the t/d term having a fractional exponent similar to Equation [9]. The coefficient of the t/d term and the two exponents were determined from the CTH results. The resulting fit is:

$$D/d = 1.0 + 1.66\,(t/d)^{0.85}\,V^{0.41} \tag{13}$$

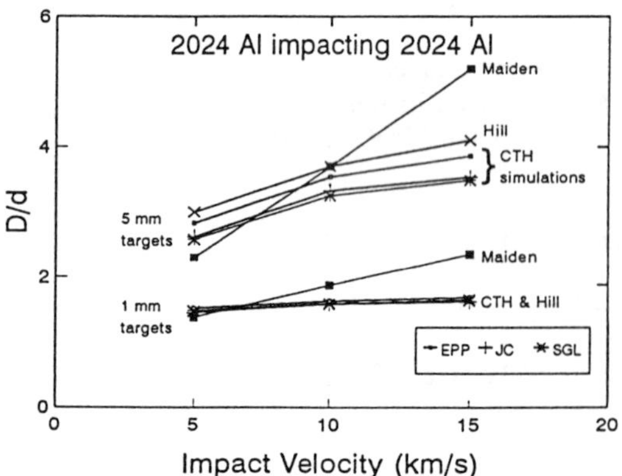

Figure 2. Ratio of perforation diameter to projectile diameter at several impact velocities for CTH results and Hill and Maiden empirical fits.

CONCLUSIONS

Impacts upon thin aluminum plates at velocities between 5 and 15 km/s were investigated using CTH simulations. The three different strength models used resulted in only minor differences in the final perforation hole size. Although the final hole size predicted by the simulations is somewhat insensitive to the model used, the strength cannot be ignored. The simulation results lead to Equation (13) which shows that perforation hole size scales by $V^{0.41}$ for velocities between 5 and 15 km/s. This, along with Equations (9) and (11), suggests that the thin target hole size scales by V^N. N is near unity for lower (1 to 5 km/s) impact velocities and decreases for larger impact velocities.

REFERENCES

[1] J. A. Zukas, *High Velocity Impact Dynamics,* New York New York: John Wiley, 1990, ch. 9

[2] S. R. Bodner and Y. Bartom, *Journal of Applied Mechanics* **42**, pp. 385-389 (1975)

[3] F. J. Zerelli and R. W. Armstrong, *J. Appl. Phys.* **61**, pp. 1816-1825 (1987)

[4] G. R. Johnson and W. H. Cook, "A Constitutive Model and Data for Metals Subjected to Large Strains, High Strain Rates, and High Temperatures," in *Seventh International Symposium on Ballistics, The Hague, Netherlands* (1983)

[5] P. A. Taylor, "CTH Reference Manual: The Steinberg-Guinan-Lund Viscoplastic Model," Sandia National Laboratories report SAND92-0716 (1992)

[6] R. L. Bell et al,"CTH User's Manual and Input Instructions, Version 1.025," Sandia National Laboratories report SAND88-0523 (revised) (1992)

[7] W. Herrman and J. S. Wilbeck, *Int. J. Impact Engng* **5**, pp. 307-322 (1987)

[8] D. C. Hill, "The Micrometeoroid Hazard in Space: Techniques for Damage Simulation By Pulsed Lasers and Environmental Modelling," *Ph. D. Thesis*, University of Kent at Canterbury, England (1990)

[9] G. I. Kerley, "CTH Reference Manual: The Equation of State Package," Sandia National Laboratories report SAND91-0344 (1991)

[10] S. A. Silling, "CTH Reference Manual: Viscoplastic Models," Sandia National Laboratories report SAND91-0292 (1991)

[11] W. H. Cubberly, *Metals Handbook, Vol. 2, Properties and Selections: Nonferrous Alloys and Pure Metals, 9th Edition*, Metals Park, OH, American Society of Metals, 1979, p. 75

[12] D. J. Steinberg, "Equation of State and Strength Properties of Selected Materials," Lawrence Livermore National Laboratory report UCRL-MA-106439 (1991)

[13] L. Davison and R. A. Graham, *Physics Reports 55, No 4*, pp 255-379, Table 3.6 (1979)

[14] C. J. Maiden and A. R. McMillan, *AIAA Journal 2*, pp. 1992-1998 (1964)

[15] A. H. McHugh, "Evaluation of Hypervelocity Impact Damage to a Thin Sheet by Regression Analysis," NAA/S&DI Report STR 152 (1966)

NUMERICAL SIMULATIONS OF IMPACT PENETRATION TESTS

T.Shibue, E.Nakayama, T.Natsumura, T.Tanaka and T.Asano
Research Institute, Ishikawajima Harima Heavy Industries Co.,Ltd.
1, Shin-Nakahara, Isogo, Yokohama 235, Japan

This paper gives one way to estimate critical strength of a steel plate against perforation failure by combinations of impact penetration tests and numerical simulations. The simulation tool employed is DYNA3D with a function to evaluate strain-rate dependency of material strength. At first, numerical simulations of a test give a set of material properties, then a series of numerical simulations reproduces a series of impact penetration tests to estimate the critical perforation velocity. The estimated critical perforation velocity is found to be 12% less than the measured value, whereas, the deformations of projectiles show a good agreement with those measured.

INTRODUCTION

Impact penetration tests are used to estimate the strength of materials against perforation failure. As a result of iterative tests, a critical perforation velocity(V_{cr}) is estimated. It is expected that numerical simulation methods are to be an alternative to impact penetration tests, but the estimation of the material properties under high strain rate, which are essential to numerical simulation methods, is difficult. One of the difficulties is that the mechanical properties measured at tests may not be applied directly to numerical simulations, because measured values contain the strain localisation effects at failure.

This paper tried to show the possibility of numerical simulation methods to be a partial alternative to impact penetration tests for the materials used for ship structures.

IMPACT PENETRATION TESTS

A series of impact penetration tests, with the same combination of the projectile and the plate, is performed with an one stage powder gun, changing the impact velocity to estimate V_{cr}. A schematic view of testing and measuring facilities is shown in Figure 1. At tests, velocities and deformations of a projectile and a target plate are measured. The velocities of a projectile before and after perforation are measured by the combination of strain gauge impulses and a high speed cinecamera. The target plates are 150mm long and 4.9mm thick square plates made of the KA, a mild steel normally used for ship structures, which is made under the specifications of NK(Nippon Kaiji Kyokai:Japan ship classification society). The configuration of projectiles, shown in figure 2, is a round bar with a cone frustum head and made of the NSCM439, a nickel chrome molybdenum steel, which is made under the specifications of JIS(Japan industry standard). The mechanical properties specifications of both projectiles and target plates are listed in table 1. The target plate is fixed on

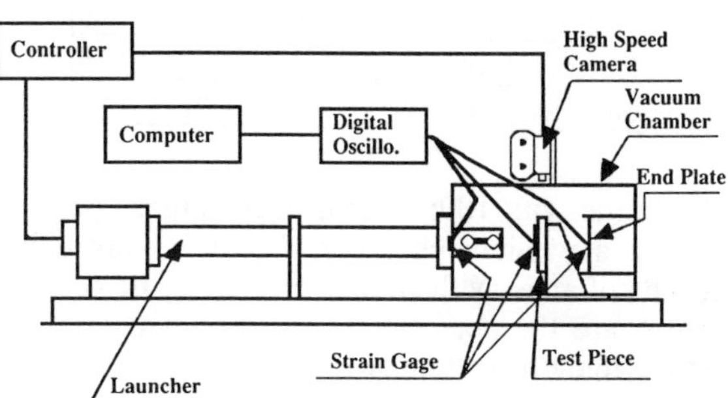

Figure 1.Testing and Measureing Facilities

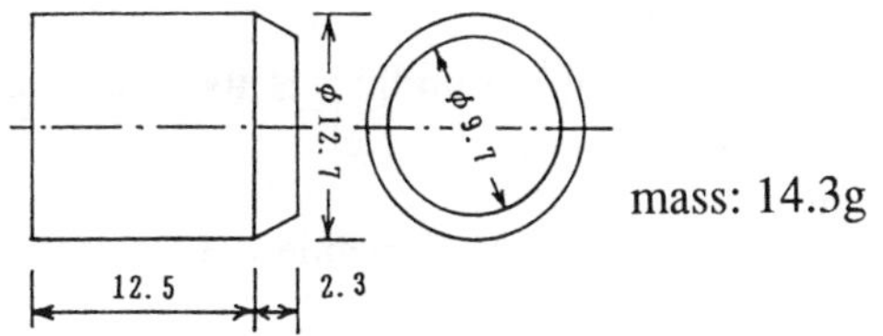

Figure 2.Configuration of Projectile

Table 1. Mechanical Properties Specifications of a Test Piece and a Projectile

	Test Piece	Projectile
Material	KA	SNCM439
Yield Stress(MPa)	235	883
Tensile Strength(MPa)	402	980
Elongation(%)	22	16

Table 2. Measured and Calculated Values at the Perforation Tests

Initial	Initial	After Perforation	
unit (m/s,mm)		Exp.	Estimate
Projectile Velocity	403	157	171
Plug Velocity	0	191	184
Projectile Diameter	12.7	13.4	13.4
Projectile Length	14.8	14.2	14.2

the frame with 100mm long rectangular opening within a vacuum chamber. Table 2 shows the results of a test with an impact velocity of 403m/s which are the objective of the parametric study with a numerical simulation tool.

NUMERICAL SIMULATION METHOD

The DYNA3D, an explicit shock code based on the finite element method[1], is used with an installed material model of an elastic plastic with failure, to reproduce the impact penetration tests. We added the strain rate dependent function to this material model.

We employed the equation(1) to show strain hardening and strain rate effects on yield stress. This equation ignores the temperature effects, because the impact velocity is not so high as to increase the plate temperature to the value enough to change its mechanical properties. Work hardening coefficients are used to represent the strain hardening effects. The power of strain rate is assumed to be in proportion to the increment of the yield stress in this equation.

$$\sigma_y = \sigma_{y0} \cdot F\left(\varepsilon_p^e\right) \cdot (1 + C \cdot \dot{\varepsilon}^n) \qquad (1)$$

where, ε_p^e :equivalent plastic strain

σ_{y0} :static yield stress

$\dot{\varepsilon}$: strain rate

The five parameters, static yield stress σ_{y0} strain rate dependence parameters C and n, work hardening coefficient and equivalent plastic strain at failure, are necessary to represent the mechanical properties. We introduce two subscripts to the five parameters to show test pieces(t) and projectiles(f) in this paper.

We assumed overall configuration of both projectile and plate to be symmetry, to make the numerical simulation model symmetry with 8 degrees of center angle, which is shown in figure 3. The total number of elements is 124 and nodes is 317.

The numerical simulations start from the initial states where the projectile contacts with the plate. The initial velocity is given to every nodes of the projectile. The sliding interface condition is applied to the intersection between the projectile and the plate, where the contact force is transmitted through the moving interface.

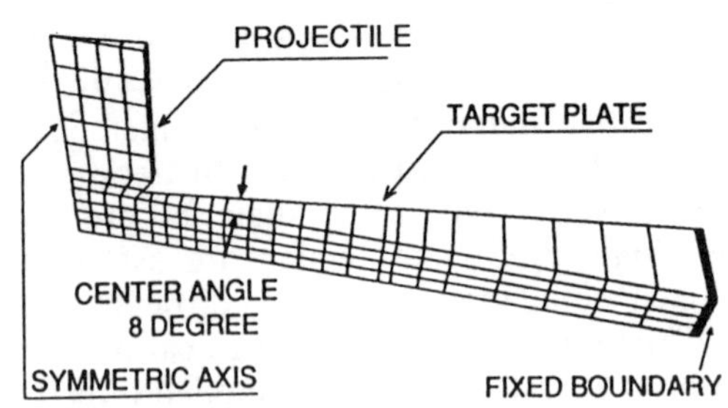

Figure 3. Numerical Simulation Model

PARAMETRIC STUDY

The static yield stresses are available from their specifications and work hardening coefficients are obtained by our former study[2]. The total parameter of the mechanical properties for both the projectile and the plate comes to 6 out of 10. The parametric study is carried out by changing one parameter out of 6 to examine the effects of a parameter on solutions. One of the results of the parametric study is shown in figure 4. The horizontal axis shows the change of each parameters. The vertical axis shows the velocity of both a projectile and a plug after perforation for (a), and the axial and the radial deformation of a projectile after perforation for (b). The horizontal solid and dotted lines show the experimental results, and the symbols show

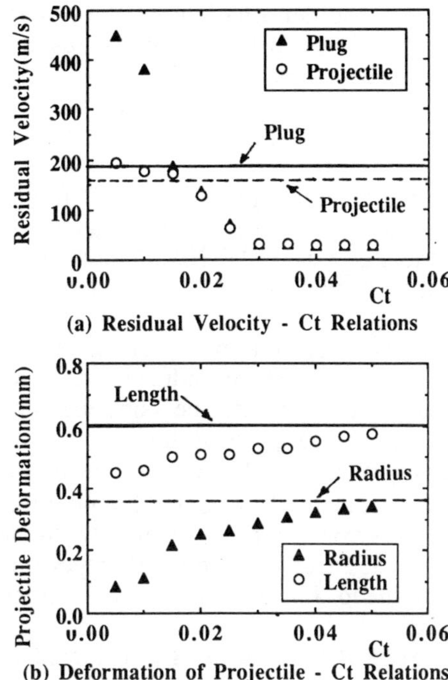

Figure 4. Effects of Ct: A Parameter of Test Piece

Table 3. Estimated Mechanical Properties of a Test Piece and a Simulated Projectile

	Test Piece	Projectile
Quasi-Static Yield Stress: (MPa)	235	883
Strain Rate Effect Parameter:C	0.015	0.010
Strain Rate Effect Parameter:n	0.45	0.50
Tangent Modulus:Ht(MPa)	735	784
Equivalent Plastic Strain at Failure	0.50	0.70

the simulated results.

Figure 4 shows the effects of Ct. As Ct increases, residual velocities decrease and deformations increase, because the increase of Ct or nt implies the increase of stiffness of the plate. The mechanical properties of both the projectile and the plate are estimated based on the parametric studies stated above, and these values are listed in table 3.

The results of the numerical simulation with the estimated mechanical properties are shown in figures 5 and 6. Figure 5 shows the simulated velocity time history of the projectile head and the plate surface. Figure 6 shows the simulated deformation time history of length and radius of the projectile. The velocities of both the

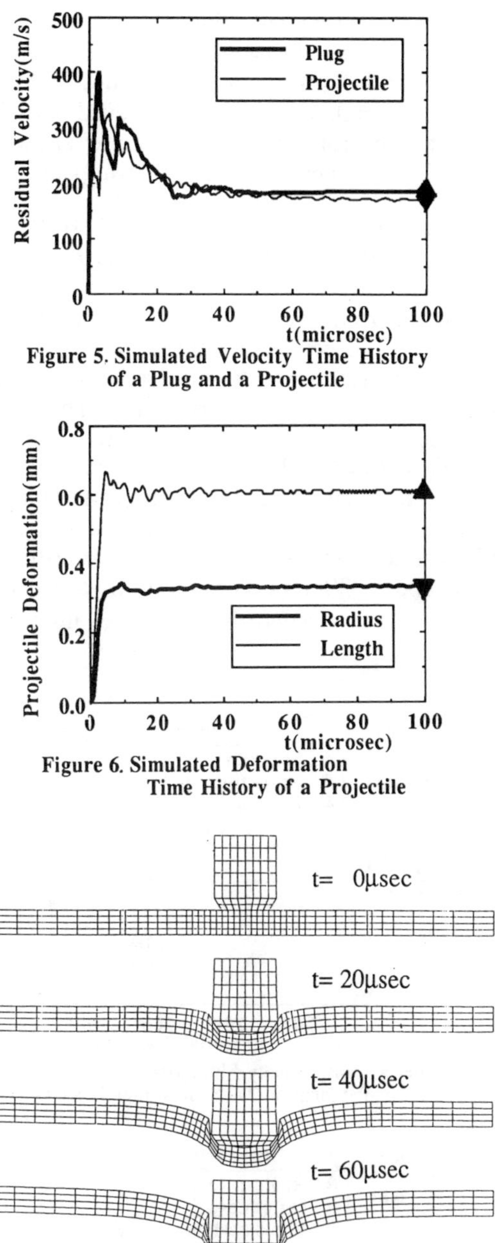

Figure 5. Simulated Velocity Time History of a Plug and a Projectile

Figure 6. Simulated Deformation Time History of a Projectile

Figure 7. Simulated Perforation Process

projectile and the plate converge to certain values at 50microseconds after impact, and they are considered to be residual velocities after perforation. The measured values are illustrated as black triangles in these figures. The numerically estimated values coincide with the measured values fairy well, showing that the experimental results can be reproduced by the numerical simulation method employed here. The simulated perforation processes are shown in figure 7 until 60microseconds after impact.

NUMERICAL ESTIMATION OF CRITICAL PERFORATION VELOCITY

We carried out a series of numerical estimations to reproduce the series of impact penetration tests with the mechanical properties obtained from the parametric study. The results of the tests and numerical estimations are shown in figures 8 and 9. Figure 8 shows the relations between residual velocities and impact velocities. Figure 9 shows the relations between projectile deformations and impact velocities. The estimated V_{cr} is about 330m/s according to the test results, and is 370m/s according to the numerical estimations. The deformations of the projectiles coincide fairly well between the test results and the numerically estimated results.

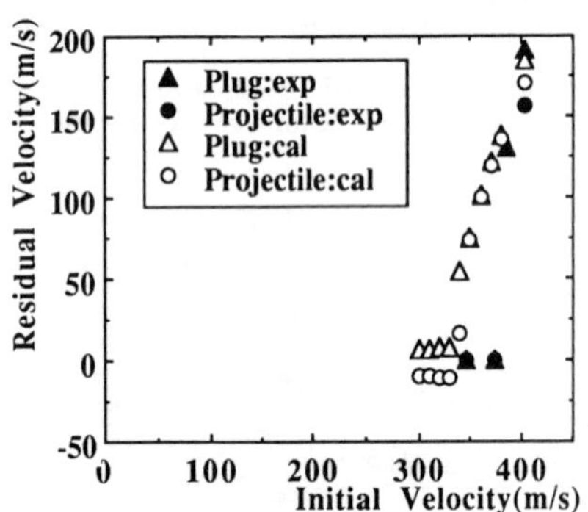

Figure 8. Numerically Simulated Perforation Tests: Residual Velocity

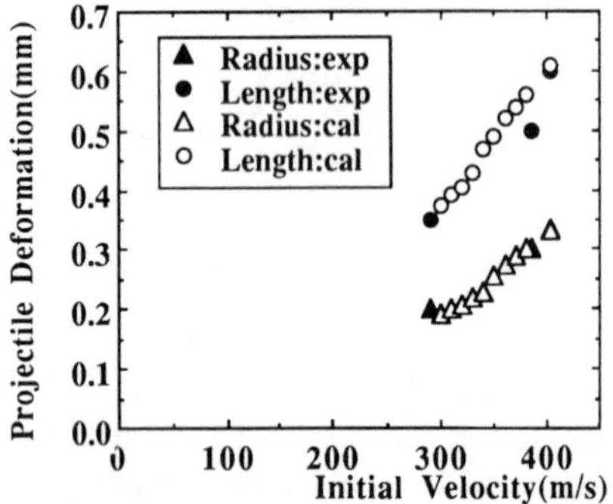

Figure 9. Numerically Simulated Perforation Tests: Deformation of Projectiles

CONCLUSIONS

The mechanical properties of both the projectile and the plate are estimated by the parametric study using DYNA3D equipped with the equation of yield stress as a function of strain rate.

The impact penetration test of the mild steel plate is shown to be reproduced well by the numerical simulation with the same method and the same mechanical properties.

The V_{cr} of the mild steel plate estimated by the numerical method gives good approximation within 12% error to what estimated by the tests. The deformation of projectiles after perforation are reproduced fairly well by the numerical estimations.

This estimation process is considered to be one method to give V_{cr} and the failure mode initiated by the high speed impact of a projectile.

ACKNOWLEDGEMENTS

Authors would like to express their acknowledgements to Mr.Y.Kato and Mr.T.Matsuyama of Japan Ministry of Defence for their kind advises. Authors are grateful to Dr.K.Fujii for his encouragement.

REFERENCES

[1]J.O.Hallquist and D.J.Benson,DYNA3D User's Manual,LLNL UCID-19592(1986)

[2]T.Shibue,E.Nakayama,T.Natsumura,T.Tanaka and T.Asano, Numerical simulations of an Impact Penetration Test (in Japanese), Proc. Society of Naval Architects Japan No.170(1991)

ANALYSIS OF PENETRATION OF STEEL AND Al_2O_3 TARGETS

David L. Littlefield, Charles E. Anderson, Jr.
Samuel R. Skaggs†

Engineering and Materials Sciences
Southwest Research Institute
6220 Culebra Road
San Antonio, TX 78238

†Los Alamos National Laboratory
P.O. Box 1663
Los Alamos, NM 87185

A series of penetration experiments was conducted to investigate the ballistic performance of steel and 99.5% pure Al_2O_3 targets using a *L/D=10* tungsten alloy projectile. The impact velocity for the experiments was nominally 1.6 km/s. Flash radiographs were used to record the positions of the nose and tail of the projectile at discrete times. The experiments have been analyzed using an analytic penetration model [1]. The steel data were matched quite well using reasonable values for the flow stress of the steel and tungsten alloy. Agreement with the ceramic data was not satisfactory, so the model was modified to account for constitutive behavior more realistic in ceramic materials. Experimental data for the ceramic target were replicated reasonably well using the modified model when the slope of the yield strength/pressure curve was 0.75.

INTRODUCTION

Critical to the evaluation of any analytical or numerical penetration model is comparison with experimental results. In traditional ballistic experiments, the data available for comparison usually consists of postmortem measurements of the projectile and target. There data might include depth of penetration, crater radius and volume, or residual penetrator length. However, time-resolved experimental data at intermediate times are also very useful to the validation of theoretical penetration models, since they allow a closer examination of the subtle details in the penetration event. Due to the inordinate expense and extensive mechanical difficulties associated with time-resolved experiments, this type of penetration data is not widely available.

One series of time-resolved penetration data has been obtained using the PHERMEX facility at Los Alamos National Laboratory [2]. In these experiments, flash radiographs were used to record positions of the projectile nose and tail as a function of time. Projectile materials included tungsten alloy and depleted uranium, and target materials included steel and 99.5% pure aluminum oxide (Al_2O_3). The projectile velocity was nominally 1.6 km/s. Data from these experiments was examined in the present study using an unsteady analytical penetration model [1]. The model was also modified to account approximately for the constitutive behavior observed in ceramic materials. Comparisons were made between analytical predictions and experimental results.

ANALYSIS

The analytical approach employed in this penetration model relies mainly on the integration of conservation equations for assumed velocity and stress distributions in the projectile and target, and on an assumed deceleration behavior for the projectile tail. The assumed velocity and stress distributions were based on observations from more complicated, two-dimensional numerical simulations of eroding penetration. For brevity, only a condensed description of the equations in the model will be given here; a more complete description may be found elsewhere [1].

Two basic equations were formulated in the model that describe the time evolution of the projectile tail and projectile/target interface velocities. The first equation conserves momentum and is derived by integration of the axisymmetric, incompressible axial momentum equation along the centerline. This relation is given by

$$\rho_p \int_{z_p}^{z_i} \frac{\partial u_p}{\partial t} dz + \rho_t \int_{z_i}^{\infty} \frac{\partial u_t}{\partial t} dz + \frac{1}{2}\rho_t u_z^2 \Big|_{z_p}^{z_i}$$

$$+\frac{1}{2}\rho_t u_z^2 \Big|_{z_p}^{\infty} - 2\int_{z_p}^{\infty} \frac{\partial \sigma_{xz}}{\partial x} dz = 0, \tag{1}$$

where u is the velocity, ρ is the density, σ_{xz} is the shear stress, x is the radial coordinate, z is the axial coordinate, and t is time. The subscripts *p, i,* and *t* refer to the projectile, interface, and target, respectively. The second equation accounts for deceleration at the rear interface of the projectile by elastic waves, and is given by

$$\dot{v} = -\frac{\sigma_p}{\rho_p(L-s)}\left[1 + \frac{v-u}{s} + \frac{\dot{s}}{c}\right], \tag{2}$$

where v, σ_p, c , L, and s are the projectile tail velocity, yield strength, elastic wave speed, length, and axial width of the plastic zone, respectively, and u is the interface velocity.

Eq. (1) can be solved together with Eq. (2) to determine u and v if velocity and stress distributions along the centerline are assumed for the target and projectile. The distributions employed were motivated by observations from the results of numerical simulations. The velocity profile in the projectile was assumed to be

$$u_z = \begin{cases} u - \dfrac{v-u}{s}(z - z_i) & (z_i - s) \le z \le z_i \\ v & z_p \le z \le (z_i - s) \end{cases}, \tag{3}$$

and in the target

$$u_z = \begin{cases} \frac{u}{\alpha^2-1}\left[\left(\frac{\alpha R}{r}\right)^2 - 1\right] & R \le z \le \alpha R \\ 0 & \alpha R \le z \end{cases}, \quad (4)$$

where R is the crater radius and α is the ratio of the plastic zone radius to the crater radius. The coordinate r is the radius of a spherical region that extends into the target from the projectile/target interface. r can be related to z by $r = z - z_i + R$. At the edge of the plastic zone $r = \alpha R$ and $z = z_i + (\alpha - 1)R$. The target material was assumed to be perfectly plastic, which allowed the shear stress in the target to be calculated. The contribution to Eq. (1) from the shear stress in the projectile was assumed negligible. Then, with the use of Eqs. (3) and (4), Eq. (1) yields

$$\rho_p \dot{v}(L-s) + \dot{u}\left[\rho_p s + \rho_t \frac{R(\alpha-1)}{\alpha+1}\right] + \frac{\rho_p \alpha s^2}{(\alpha^2-1)R}\left(\dot{u}\alpha - \frac{2u\dot{\alpha}}{\alpha^2-1}\right) + \frac{2\rho_t u \dot{\alpha} R}{(\alpha+1)^2} = \frac{1}{2}\rho_p (v-u)^2 - \frac{1}{2}\rho_t u^2 - \frac{7Y}{3}\log\alpha, \quad (5)$$

where Y is the constant yield strength in the target. Eqs. (2) and (5) represent first-order coupled equations governing the time evolution of u and v. The initial conditions for these equations were assumed to be the Rankine-Hugoniot shock jump conditions.

MODIFICATION FOR CERAMIC MATERIALS

In the development of Eq. (5), the target material was assumed to be perfectly plastic with a constant yield stress. This constitutive model is quite adequate for most metals, but is not suitable for ceramic materials. Experimental studies [3,4] have demonstrated that ceramic materials exhibit strong strength characteristics when held under confinement, but are very weak and brittle when subjected to tensile loads. Furthermore, the strength of the ceramic decreases after the material begins to crack or fail. This phenomenologically observed constitutive behavior was implemented in an approximate manner for the present model by permitting the yield stress to vary with confining pressure, so that $Y = \beta p$. This augmentation also tends to replicate the additional strength seen at early times for the intact ceramic, since the pressure is quite large during the initial stages of the penetration process.

To implement the assumed constitutive behavior for the ceramic material, the last integral in Eq. (1) was evaluated assuming the yield stress is variable. Using the velocity profiles given in Eq. (4) and allowing for variable yield stress, this integral becomes

$$2\int_{z_i}^{\infty} \frac{\partial \sigma_{xz}}{\partial x} dz = -\frac{7}{3}\int_{R}^{\alpha R} \frac{Y dr}{r}. \quad (6)$$

The pressure distribution along the centerline in the target must also be determined. This is accomplished though integration of the incompressible axisymmetric axial momentum equation from an arbitrary location inside the plastic zone to the edge of the plastic zone. Application of this procedure yields

$$p = -\frac{2Y}{3} + \rho_t \int_r^{\alpha R} \frac{\partial u_z}{\partial t} dr - \frac{1}{2}\rho_t u_z^2 + \frac{7}{3}\int_r^{\alpha R} \frac{Y dz}{r}, \quad (7)$$

where p is the pressure. The assumed constitutive behavior in the ceramic requires $p = Y/\beta$, which when combined with Eq. (7), yields an integral equation for Y. This integral equation was solved for Y using the condition that $p = 0$ at $r = \alpha R$. Once Y was determined, the integral in Eq. (6) was then evaluated. The algebraic details are quite cumbersome but, nevertheless, straightforward. Substitution of the result into Eq. (1), making use of the velocity distribution given in Eq. (4), yields the integrated form of the axial momentum equation for the ceramic, given by

$$\rho_p \dot{v}(L-s) + \dot{u}\left[\rho_p s + \rho_t \frac{R(\alpha-1)}{\alpha+1}\right] + \frac{\rho_p \alpha s^2}{(\alpha^2-1)R}\left(\dot{u}\alpha - \frac{2u\dot{\alpha}}{\alpha^2-1}\right) + \frac{2\rho_t u \dot{\alpha} R}{(\alpha+1)^2} = \frac{1}{2}\rho_p (v-u)^2 - \frac{1}{2}\rho_t u^2 - \frac{2\rho_t \delta u}{\alpha^2-1}\left[\dot{\alpha} R\left(\frac{\delta\alpha^\delta - \alpha}{\delta - 1} - 1\right) + \frac{u}{\alpha^2-1}\left\{\frac{2\delta\alpha^4}{(2-\delta)(4-\delta)} + \frac{\delta\alpha^\delta}{4-\delta} - \frac{\delta\alpha^{\delta+2}}{2-\delta} - \alpha^2 + 1\right\}\right] - \frac{\rho_t \delta R}{\alpha^2-1}\left[\frac{2u\alpha\dot{\alpha}}{\alpha^2-1} - \dot{u}\right]\left[\frac{\alpha^2}{\delta-1} + \frac{1}{\delta+1} - \frac{2\delta\alpha^{\delta+1}}{\delta^2-1}\right]. \quad (8)$$

where $\delta = 7\beta/(3+2\beta)$. When solved together with Eq. (2), Eq. (8) yields the time evolution for the velocities u and v.

Determination of α

A critical part of the analysis is the determination of α. The calculation of α is nontrivial, and is intimately coupled with the constitutive model assumed for the target. A recent study employed cavity expansion theory [5] to determine α for materials with a yield strength that varied with pressure. Furthermore, the yield strength of the intact material was assumed to be $Y = Y_0 + \beta_0 p$, where Y_0 is the yield strength of intact material at zero pressure, and β_0 is the slope of the intact yield strength/pressure curve. After steady-state, one-dimensional flow was assumed, an expression for α was derived as

$$\alpha = \left[\frac{2\sqrt{3}G}{2Y_0 + f\beta_0\rho_t u^2}\right]^{1/2}, \quad (9)$$

where G is the shear modulus. The factor f accounts approximately for the decrease in u across the plastic zone, since it was assumed to be constant in the derivation of Eq. (9). In the present study f was set to 0.5.

Further complicating the calculation of α is the fact that during the initial stages of penetration the flow is unsteady. Initial values for α should be quite small when compared to the steady-state values. In the present study it was assumed initially that the edge of the plastic zone is coincident with the shock front. α was set initially to $(u_s/u)^q$, where u_s is the initial shock velocity. The constant q was adjusted so that the initial pressure in the calculation matched the cross Hugoniot pressure. This initial value was then linearly interpolated to the steady state value given by Eq. (9).

It is evident that the shortcomings in the calculation for α presented here are numerous, and is clearly an area where the model needs to be refined in the future. Nevertheless, in spite of the obvious deficiencies in this part of the model, the analytical predictions presented in the next section compared very favorably with the experimental results for the ceramic targets.

COMPARISONS WITH EXPERIMENTS

Results from the analytic model were compared and contrasted with the experimental data. Shown in Fig. 1 are analytical predictions and experimental data for projectile tail and interface positions as a function of time, for a *L/D=10* tungsten alloy (WA) projectile penetrating semi-infinite (SI) rolled homogeneous armor (RHA). Also shown in the figure are experimental results for depleted uranium projectiles penetrating semi-infinite RHA. The initial length of the projectile in each case was 79 mm. The analytical predictions were based on the momentum balance given by Eq. (4), which assumed the target material was perfectly plastic. Agreement between the analytical predictions and the experimental data is quite reasonable and well with the experimental scatter.

Comparisons were also made between the analytic model and experimental data for WA projectiles penetrating aluminum oxide targets. Shown in Fig. 2 are tail and interface positions for a WA *L/D=10* projectile penetrating SI 99.5% pure Al_2O_3 (AD99.5, manufactured by Coors Ceramics). The initial projectile length was shortened slightly to 71 mm in the analytical prediction to account for erosion of the penetrator in the cover plate, which was located outside the ceramic. The predictions shown in the figure are based on Eq. (4). Several analytic predictions are shown for various yield strengths, ranging from 6.03 GPa (the Hugoniot elastic limit for AD99.5) to 1.51 GPa. It is apparent from the figure that the analytical predictions are not consistent with the experimental data. When the yield strength in the target is adjusted to match the penetration data at early times, excessive projectile erosion occurs at later times.

The results presented in Fig. 2 were then repeated using an analysis based on Eq. (8), which assumed the yield stress varied linearly with pressure. Shown in Fig. 3 are analytical predictions for the projectile tail and interface positions for various values of β. Most of the experimental data appears to match the analytical predicted values quite reasonably when β was set to 0.75.

To develop a better understanding of the influence the constitutive model has on penetration characteristics, it is useful to examine the velocity profiles. In Fig. 4 the projectile tail and interface velocities are shown as a function of time for β=0.75. The tail velocity v exhibits deceleration features similar to those observed in many other analytical and numerical calculations of long-rod metallic projectile penetration into SI targets [6]. The penetration velocity u, however, exhibits peculiar characteristics that are a consequence of the assumed constitutive model. At early times the penetration velocity decreases quite rapidly, followed by a short time interval where u actually increases, succeeded by a long interval exhibiting a steady, gradual decay in penetration velocity. The reason for the increase in u at early times is apparent upon examination of Fig. 5. In the figure the interface pressure, target resistance, and α are shown as a function of time. The target resistance R_t accounts for strength as well as lateral confinement in the target, and may be calculated from the stress distribution as

$$R_t = -2\int_{z_i}^{\infty} \frac{\partial \sigma xz}{\partial x} dz. \tag{11}$$

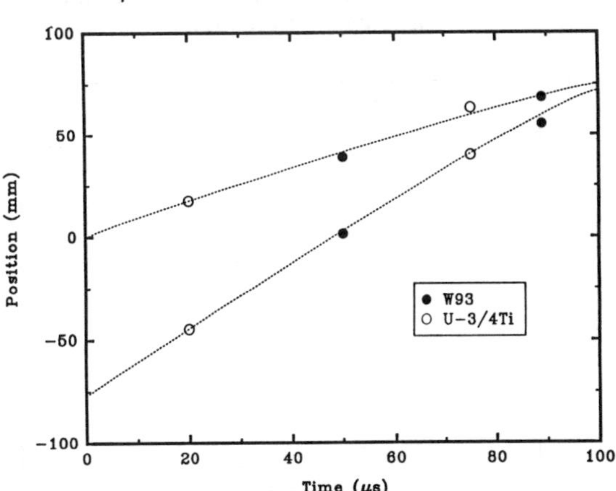

Fig. 1. Position vs. time for WA projectiles penetrating SI RHA.

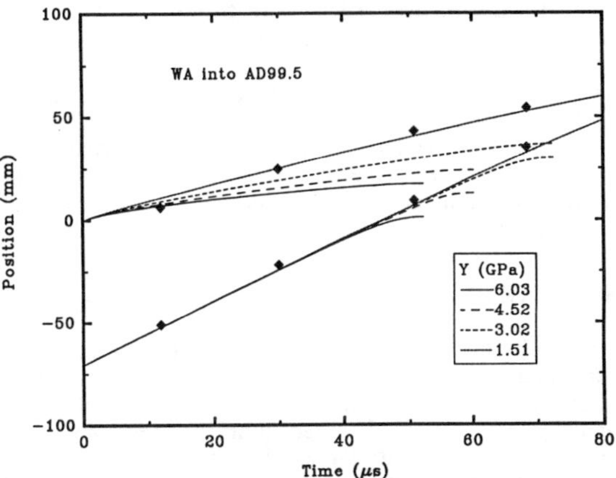

Fig. 2. Position vs. time for WA projectiles penetrating SI AD99.5.

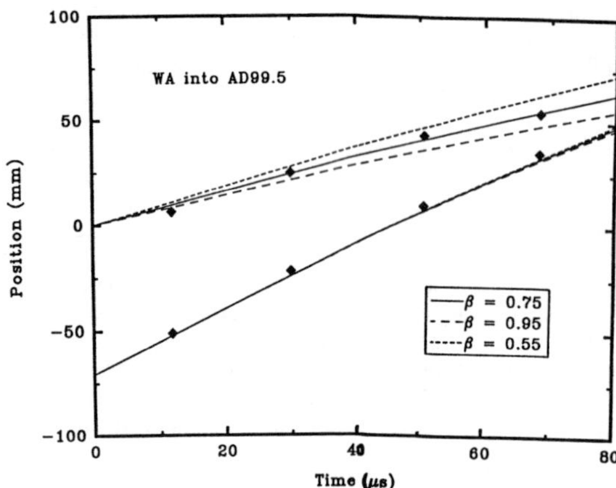

Fig. 3. Position vs. time for a WA projectile penetrating SI AD99.5.

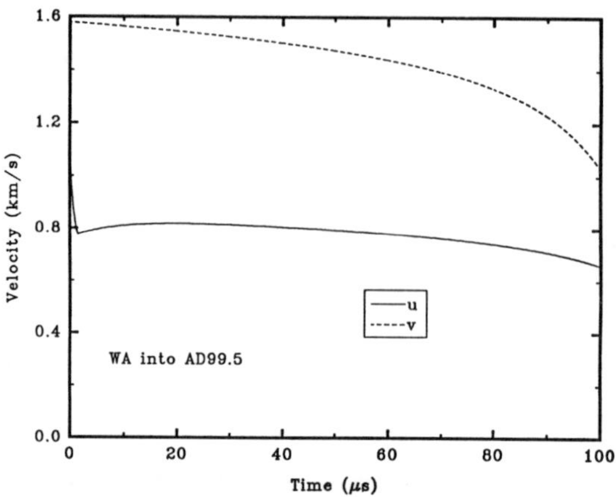

Fig. 4. Projectile tail and interface velocity vs. time for a WA projectile penetrating SI AD99.5. The value of β was 0.75.

The values of R_t and p at early times are quite large, resulting in the rapid decrease in u observed in the first few microseconds. R_t and p then diminish suddenly to their quasi steady-state values. Inertial effects associated with this decrease result in the gradual increase in u over the next 20 microseconds.

SUMMARY

Results from an analytic penetration model have been compared with time-resolved experimental data for tungsten rods penetrating steel and aluminum oxide targets. The model was augmented to account for the constitutive behavior in the ceramic target. Several shortcomings and necessary refinements to the model were identified. Nevertheless, model predictions based solely on known material properties exhibited penetration characteristics that compared favorably with the experimental results.

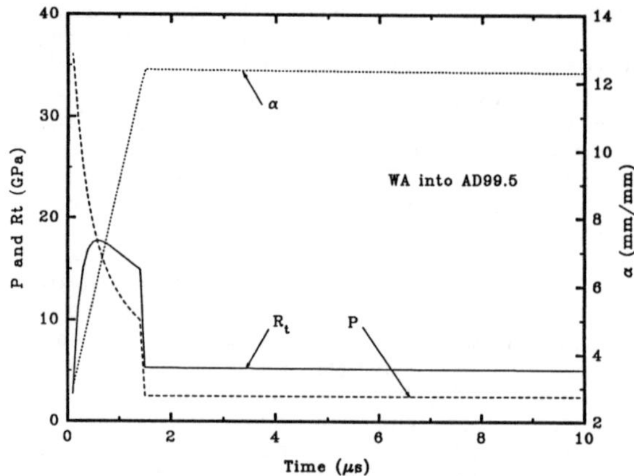

Fig. 5. R_t, p and α vs. time for a WA projectile penetrating SI AD99.5. The value of β was 0.75.

ACKNOWLEDGEMENTS

A portion of this work was supported by the U. S. Army Research Office under Contract No. DAAL03-92-K-001.

REFERENCES

[1] J. D. Walker and C. E. Anderson, Jr., "A Nonsteady-State Model for Penetration," *13th International Symposium on Ballistics*, 3, TB-1/1-8, June 1-3, 1992.

[2] S. R. Skaggs, private communication, 1992.

[3] S. J. Bless, Z. Rosenberg, and B. Yoon, "Hypervelocity Penetration of Ceramics," *Int. J. Impact Engng*, **5**, 165 (1987).

[4] C. E. Anderson, Jr., and B. L. Morris, "The Ballistic Perforation of Confined Al_2O_3 Ceramic Tiles, *Int. J. Impact Engng.*, **12**, 167, 1992.

[5] Partom, Y. A., "Ceramic Armor Resistance to Long-Rod Penetration and Its Dependence on Impact Velocity", *Institute for Advanced Technology IAT.R.0017*, March 1993.

[6] C. E. Anderson, Jr., D. L. Littlefield, and J. D. Walker, "Long Rod Penetration, Target Resistance, and Hypervelocity Impact," *Int. J. Impact Engng*, (in press).

THE INFLUENCE OF THE TARGET STRENGTH MODEL ON COMPUTED PERFORATION

John E. Reaugh
Applied Physics Division
Lawrence Livermore National Laboratory
Livermore, CA 94551

ABSTRACT

We used an axi-symmetric, two-dimensional Eulerian computer simulation program to simulate the penetration of a tungsten rod with length to diameter ratio L/D = 10 into a thick steel target, and the same rod into finite steel plates of thicknesses between 0.9 and 1.3 L. We compare the perforation limit with the semi-infinite penetration depth at the same velocity (the excess thickness) when the model for target strength is constant yield stress, and when the model incorporates work hardening and thermal softening. We also compare our computed results with available experimental results, which show an excess thickness of about 1 rod diameter.

INTRODUCTION

Computer simulations of the axi-symmetric penetration of right-circular cylinders into semi-infinite targets are routinely performed, using present day computers and computer simulation programs.[1-4] These programs solve the partial differential equations of continuum mechanics. The simulation of penetration depth is typically accurate to within 10% when compared with experiment. For a given velocity in the range 1-2 km/s, the target strength and density and the projectile density are the three most significant independent parameters.[1]

Application of these programs to armor requires the ability to simulate the perforation of finite thickness targets. Experimentally, this is accompanied by fracture. Models to describe ductile and brittle fracture have been developed for these programs.[5,6] Before applying these models to perforation, we felt it important to examine the effects of the target strength description. In this way the influence of the model on the computed result can be determined.

METHOD

We used the Eulerian computer simulation program GLO, which is under development at this laboratory, to perform these simulations. We have successfully applied this program [1,7] to projectile and target interaction for a variety of projectile and target materials. As a baseline for the simulations reported here, we recorded the penetration depth as a function of velocity for a length-to-diameter ratio L/D = 10 tungsten alloy projectile into a semi-infinite steel target.

We obtain the limit velocity for finite steel targets by a method that imitates the experimental procedure. By overmatching the target, a portion of the projectile passes through. We record the velocity of this residual projectile, V_R, as a function of the impact velocity V. These velocity pairs are then fit by the functional form.[8]

$$V_R = (AV^P - B)^{1/P}$$

with the parameters A and B chosen by the method of linear least-squares for a given P. The final value of P is selected to minimize the rms deviation. We show the results for the set of calculations that used a constant flow stress for three different target thicknesses in Fig. 1. The limit velocity V_L is given in terms of the fitted parameters

$$V_L = \left(\frac{B}{A}\right)^{\frac{1}{P}}$$

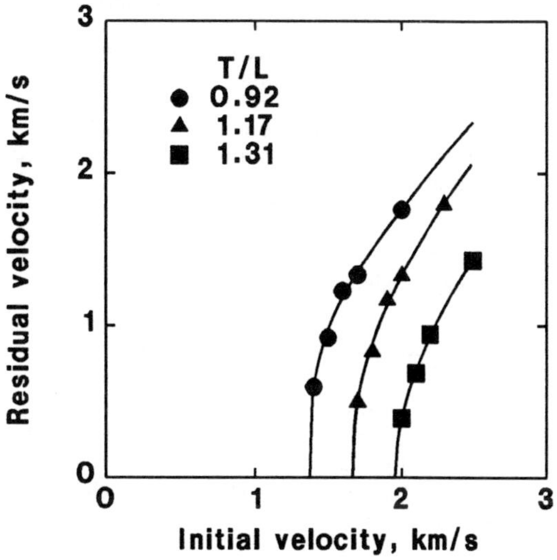

Figure 1. Computed residual velocity for three ratios of thickness T to projectile length L and fitted curves.

Perforation Without Fracture

It would seem paradoxical that a projectile could perforate a target if there were no fracture model in the computer simulation program. However, there is a tacit rupture model in GLO, and in all other Eulerian programs: if the material thins out to be less than a finite-difference zone size, it is no longer treated as intact. The details of how this happens differ in each of the programs, but they also don't matter much. When the material is stretched thin, the stress acting across the ligament is limited by the flow stress of the material. As a consequence the force transmitted across the ligament decreases with the area. With proper simulation design (i.e., small enough zones) that force will not significantly change the momentum of the residual projectile during the available time. As a consequence, refining the zone size, which would increase the time to break and effectively increase the strain at fracture, does not significantly change the residual velocity.

Material Description

We used two strength models for the target steel—constant a flow stress, and flow stress with work hardening and thermal softening.[9] With the second model, we used both the nominal value and twice that value for d(lnG)/dT where G is the shear modulus and T is temperature. (The standard model uses the same temperature dependence for both the shear modulus and flow stress.) The properties used in the simulations are given in the Appendix.

EXPERIMENTAL DATA

We use the semi-infinite and finite thickness experiments of Hohler and Stilp[10] in which L/D = 10 tungsten alloy rods were fired normally into mild steel (Brinell hardness BHN 180) and armor steel (BHN 300-360) targets. We scaled their results for penetration depth vs. velocity and thickness vs. limit velocity by the projectile length (see Fig. 2). For both steels, finite armor must be thicker to stop a given projectile at a given velocity than the penetration depth in a semi-infinite target. In the velocity range of 1-2 km/s, the average excess thickness was 1.23 $\pm$ 0.17 projectile diameters for the armor steel, and 1.06 $\pm$ 0.26 for the mild steel. The relatively large uncertainty is due to the subtraction of two nearly equal values with independent uncertainties.

COMPUTER SIMULATIONS

We fit the semi-infinite penetration depth results (Table 1) to a quadratic in impact velocity, and obtain the excess thickness by evaluating that fit at the limit velocity and subtracting from the finite plate target thickness. The results are given in Table 2.

From those data we observe that the steel 1 and 2 models show significantly larger excess thickness than the steel 0 model, but that all values are less than 1 diameter. In contrast, the experimental results of Hohler and Stilp show excess thickness of more than 1 diameter.

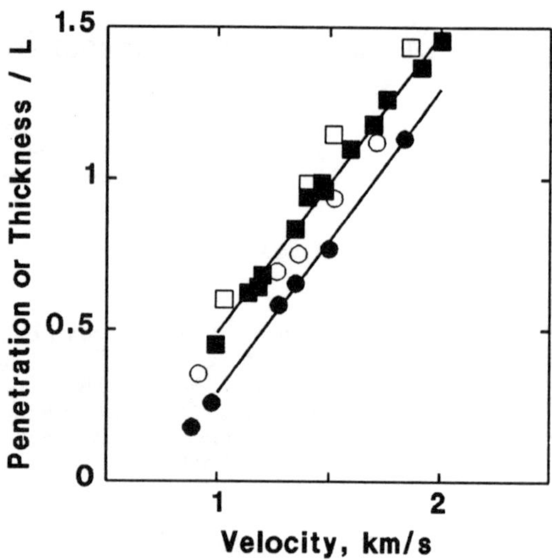

Figure 2. Experimental results[10] for semi-infinite penetration depth (filled) or limit velocity (open) for armor steel (circle) and mild steel (square).

ANALYSIS OF RESULTS

By including thermal softening in the target model, the strain localizes, which reduces the force on the projectile residue as it exits the target. For a given thickness, then, the strain localization results in a higher residual velocity.

However, the strain localization in our simulations is more like a membrane thinning than plugging, which is a lower energy deformation mode.[6] As a consequence, the target continues to exert a force on the projectile longer than it would if a plug formed.

IMPLICATIONS FOR FURTHER RESEARCH

Our simulations used models for the flow stress that are intrinsically susceptible to strain localization. Despite that, there was no evidence of any tendency toward plugging. Instead, the back surface bulge thinned and eventually localized, but only after significant stretching had occurred.

Apparently, in order for plugging to occur in our simulations, the material must fracture early near the cavity, and the fracture must initiate the strain localization that leads to plugging. If, however, the object of the simulations is to determine the residual penetration capability of the projectile residue, then a simpler method of artifically introducing a plug[6] may suffice.

Table 1. Computed semi-infinite penetration depth for L = 76.2 mm, D = 7.62 mm tungsten rods in steel.

	Velocity, km/s			
Model	1.3	1.6	1.8	2.2
Steel 0	60.1 mm	81.7	91.5	103.7
Steel 1	51.1	71.8	82.7	96.5
Steel 2	52.7	73.7	84.1	98.2

Table 2. Computed excess steel thickness for L = 76.2 mm, D = 7.62 mm tungsten rod.*

Target Strength Model	Thickness mm	Limit Velocity, km/s	Semi-infinite Penetration Depth, mm	Excess Thickness, mm
Steel 0	70	1.37 ± .005	65 ± .2	4.1 ± .3
	88.9	1.67	85.2	3.7
	100	1.95	97.7	2.3
Steel 1	70	1.49	64.7 ± .1	5.3
	100	2.19	96.3	3.7
Steel 2	70	1.47 ± .003	65.4	4.6
	100	2.09	95.3	4.9

*The uncertainty in the excess thickness is from both uncertainty in the fit to semi-infinite penetration and uncertainty in the fit to limit velocity.

SUMMARY

The strain localization that occurs with either a constant yield stress or with work-hardening and thermal softening is insufficient to cause a projectile to perforate with plugging in our simulations. Instead the rear surface bulges and thins before separation occurs. As a consequence, the computed excess thickness for perforation is only about 0.5 diameters. Experimental data for armor steel show the measured value exceeds 1 diameter.

APPENDIX: MATERIAL PROPERTY PARAMETERS

The equation of state is given by

$$P = A\mu + B\mu^2 + (\gamma_0 + b\mu)E$$

where P is the pressure, E the internal energy density per unit reference volume. The variable μ is the excess density $\mu = \rho/\rho_0 - 1$. For tungsten, ρ_0 = 17.77 g/cc, A = 2.85 Mbar, B = 2.2 Mbar, γ_0 = 1.54 and b = 1.54. The tungsten shear modulus G = 1.5 Mbar, and the yield stress is 12 kbar. For steel, ρ_0 = 7.83, A = 1.59, B = 1.9, γ_0 = 1.6, b = 0.6. The shear modulus is 0.77 Mbar. For steel 0, the yield stress is 10.3 kbar. For steel 1 and steel 2, the flow-stress Y is given by

$$Y = Y_0(1 + \beta\varepsilon)^n$$

where ε is the equivalent plastic strain, Y_0 = 10.3 kbar, β = 125, and n = 0.07. This is the work hardening measured by us for 4340 steel heat treated to Rockwell hardness HRC35. The strength corresponds approximately to a Brinell hardness BHN 330.[10] Both the shear modulus and flow stress are multiplied by the function f

$$f = 1 + bPV^{1/3} - h\,[(E-E_c)/c - 300°K)] \geq 0$$

where c is the specific heat, and E_c is the energy of cold compression found by subtracting the thermal energy density on the principal adiabat from the internal energy density. See Ref. 9 for details. For steel, c = .107 cal/g/°K, b = 2.06. For steel 1, we used the nominal value of h, $3.15 \cdot 10^{-4}$. For steel 2, we used twice that value. When the temperature exceeds the melt temperature, f is set to zero. The steel 1 model results in the strength and shear modulus being half the room temperature value just before melt is reached, whereas the steel 2 model reduces both to nearly zero there.

ACKNOWLEDGMENTS

This work was performed under the auspices of the U. S. Department of Energy by the Lawrence Livermore National Laboratory under Contract W-7405-Eng-48.

REFERENCES

[1] M. L. Wilkins and J. E. Reaugh, "Computer Simulations of Ballistic Experiments," LLNL Report UCRL-95774 (1987).

[2] R. T. Sedewich, M. G. Wilkinson, "High Velocity Long Rod Impact," in *Proceedings from the 10th International Symposium on Ballistics* (1987).

[3] P. M. Holland, J. T. Gordon, T. L. Menna, A. C. Charters, *Int. J. Impact Engng* 10, 1-4, pp 241-250 (1990).

[4] C. E. Anderson, Jr., S. A. Mullin, C. J. Kuhlman, *Int. J. Impact Engng* 13, 1 pp 35-52 (1993).

[5] D. M. Norris, J. E. Reaugh, B. Moran, D. F. Quinones, Trans. ASME, *J. Engng. Mats. Tech.* 100, 3, pp. 279-286 (1978).

[6] M. L. Wilkins, *Int. J. Engng. Sci.* 16, pp. 793-807 (1978).

[7] J. E. Reaugh, "Penetration of Yawed Projectiles," LLNL Report UCRL-ID-104890 (1990).

[8] J. A. Zukas, et al., *Impact Dynamics*, NY: Wiley and Sons, ch 5, pp 201-202 (1982).

[9] D. J. Steinberg, S. G. Cochran, M. W. Guinan, *J. Appl Phys.* 51, pp. 1498-1505 (1980).

[10] C. E. Anderson Jr., B. L. Morris, D. L. Littlefield, "A Penetration Mechanics Database," Southwest Res. Inst. Report 3593/001 (1992).

PENETRATION OF L/D=10 AND 20 TUNGSTEN ALLOY PROJECTILES INTO RHA TARGETS

Yehuda Partom and Dan Yaziv
RAFAEL Ballistics Center
P. O. Box 2250
Haifa 31021, Israel

Abstract—Penetration data for high L/D projectiles show that penetration efficiency (P/L) decreases substantially even above L/D = 10. Our data, for L/D = 10 and 20 tungsten alloy projectiles into RHA steel at 1.0 to 1.5 Km/s also show this behavior. To gain insight into the mechanism causing this reduction in P/L we performed computer simulations with the PISCES 2D code. Based on these simulations we suggest that the efficiency reduction is related to plastic flow in the projectile. By introducing a strain to failure parameter (ε_f) for the projectile it is possible to reduce the decrease in P/L in going from L/D = 10 to L/D = 20 projectiles.

INTRODUCTION

It is well known and documented that penetration efficiency (P/L) decreases substantially with L/D for L/D < 10 [1]. This behavior is sometimes understood as a diameter effect [2]. With this assumption we can express penetration as a function of velocity (V), projectile length (L) and diameter (D) by:

$$P = a(V)L + b(V)D, \tag{1}$$

where V is the impact velocity. Dividing by L we get:

$$P/L = a(V) + b(V) / \frac{L}{D}. \tag{2}$$

From Figure 47 of reference [1] we have, for a tungsten alloy projectile into steel, at V = 1.5 Km/s and L/D = 3, P/L ≅ 1.2. To get an upper bound for b(V), we ignore the contribution of a(V) for L/D = 3 (estimated maximum extent of a diameter effect). Using a = 0, we get b(1.5) ≤ 1.2 x 3 = 3.6. For L/D = 20 and 32 we then get at V = 1.5 Km/s:

$$P/L\ (L/D = 20) \le a(1.5) + 0.180. \tag{3}$$

$$P/L\ (L/D = 32) \le a(1.5) + 0.112. \tag{4}$$

$$P/L\ (L/D = 20) - P/L\ (L/D = 32) \le 0.068, \tag{5}$$

which would be an upper bound for this difference if it is a result of a diameter effect.

But from Figure 48 of reference [1] we read off at V = 1.5 Km/s that this difference is as high as 0.156. We conclude that the decrease of penetration efficiency at high L/D is too high for all of it to be explained as a diameter effect. Similar data are given by other investigators but in a less explicit way. It seems that the substantial decrease of penetration efficiency with L/D at L/D > 10 has not been identified as such and has not receive attention until recently [3]. Our data for L/D = 10 and 20 tungsten alloy projectiles also show the penetration efficiency decrease effect.

In what follows we first present our experimental data and then report the results of some computer simulations, performed for the purpose of understanding the efficiency decrease effect.

EXPERIMENTAL DATA

During the past five years we accumulated data on the penetration of tungsten alloy projectiles into RHA steel in the range of 1.0 to 1.5 Km/s. Our L/D = 10 projectiles have dimensions of 80/8 mm; and the L/D = 20 projectiles have dimensions of 120/6 mm, both with a hemispherical nose. Our results of penetration efficiency as a function of impact velocity are shown in Figure 1. Also shown are three straight interpolation lines. Line a is a fit to L/D = 10 data taken from reference [4]. Lines b and c are fits for our L/D = 10 and 20 data, respectively. The line equations are given in the figure caption. At 1.5 Km/s we get P/L (b) - P/L (c) = 0.18 which is a decrease of about 20%. Again, this is too large to be explained as a diameter effect. It is also too large to be explained by differences in tungsten alloy properties of the two projectiles.

SIMULATIONS AND DISCUSSION

To understand how penetration efficiency decreases with L/D at high L/D we ran computer simulations with the Euler processor of the PISCES 2D wavecode [5]. We ran the same configuration as in our experiments, but at a single velocity of 1.4 Km/s. We obtained that penetration efficiency did indeed decrease substantially when going from L/D = 10 to L/D = 20. Recently, some of our simulations were repeated by our colleagues [3]. They found

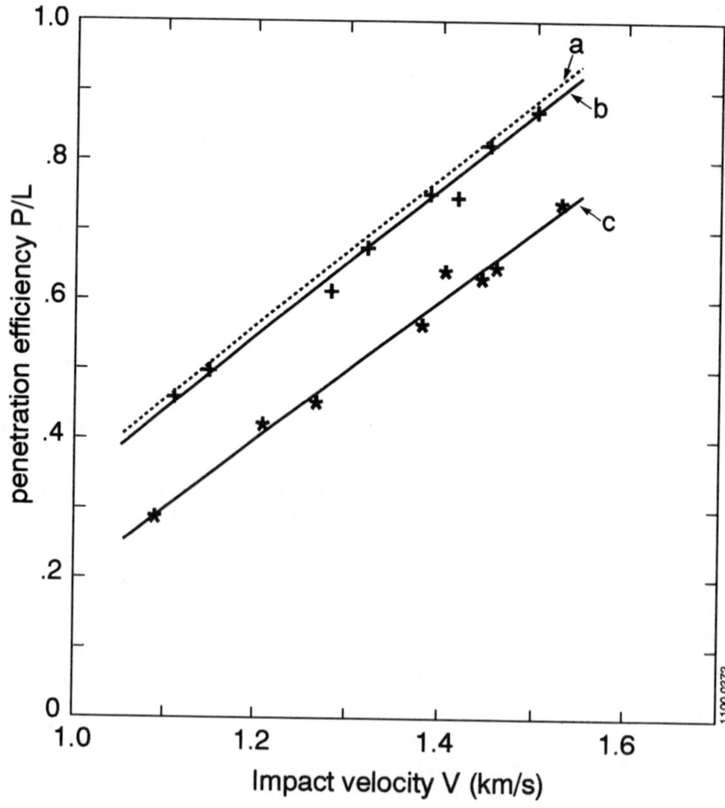

Figure 1. Penetration efficiency data and interpolation lines. + L/D = 10, * L/D = 20. a: Interpolation line from reference [4], P/L = 1.068 V - 0.716. b: P/L = 1.07 V - 0.725. c: P/L = 1.0 V - 0.8.

that we didn't have enough resolution in our simulations and because of that our results overestimated the efficiency decrease effect. In what follows we therefore use our simulations results only to indicate trends.

Observing the flow field in the simulations it seemed to us that the efficiency decrease has to do with the plastic flow of the projectile as it flows radially. To test this hypothesis we ran simulations in which we introduced a strain to failure parameter (ε_f) for the projectile. Some of our results are shown in a penetration-erosion diagram P(L) in Fig. 2. We found that as ε_f decreases, P/L increases; which shows that plastic flow in the projectile plays a role in the overall penetration process. Comparing the effect of ε_f for the two projectiles we obtained that the effect on the L/D = 20 projectile is much larger than on the L/D = 10 projectile. For ε_f = 150% the results are given in Table 1. Also given are the data from the interpolation lines in Figure 1.

Table 1. Penetration efficiency for L/D = 10 and 20 at 1.4 Km/s from simulations ($\varepsilon_f = \infty$ and 150%) and from data.

	P/L		
	L/D = 10	L/D = 20	Δ P/L
$\varepsilon_f = \infty$	0.75	0.56	0.21
ε_f = 150%	0.81	0.67	0.14
data	0.77	0.60	0.17

We see that by introducing a strain to failure of 150% for the projectile the difference in penetration efficiencies is reduced from 0.21 to 0.14. It therefore seems that by reducing the rate of plastic work in the projectile as it flows, penetration efficiency increases by a larger amount for the larger L/D projectile. By the same reasoning we conjecture that if strain hardening is introduced for the projectile, penetration efficiency decreases, and it

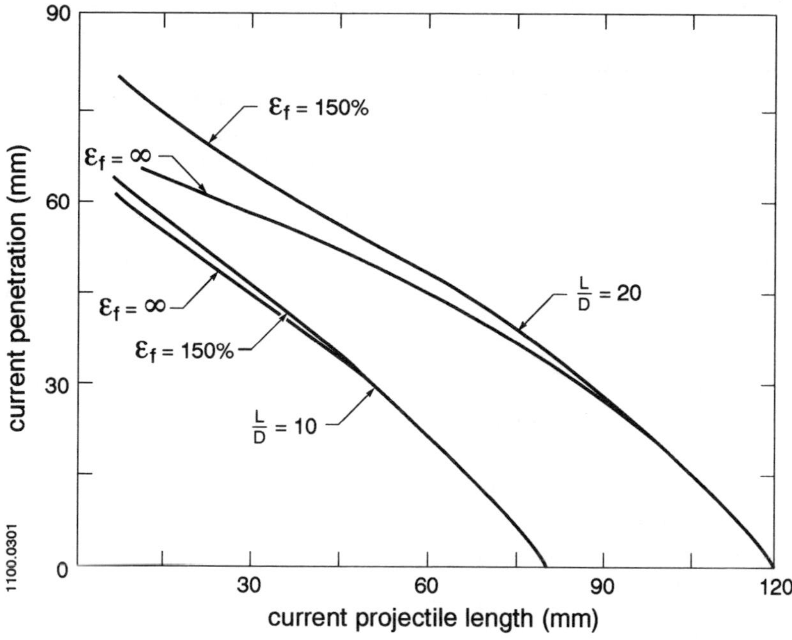

Figure 2. Computed penetration-erosion curves for V = 1.4 Km/s.

decreases by a larger amount for a higher L/D projectile. This conjecture has yet to be tested with more simulations. The increase of penetration efficiency as the strain to failure decreases is understandable. As the projectile flows radially it fails and continues to flow without resistance. It is then easier for the rest of the oncoming projectile to do work on the target. But we're not yet sure why the increase in penetration is not proportional to the projectile length. More simulation and modeling work is needed to understand this.

CONCLUSION

Available literature data and our own data show that the penetration (P/L) of long rod projectiles (L/D > 10) decreases with L/D at a rate that cannot be explained as a diameter effect. It seems that this behavior has not received attention until recently.

On the basis of computer simulations we suggest that this decrease of penetration efficiency has to do with plastic flow in the projectile. To test our hypothesis we ran computer simulations in which we introduced a strain to failure parameter (ε_f) for the projectile. This has two effects:

1. Penetration efficiency increases with decreasing values of ε_f for both L/D = 10 and L/D = 20 projectiles.

2. The increase in penetration efficiency when ε_f is reduced is much larger for L/D = 20 projectiles than that for L/D = 10 projectiles.

These results seem to support our hypothesis. More simulation work is needed to further substantiate our results and obtain insight into how they come about.

ACKNOWLEDGMENTS

The authors would like to thank the Publications and Graphics Department at the Institute for Advanced Technology, The University of Texas at Austin for assisting in the preparation of this paper.

REFERENCES

[1] V. Hohler and A. J. Stilp, *Long-Rod Penetration Mechanics, in High Velocity Impact Dynamics*, edited by J. A. Zukas, 1990, p.321 .

[2] V. Hohler and A. J. Stilp, "Hypervelocity Impact of Rod Projectiles with L/D from 1 to 32," Int. J. Imp. Engng. vol. 5, p. 323, 1987.

[3] Z. Rosenberg and E. Dekel, "The Relation Between the Penetration Capability of Long-Rods and Their Aspect Ratio," Submitted to the Int. J. Imp. Engng.

[4] C. E. Anderson and J. D. Walker, "An Examination of Long-Rod Penetration," Int. J. Imp. Engng. vol. 11, p. 481, 1991.

[5] S. L. Hancock, PISCES 2DELK Manual, Physics Int. Co., 1985.

TIME EVOLUTION OF PRESSURE FIELDS GENERATED IN IMPACT OF CYLINDRICAL PROJECTILES WITH PLATES

Anand Prakash
U.S. Army Research Laboratory
Aberdeen Proving Ground, MD 21005, U.S.A.

Three-dimensional (3-D) simulations of normal impact of 38.16-mm-long steel cylinders of L/D=6, moving at velocities of 219–876 m/s, on thin (1.59 mm) aluminum plates, which are either stationary or in lateral motion (0–160 m/s), have been carried out using the HULL code on Cray supercomputers. HULL is an Eulerian code that uses a finite difference scheme to solve partial differential equations of continuum mechanics. An elastic-perfectly plastic model was used to describe the strain response of the target and the projectile. Color-coded movies of time evolution of pressure in the system have been made from the computer output. Here, the results of the simulations are presented as graphs of time histories of the physical quantities in the rod-plate interaction.

INTRODUCTION

The rod-plate interaction, including the evolution of stress waves, involving normal impacts of cylindrical projectiles on thin plates (which are stationary or moving laterally) is investigated theoretically. It is a complex task to analytically model all features of the projectile-plate interaction physics. With the availability of modern supercomputers, large-scale problems of impact dynamics can be simulated realistically without resorting to the uncertainties of restricted modelling.

Using the Cray supercomputers, we have carried out 3-D simulations of normal impact of 38.16-mm-long steel cylinders of 6.36-mm diameter, moving at 219 m/s and 876 m/s, on a thin (1.59 mm) aluminum plate, which is moving laterally (tangentially) with velocities up to 160 m/s. The objective of our work was to find out how the projectile is affected as it perforates these plates.

THE SIMULATIONS

The simulations were carried out with the HULL code of Matuska and Osborn. HULL is an Eulerian code that uses a finite difference scheme to solve the partial differential equations of continuum mechanics. The hydro-dynamic behavior of the metals is modeled using the Mie-Grüneisen equation of state. An elastic-perfectly plastic model was used to describe the strain response of the target and projectile, with a 2.0-kb yield strength for the (2024-0 Al) plate and 3.1-kb yield strength for the (cold-rolled SAE 1010 steel) projectile. Thermal softening parameters were included. The maximum principal strain model of material failure was used. When material failure occurs in a cell, a numerically significant void is introduced in the cell by replacing the material with air which permits relaxation of the tensile forces. Subsequent recompression of the cell is permitted. Principal strain at failure was taken as 0.22 for the plate and 0.40 for the projectile. In all cases, the steel projectile was a 38.16-mm blunt cylinder of L/D=6, and the thickness of the aluminum plate was 1.59 mm.

The initial configuration of the system at the beginning of the impact is shown in Fig. 1. In the "laboratory" frame of reference, for Case I, the initial plate velocity is 40 m/s to the left (i.e., in the $-x$ direction), and the projectile is moving vertically upwards at 219 m/s. In the 3-D simulations, this initial direction of projectile velocity is taken as the positive z–axis (the positive and negative y–axis being the "fore" and "aft" directions). The problem has "fore"–"aft" symmetry so that the simulations can be done with only positive *y* values, with reflection symmetry about the *x–z* plane. However, there is no symmetry about the *y–z* plane for nonzero plate velocities. We used a 3-D Cartesian grid of 120,064 cells for this problem, with a mesh size of 0.04 cm. The simulation took 9 minutes of Gray-XMP cpu time for each microsecond of simulated (physical) time.

The problem, with the same geometry as above (see Fig. 1), was simulated for a four-fold increase in both the projectile and the plate velocity (Case II). This simulation of normal impact of the cylindrical projectile of velocity 876 m/s on the 1.59-mm-thick aluminum plate, moving transversely at 160 m/s, was carried out on a Cray-2 computer with a 3-D Cartesian grid consisting of 518,848 cells, with a mesh size of 0.0318 cm. It took 1 hour of cpu time to simulate each microsecond of physical time.

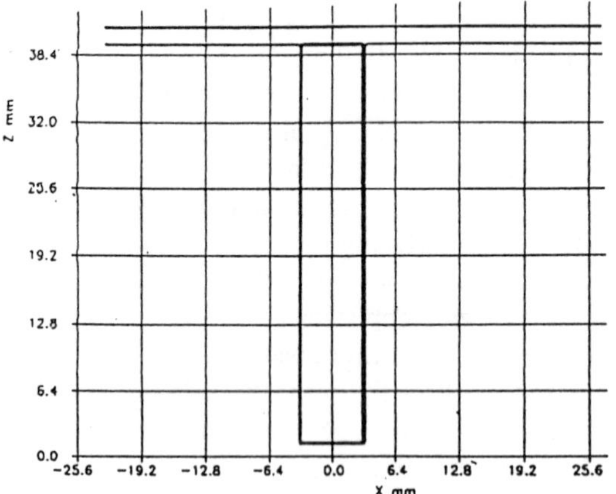

Figure 1. Projectile-plate impact at 0 μs.

Each of the previous two simulations was repeated with plate velocity set to zero (Cases III and IV).

RESULTS AND DISCUSSION

In order to study the evolution of the rod-plate interaction, density contours were plotted at an interval of a few microseconds, for Cases I and II. Figure 2 shows the process of initial plugging at 25 μs after impact, for Case I (219-m/s projectile impact velocity). Figure 3 shows the situation at 25 μs after impact for Case II. In both cases, we find that after the initial plugging, the subsequent part of the penetration process exhibits a "tearing" of the plate and transfer of transverse momentum to the projectile, a feature that does not occur if the plate were stationary.

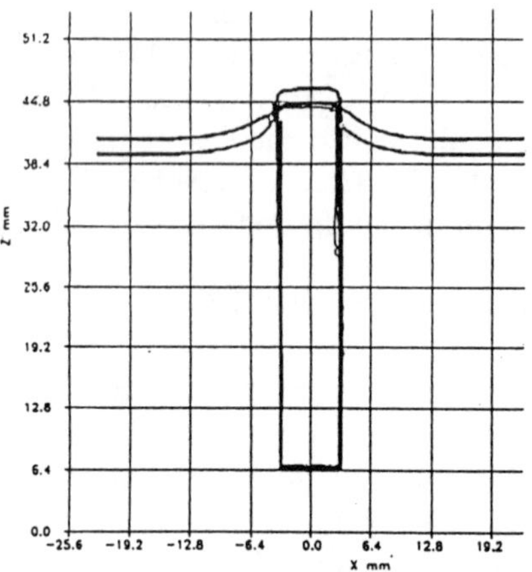

Figure 2. Case I at 25 μs after impact.

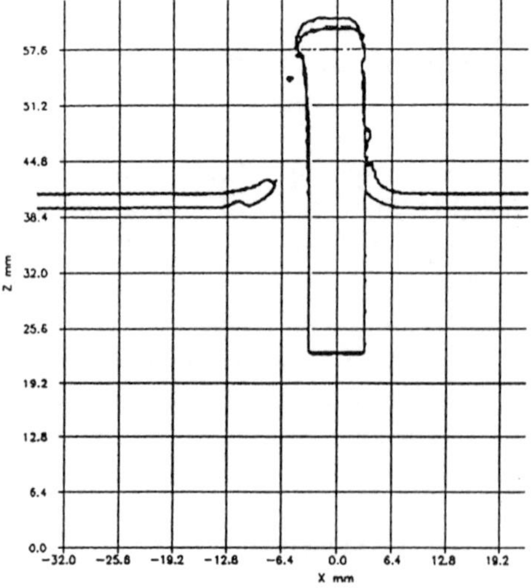

Figure 3. Case II at 25 μs after impact.

Figure 4 shows, for Case I, the time history of the vertical (*z* direction) velocity, *w*. Figure 5 shows the transverse (*x* direction) velocity, *u*, of the projectile tip, for Case II. The impact of the moving plate with the cylindrical projectile produces longitudinal waves, transverse waves, and reflected waves at material boundaries. As a material property input, the simulations used the longitudinal wave velocity in steel as 4.6 km/s. The oscillations in vertical velocity, shown in Fig. 4, with a period of approximately 16 μs, correspond to longitudinal waves induced in the projectile by the impact. Early time oscillations, seen in Fig. 4 for Case I, are produced during the process of plugging. The duration of their appearance is roughly equal to the transit time of the rod through a distance equal to the plate thickness. This nominal transit time is 7.2 μs for Cases I and III, and 1.8 μs for Cases II and IV. The compression transmitted to the plate by initial impact of the projectile is reflected as a rarefaction (tension) from the opposite (free) face of the plate, and, on reaching the rod-plate interface, it is partially transmitted into the rod and partially reflected back into the plate because of impedance mismatch at the interface. Also, lateral (radial) rarefactions emanate from the free surface of the projectile and move toward the axis. The resulting net oscillations of pressure in the rod can be seen in the time-history plots of pressure at an axial point near the tip, shown in Figs. 6 and 7, for Cases III and IV. For these cases, we also show pressure at an axial point 0.96 cm below the tip in Figs. 8 and 9.

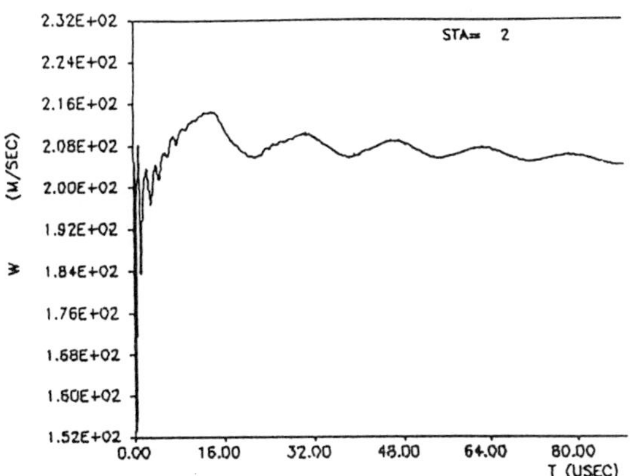

Figure 4. Vertical tip velocity, Case I.

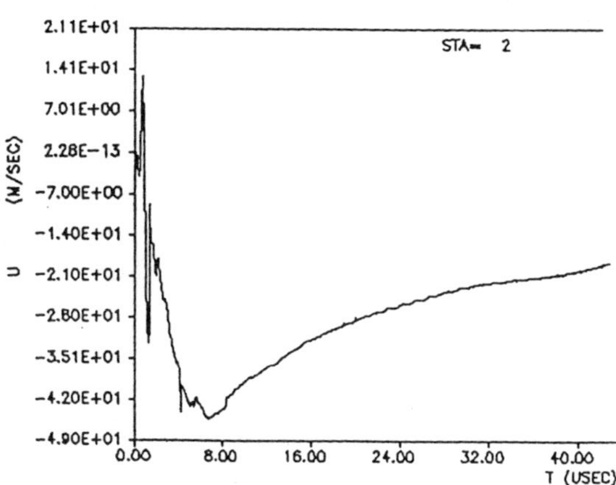

Figure 5. Horizontal tip velocity, Case II.

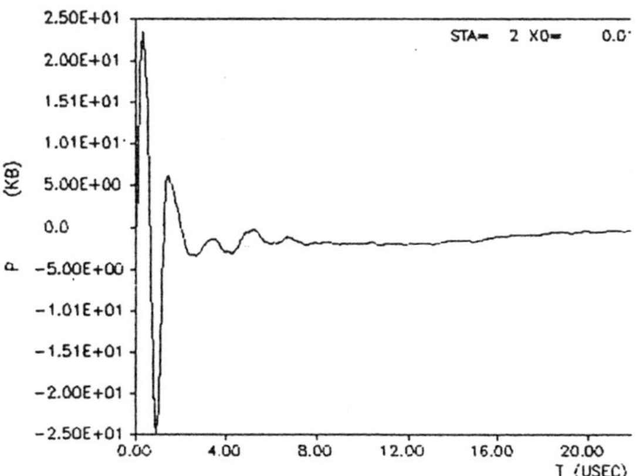

Figure 6. Tip-pressure history, Case III.

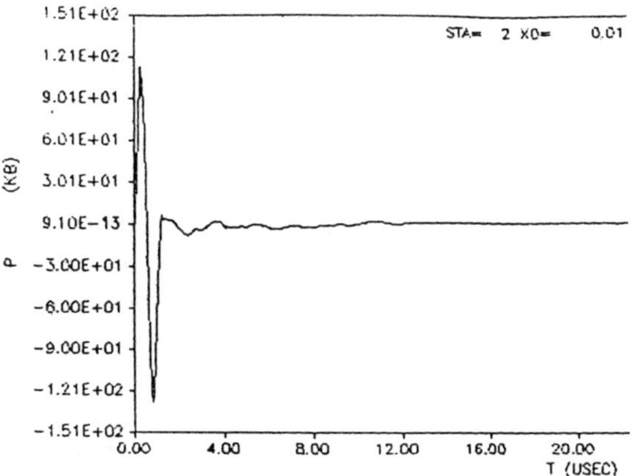

Figure 7. Tip-pressure history, Case IV.

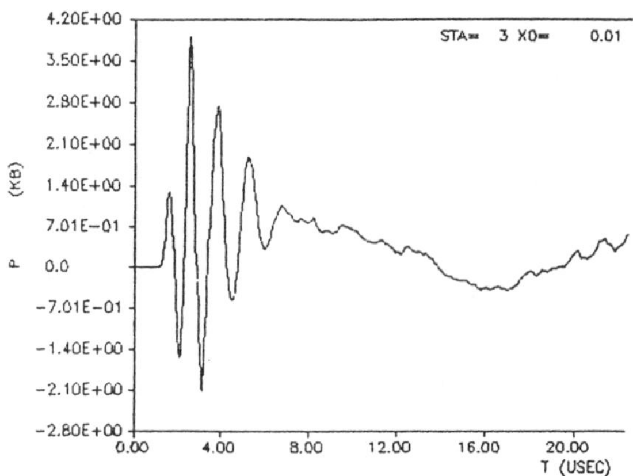

Figure 8. Pressure history at 0.96 cm from the tip, for Case III.

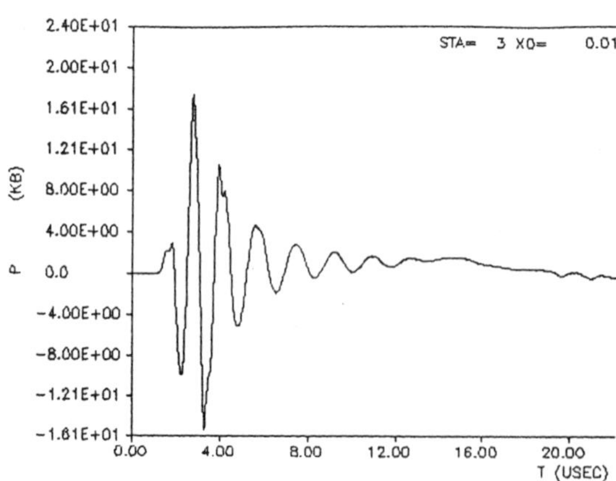

Figure 9. Pressure history at 0.96 cm from the tip, for Case IV.

Actually, the stress waves generated in the projectile are quite complicated, especially because of multiple reflections, in three dimensions, at material boundaries. Color-coded movies of time evolution of pressure have been made from the computer output. As an example, we reproduce in Fig. 10, as best as we can, a black-and-white print of the frame showing the stress wave pattern in the *y*–*z* cross-section at 3.8 µs after impact, for Case II.

Figure 10. 3.8-µs stress wave pattern, Case II.

THE PENETRATION PERFORMANCE OF SHORT L/D PROJECTILES

Charles E. Anderson, Jr., David L. Littlefield, Neil W. Blaylock
Stephan J. Bless[†], Ravi Subramanian[†]

Engineering and Materials Sciences
Southwest Research Institute
6220 Culebra Road
San Antonio, TX 78238

[†]Institute for Advanced Technology
The University of Texas at Austin
4030-2 West Braker Lane
Austin, TX 78759

The depths of penetration normalized by the original projectile length for steel, tungsten alloy, and aluminum projectiles, as a function of impact velocity have been studied to obtain scaling relationships of projectile and target densities, impact velocity, and target flow stress for relatively short length-to-diameter ratio ($L/D \le 6$) projectiles. It is demonstrated, using a fairly extensive set of experimental data, that nondimensional terms can "collapse" the data into a family of curves that differ only by the aspect ratio (L/D) of the projectiles. Regression fits were performed to provide analytical expressions for the reduced penetration efficiency in terms of the nondimensional impact terms. Finally, the results of numerical simulations and independent experiments were found to agree quite well with the regression fits.

INTRODUCTION

The penetration efficiency, defined as the depth of penetration P normalized by the initial length of the projectile L, into a semi-infinite target is a subject of fundamental interest in penetration mechanics. It has long been observed that P/L increases as the aspect ratio L/D (where D is the diameter of the projectile) of the projectile decreases; see Ref. [1-2]. However, the absolute depth of penetration is proportional to the length of the projectile. Therefore, in military applications, the emphasis has been on increasing the aspect ratio to $L/D \sim 30$. Practical armor systems have finite dimensions, with the result that a portion of the original projectile could perforate the armor system. It has been reported that the remnant projectile can contribute significantly to damage behind an armor element [3]. This remnant projectile is characterized by a residual length L_r and residual velocity V_r. It is desired to estimate the penetration capability of the residual projectile if L_r and V_r are known. The overall objective of this study was to gather existing data for short L/D projectiles and demonstrate that P/L can be estimated given L_r and V_r.

The database for heavy metal alloy projectiles impacting armor steel targets, such as rolled homogeneous armor (RHA), for low aspect ratio projectiles at relatively modest impact velocities is not particularly robust. Further, penetration is a strong function of target strength [4], and the available data are for various target strengths. The approach taken here is to use similitude modeling to form nondimensional terms, called Pi terms, that will permit a larger experimental database.

NONDIMENSIONALIZED SEMI-INFINITE PENETRATION

Experience and analytical modeling have demonstrated that the target density, projectile density, impact velocity, and target flow stress are the most important physical parameters [4-5] in determining penetration efficiency. These parameters can be formed into two Pi terms:

$$\pi_1 \equiv (\rho_p V^2/\sigma_t) \qquad \pi_2 \equiv (\rho_p/\rho_t)$$

where ρ is the density, V is the impact velocity, and σ is the flow stress. The subscripts p and t represent the projectile and target, respectively. π_1 is a nondimensional velocity, and π_2 is a nondimensional density.

Figure 1 depicts P/L versus impact velocity for $L/D = 1$ projectiles; Fig. 2 provides similar data for $L/D = 3$ projectiles. The data are from a compendium [6] of penetration data from various sources, and are for a variety of projectiles into different types and hardnesses of metallic targets. The legend indicates the projectile material (W, tungsten alloy; St, steel; Al, aluminum) impacting a target material. The number in front of the target designation gives the Brinell hardness of the target material. The letters after the target designation refer to the investigators who obtained the data: i.e., H&S, Hohler and Stilp; C&G, Christman and Gehring; AC, Alex Charters.

We will demonstrate the ability to collapse these seemingly disparate data by considering the $L/D = 1$ projectiles. First, we note that the penetration limit for hydrodynamic flow is given by the density ratio $(\rho_p/\rho_t)^{1/2}$. Much of the difference in penetration of tungsten-into-steel versus steel-into-steel can be accounted for by further normalizing the depth of penetration by this density ratio. $P/\alpha L$, where α is the square root of the density ratio, is plotted versus impact velocity in Fig. 3.

The next step is to account for target hardness. This is done by calculating the nondimensionalized impact velocity, with the flow stress given by:

$$\sigma_t\,(\text{GPa}) = 3.48 \times 10^{-3} \bullet (\text{BHN}-11.24).$$

The results are shown in Fig. 4. We have selected the exponent to be $1/3$ on this Pi term since P/L varies as $V^{2/3}$ at hypervelocities [7]. The data have collapsed quite well into a common curve; however, there is some disparity in the tungsten-into-steel versus steel-into-steel data, suggesting that all of the density dependence has not been fully accounted for in the model.

We next let the abscissa be represented by the product of the nondimensionalized velocity and nondimensionalized density. A regression analysis was performed to determine the exponent for the nondimensional density term. This was found to be approximately -0.15. The results are plotted in Fig. 5.

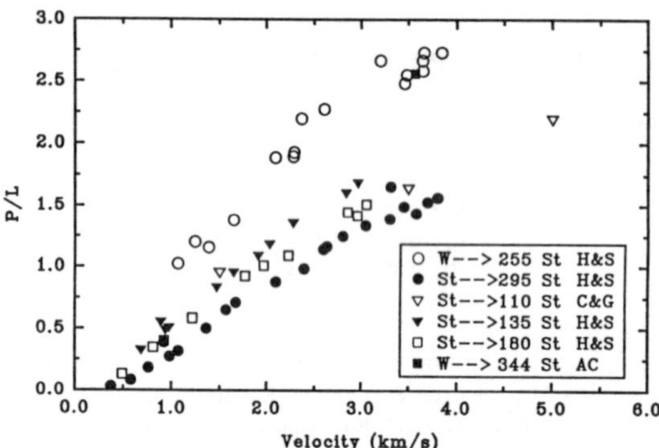

Fig. 1. *P/L* for *L/D = 1* Rods versus Impact Velocity

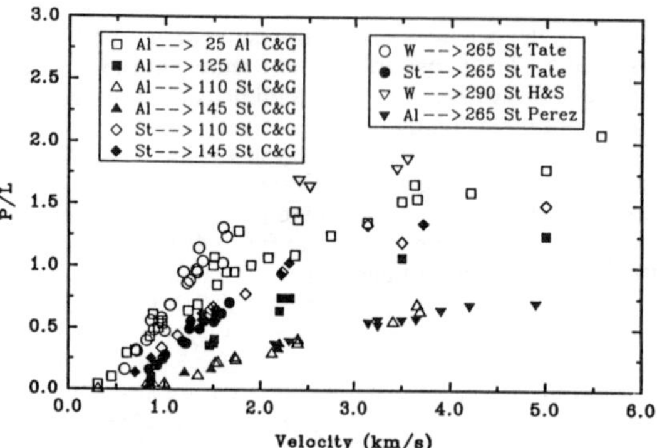

Fig. 2. *P/L* for *L/D = 3* Rods versus Impact Velocity

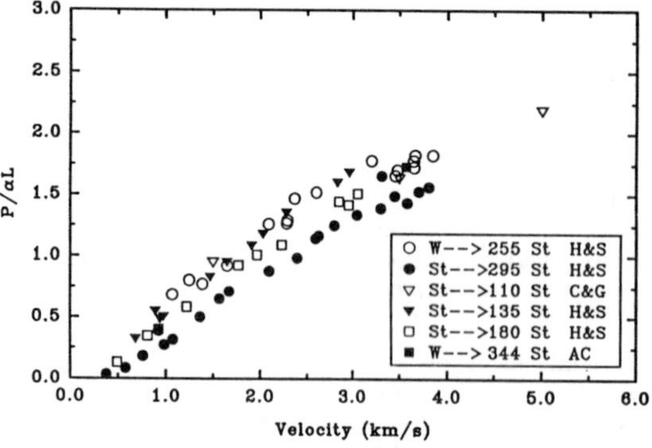

Fig. 3. *Pα/L* for *L/D = 1* Rods versus Impact Velocity

One last "adjustment" was made to a subset of the data. Christman and Gehring [2] used very soft targets in many of their experiments. In general, their data do not agree with the data of other researchers when the data are plotted in the nondimensional coordinates used here. If we assume that these very soft materials strain harden disproportionally to their initial flow stress, then a larger σ_t should be used in the denominator of the nondimensionalized velocity. The 110 BHN steel was changed to an effective 220 BHN steel; the arrows show the "movement" of the data points in Fig. 5, making these data much more consistent with the data for substantially harder targets.

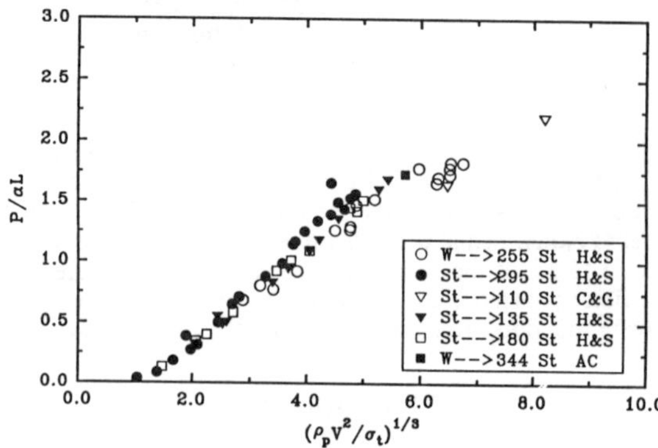

Fig. 4. *Pα/L* for *L/D = 1* Rods versus $\pi_1^{1/3}$

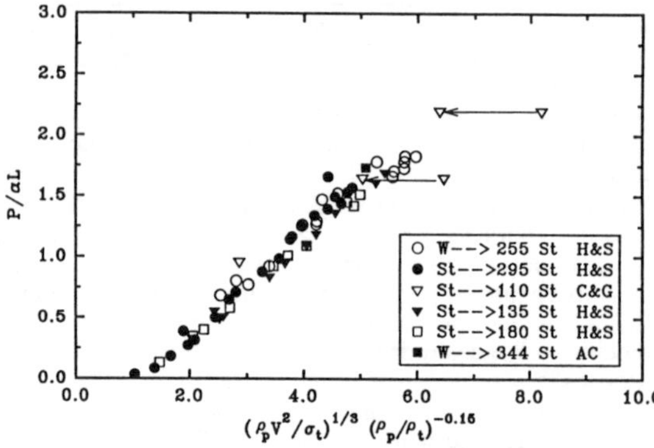

Fig. 5. *Pα/L* for *L/D = 1* Rods versus $\pi_1^{1/3}\ \pi_2^{-0.15}$

Similar analyses were performed on the *L/D = 3* and *L/D = 5 and 6* data. (There were so few *L/D =5* and *6* data that they were combined into a single data set.) The same exponents found for the *L/D = 1* case were used for the two Pi terms in the abscissa. The results are depicted in Figs. 6 and 7. Again, a "strength" adjustment was used on the very soft targets used by Christman and Gehring (110 BHN and 145 BHN steel were modified to become 220 BHN steel, and 25 BHN aluminum was modified to 50 BHN aluminum; all other hardness values were used as reported).

ANALYSIS

Two types of least-squares regression fits were made to the data using the Pi terms of Figs. 5, 6, and 7. First, a regression fit was done in order to represent the data over the entire parameter space (all impact velocities):

$$x \equiv \pi_1^{1/3}\pi_2^{-0.15} \equiv \left(\frac{\rho_p V^2}{\sigma_t}\right)^{1/3}\left(\frac{\rho_p}{\rho_t}\right)^{-0.15} \quad (1)$$

$$\frac{P}{\alpha L} = a + b\,x \quad (2)$$

$$\ln\left(\frac{P}{\alpha L}\right) = a + \frac{b}{x\sqrt{x}} \quad (3)$$

$$\ln\left(\frac{P}{\alpha L}\right) = a + b e^{-x} \quad (4)$$

The coefficients for the regression fits are summarized in Table 1; also given are the r^2 regression correlation coefficient for each curve fit and the standard error in estimating $P/\alpha L$. Second, linear, least-squares regressions, of the same form as the linear fit for *L/D = 1* above, were performed in the nominally linear range of the data. The appropriate information, with limits of applicability, is also given in Table 1.

Table 1. Parameters for Regression Analysis.

L/D	*a*	*b*	r^2	*Eq No*	*Stand. Error*	*Limits*
1	-0.433	0.400	0.970	2	0.093	$1.0 \le x \le 7.0$
3	0.821	-6.277	0.964	3	0.080	$0.5 \le x \le 9.0$
3	-0.582	0.413	0.936	2	0.067	$1.5 \le x \le 4.0$
5&6	0.264	-16.59	0.985	4	0.041	$1.0 \le x \le 6.0$
5&6	-0.912	0.496	0.965	2	0.039	$1.9 \le x \le 4.0$

Computer simulations and results from independent experiments were used to investigate how well the regression fits might be used to estimate penetration performance as a function of impact velocity. The computer simulations were performed using the Eulerian wavecode CTH [8]. The depths of penetration for a right-circular, tungsten alloy cylinder impacting RHA targets for different velocities and aspect ratios were computed. The initial conditions and results are summarized in Table 2. Four experiments were also performed where a projectile first impacted and perforated a finite-thickness (45.72-cm thick) RHA target. *L/D = 30* tungsten alloy projectiles (17.4 g/cm^3) were used for the experiments. The projectile lengths were 49.4 and 38.3 cm for the low and high velocity experiments, respectively. Orthogonal flash X-rays were employed to obtain the residual velocity and residual length of the projectile. Separate experiments were performed, with nominally identical impact conditions, to determine the depth of penetration of the residual projectile in a RHA witness pack (σ_t = 0.88 GPa). Table 3 summarizes the experimental data.

The results of the experiments and the computations are plotted in Fig. 8. The results all lie within the data scatter. The point that deviates the most from the regression fits is the *L/D = 3*, 3.0-km/s case. This point lies within the region of the *L/D = 3* data where there exists large scatter in the data. At abscissa values greater than 5, the regression fit is controlled essentially by the soft (25 BHN) aluminum targets.

We have already noted that the forming of the Pi terms using the reported strength of the very soft targets leads to results that are not consistent with the harder targets. Although using a *modified* value for the hardness appears to be consistent with other data at lower impact velocities, it would seem that such a simple "first approach" is not adequate for the higher impact velocities.

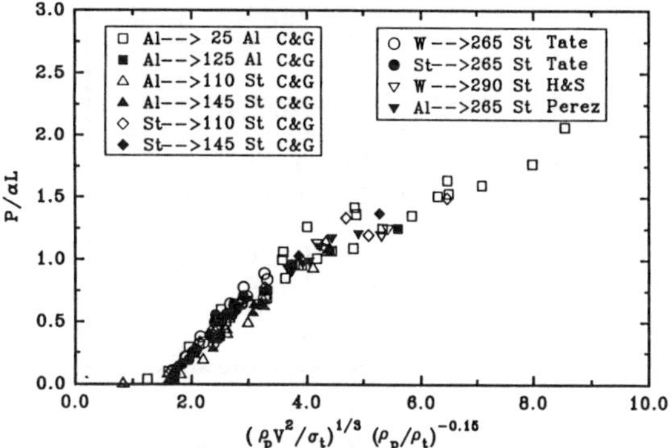

Fig. 6. ***P*α*/L* for *L/D = 3* Rods versus $\pi_1^{1/3}\,\pi_2^{-0.15}$**

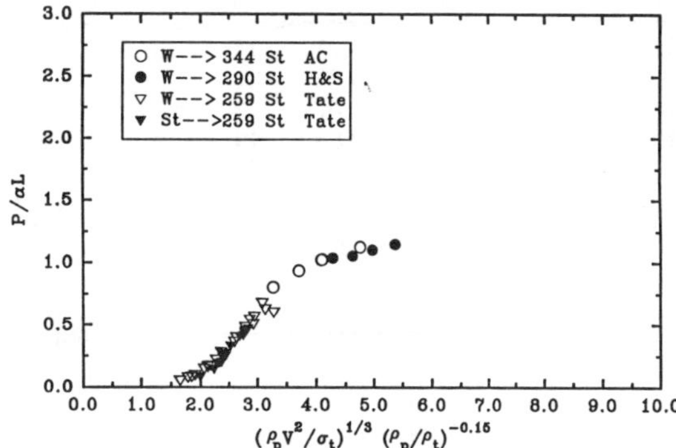

Fig. 7. ***P*α*/L* for *L/D = 5 & 6* Rods versus $\pi_1^{1/3}\,\pi_2^{-0.15}$**

SUMMARY

Penetration performance has been plotted in terms of nondimensional expressions that were formed from *a priori* knowledge of the physical parameters most important in determining depth of penetration into semi-infinite targets. We acknowledge that some other parameters that have been ignored, e.g., projectile strength, do influence penetration performance; but in general, the effects that have been ignored can be considered second-order effects. An implicit assumption in the analysis is that the impact velocities are sufficiently large that erosion of the projectile occurs during penetration. The data for relatively low aspect ratio rods have been analyzed for a fairly wide range of target strengths, projectile densities, and impact velocities. Relatively good correlation has been obtained for $P/\alpha L$ in terms of $(\rho_p V^2/\sigma_t)^{1/3}$ $(\rho_p/\rho_t)^{-0.15}$, although it was shown that the flow stress of very soft targets needs to be increased somewhat in order to bring

Table 2. Summary of Computational Results.

L/D (-)	V_s (km/s)	*P/L* (-)	*P/αL* (-)	$\pi_1^{1/3}\pi_2^{-0.15}$ (-)
1	1.3	1.143	0.772	2.848
1	1.5	1.320	0.892	3.138
1	1.8	1.500	1.013	3.538
1	3.0	2.228	1.498	4.974
3	1.3	0.977	0.660	2.848
3	1.5	1.130	0.763	3.138
3	1.8	1.383	0.935	3.538
3	3.0	1.754	1.185	4.974
5	1.3	0.872	0.589	2.848
6	1.5	1.000	0.676	3.138
5	1.8	1.283	0.867	3.538
5	3.0	1.644	1.111	4.974

Table 3. Summary of Experimental Data.

V_s (km/s)	*D* (mm)	V_r (km/s)	V_r/V_s	L_r (mm)	L_r/D (-)	*P* (mm)
1.73	16.5	1.30	0.75	77	4.67	-
1.77	16.5	1.36	0.77	82	4.97	-
1.80	16.5	1.37*	0.76*	79.5*	4.82*	69
2.53	12.8	2.23	0.88	49	3.83	-
2.57	12.8	2.26	0.88	44	3.44	-
2.59	12.8	2.28**	0.88**	46.5**	3.63**	71

* Values estimated from rows 1 & 2
** Values estimated from rows 4 & 5

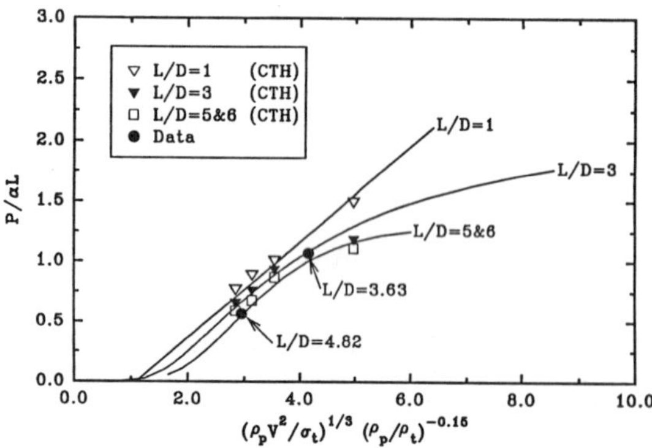

Fig. 8. *Pα/L* for versus $\pi_1^{1/3}\ \pi_2^{-0.15}$

the results of soft targets into consistent agreement with harder targets. This approach was justified by noting that strain hardening (and perhaps strain rate hardening) increases the strength of these very soft materials, relative to their initial strengths, considerably more than harder materials.

Finally, the results from numerical simulations and experiments were compared to regression fits of the nondimensionalized data. In general, these independent results agree within the data scatter. In particular, we note that the experimental results do not represent the performance of a pristine projectile; rather, the experimental results are for a rod that has undergone considerable erosion during passage and perforation of a finite-thickness target before striking a witness pack. Although not unexpected, the good agreement demonstrates that the penetration performance of a residual projectile after perforation of a target can be estimated from independent experiments that begin with an undeformed and unstressed projectile of the appropriate length and impact velocity.

ACKNOWLEDGEMENTS

A portion of this work was funded under the U. S. Army Research Office Contract DAAL03-92-K-001, and Contract DAAL03-91-C-0021.

REFERENCES

[1] V. Hohler and A. Stilp, "Hypervelocity Impact of Projectiles with L/D from 1 to 32," *Int. J. Impact Engng.*, **5**(1-4), 323-331, 1987.

[2] D. R. Christman and J. W. Gehring, "Analysis of High-Velocity Projectile Penetration Mechanics," *J. Appl. Phys.*, **37**(4), 1579-1587, 1966.

[3] P. H. Deitz and A. Ozolins, "Computer Simulations of the Abrams Live-Fire Field Testing," BRL-MR-3755, U. S. Army Ballistic Research Laboratory, Aberdeen Proving Ground, MD, May 1989.

[4] C. E. Anderson, Jr., J. D. Walker, and G. E. Hauver, "Target Resistance for Long-Rod Penetration into Semi-Infinite Targets," *Nucl. Engng. And Design*, **138**, 93-104, 1992.

[5] C. E. Anderson, Jr., S. A. Mullin, and C. J. Kuhlman, "Computer Simulation of Strain-Rate Effects in Replica Scale Model Penetration Experiments," *Int. J. Impact Engng.*, **13**(1), 35-52, 1993.

[6] C. E. Anderson, Jr., B. L. Morris, and D. L. Littlefield, "A Penetration Mechanics Database," SwRI Report 3593/001, Southwest Research Institute, San Antonio, TX, 1992.

[7] W. Herrmann and J. S. Wilbeck, "Review of Hypervelocity Penetration Theories," *Int. J. Impact Engng.*, **5**(1-4), 307-322, 1987.

[8] J. M. McGlaun, S. L. Thompson, and M G. Elrick, *Int. J. Impact Engng.*, **10**(1-4), 351-360, 1990.

IMPACT INDUCED FRACTURE OF GLASS BARS

Stephan J. Bless
Institute for Advanced Technology, University of Texas at Austin, Austin TX 78759, USA
N. S. Brar
Impact Physics Laboratory, University of Dayton Research Institute,
Dayton, OH 45469-0182, USA

Soda lime and pyrex glass bars are impacted with glass bars at impact velocities to 300 m/sec. Manganin gauges are embedded 10 diameters away from the impact face to measure stress-time profile. An Imacon camera, at a framing rate of 10^5 f/s, is used to monitor the impact induced fracture front in the bar. Glass bars fail through a fracture or failure front propagating across the cross section of the bar. The speed of the fracture front in pyrex bar is a function of the impactor velocity. The speed increases from 2.3 mm/μs, corresponding to impact velocity of 125 m/s, to 5.2 mm/μs for impact velocity of 330 m/s[1]. In two experiments a 1.6 mm thick round aluminum disk was glued on the impact face of the target bar. In the experiment on soda lime glass bar target in this configuration we observed two fracture fronts, one originating at the impact face and the other originating about 30 μs after the impact, from the gauge interface 10 diameters away, where the manganin gauge is embedded.

INTRODUCTION

There have been a number of investigations on the brittle failure of ceramic and glass bars under uniaxial stress[1-4]. In the case of alumina bars we have shown that the highest peak stress of a stable 1-d stress wave is approximately equal to its compressive strength. Cosculluela et al have obtained similar results on alumina bars[5]. We have recently reported the mechanisms of impact induced failure waves in soda lime glass plates and pyrex bars[1]. Pyrex bars fail through fracture front that propagate across the cross section of the bar. The objective of the present paper is to study the mechanisms and speeds of failure or fracture front in soda lime and pyrex glass bars impacted by glass bars.

EXPERIMENTAL METHOD AND RESULTS

Pyrex bars, 12.7 mm in diameter, were obtained from Corning Glass Works, Corning, New York. Soda lime glass bars (14 mm in diameter) were purchased from Schott America Glass and Scientific Products, Yonkers, New York. The bars, 125 mm in length, were impacted with glass bars as shown schematically in Figure 1. One-dimensional stress was measured by embedding commercially available manganin gauges
(Type C-880113-B) at 10 diameters away from the impact face. High speed framing camera (Imacon 790) was used to monitor the propagation of failure or fracture fronts. Experiments were performed using the 50-mm gas/powder gun at the University of Dayton Research Institute. Impact parameters are summarized in Table 1. The calibration of manganin gauges under shock loading was taken from References[6].

RESULTS AND DISCUSSION

The results from our study on the speed of fracture fronts in pyrex bars are shown in Figure 2[1]. We plot the position of the fracture front as function of time for three impact velocities. Fracture front velocities are 2.3 mm/μs and 5.2 mm/μs in pyrex bars when impacted with

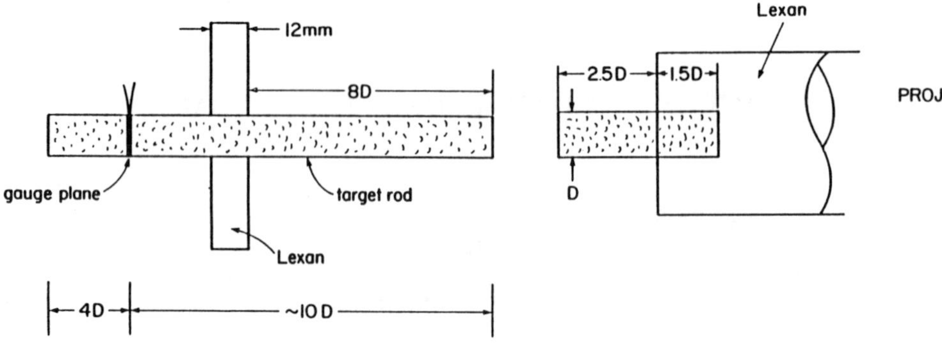

Figure 1. Schematic of experimental configurations.

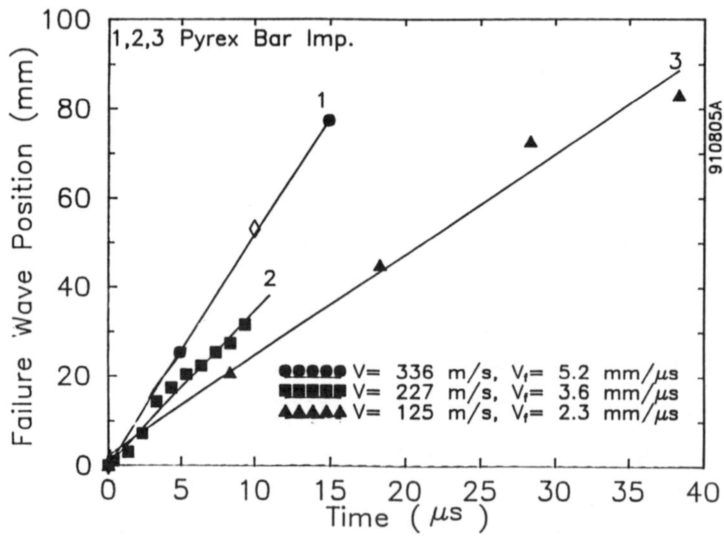

Figure 2. Fracture wave position in 12.7-mm diameter pyrex bar.

a similar bar at 125 m/s and 330 m/s. Impact stresses corresponding to impact velocities of 125 m/s, 227 m/s, and 336 m/s for the glass bar on bar tests, from impedance matching are about 8 kbar, 14 kbar, and 20 kbar respectively. This result suggests that failure wave velocity is a simple function of impact stress.

A sequence of photographs of the soda lime glass bar impact taken at 10 μs/frame in shot 7-1661 from the present experiments is shown in Figure 3. The fiducial (wire) is 25 mm from the impact face. Impact takes place in the fourth frame and the fracture front originating at the impact face propagates about 50-mm away from the impact face in the fifth frame. In frame 7 an initiation of the fracture front from the interface at the gauge location is seen. This second fracture front propagates about 40 mm towards the impact face, as seen in the eighth frame, and stops. The first fracture front propagates about 75 mm along the

Table 1. Summary of the impact data

Shot #	Impactor/ Velocity (m/sec)	Target Configuration	Peak Stress Calculated (Kbar)	Peak Stress Measured (Kbar)
7-1661	Glass bar / 210	1.6 mm aluminum disk+125 mm soda lime glass bar +gauge+50 mm glass bar	14	9
7-1733	Glass bar / 208	125 mm glass bar+gauge+50 mm soda lime glass bar	14	*
7-1734	Pyrex bar / 204	1.6 mm aluminum disk+125 mm pyrex glass bar+ gauge+38 mm glass bar	13.5	8.4

* Not measured

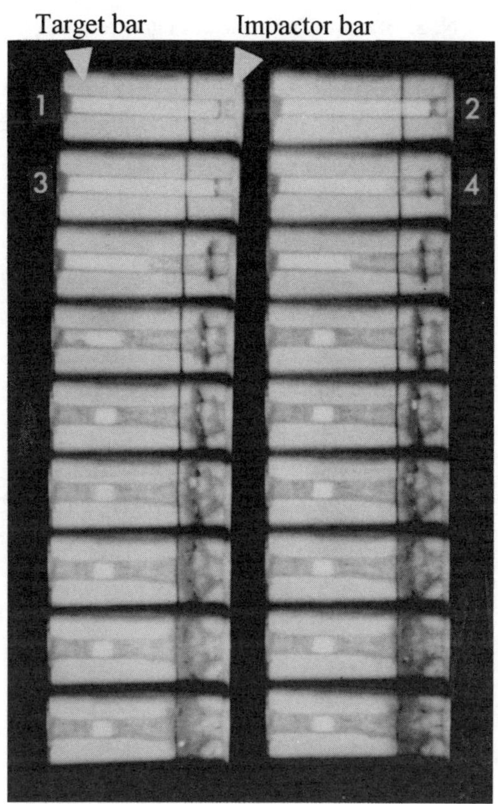

Figure 3. Framing camera pictures of a fracture front in a 14 mm diameter soda lime glass bar on impact with a bar at 210 m/s. Frame are numbered sequentially and are 10 μs apart.

bar and stops as well. A 20 mm long segment of the target bar remains intact through out the observation time of 160 μs. Manganin gauge profile from this shot is shown in Figure 4. Unloading of the stress wave takes place from the far end of the 50 mm bar. This profile corresponds to a peak stress of 9 kbar, whereas the calculated stress assuming one-d stress condition is 14 kbar.

A sequence of photographs of the pyrex bar impact in shot 7-1734 taken at 10 μs/frame is shown in Figure 5. Impact takes place in the 3nd frame. The fracture front originating at the impact face propagates about 60 mm, as seen in the sixth frame, and stops there. In the eighth

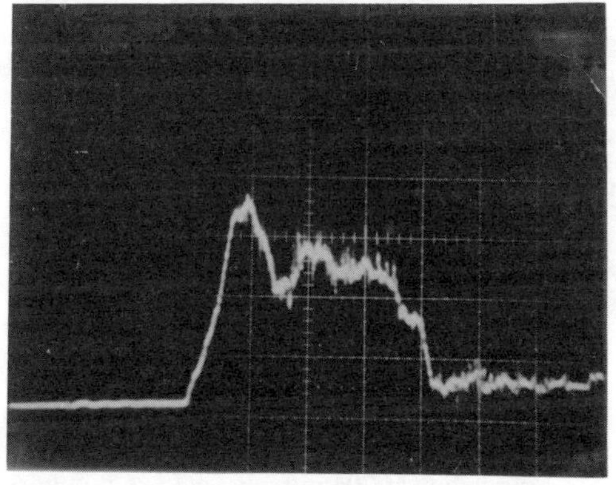

Figure 4. Manganin gauge profile shot 7-1661; (0.1 v/div, 5 μs/div).

frame we see that the whole bar is fractured. It appears that between seventh and eighth frames, second fracture front originates at the gauge interface and propagates towards the first fracture front. These two fracture fronts meet and the whole bar is fractured.

We do not fully understand the cause for the origin of the second fracture front, but Kanel[7] has an indirect evidence of such a fracture taking place in glass plate targets. More experiments are needed to investigate the phenomenon for the origin of the second fracture.

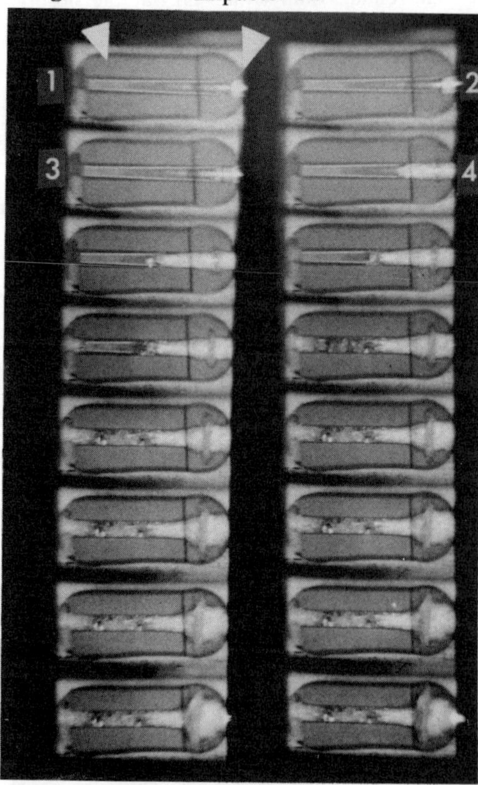

Figure 5. Framing camera pictures of a fracture front in a 12.7-mm diameter pyrex bar on impact with pyrex bar at 204 m/s. Frame are numbered sequentially and are 10 μs apart.

ACKNOWLEDGMENTS

This work was supported by the Army Research Office under Contract DAAL-03-88-K-0203 and the U. S. Army Aramament Research and Development Engineering center. The authors would like to thank
Dr. Zvi Rosenberg for technical discussions and
Mr. Mark Laber for his help in with the experiments.

REFERENCES

[1] N. S. Brar and S. J. Bless, High Pressure Research, 10, 773-784 (1992).

[2] N. S. Brar and S. J. Bless, in Shock-Wave and High-Strain-Rate Phenomena in Materials, Eds. M. A. Mayers et al., Marcel Dekker, Inc., New York, 1041, 1992.

[3] S. J. Bless, N. S. Brar, and Z. Rosenberg, in Shock Compression of Condensed Matter-1989, Eds., S. C. Schmidt et al., Elsevier Science publishers, 939, 1990.

[4] N. S. Brar, S. J. Bless, and Z. Rosenberg, J. de Physique 49, coll. C3, suppl. no. 9, C3-607, 1988.

[5] A. Cosculluela, J. Cagnoux, and F. Collombet, in Shock Compression of Condensed Matter-1991, Eds., S. C. Schmidt et al., North Holland, Amsterdam, 951, 1992.

[6] Z. Rosenberg, D. Yaziv, and Y. Partom, J. Appl. Phys. 51, 3702 (1980).

[7] G. I. Kanel, Private Communication, 1991.

COMPUTATIONAL SIMULATIONS OF EXPERIMENTAL IMPACT DATA OBTAINED AT 7 TO 11 KM/S WITH ALUMINUM AND ZINC

Scott A. Mullin
David L. Littlefield
Southwest Research Institute
San Antonio, Texas 78228

Lalit C. Chhabildas
Sandia National Laboratories
Albuquerque, New Mexico 87185

Andrew J. Piekutowski
University of Dayton Research Institute
Dayton, Ohio 45469

A combined experimental/computational program was conducted to assess the physical characteristics of impacts at speeds above those attainable using conventional light-gas guns, but within the realm of impact encounters in space, where velocities can range from 7 to 15 km/s. A major goal of the program was to assess the capability of state-of-the-art hydrocodes to reproduce damage and loading characteristics seen in hypervelocity impacts that produce diffuse molten or vaporous debris clouds. In this study the Eulerian hydrocode CTH was used. Comparisons have been made to experiments conducted with aluminum projectiles traveling from 7.4 to 11.4 km/s. A three-stage light-gas gun launcher was used to launch 17 x 1 mm aluminum disks, and an inhibited shaped charge launcher was used to launch 20 x 5 mm aluminum rods. Additional experiments were conducted at velocities from 3.5 to 6.6 km/s using zinc. In that range, scale modeling analysis predicts that a response similar to aluminum impacting at roughly twice the velocity should be attained. Comparisons between observed experimental results and computational simulations are highlighted.

INTRODUCTION

This paper is concerned with numerical simulations of hypervelocity impacts which are of sufficient velocity to produce vaporous states in the debris cloud. A significant portion of impacts into spacecraft are likely to occur at 7 km/s to 15 km/s, which will cause engineering materials such as aluminum to melt and vaporize. This study was motivated by the need to further the understanding of material behavior under such conditions. Since current ground-based launcher facilities are almost entirely limited to striking velocities below 8 km/s, other techniques must be employed to investigate the 7 to 15 km/s velocity regime.

One method that has been successfully employed to study hypervelocity impact phenomena involves the use of dissimilar material substitution in physical experiments. This technique is known as velocity scaling, developed previously by Southwest Research Institute (SwRI) [1]. Another technique involves the use of specialized launchers. Impact velocities of 11 to 12 km/s have been achieved with launcher techniques that are currently restricted to rather simple projectile geometries and materials: The inhibited shaped charge (ISC) launcher developed at SwRI [2] and the three stage light-gas gun hypervelocity launcher (HVL) system developed at Sandia National Laboratories [3]. A third method that has been used to study hypervelocity impact phenomena is numerical simulation using hydrocodes [4].

In this paper results from numerical simulations are compared to experiments performed using the previously mentioned techniques: a series of velocity scaling experiments performed at velocities from 3.5 to 5 km/s with zinc; an aluminum disk launched to 7.4 km/s with the HVL, and an aluminum rod launched to 11.4 km/s by the ISC. In all the experiments the projectile was impacted onto a bumper plate, with the resulting debris cloud then striking a secondary target. The ability of the hydrocode to simulate features and damage observed in the experiments was investigated.

COMPUTATIONAL DESCRIPTION OF THE PROBLEM

Hydrocode simulations of hypervelocity impact were performed using CTH [5]. CTH is a hydrocode used by many researchers in the community to solve a wide range of solid dynamics problems involving shock wave propagation. A two-step Eulerian scheme is employed in the code to integrate the conservation equations in time. The first step is a Lagrangian step, where integration of equations is performed. This is followed by an Eulerian remap step, where the distorted computational grid is restored to its original position. A wide variety of equation of state options are available in the code, which can be used to model melting and vaporization of metals and alloys. Several new strength and fracture models have also been recently implemented.

The computational grid employed in the present calculations consisted of five zones across the thin bumper plate shown in Fig. 1. Zones were square in strong interaction regions, then gradually increased in size both the radial and axial directions. The full ANEOS analytical equation of state was used to model the complete phase transitions for the materials used in the simulations. An elastic-viscoplastic constitutive model was used for material strength. A simple maximum principle stress based fracture model was employed to model material failure.

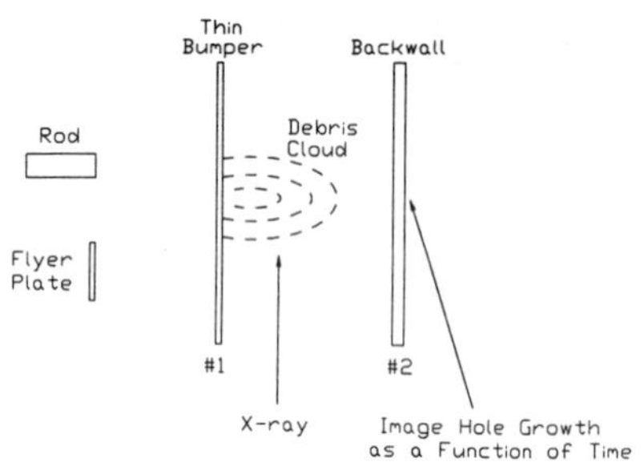

Figure 1. Experimental Impact Test Configuration.

COMPARISON TO EXPERIMENTS

Zinc Impacts into Zinc

Figure 1 depicts the setup used in the experiments. Zinc disk and rod projectiles were impacted onto a zinc bumper plate. The debris cloud generated from impact traversed an evacuated gap, then struck an aluminum 6061-T6 alloy back wall plate. Geometrical dimensions of the plates and projectiles employed in the test configuration are provided in Table 1. Three tests were numerically simulated using the hydrocode, including disk-shaped zinc projectiles impacting the bumper plate at velocities of 3.53 and 6.61 km/s, and a rod-shaped projectile striking the bumper at 4.97 km/s [6]. A previous analysis [1] employed in a velocity scaling study predicted that fully shocked zinc reaches incipient melt, complete melt and incipient vaporization states at impact velocities of 2.7, 3.4 and 4.5 km/s, respectively. Consequently, the debris cloud generated from impact in these experiments was expected to produce significant portions of molten and/or vaporous material.

In Fig. 2 an image of the debris cloud taken by flash X-ray during the experiments is presented together with the corresponding results calculated from the numerical simulations. It is evident that certain features compare favorably between the experiment and simulation, while others are different. For example, in Fig. 2a the residual rod is visible in both X-ray and simulation, and results for the length of the rod appear to match quite reasonably. The leading edge of the debris cloud exhibits slightly different characteristics in the calculation. In Figs. 2b and 2c, the central column of higher-density material that results from disk impacts is observed in both the experiments and the numerical calculations. However, the overall extent of the cloud (outer debris veil) appears to have a different geometry.

Comparisons were also made between data obtained from the experiments and the numerical simulations. In Table 1 lateral and axial positions and velocities are shown at various times during propagation of the debris cloud through the gap. The size of the hole generated in both the bumper plate and the back wall are listed at selected times. Intermediate time and postmortem hole sizes in the backwall are also given. Postmortem hole sizes listed in the table from the calculation were taken at times after which no observable deformation in the backwall occurred. Obviously this does not account for damage that might have occurred to the backwall on a millisecond or greater time scale.

Results from the table indicate that the numerical predictions for debris cloud axial and lateral position and velocity exceeded the values obtained from the experimental measurements. Furthermore, the numerical calculations predicted an axial acceleration of the debris cloud, whereas the experimental results clearly indicate the cloud velocity decreases with time. At early times, the axial velocity in the simulations exceeded the corresponding experimental values by about 5%, and at later times the disparity increases to about 20%. The result of the higher velocity is that the debris cloud positions are also larger in the numerical simulation. The hole diameters, on the other hand, compared quite favorably between the code calculations and the experiments. Disparities between the numerical and test results for hole diameter were generally less than 5%.

Aluminum Impacts into Aluminum

Experiments were also conducted with aluminum rods and disks using the HVL and the ISC. The disk and rod were launched to 7.4 km/s and 11.4 km/s, respectively. The experimental configuration is described in Fig. 1 and the corresponding physical dimensions are documented in Table 1. Debris cloud motion and hole sizes in the impacted plates were compared at selected times. Fewer data points were available for comparison with the aluminum tests as a result of the limited number of X-ray heads used in the experiments.

As was observed in the zinc impacts, numerical simulations for the aluminum tended to over-predict the debris cloud axial velocity for both projectile geometries. Calculated values for velocity were about 6% higher than the test measurements. Hole sizes reported for the bumper plate compared quite favorably. The calculated hole sizes in the backwall, however, were quite different from the test results, with the simulations under-predicting the diameter by an average of 50%.

SUMMARY

The hydrocode simulations performed with CTH tended to predict the response seen in the experiments well for most comparisons available. The simulations tended to over-predict the debris cloud lateral and axial velocity, but the disparities were not excessive. This result applies to both zinc and aluminum, and for the rod and disk shaped projectiles. A difficult task for the hydrocode is to exactly match the spread of the diffuse regions of the debris cloud because it involves mixed phase motion. The code does not properly model the flow in mixed phase regions, which might contribute to the observed discrepancies in debris cloud velocity and extent.

The size of holes measured in the bumper and back wall plates were comparable in magnitude for the zinc experiments and calculations. This was observed from the results of both projectile geometries, and at both intermediate and postmortem times. This similarity indicates that hole sizes are not overly sensitive to the discrepancies noted previously in the debris cloud lateral and axial velocities. It is also noteworthy that the zinc

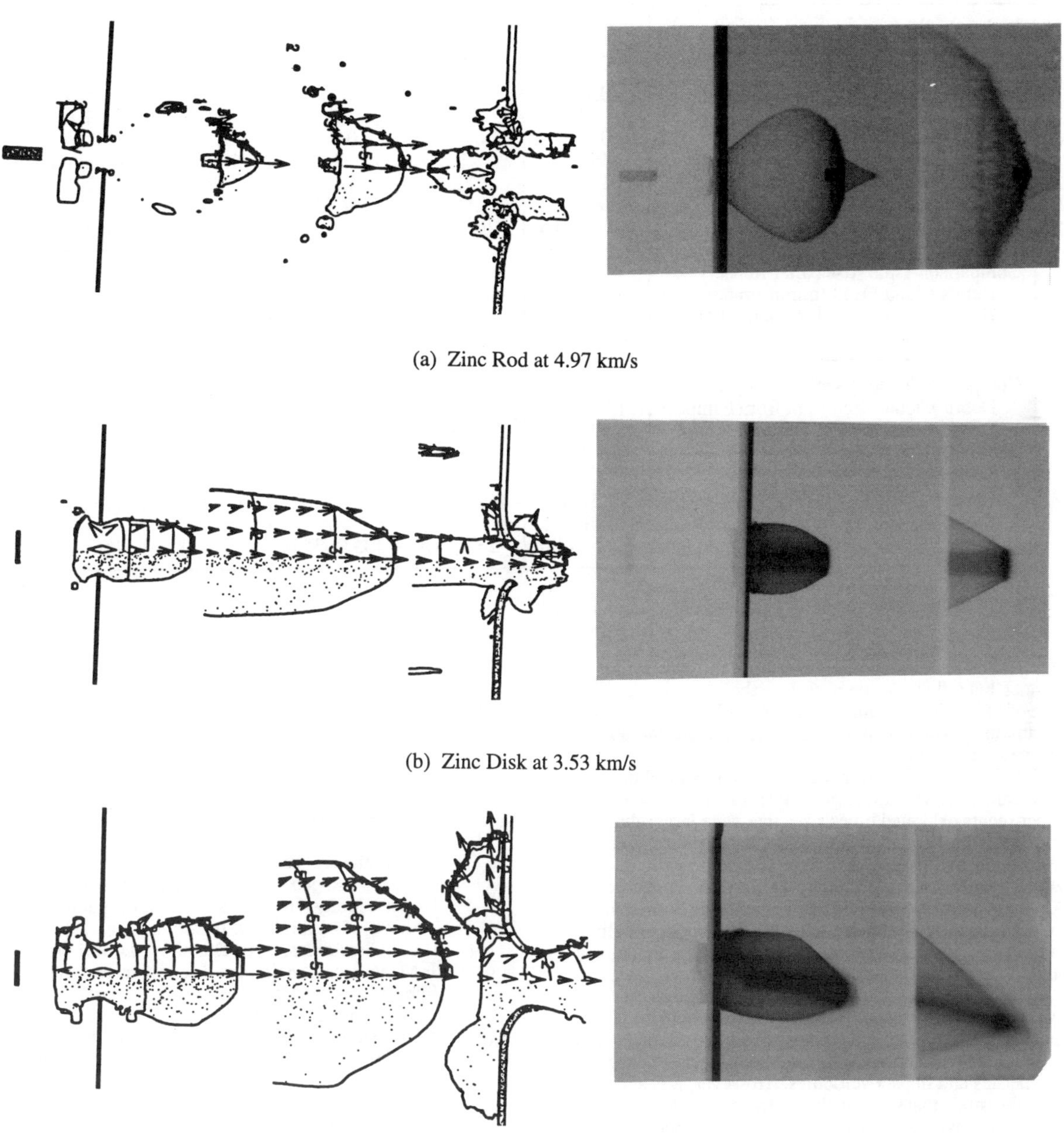

(a) Zinc Rod at 4.97 km/s

(b) Zinc Disk at 3.53 km/s

(c) Zinc Disk at 6.61 km/s

Figure 2. Comparison of Zinc Experimental Debris Cloud and CTH Calculations.

Table 1. Comparison of Experimental Data and Computational Simulations

Projectile Shape	Disk	Disk	Rod	Rod	Disk
Material	Zinc	Zinc	Zinc	Aluminum	Aluminum
Diameter (mm)	13	13	3.98	4.9	17
Length (mm)	0.759	0.759	14.15	22.2	0.92
Impact Velocity (km/s)	3.53	6.61	4.97	11.4	7.4
Bumper Thickness (mm)	0.965	0.965	0.965	1.27	1.27
Bumper Material	Zinc	Zinc	Zinc	Aluminum	Aluminum
Gap Distance (mm)	152.4	152.4	152.4	200	203
Back Wall Thickness(mm)	2.44	2.34	2.54	3.17	3.17
Back Wall Material	Al6061-T6	Al6061-T6	Al6061-T6	Al6061-T6	Al6061-T6
Comparison Time (μsec after impact)	9.2	7.0	10.5	13.6	7.5
Debris Cloud Front (mm from bumper)	[34.5]/32.0	[52.4]/53.8	[58.3]/55.4	[178.4]/164.1	[60.0]/55.8
Debris Cloud Frontal Velocity (km/s)	[3.73]/3.56	[7.67]/7.66	[5.67]/5.38	[13.4]/12.6	[7.9]/7.5
Debris Cloud Lateral Velocity (km/s)	[0.58]/0.58	[2.28]/1.32	[1.89]/1.93		
Comparison Time (μsec after impact)	30.1	16.6	25.9		
Debris Cloud Front (mm from bumper)	[112.8]/105.2	[129.6]/123.7	[150.0]/135.4		
Debris Cloud Frontal Velocity (km/s)	[3.72]/3.44	[8.21]/6.71	[6.08]/5.01		
Hole Diameters:					
Bumper (mm)	[17.5]/18.5	[19.0]/NA	[10.0]/10.0	[12]/NA	[23]/26.8
Back Wall (mm, midtime)	[11.0]/12.8	[13.0]/13.0	NA		
Back Wall(mm, postmortem)	[12.5]/14.0	[23.0]/NA	[35.0]/35.6	[15]/38	[16.5]/28

NOTE: Calculation results are enclosed in square brackets.

bumper and backwall plates did not fail in a petalling type manner, but rather in a punch-through hole type mode. This type of failure is more amenable to modeling in hydrocode calculations, which do not simulate gross material failures like petalling well.

The size of the late-time hole diameter in the aluminum backwall plates was not in good agreement, however. The experiments exhibited holes sizes that were larger than the corresponding computed values. Some of the disagreement was due to obliquity of the projectile in the experiments, which would have a tendency to produce larger holes. Another possible source of disagreement may be unrealistic failure modeling of aluminum by the hydrocode, or slight inaccuracies in the equation of state. Further computational study is required to identify the source of error.

This study has not been definitive enough to fully evaluate the performance of the equation of state or failure models for aluminum and zinc. More experiments and simulations will be required, and should include different geometries and impact velocities. However, it is apparent from this study that state-of-the-art hydrocodes can provide qualitative overall agreement for hypervelocity impact simulations that involve molten and vaporous debris clouds. For the case of zinc projectiles and bumper plates, quantitative agreement was also obtained between experiment and simulation.

ACKNOWLEDGEMENTS

The work reported in this paper was supported by Defense Nuclear Agency and Sandia National Laboratories under contract AB-6221.

REFERENCES

[1] S. A. Mullin, C. E. Anderson, Jr., J. S. Wilbeck, D. K. Apo, "Dissimilar Material Velocity Scaling for Hypervelocity Impact," *Proceedings from the Classified Session of the 1989 Hypervelocity Impact Symposium*, published by Southwest Research Institute, 1990.

[2] J. D. Walker, D. J. Grosch, S. A. Mullin, "A Hypervelocity Fragment Launcher Based on an Inhibited Shaped Charge," proceedings of the 1992 Hypervelocity Impact Symposium, published in Volume 14 of the *Int. J. Impact Engng.*, 1993.

[3] L. C. Chhabildas, J. E. Dunn, W. D. Reinhart and J. M. Miller, "An Impact Technique to Accelerate Flier Plates to Velocities Over 12 km/s," *Int. J. Impact Engng.*, **14**, 1993.

[4] E. S. Hertel, L. C. Chhabildas and S. A. Hill, "Whipple Bumper Shield Simulations," *Proceedings of the APS Topical Conference*, Williamsburg, VA., June 17-20, 1991.

[5] J. M. McGlaun, S. L. Thompson, and M. G. Elrick, "CTH-A Three-Dimensional Shock Wave Physics Code," *Int. J. Impact Engng.*, **14**, 1990.

[6] C. H Konrad, L. C. Chhabildas, M. B. Boslough, A. J. Piekutowski, K. L. Poorman, S. A. Mullin, D. L. Littlefield, "Dependence of Debris Cloud Formation on Projectile Shape," *Proceedings of the Joint AIRAPT/APS Conference,* Colorado Springs, CO., June 28-July 2, 1993.

INVESTIGATION OF ANOMALOUS PENETRATION

Robert D. Young and David L. Littlefield
Southwest Research Institute
San Antonio, TX 78238

Y. Horie
North Carolina State University
Rayleigh, NC

Numerical experiments were performed as part of an ongoing effort to understand the Russian claims of anomalous or super-deep penetration. The claim is that unusually large penetration to particle diameter ratios are obtained for a few particles when a large number of particles bombard a solid target. As a first step in this process, cumulation effects were examined to determine their potential mechanistic role in the interaction. Two-dimensional hydrocode analyses were used to simulate simultaneous particle impact into a semi-infinite target. As a consequence of the chosen axisymmetric model, impacting particles were rings, collapsing to a single sphere when the modeled particles were centered on the axis of symmetry. Results of the analysis indicate that when the distance between particle centers is nonzero, cylindrical shock waves form which have propagation components both converging to and diverging from the axis of symmetry. Energy density cumulation results due to the decreasing volume of converging shock waves approaching the symmetry axis. Numerical results show a four fold increase in shock wave amplitude at the time of convergence with respect to the shock amplitude produced at impact. Surprisingly, the amplitude of the converged shock is only a weak function of the particle distance from the symmetry axis. As a result of the convergence, a tunnel forms along the axis of symmetry which, upon release, changes phase to liquid and vapor which possesses high velocity components. This phenomenon was observed at impact velocities as low as 3 km/s.

INTRODUCTION

There have been numerous claims in the Russian literature concerning the concept of anomalous or super-deep penetration of particles into solid targets [1-3]. Conspicuous by its absence is the discussion of this phenomenon in the Western literature. As part of an ongoing effort to understand the Russian claims, computer simulations were performed to examine the interactions of multiple shock waves formed by the impact of multiple particles onto solid surfaces. Of particular interest in this investigation is the claim of Buravova [4-7], who states that super-deep penetration is a special class of the erosion damage problem, caused by the flux of particles. The claim states that channels observed in super-deep penetration are not the trajectories of particles penetrating the target, but rather the result of focusing rarefaction waves.

The model chosen to investigate this hypothesis is similar in nature to Barkhudarov's reflection of an annular shock wave [8]. Instead of producing an annular shock wave in air with a gas-discharge source that interacts with a free surface target producing an axisymmetric converging shock wave, a steel annular ring was impacted onto a copper surface. Upon initial impact, shock waves of ordinary magnitude emanated from the contact source. Degradation of the shock amplitude was observed in the direction away from the axis of symmetry, and marginally increasing amplitude in the direction toward the axis. Upon convergence of the shock wave along the symmetry axis, the amplitude dramatically increases and then inverts into a high intensity release wave causing the material in the near vicinity to liquify and vaporize.

NUMERICAL ANALYSIS

A series of numerical experiments were performed to investigate the possibility of producing deep channels with converging shock waves. The hydrocode CTH [9] was used in the simulations. CTH is an eulerian code used to investigate physical phenomena involving strong shock waves and large strain rates. A variety of equation-of-state, constitutive, reactive material and failure models are available in the code. Improvements and/or augmentations have been continually implemented as new material physical models have become available.

The geometrical configuration employed in this study is depicted in Fig. 1. A ring of steel is shown impacting a semi-infinite copper target. The cross section of the ring was circular with a diameter D of 20 μm in planes parallel to the axis of symmetry. The ring diameter normal to the axis (henceforth referred to as the major diameter) varied from 0 to 6D. This ring geometry was intended to simulate the effects of simultaneous impact of many particles in a circular arrangement. Impact velocities for the ring ranged from 3 to 5 km/s. The mesh employed in the calculation consisted of square zones 0.5 μm in length in strong interaction regions. Outside these regions the mesh size was permitted to grow at a rate of 4%. The Mie-Gruneisen equation of state was used for the steel , and the ANEOS analytical equation of state for copper. ANEOS includes models for complete equations of state in the solid, liquid and gas phases of the material, including the mixed phase and ionization regimes. A linearly elastic-perfectly plastic constitutive model was used for material strength. Fracture was simulated using a simple maximum principal stress-based model.

Shown in Fig. 2 are pressure and temperature contours for a steel sphere impacting a copper target at 5 km/s. The time was 14 ns after initial impact. This calculation represents a baseline condition for comparison with other computational results that employed converging geometries.

Pressures shown in the figure are moderate, limited to 100 GPa or less at the shock front and 1 GPa at the penetration interface. Temperature contours indicate that no phase change has taken place in the target at this time. Normally a phase change region might be expected behind the leading shock front, since a momentary pressure release occurs in this region. The impact velocity, however, was too low in this situation to initiate a phase change in the target.

When the ring major diameter is nonzero the numerical calculations exhibit striking physical features that result from the convergence and interaction of shock waves. Shown in

Fig. 3 are pressure and temperature contours for an annular ring with major diameter of 6D striking semi-infinite copper at 5 km/s. The time was 20 ns after impact. It is evident from the figure that pressures in the copper are much higher both at the shock front and behind the shock front. A 0.7Mb pressure region is evident as deep as 5.5D below the original interface. In addition, the presence of a vaporized tunnel nearly 3D in depth is evident at this time. Also present are void regions collected near the centerline of impact. These voids are a result of tensile stresses induced by jetting that occurs in a direction opposite to the penetration. Shown in Fig. 4 are velocity vectors and density contours for this ring configuration. The presence of a high velocity jet emanating from the central regions of the target is evident. The magnitude of the jet tip velocity is several km/s, and the jet is comprised almost entirely of vaporized copper.

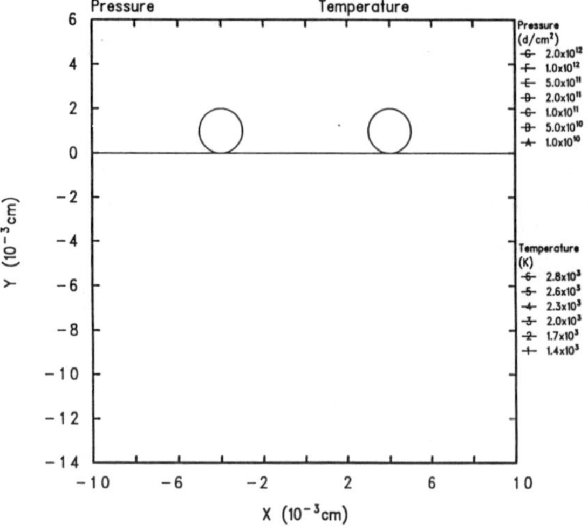

Figure 1. Geometrical configuration.

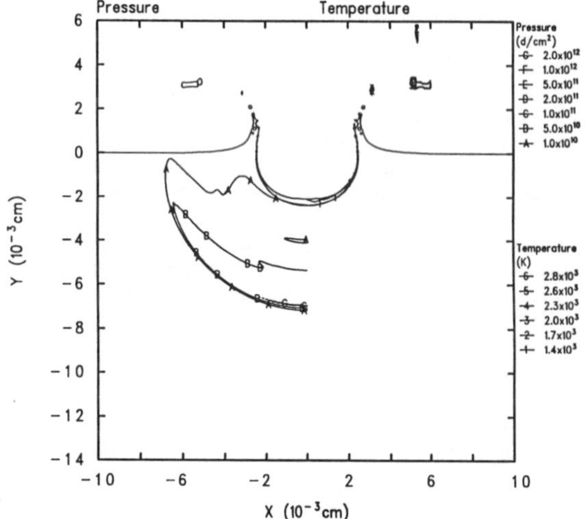

Figure 2. Pressure and temperature contours at 14 ns for a steel sphere impacting a semi-infinite copper target at 5 km/s.

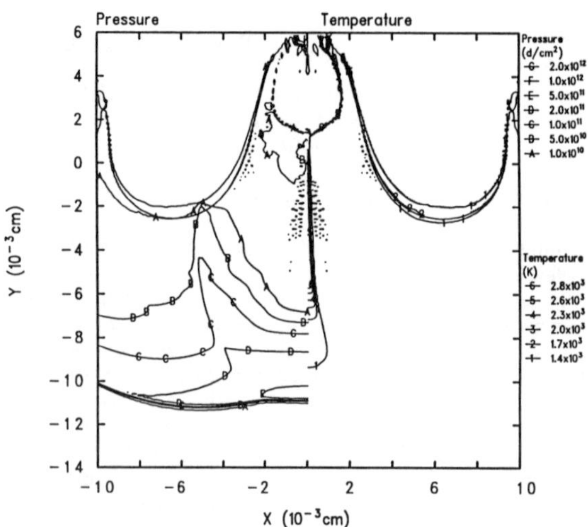

Figure 3. Pressure and temperature contours at 20 ns for a steel ring impacting a semi-infinite copper target at 5 km/s.

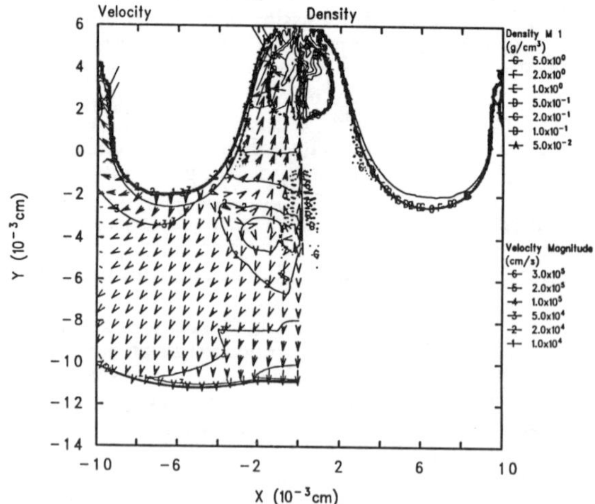

Figure 4. Velocity and density contours at 20 ns for a steel ring impacting a semi-infinite copper target at 5 km/s.

Pressure distributions along the converging axis vary appreciably as the major diameter is changed. Shown in Figs. 5a and 5b are pressure histories at several points in the target for ring impactors with major diameters of 2D and 6D, respectively. Pressures are shown at lagrangian tracer points that move with the material. When the ring diameter is 2D, the maximum pressure is about 6.3 Mb and occurs about .5D below the interface. This value is about four times higher than the baseline value observed for a sphere. It is noteworthy that the impact velocity of a sphere would have to be about 12 km/s to achieve an impact pressure in this range. At deeper depths in the target, the pressure diminishes quite rapidly.

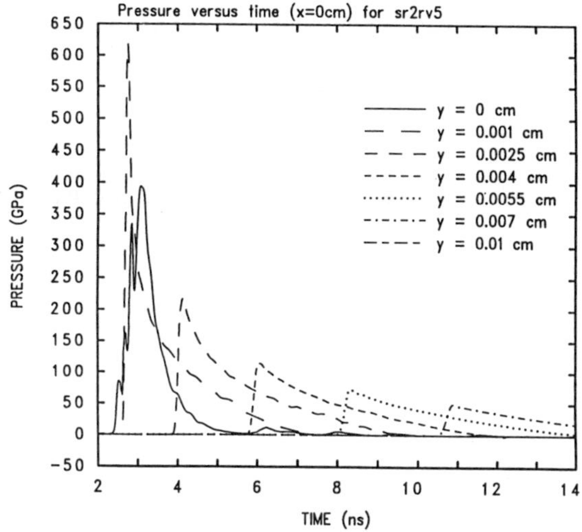

Figure 5a. Effect of ring diameter on the pressure distribution in the target: 2D.

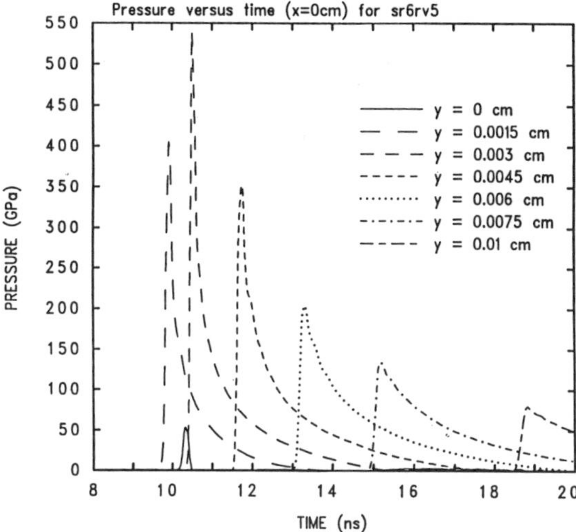

Figure 5b. Effect of ring diameter on the pressure distribution in the target: 6D.

When the ring diameter is 6D, on the other hand, the pressure decreases less dramatically with depth. The maximum pressure occurs approximately 1.5 major diameters below the original target interface. Fig. 6 demonstrates the effect ring diameter has on the state of material along the centerline. The pressure, for instance, starts out at 1.6 Mb for a sphere, then jumps up rapidly to 6.2 Mb for rings with small major diameters. Evidently, this maximum pressure stays relatively constant as the ring diameter increases, decreasing to only about 5.5 Mb when the major diameter is 6D. The location where this maximum pressure occurs and the depth of the vapor channel formed also both increase with ring diameter. Obviously the depth of the vapor channel will eventually reach a maximum and subsequently decrease as the ring diameter is increased further. Nevertheless, the calculations demonstrate that the channel depth continues to increase even at diameters of 6D.

The impact of multiple rings can also act in a cooperative manner to produce even deeper channels in the target. Shown in Fig. 7 are pressure and temperature profiles for the impact of two rings initially spaced 5D apart. The ring major diameter was 6D, and the time is 48 ns after impact. The depth of the vapor channel formed is about 5D.

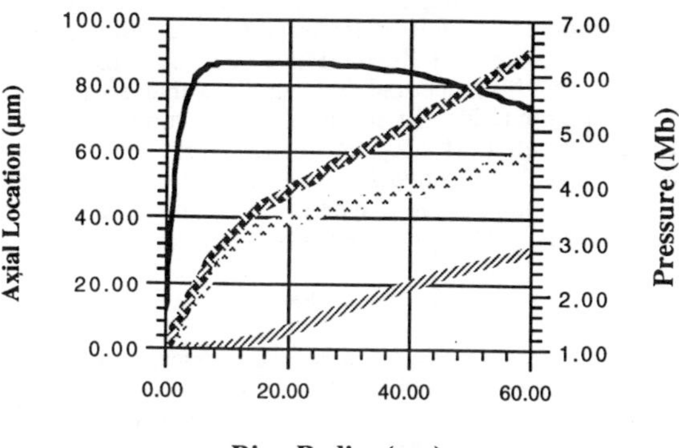

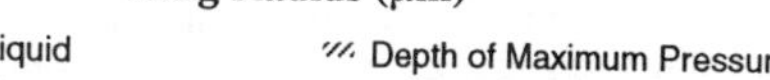

Figure 6. Effect of ring diameter on depth of liquid channel, depth of vapor channel, maximum pressure and location of maximum pressure.

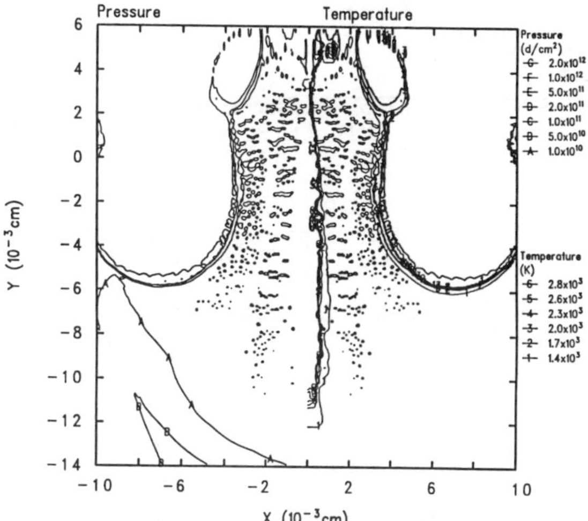

Figure 7. Pressure and temperature contours at 48 ns for two steel rings impacting a semi-infinite copper target at 5 km/s.

DISCUSSION

Although most of the computational effort in this study was performed at an impact velocity of 5 km/s, the Russian claims focus on bulk particle velocities between 1 and 3 km/s.

Statistically, however, a body of particles traveling at a bulk velocity of 3 km/s will contain some particles traveling faster. A more comprehensive look at this phenomena for lower velocities will be undertaken in the future. A surprising result indicated the presence of vaporized material along the axis of symmetry for an impact velocity of 3 km/s. The extent of the channels was not as extensive as those obtained at 5 km/s.

The calculations seem to suggest the plausibility of converging shock waves in producing deep narrow channels in copper targets along the axis of symmetry. However, the penetration to particle diameter ratios of 500 or more observed experimentally have not been demonstrated or validated by this numerical exercise. This analysis was only a first attempt to identify mechanisms that might contribute to the formation of deep channels. Moreover, it seems conceivable that the impacts of several thousands of particles could potentially act in a synergistic manner to form very deep channels. Clearly more study is needed.

CONCLUSIONS

The impact of a ring onto a surface produces a shock wave that propagates both outward and inward with reference to the axis of symmetry. Upon convergence a mach stem is formed and the pressures become extremely large enabling the focused region to undergo melting and vaporization. The radius of the impacting ring can be quite large and still show this phenomenon. As the ring radius increases, the depth below the surface at which focusing occurs also increases. Furthermore, the extent of the vaporized channel increases with ring radius. The channels left behind by this process are, in concept, similar in description to the longitudinal channels detailed by Buravova.

REFERENCES

[1] G. G. Chernyi, "Mechanism of Anomalously Low Resistance to the Motion of a Body in a Solid Medium", *Sov. Phys. Dokl*, 32, 2, pp. 168-170 (1987).

[2] S. K. Andilevko, G. S. Romonov, S. M. Usherenko, and V. A. Shilkin, "Some Superdeep Penetration Effects", *Sov. Tech. Phys. Lett.*, 16, 11, p. 864,(1990).

[3] S. S. Grigoryan, "Nature of 'Ultradeep' Penetration of Solid Microparticles into Solids", *Sov. Phys. Dokl.*, 32, 2, pp. 124-126, (1987).

[4] S. N. Buravova, "Focusing of Stress-Relief Waves and Damage to Obstacles in Particle Flux", *Sov. Tech. Phys. Lett.*, 15, 9, pp. 689-690 (1989).

[5] S. N. Buravova, "Erosive Damage of the Surface of a Solid By a Stream of Particles", *Sov. Tech. Phys. Lett.*, 16, 10, pp. 734-736, (1990).

[6] S. N. Buravova, "Scabbing Model of Erosion Wear of Surfaces Bonbarded by Particle Beams", *Sov. Phys. Tech. Phys.*, 37, 8, pp. 859-862 (1992).

[7] S. Buravova, "Surface Erosion Under Impact Action of Particles", in Shock Compression of Condensed Matter 1991, 1992, pp. 1007-1009.

[8] E. M. Barkhudarov, M. O. Mdivnishvili, I. V. Sokolov, M. I. Taktakishvili, and V. E. Terekhin, "Formation of Quasispherical Converging Implosion Shock Waves Upon the Reflection of an Annular Shock Wave From a Solid", *JETP Lett.*, 52, 7, pp. 379-382 (1990).

[9] J. M. McGlaun, S. L. Thompson, and M. G. Elrick, "CTH: A Three Dimensional Shock Wave Physics Code," *Int. J. Impact Engng.*, 14 (1990).

A SIMPLE HYDRODYNAMIC MODEL FOR JETTING FROM TUBULAR HYPERVELOCITY PENETRATORS

James R. Kamm
Geophysics Group, MS F659
Los Alamos National Laboratory, Los Alamos, NM 87545 USA

Recent experimental results of Franzen & Schneidewind [1] for impacts of tubular penetrators at 2–4 km/s show the formation of a jet of material ejected from the interior cavity of the penetrator. Using a simple hydrodynamic model based on the tubular penetration theory of Franzen [2], we calculate steady configurations of outflowing penetrator and target material. Limiting velocities of jetting material are obtained and compared with Franzen & Schneidewind's experimental data.

INTRODUCTION

Franzen & Schneidewind [1] (F & S) give a brief review of previous work on tubular penetrators. F & S present results of reverse ballistic experiments for the normal impact of tungsten, steel, and aluminum tubular penetrators with steel and aluminum targets, including radiographs of experimental impacts that show the presence of a jet of material ejected from the hollow interior of the penetrator. The jet, consisting of a high-speed precursor element followed by the main body, was not present in all experiments, a fact attributed to interaction between the jet and the penetrator inner wall.

In this work we present a simple hydrodynamic model of tubular rod penetration that is based closely on the formulation developed by Franzen [2], which we modify to allow jetting from within the penetrator cavity. From the assumption of steady, incompressible flow, we obtain values for the velocity of the jet of material that is ejected during the steady penetration process. We compare these results with the experimentally measured velocities of the precursor jet and the tip of the main jet body.

STEADY HYDRODYNAMIC MODEL

The hydrodynamic model to be considered is based on the assumption that the flow velocities are sufficiently great so that material strength effects can be neglected. With this assumption, the constant penetration velocity U_0 is related to the impact velocity V and the densities of the target ρ_t and penetrator ρ_p as [3]:

$$U_0 = V/[1 + (\rho_t/\rho_p)^{1/2}]\,. \tag{1}$$

Assuming that the penetration velocity is less than the sound speed of the target material, we model the steady penetration process as the flow of an inviscid, incompressible fluid. By a uniform translation at the penetration velocity U_0 we obtain a frame of reference in which the bottom of the crater is not moving. The side view of this steady penetration configuration above the axis of symmetry is presented in Fig. 1. We assign the penetrator outer radius to be unity, and denote the inner radius of the penetrator by μ.

Following Franzen [2], the contours of the outflowing penetrator material in Fig. 1 are identified with the subscript i for flow inside the hollow cavity of the penetrator, and the subscript o for flow outside. The widths of the layers of outgoing penetrator material, denoted by τ_i and τ_o, are assumed symmetric about the centerline curves (x_i, y_i) and (x_o, y_o). These quantities are functions of the angle β between the tangent to the local centerline of the outflowing penetrator material and the axis of symmetry, where $-\pi/2 \leq \beta \leq 0$ for flow inside the penetrator, and $0 \leq \beta \leq \pi/2$ for flow outside.

The fraction of penetrator material flowing inside the penetrator cavity is denoted q, so that the fraction flowing outside is $1-q$. Mass conservation implies that the inner and outer widths are given by

$$\tau_i(\beta) = \frac{q\,(1-\mu^2)}{2\,y_i(\beta)}\,, \quad \tau_o(\beta) = \frac{(1-q)\,(1-\mu^2)}{2\,y_o(\beta)}\,. \tag{2}$$

The contours of the outflowing penetrator material inside the cavity can be expressed as:

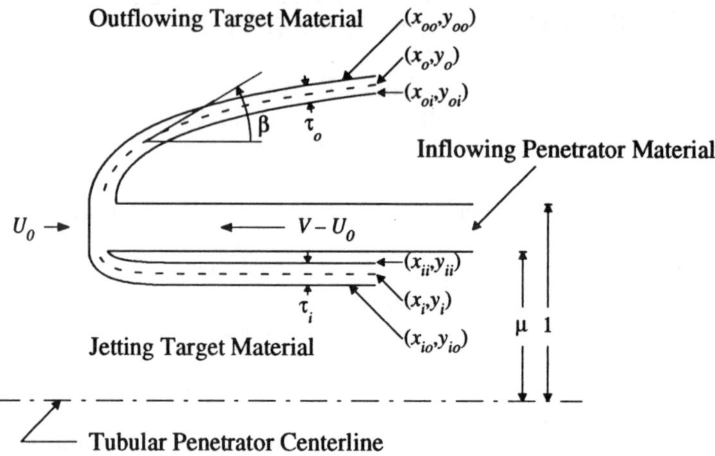

Figure 1. Side view of the impact of a tubular penetrator in the steady reference frame.

$$\left.\begin{matrix} x_{ii}(\beta) \\ x_{io}(\beta) \end{matrix}\right\} = x_i(\beta) \mp \frac{1}{2}\tau_i(\beta)\sin\beta\,,$$

$$\left.\begin{matrix} y_{ii}(\beta) \\ y_{io}(\beta) \end{matrix}\right\} = y_i(\beta) \pm \frac{1}{2}\tau_i(\beta)\cos\beta\,. \qquad (3)$$

The radius of target material flowing through the cavity assumes the value μ at the entrance, decreasing to the value μ^* infinitely far downstream. The mass fraction q of penetrator material flowing inside the cavity is given by [2]

$$q = \left[2 + p_{s,ent}/(\rho_t U_{ent}^2)\right]^{-1}, \qquad (4)$$

where p_s is the static pressure, U is the flow velocity, and ent denotes cavity entrance values.

We make the following assumption to determine the inner flow contour: in the frame of reference in which the interface between target and penetrator at the bottom of the crater is not moving, *the flow of target material into the cavity occurs at the penetration velocity, i.e.,* $U_{ent} = U_0$. This condition differs from that posited by Franzen [2], who requires that the target material flow into the cavity at an undetermined velocity (less than U_0) and reach the velocity U_0 infinitely far downstream.

The jet velocity at any downstream position is related to the local cavity radius and the inflow penetration velocity and radius as

$$U(\beta) = \left(\frac{\mu}{y_{io}(\beta)}\right)^2 U_0 \;\rightarrow\; U^* \equiv \left(\frac{\mu}{\mu^*}\right)^2 U_0, \qquad (5)$$

where the limiting value U^* is the velocity infinitely far downstream (i.e., as $\beta \rightarrow 0^-$). The static pressure p_s of the outflowing target material decreases from its initial value $p_{s,ent}$ to the value zero as $\beta \rightarrow 0^-$ according to the Bernoulli relation $p_{s,ent} + \frac{1}{2}\rho_t U_0^2 = \frac{1}{2}\rho_t U^{*2}$. From Eqs. 4 and 5, the following expressions for the pressure at the cavity entrance and for the inward flowing penetrator mass fraction are obtained:

$$p_{s,ent} = \frac{1}{2}\rho_t U_0^2\left[(\mu/\mu^*)^4 - 1\right],$$

$$q = \frac{2}{3 + (\mu/\mu^*)^4}\,. \qquad (6)$$

There are two limits for which these expressions are easily examined: (1) the "cookie cutter" limit of a tubular penetrator with a vanishingly thin wall: $\mu \rightarrow 1^-$, and (2) the solid rod limit: $\mu \rightarrow 0^+$. In the first case, assuming that the jet radius also approaches unity implies that the jet velocity reduces to the penetration velocity (i.e., there is no jetting in the laboratory frame of a zero-velocity target), the static pressure at the cavity entrance goes to zero, and half of the penetrator material flows inside the cavity. In the solid rod case, assuming that the jet radius vanishes faster than the cavity inflow radius (i.e., $\mu^* = o(\mu)$ as $\mu \rightarrow 0^+$) implies that both the jet velocity and the static pressure at the cavity entrance grow without bound, and all penetrator material flows outside of the cavity; these limiting values for the jet velocity and cavity entrance pressure are clearly unphysical, indicating that this model is inappropriate in the solid rod limit.

Following Franzen [2], we assume that the internal flow is governed by the balance between the normal force due to the dynamic and static pressures in the outflowing target material and the normal force due to the centripetal acceleration of the outflowing penetrator material. This balance is expressed in the equation

$$\frac{1}{2}\rho_t U^2(\beta)\sin^2\beta + p_s(\beta) = \tau_i(\beta)\,\rho_p\,\frac{(V-U_0)^2}{R(\beta)}, \quad (7)$$

where $R(\beta) \equiv \csc\beta\,(dy_i/d\beta)$ is the radius of curvature of the inner centerline curve. Using Eqs. 1, 2, 3, 5, and the Bernoulli relation, this equation simplifies to the following ODE for the centerline y-coordinate of the interior flow contour:

$$\frac{dy_i}{d\beta} = \frac{1}{y_i}\left[(1-\mu^2)\,q\,\sin\beta\right] \times \left\{\left(\frac{\mu}{\mu^*}\right)^4 - \frac{\mu^4\,y_i^4\,\cos^2\beta}{\left[y_i^2 - \frac{1}{4}(1-\mu^2)\,q\,\cos\beta\right]^4}\right\}^{-1}. \quad (8)$$

This equation is subject to two boundary conditions: (1) at inflow, the centerline value is the inner radius of the penetrator; and (2) at outflow, the inner contour height is the jet radius; these are expressed mathematically as:

$$y_i(-\pi/2) = \mu\,,$$
$$y_i(0) = \frac{\mu^*}{2}\left\{1 + \sqrt{1 + \left[q(1-\mu^2)\right]/\mu^{*2}}\right\}. \quad (9)$$

Eqs. 8 and 9 constitute a two-point boundary value problem for y_i with the eigenvalue μ^*. The axial coordinates of the associated flow contours are related to the radial coordinates through the geometric relation $dy_i/dx_i = \tan\beta$.

Substitution of the following variables:

$$w \equiv y_i^2, \quad \lambda \equiv \mu^2, \quad \lambda^* \equiv \mu^{*2}, \quad \xi \equiv \cos\beta, \quad (10)$$

simplifies Eqs. 8–9 to the following form:

$$\frac{dw}{d\xi} = -2\,(1-\lambda)\,q \times \left\{\left(\frac{\lambda}{\lambda^*}\right)^2 - \left(\frac{\lambda\,w\,\xi}{\left[w - \frac{1}{4}(1-\lambda)\,q\,\xi\right]^2}\right)^2\right\}^{-1}, \quad (11)$$
$$w(0) = \lambda\,,\; w(1) = \frac{\lambda^*}{4}\left\{1 + \sqrt{1 + \left[q\,(1-\lambda)\right]/\lambda^*}\right\}^2.$$

These equations can be analyzed for $\lambda \to 1^-$ (the "cookie cutter" limit). Assuming that λ^* decreases from the limiting value of unity faster than λ, we employ the following expansions:

$$w = 1 - \varepsilon\,v + \cdots, \quad \lambda = 1 - \varepsilon + \cdots, \quad 0 < \varepsilon \ll 1. \quad (12)$$

Substituting these quantities into Eq. 11 and imposing the boundary condition at $\xi = 0$ yields the following solution for the leading term:

$$v = 1 + \frac{2\,\lambda^{*3}}{1 + 3\,\lambda^{*2}}\,\log\left(\frac{1 + \lambda^*\,\xi}{1 - \lambda^*\,\xi}\right). \quad (13)$$

Analysis of the boundary condition at $\xi = 1$ implies that the expansion for λ^* is of the form

$$\lambda^* = 1 + \ell_1\,\varepsilon\,\log\varepsilon + \ell_2\,\varepsilon\,\log|\log\varepsilon| + \ell_3\,\varepsilon + \cdots. \quad (14)$$

Substituting this expression into the boundary condition at $\xi = 1$ given in Eq. 11, expanding, equating like terms, and solving the resulting equations yields the perturbation coefficients:

$$\ell_1 = \frac{1}{2},\; \ell_2 = \frac{1}{2},\; \ell_3 = -\left(\frac{5}{4} + \log 2\right) \approx -1.94. \quad (15)$$

RESULTS

An initial solution to Eqs. 8 and 9 was found using the relaxation method for a value of μ near unity with an initial guess for μ^*; other solutions were obtained by continuation in μ away from the converged solution. The results for the limiting jet radius as a function of the ratio of penetrator inner radius to outer radius are given in Figure 2. When μ approaches the "cookie cutter" value of unity, the jet radius also approaches unity; as the thickness of the penetrator wall increases, the jet radius decreases. Numerical solutions were obtained down to the value of $\mu = 0.1$; below this value, the computed limiting jet velocity is almost an order of magnitude greater than the penetration velocity, which is physically unlikely. Plotted as the dashed line is the value of μ^* computed by Franzen [2] under the assumption that there is no hydrodynamic jetting. Whereas the present model gives a nonzero limiting jet radius for tubular penetrators of all thickness ratios considered, the zero-jet assumption implies that the center cavity converges on axis for $\mu \lesssim 0.69$. The dotted line in the inset is the perturbation solution, through and including the $O(\varepsilon)$ term, for $0 < \varepsilon \leq 0.1$.

Figure 3 shows the results for the computed jet velocity normalized by the hydrodynamic penetration velocity in the laboratory frame (i.e., the frame in which the penetrator has speed V and the target is stationary) as a function of the ratio of penetrator inner radius to outer radius. There is no jetting in the "cookie cutter" limit, and the limiting jet velocity in-

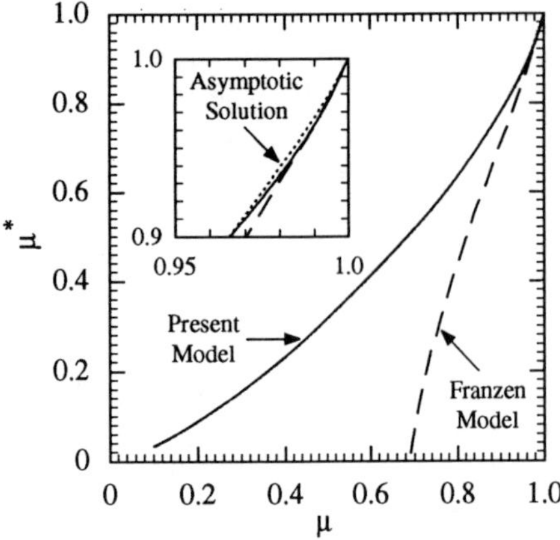

Figure 2. Computed limiting nondimensional jet radius versus the ratio of inner radius to outer radius of the tubular penetrator.

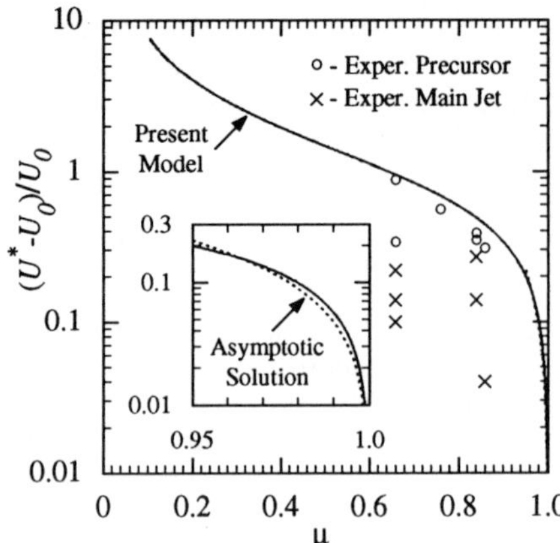

Figure 3. Computed limiting nondimensional lab frame jet velocity versus the ratio of inner to outer radius of the tubular penetrator.

Table 1. Experimental and computed jet velocities for the impact of tubular penetrators.

F & S Test #	Pen. Material	Target Material	μ	V (km/s)	U_0 (km/s)	Experimental U_{tip}/U_0	U_{prec}/U_0	Comp. U_{jet}/U_0
HT-15	W	Steel	0.84	2.17	1.33	0.26	0.35	0.49
HT-16	W	Steel	0.84	2.26	1.38	0.14	0.39	0.49
HT-17	W	Steel	0.66	2.04	1.25	0.22	0.88	0.95
HT-18	W	Steel	0.66	2.04	1.25	0.14	—	0.95
HT-24	Steel	Al	0.86	3.59	2.26	0.04	0.31	0.44
HT-25	Steel	Al	0.76	3.63	2.29	—	0.56	0.69
HT-27	Al	Al	0.66	4.00	2.00	0.10	0.34	0.95

creases as the inner radius of the penetrator decreases. The dotted line in the inset is the perturbation solution, through and including the $O(\varepsilon)$ term, for $0 < \varepsilon \leq 0.1$. Also plotted on this diagram are the experimental values [1] for the precursor velocity ($\circ$) and the velocity of the tip of the main jet ($\times$), normalized by the hydrodynamic penetration velocity computed according to Eq. 1 for the materials involved, assuming these mass densities: $\rho_W = 19.2$ g/cc, $\rho_{steel} = 7.8$ g/cc, and $\rho_{Al} = 2.7$ g/cc. The numerical values of the experimental data and the corresponding model results are presented in Table 1. The limiting jet velocities given by the model compare moderately well with those for the experimental precursor jet, which may consist of ejected target material liberated by high tensile stresses. This favorable comparison is interesting, as we have neglected the effects of compressibility and material strength, both of which play significant roles in cratering and ejecta formation. The "ballpark" agreement between the computed jet velocity and experimental precursor velocity suggests that basic hydrodynamics may provide a useful model for the jetting of material during the quasi-steady phase of penetration following the impact of tubular rods at moderately high velocities.

ACKNOWLEDGEMENTS

This work was begun when the author was at SAIC. The author thanks R. Stoughton for his support of this investigation, J. Rotenberry for helpful insights into the perturbation analysis, K. McCall for valuable suggestions on the text, and M. Scharff for the introduction to hypervelocity impact phenomenology.

REFERENCES

1. R. R. Franzen and P. N. Schneidewind, Observations Concerning the Penetration Mechanics of Tubular Hypervelocity Penetrators, *Int. J. Impact. Engng* **11**, No. 3, pp. 289–303 (1991).
2. R. R. Franzen, "Notes on Tubular Hypervelocity Penetrators," in *Proceedings of the 10th International Symposium on Ballistics*, San Diego, CA 1987.
3. G. Birkhoff, D. P. MacDougall, E. M. Pugh and G. I. Taylor, Explosives with Lined Cavities, *J. Appl. Physics* **19**, pp. 563–582 (1948).

EFFECT OF PHASE CHANGE IN A DEBRIS CLOUD ON A BACKWALL STRUCTURE [1]

L. N. Kmetyk, L. C. Chhabildas, M. B. Boslough, R. J. Lawrence
Sandia National Laboratories
Albuquerque, New Mexico 87185

The physical state of a debris cloud generated upon impact of a thin flier plate with a thin bumper depends on the impact velocity. At impact velocities of 10km/s, the debris cloud is expected to be primarily molten with some vapor present. A series of calculations using the finite-difference code CTH has been used to evaluate the effect of phase change (*i.e.*, higher concentrations of vapor) in debris clouds and their subsequent impact on a backwall structure. In these calculations, the higher concentrations of vapor is achieved by increasing the initial temperature of the impactor and the bumper material while keeping the same impact velocity. The nature of the interaction of the debris cloud and the subsequent loading on the backwall depends on its thermophysical state. This interaction (with a backwall) can cause either spallation, rupture, or simply bulging of the backwall structure. These results will be discussed and compared with an impact experiment performed at ≈10km/s on the Sandia hypervelocity launcher. In the experiment, the debris cloud was generated by the impact of a titanium plate with a titanium bumper.

INTRODUCTION

Protection sheets, commonly referred to as Whipple bumper shields, were proposed for deployment with early spacecraft. In the early sixties, these sheets were designed to protect the spacecraft from micrometeoroid debris, which is primarily dust-type 100μm-size silicate particles. It is recognized that the threat to spacecraft has progressively increased due to the abundance of man-made space-debris in the environment. The space-debris environment, also referred to as orbital debris, is presumed to be gram-mass mm- or cm-diameter metallic plate-like particles with average impact interaction velocities of ≈10km/s. The prossibility of impact on spacecraft by these heavier plate-like objects is not negligible. The requirements for an adequate bumper shield are quite demanding for a variety of reasons, including the uncertainty in the size, shape, and density of the orbital debris particulate and the high interaction velocities.

At higher impact velocities, *i.e.* at velocities in excess of 7km/s, most of the impact generated debris (from the Whipple shield) will consist of molten liquid with some vaporized material present. There is considerable speculation that, for Whipple shields to be effective, there should be a greater mass fraction of vaporized debris in the debris cloud. It is the purpose of this paper to use the results of an experiment conducted at ≈10km/s [1] to validate the use of the CTH hydrodynamics code [2] for these types of problem, and further evaluate the effect of having more vapor in the impact-generated debris cloud and of changing the density of the bumper material on the physical integrity of the backwall structure. Results of this study indicate that it is not merely sufficient to have more vaporized debris in an impact-generated debris cloud for the survival of a backwall structure; the density and relative kinetic energy of the debris also have an effect on determining the integrity (*i.e.*, the survivability) of a backwall structure.

PROBLEM DESCRIPTION

Experiment XH-9 Base Case

In the XH-9 experiment, a thin, flat flier plate impacted a thin, flat bumper shield at a velocity of 9.66km/s. The flier plate material was Ti-6Al-4V and the geometry was a circular disk 12.629mm in diameter and 0.98mm thick, with a mass of 0.529gm. The bumper shield was 0.7366mm thick, and also made of Ti-6Al-4V. The backwall was 4.0132mm thick, and separated from the bumper shield by a distance of 15.24cm. The backwall was made of 6061-T6 aluminum. More details on the experiment procedure and results can be found in [1].

Sensitivity Studies

Three different studies were done on the problem described above. In the first study, the materials, dimensions and impact velocity were left unchanged, while the initial temperatures of the flier plate and/or bumper shield were varied as shown in Table 1 (to increase the vapor content in the the debris cloud):

Table 1. Initial Temperature Variations

Case ID	Flier Temperature	Bumper Temperature
Base	300K	300K
"Hot Bumper"	300K	1923K
"Hot"	1923K	1923K
"Very Hot"	3513K	3513K

where the melting temperature of Ti-6Al-4V is 1943K and the vaporization temperature is 3533K. In the second study, the materials, dimensions and initial temperatures were unchanged, but the impact velocity was progressively increased to ≈20 and ≈30km/s. In the third study, the flier material, dimensions and the impact velocity were unchanged but the bumper shield

[1]This work performed at Sandia National Laboratories supported by the U. S. Department of Energy under contract DE-AC04-76DP00789.

material was changed to plexiglass and to cadmium. These materials were selected as lower- and higher-density materials than Ti-6Al-4V but with similar, low melt points. The thickness of the bumper shield was adjusted to maintain constant areal densities, so the cadmium bumper was 0.381mm thick and the plexiglass bumper 2.667mm thick. (The backwall was identical in all cases.)

CTH INPUT MODELS

The CTH calculations were performed using a two-dimensional, cylindrical geometry. These impact calculations were run in two stages.

The impact of the flier plate onto the bumper shield was simulated first, using fine resolution. The **x**-direction (radial) mesh was started at **x**=0, the axis of symmetry, while the **y**-direction (axial) mesh was started at **y**=-0.5cm with the initial contact surface between the flier plate and the bumper shield defined to be **y**=0. A subgrid of 400×750 0.01cm-square cells was used in an initial interaction region 8cm in diameter and 7.5cm in length (with additional cells growing at a 5% rate used outside this subgrid).

The initial impact calculation was run until the debris cloud had expanded to fill nearly the entire 400x750 square-cell subgrid which, for impacts of ≈10km/s, took ≈6μs. The material distribution at that time was then manually rezoned into a larger, coarser mesh which included the backwall. This mesh used a larger subgrid of 100×474 0.04cm-square cells in a larger, later interaction region 8cm in diameter but 19cm in length (again with additional cells growing at a 5% rate used to model further regions). This second part of the calculation was run until backwall bulging and/or rupture was predicted.

RESULTS

Base Case Results vs Experiment

Photographs from the XH-9 experiment [1] at ≈5.8μs show the leading edge of the debris cloud travelling at ≥11km/s while radiographs at the same time give a velocity of ≈10km/s; this indicates that the low-density vaporized debris front is travelling faster than the relatively higher density cloud imaged using X-rays. The base case CTH analysis predicts the leading edge of the debris cloud ($\varrho \geq 10^{-6}$gm/cm^3) to be travelling at ≈12km/s and the higher-density inner core ($\varrho \geq 10^{-1}$gm/cm^3) to be travelling at ≤11km/s, in reasonable agreement with test data.

Initial Temperature Variations

The debris cloud propagation seen in the first set of calculations (increasing the initial temperature of the flier plate and/or bumper shield) differs due to the varying amounts of molten and vaporized material produced in the initial impact. Figure 1 shows the debris cloud extent predicted by CTH at 5μs after initial impact of the flier plate with the bumper shield, for the base case problem and for the three sensitivity studies as identified in Table 1. Contours showing order-of-magnitude changes in the density are included to highlight the debris cloud internal structure.

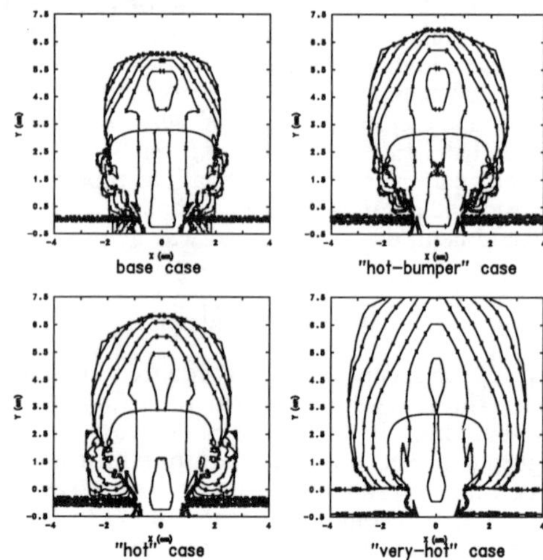

Figure 1. Debris Cloud with Density Contours at 5μs for Base Case and Initial-Temperature Variations

At 5μs after impact, the flier-plate debris consists of about equal amount of molten and vaporized material in the base case analysis; in the "very-hot" calculation, in contrast, the flier plate debris is about 67%-vapor at this time, due to the higher initial temperatures. (Note that the fraction of material molten or vaporized is estimated simply based upon the amount of material above the melt or vaporization temperature.)

The debris cloud in the base case analysis travels the slowest and has dispersed the least, while the debris cloud in the "very-hot" case travels the fastest and has dispersed the most.

As a result, the impulse imparted to the backwall is distributed differently in each of these four cases, in both space and in time, as shown in Figure 2 for a typical point in the backwall 0.25cm from the impact centerline. For all distances ≤0.5cm from the impact, the impulse is significantly higher in the base case, and most of that impulse is accumulated in a relatively brief period (from ≈12.5μs to ≈17.5μs). In the "very-hot" calculation, due to the higher fraction of vaporized material, the impulse is significantly lower and is accumulating slowly. In the two intermediate cases, the final impulse in the region ≤0.25cm from the impact centerline is ≈65-80% lower than in the base case, and is accumulated over a somewhat longer period (from ≈12.5μs to ≈22.5μs).

The final configuration of the backwall in these four cases is shown in Figure 3. The greater, more localized and more rapid impulsive loading predicted by the base case results in late-time rupture of the backwall, while the lower and slower loadings predicted by the other

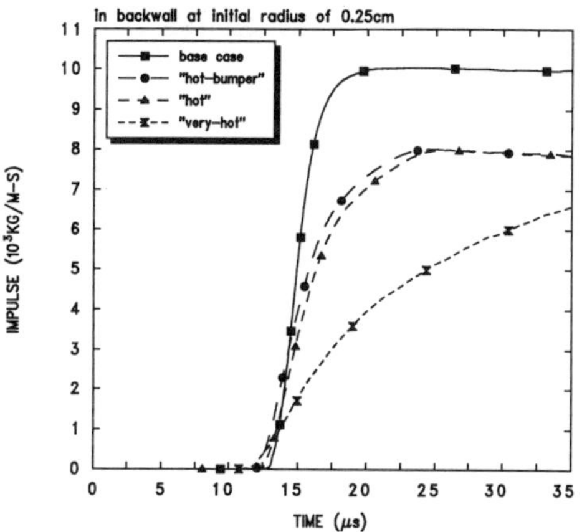

Figure 2. Impulse on Backwall for Base Case and Initial-Temperature Variations

three, elevated-temperature cases merely flex or bulge the backwall slightly.

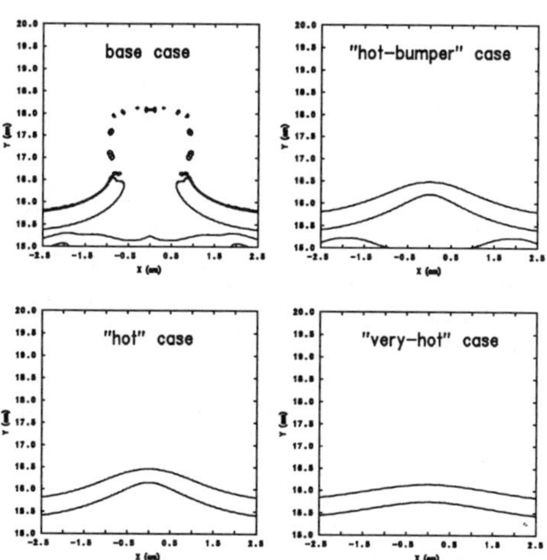

Figure 3. Backwall Configuration at 35μs for Base Case and Initial-Temperature Variations

Impact Velocity Variations

An alternate way to generate more vaporized material in a debris cloud is to have the initial impact occur at higher velocities. Figure 4 shows the debris cloud resulting from a ≈20km/s impact at a time (2.5μs) corresponding to the debris cloud at 5μs in the base case ≈10km/s impact. The flier plate material in this debris cloud is ≈78% vapor, compared to ≈50% vapor in the basecase. However, since the leading edge of the vapor is travelling much faster in this case, it does not have sufficient time to disperse the debris as efficiently as in the initial-temperature variations. Therefore, a greater impulse is imparted to the backwall more rapidly for higher initial impact velocities, as shown in Figure 5 for a typical point in the backwall.

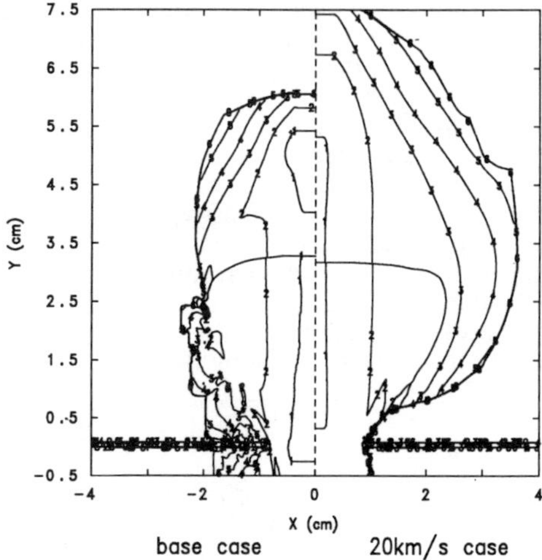

Figure 4. Debris Cloud at 5μs for ≈10km/s Impact (Base Case) and at 2.5μs for ≈20km/s Impact

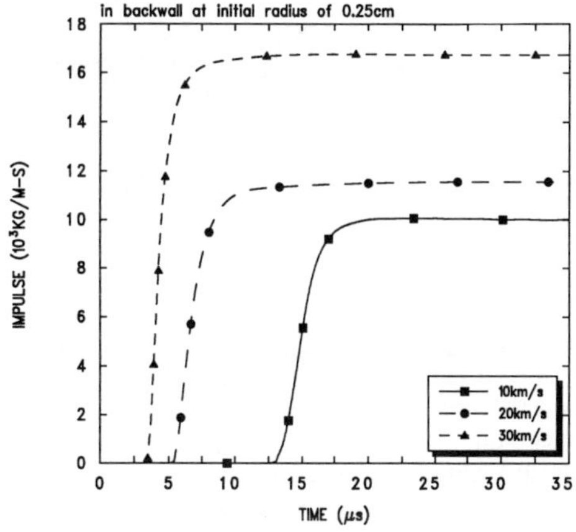

Figure 5. Impulse on Backwall for Base Case and Impact-Velocity Variations

Thus, although the thermal state of debris clouds resulting from higher-velocity impacts may be such that more vapor is present, the debris cloud has sufficient concentrated kinetic energy to rupture the back wall. The diameter of the resulting hole was predicted to be

2.06cm and 3.10cm, respectively, for initial impact velocities of ≈20km/s and ≈30km/s, compared to a final hole diameter of 1.25cm in the base case analysis.

Bumper Material Variations

Figure 6 shows the debris cloud structure predicted at 5μs assuming equal-mass bumper shields made of cadmium and plexiglass instead of titanium alloy. At the time shown, the debris cloud produced by impact with a thin, high-density, cadmium bumper has propagated slightly further both radially and axially and is slightly more spherical in shape than the debris cloud in the base case analysis; the debris cloud produced by impact with a thick, low-density, plexiglass shield has propagated much further axially and is much more elongated. With the cadmium shield, ≈55% of the flier material is vapor at this time (compared to ≈50% in the base case). With the plexiglass bumper, almost all of the flier material is molten by this time.

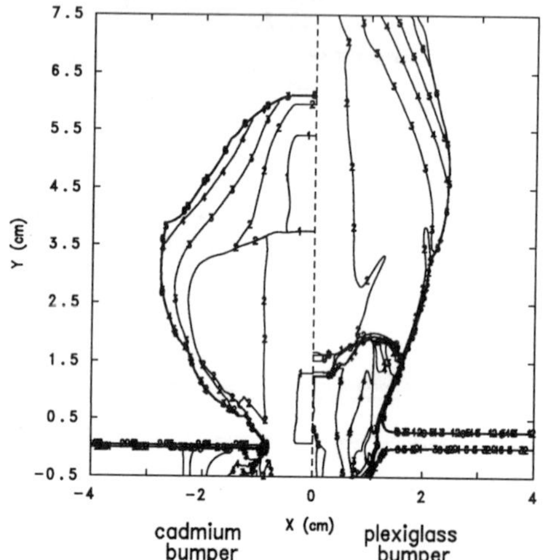

Figure 6. Debris Cloud with Density Contours at 5μs for Bumper-Material Variations

The more-rapidly expanding debris cloud generated by impact with a plexiglass bumper reaches the backwall earliest, while the leading edges of debris clouds generated by impacts with titanium and with cadmium shields arrive at about the same time, as shown in Figure 7 for a typical point in the backwall. All of these debris clouds have enough concentrated kinetic energy to rupture the backwall, with the hole size roughly proportional to the impulse loading delivered to the backwall in each case (as would be expected). The diameter of the resulting hole was predicted to be 1.75cm and 1.05cm, respectively, for the cadmium and plexiglass bumper shields, compared to a final hole diameter of 1.25cm in the base case analysis.

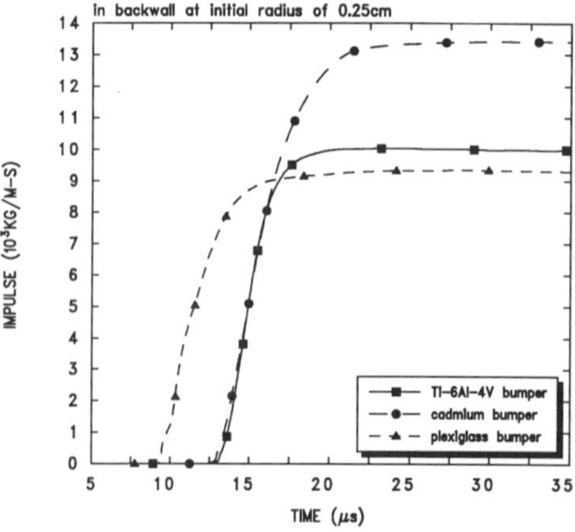

Figure 7. Impulse on Backwall for Base Case and Bumper-Material Variations

CONCLUSIONS

A series of calculations using the finite difference code CTH has been used to evaluate the effect of phase change (*i.e.*, higher concentrations of vapor) in a debris cloud and subsequent impact on a backwall structure. In these calculations, higher concentrations of vapor were achieved by increasing the initial temperature of the impactor and the bumper material while keeping the same impact velocity. The results showed that generating more vapor in the debris cloud did assist in backwall survival, by distributing the impact load over a wider surface area and longer time frame. The results of other calculations, assuming higher impact velocities, showed that the presence of a higher proportion of vaporized material in the debris cloud is not a sufficient condition for backwall survival, if the vaporized debris does not have enough time and/or space to disperse adequately before loading the backwall. Finally, calculations with different bumper shield materials indicate that individual material properties also affect debris cloud propagation and backwall damage.

REFERENCES

1. L. C. Chhabildas, M. B. Boslough, "Experimental Technique to Launch Flier-Plates Representing Orbital Debris to Hypervelocities", Proceedings, 1993 SPIE Conference, Orlando, Florida, April 1993 (to be published).
2. J. M. McGlaun, S. L. Thompson, L. N. Kmetyk, M. G. Elrick, "A Brief Description of the Three-Dimensional Shock Wave Physics Code CTH", Sandia National Laboratories, SAND89-0607, July 1990.

PVDF GAUGE CHARACTERIZATION OF HYPERVELOCITY-IMPACT-GENERATED DEBRIS CLOUDS

M.B. Boslough, L.C. Chhabildas, W.D. Reinhart, C.A. Hall, J.M. Miller, R. Hickman
Experimental Impact Physics Department 1433
Sandia National Laboratories
Albuquerque, New Mexico, USA 87185-5800

S.A. Mullin, and D.L. Littlefield
Southwest Research Institute
San Antonio, Texas, USA 78228-0510

We have used PVDF gauges to determine time-resolved stresses resulting from interaction between hypervelocity-impact-generated debris clouds and various target gauge blocks. Debris clouds were generated from three different impact configurations: 1) steel spheres impacting steel bumper sheets at 4.5 to 6.0 km/s, 2) aluminum inhibited shaped-charge jets impacting aluminum bumper sheets at 11.4 km/s, and 3) titanium disks impacting titanium bumper sheets at 7.6 to 10.1 km/s. Additional data were collected from the various experiments using flash X-ray radiography, pulsed laser photography, impact flash measurements, time-resolved strain gauge measurements, and velocity interferometry (VISAR). Data from these various techniques are in general agreement with one another and with hydrocode predictions, and provide a quantitative and comprehensive picture of impact-generated debris clouds.

INTRODUCTION

There have been many experimental characterization studies of hypervelocity debris clouds using a number of diagnostic methods [*e.g.* 1-3]. Techniques have included recovery of witness plates, collection of flash X-ray images, and fast framing photography. More recently, pulsed-laser, open-shutter photography and holography have been used in an effort to provide higher-resolution data on spatial and size distributions of particles.

The purpose of the present work is to continue to develop quantitative methods for the characterization of hypervelocity-impact generated debris. Polyvinyidene difluoride (PVDF) gauges have been shown to be reliable and convenient for collecting time-resolved stress data in a number of applications, particularly those involving very fast loading rates under uniaxial strain [4]. By embedding them inside a solid material placed in the path of a debris cloud moving at hypervelocity, information about the structure of the debris cloud can be *inferred* from the measured stress histories. In addition, hydrocode simulations of impact-generated debris clouds can include their effect on a solid gauge block. By comparing measured stress histories to those predicted by the code, the experiments can be used to validate hydrodynamic codes in a quantitative way.

EXPERIMENTAL METHODS

Three sets of experiments were performed using three different launch systems. The general configuration is shown in Figure 1. A bumper plate is impacted by a hypervelocity projectile, generating a debris cloud which subsequently impacts upon a solid gauge block. The hypervelocity projectiles included steel spheres, aluminum shaped charge jets, and titanium disks.

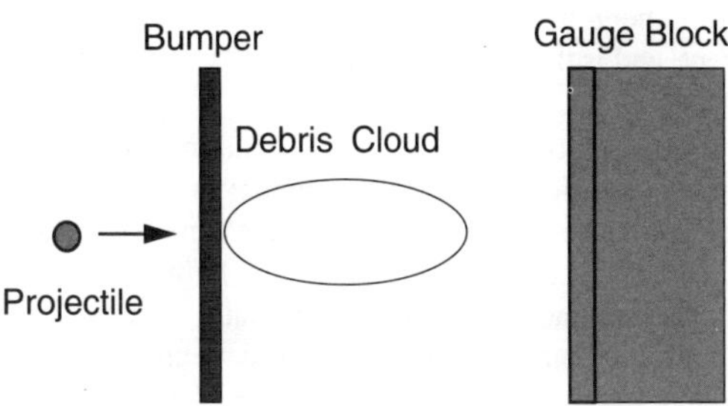

Figure 1. General Experimental Configuration

PVDF Gauges

There is more than one type of PVDF gauge, and there are several modes in which they can be operated. For these experiments we made use of both Bauer [*e.g.*, 4] and Dynasen [5] gauges. For applications in which extremely fast (ns) response is required, gauges are typically operated in current mode. A precision current-viewing resister (CVR) is placed in parallel with the gauge at the target, and the measured current is mathematically integrated to yield charge, from which stress can be determined.

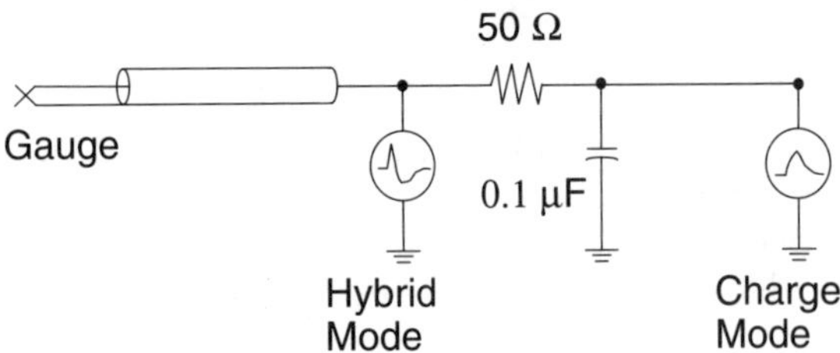

Figure 2. Circuit diagram for PVDF gauges

For the present experiments, in which stress rise times are hundreds of nanoseconds to microseconds, it was found that charge-mode recording was more useful. In charge mode, the signal from the gauge is input into a low-inductance hardware charge integrator (HCI) which contains a 0.1 μF capacitor. The charge is recorded directly as a voltage drop across the capacitor (Figure 2). By measuring the voltage difference across the top side of the HCI (looking across a 50 ohm resistor), an effective current-mode measurement can be made simultaneously. Because of the back voltage due to the charge on the capacitor, this measurement is the sum of voltages due to charge and current, and is therefore referred to as "hybrid mode" in this paper.

There are two methods of determining the equivalent current mode signal from hybrid mode: 1) if a good charge mode record was made using the same time base, it can be subtracted directly, or 2) the integrated hybrid mode record can be subtracted (with appropriate constants from calibration) from the original record. This procedure is repeated iteratively until convergence. The advantage in combined hybrid/charge mode recording is that it is very forgiving of sensitivity settings, which is important for experiments such as these, in which peak stresses and risetimes are difficult to predict.

Most of the development and application of PVDF gauges has been limited to environments of uniaxial strain conditions generated by planar loading experiments. In the present applications, the debris clouds have a more complicated geometry and contain discrete solid fragments, liquid droplets, and vapor, generally giving rise to non-uniaxial loading conditions within the target. The fact that thin-film PVDF gauges respond to lateral strain as well as normal stress needs to be considered. As will be seen in the following section, this was done on a case-by-case basis.

RESULTS AND DISCUSSION

Because of the large number of experiments carried out using a variety of geometries, loading conditions, and materials, only selected shots from each of the three series will be discussed.

I. Steel Spheres onto Steel Plates

In the first series, steel spheres were launched with the Terminal Ballistics Facility (TBF) gun at Sandia's STAR Facility. They impacted onto steel plates, and the resulting debris clouds impacted PMMA disks containing four embedded PVDF gauges. Additional data were collected using flash X-ray radiography, pulsed-laser photography, and impact flash measurements for timing.

Experiment XT-9

Shown in Figure 3 are a pulsed laser photograph and a flash X-ray image of a debris cloud generated by the impact of a 6.35 mm sphere at 4.50 km/s. These two images were obtained simultaneously, approximately 23 μs after impact on the bumper plate. The time of impact was precisely determined by measuring the light emission (impact flash) with a photomultiplier tube. By measuring the positions of the debris front on the visible and X-ray images, the debris front velocity was determined to be 4.28 and 4.31 km/s, respectively. This velocity was independently confirmed with the time-of-arrival of the first compression wave to the PVDF gauges, which yielded a debris velocity of 4.29 km/s.

Experiment XT-5

This experiment was identical to XT-9 except that the impactor was smaller (4.76 mm diameter). The PMMA gauge block contained four PVDF gauges in an array, with one at the center and the other three approximately equally spaced on a 25.4 mm radius.The projectile trajectory was about 18 mm below and 10 mm to the left of the center line of the target, so that each gauge was a different distance from the axis of the debris cloud. The measured stress histories from each gauge are presented in Figure 4. The time of arrival of the stress peak at each gauge increases with that gauge's distance from the center axis of the debris cloud, as can be seen in the inset plot in Figure 4.

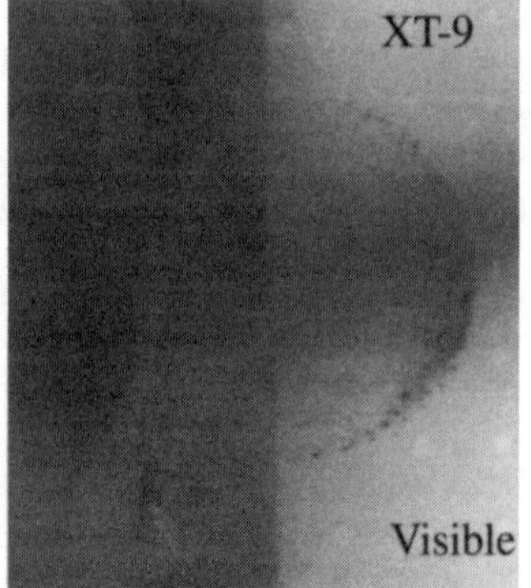

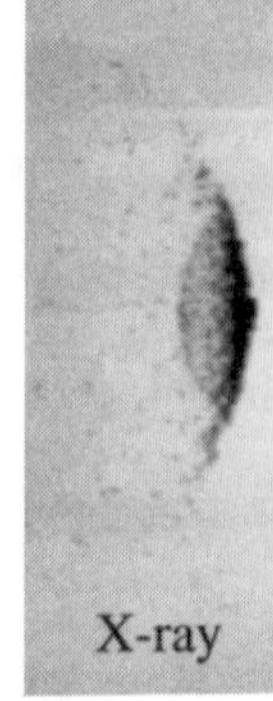

Figure 3. Visible and X-ray images of steel debris

Integrating the stress history with respect to time yields an impulse history, which contains information about the structure of the debris cloud. A set of impulse histories is displayed in Figure 5. In the inset, the impulse at the time peak pressure is achieved at each gauge is displayed as a function of that gauges radial distance from the axis of the debris cloud. This plot demonstrates that the momentum density is approximately symmetric within the debris cloud, consistent with the images in Figure 3. In this set of experiments, it was assumed *a priori* that the contribution from lateral strain to the gauge output was not important for the first one or two microseconds.

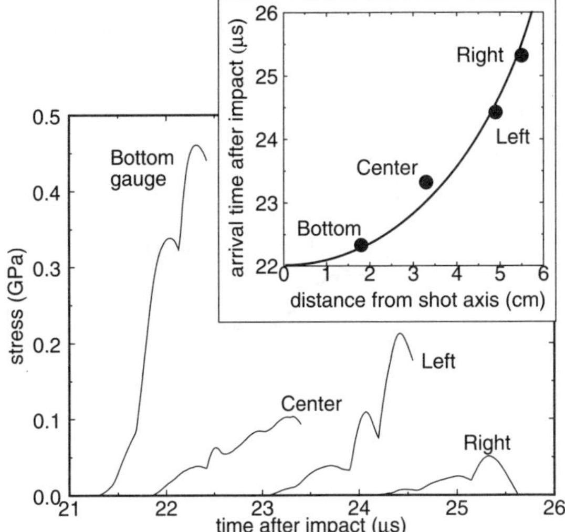

Figure 4. Four stress histories from XT-5

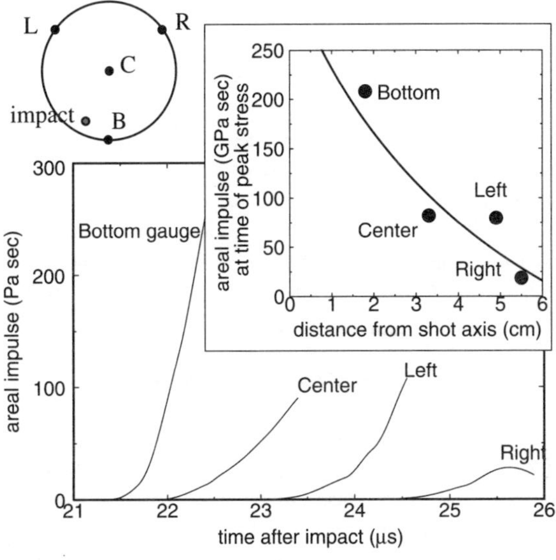

Figure 5. Four impulse histories from XT-5

II. Aluminum Jets onto Aluminum Plates

Experiments using aluminum inhibited shaped charge jets were performed at Southwest Research Institute. The 4.6 mm diameter (L/D=3) aluminum projectiles were launched at speeds of 11.4 km/s, and impacted onto a 1.27 mm-thick aluminum sheet. An aluminum gauge block was placed 200 mm away from the bumper, and had two Bauer PVDF gauges embedded 30 mm behind its front surface to measure the stress profile generated by the impact of the aluminum debris cloud. In addition, orthogonal flash X-ray images were obtained of both the projectile and the debris cloud.

Experiment T-37

In preparation for these experiments a series of CTH hydrocode simulations was performed for various impact/target configurations. One purpose of these calculations was to provide an estimate of the expected shock pressures and risetimes. A second goal was to determine the optimal depth at which the gauges should be embedded in the target, so they would be deep enough that lateral strain would be small, but sufficiently shallow that they would still be sensitive to the structure of the debris cloud. Based on the results of the simulations we chose to embed the gauges 30 mm from the front surface of the target.

Figure 6 displays X-ray images of the shaped-charge jet prior to impact, and the resulting debris cloud. As can be seen, the projectile is not a perfect right circular cylinder, and the spatial distribution of the debris departs from the ideal axial symmetry of the CTH simulation. Nevertheless, a comparison of the PVDF gauge output to the predicted stress history for a 11.1 km/s, axially symmetric impact shows remarkable agreement (Figure 7). The center of the crater in the recovered target was about 15 mm away from the gauge position, so the stress tracer at that point was chosen for comparison. While the exceptional agreement may be somewhat fortuitous, this comparison underscores the fact that PVDF gauges can provide a strong quantitative tool for hypervelocity impact code validation.

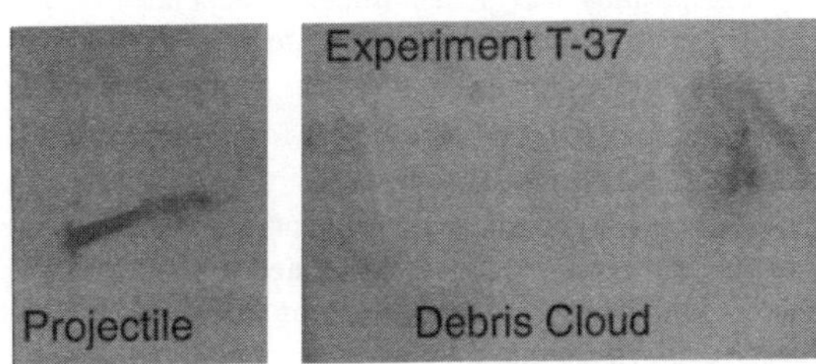

Figure 6. X-ray images of aluminum jet and debris

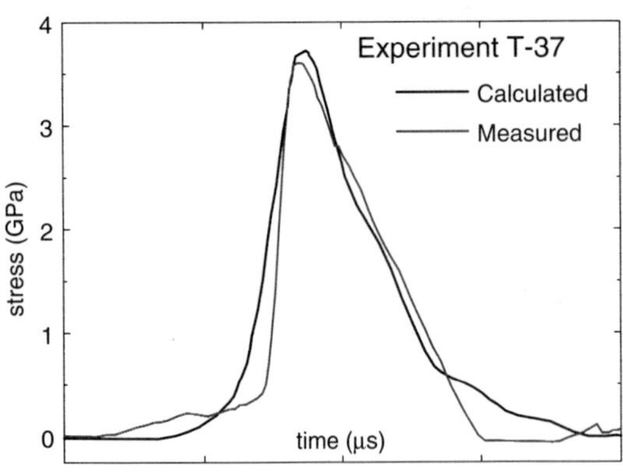

Figure 7. Calculated and measured stress

III. Titanium Disks onto Titanium Plates

These experiments made use of Sandia's Hypervelocity Launcher (HVL). Titanium disks 17 mm in diameter and about 0.5 mm thick were launched to speeds of 7.6 to 10.1 km/s. The debris cloud generated upon impact with a titanium bumper plate was allowed to impact a PMMA gauge block mounted 305 mm away. This target contained two PVDF gauges, each overlying two strain gauges for a time-resolved measurement of lateral strain at the gauge locations. A simultaneous VISAR measurement was made from a location directly behind one of the PVDF gauges, separated by a thin (0.7-mm thick) PMMA buffer. The strain measurements and VISAR measurements were made to determine the magnitude of strain compensation required. Flash X-rays were also obtained of the flyer and of the debris cloud after impact.

Experiment HTI-7

Figure 8 shows x-ray images of a titanium disk about to impact at 7.6 km/s, and the resulting debris cloud. The disk was damaged during launch, and is rotated. In Figure 9, preliminary VISAR, PVDF, and strain data are plotted on the same time scale. This test was completed very recently, and has not yet been fully analyzed; however, it is noteworthy that the lateral strain is significant. The stress at the gauge position will be determined independently from VISAR data and from strain-compensated PVDF data.

SUMMARY

PVDF gauges provide a convenient quantitative means of characterizing debris clouds generated by hypervelocity impacts, with compensation for strain required in some cases. We anticipate that they will become an increasingly-used tool for the experimental validation of hydrodynamic code simulations of hypervelocity impact events.

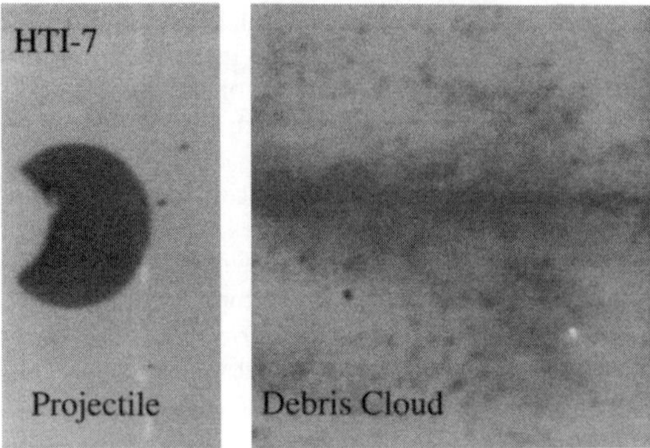

Figure 8. X-ray images of titanium disk and debris

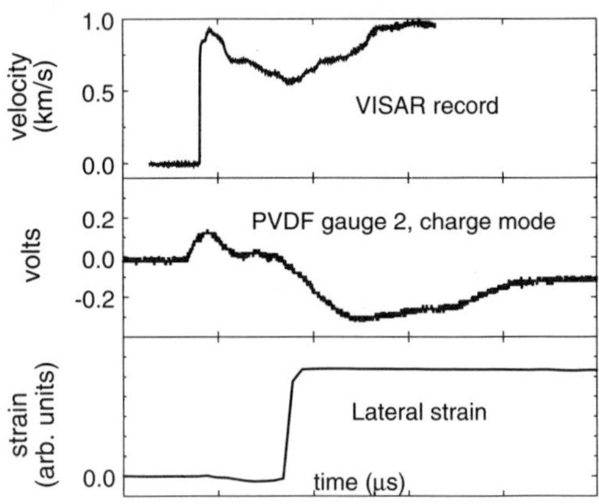

Figure 9. Preliminary data on HTI-7.

REFERENCES

[1] M. Boslough *et al.*, *Intl. J. Impact. Engng.*, 14, (1993).

[2] L.C. Chhabildas *et al.*, "Debris Cloud Characterization at Impact Velocities over 5 to 11 km/s," this volume.

[3] C.H. Konrad *et al.*, "Dependence of Debris Cloud Formation on Projectile Shape," this volume.

[4] F. Bauer, *et al.*, in *Shock Compression of Condensed Matter 1991*, ed. by S.C. Schmidt et al., p. 887, (1992).

[5] J.A. Charest and C.S. Lynch, in *Shock Compression of Condensed Matter 1991*, ed. by S.C. Schmidt et al., p. 897, (1992).

ACKNOWLEDGMENTS

M.U. Anderson, D.E. Wackerbarth, D.A. Crawford, D.K. Johnson, D.J. Grosch, J.A. Charest, and C.S. Lynch provided expert technical advice and help. This work was performed at Sandia National Laboratories supported by the U.S. Department of Energy under contract DE-AC04-76DP00789.

ANALYTIC MODELS FOR HYPERVELOCITY PARTICLE SHIELD ANALYSIS

R. Jeffery Lawrence
Special Projects Division
Defense Nuclear Agency
6801 Telegraph Road
Alexandria, Virginia 22310-3398 USA

Stand-off or "Whipple bumper" shields provide the most efficient protection for space-based assets against the increasing threat posed by orbital debris. By correlating target response with delivered impulse, simple engineering models for the behavior, design, and optimization of these shields have been developed. Previous applications of this approach are summarized and several new extensions are described.

INTRODUCTION

The most efficient protection of space-based assets against the increasing risks presented by orbital debris is afforded by stand-off or "Whipple bumper" shields. These shields function by allowing an impacting projectile to penetrate, but in the process, to breakup into an expanding cloud of fragmented, melted, or vaporized material. If the stand-off distance is large enough, the point load of the projectile is spread over a much larger area of the target surface, hopefully reducing the specific load to a level that will preclude failure.

There are several approaches for analyzing and designing these types of shields. They range from full experimental measurements, through analyses employing elaborate multi-dimensional hydrocodes, to the use of simple analytic models and scaling laws. The more sophisticated design methods can serve for both validation and calibration of the simpler engineering models, but are not appropriate for the many parametric studies that are required for shield design and optimization. In addition, many of the operational conditions under which these shields must function are not readily accessible to experiment. It is thus important both to develop and to justify the use of the simpler models so that a complete suite of analysis tools is available.

Simple descriptions of the processes associated with the operation of stand-off shields were presented as early as 1959 by Lull,[1] and have been expanded on and further developed since that time by Richardson,[2] Cour-Palais,[3] Swift *et al.*, and Lawrence.[5-7]

In the present paper we summarize some of these recent models and show that they can be used to predict the failure of the structure under consideration. Ballistic limit analysis, in conjunction with limited experimental observations on actual space station design configurations, then suggests that with an optimized balance between stand-off distance and shield thickness, total shield weights can be reduced by a factor of two or more over current designs. Finally, we describe model extensions that have the potential for predicting the actual *extent* of target failure and show that they are qualitatively substantiated by experimental observations of witness plate damage patterns.

DESCRIPTION OF MODEL

The interaction of hypervelocity particles with solid targets leads to two types of phenomena. If the impact velocity is sufficiently high and the target is thick, the material in the immediate vicinity of the impact site will be vaporized and blown back in the upstream direction, enhancing the momentum produced in the target. On the other hand, if the target is thin, the particle will penetrate, breakup, and form an expanding cloud of fragmented, melted, or vaporized debris. It is this latter situation that we are interested in for studying stand-off shields.

We begin by assuming that the expanding debris cloud takes the form of a translating and expanding uniform hollow shell, a shape that has been qualitatively verified by many observations. The mass of the debris cloud is comprised of two parts, the mass swept out of the shield m_S, and the mass of the incident spherical projectile m_P. Using the parameters as defined in Figure 1, these masses are given by

$$m_s = \pi (D_s/2)^2 t_s \rho_s , \tag{1}$$

and

$$m_p = (\pi/6) D_p^3 \rho_p , \tag{2}$$

where ρ_p is the density of the projectile and ρ_S is the density of the shield. A nondimensional shield thickness or mass ratio M is then defined from these masses as

$$M = \frac{m_s}{m_p} = \frac{3\beta^2}{2}\left(\frac{\rho_s t_s}{\rho_p D_p}\right) , \tag{3}$$

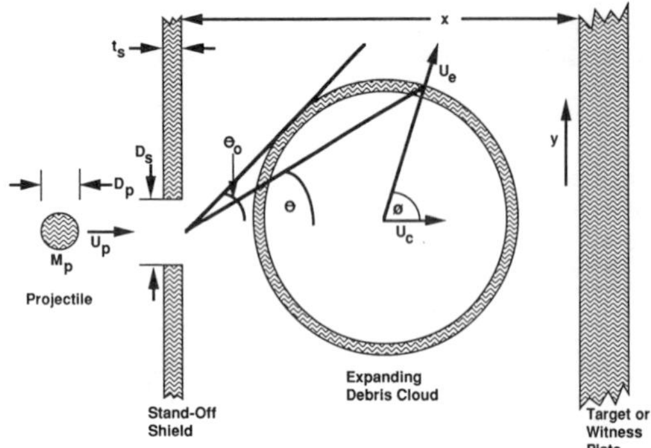

Figure 1. Schematic for stand-off shield analysis.

where β is the ratio of the hole diameter to the projectile diameter, i.e., $\beta = D_s/D_p$. For a second major independent variable we nondimensionalize the projectile velocity u_p with the effective decomposition energy per unit mass ε_b needed to breakup or vaporize the materials of the shield and projectile,

$$V_p = u_p^2/2\varepsilon_b \ , \tag{4}$$

which is then a dimensionless kinetic energy per unit mass characterizing the projectile. Much of the subsequent analysis will be given in terms of these two dimensionless variables, M and V_p.

The motion of the debris cloud can be described by its center- of-mass velocity u_c,

$$u_c = u_p/(1+M) \ , \tag{5}$$

and its expansion velocity u_e about this point,

$$u_e = u_p\sqrt{\frac{M}{(1+M)^2} - \frac{1}{V_p}} \ . \tag{6}$$

The former arises from conservation of momentum, and the latter follows from conservation of energy. The debris divergence angle Θ_o can then be found from $\sin\Theta_o = u_e/u_c$, or

$$\theta_o = \sin^{-1}\sqrt{M - \frac{(1+M)^2}{V_p}} \ , \tag{7}$$

where we note that an experimental measurement of Θ_o yields an unambiguous determination of the most uncertain model parameter, ε_b.

One of the important assumptions of this model is that the relevant target loading can be expressed in terms of the specific impulse or momentum per unit area delivered to the target by the debris cloud. By summing the momentum in both the front and rear of the debris cloud, the axial value of this impulse, I_{axial}, becomes

$$I_{axial} = \frac{m_p u_p}{2\pi x^2}\left(\frac{1}{U} + 3\right) \ , \tag{8}$$

where $U = M - (1 + M)^2/V_p$, and x is the stand-off distance between the shield and the target. It is this axial loading that will be correlated with "ballistic limit" failure of the target.

The model results presented above are simply a summary of previously developed material.[5] We now extend the analysis to provide a description of the *extent* of failure of the underlying target. To accomplish this the impulse delivered to the target must be determined as a function of the distance y from the axis of symmetry. We first note that the two angles Θ and ϕ, as defined in Figure 1, can be related through

$$\theta = \tan^{-1}\left(\frac{U^{1/2}\sin\phi}{1 + U^{1/2}\cos\phi}\right) \ , \tag{9}$$

where we see that when Θ is at its limiting value Θ_o, representing the debris divergence angle, we have $\phi = \phi_o = \Theta_o + \pi/2$. Now, as a function of ϕ, the impact area on the target, A_n, for a unit area on the surface of the debris cloud can be shown to be given by

$$A_n = |\cos\phi| + \frac{U^{1/2}\sin^2\phi}{1 + U^{1/2}\cos\phi} \ , \tag{10}$$

which will be appropriate for both the front and back portions of the debris cloud. The target impulse associated with this area is then

$$I(\phi) = \frac{m_p u_p}{4\pi x^2}\frac{1}{A_n}\frac{(1 + U^{1/2}\cos\phi)^3}{U} \ . \tag{11}$$

$I(y)$ can be found by using Eq (9) and the fact that $y = x \tan\Theta$. If we set ϕ equal to 0° and 180° and sum the results, Eq (8) is obtained, as anticipated.

To use these expressions we first obtain values for the engagement parameters u_p, D_p, t_s *and* x; for the material properties ρ_s and ρ_p; and for the additional parameters β and ε_b. The latter two values should be based on experimental observations or whatever other evidence is available. More specifically, the shield hole-size ratio β depends on both the impact velocity and the shield thickness, and can vary somewhat. However, for parameter ranges characteristic of optimized shield designs, it is typically a constant between one and two. Previous analysis has suggested that ε_b should be near the vaporization energy of the relevant materials.[6] Equations (8) and (11) are then available for predicting the axial load on the target and the overall distributed load, respectively. Any of the parameters can then be varied or we can compare the predictions with measurements to determine the loads that correlate with target failure. Extrapolations to other conditions can be accomplished, and the model can then be use for design and optimization purposes.

MODEL APPLICATIONS

The present model has been applied to a design for the stand-off orbital debris shield proposed for the protection of one module of the space station. Because it is not a first-principle model, some method must be employed for its calibration. To accomplish this we use a pair of experiments conducted recently by Chhabildas *et al.*[8] In these tests representative stand-off shield configurations were subjected to 0.65-g and 0.32-g projectile impacts at velocities just over 10 km/s, and showed penetration and no penetration of the target, respectively. From these tests and their accompanying hydrocode analyses it was concluded that for a current space station shield design, penetration of the target structure would occur at a specific impulse between 2.7 and 9.2 ktaps.[7]

Application of the model then leads to the ballistic limit curves shown in Figure 2.[7] Numerical data due to Hertel *et al.*[9] are also included, and qualitatively substantiate these results. Several features of this figure should be noted. First, the results apply only to the specific target and shield combination indicated, and, because of the limited number of experiments, they exhibit a rather large band of uncertainty. Second, and most important, there is a ballistic limit threshold at an impact velocity in the vicinity of 8 km/s, below which stand-off shields are no more effective than comparable conventional monolithic shields. This threshold can be correlated with the onset of projectile breakup, melting, and vaporization. Note that extrapolation of either experimental or numerical date across this "ballistic limit anomaly" could lead to erroneous conclusions.

Using these results, the curves shown in Figure 3 can be generated. They indicate that since the space station shield design under consideration is on the very steep portion of these curves, relatively small increases in the stand-off distance can lead to significant reductions in the total shield mass. For example, increasing the stand-off from 107 mm to 150 mm would reduce the nominal 550-kg shield mass by half, to 280 kg. Balancing the shield thickness with stand-off in this fashion allows the model to facilitate shield optimization.

In some situations we may want to determine the extent of failure as well as the nominal ballistic limit. Although we have not performed quantitative comparisons with experimental measurements, the model, as described here, can provide the relevant predictions. To illustrate, we plot the results of applying Eq (11) to the data for the two experiments on which Figure 2 is based. As shown in Figure 4, the impulse profiles associated with the fronts of the debris clouds are broadly peaked on the axis, as expected. However, because of the shell-like structure assumed and observed for the debris clouds, all the profiles exhibit narrower peaks demarking their outer edges. Also, as anticipated, the fronts of the debris clouds deliver by far the majority of the impulse. The two curves representing penetration show a smaller overall divergence and a substantially larger total specific impulse. To indicate that this description is qualitatively correct, Figure 5 shows the damaged region produced on a witness plate for conditions similar to those discussed above.[10] The edge of the pattern is sharp and suggests a localized increase in the impulse consistent with the profiles of the previous figure.

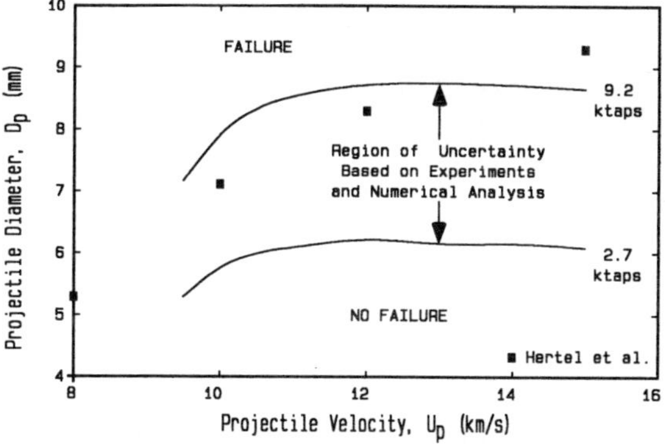

Figure 2. Ballistic limit curves for representative stand-off shield configuration. The information is for projectiles incident on a 1.27-mm-thick shield spaced 114 mm from a 3.2-mm-thick target; all materials are aluminum.

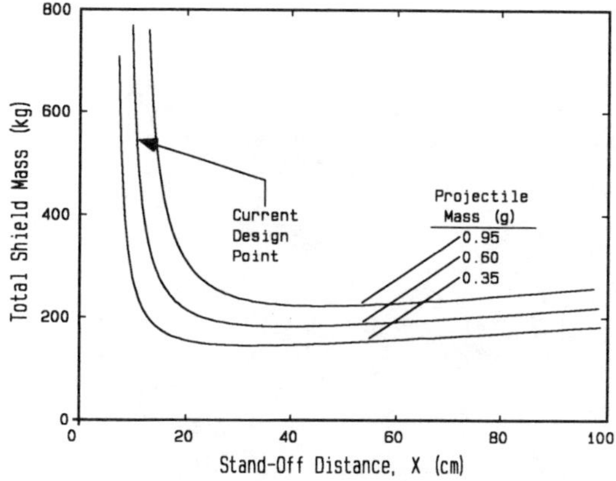

Figure 3. Total stand-off shield mass for a representative space station module. Curves are drawn for a projectile impact velocity of 12 km/s and for the three indicated projectile masses. The current design consists of a 3.2-mm-thick target, and a 1.27-mm-thick shield with a 107-mm stand-off. All components are aluminum.

CLOSURE

We have described a simple analytic model that can be used to optimize the design of stand-off hypervelocity particle shields. In addition to characterizing target failure through a calibrated ballistic limit analysis, it is capable of predicting the extent of failure of the underlying structural target, an application that could be important for many space-based systems. Although it is extremely simple, the model captures all the major features of the phenomena associated with the operation of these shields. The model undoubtedly contains large uncertainties, but when it is properly tied to limited experiments and other, more elaborate analyses, it should prove to be a reliable and valuable tool for the analysis of this class of hypervelocity particle shield.

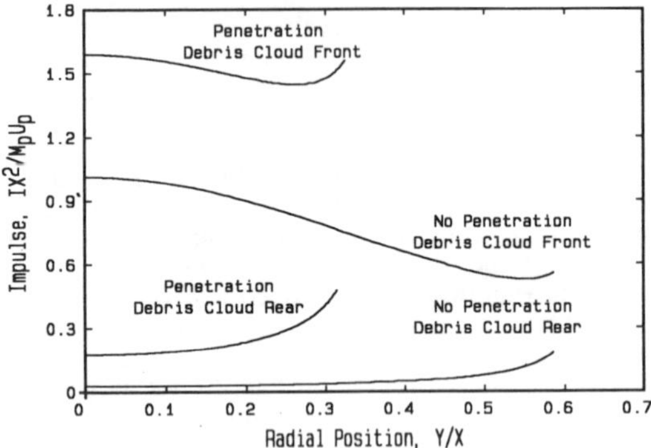

Figure 4. Dimensionless impulse profiles as a function of position on target witness plate. Curves are for the front and rear of the two experimental debris clouds associated with Figure 2.

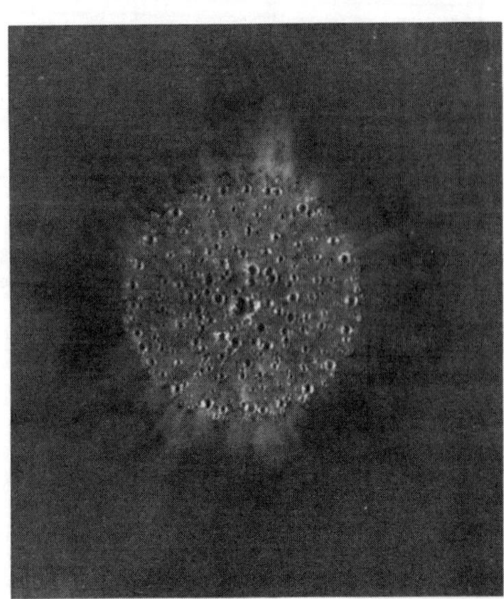

Figure 5. Observed debris pattern on target witness plate. The sharp periphery of the damaged region, as predicted by the model, is clearly visible. The experiment involved a 6.5-km/s, 3-mm-diameter projectile incident on a 0.5-mm-thick shield at a stand-off of 100 mm from the witness plate. Projectile and shield were both aluminum.

REFERENCES

[1] D. B. Lull, "Analysis of Impact of Hypervelocity Pellet With a Thin Shield," Memo, A. D. Little Corp. (December 1959), as quoted in W. Herrmann and A. F. Jones, *Survey of Hypervelocity Impact Information,* ASRL Report No. 99-1, Aeroelastic and Structures Laboratory, MIT, Cambridge, MA (September 1961).

[2] A. J. Richardson, "Theoretical Penetration Mechanics of Multisheet Structures Based on Discreet Debris Particle Modeling," *AIAA Hypervelocity Impact Conference,* AIAA, New York (1969).

[3] B. G. Cour-Palais, "Meteoroid Protection by Multiwall Structures," *AIAA Hypervelocity Impact Conference*, AIAA, New York (1969).

[4] H. F. Swift, R. Bamford, and R. Chen, *Designing Dual-Plate Shields--A New Analysis*, JPL Publication 82-39, Jet Propulsion Laboratory, Pasadena, CA (March 1982).

[5] R. J. Lawrence, "A Simple Model for the Optimization of Stand-Off Hypervelocity Particle Shields," *Int. J. Impact Engng,* Vol. 5, pp. 451-461 (1987).

[6] R. J. Lawrence, *Stand-Off Hypervelocity Particle Shields for Fixed Structures,* Report No. SAND 89-0442, Sandia National Laboratories, Albuquerque, NM (April 1989).

[7] R. J. Lawrence, *A Simple Approach for the Design and Optimization of Stand-Off Hypervelocity Particle Shields,* AIAA Paper No. 92-1465, AIAA, Washington, DC (1992).

[8] L. C. Chhabildas, E.S. Hertel, and S. A. Hill, "Hypervelocity Impact Tests and Simulations of Single Whipple Bumper Shield Concepts at 10 km/s," *Int. J. Impact Engng,* Vol. 14 (1993).

[9] E. S. Hertel, L. C. Chhabildas, and L. Yarrington, "Computational Determination of Ballistic Limits for a Simple Whipple Bumper Shield,"*Proceedings of the Workshop on Hypervelocity Impacts in Space,* J. A. M. McDonnell, Ed., University of Kent, Canterbury, UK (July 1991).

[10] C. H. Yew, University of Texas, J. L. Crews, NASA/Johnson Space Center (private communication).

DEBRIS CLOUD CHARACTERIZATION AT IMPACT VELOCITIES OF 5 TO 11 KM/S

L. C. Chhabildas, M. B. Boslough, W. D. Reinhart and C. A. Hall
Experimental Impact Physics Department 1433
Sandia National Laboratories
Albuquerque, New Mexico, USA 87185-5800

A series of experiments has been performed on the Sandia Hypervelocity Launcher to impact a 1.25-mm thick aluminum bumper by an aluminum flier plate 17-mm diameter by 0.92-mm thick over the velocity range of 5 km/s to 11 km/s. Radiographic techniques were employed to record the debris cloud generated upon impact. The shape of the debris cloud is found to depend on the flier plate tilt. Generally—the data indicate a central core of higher density surrounded by a diffused layer. These experiments allow measurements of debris cloud expansion velocities as the material undergoes a phase change from solid fragments at impact velocities of 5 km/s to a mixture of liquid and vapor phase at higher impact velocities. The expansion velocity of the debris cloud increases with increasing impact velocity, with the high-density leading edge travelling faster than the impact velocity. There is a difference between the X-ray and photographic measurements of expansion velocities at higher impact velocities. This is believed to be due to the presence of very low-density vapor in the photographic records that are not detected using X-ray techniques.

INTRODUCTION

There is considerable interest in characterizing debris clouds that are generated upon impact of a projectile on a target plate. When the target is thin compared to the size of the projectile the geometry approximates the Whipple bumper shield configuration. If the target is thick then it can represent an armor configuration. The debris cloud that is generated upon impact depends on several factors, including the velocity, size and shape of the projectile [1, 2], and the relative thickness of the target to the projectile dimensions. In this paper, the results of a systematic study conducted to characterize debris clouds generated upon impact of a thin aluminum plate on a thin aluminum bumper shield are summarized. The experiments were performed over an impact velocity range of 5 km/s to 11 km/s. Aluminum was chosen in this study, since it is representative of aerospace materials. The experiments allow measurements of debris cloud properties as the material undergoes a phase change from solid/liquid fragments at impact velocities of 5 km/s to a mixture of liquid and vapor phase at higher impact velocities.

EXPERIMENTAL TECHNIQUE

Sandia's newly developed HyperVelocity Launcher, HVL, [3] was used to conduct these experiments. The HVL is based on the principle that structured, time-dependent (shockless), megabar driving pressures are needed to launch a flier plate without inducing melt or fracture in the flier plate. This is accomplished by using a graded-density material to impact a stationary flier plate at high velocities on a two-stage light-gas gun. Two-stage light-gas gun impact velocities over the range of 3 to 6.9 km/s will launch a nominally 1-mm thick aluminum flier plate to velocities over the range of 5 to 11 km/s [3]. The mass of the flier plate is controlled by the diameter of the impacting plate. The velocity of the flier plate is measured using radiographic techniques. Due to two-dimensional effects and the large deformation that the flier-plate undergoes upon acceleration, the flier plate is generally bowed after long flight distances.

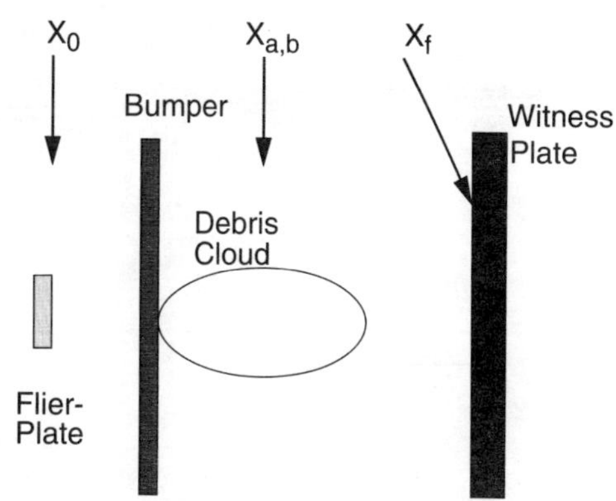

Figure 1. Experimental Impact Configuration

The experimental configuration used to generate debris clouds upon impact is indicated in Figure 1. Aluminum flier plates 17-mm diameter by 0.92-mm thick impacted 1.27 mm thick aluminum bumper plates. Aluminum witness plates 3.18 mm thick were positioned 203 mm behind the bumper plate. The debris cloud is viewed between the bumper shield and the witness plate using flash X-ray radiographic techniques. The back surface of the witness

Table 1. Summary of Debris Cloud Experiments

Shot No	Impact Velocity (km/s)	Time after bumper impact (μs)	Debris Length f (mm)	Debris Diameter d (mm)	Aspect Ratio f/d	Front Velocity f/t (km/s)	Lateral Velocity d/t (km/s)	Bumper hole h_b (mm)	Plate hole h_p mm x mm
hal5	4.99	8.63	43.2	34.2	1.26	5.09	2.0	27.2	45 x 58
hal4	7.43	7.44	55.8	40.3	1.38	7.5	3.2	26.8	26 x 31
hal2	9.56	6.27	62.9	42.1	1.49	10.2	4.0	26.2	-
hal6	11.1	5.1	57.9	42.2	1.37	11.4	5.3	42.7	11 x 15

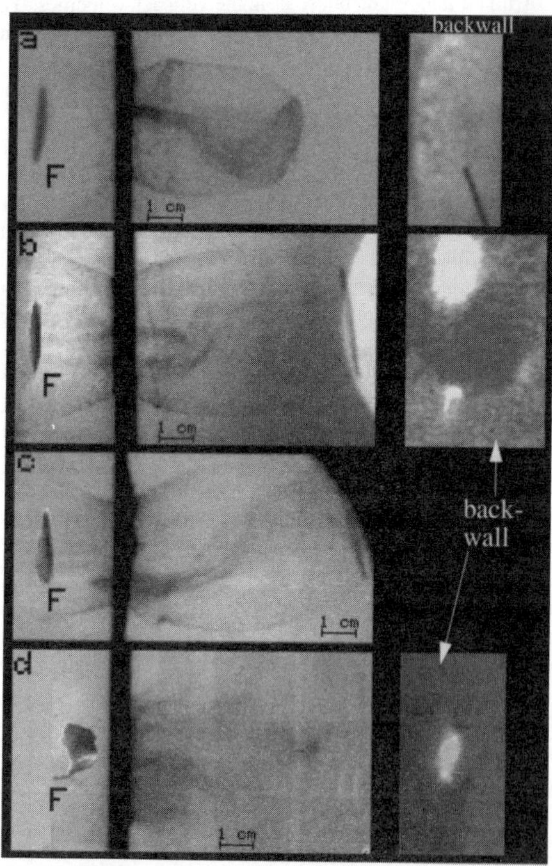

Figure 2. Radiographs of the debris cloud formed upon impact of an aluminum flier plate (F) with an aluminum bumper plate at (a) 5 km/s, (b) 7.43 km/s, (c) 9.56 km/s, and (d) 11.1 km/s.

plate was also radiographed at an angle to determine the effect of subsequent loading by the impact-generated debris cloud. The X-ray measurements of the debris cloud are indicated in Figure 2. Only those X-rays that are not absorbed by the debris cloud *i.e.*, the relatively higher density material within the cloud, are being imaged. A sensitivity analysis on the minimum areal density of the debris cloud that can be imaged using current radiographic capabilities has not been performed for these studies.

RESULTS

Results of experiments performed to characterize the debris cloud are summarized in Table 1. The impact velocity of the flier plate is determined very accurately using multiple radiographic measurements over distances of 350 mm. The X-ray of the flier plate shown in Figure 2 is taken ~ 250 mm prior to impact. The flier plate appears to be severely deformed for experiment hal6 prior to impact. This is because the temperature of the flier plate material is very close to the melt boundary. The debris cloud dimensions indicated in Table 1 are those measured from the radiographs that are shown in Figure 2. Both the debris front location (its length) and the maximum debris diameter are given in the table. The ratio of the debris front length dimension to its diameter, defined as the aspect ratio, should be a very accurate estimate. The variation of aspect ratio with impact velocity is shown in Figure 3.

The impact time on the bumper is defined to be zero in this study. The debris exposure time, which is the time after impact in the table when the X-ray is taken, is accurate to within an uncertainty of three hundred nanoseconds, due to the uncertainty in estimating the impact time on the bumper. This will introduce ~ 6% uncertainty in estimating the debris front and lateral velocities indicated in Table 1. The variation of both the debris front velocity and the lateral velocity with impact velocity is indicated in Figure 4. The debris front velocity for experiment hal5 is very accurate because multiple X-rays (not shown) over long distances were used to estimate the velocity. The lateral velocity of the debris cloud is calculated assuming that the debris expands linearly from its pre-impact diameter of 17 mm to the diameter measured at the exposure time. Multiple X-ray exposures are needed to verify this assumption.

The hole size in the bumper plate is determined by averaging the "width" of the debris cloud from both front

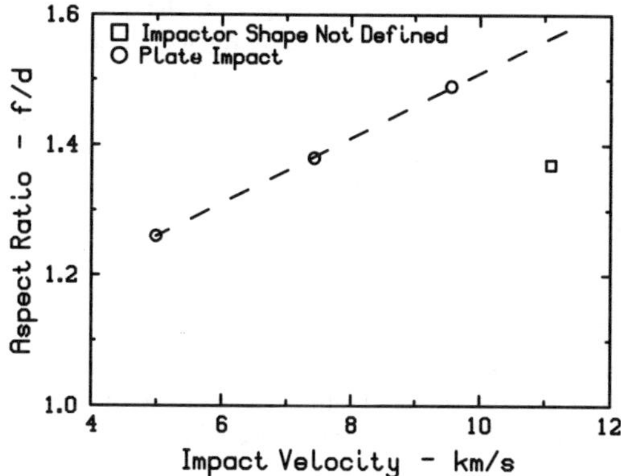

Figure 3. The ratio of the leading edge of the debris front to its diameter f/d *versus* impact velocity.

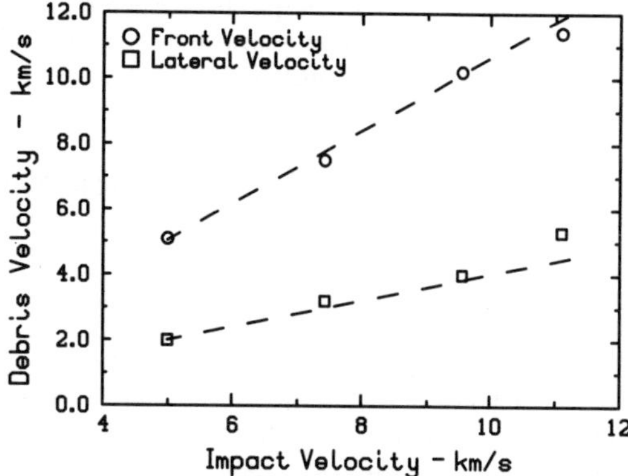

Figure 4. Debris front and lateral velocity variation with impact velocity.

and back surface ejection at the bumper plate. Since an orthogonal view is absent, it is assumed for current discussions that the hole in the bumper plate is symmetrical and circular. This assumption is especially reasonable for normal impact by a plate into thin bumper plates.

The hole size in the witness plate is determined experimentally using an oblique X-ray source. Pre-calibration of the experimental set up is necessary to estimate the hole size. The witness plate radiograph is generally taken approximately 50 μs after impact interaction of the debris cloud with the witness plate. It is taken sufficiently early to eliminate interactions from the arrival of the slower moving two-stage light-gas gun projectile debris. Although the measurement of a rupture in the witness plate was not successful in experiment hal2, previous experiments [5] conducted at similar impact conditions have indicated a backwall rupture.

DISCUSSIONS

Thermodynamic States

Assuming a flat-plate impact, the peak stress states in the aluminum flier and the bumper will be ~ 58 GPa, 102 GPa, 150 GPa, and 190 GPa at impact velocities of 4.99, 7.43, 9.56, and 11.1 km/s, respectively. Accordingly, the corresponding release temperatures of aluminum [4] shocked to 60 GPa will be very close to the melt temperature of 930 K, while the release temperature of aluminum that has been shocked to 190 GPa will be over 3000 K, which is well above its boiling temperature of 2700 K. Therefore, the aluminum debris will be in the solid/liquid phase at an impact velocity of 5 km/s, liquid phase at 7.43 km/s, and liquid phase with increased quantity of vapor fraction at the higher impact velocities of 9.56 and 11.1 km/s, respectively.

Debris Cloud Shape

The flier plate mass used in this study is ~ 0.53 g, and its undeformed *aspect ratio i.e.*, thickness-to-diameter ratio is ~ 0.05. After impact, the free-surface stress relief dominates. The diameter of a sphere representing an equivalent mass of the flier plate would be 7.2 mm. The wave interaction time for a plate impact will be one-eighth the time compared to a spherical impact. Therefore, one-dimensional effects control the impact interaction. This is indicated by the shape of the debris cloud observed in the radiographs. The leading edge of the debris cloud in all instances has the highest density mass. The shape of the debris cloud generated upon impact is found to depend on the flier plate tilt. The data indicate a central core of higher density surrounded by a diffused layer. The variation of the aspect ratio with impact velocity is shown in Figure 3. The ratio of the debris front dimension to its diameter, defined as the aspect ratio, is an accurate estimate. If the debris propagation effects are influenced strictly by one-dimensional processes then this ratio is expected to increase with time. For spherical propagation this ratio is expected to be close to unity. Note in experiment hal6, where the flier plate impactor is not well defined, the aspect ratio is lower than the expected result.

Solid fragments are observed in Figure 2a for the impact experiment at 5 km/s. It is surprising to observe a disc shaped leading edge for the two experiments at 7.44 km/s and 9.56 km/s, considering that the bumper material is expected to be completely molten. Any low density vapor preceding the debris cloud is not observable on the radiographs. Since the flier plate is significantly deformed in experiment hal6 (Figure 2d), its shape prior to impact is not well defined. Consequently, the debris cloud in figure 2d is not similar to those indicated in Figures 2a, 2b, and 2c. It can be shown that low density debris of approximately 0.008 g/cm^3 would fill uniformly into a cylinder having an aspect ratio of 1.42. In all instances, low energy X-ray sources are needed to accurately/precisely define the true "shape" of the debris cloud.

Debris Velocities

The debris front and lateral velocities of the experiments (shown in Figure 2) are indicated in Figure 4. As indicated in the figure, the high density leading edge of the debris front is travelling faster than the impact velocity. Previous impact experiments at 10 km/s diagnosed using fast framing photographic techniques [5] have indicated a vapor front (preceding the debris cloud) travelling at velocities of 14 km/s. It is, therefore, crucial that both X-rays and photography be used if possible to obtain a detailed description of the debris cloud. An alternate approach is to develop low energy X-rays to allow the imaging of the entire debris cloud. The lateral velocity of the debris cloud resulting from plate impact also increases with impact velocity; when expressed as a fraction of the impact velocity the lateral velocity appears to be relatively constant and ~ 40% of the impact velocity. Note the radial expansion velocity will be ~ 20% of the impact velocity. In experiment hal6 the impactor is not well defined; the debris front velocity appears to be lower than anticipated, while the lateral velocity appears to be higher than the expected measurement.

SUMMARY

A series of experiments has been performed to characterize the debris generated from plate impacts over the velocity range of 5 km/s to 11 km/s. Radiographic techniques were employed to record the debris clouds generated. The shape of the debris cloud is found to depend on the flier plate tilt, but the data also indicate a central core of higher density material surrounded by a diffused layer. These experiments allow measurements of debris cloud expansion velocities as the material undergoes a phase change from solid fragments at impact velocities of 5 km/s to a mixture of liquid and vapor phase at higher impact velocities. The expansion velocity of the debris cloud appears to increase with increasing impact velocity. At higher impact velocities there is a discrepancy between the present X-ray and previous photographic measurements [5] of expansion velocities. This is believed to be due to the presence of very low-density vapor in the photographic records that are not detected using X-ray techniques.

Although not discussed above, the hole size in the bumper plate is estimated to be ~ 26.5 mm, and is independent of the impact velocity when the integrity of the flier plate is maintained. When compared to the original flier plate dimensions of 17 mm, this is an amplification by a factor of 1.5 to 1.6 in these studies.

The rupture damage to the witness plate is listed in Table 1. It should be noted that although there is presence of molten and vaporized aluminum in the debris cloud, the backwall is still ruptured—mainly because of the high-density leading edge and the presence of what appears to be a central high density core.

Studies in the past have concentrated on impacting spheres onto thin bumper plates at lower velocities than this study, because the capability to launch spheres is available. Spherical impact also provides well-controlled boundary conditions for numerical analysis of the experiments. Our experiments, primarily due to their plate geometry, will also serve to validate hydrodynamic codes in the impact regime where very few experiments are available.

ACKNOWLEDGMENTS

This work performed at Sandia National Laboratories supported by the U.S. Department of Energy under contract DE-AC04-76DP00789. We would also like to acknowledge Tom Tsai and John Connell, Defense Nuclear Agency, for their interest in this work.

REFERENCES

[1] E. S. Hertel, L. C. Chhabildas, L. Yarrington, "Computational Determination of Ballistic Limits for a Simple Whipple Bumper Shield," in *Proceedings of the Workshop on Hypervelocity Impacts in Space-1991,* ed. by J. A. M. McDonnell, 1992, pp. 15-18.

[2] C. H. Konrad, L. C. Chhabildas, M. B. Boslough, A. J. Piekutowski, K. L. Poormon, S. A. Mullin, D. L. Littlefield, "Dependence of Debris Cloud Formation on Projectile Shape," this volume.

[3] L. C. Chhabildas, J. E. Dunn, W. D. Reinhart, J. M. Miller, *Intl. J. Impact Engng.,* V14, 1993.

[4] G. I. Kerley, *Intl. J. Impact Engng.,* V5, pp. 441-449, 1987.

[5] L. C. Chhabildas, E. S. Hertel, S. A. Hill, *Intl. J. Impact Engng.,* V14, 1993.

Dependence of Debris Cloud Formation on Projectile Shape

C. H. KONRAD, L. C. CHHABILDAS, M. B. BOSLOUGH
Department 1433, Sandia National Laboratories
Albuquerque, New Mexico, 87185-5800

A. J. PIEKUTOWSKI, K. L. POORMON
University of Dayton Research Institute
300 College Park, Dayton, Ohio, 45469-0180

S. A. MULLIN, D. L. LITTLEFIELD
Southwest Research Institute,
6220 Culebra Road, San Antonio, Texas, 78228-0510

A two-stage light-gas gun has been used to impact thin zinc bumpers by zinc projectiles over the velocity range of 2.4 km/s to 6.7 km/s to determine the propagation characteristics of the impact generated debris. Constant-mass projectiles in the form of spheres, discs, cylinders and rods were used in these studies. Radiographic techniques were employed to record the debris cloud generated upon impact and the dynamic formation of the resulting rupture in an aluminum backing plate resulting from the loading of the debris cloud. The characteristics of the debris cloud generated upon impact is found to depend on the projectile shape. The data indicate that the debris front velocity is independent of the shape of the projectile, whereas the debris lateral/ radial velocity is strongly dependent on projectile geometry. Spherical impactors generate the most radially dispersed debris cloud while the normal plate impactors result in column-like debris. It has been observed that the debris generated by the impact of thin plates on a thin bumper shield is considerably more damaging to a backwall than the debris generated by an equivalent-mass sphere.

INTRODUCTION

There has been considerable attention given to evaluate the effects of projectile shape in thick-plate penetration experiments. These studies have employed projectile shapes such as long rods or spheres. Very little data/analyses exist in which the penetration capability of debris resulting from impact of thin plates has been studied. In a computational study, it has been noted that the debris generated by the impact of thin plates on a thin bumper shield is considerably more damaging to a backwall than the debris generated by an equivalent mass sphere[1]. To determine these effects we have performed a series of systematic studies in which a constant mass zinc projectile impacts a thin zinc bumper sheet. The damage to a backwall plate resulting from subsequent loading by the debris generated by the bumper impact is measured. Zinc was selected in this study, because of its low melting and boiling temperature; it will melt and vaporize at relatively low impact velocities of 2.5 to 7 km/s. These experiments, combined with hypervelocity impact experiments in aluminum up to 11 km/s [2] will evaluate velocity scaling concepts [3].

EXPERIMENTAL CONFIGURATION

The experimental arrangement for the impact tests is illustrated in Figure 1. The zinc projectiles consisted of four different geometries—disk, sphere, cylinder and a rod. They made normal impacts on a thin zinc bumper plate. A 6061-T6 aluminum backwall was positioned 152.4 mm behind the zinc bumper. The mass of the projectiles was kept constant except in the case of a long rod. Fine source, soft x-

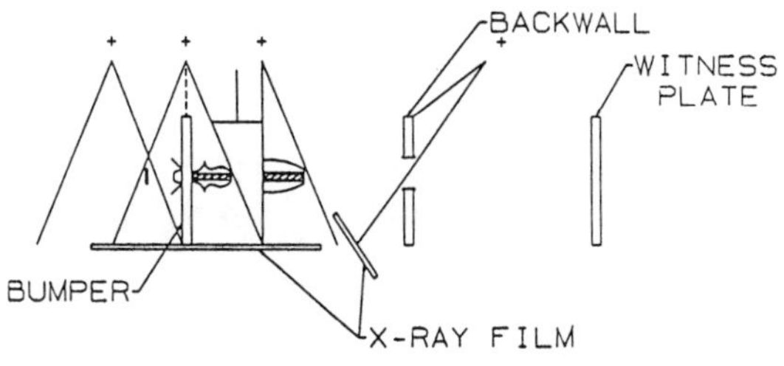

Figure 1. Experimental Impact Configuration

rays were used to observe the projectile and the debris cloud formation resulting from impact [4]. As indicated in

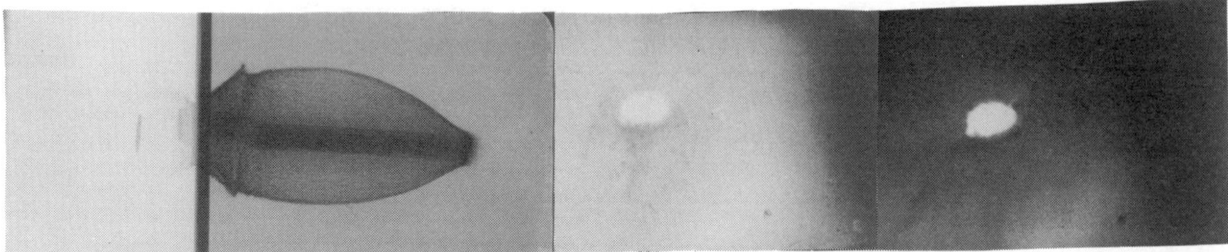

Figure 2a. The plate at left 5.9 μs before impact, and the debris cloud formation at 18.3 μs after impact. Dynamic hole formation is displayed at 51.2 μs after impact of the bumper plate and is compared to the hole size in the recovered plate at right.

NO BACKWALL PENETRATION

Figure 2b. The sphere at left 5.2 μs before impact, and the debris cloud formation a 19.4 μs after impact. No penetration of the backwall is achieved for the spherical impact.

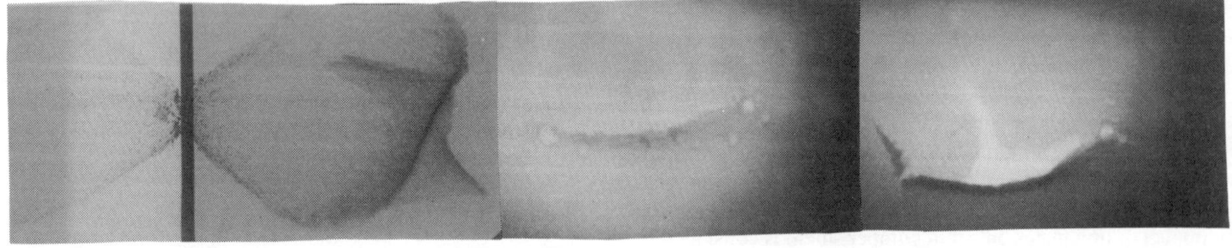

Figure 2c. The cylinder at left 2.7 μs before impact and the debris cloud formation at 21.4 μs after impact. Dynamic hole formation is displayed at 49.4 μs after impact of the bumper plate and is compared to the hole size in the recovered plate at right.

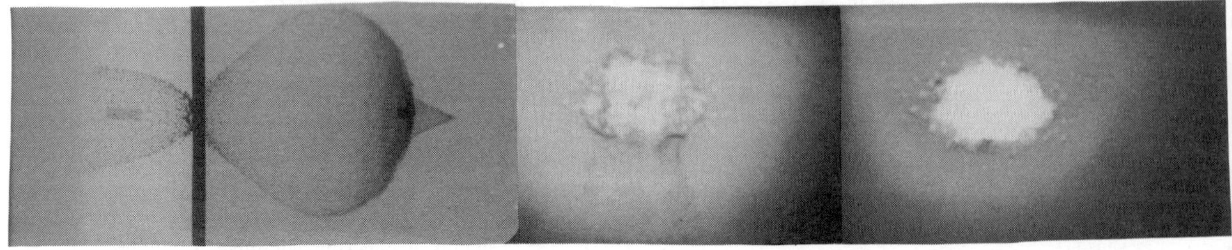

Figure 2d. The rod at left 5.9 μs before impact and the debris cloud formation at 18.2 μs after impact. Dynamic hole formation is displayed at 51.2 μs after impact of the bumper plate and is compared to the hole size in the recovered plate at right.

Table 1. Summary of Experiments

Shot No.	Impactor Shape	Impactor Dimensions diam. x thick. (mm x mm)	Impactor Mass (gm)	Impactor Velocity (km/s)	Front Velocity (km/s)	Lateral/ Radial Velocity (km/s)	Bumper Hole Size diam. x diam. (mm x mm)	Dynamic Hole Size diam. x diam. (mm x mm)	Recovered Hole Size diam. x diam. (mm x mm)
1511	Plate	13 x 0.759	0.731	5.01	5.22	0.92	20 x 20	14.5 x 13.5	14.5 x 13.5
1515	Sphere	5.77	0.719	4.98	4.71	2.84	12.0 x 11.4	No Hole	No Hole
1553	Cylinder	5.05 x5.05	0.716	5.22	5.22	Tilted	14.4x14.4 Torn	6.1 x 50	26.2x56.1
1554	Rod	3.98 x 14.2	1.241	4.97	5.28	1.93	10.1 x 10.1	38.1x36.3	35.6x35.6

Figure 2, the projectile orientation is determined prior to bumper plate impact. In addition, the debris cloud formation at ~ 19 µs after impact is also indicated. (Multiple exposures were taken to determine the debris evolution but are not displayed in Figure 2.) Radiographic measurements of the backwall were also made during the experiment to determine the *in-situ (i.e., the dynamic*) formation of a hole in the backwall. This x-ray was exposed at an oblique angle.

RESULTS

The summary of the experiments reported in this paper is given in Table 1. A detailed summary of all experiments conducted is reported elsewhere [5]. Multiple exposures taken to determine the debris cloud evolution are also reported in reference 5. Figure 2 indicates the debris cloud evolution for different projectile shapes at ~ 19 µs after impact.

The debris front velocity indicated in the table is an average of the three different radiographic measurements taken at three different times [5]. Likewise, the lateral velocity reported in the paper is determined at the maximum radius of the debris cloud as determined by the multiple x-ray exposures. It represents the rate of change of radius with time. The debris front velocity and the lateral velocity are displayed in Figure 3 for all experiments performed in this investigation.

The hole size in the recovered backwall plate (see Table 1) are indicated in Figure 4 for plate and spherical projectiles as a function of impact velocity. The hole size shown in Figure 4 is transformed to an equivalent areal dimension. The hole size in the bumper plate is also given in Table 1. Because the impactor in the cylinder experiment is considerably tilted prior to impact, the hole size is not symmetrical as in the other experiments, and the bumper is torn.

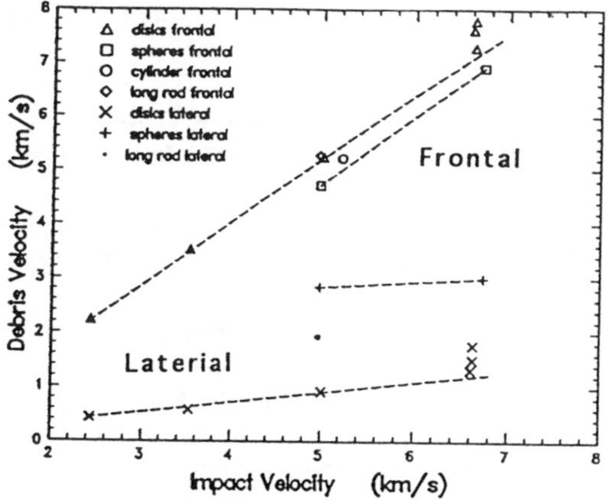

Figure 3. Debris Front and Lateral Velocity variation with impact velocity for all projectiles

DISCUSSIONS

Size and Shape Dependence of the Debris Cloud

The debris clouds generated upon impact of different projectiles are indicated in Figure 2. As summarized in Table 1, these experiments were performed for a constant

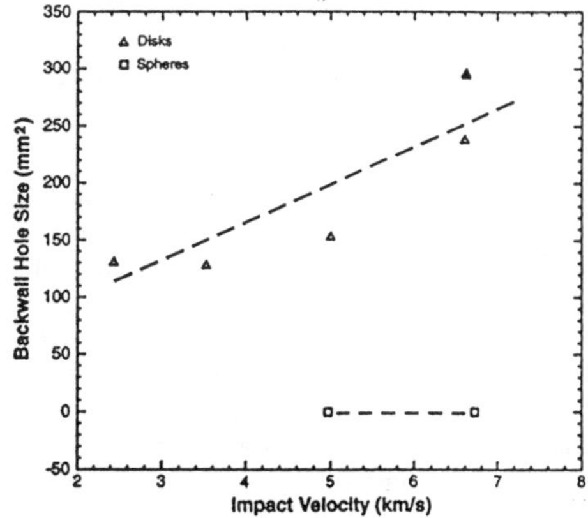

Figure 4. Backwall hole size as a function of impact velocity for plate and spherical projectiles.

mass projectile and at an impact velocity of ~ 5 km/s. For plate impact, the distinct features of the observed debris cloud consist of a leading edge resembling a high density plate followed by a lower density column over the remaining length. The shape of the debris cloud is tilted similar to the impactor tilt angle. The central column does not appear to radially expand with time, suggesting the one-dimensional nature of propagation for the central column. The central column is surrounded by a lower density cloud which is presumably vapor. The lateral dispersion for the plate impact is the least when compared to the debris cloud generated by other projectile shapes. This is graphically illustrated in Figure 3 where the radial velocity for the plate is the lowest of all the other projectile shapes. Since the cloud has not dispersed sufficiently, this central column is quite detrimental when it interacts with the backwall.

The debris cloud in Figure 2b is for a spherical impact configuration with a similar mass at the same velocity. The debris cloud has a high-density diffused leading edge that is considerably dispersed within the debris cloud. Two-dimensional effects resulting from the impact of the sphere and bumper shield disperses the debris cloud more efficiently, and imparts a large radial velocity component. This is indicated in Figure 3. For this reason, the backwall is not penetrated due to the spherical nature of the debris cloud, since the impulse is spread over a larger surface area of the backwall.

Figures 2c and 2d show the debris cloud that results from impact of a cylinder(L/D=1) and a rod(L/D=3.6). Even though the masses of the two projectiles are not identical, some features of the debris cloud appear to be common to both. They both have a distinct conical leading edge separated from the spherical debris cloud. In the case of the cylinder, it sees sufficiently high loading stresses resulting in total fragmentation; however, due to stress attenuation effects in the long rod the back end of the rod remains intact. This results in a remnant rod, travelling unperturbed at the impact velocity, as indicated in Figure 2d. (There are also some solid fragments along the periphery of the spherical front which are not clearly distinguishable in Figure 2d.)

In both the examples shown in Figures 2c and 2d, the backwall is ruptured. As a result of significant tilt for cylinder impact, the backwall appears to be torn. It is anticipated that rupture would have occurred under ideal impact conditions [6], but with a smaller hole compared to plate impact since the debris cloud in Figure 2c appears to be dispersed. The experiment needs to repeated to address this issue. It is not surprising that a rupture was caused by the debris generated in the long rod impact of Figure 2d. The remnant rod in the debris cloud travelling at 5 km/s can cause the backwall structure to rupture; this is further compounded by solid fragments that are also present in the debris.

Debris Velocities

Figure 3 shows the propagation characteristics of the debris cloud that are indicated in Figure 2. In all experiments, the leading edge of the debris front (defined as the frontal velocity) is traversing at the impact velocity. The lateral velocity, however, is more dependent on the impactor geometry. For the debris cloud formed by the plate impact the lateral velocity was 0.92 km/s (~ 18% of the impact velocity) while the sphere impact had a lateral velocity of 2.84 km/s (~ 57% of the impact velocity). As mentioned before, one dimensional effects dominate the debris cloud propagation processes in plate impact geometry, while two-dimensional effects influence the spherical impact configuration, resulting in a large lateral velocity component. No lateral velocity could be obtained for the cylinder impact because the skewed debris cloud resulting from the tilted impact made measurements difficult. The rod lateral velocity of 1.93 km/s (~ 39% of the impact velocity) falls between the plate and the disk.

ACKNOWLEDGMENTS

This work performed at Sandia National Laboratories supported by the U.S. Department of Energy under contract DE-AC04-76DP00789. We would also like to acknowledge Tom Tsai and John Connell, Defense Nuclear Agency for their interest and partial support provided for this work.

REFERENCES

[1] E. S. Hertel, L. C. Chhabildas, L. Yarrington, "Computational Determination Of Ballistic Limits For A Simple Whipple Bumper Shield," in *Proceedings of the Workshop on Hypervelocity Impacts in Space-1991,* ed. by J. A. M. McDonnell, 1992, pp. 15-18.

[2] L. C. Chhabildas, M. B. Boslough, W. D. Reinhart, C. A. Hall, "Debris Cloud Characterization at Impact Velocities over 5 to 11 km/s", this volume.

[3] S. A. Mullin, D. L. Littlefield, C. E. Anderson, Jr., N. T. Tsai, Velocity Scaling of Impacts into Spacecraft Targets at 8 to 15 km/s, private communication.

[4] A. J. Piekutowski, *Intl. J. Impact Engng.,* V10, pp. 453-471, (1990).

[5] C. H. Konrad, L. C. Chhabildas, M. B. Boslough, A. J. Piekutowski, K. L. Poormon, S. A. Mullin, D. L. Littlefield, Sandia National Laboratories Report (unpublished).

[6] R. H. Morrison, "A Preliminary Investigation Of Projectile Shape Effects In Hypervelocity Impact Of Double-sheet Structures," NASA Technical Note NASA TN D-6944, 1972.

TARGET RESPONSE TO DEBRIS CLOUD INCIDENCE

Marlin E. Kipp
Sandia National Laboratories
Computational Physics and Mechanics Department 1432
Albuquerque, NM, USA, 87185-5800*

The extent of penetration and/or perforation of a target layer by a debris cloud, whose particle mass distribution and velocities were calculated from a previous impact, was determined with two computational approaches. First, the size of single or paired particles required for target perforation was calculated and compared with the largest particle expected based on the fragment size distribution in the debris cloud. A second approach used a three-dimensional shock-wave code to calculate the explicit interaction of individual particles in the debris cloud with the target. The cloud was represented by randomly locating the particles within an envelope, maintaining the mass and size distribution of the particles. This interaction of the cloud of particles produced target surface craters and penetration comparable to recovered witness plates from impact experiments.

INTRODUCTION

When a projectile perforates the initial layer of a spaced target array, fragmented projectile and target material combine to form an expanding debris cloud. Analysis of the damage to a subsequent target caused by this debris has been the subject of considerable study (*e.g.* [1]). If the targets are relatively close, the numerical analysis has typically convected the ejecta from the first impact to the second target, and computed the impact effects of this expanding, rarified material. This provides insight into the damage to the primary target, expansion characteristics of the debris cloud, and some information about the integrity of secondary targets.

In order to capture the details characterizing ejected solid or liquid fragments and their interaction with subsequent targets, additional computational refinement is required. This is particularly necessary if the target separation is large enough for the fragments to form a dispersed cloud. Under these conditions, the fragments impact a secondary target as discrete particles, and the cloud cannot be represented as a distributed mass of low mean density.

A quantitative definition of the particle size and mass distribution of the debris cloud that results from the initial target impact can be determined from current fragmentation theories, using material state information calculated at the time of fracture (*e.g.* [2],[3]). An estimate of the envelope of the cloud can be obtained using the residual axial and radial expansion velocities of the material ejecta, and extrapolating to the position of incidence with the next target plate; guidance is also provided by radiographic and holographic diagnostics of debris clouds ([2],[4]).

Two computational paths were pursued for evaluating the extent of penetration and/or perforation this debris cloud would have on a subsequent target layer. The first method calculated the size of single or paired particles required to perforate the target, and compared it with the largest expected size determined by the fragment distribution. A second approach used a three-dimensional shock-wave code to calculate the explicit interaction of individual particles in the cloud with the target.

DEBRIS CLOUD DEFINITION

The specific configuration chosen to illustrate these computational techniques is that of a 6.35 mm hard steel sphere of mass $M = 1.05$ g and initial velocity of 4570 m/s impacting a 3.38 mm PMMA (polymethylmethacrylate) primary target at normal incidence, with an aluminum witness plate to intercept the debris cloud [2]. The 12.7 mm aluminum witness plate is 470 mm directly behind and parallel to the PMMA target. The steel sphere is shattered during impact with the PMMA, and the debris prop-

*This work performed at Sandia National Laboratories supported by the U.S. DOE under contract #DE-AC04-76DP00789.

agates to the aluminum witness plate, diverging both radially and axially during the time of transit to form a clearly defined disk-like cloud [2]. The residual axial velocity was 4300 m/s, and the radial expansion velocity of the cloud was 270 m/s. The statistics of the particle sizes were calculated and found to compare favorably with radiographic data. The calculated particle size distribution can be represented analytically as an exponential function, N_m, of the particle mass, m,

$$N_m = A\frac{N_0 m^2}{\mu^3}e^{-3m/\mu}, \qquad (1)$$

where A is a constant, N_0 is the number of particles in the cloud, and μ is the average particle mass, defined by $\mu = M/N_0$. The coefficient A is 13.5, which normalizes the distribution to the correct total mass. In this experiment, the number of particles is about 300, the average particle mass is 3.5 mg, and the largest mass is about 7 mg; assuming spherical fragments, the average particle diameter is 0.95 mm. The largest number of particles have a diameter of about 0.7 mm (Figure 1).

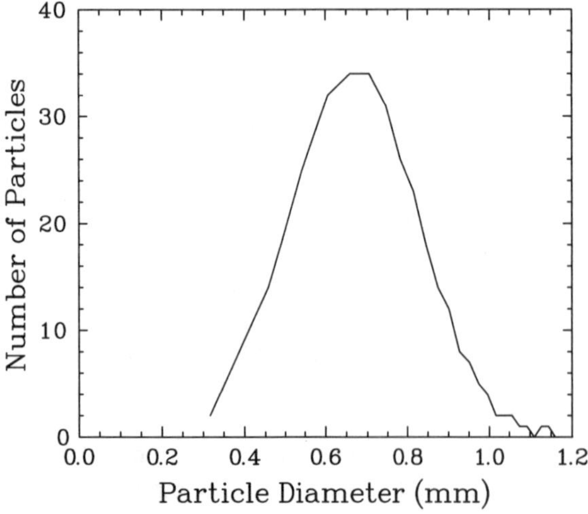

Figure 1. Fragment number *vs.* size distribution for 300 steel particles, formed by impact with a PMMA target.

The dimensions of the debris cloud envelope at the location of the aluminum witness plate were determined from the calculated expansion and transit velocities of the debris, and adjusted with radiograph data. This cloud is defined by a circular disk of diameter about 55 mm and thickness about 10 mm.

The coordinate positions of each particle were assigned in the envelope of the cloud with a random number generator. The particles are then fairly uniformly distributed within the cloud. No attempt was made to represent the preferential spatial positions or shapes of particular particle sizes that are observed in the radiographs of these events. The axial velocity of the particles at impact with the witness plate is 4300 m/s; each particle was also assigned a radial expansion velocity scaled to the outer expansion velocity of 270 m/s.

SECONDARY TARGET RESPONSE

The debris cloud of steel fragments defined in the previous section - particle location and velocity - was used as the initial condition to evaluate the extent of penetration and/or perforation resulting from impact with the aluminum witness plate. All of the calculations were made with the Eulerian shock-wave propagation code, CTH [5]. The materials were modeled with a Mie-Gruneisen equation of state, with elastic perfectly plastic deviatoric behavior (see Table 1). The primary focus of these numerical approaches is on the integrity of the aluminum witness plate when impacted by debris.

Table 1: Material Parameters for CTH Calculations

Property / Material	Aluminum	Steel
Density, ρ_0 (kg/m^3)	2785	7850
Bulk Sound Speed, C_0 (m/s)	5238	4610
Slope of U_s - U_p Hugoniot, s	1.338	1.73
Gruneisen Coefficient, γ_0	2.00	1.67
Specific Heat, C_v (J/kg-K)	948	464
Yield Stress, Y_0 (GPa)	0.3	2.0
Poisson Ratio, ν	0.333	0.2897
Fracture Stress, σ_f (GPa)	1.5	4.0

Single and Paired Particle Analyses

Two-dimensional axisymmetric analyses of spherical particle impacts on a 12.7 mm aluminum target were made to determine the threshold particle size for perforation of the target, and to compare that size with the sizes available in the distribution. This study was done numerically, since directly applicable penetration data or verified analytic formulae for the target perforation limits were not available. The particle impacts were assumed to be events uncoupled from other regions of the debris impact on the target. Of the many possible impact configurations of particles in a debris cloud, two were considered: (1) a single particle, and (2) two identical particles on the same trajectory, separated by the cloud thickness of 10 mm (the largest separation that can occur). For a single spherical particle, a diameter greater than 2.5 mm is required to perforate this target; for two spherical particles, a diameter greater than 1.6 mm is required to perforate the same target (Figure 2). In either case the particle size required for perforation is larger than the maximum fragment size defined by the debris cloud distribution (1.2 mm, Figure 1). A 1.2 mm spherical particle penetrates only one-half the thickness of the aluminum target.

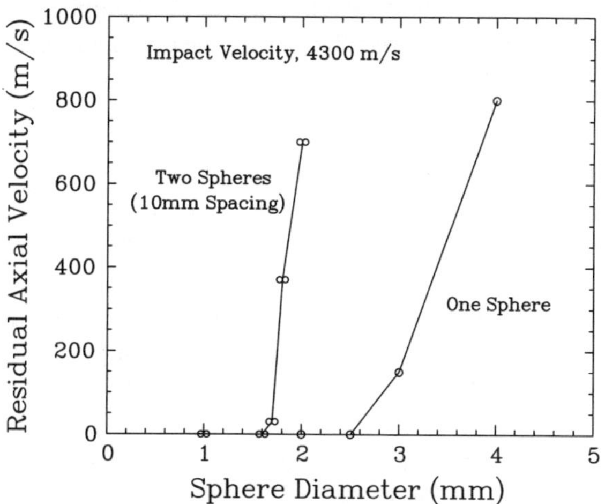

Figure 2. Calculated residual velocity after penetration, for one and two spheres impacting 12.7 mm aluminum at 4300 m/s.

One variation on particle shape is that of a splinter, or long rod. The longest possible fragment from the original spherical projectile is 6.35 mm. The largest mass allowed by the distribution, 7 mg, limits the rod diameter to 0.42 mm. Normal impact of this particle at 4300 m/s is calculated to be at the threshold for perforation of the aluminum witness plate.

Full Debris Cloud Analysis

The second approach is a three-dimensional numerical simulation of the complete cloud of particles impacting the aluminum target. The physical space of the debris cloud and 12.7 mm aluminum witness plate was defined by uniform 0.3 mm cubical cells, resulting in about 6.25 million cells in the calculation. The resolution of the calculation provides about 2 cell widths to define the diameter of the particles of average size in the distribution. Consequently, some of the particles will be shapeless masses impacting the target rather than well-defined spheres. Views of the initial conditions are shown in Figure 3.

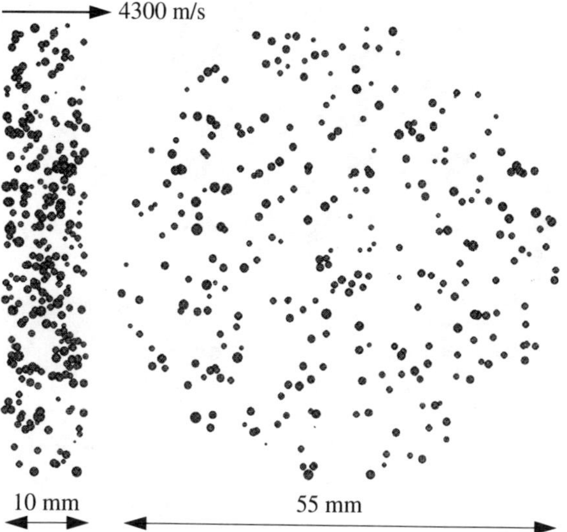

Figure 3. Debris cloud of 300 steel particles, randomly placed within the envelope of a disk (10 mm x 55 mm), prior to impact with an aluminum target (edge and top views).

By 10 μs after impact the craters have all been formed and the steel particles have transferred their momentum to the aluminum witness plate. Edge and surface views of the target at this time are shown in Figure 4, in which both the jagged impact crater lips and the significant rear surface bulge are evident. No perforation of the aluminum target has occurred, although there are crater depths to within 4 mm of the rear surface. Extensive void formation resulting from internal fractures is within 1 mm of the rear surface. An estimate of the computed excavation (crater) volume of aluminum is 3 cm^3.

Figure 4. Views of the calculated aluminum target plate at 10 μs: an edge view of the target (upper), and a perspective view of the target (lower).

Computational and Experimental Observations

Both numerical analyses indicate that the particles in this debris cloud will not perforate the aluminum target; however the calculated single rod and debris cloud results suggest that the threshold for perforation has nearly been reached. This principal conclusion is verified by experimental results: in two nearly identical experiments, one witness plate was not perforated, and the other was perforated with a single small hole [2]. Other aspects calculated for the full debris cloud impact, such as the target impact surface features and rear surface bulge, are similar to what is observed on the recovered witness plates. The actual volume of excavation and extent of crater coupling in the plates appears to be somewhat greater than what has been calculated [2].

CONCLUSIONS

The analyses described here provide two complementary methods to determine the effects of debris on secondary targets, both leading to correct assessment of the extent of protection offered by the secondary target. Analysis with the full debris cloud present is the more comprehensive approach. Coupling the debris characterized from an initial impact event to the numerical simulation of the resulting debris cloud of discrete particles impacting a secondary target provides a view of the entire impact process in unparalleled detail. Analyses with variations in the size distribution and particle shape for the full debris cloud would provide support for the proximity to threshold that has been calculated here.

ACKNOWLEDGEMENT

The author is grateful to D. E. Grady for providing radiographs of debris clouds and examples of recovered secondary targets, and to D. L. Campbell for assistance in the visualization of the computations.

REFERENCES

[1] L. C. Chhabildas, E. Hertel, and S. Hill, Hypervelocity Impact Tests and Simulations of Single Whipple Bumper Shield Concepts at 10 km/s, *Int. J. Impact Engng.*, in press (1993).

[2] M. E. Kipp, D. E. Grady, and J. W. Swegle, Experimental and Numerical Studies of High-Velocity Impact Fragmentation, Sandia National Laboratories Report SAND93-0773, July 1993.

[3] G. R. Johnson, R. A. Stryk, T. J. Holmquist, and O. A. Souka, Recent EPIC Code Developments for High Velocity Impact: 3D Element Arrangements and 2D Fragment Distributions, *Int. J. Impact Engng.*, 10, pp. 281-294 (1990).

[4] J. A. Ang, B. D. Hansche, C. H. Konrad, W. C. Sweatt, S. M. Gosling, and R. Hickman, Pulsed Holography for Hypervelocity Impact Diagnostics, *Int. J. Impact Engng.*, in press (1993).

[5] J. M. McGlaun, S. L. Thompson, and M. G. Elrick, CTH: A Three-Dimensional Shock Wave Physics Code, *Int. J. Impact Engng.*, 10, pp. 351-360 (1990).

HIGH-SPEED IMPACT OF DRY-ICE PROJECTILES ON THIN PLATES

Koichi Tanaka and Teiichi Ookouchi
Department of Mechanical Engineering,
Nagoya Institute of Technology
Gokiso-cho,Showa-ku,Nagoya 466, Japan

This paper is a report of an experimental investigation on the high-speed impact of cylindrical dry-ice projectiles on thin circular plates of stainelss alloy. One of the purposes of the present study is to develop, from an engineering point of view, ways of metal forming such as deep drawing and forging by the use of the kinetic energy of high-speed projectiles, and another is to elucidate the shock phenomena of dry-ice, the dynamic physical properties of which are not understood. Our main interest is devoted to the deep drawing of plates and the deformation process of plates and dry-ice projectiles, which are numerically simulated by means of the hydro-code.

INTRODUCTION

Dry-ice is usually used for low-temperature preservation and the refrigeration of food and other things, and is rarely used for industrial purposes. Utilizing the fact that dry-ice is pure solid carbon dioxide and is easily sublimed, we intend to use it as a high-speed projectile for metal forming such as deep drawing and forging which differ from the usual methods of processing which use solid punches and dies[1].

In this paper, an experimental investigation is reported on the direct impact of dry-ice projectiles on thin circular plates of stainless alloy (SUS304) which were set up on a cup-like deep drawing die. The relationship between the initial kinetic energy of the projectiles and the deformation of the thin plates is discussed as the central topic.

The processes of the deep drawing were also numerically simulated by means of the computer code AUTODYN-2D(Century Dynamics Inc.). Paraffin projectiles were used successfully instead of dry-ice projectiles although the effect of sublimation on the impact phenomena could not be taken into account.

The hydrodynamic pressure generated by the impact of dry-ice projectiles on flat and rigid surfaces was observed, and as anticipated the dry-ice disintegrated and sublimed owing to the high stress intensity and high temperature at the impact surface.

EXPERIMENTS IN DEEP DRAWING

As depicted in Figure 1, thin circular plates of SUS304 were set up in a cavity of $110mm$ diameter and $2mm$ depth between the axisymmetrical nozzle and the cup-like die. The shape and dimensions of the die and dry-ice projectiles are shown in Figure 2. Dimensions of specimens used in the experiments are listed in Table 1. The dry-ice projectile, which is accelerated by a nitrogen gas gun of $100mm$-inner diameter and $4m$-length, enters the mouth of the nozzle, is compressed and deformed, and then impacts diretly on the plate surface. Each of the projectiles has a ring of slender steel wire buried in it and the speeds of the projectiles are measured by two B-dot type magnetic in-

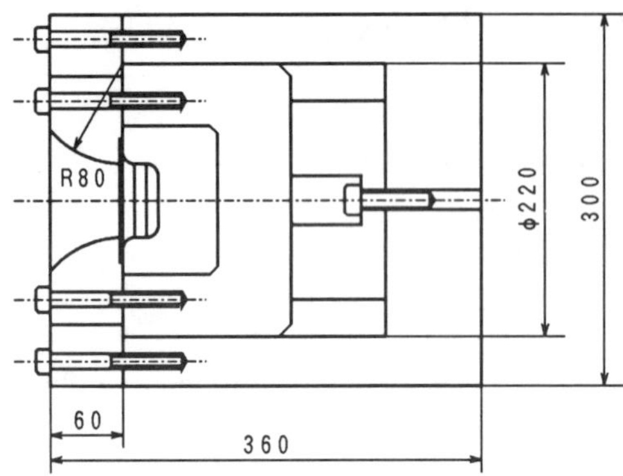

Figure 1. Equipment for deep drawing

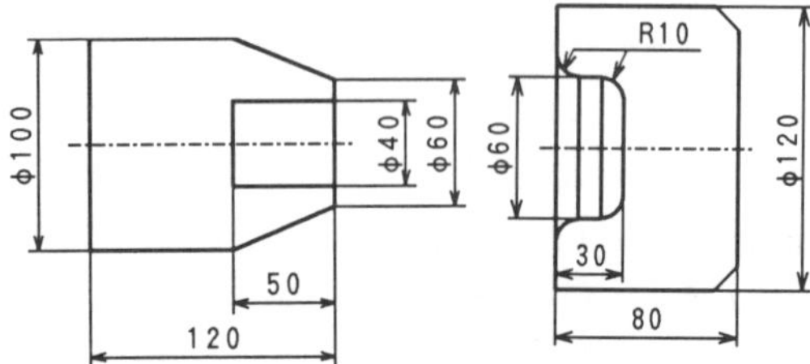

Figure 2. Profiles of the die and projectile

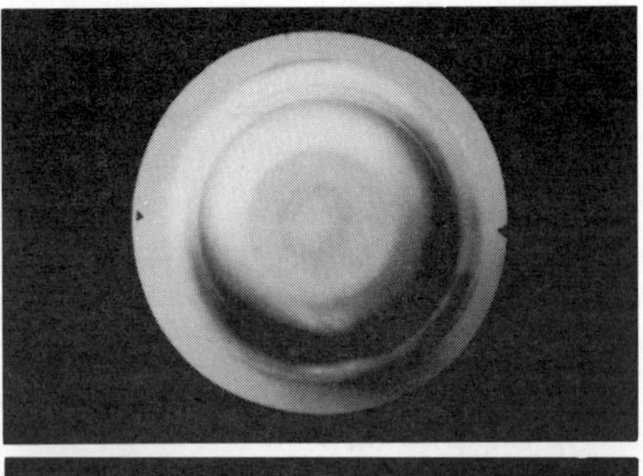

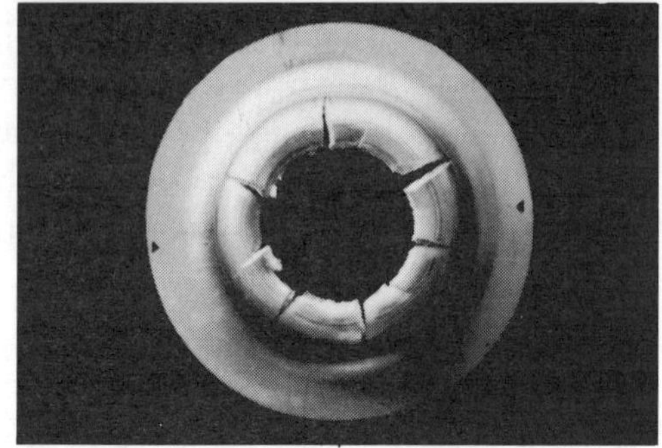

Figure 3. Examples of the drawn plates

ductance coils located just in front of the muzzle.

Figure 3 shows samples which are drawn in different kinetic energies. As the impact speed is increased, the deformation develops from shallow dishes to deep cups which completely fill the die profile. For exceedingly large impact speeds circular failure and radial cracks occur near the bottom of the cup. Among the many factors which would affect deep drawing, the main interests are focused on the relationship between the initial kinetic energy of the projectiles and the plastic deformation of the plates.

Table 1. Dimensions of test pieces

Thickness [*mm*]	Blank Diameter [*mm*]
2.0	100
	105
	110
1.4	110
1.0	110

Figure 4 shows the relationship between the initial kinetic energy of the projectile and the depth of drawn cups of various thicknesses. The depth is increased as the energy is increased. As the energy reaches a certain value the depth is increased abruptly, but further increase of energy causes a decrease of the depth reversely, because a spring-back occurs at the bottom. If the energy is too great, fracture occurs near the bottom. The smaller the thickness of the plate, and the smaller the drawing ratio, the better the drawing the less the failure that occurs.

As the plate is drawn the diameter of the flange decreases owing to the draw-in. However, when the kinetic energy reaches a certain value the draw-in ceases and the flange diameter increases reversely as depicted in Figure 5. Reduction of the flange diameter is larger in the parallel and perpendicular directions than

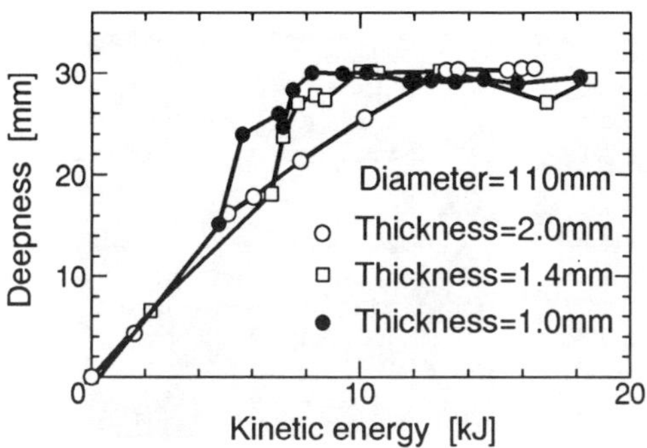

Figure 4. Deepness of cups *versus* kinetic energy

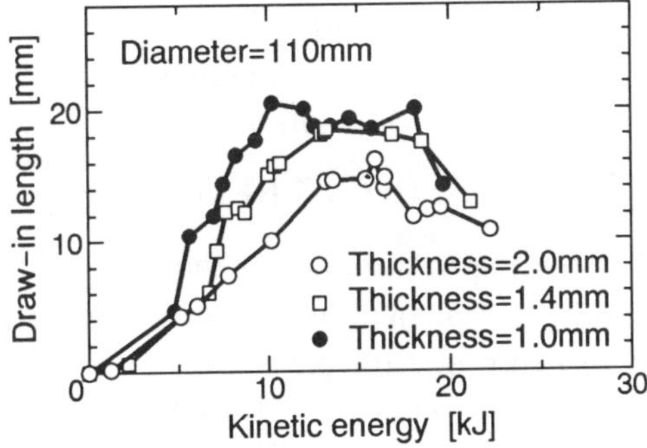

Figure 5. Draw-in length *versus* kinetic energy

it is in the direction of an angle 45° to the rolling direction of the plates. Although only a few graphs can be shown here, from these figures of the curves of the depth and the flange diameter of the cup, it is possible to determine the appropriate energy level of projectiles.

NUMERICAL SIMULATION OF DEEP DRAWING

In order to examine the dynamical behavior of plates and projectiles during the drawing process,the computer simulations were made by means of AUTODYN-2D. Please note that paraffin was used instead of dry-ice for the projectile,since the constitutive equation and the Hugoniot relation of dry-ice are little known at present[2,3,4]. Material constants used in the calculations are quoted from the material library involved in AUTODYN-2D, where Lagrangian elements are used for stainless plates and other metallic parts and a Eulerian element is used for paraffin.

Figure 6 dispalys the deformation process, where the diameter and the thickness of the plate is $100mm$ and $2.0mm$ respectively, and the speed of the projectile is $120m/s$.

As the projectile rushes into the nozzle, deforms itself along the nozzle profile, and impacts the central part of the plate the plate begins deformation momentarily. The central portion and the rear side of the plate is subjected to tensile stress, while the flange and the impacted surface are subjected to compressional stress. After a while, the front surface of the projectile contacts the whole surface of the plate and the plates are subjected entirely to tensile stress. The center of the plate first touches the bottom of the die and then the plate is expanded radially and pressed against the inner wall of the die. Finally, the projectile detaches from the plate and the drawing is completed. As mentioned above it can be seen that the flange diameter is gradually decreased while the deformation is progressing. It can also be understood from the simulation that fractures near the bottom are caused by high tensile stress when excessive kinetic energy is applied. The deformation process shown in Figure 3 was simulated successfuly, although the sublimation effect of dry-ice could not be taken into account. It must be emphasized that, in the present method, drawing is carried out by both the axial and radial forces exerted by dry-ice projectiles having fluidity and little friction in contrast with common deep drawing where the unidirectional and frictional movement of solid punches is used.

IMPACT OF DRY-ICE PROJECTILES ON A RIGID SURFACE

As has been shown above, dry-ice projectiles are deformed and subjected to high stress

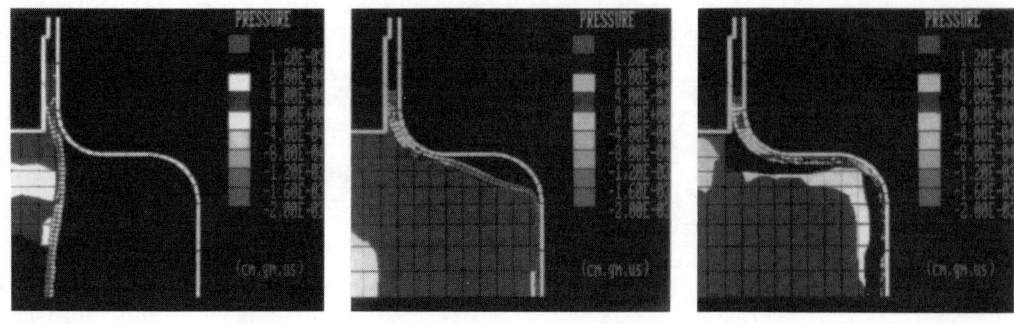

Figure 6. Numerical simulation of the deep drawing process

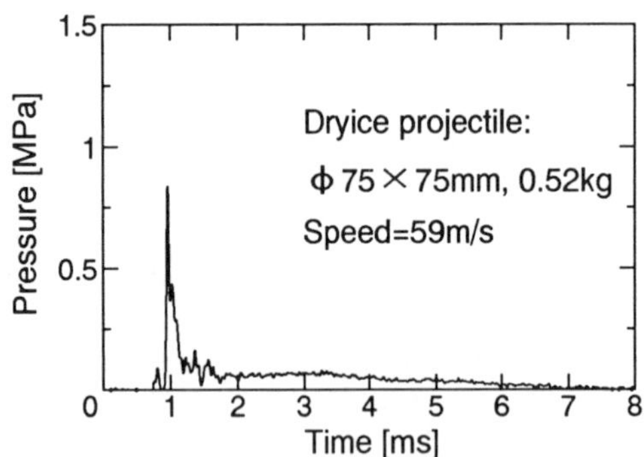

Figure 7. A pressure wave at the impact surface

intensity and high temperature at the contact surface, where sublimation occurs. Therefore, there may be a highly pressurized cavity of CO_2 gas between the dry-ice, and the plate and the hydrodynamic pressure serves to expand the plate radially in addition to the action of the axial momentum of the projectiles. In this connection, the hydrodynamic pressure generated at the impact surface is measured by a pressure gauge which is set behind a narrow hole drilled in a heavy solid target with a flat surface on which cylindrical dry-ice projectiles impact.

The pressure is increased abruptly and then decreased, but the trailing wave of relatively long duration observed clearly in Figure 7 is due to sublimation at the contact surface. If abrupt and explosive sublimation occured in a closed vessel, the pressure would be much greater than that observed here, since pressure leakage would be prevented.

CONCLUDING REMARKS

The high-speed impact phenomena of cylindrical dry-ice projectiles centered around the deep drawing of thin plates were invetigated. The relationship between the deformation process of the plates and the initial kinetic energy of the dry-ice projectiles was elucidated by experiments and numerical simulations. Dry-ice projectiles play the roles of both a high-speed solid punch with large momentum and small friction, and an explosive which expands in all directions and generates high pressure.

REFERENCES

[1] T.Z.Blazynski, *Plasticity and Modern Metal-Forming Technology*, London; Elsevier Appllied Science, 1989, ch.4, 7, and 8.

[2] K.Tanaka and T.Ookouchi, "Impact of Dry-ice Projectiles on Elastic Plastic Bodies", in *Shock Compression of Condensed Matter-1991*, Amsterdam; North-Holand, 1992, pp.1003-1006.

[3] Lin-gun Liu, Compression and Phase Behavior of Solid CO_2 to Half Megabar,*Earth and Planetary Science Letters*, 71(1984), pp.104-110.

[4] V.N.Zubarev and G.S.Telegin, The Impact Compressibility of Liquid Nitrogen and Solid Carbon Dioxide,*Soviet Physics-Doklady*, 7-1(1962), pp.34-36.

THE EFFECT OF THE CONSTITUTIVE RESPONSE ON THE PREDICTED TEMPERATURES IN COPPER JETS

D. J. Nikkel, Jr. and D. H. Lassila
University of California
Lawrence Livermore National Laboratory
P.O. Box 808, L-342, Livermore, CA 94551

This paper examines the effect of various elements in a set constitutive equations on the predicted stress and temperature response of material undergoing pressure and strain histories representative of those in copper jets formed by shaped charges. It is found that the dependence of the flow stress on hydrostatic pressure, which enters here through the pressure dependence of the shear modulus, has a significant effect on the predicted flow stress and hence temperature.

INTRODUCTION

Metallurgical phenomena which effect the performance of shaped charge jets [1,2], such as high temperature embrittlement in copper, are influenced by the temperature history which the material undergoes. Numerical codes have been successful in predicting motions and pressures occurring from the detonation of shaped charges, which is primarily a hydrodynamically driven phenomena. The temperature of material in a shaped charge jet is mainly a result of heating from mechanical work (shock heating is minimal), and hence it is a direct function of the flow stress. Here the effects of various elements in the constitutive equations on the prediction of temperature in a shaped charge jet are examined. In particular, we examine the effects on the predicted stress and temperature response due to the dependence of the flow stress on hydrostatic pressure (entering through the pressure dependence of the shear modulus) and to the temperature dependence of the specific heat. Comparison is also made between the predictions of the Steinberg-Guinan constitutive equation for the flow stress [3] and that of the Mechanical Threshold Stress (MTS) model [4–6].

METHODOLOGY

In order to isolate the effects of a particular aspect of the constitutive equations, we will focus on the prediction of the stress and temperature at one material point in a copper liner of a shaped charge which ultimately ends up in the jet (Figure 1). An Eulerian hydrocode provided predictions of the pressure and equivalent plastic strain histories to which that material particle was subjected (Figure 2). The pressure shown in the HE shock is higher than the code prediction, but is more representative of experimental values. Since this process is primarily driven by

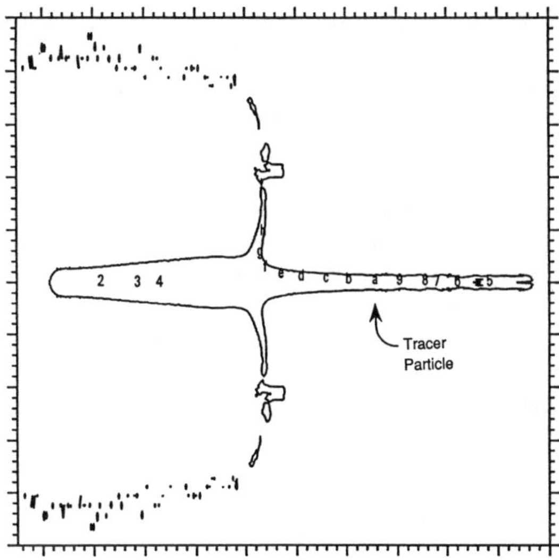

Figure 1. Eulerian hydrocode calculation of the shape of a shaped charge liner 40 μs after HE detonation. This calculation is relatively insensitive to flow stress.

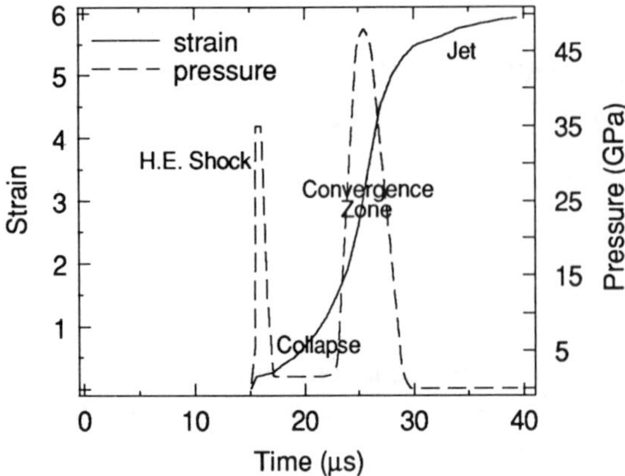

Figure 2. Calculated strain and pressure histories for the tracer particle in the shaped charge liner.

hydrodynamics, such predictions are relatively insensitive to the constitutive equations for the deviatoric part of the response (i.e., the "strength model"). It is these later constitutive equations which we examine, hence the strain and pressure histories in Figure 2 are used as the input for all of the calculations which follow.

In order to calculate the stress and temperature once a strain and pressure history are known, constitutive equations are required for the yield stress (or "strength"), the relationship between applied pressure, volume change and temperature (or energy), and the relationship between internal energy and temperature. These equations are also supplemented by a relation giving the melting temperature as a function of the compression of the material. These basic equations are briefly summarized below. For more details and background refer to the cited references (noting differences in notation).

The Steinberg-Guinan Model

A commonly used equation for the flow stress (σ) of metals, which depends on the strain (ε), temperature (T), and pressure (p), is given by [3]:

$$\sigma = Y_0[1 + \beta(\varepsilon_i + \varepsilon)]^n \frac{G(p,T)}{G_0} , \qquad (1)$$

where the flow stress has an upper bound

$$\sigma \leq \frac{G(p,T)}{G_0} Y_{max} . \qquad (2)$$

The quantities Y_0, β, ε_i, n, G_0 and Y_{max} are constants. The flow stress scales with the shear modulus G, which is taken to depend on pressure, temperature and density (ρ) according to

$$\frac{G(p,T)}{G_0} = 1 + \mathcal{A} p \left(\frac{\rho_0}{\rho}\right)^{1/3} - \mathcal{B}(T - 300) , \qquad (3)$$

where $\mathcal{A}$ and $\mathcal{B}$ are constants.

Flow Stress from the MTS Model

An alternative equation for the flow stress is given by the strain rate and temperature dependent MTS model as [7]:

$$\sigma = \left\{ \sigma_a + \hat{\sigma} \left[1 - \left(\frac{kT}{b^3 g_0 G(p,T)} \ln\left(\frac{\dot{\varepsilon}_0}{\dot{\varepsilon}}\right)\right)^{1/q} \right]^{1/\varphi} \right\} \frac{G(p,T)}{G_0} , \qquad (4)$$

where $\hat{\sigma}$ is an additional state variable which is governed by the evolution equation

$$\frac{d\hat{\sigma}}{d\varepsilon} = \left[1 - \frac{\tanh\left(\frac{2\hat{\sigma}}{\hat{\sigma}_s}\right)}{\tanh(2)} \right] \{C_1 + C_2 \log(\dot{\varepsilon}) + C_3\, \dot{\varepsilon}\} ,$$
$$\hat{\sigma}_s = \hat{\sigma}_{s0} \left(\frac{\dot{\varepsilon}}{\dot{\varepsilon}_{s0}}\right)^{\frac{kT}{b^3 A G(p,T)}} . \qquad (5)$$

The quantities σ_a, k, b, g_0, $\dot{\varepsilon}_0$, φ, q, C_1, C_2, C_3, $\hat{\sigma}_{s0}$, $\dot{\varepsilon}_{s0}$, and A are constants. The shear modulus is again taken to be dependent on the pressure and temperature as given by (3). Note that previous work using the MTS model [4–8] has not included the pressure dependence in the shear modulus, although temperature dependence has been incorporated and shown to be a dominating effect in some applications [8]. The previously used form of G in the MTS model is recovered by setting $\mathcal{A}$=0 in (3).

Grüneisen Equation of State

The relation between the pressure, the change in density or compression ($\mu \equiv \rho/\rho_0 - 1$), and internal energy per unit reference volume (E) is given by [9]:

$$p = \begin{cases} \dfrac{\rho_0 C_0^2 \mu \left[1 + \left(1 - \frac{\gamma_0}{2}\right)\mu - \frac{b}{2}\mu^2\right]}{\left[1 - (S_1 - 1)\mu - S_2 \frac{\mu^2}{\mu + 1} - S_3 \frac{\mu^3}{(\mu + 1)^2}\right]^2} \\ \quad + (\gamma_0 + b\mu)E \ , \qquad \text{if } \mu > 0 \ , \\ \rho_0 C_0^2 \mu + \gamma_0 E \ , \qquad \text{if } \mu < 0 \ , \end{cases} \tag{6}$$

where C_0, γ_0, b, S_1, S_2, and S_3 are constants.

Thermal Effects

The deformation process takes place so quickly that it may be viewed as being adiabatic, and the energy is calculated from

$$\dot{E} = \frac{\rho_0}{\rho}(\sigma\dot{\varepsilon} + \frac{p}{\rho}\dot{\rho}) \ . \tag{7}$$

As is typical in hydrocodes, the temperature is computed from the energy as $T = (E - E_c)/\rho_0 C$, where E_c is the cold-compression energy (see [3], eqn. 4) and C is the temperature dependent specific heat which here is of the form

$$C = \bar{A} + \bar{B}T \ . \tag{8}$$

The temperature at which the material melts is assumed to be given by a modified Lindemann law [9]:

$$T_{\text{melt}} = T_{m0} \exp\left\{2a\left(1 - \frac{\rho_0}{\rho}\right)\right\}\left(\frac{\rho}{\rho_0}\right)^{2(\gamma_0 - a - 1/3)} \ , \tag{9}$$

where T_{m0} and a are constants.

RESULTS

Using the strain and pressure histories $\varepsilon(t)$ and $p(t)$ shown in Figure 2, the constitutive equations (3)–(5) for the MTS model, or (1)–(3) for the Steinberg-Guinan model, along with (6)–(9) are used to calculate the corresponding stress and temperature histories. The values of the constants used in the calculations are taken from [7] for OFE copper and from [9] for OFHC ½-Hard copper. Various calculations are presented which contrast the effect of including pressure dependence of the shear modulus and including temperature dependence of the specific heat. Cases in which the pressure dependence of the shear modulus is suppressed are obtained by setting $\mathcal{A}$=0 in (3); for cases with constant specific heat, C is obtained from (8) with T=300.

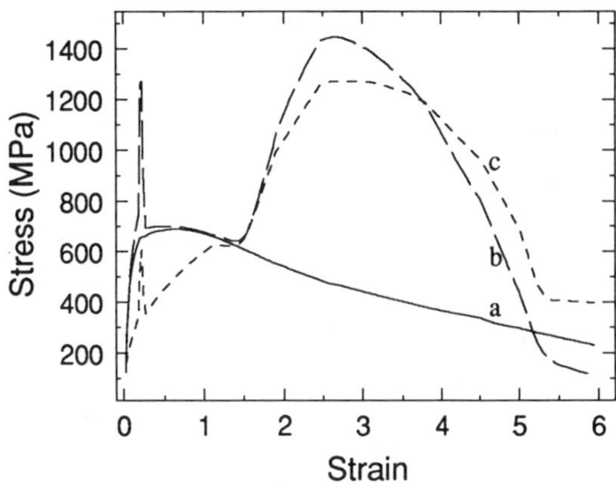

Figure 3. Predicted flow stress from various forms of the constitutive equations: (a) MTS model, G indep. of p; (b) MTS model, G depends on p; (c) Steinberg-Guinan model.

The calculated stress vs. strain for various forms of the constitutive equations is shown in Figure 3. The lowest (solid) curve, denoted by (a), is the prediction of the MTS model with temperature dependent specific heat and shear modulus independent of the pressure. When the shear modulus is taken to depend on pressure, the prediction shown by the dashed curve (b) is obtained. Comparing (a) and (b) in Figure 3 shows the significant effect on the predicted stress due to including the dependence of the shear modulus on pressure. Suppressing the temperature dependence of the specific heat in the cases shown in (a) and (b), namely the MTS model without and with a pressure dependent shear modulus, the predictions are similar but become slightly lower after roughly 200% strain (curves not shown for clarity in Figure 3). The difference in the predictions with and without temperature dependence of the specific heat is never more than roughly 5% of the maximum stress. The prediction of the Steinberg-Guinan model is shown by curve (c) in Figure 3, which

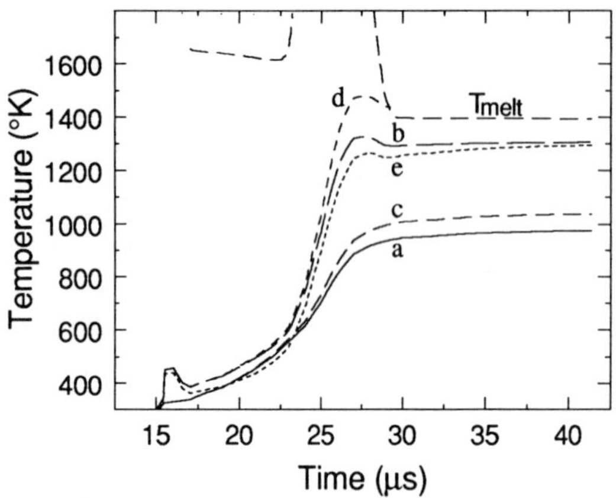

Figure 4. Predicted temperature from various forms of the constitutive equations: (a) MTS model, G indep. of p, C depends on T; (b) MTS model, G depends on p, C depends on T; (c) MTS model, G indep. of p, C const.; (d) MTS model, G depends on p, C const.; (e) Steinberg-Guinan model, C depends on T.

may be compared with the corresponding prediction of the MTS model, curve (b).

The calculated temperature vs. time for various forms of the constitutive equations is shown in Figure 4. In addition to the cases shown in Figure 3, the curves for the MTS model with the temperature dependence of the specific heat suppressed are also shown. The upper curve is the melting temperature given by (9). Again, the largest effect is seen to be due to the pressure dependence of the shear modulus, the inclusion of the temperature dependence of the specific heat having a less significant effect.

DISCUSSION

A main feature of the Steinberg-Guinan (S-G) model, important in matching shock wave profile data in copper, is the pressure dependence of the shear modulus. With a shear modulus independent of pressure, the MTS model has been extended to more accurately represent structure evolution during shocked conditions by refining the evolution of $\hat{\sigma}$ [10]. The S-G and MTS models approach matching shock data from different points of view. It is of interest to note that the peak stress during the HE shock in the S-G prediction is quite close to the prediction of the MTS model without pressure dependence in the shear modulus (Figure 3, curves (a) and (c)).

Dislocation phenomena which accommodate plastic deformation of copper are invariably related to the elastic moduli of the crystal structure. Because of this, elastic moduli in constitutive descriptions should be allowed to vary with deformation conditions such as hydrostatic pressure and temperature. The accuracy of the constitutive models appearing in this work, with regard to their dependence on shear modulus at very large strains, is not known and needs to be validated experimentally.

ACKNOWLEDGEMENT

Work performed under the auspices of the U.S. Department of Energy by the Lawrence Livermore National Laboratory under contract number W-7405-ENG-48.

REFERENCES

[1] M. L. Duffy and S. K. Golaski, U. S. Army Ballistics Research Laboratory Technical Report BRL-TR-2800, (1987).

[2] D. H. Lassila, in *Proceedings of the Ballistics '92 13th International Symposium*, Stockholm, Sweden, **2**, pp. 549-556, (1992).

[3] D. J. Steinberg, S. G. Cochran and, M. W. Guinan, *J. Appl. Phys.*, **51**, pp. 1498–1504, (1980.)

[4] U. F. Kocks, *J. Eng. Mater. Technol.*, **98**, p. 76, (1976).

[5] H. Mecking and U. F. Kocks, *Acta Metall.*, **29**, p. 1865, (1981).

[6] P. S. Follansbee and U. F. Kocks, *Acta Metall.*, **38**, p. 81, (1988).

[7] W. H. Gourdin D. H. Lassila, *Acta Metall.*, **39**, pp. 2337–2348, (1991).

[8] W. H. Gourdin D. H. Lassila, *Mat. Sci. and Engr.*, **A151**, pp. 11–19, (1992).

[9] D. J. Steinberg, Lawrence Livermore National Laboratory, UCRL-MA-106439, (1991).

[10] P. S. Follansbee, in *Shock Compression of Condensed Matter 1991*, S. C. Schmidt *et al.* eds., Elsevesier Publ., pp. 415–418, (1992).

AN ANALYTICAL EXPRESSION FOR THE VELOCITY DIFFERENCE BETWEEN JET PARTICLES FROM A SHAPED CHARGE

William P. Walters and Richard L. Summers
Warhead Technology Directorate
U.S. Army Research Laboratory
Aberdeen Proving Ground, MD 21005-5066

A model was derived to predict the velocity difference between particulated shaped charge jet particles. The model is based on the "wire drawing" formula presented by Kolsky, the plastic instability criterion, and the Zerilli-Armstrong constitutive equation for face-centered-cubic (fcc) materials. The velocity difference expression is strongly dependent on the jet temperature and weakly dependent on the jet strain rate. Calculations were also made using the Johnson-Cook constitutive model. The velocity difference between jet particles was calculated using several variants of the model. Velocity difference comparisons with experimental data were made for several shaped charge designs with copper liners of various geometries.

INTRODUCTION

A shaped charge consists of a cylinder of explosive with a hollow cavity in one end and a detonator at the opposite end. The hollow cavity, which may assume almost any geometric shape, is usually lined with a thin layer of metal. The liner forms a jet when the explosive charge is detonated. Upon initiation, a spherical wave propagates outward from the point of initiation. This high pressure shock wave moves at a very high velocity, typically around 8 km/s. As the detonation wave engulfs the lined cavity, the material is accelerated under the high detonation pressure, collapsing the liner. During this process, the liner material is driven to very violent distortions over very short time intervals, at strain rates of 10^4–10^7 s^{-1}. For conical liners, the collapse of the liner material onto the centerline forces a portion of the liner to flow in the form of a jet where the jet tip velocity can travel in excess of 10 km/s. The jet temperature is about 500–900 K according to the measurements of von Holle and Trimble (see [1]). Also, there are undoubtedly temperature gradients along and through the jet. Due to the axial velocity gradient, the jet will stretch until it fractures into a column of particles. This is known as jet breakup or particulation. Associated with the particulation of a shaped charge jet, there exists an average particle length of the particulated jet segments with an average velocity difference between them.

There are at least three reasons for attempting to calculate the velocity difference (ΔV) between particulated shaped charge jet particles. First, this ΔV is usually 0.1 km/s for most jets from copper conical liners. Thus, attempting to calculate a known (or approximately known) quantity may serve to verify the calculational and modeling method used to characterize the liner material and the particulation process. Second, the ΔV between particulated jet particles may be linked to the calculation of jet breakup time if $\Delta V = \Delta L/\tau$, where ΔL is the characteristic length or change in particle length which occurs over the interval ΔV, and τ is the average jet breakup time, measured from some reference point. Third, if the penetration of a particulated jet is calculated incrementally, i.e., particle by particle, then the separation distance and velocity between jet particles must be known.

The velocity difference between particles for a jet from a copper liner typically ranges from nearly 0 to 0.250 km/s. The highest values of ΔV are observed between two particles which separate earlier than the neighboring particles. This variation in separation time and ΔV is attributed to inhomogeneities in the shaped charge jet material. The average ΔV between jet particles over all particles from a single jet is relatively constant, between 0.080 km/s and 0.130 km/s, for most copper jets regardless of the liner size or geometry.

Previous Analytical Models

Several analytical models are available to estimate the velocity difference (ΔV) between jet particles and are summarized in Walters and Summers [2]. These ΔV models are primarily semi-empirical and are of the form $\Delta V/\sqrt{\sigma/\rho}$ = constant. The constant is usually less than 1. Thus, the existing ΔV models cannot account for variations in liner geometry, type of explosive fill, etc. These models account for liner material differences through the liner density (ρ) and the liner material dynamic yield stress (σ).

Other studies exist that are related to jet breakup time, but provide some insight into mechanisms behind jet particulation, jet ductility, and/or the velocity difference between particulated jet particles. In most breakup time models, the average jet breakup time is also dependent on $\sqrt{\sigma/\rho}$ and, hence, ΔV. These studies are reported in Walters and Summers [2].

THE ANALYTICAL MODEL

Constitutive Equations

The particulation process, and the resulting average velocity difference between particulated jet particles, must depend on the constitutive behavior of the material, i.e., the stress-strain-strain rate interdependency. The constitutive relationships chosen for this study were the Zerilli-Armstrong and the Johnson-Cook models since the exact functional forms and the values of the coefficients used in the equations are available (see [2]). The Zerilli-Armstrong constitutive equation for fcc materials is

$$\sigma = C_0 + k\lambda^{-1/2} + C_2\varepsilon^{1/2}\exp(-C_3T + C_4T\ln\dot{\varepsilon}). \quad (1)$$

The stress, σ, is in MPa, the strain rate, $\dot{\varepsilon}$, is in s^{-1}, the grain size, λ, is in mm, and the temperature, T, is in K.

The Johnson-Cook constitutive equation was also investigated. Johnson reports

$$\sigma = (A + B\varepsilon^n)(1 + C\ln\dot{\varepsilon})(1 - T^{*m}), \quad (2)$$

where $T^* = (T - T_{room})/(T_{melt} - T_{room})$. Any constitutive equation may be used in this analysis, assuming of course that the parameters used in the equation are available and do not introduce additional unknowns.

The Zerilli-Armstrong and Johnson-Cook constitutive equations are used to provide the values of stress and strain at the onset of plastic instability, or necking. The critical strain at necking is determined by the plastic stability criterion which states that

$$d\sigma \geq \sigma d\varepsilon. \quad (3)$$

The strain at the necking onset is calculated where

$$d\sigma = \sigma d\varepsilon, \quad (4)$$

and $d\sigma/d\varepsilon$ and σ are obtained from Equation 1 or 2 or any other appropriate constitutive equation.

The initial strain rate, $\dot{\varepsilon}_0$, is taken to be the difference in velocity between the fastest and the slowest jet particles divided by the initial jet length. The initial jet length, ℓ_0, is taken to be the initial length of the jet available prior to stretching. In general, the initial jet length is taken as:

$$\ell_0 = \ell_s(V_{jo} - V_R)/V_{jo}. \quad (5)$$

For a conical liner, ℓ_s is the slant height of the cone. This is essentially the jet length considered in the steady-state jet formation theory of Birkhoff, MacDougall, Pugh, and Taylor described in Walters and Zukas [1]. For nonconical liners, ℓ_s is one-half the perimeter of the inside surface of the liner obtained by taking a cross section along the axis of the liner. The ratio $(V_{jo} - V_R)/V_{jo}$ is introduced to account for the fact that the flash radiograph may not provide information on the entire length of the shaped charge jet. However, this ratio does not account for the portion of the apex region of a conical liner which may only contribute to the mass of the jet tip particle or the portion of the base region of the liner which may not contribute to the jet. However, ΔV calculations are relatively insensitive to the initial strain rate [2].

ΔV Equations

The ΔV between particulated jet particles is calculated based on the equation for the propagation of plastic deformation along a wire [3]. This equation is used to determine the velocity at which a wire would break during the wire drawing fabrication process. This equation, as applied to a stretching shaped charge jet [2], provides an expression for the velocity difference ΔV as

$$\sqrt{\rho}\ \Delta V = \int_0^{\varepsilon_{N_e}} \sqrt{\frac{d\sigma_e}{d\varepsilon_e}}\, d\varepsilon_e = \int_0^{\varepsilon_N} \sqrt{\frac{d\sigma}{d\varepsilon} - \sigma}\, d\varepsilon \ , \quad (6)$$

where ρ is the initial density of the jet. The subscript N denotes the strain at the onset of necking and the subscript e denotes an engineering stress or strain. The strain, ε_{N_e}, corresponds to the ultimate tensile strength of the jet, and the velocity corresponding to ε_{N_e} is the velocity at which the jet will break. This formula can be extended to account for a reduction in the cross-sectional area of the wire (or jet) [2].

A closed form analytical expression may be obtained by assuming isothermal deformation, $d\sigma/d\varepsilon >> \sigma$, and $\dot{\varepsilon} = \dot{\varepsilon}_0$. This gives

$$\Delta V = \left(\frac{2}{n+1}\right) \sqrt{\frac{n\,\kappa}{\rho}}\ \varepsilon_N^{\frac{n+1}{2}} \ , \quad (7)$$

where $\kappa = C_2 \exp(-C_3 T)\ \dot{\varepsilon}_0^{C_4 T}$ for the Zerilli-Armstrong fcc constitutive equation, and $\kappa = B\ (1 + C \ln \dot{\varepsilon}_0)\ (1 - T^{*m})$ for the Johnson-Cook constitutive equation. If ΔV is expressed in terms of the true stress, then

$$\Delta V = \left(\frac{2}{n+1}\right) \sqrt{\frac{n}{\rho}}\ (\kappa)^{-\frac{1}{2n}} \left(\sigma_N - \sigma_0\right)^{\frac{n+1}{2n}} , \quad (8)$$

where $\sigma_0 = C_0 + k\lambda^{-½}$ for the Zerilli-Armstrong fcc relation and $\sigma_0 = A\ (1 + C \ln \dot{\varepsilon}_0)\ (1 - T^{*m})$ for the Johnson-Cook constitutive equation. This expression, when compared to the results of other investigators, shows the same dependence on $\rho^{-½}$ but varies as $(\sigma - \sigma_0)^{(n+1)/2n}$ instead of $\sigma^{½}$. The Zerilli-Armstrong equation predicts the velocity difference between particulated jet particles will decrease with decreasing grain size, as expected.

RESULTS

Equation 8 used in conjunction with the Zerilli-Armstrong constitutive equation gave the best agreement to the measured average velocity difference between jet particles. Table 1 lists the measured tip velocity, tail velocity, and average ΔV for several copper shaped charge liner designs. In addition, the ΔV calculated using Equation 8 and the Zerilli-Armstrong constitutive equation with an assumed jet temperature of 500 K is given. The Zerilli-Armstrong equation yields average ΔV values in closer agreement with the experimental data than the Johnson-Cook based models.

Table 1. Comparison of Experimental and Analytical ΔV Values for Several Shaped Charge Designs.

Liner	V_{jo}	V_R	Avg. ΔV	Model ΔV
	(km/s)			
65-mm Cone	9.20	4.16	0.12	0.100
76-mm Hemisphere	4.21	2.01	0.10	0.099
81-mm Cone	7.68	2.13	0.11	0.098
102-mm Cone	8.82	4.26	0.13	0.098
163-mm Trumpet	10.00	4.67	0.10	0.096

The predicted values of ΔV are strongly dependent on jet temperature when the Zerilli-Armstrong constitutive equation is used. A very close match to the experimental data can be obtained if the jet temperature is assumed to be lower than the experimental values quoted by von Holle and Trimble. The copper predictions indicate that ΔV decreases with increasing jet temperature. These trends are in agreement with experimental observations of the strain at the onset of plastic instability, i.e., copper begins to neck at lower strains when tested at higher temperatures [4]. The ΔV predictions using the Johnson-Cook model and Equation 8 are only slightly dependent on jet temperature.

The velocity difference predicted by the current model stems from the "wire-drawing" equation. This equation is used to determine the maximum velocity at which a wire (jet) may be stretched without breaking. Therefore, this equation predicts the minimum velocity at break. Figure 1 shows the experimentally determined values of ΔV, measured for each jet particle, from the 81-mm copper cone. The dashed line represents the average ΔV for the experiment, which corresponds to the experimental value given in Table 1. The solid curves in Figure 1 show the incremental ΔV calculated using Equation 6 in conjunction with a jet formation code. The jet temperature was taken to be 900 K. Isothermal deformation is assumed. The analytical curve is most directly comparable to the lower magnitude of the experimental data since the minimum velocity at break is predicted. The values of minimum ΔV predicted using the Zerilli-Armstrong constitutive equation compare favorably to the experimental data. The Johnson-Cook relation predicted lower values of ΔV than Zerilli-Armstrong, but also compared well to the experimental data.

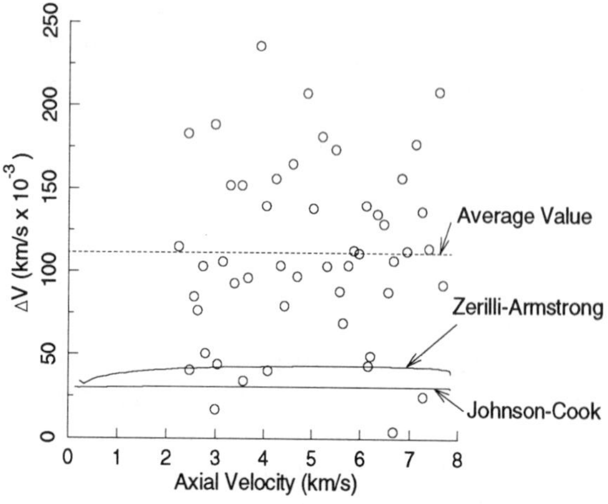

Figure 1. Experimental and predicted ΔV for the 81-mm copper conical liner.

CONCLUSIONS

A model was derived to predict the ΔV between particulated jet particles. The model was derived from the "wire drawing" equation reported by Kolsky, the criterion for plastic instability, and an appropriate constitutive equation. The calculated results were well within the range of the experimental data for the six different copper shaped charge designs studied. However, the calculated average ΔV value was below the experimental average.

The model allows for variation in initial strain rate and can, thus, distinguish between different liner designs, unlike other models. The ΔV calculations are also dependent on temperature and may be better than indicated once accurate calculations or experiments are conducted to determine the jet temperature gradients.

REFERENCES

[1] W. P. Walters and J. A. Zukas, *Fundamentals of Shaped Charges*, New York: John Wiley and Sons, 1989.

[2] W. P. Walters and R. L. Summers, *The Velocity Difference Between Particulated Shaped Charge Jet Particles for Face-Centered-Cubic Liner Materials*, ARL-TR-8, U.S. Army Research Laboratory, APG, MD, November 1992.

[3] H. Kolsky, *Stress Waves in Solids*, New York: Dover, 1963, ch. 7.

[4] F. Zerilli and R. Armstrong, "Description of Tantalum Deformation Behavior by Dislocation Mechanics Based Constitutive Relations," *Journal of Applied Physics*, 68, pp. 1580–1591 (August 1990).

SHAPED CHARGE VIRTUAL PRIMING CENTERS DETERMINATION BY IMAGE PROCESSING

Véronique FRACHET, Patrick MERCIER
Commissariat à l'Energie Atomique
Centre d'Etudes de Vaujours
BP 7
COURTRY, FRANCE, 77181

In order to provide fictive priming points determination for a hundred millimeters diameter shaped charge, a Doppler Laser Interferometry (D.L.I.) measurement joined to a X-ray observation was carried out. Detonation wave shape was obtained by image processing and tomographic reconstruction on the radiographs. It allows the accurate localization of the fictitious priming points and the determination of the porous material screen shape at the considered time. As the charge is punctually primed, the detonation wave passes around the porous screen and emerges on both sides of it. This detonation, divided in two torical waves, reaches the copper liner with a planar shape after a few microseconds. Measurement enables us to accurately determine the fictitious priming centers. These ones can be compared with the centers determined by simulation. This comparison allows us to introduce the accurate location of the virtual centers in the previous calculations.

INTRODUCTION

Experiments we have achieved till now on shaped charges were mainly aimed to observe the produced jet and its effects. They enabled us to validate the numerical codes and the equations of state of different classical shaped charges constitutive materials we have studied at "Centre d' Etudes de VAUJOURS" (fragmentation study, speed of different elements and perforation measurements) [1].

But presently, new constraints, due to new pyrotechnic safety rules lead us to use explosives which detonate in a non-ideal way. Consequently, our knowledge of priming, initiation, and detonation wave propagation and eventually of liner attacking is not perfect. These parameters cannot be so easily introduced in the hydrodynamic codes, and are still uneasily handled in numerical processing. So, different steps should be observed in an experimental way, in order to determine elements for conceiving numerical tools, used for foreseeing and optimization of such shaped charges.

Two complementary measurement techniques are laid out together on the same experiment, D.L.I. for velocity measurement and flash radiography to obtain detonation wave shape. The aim of D.L.I. is to measure as long as possible (3 μs) liner speed on several points of the free surface. Radiographic observation associated to image processing allows to get on one hand the detonation wave shape, on the other hand the shape of porous material screen. From these measurements results we deduce fictitious priming points location, and so we reach the goal for what the radiographic experiment has been conceived.

EXPERIMENT CONCEIVING

The scheme of the shaped charge with its instrumentation is shown on Figure 1.

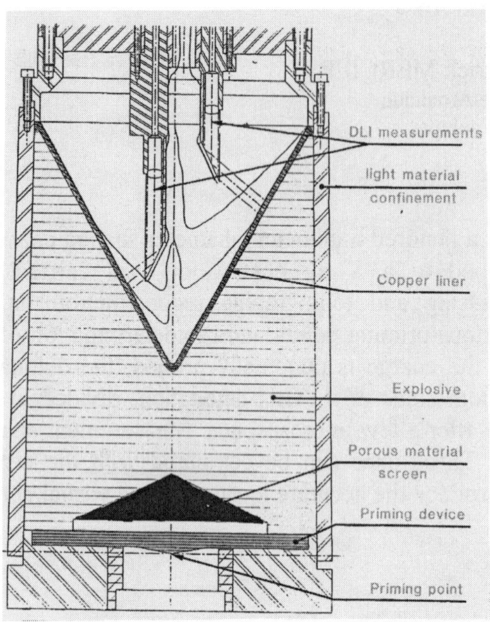

Figure 1. Scheme of the shaped charge

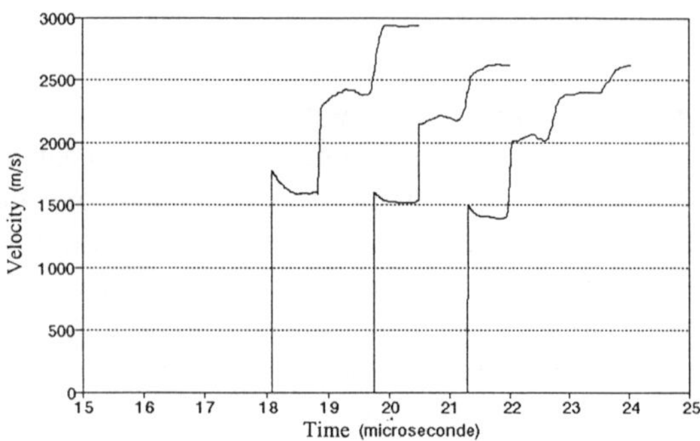

Figure 2. D.L.I. results

D.L.I. measurements implementation

We wish to measure as long as possible the liner expansion on several points, taking into account :

- preliminary calculations which describe the liner free surface evolution, the jet head progression (early destroyed) and speed evolution,
- the fact that the experiment needs a miniature D.L.I. head.

Three measurements along selected azimuths, and different distances from the cone basis have been implemented. D.L.I. recordings have been achieved by means of B.M.I. lasers and T.S.N. 506 electronic cameras.

Records exploitation shown on Figure 2 enables us to say that :

- three speed curves show similar behavior,
- they globally decrease from the top to the bottom of the cone,
- speed steps are well marked,
- the two first shocks are very strong.

Radiographic measurements implementation

The main advantage of flash radiography lies in the fact that it observes very fast flows or objects without disturbing them.

The geometry of radiographic observation is shown in Figure 3. Radiographic viewing axis, perpendicular to charge revolution axis which is horizontal, is defined by a straight line between X-ray source center and reception device center.

TRIMEV flash X-ray machine emits photons maximal energy of which is 3 MeV and provides a 0.08 Gy dose at 1 meter.

Pyrotechnic shieldings are set in front of emissive source and reception system in order to protect them against mechanical aggressions due to charge functioning.

Radiographic observation instant has been chosen so that detonation wave gets out on each side of porous material screen before attacking the liner.

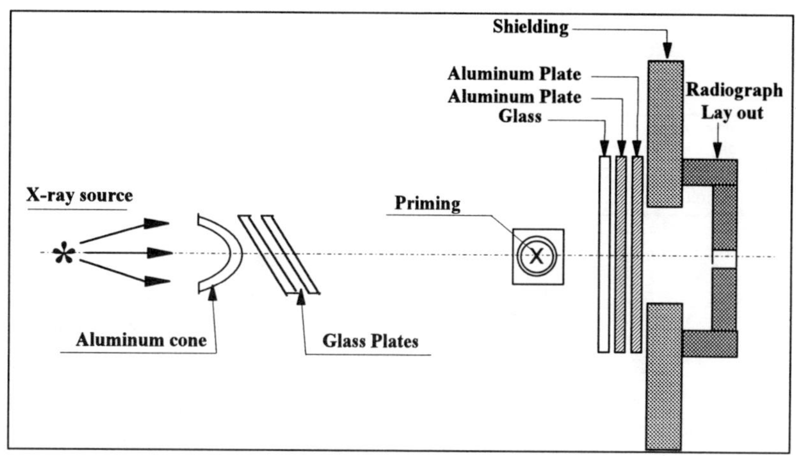

Figure 3. Geometry of radiographic observation

RADIOGRAPHIC MEASUREMENTS HANDLING

Radiographic films impressed during the experiment are scanned by a flat bed micro-densitometer (Perkin-Elmer PDS 2020). Images are then analysed according to following steps :

- optical densities conversion into areal masses,
- getting rid of a part of scattered rays,
- tomographic reconstruction,
- interfaces extraction.

These different steps are shown in Figure 4.

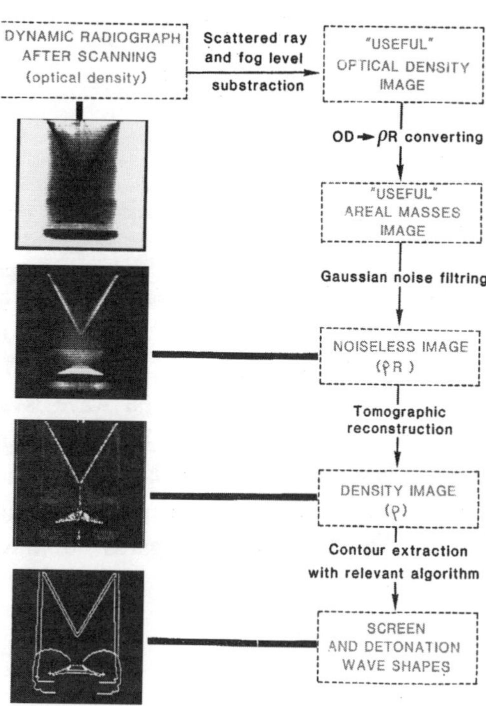

Figure 4. Different steps of image processing

RESULTS

Image processing makes obvious porous material screen compacting and enables the visualization of detonation wave at t=12 μs (seen Figure 5).

From this result, we determine detonation wave radius (3.25 cm) at this observation instant, and fictitious priming center location (ring shaped and symmetrical as regards to shaped charge revolution axis). Knowing annular priming fictitious center will enable the accurate initialization of simulation codes.

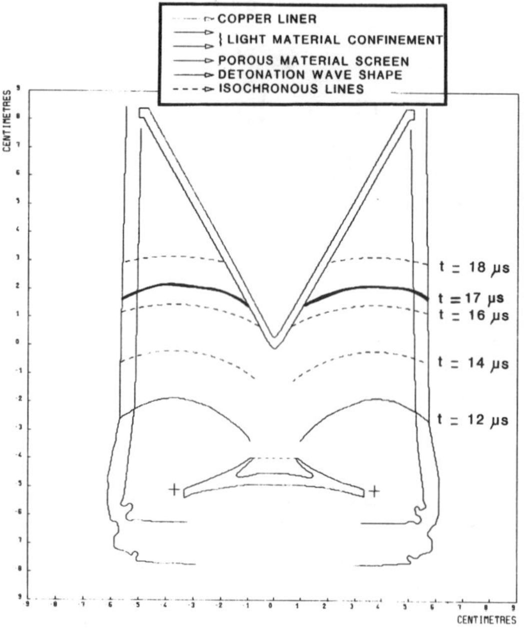

Figure 5. Priming centers determination

On this Figure 5, we present not only the experimental wave front but the extrapolation of this front location at sequential instants. The evolution versus time, of detonation wave is so visualized (t=14, 16 and 18 µs). A complementary experiment has been achieved later at instant t=17 µs : we notice a good agreement with previously shown results as regards to wave location and shape.

CONCLUSION

Thanks to the tomographic reconstruction of flash radiograph, we can reach parameters characteristic of the charge priming, such as wave and screen shapes that we cannot reach by other means.

Radiographic measurements enabled us to validate fictitious priming points assumption. This simplifies calculation code initialization by means of an experimentally fitted parameter which accounts for complex initial conditions bound with screen passing round.

On the other hand, the results enable us to conclude that calculation method by the geometrical motion of wave front could be used to deal with detonation propagation in such shaped charges by determining fictitious priming centers.

REFERENCES

[1] Eric BOTTET and Dominique PIROTAIS "Commissariat à l'Energie Atomique - Centre d'Etudes de Vaujours" *Numerical simulation of the dynamic behavior of materials with the two-dimensional Eulerian code CEE* - Computational Plasticity - April 6-10, 1987 - Barcelona - Spain.

INCOHERENCE OF SHAPED CHARGE JETS

James D. Walker
Engineering and Materials Sciences
Southwest Research Institute
6220 Culebra Road
San Antonio, TX 78238

It has been known for many years that some shaped charge geometries produce a radially expanding jet, referred to as jet incoherence. Incoherence greatly reduces the penetration capability of a jet. Experimentally, incoherence has been related to the sound speed of the material. In this paper, it is shown that the radial expansion is due to the conditions of the jet upon emergence of jetting material from the collapse region. A large rise in axial velocity of the jet occurs in a small volume adjacent to the collapse region. Radial expansion of the jet will occur if the flow is supersonic (relative to the reference frame of the collapse point) at some point within this volume. No radial expansion will occur if the flow is subsonic in this region. In this way, the material flow is similar to that seen in a duct. It is shown that the relevant sound speed is the longitudinal sound speed for elastic-plastic solids. The radial velocities are not due to the formation of shocks from supersonic collision as had been hypothesized by previous researchers.

INTRODUCTION

Shaped charges have been used for many years in military systems as warheads, and in industrial work as well perforators and demolition devices [1]. The term *shaped charge* refers to a hollow cavity in an explosive, that is usually lined with metal (Fig. 1). When the explosive is detonated, the expansion of the explosive product gases results in a collapse of the cavity and the metal liner. The geometry of the cavity and detonation is designed so that the collapse of the metal liner produces a metal jet. A velocity gradient stretches the jet as it travels downrange. This long metal jet produces large penetrations.

However, it has been observed experimentally that for some shaped charge geometries the jet is radially expanding (Fig. 2 and [2]). This is referred to as *incoherence* of the jet. The radial expansion produces a much broader crater at considerable expense in crater depth, and is therefore avoided in shaped charge designs.

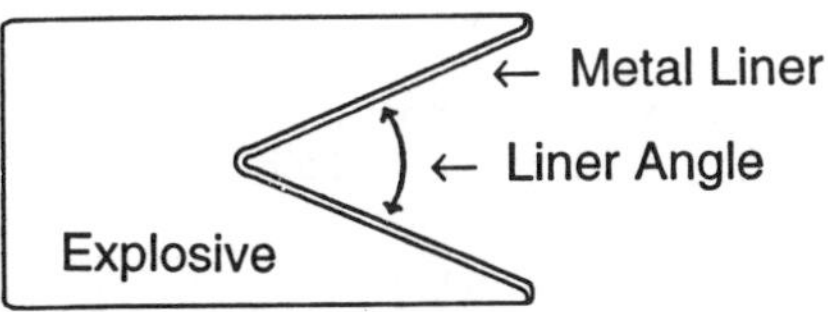

Figure 1. Shaped charge geometry.

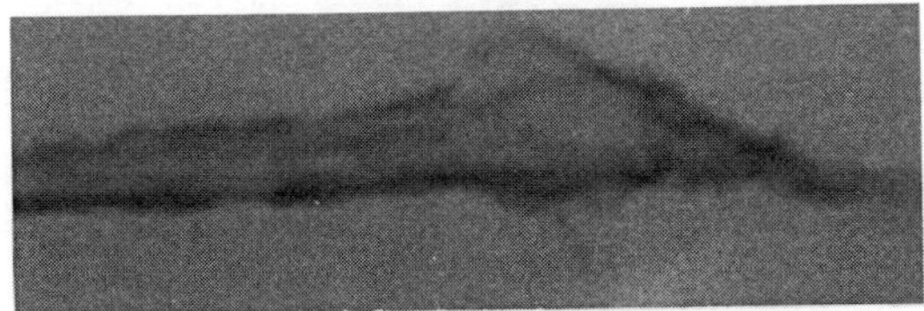

Figure 2. Incoherent jet from 20° Al liner.

The arguments that follow are best understood by moving from the laboratory frame of the experiment into a frame that is moving with the collapse point of the shaped charge. The collapse point is the high pressure region at the center of the collapse process. In the frame of the collapse point, the material appears to be flowing directly towards the collapse point at the collapse velocity (or flow velocity), as in Fig. 3. If the collapse process were steady state, then the assumption that little energy is dissipated in collapse implies the asymptotic velocity of the material exiting the collapse region in the axial directions does so at the collapse velocity [3].

Experimentation led early researchers to conclude that incoherence was related to a material's sound speed. Engineering formulae arose to aid in the design of shaped charges, the most famous being the BRL design criteria that the collapse velocity needs to be less than 1.23 times the bulk sound speed of the liner material [4].

Early work on the impact of plates, and subsequent development of criteria for when jetting occurs, led to arguments that a similar process was occurring in shaped

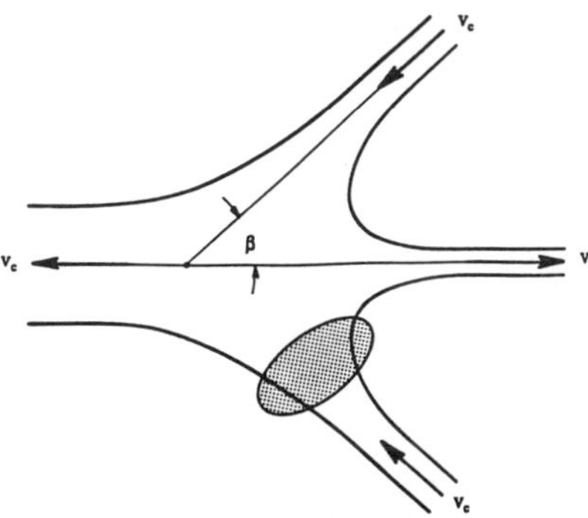

Figure 3. Material flow in collapse reference frame.

charge collapse [5]. The hypothesis on incoherence was that a detached shock is formed (in the shaded region in Fig. 3) for a supersonic collision. This then leads to an instability and then radial expansion of the jet.

We performed numerical simulations of the collapse process, and no such detached shock was observed, whether a coherent jet formed or not. There are very high pressures in the collapse region (on the order of 0.5 Mbar), but no shocks are evident. The shaped charge collapse process is relatively smooth, and the behavior is dominated by steady-state flow.

NUMERICAL CALCULATIONS

A number of calculations were done with the hydrocode CALE [6], with the geometry in Fig. 1. Aluminum was modeled as an elastic-perfectly plastic solid with a pressure-density relation of the form

$$P(\rho, E) = K_1\mu + K_2\mu^2 + K_3\mu^3 + (\Gamma_0 + b\mu)E \qquad (1)$$

where $\mu = \rho/\rho_0 - 1$, $K_1 = 74.2$ GPa, $K_2 = 60.5$ GPa, $K_3 = 18.7$ GPa, $\Gamma_0 = 1.97$, b = 0.48, and $\rho_0 = 2.7$ g/cm^3. The shear modulus was 27.6 GPa and the constant flow stress was 34 MPa (roughly 5 ksi—experiments were with a soft 1100-O aluminum). This aluminum will be referred to as standard aluminum. One of the powerful aspects of using numerical simulations to gain an understanding of physical phenomena is the ability to artificially alter a material property, and examine the subsequent system behavior. A second "aluminum" was used in calculations, where the K_i were divided by 4 to approximately give rise to half the sound speed, since

$$c = \sqrt{\left(\frac{\partial P}{\partial \rho}\right)_s} \qquad (2)$$

(s is the entropy). This material will be referred to as "low-sound-speed aluminum." Its purpose was to help determine the role of material sound speed in shaped charge collapse.

The Octol explosive was modeled with the JWL equation of state, with equation of state values found in [7]. In the computations, the detonation front reaches the apex of the cone at approximately 7 μs.

COMPUTATIONAL RESULTS

Two calculations with a liner angle of 45° will be focused on, one with standard aluminum and one with the low-sound-speed aluminum. The calculated jet had 8 to 10 computational cells across the radius.

Pressure contours at 12 μs for the standard aluminum are shown in Fig. 4, and in Fig. 5 for the low-sound-speed aluminum. There are no visible shock fronts near the collapse region in either figure. (The pressure rise in the collapse region occurs over 6—10 computational cells. In the upper right hand corner of each figure is the detonation front which *is* a shock: there the pressure rise occurs over two computational cells.) Though the pressures are similar, the densities in the collapse region differ greatly, due to the much higher compressibility of the low-sound-speed aluminum. Figures 6 and 7 are density plots for the two cases at 16 μs. The densities of the standard aluminum in the collapse point are on the order of 3.4 g/cm^3, while densities in the low-sound-speed aluminum are on the order of 4.5 g/cm^3. The standard aluminum jet is coherent, while the low-sound-speed aluminum jet is hollow.

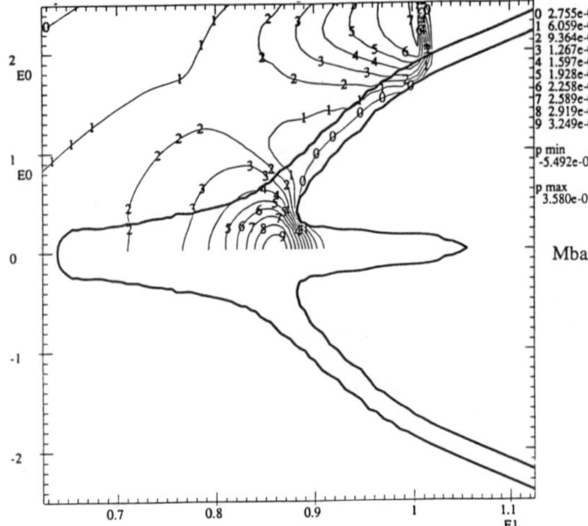

Figure 4. Pressure for standard aluminum.

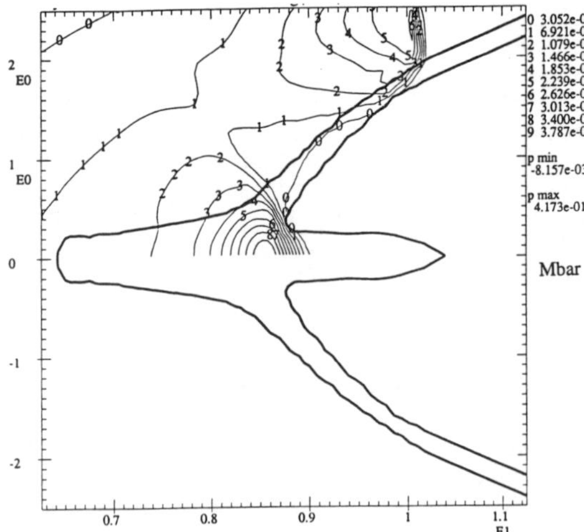

Figure 5. Pressure for slow-sound-speed aluminum.

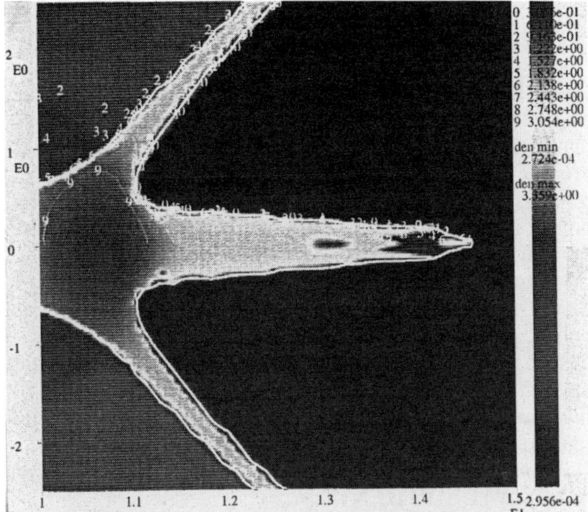

Figure 6. Density for standard aluminum.

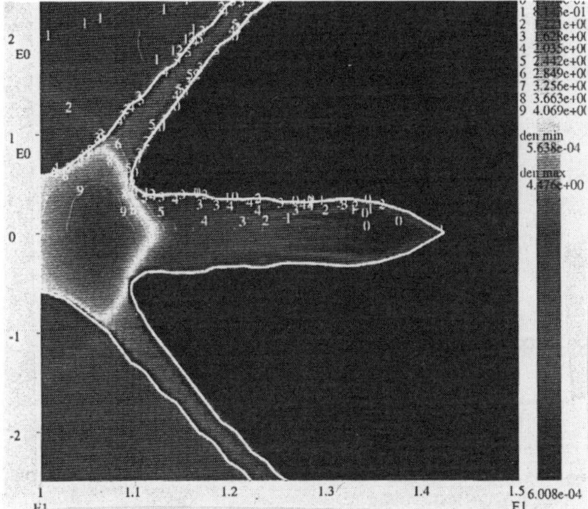

Figure 7. Density for slow-sound-speed aluminum.

The axial velocity along a short region of the jet as it emerges from the collapse point is shown in Fig. 8 for both examples. The axial velocity rises from the collapse region to the asymptotic jet velocity. The axial extent of the region where the velocity rises is on the order of the jet radius. The whole question of coherence centers on this short section.

The axial velocity is roughly independent of radius through the jet, as shown in Fig. 9, taken at 11.2 cm, midway between the jet emergence location and the point where the axial velocity reaches its asymptotic value. The density values do show some variation, but not a great deal.

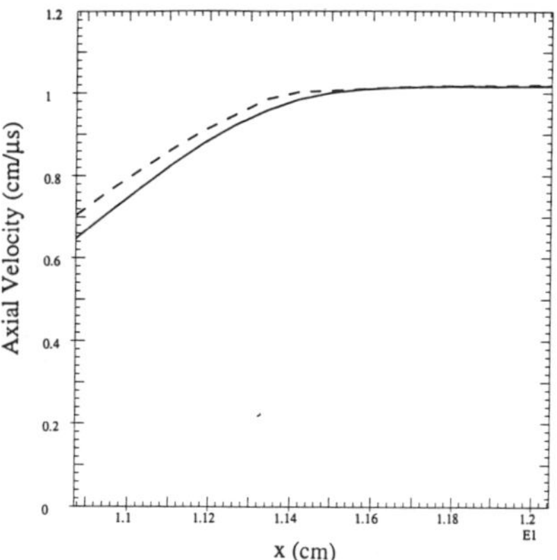

Figure 8. Centerline axial velocity in jet.

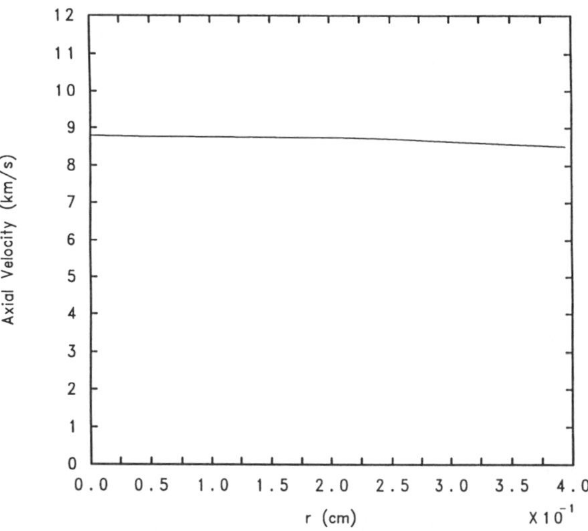

Figure 9. Jet axial velocity through radial section.

NEW THEORY

Assuming uniform density and axial velocity through the radius of the jet permits a simplification in the analysis of the behavior of the jet. The cross sectional area of the jet will be denoted by A. In the reference frame moving with the collapse point, the material flow approximates steady state. Mass conservation is

$$\frac{\partial}{\partial x}(A\rho \text{v})=0 \tag{3}$$

The momentum balance along the centerline is

$$-\frac{\partial P}{\partial x}=\rho\frac{D\text{v}}{Dt}=\rho \text{v}\frac{d\text{v}}{dx} \tag{4}$$

If the pressure term is viewed as being a function of density only, Eqs. (2), (3) and (4) combine to give

$$\frac{1}{A}\frac{dA}{dx}=\left(\frac{\mathrm{v}^2}{c^2}-1\right)\frac{1}{\mathrm{v}}\frac{d\mathrm{v}}{dx} \tag{5}$$

On the right hand side of Eq. (5), both v and dv/dx are positive. We arrive at the surprisingly simple conclusion that if $\mathrm{v} > c$ in the collapse point reference frame (hence supersonic), then the area of the jet is an increasing function of distance, while if $\mathrm{v} < c$ (hence subsonic), then the area of the jet is decreasing. Thus, whether the jet radially diverges is completely determined by the velocity in the collapse frame versus the local sound speed of the jet material. This result is similar to that for gaseous flow within a duct [8]. Incoherency is not due to transient effects, but results from the steady-state flow.

If the radial expansion is not too great, the jet material may be tough enough to resist further expansion, giving rise to a hollow jet. An example of an aluminum hollow jet tip is given in Fig. 10. If, on the other hand, the radial expansion is large, the jet material will fragment, giving rise to expanding fragmented jet material of the incoherent jet (as in Fig. 2). Thus, hollow jets are to be expected when a charge produces a jet that is nearly incoherent.

Previous hypotheses generated considerable discussion on which "sound speed" was appropriate in deciding jet incoherence, since the region of the collapse has very high pressures. However, the above clearly indicates which sound speed is relevant for coherence. As a shaped charge geometry is slightly altered so that a coherent jet approaches incoherency, $dA/dx \to 0$. Thus, the strain state in the jet on the borderline between coherency and incoherency is one of uniaxial strain. The pressure in the jet decreases rapidly as it moves away from the collapse region. Therefore, the sound speed in question is the low pressure longitudinal sound speed for a solid. In terms of the bulk sound speed, this is given by

$$c_L=\sqrt{3\frac{1-\nu}{1+\nu}}\,c_0, \qquad c_0=\sqrt{K/\rho_0} \tag{6}$$

where ν is Poisson's ratio and K the bulk modulus. For copper, $\nu = 0.35$ and so $c_L = 1.20c_0$. The value of 1.20 is somewhat less that the experimentally determined value of 1.23 (the aforementioned BRL design criterion). Further details can be found in [9].

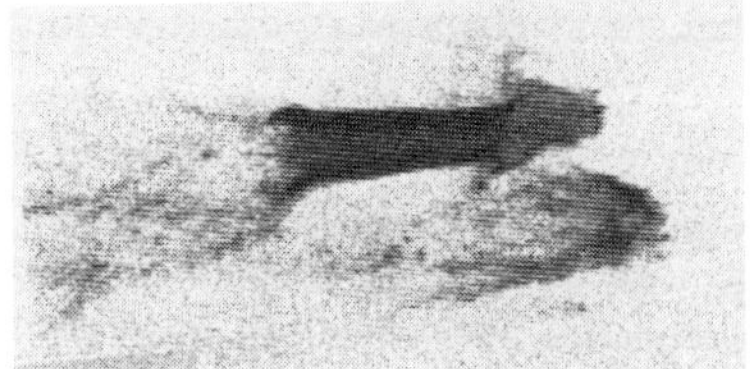

Figure 10. Hollow jet tip from 30° Al liner.

CONCLUSION

The coherence criteria for a shaped charge jet arises from the conditions in the jet as it emerges from the collapse region. If the velocity of the jet, as seen in the frame of reference moving with the collapse point, is greater than the longitudinal sound speed of the jet material, then the jet will have a radially diverging component. This component may be arrested by the ductility of the jet material for jets close to incoherence, giving rise to hollow jets. If the velocity of the jet is less than the longitudinal sound velocity, then the jet is coherent. This explanation is consistent with the BRL design criteria for shaped charges. It is interesting that the coherency question for a jet is determined by a small region of the jet, with axial extent on the order of the jet radius.

ACKNOWLEDGMENTS

The author would like to acknowledge many helpful discussions with Jack Riegel, Don Grosch, Scott Mullin, and Charlie Anderson, all of Southwest Research Institute.

REFERENCES

[1] W. P. Walters and J. A. Zukas, *Fundamentals of Shaped Charges,* New York, John Wiley & Sons, 1989.

[2] P. Y. Chanteret, "Studies of Maximum Velocities for Coherent Shaped Charge Jets," 13th International Ballistics Symposium, Stockholm, Sweden, pp. 327-334, 1992.

[3] E. M. Pugh, R. J. Eichelberger, and N. Rostoker, "Theory of Jet Formation by Charges with Lined Conical Cavities," *Journal of Applied Physics*, 23(5), pp. 532-536, 1952.

[4] J. T. Harrison, "BASC, An Analytical Code for Calculating Shaped Charge Properties," 6th International Ballistics Symposium, Orlando, Florida, pp. 253-261, 1981.

[5] P. C. Chou, J. Carleone, and R. R. Karpp, "Criteria for jet formation from impinging shells and plates," *Journal of Applied Physics*, 47(7), pp. 2975-2981, 1976.

[6] R. Tipton, "CALE Users Manual," Lawrence Livermore National Laboratory, Livermore, California, November, 1990.

[7] B. M. Doboratz and P. C. Crawford, *LLNL Explosives Handbook*, Lawrence Livermore National Laboratory, 1985.

[8] R. E. Meyer, *Introduction to Mathematical Fluid Dynamics,* New York, Dover Publications, Inc., 1982.

[9] J. D. Walker, "Incoherence of Shaped Charge Jets," 14th International Ballistics Symposium, Quebec City, Quebec, 1993.

SHAPED CHARGE JET PARTICULATION

William P. Walters and Richard L. Summers
Warhead Technology Directorate
U.S. Army Research Laboratory
Aberdeen Proving Ground, MD 21005-5066

An analytical model was developed to predict the breakup time of the jet from a shaped charge liner. The model is based on three presumptions. First, a kinematic expression for the breakup time; second, an expression related to plastic stability; and finally, a material-based constitutive equation relating the stress, strain, strain rate, and temperature. In other words, the jet from a shaped charge liner will particulate when it becomes plastically unstable, and the breakup time will depend on the stress, strain, strain rate, and temperature at failure (particulation).

INTRODUCTION

A cylinder of explosive with a hollow cavity in one end and a detonator at the opposite end is known as a shaped charge. The hollow cavity (which may assume almost any geometric shape) is usually lined with a thin layer of metal. When the explosive charge is detonated, the collapse of the liner material onto the centerline forces a portion of the liner to flow in the form of a jet where the jet tip can travel in excess of 10 km/s. Because of the presence of an axial velocity gradient, the jet will stretch until it fractures into a column of particles. This fracture of the jet into a series of particles is termed jet breakup or particulation.

The penetration of a shaped charge jet into most target materials increases to a maximum and then decreases as the standoff distance (distance from the front of the shaped charge to the target) increases. This penetration peak occurs just prior to the onset of jet breakup due to the dispersion, spread, and tumbling of the jet particles after particulation. As a result, it would be advantageous to the shaped charge designer to predict and control the jet breakup time.

The jet breakup time can be experimentally determined in several ways with varying results. The most common method of calculating an aggregate jet breakup time is to divide the cumulative jet length by the change in the jet velocity from the tip particle to the slowest jet particle characterized in the experiment. This "slowest" particle may or may not be the rear of the jet. This method provides a single value, termed the "cumulative breakup time," for the entire jet. The cumulative breakup time is based on several assumptions. The jet is assumed to stretch from an initial length of zero at a constant, uniform rate. In addition, the jet is assumed to break simultaneously, from tip to tail, at the time it reaches its maximum length. Conversely, the breakup time can also be calculated under the assumption that the jet particles travel at a constant velocity after the jet particulates. Thus, the time at which two jet particles separate from one another can be derived from the distance between the two particles at a known time and the velocity of the particles.

THE ANALYTICAL MODEL

The kinematic expression for the cumulative jet breakup time is derived as follows. An initial length of jet, ℓ_o, eventually stretches to length ℓ where it fractures at the breakup time, τ. Then

$$\ell = \ell_o + \tau(V_{jo} - V_R), \tag{1}$$

where V_{jo} is the tip velocity of the jet and V_R is the rear or tail velocity of the jet. Thus,

$$\tau = \varepsilon_e/\dot{\varepsilon}_o, \tag{2}$$

where $\varepsilon_e = (\ell-\ell_o)/\ell_o$ and $\dot{\varepsilon}_o=(V_{jo}-V_R)/\ell_o$.

The experimental calculation of cumulative breakup time neglects ℓ_o and yields:

$$\tau_e = (\varepsilon_e + 1)/\dot{\varepsilon}_o. \tag{3}$$

The plastic stability criterion requires that

$$d\sigma \geq \sigma \, d\varepsilon \tag{4}$$

for stability, otherwise the jet necks and eventually breaks [1]. In order to implement the model, Equation 4 is used with the equality sign, and is integrated between the limits $\varepsilon = 0$ to $\varepsilon = \varepsilon_F$ and $\sigma = \sigma_o$ to $\sigma = \sigma_F$, where σ_o is the value of σ at $\varepsilon = 0$ and the subscript F denotes values at failure. Thus,

$$\sigma_F = \sigma_o \exp \varepsilon_F. \tag{5}$$

The true strain at failure is determined using Equation 5 and an appropriate constitutive equation. The Zerilli-Armstrong constitutive equation for face-centered-cubic (fcc) materials [3] is used due to its popularity in many hydrocodes and the fact that the material coefficients are available for most materials of interest in shaped charge liner design.

Two methods are presented for calculating cumulative jet breakup time. The first method involves a single calculation utilizing the jet tip and rear velocity and an estimate of the total initial jet length. This method provides a single representative breakup time for the entire jet. The initial jet length, ℓ_o, is taken to be the initial length of the jet available prior to stretching. In general, the initial jet length is taken as:

$$\ell_o = \ell_s (V_{jo} - V_R)/V_{jo}. \tag{6}$$

For a conical liner, ℓ_s is the slant height of the cone. This is essentially the jet length considered in the steady-state jet formation theory of Birkhoff, MacDougall, Pugh, and Taylor described in Walters and Zukas [2]. For nonconical liners, ℓ_s is one-half the perimeter of the inside surface of the liner obtained by taking a cross section along the axis of the liner. The ratio $(V_{jo} - V_R)/V_{jo}$ is introduced to account for the fact that the flash radiograph may not provide information on the entire length of the shaped charge jet. However, this ratio does not account for the portion of the apex region of a conical liner which may only contribute to the mass of the jet tip particle or the portion of the base region of the liner which may not contribute to the jet. The initial jet length for a hemispherical liner was taken to be $\pi(d)/4$ where d is the inner liner diameter.

The calculation of ℓ_o and $\dot{\varepsilon}_o$, based on the slant height of the liner and the tip to tail velocity difference, allows a direct calculation of the final true strain and, thus, the total jet length and cumulative breakup time. However, this method only provides a prediction of the average strain attained by the entire jet and a single cumulative breakup time. Alternatively, this model may be employed in conjunction with a jet formation code. In the jet formation code, the value of ℓ_o is defined to be the length of a segment of the jet at the time it reaches the liner axis of symmetry. The velocity difference, used to calculate initial strain rate, is defined as the velocity of the preceding jet segment less the velocity of the succeeding element.

RESULTS

Table 1 presents the experimentally determined jet tip velocity, jet tail velocity, total jet length, final true strain, and cumulative jet breakup time for several copper shaped charge liner designs. The value of final true strain given in Table 1 is based upon the measured total jet length and the calculated initial jet length from Equation 6. Note that for the conical and trumpet liners the average final true strain of the jet is nearly constant, approximately 2.3. The value of ε_F reported for the copper hemispherical liner is lower, namely 1.95. This difference in the value of ε_F may be due to the different jet collapse and formation mechanics between hemispherical and conical (or conical-like) liners or it may relate to the method used to calculate initial jet length for hemispherical liners. Simple jet formation codes are not available for hemispherical liners, but hydrocode simulations could be employed to determine the length of various segments of the jet at the time they reach the axis of symmetry.

Table 1 also presents the predicted values of total jet length and cumulative breakup time for each shaped charge design. Predictions for the conical liners were obtained using a jet formation code. Trumpet and hemispherical calculations were based on the slant length approximation. The final

Table 1. Experimental and Predicted Values for Several Copper Shaped Charge Designs.

Liner	Experimental Data					Predictions		
	V_{jo} (km/s)	V_R (km/s)	ε_F	L_T (mm)	τ_e (μs)	T (K)	L_T (mm)	τ_e (μs)
65-mm Cone	9.20	4.16	2.30	500.1	99.2	450	508.2	101.9
76-mm Hemisphere	4.21	2.01	1.95	419.6	190.7	450	601.8	273.5
81-mm Cone	7.68	2.13	2.31	820.3	147.8	450	808.4	140.4
102-mm Cone	8.82	4.26	2.35	772.1	169.3	450	730.3	154.6
163-mm Trumpet	10.00	4.67	2.33	1,363.2	255.8	450	1,341.7	251.7

true strain predicted for copper slowly increases with increasing strain rate. The copper results presented in Table 1 show excellent agreement with the experimental data at an assumed uniform jet temperature of 450 K. This temperature is below the measured values of von Holle and Trimble (see [2]) for a shaped charge with a copper, conical liner. However, the experimental temperature measurements were taken near the tip region of the jet. There may be a temperature gradient along length of the jet (from tip to tail) as well as a temperature gradient through the jet thickness [4]. A temperature gradient from the jet tip to the jet tail could result in lower temperatures near the rear of the jet which may undergo less plastic deformation and less shock heating than the jet tip region. The ductility of copper is predicted to decrease with increasing jet temperature. This trend is due to the constitutive equation and the observation that, for fcc materials, the strain at maximum load decreases with increasing temperature [3]. Ideally, the individual breakup time could be calculated from a jet formation code with temperatures for each element of the jet (obtained from hydrocode calculations perhaps) used as input.

The use of the breakup time model in conjunction with a jet formation model also allows for the prediction of individual breakup times, actual separation times, and the distance a segment of jet travels before particulation. Figure 1 is a plot of separation time of each jet particle as a function of the jet particle's velocity for, as a representative example, the 81-mm copper cone. Figure 1 indicates the actual particulation time tends to increase with decreasing jet velocity. It is not evident from the experimental data points that the jet breakup proceeds uniformly from the jet tip to tail. The model predicts a first break near the front of the jet but away from the tip region for this warhead design. The analytical prediction agrees well with the experimental data, however, the model is clearly not sophisticated enough to predict

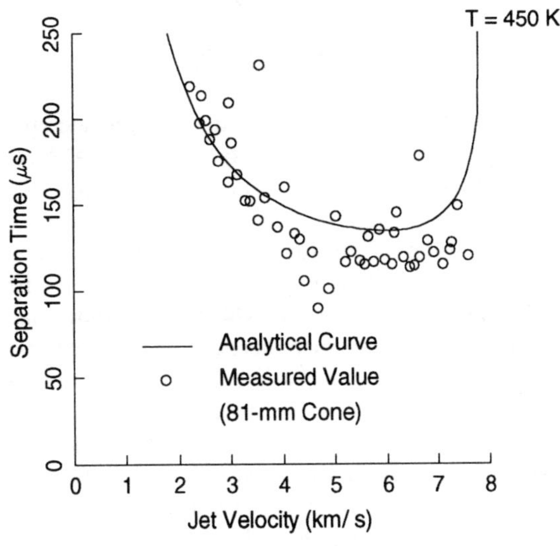

Figure 1. Comparison of Measured and Predicted Separation Times for the Copper 81-mm Conical Liner.

the variations which occur from particle-to-particle. The predicted value of true strain at failure is an average value calculated for discrete jet segments. Stress concentrations in the necked regions of the jet are not included in the model nor are release waves or liner inhomogeneities.

An alternate failure model may simply be to set the strain at failure to 2.3. In this case, *a priori* knowledge of the jet temperature is not required. Other researchers have claimed failure occurs at a stress of approximately 300 MPa for a copper jet [1]. For a strain of 2.3, the Zerilli-Armstrong constitutive equation for copper predicts a stress of 300 MPa when the jet temperature is approximately 980 K. The Johnson-Cook model predicts a stress of 300 MPa at a strain of 2.3 for a copper jet temperature of approximately 830 K. Both of these jet temperatures are higher than the measurements of von Holle and Trimble.

CONCLUSIONS

A technique was derived to calculate the breakup time for a shaped charge with a face-centered-cubic liner material. The approach involved an equation for plastic stability; a kinematic relationship for the jet breakup time; and a material-dependent constitutive equation. The study was limited to data which the authors had personally analyzed since there are several possible ways to express a distribution of jet breakup times and it is often not clear as to the time origin involved or the experimental data reduction methods used. Also, the constitutive equation used must be expressed in terms of known coefficients.

The jet breakup time predictions were shown to be very good for several shaped charge designs. Using the model in conjunction with a jet formation code revealed good agreement between calculated and experimental jet breakup time distributions for an assumed uniform temperature. The temperature is probably not uniform through the jet and may vary depending upon the liner design and the initial strain rate. However, no attempt was made to vary the jet temperature for different liner designs to obtain better agreement with the measured jet breakup time. The breakup time model could be simplified further by noting that the average true strain at failure of the majority of the shaped charge designs is approximately a constant.

REFERENCES

[1] W. P. Walters and R. L. Summers, "The Particulation of a Shaped Charge Jet for Face-Centered-Cubic Liner Materials," ARL-TR-114, U.S. Army Research Laboratory, APG, MD, April 1993.

[2] W. P. Walters and J. A. Zukas, *Fundamentals of Shaped Charges*, New York: John Wiley and Sons, 1989.

[3] F. Zerilli and R. Armstrong, "Dislocation-Mechanics-Based Constitutive Relations for Material Dynamics Calculations," *Journal of Applied Physics*, 61, pp. 1816–1825 (March 1987).

[4] L. Zernow and L. Lowry, "High-Strain-Rate Deformation of Copper in Shaped Charge Jets," in *Shock Wave and High-Strain-Rate Phenomena in Materials*, Edited by M. A. Meyers, L. E. Murr, and K. P. Staudhammer, New York, 1992.

PHASE DETONATED SHOCK TUBE (PFST)*

W. D. Zerwekh, S. P. Marsh and T.-H. Tan

Group M-6, Los Alamos National Laboratory, Los Alamos, NM 87545 USA

I. INTRODUCTION

The simple, cylindrically imploding and axially driven fast shock tube (FST) has been a basic component in our high velocity penetrator (HVP) program. It is a powerful device that is capable of delivering a directed and very high pressure output that we have successfully employed to drive hypervelocity projectiles. The FST is configured from a hollow, high-explosive (HE) cylinder, a low-density Styrofoam core, and a one-point initiator at one end. A Mach stem is formed in the core as the forward-propagating, HE detonation wave intersects the reflected radial wave. By proper arrangement of HE length and diameters, a steady-state Mach stem is readily achieved at the output end. Predetonation of HE is prevented by underdriving the Mach stem as it is being developed and this is most easily done by varying the foam density. The strength of the Mach stem is dependent on the effective energy transfer from the HE and this can be scaled geometrically. We have found this simple FST to be a powerful pressure multiplier. Typically, up to 1-Mbar output pressure can be obtained from this device. Further increase in the output pressure can be achieved by increasing the HE detonation velocity.

Over the last few years the FST has been fine tuned to drive a thin plate to very high velocity under an impulse per unit area of about 1 Mbarμs/cm^2. Typically, a 1.5-mm-thick stainless steel disk has been accelerated intact to 0.8 cm/μs under a loading pressure rate of several Mbar/μs. By making the plate curvature slightly convex at the loading side we have successfully accelerated it to almost 1.0 cm/μs. By placing a 1-mm layer of sapphire as a buffer, a thin stainless steel or titanium plate with an equivalent composite mass as before has been accelerated to above 1.1 cm/μs. We have found the incorporation of a barrel at the end of the FST to be important. The confinement of the propellant gas by the barrel tends to accelerate the projectile to higher velocity. Furthermore, the standoff in the barrel between the plate and the FST allows the expanding gas to load more gently on the plate and thus reduces the loading pressure rate. A shockless acceleration is highly desirable to prevent the plate from being broken up prematurely. However, presence of a large standoff volume tends to introduce wall affects and generates serious perturbations from the not-well-understood, high-pressure gas flow dynamics. We try to mitigate this difficulty by keeping the standoff distance as short as can be tolerated by experimental tests. In general we have found good agreements between the 2D numerical simulations and measurements. Even scaling tests appear to be satisfactory. A factor of three increase in the geometric dimensions of the FST, barrel, standoff, and plate, yields similar results in both the calculations and experiments.

The desire to accelerate the plate above 1.0 cm/μs provides the impetus to develop a more advanced fast shock tube that will deliver a much higher output pressure. We decided to investigate a relatively simple air-lens phase-detonation system (PFST) with fifty percent higher phase-detonation velocity and a modest 2 Mbar output. Code calculations show that this PFST acceleration of a plate to about 1.2 cm/μs can be achieved. The performance of these PFSTs has been evaluated and the details are discussed below.

II. DESCRIPTION OF PHASE-DETONATED FST

The phase-detonated FST is shown in Figure 1a. The fast detonation-velocity component of a P078 explosive HE lens is detonated on the left of the figure

*This work supported by the US Department of Energy.

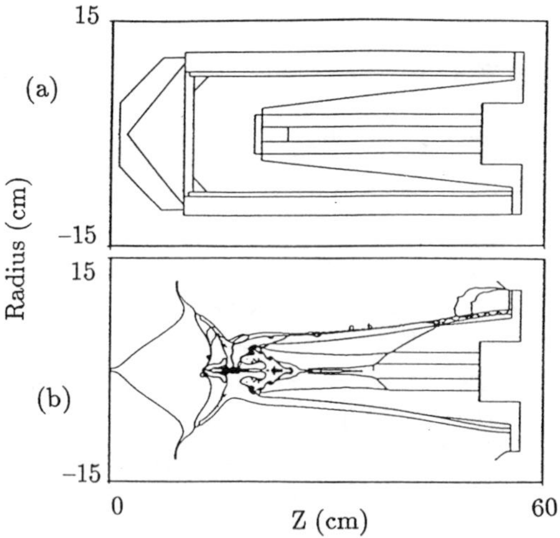

FIGURE 1
Phase-detonated FST with isobars showing (a) setups and (b) Mach-disk formation process

and this detonates the cylinder of Composition B-3 on the outside surface of the FST. As its detonation proceeds to the right, a cylindrical shell of 304 stainless steel (SS) is propelled radially inward. It impinges on the conical surface of a 6061 aluminum phasing lens, the angle of which determines the phase-velocity of the system (Figure 2). This lens transmits a shock to a cylindrical shell of PBX 9501 explosive and detonates it at an axial velocity determined by the phasing lens angle. An axial cylinder of Styrofoam is then shock-compressed by this travelling detonation front resulting in a Mach disk travelling at the same phase velocity. It ultimately breaks out of the system at the right-hand face and causes the acceleration of a 304SS plate placed against that face or suspended in a 304SS barrel that rests against that face.

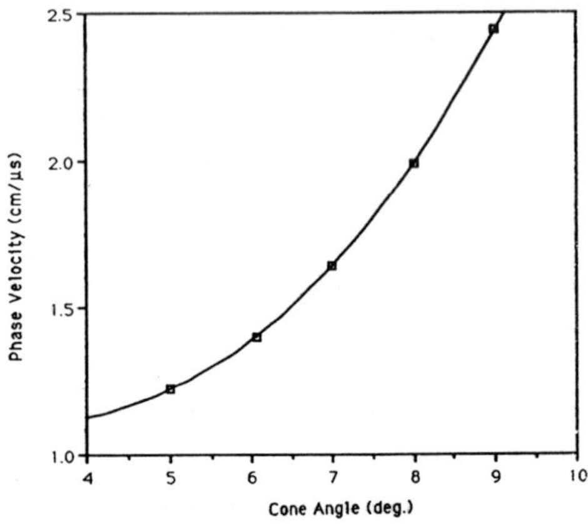

FIGURE 2
Calculated phase velocity as a function of cone angle for a PFST.

The purpose of the steel plate against the base of the P078 lens, the polyethylene wedge against its periphery, and the polyethylene disk at the left face of the phasing lens are to prevent the predetonation of the PBX 9501 explosive before the shock from the collapsing 304SS cylinder detonates it. The plug of polyethylene on the left face of the Styrofoam results in a shorter run-distance for the full diameter formation of the Mach disk.

III. PHASE-DETONATION/MACH DISK PERFORMANCE

The hydrocode, Mesa2D, has been used in modeling the overall performance of the phase-detonated FST. It is a 2D, Eulerian, second-order code that can handle multimaterial problems and can treat the programmed detonation of high explosives. The results shown here have been obtained using a Cray Y-MP computer.

The modeling of a phase-detonated FST with isobars is shown in Figure 1b showing collapse of the 304SS cylinder onto the 6061Al phasing lens, shock in the lens, phase detonation of the PBX 9501 explosive and Mach disk position. The angle of the phasing lens in this problem is six degrees and the resulting phase velocity of the PBX 9501 detonation front is 1.40 cm/μs, an increase of 59% over the normal detonation velocity of 0.88 cm/μs. The shock velocity of the Mach disk in the Styrofoam is the same value of 1.40 cm/μs.

Microwave-interferometry experiments have been performed to measure the phase velocity in the system shown in Figure 1a. To accomplish this, twelve small diameter coaxial cables were imbedded at equally spaced intervals around an aluminum rod (microwave-interferometry probe) that replaced the foam/polyethylene cylinders shown in the figure. They were imbedded in small semi-circular (cross-section) longitudinal grooves machined into the aluminum rod and then had their protruding outer conductors carefully scraped off, exposing the central coaxial conductor (Figure 3). As the phase-detonation proceeded along the PBX 9501 explosive, the cables were shorted and through an interferometry circuit the position vs. time data of the twelve cables was determined. The velocity was then extracted from the x-t data.

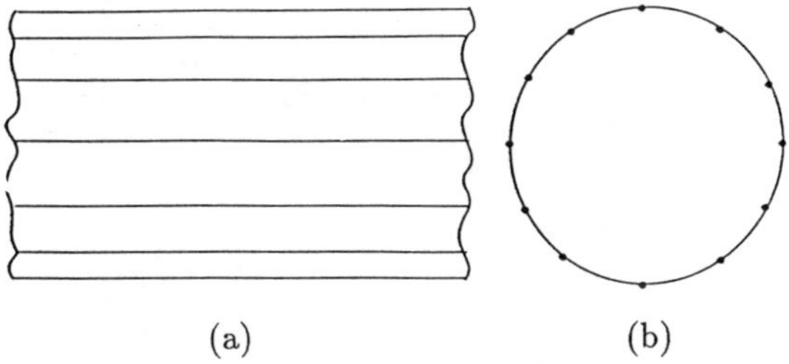

FIGURE 3
Side (a) and end (b) views of microwave-interferometer probe used to determine phase velocity.

A plot of the detonation-velocity averages of the channels is shown in Figure 4. The phase velocity is seen to be 1.42 cm/μs which is acceptably close to the design phase velocity of 1.40 cm/μs. This shot was fired vertically downward.

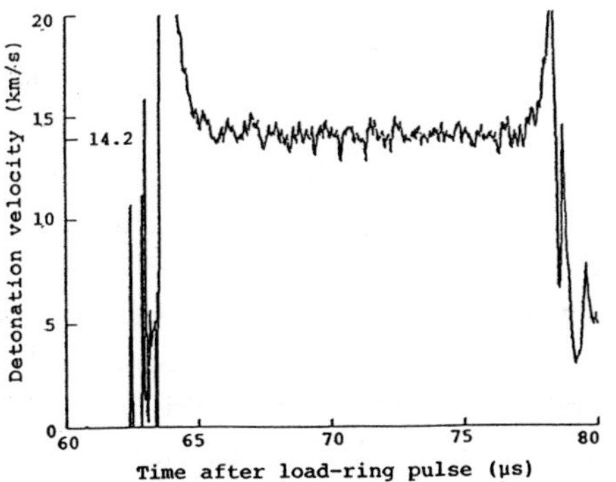

FIGURE 4
V-t plots obtained from x-t data of microwave interferometer.

IV. PLATE-ACCELERATION PERFORMANCE

Because of the poor results obtained when trying to accelerate a plate down a barrel it was decided to attempt (with a vertical axis system) to accelerate a plate initially in contact with the shock-tube face and having convex plate curvature toward the shock-tube face as shown in Figure 5. The plate is 0.15-cm-thick 304SS and for the two systems studied the radii of curvature of the plate faces against the shock tube were 11.37 cm and 5.72 cm. Hydrocalculations in these two systems are shown in overlays on Figure 5. The effect of decreasing the radius of curvature is evident in the greater consolidation, thickness, and increased forward bowing. The plate velocities are 1.26 and 1.20 cm/μs for the long and the short radius-of-curvature plates, respectively.

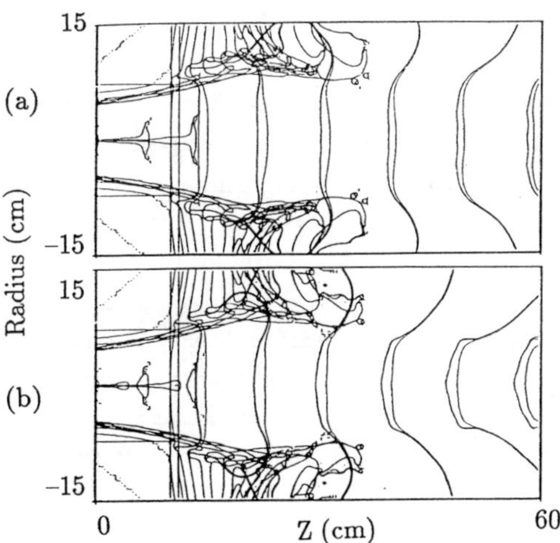

FIGURE 5
Overlays of calculated plate contours at 1-μs intervals for phase-detonated FST w/no barrel. The radii of curvature of the plate are (a) 11.37 cm and (b) 5.72 cm.

Experiments were performed on shock tubes with these two radii of curvature machined on the plate surfaces. A light grease was used to fill any gap between the Styrofoam and PBX 9501. The shots 57-4797 and 57-4795, had radii of curvature of 11.37 cm and 5.72 cm, respectively.

The experimental setup for these shots is shown in Figure 6. The assemblies accelerated the plates vertically downward. The displacements of the plates at flash x-ray times (9.5 and 36.1 cm) were greater than the largest displacements shown in the hydrocalculation (6.3 cm in both calculations) in order to protect the x-ray head and the film cassettes from blast and shrapnel.

The radiographic results for these shots are given in Figure 7. Only one exposure was obtained for shot 57-4795 because only one channel of the flash x-ray unit triggered. But a plate velocity was obtained for this shot by using information on initial motion time obtained from hydrocalculations and the earlier shot fired. The velocity of the plate in shot 57-4797 is 1.18 cm/μs and the velocity of the massive part of the tip in shot 57-4795 is 1.16 cm/μs.

The difference in the calculated and experimental plate contours for the plate with 11.37-cm radius of curvature (Figures 5a and 7a) is caused by early fracture of the plate at its periphery (not modelled by the hydrocode) reducing the driving pressure in that region and causing it to lag behind the plate center, which can be seen in Figure 7a. Although the same peripheral pressure drop exists for the plate with the smaller radius of curvature, the convergence is so much greater that it folds forward and collapses on axis (Figure 7b) as its much greater displacement is reached by x-ray time. The plates in both of these shots may be melted by the residual internal energy after the initial

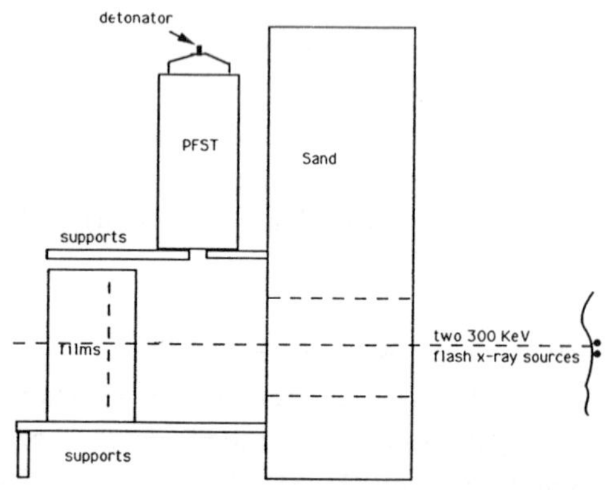

FIGURE 6
Experimental setup for vertical shots 57-4797 and 57-4795.

(a)

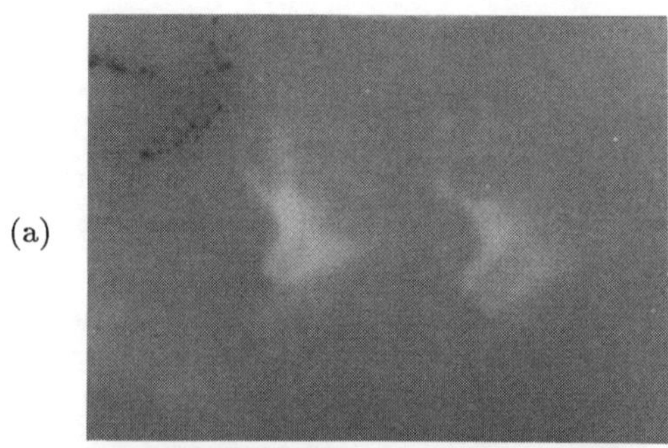

(b)

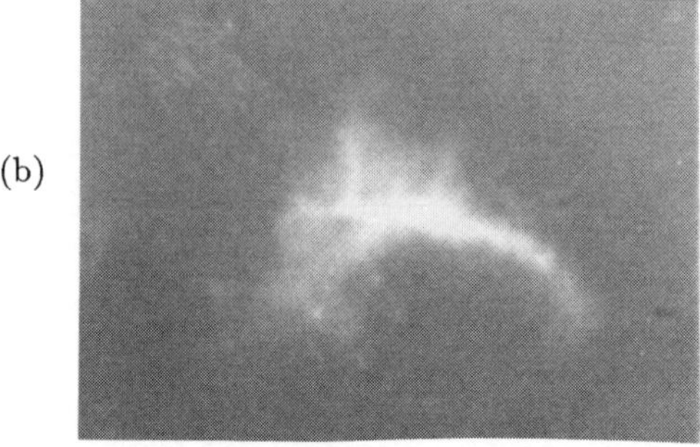

FIGURE 7
Radiograph of stainless steel plates moving to the rignt in (a) shot 57-4797 and (b) shot 57-4795. Over-consolidation of plate in (b) can be seen to form a rod.

shock and rarefactions are completed and the plate is back at zero pressure.

V. CONCLUSIONS

Detonation of PBX 9501 at a phase velocity of 1.40 cm/μs has been observed, and its detonation velocity was uniform at 12 positions around the inner cylindrical interface. A Mach disk in an axial Styrofoam cylinder within the explosive was formed and travelled at the same phase-velocity. Precursor shocks or jets caused by the foam/explosive interface were eliminated by firing the shots vertically and placing a low viscosity grease in the interface gap. A radius of curvature of 11.37 cm on the driving face of a SS plate in contact with the foam/HE face of a shock tube produced plate convergence during acceleration and allowed the plate to reach a velocity of 1.18 cm/μs. The indistinct edge of the plate indicates it may have melted. Arrangement with a barrel and appropriate standoff still offers the possibility to accelerate a plate shocklessly and intact.

CHAPTER XXV

RADIATION-MATTER INTERACTION

GENERATION OF EXTREME STATES IN CONDENSED MATTER WITH HIGH ENERGY PARTICLE BEAMS

V.E.Fortov, V.V Kostin, O.Yu.Vorob'ev*

High Energy Density Reseach Center, IVTAN, Izhorskaya 13/19, 127412 Moscow, Russia

* Institute of Chemical Physics , 142432 Chernogolovka. Moscow region, Russia

Results of numerical simulation of intense laser and light ion beams action on condensed targets are presented in comparison with experimental data on dynamic response of the targets. High pressure generation in the matter as a result of both direct beam action and so converted into x-ray radiation or kinetic energy of an accelerated foil is considered.

INTRODUCTION

Intense light ion and laser beams are of great interest in high energy density physics due to possibility of extreme states generation in the matter in a wide range of pressures and temperatures: from nonideal plasma (energy deposition region) to strongly compressed condense states behind the shocks generated. Experimental study of the matter properties in extreme states produced with the beams become possible owing to the appearance of high resolution diagnostic methods [1]. Numerical simulation based on the realistic physical model is necessary here to predict the range of parameters to be measured and to choose the optimal conditions for the experiment.

In this paper, computer simulation was used to study the high pressure generation in the matter both by direct beam action and so by converted into x-ray radiation or accelerated foil actions. Laser pulse parameters considered were in the range: $I=10^8-10^{15}$ W/cm^2, τ=100 ps-1 mks, E=1-100J. For light ion beams power density was in the range 0.01-10TW/cm^2, at beam duration 20-80ns.

PHYSICAL MODEL AND NUMERICAL METHODS

To describe the dynamics of condensed matter under the beam actions equations of motion were used both as in Eulerian (for ion beams) and so in Lagrangian coordinates. They were closed by wide-range semiempirical equations of state, which describe the states of the medium in condensed and gaseous phases [2]. Energy transfer by radiation was treated in the approximation of radiation-heat conduction for ion beams and in the multigroup radiation transport approximation for laser beams. Electron conductivity coefficient and Rosseland mean free path were determined by wide range semiempirical formulas developed in [3]. Ion beam deposition into the target was calculated in the single- particle approximation according to [4]. The laser beam-target interaction was simulated by two methods: first with the help of scaling laws, which gives the ablation pressure on irradiated surface [5], second by the use of Buggers law (the same law was used for soft x-rays deposition calculation). To describe spallation in release waves continuous kinetic model was used. This model is empirical and uses a few constants of the material obtained choosing by comparison between experimental and numerical results [1]. Elastoplastic behavior was included in Lagrangian codes [5], which were used to laser beam target interaction simulations. The calculations of light ion beam interactions with matter were done by Godunov code in a moving grid [1] using hydrodynamic approach, as pressures generated in the targets considerably exceeded the yield stress.

SIMULATION RESULTS

Ion beams

Simulations presented here were done in assumption of a constant beam power density during the beam pulse. Really, power temporal profile is more complicated and depends on the type of diode. Simulation results as functions of maximal pressure on beam power density are plotted in Fig.1 by thick line. Changing of proton energy from 1 MeV to 10 MeV does not influence greatly on the value of maximal pressure. High pressure relaxation time nevertheless is proportional to the proton range. Conversion of beam energy into x-rays radiation gives more steep dependence of pressure upon power density, which is shown in fig.1 with dashed line together with experimental point [6]. More high pressures can be achieved using flyer impact techniques [7]. In this case thermal pressure generated by ion energy deposition propels the payload, which then impacts on the solid target producing the high pressures. Curves designed in fig.1 with figures correspond to impact of accelerated with different beams 10 mkm aluminum payload with an aluminum target. The length of absorber (aluminum) was chosen to be equal to the proton range. In accordance with results obtained previously [7,8], **KALIF** beam gives the maximum efficiency of beam energy transformation into kinetic energy of 10 mkm aluminum payload (μ=0.03) due to the optimal proportion between the masses of target and payload (m_p/m=0.27). Beam power density increase up to about 1TW/cm^2 leads to payload melting in release waves during the acceleration. This may be one of the possible restriction on the maximum velocity attainable with the help of ion beams for solid payload.

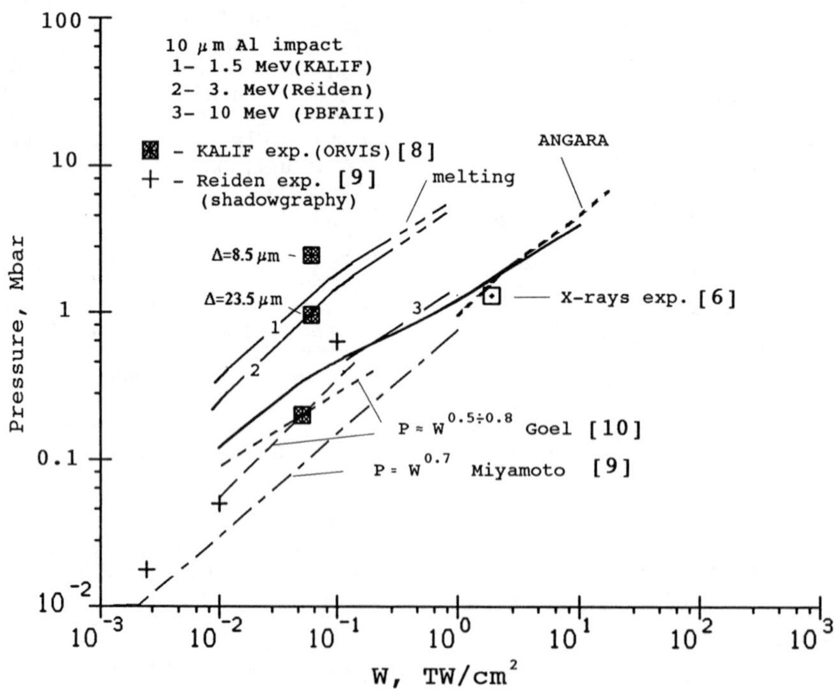

Figure 1. Pressure generation with light ion beams.

Laser beams

Data, presented here, were obtained for Al samples with thickness h = 5 - 1000 μm. Restrictions on a laser beam parameters considered here were determined by the region of the physical model validity. Minimum pulse duration can be estimated by the electron-ion thermal relaxation time (of order of 10^{-12}s). The shock wave formation regime is provided under conditions, when $h_t > h_a$ (here h_t is the sample thickness, h_a - absorption depth of the laser irradiation). In this case the shock wave width depends on the pulse duration and its intensity, mainly. This regime has been used for spallation phenomena investigation in [5] where the spall strength value for a very high strain rates (10^7 s^{-1} and more) have been obtained . Maximal ablation pressure as a function of laser beam intensity is presented in Fig.2. There are also plotted experimental data of another authors and scaling laws. Obtained results show, that in accordance with [12] less than 15% of deposited energy transforms into kinetic energy of the condensed matter motion. Hydrodynamic efficiency of laser beam action depends on power intensity of the laser irradiation and foil thickness. Carried out calculations allow to estimate the value of the energy conversion into the laser plasma irradiation. Data show, that this parameter is in the range 1-50 % depending on the beam power.

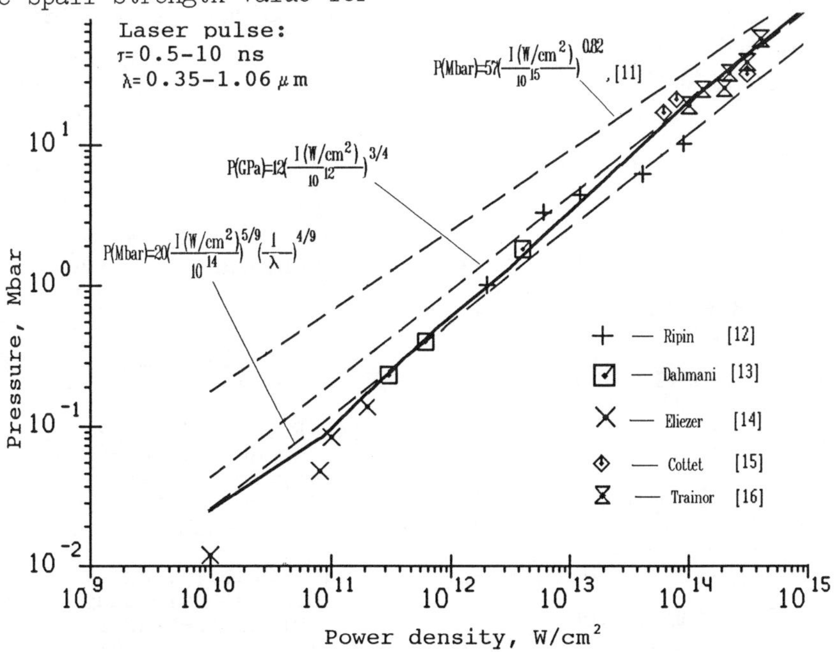

Figure 2. Pressure generation with laser beams.

CONCLUSIONS

Pressures of order of several hundreds of Mbars can be reached in the plasma using intense laser beams at power densities 100-1000 TW/cm². Numerical calculations show good agreement with experiments in a wide range of beam power.

Acceleration of the projectiles with light ion beams is profitable for generation of high pressures in comparison with the direct action especially at moderate beam intensities (0.1-1 TW/cm²). By that light payload produces more high pressures than in the case of heavy one at the same thickness of the payload due to higher velocity. At a fixed mass of payload using of heavy substance for payload is more effective but it appears to be too thin to carry out experiments (less than 1 mkm).

Conversion of ion beam energy into x-rays seems to be profitable also from the point of high pressure generation in the targets. Using ANGARA facilities for example, the pressures of order of 10 Mbar can be reached in solid target.

REFERENCES

[1] A.V.Bushman, G.I.Kanel, A.L.Ni, V.E.Fortov, *Thermal Physics and Dynamics of Intence Pulse Action*, Chernogolovka, Inst.of Chemical Physics, 1988

[2] A.V.Bushman, V.E.Fortov, I.V.Lomonosov,"Wide-Range Equation-of-State Models for Matter", in *High Pressure Equations of State: Theory and Applications*, Amsterdam, North Holland, 1991, pp.249-262.

[3] A.Ya.Polyshchuk, Moscow, Preprint IVTAN SSSR No.1-267, 1989.

[4] A.Ya.Polyshchuk et.al., *Soviet J. Plasma Phys* 17, pp. 523 (1991)

[5] V.E.Fortov, V.V.Kostin, S.Eliezer, "Spallation of metals under laser irradiation", *J.Appl.Phys.* 70, pp.4524-4531(1991).

[6] T.Endo,H.Shiraga,K.Shiloyama,Y.Kato, "Generation of a shock wave by soft-x-ray-driven ablation", *Phys. Rev.Lett.* 60, pp.1022-1025 (1988).

[7] A.R.Piriz, "Ion Beam Driven Expansion of Super-range Multilayer Plane Targets", *Plasma Phys. and Contr.Fusion* 30, pp.793-799, (1988).

[8] K.Baumung et al., "Hydrodynamic Target Experiments with Proton Beams at KALIF", in *Proc. Ninth International conference on High-Power Particle Beams*, Washington DC, USA, May 25-30, 1992.

[9] S.Miyamoto et.al, "Ablative acceleration of thin foil targets by intense proton beams", in Proc. of Topical Seminar on Particle Beam Application to Fusion Reseach", Institute of Plasma Physics, Nagoya University, 1981, pp.166-177.

[10] B.Goel, "Influence of beam profile on the pressure generated by LIB", in *Proceeding of the 8th Int. Conf. on High-Power Particle Beams*, Novosibirsk, Russia, 1990, pp.715-720.

[11] Anisimov S.I., Prockorov A.M., Fortov V.E. "Application of a high power laser installations for a matter investigation by extreem pressures" *Soviet J. UFN (in russian)* 142, pp. 395-434 (1984).

[12] Ripin B.H., Decoste R. et al.,"Laser-plasma interaction and ablative acceleration of thin foils at 10^{12}-10^{15}W/cm^2" *Physics of Fluids* 23, pp. 1012-1045 (1980).

[13] Dahmani F., Kerdja T.,"Measurements and laser-wavelength dependence of mass-ablation rate and ablation pressure in planar layered targets", *Laser and Particle Beams* 9, pp. 769-778 (1991).

[14] Eliezer S., Gazit Y., Gilath I., "Shock wave decay and spall strength in laser-matter interaction", *J.Appl.Phys.* 68, pp.356-358 (1990).

[15] Cottet F., Marty L. et al.,"Two-dimensional study of shock break-out at therear face of laser irradiated metallic targets", *J.Appl.Phys.* 64, pp.4474-4482 (1988).

[16] Trainor R.J., Holmes N.C., "Measurement of laser induced ablation pressure" In.: *Shock Waves Condenced Matter*, New York, USA, Amer.Inst.Phys., 1981, pp.145-150.

HIGH-POWER LIGHT ION BEAMS AND INTENSE SHOCK WAVES.

G. Kesler, H. U. Karow, K. Baumung

Kernforschungszentrum Karlsruhe,
Institute of Neutron Physics and Reactor Technic
Karlsruhe, Germany, 7500

V.E. Fortov, G.I. Kanel

High Energy Density Research Center, Russia Academy of Sciences
Moscow, Russia, 127412

V. Licht
University of Karlsruhe, Karlsruhe, Germany

Measurements of particle velocity profiles during the high-power proton beam interaction with solid targets have been performed at the Karlsruhe Light-Ion Facility (KALIF) with ORVIS velocimeter of subnanosecond time resolution. The peak ablation pressure and maximum velocity of foil accelerated by ablation pressure correlate with a beam power. The ultimate Al foil velocity of 12.5 km/s creates new possibilities for the equations of state measurements in a megabar pressure region. A new methods of the Hugoniot measurements with impactors of micron thickness and transparent barriers was tested successfully. New results for the spall strength in a nanosecond load duration range and shock front rise times have been obtained during the first experimental series. Monitoring the velocity profiles with high temporal resolution can be used to diagnose the beam properties also.

INTRODUCTION

The beams technique offers wide opportunities to study equations of state, mechanical and other properties of condensed matter. Considerable progress in ion beam production and focusing was achieved within the past years at the Karlsruhe Light Ion Facility "KALIF" [1]. KALIF is a 1.7 MeV, 600 kA, 50 ns pulse power generator. Depending on the beam source used ("ion diode") [2] - the proton beam pulse generated in KALIF has an energy content of several tens kJ, a pulse duration of the energy incident on the target of about 40 ns, and a beam power density up to 1 TW/cm^2 at the focus spot of about 0.5 cm diameter. The kinetic energy of the singly charged ions of the beam reaches 2 MeV.

An ORVIS-type laser velocimeter [3] was set up to study the beam-target interaction at KALIF. The main goals of performed experimental series were: development of new methods of ion beam diagnostics, an achievement by ablative acceleration of high (>10 km/s) velocity of plate impactors to create intense shock waves in condensed matter, measurements of material behavior in the nanosecond time scale. Preliminary results are discussed here.

EXPERIMENTS

Most of experiments were carried out with the B_θ proton beam diodes [2] which provided 0.25 TW/cm^2 beam power density on the target. Several shots were performed with more advanced B_{appl} diode [4] of 1 TW/cm^2 maximum power density.

Targets were metal or polymer foils 10 to 100 μm thick. Velocity histories of the target rear free surface or interface between target and transparent window were monitored by ORVIS. LiF and sapphire single crystals were used as window materials [5]. Targets were placed at the focal plane of diode.

Argon ion laser of 1 W power in the one frequency mode and Imacon 675 streak camera used in ORVIS provide 200 ps temporal resolution at the maximum streak rate of 0.3 ns/mm. One very important aspect of the experimental arrangement is the possibility to exactly synchronize the velocimeter record with the KALIF pulse. The trigger signal picked up from pulse line shows a jitter relative to the ion beam impact on target of < ±7 ns and allows to fully utilize the high time resolution. The fringe constant of ORVIS can be varied from 180 m/s to about 11 km/s. The velocity can be measured with an uncertainty of a few percents.

RESULTS

Figure 1 shows pressure histories deduced from particle velocity measurements performed with aluminum targets 33 μm thick backed by LiF windows. Due to coincidence of the aluminum and LiF dynamic impedances, shown profiles are practically ablation pressure histories in the

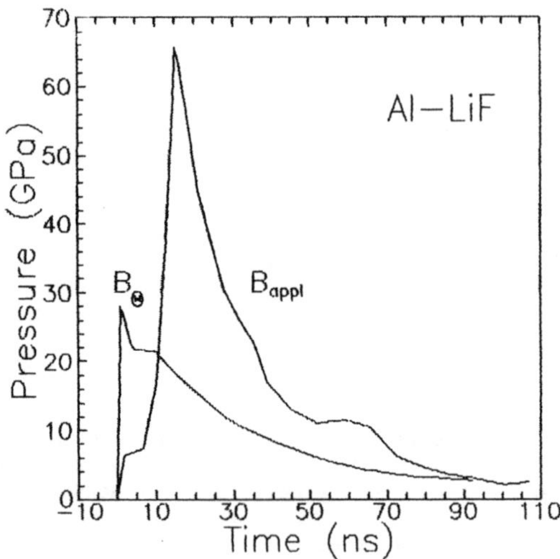

Figure 1. Ablation pressure in aluminum targets induced by the B_θ diode (0.25 TW/cm^2) and B_{appl} diode (1 TW/cm^2).

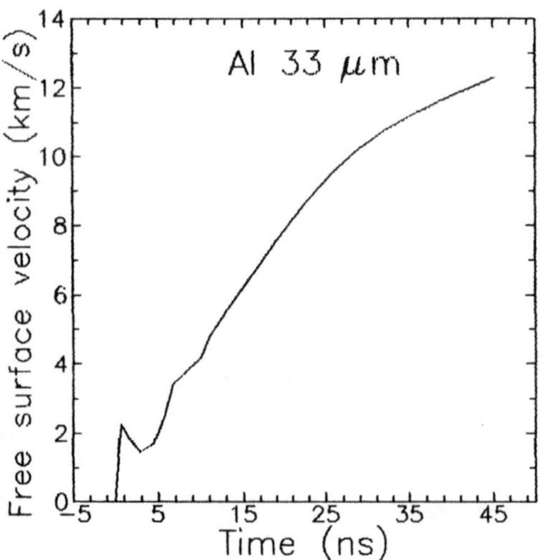

Figure 2. Ablative acceleration of the aluminum foil 33 μm thick with B_θ diode.

aluminum. Both B_θ and B_{appl} diodes were used as the beam sources. Relation between maximum pressure is approximately proportional to the relation between power of the ion beams. The B_{appl} diode needs ~10 ns to establish nominal operating conditions. During this period, the ion current and, correspondingly, beam power are relatively low. This is a reason of "preshock" in the ablation pressure profile.

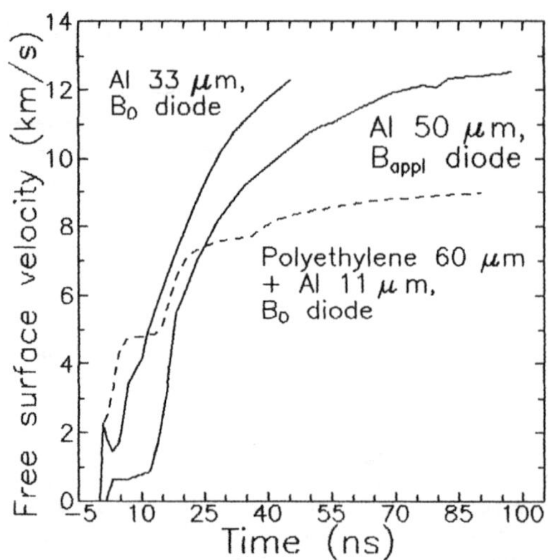

Figure 3. Velocity histories of the aluminum and composite targets obtained with two diodes.

Figure 2 shows acceleration of aluminum foil 33 μm thick by the ablation pressure. Acceleration is not monotonous. Initial phase consists from several clear visible steps, which are result of wave reverberation inside the foil between its rear surface and boundary with plasma. The first step on the velocity profile contains also a short spike. These peculiarities are analyzed in ref. [6] and can be used for estimation of the energy deposition range in target as a function of time, and for measurements of the bunched beams front structure.

Aluminum foil velocity histories obtained with two kinds of diodes are compared in Figure 3. About 12.5 km/s ultimate velocities were reached for 50 μm foil with B_{appl} diode and for 33 μm thick foil with B_θ diode. Due to the ablation, a residual thickness of foils at the moment of ultimate velocity was ~25 μm and ~8 μm correspondingly. Result of experiment with combined Al backed by polyethylene target is presented in Figure 3 also. Acceleration of the combined target with the same mass per unit of area is higher at the beginning of process and becomes smaller after 20 ns in comparison with Al foil 33 μm thick.

APPLICATIONS

The foil velocities reached are enough high for the equations of state investigation in a megabar shock pressures range. The main problem here is an accuracy of measurements. Two kinematical parameters of shock wave have to be measured to determine a point on the Hugoniot. Usually it is shock velocity and particle

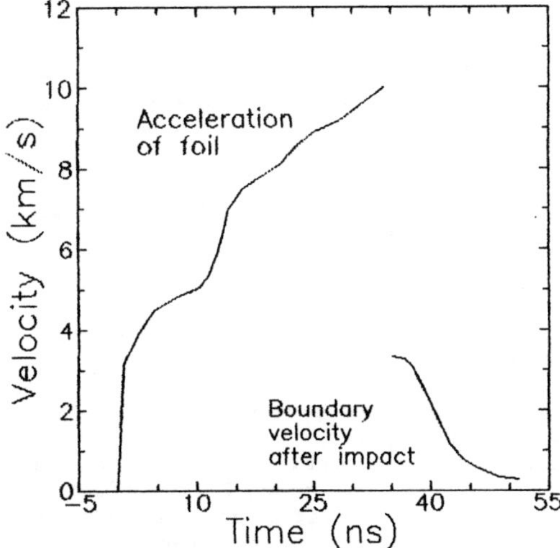

Figure 4. Impact of the polyethylene foil accelerated by the ablation pressiure on the LiF barrier.

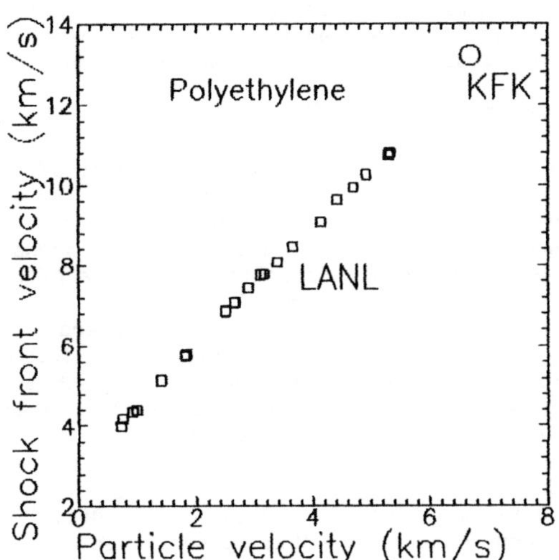

Figure 5. Result of the Hugoniot measurement of polyethylene at 84.4 GPa in comparison with the LANL Compendium of Shock-Wave Data.

velocity, and error for these values can not exceed 1.5%. But as a result of small impactor thickness, shock wave begins to decay in target very soon. This accuracy is not available for usual methods in the microns/nanoseconds distance/time scale. The same problem exists for laser driven shock waves.

Fast interferometry permits to solve this problem in experimental schemes described below. The main idea is based on use of a transparent barrier on the way of flyer plate accelerated by the ion beam. Hugoniot of one material (the flyer plate or the barrier) has to be known.

If the barrier material keeps a transparency after shock compression, the impact velocity and boundary velocity after impact can be measured at one shot. With known Hugoniot of one material, it is enough to calculate the shock pressure, shock velocity, etc. of the material tested. One example of similar measurements is shown in Figures 4, 5 where results of experiment with polyethylene flyer and LiF barrier are presented.

If a barrier material does not keep the transparency in a shock wave, a shock front velocity can be measured by ORVIS. The idea is based on monitoring the laser light reflection from shock front. A jump of the refractory index accompanies a density discontinuity in the shock front. For intense shock waves a reflectivity of shock front reaches few percents, what is enough for ORVIS. An example of this kind measurements for the aluminum flyer plate and PMMA barrier is shown in Fig.6.

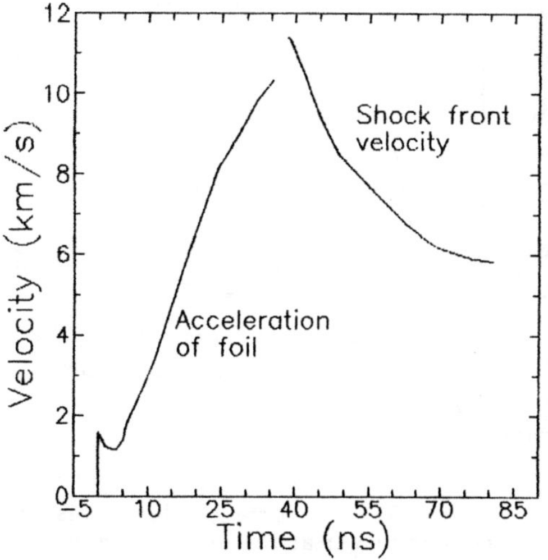

Figure 6. Impact of the aluminum foil on a PMMA barrier. Impact velocity and shock front velocity in PMMA were measured.

Transparent barriers were used also to verify the free surface velocity measurements. The velocity histories often contain jumps which introduce an uncertainty into the final data evaluation. In case of barrier installed on the way of target surface, a moment of collision of target and barrier is well determined in the interferogramm. After that the amount of lost fringes in jump can be determined through the comparison of initial

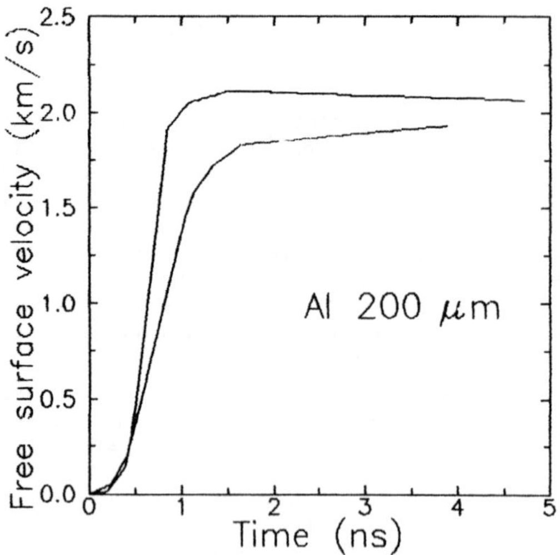

Figure 7. Shock front rise time in aluminum.

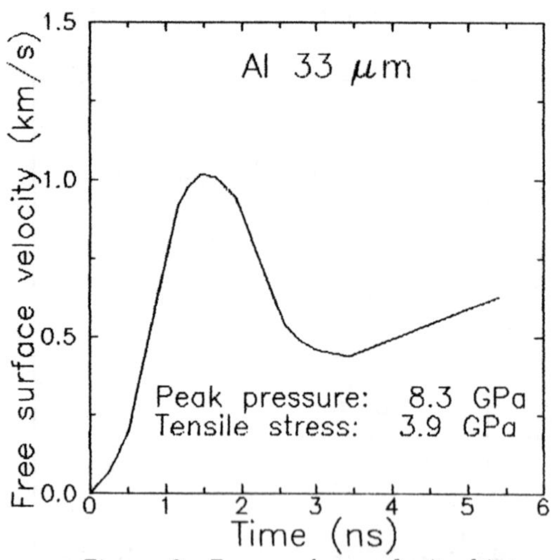

Figure 8. Free surface velocity history of the aluminum target at the lowered beam power.

distance between the target and barrier and the target surface displacement calculated by integrating of the velocity profile.

High temporal resolution of the KALIF/ORVIS installation permits us to make traditional shock wave physics measurements in a new time scale. One example of similar measurements is a shock front rise time. The shock front rise time was measured here for aluminum 0.2 mm thick at peak pressure 18.2 GPa. Figure 7 shows free surface velocity profiles for two shots. The shock front rise time is equal to 0.6±0.2 ns. A possible reason of the discrepancy between two shots can be related with some tilt of the shock front in the target.

Tensile stresses and a spall fracture are created inside a body after shock pulse reflection from the free surface. Previous measurements of the spall strength were performed up to maximum strain rates of 10^6 s^{-1}. In experiments with ion beams the strain rate reached 10^8 s^{-1} (Figure 8). Results are described in other paper of this proceeding [7].

CONCLUSION

The proton beam pulses with high energy contents have opened up new possibilities to experimental research. Besides the beam diagnostics, we hope to apply the KALIF/ORVIS installation to investigations in fields of equations of state, phase transitions, and non-equilibrium processes in condensed matter. Most interesting task is diagnostics of the ablation plasma, but it is not quite clear today how to determine all parameters of the plasma state simultaneously. In the following work we plan to investigate the stability of thin foils accelerated by the ion beam, which is very important for future applications.

ACKNOWLEDGMENT

This work was performed with the support of the Bundesministerium fur Forschung und Technologie, Germany, and Russia Ministry of Science and Technical Strategy in the framework of the Bilateral Scientific and Technical Cooperation, contract no. WTZ VI.20.

The authors would like to acknowledge the participation in experiments of V.Licht (Karlsruhe University) and the technical assistance by J. Singer and O. Stoltz (KFK/INR), and the KALIF operators.

REFERENCES

[1] H.Bluhm, K.Bohnel, L.Buth, et al. Dig. Tech. Papers, 5th IEEE Pulsed Power Conf., Alington, VA, June 10-12, 1985, pp 114-117.

[2] W.Schimassek, W.Bauer, and O.Stoltz. Rev. Sci. Instrum., 62, 168 (1991).

[3] D.D.Bloomquist, S.A.Sheffield. J. Appl. Phys., 54(4), 1717 (1983).

[4] H.Bluhm, P.Hoppe, H.P.Laqua, and D.Rush. Proc. of the IEEE, 80, 995 (1992).

[5] J.L.Wise and L.C.Chhabildas. In: Shock Waves in Condensed Matter - 1985, Y.M.Gupta ed., (Plenum Publ., 1986), p. 441.

[6] A.V.Utkin, G.I.Kanel, K.Baumung, H.U.Karow, D.Rusch. Ion Beam Diagnostics by Methods of Shock-Wave Physics. In this book.

[7] G.I.Kanel, S.V.Razorenov, A.V.Utkin, K.Baumung, H.U.Karow, V.Licht. Spallations Near the Ultimate Strength of Solids. In this book.

ION BEAM DIAGNOSTICS BY METHODS OF SHOCK-WAVE PHYSICS

A.V.Utkin, G.I.Kanel
Institute of Chemical Physics, Russian Academy of Sciences,
Chernogolovka, Russia, 142432

K.Baumung, H.U.Karow, D.Rusch
Kernforschungszentrum Karlsruhe, Institute of Neutron Physics and Reaktor Technik
Karlsruhe, Germany, 7500

V. Licht
University of Karlsruhe, Karlsruhe, Germany

Response of plane targets to the high-power proton beam has been investigated using time-resolved laser Doppler velocimetry with sub-nanosecond temporal resolution. An acoustic model was established for a semi-quantitative interpretation of the phenomena observed. It was shown the wave dynamics in a target reflects the energy distribution in the ion beam and its evolution. The evolution in time of the energy deposition zone has been deduced from performed experiments.

INTRODUCTION

Intense ion beams represent a powerful tool for the investigation of material behavior under extreme conditions. A basic requirement in this context is the knowledge of the beam-target interaction mechanisms. The methods of shock wave physics can be useful here not only to diagnose a response of matter hit by a high-power beam but also for the analysis of beam parameters. Such experiments were performed at the Karlsruhe Light Ion Facility "KALIF".

EXPERIMENTAL TECHNIQUE

KALIF [1] is a 1.8 MV, 600 kA, 50 ns FWHM pulsed power accelerator delivering up to 40 kJ proton beam energy at a peak power density of 1 TW/cm^2 in a diameter focus of 6 to 8 mm. With proton ranges of ~10 μm in condensed matter a bulk energy deposition of up to 4 MJ/g at deposition rates of >100 TW/g can be achieved.

In most of our experiments we used the so-called "B_θ-diode" [2] as an ion source which provides a proton beam with a power density of ~0.25 TW/cm^2. Targets were Al foils 10 to 100 μm thick which were placed in the focal plane of the diode.

Monitoring of wave processes in target was realized with ORVIS [3] velocimeter. Velocity histories were recorded of the target rear free surface and the interface between the target and LiF or sapphire window [4] in close contact with the target rear surface. The maximum time resolution of the velocity histories measurements is estimated to be < 200 ps. The fringe constant of the ORVIS can be varied in multiple steps between 180 m/s and >10 km/s. The accuracy of the velocity measurements in performed experiments is estimated to be 5 to 50 m/s.

RESULTS OF ENERGY DEPOSITION RANGE MEASUREMENTS

Figure 1 shows an example of an ablation pressure measurement with a 33-μm-thick aluminum foil backed by a LiF window. Using the known equation of state of LiF, the pressure at the aluminum surface and thus at the nearby boundary of the ablation plasma has been calculated. In the same figure are presented

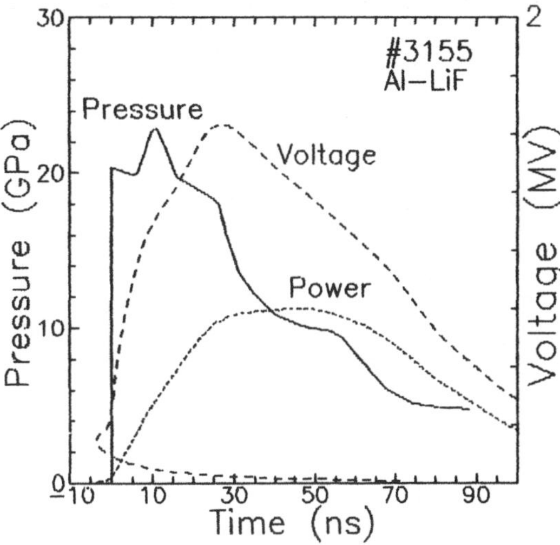

Figure 1. Ablation pressure in aluminum. LiF window was used. Voltage and power histories have been corrected for bunching.

the electrical parameters of the beam corrected for the bunching effect to the place of the target. The bunching of the proton beam occurs during the voltage rise of the generator pulse: on the way of 15 cm to focal spot protons starting later but with a higher velocity overtake slower protons which started earlier at a lower acceleration voltage. Depending on the particular pulse shape, the beam front may consists of ions of different energies or even energy intervals.

One can see the ablation pressure profile contains the steep front and series of details in the unloading part which are obviously related with the ion beam structure. Unfortunately measurements with solid windows were not quite sure for several first nanoseconds. A thickness of the glue layer between foil and window was small enough but nevertheless finite. As a result, the wave reverberations took place in the glue between surfaces of target and window. Experiments with free foil targets do not contain these distortions.

Figure 2 shows initial parts of two typical free surface velocity histories of aluminum targets 33 μm thick. These two shots were some different in the shape of KALIF voltage pulses. As can be seen the acceleration of target is not monotonous. The measured profiles often show a characteristic spike - like e.g. shot 3329 in Fig. 2 - which may be rounded or even plateau-shaped (cf. shot 3334 in Fig. 2). Several steps can be discerned which are related to reflections of the compression wave inside the target foil between the rear free surface and the boundary to the ablation plasma. A similar behaviour occured for all

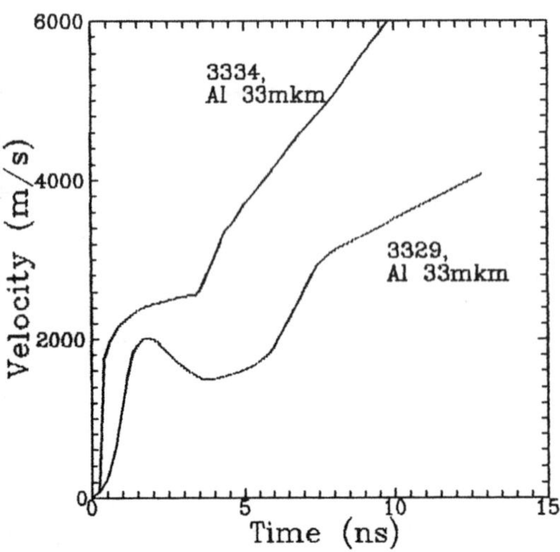

Figure 2. Free surface velocity histories of aluminum targets 33 μm thick for different parameters of ion beam.

foil thicknesses ranging from 10 to 100 μm.

Obviously, particularities in the ablation pressure profile are related with the respective structure of the ion beam.

ACOUSTIC ANALYSIS OF THE PRESSURE PULSE PROFILE

A more detailed analysis is necessary to understand the fine structure in the ablation pressure profile. With this goal an analysis of the wave process related with fast bulk energy deposition has been performed in the acoustic approach.

The simplified situation is following. Energy deposition with constant or linearly increasing power takes place in a plane layer of thickness δ at the surface of a semi-infinite target. In the initial phase, the energy deposition occurs with constant volume, and, due to heating, the pressure increases as

$$P = \frac{\Gamma}{V} E, \tag{1}$$

where Γ is the Gruneisen parameter, and P, V, E are pressure, specific volume, and specific energy. With the beginning of the process, unloading waves C_+ and C_- start from the free surface of the energy deposition zone and from its boundary to the undisturbed material (Figure 3). The circulation of these waves in the absorbing layer defines the shape of the compression pulse which is induced into the adjacent matter by the ion beam. It is necessary to establish a relation between the energy deposition rate and the wave profile at the ablation boundary.

The mass flow is described in Lagrangian coordinates by the equation of continuity, Newton's law, and the linearized Mie-Grneisen equation of state:

$$\frac{\partial V}{\partial t} = V_o \frac{\partial u}{\partial h}, \qquad \frac{\partial u}{\partial t} = -V_o \frac{\partial P}{\partial h}, \tag{2}$$

$$P = \rho_o^2 c_o^2 (V_o - V) + \frac{\Gamma}{V} E(t),$$

where u is the particle velocity, $\rho = 1/V$ is the density, h is the Lagrangeian coordinate, and $\Gamma/V = \Gamma_o/V_o = const$. By eliminating the specific volume V and applying the Laplace transformation in time for the energy deposition zone one obtains the system of usual differential equations. A solution must satisfy to the boundary conditions (P=0 at h=0, and the Rieman invariant I_-=0 at the boundary $h=\delta$).

Applying the reverse Laplace transformation for this solution we find distributions of particle velocity and pressure in the energy deposition zone. For $h=\delta$ it is:

$$u(t,\delta) = \frac{\Gamma_0}{2c_0}\Big[E(t)\theta(t)-2E(t-\tau_i)\theta(t-\tau_i)+$$

$$E(t-2\tau_i)\theta(t-2\tau_i)\Big],\ p(t,\delta)=\rho_0 c_0 u(t,\delta) \quad (3)$$

where $\tau_i=\delta/c_0$ is the period of a wave circulation, and $\theta(x)$ is the Haviside unit function. Since the flow in cold matter (for $h>\delta$) is described by a simple wave, the pressure and particle velocity at the boundary $h=\delta$ are connected by the simple relation $P = \rho_0 c_0 u$.

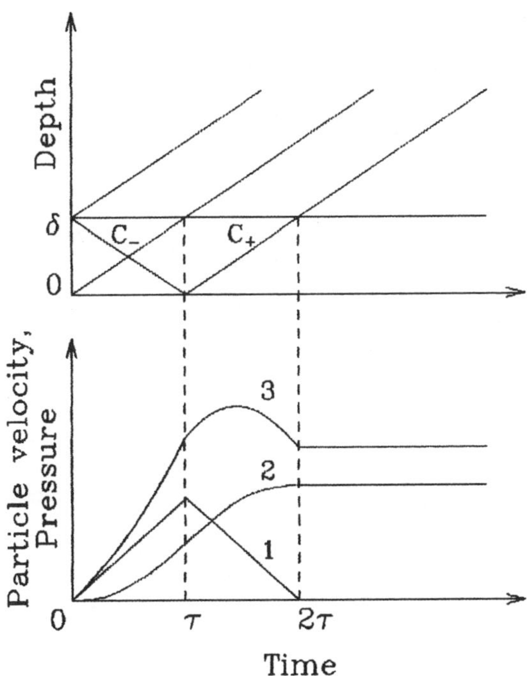

Figure 3. The time-distance diagramm and pressure profiles of the bulk energy deposition process.

Let us consider the influence of deposition energy power $W(t)=dE(t)/dt$ on the pressure and particle velocity at $h=\delta$ for dependence of power vs time as:

$$W(t)=W_0+W_1 t.$$

1. $W_1= 0$: after an initial jump to W_0 the power is constant. In this case according to (3) the velocity and pressure profiles show a triangular shape as displayed in Fig. 3 (curve 1). The velocity increases as $u = \Gamma_0 W_0 t/(2c_0)$ up to the moment $t = \tau_i$. The front of unloading wave from irradiated surface reaches the zone boundary at the moment $t = \tau_i$; after that the velocity decreases as $u = \Gamma_0 W_0 (2\tau_i-t)/(2c_0)$. For $t>2\tau_i$ the velocity is equal to zero.

2. $W_0= 0$: a power starting from the initial zero value rises linearly in time. In this case the velocity increases monotonously from zero to its maximal value $u_s = \Gamma_0 W_0 \tau_i^2/(2c_0)$ when $t = 2\tau_i$, after that it remains constant (Figure 3, curve 2). The velocity amounts to half the maximum value at $t=\tau_i$.

3. $W_0>0$ and $W_1>0$. For the general case we obtain velocity profiles as shown in Fig. 3 by curve 3. The velocity increases monotonously up to the arrival of the unloading wave $(0<t<\tau_i)$. The further evolution depends on the relation between W_0 and W_1. If $W_1\tau_i \le W_0$ the velocity reaches a maximum value of $\Gamma_0(W_0+W_1\tau_i/2)\tau_i/(2c_0)$ at moment $t = \tau_i$, decreases during $t_i< t < 2t_i$, and then remains constant and equal to $u_s = \Gamma_0 W_1^2 \tau_i/(2c_0)$ during the next circulation. If $W_1\tau_i>W_0$, the velocity, after changing the slope at $t=\tau_i$, continues increasing and reaches a maximum value $u_m = \Gamma_0(W_0^2/W_1 + 2W_1\tau_i^2)/(4c_0)$ at the moment $t_m = 2\tau_i-W_0/W_1$, and only after that begins to decrease.

So, in all cases, for times $t>2\tau_i$, the velocity depends on the increase of the energy deposition rate W_1 only.

APPLICATION OF THE ACOUSTIC ANALYSIS TO THE EXPERIMENTAL DATA

Coming back to Figure 2, one can see the velocity profile for shot 3329 shows the characteristic spike and resembles case 3 in Fig. 3 whereas the shot 3334 is similar to the case 2 where $W_0= 0$. From the characteristic times τ_i of these two shots - ~1.6 ns for shot 3329 and ~0.5 ns for shot 3334 - one deduces initial ion ranges of ~8 μm and ~3 μm, respectively. This corresponds to ion energies of 0.7 MeV and 0.3 MeV. These values are in good agreement with the mean energies of the bunched ion beam at the place of target as calculated from the measured diode voltage histories.

The values of the free surface velocity after the first increase can be used to estimate the power density $I = \rho_0 \delta\ W$ [TW/cm2]. For shot 3329, we find a jump of the power density due to the bunching of I_0~ 0.01 TW/cm^2

and an increase rate of $I_1 \sim 0.001$ TW/(cm^2·ns). For shot 3334 the initial jump of the power density is close to zero. The increase rate of the power density of $I_1 \sim 0.02$ TW/(cm^2·ns) is significantly higher than in the preceding example and results in a stabilization of the velocity at a higher level.

For times considerably longer than one wave circulation period, the correlation between the beam parameters and the ablation pressure history is displayed by experiments with windows (Fig. 1). The energy deposition of the steep bunched beam front causes the pressure to rise at a very fast rate up to 25 GPa. After that, since the energy deposition rate continues to rise the ablation pressure is approximately maintain during the rise time of the power pulse. After ~25 ns the fast power increase is stopped and the expansion of the ablation plasma begins to outweigh the futher energy input. As a result, the pressure starts falling off.

Figure 4 shows the energy deposition depth as a function of time. The dependence was constructed using results of experimental series with parameters of electrical pulse in KALIF similar to shot 3329. An estimation of the initial - during the first couple of nanoseconds - range of the ions was made on the basis of rise time measurements for thinest (11 μm) foils according to acoustic analysis presented above. The analysis of the pressure pulse reverberations in the residual part of the targets yields the range values at later times.

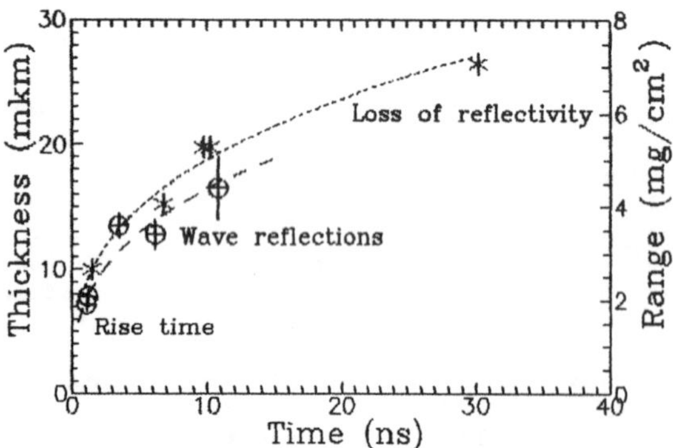

Figure 4. The dependence of the energy deposition depth vs time. Dashed lines present the results of power approximation.

The total recording time for thin foils is limited by loss of intensity of the reflected laser light. This may be caused by vaporization of the target when the ion range exceeds the foil thickness, or when a heat wave reaches the rear surface, or by hydrodynamic instabilities developing during the acceleration process. The duration of light reflection was significantly longer in experiments using a solid window. In this latter case reflectivity should disappear only due to material evaporation. So, measuring the time elapsed up to loss reflectivity for foils of different thicknesses backed by solid windows also yields the evolution in time of the ablation zone. Results of such estimations are presented in Figure 4 also.

CONCLUSION

Results of the investigation presented here demonstrate that the time-resolved measurements is a useful tool for the analysis of the beam-target interaction. It allows to determine the temporal evolution of the ablation pressure and to relate it with the details of the ion beam structure. Estimations of the ion penetration depth vs time and bunching effect have been made through measurements of wave processes in targets.

REFERENCES

[1] W.Bauer,H.Baumung,H.J.Bluhm,H.U.Karow. Diagnostische Verfahren zur Untersuchung intensiver Ionenstrahlen und der Strahl - Target-Wechselwirkungen. KfK-Nachrichten, 1992, 24, S. 19-28.

[2] W.Schimassek. Erzeugung und Fokussierung eines intensiven gepulsten Protonen-Strahles mit einer selbstmagnetisch B_θ-isolierten Ionendiode. Dissertation, KfK 455, 4, 1989.

[3] D.D.Bloomquist, S.A.Sheffield. J. Appl. Phys, v.54, pp.1717-1722 (1983)..

[4] J.L.Wise, L.C.Chhabildas. "Laser Interferometer Measurements of Refractive Index in Shock-Compressed Materials", in Shock waves of condensed matter, ed. by Gupta, 1989.

KINETIC AND OPTICAL PROPERTIES OF CONDENSED MATTER IN ULTRA STRONG LASER FIELD.

A.YA.POLISHCHUK

Max-Planck-Institut für Quantenoptik, Ludwig-Prandtl-Str. 10, Postfach 1513 , D-8046 Garching, Germany

on leave from High Energy Density Reseach Center, Institute for High Temperatures, Izhorskaya 13/19, 127412 Moscow, Russia.

Interaction of ultra-intense ultra-short laser pulses with condensed matter can create strongly nonisothermal two-component plasma. It is shown that electron-electron interactions are important at such conditions and kinetic equation is analytically solved. The influence of the laser fieldon the energy exchange between electrons and ions is investigated.

Kinetic equation for strongly non-isothermal two- component plasma.

In Silin's paper [1] it was demonstrated that, for a strongly nonisothermal plasma ($T_e \gg T_i$), electron–electron interaction via plasma ion sound waves dominates in the e-e collision integral rather than conventional e-e binary collisions. Such an effect is negligible in e-i interaction because the ion sound velocity is much greater than the ion thermal velocity.

Silin and coworkers solved the electron kinetic equation for nonisothermal plasma approximately, using the Sonine-Laguerre polynomial expansion . Unfortunately such an approach in the limiting case when e-e collisions dominate leads to the unphysical result for the electrical conductivity [2].

The purpose of the present paper is to demonstrate that using Silin's result for e-e collision integral in the case of a strongly nonisothermal plasma one can solve the kinetic equation exactly analytically . This gives another example of an exact solution of the kinetic equation in addition to the well–known Lorentz model, but in a rather complicated case when light-particle light-particle collisions are considered side by side with light-particle heavy-particle collisions. It is now possible to observe directly , unlike in the well-known Spitzer's solution , theinfluence of the e-e collisions on the electron free path separately.

The results of the present paper can be of importance in analysis of experimental results of ultra–short powerful laser pulses interactions with matter, especially, in reflectivity calculations [3].

The Boltzmann kinetic equation for the electron distribution function $f(p_j,t)$ in the external electric field E_j can be written in the following form:

$$eE_j\frac{\partial f}{\partial p_j} = I_{ei} + I_{ee}, \qquad (1)$$

where I_{ei} and I_{ee} denote respective collision integrals, e – is electron charge.

Since the ion mass M is assumed to be much larger then the electron mass m, we can write :

$$I_{ei} = n_i\frac{\partial}{\partial p_\alpha}B^{ei}_{\alpha\beta}\frac{\partial}{\partial p_\beta}f \qquad (2)$$
$$B^{ei}_{\alpha\beta} = B\Lambda(\delta_{\alpha\beta} - \frac{p_\alpha p_\beta}{p^2})$$
$$B = \frac{2\pi e^4 Z^2 m}{p}$$

where Z is ion charge, n_i –ion number density, Λ – conventional Coulomb logarithm.

In the case ($T_e \gg T_i$) considered here we use the Silin's formula [1] for e-e collision integral:

$$I_{ee} = n_e\frac{\partial}{\partial p_\alpha}\int d^3p' B^{ee}_{\alpha\beta}(\frac{\partial}{\partial p_\beta} - \frac{\partial}{\partial p'_\beta})\, f(\mathbf{p},t)\, f(\mathbf{p}',t) \quad (3)$$

$$B^{ee}_{\alpha\beta} = \frac{n_\alpha\, n_\beta}{|\mathbf{p}\times\mathbf{p}'|}\, C$$
$$C = \frac{2\,(2\pi)^{1/2}e^4 Z T_e^{3/2} m^{3/2}}{T_i\,\Lambda_1}$$

where n_α – unit vector perpendicular to $\mathbf{p}$ and $\mathbf{p}'$, and $\Lambda_1 = \ln(Z^2 M\, T_e^3/\, m\, T_i^3)$

It was shown that the solution of equation (1) in linear approximation with respect to the electric field can be expressed in the form:

$$g(p) = \frac{1}{\alpha}\,(p^3 + \beta\gamma), \qquad (4)$$

where

$$\alpha = \frac{2T_e}{e}(\, n_i B + \pi^2\, C\, \int_0^\infty dp\; p\; f_0(p)\,) \qquad (5)$$
$$\beta = \frac{2T_e}{e}\pi^2\, C$$

and γ can be calculated from equation:

$$\gamma = \frac{1}{\alpha} \int_0^\infty dp\, f_0(p)\, (p^4 + p\beta\gamma). \qquad (6)$$

Now it is not difficult to calculate the electric conductivity via the conventional expression:

$$\sigma = \frac{4\pi e}{3m^2} \int_0^\infty p^4\, g(p)\, f_0(p)\, dp \qquad (7)$$

After calculating all integrals one obtains:

$$\sigma = \frac{8(T_e/\pi)^{3/2}}{Z\, e^2\sqrt{2m_e}\,\Lambda} \frac{\Lambda\Lambda_1 + \frac{\pi}{64Z}\frac{T_e}{T_i}}{\Lambda\Lambda_1 + \frac{1}{2}\frac{T_e}{T_i}} \qquad (8)$$

It can be observed from this result that, if e-e collisions are neglected, expression (11) coincides with the well-known result for the Lorentz plasma. If e-e collisions are very strong (collision integral tends to infinity , for instance when $T_e \gg T_i$, conductivity does not vanish, it is reduced by a large, but nevertheless finite, factor $32Z/\pi$ in comparison to the Lorentz value. If e-i collisions are neglected, but e-e ones are not,the conductivity becomes infinite, as it should be from the common point of view, because e-e collisions do not change the total momentum of the electron subsystem. This result does not arise in [2], where the expansion in Sonine-Laguerre polynomials was used to solve the kinetic equation.

It is also possible to solve the kinetic equation , when space gradients of the plasma parameters exist.

For instance, for the entire electron energy flux Q_j one obtains:

$$Q_j = \int \frac{p_j}{m}\frac{p^2}{2m}\delta f d^3p = -\nabla_j T_e \frac{5!\sqrt{2}T_e^{5/2}}{3\pi^{3/2}\sqrt{m}e^4 Z\Lambda} \times \frac{1}{1 + \frac{1}{2\Lambda\Lambda_1}\frac{T_e}{T_i}} \qquad (9)$$

It is seen from (9) that, unlike the electrical charge flux , the energy flux remains finite even when e–i collisions are neglected.

Electron-ion relaxation in plasma exposed to ultra-intense laser radiation.

This section is concerned with the heating of ions through electron-ion collisions in the presence of laser radiation. This important problem has been recently studied in a weak field limit [4]. The aim of the present paper is to consider the case of very intense fields and to propose an interpolation formula for the whole region of intensities. We consider electron-ion plasma in a high-frequency field $\mathbf{E}cos\omega t$. The wave function of a free electron with canonical momentum k can be written as:

$$\psi_k = \frac{1}{\sqrt{\Omega}} exp(i\mathbf{kr} - \frac{i}{2m}\int^t (\mathbf{k} + \frac{e\mathbf{E}}{\omega} sin\omega t')^2\, dt') \qquad (10)$$

where Ω is the volume of the system, e-the electron charge. The influence of the electric field on the ion motion can be neglected due to the small ratio m/M of electron and ion masses.

Let the colliding electron and ion have initial momenta $\mathbf{k}$ and $\mathbf{p}$ and final momenta $\mathbf{k}'$ and $\mathbf{p}'$ respectively. Then using conventional perturbation theory for electron-ion scattering problem we can calculate the transition probability per unit time:

$$W(\mathbf{p}', \mathbf{k}'|\mathbf{p}, \mathbf{k}) = \sum_{-\infty}^{\infty} J_n^2(\rho) \frac{(2\pi)^4}{\Omega^3} \delta(\mathbf{p}' + \mathbf{k}' - \mathbf{p} - \mathbf{k}) \times |V(\mathbf{k} - \mathbf{k}')|^2 \delta(\frac{k'^2 - k^2}{2m} - \frac{p'^2 - p^2}{2M} + n\omega) \qquad (11)$$

Here, J_n are Bessel functions,$\rho = (\mathbf{k} - \mathbf{k}')e\mathbf{E}/m\omega^2$, $V_q = 4\pi e^2 Z/q^2$, with Z being ion charge.

We will concentrate on the calculation of the rate of variation of the ion subsystem energy E_i' due to electron-ion collisions. We therefore can write

$$E_i' = \sum_{\mathbf{kk'pp'}} F(\mathbf{p}) f(\mathbf{k}) W(\mathbf{p}', \mathbf{k}'|\mathbf{p}, \mathbf{k}) \frac{p'^2 - p^2}{2M}, \qquad (12)$$

where F,f are ion and electron distribution functions, respectively. Substituting (11) into (12), we can write the expression for E_i' in the following form:

$$E_i' = \sum_{n=0}^{\infty} E_i'(n)$$

$$E_i'(n) = \frac{N_i}{8(2\pi)^6} \int d\mathbf{Q} \int d\mathbf{q} \times |V_q|^2 (2\pi) (\delta(\frac{\mathbf{qQ}}{2m} - n\omega) + \delta(\frac{\mathbf{qQ}}{2m} + n\omega)) \times J_n^2(\rho) f(\frac{1}{2}(\mathbf{Q} + \frac{2m}{M}\mathbf{p} - \frac{m}{M}\mathbf{q} - \mathbf{q}))(\frac{\mathbf{pq}}{M} - \frac{q^2}{2M}) \qquad (13)$$

Here $\rho = \mathbf{q}\mathbf{E}e/m\omega^2$, N_i is the total number of ions, and averaging over ion momenta $\mathbf{p}$ is assumed. The presence of δ-functions in (13) is due to the energy transfer from electrons to ions which can be accompanied by n-photon emission or absorption processes. When $n = 0$, only one δ-function is assumed in (13). For the particular analysis in the present paper, we assume Maxwellian distribution functions for ions and electrons with temperatures T_i and T_e respectively, in particular, $f(k) = A_T exp(-k^2/2mT_e)$, n_e is electron number density, $A_T = n_e(2\pi/mT_e)^{3/2}$

Let us now take into account the existence of a small parameter m/M and consider the expansion of (13) in powers of $1/M$. Expression can be considerably simplified in the limit of strong fields. Instead of (13) we obtain:

$$E_i'(n) = \frac{N_i m^2 A_T}{(2\pi)^4} \int_{q_1}^{\infty} dq |V_q|^2 4\frac{\omega}{v_E} \ln\frac{q v_E}{\omega} \times e^{-\frac{m\omega^2 n^2}{2q^2 T_e} - \frac{q^2}{8mT_e}} \times ((e^{n\omega/2T_e} + e^{-n\omega/2T_e})\frac{q^2}{2M}(T_e - T_i) \times + T_i \frac{n\omega m}{M}(e^{n\omega/2T_e} - e^{-n\omega/2T_e})) \qquad (14)$$

Here we introduced the amplitude of electron velocity oscillations in the high-frequency field $v_E = |eE|/m\omega$. It is assumed that mv_E^2 is much greater than mv_e^2 and $\hbar\omega$. Here v_e is electron thermal velocity.

Calculating integral in (14) and then summing up the series in (13), which can be done by replacing sum by integral, one obtains:

If $\omega \gg T_e$:

$$\frac{dT_i}{dt} = n_e \frac{3}{2} \frac{C_0}{\sqrt{2\pi}} \frac{T_e}{v_e^2 v_E} (\ln \frac{mv_E^2}{\omega})^2 \qquad (15)$$

If $\omega \ll T_e$:

$$\frac{dT_i}{dt} = n_e \frac{2C_0}{\sqrt{2\pi}} \frac{1}{v_e^2 v_E} [T_e((\ln \frac{mv_E^2}{\omega})^2$$

$$- \frac{1}{2}(\ln \frac{v_E}{v_e})^2) - T_i(\frac{3}{16}(\ln(\frac{T_e}{\omega}\frac{mv_E^2}{\omega}))^2 + \frac{3}{4}\ln(\frac{v_E}{v_e})^2)] \qquad (16)$$

For practical aims the case $T_e \gg \omega, T_e \gg T_i$ is most important and the following interpolation formula is suggested (compare with the formula in the zero field limit [5]):

$$\frac{dT_i}{dt} = \frac{8\sqrt{2\pi} n_e e^4 Z^2}{3M(v_e + v_E)} \ln(\frac{mv_E^2}{\omega} + \frac{mv_e^2}{\omega_p}) \ln(1 + \frac{mv_E^2}{\omega}) \qquad (17)$$

It is seen from that formula that the effect of an external field is physically reduced to the substitution of the electron thermal velocity v_e by the quiver velocity v_E. Of course, numerical factors as well as more complicated logarithmic terms can not be deduced from such a qualitative argument .

Acknowledgments

The author (A.Ya.P) is grateful to Alexander von Humboldt Foundation (Germany) for the valuable support during this work. professor J. Meyer-ter-Vehn and professor S. Witkowsky for their hospitality in Max Planck Institut fuer Quantenoptik.

References.

1. V.P.Silin, Nuclear Fusion 2, p. 125 (1962)
2. L.M. Gorbunov and V.P. Silin, Sov. Phys. - Techn. Phys. 9 , p. 305 (1964)
3. A.Ya. Polishchuk, V.S. Hloponin and V.E. Fortov, Phys. Lett. A, 157, 406 (1991).
4. R. Balesku, J. Plasma Phys 27, p. 553 (1982)
5. E.M. Lifshitz and L.P. Pitaevskii, Physical Kinetics, Pergamon Press, 1988.

AN ANALYTICAL MODEL FOR LASER-SUPPORTED DETONATION WAVES ON A TARGET

Gang Yuan*, Zhou Guang-quan, Z.P Tang and L.L. Wang
Department of Modern Mechanics, University of Science and Technology of China, Hefei 230026, P. R. China

An analytical model of laser-supported detonation (LSD) wave on the target surface is described. The parameters on the shock wave front are obtained from the stability analysis of the detonation wave. The parameters of the flowfield between the shock wave front and target surface have been solved completely by Taylor's theory. The results agree well with the experiments.

INTRODUCTION

The dynamic process of the plasma generated by a pulsed laser beam irradiating on a metal target in air is a function of incident flux level, ambient gas conditions above the surface, laser spot geometry, and pulse duration [1]. When the incident laser intensity slightly excesses to the plasma threshold, a subsonic laser-supported combustion (LSC) wave will be generated. For CO_2 lasers at 10.6 μm, this threshold has been observed at intensity level in excess of 3 x 10^4 W/cm^2 [2]. An analytical model of LSC wave has been described by Pirri [3]. Since the system of equations was not closed until the radiative transport relations for LSC wave propagation were included, the model can not give a complete solution. When the laser intensity gets higher, the short absorption length of the radiation allows a laser-supported detonation (LSD) wave to form. For CO_2 laser at 10.6 μm and Nd-glass lasers at 1.06 μm, thresholds of ignition of the detonation wave are larger than 10^7 W/cm^2 [3] and 6.5 x 10^7 W/cm^2 [4], respectively. Raizer first described the laser-supported detonation wave for air breakdown at laser light focus [5]. The detonation wave velocity is proportional to the cube root of the incident laser intensity divided by the ambient density. In this study, we will not deal with the laser light breakdown at the focus point but with a pulsed laser interacts with a target in air, so that the whole flowfield on the target should be considered. The analysis of stabilities of Chapman-Jougnet (C-J) detonation has been used to investigate the detonation shock front and Taylor's theory was used to investigate the flowfield between the shock and the target. The parameters of the detonation wave front and whole flowfield are determined completely.

LASER-SUPPORTED DETONATION WAVE

One-dimensional laser-induced detonation wave is illustrated in Figure 1. The intense laser pulse vaporizes the target material resulting in ionization. The plasma zone absorbs laser energy and travels toward the laser. We suppose that all laser energy is absorbed by the plasma zone. The conservation of mass, momentum, and energy across the shock front can be expressed as

$$\rho_0 D = \rho_1 (D-u_1) \tag{1}$$

$$P_0 + \rho_0 D^2 = P_1 + \rho_1 (D-u_1)^2 \tag{2}$$

$$\rho_0 D\left(h_0 + \frac{D^2}{2}\right) + I_0 = \rho_1 (D-u_1)\left(h_1 + \frac{(D-u_1)^2}{2}\right) \tag{3}$$

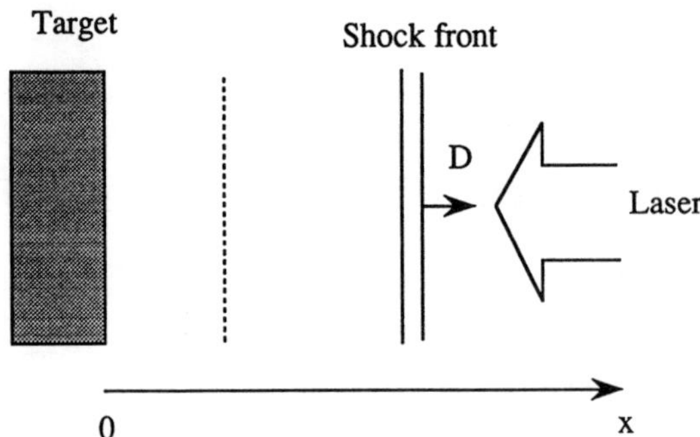

Figure 1. The model of laser-induced detonation wave.

where D, ρ, u, P and h are shock velocity, density, particle velocity, shock pressure and specific enthalpy respectively; I_0 is the incident laser intersity as indicated in Figure 1. The subscripts 0 and 1 refer to the states in front and behind the shock wave, respectively. The plasma zone can be expresszed as perfect gas

$$P_1 = \frac{k-1}{k}\rho_1 h_1 \tag{4}$$

where k is the specific heat ratio of the air plasma. From the equations (1) to (4) and based on the C-J theory of the detonation, we obtain parameters behind the shock

$$D = \left(\frac{2(k^2-1)\, I_0}{\rho_0}\right)^{1/3} \tag{5}$$

$$P_1 = \frac{\left(2(k^2-1)\, I_0\right)^{2/3}}{k+1}\rho_0^{1/3} \tag{6}$$

$$\rho_1 = \frac{k+1}{k}\rho_0 \tag{7}$$

$$h_1 = \frac{kI_0}{\rho_0 D} \tag{8}$$

For the constant target materials, the shock velocity D and pressure P_1 on the shock front are proportional to $I_o^{1/3}$ and $I_o^{2/3}$, respectively.

DETERMINATION OF FLOWFIELD BETWEEN THE SHOCK FRONT AND THE TARGET SURFACE

For the investigation of laser-induced shock wave in the target, it is necessary to know the pressure history on the target surface. Since the particle velocity of the solid surface is much smaller respect to the expansion velocity of the plasma, it is assumed that the particle velocity at the target surface is zero, that is u_s=0. (see Figure 1). The flowfield between the shock front target surface can be taken as a quasi-steady flowfield. Based on the Taylor's theory [6], a single variable of velocity is introduced

$$Z = x/t \tag{9}$$

Because every particle moving through the C-J point is isentropic, and flowfield between the shock front and target surface is homoentropic

$$dP = a^2 d\rho \tag{10}$$

The continuity and momentum equations for homoentropic are

$$\frac{\partial \rho}{\partial t} + u\frac{\partial \rho}{\partial x} + \rho\frac{\partial u}{\partial x} = 0 \tag{11}$$

$$\frac{\partial u}{\partial t} + u\frac{\partial u}{\partial x} + \frac{a^2}{\rho}\frac{\partial \rho}{\partial x} = 0 \tag{12}$$

To consider the quasi-steady flowfield condition, (11) and (12) become:

$$(u-Z)\frac{d\rho}{dZ} + \rho\frac{du}{dZ} = 0 \tag{13}$$

$$(u-Z)\frac{d\rho}{dZ} + \frac{a^2}{\rho}\frac{d\rho}{dZ} = 0 \tag{14}$$

Since u_s=0 in the region $0 \leqq Z \leqq D$, the equation of (13) and (14) should satisfy the following boundary conditions:

$$P(D) = \rho_1,\ u(D) = u_1 \tag{15}$$

$$u(0) = 0 \tag{16}$$

where ρ_1 and u_1 refer to the parameters on the C-J point.
Riemainn invariant is defined as

$$y=\int_0^{\rho} a d\rho/\rho = \int_0^{P} dP/(a\rho) \quad (17)$$

Substitute (17) into (13)-(14)

$$(u-Z+a)\frac{d(y+u)}{dZ} = 0 \quad (18)$$

$$(u-Z-a)\frac{d(y-u)}{dZ} = 0 \quad (19)$$

$$a=a(y) \quad (20)$$

for perfect gas and homoentropic flow P/ρ^{k1}= constant

$$a = (k_1-1)y/2 \quad (21)$$

where k_1 is the specific heat ratio of homoentropic flow. It is clear that equations (18), (21) have trivial solutions:

u=0; ρ=constant; P=constant; a=constant and y=constant (22)

So the boundary condiction (15) and (16) cannot be met. We have to choose u and Z at a proper point:

$$u=u_f \text{ and } Z=Z_f \quad (23)$$

to match the trivial and non-trivial solution, the trivial solution (22) is suitable for $0 \leqq Z \leqq Z_f$ and non-trivial solution satisfies in the region of $Z_f < Z \leqq D$. At the point of Z=D, from C-J conditions, we have,

$$Z = u+a$$

and

$$u-Z-a \neq 0$$

From (19), we have

$$\frac{d(y-u)}{dZ} = 0$$

or

$$y-u = y_1-u_1 \quad (24)$$

On the other hand

$$\frac{d(y+u)}{dZ} \neq 0$$

So

$$u - Z + a = 0 \quad (25)$$

The flowfield behind the shock wave is a simple rarefaction waves region. There is a constant pressure region between the target and matching point Z=D/2.
Based on the C-J condition, we obtain

$$y_f=y_1-u_1; \quad Z_f=a_f(y_f) \quad (26)$$

$$Z_f=D; \; u_1=D/(k+1); \; y=2kD/(k^2-1) \text{ and}$$

$$a_1=kD/(k+1) \quad (27)$$

from (20), (24) and (25), we obtain

$$y_f=y_1-u_1=D/(k-1); \; Z_f=D/2; \; a_f=D/2 \quad (28)$$

$$(P_s/P_1) = (a_s/a_1)^{2k_1/(k_1-1)} = \left(\frac{k_1+1}{k_1}\right)^{2k_1/(k_1-1)} \quad (29)$$

$$(\rho_s/\rho_1) = (a_s/a_1)^{2/(k_1-1)} = \left(\frac{k_1+1}{2k_1}\right)^{2/(k_1-1)} \quad (30)$$

where subscripts s and 1 refer to the states of target and C-J point, respectively.

RESULTS AND CONCLUSIONS

The plasma parameters on the shock wave front have been calculated in the case of CO_2 laser as the incident laser intensity varying from 10^7-10^{10} W/cm^2. The numerical values are ρ_0=1.3 kg/m^3 and k=1.33. As shown in Figure 2, shock velocity D is 5-40 km/s and the pressure on the shock front is 1.3-9 x 10^7 N/m^2.

As the plasma shock wave propagates into the air, rarefaction waves are produced behind the shock wave since the particle velocity at the target surface is zero. The simple rarefaction waves reduced the shock pressure from P_1 to P_s

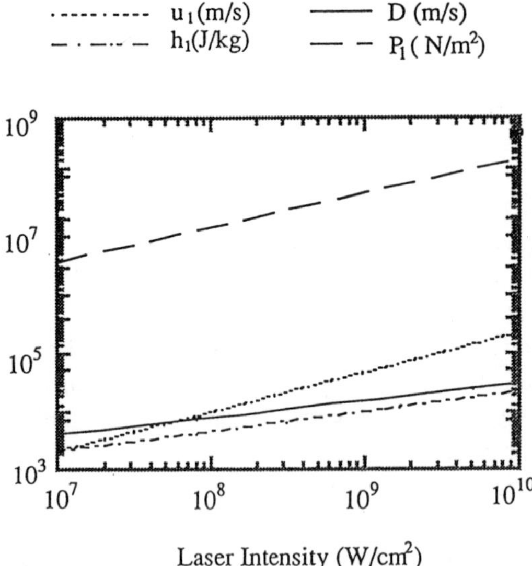

Figure 2. Plasma parameters on the shock front (k=1.33).

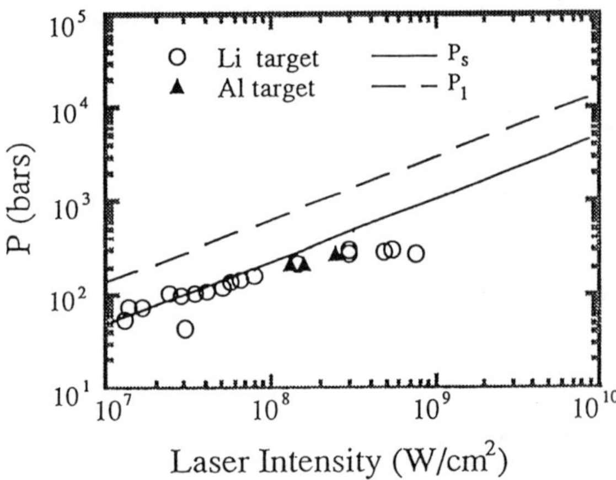

Figure 3. Plasma parameters on the target surface (k_1=1.2) and comparison of pressure on the target surface with experimental results of CO_2 laser. Solid line: the pressure on the target surface; broken line: the pressure on the shock front. The solid triangles and open circles are the experimental data of different targets.

and then there is a constant pressure (P_s) zone from the matching point Z=D/2 to the target surface. Here k_1=1.2. The results are given in Figure 3.

It is clear that the pressure on the target surface is much smaller than that on the shock front. The model gives consistent results of pressure on the target surface in comparison with the experimental results [7]. When incident laser intensity is in 10^7-10^8 W/cm^2, the calculated data agree with the experiment very well. As laser intensity gets higher($>10^8$ W/cm^2), the model predicts higher values of pressure on the target surface in comparison with the experimental data. This means that the laser-induced detonation wave is transferring to the superdetonation regime [5].

In summary, an analytical model of laser-supported detonation wave has been developed. It can be used to describe the whole flowfield of the detonation wave above the target. The intensity of the shock is reduced by the simple rarefaction waves between the moving point Z=D/2 and shock front. There is a constant pressure zone from the moving point to the target surface. The pressure on the target surface calculated by the model agrees with the experimental data.

* Present address: Institute of Laser Engineering, Osaka University, 2-6 Yamada-oka, Suita, Osaka 565, Japan

REFERENCES

[1] G.Yuan and G.Q. Zhou, *Chinese J. of High Pressure Phys.* 2,188 (1988)
[2] E.L. Klosterman and S.R. Byron, *J. of Appl. Phys.*, 45, 4751 (1974)
[3] A.N. Pirri, R.G. Root and p.K.S. Wu, *AIAA J.* 16,1296 (1978)
[4] G. Yuan, Ph.D thesis, USTC (1993)
[5] Y.P. Raizer, *Sov. Phys. JETP,* 21,1009 (1965)
[6] H.D. Gruschka and F.Wecken, Gasdynamic *Theory of Detonation*, Gordon and Breach Science Publish, New York (1971)
[7] A.V. Danilychev, et al, *J. of Sov. Laser Research*, 5, 667 (1984)

DYNAMIC FRACTURE OF IRON UNDER SHOCK LOADING INDUCED BY PULSED LASER BEAM*

Zhuang Shiming, Liu Cangli, Wang Chunyan, Sun Chengwei
Southwest Institute of Fluid Physics
P.O.Box 523 Chengdu, Sichuan 610003, CHINA

The ultra high pressure and short duration of stress wave induced by high power laser beam allows us to study the dynamic fracture behaviors of materials at strain rate over $10^7 s^{-1}$. In this experiment Nd:glass laser beam with pulse width of 750ps (FWHM) is focused on iron targets in vacuum chamber. The threshold laser flux for 400μm thickness targets to spall is about 4×10^{12} W / cm^2. The detailed microscopic observation of the recovered samples reveal that the main damage mechanism of iron under this loading condition is the microcracks' nucleation, growth, and coalescence. The microcracks can nucleate both inside the grains or at the plastic deformation area at / or near grain boundaries. The spall thickness is about 55 ± 10 μm, and the width of the damage zone is in the range of 50 ± 8 μm. In addition, corresponding to the laser irradiated area, there is a twinning zone which appears not far from the loading surface and disappears in front of the damage area.

INTRODUCTION

The interaction of laser beam with materials mainly induces two kinds of physical effects: the thermal effects of the continuous wave or long pulse laser beam, such as stress relaxation, thermal ablation, etc, and the shock effects of the short duration laser pulses. The application of the second effects made it possible for us to study the state–equations of materials at ultra high pressure[1,2]and the dynamic fracture behaviors of materials at ultra high strain rate over $10^7 s^{-1}$. [3~6]

When the laser beam radiates on the targets and is absorbed , the surface of target is ablated rapidly , so that the vapor plasma is produced. The intense recoil of vapor plasma results in a ultra high shock pressure and short duration stress pulse inside the target, which will attenuate during propagation and be reflected as reaching the rear free surface. This reflected rarefraction wave interacts with that coming from the incident surface, a tensile stress wave forms. if the amplitude and duration of the tensile stress pulse are sufficient, internal damage will occur in the target, consequently a layer of materials parallel / near to the free surface will be split out from the target body, which is called spall.

In this work the dynamic fracture of iorn has been investigated experimentally with the shock loading induced by short duration Nd:glass laser pulse of 750ps FWHM (full width of half maximum), the detailed metallurgical analysis indicates that the damage mechanism of iron at strain rate up to $10^7 s^{-1}$ is still the brittle fracture in the way of the microcracks' nucleation, growth, and coalescence, the number of nucleated microcracks per cubic centimeter is about $1\sim 2$ order higher than that obtained at lower strain rate by the plane plate impact, which implies that the brittle spall strength of iron certainly increases with the loading strain rate, meanwhile a twinned zone is observed on path of compressive wave propagation.

EXPERIMENT ARRANGEMENT

The high power laser facility employed to perform this experiment is capable of outputing the Gaussian–shaped Nd:glass laser pulse of 750ps FWHM with energy up to 80J, and the beam has a smooth Gaussian space intensity distribution. This facility consists of three stages: the forming and preamplifying, the filtering and amplifying stage, and the main amplifying stage.

The amplified beam by the third stage is focused

* This work is supported by the National Natural Science Foundation of China.

on the targets through a f / 300mm lens in vacuum chamber. For this spall experiment the beam intensity on the targets are in the range of $10^{11} \sim 10^{13}$W / cm^2. The target material used in this experiment is annealed 99.95% pure iron, the thickness of targets is 400μm, the spot diameter of laser beam on the targets surface is set to 1.2 mm, which is three times the target thickness, so a planar shock wave propagation can been ensured approximately. All the experiments were performed under the vacuum condition of 10^{-3}torr.

RESULTS AND DISCUSSION

After each shot, the internal damage of the samples is revealed by optical or scanning electron microscope (SEM) measurement on recovered samples by metallurgical cross–sectioning and polishing. Fig. 1 shows the optical metallurgical cross–sectioned micrograph of the 400μm thickness sample irradiated by the laser pulse with flux of 4.7×10^{12} W / cm^2. It can be clearly seen that the spall area corresponds to the irradiated area and the damage zone (on which the fracture plane will form) is parallel to the irradiated surface or the free surface, indicating that the planar shock wave propagates through the target. The spall thickness is about 55 ± 10μm, and the width of damage zone is in the range of 50 ± 8μm. The very thin spall thickness and narrow width of damage zone is attributed to the very short duration of the stress pulse induced by the laser pulse. It is this short duration of stress pulse in the order of nanoseconds to tens nanoseconds that make the materials fractured at the strain rate over 10^7s^{-1}.

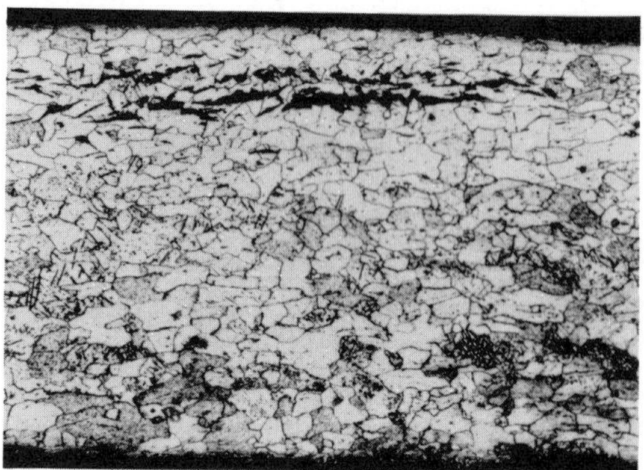

Figure 1. Optical micrograph of metallurgical cross section of 400μm thickness pure iron target irradiated by laser laser pulse of 4.7×10^{12} W / cm^2.

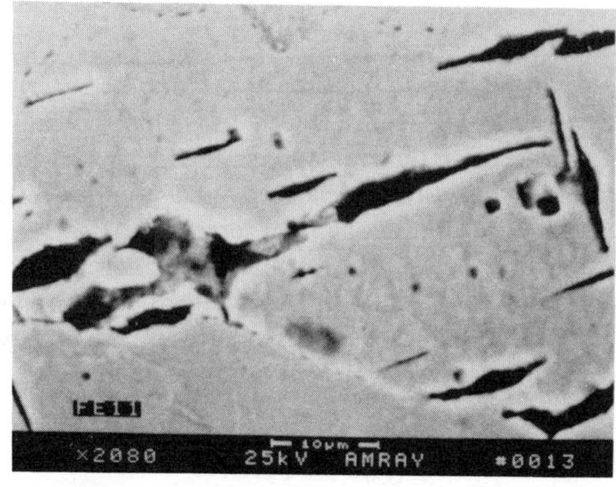

Figure 2. The SEM micrograph of the damage area.

Fig.2 is the SEM micrograph of the damage area in the same sample of Fig.1, which shows more clearly that the damage mechanism of the pure iron under this loading condition is the brittle fracture in the way of microcrack nucleation, growth, and coalescence to form fracture plane.The microcracks nucleate in two ways: the cleavage–type fracture of individual grains and the connection of the microvoids along the grain boundaries. The first is controlled by the presence of weak cleavage planes in the grains under the action of tensile stress field, the microcrack nucleates firstly on the weakest cleavage plane, then expands along this cleavage plane. Most microcracks arrest at grain boundaries during growth, which is due to that large deviations from crystallograghic match–up between grains makes it difficult for a cleavage crack to form in an adjacent grains. Furthermore, the nucleated microcracks inside the grain parallel each other, indicating that that group of crystal lattice planes of the grain is the weakest cleavage planes. However, on the whole view the observed microcracks are randomly oriented, is attributed to that the grains and hence the cleavage planes are nearly randomly oriented in the solids. The second nucleated way is due to the plastic deformation at the grain boundaries, the microfractures nucleate in this plastic defomation area, grow spherecally, and coalesce with one another to result in the observed microcracks.

The observed microcracks on the cross–sectioned surface were measured and counted and assembled into the surface distributions of number versus length, the transformaton from the surface distribution n(c) to the volume distribution N(R) is done by the first approximation transformation method proposed by Seaman[7]:

$$N(R) = n(c) / c \qquad (1)$$

here the orientations were suppressed by summing cracks number over all orientation. The R and c in eq.(1) are the true crack radius and half of microcracks' apparent length, respectively. Because the damage area is very narrow , the statistic of cracks distribution is made as only one zone for the whole damage area, the results are shown in Fig. 3, and can be approximatally expressed as follow:

$$N(R) = 1.12 \times 10^9 e^{-R/0.00058} \qquad (2)$$

where the units of N and R are cm^{-3} and cm,

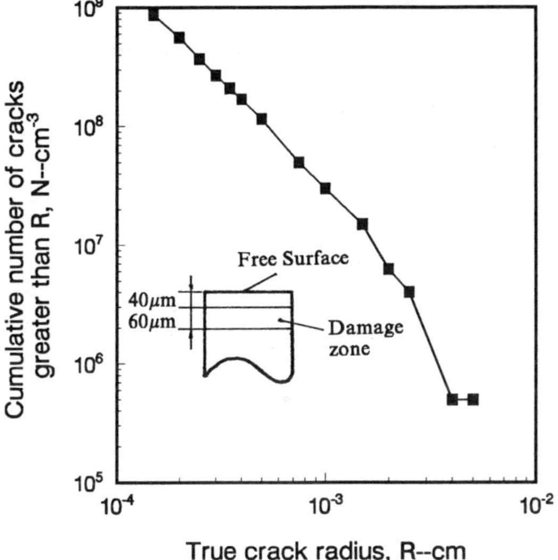

Figure 3. Crack size distribution in the damage zone of iron.

respectively. Comparing with the result obtained by the plane plate impact experiment[7], the total number of microcracks per cubic centimeter obtained in this experiment is higher about one to two order, reaching up to $10^9 / cm^3$.

By using above statistical data we can make an estimatiom for the strain rate and the spall strength of iron under this loading condition by Grady's theoretic analysis model[8].

According to Grady's energy–limited spall model, the spall occurs only at the condition that the potential and kinectic energy associated with the tensile loading process exceed the fracture energy of the materials. For the brittle solids the energy–limited spall is determined by the material fracture toughness K_c, the brittle spall strength P_s and the fragment sizes can be related to the loading strain rate $\dot{\varepsilon}$ with following expresses:

$$P_s = (3\rho c_0 K_c^2 \dot{\varepsilon})^{1/3} \qquad (3)$$

$$s = 2(3K_c / \rho c_0 \dot{\varepsilon})^{2/3} \qquad (4)$$

where ρ, c_0 are the density and sound velocity of solids. For the sake of simplifying, assuming that the new surfaces of all fragments are contributed by those cracks with the radius greater than the characteristic radius of size distribution (here is 5.8μm) , then the number of fragments in uint volume is about $1.12 \times 10^9 e^{-1} / 3$ by eq.(2), and assuming that the fragments are cube, the average size of the fragments will be the order of 20 μm. For iron taking $\rho = 7.9\ g/cm^3$, $c_0 = 0.458\ cm/\mu s$, $K_c \approx 6 \times 10^{-2} GPa \cdot cm^{1/2}$, and s = 0.002 cm, by eq.(4) and eq.(3), the strain rate $\varepsilon \approx 10^7 s^{-1}$, and the spall strength $P_s \approx 3.4$ GPa.

From Fig.1 it also can seen that there is a twinning zone corresponding to the laser irradiated area, which is shown more clearly in Fig.4 by the SEM micrograph. The twins, which are produced by the elastic precursor, appear at about 60μm from the ablated surface , extending for about 180 μm, and disappear in front of damage zone. The density of twins decreases with distance increasing, which corresponding to the decay of shock amplitude. The front end of twinned zone, somewhat like the humps of a camel, is attributed to the space intensity distribution of laser beam.

As shown in Fig.1, the spall damage of target is in the incipient stage corresponding to incident laser flux

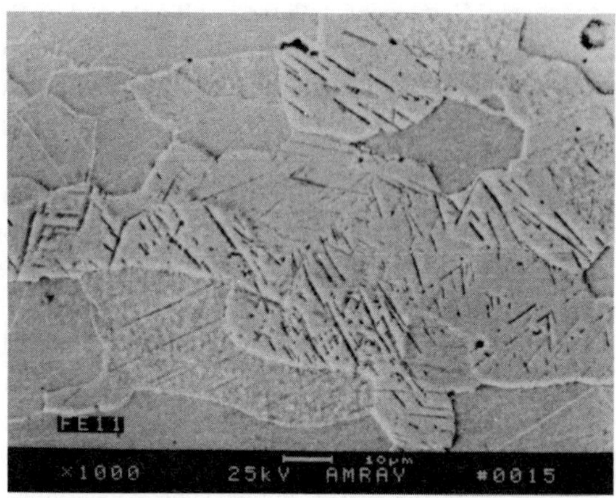

Figure 4. The SEM micrograph of the twinned zone.

of 4.7×10^{12} W / cm^2. For the lower laser intensity the spall damage will not occur, but the twins may still be produced, so the threshold laser intensity for 400μm thickness iron targets to spall is about 4×10^{12} W / cm^2.

SUMMARY

Under the shock loading induced by short duration Nd:glass laser pulse of 750ps (FWHM), the dynamic fracture behaviors of 400μm thickness iron targets is studied. The main damage mechanism of iron under this loading condition is the brittle fracture in the way of microcrack nucleation, growth, and coalescence. The microcracks nucleate in two ways: the cleavage–type fracture of individual grains and the connection of the microvoids along the grain boundaries.

Corresponding to this loading condition, the estimated strain rate can reach up to $10^7 s^{-1}$, and the brittle spall strength of iron goes up to about 3.4 GPa. For the 400μm thickness iron target, the spall thickness is about $55\pm 10\mu$m, and the width of damage zone is in the range of $50\pm 8\mu$m, the threshold laser flux is about 4×10^{12} W / cm^2.

In addition, corresponding to the laser irradiated area, a twinned zone is observed, which appears not far from the loading surface and disappears in front of the damage area.

REFERENCES

1. S.I.Anisimov, et al., Sov.Phys.Usp. 27(3), pp. 181–205 (1984).
2. R.J.Trainor, et al., Lawrence Livermore Lab. Report UCRL–52562, 1978.
3. J.A.Fox and D.N.Barr, Appl.Phys.Lett. 22, pp. 594–596 (1973).
4. S.Eliezer, I.Gilath and T.Bar–Noy, J.Appl.Phys. 67(2), pp. 715–724 (1990).
5. M.Boustie and F.Cottet, J.Appl.Phys. 69(11), pp. 7533–7538 (1991)
6. Zhuang Shiming, et al., SPIE Proc. 1761, pp. 141–149 (1992).
7. L.Seaman, et al., J.Appl.Phys. 49(10), pp. 5221–5229 (1978).
8. D.E.Grady, J.Mech.Phys.Solids 36(3), pp. 353–384 (1988)

THERMAL EFFECTS IN LASER INDUCED STRONG SHOCK WAVES

Xin-Zen Li Zhi-Ping Tang Gunag-Quan Zhou Sheng-Bin Lin
Department of Modern Mechanics
University of Science & Technology of China
Hefei, Anhui 230026, PRC.

Laser induced shock waves were originated by surface energy absorption, the thermal effects should be examined carefully. Work reported here was endeavored to improve the present shock theory to include the external heat source. A model with a moving boundary as ablation front of laser was used to avoid the complexity of plasma. Hyperbolic heat conduction equations were adopted due to the small time and space range. The thermal terms were coupled into Gruneisen EOS through internal energy. Approximate difference analysis to aluminum shows that the laser heating was limited near the ablation surface, and the shock pulse did not show obvious change compared with conventional case because the pressure - volume relation is not sensitive to temperature. Our results also indicated that unloading melting or structural transition may take place in the thermal and pressure coupling region. These might have obvious influence to the shock pulse behavior.

INTRODUCTION

High-power laser pulse have been used to generate strong shock waves in solid target for these two decades. One of the key problem in the process is the precise description of the shock profiles. Some researches kept on the effort to directly detect the pressure profiles,[1,2,3] but it was proved to be a very difficult work due to the space and time limitation, the ablation on the target surface, the linear range of the transducer and other factors. The peak pressure generated by laser was reported over TPa level,[4] while the highest direct measured pressure was only several tens of GPa. Another approach was to obtain empiric law and was the most popular way in dealing with this problem so far. However, such formulas have the shortcoming that they could not provide thedetailsof the pressure profiles. Finally, there was numerical simulation using special constructed computer code such as MEDUSA.[5] Unfortunately, the EOS model engaged by MEDUSA in the solid medium was too simple.

Since the shock pressure is originally induced by surface heating, the heat conduction problem should be considered carefully. This was not included in MEDUSA, as well as other approaches mentioned above, either.

On the other hand, there are considerable amounts of works dealing with the heat pulse conduction in solid using hyperbolic heat conduction model (due to the small time and space ranges) [6,7], or by MD method.[8] Nevertheless, they did not consider the ablation on the surface and could only be applied to laser energy intensity below about 10^8 W/cm^2 where shock wave may not be formulated.

From physics point of view, pulsed laser introduced a transient temperature field and a shock wave simultaneously. The temperature may affect the shock propagation in the aspects of material softening (decrease of unloading isentropic sound speed), unloading melting condition and other parameters linked with temperature. In this work, we tried to improve the shock wave theory to include heat conduction from external source.

PROBLEM FORMULATION

To deal with this problem, we use EOS of energy type. One of the conventional form may be written as

$$E = E_c(v) + E_T(T,v) + E_e(T,v) \tag{1}$$

$$P = P_c(v) + P_T(T,v) + P_e(T,v) \tag{2}$$

where E is energy, P, v, T denote pressure, specific volume and temperature, respectively. The subscript c, T, e represent the "cold" term, the contribution of thermal vibration of atoms and the contribution of electrons, respectively. And there has a relation between cold pressure and cold energy

$$P\,(v) = -\frac{d\,E_c(v)}{dv} \tag{3}$$

We then specify a special boundary condition for strong laser interaction with solid targets. We assume the existence of a ablation front x_f that marks the phase transition plane of target substance from solid to liquid, gas or plasma. In front of this boundary is the solid medium in which pressure and heat waves will propagate. A region of dense plasma supported by laser is behind the ablation front and apply pressure and thermal constraints on it. We further assume that the ablation front may maintain a constant temperature level T_m due to phase transition. Here T_m may be the melting point of target material in such circumstance. We may in turn find out this ablation front using

$$T=T_m|_{x=x_f} \tag{4}$$

In this approach, we can pay attention only on the solid medium, and the total temperature rise has two terms as:

$$T(h,t)= T_p(h,t) + T_t(h,t) \tag{5}$$

where T_p is shock heating due to unreversible compression. h and t are Largarange coordinate and time, respectively. T_t is heat conduction term governed by hyperbolic equation considering the small time and space range.

$$\frac{\partial^2 T_t}{\partial x^2} = \frac{1}{c^2}\frac{\partial^2 T_t}{\partial t^2} + \frac{1}{\alpha}\frac{\partial T_t}{\partial t} \tag{6}$$

where α is thermal diffusivity. c is the heat wave speed. x is Eulerian coordinate.

One character in laser shock pulse is that the thermodynamic process could be described as an adiabatic compression followed by an isentropic rarefaction. We can find out the temperature path in shock loading as

$$T_p= T_D|_{\text{adiabatic process}} \tag{7}$$

and isentropic path as

$$T_p= T_s|_{s = \text{const.}} \tag{8}$$

Here s denotes entropy. T_D, T_s are defined by temperature path of adiabatic and isentropy condition, respectively. Thus we construct a set of complete equations for the analysis of the thermal effects in laser induced shock waves.

If specific heat of constant volume Cv and the ratio γ/v are assumed to be constants, we may write[9]

$$T_D = T_0 \exp[\, \gamma_0\eta \,(1+ \frac{1 + \lambda}{6T_0\alpha}\eta^2)] \tag{9}$$

$$T_s = T^* \exp\,(\,\gamma_0\eta) \tag{10}$$

Where T_0 is initial temperature. γ_0 is the initial Gruneisen coefficient. α is bulk linear expansion coefficient, λ is the linear factor in Hugoniot shock speed - particle velocity relationship. $\eta= 1-v/v_0$. T^* is an arbitrary value on the T_s curve. If we assume ablation velocity

$$u = dx /dt \tag{11}$$

to be a constant, and α, c do not change with temperature, T_t could be found out analytically.[10] Under same assumptions, Eqs.(1-2) can be written as[11]

$$P= P_c + \frac{\gamma}{v}[\, Cv(T-T_0)+E_0]+ \frac{1}{4}\frac{\beta}{v_0}(\frac{v_0}{v})^{1/2}T^2 \tag{12}$$

$$E= - \int_{v_{0c}}^{v} P_c dv +Cv(T-T_0) + E_0+ \frac{1}{4}\frac{\beta}{v_0}(\frac{v_0}{v})^{1/2}T^2 \tag{13}$$

NUMERICAL SIMULATION TO ALUMINUM TARGET

Conventional 1-D difference method was engaged to simulate the problem in aluminum target in Largrange system. Eulerian coordinates were transferred to Largrange ones through

$$dx/dh =1 +\eta \tag{14}$$

We also move the initial difference net point along ablation velocity u_f so to make out an ablation front. Aluminum may be the only material that its EOS and thermal constants are available so far. We took the EOS constants directly from Ref.11, with initial sound speed of 0.538cm/μs, γ_0=2.09 and λ = 1.338. Other parameters were listed in Table 1. The laser pressure was 0.2Mbar correspond to energy intensity of 10^{11} W/cm^2 order according to Phipps et al's work.[2] The laser pulse shape was taken as a rectangular one with a duration of 1ns. The temperature on the ablation front was assumed to be 900k. We chose u_f=0.11 cm/μs.

Fig.1 gives the results of pressure and temperature distribution during the laser pulse. The pressure profiles did not show obvious change while the temperature near the ablation front had a higher level. Noticing the scale of heat wave affected region was μm order. Fig.2 gives the distribution of pressure and temperature of same quantities as Fig.1 when the laser pulse was over. The effective heat conduction depth was also μm scale and had no obvious influences on shock behavior. Boustie et al[12] suggested an elongation region on the tail of shock pulse.

Table 1. Material Coefficients Used In The Calculation

Cv	J/g K	8.96x10^{-6}
α	cm^2/μs	2.43x10^6
c	cm/μs	0.55
α_0	1/ K	6.93x10^{-5}

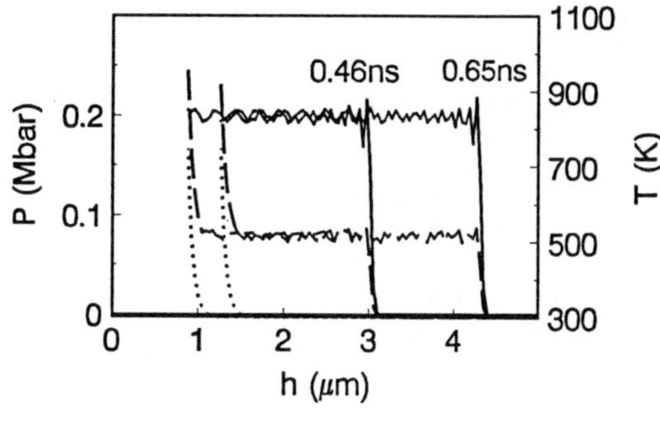

—— P --- T .... T_t

Figure 1. Pressure and temperature distribution in loading process for t= 0.46ns and 0.65ns. The start points indicate the location of ablation front.

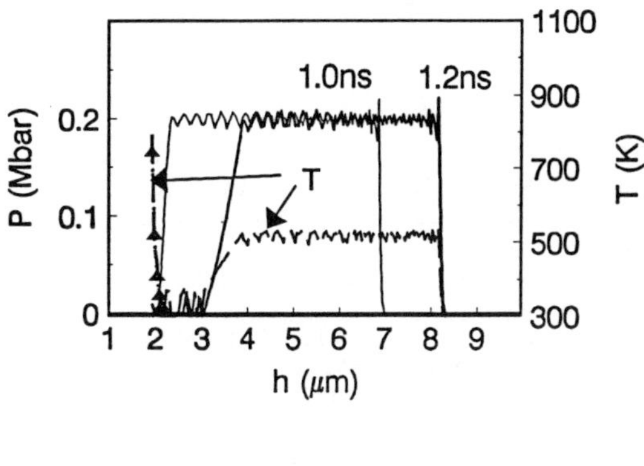

—— P --- T Δ Δ T_t

Figure 2. Presure and temperature distribution in unloading process for t=1ns and pressure for t=1.2ns .

The space scale of their elongation region was about 50μm. Our present work shows that heat conduction could not affect their results.

FURTHER DISCUSSIONS TO OTHER MATERIALS

We can see a clear pattern from above results. There is a heat conducting layer in front of the ablation surface. Outside this layer, the shock wave behavior was not affected by the surface heating. Although the heat wave speed seems the same order as shock wave, this layer could only be μm range due to the rapid dissipation of heat wave. Even in the small conduction affected region, over 80% of the pressure comes from cold contribution. The pressure - volume relation, which determine the shock wave behavior, is not sensitive to temperature. In general cases, we cannot expect to find any detectable effects in shock loading due to the heat conduction from surface.

The heat conduction could coupled with unloading process to increase the possibility of unloading melting or increase the melting depth. Romain et al[13] had reported a μm scale recrystalling layer at the bottom of the laser ablation crater in iron target. This might be caused by the coupling effects of heat conduction and shock unloading. One reason is that the recystalling space scale was the same order as present work, another is that if this layer was melted during ablation, it should be blown off.

The thermal effects may indeed have some important influence to structure phase transition material like iron or abnormal melting material like lead. The reverse phase transition in the unloading process would produce a curvature on the pressure - volume plane and resulting an unloading shock. This effect may change the shock wave behavior obviously as illustrated by Bertholf's famous work.[14] For temperature change of 100K, the phase transition pressure may have a shift of 30%.[9] For later works of laser induced shock wave study on such materials, the thermal effects should be carefully examined.

Heat energy may have another propagation approach through hot electrons in case of strong laser pulse and produce preheating effects. A simple calculation of Eqs.(12-13) shows that electrons contribution to pressure is only one percent of the whole value. Its effect will be even smaller.

One idea may be drawn from resent work that latent heat can be introduced in models of MEDUSA and other similar works.. We can expect a phase platform which indicate the location of ablation front on the space coordinates.

CONCLUSION

A model including moving ablation boundary and heat wave conduction for the study of laser shocks was established in this work. One - dimensional difference calculation were carried out to aluminum target. Our results showed that the laser heating effect was mainly limited to a μm layer near the boundary. And the shock pulse did not show obvious change compared with conventional cases. This conclusion was obtained through a relatively reasonable way from physics point of view.

The heat conduction effects, if it could be observed, may expect to be found in reverse transition process of structural phase transition materials. This needs to be verified further.

This work was supported by National High Tech Project.

REFERENCES

[1] C.T.Walter, " Laser Generation of 100 kbar Shock Waves in Solid", in Proceeding of Shock Compression of Condensed Matter-1991, pp797-780.

[2] C.R.Phipps et al, J. Appl. Phys., **64**, pp1083 -1096 (1988)

[3] T.P.Romain, D. Zagouri, "Laser-Shock Studies Using an Electromagnetic Gauge for Particle Velocity Measurements", ditto as Ref.1, pp801-804.

[4] Gu Yuan et al,"Progress of the Laser EOS Research at SLIP", in Proceedings of 2nd Intel. Symp. on Intense Dynamic Loading and Its Effects. Sichuan Univ. Press, 1992. pp57 -61.

[5] J.P.Christiansen, D.E.T.F.Ashby & K.V.Robert Comput. Phys. Comm.,**7**, pp271-283(1974)

[6] W.S.Kim et al, J. Appl. Phys., **68**, pp5478 - 5485(1990)

[7] M.J.Maurer, H.A.Thomson, J. Heat Transf. **5**, pp284-286(1973)

[8] R.A MacDonald, D.H.Tsai, Physics Reports, **46**, pp1-41(1971)

[9] G.R.Duvall, K.A.Graham, Rev. Modern Phys. **49**, pp523-580(1977)

[10] X.Z.Li, Z.P.Tang, G.Q.Zhou, to be published

[11] S.Eliezer, A.Ghatak, H.Hora & E.Teller, *Equations of State*,Cambridge Univ. Press, 1986, ch.13,pp197-220.

[12] M.Boustie, F.Cottet, and J.P.Romain, "Spall -ing Due to a Strong Shock Wave Decay Process in Solid Targets Irradiated by a pulsed laser", Ditto as Ref.1, pp805-808.

[13] J.P.Romain et al, " $\alpha \Rightarrow \varepsilon$ Phase Transition in Iron Induced by Laser Generated Shock Waves", in Proceeding of Shock Waves in Condensed Matter, Elsevier Science Publisher, 1988. pp787-790.

[14] L.D.Bertholf et al, J. Appl. Phys., **46**, p3776 (1975).

PVDF MEASUREMENT OF SOFT X-RAY INDUCED SHOCK AND FILTER DEBRIS IMPULSE

D.E. Johnson and L.M. Lee
Ktech Corporation, 901 Pennsylvania NE, Albuquerque, NM 87110

M.A. Hedemann
Sandia National Laboratories, P.O. Box 5800, NM 87185

F. Bauer
Institut franco-allemand de Recherches, 68301 Saint Louis, France

PVDF piezoelectric polymer shock stress sensors have been used to measure the shock and impulse generated by soft X-rays and by filter debris in the SATURN Plasma Radiation Source at Sandia National Laboratories, NM. SATURN was used to generate 30 to 40 kJ, 20-ns duration, line radiation at 2 to 3 keV. Fluence on samples was nominally 40, 200, and 400 kJ/m^2 (1, 5, and 10 cal/cm^2). Measurements of X-ray induced material shock response exposing both aluminum and PMMA acrylic samples agree well with companion measurements made with single crystal X-cut quartz gauges. Time-of-flight, stress, and impulse produced by Kimfol (polycarbonate/aluminum) filter debris were also measured with the PVDF gauges.

INTRODUCTION

One-dimensional piezoelectric X-cut quartz gauges have been a standard for material stress measurement in impact physics experiments since 1965 when Graham described their potential accuracy when properly used.[1] Piezoelectric gauges still offer the best performance in material response studies when the tradeoffs between accuracy, cost, and the complexity of setting up tests are evaluated.

In addition to using X-cut quartz gauges, we are developing stress gauges that use the piezoelectric polymer film, polyvinylidene fluoride (PVDF), as the active stress-sensing element. The primary advantage of PVDF over quartz in this application is that smaller gauges can be built to record for several microseconds or more. Several experiments, one which will be described in this paper, require the ability to record for several microseconds.

While testing a new PVDF stress gauge at SATURN[2], we conducted a short series of experiments to measure the stress and impulse generated by a vaporized Kimfol filter. The results of these experiments illustrate the longer recording time available with the PVDF gauges and provide preliminary measurements of stress and impulse generated both by ablation of the sample and by the impact of the Kimfol filter debris on the sample being irradiated.

PVDF GAUGE DESIGN

The PVDF stress gauges used at SATURN use PVDF shock sensors produced using the polymer material source and electrical poling treatment developed by Bauer.[3] These sensors have been shown to respond in a reproducible manner to shock loading over a stress range from 10^4 to 10^{10} Pa.[4,5] In these gauges, the sensors, 0.25 cm^2 in area, were epoxy-bonded onto a PMMA (polymethylmethacrylate or acrylic) backer and covered by 0.6-mm thick PMMA sample. The PMMA/PVDF subassembly was epoxy-potted into a 25-mm diameter aluminum canister that included a coaxial electrical connector. Figure 1 shows the gauge

Supported by Sandia National Laboratories/New Mexico Contract SNLA 87-6392. Funded by DOE Contract DE-AC04-76-DP00789

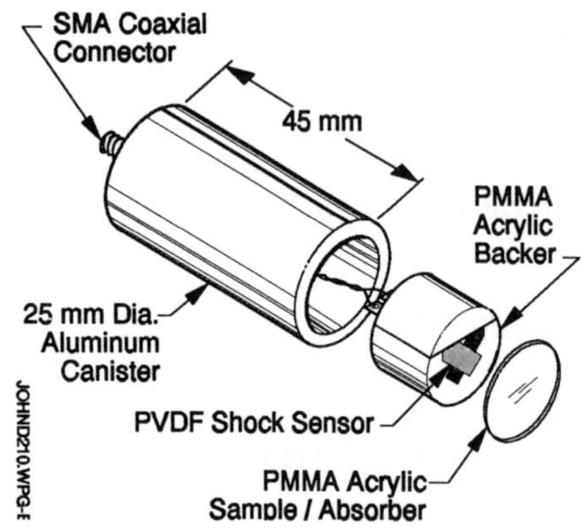

Figure 1. PVDF Stress Gauge Components.

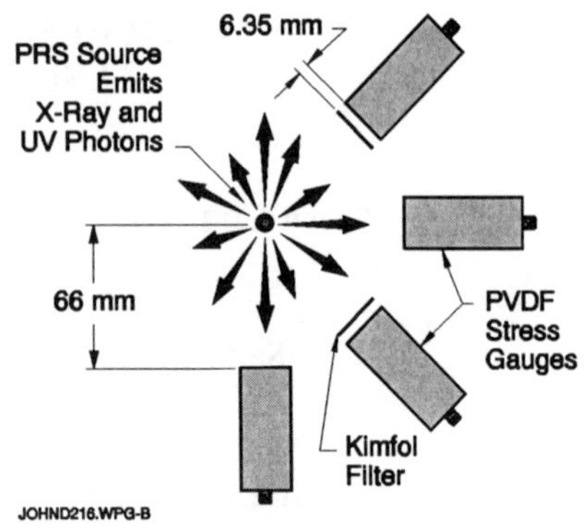

Figure 2. SATURN can irradiate many samples simultaneously.

components.

These gauges were set up such that the sensor was connected directly to a high-quality 50-Ohm cable that was then terminated at the recorder with a matching impedance of 50-Ohms. The voltage recorded in this setup is 50 times the current produced by the sensor. The current is proportional to the time rate of stress change, or stress rate, in the sensor. The recorded signal is then software integrated and scaled appropriately to determine stress.

TESTS AND MEASUREMENTS AT SATURN

The SATURN radiation simulator at Sandia National Laboratories is a large pulse power machine used to generate either Bremstrahhlung or soft (2 to 3-keV) X-rays to evaluate the response of materials and electronic circuits to high levels of radiation. In these tests, SATURN was set up as a *Plasma Radiation Source* to produce 20-ns duration pulses of 3.1 keV line radiation. The total energy is quite high, 30 to 40 kJ, allowing many samples to be placed around the source and simultaneously irradiated as shown in Figure 2.

Several tests were conducted at SATURN in which PVDF gauges and X-cut quartz gauges were placed in the diode and exposed to 3 keV line radiation (argon gas puff) at fluences from 45 to 450 kJ/m^2 (1 to 10 cal/cm^2). The quartz and PVDF gauges both used PMMA samples and were set up to provide nearly identical exposure to four or more gauges on each shot. The stress measured by the PVDF gauges compared very well with that measured by the quartz gauges as illustrated by Figure 3 in which the results from Shot 1610 are compared. The chief difference in the records when the full time window is compared is that the stress pulse has reached the back surface of the quartz gauge at about 0.33 μs and the resulting reflections prevent further stress measurement. The PVDF gauge, in contrast, continues to record for several microseconds.

The radiation pulse contains 30 to 40 kJ of radiation at 3.1 keV and about 300 kJ of lower energy photons primarily in the ultraviolet range. The UV photons are usually prevented from reaching the material samples (filtered) by placing two or three layers of Kimfol (2-μm thick polycarbonate metalized with aluminum) between the source and the irradiated samples. These filters vaporize, generating a rapidly expanding cloud of plasma and gas debris. The filters are therefore normally placed as far from the sample as possible and angled to minimize the amount of debris that strikes the sample.

Four shots were taken in which PVDF stress gauges were set up with and without Kimfol filters as was shown in Figure 2. In one of the shots, Shot 1613, two gauges included the Kimfol filters and two gauges were set up as controls

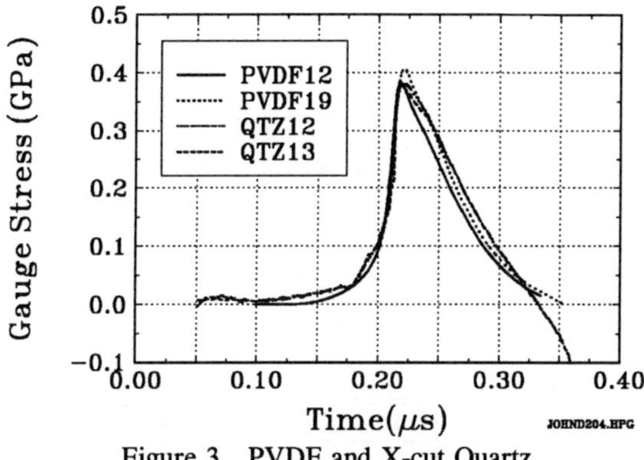

Figure 3. PVDF and X-cut Quartz Records.

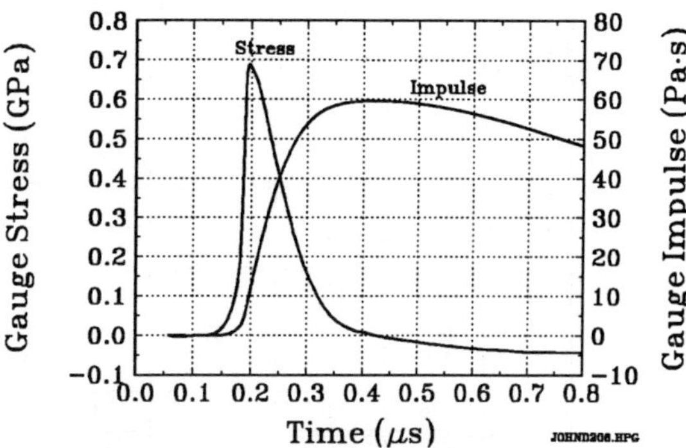

Figure 5. Blow-off induced sample stress and impulse.

with identical hardware except the filters. The filters were placed 6.35 mm in front of the samples and oriented so that they were parallel to the sample face. (This orientation and spacing is not typical, but chosen to improve the ability to identify the debris impact and measure a potentially low stress.)

A typical record, shown in Figure 4, clearly illustrates how PVDF can provide a long recording time free of internal reflections. The first spike, negative-going at 0 μs, was generated by electrical noise in the gauge while the machine was producing X-rays. The stress pulse was generated in the front surface of the sample at the same time and began propagating through the sample thickness. When the stress pulse arrived at the back of the sample, the PVDF sensor was stressed producing the initially positive spike at 0.2 μs. The output then went to zero until 1.2 μs, when a second initially positive spike was observed. This second spike was caused by the filter debris. On gauges with filters, a very similar spike was always recorded at about 1.2 μs while no spike was observed on the control gauges without filters.

Figure 5 shows the integration of the first initially positive spike caused by vaporization of the sample face by radiation. The fluence on sample was 494 kJ/m^2 (7 cal/cm^2)and produced 0.7 GPa (7 kbar) at the rear face of the sample. A second software integration yields the sample impulse, about 60 Pa-s (0.6 ktap).

Figure 6 shows the integration of the second slower spike caused by the filter debris cloud hitting the sample face. The stress peaks at only 0.22 GPa (0.22 kbar) but produces 50 Pa-s (0.5 ktap) of impulse. (Note that filter stress and impulse would generally be much smaller

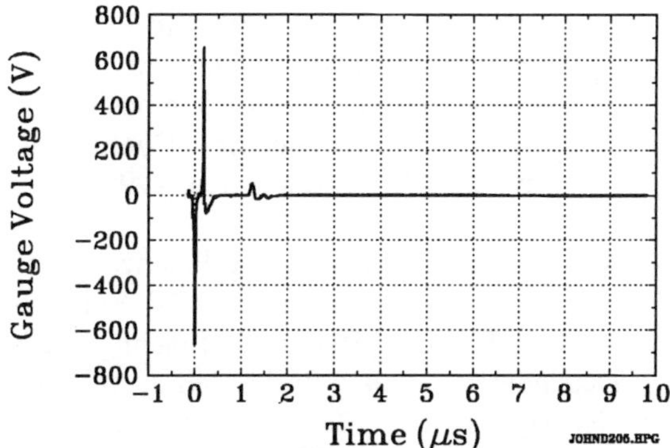

Figure 4. Raw voltage record from PVDF gauge at SATURN.

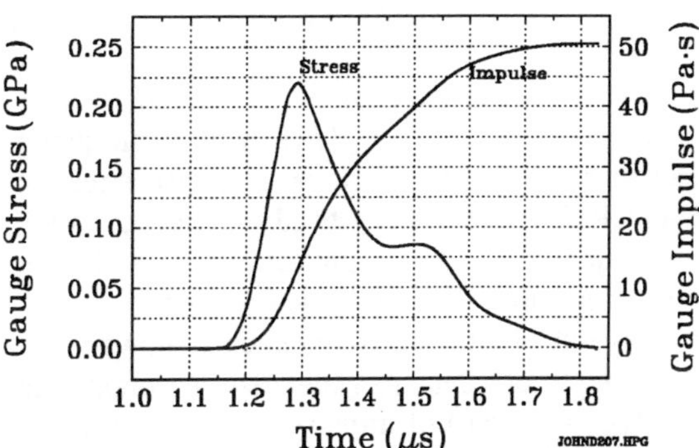

Figure 6. Filter debris stress and impluse.

Table 1. Saturn Debris Summary.

Shot	Gauge s/n	Sample Fluence (kJ/m²)	Blowoff Stress (GPa)	Blowoff Impluse (Pa-s)	Kimfol Fluence (kJ/m²)	Debris Stress (GPa)	Debris Impulse (Pa-s)	Kimfol Flight Distance (mm)	Debris TOA (μs)	Minimum Debris Vel (km/s)
1611	004	273	+	-	341	.22	37	6.35	1.05	6.05
	005	273	+	-	341	.05	8	6.35	1.20	5.29
1612	006	236	.38	24	295	.10	18	6.35	1.28	4.96
	007	210	.39	27	260	*	-	12.7	-	-
	008	236	.40	26	295	.12	37	6.35	1.04	6.14
	010	210	.33	19	260	*	-	12.7	-	-
1613	009	494	.69	60	652	.22	51	6.35	1.04	6.13
	011	544	+	-	no kimfol	-	-	-	-	-
	013	494	+	-	652	.23	42	6.35	1.00	6.36
	014	544	.99	92	no kimfol	-	-	-	-	-
1614	015	564	.89	96	960	.18	36	6.35	1.35	4.71

*insufficient recording resolution +baseline shift

because the filter-to-sample spacing would be greater and the filter would be tilted to direct the debris away from the sample.)

The time of arrival of the filter debris divided by the initial distance separating the filter and the sample yield a minimum velocity at which the debris must have been traveling. This minimum velocity calculated from the preceding records was 6.36 km/s. The same calculation for six other tests ranged from 4.7 to 6.1 km/s as shown in Table 1. The narrow debris velocity range is interesting considering that the fluence at the filter was doubled and tripled on some of the shots.

SUMMARY

Stress gauges using Bauer-type PVDF sensors have been shown to agree well with X-cut quartz gauges in measuring material response stress at SATURN. The principle advantage of PVDF over quartz in this application is a longer recording time of several microseconds.

Several preliminary experiments showed that Kimfol filter debris generated a maximum 50 Pa-s (0.5 ktap) of impulse. The arrival times recorded show a minimum filter debris velocity of about 6 mm/μs over a 6.35 mm flight distance.

REFERENCES

[1] R.A. Graham, F.W. Neilson, and W.B. Benedick, *Journal of Applied Physics* 36, pp. 1775-1783 (1965).

[2] L.M. Choate, *The Saturn X-Ray Simulation Facility, A Technical and Logistical Information Guide for Users,* Albuquerque: Sandia National Laboratories, 1989.

[3] F. Bauer, *Amer. Inst. Phy.*, pp. 251 (1982).

[4] F. Bauer, "Piezoelectric Response of Precisely Poled PVDF to Shock Compression Greater Than 10 GPa," presented at the International Symposium on Application of Ferroelectrics Conference, Greensville, SC, 30 Aug-2 Sep, 1992.

[5] R.A. Graham, "Piezoelectric Polarization of the Ferroelectric Polymer PVDF from 10 MPa to 10 GPa: Studies of Loading -Path Dependence," in *Preceedings of the Conference on Shock Compression of Condensed Matter*, 1991, pp. 883-886.`

MEASUREMENTS OF LASER INDUCED SHOCK PRESSURES USING PVDF GAUGES☆

J.P.ROMAIN[1], F. BAUER[2], D. ZAGOURI[1] and M. BOUSTIE[1]
1: L.E.D., ENSMA, 20 rue Guillaume VII, 86034 Poitiers Cédex, France.
2: Institut Saint Louis, 12 rue de l'Industrie, 68301 Saint-Louis, France

Shock Pressure measurements are made with the use of PVDF gauges applied on the back face of 0.1 to 1 mm thick targets, covered with glass windows and irradiated by laser pulses of 25 ns duration, at incident intensity between 10^8 and 10^{10} W/cm^2. Standard PVDF gauges of 25 µm thickness and also new copolymer gauges of 450 µm thickness are used. Results obtained from thin and thick gauges are quite consistent. From the experimental results, a complete description of the shock evolution through the target is obtained, including a determination of induced peak pressures (1to 50 kbar) and estimates of pressure decay during the shock propagation. Multiple reverberations of shock and release waves are also observed. The experimental results are analysed by the way of computer simulations, reproducing features of the measured shock profile evolution.

INTRODUCTION

Nowadays, laser induced shocks are widely used for getting information on the behavior of materials under high dynamic pressure, as well as for material processing. All these investigations are strongly related to the loading profile induced by the laser irradiation and the mechanisms governing the laser matter interaction. Instead of a direct irradiation of the targets, a confined irradiation can be used in order to increase the amplitude as well as the duration of the applied pressure pulse. We have performed shock pressure measurements in this configuration, using a Nd-glass laser with a pulse duration of 25ns and thin PVDF or thick copolymer gauges, whose piezoelectric properties have been widely studied[1]. By this way, we can relate the peak pressure induced into the material to the laser incident intensity confined through a glass window.

☆ Study supported by "Direction des Recherches et Etudes Techniques" under contract n° 91/1244A

EXPERIMENTS

The PVDF gauges developed at I.S.L. are now used under a wide range of shock loading conditions : plate impact, explosives, Hopkinson bars [2 ,3 ,4]. Their good reproducibility on a wide range of pressure, up to 200kbars [5], makes them a strong candidate for measuring laser induced pressure of high amplitude and short duration. We have used two kinds of gauges, testing at the same time their reliability by comparison of the results they could give. These gauges are presented on figure 1 :

- PVDF film of 25µm thickness
- copolymer gauges of 450µm thickness.

The PVDF film is stretched biaxially in order to get 50% amorphous, 50% cristalline phase and its structure is rearranged by the patented poling Bauer process, leaving a remanent polarization of 9.2µC/cm^2. The electrodes on both sides are constituted by sputtered Pt/Au. The active area is ranging between 1mm^2 for thin gauges to 4mm^2 for thick gauges. These gauges are applied at the rear face of thin aluminum foil on the front face of which the shock is generated. The front face of the gauge is insulated by a 25µm teflon foil and an anvil of KelF is applied on the back face of the gauge in order to avoid reverberations.

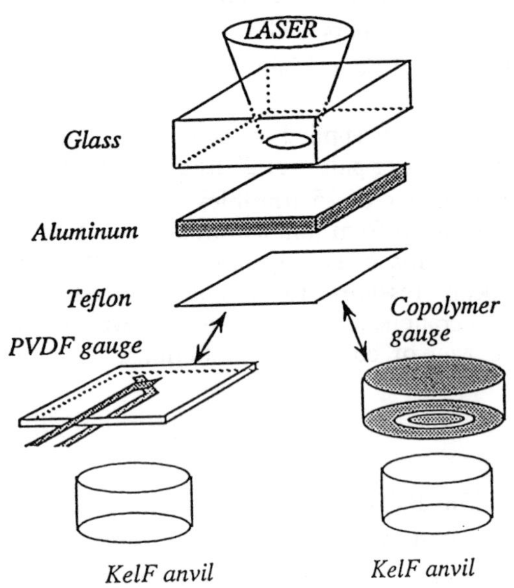

Figure 1. Sketch of the experimental set-up for measuring laser induced pressure, using PVDF and copolymer gauges

DIAGNOSTICS

The gauges deliver a current of intensity i(t) proportional to the stress difference between both electrodes :

$$i(t) = \frac{d_{33}Av}{e}[\sigma_1(t) - \sigma_2(t)] \qquad (1)$$

e : gauge thickness (25μm ou 450μm)
A : active area
v : shock velocity
d_{33} : piezoelectric constant

The signal is recorded on a DSA 602 Tektronix oscilloscope at a sampling rate of $0.5ns^{-1}$. From this signal, the stress σ_1 on the front face of the gauge is reconstituted step by step from the direct record during the transit time of the shock through the gauge. By using thin aluminum foil targets (<300μm), there is no significant attenuation of the peak pressure at the back of the target with irradiation conditions of intensity from 0.1 to 10 GW/cm^2 and a pulse duration of 25ns. Hence, taking into account the impedance mismatch between Al and PVDF, the measured pressure at the front face of the PVDF gauge gives the peak pressure applied on the front face of the target.

RESULTS

From the recorded signals, the induced peak pressure is measured and also the time history of the pulse propagation is obtained. This time history can be compared with the results of simulations using the hydro code SHYLAC[5] which describes the shock profile evolution from initial conditions given by laser energy deposition at the target-confinement interface.

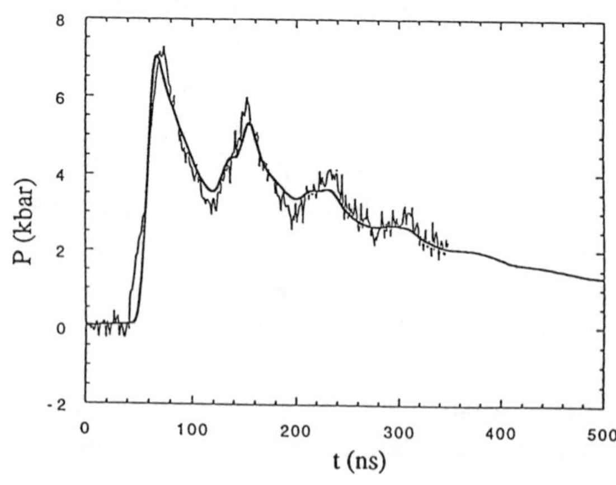

Figure 2. Pressure evolution on the front face of a 25μm PVDF gauge applied on the back face of a 240μm Al foil covered with glass and irradiated at 0.8GW/cm^2 incident intensity

— experimental result
— SHYLAC simulation

For example, the reconstituted signal of figure 2. shows a maximum pressure in PVDF of 7 kbar corresponding to an induced pressure of about 15 kbar in the aluminum. Successive reloadings at 100ns time interval are well evidenced. They are due to the reflection of the incident shock at the Al-PVDF interface, and consequently to the reverberations between the front and the back face of the Al foil. A very good agreement is observed between the experimental and numerical results.

The stress at the back face of a gauge is zero during the transit time of the shock through it; the intensity i(t) is directly related to the incident stress during that time, which is approximately 200ns for the thick copolymer gauges, and no signal reconstitution is required. Such a signal is shown on figure 3. and compared with the results of SHYLAC simulations in the same irradiation conditions. The agreement is reasonable as long as the shock has not reached the back of the gauge.

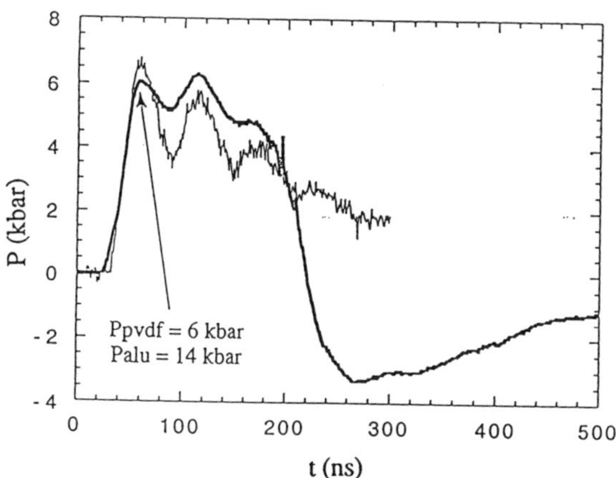

Figure 3. Pressure evolution on the front face of a 450μm copolymer gauge applied on the back face of a 160μm Al foil covered with glass and irradiated at 0.7GW/cm^2 incident intensity

— experimental result

— SHYLAC simulation

The experimental results of the induced peak pressure in the target as a function of incident laser intensity at λ=1.06μm and 25ns pulse duration in confined interaction, obtained with the use of both gauges are reported on figure 4. Both series of measurements are quite consistent. This curve shows the pressure saturation above 3GW/cm^2. This effect is due to the breakdown of glass beyond this irradiance.

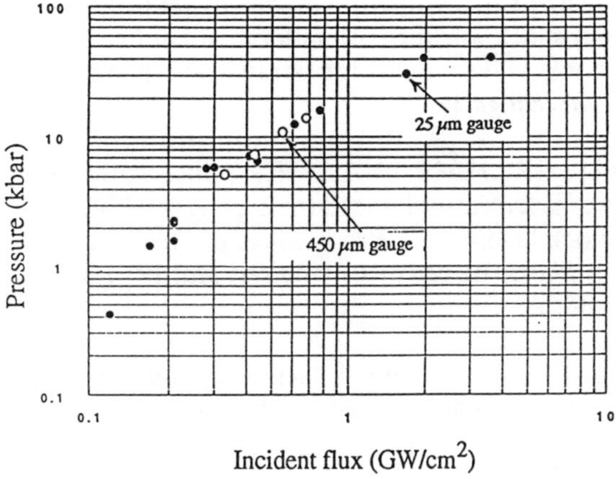

Figure 4. Induced peak pressure in aluminum targets confined by glass, versus laser incident intensity, at λ=1.06μm and 25ns laser pulse duration

CONCLUSION

In this study, the efficiency of PVDF and copolymer gauges is demonstrated for measuring shock pressure up to 50kbar at short pulse duration, such as those induced by laser irradiation. This opens up an interesting field of applications for these gauges which have been successfully used for determining the relation between shock amplitude and laser incident intensity in confined interaction. This result is of interest for laser shock applications using this configuration.

ACKNOWLEDGEMENTS

We would like to thank especially MM. Simonnet, Harnischmacher and Riha and for all their care in preparing the gauges.

REFERENCES

[1] BAUER F., Ferroelectric polarization of PVDF and VF_2/C_2F_3H copolymers : piezoelectric properties under dynamic pressure and shock loading - Metallurgical applications of shock waves and high strain rate phenomena 1985, pp1071-1082

[2] GRAHAM R.A., "Response of Bauer piezoelectric polymer stress gauges (PVDF) to shock loading", in *Proceedings of the Conference on Shock Waves in Condensed Matter, 1987, pp 619-622*

[3] BAUER F., MOULARD H., "State of the art in the research work of piezoelectric PVF_2 polymer shock gauges", in *Proceedings of the Conference on Shock Waves in Condensed Matter, 1987, pp 627-630*

[4] BAUER F., LICHTENBERGER A., "Use of PVF_2 shock gauges for stress measurements in Hopkinson bar", in *Proceedings of the Conference on Shock Waves in Condensed Matter, 1987, pp 631-635*

[5] COTTET F, BOUSTIE M, "Spallation studies in aluminum targets using shock waves induced by laser irradiation at various pulse durations", *J. Appl. Phys.* ***66*** *(9), 1989, pp 4067-4073*

SIMULATED X-RAY STREAK CAMERA DATA OF *IN SITU* DIFFRACTION FROM LASER-SHOCKED SINGLE CRYSTALS*

N. C. Woolsey and J. S. Wark

Department of Physics
Clarendon Laboratory
University of Oxford
Parks Road
Oxford, OX1 3PU, United Kingdom.

The computation time taken to simulate the *in situ* x-ray diffraction from laser-shocked single crystals has been reduced by two orders of magnitude by use of a kinematic, rather than dynamical, diffraction theory. Incorporation of the diffraction routine into an hydrocode allow the direct generation of x-ray streak camera data. A comparison of simulated and experimental data shows excellent qualitative agreement for different pulse lengths.

INTRODUCTION

In situ x-ray diffraction has become a valuable tool in the diagnosis of laser-driven shock waves in crystalline solids.[1-3] The change in diffraction angle with compression or tension within the crystal gives direct information about the elastic strain within the crystal. X-Ray streak camera records can yield such diffraction data on timescales of order 10 psec. However, apart from the simple task of extracting peak compressive or tensile strains within the crystal, analysis of the diffraction data is complicated by the fact that the probe depth of the x-rays (typically of order 10 μm) is of the same magnitude as the perturbed region of laser-shocked crystal, due to the 0.1 - 1.0 nsec laser pulse lengths used for shock generation. This means that over the probe depth of the x-rays there is a whole range of lattice strains that diffract the x-rays at different Bragg angles; the intensity of the diffraction at each angle being a function of the depth at which diffraction is taking place, and the strain gradient at that point. The capability to model the diffraction from the laser-shocked crystal is therefore useful in data analysis. We have been especially interested in the possibility of coupling such a diffraction model to the time-dependent strain gradients predicted by an hydrocode, so that we can directly generate simulated streak camera data to compare with that from experiments.

X-RAY DIFFRACTION FROM LASER-SHOCKED CRYSTALS

The theory of X-ray diffraction from strained media was developed 20 years ago by Takagi[4] and independently by Taupin[5]. The Tagaki-Taupin formulation extends the dynamic theory of x-ray diffraction to a strained crystal by allowing the Bragg angle to vary as a function of depth below the crystal surface. The dynamic theory takes account of absorption (photoelectric effect and Compton scattering) and extinction (coherent scattering) of the wave fields within a crystal. We have used this theory successfully in the past to model the diffraction from laser-shocked crystals for a given strain-profile at a given point in time, and details of the theory can be found within these references.[2] However, it has not been possible to incorporate this model into the hydrocode, as it is too computationally expensive.

One of the main features of the dynamical theory is that it takes into account extinction, i.e. a reduction of the intensity of the incident beam due to efficient diffraction. This is an important effect in unstrained perfect crystals, and in strained crystals with small strain gradients. However, it is known to be inaccurate in the case of imperfect crystals, where the single crystal can better be portrayed as a mosaic of small crystallites, each with some small, random distribution of angles around the mean. In this case the incident x-ray beam is absorbed by photoelectric absorption until it reaches a crystallite oriented with the correct angle to match the Bragg angle. Due to the small thickness of the crystallite the reduction of intensity of the incident beam due to diffraction is negligible compared to that due to absorption in the bulk of the crystal traversed in reaching the point of diffraction. The theory describing the diffraction from imperfect crystals is known as the kinematic theory. It can be seen that this theory should be adaptable to the case of laser-shocked crystals: the high strain-gradients involved ensure that for a given angle, diffraction only takes place within a thin layer of crystal with the appropriate strain, up until that point the incident and diffracted x-rays are simply attenuated by photoelectric absorption. Thus we should be able to neglect the effects of extinction. We show this to be the case below, where we compare the diffraction profiles for a simulated laser-shocked crystal for the full dynamical and approximate kinematic theories in the presence of strain gradients.

The crystal is divided into a number of parallel laminae, each of constant strain. We assume the x-ray beam enters the crystal and is reflected by a layer at depth T, the absorption within the layer is ignored. The integrated reflectivity of the layer is[6]

$$\delta P = \left(\frac{4w_s}{3}\right)\tanh[A] \tag{1}$$

Where w_s is the dynamical width of the laminaes' rocking curve, and A is a dimensionless depth. The incident and reflected beams are attenuated by ordinary absorption (this is essentially the kinematical approximation since extinction is ignored). The reflectivity is assumed constant over the angular range w_s centred on the Bragg angle of the strained laminae. The angular change in Bragg angle from one strained laminae to the next is fixed to be the same as the dynamical width. This requires re-zoning of the mesh used in the hydrocode.

Strain profiles within laser-shocked crystals were generated by use of a modified version of the 'Medusa' hydrocode.[7] The modifications incorporate a Mie-Grüneisen equation of state to allow accurate modelling of the solid material. At this stage plastic response of the material is ignored in the code: this should not be important for simply qualitatively comparing the results from typical strain-depth profiles.

A typical strain profile calculated with the code on a 150 cell grid is shown in Fig. 1. The simulation shows the shock wave during shock breakout from a free surface, a rarefaction is travelling back into the bulk of the target, the material close to the surface is in tension whilst material deeper in the target is still compressed.

The diffracted intensity as a function of dimensionless angle for both the dynamical and kinematic theories is shown in Fig. 2. It can be

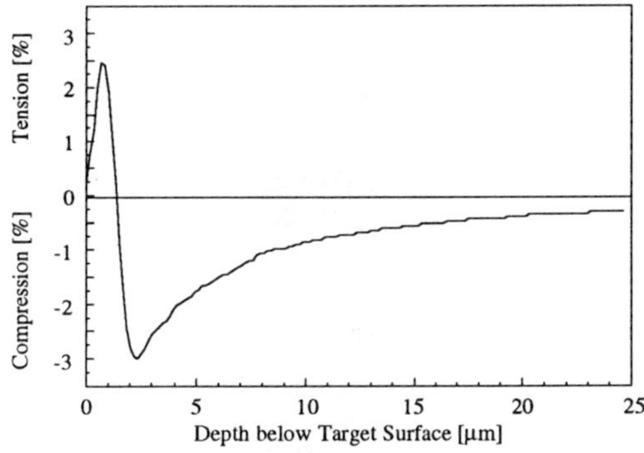

Figure 1. Output from Medusa, 150 cell simulation of a shock wave breaking out from the rear surface of a crystal.

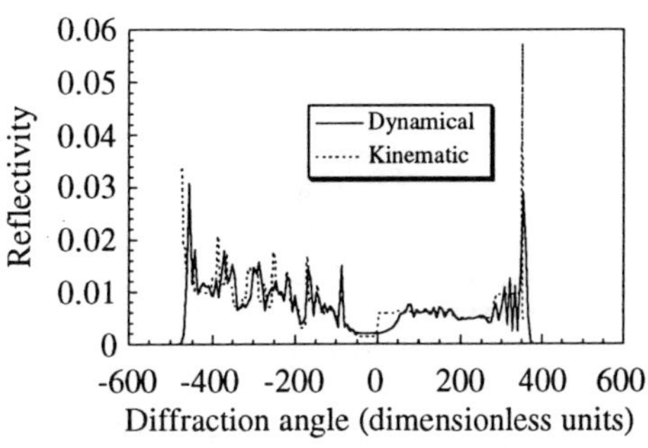

Figure 2. Rocking curves calculated from the strain profile shown in Figure 1. The units used in the x-axis are in terms of the diffraction width of a perfect crystal.

seen that there is excellent agreement between the two cases - there is both good agreement as to the shape of the profile, and also the total reflectivity integrated over angle differs by only 2.5%. In addition it should be noted that due to the simplicity of the kinematic approximation, computationally it is up to two orders of magnitude faster than the dynamical case, making incorporation into an hydrocode a viable proposition.

SIMULATED STREAK CAMERA DATA

Simulated streak camera data were generated by incorporating the kinematic theory into the hydrocode. The x-ray diffraction profile was computed every 10 psec of simulation time. Simulations were performed for laser-pulses of both 0.1 and 1.0 nsec duration, and of intensity sufficient to produce a compressive elastic strain of approximately 6% at the rear surface of a 50 μm thick (111) silicon single crystal (typically several x 10^{10} W cm^{-2}). The x-rays were taken to be from the resonance line of helium-like titanium (2.6Å). Further details concerning the laser system used and the experiments can be found elsewhere.[3]

Figs. 3 and 4 show the simulated streak camera diffraction records for the two laser pulses. Note that the simulated data is for diffraction for a perfectly monochromatic x-ray beam. In the experiment the diffracted x-rays consist of three lines - the resonance, intercombination, and unresolved dielectronic satellites of helium-like titanium (these can be seen at early time in Fig.3 before the shock arrives, when we are diffracting from unperturbed crystal) - for a full comparison we would need to convolve the simulated data with such a line profile.

It can be seen that there is excellent qualitative agreement between experiment and simulation. The main features to note are that for the 1.0 nsec pulse the diffraction from the compressed region is less smeared out over angle, indicating a high strain gradient rising to a plateau of strain, whereas for the 0.1 nsec case the diffracted signal is smeared out over a wide range of compressive strains, indicating lower strain gradients. This contrast may be due to the larger hydrodynamic decay experienced by the shorter pulse; the precise reasons for these differences are presently being analysed: the main point of this paper being to demonstate that such features can

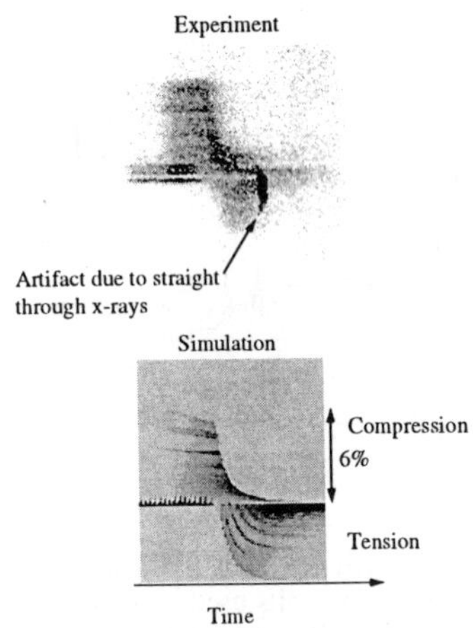

Fig. 3. A comparison of simulated and experimental x-ray streak camera data for a 0.1 nsec laser pulse. The total experimental x-ray pulse is on for approximately 1.0 nsec.

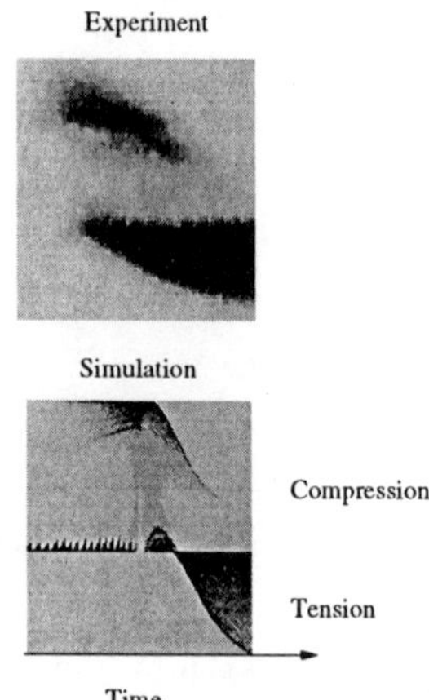

Fig. 4. As for Fig. 3 except with a laser shock driving pulse of 1.0 nsec.

be reproduced and that study of the strain profiles that produce them hopefully will lead to a greater understanding of the shock profiles that cause them.

CONCLUSION

We have used kinematic diffraction theory to model in situ x-ray diffraction from laser-shocked crystals. A comparison with the full dynamical theory shows good quantitative agreement, whilst the time-dependent simulation data produced by incorporating the diffraction routine into an hydrocode produces results that agree well qualitatively with experimental data.

The capability to simulate the diffraction profiles in a time-dependent manner will assist greatly in the interpretation of streak camera data. The next step in the analysis of these results is to try to extract strain-depth profiles from the streak-camera data, using our knowledge of the x-ray diffraction process.

REFERENCES

* This paper was presented in place of the advertised paper in session C2.2.

1. J. S. Wark, R. R. Whitlock, A. A. Hauer, J. E. Swain, and P. J. Solone, Phys. Rev. B35, 9391 (1987).
2. J. S. Wark, R. R. Whitlock, A. A. Hauer, J. E. Swain, and P. J. Solone, Phys. Rev.. B40, 5705 (1989).
3. J. S. Wark, G. Khein, R. R. Whitlock, D. Riley, and N. C. Woolsey, J. Appl. Phys., 68, 4531 (1990).
4. S. Tagaki, Acta Crystallog. 15, 1311 (1962).
5. D. Taupin, Bull. Soc. Franç. Minér. Crist. 87, 469 (1964).
6. W. H. Zachariasen, *Theory of X-ray Diffraction in Crystals*, New York.(1945).
7. J. P. Chritiansen, D. E. F. T. Ashby, and K. Roberts, Comp. Phys. Comm. 7, 271, (1974).

AUTHOR INDEX

SUBJECT INDEX